TOP QUALITY

HAY

ENGLISH
AMERICAN SOUTH AFRICAN

TIMOTHY   ALFALFA   CLOVER   RYEGRASS

SUPPLIERS TO LEADING TRAINERS AND STUD FARMS

J. & J. Ransley

Contact Philip Ransley
Golden Wood Farm, Brisley Lane, Ruckinge, Ashford, Kent, TN26 2PW
Tel: (01233) 731001/733189
Fax: (01233) 731002

PW Piper Ltd
Forage Merchant

Suppliers of Top Quality Racehorse & Stud Hays
English Mixtures & Leys
Samples available

Philip Piper will be happy to discuss your individual
forage requirements.

Telephone: 01438 811720
Mobile: 07721 571020
E-mail: pwpiper.forage@onetel.net

CUSHION TRACK PREMIER RACING

Endorsed by champion trainer Paul Nicholls, Charlie Mann, Nicky Richards, James Given, Heather Dalton, Ian Semple, M J Coombe, Daniel O'Brien, Tom Hogan, and A J Martin.

Equestrian Surfaces have now received approval from the British Horse Racing Authority to instal Cushion Track Premier on racecourses throughout the UK.

Racetracks worldwide include Hollywood Park in the U.S.A. Queensland Racing, Australia have also chosen Cushion Track for Sunshine Coast Turf Club, Gold Coast Turf Club and Toowoomba Turf Club.

Our ability to move equestrian properties is outstanding.

That's because our specialised team has a wealth of contacts and experience across the country, all supported by our nationwide network of offices.

Potentlal purchasers recognise we can bring them properties even before they come to market. And so they come to us first.

If you're looking to place your property on the market, hand it to us. We will be delighted to act on your behalf.

**Contact: Robert Fanshawe
on 020 7629 8171 or email
robert.fanshawe@knightfrank.com**

www.knightfrank.com

Head
and
hands
above
the
rest

**Knight
Frank**

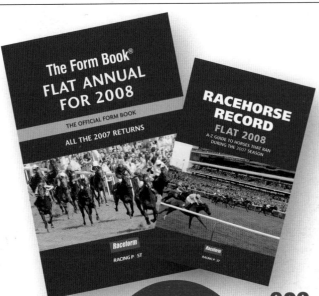

HORSES
IN TRAINING 2008

115th YEAR OF PUBLICATION

Raceform

INDEX TO GENERAL CONTENTS

Editor	Richard Lowther; Raceform Ltd., Compton, Newbury, RG20 6NL. Fax: 01635 578101 E-mail: richard.lowther@racingpost.co.uk
Assistant Editor	Simon Turner
Production Editor	Richard Scoble; Bloodstock Services, Weatherbys
Typesetting	Maggie Elvie; Printing Services, Weatherbys, Sanders Road, Wellingborough, NN8 4BX.
Orders	Raceform Ltd., High Street, Compton, Newbury, RG20 6NL. Tel: 01635 578080 www.racingpost.co.uk/bookshop Fax: 01635 578101
Advertisements	Julian Brown; Raceform Ltd., Compton, Newbury, RG20 6NL. Tel: 01635 577603 E-mail: julian.brown@racingpost.co.uk
ISBN	978-1-905153-70-1

Printed in Great Britain by William Clowes Ltd., Beccles, Suffolk, NR34 7TL.

© Raceform Ltd 2008

INDEX TO ADVERTISERS

INDEX TO TRAINERS

†denotes Permit to train under N.H. Rules only

Name	Team No.
BRADBURNE, MRS S. C.	057
BRADLEY, MR J. M.	058
BRADSTOCK, MR M. F.	059
BRAVERY, MR G. C.	060
BRENNAN, MR OWEN	061
†BREWIS, MISS R. G.	062
BRIDGER, MR J. J.	063
BRIDGWATER, MR D. G.	064
BRIDGWATER, MR G. F.	065
BRISBOURNE, MR W. M.	066
BRITTAIN, MR C. E.	067
BRITTAIN, MR M. A.	068
BROCKBANK, MR J. E.	069
†BROOKE, LADY S.	070
†BROOKHOUSE, MR R. S.	071
BROOKS, MRS A. E.	072
BROOKSHAW, MR S. A.	073
BROTHERTON, MR R.	074
†BROWN, MR I. A.	075
†BROYD, MISS A. E.	076
†BRYANT, MISS M. P.	077
BUCKLER, MR R. H.	078
BUCKLEY, MR M. A.	079
BURCHELL, MR W. D.	080
BURGOYNE, MR P. V. J.	081
BURKE, MR K. J.	082
BURKE, MR K. R.	083
BURROUGH, MR S.	084
BUTLER, MR P.	085
BUTT, MR T.	086
BYCROFT, MR N.	087

C

Name	Team No.
CALDWELL, MR T. H.	088
CALLAGHAN, MR S. A.	089
CAMACHO, MISS J. A.	090
CAMPION, MR A. M.	091
CANDLISH, MS JENNIE	092
CANDY, MR HENRY D. N. B.	093
CARR, MRS RUTH A.	094
CARROLL, MR A. W.	095

Name	Team No.
CARROLL, MR D.	096
†CARSON, MR R. M.	097
CASE, MR B. I.	098
CECIL, MR H. R. A.	099
†CHADWICK, MR S. G.	100
CHAMBERLAIN, MR A. J.	101
CHAMINGS, MR P. R.	102
CHANCE, MR N. T.	103
CHAPMAN, MR M. C.	104
CHAPPLE-HYAM, MR P. W.	105
CHARLTON, MR G. A. G.	106
CHARLTON, MR ROGER J.	107
†CLARK, MR R. M.	108
CLEMENT, MR NICOLAS	109
CLINTON, MR P. L.	110
CLUTTERBUCK, MR K. F.	111
COAKLEY, MR D. J.	112
†COBB, MRS H. J.	113
COLE, MR P. F. I.	114
COLLET, MR ROBERT	115
COLLINGRIDGE, MR H. J.	116
COLTHERD, MR W. S.	117
†CONNELL, LADY	118
COOGAN, MR A. B.	119
COOMBE, MR M. J.	120
CORCORAN, MR L. A.	121
CORNWALL, MR J. R.	122
COUPLAND, MR J. F.	123
COWELL, MR R. M. H.	124
COWLEY, MR P. E.	125
COX, MR C. G.	126
CRAGGS, MR R.	127
CREIGHTON, MR E. J.	128
CROOK, MR A.	129
CROWLEY, MISS J. P.	130
CUMANI, MR L. M.	131
CUNDELL, MR P. D.	132
CUNNINGHAM, MR M.	133
CURRAN, MR J. M. S.	134
CURTIS, MR R.	135
CUTHBERT, MR T. A. K.	136

Name	Team No.	Name	Team No.
GASK, MR J. R.	211	HAMMOND, MR M. D.	250
GEAKE, MR J.	212	HAMMOND, MR M. P.	251
GEORGE, MR T. R.	213	†HANDLEY, MRS S. E.	252
GIBNEY, MISS J. R.	214	HANNON, MR R.	253
GIBSON, MR RICHARD	215	HARKER, MR G. A.	254
GIFFORD, MR N.	216	†HARKIN, MRS P. E.	255
GILLARD, MR M. A.	217	†HARPER, MR R. C.	256
GILMORE, MR S. J.	218	HARRINGTON, MRS JESSICA	257
GINGELL, MR M. J.	219	HARRIS, MR J. A.	258
GIVEN, MR JAMES	220	HARRIS, MR M.	259
GOLDIE, MR J. S.	221	HARRIS, MR R. A.	260
†GOLDIE, MR R. H.	222	HASLAM, MR PATRICK	261
GOLDSWORTHY, MR K.	223	HAWKE, MR N. J.	262
GORDON, MR C. E.	224	HAYDEN, MR JOHN C	263
GOSDEN, MR J. H. M.	225	HAYDN JONES, MR D.	264
GRAHAM, MRS H. O.	226	HAYNES, MR A. B.	265
GRANT, MR C.	227	HAYNES, MR H. E.	266
GRASSICK, MR L. P.	228	†HAYNES, MR J. C.	267
GRASSICK, MR M. J.	229	HEAD, MRS C.	268
GRAY, MR C. J.	230	HENDERSON, MR N. J.	269
GRAYSON, MR P. M.	231	†HENDERSON, MR P. F.	270
GREEN, MR P.	232	HERRIES, LADY	271
†GREENWAY, MR V. G.	233	†HEWITT, MR R. J.	272
†GRIFFITHS, MRS S. G.	234	HIATT, MR P. W.	273
GRISSELL, MR D. M.	235	HILL, MR M. E.	274
GROUCOTT, MR J. B.	236	HILL, MRS T. J.	275
GUBBY, MR BRIAN	237	HILLS, MR B. W.	276
GUEST, MR R.	238	HILLS, MR J. W.	277
		HOAD, MR M. R.	278
		HOBBS, MR P. J.	279

H

Name	Team No.	Name	Team No.
HAGGAS, MR W. J.	239	HODGES, MR R. J.	280
HAIGH, MISS V.	240	†HOGAN, MR M. J.	281
HALDANE, MR J. S.	241	HOGAN, MR TOM	282
HALES, MR A. M.	242	†HOGARTH, MR H. P.	283
HALL, MISS S. E.	243	HOLLINGSWORTH, MR A. F.	284
HALL, MR S. W.	244	HOLLINSHEAD, MR R.	285
HAM, MR G. A.	245	HOLT, MR J. R.	286
HAMBRO, MRS M. C.	246	HONEYBALL, MR A.	287
†HAMILTON, MRS A.	247	HORGAN, MR CON	288
†HAMILTON, MRS A. C.	248	HOURIGAN, MR M.	289
HAMILTON-FAIRLEY, MOUSE.	249	HOWE, MR H. S.	290

Name	Team No.	Name	Team No.
HOWLING, MR P.	291	KELLETT, MR C. N.	325
HUGHES, MR D. T.	292	KELLEWAY, MISS G. M.	326
†HUGHES, MR S. A.	293	KELLY, MR G. P.	327
†HUGO, MS N. M.	294	†KELSALL, MR P.	328
†HUMPHREY, MRS S. J.	295	†KERR, MRS C. J.	329
		KEY, MISS K.	330
		KING, MRS A. L. M.	331
I		KING, MR ALAN	332
†IKIN, MRS C. J.	296	KING, MR N.	333
INGRAM, MR R.	297	†KIRBY, MR F.	334
IVORY, MR D. K.	298	KIRK, MR S. A.	335
		KITTOW, MR W. S.	336
		KNIGHT, MISS H. C.	337
J		KNIGHT, MR W. J.	338
†JACOBS, MR S. M.	299	KNIPE, MR R. F.	339
JAMES, MR L. R.	300		
JARVIS, MR A. P.	301		
JARVIS, MR M. A.	302	**L**	
JARVIS, MR W.	303	LAFFON-PARIAS, MR C.	340
JEFFERSON, MR J. M.	304	LAMYMAN, MRS S.	341
JENKINS, MR J. R. W.	305	LANIGAN, MR D. R.	342
†JESSOP, MR A. E. M.	306	LAVELLE, MISS E. C.	343
†JESTIN, MR F.	307	†LAY, MR B. L.	344
JEWELL, MRS L. C.	308	LE BROCQ, MRS J. L.	345
JOHNSON, MR B. R.	309	LEE, MR RICHARD	346
JOHNSON HOUGHTON, MISS E. A.	310	LEECH, MRS S. V. O.	347
JOHNSON, MR J. H.	311	LELLOUCHE, MR ELIE	348
JOHNSON, MR ROBERT W.	312	LEWIS, MISS H.	349
JOHNSON, MRS S. M.	313	†LEWIS, MR R. W.	350
JONES, MR A. E.	314	LIDDERDALE, MR A. J. D.	351
†JONES, MR G. ELWYN	315	LIDDIARD, MRS S. A.	352
†JONES, MR P. J.	316	LITTMODEN, MR N. P.	353
JONES, MR T. M.	317	†LLEWELLYN, MR B.	354
JORDAN, MR F. T. J.	318	LLEWELLYN, MR B. J.	355
JUCKES, MR A. G.	319	LLEWELLYN, MR C.	356
		LOCKWOOD, MR A. J.	357
		LONG, MR J. E.	358
K		LONGSDON, MR C.	359
KEANE, MR D. P.	320	LUNGO, MR L.	360
KEDDY, MR T.	321	†LURCOCK, MR M. J.	361
KEEVIL, MRS C.	322	LYCETT, MR S.	362
†KEHOE, MRS F. J.	323	LYONS, MR GER	363
KEIGHLEY, MR M. H.	324		

Name	Team No.
M	
MACAIRE, MR G.	364
MACKIE, MR W. J. W.	365
MACTAGGART, MR A. B.	366
†MACTAGGART, MR A. H.	367
†MADDISON, MR P.	368
MADGWICK, MR M. J.	369
MAGNUSSON, MR M. A.	370
MAKIN, MR P. J.	371
MALETROIT, MR R.	372
MALZARD, MRS ALYSON	373
MANGAN, MR JAMES J.	374
MANN, MR C. J.	375
†MANN, MRS J. M. E.	376
MANNERS, MR H. J.	377
MARGARSON, MR GEORGE	378
†MARSHALL, MR S. J.	379
MASON, MR S. T.	380
†MATHEW, MR R.	381
MCCABE, MR A. J.	382
MCCAIN, MR D. R.	383
MCCORMACK, MR N. P.	384
MCGRATH, MR M.	385
MCGREGOR, MRS J. C.	386
MCINNES, MR I. W.	387
MCLINTOCK, MS K. J.	388
MCMAHON, MR E. S. A.	389
MCMATH, MR B. J.	390
MCMATH, MR I.	391
†MCMILLAN, MR M. D.	392
†MCPHERSON, MR G. P.	393
MEEHAN, MR B. J.	394
†MEEK, MS M. A.	395
†MIDDLETON, MR A.	396
MIDGLEY, MR P. T.	397
MILLIGAN, MISS M. K.	398
MILLMAN, MR B. R.	399
MILLS, MR T. G.	400
MITCHELL, MR N. R.	401
MOFFATT, MR D. J.	402
MONGAN, MRS L. J.	403

Name	Team No.
MONTEITH, MR PETER	404
MOORE, MR A. L.	405
MOORE, MR G. L.	406
MOORE, MR G. M.	407
MOORE, MR J. S.	408
MORGAN, MR K. A.	409
MORLOCK, MR C. P. H.	410
MORRIS, MR M.	411
MORRIS, MRS THERESA	412
MORRISON, MR H.	413
MOSS, MR G. P.	414
MOUNTAIN, MISS D.	415
MUIR, MR WILLIAM R.	416
MULHALL, MR C. A.	417
MULLINEAUX, MR M.	418
MULLINS, MR J. W.	419
MULLINS, MR WILLIAM P.	420
MURPHY, MR F.	421
MURPHY, MR P. G.	422
MURPHY, MR P. T. J.	423
MURRAY SMITH, MR D. J. G.	424
MURTAGH, MR F.	425
MUSSON, MR W. J.	426
N	
NAUGHTON, MRS A. M.	427
NAYLOR, DR J. R. J.	428
†NEEDHAM, MR J. L.	429
†NEEDHAM, MR P.	430
NELMES, MRS H. R. J.	431
†NENADICH, MR C.	432
NEWCOMBE, MR A. G.	433
NEWLAND, DR R. D. P.	434
NEWTON-SMITH, MISS A. M.	435
NICHOLLS, MR D.	436
NICHOLLS, MR P. F.	437
NIVEN, MR P. D.	438
†NIXON, MR G. R. S.	439
†NOCK, MRS S.	440
NOLAN, MR D. A.	441
NORMILE, MRS L. B.	442

Name	Team No.	Name	Team No.
NORTON, MR J. R.	443	POOK, MRS N. N. M.	479
NOSEDA, MR J. J.	444	POPHAM, MR C. L.	480
		PORTMAN, MR J. G. B.	481
O		POWELL, MR B. G.	482
O'BRIEN, MR D. C.	445	†POWELL, MR G. J.	483
O'GRADY, MR E. J.	446	†PRENDERGAST, MR K. M.	484
O'KEEFFE, MR J.	447	PRENDERGAST, MR P. J.	485
O'LEARY, MR RONNIE	448	PRESCOTT BT, SIR MARK	486
†O'NEILL, MR J. G.	449	†PRICE, MRS A.	487
O'NEILL, MR J. J.	450	PRICE, MR A. E.	488
O'SHEA, MR J. G. M.	451	†PRICE, MR J. K.	489
OLD, MR J. A. B.	452	PRICE, MR RICHARD J.	490
OLDROYD, MR G. R.	453	PRIEST, MISS J.	491
OSBORNE, MR J. A.	454	PRITCHARD, DR P. L. J.	492
OXX, MR JOHN M.	455	PRODROMOU, MR G.	493
		PURDY, MR P. D.	494
P			
PALLING, MR BRYN	456	**Q**	
PANVERT, MR J. F.	457	QUINLAN, MR M.	495
PARKER, MR ANDREW	458	QUINN, MR J. J.	496
†PAYNE, MR J. R.	459	QUINN, MR M.	497
†PAYNE, MR P. S.	460		
PEACOCK, MR R. E.	461	**R**	
PEARCE, MR J.	462	RATCLIFFE, MR W. J. H.	498
PEARS, MR O. J.	463	†REED, MR W. J.	499
†PEARSON, MR D.	464	REES, MR D.	500
PEILL, MR M. A.	465	REES, MRS G. S.	501
PERRATT, MISS L. A.	466	†REES, MRS H. E.	502
PERRETT, MRS A. J.	467	REID, MR A. S.	503
†PEWTER, MR G. R.	468	REVELEY, MR K. G.	504
PHELAN, MR P. M.	469	RICHARDS, MRS LYDIA	505
PHILLIPS, MR R. T.	470	RICHARDS, MR N. G.	506
PICKERING, MR J. A.	471	†RIGBY, MRS P. A.	507
†PIKE, MR STEWART	472	RIMELL, MR M. G.	508
PINDER, MR DAVID	473	ROBESON, MRS P.	509
PIPE, MR D. E.	474	ROBSON, MISS P.	510
PITT, MR T. J.	475	RODFORD, MR P. R.	511
†POGSON, MR C. T.	476	ROPER, MR W. M.	512
POLLOCK, MR B. N.	477	ROUGET, MR J-C	513
POMFRET, MR N. J.	478	ROWE, MR R.	514

Name	Team No.
ROWLAND, MISS M. E.	515
RUSSELL, MRS L. V.	516
RYALL, MR B. J. M.	517
RYAN, MR J. B.	518
RYAN, MR K. A.	519

S

Name	Team No.
SADIK, MR A. M.	520
†SANDERSON, MRS K. M.	521
SAUNDERS, MR M. S.	522
SAVILLE, MR J.	523
SAYER, MRS H. D.	524
SCARGILL, DR J. D.	525
†SCOTT, MR D. D.	526
SCOTT, MR J.	527
†SCRASE, MRS J.	528
†SCRIVEN, MR B.	529
SCUDAMORE, MR M. J.	530
SHAW, MR D.	531
SHEPPARD, MR M. I.	532
SHERWOOD, MR O. M. C.	533
SHERWOOD, MR S. E. H.	534
†SHIELS, MR R.	535
SHIRLEY-BEAVAN, MR S. H.	536
SIDDALL, MISS L. C.	537
SIMCOCK, MR D. M. I.	538
SIMPSON, MR RODNEY	539
†SLACK, MRS D. E.	540
SLY, MRS P. M.	541
SMAGA, MR D.	542
SMART, MR B.	543
SMITH, MR G. J.	544
SMITH, MR JULIAN SIMON	545
SMITH, MR M.	546
SMITH, MRS NADINE	547
SMITH, MISS S.	548
SMITH, MRS S. J.	549
†SMITH, MRS S. J.	550
SMITH, MR V.	551
SOUTHCOMBE, MISS J. A.	552
SOWERSBY, MR M. E.	553

Name	Team No.
SPEARING, MR J. L.	554
SPEARING, MISS T. S.	555
STACK, MR T.	556
†STEPHENS, MR D. O.	557
STIMPSON, MR J. T.	558
†STIRK, MRS M. K.	559
STOKELL, MISS ANN	560
†STONE, MR W. B.	561
STOREY, MR B.	562
STOREY, MR W.	563
†STRETTON, MRS S. P.	564
STRONGE, MR R. M.	565
STUBBS, MRS L.	566
STURGIS, MISS V. C.	567
SUMMERS, MR B. R.	568
SWAN, MR CHARLIE	569
†SWEETLAND, MR M. S.	570
SWINBANK, MR G. A.	571
SWINBURN, MR W. R. J.	572

T

Name	Team No.
TAAFFE, MR T. J.	573
TATE, MR T. P.	574
TEAGUE, MR COLIN	575
TEAL, MR R. A.	576
THOMAS, MRS D.	577
†THOMAS, MR KEITH S.	578
THOMPSON, MR D. W.	579
THORNTON, MR C. W.	580
THORPE, MRS A. M.	581
TIZZARD, MR C. L.	582
TODHUNTER, MR D. M.	583
TOLLER, MR J. A. R.	584
TOMPKINS, MR M. H.	585
TOOTH, MISS J. R.	586
†TORK, MR K.	587
TOWNSLEY, MRS P.	588
TREGONING, MR M. P.	589
TUER, MR E.	590
TUER, MR G. F.	591
†TULLIE, MRS A. F.	592

Name	Team No.
TURNELL, MR ANDREW	593
†TURNER, MR D. C.	594
TURNER, MR J. R.	595
TURNER, MR W. G. M.	596
TUTTY, MRS K. J.	597
TWISTON-DAVIES, MR N. A.	598

U

Name	Team No.
UPSON, MR J. R.	599
USHER, MR M. D. I.	600

V

Name	Team No.
VAUGHAN, MR E. F.	601
VAUGHAN, MR N. J.	602
VAUGHAN, MR T. E.	603
VON DER RECKE, MR CHRISTIAN	604

W

Name	Team No.
WADE, MR J.	605
WADHAM, MRS L. A. M.	606
†WAGGOTT, MR N.	607
WAGGOTT, MISS T.	608
WAINWRIGHT, MR J. S.	609
WALDRON, MRS K.	610
†WALEY-COHEN, MR R. B.	611
WALFORD, MR T. D.	612
WALL, MR C. F.	613
†WALL, MRS S.	614
WALL, MR T. R.	615
WALTON, MRS K.	616
WARING, MRS BARBARA	617
WATSON, MR F.	618
†WATSON, LADY S.	619
WATT, MRS S. A.	620
†WEBB-BOWEN, MR R. I.	621
WEBBER, MR P. R.	622
WEEDEN, MISS D. E.	623
WEGMANN, MR P.	624
WELD M.V.B. M.R.C.V.S., MR D. K.	625
WELLINGS, MR MARK	626

Name	Team No.
WELLS, MR L.	627
WEST, MISS S.	628
WEYMES, MR J. R.	629
WHEELER, MR E. A.	630
WHILLANS, MR D. W.	631
WHITAKER, MR R. M.	632
†WHITEHEAD, MR A. J.	633
WIGHAM, MR M.	634
WILESMITH, MR M. S.	635
WILLIAMS, MR IAN	636
WILLIAMS, MR N. S. L.	637
WILLIAMS, MR R. E. R.	638
WILLIAMS, MR S. C.	639
WILLIAMS, MISS V. M.	640
WILLIAMSON, MRS L. V.	641
†WILSON, MR A. C.	642
WILSON, MR A. J.	643
WILSON, MR C. R.	644
WILSON, MR N.	645
WINGROVE, MR K. G.	646
WINKWORTH, MR P. L.	647
WINTLE, MR D. J.	648
WOOD, MR I. A.	649
WOODHOUSE, MR R. D. E.	650
WOODMAN, MR S.	651
†WOODROW, MRS A. M.	652
WOODWARD, MR G.	653
WRAGG, MR GEOFFREY	654

Y

Name	Team No.
YARDLEY, MR G. H.	655
YORK, MR R. H.	656
†YOUNG, MR W. G.	657

PROPERTY OF HER MAJESTY

The Queen

Colours: Purple, gold braid, scarlet sleeves, black cap with gold fringe

Trained by **Sir M. Stoute**, Newmarket

THREE-YEAR-OLDS

1 **BEAUTIFUL DREAMER**, br f Red Ransom (USA)—Flight of Fancy
2 **CRITERION**, b g Dr Fong (USA)—Film Script
3 **DRUM MAJOR (IRE)**, b c Sadler's Wells (USA)—Phantom Gold
4 **KINGDOM OF FIFE**, b c Kingmambo (USA)—Fairy Godmother
5 **NAVAL REVIEW (USA)**, b br c Storm Cat (USA)—Arutua

TWO-YEAR-OLDS

6 **ENTICEMENT**, b f 13/2 Montjeu (IRE)—Ecoutila (USA) (Rahy (USA)) (310000)
7 **GOLDEN STREAM (IRE)**, b f 25/4 Sadler's Wells (USA)—Phantom Gold (Machiavellian (USA))
8 **HARVEST SONG (IRE)**, b c 5/4 Sadler's Wells (USA)—La Mouline (IRE) (Nashwan (USA)) (290000)
9 **HIGHLAND GLEN**, b c 25/1 Montjeu (IRE)—Daring Aim (Daylami (IRE))
10 **PIED PIPER**, b c 2/3 Pivotal—Flight of Fancy (Sadler's Wells (USA))

Trained by **Roger J. Charlton**, Beckhampton

THREE-YEAR-OLDS

11 **CARDINAL**, ch c Pivotal—Fictitious
12 **CHORAL SYMPHONY**, ch c Singspiel (IRE)—Celtic Cross
13 **TRIANON**, ch f Nayef (USA)—Trying For Gold (USA)

TWO-YEAR-OLDS

14 **BROAD CAIRN**, b c 28/1 Green Desert (USA)—Celtic Cross (Selkirk (USA))
15 **GOING FOR GOLD**, b f 1/2 Barathea (IRE)—Flash of Gold (Darshaan)
16 **MORNING CALM**, b f 11/2 Montjeu (IRE)—Tempting Prospect (Shirley Heights)
17 **SALLY FORTH**, b f 29/4 Dubai Destination (USA)—Daralbayda (IRE) (Doyoun)

Trained by **R. Hannon**, Marlborough

THREE-YEAR-OLDS

18 **FIRESTREAK**, b g Green Desert (USA)—Flash of Gold
19 **ISLE OF CAPRI**, b f Cape Cross (IRE)—Zenith
20 **VICTORIA REEL**, ch f Danehill Dancer (IRE)—New Assembly (IRE)

TWO-YEAR-OLDS

21 **EVALUATION**, gr f 4/5 El Prado (IRE)—Day of Reckoning (Daylami (IRE))
22 **FREE AGENT**, b c 13/5 Dr Fong (USA)—Film Script (Unfuwain (USA))
23 **FULL TOSS**, b c 8/2 Nayef (USA)—Spinning Top (Alzao (USA))
24 **INSTALMENT**, b c 18/3 Cape Cross (IRE)—New Assembly (IRE) (Machiavellian (USA))

PROPERTY OF HER MAJESTY

The Queen

Trained by **N. J. Henderson**, Lambourn

25 **BARBERS SHOP**, 6, b g Saddlers' Hall (IRE)—Close Harmony
26 **FIRST LOVE**, 12, br g Bustino—First Romance
27 **GOLD AWARD**, 5, b g Daylami (IRE)—Trying For Gold (USA)
28 **MIDSUMMER MAGIC**, 4, b f Muhtarram (USA)—Romantic Dream
29 **MOONLIT PATH**, 5, b m Shambo—Lunabelle
30 **PIPE BANNER**, 4, b g Silver Patriarch (IRE)—Bella Macrae
31 **SEA CAPTAIN**, 8, b g Oscar (IRE)—Calabria

Trained by **A. M. Balding**, Kingsclere

32 **BANKNOTE**, 6, b c Zafonic (USA)—Brand

THREE-YEAR-OLD

33 **PROVISION**, ch f Cadeaux Genereux—Brand

TWO-YEAR-OLD

34 **BRANDY BUTTER**, ch c 9/2 Domedriver (IRE)—Brand (Shareef Dancer (USA))

Trained by **Miss H. C. Knight**, Wantage

35 **BRIGHT SPIRIT**, 7, b g Petoski—Lunabelle
36 **DESERT STAR**, 8, b g Green Desert—Phantom Gold

---

1 **MR JONATHAN AKEHURST, Epsom**
Postal: **Tattenham Corner Stables, Tattenham Corner Road, Epsom Downs, Surrey, KT18 5PP**
Contacts: **PHONE** (01737) 360066 **FAX** (01737) 360055
WEBSITE www.jakehurst.co.uk

1 **AUDIENCE**, 8, b g Zilzal (USA)—Only Yours **Canisbay Bloodstock**
2 **AZYGOUS**, 5, ch g Foxhound (USA)—Flag **The Grass Is Greener Partnership V**
3 **BABA GHANOUSH**, 6, ch m Zaha (CAN)—Vrennan **Canisbay Bloodstock**
4 **BLU MANRUNA**, 5, ch g Zaha (CAN)—Vrennan **Canisbay Bloodstock**
5 **CALABAZA**, 6, ch g Zaha (CAN)—Mo Stopher **Canisbay Bloodstock**
6 **CAPRICHO (IRE)**, 11, gr g Lake Coniston (IRE)—Star Spectacle **Canisbay Bloodstock**
7 **CAPTAIN MARRYAT**, 7, ch g Inchinor—Finlaggan **Canisbay Bloodstock**
8 **COMPETITOR**, 7, b h Danzero (AUS)—Ceanothus (IRE) **John Akehurst**
9 **DIANE'S CHOICE**, 5, ch m Komaite (USA)—Ramajana (USA) **The Grass Is Greener Partnership II**
10 **DR SYNN**, 7, br g Danzero (AUS)—Our Shirley **Canisbay Bloodstock**
11 **EAU SAUVAGE**, 4, ch f Lake Coniston (IRE)—Mo Stopher **Canisbay Bloodstock**
12 **GLENCALVIE (IRE)**, 7, ch g Grand Lodge (USA)—Top of The Form (IRE) **Tattenham Corner Racing**
13 **GRIZEDALE (IRE)**, 9, ch g Lake Coniston (IRE)—Zabeta **Canisbay Bloodstock**
14 **L'HIRONDELLE (IRE)**, 4, b c Anabaa (USA)—Auratum (USA) **Canisbay Bloodstock**
15 **MIXING**, 6, gr g Linamix (FR)—Tuning **Canisbay Bloodstock**
16 **PRIME NUMBER (IRE)**, 6, gr g King's Best (USA)—Majinskaya (FR) **A. D. Spence**
17 **PRINCE OF THEBES (IRE)**, 7, b g Desert Prince (IRE)—Persian Walk (FR) **Canisbay Bloodstock**
18 **SALIENT**, 4, b c Fasliyev (USA)—Savannah Belle **Canisbay Bloodstock**
19 **SPIRIT'S AWAKENING**, 9, b g Danzig Connection (USA)—Mo Stopher **Canisbay Bloodstock**
20 **STARK CONTRAST (USA)**, 4, ch g Gulch (USA)—A Stark Is Born (USA) **A. D. Spence**
21 **SUPER FRANK (IRE)**, 5, b g Cape Cross (IRE)—Lady Joshua (IRE) **A. D. Spence**
22 **TORQUEMADA (IRE)**, 7, ch g Desert Sun—Gaelic's Fantasy (IRE) **Canisbay Bloodstock**
23 **TRAFALGAR SQUARE**, 6, b g King's Best (USA)—Pat Or Else **Canisbay Bloodstock**

MR JONATHAN AKEHURST—continued

THREE-YEAR-OLDS

24 **BAD MOON RISING,** ch c Piccolo—Janette Parkes **Advance Digital Print Limited**
25 **MISS MUJANNA,** b f Mujahid (USA)—Robanna **Green Pastures Partnership**
26 **SWEET REFRAIN,** ch f Tobougg (IRE)—Steppin Out **Canisbay Bloodstock**
27 **THUNDERONTHEMOUNT,** ch c Zaha (CAN)—Vrennan **Canisbay Bloodstock**
28 **TIEPIE,** ch c Tomba—Contrary Mary **Green Pastures Farm**

TWO-YEAR-OLDS

29 Ch f 1/2 Dr Fong (USA)—Chiasso (USA) (Woodman (USA)) **John Akehurst**
30 B c 3/4 Zilzal (USA)—Robanna (Robellino (USA)) (761) **John Akehurst**
31 Gr f 15/4 Hawk Wing (USA)—To The Skies (USA) (Sky Classic (CAN)) (6000) **John Akehurst**

Other Owners: Mr P. A. Allard, N. Boyce, Mr P. J. Caswell, Mr Gus Gordon, G. B. Griffin, Mr R. G. Harrington, Mr R. F. Kilby, Mr Anthony Pitt, Mrs Jane Pitt, Mr P. Rose, Mr Roger Stickells, Miss Maureen Stopher, Mr D. G. Worley.

2
MR N. W. ALEXANDER, Leslie
Postal: **Kinneston, Leslie, Glenrothes, Fife, KY6 3JJ**
Contacts: **PHONE (01592) 840774 MOBILE (07831) 488210**
E-MAIL kinneston@aol.com

1 **AMULREE,** 5, b m Dancing High—Harrietfield **The Ladies Who**
2 **ART INVESTOR,** 5, b g Sinndar (IRE)—Maid For Romance **N. W. Alexander**
3 **CONTENDO,** 7, ch g Classic Cliche (IRE)—Madam Ross **Alexander Family**
4 B, g Dushyantor (USA)—Dalkey Pride **The Peglegs**
5 **FEARLESS FOOTSTEPS,** 4, b f Dancing High—Harriettield **Alexander Family**
6 **FOODBROKER FOUNDER,** 8, ch g Groom Dancer (USA)—Nemea (USA) **Alexander Family**
7 5, B m Milieu—Miss Colette **Kinneston Racing**
8 **NATIVE COLL,** 8, ch g Primitive Rising (USA)—Harrietfield **Alexander Family**
9 **SEEKING POWER (IRE),** 7, b g Supreme Leader—Seeking Gold (IRE) **Alexander Family**
10 **SKIPPING CHAPEL,** 7, ch g Minster Son—Harrietfield **Alexander Family**
11 **WHISPERING MOOR,** 9, br g Terimon—Larksmore **Mrs L. C. A. Stanistreet**
12 **WISE MAN (IRE),** 13, ch g Mister Lord (USA)—Ballinlonig Star **Alexander Family**

Other Owners: Mrs S. R. Alexander, J. F. Alexander, Miss E. M. Barlow, N. D. A. Stanistreet.

Assistant Trainer: Francesca MacManaway

Amateur: Miss Lucy Alexander.

3
MR J. S. ALLEN, Alcester
Postal: **Alne Park, Park Lane, Great Alne, Alcester, Warwickshire, B49 6HS**
Contacts: **STABLES (01789) 488469 OFFICE (01789) 299492**
FAX (01789) 415330 MOBILE (07836) 725931

1 **BOUNCING BOB,** 7, ch g Florida Son—Dancing Dove (IRE) **J. S. Allen**
2 5, B m Cyborg (FR)—Cle de Lune (FR) **J. S. Allen**
3 5, Gr m Silver Patriarch (IRE)—Consuelo **J. S. Allen**
4 **GO GUNNER (IRE),** 6, b g Needle Gun (IRE)—Highland Spirit **J. S. Allen**
5 **LA LUNE BLEU (FR),** 6, gr m Cyborg (FR)—Cle de Lune (FR) **J. S. Allen**
6 5, Ch m Shahrastani (USA)—Linguistic Dancer **J. S. Allen**
7 5, B g Shahrastani (USA)—Nordic Crown (IRE) **J. S. Allen**
8 5, B g Roi de Rome (USA)—Sainte Etoile (FR) **J. S. Allen**
9 **SAND IRON (IRE),** 6, b m Desert Style (IRE)—Mettlesome **J. S. Allen**
10 **SARGENTOS (GER),** 6, gr g Linamix (FR)—Subia (GER) **J. S. Allen**
11 5, B g Silver Patriarch (IRE)—Severn Gale **J. S. Allen**
12 **SKIPPING SUZY,** 7, ch m Double Trigger (IRE)—Singing Hills **J. S. Allen**

Assistant Trainer: Susan Watt

Jockey (NH): C. Poste, T. J. Phelan. **Amateur:** Miss Clare Dyson, Miss Hannah Watson.

4 MR M. A. ALLEN, Findon
Postal: **Windrush Stables, Findon, Worthing, West Sussex, BN14 0RQ**
Contacts: **PHONE (01903) 877061 FAX (01903) 872051 MOBILE (07939) 262353**
E-MAIL carol_lowman@yahoo.com

1 DONT CALL ME DEREK, 7, b g Sri Pekan (USA)—Cultural Role **Miss S. A. Phillips**
2 HIGH 'N DRY (IRE), 4, ch f Halling (USA)—Sisal (IRE) **Miss S. A. Phillips**
3 I'M LOVIN IT (IRE), 8, b g Supreme Leader—Sparky Mary (IRE) **Mrs C. Lowman**
4 MONASHEE BRAVE (IRE), 5, b g Monashee Mountain (USA)—Miss Butterfield **Miss S. A. Phillips**
5 PIPPINS CORNER, 6, b m Piccolo—Newlands Corner **C. N. H. Foster**
6 PROSPECT PLACE, 4, b g Compton Place—Encore My Love **Miss S. A. Phillips**
7 ROYALTIES, 6, b m Mujahid (USA)—Rock Face **G. C. Lowman N. Hoad**
8 TEQUILA SHEILA (IRE), 6, ch m Raise A Grand (IRE)—Hever Rosina **Miss S. A. Phillips**
9 THOMAS HARDY, 5, ch g Fleetwood (IRE)—Miss Hardy **The Hardy Partners**

Other Owners: Miss L. M. Footner, Mr N. Hoad, T. L. Parry.

Jockey (flat): Paul Doe. **Jockey (NH):** Sean Curran. **Conditional:** Lee Edwards.

5 MR R. H. & MRS S. ALNER, Blandford
Postal: **Locketts Farm, Droop, Blandford, Dorset, DT11 0EZ**
Contacts: **PHONE (01258) 817271 MOBILE (07767) 436375**
E-MAIL robertalner@btopenworld.com

1 ANNA PANNA, 7, b m Piccolo—Miss Laetitia (IRE) **Chasing Gold**
2 ANNIE FLEETWOOD, 10, ch m Anshan—Gold Luck (USA) **Mrs S. F. Maude**
3 ANSOME, 5, b h Sovereign Water (FR)—Mabel's Memory (IRE) **A. J. M. Trowbridge**
4 BLACK DE BESSY (FR), 10, b g Perrault—Emerald City **Mrs Derek Fletcher**
5 BOWLEAZE (IRE), 9, br g Right Win (IRE)—Mrs Cullen **M. Short**
6 CHARLIES FUTURE, 10, b g Democratic (USA)—Fausterlerie **M. L. Lewis-Jones**
7 CLOUD NINE (IRE), 5, b g Saddlers' Hall (IRE)—Park Breeze (IRE) **Old Moss Farm**
8 COOLERS QUEST, 9, b m Saddlers' Hall (IRE)—Lucidity **K. B. Snook**
9 EVEN MORE (IRE), 13, b g Husyan (USA)—Milan Moss **G. F. Keirle**
10 FALCONS GIFT (IRE), 6, b m Zaffaran (USA)—Falcon Crest **Mr J. Halliday**
11 FARMER'S LAD (IRE), 6, b g Leading Counsel (USA)—Lucky Dante (IRE) **P. Partridge**
12 FREE GIFT, 10, b g Presenting—Gladtogetit **Tom Chadney Val Chadney Doug Guyer**
13 HARRY'S DREAM, 11, b g Alflora (IRE)—Cheryls Pet (IRE) **P. Partridge**
14 IBBERTON, 8, b g Sovereign Water (FR)—Betty Hayes **Lady Talbot of Malahide & Mr P. Lambert**
15 JEANQUIRI (FR), 4, b f Mansonnien (FR)—J'y Reste (FR) **G. L. Porter**
16 LADY VOLDEMORT, 5, b m Josr Algarhoud (IRE)—Miss Laetitia (IRE) **Chasing Gold Limited**
17 LAUDAMUS, 10, ch g Anshan—Faint Praise **Lady Cobham**
18 LIBERTY BEN (IRE), 8, b g Beneficial—Silver Fairy (IRE) **P. M. De Wilde**
19 LINDOP, 8, ch g Nashwan (USA)—Footlight Fantasy (USA) **R. H. Alner**
20 MACMAR (FR), 8, b g Ragmar (FR)—Ex des Sacart (FR) **E. W. Carnell**
21 MAGOT DE GRUGY (FR), 8, b g Tzar Rodney (FR)—Hirlish (FR) **P. M. De Wilde**
22 MASTER MEDIC (IRE), 7, b g Dr Massini (IRE)—Name A Reason (IRE) **Pell-Mell Partners**
23 MIBLEU (FR), 8, b g Agent Bleu (FR)—Eauseille (FR) **Chasing Gold Limited**
24 MIGHT AS WELL, 5, b g Terimon—Might Be **Dr & Mrs John Millar**
25 MIKO DE BEAUCHENE (FR), 8, b g Nashamaa—Chipie d'angron (FR) **A. O. Wiles**
26 MILLBROOK MEADOW, 6, b g Meadowbrook—Sulamar **Miss M. J. Aplin**
27 MISS CEKA (IRE), 6, gr m Rudimentary (USA)—Party Woman (IRE) **D. Brennan**
28 MISS MITCH (IRE), 7, b br m King's Theatre (IRE)—Party Woman (IRE) **Clipper Group Holdings Ltd**
29 MISTER SHER (IRE), 9, b g Shernazar—Running River (IRE) **Mrs Sally White**
30 MORT DE RIRE (FR), 8, gr g Luchiroverte (IRE)—Fia Rosa (FR) **A. O. Wiles**
31 NEMETAN (FR), 7, ch g Port Lyautey (FR)—Annabelle Treveene (FR) **P. M. De Wilde**
32 NEW TEAM (FR), 7, ch g Green Tune (USA)—Fortuna Jet (FR) **G. L. Porter**
33 NICTO DE BEAUCHENE (FR), 7, b g Nashamaa—Chipie d'angron (FR) **P. M. De Wilde**
34 NILS ANDERSON (FR), 7, b br g Franc Bleu Argent (USA)—Fee du Lac (FR) **P. M. De Wilde**
35 ONYONGARD (IRE), 6, b g Gulland—Gusserane Princess **Ray & Sue Dodd Partnership**
36 PIMBURY (IRE), 6, b g Pistolet Bleu (FR)—Duchess of Kinsale (IRE) **Old Moss Farm**
37 PISTOL DESBOIS (FR), 5, gr g Smadoun (FR)—Tarpeia (FR) **G. L. Porter**
38 PORTLAND BILL (IRE), 8, ch g Zaffaran (USA)—Donegal Moss **A. J. M. Trowbridge**
39 PRESENT M'LORD (IRE), 8, b g Presenting—The Red Side (IRE) **Chasing Gold Limited**
40 ROCK STAR APPEAL, 7, b g Rock City—Turkish Star **H. Wellstead**
41 SILVER INNGOT (IRE), 8, gr g Gothland (FR)—
Hotel Saltees (IRE) **J.Browne,Mrs C.Robertson,Mrs E.Woodhouse**

MR R. H. & MRS S. ALNER—continued

42 **SUNSET BOULEVARD (IRE)**, 5, b g Montjeu (IRE)—Lucy In The Sky (IRE) **Ray & Sue Dodd Partnership**
43 **THE LISTENER (IRE)**, 9, gr g Roselier (FR)—Park Breeze (IRE) **Old Moss Farm**
44 **TOMS GONE GREY (IRE)**, 9, gr g Gothland (FR)—Cpv Lady **Chasing Gold Limited**
45 **VODKA BROOK (IRE)**, 5, b g Alderbrook—Another Vodka (IRE) **H. Wellstead**
46 **WAZALINO**, 6, b g Wace (USA)—Voolino **Mrs V. E. Nock-Sampson**
47 **WORBARROW BAY (IRE)**, 6, b m Zaffaran (USA)—Cribaline (FR) **M. Short**

Other Owners: Mr J. C. Browne, Mr T. H. Chadney, Mrs V. J. Chadney, Mr J. Chromiak, Mr Ray Dodd, Mrs Sue Dodd, Mr T. C. Frost, Mrs E. M. Frost, Mr Richard Gilder, Mr Douglas Guyer, Mrs B. P. Hall, Mr R. W. Humphreys, Mrs Susan Humphreys, Mr R. M. Kellow, Mr Peter Lambert, Mrs C. A. Lewis-Jones, Dr John Millar, Mrs John Millar, Mrs J. M. Miller, Mr Paul Murphy, Mrs C. H. Robertson, Lady Talbot of Malahide, Mr Frank Watson, Mrs J. R. Webber, Mrs G. E. S. Woodhouse.

Assistant Trainer: Mrs S Alner, Nick Mitchell & Mrs S A Old

Jockey (NH): D. Jacob, A. Thornton, R. Walford. **Amateur:** Mr I. Chanin, Mr J. Derham.

---

6 MR E. J. ALSTON, Preston
Postal: **Edges Farm Stables, Chapel Lane, Longton, Preston, Lancashire, PR4 5NA**
Contacts: **PHONE (01772) 612120 FAX (01772) 619600 MOBILE (07879) 641460**
E-MAIL eric1943@supanet.com

1 **DIPLOMATIC DAN (IRE)**, 5, b g Imperial Ballet (IRE)—Yaqatha (IRE) **D. Mossop**
2 **ELLA WOODCOCK (IRE)**, 4, b g Daggers Drawn (USA)—Hollow Haze (USA) **D. Mossop**
3 **INVINCIBLE LAD (IRE)**, 4, b g Invincible Spirit (IRE)—Lady Ellen **C. F. Harrington**
4 **JOHNSTON'S GLORY (IRE)**, 4, b f Desert Sun—Clos de Tart (IRE) **Mollington Golf Club Boys**
5 **MAISON DIEU**, 5, b g King Charlemagne (USA)—Shining Desert (IRE) **Whitehills Racing Syndicate**
6 **ME NO PUPPET**, 4, b f Mtoto—Puppet Play (IRE) **Mrs P. A. McAuley**
7 **PIANOFORTE (USA)**, 6, b g Grand Slam (USA)—Far Too Loud (CAN) **Edges Farm Racing Stables Ltd**
8 **REVERENCE**, 7, ch g Mark of Esteem (IRE)—Imperial Bailiwick (IRE) **Mr & Mrs G. Middlebrook**

THREE-YEAR-OLDS

9 **DALAROSSIE**, br g Kyllachy—Damalis (IRE) **Liam & Tony Ferguson**
10 **QUIET ELEGANCE**, b f Fantastic Light (USA)—Imperial Bailiwick (IRE) **Mr & Mrs G. Middlebrook**

TWO-YEAR-OLDS

11 **BALLARINA**, b f 23/2 Compton Place—Miss Uluwatu (IRE) (Night Shift (USA)) (25740) **Mrs P. O. Morris**
12 Br f 27/3 Lend A Hand—Damalis (IRE) (Mukaddamah (USA)) (8000)
13 **DARK VELVET (IRE)**, b f 17/3 Statue of Liberty (USA)—
                                    Lovingit (IRE) (Fasliyev (USA)) (3217) **The Five Go Racing Partnership**
14 **IMPRESSIBLE**, b f 4/4 Oasis Dream—
                        Imperial Bailiwick (IRE) (Imperial Frontier (USA)) **Mr & Mrs G. Middlebrook**
15 Ch c 27/4 Daggers Drawn (USA)—Paganina (FR) (Galetto (FR)) (10295) **P. J. Davies**
16 **STAR ADDITION**, ch c 18/1 Medicean—Star Cast (IRE) (In The Wings) (18000) **John & Maria Thompson**
17 B f 24/2 Mark of Esteem (IRE)—Turf Moor (IRE) (Mac's Imp) **Valley Paddocks Racing Limited**

Other Owners: P. G. Buist, M. L. Ferguson, Mr C. A. Ferguson, M. S. Kelly, J. W. D. R. Lightfoot, Mr T. D. Lloyd, G. Middlebrook, Mrs L. A. Middlebrook, Dr J. G. Randall, Mrs J. E. Rimmer, Mrs S. Rimmer, G. Sheridan, M. Sheridan, J. Thompson, Mrs M. T. Thompson.

Assistant Trainer: Mrs Sue Alston

Jockey (flat): D. Allan, W. Supple. **Amateur:** Miss Sheree Siddall.

---

7 MR W. AMOS, Hawick
Postal: **Broadhaugh Farm, Newmill on Teviot, Hawick, Roxburghshire, TD9 0JX**
Contacts: **PHONE (01450) 850323 MOBILE (07810) 738149**

1 **ALSO JO**, 5, gr g Cloudings (IRE)—Forgotten Empress **Mrs S. Gray, Mr I. Gray**
2 **BOB'S DREAM (IRE)**, 6, b g Bob's Return (IRE)—Back In Kansas (IRE) **R. J. Kyle**
3 **BORDER MIST (IRE)**, 5, br gr m Mull of Kintyre (USA)—Caroline Lady (JPN) **Mrs E. H. Aitchison**
4 **CHIRAPATRE**, 6, b m Alflora (IRE)—Tenella's Last **S. Bonney**
5 **COOL DESSA BLUES**, 9, br m Cool Jazz—Our Dessa **Mrs D. S. Alder, Stewart Bonney**
6 **FISHING INSTRUCTOR**, 5, gr g Silver Patriarch (IRE)—Super Malt (IRE) **G. W. Murray**

MR W. AMOS—continued

7 **GALLANT GIRL**, 7, ch m Topanoora—High 'b' **Mrs C. Moore**
8 **GUNSON HIGHT**, 11, b g Be My Chief (USA)—Glas Y Dorlan **J. L. Gledson**
9 **HAIR OF THE DOG**, 4, b g Foxhound (USA)—Bebe de Cham **J. L. Gledson**
10 **LIE FORRIT (IRE)**, 4, b g Subtle Power (IRE)—Ben Roseler (IRE) **J. W. McNeill**
11 **MAKE A MARK (IRE)**, 8, b g Victory Note (USA)—Election Special **Fourward Racing**
12 **NEW SOURCE (IRE)**, 6, ch m Old Vic—Saucy Nun (IRE) **Mr A. Dawson & Mrs K. Campbell**
13 **OLEOLAT (FR)**, 6, ch g Art Bleu—Contessina (FR) **J. L. Gledson**
14 6, B m El Conquistador—Orange Spice **W. Amos**
15 **OVER THE BORDER**, 5, gr g Overbury (IRE)—Copper Castle **W. M. Aitchison**
16 **TEVIOT LASS**, 6, b m Minster Son—Here Comes Tibby **W. Amos**
17 **TYHOLLAND (IRE)**, 9, br g Up And At 'em—Spanish Gypsy (IRE) **J. E. Curry**
18 **WENSLEY BLUE (IRE)**, 9, b g Blues Traveller (IRE)—Almasa **Northumberland Jumpers**

Other Owners: Mr W. M. Aitchison, Mrs D. S. Alder, Mr Stewart Bonney, Mrs Kate Campbell, Mr A. Dawson, Mr Ian J. Gray, Mrs Sheila Gray, Mrs G. Mawston, Miss J. M. Murray, Mr R. Smoult.

---

8   MR M. APPLEBY, Compton Verney
Postal: **Home Farm, Compton Verney, Warwick**
Contacts: **HOME (01926) 691122 MOBILE (07884) 366421**
E-MAIL appleby477@aol.com

1 **BLACKTHORN**, 9, ch g Deploy—Balliasta (USA) **M. T. Hughes**
2 **BLANDFORD FLYER**, 5, b g Soviet Star (USA)—Vento Del Oreno (FR) **Mr T. J. McEnery**
3 **BRAVE BUGSY (IRE)**, 5, b g Mujadil (USA)—Advancing (IRE) **West Mercia Fork Trucks Ltd**
4 **FASHION ACCESSORY**, 4, b f Muthahb (IRE)—Queen of Fashion (IRE) **R. Smith**
5 **ROYMAR**, 4, b f Muthahb (IRE)—Tapper (IRE) **R. Smith**
6 **TANNING**, 6, b m Atraf—Gerundive (USA) **D. K. Maughan**
7 **TRACKATTACK**, 6, ch g Atraf—Verbena (IRE) **M. Appleby**
8 **WESTERN ROOTS**, 7, ch g Dr Fong (USA)—Chrysalis **Sarnial Racing**
9 **YOU ME AND THEBOYS**, 6, b g Overbury (IRE)—La Bella Villa **K. D. Pugh**
10 **ZACH'S HARMONEY (USA)**, 4, ch c Diesis—Cool Ashlee (USA) **Sarnian Racing**

THREE-YEAR-OLDS

11 **MUSHARAHB**, b c Muthahb (IRE)—Naz (IRE) **R. Smith**
12 Ch f Ballet Master (USA)—Over The Moon **Mr E. P. Spain**

Other Owners: Mr C. Langley, Mr A. W. Le Page.

Assistant Trainer: Mr Lee Moulson

Jockey (flat): G. Baker, N. Chalmers. **Jockey (NH):** R. Greene. **Amateur:** Mr Jamie Goss, Mr Rob Kirk, Miss Hannah Watson.

---

9   MR D. W. P. ARBUTHNOT, Compton
Postal: **Uplands Stables, Downs Road, Compton, Newbury, Berkshire, RG20 6RE**
Contacts: **PHONE (01635) 579090 FAX (01635) 578000 MOBILE (07836) 276464**
E-MAIL david@uplandsstables.com WEBSITE www.uplandsstables.com

1 **ARABIAN CORAL (IRE)**, 4, b f Intikhab (USA)—Tropical Dance (USA) **Bonusprint Ltd**
2 **BANOO (IRE)**, 5, b m Hernando (FR)—Toi Toi (IRE) **N. D. Cronin**
3 **BOB MOUNTAIN (IRE)**, 7, b br g Bob Back (USA)—Honey Mountain **Lucky Seven R Us**
4 **BOB RUN (IRE)**, 4, ch g Bob Back (USA)—Rith Ar Aghaidh (IRE) **Mr & Mrs George Ward**
5 **CALL OSCAR**, 9, b g Oscar (IRE)—Athy Princess (IRE)
6 **CALMING WATERS**, 5, ch g Dr Fong (USA)—Faraway Waters **Mr R. E. Crutchley**
7 **CODA AGENCY**, 5, b g Agnes World (USA)—The Frog Lady (IRE) **Banfield, Thompson & Crown**
8 **CRASHTOWN HALL (IRE)**, 7, b h Saddlers' Hall (IRE)—Crashtown Lucy **George Ward**
9 **DESERT SEA (IRE)**, 5, b g Desert Sun—Sea of Time (USA) **Bonusprint Ltd**
10 **DOMINICAN MONK (IRE)**, 9, b g Lord Americo—Ballybeg Katie (IRE) **George Ward**
11 **DON'T TELL SUE**, 5, ch g Bold Edge—Opopmil (IRE) **Lady Whent**
12 **FORAGER**, 9, ch g Faustus (USA)—Jolimo **Avondale Construction Ltd**
13 **GIMME SOME LOVIN (IRE)**, 4, b f Desert Style (IRE)—Licence To Thrill **C. N. Wright**
14 **GLACIAL SUNSET (IRE)**, 13, ch g Glacial Storm (USA)—Twinkle Sunset **George Ward**
15 **JOHNNY BISSETT (IRE)**, 7, br g Oscar (IRE)—Millers Run **George Ward**

MR D. W. P. ARBUTHNOT—continued

16 **KING AR AGHAIDH (IRE)**, 7, b g King's Theatre (IRE)—Shuil Ar Aghaidh **George Ward**
17 **LAVENDER TRACK (IRE)**, 6, ch m Pistolet Bleu (IRE)—Tracker **George Ward**
18 **LAWDY MISS CLAWDY**, 4, ch f Bold Edge—Long Tall Sally (IRE) **N. D. Cronin**
19 **MON PETITE AMOUR**, 5, b m Efisio—Food of Love **N. D. Cronin**
20 **OSCAR PARK (IRE)**, 9, b g Oscar (IRE)—Parkavoureen **George Ward**
21 **PRESENT GLORY (IRE)**, 9, br g Presenting—Prudent Rose (IRE) **George Ward**
22 **RITH BOB (IRE)**, 5, b m Bob Back (USA)—Rith Ar Aghaidh (IRE) **George Ward**
23 **ROMANTIC BRIDGE (IRE)**, 6, b m Bob Back (USA)—Henry G's (IRE)
24 4, B g Mind Games—Sequin Slippers (IRE) **Mr F. P. Fry**
25 **SHADED EDGE**, 4, b g Bold Edge—Twilight Mistress **Lady Whent & Friends**
26 **SOPHIA GARDENS**, 4, ch f Barathea (IRE)—Lovely Lyca **D. C. Broomfield**
27 **SOUND ACCORD (IRE)**, 7, br g Accordion—Shuil Na Lee (IRE) **George Ward**
28 **STAR AR AGHAIDH (IRE)**, 4, b f Soviet Star (USA)—Shuil Ar Aghaidh **Mr & Mrs George Ward**
29 **THATS CONFIDENTIAL (IRE)**, 6, b g Saddlers' Hall (IRE)—
                                     New Legislation (IRE) **The Unconventionals Racing Syndicate**
30 **THEATRE DANCE (IRE)**, 7, b g King's Theatre (IRE)—Dance Alone (USA)
31 **TOP FLOWER (IRE)**, 4, b f Alflora (IRE)—Top Ar Aghaidh (IRE) **Mr & Mrs George Ward**
32 **TROPICAL STRAIT (IRE)**, 5, b g Intikhab (USA)—Tropical Dance (USA) **Mr Francis Ward & Mr Anthony Ward**
33 **VALLEY RIDE (IRE)**, 8, b br g Glacial Storm (USA)—Royal Lucy (IRE) **George Ward**

THREE-YEAR-OLDS

34 **BLUEBELL RIDGE (IRE)**, b f Distant Music (USA)—Miss Indigo **The Bluebell Ridge Partnership**
35 **ONE OI**, b c Bertolini (USA)—Bogus Penny (IRE) **Saxon Gate Partnership**
36 **SILK HALL (UAE)**, b c Halling (USA)—Velour Bonusprint Ltd
37 **SOVIET CAT (IRE)**, b g Soviet Star (USA)—Forest Kitten (IRE) **George Ward**
38 **TROPICAL TRADITION (IRE)**, ch g Traditionally (USA)—Tropical Coral (IRE) **George Ward**

TWO-YEAR-OLDS

39 Br c 2/3 Captain Rio—Alley Kitten (IRE) (Alzao (USA)) (8364)
40 Ch f 15/3 Bold Edge—Floppie Disk (Magic Ring (IRE)) (9000)
41 B c 13/3 Traditionally (USA)—Forest Kitten (IRE) (Marju (IRE)) **George Ward**
42 Ch c 4/3 Compton Place—Miriam (Forzando) **George Ward**
43 **PLACE THE DUCHESS**, b f 12/2 Compton Place—Barrantes (Distant Relative) (25000) **Mr & Mrs George Ward**
44 Ch c 5/3 Needwood Blade—Roonah Quay (IRE) (Soviet Lad (USA)) (20591) **Mr Paul Claydon**
45 **RUMBLE OF THUNDER (IRE)**, b c 11/3 Fath (USA)—
                           Honey Storm (IRE) (Mujadil (USA)) (15000) **Mr Francis Ward & Mr Anthony Ward**
46 Ch c 25/1 Compton Place—Simply Sooty (Absalom) (16000)
47 B c 5/4 Bachelor Duke (USA)—Tropical Coral (IRE) (Pennekamp (USA)) **George Ward**
48 Ch c 5/3 Bachelor Duke (USA)—Tropical Dance (USA) (Thorn Dance (USA)) **George Ward**

Other Owners: Mr Philip Banfield, Mr Derrick C. Broomfield, Mrs Zara Campbell-Harris, Mr Noel Cronin, Mr Stephen Crown, A. F. S. Haynes, Wing Comdr A. Howie, Mr B. F. Macken, Mr M. A. March, Mr G. March, Mr A. Parker, Mr W. L. Smith, Mr George S. Thompson, Mrs George Ward, Mr Francis Ward, Mr Anthony Ward, Lady Whent, Mr A. Whiteley, Mr Godfrey Wilson, Mrs Caroline Wilson, Mr N. A. Wyman.

Jockey (flat): Fergus Sweeney. **Jockey (NH):** Seamus Durack. **Apprentice:** Antonio Alonso Gallardo.

10	**MR R. J. ARMSON, Melbourne**

Postal: **Scotlands Farm, Burney Lane, Staunton-Harold, Melbourne, Derbyshire, DE73 8BH**
Contacts: **OFFICE** (01332) 865293 **HOME** (01332) 865383 **MOBILE** (07811) 827678

1 **BURN BROOK**, 8, br m Alderbrook—One of Those Days **R. J. Armson**
2 **RED ALF**, 9, ch g Alflora (IRE)—Red Dust **R. J. Armson**

Assistant Trainer: Mrs S Armson

Amateur: Mr R. J. Armson.

11 MR P. G. ATKINSON, Northallerton
Postal: Yafforth Hill Farm, Yafforth, Northallerton, North Yorkshire, DL7 0LT
Contacts: PHONE (01609) 772598 MOBILE (07751) 131215

1 FLAG HILL, 5, b g Minster Son—Dreamago **D. G. Atkinson**
2 MINI MINSTER, 6, b m Minster Son—Dreamago **D. G. Atkinson**

Jockey (NH): P. Kinsella.

12 MR M. J. ATTWATER, Epsom
Postal: 62 Woodstone Avenue, Epsom, Surrey, KT17 2JP
Contacts: MOBILE (07725) 423633
E-MAIL attwaterracing@hotmail.co.uk

1 ABOUNDING, 4, b f Generous (IRE)—Ecstasy **The Attwater Partnership**
2 JOY AND PAIN, 7, b g Pursuit of Love—Ice Chocolate (USA) **Phones Direct Partnership**
3 KISSI KISSI, 5, b m Paris House—Miss Whittingham (IRE) **Mrs M. Tanner**
4 MARMOOQ, 5, ch g Cadeaux Genereux—Portelet **The Attwater Partnership**
5 ONLY IF I LAUGH, 7, ch g Piccolo—Agony Aunt **Phones Direct Partnership**
6 TUNING FORK, 8, b g Alzao (USA)—Tuning **Canisbay Bloodstock**

Other Owners: Mr B. M. Attwater, Mrs C. J. Attwater, Mr R. A. Hunt, R. F. Kilby, Mr D. Robinson, Miss M. E. Stopher.

Assistant Trainer: K. F. Latchford

13 MR JEAN-RENE AUVRAY, Upper Lambourn
Postal: Frenchman's Lodge Stables, Upper Lambourn, Hungerford, Berkshire, RG17 8QT
Contacts: PHONE (01488) 73740 FAX (01488) 72742 MOBILE (07798) 645796
E-MAIL jr.auvray@lambournracing.com WEBSITE www.lambournracing.com

1 BRISTOL DELAURIERE (FR), 4, b g Epistolaire (IRE)—Shenedova (FR)
2 BULKAWA BELLEVUE (FR), 4, b g Bulington (FR)—Strakawa (FR) **Aldridge, Collins and Keir**
3 CASEWICK MIST, 8, ch m Primitive Rising (USA)—Buckmist Blue (IRE) **J. M. Cleeve**
4 COOL ALICE, 6, ch m Cool Jazz—Dominion's Dream **Lady Eliza Mays-Smith**
5 COUNTY KERRY (UAE), 4, b f Jade Robbery (USA)—Limerick Belle (IRE) **The Sw1ft Buck Partnership**
6 DOUBLE SPECTRE (IRE), 6, b g Spectrum (IRE)—Phantom Ring **The Dragon Partnership**
7 FRANKLY FANTASTIC, 4, gr g Fantastic Light (USA)—Fracassina **The Cross Keys Racing Club**
8 IMPERIUM, 7, b g Imperial Ballet (IRE)—Partenza (USA) **The Cross Keys Racing Club**
9 IRISHKAWA BELLEVUE (FR), 10, b br g Irish Prospector (FR)—Strakawa (FR) **The Magpie Partnership**
10 IT'S RUMOURED, 8, ch g Fleetwood (IRE)—Etourdie (USA) **The Simpsons Partnership**
11 KING OF DIAMONDS, 7, b g Mtoto—Capricious Lass **Lambourn Racing**
12 KITCHEN SINK (IRE), 6, ch g Bold Fact (USA)—Voodoo Rocket **Lambourn Racing**
13 LABELLED WITH LOVE, 8, ch g Zilzal (USA)—Dream Baby **Lambourn Racing**
14 POCKETWOOD, 6, b g Fleetwood (IRE)—Pocket Venus (IRE) **Jean-Rene Auvray**
15 RAGDOLLIANNA, 4, b f Kayf Tara—Jupiters Princess **Mr D. M. & Mrs M. A. Newland**
16 REGAL ANGEL, 5, ch m Roi de Rome (USA)—Dominion's Dream **Nigel Kelly & Alison Auvray**
17 RUSSIAN ANGEL, 4, gr f Baryshnikov (AUS)—Eventuality **Nigel Kelly & Alison Auvray**
18 STROPPI POPPI, 4, b f Mtoto—Capricious Lass **Mr D. M. & Mrs M. A. Newland**
19 TASK COMPLETE, 5, ch m Bahamian Bounty—Taskone **Task Limited**

THREE-YEAR-OLDS

20 CODE VIOLATION, gr f Silver Patriarch (IRE)—Lady High Sheriff (IRE) **Dan George & Sara Collie**
21 PETER'S JOY (USA), b g Stravinsky (USA)—Jadarah (USA) **The Dragon Partnership**

TWO-YEAR-OLDS

22 DITZY DIVA, b f 18/3 Imperial Dancer—
Runs In The Family (Distant Relative) (2619) **The Sw1ft Buck Partnership**
23 Ch f 15/4 Hawkeye (IRE)—Don't Tell Trigger (IRE) (Mujadil (USA)) (2800)

MR JEAN-RENE AUVRAY—continued

24 Br f 24/3 Mull of Kintyre (USA)—Night Delight (IRE) (Night Shift (USA)) (4500)
25 **SECOND TO NUN (IRE)**, b f 16/2 Bishop of Cashel—One For Me (Tragic Role (USA)) **M. J. Lewin & D. Grieve**

Other Owners: Mrs A. L. Auvray, Mr Jean-Rene Auvray, David Cannings, Mr & Mrs Drury, Mr R. C. C. Gait, B. Kenworthy, Jackie Kleimunt, Mr & Mrs Lake, Mr D. W. Lord, Ms Joan Major, Mr M. McAuley, David Pryor, Mr Andrew V. Roper, Mr A. Slattery, Ms L. Stoten.

Conditional: K. Tobin. **Amateur:** Miss J. Hindle.

---

14 **MR N. G. AYLIFFE, Minehead**
Postal: **Glebe Stables, Little Ham, Winsford, Minehead, Somerset, TA24 7JH**
Contacts: **PHONE (01643) 851265 MOBILE (07975) 657839**

1 **BLUES STORY (FR)**, 10, b g Pistolet Bleu (IRE)—Herbe Sucree (FR) **R. Allatt**
2 **BUBBS**, 6, b m Robellino (USA)—Llancillo Lady (IRE) **Mrs M. A. Barrett**
3 **FAIRLY HIGH (IRE)**, 8, b m Sri Pekan (USA)—Ecco Mi (IRE) **Mrs M. A. Barrett**
4 **LISTEN SON (IRE)**, 6, b g Desert Sun—Hear Me **M. J. Hayes & W. G. Winzer**
5 **NENETTE DU BOIS (FR)**, 7, b m Lost World (IRE)—Besborge (FR) **D. T. Hooper**
6 **OXYBAU (FR)**, 9, ch g Beaudelaire (USA)—Foxy (FR) **R. Allatt**
7 **TOMEROSE (IRE)**, 5, ch g Tel Quel (FR)—Ag Rith Abhaile **D. T. Hooper**
8 4, B g Winged Love (IRE)—Wind Scarlet (IRE)

Other Owners: Mr Michael J. Hayes, Mr G. Winzer.

Assistant Trainer: Mrs C. Winzer.

---

15 **MR J. W. F. AYNSLEY, Morpeth**
Postal: **Rye Hill Farm, Thropton, Morpeth, Northumberland, NE65 7NG**
Contacts: **PHONE (01669) 620271**

1 **JUPSALA (FR)**, 11, ch g Video Rock (FR)—Belle d'avril V (FR) **Heads Or Harps Syndicate**
2 **KNOW THE ROPES (IRE)**, 8, b g Muroto—Bobs My Uncle **R. L. Miller-Bakewell**
3 **MOLLY MISCHIEF**, 7, b m Endoli (USA)—Eve Pet **J. W. F. Aynsley**
4 **OLD NODDY (IRE)**, 8, ch g Duky—General Run **J. W. F. Aynsley**
5 **VAGABONDO MAN (IRE)**, 7, b br g Kadastrof (FR)—Tacmahack (IRE) **J. W. F. Aynsley**

Other Owners: Miss Victoria Burrell-Corey, Mr E. Fahy, R L Miller-Bakewell.

Assistant Trainer: J R Aynsley

---

16 **MR A. BAILEY, Newmarket**
Postal: **Cavendish Stables, Hamilton Road, Newmarket, Suffolk, CB8 7JQ**
Contacts: **PHONE (01638) 664546 MOBILE (07808) 734223**

1 **AMICUS MEUS (IRE)**, 4, b c Danehill Dancer (IRE)—Top Brex (FR) **North Cheshire Trading & Storage Ltd**
2 **ANDORRAN (GER)**, 5, b g Lando (GER)—Adora (GER) **P. Buchanan**
3 **EARLSTOWN**, 4, b c Beat All (USA)—Miss Cashtal (IRE) **P. Boyers, P. Lockie**
4 **GIFTED HEIR (IRE)**, 4, b c Princely Heir (IRE)—Inzar Lady (IRE) **P. Buchanan**
5 **HIGH ARCTIC**, 6, b g Pivotal—Ladykirk **North Cheshire Trading & Storage Ltd**
6 **IMPRIMIS TAGULA (IRE)**, 4, b g Tagula (IRE)—Strelitzia (IRE) **N.Davies,J.McMahon,S.Costello,P.Donlan**
7 **LAW MAKER**, 8, b g Case Law—Bo' Babbity **North Cheshire Trading & Storage Ltd**
8 **LILY OF TAGULA (IRE)**, 4, b f Tagula (IRE)—At Amal (IRE) **Middleham Park Racing X**
9 **STARR FLYER**, 4, b g Star of Persia (IRE)—Madame Butterfly **Mrs B. May**

THREE-YEAR-OLDS

10 **BALLYCROY BOY (IRE)**, b g Captain Rio—Royal Baldini (USA) **R. T. Collins**
11 **BEAT THE BELL**, b c Beat All (USA)—Bella Beguine **M. Turner**
12 **CURLY BROWN**, b c Lujain (USA)—Shearwater **Mr G. Maher**
13 **RUNNING BUCK (USA)**, b c Running Stag (USA)—Dinghy (USA)
14 **SYRIANA**, b f Dubai Destination (USA)—Syrian Dancer (IRE) **P. T. Tellwright**

MR A. BAILEY—continued

TWO-YEAR-OLDS

15 **ASPEN DARLIN (IRE)**, b f 20/3 Indian Haven—
Manuka Magic (IRE) (Key of Luck (USA)) (6434) **Indian Haven Syndicate**
16 **BETWS Y COED (IRE)**, br f 27/1 Indian Haven—Tommys Queen (IRE) (Ali-Royal (IRE)) (2251)
17 B f 25/4 Needwood Blade—Ever So Lonely (Headin' Up)
18 B c 22/4 Captain Rio—Fahan (IRE) (Sri Pekan (USA)) (6000)
19 **FUAIGH BEAG**, gr c 10/4 Intikhab (USA)—Tennessee Valley (USA) (Quiet American (USA)) (4503)
20 **FUAIGH MOR (IRE)**, ch f 14/3 Dubai Destination (USA)—Marl (Lycius (USA)) (3860) **P. Buchanan**
21 **MA DAME MYTTON**, b f 1/4 Hunting Lion (IRE)—Lady Mytton (Lake Coniston (IRE)) **G. Mytton**
22 **MYTTONS MAID**, b f 24/2 Bertolini (USA)—The In-Laws (IRE) (Be My Guest (USA)) (15000) **G. Mytton**
23 **OMEGA WOLF (IRE)**, bc 13/3 Spartacus (IRE)—Brave Cat (IRE) (Catrail (USA)) (21878) **P. Buchanan**
24 **STRONGARM**, b g 26/2 Refuse To Bend (IRE)—Surf The Net (Cape Cross (IRE)) **P. T. Tellwright**

Other Owners: Mr A. Bailey, L. Conway, Mr J. J. S. Costello, Mr N. J. Davies, Ms J. Davies, Mr P. A. Donlan, P. J. Gleeson, N. P. Littmoden, Mr J. J. McMahon, T. S. Palin, K. R. Parker, M. Prince.

Assistant Trainer: Mrs J. P. Bailey

Apprentice: Natalie Hassall.

---

17 MRS C. BAILEY, Holdenby
Postal: **37 Eastfield Road, Brixworth, Northampton, Northamptonshire, NN6 9ED**
Contacts: **PHONE (01604) 883729 (Home) (01604) 770234 (Yard)**
FAX (01604) 770423 MOBILE (07831) 373340
E-MAIL caroline.bailey4@btinternet.com WEBSITE www.carolinebaileyracing.co.uk

1 **ARNOLD LAYNE (IRE)**, 9, gr g Roselier (FR)—Cotton Gale **Mr & Mrs R. Scott**
2 **ASTROP ROAD**, 6, b g Kayf Tara—Lady Confess
3 **DOCTOR DAVID**, 5, gr g Zilzal (USA)—Arantxa **Dr D. S. Myers**
4 **DONALD WILL DO (IRE)**, 8, ch g Zaffaran (USA)—Jersey Pearl **Mr J. Hilsdon**
5 **DOUBLY SHARP (USA)**, 5, ch g Diesis—La Soberbia (ARG) **Mrs S. Carsberg**
6 **EARLSFIELD RAIDER**, 8, ch g Double Trigger (IRE)—Harlequin Walk **Ferrybank Properties Limited**
7 **GLEN THYNE (IRE)**, 8, b g Good Thyne (USA)—Glen Laura **Mrs S. Carsberg**
8 **JALOUX D'ESTRUVAL (FR)**, 11, b g Kadalko (FR)—Pommette III (FR) **Mrs L. C. Taylor**
9 **KILLARD POINT (IRE)**, 9, b g Old Vic—Chic And Elite **Mrs S. Carsberg**
10 **SUPERCILIOUS (IRE)**, 6, b g Zafonic (USA)—Queen of Dance (IRE) **Mr & Mrs R. Scott**

Other Owners: A. S. Reid, R. Scott, Mrs P. M. Scott.

---

18 MR K. C. BAILEY, Cheltenham
Postal: **Thorndale Farm, Withington Road, Andoversford, Cheltenham, Gloucestershire, GL54 4LL**
Contacts: **PHONE (01242) 890241 FAX (01242) 890193 MOBILE (07831) 416859**
E-MAIL info@kimbaileyracing.com WEBSITE www.kimbaileyracing.com

1 **ALL ABOUT TRIGGER (FR)**, 6, ch g Double Trigger (IRE)—Gaye Fame **Martyn & Elaine Booth**
2 **BASIS POINT (FR)**, 5, b g Take Risks (FR)—Caraveine (FR) **Martyn & Elaine Booth**
3 **BAY KETCH**, 7, b g Karinga Bay—Suilven **I. F. W. Buchan**
4 **BRAYBROOKE LADY (IRE)**, 5, br m Presenting—Menedreams (IRE) **N. R. Jennings**
5 **BUFFALO BOB (IRE)**, 5, b g Bob's Return (IRE)—Back In Kansas (IRE) **The GFH Partnership**
6 **CAMPAIGN CHARLIE**, 8, b g Rakaposhi King—Inesdela **P. J. H. Wills**
7 **CONSTANTIUS**, 7, b g Halling (USA)—Premier Night **The Churston Family**
8 **DOUBLE MEAD**, 6, b m Double Trigger (IRE)—Normead Lass **Dream Makers Partnership**
9 **GALAXIA (IRE)**, 6, b g Fourstars Allstar (USA)—Cool N Calm **A. N. Solomons**
10 **GOOD OLD DAYS (IRE)**, 9, b g Bob Back (USA)—Idealist **Mr & Mrs K. R. Ellis**
11 **HEARTOFMIDLOTHIAN (IRE)**, 9, ch g Anshan—Random Wind **L. J. Haugh**
12 **KATY'S CLASSIC (IRE)**, 8, b g Classic Cliche (IRE)—Mrs Jennifer **W. J. Ives**
13 **KAY FOR KARBIA**, 5, b m Kayf Tara—Carbia's Last **K F K Partnership**
14 **LADY SAMANTHA**, 5, ch m Fraam—Lady Rebecca **C. J. Courage**
15 **LONGSHANKS**, 11, b g Broadsword (USA)—Brass Castle (IRE) **D. A. Halsall**
16 **LORD OF THE BRIDGE (IRE)**, 6, br g Mister Lord (USA)—Costly Alyse **Mr & Mrs K. R. Ellis**
17 **LORD SEAMUS**, 13, b g Arctic Lord—Erica Superba **K. C. Bailey**
18 **LUCKY LUK (FR)**, 9, ch g Lights Out (FR)—Citronelle II (FR) **Mrs E. A. Kellar**
19 **MAX BYGRAVES**, 5, ch g Midnight Legend—Smokey Diva (IRE) **J. F. Perriss**

MR K. C. BAILEY—continued

20 **MOONLIGHT MUSIC (IRE)**, 5, ch m Rossini (USA)—Jarmar Moon **Quicksilver Racing Partnership**
21 **OSHKOSH (IRE)**, 7, ch g Shernazar—Lucy Mews (IRE) **Mrs C. Bailey**
22 **PERSIAN GAYE (IRE)**, 5, b m Kahyasi—Gaye Fame **N. D. Cronin**
23 **PREDESTINE (FR)**, 8, ch g Signe Divin (USA)—Smyrna (FR) **The Predestine Partnership**
24 **PTIBABY (FR)**, 5, b g Funny Baby (FR)—Daytona II (FR) **Quicksilver Racing Partnership**
25 **RED GRANITE**, 8, gr g Rock City—Cherry Side **K. C. Bailey**
26 **REGAL APPROACH (IRE)**, 5, b g Bob Back (USA)—Crash Approach **P. J. Vogt**
27 **RUBY CROWN**, 6, b m Rakaposhi King—Suilven **I. F. W. Buchan**
28 **SARDE (FR)**, 4, b g Lost World (IRE)—Stenoree (FR) **W. J. Ives**
29 **SILVER MISSILE**, 6, ch m Silver Patriarch (IRE)—Lunar Missile **Alec J. Byrne**
30 **THE GOOD GUY (IRE)**, 5, b g Lord Americo—Lady Farnham (IRE) **The Cotswold Hunt Partnership**
31 **TWENTI TWENTI (IRE)**, 7, ch g Topanoora—Ar Ais Aris (IRE) **Mad Batters Partnership**
32 **WILLING WEASEL (IRE)**, 6, b g Rudimentary (USA)—Final Peace (IRE) **The Willing Partnership**
33 **YA I KNOW (IRE)**, 7, b g Oscar (IRE)—Strong Rosejen (IRE) **Mr J. Burgess**

Other Owners: D. C. R. Allen, Mr H. Bevan, M. Booth, Mrs E. Booth, Mrs L. S. Buttery, D. G. Churston, K. R. Ellis, Mrs E. Ellis, T. R. Gittins, D. A. Hibbert, B. Kitcherside, Mr J. A. J. Price, M. A. Sherwood, J. R. Stephens, Mr G. Sturgeon, G. D. W. Swire, Mrs C. A. T. Swire, Major R. G. Wilson.

Conditional: Nathan Smith.

---

19 **MRS L. P. BAKER, Maidstone**
Postal: **1 Big Allington Farm, Pilgrims Way, Hollingbourne, Maidstone, Kent, ME17 1RD**
Contacts: **PHONE (01622) 880655 FAX (01622) 880235 MOBILE (07890) 328745**
E-MAIL mrslesleybaker@hotmail.co.uk

1 **CARRICK CEILIDH**, 7, b m Silver Patriarch (IRE)—Black Pearl (HOL)
2 **RATHCANNON BEAUTY**, 6, b m Muhtarram (USA)—Bint Alhabib **Mrs L. P. Baker**

Assistant Trainer: Michael Baker

Jockey (NH): M. Goldstein.

---

20 **MR A. M. BALDING, Kingsclere**
Postal: **Park House Stables, Kingsclere, Newbury, Berkshire, RG20 5PY**
Contacts: **PHONE (01635) 298210 FAX (01635) 298305 MOBILE (07774) 633791**
E-MAIL admin@kingsclere.com WEBSITE www.kingsclere.com

1 **ALBINUS**, 7, gr g Selkirk (USA)—Alouette **Kingsclere Stud**
2 **ALECIA (IRE)**, 4, gr f Keltos (FR)—Ahliyat (USA) **The Grey Lady Partnership**
3 **BANKNOTE**, 6, b h Zafonic (USA)—Brand **Her Majesty The Queen**
4 **BORDER MUSIC**, 7, b g Selkirk (USA)—Mara River **Kingsclere Stud**
5 **BRIAREUS**, 8, ch g Halling (USA)—Lower The Tone (IRE) **Miss E. Lambourne**
6 **BUCCELLATI**, 4, ch c Soviet Star (USA)—Susi Wong (FR) **P. C. & Mrs J. A. McMahon**
7 **BUZBURY RINGS**, 4, b g Piccolo—Mory Kante (USA) **Michael E. Wates**
8 **CORRIOLANUS (GER)**, 8, b g Zamindar (USA)—Caesarea (GER) **K R C**
9 **DARK MISSILE**, 5, b m Night Shift (USA)—Exorcet (FR) **J. C. Smith**
10 **DINGAAN (IRE)**, 5, b g Tagula (IRE)—Boughtbyphone **Lady C. S. Cadbury**
11 **DRUMMING PARTY (USA)**, 6, b br g War Chant (USA)—Santaria (USA) **Mrs Peter Hastings**
12 **FREE TO AIR**, 5, b g Generous (USA)—Petonica (USA) **Miss C. V. Balding**
13 **HATTON FLIGHT**, 4, b g Kahyasi—Platonic **D. Brownlow**
14 **HOLBECK GHYLL (IRE)**, 6, ch g Titus Livius (FR)—Crimada (IRE) **Halsall Nicholson Partnership**
15 **IRONY (IRE)**, 9, gr g Mujadil (USA)—Cidaris (IRE) **John Nicholls Ltd/Mobley Homes**
16 **ISPHAHAN**, 5, b g Diktat—Waltzing Star (IRE) **Mr M. Rafique**
17 **KERVRIOU (FR)**, 5, ch g Pennekamp (USA)—Good Blend (FR) **Mr & Mrs Guy Luck**
18 **LOCH VERDI**, 5, b m Green Desert (USA)—Lochsong **J. C. Smith**
19 **LOCHSTAR**, 4, b c Anabaa (USA)—Lochsong **J. C. Smith**
20 **LUNDY'S LANE (IRE)**, 8, b g Darshaan—Lunda (IRE) **Dubai Thoroughbred Racing**
21 **MY LEARNED FRIEND (IRE)**, 4, b g Marju (IRE)—Stately Princess **Dr E. Harris**
22 **NIGHT ROCKET (IRE)**, 4, b f Night Shift (USA)—Exorcet (FR) **J. C. Smith**
23 **NORMAN TRADITION**, 4, ch f Traditionally (USA)—Normandy (CHI) **The Hon R. W. Hanson**
24 **OCEANA GOLD**, 4, ch g Primo Valentino (IRE)—Silken Dalliance **The C H F Partnership**
25 **OLLIE GEORGE (IRE)**, 5, ch g Fruits of Love (USA)—The Iron Lady (IRE) **P. Grubb**
26 **PINCH OF SALT (IRE)**, 5, b g Hussonet (USA)—Granita (CHI) **The Hon R. W. Hanson**

MR A. M. BALDING—continued

27 **RAMBLING LIGHT,** 4, b g Fantastic Light (USA)—Rambler **G. W. Chong**
28 **SEAFLOWER REEF (IRE),** 4, b f Robellino (USA)—Sankaty Light (USA) **Kingsclere Stud**
29 **SHOW WINNER,** 5, b g Mtoto—Rose Show **Sir Gordon Brunton**
30 **SIREN'S GIFT,** 4, ch f Cadeaux Genereux—Blue Siren **J. C. Smith**
31 **VANDERLIN,** 9, ch g Halling (USA)—Massorah (FR) **J. C. & S. R. Hitchins**
32 **WHISKEY JUNCTION,** 4, b g Bold Edge—Victoria Mill **K R C**
33 **YEAMAN'S HALL,** 4, b g Galileo (IRE)—Rimba (USA) **George Strawbridge Jnr**

THREE-YEAR-OLDS

34 **ABSTRACT COLOURS (IRE),** b br g Kalanisi—St Bride's Bay **Auto Body Supplies & Mrs M A Raesmith**
35 **ADA RIVER,** b f Dansili—Miss Meltemi (IRE) **G. B. Russell**
36 **AMANJENA,** b f Beat Hollow—Placement **Mrs M. E. Wates**
37 **ARREWIG LISSOME (USA),** b c Black Tie Affair—Lissome (USA) **Mick and Janice Mariscotti**
38 **BID ART (IRE),** b g Hawk Wing (USA)—Crystal Theatre (IRE) **M. R. Green**
39 **BLUE SKY BASIN,** b g Desert Prince (IRE)—Kimba (USA) **George Strawbridge Jnr**
40 **BORDES LANE,** b g Olden Times—Rimba (USA) **George Strawbridge Jnr**
41 **DONEGAL (USA),** b br g Menifee (USA)—Vickey's Echo (CAN) **The Donegal Partnership**
42 **DREAM EATER (IRE),** gr c Night Shift (USA)—Kapria (FR) **J. C. Smith**
43 **ERICARROW (IRE),** b f Bollin Eric—Floriana **K R C**
44 **EVER DREAMING (USA),** b f Dynaformer (USA)—Slept Thru It (USA) **D. H. Caslon**
45 **FAR SONG (IRE),** ch f Distant Music (USA)—Charlene Lacy (IRE) **The Dim & Distant Racing Partnership**
46 **FIRST IN SHOW,** b f Zamindar (USA)—Rose Show **Sir Gordon Brunton**
47 **FLYING INDIAN,** ch f Hawk Wing (USA)—Poppadam **D. H. Caslon**
48 **HONESTY PAYS,** b f Dr Fong (USA)—Absolve (USA) **Miss A. V. Hill**
49 **ISABELONABICYCLE,** b f Helissio (FR)—Santa Isobel **J. C. & S. R. Hitchins**
50 **JEDEDIAH,** b g Hernando (FR)—Penelewey **Mr & Mrs P McMahon Mr& Mrs Peter Pausewang**
51 **KALAHARI GOLD (IRE),** ch g Trans Island—Neat Shilling (IRE) **The Toucan Syndicate**
52 **KARATE QUEEN,** b f King's Best—Black Belt Shopper (IRE) **Axom (VI)**
53 **LADY BRORA,** b f Dashing Blade—Tweed Mill **W. Aeberhard**
54 **MA VIE EN ROSE (IRE),** b f Red Ransom (USA)—Stop Out **Mrs P. Grimes**
55 **MAGPIE (IRE),** br g Hawk Wing (USA)—Swilly (USA) **Mr P. C. McMahon**
56 **MY AUNT FANNY,** b f Nayef (USA)—Putuna **J. C. & S. R. Hitchins**
57 **OCEANA BLUE,** b f Reel Buddy (USA)—Silken Dalliance **The C H F Partnership**
58 **ONE NIGHT IN MAY (IRE),** b f Choisir (AUS)—Dream Genie **G. W. Chong**
59 **PRAIRIE STORM,** b g Storming Home—Last Dream (IRE) **W.V. & Mrs E.S. Robins**
60 **PRINCESS AUGUSTA (USA),** b f Silic (FR)—Tri Anytime (USA) **Mr L. L. Register**
61 **PROVISION,** ch f Cadeaux Genereux—Brand **Her Majesty The Queen**
62 **RABEERA,** b f Beat Hollow—Gai Bulga **J. Dwyer**
63 **RELATIVE STRENGTH (IRE),** ch c Kris Kin (USA)—Monalee Lass (IRE) **D. H. Caslon**
64 **RESTLESS GENIUS (IRE),** b g Captain Rio—Mainmise (USA) **Favourites Racing IV**
65 **ROYAL STRAIGHT,** ch g Halling (USA)—High Straits **J. C. Smith**
66 **SEEDLESS,** br f Mtoto—Unseeded **Mr C. J. Spence**
67 **STARBURST,** b f Fantastic Light—Rasmalai **Holistic Racing**
68 **STREET CRIME,** b g Tagula (IRE)—Brandon Princess **K R C**
69 **TOP LOCK,** b c Nayef (USA)—Ermine (IRE) **D. Brownlow**
70 **TRANSFER,** br g Trans Island—Sankaty Light (USA) **D. H. Back**
71 **VENI BIDI VICI,** ch f Horse Chestnut (SAF)—Wily Bid (USA) **Mike Webley & Stuart McPhee**
72 **VICTORIA MONTOYA,** br f High Chaparral (IRE)—Spurned (USA) **K R C**
73 **WALTON HOUSE (USA),** ch g Mutakddim (USA)—Dominant Dancer **Another Bottle Racing**
74 **WIGRAM'S TURN (USA),** ch c Hussonet (USA)—Stacey's Relic (USA) **D. Brownlow**
75 **YOUR PLEASURE (USA),** b f Forest Wildcat (USA)—Pleasure Center (USA) **George Strawbridge Jnr**

TWO-YEAR-OLDS

76 B g 18/2 Passing Glance—Averami (Averti (IRE)) (1238) **K R C**
77 Ch f 13/3 Saffron Walden (FR)—Bellagio Princess (Kris) (7000) **G. W. Chong**
78 B f 11/4 King's Best—Blue Siren (Bluebird (USA)) **J. C. Smith**
79 B g 22/5 Passing Glance—Brandon Princess (Waajib) (1619) **K R C**
80 **BRANDY BUTTER,** ch c 9/2 Domedriver (IRE)—Brand (Shareef Dancer (USA)) **Her Majesty The Queen**
81 **CAVERA (USA),** b f 7/5 Not For Love (USA)—Spelling (USA) (Alphabet Soup (USA)) **G. Strawbridge**
82 **CELTIC SPUR (IRE),** b c 18/4 Celtic Swing—
          Kart Star (IRE) (Soviet Star (USA)) (12000) **Mick and Janice Mariscotti**
83 **CHERRY PLUM,** ch f 4/4 Medicean—Putuna (Generous (IRE)) **J. C., J. R. & S. R. Hitchins**
84 **DAY CREEK,** gr f 12/5 Daylami (USA)—With Fascination (USA) (Dayjur (USA)) **G. Strawbridge**
85 B c 12/4 Trans Island—Decatur (Deploy) (5000) **K R C**
86 **DER ROSENKAVALIER (IRE),** b c 10/3 Captain Rio—Brooks Masquerade (Absalom) (30000) **D. Brownlow**

MR A. M. BALDING—continued

87 **DEYAS DREAM**, b f 20/4 Clodovil (IRE)—Dream On Deya (IRE) (Dolphin Street (FR)) (22857) **Miss A. V. Hill**
88 **FARLEIGH**, b f 7/4 Trans Island—Medway (IRE) (Shernazar) (5000) **The Farleigh Partnership**
89 **FINAL VICTORY**, ch c 4/4 Generous (IRE)—Persian Victory (IRE) (Persian Bold) **Sir Gordon Brunton**
90 Ch c 10/2 Tagula (IRE)—Floriana (Selkirk (USA)) **K R C**
91 **GEORGINA MACRAE**, b f 1/1 Bahamian Bounty—
　　　　　　　　　　　　　　Sadly Sober (IRE) (Roi Danzig (USA)) (25000) **Mr E. Sutherland**
92 B c 27/2 King's Best (USA)—Glam Rock (Nashwan (USA)) (30000) **Pink Hat Partnership**
93 B c 15/3 Sinndar (IRE)—Imitation (Darshaan) (65000) **Mr P. C. McMahon**
94 **JOSIE MAY (USA)**, gr f 1/2 Aljabr (USA)—Aqaarid (USA) (Nashwan (USA)) (26000) **Mr P. J. Eaton**
95 B br c 27/1 Pyrus (USA)—Just One Look (Barathea (IRE)) (32000) **Thurloe Thoroughbreds XXII**
96 B c 27/2 Montjeu (IRE)—Kicking Bird (FR) (Darshaan) (47000) **P. C. & Mrs J. A. McMahon**
97 B c 27/2 Selkirk (USA)—Legend Has It (IRE) (Sadler's Wells (USA)) (130000) **George Strawbridge Jnr**
98 B f 13/2 Oasis Dream—Lochangel (Night Shift (USA)) **J. C. Smith**
99 B f 7/2 Xaar—Lochridge (Indian Ridge) **J. C. Smith**
100 B c 26/4 Anabaa (USA)—Lochsong (Song) **J. C. Smith**
101 B f 2/2 Kyllachy—Luxurious (USA) (Lyphard (USA)) **Horses For Causes**
102 B f 26/1 Dashing Blade—Mara River (Efisio) **K R C**
103 B c 8/4 Dubai Destination (USA)—Maria Theresa (Primo Dominie) (37000) **A. Taylor**
104 B br c 3/3 Reset (AUS)—Masrora (USA) (Woodman (USA)) **Favourites Racing**
105 B c 20/2 Fantastic Light (USA)—Memsahib (Alzao (USA)) **Sir Gordon Brunton**
106 Ch f 20/4 Distant Music (USA)—Miss Indigo (Indian Ridge) (5000) **CHF Partnership**
107 B br c 24/2 Ten Most Wanted (USA)—Miss Orah (Unfuwain (USA)) (25000) **Calzaghe Partnership**
108 B c 3/3 Passing Glance—Mory Kante (USA) (Icecapade (USA)) **M. E. Wates**
109 B f 19/4 Reset (AUS)—Mountain Ash (Dominion) (30000) **Mrs P. Grimes**
110 **PERFECT SECRET**, b f 6/2 Spinning World (USA)—Sharp Secret (IRE) (College Chapel) **Mr J. & Dr B. Drew**
111 B f 20/4 Trans Island—Pictina (Petong) **K R C**
112 **PRINCE SIEGFRIED**, b c 24/3 Royal Applause—Intrum Morshaan (IRE) (Darshaan) (38000) **D. Brownlow**
113 **PRIVATE ICE**, br f 30/3 Pivotal—Midnight Air (USA) (Green Dancer (USA)) **G. Strawbridge**
114 **REGAL BLUSH**, b f 5/5 Bachelor Duke (USA)—Royale Rose (FR) (Bering) (48000) **Horses For Causes**
115 B f 14/4 Passing Glance—Sankaty Light (USA) (Summer Squall (USA)) **K R C**
116 Ch c 14/2 Piccolo—Silken Dalliance (Rambo Dancer (CAN)) (30000) **The C H F Partnership**
117 Br f 28/4 Pursuit of Love—Society Rose (Saddlers' Hall (USA)) (40000) **Mr & Mrs W. Clifford**
118 Br c 28/4 Nayef (USA)—Spurned (USA) (Robellino (USA)) **K R C**
119 B c 5/5 Halling (USA)—Velour (Mtoto) (6500) **I. A. Balding**
120 **WARRANTS ATTENTION (IRE)**, b c 17/3 Fruits of Love (USA)—
　　　　　　　　　　　　　　Irish Lover (USA) (Irish River (FR)) (16000) **R. Parry**
121 **YEOMAN BLAZE**, b c 18/3 Needwood Blade—Gymcrak Flyer (Aragon) (24000) **Yeoman Homes Limited**

Other Owners: Mr S. Alansari, Mrs D. J. Arstall, Mr L. Arstall, Auto Body Supplies Ltd, Axom, Mrs I. A. Balding, Mrs A. L. Balding, Mrs Andrew Bays, Mr Peter Box, Mr A. Brooke Rankin, Mr I. G. Burbidge, Mr Dan Downie, Mrs John Duncan, Mr J. R. Eburne, Mr Michael K. Elliott, Mr P. E. Felton, Mr K. H. Fischer, Mr C. H. Fischer, Mr B. J. R. Greenwood, D. A. Halsall, Mr Arthur B. Hancock III, Mr Tony Hill, Mr J. C. Hitchins, Mr S. R. Hitchins, Ms Kate James, John Nicholls (Trading) Ltd, Mr David N. King, Mr Guy Luck, Mrs Guy Luck, Mr Mick Mariscotti, Mrs Janice Mariscotti, Mr R. D. McDougall, Mrs J. A. McMahon, Mr Stuart McPhee, R. P. B. Michaelson, Mobley Homes, Mr D. Nicholson, Miss M. Noden, Mr Peter Pausewang, Mrs Peter Pausewang, O. J. W. Pawle, Mrs M. A. Rae Smith, Mr W. V. Robins, Mrs Shirley Robins, Mr G. H. Skeats, Mrs N. H. Stafford, Mr Tim Walker, Dr Mike Webley.

Assistant Trainer: C. Bonner

Jockey (flat): F. Norton, N. Chalmers, L. Keniry. **Apprentice:** D. Probert, W. Buick. **Amateur:** Mr Karl Poole.

---

21 MR J. BALDING, Doncaster
Postal: **Mayflower Stables, Saracens Lane, Scrooby, Doncaster, South Yorkshire, DN10 6AS**
Contacts: **HOME (01302) 710096 FAX (01302) 710096 MOBILE (07816) 612631**
E-MAIL j.balding@btconnect.com

1 **DUNN DEAL (IRE)**, 8, b g Revoque (IRE)—Buddy And Soda (IRE) **D. A. Davies**
2 **FIONA FOX**, 4, b f Foxhound (USA)—First Play **Mr D. A. Dickinson**
3 **GIFTED LASS**, 6, b m Bold Edge—Meeson Times **Bawtry Racing Partnership**
4 **HAROLDINI (IRE)**, 6, b g Orpen (USA)—Ciubanga (IRE) **Tykes & Terriers Racing Club**
5 **NITEOWL LAD (IRE)**, 6, ch g Tagula (IRE)—Mareha (IRE) **Burntwood Sports Ltd**
6 **SOBA JONES**, 11, b g Primer Jones (USA)—Soba **R. L. Crowe**
7 **THE CUBE**, 4, b g Mind Games—Nite-Owl Dancer **Burntwood Sports Ltd**
8 **TURN ON THE STYLE**, 6, ch g Pivotal—Elegant Rose **The Haydock Badgeholders**

MR J. BALDING—continued

THREE-YEAR-OLDS

9 **BE SUPERIOR,** b f Superior Premium—Miss Tun **Mrs O. Tunstall**
10 **LAUGHING GRAVY,** b c Forzando—Elegant Rose **Arnold Robinson Racing**
11 **RUBY'S RAINBOW (IRE),** b f Fayruz—Sweet Finesse (IRE) **Mr P. Balding**

Other Owners: Mrs Stella Barclay, Mr D. C. Bichan, Mr Robert Brackenridge, Mr Thomas Laurence Byrne, Mr Paul Clarkson, Mr T. J. Crehan, Mr M. V. Firth, Mr D. N. Freeman, Mr Bob Leach, Mr David Robinson (Preston), Mr Gerard Dominic Wood.

Assistant Trainer: Claire Edmunds

Jockey (flat): J. Edmunds.

22

MRS A. BARCLAY, Moreton-in-Marsh
Postal: **Fotherop, Oddington, Moreton-In-Marsh, Gloucestershire, GL56 0XF**
Contacts: **PHONE (01451) 830680 FAX (01451) 870572 MOBILE (07850) 729000**

1 **CURRADOON (IRE),** 7, b g Lord Americo—Clara Petal (IRE) **Mrs A. Barclay**
2 **GERRARD (IRE),** 10, b g Jurado (USA)—Vienna Waltz (IRE) **Mrs A. Barclay**
3 **OWN UP,** 6, b g Petoski—My Little Doxie (IRE) **Mrs A. Barclay**
4 **QUAPRILAND (FR),** 4, br f Dark Moondancer—Falkland III (FR) **Mrs A. Barclay**

23

MR J. BARCLAY, Milnathort
Postal: **St Serf's, The Cobbles, Kinnesswood, Kinross**
Contacts: **PHONE (01592) 840331 MOBILE (07709) 878676**
E-MAIL Barclay.jim@hotmail.co.uk

1 **MR TWINS (ARG),** 7, ch g Numerous (USA)—Twins Parade (ARG) **A. Singer**
2 **SWORDS AT DAWN (IRE),** 7, ch m Daggers Drawn (USA)—Caraway J. **Barclay**
3 **THE WEAVER (FR),** 9, ch g Villez (USA)—Miss Planette (FR) **A. Singer**
4 **ULYSEES (IRE),** 9, b g Turtle Island (IRE)—Tamasriya (IRE) **Mr J. C. Higgins**

Assistant Trainer: Miss Caroline Barclay & James Barclay Jnr

24

MRS T. M. BARFOOT-SAUNT, Wotton-under-Edge
Postal: **Cosy Farm, Huntingford, Charfield, Wotton-under-Edge, Gloucestershire, GL12 8EY**
Contacts: **PHONE (01453) 520312 FAX (01453) 810306 MOBILE (07976) 360626**

1 **ELBOW LANE (IRE),** 8, b g Oscar (IRE)—Ah Donna **Mr P. J. Sturgess**
2 **MIXSTERTHERIXSTER (USA),** 12, b g Alleged (USA)—Parliament House (USA) **Mrs T. M. Barfoot-Saunt**
3 **STERLING HEIGHTS (NZ),** 9, br g Rainbow Myth (NZ)—
Amrita (NZ) **Mr & Mrs Scholfield & Mr & Mrs Slocombe**
4 **THE MYSTERY MAN (IRE),** 9, ch g Roselier (FR)—Christys Best (IRE) **A Good Days Racing**

Other Owners: Mrs Tracey Barfoot-Saunt, Mr T. S. Ide, Mrs S. Scholfield, Mrs Y. J. Slocombe.

Jockey (NH): H. Oliver. **Amateur:** Mr Geoff Barfoot-Saunt.

25

MR D. W. BARKER, Richmond
Postal: **Tancred Grange, Scorton, Richmond, North Yorkshire, DL10 6AB**
Contacts: **HOME (01748) 811371 WORK (01325) 378266**
FAX (01325) 378266 MOBILE (07836) 260149
E-MAIL david.barker223@virgin.net WEBSITE www.davidbarkerracing.co.uk

1 **BRUT,** 6, b g Mind Games—Champenoise **D. W. Barker**
2 **CELTIC MILL,** 10, b g Celtic Swing—Madam Millie **P. Asquith**
3 **CHAMPAGNE SUE,** 4, ch f Foxhound (USA)—Pigeon **Mr A. Turton**
4 **CHEERY CAT (USA),** 4, b br g Catienus (USA)—Olinka (USA) **Cataractonium Syndicate**
5 **DARCY'S PRIDE (IRE),** 4, b br f Danetime (IRE)—Cox's Ridge (IRE) **Ms J. Hanson**
6 **DENDOR,** 4, b g Warningford—Dolphin Dancer **D. G. Clayton**
7 **DORN DANCER (IRE),** 6, b m Danehill Dancer (IRE)—Appledorn **The Ebor Partnership**
8 **HYPNOSIS,** 5, b m Mind Games—Salacious **R. W. Snowden**

MR D. W. BARKER—continued

9 **MR WOLF**, 7, b g Wolfhound (USA)—Madam Millie **P. Asquith**
10 **REBEL DUKE (IRE)**, 4, ch g Namid—Edwina (IRE) **Mr I. Bishop**
11 **STIR CRAZY (IRE)**, 4, b g Fath (USA)—La Captive (IRE) **D. W. Barker**
12 **TOP JARO (FR)**, 5, b g Marathon (USA)—Shahmy **D. W. Barker**
13 **WAHOO SAM (USA)**, 8, ch g Sandpit (BRZ)—Good Reputation (USA) **Mr J. Holland**
14 **WASALAT (USA)**, 6, b m Bahri (USA)—Saabga (USA) **Miss D. Downes**
15 **WHINHILL HOUSE**, 8, ch g Paris House—Darussalam **Destiny Racing Club**
16 **WOVOKA (IRE)**, 5, b g Mujadil (USA)—Common Cause **D. W. Barker**
17 **WULIMASTER (USA)**, 5, br g Silver Hawk (USA)—Kamaina (USA) **Mr Andrew Turton & Mr David Barker**

THREE-YEAR-OLDS

18 **BARONOVICI (IRE)**, b c Namid—Allegrina (IRE) **D. W. Barker**
19 **CAPTAIN TURBOT (IRE)**, ch g Captain Rio—Kiriwas (ITY) **Mr Andrew Turton & Mr David Barker**
20 **DOLLY NO HAIR**, ch g Reel Buddy (USA)—Champagne Grandy **Dolmar Limited**
21 **GIOACCHINO (IRE)**, b g Rossini (USA)—Gareyba (IRE) **D. W. Barker**
22 **GRUDGE**, b c Timeless Times (USA)—Envy (IRE) **Mark Sumner & Partners I**
23 **HALF A CROWN (IRE)**, b c Compton Place—Penny Ha'penny **G. N. Parker**
24 **LEGENDARY GUEST**, b c Bahamian Bounty—Legend of Aragon **D. W. Barker**
25 **ZABOUGG**, b g Tobougg (IRE)—Double Fault (IRE) **D. W. Barker**
26 **ZAPLAMATION (IRE)**, b c Acclamation—Zapatista **Mr Andrew Turton & Mr David Barker**

TWO-YEAR-OLDS

27 B c 18/4 Reel Buddy (USA)—Amber's Bluff (Mind Games) (8000)
28 **CELTIC SOVEREIGN (IRE)**, b c 7/5 Celtic Swing—Penny Ha'penny (Bishop of Cashel) (26000) **P. Asquith**
29 **EASTER BUNNY**, ch f 18/4 Compton Place—Sweet Myrtle (USA) (Mutakddim (USA)) **P. Asquith**
30 Br f 13/3 Danetime (IRE)—Shining Desert (IRE) (Green Desert (USA)) (17000)
31 B f 19/2 Reel Buddy (USA)—Tancred Arms (Clantime) (8500)

Other Owners: Mrs Judy Allan, Mr P. Asquith, Mr D. W. Barker, Mrs S. J. Barker, Mr D. Clayton, Ms Jenny Hainson, Mr C. Simpson, Mrs Debbie Stefanou, Mr Andrew Turton.

Assistant Trainer: Samantha Barker

---

26 | **SIR J. BARLOW, Nantwich**
Postal: Ash House, Brindley, Nantwich, Cheshire, CW5 8HX
Contacts: OFFICE (01270) 524339 FAX (01270) 524047

1 **BOSTON MONDAIN (FR)**, 7, b g Le Pommier d'or—Armalita (FR) **Sir John & Lady Barlow**
2 **FAIR KALD (FR)**, 7, b g Exit To Nowhere (USA)—Kaldona (FR) **Sir John Barlow**
3 **FLYING JODY (IRE)**, 9, b g Frimaire—Flying Flo Jo (USA) **Sir John & Lady Barlow**

---

27 | **MR M. A. BARNES, Brampton**
Postal: Tarnside, Farlam, Brampton, Cumbria, CA8 1LA
Contacts: PHONE/FAX (01697) 746675 MOBILE (07760) 433191

1 **CURRAHEE**, 4, b g Efisio—Dixie Favor (USA) **Abbadis Racing Club**
2 **DANTOR**, 6, b g Dansili—Shallop **T. A. Barnes**
3 **FILEY BUOY**, 6, b g Factual (USA)—Tugra (FR) **J. M. Carlyle**
4 **FIRST STOP**, 5, b g Chocolat de Meguro (USA)—One Stop **Mr R. Burgan**
5 **HAPPY BOY (IRE)**, 7, b g Victory Note—Pepper And Salt (IRE) **T. A. Barnes**
6 **HUGS DESTINY (IRE)**, 7, b g Victory Note (USA)—Embracing **J. G. K. White**
7 **JALAMID (IRE)**, 6, b g Danehill (USA)—Vignelaure (IRE) **D. Maloney**
8 **LORD SAMPOSIN**, 7, b g I'm Supposin (IRE)—Skiddaw Samba **J. R. Wills**
9 **MIDNIGHT MAGGIE**, 7, b m Midnight Legend—I'm Maggy (NZ) **S. C. Brown**
10 **MISS TARANTELLA**, 5, ch m Minster Son—Granham Charm (IRE) **Mr A. Smithson**
11 **ODDSMAKER (IRE)**, 7, b g Barathea (IRE)—Archipora (IRE) **D. Maloney**
12 4, B g Chocolat de Meguro (USA)—One Stop **Mr M. Barnes**
13 **OVERBAY**, 4, b f Overbury (IRE)—On The Bay **M. D. Townson**
14 **SADDLERS SINGER (IRE)**, 5, b g Saddlers' Hall (IRE)—Parsons Law **Alex Singer**
15 **SCUZME (IRE)**, 5, br g Xaar—Decatur **S. C. Brown**
16 **SILVER ALIDANTE**, 5, gr m Silver Patriarch (IRE)—Aubade **Lowther Coates Nicholson Anderson**
17 **SKIDDAW JONES**, 8, b g Emperor Jones (USA)—Woodrising **J. R. Wills**
18 **SOUBRIQUET (IRE)**, 5, b g Daylami (IRE)—Green Lucia **Minstrel's Double Racing**

MR M. A. BARNES—continued

19 TORKINKING (IRE), 9, b g Supreme Leader—Nicola's News (IRE) **Mr J. G. Graham, Mr Scott Lowther**
20 TSALA, 6, b br g Alflora (IRE)—I'll Skin Them (IRE) **Miss A. P. Lee**
21 VALDAN (IRE), 4, b g Val Royal (FR)—Danedrop (IRE) **D. Maloney**

TWO-YEAR-OLDS

22 Ch f 13/4 Nayef (USA)—Mindanao (Most Welcome) **Mr T. Noble**
23 B f 22/4 Chocolat de Meguro (USA)—One Stop (Silly Prices) **Mr M. Barnes**

Other Owners: Mr D. Anderson, Mr M. Barnes, Mr Robin Coates, Mr Harold Fogg, Mr J. G. Graham, Mr D. Graham, Mr Ian Gray, R. E. Jackson, Mr Scott Lowther, Mr T. Nicholson, Mrs Anna Noble.

Jockey (flat): J. Crowley. **Amateur:** Miss Angela Barnes.

---

28 MR R. E. BARR, Middlesbrough
Postal: **Carr House Farm, Seamer, Stokesley, Middlesbrough, Cleveland, TS9 5LL**
Contacts: **PHONE (01642) 710687 MOBILE (07711) 895309**
E-MAIL christinebarr1@aol.com

1 ATOMIC BREEZE (IRE), 14, b br g Strong Gale—Atomic Lady **R. E. Barr**
2 BAYBSHAMBLES (IRE), 4, b g Compton Admiral—Payvashooz **Miss S. Haykin**
3 BLACK EYED PEA, 6, gr m Grey Desire—Cheeky Pigeon **Mrs C. Barr**
4 BORODINSKY, 7, b g Magic Ring (IRE)—Valldemosa **Mrs C. Barr**
5 CRUX, 6, b g Pivotal—Penny Dip **Mrs C. Barr**
6 DARK CHAMPION, 8, b g Abou Zouz (USA)—Hazy Kay (IRE) **A. Suddes**
7 FRIMLEY'S MATTERRY, 8, b g Bluegrass Prince (IRE)—Lonely Street **Mrs C. Barr**
8 LA MARMOTTE (IRE), 4, b f Mujadil (USA)—Zilayah (USA) **P. Cartmell**
9 LEWIS LLOYD (IRE), 5, b g Indian Lodge (IRE)—Sandy Fitzgerald (IRE) **B. Morton**
10 LOCH AWE, 5, b m Inchinor—Lochbelle **Mrs C. Barr**
11 MACCHIATO, 7, br m Inchinor—Tereyna **D. R. E. McDuffie**
12 NEARDOWN BEAUTY (IRE), 5, br m Bahhare (USA)—Habla Me (IRE) **B. Morton**
13 NEXT FLIGHT (IRE), 9, b g Woodborough (USA)—Sans Ceriph (IRE) **Mrs C. Barr**
14 PAY TIME, 9, ch m Timeless Times (USA)—Payvashooz **Mrs C. Barr**
15 ROSE OF INCHINOR, 5, b m Inchinor—Rosa Canina **M. W. Mitchell**
16 SILLY GILLY (IRE), 4, b f Mull of Kintyre (USA)—Richly Deserved (IRE) **M. Omair**
17 STRENSALL, 11, b g Beveled (USA)—Payvashooz **R. E. Barr**
18 THE KEEP, 6, ch m Shinko Forest (IRE)—Poyle Amber **D. Thomson**

THREE-YEAR-OLDS

19 KYZER CHIEF, b g Rouvres (FR)—Payvashooz **B. Morton**

Other Owners: Mrs R. E. Barr, Mr R. E. Barr, Miss J. A. Sawney.

Assistant Trainer: Mrs C Barr

Amateur: Miss V. Barr.

---

29 MR T. D. BARRON, Thirsk
Postal: **Maunby House, Maunby, Thirsk, North Yorkshire, YO7 4HD**
Contacts: **PHONE (01845) 587435**

1 A BIG SKY BREWING (USA), 4, b g Arch (USA)—Runalpharun (USA) **Mr T. Boanas**
2 BABIECA (USA), 4, gr g Tactical Cat (USA)—Secret Mountain (USA) **Mr R. G. Toes & Mr Patrick Toes**
3 BY THE EDGE (IRE), 4, b f Shinko Forest (IRE)—Magic Annemarie (IRE) **J. Starbuck**
4 CARNIVORE, 6, ch g Zafonic (USA)—Ermine (IRE) **The Meat Eaters**
5 DISPOL ISLE (IRE), 6, gr m Trans Island—Pictina **W. B. Imison**
6 DOUBTFUL SOUND (USA), 4, b c Diesis—Roam Free (USA) **Miss N. J. Barron**
7 FLIPANDO (IRE), 7, b g Sri Pekan (USA)—Magic Touch **Mrs J. Hazell**
8 FLORES SEA (USA), 4, ch g Luhuk (USA)—Perceptive (USA) **T. D. Barron**
9 HOW'S SHE CUTTIN' (IRE), 5, ch m Shinko Forest (IRE)—Magic Annemarie (IRE) **Mr C. McHale**
10 IMPERIAL SWORD, 5, b g Danehill Dancer (IRE)—Hajat **Harrowgate Bloodstock Ltd**
11 INGLEBY ARCH (USA), 5, b g Arch (USA)—Inca Dove **D. Scott**
12 INGLEBY PRINCESS, 4, br f Bold Edge—Bob's Princess **D. Scott**
13 INSPAINAGAIN (USA), 4, ch g Miswaki (USA)—Counter Cat (USA) **Jim Beaumont & Douglas Pryde**

MR T. D. BARRON—continued

14 **INTEREST (USA)**, 4, ch g Banker's Gold (USA)—Princess Kris **Harrowgate Bloodstock Ltd**
15 **KING OF THE MOORS (USA)**, 5, b g King of Kings (IRE)—Araza (USA) **Mr G. Fawcett**
16 **MY GACHO (IRE)**, 6, b g Shinko Forest (IRE)—Floralia **G. Mercer**
17 **PARTNERS IN JAZZ (USA)**, 7, gr g Jambalaya Jazz (USA)—

Just About Enough (USA) **Sporting Occasions Racing No 2**
18 **PIETERSEN (IRE)**, 4, ch g Redback—Faye **Sporting Occasions No 8**
19 **RIGAT**, 5, b g Dansili—Fudge **Mrs J. M. MacPherson**
20 **SINGLEB (IRE)**, 4, b g Intikhab (USA)—Bubble N Squeak (IRE) **The JTM**
21 **SKHILLING SPIRIT**, 5, b g Most Welcome—Calcavella **Mr I. Hill**
22 **SPINNING**, 5, ch g Pivotal—Starring (FR) **Mrs J. Hazell**
23 **STAKED A CLAIM (IRE)**, 4, ch g Danehill Dancer (IRE)—Twany Angel **Mr C. McHale**
24 **THORNABY GREEN**, 7, b g Whittingham (IRE)—Dona Filipa **K. J. Alderson**
25 **TRANCE (IRE)**, 8, ch g Bahhare (USA)—Lady of Dreams (IRE) **N. R. Shields**
26 **ZERO TOLERANCE (IRE)**, 8, ch g Nashwan (USA)—Place de L'opera **The Hornsey Warriors Racing Syndicate**

THREE-YEAR-OLDS

27 **BORASCO (USA)**, ch f Stormy Atlantic (USA)—Seek (USA) **Mr Patrick Toes & Mr R. G. Toes**
28 **CHAMPAGNE LAWN (USA)**, gr f Aljabr (USA)—Quality Gift **Harrowgate Bloodstock Ltd**
29 **CHESHIRE ROSE**, ch f Bertolini (USA)—Merch Rhyd-Y-Grug **D. C. Rutter P. J. Huntbach**
30 **CROSSING BRIDGES**, ch f Dr Fong (USA)—Pontressina (USA) **Messinger Stud Ltd**
31 **ELIJAH PEPPER (USA)**, ch g Crafty Prospector (USA)—Dovie Dee (USA) **Harrowgate Bloodstock Ltd**
32 **FLYING SOMMELIER (USA)**, b g Dixieland Band (USA)—Charming Lauren (USA) **Mrs J. Hazell**
33 **GAINSHARE**, b g Lend A Hand—Red Shareef **The Dastardly & Muttley**
34 **GRAND VALUE (USA)**, b f Grand Slam (USA)—Privyet Nadya (USA) **D. W. Armstrong**
35 **INGLEBY STAR (IRE)**, b g Fath (USA)—Rosy Scintilla (IRE) **D. Scott**
36 **JACONET (USA)**, ch f Hussonet (USA)—Radiant Rocket (USA) **Mr R. G. Toes**
37 **LITTLE EDEN (IRE)**, b g Piccolo—Paradise Eve **Mr C. A. Washbourn**
38 **LOW FLYER (USA)**, gr ro g Runaway Groom (CAN)—To The Right (USA) **K. Shaw**
39 **MEINARDUS (IRE)**, b g Noverre (USA)—Volte Face **Twinacre Nurseries Ltd**
40 **MIDNIGHT MUSE (USA)**, b c Swain (IRE)—Witching Hour (FR) **Mr C. A. Washbourn**
41 **PIVERINA (IRE)**, b f Pivotal—Alassio (USA) **D. W. Armstrong**
42 **POET'S PLACE (USA)**, b g Mutakddim (USA)—Legion of Merit (USA) **Harrowgate Bloodstock Ltd**
43 **PRESIDENT ELECT (IRE)**, b c Imperial Ballet (IRE)—Broadway Rosie **Mr C. McHale**
44 **SIRVINO**, b g Vettori (IRE)—Zenita (IRE) **Mr Theo Williams & Mr Charles Mocatta**
45 **SKHILLING PRIDE**, ch f Kyllachy—Twilight Time **Mr I. Hill**
46 **STATEN (USA)**, b c Century City (USA)—Lever To Heaven (IRE) **Mrs J. M. MacPherson**
47 **STORMIN HEART (USA)**, br c Stormin Fever (USA)—Heart Beats True (USA) **G. Mercer**
48 **SWALLOW FOREST**, b f Averti (IRE)—Sangra (USA) **Foreneish Racing**
49 **TEATIME LADY (USA)**, b br f Stormin Fever (USA)—Tea Service (USA) **D. W. Armstrong**
50 **TITO (IRE)**, b c Diktat—T G's Girl **Mrs J. M. MacPherson**
51 **TO BUBBLES**, b f Tobougg (IRE)—Effervescent **Mrs J. Hazell**

TWO-YEAR-OLDS

52 B br c 4/2 Doneraile Court (USA)—Clearwater (USA) (Seeking The Gold (USA)) (1943) **D. G. Pryde**
53 B c 31/1 Namid—Corps de Ballet (IRE) (Fasliyev (USA)) (46000) **D. W. Armstrong**
54 **DANTE DEO (USA)**, b f 3/4 Proud Citizen (USA)—Best Feature (USA) (El Gran Senor (USA)) (31584) **R. G. Toes**
55 Ch f 3/5 Presidium—Gypsy Fair (Compton Place)
56 **INGLEBY KING (USA)**, b br c 10/4 Doneraile Court (USA)—

Smart Lady Too (USA) (Clever Trick (USA)) (15549) **D. Scott**
57 **INGLEBY LADY**, ch f 30/1 Captain Rio—Petra Nova (First Trump) (24000) **D. Scott**
58 **LA ZAMORA**, b f 31/1 Lujain—Love Quest (Pursuit of Love) (4200) **J. G. Brown**
59 Ch f 11/3 Van Nistelrooy (USA)—

Los Altos (USA) (Robin des Pins (USA)) (6073) **Mount Pleasant Farm Racing Partnership**
60 B f 20/4 Arch (USA)—Marketplace (USA) (Relaunch (USA)) (4859)
61 Gr ro c 9/1 Brahms (USA)—Morning Pearl (CAN) (Morning Bob (USA)) (2915) **Twinacre Nurseries Ltd**
62 B c 18/5 Mizzen Mast (USA)—My Turn Kissin (USA) (Kissin Kris (USA)) (6802) **Twinacre Nurseries Ltd**
63 B g 17/4 Trans Island—Patricia Philomena (IRE) (Prince of Birds (USA))
64 B br c 4/4 Doneraile Court (USA)—Plateau (USA) (Seeking The Gold (USA)) (5344)
65 B c 13/3 Cactus Ridge (USA)—Queen of Humor (USA) (Distorted Humor (USA)) (4859)
66 Ch f 14/2 Beat Hollow—Questa Nova (Rainbow Quest (USA)) (2800) **Harrowgate Bloodstock Ltd**
67 **RAFFANETTI (IRE)**, b c 28/5 Raphane (USA)—Proud Boast (Komaite (USA)) **P. Savill**
68 B f 23/1 Perfect Soul (IRE)—Regal Baby (USA) (Northern Baby (CAN)) (10689) **S. C. Barron**
69 **SILVERHAY GIRL**, ch f 15/3 Compton Place—Muja Farewell (Mujtahid (USA)) (5000) **D. Rutter & P. Huntbach**

MR T. D. BARRON—continued

70 B f 28/4 Acclamation—Toldya (Beveled (USA)) (26000) **D. W. Armstrong**
71 B c 15/4 Monashee Mountain (USA)—Who's Sorry Now (USA) (Ogygian (USA)) (7288) **Dovebrace Limited**

Other Owners: Mr Tim D. Barron, Mrs Christine Barron, Miss N. J. Barron, Mr Jim Beaumont, Mrs D. Catlow, Mr Mel Catlow, Dr D. J. Forecast, Mr P. J. Huntbach, Mr John Knotts, Mr C. Mocatta, Mr Laurence O'Kane, Mr D. G. Pryde, Mr D. C. Rutter, Mr Allan Sturman, Mr R. G. Toes, Mr Patrick Toes, Mr Theo Williams.

Jockey (flat): P. Fessey, P. Makin. **Apprentice:** D. Heslop, N. Brown.

---

30   MR P. BARY, Chantilly

Postal: **5 Chemin des Aigles, 60500 Chantilly, France**
Contacts: **PHONE (0033) 3445 71403 FAX (0033) 3446 72015**
E-MAIL p-bary@wanadoo.fr

1 BERNANDO (FR), 4, b c Hernando (FR)—Beggars Belief (IRE) **D. Jacob**
2 FINGERPRINT (USA), 4, b c Maria's Mon (USA)—Helstra (USA) **K. Abdullah**
3 GLORIA DE CAMPEAO (BRZ), 5, b h Impression (ARG)—Audacity (BRZ) **S. Friborg**
4 HOLOCENE (USA), 4, b br c Lemon Drop Kid (USA)—Witching Hour (FR) **Niarchos Famille**
5 INDIAN CHOICE (USA), 4, b g With Approval (CAN)—Cheyenne Dream **K. Abdullah**
6 OBJETO DE ARTE (BRZ), 5, ch h Boatman (USA)—Adrienne (ARG) **S. Friborg**
7 PALM ACADEMY (USA), 4, ch g Royal Academy (USA)—Stormy Moud (USA) **M. Ohana**
8 SIMBAD (FR), 4, b c Danehill (USA)—Napoli **Niarchos Famille**
9 ZAMBEZI SUN, 4, b c Dansili—Imbabala **K. Abdullah**

THREE-YEAR-OLDS

10 A DEMAIN PAPA (FR), b c Lomitas—Tashira (FR) **M. A. Berghgracht**
11 ALARMED, b f King's Best (USA)—Totality **K. Abdullah**
12 ARCADIA'S ANGLE (USA), b c Aldebaran (USA)—Diane's Birthday (USA) **Niarchos Famille**
13 ATSO (USA), ch c Kingmambo (USA)—Sea of Showers (USA) **Niarchos Famille**
14 AZTLAN (USA), b c Kingmambo (USA)—Speed of Thought (USA) **Niarchos Famille**
15 BARILOCH (FR), gr f Anabaa Blue—Linamox (FR) **J.C. Seroul**
16 BEIJING OPERA (FR), b f Starborough—Equatoriale (FR) **M. Hwang**
17 BLUE CIEL, b f Oasis Dream—Blue Fern (USA) **Skymarc Farm Inc**
18 CHOBE, b c Kaldounevees (FR)—Metisse (USA) **Sanremo '85 Srl**
19 CONFERENCE CALL, b f Anabaa (USA)—Phone West (USA) **K. Abdullah**
20 CONSTABLE COUNTRY, ch c Peintre Celebre (USA)—Serene View (USA) **K. Abdullah**
21 EL ROSA (FR), ch c Green Tune (USA)—Haine Amour (FR) **Ecurie Bouchard**
22 ELBRUS (USA), b c Giant's Causeway (USA)—Timi **Allevamento La Nuova**
23 ESTRELA HELEN (FR), gr f Verglas (IRE)—Mims Return (USA) **S. Friborg**
24 FORTUNATE ISLES (USA), b f Seeking The Gold (USA)—Dragonada (USA) **Niarchos Famille**
25 GIMSPIL, b c Singspiel (IRE)—Ginevra di Camelot (FR) **Allevamento La Nuova**
26 GREY SWAN (IRE), gr f Daylami (USA)—Irish Style (IRE) **Arrowfield Stud**
27 HEART OF MAGIC (USA), b f Storm Cat (USA)—Angel In My Heart (USA) **Niarchos Famille**
28 HOW BOLD, ch c Beat Hollow—Bold Empress (USA) **K. Abdullah**
29 B f Domedriver (IRE)—Island Lady (IRE) **D. Jacob**
30 JOUEL (FR), bl f Machiavellian (USA)—Visions On Space (IRE) **Niarchos Famille**
31 KAPPA (USA), b c Storm Cat (USA)—Coup de Genie (USA) **Niarchos Famille**
32 KESARA, b f Sadler's Wells (USA)—Kaldounya **Niarchos Famille**
33 LA ARGENTINA (FR), b c Cape Cross (IRE)—Spanish Quest **P. Rossier**
34 LIFESPAN, b c Dansili—Broken Spectre **K. Abdullah**
35 LUNE ROSE, b f High Chaparral (IRE)—Lunassa (FR) **Lady O'Reilly**
36 MADONNA LILY (IRE), gr f Daylami (USA)—Maria de La Luz (USA) **R.G. Ehrnrooth**
37 NATAGORA (FR), gr f Divine Light (JPN)—Reinamixa (FR) **S. Friborg**
38 NITYA (FR), b br f Indian Ridge—Napoli **Niarchos Famille**
39 OUTER CONTINENT (IRE), b c Domedriver (IRE)—Baratheastar **Niarchos Famille**
40 PASSION PROFONDE (FR), b f Priolo (USA)—Palagene **P. Augier**
41 PERFECT HAND, ch f Barathea (IRE)—Tarocchi (USA) **K. Abdullah**
42 PRUDENZIA (IRE), b f Dansili—Platonic **Ecurie Monceaux**
43 QUIETLY WINNER (GER), b c Singspiel (USA)—Quebrada (IRE) **Ecurie Bouchard**
44 RANSOM HOPE, b c Red Ransom (USA)—Field of Hope (IRE) **Allevamento La Nuova**
45 ROATAN, b c Daylami (USA)—Celestial Lagoon (JPN) **Sanremo '85 Srl**
46 ROCK FELLOW (FR), b c High Chaparral (IRE)—Liu (IRE) **Ecurie Bouchard**
47 SAN CARLOS (FR), ch c Dr Fong (USA)—Sateen (USA) **J.P. Van Gysel**
48 SCAPEGRACE (IRE), b f Cape Cross (IRE)—Serisia (FR) **Lady O'Reilly**

MR P. BARY—continued

49 **SHEITAN,** b c Dalakhani (IRE)—Biosphere **Allevamento La Nuova**
50 **SIMPLE ACT (USA),** b f Kingmambo (USA)—Rosa Parks **S.J. & R.S. Leigh**
51 **STERN OPINION (USA),** gr ro c Mizzen Mast (USA)—Helstra (USA) **K. Abdullah**
52 **TRIANGULAR (USA),** b c Diesis—Salchow **Niarchos Famille**
53 **UPSILON (USA),** b br c Aldebaran (USA)—Sun Is Up (JPN) **Niarchos Famille**
54 **WEALD,** b c Bering—New Abbey **K. Abdullah**

TWO-YEAR-OLDS

55 **AGNES CHAMP (FR),** b c 1/1 Agnes Kamikaze (JPN)—Antilles (IRE) (Danehill (USA)) **S. Friborg**
56 B br f 21/3 Storm Cat (USA)—Angel In My Heart (FR) (Rainbow Quest (USA)) **Niarchos Famille**
57 B c 28/3 Gulch (USA)—Anja (IRE) (Indian Ridge) (64350) **Ecurie Bouchard**
58 **ANTINEA,** b f 20/3 Royal Applause—Wish (Danehill (USA)) (57915) **L. Duquesne**
59 Gr f 15/3 Linamix (FR)—Autriche (IRE) (Acatenango (GER)) **D. Camilla**
60 **BAILA MORENA (FR),** ro f 27/2 Agnes Kamikaze (JPN)—Reinamixa (FR) (Linamix (FR)) (212355) **S. Friborg**
61 Ch f 5/3 Nayef (USA)—Bayswater (Caerleon (USA)) **K. Abdullah**
62 Gr f 27/2 Verglas (IRE)—Beau Duchess (FR) (Bering) (11583) **Skymarc Farm Inc.**
63 B f 26/4 Aldebaran (USA)—Belva (USA) (Theatrical) (170068) **Ecurie Monceaux**
64 B f 11/4 Dansili—Blue Fern (USA) (Woodman (USA)) **Lady O'Reilly**
65 **CAROLINA SHOOT,** ch f 12/3 Selkirk (USA)—Oyster Catcher (IRE) (Bluebird (USA)) (96525) **E. Simian**
66 B f 30/1 Mizzen Mast (USA)—Cheyenne Dream (Dancing Brave (USA)) **K. Abdullah**
67 **DAMIANI,** ch c 8/1 Lomitas—Drifa (ITY) (Hamas (IRE)) (154440) **Allevamento La Nuova**
68 B c 7/5 Rainbow Quest (USA)—Dansara (Dancing Brave (USA)) **D. Camilla**
69 **ENTREVES,** gr f 14/3 Montjeu (IRE)—Etroubles (FR) (Indian Ridge) (77220) **Scuderia Pieffegi**
70 B f 1/3 Aptitude (USA)—Gombeen (USA) (Private Account (USA)) **K. Abdullah**
71 Ch f 30/4 Rosen Kavalier (JPN)—Green Maid (USA) (Green Dancer (USA)) (29601) **S. Friborg**
72 B c 21/2 Fasliyev (USA)—Heroine (FR) (Highest Honor (FR)) (57915) **G. Algranti**
73 Ch f 17/3 Danehill Dancer (IRE)—Hint of Silver (USA) (Alysheba (USA)) (51480) **Skymarc Farm Inc.**
74 **HOLDING (IRE),** b f 9/3 Montjeu (IRE)—Heaven Only Knows (High Top) (128700) **Allevamento La Nuova**
75 B c 27/3 Kahyasi—Imbabala (Zafonic (USA)) **K. Abdullah**
76 B f 6/4 Anabaa (USA)—Kiss Me Goodknight (First Trump) (29601) **D. Jacob**
77 Gr ro c 1/5 Mizzen Mast (USA)—Louis d'or (USA) (Mr Prospector (USA)) **K. Abdullah**
78 Gr f 1/3 Verglas (IRE)—Louve d'arabie (FR) (Loup Solitaire (USA)) (32175) **S. Friborg**
79 B f 11/4 Dalakhani (IRE)—Maria de La Luz (Machiavellian (USA)) (51480) **Mr Ehrnrooth**
80 **MISTAKEN IDENTITY (IRE),** b c 6/2 Vettori (IRE)—Misplace (IRE) (Green Desert (USA)) **Laghi Snc**
81 Ch c 26/3 Rock of Gibraltar (IRE)—Monetary (GER) (Winged Love (IRE)) (38610) **A & C Borsani**
82 B f 30/3 Pivotal—Napoli (Baillamont (USA)) **Niarchos Famille**
83 **NIGHTDANCE SUN (GER),** b f 11/3 Monsun (GER)—

Nightdance (GER) (Shareef Dancer (USA)) **Ecurie Monceaux**
84 **NOUVELLE MUSIQUE (IRE),** b f 26/4 Nayef (USA)—Contemporary (IRE) (Alzao (USA)) **Allevamento La Nuova**
85 Ch f 1/1 Sulamani (USA)—Obscura (USA) (Mr Prospector (USA)) **Niarchos Famille**
86 B f 18/2 Danehill Dancer (IRE)—Onda Nova (USA) (Keos (USA)) **Niarchos Famille**
87 **PARTY ANIMAL (FR),** b c 1/1 Dream Well (FR)—Spring Party (IRE) (Anabaa (USA)) **Ecurie Bouchard**
88 **PLACE IN THE SUN,** b c 24/2 Dubai Destination (USA)—

Star On Stage (Sadler's Wells (USA)) **Allevamento La Nuova**
89 **PLANET FIVE (USA),** b br c 28/1 Storm Cat (USA)—Six Perfections (FR) (Celtic Swing) **Niarchos Famille**
90 B c 11/2 Domedriver (IRE)—Remote Romance (IRE) (Irish River (FR)) **Niarchos Famille**
91 B c 2/2 Danehill Dancer (IRE)—Second Burst (IRE) (Sadler's Wells (USA)) (180180) **Ecurie Bouchard**
92 **SKAMAR (IRE),** b c 22/4 Marju (IRE)—Lunaska (FR) (Ashkalani (IRE)) (61132) **Sanremo '85 Srl**
93 Ch f 30/1 Diesis—Skiable (IRE) (Niniski (USA)) **K. Abdullah**
94 B c 12/2 Anabaa (USA)—Spacecraft (Distant View (USA)) **K. Abdullah**
95 **SPAMIX (IRE),** b c 24/3 Linamix (FR)—Spa (Sadler's Wells (USA)) (51480) **Allevamento La Nuova**
96 **SPECIAL GALILEO (IRE),** b c 2/3 Galileo (IRE)—Special Oasis (Green Desert (USA)) **Ecurie Bouchard**
97 Gr f 9/4 Fasliyev (USA)—Splendida Idea (IRE) (Kenmare (FR)) (19304) **P. Rossier**
98 Ch c 1/3 Verglas (IRE)—Star des Evees (FR) (Moulin) (51480) **Sanremo '85 Srl**
99 B c 8/3 Rock of Gibraltar (IRE)—Swandor (USA) (Swain (IRE)) (28957) **Mr Borsani**
100 B f 21/4 Tiger Hill (IRE)—Tango Queen (USA) (Kingmambo (USA)) **Ecurie Monceaux**
101 Gr c 26/4 Domedriver (IRE)—Three Mysteries (IRE) (Linamix (FR)) (48262) **Niarchos Famille**
102 B f 7/2 Kingmambo (USA)—Visions of Clarity (IRE) (Sadler's Wells (USA)) **Niarchos Famille**
103 **WONDER LUP (IRE),** b c 5/4 Montjeu (IRE)—

Saperlipoupette (FR) (Highest Honor (FR)) (122265) **Ecurie Bouchard**
104 **YANGON (USA),** ch c 24/3 Storm Cat (USA)—Shiva (JPN) (Hector Protector (USA)) **Niarchos Famille**
105 B c 15/3 Sadler's Wells (USA)—Yogya (USA) (Riverman (USA)) **Niarchos Famille**

Jockey (flat): C. P. Lemaire, S. Pasquier, T. Thulliez.

31   MR R. BASTIMAN, Wetherby
Postal: **Goosemoor Farm, Warfield Lane, Cowthorpe, Wetherby, West Yorkshire, LS22 5EU**
Contacts: **PHONE (01423) 359397 MOBILE (07976) 282976**

1 **BARATARIA**, 6, ch g Barathea (IRE)—Aethra (USA) **Coal Trade Partnership**
2 **BORDERLESCOTT**, 6, b g Compton Place—Jeewan **Border Rail & Plant Limited**
3 **CABOURG (IRE)**, 5, b g Danehill (USA)—Loire Valley (IRE) **Ms M. Austerfield**
4 **CONJECTURE**, 6, b g Danzig (USA)—Golden Opinion (USA) **Mrs C. B. Bastiman**
5 **ISLAND KING (IRE)**, 5, br g Turtle Island (IRE)—Love of Paris **Ms M. Austerfield**
6 **JIMLESCOTT**, 4, b g Bertolini (USA)—North Pine **Border Rail & Plant Limited**
7 **JOSAMA**, 4, br f Desert Sun—Edge of Darkness **I. B. Barker**
8 **LITTLE LILY MORGAN**, 5, gr m Kayf Tara—Cool Grey **J. E. Endersby**
9 **MAROMITO (IRE)**, 11, b g Up And At 'em—Amtico **Mrs C. B. Bastiman**
10 **MISS LIGHTNING**, 5, b m Mujahid (USA)—Salu **Mrs A. Dyer**
11 **MONSIEUR DUMAS (IRE)**, 4, b g Iron Mask (USA)—Serenity **Chris Myers & Partners**
12 **ON EVERY STREET**, 7, b g Singspiel (IRE)—Nekhbet **R. Bastiman**
13 **ONLY A GRAND**, 4, b f Cloudings (IRE)—Magic Orb **S. N. Lorimer**
14 **OWED**, 6, b g Lujain (USA)—Nightingale **R. Bastiman**
15 **SMIDDY HILL**, 6, b m Factual (USA)—Hello Hobson's (IRE) **I. B. Barker**
16 **VALIANT ROMEO**, 8, b g Primo Dominie—Desert Lynx (IRE) **Mrs P. Bastiman**

THREE-YEAR-OLDS

17 **HABBIE HEIGHTS**, b f Josr Algarhoud (IRE)—Hello Hobson's (IRE) **The McMaster Springford Partnership**
18 **WARNERS BAY (IRE)**, b c Iron Mask (USA)—Romangoddess (IRE) **P. Crabtree**

TWO-YEAR-OLDS

19 B c 28/2 Sampower Star—Fishy (Irish River (FR)) (3500) **R. Bastiman**
20 **SECRET CITY (IRE)**, b g 3/3 City On A Hill (USA)—
Secret Combe (IRE) (Mujadil (USA)) (8500) **Ms M. Austerfield**

Other Owners: Mr K. R. Barker, Mr Robin Bastiman, Mrs P. Bastiman, Mr David Dickson, Mr John Dyer, Mr C. Hopton, Mr Brown McMaster, Mrs Jean McMaster, Mr Chris Myers, Mr Paul Myers, Mr Hugh T. Redhead, Mr G. J. Smith, Mr S. M. Taylor.

Assistant Trainer: H Bastiman & Miss R Bastiman

Amateur: Miss R. Bastiman.

32   MR A. J. BATEMAN, Minehead
Postal: **Broadwood Farm, Dunster, Minehead, Somerset, TA24 6TA**
Contacts: **PHONE (01643) 822111 FAX (01643) 822111 MOBILE (07967) 367251**
E-MAIL **abrlimited@gmail.com**

1 **DUMARAN (IRE)**, 10, b g Be My Chief (USA)—Pine Needle **Old & Optimistic Partnership**
2 **FOREVER DREAM**, 10, b g Afzal—Quadrapol **Mr W. McKibbin & Mr A. Stevens**
3 **FREMANTLE DOCTOR (FR)**, 8, b g Gildoran—Glen Breeze (IRE) **Notre Cheval Partnership**
4 **GOOD BOOK (IRE)**, 10, b g Good Thyne (USA)—Book of Rules (IRE) **T. M. Evans**
5 **MILLARDS LAD (IRE)**, 9, b g Flemensfirth (USA)—Toransha **T. M. Evans**
6 **OSOKENDA**, 8, b m Teenoso (USA)—Song of Kenda **J. M. Wingfield Digby**
7 **SUPREME DE PAILLE (IRE)**, 6, b g Supreme Leader—Wondermac (IRE) **T. M. Evans**

Other Owners: Aaron Bateman Racing Ltd, Mr P. C. Browne, Mr W. McKibbin, Mr A. Stevens.

Assistant Trainer: Miss R. Booth

33   MR B. P. J. BAUGH, Stoke on Trent
Postal: **Brooklands Farm, Park Lane, Audley, Stoke on Trent**
Contacts: **STABLES (01782) 723144 HOME (01782) 723144 MOBILE (07771) 693666**

1 **AGGBAG**, 4, b g Fath (USA)—Emaura **Mr J. Singh**
2 **AIRMAN (IRE)**, 5, b g Danehill (USA)—Jiving **Saddle Up Racing**
3 **ARCHIRONDEL**, 10, b g Bin Ajwaad (IRE)—Penang Rose (NZ) **M. C. Masters**
4 **AVONCREEK**, 4, b g Tipsy Creek (USA)—Avondale Girl (IRE) **Messrs Chrimes, Winn & Wilson**
5 **BOBERING**, 8, b g Bob's Return (IRE)—Ring The Rafters **Mr J. H. Chrimes & Mr & Mrs G. W. Hannam**

MR B. P. J. BAUGH—continued

6 **BRET MAVERICK (IRE),** 4, b g Josr Algarhoud (IRE)—
Shady Street (USA) **Mr J. H. Chrimes & Mr & Mrs G. W. Hannam**
7 **GARRYA,** 4, ch c Mark of Esteem (IRE)—Sherkova (USA) **Miss S. M. Potts**
8 **JOE JO STAR,** 6, b g Piccolo—Zagreb Flyer **Mr J. Singh**
9 **JUST SPIKE,** 5, ch g Cayman Kai (IRE)—Grandads Dream **Mr C. R. Watts**
10 **KIELTY'S FOLLY,** 4, gr g Weet-A-Minute (IRE)—Three Sweeties **Saddle Up Racing**
11 **MAYS LOUISE,** 4, ch f Sir Harry Lewis (USA)—Maysimp (IRE) **Mr J. H. Chrimes & Mr & Mrs G. W. Hannam**
12 **MINNIE MILL,** 4, b f Mind Games—Sometime Never (IRE) **B. Hatton**
13 **MISTER BENJI,** 9, b g Catrail (USA)—Katy-Q (IRE) **Mr J. H. Chrimes & Mr & Mrs G. W. Hannam**
14 **REMINISCENT (IRE),** 9, b g Kahyasi—Eliza Orzeszkowa (IRE) **Miss S. M. Potts**
15 **SCAMPERDALE,** 6, br g Compton Place—Miss Up N Go **Saddle Up Racing**
16 **TANFORAN,** 6, b g Mujahid (USA)—Florentynna Bay **F. Gillespie**
17 **TOWN HOUSE,** 6, gr m Paris House—Avondale Girl (IRE) **J. H. Chrimes**

THREE-YEAR-OLDS

18 **AMBER RIDGE,** b g Tumbleweed Ridge—Amber Brown **Saddle Up Racing**
19 **JOHN POTTS,** b g Josr Algarhoud (IRE)—Crown City (USA) **Miss J. A. Price**

Other Owners: W. G. Hannam, Mrs C. Hannam, Mrs M. Robinson, Mr K. V. Robinson, J. M. Winn.

Assistant Trainer: S Potts

Apprentice: Sonia Eaton.

---

34 · MR C. C. BEALBY, Grantham
Postal: **North Lodge, Barrowby, Grantham, Lincolnshire, NG32 1DH**
Contacts: **OFFICE (01476) 564568 FAX (01476) 572391 MOBILE (07831) 538689**
E-MAIL chris@northlodgeracing.co.uk WEBSITE www.northlodgeracing.co.uk

1 **ASHWELL (IRE),** 9, gr g Anshan—Willshego **Mrs E. A. Bingley**
2 **BENNYNTHEJETS (IRE),** 6, b g Beneficial—Lucky Adventure (IRE) **Payplan Partnership**
3 **CLEARLY MAD (IRE),** 5, b g Houmayoun (FR)—Madness In Motion **C. C. Bealby**
4 **DOCTOR KILBRIDE (IRE),** 5, ch g Fruits of Love (USA)—Kilbride Lass (IRE) **Michael Hill**
5 **DONT BE CROSS (IRE),** 5, b g Cape Cross—Doitmyway (IRE) **C. C. Bealby**
6 **EUMENE (IRE),** 5, ch g Grand Lodge (USA)—Pelagic **P. J. Vogt**
7 **EXTRA SMOOTH,** 7, gr g Cloudings (IRE)—Miss Ondee (FR) **Mr C. Martin Miss Claire Knight**
8 **GUS,** 5, b g Dr Fong (USA)—Tender Moment (USA) **A. Boughen**
9 **HARLAXTON (IRE),** 5, b g Lahib (USA)—Tweet Tweet **C. C. Bealby**
10 **JEANANN'S FIRST,** 5, ch m Shahrastani (USA)—Jeanann **T. Evans**
11 **LEYTE GULF (USA),** 5, b g Cozzene (USA)—Gabacha (USA) **R. A. Jenkinson**
12 **MACAMOTO (IRE),** 6, b g Muroto—Amach An Doras **Mrs E. A. Bingley**
13 **MOUSTIQUE DE L'ISLE (FR),** 8, gr g Dom Alco (FR)—Gratiene de l'Isle (FR) **Michael Hill**
14 **PASAGAI (FR),** 6, b g Panoramic—Saragay (FR) **I. S. Naylor**
15 **PERSIAN NATIVE (IRE),** 8, br g Anshan—Natina (IRE) **The Huntingdon Hopefuls**
16 **QUALIN DES BROSSES (FR),** 4, bl g Ungaro (GER)—Rosy des Brosses (FR) **The Glengarry Partnership**
17 **SPARROW HILLS (IRE),** 4, b g Moscow Society (USA)—Glenstal Forest (IRE) **The Glengarry Partnership**
18 **ST PANCRAS (IRE),** 8, b g Danehill Dancer (IRE)—Lauretta Blue (IRE) **Michael Hill**
19 **SURFACE TO AIR,** 7, b g Samraan (USA)—Travelling Lady **T. Urry**
20 **THE HERO SULLIVAN (IRE),** 7, b br g Muroto—You'll Never Know (IRE) **M. G. Kelly**
21 **THISTLECRAFT (IRE),** 9, b g Warcraft—Thistletopper **The Wally Partnership**
22 **TROOP THE COLOUR (USA),** 5, b br g Theatrical—Winsome **Mr J. A. Barson**
23 **WICKED NICE FELLA (IRE),** 10, b g Warcraft (USA)—Down Town To-Night **Mrs F. J. Martin**
24 **ZENDARO,** 6, b g Danzero (AUS)—Countess Maud **The Old Coat Partnership**

THREE-YEAR-OLDS

25 **CHEROKEE STAR,** br g Primo Valentino (IRE)—Me Cherokee **Triumph In Mind**
26 B g Mull of Kintyre (USA)—Fantastic Bid (USA) **Michael Hill**
27 **MAGIC OF THE ISLES,** ch g Kirkwall—Just Magic **Triumph In Mind**
28 **SULTAN OF THE SAND,** b g High Estate—Desert Bloom (FR) **Triumph In Mind**

MR C. C. BEALBY—continued

Other Owners: P. R. Armour, P. W. R. Bagshaw, M. H. Chatterton, P. M. Clarkson, Mrs I. A. Coles, Miss C. Knight, Mr C. L. Martin, Mr G. P. D. Rann, Mrs L. E. Rann, Mrs L. E. Tapson, Mr T. Wendels, R. F. Wright.

Assistant Trainer: Andrew Corbett

Jockey (flat): P. Makin. **Jockey (NH):** N. Fehily. **Conditional:** T. Messenger. **Amateur:** Mr M. Seston.

---

35 **MR P. BEAUMONT, Brandsby**
Postal: **Foulrice Farm, Brandsby, York, YO61 4SB**
Contacts: **PHONE (01347) 888208 FAX (01347) 889033 MOBILE (07801) 529783**
E-MAIL peter@peterbeaumontracing.com WEBSITE peterbeaumontracing.com

1 **ANOTHER CHARMER (IRE),** 7, b g Charmer—Avransha **Gay & Peter Hartley**
2 **BRADDOCK DASH,** 5, b g Rock City—Small **Mrs S. C. Sunter**
3 **CLASSIC HARRY,** 7, b g Classic Cliche (IRE)—Always Shining **N. W. A. Bannister**
4 **CLOUDLESS DAWN,** 8, b m Cloudings (IRE)—Charlotte's Emma **Us Lot**
5 **CURRAN (IRE),** 6, b g Good Thyne (USA)—Weather Along **Mrs C. M. Clarke**
6 **DIVVYS DREAM,** 6, gr g Environment Friend—Oriel Dream **M. T. Goulding**
7 **DOUBLE PAST,** 6, b g Yaheeb (USA)—Gale Blazer **Percy's Punters**
8 **DUN NA NGALL (IRE),** 6, ch g Fourstars Allstar (USA)—Aiguille (IRE) **D. R. & E. E. Brown**
9 **EMILY'S FLORA,** 5, ch m Alflora (IRE)—Emilymoore **Mrs A. E. Dixon**
10 **FALCON'S GUNNER,** 6, ch m Gunner B—Broadcast **Falcons Line Ltd**
11 **FALCON'S TRIBUTE (IRE),** 6, b m Beneficial—Early Storm (IRE) **Falcons Line Ltd**
12 **FENCOTE GOLD,** 8, ch g Bob's Return (IRE)—Goldaw **Mrs K. M. Richardson**
13 **FENCOTE MYSTERY,** 6, b g Classic Cliche (IRE)—Soupinette (FR) **Mrs K. M. Richardson**
14 **FINE PARCHMENT (IRE),** 5, b g Presenting—Run For Cover (IRE) **N. W. A. Bannister**
15 **I'M GUNNER BE FINE,** 6, ch g Gunner B—I'm Fine **Destiny Racing Club**
16 **ITALIANO,** 9, b g Emperor Jones (USA)—Elka (USA) **Mrs M. Turner**
17 **JAASSEY,** 5, b g Josr Algarhoud (IRE)—Saaryeh **Opal Racing**
18 **KING MAK,** 6, gr g Makbul—Miss Nova **Mrs M. Turner**
19 **MOOR SPIRIT,** 11, b g Nomadic Way (USA)—Navos **Mrs J. M. Plummer**
20 **MR PRICKLE (IRE),** 8, ch g Carroll House—Auntie Prickle Pin (IRE) **Smith Bannister Bowring**
21 **PEKIN (FR),** 5, b g Useful (FR)—Bayokalie (FR) **N. W. A. Bannister**
22 **SHERIFF'S FALCON (IRE),** 5, b m Presenting—Gale Eight (IRE) **Falcons Line Ltd**
23 **TIMMY MY BOY,** 7, b g Rakaposhi King—I'm Fine **Fellowship Of The Rose Partnership**
24 **WEE GEORGE,** 6, ch g Alflora (IRE)—Cherry Dee **Mrs M. Dilger**

Other Owners: Mr P. Allison, Mr Phillip Ambler, Mr N. W. A. Bannister, Mr Peter Beaumont, Mr Andrew Bird, Mr D. S. Bowring, Mr D. R. Brown, Mrs E. E. Brown, Mr J. M. Davenport, Mr J. Dent, Mrs P. A. H. Hartley, Mr P. A. H. Hartley, Mrs D. Lesley Holloway, Miss C. Hugill, Miss D. Midwinter, Mr S. M. Roberts, Mr W. L. Smith, Mr Colin Stirling, Mr Antony Wakeham, Mr P. Woodcock-Jones.

Assistant Trainer: Patrick Holmes

Jockey (NH): Paddy Aspell, Gary Berridge, Padge Whelan. **Amateur:** Mr Guy Brewer, Mr Miles Seston.

---

36 **MR R. M. BECKETT, Whitsbury**
Postal: **Whitsbury Manor Stables, Whitsbury, Fordingbridge, Hampshire, SP6 3QQ**
Contacts: **PHONE (01725) 518889 FAX (01725) 518747 MOBILE (07802) 219022**
E-MAIL trainer@rbeckett.com WEBSITE www.rbeckett.com

1 **COME ON JONNY (IRE),** 6, b g Desert King (IRE)—Idle Fancy **A. E. Frost**
2 **LIPOCCO,** 4, br g Piccolo—Magical Dancer (IRE) **The Anagram Partnership**
3 **LOOK SO,** 4, b f Efisio—Last Look **J. H. Richmond-Watson**
4 **MASKED (IRE),** 7, b g Soviet Star (USA)—Moon Masquerade (IRE) **P. G. Weeks**
5 **PLAYFUL,** 5, b m Piccolo—Autumn Affair **Mrs L. M. Aykroyd**
6 **PRINCE OF DELPHI,** 5, b g Royal Applause—Princess Athena **L. G. Albertini**

THREE-YEAR-OLDS

7 **BETONART,** b f Tamure (IRE)—Heather Honey **M. R. Green**
8 **BILLY HOT ROCKS (IRE),** b c Intikhab (USA)—Rock Abbey (IRE) **Chimera Racing**
9 **CALAMANSAC,** ch f Alhaarth (IRE)—Bistranova (USA) **Lady Cobham**
10 **CANDIDA'S BEAU,** b g Bertolini (USA)—Breezy Louise **Lynch, Nadir & Lycett Green**

MR R. M. BECKETT—continued

11 **CELTIC SLIPPER (IRE)**, b f Anabaa (USA)—Celtic Silhouette (FR) **P. D. Savill**
12 **DIVINE POWER**, b f Kyllachy—Tiriana **Mrs J. Minton**
13 **FR DOMINIC (USA)**, b br c Arch (USA)—Collodia (USA) **R. A. Pegum**
14 **HEARTBUSTER (IRE)**, gr g Alhaarth (IRE)—Special Lady (FR) **A. E. Frost**
15 **HOBBY**, b f Robellino (USA)—Wydah **Larksborough Stud Limited**
16 **HOURI (IRE)**, b f Alhaarth (IRE)—Witching Hour (IRE) **Mrs L. M. Aykroyd**
17 **ISINKSO (IRE)**, gr c Clodovil (IRE)—Storm Pearl (IRE) **Mr J. F. Perryman**
18 **ISTRIA (USA)**, b f Zavata (USA)—Estri (USA) **Morecombe and Not So Wise**
19 **LOOK HERE**, b f Hernando (FR)—Last Look **J. H. Richmond-Watson**
20 **LOWRY'S ART**, b f Night Shift (USA)—Creme Caramel (USA) **M. R. Green**
21 **MARCHPANE**, b f Olden Times—Ecstasy **A. D. G. Oldrey**
22 **MILLE FEUILLE (IRE)**, b f Choisir (AUS)—Watch The Clock **P. K. Gardner**
23 **MISTIC ACADEMY (IRE)**, ch f Royal Academy (USA)—Mistic Sun **Roberts & Milner**
24 **MIZOOKA**, b f Tobougg (IRE)—Tetravella (IRE) **M S T Partnership**
25 **MOUNT LAVINIA (IRE)**, b f Montjeu (IRE)—Havinia **Thurloe Thoroughbreds XX**
26 **MULLEIN**, b f Oasis Dream—Gipsy Moth **Landmark Racing Limited**
27 **MY MATE PETE (IRE)**, b g Captain Rio—Lady Peculiar (CAN) **R. A. Pegum**
28 **POYLE DEE DEE**, b f Oasis Dream—Poyle Fizz **C. Wiggins**
29 **PRINCE AFRAM**, b c Fraam—Miletrian Cares (IRE) **Young Guns Syndicate**
30 **PSYCHO KILLER**, b f Best of The Bests (IRE)—Kasamba
31 **PURELY BY CHANCE**, b f Galileo (IRE)—Sioux Chef **Lady Green**
32 **QUICK FLASH**, b f Fantastic Light (USA)—Brief Glimpse (IRE) **Jock Strap Partners**
33 **RED ICON**, b f Red Ransom (USA)—Blue Icon **J. H. Richmond-Watson**
34 **RED RUMOUR (IRE)**, b c Redback—Church Mice (IRE) **Mr R. J. Roberts**
35 **RICHCAR (IRE)**, b c Almutawakel—Gerobies Girl (USA) **Mr R. J. Roberts**
36 **SPELL CASTER**, ch f Bertolini (USA)—Princess Claudia (IRE) **Mr D. P. Barrie & Mr M. J. Rees**
37 **SPIN AGAIN (IRE)**, b c Intikhab (USA)—Queen of The May (IRE) **R. H. W. Morecombe**
38 **SPOTTY MULDOON (IRE)**, b c Mull of Kintyre (USA)—Fashion Guide (IRE) **Axis Partnership**
39 **TACTFUL (IRE)**, b f Intikhab (USA)—Crozon **Mrs L. M. Aykroyd**
40 **TAMRAI DANCER**, b f Tamure (IRE)—Rail Cat **Whitsbury Hopefuls**
41 **TURN LEFT (IRE)**, b c Xaar—Stamatina **R. S. G. Jones & Norman Brunskill**
42 **WITHOUT A PRAYER (IRE)**, ch c Intikhab (USA)—Prayer (IRE) **McDonagh Murphy & Nixon**
43 **ZIPPI JAZZMAN (USA)**, ch c Dixieland Band (USA)—Redeem (USA) **Jones, Adams & Williams**

TWO-YEAR-OLDS

44 B c 26/2 Nayef (USA)—Agony Aunt (Formidable (USA)) (46331) **R. A. Pegum**
45 **AKABAR**, b c 14/4 Piccolo—Fredora (Inchinor) (24000)
46 B c 12/4 One Cool Cat (USA)—Alpine Park (IRE) (Barathea (IRE)) (3000) **M. R. Green**
47 **AMEN TO THAT (IRE)**, b f 4/3 Acclamation—In Time (Generous (IRE)) (30243) **R. A. Pegum**
48 **ASAINT NEEDS BRASS (USA)**, b br c 23/1 Lion Hearted (USA)—
British Columbia (Selkirk (USA)) (24000) **Mrs I. M. Beckett**
49 **AUGUST DAYS (IRE)**, ch f 18/3 Noverre (USA)—
Vitesse (IRE) (Royal Academy (USA)) **Pump & Plant Services Ltd**
50 B f 1/4 Tobougg (IRE)—Barakat (Bustino) (72000) **D. B. Clark**
51 **BELLE DES AIRS (IRE)**, ch f 18/3 Dr Fong (USA)—Belle Reine (King of Kings (IRE)) **Mrs H. I. Slade**
52 **BLUE NYMPH**, ch f 17/3 Selkirk (USA)—Blue Icon (Peintre Celebre (USA)) **J. H. Richmond-Watson**
53 **BOHO CHIC**, b f 28/3 Kyllachy—Summer Lightning (IRE) (Tamure (IRE)) **P. K. Gardner**
54 **BOTHY**, ch c 5/3 Pivotal—Villa Carlotta (Rainbow Quest (USA)) **J. H. Richmond-Watson**
55 **CRESHENDO**, b c 3/4 Kyllachy—Dry Wit (IRE) (Desert Prince (IRE)) (1428) **Mrs L. M. Aykroyd**
56 B c 4/4 Tobougg (IRE)—Cumbrian Concerto (Petong) (14156) **Mrs I. M. Beckett**
57 **DREAMWALK (IRE)**, b c 24/4 Bahri (USA)—Celtic Silhouette (FR) (Celtic Swing) (50000) **P. D. Savill**
58 B f 8/3 Fantastic Light (USA)—Ecstasy (Pursuit of Love) **A. D. G. Oldrey**
59 **GILBERTIAN**, b c 20/2 Sakhee—Fudge (Polar Falcon (USA)) **The Turf Club**
60 B c 20/4 Intikhab (USA)—Institutrice (IRE) (College Chapel) (16730) **G. R. Pooley**
61 **IT'S TOAST (IRE)**, b f 25/3 Diktat—Kapria (FR) (Simon du Desert (FR))
62 B f 3/4 Intikhab (USA)—Kalimar (IRE) (Bigstone (IRE)) (41826) **P. K. Gardner**
63 **KAYCEEBEE**, b c 3/3 Cyrano de Bergerac—
Twice Upon A Time (Primo Dominie) (11000) **The Millennium Madness Partnership**
64 Ch c 6/3 Bertolini (USA)—Miss Honeypenny (IRE) (Old Vic) **D. J. M. Newell**
65 **MR UDAGAWA**, b c 3/3 Bahamian Bounty—Untold Riches (Red Ransom (USA)) (28000) **Mr B. R. Ingram**
66 B c 19/2 Selkirk (USA)—Never A Doubt (Night Shift (USA)) (100000) **Thurloe Thoroughbreds XXIII**
67 **OLYNARD (IRE)**, b c 7/5 Exceed And Excel (AUS)—Reddening (Blushing Flame (USA)) (33461) **Mr R. J. Roberts**
68 **OUTOFOIL (IRE)**, b c 18/2 King's Best (USA)—Simplicity (Polish Precedent (USA)) (20591) **I. J. Heseltine**
69 **PERFECT AFFAIR (USA)**, b c 18/4 Perfect Soul (IRE)—
Caribbean Affair (USA) (Red Ransom (USA)) (37000) **I. J. Heseltine**

MR R. M. BECKETT—continued

70 **PICK A PURSE**, ch c 12/4 Piccolo—Silver Purse (Interrex (CAN)) (9000)
71 **POYLE MEG**, b f 22/1 Dansili—Lost In Lucca (Inchinor) (35000) **C. Wiggins**
72 **RAGGLE TAGGLE (IRE)**, b f 24/2 Tagula (IRE)—Jesting (Muhtarram (USA)) (15000) **Lady Marchwood**
73 **RHYDIAN**, ch c 11/1 Monsieur Bond (IRE)—Miss Flirtatious (Piccolo) (6434) **Mr R. J. Roberts**
74 B c 19/1 Efisio—Royal Jade (Last Tycoon) (40000)
75 **ROYAL SUPERLATIVE**, b f 10/1 King's Best—Supereva (IRE) (Sadler's Wells (USA))
76 B f 17/3 Bahri (USA)—Sea Nymph (IRE) (Spectrum (IRE)) (5000)
77 B c 17/4 Lomitas—Silvertone (FR) (Highest Honor (FR)) **A. E. Frost**
78 **STEEPLE CASTER**, ch c 24/4 Compton Place—
                      Antonia's Double (Primo Dominie) (24000) **Mr D. P. Barrie & Mr M. J. Rees**
79 **SUCH OPTIMISM**, b f 21/3 Sakhee (USA)—Optimistic (Reprimand) (20000) **G. C. Myddelton**
80 B c 22/2 Johannesburg (USA)—Sweet Deimos (Green Desert (USA)) (50000) **M. R. Green**
81 **TIPONI (IRE)**, b f 23/3 Traditionally (USA)—Capestar (IRE) (Cape Cross) **D. J. M. Newell**
82 **TOP BIRD**, b f 25/4 Robellino (USA)—High Bird (IRE) (Polar Falcon (USA)) (1238) **Mrs J. Langton**
83 **TOP TOWN GIRL**, b f 17/2 Efisio—Halland Park Girl (IRE) (Primo Dominie) **Landmark Racing Limited**
84 **WETHERBY PLACE (IRE)**, ch f 19/4 King's Best (USA)—
                      Summer Sunset (IRE) (Grand Lodge (USA)) (35392) **R. A. Pegum**
85 B f 22/4 Xaar—Zanella (IRE) (Nordico (USA)) (6000) **The Turf Club**

Other Owners: D. P. Barrie, Mr E. Bonsor, N. Brunskill, Miss S. Davis, P. A. Deal, G. J. Head, B. E. Holland, R. S. G. Jones, Mr G. N. D. Locock, R. Lycett Green, Mr M. Lynch, W. R. Milner, Mr P. G. Murphy, O. J. W. Pawle, D. F. Powell, Mr D. Redvers, M. J. Rees, S. Smith, Mrs H. L. Smyly, Mr J. I. Spence, J. A. B. Stafford, D. J. Taylor, Major I. M. Thompson, E. M. Thornton, Mrs S. Thornton, Miss L. J. Whitehorn, C. Wilson.

Assistant Trainer: J Trim

Jockey (flat): S. Sanders. **Apprentice:** R. Felton.

---

37 MR M. L. W. BELL, Newmarket
Postal: Fitzroy House, Newmarket, Suffolk, CB8 0JT
Contacts: **PHONE (01638) 666567 FAX (01638) 668000 MOBILE (07802) 264514
E-MAIL mlwbell.racing@virgin.net WEBSITE www.michaelbellracing.co.uk**

1 **DIRECT DEBIT (IRE)**, 5, b g Dansili—Dimple **W. Maguire**
2 **FLY FREE**, 4, b f Halling (USA)—Gipsy Moth **Sir M. W. J. Smurfit**
3 **FURNACE (IRE)**, 4, b g Green Desert (USA)—Lyrical Dance (USA) **Highclere Thoroughbred Racing XXXV**
4 **GAVROCHE (IRE)**, 7, b h Docksider (USA)—Regal Revolution **M Khan X2**
5 **GOLD PROSPECT**, 4, b br g Rainbow Quest (USA)—Grain of Gold **B. J. Warren**
6 **GULL WING (IRE)**, 4, ch f In The Wings—Maycocks Bay **Lady Bamford**
7 **HIGHLAND LEGACY**, 4, ch c Selkirk (USA)—Generous Lady **B. J. Warren**
8 **HOH MIKE (IRE)**, 4, ch c Intikhab (USA)—Magical Peace (USA) **Mr M. Lynch & the late Mr D. Allport**
9 **JUNIPER GIRL (IRE)**, 5, b m Revoque (IRE)—Shajara (FR) **M. B. Hawtin**
10 **KING'S BASTION (IRE)**, 4, b g Royal Applause—Aunty Mary **E. J. Ware**
11 **METAPHORIC (IRE)**, 4, b g Montjeu (IRE)—Virgin Hawk (USA) **The Royal Ascot Racing Club**
12 **MONTRACHET**, 4, ch f Singspiel (IRE)—Riberac **Mr & Mrs G. Middlebrook**
13 **OAT CUISINE**, 4, b f Mujahid (USA)—Gazebo **Mrs G. E. Rowland-Clark**
14 **RAWDON (IRE)**, 7, b g Singspiel (IRE)—Rebecca Sharp **E. J. Ware**
15 **REGIME (IRE)**, 4, b c Golan (IRE)—Juno Madonna (IRE) **Highclere Thoroughbred Racing XL**
16 **SPICE ROUTE**, 4, ch g King's Best (USA)—Zanzibar (IRE) **Mrs G.Rowland-Clark & Mr K.J.Mercer**

THREE-YEAR-OLDS

17 **AFRICAN FLIGHT**, b f Hawk Wing (USA)—Valiantly **Mr L. C. Baxter**
18 **ALLIED POWERS (IRE)**, b c Invincible Spirit (IRE)—Always Friendly **Mr David Fish & Mr Edward Ware**
19 **AMBER MOON**, ch f Singspiel (IRE)—Merewood (USA) **Mr & Mrs G. Middlebrook**
20 **ARTSU**, b g Bahamian Bounty—War Shanty **Mrs M. S. Gershinson**
21 **AURA**, b f Barathea (IRE)—Finger of Light **Highclere Thoroughbred Racing**
22 **BADALONA**, b f Cape Cross (IRE)—Badawi (USA) **Marwan Al Maktoum**
23 **BARBARY BOY (FR)**, b c Rock of Gibraltar (IRE)—Don't Worry Me (IRE) **Thurloe Thoroughbreds XX**
24 **BONNE**, b f Namid—Jouet **Mr and Mrs R. Tooth**
25 **CALYPSO CHARMS**, b f Dansili—Chrysalis **Mr & Mrs Christopher Wright**
26 **DANCING ABBIE (USA)**, ch f Theatrical—Sicy d'alsace (FR) **Marwan Al Maktoum**
27 **DRESDEN DOLL (USA)**, ch f Elusive Quality—Crimson Conquest (USA) **Marwan Al Maktoum**
28 **FAR GONE**, b f Diktat—Fairy Jackie (IRE) **R. Frisby**

MR M. L. W. BELL—continued

29 **GLITZ (IRE)**, b f Hawk Wing (USA)—Lunar Lustre (IRE) **Highclere Thoroughbred Racing (VCI)**
30 **GOLDEN BISHOP**, ch g Medicean—Hen Harrier **Sir Thomas Pilkington**
31 **GREAT CHARM (IRE)**, b g Orpen (USA)—Briery (IRE) **Mr & Mrs G. Middlebrook**
32 **GUNNADOIT (USA)**, b br g Almutawakel—Gharam (USA) **The One Carat Partnership**
33 **HONKY TONK SALLY**, b f Dansili—Flower Girl **W. J. Gredley**
34 **HOUSE OF LORDS (USA)**, b br c Doneraile Court (USA)—Farrfesheena (USA) **Marwan Al Maktoum**
35 **I'LL GET BY**, b g Red Ransom (USA)—Way O'gold (USA) **W. J. Gredley**
36 **INK SPOT**, b g Diktat—Good Girl (IRE) **Mrs L. B. K. Bone**
37 **ITALIAN GODDESS**, ch f Medicean—Little Italy (IRE) **The Hon James Broughton & Lord Fairhaven**
38 **JUST LIKE A WOMAN**, b f Observatory (USA)—Always On My Mind **Mascalls Stud**
39 **LOVEINANELEVATOR**, ch f Dr Fong (USA)—Londonnetdotcom (IRE) **R. Frisby**
40 **MARYQUEENOFSCOTS (IRE)**, b f Fantastic Light (USA)—Marie de Blois (IRE) **Mrs M. Bryce**
41 **MEZZANISI (IRE)**, b g Kalanisi (IRE)—Mezzanine **Mr T. Redman & Mr P. Philipps**
41 **MILANOLLO**, b f Soviet Star (USA)—Military Tune (IRE) **R. Frisby**
43 **MISS BROWN TO YOU (IRE)**, b f Fasliyev—Almaaseh (USA) **W. J. Gredley**
44 **PAYNE RELIEF (IRE)**, b br f Desert Prince (IRE)—Saffron Crocus **D. W. & L. Y. Payne**
45 **POULAINE BLEUE**, b f Bertolini (USA)—Blue Indigo (FR) **G.Rowland-Clark,C.Rhodes & A.Buxton**
46 **PROFUMO AFFAIR**, b c Oasis Dream—Affair of State (IRE) **W. Maguire**
47 **RAMPRAKASH**, b c Best of The Bests (IRE)—Missy Dancer **Scotney,Asplin,Symonds & Chellingworth**
48 **RED EXPRESSO (IRE)**, ch g Intikhab (USA)—Cafe Creme (IRE) **T. Neill**
49 **RED LINNET**, b f Cape Cross (IRE)—Red Conquest **Marwan Al Maktoum**
50 **REDFORD (IRE)**, b c Bahri (USA)—Ida Lupino (IRE) **Highclere T'bred Racing (Housemaster)**
51 **SAKHEELA**, br f Sakhee (USA)—Salinova (FR) **Baron Von Oppenheim**
52 **SAVANNAH POPPY (IRE)**, b f Statue of Liberty (USA)—Refined (IRE) **C. N. Wright**
53 **SEA CHORUS**, b f Singspiel (IRE)—Island Race **The Eclipse Partnership**
54 **SHAKER (IRE)**, b f Key of Luck (USA)—Gravieres (FR) **T. G. N. Burrage**
55 **SILK GALLERY (USA)**, b f Kingmambo (USA)—Moon Flower (IRE) **Mr & Mrs G. Middlebrook**
56 **STAR CHOICE**, ch c Choisir (AUS)—Bay Queen **B. J. Warren**
57 **STATUS (IRE)**, b c Pivotal—Hidalguia (IRE) **Highclere Thoroughbred Racing (Lake Con)**
58 **SUMMERS LEASE**, b f Pivotal—Finlaggan **Mrs C. R. Philipson & Mrs H. G. Lascelles**
59 **THAT'S ALL (IRE)**, b c Rock of Gibraltar (IRE)—Marigold (FR) **W. J. Gredley**
60 **THE BETCHWORTH KID**, b g Tobougg (IRE)—Runelia **W. H. Ponsonby**
61 **TOP DRAW (USA)**, b f Elusive Quality (USA)—Cala (FR) **Marwan Al Maktoum**
62 **TOPAZES**, ch c Cadeaux Genereux—Topkamp **Baron Von Oppenheim**
63 **WOOD CHORUS**, b f Singspiel (IRE)—Woodbeck **H. J. P. Farr**
64 **WRITINGONTHEWALL (IRE)**, b c Danetime (IRE)—Badee'a (IRE) **M. Tabor**

TWO-YEAR-OLDS

65 **ADBURY**, ch c 12/3 Compton Place—Science Fiction (Starborough)
66 **ADVISOR**, gr c 24/4 Anabaa (USA)—Armilina (FR) (Linamix (FR)) (77220) **The Royal Ascot Racing Club**
67 **ART CONNOISSEUR (IRE)**, b c 20/3 Lucky Story (USA)—
              Withorwithoutyou (IRE) (Danehill (USA)) (55000) **Mr Richard Green**
68 B c 27/3 Fath (USA)—Auriga (Belmez (USA)) (32000) **Thurloe Thoroughbreds**
69 **BAHAMIAN BABE**, ch f 7/2 Bahamian Bounty—
              Baby Bunting (Wolfhound (USA)) (5500) **Mrs P. D. Gray & Mr H. Farr**
70 **BALLANTRAE (IRE)**, b f 24/3 Diktat—Badawi (USA) (Diesis)
71 **BIN END**, b c 2/3 King's Best (USA)—
              Overboard (IRE) (Rainbow Quest (USA)) **The Hon Mrs J. M. Corbett & Mr Chris Wright**
72 **BRIGHT WIRE**, b c 14/3 Elusive City (USA)—Alinga (IRE) (King's Theatre (IRE)) (61132) **T. G. N. Burrage**
73 **BUBSES BOY**, ch c 5/4 Needwood Blade—Welcome Home (Most Welcome) (27000) **Mr C. Gershinson**
74 B f 14/4 Elusive Quality (USA)—Cala (FR) (Desert Prince (IRE)) **Marwan Al Maktoum**
75 **CAUGHT ON CAMERA**, b f 26/4 Red Ransom (USA)—Colorsnap (Shirley Heights) **Helena Springfield**
76 B f 8/2 Selkirk (USA)—China (Royal Academy (USA)) (65000) **Highclere Thoroughbred Racing(Persimmon)**
77 **DOVE MEWS**, b f 24/2 Namid—Flying Fulmar (Bahamian Bounty) **Sir Thomas Pilkington**
78 **EDDIE BOY**, b c 3/5 Tobougg (IRE)—Maristax (Reprimand) (80000) **Mr C. Gershinson**
79 B c 8/4 Mark of Esteem (IRE)—
              Granted (FR) (Cadeaux Genereux) (15000) **P.Deal, E.Kessly, A.Jenkins & J.Thompson**
80 **LA ADELITA (IRE)**, b f 11/4 Anabaa (USA)—Aiming (Highest Honor (FR)) (140000) **Mrs M. Bryce**
81 **LADY ARTEMISIA (IRE)**, b f 29/4 Montjeu (IRE)—
              Crimson Glory (Lycius (USA)) (26000) **Marco & Sarah Moretti**
82 **LOCHAN MOR**, b c 13/2 Kyllachy—Bright Moll (Mind Games) **Mr Andrew Buxton**
83 B f 14/2 Pivotal—Maycocks Bay (Muhtarram) (USA) **Lady Bamford**
84 Ch f 22/1 Dr Fong (USA)—Merewood (USA) (Woodman (USA)) **Mr & Mrs G. Middlebrook**
85 B f 6/3 Reel Buddy (USA)—Night Gypsy (Mind Games) (31000) **Mr R. P. B. Michaelson & Mr John Thompson**

MR M. L. W. BELL—continued

86 **NIGHT KNIGHT**, b c 13/3 Bachelor Duke (USA)—
Dark Albatross (USA) (Sheikh Albadou) (28313) **Scotney, Asplin, Symonds, Ball & Chelingworth**
87 B f 6/4 Red Ransom (USA)—Painted Moon (USA) (Gone West (USA)) **Marwan Al Maktoum**
88 Ch c 21/3 Stravinsky (USA)—
Peanut Gallery (USA) (Mister Baileys) (45000) **Bamber, Barnett, Cole, Hart, Manasseh, King**
89 B f 12/3 Alhaarth (IRE)—Pilgrim's Way (USA) (Gone West (USA)) (57914) **M. B. Hawtin**
90 **RED HORSE (IRE)**, ch c 20/3 Bachelor Duke (USA)—Miss Childrey (IRE) (Dr Fong (USA)) (65000) **R. I. Morris**
91 **RED ZOE (USA)**, b br f 22/3 Danehill Dancer (IRE)—Starbourne (IRE) (Sadler's Wells (USA)) (80000) **T. Neill**
92 B f 8/2 Pivotal—Sabreon (Caerleon (USA)) (75000) **M. L. W. Bell Racing Ltd**
93 B f 7/5 Elusive Quality (USA)—Saraa Ree (USA) (Caro) **Mr Christopher Wright**
94 **SECRET SOCIETY**, b c 18/4 Exceed And Excel (AUS)—Shady Point (IRE) (Unfuwain (USA)) **Marwan Al Maktoum**
95 **SICILIANDO**, b c 2/2 Bertolini (USA)—Donna Vita (Vettori (IRE)) (20000) **Mr W. J. Gredley**
96 B f 12/4 Beat Hollow—Sismique (Warning) **The Eclipse Partnership**
97 **SOFONISBA**, b f 4/3 Rock of Gibraltar (IRE)—
Lothlorien (USA) (Woodman (USA)) (22000) **Marco & Sarah Moretti**
98 **STEEL FREE (IRE)**, b f 21/1 Danehill Dancer (IRE)—Candelabra (Grand Lodge (USA)) (96524) **T. G. N. Burrage**
99 B c 15/3 Royal Applause—Subya (Night Shift (USA)) (62000) **R. Green**
100 B f 8/2 Hernando (FR)—Tawoos (FR) (Rainbow Quest (USA)) (20000) **Mr and Mrs R. Tooth**
101 B f 9/5 One Cool Cat (USA)—Termania (IRE) (Shirley Heights) (90089) **Mr. M. Tabor**
102 **TRI TO COLLECT**, b c 2/3 Intikhab (USA)—Tri Pac (IRE) (Fairy King (USA)) (12000) **The Player Syndicate**
103 B c 1/4 Baratheca (IRE)—
Urgent Liaison (IRE) (High Estate) (110000) **Highclere Thoroughbred Racing (Munnings)**
104 **VODKA SHOT (USA)**, b br f 16/4 Holy Bull (USA)—Absoluta (IRE) (Royal Academy (USA)) (16000) **C. N. Wright**
105 B f 8/2 Mujadil (USA)—Waaedah (USA) (Halling (USA)) (28000)
106 B c 10/3 Dubai Destination (USA)—Zanzibar (IRE) (In The Wings) (43000)
107 B br f 7/2 Highest Honor (FR)—
Zither (Zafonic (USA)) (32000) **Mr Luke Lillingston, Mr B. Burrough & Mr J. Root**

Other Owners: Estate of the Late Mr D. F. Allport, Mr D. Aspin, Mrs Michael Bell, Mr J. H. A. Broughton, Mrs S. Broughton, Mr K. E. Bushnell, A. R. F. Buxton, Miss H. P Chellingworth, C. Conroy, The Hon Mrs J. M. Corbett, S. M. Crown, P.A. Deal, D. W. Dennis, P. N. Dodding, Lord Fairhaven, Mr David Fish, N. J. Forman Hardy, Mrs R. M. Gray, Mrs S. J. Hearn, B. M. W. Hearn, The Hon H. Herbert, Mr D. T. Herbert, Highclere Thoroughbred Racing Ltd, Mrs A. M. Jenkins, Edward David Kessly, M. Khan, M. Khan, Mrs J. C. Lascelles, Mr Michael T. Lynch, C. G. Mackenzie, M. Manasseh, K. J. Mercer, Mrs S. Mercer, R. P. B. Michaelson, Mr G. Middlebrook, Mrs L. Middlebrook, Mr Oliver Pawle, Mr D. W. Payne, Mrs L. Y. Payne, P.A. Philipps, Mrs C. R. Philipson, T. S. Redman, Major C. E. R. C. Rhodes, Paul Robson, Mrs Audrey Scotney, Mr J. A. B. Stafford, Mr A. Symonds, Mr D. J. Taylor, J. A. Thompson, Mr Raymond Tooth, Mrs Debbie Tooth, Mrs J. A. Wright.

Assistant Trainer: Amy Weaver

Jockey (flat): H. Turner, J. Spencer. **Apprentice:** Luke Morris, Chris Hough.

---

38 MR J. A. BENNETT, Wantage
Postal: **2 Filley Alley, Letcombe Bassett, Wantage, Oxfordshire, OX12 9LT**
Contacts: **PHONE** (01235) 762163 **FAX** (01235) 762163 **MOBILE** (07771) 523076

1 **DARNAY'S BREEZE (IRE)**, 6, br m Darnay—Lomond's Breeze **Miss J. C. Blackwell**
2 **JAYED (IRE)**, 10, b br g Marju (IRE)—Taqreem (IRE) **Miss J. C. Blackwell**
3 **KING OF JAVA**, 7, br g Priolo (USA)—Krakatoa **Miss J. C. Blackwell**

Assistant Trainer: Miss J Blackwell

---

39 MR A. BERRY, Cockerham
Postal: **Moss Side Racing Stables, Crimbles Lane, Cockerham, Lancaster, LA2 0ES**
Contacts: **PHONE** (01524) 791179 **FAX** (01524) 791958 **MOBILE** (07880) 553515
E-MAIL mosssideracing@tiscali.co.uk **WEBSITE** www.alanberryracing.co.uk

1 **BOVERED (IRE)**, 4, b f Fayruz—Lucky Pick **A. Berry**
2 **CAMPO BUENO (FR)**, 6, b g Septieme Ciel (USA)—Herba Buena (FR) **Sporting Kings**
3 **GEORDIE DANCER (IRE)**, 6, b g Dansili—Awtaar (USA) **A. Berry**
4 **GRETHEL (IRE)**, 4, b f Fruits of Love (USA)—Stay Sharpe **Mrs L. White**
5 **KATIE BOO (IRE)**, 6, br m Namid—Misty Peak (IRE) **The Early Doors Partnership**
6 **MANGANO**, 4, b g Mujadil (USA)—Secret Dance **A. R. White**
7 **NEVERONAMONDAY (IRE)**, 4, br f Night Shift (USA)—Appalachia (IRE) **A. Berry**
8 **OBE ONE**, 8, b g Puissance—Plum Bold **A. Berry**

MR A. BERRY—continued

9 **PETER'S IMP (IRE)**, 13, b g Imp Society (USA)—Catherine Clare **A. Berry**
10 **PHOENIX NIGHTS (IRE)**, 8, b g General Monash (USA)—Beauty Appeal (USA) **I. A. Bolland**
11 **SCOTTY'S FUTURE (IRE)**, 10, b g Namaqualand (USA)—Persian Empress (IRE) **A. Berry**
12 **SIGNOR WHIPPEE**, 5, ch g Observatory (USA)—Revoltosa (IRE) **A. Berry**
13 **TELEPATHIC (IRE)**, 8, b g Mind Games—Madrina **A. Berry**
14 **THROW THE DICE**, 6, b g Lujain (USA)—Euridice (IRE) **E. R. H. Nisbet**
15 **WICKED WILMA (IRE)**, 4, b f Tagula (IRE)—Wicked **Auldyn Stud Limited**

THREE-YEAR-OLDS

16 **ANDRASTA**, b f Bertolini (USA)—Real Popcorn (IRE) **A. B. Parr**
17 **COMEONOVERVALERIE (IRE)**, b f Lend A Hand—Sky Pink **Galaxy Moss Side Racing Clubs**
18 **LOOK BUSY (IRE)**, b f Danetime (IRE)—Unfortunate **Mr A. Underwood**
19 **MAGNUSHOMESTWO (IRE)**, b g Val Royal (FR)—Classy Act **Pentakan Ltd**
20 **NEXT BEST**, b f Best of The Bests (IRE)—Lone Pine **W. Burns**
21 **NORTHWEST**, b g Reel Buddy (USA)—Adorable Cherub (USA) **Galaxy Moss Side Racing Clubs**
22 **TENDULKAR'S DIVA (IRE)**, b f Tendulkar (USA)—Daring Connection **South Yorkshire Racing**

TWO-YEAR-OLDS

23 B f 10/3 Intikhab (USA)—Algaira (USA) (Irish River (FR)) (5000) **P. Renoso**
24 B f 10/4 Tagula (IRE)—Ali Fortuna (IRE) (Ali-Royal (IRE)) (771)
25 Gr c 11/2 Verglas (IRE)—American Queen (IRE) (Fairy King (USA)) (642) **Mr Adrian Parr**
26 Br c 14/2 Mull of Kintyre (IRE)—Capetown Girl (Danzero (AUS)) (4503)
27 **CHEEKY CRUMPET**, b f 7/2 Mind Games—Woore Lass (IRE) (Persian Bold) (3500) **Mrs M. Forsyth**
28 B f 14/2 Pyrus (USA)—Columbine (IRE) (Pivotal) **Mr Eric Nisbet**
29 **DESDAMONA (IRE)**, b f 5/3 Desert Style (IRE)—
                                    Tattymulmona Queen (USA) (Royal Academy (USA)) (5791) **Mrs L. White**
30 B f 13/3 Tagula (IRE)—Dusty Diamond (IRE) (Royal Abjar (USA)) (3217)
31 B f 21/3 Tagula (IRE)—Fiore d'acciaio (IRE) (Thatching) (964)
32 **GRISSOM (IRE)**, b c 20/4 Desert Prince (IRE)—Misty Peak (IRE) (Sri Pekan (USA)) (10295) **Jim & Helen Bowers**
33 Ch c 31/3 Presidium—Lady Magician (Lord Bud) (3200) **Mr Jack Berry**
34 B f 22/4 Makbul—Lone Pine (Sesaro (USA)) (1800) **Mr Willie Burns**
35 **PENNINE ROSE**, b f 29/4 Reel Buddy (USA)—Adorable Cherub (USA) (Halo (USA)) (7000) **Pennine Racing**
36 **POLLISH**, b f 20/2 Polish Precedent (USA)—Fizzy Fiona (Efisio) (2500) **Lord Crawshaw**
37 B f 16/3 Pyrus (USA)—Red Millennium (IRE) (Tagula (IRE)) (10000) **Sporting Kings**

Other Owners: Mr Steve Allen, Mrs J. M. Berry, Mrs H. M. Bowers, J. F. Bowers, Mr R. Crean, Mr G. Daniels, Mr A. M. Day, C. P. Devitt, Mr D. M. Fox, Mr Bruce Hellier, Mr Ian Johnson, Mr A. Jones, Mr R. G. Knight, Mr Ian Mackintosh, Mr Andrew James Murphy, Mr Nigel Taylor.

Jockey (flat): F. Lynch, F. Norton. **Jockey (NH):** N. Mulholland.

MR J. C. DE P. BERRY, Newmarket
Postal: **Beverley House Stables, Exeter Road, Newmarket, Suffolk, CB8 8LR**
Contacts: **PHONE (01638) 660663**
WEBSITE www.beverleyhousestables.com

1 **BELLE ANNIE (USA)**, 4, b f Aptitude (USA)—Call Me **D. J. Huelin**
2 **BEN BHRAGGIE (IRE)**, 4, b g Benny The Dip (USA)—Kelpie (IRE) **J. C. De P. Berry**
3 **BRIEF GOODBYE**, 8, b g Slip Anchor—Queen of Silk (IRE) **Miss L. I. McCarthy**
4 **EXTREME CONVICTION (IRE)**, 4, b g Danehill Dancer (IRE)—Nousaiyra (IRE) **All Points West Partnership**
5 **JILL DAWSON (IRE)**, 5, b m Mull of Kintyre (USA)—Dream of Jenny **Joe McCarthy & Friends**
6 **LADY SUFFRAGETTE (IRE)**, 5, b m Mull of Kintyre (USA)—Miss Senate (IRE) **Mr S Leadley-Brown**
7 **MY OBSESSION**, 6, b g Spectrum (IRE)—Little Love **J. Berry & D. Huelin**
8 **PANTOMIME PRINCE**, 5, b g Royal Applause—Floppie (FR) **Mrs E. L. Berry**
9 **SOMEWHERE SAFER (NZ)**, 5, ch m Postponed (USA)—Security (NZ) **Mr & Mrs M. Tidmarsh**

THREE-YEAR-OLDS

10 **ANIS ETOILE**, b f Helissio (FR)—French Spice **Tri-Nations Partnership**
11 **FILEMOT**, ch f Largesse—Hickleton Lady (IRE) **Mr & Mrs H. R. Moszkowicz**
12 **IMPERIAL DECREE**, b f Diktat—Docklands Princess (IRE) **The Principes Formation**
13 **POLYCHROME**, b f Polish Precedent (USA)—Pantone **J. C. De P. Berry**
14 **RUN FROM NUN**, b f Oasis Dream—Nunatak (USA) **Mrs Emma Berry**

MR J. C. DE P. BERRY—continued

TWO-YEAR-OLDS

15 B f 17/4 Key of Luck (USA)—Aqraba (Polish Precedent (USA)) (5147) **Mr A. Fordham**
16 B f 1/5 Halling (USA)—Clarinda (IRE) (Lomond (USA)) (1200)
17 B f 15/3 Catcher In The Rye (IRE)—Dream of Jenny (Caerleon (USA)) (6434)
18 **ETHICS GIRL (IRE),** b f 6/2 Hernando (FR)—Palinisa (FR) (Night Shift (USA)) (12869) **1997 Partnership**

Other Owners: Mr W. Benter, Mr C. de P. Berry, Mr Jeremy Bond, Mr R. Byrne, Mr D. Casey, Mr L. Casey, Ms Alix Choppin, Mr J. Colbert, Mr D. Collings, Mr P. Devereaux, Mr J. Dumas, Mrs J. Duscherer, Mr D. Enright, Mr Ken Gibbs, Golden Vale Stud, Mr G. Grimstone, Mr Jason Hathorn, Mrs F. K. Hathorn, Mr D. J. Huelin, Mr R. Jones, Mr K. Leggatt, Mr B. McAllister, Mrs I. E. McCarthy, Mrs S. McCormick, Mr B. McMahon, Mr. A. Merriam, Mr N. Morrissey, Mrs M. Parker, Mr C. Plant, Mr T. Richardson, Mr L. Richardson, Mrs A. J. Ridges, Mr T. Stack, Mr T. Trounce, Mr L. C. Wadey.

Assistant Trainer: David Knights

Jockey (flat): N. Pollard, G. Baker, B. Doyle, T. E. Durcan, M. Fenton. **Jockey (NH):** W. Kennedy.

41

MR J. J. BEST, Lewes
Postal: **Grandstand Stables, The Old Racecourse, Lewes, East Sussex, BN7 1UR**
Contacts: **PHONE (01273) 480205 (01273) 480249 MOBILE (07968) 743272**
E-MAIL jimandtombest@btconnect.com WEBSITE www.jimandtombestracing.co.uk

1 **BRENDAR (IRE),** 11, b g Step Together (USA)—Willabelle **Chipstead Racehorse Owners Club**
2 **CHOREOGRAPHY,** 5, ch g Medicean—Stark Ballet (USA)
3 **DANCE WITH WOLVES (FR),** 8, ch g Tel Quel (FR)—La Florian (FR) **L. Best**
4 **DOT'S DELIGHT,** 4, b f Golden Snake (USA)—Hotel California (IRE) **M. Kelly**
5 **DOUBLE MAGNUM,** 8, b g Double Trigger (IRE)—Raise The Dawn **L. Best**
6 **DUNDRIDGE NATIVE,** 10, b m Be My Native (USA)—Fra Mau **C. Sullivan**
7 **GREEN PROSPECT (FR),** 8, b g Green Tune (USA)—City Prospect (FR) **R. Howitt**
8 **HIDDEN WEAPON,** 11, b g Charmer—Bustellina **M. J. Hills**
9 **JUST SUPERB,** 9, ch g Superlative—Just Greenwich **JB Racing**
10 **KING CYRUS (IRE),** 6, br g Anshan—Miss Eurolink **The Gascoigne Brookes Partnership II**
11 **KISHA KING (IRE),** 7, b g Dr Massini (IRE)—Lady Elise (IRE) **Muerren Racing**
12 **LADY PILOT,** 6, b m Dansili—Mighty Flyer (IRE) **Odds On Racing**
13 **LAKIL BOY (IRE),** 8, b g Presenting—Tinerana Noble (IRE) **Chipstead Racehorse Owners Club**
14 **MISBEHAVIOUR,** 9, b g Tragic Role (USA)—Exotic Forest **The Bad Boys**
15 **MOUNTAIN CREEK (IRE),** 6, ch h Monashee Mountain (USA)—Forest Child (IRE)
16 **NOBLE MINSTREL,** 5, ch g Fantastic Light (USA)—Sweetness Herself **Never Stop Out Racing**
17 **NOD'S STAR,** 7, ch m Starborough—Barsham **Mr A. C. Clarke**
18 **PEEPHOLE,** 5, ch g Pursuit of Love—Goodwood Lass (IRE) **The Bad Boys**
19 **QUEEN OF SONG,** 6, b m Singspiel (IRE)—Fascination Waltz **The Bad Boys**
20 **RAPSCALLION (GER),** 9, b g Robellino (USA)—Rosy Outlook (USA) **Mr W. A. Scott Mr L. Best**
21 **ROSE OF YORK,** 8, b m Emarati (USA)—True Ring **The Bad Boys**
22 **STARS DELIGHT (IRE),** 11, ch g Fourstars Allstar (USA)—Celtic Cygnet **L. Best**
23 **THE WOODEN SPOON (IRE),** 10, b g Old Vic—Amy's Gale (IRE) **Mr W. A. Scott Mr M. J. Hills**
24 **THREE SHIPS,** 7, ch g Dr Fong (USA)—River Lullaby (USA) **JB Racing**
25 **TOCCATA (IRE),** 4, b f Cape Cross (USA)—Sopran Marida (IRE) **The Sporting Divots**
26 **VICTOR TRUMPER,** 4, b g First Trump—Not So Generous (IRE) **N. J. Sillett**
27 **WOTCHALIKE (IRE),** 6, ch g Spectrum (IRE)—Juno Madonna (IRE) **J. D. Sells**

Other Owners: Mr J. Baker, Mrs D. R. Baker, K. Barker, L. Brakes, J. N. W. Brookes, Mr J. J. Buff, D. F. P. Callaghan, Mr P. J. Gardner, D. A. Gascoigne, Mr P. Gillam, S. R. Harman, Mr N. Mandry, J. Noonan, Mr G. C. Sales, W. A. Scott, Mr P. J. Seymour, Mr J. F. Sharpless, Mr J. R. Staite, D. M. Woodward.

Assistant Trainer: Mr T. Best

Jockey (flat): R. Thomas. **Jockey (NH):** R. Lucey-Butler.

42 **MR J. R. BEST, Maidstone**
Postal: **Scragged Oak Farm, Scragged Oak Road, Hucking, Maidstone, Kent, ME17 1QU**
Contacts: **PHONE (01622) 880276 FAX (01622) 880525 MOBILE (07889) 362154**
E-MAIL john.best@johnbestracing.com WEBSITE www.johnbestracing.com

1 **BERTIE SOUTHSTREET,** 5, b br g Bertolini (USA)—Salvezza (IRE) **A. R. Bell**
2 **CHARLIES DOUBLE,** 9, b g Double Eclipse (IRE)—Pendil's Niece **The Highly Hopeful Club**
3 **DARASUN (IRE),** 4, ch c Desert Sun—Darabaka (IRE) **R. Hornbuckle B. Cains P. Rooks**
4 **FALCON FLYER,** 4, br f Cape Cross (IRE)—Green Danube (USA) **Mr & Mrs R. Dawbarn**
5 **FASTRAC BOY,** 5, b g Bold Edge—Nesyred (IRE) **P O'Connell**
6 **FORELAND SANDS (IRE),** 4, b g Desert Sun—Penrose (IRE) **Mr J. Ward & Mr D. Goulding**
7 **HALSION CHANCER,** 4, br g Atraf—Lucky Dip **Halsion Ltd**
8 **HUCKING HEIST,** 4, b g Desert Style (IRE)—Oriental Queen (GER) **Hucking Horses**
9 **HUCKING HILL (IRE),** 4, ch g City On A Hill (USA)—Con Dancer **Hucking Horses**
10 **HURRICANE SPIRIT (IRE),** 4, b c Invincible Spirit (IRE)—Gale Warning (IRE) **The Little House Partnership**
11 **HYTHE BAY,** 4, b f Auction House (USA)—Ellway Queen (USA) **Eastwell Manor Racing Ltd**
12 **KING AFTER,** 6, b g Bahamian Bounty—Child Star (FR) **Miss S. J. Furnival**
13 **LADY FIRECRACKER (IRE),** 4, b f Almutawakel—Dazzling Fire (IRE) **Let's Give It A Go Racing & S. Furnival**
14 **MIND HOW YOU GO (FR),** 10, b g Hernando (FR)—Cos I Do (IRE) **A Fiver In Mind Partnership**
15 **MINE BEHIND,** 8, b g Sheikh Albadou—Arapi (IRE) **M. Folan R. Lees R. Crampton**
16 **MONASHEE PRINCE,** 6, ch g Monashee Mountain (USA)—
Lodema (IRE) **Michael Hurd, Ray Rooks, Paul Rooks**
17 **MUJOBLIGED (IRE),** 5, b g Mujadil (USA)—Festival of Light **One More Syndicate**
18 **OASIS SUN (IRE),** 5, ch m Desert Sun—Albaiyda (IRE) **Mrs J. A. Schabacker**
19 **PAPRADON,** 4, b g Tobougg (IRE)—Salvezza (IRE) **Donna Rooks & Pam Rooks**
20 **PRINCE OF MEDINA,** 5, ch g Fraam—Medina de Rioseco **G G Racing**
21 **SAMSONS SON,** 4, b g Primo Valentino (IRE)—Santiburi Girl **M. Folan**
22 **SMOKIN JOE,** 7, b g Cigar—Beau Dada (IRE) **G G Racing**
23 **WEYBA DOWNS (IRE),** 4, b g Daggers Drawn (USA)—Jarmar Moon **Mr & Mrs R. Dawbarn**
24 **WHITE COCKADE,** 5, gr g Compton Place—Swissmatic **Karma Row Racing**
25 **WILLHEGO,** 7, ch g Pivotal—Woodrising **G G Racing**

THREE-YEAR-OLDS

26 **BOLLYWOOD STYLE,** b f Josr Algarhoud (IRE)—Dane Dancing (IRE) **Miss S. J. Furnival**
27 **CLEAR DAYLIGHT,** b c Daylami (IRE)—Barbara Frietchie (IRE) **Heart Of The South Racing**
28 **HALSION CHALLENGE,** b c King's Best—Zaynah (IRE) **Mr C. Powell**
29 **HOWDIGO,** b c Tobougg (IRE)—Woodrising **G G Racing**
30 **HUCKING HARKNESS,** ch c Dr Fong (USA)—Dalaauna **Hucking Horses**
31 **HUCKING HARMONY (IRE),** b f Spartacus (IRE)—Gute (IRE) **Hucking Horses**
32 **HUCKING HARRIER (IRE),** ch c Hawk Wing (USA)—Dangerous Mind (IRE) **Hucking Horses**
33 **HUCKING HERO (IRE),** b c Iron Mask (USA)—Selkirk Flyer **Hucking Horses**
34 **IMPURE THOUGHTS,** b c Averti (IRE)—Blooming Lucky (IRE) **Blooming Lucky Racers**
35 **KINGSGATE CASTLE,** b c Kyllachy—Ella Lamees **J. H. Mayne**
36 **KINGSGATE NATIVE (IRE),** b c Mujadil (USA)—Native Force (IRE) **J. H. Mayne**
37 **LIBERTY BELLE (IRE),** b br f Statue of Liberty—Enaya **Heading For The Rocks Partnership**
38 **MCCONNELL (USA),** ch c Petionville (USA)—Warsaw Girl (IRE) **Market Avenue Racing Club Ltd**
39 **MEYDAN DUBAI (IRE),** b c Alzao (USA)—Rorkes Drift (IRE) **Mr A. A. A. Al Shafar**
40 **MISS CRUISECONTROL,** b f Hernando (FR)—Wenda (IRE) **Miss S. Furnival & Mr D. Standbridge**
41 **REALLY REALLY WISH,** b c Bertolini (USA)—Shanghai Lil **M. J. Ward**
42 **RUFF DIAMOND (USA),** b br c Stormin Fever (USA)—Whalah (USA) **Mr John Griffin Mr Owen Mullen**
43 **VICTORY SHOUT (IRE),** b g Victory Gallop (CAN)—Lu Lu's Lullaby (USA) **Kingstonian Partnership**

TWO-YEAR-OLDS

44 B f 28/1 Johar (USA)—Crimson Native (The Name's Jimmy (USA)) (14577) **Kent Bloodstock**
45 **DIAMOND TWISTER (USA),** b c 6/4 Omega Code (USA)—
King's Pact (USA) (Slewacide (USA)) (34985) **J. Griffin, Owen Mullen**
46 **GOOD BUY DUBAI (USA),** gr c 2/3 Essence of Dubai (USA)—
Sofisticada (USA) (Northern Jove (CAN)) (17006) **Mr J. A. Keaty**
47 B c 27/3 Mr Greeley (USA)—Jo Zak (USA) (Vilzak (USA)) **Mr D. Gorton**
48 **KINGSGATE STORM (IRE),** gr c 21/4 Mujadil (USA)—In The Highlands (Petong) (65000) **J. H. Mayne**
49 B c 10/2 Mull of Kintyre (USA)—Lady Lucia (IRE) (Royal Applause) (26000) **Kent Bloodstock**
50 B c 14/4 Officer (USA)—Morganza (Clever Trick (USA)) (80174) **Kent Bloodstock**
51 B c 30/1 Chapel Royal (USA)—Velvet Tulip (Valid Appeal (USA)) (13119) **Kent Bloodstock**
52 **YALDAS GIRL (USA),** gr ro f 20/3 Unbridled's Song (USA)—
Marina de Chavon (USA) (Exploit (USA)) (97181) **Mr D. Gorton**
53 B c 2/4 Noverre (USA)—Zanoubia (USA) (Our Emblem (USA)) (34013) **Kent Bloodstock**

MR J. R. BEST—continued

Other Owners: Mr G. K. Aldridge, Mr S. J. Best, Mr B. T. Blake, Mr B. Cains, Mrs Carolyn Chamberlain, Chegwidden Systems Ltd, Mr R. A. Cluley, Mrs J. Coombs, Mr Dean Coombs, Mr Rob Crampton, Mr R. B. Dawbarn, Mrs S. P. Dawbarn, Mrs J. L. Elsom, Mr M. Folan, Miss Sara Furnival, Mr P. M. A. Gazeley, Mr. Frank Gilmour, Mrs Deana Godmon, Mr. G. Godmon, Mr D. Goulding, Mr John Griffin, Mr Bob Hornbuckle, Mr M. Hurd, Mr John A. T. Jones, Mr R. I. H. Lees, Mr M. P Long, Mr Owen Mullen, Mr Peter Nelson, Mr Steve Nelson, Mr Christopher Newing, Mr D. T. Norton, Mr John Penny, Mrs Caroline Penny, Mrs Donna Rooks, Mrs Pam Rooks, Mr R. Rooks, Mr Paul Rooks, Mr Dave Standbridge, Mr Paul Tindall, Mr James Ward, Mr Trevor Wells, Mr S. J. Whelan, Miss H. Williams, Mr M. J. Winwright, Mr T. Yorke.

Assistant Trainer: Martin Smith

Apprentice: Kieren Fox.

---

43 **MR J. D. BETHELL, Middleham**
Postal: **Thorngill, Coverham, Middleham, North Yorkshire, DL8 4TJ**
Contacts: **PHONE (01969) 640360 FAX (01969) 640360 MOBILE (07831) 683528**
E-MAIL jamesbethell@aol.com WEBSITE www.clarendonracing.co.uk
and www.jamesbethell.co.uk

1 ABSTRACT FOLLY (IRE), 6, b g Rossini (USA)—Cochiti **Clarendon Thoroughbred Racing**
2 CASUAL AFFAIR, 5, b g Golden Snake (USA)—Fontaine Lady **Mr P. J. Mitchell**
3 FOSSGATE, 7, ch g Halling (USA)—Peryllys **Mrs S. Bethell**
4 GRANSTON (IRE), 7, gr g Revoque (IRE)—Gracious Gretclo **The Four Players Partnership**
5 KASTHARI (IRE), 9, gr g Vettori (IRE)—Karliyka (IRE) **Elliott Brothers**
6 KING HARSON, 9, b g Greensmith—Safari Park **C. J. Burley**
7 LITTLE BOB, 7, ch g Zilzal (USA)—Hunters of Brora (IRE) **R. F. Gibbons**
8 MICKLEBERRY (IRE), 4, b f Desert Style (IRE)—Miss Indigo **Clarendon Thoroughbred Racing**
9 MINE (IRE), 10, b h Primo Dominie—Ellebanna **M. J. Dawson**
10 NESNO (USA), 5, ch g Royal Academy (USA)—Cognac Lady (USA) **Elliott Brothers**
11 SENDALI (FR), 4, b g Daliapour (IRE)—Lady Senk (FR) **Elliott Brothers**
12 SNOWED UNDER, 7, gr g Most Welcome—Snowy Mantle **Mrs G. Fane**
13 STRETTON (IRE), 10, br g Doyoun—Awayil (USA) **M. J. Dawson**
14 WISDOM'S KISS, 4, b g Ocean of Wisdom (USA)—April Magic **Ms L. Hipkiss**
15 YOUNG SCOTTON, 8, b g Cadeaux Genereux—Broken Wave **Elliott Brothers**

THREE-YEAR-OLDS

16 BAHAMIAN BALLAD, ch f Bahamian Bounty—Record Time **Scotyork Partnership**
17 BELLANISI (IRE), b f Kalanisi (IRE)—Marie de Bayeux (FR) **Hornblower Racing**
18 HONEYCOTT (IRE), ch f King's Best (USA)—Kingsridge (IRE) **Clarendon Thoroughbred Racing**
19 KISS ME HARDY, b f Storming Home—Hunters of Brora (IRE) **R. F. Gibbons**
20 LIBERTY SHIP, b g Statue of Liberty (USA)—Flag **M. W. Territt**
21 RICH JAMES (IRE), b g Ishiguro (USA)—Mourir d'aimer (USA) **Mrs J. E. Vickers**
22 TEMPLETUOHY MAX (IRE), b g Orpen (USA)—Eladawn (IRE) **C. Monty**
23 TRANSCENDENT (IRE), b c Trans Island—Shannon Dore (IRE) **Ms L. Hipkiss**
24 WANDER LUST, b c Where Or When (IRE)—Surf Bird **L. B. Holliday**
25 WHASTON (IRE), b g Hawk Wing (USA)—Sharafanya (USA) **Clarendon Thoroughbred Racing**

TWO-YEAR-OLDS

26 B c 9/4 Lucky Story (USA)—Arctic Song (Charnwood Forest (IRE)) (17000)
27 Ch c 27/4 Gulch (USA)—Carr Shaker (USA) (Carr de Naskra (USA)) (16730)
28 INVENTING PARADISE, ch f 24/1 Bahamian Bounty—Phi Beta Kappa (Diesis) (8500)
29 LEGBEFOREWICKET, gr f 9/3 Silver Patriarch (IRE)—Shazana (Key of Luck) (USA)
30 B f 13/3 Mark of Esteem (IRE)—Matisse (Shareef Dancer (USA)) (8000)
31 ROWAYTON, br gr f 28/3 Lujain (USA)—Bandanna (Bandmaster (USA)) (14000)

Other Owners: Mr Mohammed Ali, Mr G. A. Barnes, Mr J. D. Bethell, Mr J. Carrick, Mr J. A. Elliott, Mr Colin Elliott, Mr John Elliott, Mr M. C. Gibson, Mr K. Hunt, Mr M. D. Pearson, Mr Richard T. Vickers, D. A. West.

Assistant Trainer: Jessica Bethell

44

MR J. R. BEWLEY, Jedburgh
Postal: **Newhouse Cottage, Camptown, Jedburgh, Roxburghshire, TD8 6RW**
Contacts: **PHONE (01835) 840273 MOBILE (07974) 831668**
E-MAIL overtonbush@aol.com

1 ABERDARE, 9, b m Overbury (IRE)—Temple Heights **J. R. Bewley**
2 6, Br g Taipan (IRE)—Baby Fane (IRE) **J. R. Bewley**
3 5, B g City Honours (USA)—Clara Petal (IRE) **J. R. Bewley**
4 4, Ch g Double Eclipse (IRE)—Go Hunting (IRE) **J. R. Bewley**
5 RAMBLING BROOK, 5, b g Rambling Bear—Apollo's Daughter **J. R. Bewley**

Assistant Trainer: Mrs K Bewley

Jockey (NH): K. Renwick. **Conditional:** Gary Berridge.

45

MR K. BISHOP, Bridgwater
Postal: **Barford Park Stables, Spaxton, Bridgwater, Somerset, TA5 1AF**
Contacts: **PHONE/FAX (01278) 671437 MOBILE (07816) 837610**

1 ASHLEY BROOK (IRE), 10, ch g Magical Wonder (USA)—Seamill (IRE) **Mrs E. K. Ellis**
2 BARREN LANDS, 13, b g Green Desert (USA)—Current Raiser **Mrs E. K. Ellis**
3 BERNARD, 8, b g Nashwan (USA)—Tabyan (USA) **K. Bishop**
4 BERTIE MAY, 6, gr g Terimon—Kalogy **J. M. Wingfield Digby**
5 CHILBURY HILL (IRE), 5, b g Bahhare (USA)—Fire Goddess **Mrs E. K. Ellis**
6 DODGER McCARTNEY, 10, ch g Karinga Bay—Redgrave Girl **W. Davies**
7 GARLETON (IRE), 7, b g Anshan—Another Grouse **J. W. Stephenson**
8 GRAVE DOUBTS, 12, ch g Karinga Bay—Redgrave Girl **W. Davies**
9 GUMLEY GALE, 13, b g Greensmith—Clodaigh Gale **Portcullis Racing**
10 HIGH SEASONS, 5, b g Fantastic Light (USA)—El Hakma **Mr R. J. Gibbons**
11 KAROO, 10, b g Karinga Bay—Cupids Bower **R. D. Cox**
12 LETS GO DUTCH, 12, b m Nicholas Bill—Dutch Majesty **Mrs E. K. Ellis**
13 PRIMROSE PARK, 9, b m Thowra (FR)—Redgrave Rose **K. Bishop**
14 SEEMARYE, 6, ch m Romany Rye—Shepani **J. A. G. Meaden**
15 SILVER ISLAND, 7, ch g Silver Patriarch (IRE)—Island Maid **Roxanne, Sharlie, Tianna Syndicate**
16 TIMYNOMATES (IRE), 5, b g Bahhare (USA)—Mimandi (IRE) **M. Smith**

Other Owners: Mr Ed Byrne, Mrs Julie Green, Mr R. C. Hicks, Mr T. O'Malley, Mr Paul Sollars, Mr R. J. Whatley.

Assistant Trainer: Heather Bishop

Jockey (NH): P. J. Brennan, R. Greene. **Conditional:** Darren O'Dwyer.

46

MISS L. A. BLACKFORD, Tiverton
Postal: **Shortlane Stables, Rackenford, Tiverton, Devon, EX16 8ED**
Contacts: **PHONE (01884) 881589 MOBILE (07887) 947832**
E-MAIL overthelast@talktalk.net WEBSITE www.overthelast.com

1 AS COLD AS ICE, 8, b m Millkom—Miss Krispy (FR) **Over De Last Racing**
2 BLEU REEF (IRE), 6, b g Pistolet Bleu (IRE)—Khaiylasha (IRE) **The Profile Partnership**
3 RIVER DANTE (IRE), 11, ch g Phardante (FR)—Astral River **Over De Last Racing**
4 RULES APPLY (IRE), 6, ch g Moscow Society (USA)—Some Bird (IRE) **18 Red Lions Partnership**

Other Owners: Miss L. A. Blackford, Mrs Sarah Child, Mr David Cocks, Mr N. D. Littlejohn, Mr M. J. Vanstone, Mr Terry Wheatley.

Assistant Trainer: M J Vanstone

Jockey (NH): Joe Tizzard. **Amateur:** Mr J. Guerriero, Mr W. Biddick.

47 MR A. G. BLACKMORE, Hertford

Postal: 'Chasers', Stockings Lane, Little Berkhamsted, Hertford
Contacts: PHONE (01707) 875060 MOBILE (07803) 711453

1 **COOL CONTENDER (IRE)**, 4, b br g Environment Friend—Island Native (IRE) **A. G. Blackmore**
2 **COOL ROXY**, 11, b g Environment Friend—Roxy River **A. G. Blackmore**
3 **FLAMING CHEEK**, 10, b g Blushing Flame (USA)—Rueful Lady **A. G. Blackmore**

Assistant Trainer: Mrs P M Blackmore

Jockey (NH): C. Honour. **Amateur:** Miss Emily Crossman.

48 MR M. T. W. BLANSHARD, Upper Lambourn

Postal: Lethornes Stables, Upper Lambourn, Hungerford, Berkshire, RG17 8QP
Contacts: PHONE (01488) 71091 (01488) 71315 (Home) FAX (01488) 73497
MOBILE (07785) 370093 E-MAIL blanshard.racing@virgin.net

1 **ALEXANDER GURU**, 4, ch g Ishiguru (USA)—Superspring **J. M. Beever**
2 **CHARLES DARWIN (IRE)**, 5, ch g Tagula (IRE)—Seymour (IRE) **J. M. Beever**
3 **GAVARNIE BEAU (IRE)**, 5, b g Imperial Ballet (IRE)—Mysticism **W. L. Hill**
4 **MAE CIGAN (FR)**, 5, gr g Medaaly—Concert **A. D. Jones**
5 **MERRYMADCAP (IRE)**, 6, b g Lujain—Carina Clare **Mrs N. L. Young**
6 **MOYOKO (IRE)**, 5, b m Mozart (IRE)—Kayoko (IRE) **Mrs N. L. Young**
7 **SEW'N'SO CHARACTER (IRE)**, 7, b g Imperial Ballet (IRE)—Hope And Glory (USA) **Aykroyd & Sons Limited**
8 **SYNONYMY**, 5, b g Sinndar (IRE)—Peony **G.H.Phillips,J.M.Beever & D.G.Chambers**
9 **THE COMPOSER**, 6, b g Royal Applause—Superspring **A. D. Jones**
10 **THE JOBBER (IRE)**, 7, b g Foxhound (USA)—Clairification (IRE) **Mrs Rosemary Wilkerson & Partners**
11 **THE TRADER (IRE)**, 10, ch g Selkirk (USA)—Snowing **Mrs C. J. Ward & D. Chambers**

THREE-YEAR-OLDS

12 **ASTON BOY**, ch c Dr Fong (USA)—Hectic Tina **Mrs R. K. Wilkerson**
13 **COPPERWOOD**, ch c Bahamian Bounty—Sophielu **Mrs R. K. Wilkerson**
14 **LUCULLUS**, b g Bertolini (USA)—Calcavella **Messrs Oliver, Gale, Ward & Roberts**
15 **MISS BOUGGY WOUGGY**, b f Tobougg (IRE)—Polly Golightly **D. Sykes**
16 **PERFECT FLIGHT**, b f Hawk Wing (USA)—Pretty Girl (IRE) **J. R. Drew**
17 **PLUMAGE**, b f Royal Applause—Cask **Mrs N. L. Young**
18 **RED SONJA (IRE)**, b f Kalanisi (IRE)—Pink Stone (FR) **J. M. Beever**
19 **SEVENTH HILL**, ch c Compton Place—Dream Baby **S. Hinton**
20 **TARA'S GARDEN**, b f Dr Fong (USA)—Tremiere (FR) **Lady Bland**

TWO-YEAR-OLDS

21 **JAQ'S SISTER**, b f 14/3 Bertolini (USA)—Polly Golightly (Weldnaas (USA)) **Mr David Sykes**
22 B c 5/3 Bertolini (USA)—Lihou Island (Beveled (USA)) (2000) **The Breeze In Partnership**
23 **LUCKY OMAN**, b br f 18/1 Key of Luck (USA)—Oman Sea (USA) (Rahy (USA)) (18000)
24 Br f 2/2 Diktat—Milly Fleur (Primo Dominie) (20000) **John Gale & Partners**
25 B c 27/1 Hawk Wing (USA)—Peep Show (In The Wings) (6000) **C. Millar, M. Pallas, K. Bartlett, J. M. Beever**
26 B f 22/3 Compton Place—Plumeria (Revoque (IRE)) (4000)
27 B f 5/4 Muhtarram (USA)—Pretisoa (IRE) (Royal Abjar (USA))
28 Ch c 15/4 Lucky Story (USA)—Seymour (IRE) (Eagle Eyed (USA)) (39000) **J. M. Beever**
29 **SONG OF PRAISE**, b f 2/4 Compton Place—Greensand (Green Desert (USA)) (12000) **T. W. Wellman**
30 B f 30/4 Efisio—Trounce (Barathea (IRE)) (14000) **The First Timers**
31 B c 12/3 Orpen (USA)—Truly Lonely (IRE) (Desert King (IRE)) (9000)
32 **WINTERBOURNE**, ch f 6/3 Cadeaux Genereux—Snowing (Tate Gallery (USA)) **Lady Bland**

Other Owners: Mr P. Berg, Mrs J. Breton, Mr D. G. Chambers, Mr A. Ellis, Mrs W. Gilbert, Mr D. Hampson, Mr D. Hughes, Mr B. Maynard, Mr B. Mitchell, Mrs J. Mitchell, Mr J. A. Oliver, Mr G. H. Phillips, Mr Peter Roberts, Mr R. Sutcliffe, Mr Vincent Ward.

49   MR P. A. BLOCKLEY, Lambourn
Postal: **Felstead Court Stables, Folly Road, Lambourn, Berkshire, RG17 8QE**
Contacts: **PHONE (01488) 71444 MOBILE (07778) 318295**
E-MAIL **paulblockley@hotmail.co.uk**

1 ACTION SPIRIT (GER), 6, ch g Dashing Blade—Action Art (IRE) **Miss J. Oakey**
2 BALMORAL STAR, 7, b m Wizard King—Balmoral Princess **Mr H. S. Maan**
3 BYWAYS BOY, 5, ch g Groom Dancer (USA)—Fuwala **Mrs A. P. Balderstone**
4 CHARMING FELLOW (IRE), 8, b g Taipan (IRE)—Latest Tangle **Blott, Newby & Brooks**
5 COME OUT FIGHTING, 5, b h Bertolini (USA)—Ulysses Daughter (IRE) **M. J. Wiley**
6 DRAGON SLAYER (IRE), 6, ch g Night Shift (USA)—Arandora Star (USA) **Mr C. Would**
7 FRIENDS HOPE, 7, ch m Docksider (USA)—Stygian **Mrs J. F. Hughes**
8 HURLERS CROSS (IRE), 10, b g Jurado (USA)—Maid of Music (IRE) **P. J. Hughes Developments Ltd**
9 INTENSIFIER (IRE), 4, b c Sinndar (IRE)—Licorne **M. J. Wiley**
10 ISTEAD RISE (IRE), 4, b g Mull of Kintyre (USA)—Tommys Queen (IRE) **J. P. McCarthy**
11 JAJOLEEN (IRE), 5, ch m Titus Livius (FR)—Radeda (IRE) **Mrs J. F. Hughes**
12 KEY PARTNERS (IRE), 7, b g Key of Luck (USA)—Teacher Preacher (IRE) **T. J. Wardle**
13 MARIA ANNINA (IRE), 5, ch m King's Best (USA)—Annieirwin (IRE) **P. Rosas**
14 MISS PORCIA, 7, ch m Inchinor—Krista **Miss S. Clough**
15 OH SO (IRE), 4, ch f Mark of Esteem (IRE)—Manuetti (IRE) **Miss J. Oakey**
16 SURFBOARD (IRE), 7, ch g Kris—Surfing **Ashton Racing Club II**
17 TARKESAR (IRE), 6, b g Desert Prince (IRE)—Tarwila (IRE) **P. J. Hughes Developments Ltd**
18 THOMAS LAWRENCE (USA), 7, ch g Horse Chestnut (SAF)—Olatha (USA) **Thomas Lawrence Experience**
19 WEET FOR EVER (USA), 5, b br g High Yield (USA)—
Wild Classy Lady (USA) **Ed Weetman (Haulage & Storage) Ltd**

THREE-YEAR-OLDS

20 BLUE EYED MISS, b f Statue of Liberty (USA)—Classic Jenny (IRE) **M. J. Wiley**
21 BORDER DEFENCE (IRE), b br g Princely Heir (IRE)—Dakhira **Bacon Isaac Gooding Booth Claridge**
22 DANSE DE SIOUX (IRE), ch f Frenchmans Bay (FR)—Purty Dancer (IRE) **Mrs U. Towell**
23 DON PICOLO, b c Bertolini (USA)—Baby Come Back (IRE) **P. Rosas**
24 EASTERN PRIDE, b f Fraam—Granuaile O'malley (IRE) **Isla & Colin Cage**
25 INDIAN DIVA (IRE), b f Indian Danehill (IRE)—Katherine Gorge (USA) **B. H. Downs**
26 LADY DEAUVILLE (FR), gr f Fasliyev—Mercalle (FR) **P. J. Hughes Developments Ltd**
27 LECHERO (IRE), ch c Millkom—Lovely Ali (IRE) **Mr C. Would**
28 MAGICAL SONG, ch c Forzando—Classical Song **The Classical Syndicate**
29 NO POINT (IRE), ch f Point Given (USA)—Youngus (USA) **Mrs Jo Hughes & Mrs Gill White**
30 OFFSHORE STAR (IRE), b c Spartacus (IRE)—Alvilda (IRE) **Mr Joseph & Mrs Georgina Kinnane**
31 ROMAN LEGION (IRE), gr c Spartacus (IRE)—Singhana (IRE) **T. W. Hosier**
32 RUB OF THE RELIC (IRE), b c Chevalier (IRE)—Bayletta (IRE) **M. J. Wiley**
33 STREET DIVA (USA), ch f Street Cry (IRE)—Arctic Valley (USA) **B. H. Downs**

TWO-YEAR-OLDS

34 B f 7/5 Kyllachy—Granuaile O'malley (IRE) (Mark of Esteem (IRE)) (1142) **Isla & Colin Cage**
35 B c 28/4 Fraam—Heneseys Leg (Sure Blade (USA)) (13333) **Mrs J. Hughes**
36 Ch g 11/4 Monsieur Bond (IRE)—Mighty Squaw (Indian Ridge) (2380) **Mr R. Bedford**

Other Owners: Mr Keith Bacon, Mr D. Blott, Mr M. Booth, Mr William Brooks, Mrs I. Cage, Mr C. J. Cage, Mr D. Claridge, Mr R. Gooding, Mr D. Goult, Mr P. Green, Mr T. Hosier, Mrs Joanna Hughes, Mr R. Isaac, Mr Chris King, Mr J. Kinnane, Mrs G. Kinnane, Mr Joe McCarthy, Mr A. R. Neilson, Mr A. Newby, Mr M. J. Tranter, Mrs Gill White.

Assistant Trainer: Jo Hughes

Jockey (flat): Frankie McDonald, G. Hannon, M. Nem, T. P. O'Shea. **Jockey (NH):** M. Bradburne. **Conditional:** Michael Murphy. **Amateur:** Mr A. Price.

50   MRS MYRIAM BOLLACK-BADEL, Lamorlaye
Postal: **20 Rue Blanche, 60260 Lamorlaye, France**
Contacts: **PHONE (0033) 3442 14966 (0033) 960 53602**
FAX **(0033) 3442 13367 MOBILE (0033) 6108 09347**
E-MAIL **myriam.bollack@wanadoo.fr**

1 ALIX ROAD (FR), 5, gr m Linamix (FR)—Life On The Road (IRE) **Mme. de Chatelperron**
2 BERENICE PANCRISIA (FR), 4, b f Kendor (FR)—Entretenue (FR) **Scuderia Mirabella**
3 CLAIRE ET BLEU (FR), 4, b f Anabaa Blue—Clarte du Soir (FR) **Mme. de Chatelperron**

MRS MYRIAM BOLLACK-BADEL—continued

4 **CYCNOS (FR)**, 4, ch g Silvano (GER)—Polish Queen **Mme. C. Niedenhausen**
5 **DEHRADOUN**, 5, b h Primo Valentino (IRE)—Pondicherry (USA) **Dwayne Woods**
6 **DESERT PLUS (IRE)**, 9, b h Desert King (IRE)—Welcome Break **Scuderia Mirabella**
7 **HAZEM (FR)**, 5, b g Singspiel (IRE)—Heroine **Mme. Seydoux**
8 **HENRY MORGANN (FR)**, 4, gr c Take Risks (FR)—Hokhmah **P. Valentiner**
9 **HORTANSE (FR)**, 4, gr f Linamix (FR)—Heroine **Mme. Seydoux**
10 **HOT SPOT (FR)**, 4, b c Kahyasi—Hokey Pokey (FR) **Mr C. Motschmann**
11 **ISAURE (FR)**, 4, b f Daliapour (IRE)—Logica (IRE) **Mme. de Chatelperron**
12 **JARDIN BLEU**, 9, b h Diesis—Cask **Mr K. Yoshida**
13 **JOHN D'AO (FR)**, 7, b h Johann Quatz (FR)—Flutiskoa **Myriam Bollack-Badel**
14 **KENDOROC (FR)**, 5, gr h Kendor (FR)—Rocade (IRE) **Scuderia Mirabella**
15 **L'AN DEUX (FR)**, 6, b h Revoque (IRE)—Lune Et L'autre **Myriam Bollack-Badel**
16 **LAST STORM**, 4, b f Marju (IRE)—Trombe **Mme. J. Mihslop**
17 **SONIC WINE**, 5, b m Grape Tree Road—Saiga (FR) **Jeffrey C. Smith**
18 **THOMAMIX (FR)**, 5, b h Linamix (FR)—Thomasina (USA) **Philippe Erzi**
19 **TIME FOR GOLD (IRE)**, 4, b f Danetime (IRE)—Gold Shift (USA) **Jeffrey C. Smith**
20 **VADLIX (FR)**, 5, gr g Linamix (FR)—Vadlawysa (FR) **Philippe Erzi**
21 **ZIMRI (FR)**, 4, b g Take Risks (FR)—Zayine (IRE) **Myriam Bollack-Badel**

THREE-YEAR-OLDS

22 **ACTE DEUX (FR)**, gr f Act One—Innocentines (FR) **Mme. de Chatelperron**
23 **ALAS (FR)**, b g Anabaa (USA)—Anysheba (USA) **Myriam Bollack-Badel**
24 **LA FRESCA**, b f Peintre Celebre (USA)—Lanaba (IRE) **Mme. de Chatelperron**
25 **MIRAMIX (FR)**, gr c Linamix (FR)—Green Bonnet (IRE) **Scuderia Mirabella**
26 **PARTY LOVER (FR)**, ch f Tobougg—Zaneton (FR) **Jeffrey C. Smith**
27 **SIWAH (FR)**, ch f Golan (FR)—Miranda (USA) **Mme. C. Niedenhausen**
28 **THE COUNTESS**, b f Numerous (USA)—Nachtigall (FR) **Jeffrey C. Smith**
29 **WAVE GOODBYE (FR)**, gr f Linamix (FR)—Bressay (USA) **Jeffrey C. Smith**
30 **ZIA SOFI (FR)**, b f Le Balafre (FR)—Zayine (IRE) **Myriam Bollack-Badel**

TWO-YEAR-OLDS

31 **DEVIL RAPIDS (FR)**, b c 14/2 Diableneyev (USA)—Orkney Rapids (Kirkwall) **Jeffrey C. Smith**
32 **DIANE DE POITIERS (IRE)**, b f 10/4 High Chaparral (IRE)—
                                    Tambura (FR) (Kaldoun (FR)) (83655) **Katsumi Yoshida**
33 **HONEY GEM (FR)**, b f 29/4 Gold Away (IRE)—Hokey Pokey (FR) (Lead On Time (USA)) **Mr C. Motschmann**
34 B c 26/1 Dubai Destination (USA)—Lusitanie (IRE) (Barathea (IRE)) (19948) **R. G. Fell**
35 B f 14/4 Elusive City (USA)—Saiga (FR) (Baryshnikov (AUS)) (12870) **Scuderia Mirabella**

Jockey (flat): Alexis Badel, Thierry Thuilliez, Johan Victoire.

---

51   MR M. R. BOSLEY, Marlborough
Postal: **The American Barn, White Barn Farm, Lockeridge, Marlborough, Wiltshire, SN8 4EQ**
Contacts: **PHONE (01672) 861200 FAX (01672) 861200 MOBILE (07778) 938040**
E-MAIL martin@martinbosley.com WEBSITE martinbosleyracing.com

1 **BOB'S SISTER (IRE)**, 5, b m Pasternak—Sousse **de Bugar Partnership**
2 **CASTLEMAINEVILLAGE (IRE)**, 8, b g Supreme Leader—Jennys Castle **Mrs J. M. O'Connor**
3 **CHARIOT (IRE)**, 7, ch g Titus Livius—Battle Queen **Mrs J. M. O'Connor**
4 **CLASSIC RUBY**, 8, b m Classic Cliche (IRE)—Burmese Ruby **Mrs J. M. O'Connor**
5 **DUALAGI**, 4, b f Royal Applause—Lady Melbourne (IRE) **Inca Financial Services**
6 **FINE RULER (IRE)**, 4, b g King's Best (USA)—Bint Alajwaad (IRE) **Mrs J. M. O'Connor**
7 **LOPINOT (IRE)**, 5, br g Pursuit of Love—La Suquet **Mrs J. M. O'Connor**
8 **MIALYSSA**, 8, b m Rakaposhi King—Theme Arena **The Blowingstone Partnership**
9 5, br m King Charlemagne (USA)—New Fortune (FR) **P. B. Woodley**
10 **SILVER PROPHET (IRE)**, 9, gr g Idris (IRE)—Silver Heart **Mrs J. M. O'Connor**

THREE-YEAR-OLDS

11 **DICKIE VALENTINE**, b g Diktat—Passionelle **Mrs J. M. O'Connor**
12 **LIDO SHUFFLE**, ch g Band On The Run—June The Eighth (IRE)

Other Owners: Mrs A Ballard, Miss Claire Edgecombe, Mrs M. P. Johnson, Mr D. P. Thompson, Mrs K. Whitaker.

Jockey (flat): G. Baker.

52 MR M. BOTTI, Newmarket

Postal: **Green Ridge Stables, Hamilton Road, Newmarket, Suffolk, CB8 7JQ**
Contacts: **PHONE (01638) 662416 FAX (01638) 662417 MOBILE (07775) 803007**
E-MAIL marcobotti06@btconnect.com WEBSITE www.marcobotti.co.uk

1 **ACTILIUS (IRE)**, 4, gr c Medicean—Afto (USA) **Dioscuri SRL**
2 **CEREMONIAL JADE (UAE)**, 5, b g Jade Robbery (USA)—Talah **G. Manfredini**
3 **DUSHSTORM (IRE)**, 7, b g Dushyantor (USA)—Between The Winds (USA) **G. Manfredini**
4 **NOLAS LOLLY (IRE)**, 4, gr f Lomitas—Holy Nola (USA) **Mrs R. J. Jacobs**
5 **ORAMA'S GHOST**, 4, b f Golan (IRE)—Orange Sunset (IRE) **Mrs R. J. Jacobs**
6 **ORPENINDEED (IRE)**, 5, b br h Orpen (USA)—Indian Goddess (IRE) **G. Manfredini**
7 **PRINCESS TAYLOR**, 4, ch f Singspiel (IRE)—Tapas En Bal (FR) **Rothmere Racing Limited**
8 **RE BAROLO (IRE)**, 5, b h Cape Cross (IRE)—Dalaiya (USA) **Effevi Snc Di Villa Felice & C.**
9 **SATYRICON**, 4, b c Dr Fong (USA)—Belladera (IRE) **Effevi Snc Di Villa Felice & C.**
10 **SILVER MITZVA (IRE)**, 4, b f Almutawakel—Ribblesdale **Mr J. Erhardt**
11 **STRAWBERRY LOLLY**, 5, b m Lomitas—Strawberry Morn (CAN) **Mrs R. J. Jacobs**
12 **SUBADAR**, 4, b g Zamindar (USA)—Valencia **G. Manfredini**
13 **WITHOUT EXCUSE (USA)**, 4, ch g Woodman (USA)—Dixie Jewel (USA) **Mr A. Nencini**

THREE-YEAR-OLDS

14 **ARABESQUE DANCER**, b f Dubai Destination (USA)—Seven of Nine (IRE) **Effevi Snc Di Villa Felice & C.**
15 **AVERTIS**, b c Averti (IRE)—Double Stake (USA) **Mrs O. Carlini Cozzi**
16 **BERTBRAND**, b c Bertolini (USA)—Mi Amor (IRE) **G. Manfredini**
17 **BLACK HEART**, b c Diktat—Blodwen (USA) **Mrs R. Manganelli**
18 **BRUKI (IRE)**, b f Captain Rio—Coup de Coeur (IRE) **The Second Great Partnership**
19 **CALISTOS QUEST**, b c Rainbow Quest (USA)—Carambola (IRE) **Mrs R. J. Jacobs**
20 **CROSSTAR**, b c Cape Cross (IRE)—Pie High **G. Manfredini**
21 **EXPRESS PRINCESS (IRE)**, b f Desert Prince (IRE)—Nashwan Star (IRE) **Mr E. Bulgheroni**
22 **FIRESPIN (USA)**, ch f Luhuk (USA)—Happy Numbers (USA) **Miss N. G. Sexton**
23 **FIULIN**, ch c Galileo (IRE)—Fafinta (IRE) **Scuderia Rencati Srl**
24 **FLOWERBUD**, b f Fantastic Light—Maidment
25 **FRATAZZ**, b c Pivotal—Lorne Lady **Scuderia Rencati Srl**
26 **GINOS DESTINATION**, ch f Dubai Destination (USA)—Gino's Spirits **Mrs R. J. Jacobs**
27 **HENRY JAMES (IRE)**, b c Iron Mask (USA)—Izibi (FR)
28 **MASETTOS FUN**, b g Dr Fong (USA)—Macina (IRE) **Mrs R. J. Jacobs**
29 **MONTEFIORE (IRE)**, b c Orpen (USA)—Tokurama (IRE) **P. M. Zambelli**
30 **MUJAHOPE**, b g Mujahid (USA)—Speak **G. Manfredini**
31 **NAUGHTY FRIDA (IRE)**, b f Royal Applause—Nausicaa (USA) **G. Manfredini**
32 **PRINCESS RAYA**, b grr f Act One—Tapas En Bal (FR) **Rothmere Racing Limited**
33 **RAYMI COYA (CAN)**, b f Van Nistelrooy (USA)—Something Mon (USA) **Mr C. Pizarro**
34 **SENDEFAA (IRE)**, b br f Halling (USA)—Patruel **Scuderia Rencati Srl**
35 **SHRAAYEF**, b f Nayef (USA)—Gorgeous Dancer (IRE) **Rabbah Bloodstock**
36 **SISTOS FASCINATION**, b c Fasliyev (USA)—Sierra Virgen (USA) **G. Manfredini**
37 **TEWIN GREEN**, ch f Zaha (CAN)—Green Run (USA) **The Perle d'Or Partnership**
38 B c Rahy (USA)—The Franchise (USA) **S. Misfer**
39 **TIA MIA**, ch f Dr Fong (USA)—Giusina Mia (USA) **Dachel Stud**
40 **TURTLE DOVE**, b f Tobougg (IRE)—Inseparable **Dioscuri SRL**
41 **VETTORENJOY**, b g Vettori (IRE)—Veiled Beauty (USA) **G. Manfredini**

TWO-YEAR-OLDS

42 Br f 10/4 One Cool Cat—Aly McBe (USA) (Alydeed (CAN)) (9000) **Dachel Stud**
43 **CALLING VICTORY (FR)**, b f 1/3 Vettori (IRE)—Calling Carat (Bering) (28957) **Mrs R. J. Jacobs**
44 **DENICES DESERT**, b f 17/3 Green Desert (USA)—Denice (Night Shift (USA)) (100000) **Mrs R. J. Jacobs**
45 **GEANT (GER)**, b c 18/4 Anabaa (USA)—Gleefully (USA) (Septieme Ciel (USA)) (15000) **Mrs R. J. Jacobs**
46 Ch c 14/3 Hernando—Gino's Spirits (Perugino) (25740) **Mrs R. J. Jacobs**
47 **HOLAMO (IRE)**, b f 21/1 Montjeu (IRE)—Holy Nola (USA) (Silver Deputy (CAN)) (110000) **Mrs R. J. Jacobs**
48 **KIYARI**, b f 16/3 Key of Luck (USA)—Ashford Castle (USA) (Bates Motel (USA)) (23000) **El Catorce**
49 **LOST IN THE DESERT (IRE)**, b c 9/2 Nayef (USA)—
Desert Harmony (Green Desert (USA)) (35392) **Effevi Snc Di Villa Felice & C.**
50 **MOSQUERAS ROMANCE**, gr f 9/4 Rock of Gibraltar (IRE)—
Mosquera (GER) (Acatenango (GER)) (33462) **Mrs R. J. Jacobs**
51 **RED PARISI (IRE)**, b f 30/4 Red Ransom (USA)—Rebecca Parisi (IRE) (Persian Heights) **Scuderia SIBA**
52 B br c 30/1 Johannesburg (USA)—Rock Salt (Selkirk (USA)) (25000) **E. Bulgheroni**
53 Ch c 24/3 Falbrav (IRE)—Scostes (Cadeaux Genereux) **Scuderia Rencati SRL**
54 **SOLO ATTEMPT**, b f 14/4 Anabaa (USA)—Sonja's Faith (IRE) (Sharp Victor (USA)) (19000) **Mrs R. J. Jacobs**

MR M. BOTTI—continued

Other Owners: Mr Keith J. Bradley, Mr L. Cashman, Dioscuri SRL, Mrs Sally Doyle, Mr P. D. Ebdon, Mr O. H. Kingsley, Mrs Rosalynd Norman, Mr A. Panetta, Mrs K. Pizarro, Mr Pietro Somaini, Miss A. Watson.

Assistant Trainer: Lucie Cechova

---

53 MR P. BOWEN, Haverfordwest
Postal: Yet-Y-Rhug, Letterston, Haverfordwest, Pembrokeshire, SA62 5TB
Contacts: **PHONE** (01348) 840118/840486 **FAX** (01348) 840486 **MOBILE** (07811) 111234
E-MAIL info@peterbowenracing.com **WEBSITE** www.peterbowenracing.com

1 ALWAYS WAINING (IRE), 7, b g Unfuwain (USA)—Glenarff (USA) **Mr & Mrs Peter James Douglas**
2 AMAZING VALOUR (IRE), 6, b g Sinndar (IRE)—Flabbergasted (IRE) **G. J. Morris**
3 BALLYCASSIDY (IRE), 12, br g Insan (USA)—Bitofabreeze (IRE) **R. Owen & P. Fullagar**
4 BLUE SPLASH (FR), 8, b g Epervier Bleu—Harpyes (FR) **Walters Plant Hire Ltd**
5 BURNBANK (IRE), 5, ch g Danehill Dancer (IRE)—Roseau
6 CADOULOR (FR), 5, b br g Cadoudal (FR)—Bright Idea (FR) **Sir Robert Ogden C.B.E., LLD**
7 CONSERVATION (FR), 5, b g Green Desert (USA)—Lightly Dancing (FR) **The Irish Partnership**
8 CONTACT DANCER (IRE), 9, b g Sadler's Wells (USA)—Rain Queen **The Hedonists**
9 COQ HARDI (FR), 7, b g Panoramic—Matagirl (FR) **Sir Robert Ogden C.B.E., LLD**
10 DIVINE WHITE, 5, ch m College Chapel—Snowy Mantle **Homebred Racing**
11 DUNBRODY MILLAR (IRE), 10, b br g Lord Americo—Salt Mills **Dundon Else Partnership**
12 ELLERSLIE TOM, 6, br g Octagonal (NZ)—Tetravella (IRE) **D. Jones**
13 FLEUR BABE, 5, b m Alflora (IRE)—Tui **Mrs L. J. Williams**
14 FOOTBALL CRAZY (IRE), 9, b g Mujadil (USA)—Schonbein (IRE) **Mrs K. Bowen**
15 GRAHAM (IRE), 8, b g Flemensfirth (USA)—Prudence Sarn (IRE) **Ms J. Day**
16 IRISH WOLF (FR), 8, b g Loup Solitaire (USA)—Erins Run (USA) **The Hacking Partnership**
17 IRON MAN (FR), 7, ch g Video Rock (FR)—Key Figure (FR) **R. Owen & P. Fullagar**
18 KILCANNON SUPREME (IRE), 6, b g Supreme Leader—Windfields Native (IRE) **J. Phelan**
19 LADY ROANIA (IRE), 8, b m Saddlers' Hall (IRE)—Ahead of My Time (IRE) **Mrs T. S. P. Stepney**
20 LANKAWI, 6, ch g Unfuwain (USA)—Zarma (FR) **Ms J. Day**
21 LAWYER DES ORMEAUX (FR), 9, ch g Sky Lawyer (FR)—Chaouia (FR) **C. B. Brookes & Dr T. J. Winning**
22 LEGALLY FAST (USA), 6, b g Deputy Minister (CAN)—Earthly Angel (USA) **Mrs T. S. P. Stepney**
23 MARKINGTON, 5, b g Medicean—Nemesia **R. C. Stepney**
24 MCKELVEY (IRE), 9, b g Anshan—Chatty Actress **N. Elliott**
25 MEGATON (IRE), 7, ch g Nashwan (USA)—Pan Galactic (USA) **Swansea Bay Syndicate**
26 MICHABO (IRE), 7, b g Robellino (USA)—Mole Creek **Nae Maer**
27 MILLENNIUM PRYDE (IRE), 7, ch m Dreams End—Landsker Pryde **Waldo's Dream Syndicate**
28 MOHAWK STAR (IRE), 7, ch g Indian Ridge—Searching Star (USA) **Richard Abbott & Mario Stavrou**
29 MONASHEE GREY (IRE), 5, gr g Monashee Mountain (USA)—Ex-Imager **B. A. Crumbley & L. M. Rutherford**
30 MR ED (IRE), 10, ch g In The Wings—Center Moriches (IRE) **G. J. Morris**
31 MUJAHAZ (IRE), 4, b g Act One—Sayedati Eljamilah (USA) **P. Bowling, S. Scott & Mrs R. Harvey**
32 NAGANO (FR), 10, b g Hero's Honor (USA)—Sadinskaya (FR) **A. Stennett**
33 NO PANIC (IRE), 5, b g Dushyantor (USA)—Afon Alwen **L. Mulryan**
34 PARTICLE (IRE), 5, ch g Selkirk (USA)—Bernique (USA) **XRMO Racing**
35 PROFESSOR HEGARTY (IRE), 8, b g Dr Massini (IRE)—Preview Days (IRE) **D. A. Smith**
36 RED CANYON, 11, b g Zieten (USA)—Bayazida **Miss Jayne Brace & Mr Gwyn Brace**
37 SANTANDO, 8, b g Hernando (FR)—Santarem (USA) **Mr J. A. Martin**
38 SERABAD (FR), 4, gr g Priolo (USA)—Serasia (FR) **Walters Plant Hire Ltd**
39 SHOUDAWOUDACOUDA (IRE), 7, b br g Oscar (IRE)—Madame Champvert (IRE) **Mr T. J. Healy & Ms Y. M. Hill**
40 SIR MONTY (USA), 6, ch g Cat's Career (USA)—Lady of Meadowlane (USA) **Saith O Ni & Karen Bowen**
41 SNOOPY LOOPY (IRE), 10, ch g Old Vic—Lovely Snoopy (IRE) **Walters Plant Hire Ltd Egan Waste Ltd**
42 SOUFFLEUR, 5, b g In The Wings—Salinova (FR) **Mrs K. Bowen**
43 SPECIAL ENVOY (FR), 6, gr g Linamix (FR)—Pawnee Dancer (IRE) **Walters Plant Hire Ltd**
44 SWEEP HOME, 3, ch g Safawan—Royal Brush **Homebred Racing**
45 TAKE THE STAND (IRE), 12, b g Witness Box (USA)—Denys Daughter (IRE) **David Robbins, Frank Ridge**
46 THE ABBOTS HABIT (IRE), 7, b g Taipan (IRE)—Thats Gospel (IRE) **Mr & Mrs Peter James Douglas**
47 TIGHE CASTER, 9, b g Makbul—Miss Fire **D. Jones**
48 TIME TO PANIC (IRE), 5, b g Broken Hearted—Supreme Style (IRE) **L. Mulryan**
49 TOMMY SPAR, 8, b g Silver Owl—Lady of Mine **R. Morgans**
50 TRINITY ROSE, 5, ch m Generous (IRE)—Stylish Rose (IRE) **D. J. Robbins**
51 TYCOON HALL (IRE), 8, ch h Halling (USA)—Tycooness (IRE) **Mrs K. Bowen**
52 YES SIR (IRE), 9, b g Needle Gun (IRE)—Miss Pushover **Ms Y. M. Hill & Mr T. J. Healy**

MR P. BOWEN—continued

Other Owners: Mr Richard Abbott, V. T. Beynon, Mrs Karen Bowen, Mr B. G. Bowen, Mr Peter Bowling, Miss Jayne Brace, Mr Gwyn Brace, Mr C. B. Brookes, Mr W. Bryan, Mr J. C. Bunyan, Mr T. Connop, Mr B. A. Crumbley, Mr Philip J. Dillon, Mr Peter J. Douglas, Mrs L. Douglas, Mr W. E. Dundon, Egan Waste Services Ltd, Mr A. R. G. Else, Mr P. Fullagar, Mr David Garahy, Mr Roger Goodwin, Mrs Rachael Harvey, Mrs Susan Haynes-Kellitt, Mr T. J. Healy, Ms Y. M. Hill, Mr Adrian Hill, Mr Gordon E. Innes, Mr E. O. Morgan, Mrs Shirley Norgrove, Mr R. Owen, Mr P. J. Owen, Mr T. Peckham, Mr V. J. Pennington, Mr B. S. Port, Mr S. D. Reeve, Mr L. M. Rutherford, Mr Simon Scott, Mr M. Stavrou, Mr Chris Wall, Mrs Sarah Wall, Mrs Debbie Wallace, Walters Plant Hire Ltd, Dr T. J. Winning, Mr P. L. Young.

Assistant Trainer: K Bowen

Jockey (NH): T. J. O'Brien, A. P. McCoy, P. J. Brennan, R. Johnson. **Conditional:** P. Merrigan, **Amateur:** Mr Donal Deveraux.

---

54 MRS A. J. BOWLBY, Wantage
Postal: **Gurnsmead Farm, Kingston Lisle, Wantage, Oxfordshire, OX12 9QT**
Contacts: **PHONE (01367) 820888 FAX (01367) 820880 MOBILE (07768) 277833**
E-MAIL mandy@mandybowlby.com

1 **GIGGLES O'SHEA (IRE)**, 6, b g Clerkenwell (USA)—Carrick Shannon **Mrs M. J. Bone**
2 **HERAKLES (GER)**, 7, b g Lagunas—Haraka (FR) **Mrs Maureen Buckley & Mrs A. M. Halls**
3 **LADY RACQUET (IRE)**, 9, b m Glacial Storm (USA)—Kindly Light (IRE) **The Norman Partnership**
4 **MIST AGAIN**, 5, ch m Double Trigger (IRE)—Idiot's Lady **D. & J. Houston**

Other Owners: Mrs M. Buckley, Mr D. J. Erwin, Mrs A. Halls, Mr D. J. Houston, Miss J. Houston.

Assistant Trainer: Michael Bowlby

Jockey (NH): A. Tinkler.

---

55 MR S. R. BOWRING, Edwinstowe
Postal: **Fir Tree Farm, Edwinstowe, Mansfield, Nottinghamshire, NG21 9JG**
Contacts: **PHONE (01623) 822451 MOBILE (07973) 712942**

1 **BARZAK (IRE)**, 8, b g Barathea (IRE)—Zakuska **Clark Industrial Services Partnership**
2 **EASTFIELDS LAD**, 6, b g Overbury (IRE)—Honey Day **S. R. Bowring**
3 **FIFTH ZAK**, 4, b g Best of The Bests (IRE)—Zakuska **Clark Industrial Services Partnership**
4 **HIGH FIVE SOCIETY**, 4, b g Compton Admiral—Sarah Madeline **The High Five Partnership**
5 **KINGSMAITE**, 7, b g Komaite (USA)—Antonias Melody **S. R. Bowring**
6 **MARINA'S OCEAN**, 4, b f Beat All (USA)—Ocean Song **S. R. Bowring**
7 **MASTER BEN (IRE)**, 5, b g Carrowkeel (IRE)—Java Jive **P. M. Sedgwick**
8 **PENNYGEE**, 4, b f Bertolini (USA)—Samadilla (IRE) **Mrs Anne & Mr Fred Cowley**
9 **RAMBLING SOCKS**, 5, ch m Rambling Bear—Cledeschamps **P. M. Sedgwick**
10 **SAMRAM**, 4, b g Samraan (USA)—Antonias Melody **S. R. Bowring**
11 **SILVER MONT (IRE)**, 5, b g Montjeu (IRE)—Silvernus **Clark Industrial Services Partnership**
12 **THE GEESTER**, 4, b g Rambling Bear—Cledeschamps **Mrs Anne & Mr Fred Cowley**
13 **WEST END LAD**, 5, b g Tomba—Cliburnel News (IRE) **K. Nicholls**
14 **XPRES BOY (IRE)**, 5, b g Tagula (IRE)—Highly Motivated **Charterhouse Holdings Plc**
15 **XPRES MAITE**, 5, b g Komaite (USA)—Antonias Melody **Charterhouse Holdings Plc**
16 **ZIL UP**, 4, ch c Zilzal (USA)—Sharpthorne (USA) **S. R. Bowring**

THREE-YEAR-OLDS

17 **DANCING MAITE**, ch c Ballet Master (USA)—Ace Maite **S. J. Burgan**
18 **SIXTH ZAK**, br c Fantastic Light (USA)—Zakuska **Clark Industrial Services Partnership**
19 **WHISTON PAT**, ch g Lomitas—Fille de Bucheron (USA) **Clark Industrial Services Partnership**

TWO-YEAR-OLDS

20 Ch c 15/3 Needwood Blade—Antonias Melody (Rambo Dancer (CAN)) **Mr S. R. Bowring**
21 B c 5/5 Ishiguru (USA)—Miss Twiddles (IRE) (Desert King (IRE)) **Clark Industrial Services Partnership**

Other Owners: Mr S. R. Bowring, Mr J. D. Chilton, Mr Jim Clark, Mr A. W. Clark, Mrs Anne Cowley, Mr Fred Cowley, Mr Ken Sweales.

Amateur: Mrs M. Morris.

56 MR J. R. BOYLE, Epsom

Postal: **South Hatch Stables, Burgh Heath Road, Epsom, Surrey, KT17 4LX**
Contacts: **PHONE (01372) 748800 FAX (01372) 739410 MOBILE (07719) 554147**
E-MAIL info@jamesboyle.co.uk WEBSITE www.jamesboyle.co.uk

1 **ALFIE TUPPER (IRE)**, 5, ch g Soviet Star (USA)—Walnut Lady **M Khan X2**
2 **ALONSO DE GUZMAN (IRE)**, 4, b g Docksider (USA)—Addaya (IRE) **M Khan X2**
3 **ARENA'S DREAM (USA)**, 4, gr ro g Aljabr (USA)—Witching Well (IRE) **J-P Lim & Mr Keith Marsden**
4 **BONNE D'ARGENT (IRE)**, 4, b f Almutawakel—Petite-D-Argent **The Fourtunes**
5 **CAVALRY GUARD (USA)**, 4, ch g Officer (USA)—Leeward City (USA) **Inside Track Racing Club**
6 **CINEMATIC (IRE)**, 5, b g Bahhare (USA)—Eastern Star (IRE) **Inside Track Racing Club**
7 **COMPTON CLASSIC**, 6, b g Compton Place—Ayr Classic **M Khan X2**
8 **DESERT REIGN**, 7, ch g Desert King (IRE)—Moondance **A. B. Pope**
9 **HUCKING HEAT (IRE)**, 4, b g Desert Sun—Vltava **M Khan X2**
10 **IDLE POWER (IRE)**, 10, b g Common Grounds—Idle Fancy **The Idle B'S**
11 **MR GARSTON**, 5, b g Mull of Kintyre (USA)—Ninfa of Cisterna **Mr A. R. O'Donnell**
12 **MRS SOLESE (IRE)**, 5, b m Imperial Ballet (IRE)—Sugar **John Hopkins (T/A South Hatch Racing)**
13 **NEWNHAM (IRE)**, 7, ch g Theatrical—Brief Escapade (IRE) **M Khan X2**
14 **ONENIGHTINLISBON (IRE)**, 4, br f Bold Fact (USA)—Mickey Towbar (USA) **Inside Track Racing Club**
15 **PONTE VECCHIO (IRE)**, 4, b g Trans Island—Gino Lady (IRE) **M Khan X2**
16 **PRESS THE BUTTON (GER)**, 5, b g Dansili—Play Around (IRE) **B. McAtavey**
17 **RAVI RIVER (IRE)**, 4, ch c Barathea (IRE)—Echo River (USA) **M Khan X2**
18 **SHANTINA'S DREAM (USA)**, 4, b f Smoke Glacken (USA)—J'aime Jeblis (USA) **Mr D. R. Grieve**
19 **SKY QUEST (IRE)**, 10, b g Spectrum (IRE)—Rose Vibert **M. C. Cook**
20 **ST PETERSBURG**, 8, ch g Polar Falcon (USA)—First Law **Inside Track Racing Club**
21 **SUNOVERREGUN**, 4, b c Noverre (USA)—Jumairah Sun **Inside Track Racing Club**
22 **SWEET PICKLE**, 7, b m Piccolo—Sweet Wilhelmina **M Khan X2**
23 **THE FIFTH MEMBER (IRE)**, 4, b c Bishop of Cashel—Palace Soy (IRE) **Mr Chris Simpson, Miss Elizabeth Ross**
24 **TOUCH OF STYLE (IRE)**, 4, b g Desert Style (IRE)—No Hard Feelings (IRE) **Inside Track Racing Club**
25 **TREBELLO**, 7, b g Robellino (USA)—Trempkate (USA) **John Hopkins (T/A South Hatch Racing)**

THREE-YEAR-OLDS

26 **AL GILLANI (IRE)**, b g Monashee Mountain (USA)—Whisper Dawn (IRE) **The Paddock Space Partnership**
27 **BLITZEN (IRE)**, b br g Indian Danehill (USA)—Notable Dear (ITY) **M Khan X2**
28 **CLASSICAL RHYTHM (IRE)**, ch g Traditionally (USA)—Golden Angel (USA) **Inside Track Racing Club**
29 **COPPERBOTTOMED (IRE)**, ch g Redback—Stoneware **M Khan X2**
30 **CROSS FELL (USA)**, b c Cherokee Run (USA)—Campsie Fells (UAE) **M Khan X2**
31 **ELISIARIO (IRE)**, b g Clodovil (IRE)—Kahla **John Hopkins, J-P Lim & Keith Marsden**
32 **HAWKSTAR EXPRESS (IRE)**, b g Hawk Wing (USA)—Band of Angels (IRE) **Inside Track Racing Club**
33 **HIBOU DE NUIT (IRE)**, b g Night Shift (USA)—Mrs Pertemps **James Burley & Jon Hughes**
34 **HOME**, b c Domedriver (IRE)—Swahili **M Khan X2**
35 **IKE QUEBEC (FR)**, ch c Dr Fong (USA)—Avezia (FR) **J-P Lim & Mr Keith Marsden**
36 **JERMAJESTY (IRE)**, b c Touch of The Blues (FR)—Mystic Dispute (IRE) **The Paddock Space Partnership 2**
37 **L'ART DU SILENCE (IRE)**, b c Xaar—Without Words **M Khan X2**
38 **MICHEALS BOY (IRE)**, ch g Bertolini (USA)—Red Storm **B. McAtavey**
39 **MISSION CONTROL (IRE)**, ch c Dubai Destination (USA)—Stage Manner **M Khan X2**
40 **PIPPBROOK GOLD**, ch g Golden Snake (USA)—Chiaro **Prosser Family Partnership**
41 **ROWAN DANCER**, b f Medicean—Golden Seattle (IRE) **Rowan Stud Partnership 1**
42 **SERIOUS CHOICE (IRE)**, b g Choisir (AUS)—Printaniere (USA) **The Serious Choice Partnership**
43 **THE GAME**, b c Compton Place—Emanant **M Khan X2**
44 **THREESTONEBURN (USA)**, b f Johannesburg (USA)—White Bridle (USA) **The Brignon Strollers**

TWO-YEAR-OLDS

45 B c 23/3 Diktat—Additive (USA) (Devil's Bag (USA)) (11000) **M Khan X2**
46 **ALLEXES (IRE)**, b br f 11/4 Exceed And Excel (AUS)—
　　　　　　　　　　　　　　　　　　Lizanne (USA) (Theatrical) (20591) **The Allexes Partnership**
47 Ch c 26/3 Lucky Story (USA)—Concubine (IRE) (Danehill (USA)) **South Hatch Racing**
48 B f 20/3 Josr Algarhoud (IRE)—Den's-Joy (Archway (IRE)) (4285) **Joy Racing**
49 B c 25/2 Noverre (USA)—Duchcov (Caerleon (USA)) (23165) **Mr D. Reynolds & Mr C. Watkins**
50 **FINE TOLERANCE**, b f 18/2 Bertolini (USA)—Sashay (Bishop of Cashel) (1200) **Calne Engineering**
51 B f 18/4 Elusive City (USA)—Happy Talk (IRE)—Hamas (IRE)) (12000) **New Partnership**
52 **HI-TEC CLASSIC**, b c 31/3 Captain Rio—Dry Lightning (Shareef Dancer (USA)) (22521) **Mr A. Kwok**
53 B c 18/4 Tiger Hill (IRE)—Lemon Tree (USA) (Zilzal (USA)) **Rowan Stud Partnership**
54 **OISEANS BOY**, b c c 21/4 Catcher In The Rye (IRE)—Red Storm (Dancing Spree (USA)) **Mr B. McAtavey**
55 B c 1/4 Val Royal (FR)—Palace Soy (IRE) (Tagula (IRE)) **Mr Chris Simpson & Miss Elizabeth Ross**
56 B g 19/4 Lujain (USA)—Simonida (IRE) (Royal Academy (USA)) (3000) **Mr I. Stevenson**

MR J. R. BOYLE—continued

Other Owners: Mr J. R. Boyle, J. Burley, Mr A. Chambers, Mr J. Douglas-Watson, A. R. Harrison, Ms J. E. Harrison, Mr John Hopkins, Mrs D. Hopkins, Mr E. J. Hughes, Mr M. Khan, Mr Mustafa Khan, Mr R. Kolien, Mr J-P Lim, Mr K. Marsden, Mr Roger May, Miss Pippa Muggeridge, Sir David Prosser, Lady Prosser, Mrs R. Ridout, Mr J. S. Ridout, Miss E. Ross, Mr E. Sames, Mr Martin Shenfield, A. C. Simpson.

Conditional: B. Adams. **Apprentice:** H. Poulton.

---

57 MRS S. C. BRADBURNE, Cupar

Postal: **Cunnoquhie Cottage, Ladybank, Cupar, Fife, KY15 7RU**
Contacts: **PHONE** (01337) 810325 **FAX** (01337) 810486 **MOBILE** (07769) 711064/(07768) 705722
E-MAIL susanbradburne@aol.com **WEBSITE** www.susanbradburne.co.uk

1 ALMIRE DU LIA (FR), 10, ch g Beyssac (FR)—Lita (FR) **Cornelius Lysaght, Quandt & Cochrane**
2 CHIEF SCOUT, 6, b g Tomba—Princess Zara **Black & White Communication (Scotland) Ltd**
3 GREAT JANE (FR), 6, b m Great Palm (USA)—Gaelic Jane (FR) **Mark Fleming & Jane Cameron**
4 KIRKSIDE PLEASURE (IRE), 7, ch g Grand Plaisir (IRE)—
Caledon Mist (IRE) **Hardie, Cochrane, Yeaman & Mitchell**
5 LADY CHATELAINE (IRE), 6, b m Supreme Leader—Lady Lock (IRE) **Turcan, Barber, Fletcher & Dunning**
6 LOCHIEL, 4, b g Mind Games—Summerhill Special (IRE) **A. Campbell**
7 MISTER JUNGLE (FR), 6, b g Saint Cyrien (FR)—Fabuleuse Histoire (FR) **W. Powrie**
8 NO PICNIC (IRE), 10, ch g Be My Native (USA)—Emmagreen **Broad & Cochrane**
9 NOT A TRACE (IRE), 9, b g Gothland (FR)—Copmenow (IRE) **Mark Fleming & Jane Cameron**
10 OR DE GRUGY (FR), 6, b g April Night (FR)—Girlish (FR) **Lord Cochrane & Partners**
11 PLATOON (FR), 5, b g Le Triton (USA)—
Divette (FR) **Mr H. W. Turcan, Sir Simon Dunning, Mr M. O. C. Wauchope**
12 SHARP REPLY (USA), 6, b g Diesis—Questonia **Mr H. W. Turcan, Mrs R. Noel Paton & Sir S. Dunning**
13 SOUTH BRONX (IRE), 9, br g Anshan—Tender Tan **Mrs S. M. Irwin**
14 STAINLEY (IRE), 5, b g Elnadim (USA)—Fizz Up **Grant, Jacobs, Howel & Cumming**
15 WATER MUSIC (FR), 5, b g Selkirk (USA)—Royal Song **Mark Fleming & Jane Cameron**
16 YANKEE HOLIDAY (IRE), 8, b g Oscar (IRE)—Parloop (IRE) **Robb Cooper Mcintosh & Hardie**

Other Owners: J. M. Barber, Mrs C. J. Broad, Ms C. J. S. Cameron, The Hon T. H. V. Cochrane, Lord Cochrane of Cults, Mrs M. Cumming, Sir Simon Dunning, Mr M. R. D. Fleming, Miss F. M. Fletcher, Mrs P. Grant, T. G. Hardie, Mr D. Howel, Mr R. A. Jacobs, C. Lysaght, Mrs P. A. Noel-Paton, Miss S. Quandt, Mrs L. Robb, H. W. Turcan, M. O. C. Wauchope, Ms D. L. Whytock.

Assistant Trainer: J G Bradburne

Jockey (NH): M. Bradburne.

---

58 MR J. M. BRADLEY, Chepstow

Postal: Meads Farm, Sedbury Park, Chepstow, Gwent, NP16 7HN
Contacts: **PHONE** (01291) 622486 **FAX** (01291) 626939
E-MAIL j.m.bradley@virgin.net

1 BLUEBOK, 7, ch g Indian Ridge—Blue Sirocco **E. A. Hayward**
2 BLUSHING RUSSIAN (IRE), 6, b g Fasliyev (USA)—Ange Rouge **J. M. Bradley**
3 BREAK OUT, 4, b c Kayf Tara—Clifton Girl **Mr J. G. Fisher**
4 BRIERY LANE (IRE), 7, ch g Tagula (IRE)—Branston Berry (IRE) **Delamere Cottage Racing Partners (1996)**
5 CAPE ROYAL, 8, b g Prince Sabo—Indigo **E. A. Hayward**
6 CAYMAN BREEZE, 8, b g Danzig (USA)—Lady Thynn (FR) **Mr G. & L. Johnson**
7 CHARLIE DELTA, 5, b g Pennekamp (USA)—Papita (IRE) **M. P. James**
8 CONVINCE (USA), 7, ch g Mt Livermore (USA)—Conical **The Lovely Jubbly's**
9 CORANGLAIS, 8, ch g Piccolo—Antonia's Folly **J. Brookman**
10 CORRIDOR CREEPER (FR), 11, ch g Polish Precedent (USA)—Sonia Rose (USA) **Mr G. & L. Johnson**
11 CURRENCY (IRE), 7, b g Sri Pekan (USA)—On Tiptoes **R. M. Bailey**
12 DECIDER (USA), 5, ch h High Yield (USA)—Nikita Moon (USA) **R. M. Bailey**
13 DICKIE DEANO, 4, b g Sooty Tern—Chez Bonito (IRE) **Mrs J. K. Bradley**
14 ENJOY THE BUZZ, 9, b h Prince of Birds (USA)—Abaklea **Miss F. D. Fenley**
15 EXPONENTIAL (IRE), 6, b g Namid—Exponent (USA) **Spitting Mick Partnership**
16 FERVENT, 4, b g Kyllachy—Romancing **E. A. Hayward**
17 FINSBURY, 5, gr g Observatory (USA)—Carmela Owen **M. Mackay & S. Bruce**
18 GOODWOOD SPIRIT, 6, b g Fraam—Rechanit (IRE) **J. M. Bradley**
19 HARRISON'S FLYER (IRE), 7, b g Imperial Ballet (IRE)—Smart Pet **racingshares.co.uk**

MR J. M. BRADLEY—continued

20 **HIGH RIDGE**, 9, ch g Indian Ridge—Change For A Buck (USA) **The Lovely Jubbly's**
21 **LITHAAM (IRE)**, 4, ch g Elnadim (USA)—Elhida (IRE) **JMB racing.co.uk**
22 **LOYAL ROYAL (IRE)**, 5, b g King Charlemagne (USA)—Supportive (IRE) **JMB racing.co.uk**
23 **MERLINS QUEST**, 4, b c Wizard King—Wonderland (IRE) **racingshares.co.uk**
24 **MILTONS CHOICE**, 5, b g Diktat—Starosta **racingshares.co.uk**
25 **MISTER INCREDIBLE**, 5, b g Wizard King—Judiam **racingshares.co.uk**
26 **MOON FOREST (IRE)**, 6, br g Woodborough (USA)—Ma Bella Luna **Mrs A. Mooney**
27 **MR FORTHRIGHT**, 4, b c Fraam—Form At Last **E. A. Hayward**
28 **MR REV**, 5, b g Foxhound (USA)—Branston Berry (IRE) **J. M. Bradley**
29 **NORDIC LIGHT (USA)**, 4, b br g Belong To Me (USA)—Midriff (USA) **Mr G. S. Thompson & Mr P. Banfield**
30 **ONE WAY TICKET**, 8, ch h Pursuit of Love—Prima Cominna **Saracen Racing**
31 **OUTER HEBRIDES**, 7, b g Efisio—Reuval **Asterix Partnership**
32 **PARKSIDE PURSUIT**, 10, b g Pursuit of Love—Ivory Bride **J. M. Bradley**
33 **PEOPLETON BROOK**, 6, b h Compton Place—Merch Rhyd-Y-Grug **Mr G. S. Thompson & Mr P. Banfield**
34 **PERUVIAN STYLE (IRE)**, 7, b g Desert Style (IRE)—Lady's Vision (IRE) **C. M. Hunt**
35 **PUSKAS (IRE)**, 5, b g King's Best (USA)—Chiquita Linda (IRE) **E. A. Hayward**
36 **SEVEN NO TRUMPS**, 11, ch g Pips Pride—Classic Ring (IRE) **J. M. Bradley**
37 **SPANISH ACE**, 7, b g First Trump—Spanish Heart **racingshares.co.uk**
38 **SUMMER RECLUSE (USA)**, 9, gr g Cozzene (USA)—Summer Retreat (USA) **C. M. Hunt**
39 **TATILLIUS (IRE)**, 5, ch g King Charlemagne (USA)—Aunty Eileen **J. M. Bradley**
40 **THABAAT**, 4, ch g Pivotal—Maraatib (IRE) **E. A. Hayward**
41 **THE GREY ONE (IRE)**, 5, gr g Dansili—Marie Dora (FR) **K. R. Miles**
42 **THE TATLING (IRE)**, 11, b br g Perugino (USA)—Aunty Eileen **J. M. Bradley**
43 **TREVIAN**, 7, ch g Atraf—Ascend (IRE) **Folly Road Racing Partners (1996)**
44 **TURKISH SULTAN (IRE)**, 5, b g Anabaa (USA)—Odalisque (IRE) **The Lovely Jubbly's**
45 **VLASTA WEINER**, 8, b g Magic Ring (IRE)—Armaiti **Miss D. Hill**
46 **YENALED**, 11, gr g Rambo Dancer (CAN)—Fancy Flight (FR) **JMB racing.co.uk**

THREE-YEAR-OLDS

47 **GILLANS INN**, b g Rambling Bear—Strat's Quest **P. Banfield**
48 B c Sooty Tern—Miss Money Spider (IRE) **Mrs R. Bradley**
49 **OXBRIDGE**, ch g Tomba—Royal Passion **Mr M. Carver**
50 Ch c Zahran (IRE)—Pageant **J. M. Bradley**
51 **SANDY PAR**, ch g No Excuse Needed—Nesting
52 **SOLEMN**, b c Pivotal—Pious **E. A. Hayward**

TWO-YEAR-OLDS

53 Ch c 27/3 Gold Away (IRE)—All Square (FR) (Holst (USA)) (5500) **Mr R. D. Willis**
54 B g 9/4 Josr Algarhoud (IRE)—Double Fault (IRE) (Zieten (USA)) (3300)
55 B f 16/4 Kyllachy—Feather Circle (IRE) (Indian Ridge) (5500)
56 B f 16/2 Orpen—Gargren (IRE) (Mujtahid (USA)) (3600)
57 B f 8/4 Kyllachy—Highland Gait (Most Welcome) (4000)
58 B f 4/2 Beat All (USA)—Lady Ezzabella (Ezzoud (IRE)) (952) **Mr R. D. Willis**
59 B c 16/5 Trans Island—Legand of Tara (USA) (Gold Legend (USA)) (2500) **Mrs R. Bradley**
60 B c 20/3 Zahran (IRE)—Miss Money Spider (Statoblest) **Mrs R. Bradley**
61 B f 3/5 Domedriver (IRE)—Preceder (Polish Precedent (USA))
62 **RUBY'S SONG (IRE)**, b f 6/4 Clodovil (IRE)—Gales Bridge (IRE) (Mujadil (USA)) (5500) **Mr G. Fry**
63 B f 30/1 Needwood Blade—You Found Me (Robellino (USA)) (3500) **racingshares.co.uk**

Other Owners: Mr Philip Banfield, Mr J. M. Bradley, Mrs J. K. Bradley, Mr S. Bruce, S. Champ, Mr P. Crawford, Mr F. M. Green, Mr G. W. Holland, Mr Martyn James, Mr T. W. James, Mr G. Johnson, Mr L. Johnson, Mr P. L. Jones, Mr G. T. Lever, Mr Michael Mackay, Mr Stephen McAvoy, Mr G. A. Roberts, Mr Mark Savidge, Mr Derek Shinton, Mr Philip Sinfield, Mrs Lisa Sinfield, Mr Pete Smith, Mr George S. Thompson, Mr E. B. Whittal-Williams, Mr R. D. Willis, P. L. Winkworth.

Assistant Trainer: Miss Hayley Davies

Jockey (flat): N. Callan, L. Keniry, G. Baker, S. Drowne, S. Kelly, P. Fitzsimons. **Jockey (NH):** W. Marston, R. Johnson. **Conditional:** C.J. Davies. **Apprentice:** Barry Savage, Pietro Romeo, Jake Payne. **Amateur:** Miss Sarah-Jayne Bradley, Miss Hayley Davies.

59 MR M. F. BRADSTOCK, Wantage

Postal: **The Old Manor Stables, Letcombe Bassett, Wantage, Oxfordshire, OX12 9NB**
Contacts: **PHONE (01235) 760780 FAX (01235) 760754 MOBILE (07887) 686697**
E-MAIL mark.bradstock@btinternet.com

1 ALINGHI (GER), 5, ch m Tertullian (USA)—Alte Garde (FR)
2 CARRUTHERS, 5, b g Kayf Tara—Plaid Maid (IRE) **The Oaksey Partnership**
3 CHIMICHURRI (FR), 6, ch g Nikos—Wackie (USA) **The Blick Partnership**
4 CHOUROMANESCO (FR), 5, ch g Maresca Sorrento (FR)—Fleur de Chou (FR) **J. B. G. Macleod**
5 COSSACK DANCER (IRE), 10, b g Moscow Society (USA)—Merry Lesa **The United Front Partnership**
6 CUCKOO PEN, 4, b g Alflora (IRE)—Plaid Maid (IRE) **The Hill Farm Partnership**
7 GAELIC MUSIC (IRE), 9, b g Accordion—Cuilin Bui (IRE) **P. J. Constable**
8 KING HARALD (IRE), 10, b g King's Ride—Cuilin Bui (IRE) **Piers Pottinger & P B-J Partnership**
9 NEARLY SIXTY, 5, b g Lujain (USA)—Gifted **Mr T. A. Killoran**
10 PARADIS BLUE (FR), 5, b g Lute Antique (FR)—Honey Blue (FR) **Mr A. Alshinbayev**
11 RADETSKY MARCH (IRE), 5, b g Taipan (IRE)—Jane Jones (IRE) **P. J. D. Pottinger**
12 4, B f Kayf Tara—Star Diva (IRE)
13 TAMBO (IRE), 13, b g Shardari—Carmen Lady **M. S. Tamburro**
14 TETBURY (IRE), 7, b g Saddlers' Hall (IRE)—Rainbow Light **Ormonds Head Partnership**
15 TOEMAC, 9, b g Slip Anchor—Bobanlyn (IRE) **J. B. G. Macleod**
16 VIAL DE KERDEC (FR), 5, b g Poliglote—Love For Ever (FR) **Orion Partnership**

Other Owners: P Bennett-Jones, Lady Dundas, C. Elgram, Mr A.P. Farnham, P. D. Hunt, D. King, A. T. A. Manning, Lord Oaksey, A. M. Waller.

Assistant Trainer: Sara Bradstock

Jockey (NH): M. Batchelor.

60 MR G. C. BRAVERY, Newmarket

Postal: **Long Acre, Lambfair Green, Cowlinge, Newmarket, Suffolk, CB8 9HY**
Contacts: **PHONE (01440) 821873 MOBILE (07711) 112345**
E-MAIL braverygc@aol.com

1 ASTORYGOESWITHIT, 5, b g Foxhound (USA)—La Belle Mystere
2 BUSTAN (IRE), 9, b g Darshaan—Dazzlingly Radiant
3 CHASE THE FOX, 5, ch m Foxhound (USA)—La Belle Dominique
4 DANCE STEPS, 4, b f Golan (IRE)—Swift Baba (USA)
5 DUKE OF MILAN (IRE), 5, ch g Desert Prince (IRE)—Abyat (USA)
6 ESTER ROSE, 4, b f Tobougg (IRE)—Perle de Sagesse
7 GRAND ASSAULT, 5, b g Mujahid (USA)—As Mustard
8 HAMMER OF THE GODS (IRE), 8, ch g Tagula (IRE)—Bhama (FR)
9 HUGGLE, 5, b g Groom Dancer (USA)—Perle de Sagesse
10 KARAOKE QUEEN, 4, ch f Tumbleweed Ridge—Sodelk
11 KINDALLACHAN, 5, b m Magic Ring (IRE)—Moore Stylish
12 LOVE AND AFFECTION, 5, b g Groom Dancer (USA)—Fox Star (IRE)
13 MASSAMS LANE, 4, b g Lahib (USA)—Night Trader (USA)
14 SCARAMOUSHCA, 5, gr g Most Welcome—Kinraddie
15 THOUGHTSOFSTARDOM, 5, b g Mind Games—Alustar
16 TILLY'S DREAM, 5, ch m Arkadian Hero (USA)—Dunloe (IRE)
17 TIME SHARE (IRE), 4, b f Danetime (IRE)—Clochette (IRE)
18 UNCLE BULGARIA, 6, b g Alhaarth (IRE)—Istibshar (USA)
19 WELCOME RELEAF, 5, ch g Most Welcome—Mint Leaf (IRE)

THREE-YEAR-OLDS

20 BAYTOWN BLAZE, ch f Zaha (CAN)—Lightning Blaze
21 Ch c Tipsy Creek (USA)—Blowing Away (IRE)
22 CHINESE PROFIT, b c Acclamation—Tancholo
23 B f Bahamian Bounty—Fox Star (IRE)
24 B f Tipsy Creek (USA)—Kinraddie
25 Ch f Viking Ruler (AUS)—La Belle Mystere
26 B f Compton Place—Marie La Rose (FR)
27 OUR LAMENT, ch c Compton Place—Glider (IRE)
28 B c Bahamian Bounty—Perle de Sagesse
29 RUBY ROCKS, ch f Zaha (CAN)—Natural Grace

MR G. C. BRAVERY—continued

30 **SHE'S THE BEST**, ch f Best of The Bests (IRE)—Myrrh
31 B c Zaha (CAN)—Silent Scream (IRE)

TWO-YEAR-OLDS

32 B f 1/1 Prince Sabo—Blowing Away (IRE) (Last Tycoon)
33 B c 1/1 Monsieur Bond (IRE)—Ejay (Emperor Jones) (USA)
34 Ch c 1/1 Monsieur Bond (IRE)—En Fin (FR) (Loup Solitaire (USA))
35 Ch c 31/3 Compton Place—Form At Last (Formidable (USA))
36 **INDIAN STORY (IRE)**, b f 14/2 Indian Ridge—Law Tudor (IRE) (Law Society (USA))
37 Ch f 1/1 Prince Sabo—Kinraddie (Wuzo (IRE))
38 B f 29/3 Intikhab (USA)—Lamees (USA) (Lomond (USA)) (24000)
39 B c 1/1 Soviet Star (USA)—Mint Leaf (IRE) (Sri Pekan (USA))
40 Ch c 1/1 Monsieur Bond (IRE)—Samar Qand (Selkirk (USA))

Owners: Mr Richard Archer, Mr Danny Berry, Mrs F. E. Bravery, Mr Neil Burns, Mr Daniel Jonathon Clark, Mr Stephen Cox, Mr M. Dunn, Mrs Suzy Harvey, Mr Mark Andrew Humphris, Mr Keith Ingram, Mr Trevor David Johnson, Mrs T. S. Macdonald Johnston, Mr G. D. Newton, Mr Richard Payne, Mrs Elizabeth Reed, Mr Mick Robinson, Mr R. Wade, Mrs Mandy Wade, Mr Richard Withers, Mr A. P. D. Wyke.

---

61 **MR OWEN BRENNAN, Worksop**
Postal: **Sloswicks Farm, Broad Lane, Worksop, Nottinghamshire, S80 3NJ**
Contacts: **PHONE (01909) 473950**

1 **COMMON GIRL (IRE)**, 10, gr m Roselier (FR)—Rumups Debut (IRE) **Mr J. Goodman**
2 **ELLERSLIE ALI (IRE)**, 6, b m Zaffaran (USA)—Garrisker (IRE) **Mr P. Mina**
3 **ELLERSLIE LISA**, 6, b m Kayf Tara—Vax Rapide **Mrs P. N. Brennan**
4 **GEMINI STORM**, 8, br g Jendali (USA)—Fanny Adams **The Christmas Box Partnership**
5 **GOLDSMEADOW**, 9, b g Thowra (FR)—Fanny Adams **Mrs P. N. Brennan**
6 **LUCKY PEARL**, 7, b m Jendali (USA)—Fardella (ITY) **Owen Brennan**
7 **MISTER MAGEE**, 7, b g Case Law—Pennine Star (IRE) **Mrs P. N. Brennan**
8 **MY FRIEND PAUL**, 8, b g Bold Fox—Annie Bee **Owen Brennan**
9 **NANNYS GIFT (IRE)**, 9, b m Presenting—Last Royal **Owen Brennan**
10 **PENNINE MOON**, 8, b g Defacto (USA)—Emerald Queen **Mr Richard J. Marshall & Mr Owen Brennan**
11 **SAM MCCOOMBE (IRE)**, 7, b g Roseberry Avenue (IRE)—
Runaway Mary (IRE) **Owen Brennan & The Christmas Box Partnership**
12 **TIMBER DEALER (IRE)**, 6, br g Charnwood Forest (IRE)—Sevens Are Wild **Mrs P. N. Brennan**

Other Owners: Mrs Pat Brennan, Mr O. Brennan, Mr Kevin Orchard.

Jockey (NH): N. Fehily.

---

62 **MISS RHONA BREWIS, Belford**
Postal: **Chester Hill, Belford, Northumberland, NE70 7EF**
Contacts: **PHONE (01668) 213239/213281**

1 **CHANELLY**, 5, b m Alflora (IRE)—Chantilly Rose **Miss Rhona Brewis**
2 **CRACKADEE**, 9, b br g Alflora (IRE)—Carnetto **Miss Rhona Brewis**
3 **KEPPEL**, 8, b g Sir Harry Lewis (USA)—Kimberley Rose **Miss Rhona Brewis**

Other Owners: Mrs G. E. Brewis, Mr R. Brewis.

---

63 **MR J. J. BRIDGER, Liphook**
Postal: **Upper Hatch Farm, Liphook, Hampshire, GU30 7EL**
Contacts: **PHONE (01428) 722528 MOBILE (07785) 716614**
E-MAIL jbridger@btconnect.com

1 **BINNION BAY (IRE)**, 7, b g Fasliyev (USA)—Literary **J. J. Bridger**
2 **BOLLYWOOD (IRE)**, 5, ch g Indian Rocket—La Fille de Cirque **J. J. Bridger**
3 **BORDER EDGE**, 10, b g Beveled (USA)—Seymour Ann **Allsorts**
4 **ELMASONG**, 4, ch f Elmaamul (USA)—Annie's Song **Double-R-Racing**
5 **INQUISITRESS**, 4, b f Hernando (FR)—Caribbean Star **Mr C Marshall Mr T Wallace Mr JJ Bridger**
6 **ISHIBEE (IRE)**, 4, b f Ishiguru (USA)—Beauty (IRE) **Clarke Gammon Wellers I**

MR J. J. BRIDGER—continued

7 KEMPSEY, 6, ch g Wolfhound (USA)—Mockingbird J. J. Bridger
8 LOVE ANGEL (USA), 6, b br g Woodman (USA)—Omnia (USA) R. A. Brimacombe
9 MEGALALA (IRE), 7, b g Petardia—Avionne T. Ware
10 MTOTO GIRL, 4, b f Mtoto—Shalati (FR) G. W. Chambers
11 MYTHICAL CHARM, 9, b m Charnwood Forest (IRE)—Triple Tricks (IRE) T. Ware
12 PLAY UP POMPEY, 6, b g Dansili—Search For Love (FR) Double-R-Racing
13 TURTLE SOUP, 12, b g Turtle Island (IRE)—Lisa's Favourite M. K. George
14 WHITE GATE (IRE), 6, br g Bob Back (USA)—Mount Sackville Mrs M. J. George
15 ZAZOUS, 7, b g Zafonic (USA)—Confidentiality (USA) J. J. Bridger

THREE-YEAR-OLDS

16 ESTELLA MAI, ch f Fleetwood (IRE)—Hill Farm Dancer G. W. Chambers
17 TOO GRAND, ch f Zaha (CAN)—Gold Linnet Clarke Gammon Wellers

Other Owners: Mr S. R. Cook, P. J. Hague, Mrs J. E. Lunn, C. Marshall, Mr T. A. Pasquale, Mr M. P. Steward, Mr T. Wallace.

Assistant Trainer: Rachel Cook

---

64 MR D. G. BRIDGWATER, Stow-on-the-Wold
Postal: Wyck Hill Farm, Wyck Hill, Stow-on-the-Wold, Cheltenham, Gloucestershire, GL54 1HT
Contacts: PHONE (01451) 830349 FAX (01451) 830349 MOBILE (07831) 635817

1 BABE HEFFRON (IRE), 7, ch g Topanoora—Yellow Ochre (IRE) Mr S. W. Clarke
2 BERTIES BROTHER, 5, ch g Forzando—Sweets (IRE) R. W. Neale
3 COLWYN BAY (IRE), 6, b g Sadler's Wells—Stolen Tear (FR) D. J. Smith
4 COUNTRY AFFAIR (USA), 5, ch g Vettori (IRE)—Nany's Affair (USA) Mr D. J. Smith & Mr D. J. Ellis
5 ESTEEM, 5, b g Mark of Esteem (IRE)—Please Mr D. J. Smith & Mr D. J. Ellis
6 FIRST AMONG EQUALS, 5, b m Primo Valentino—Margarets First Mrs M. A. Bridgwater
7 FOREVER AUTUMN, 5, b g Sinndar (IRE)—Photo Call Bourton Vale Racing
8 HE'S MINE TOO, 4, b g Indian Ridge—Screen Idol D. A. Thorpe
9 JUST DENNIS, 4, b g Superior Premium—Sweets (IRE) R. W. Neale
10 LADY ROMANOV (IRE), 5, br m Xaar—Mixremember (FR) Mrs S. Hunt
11 PAGAN SWORD, 6, ch g Selkirk (USA)—Vanessa Bell (IRE) Terry & Sarah Amos
12 PRIVATE GARCIA (IRE), 8, b g Erins Isle—Southern Song (IRE) Mr D. J. Smith & Mr D. J. Ellis
13 QUENZO CONTI (FR), 4, b g Franc Bleu Argent—Cantagrel (FR) D. A. Thorpe
14 RUN ON, 10, b h Runnett—Polar Storm (IRE) Miss V. B. H. Evans
15 RUNSHAN (IRE), 8, ch g Anshan—Whitebarn Run Terry & Sarah Amos
16 WINNIE'S SPIRIT, 7, ch m Commanche Run—Winnie The Witch Mrs M. A. Bridgwater
17 ZELOS (IRE), 4, b g Mujadil (USA)—First Degree Mr D. J. Smith
18 ZIG ZAG ZOE (IRE), 4, b f Bertolini (USA)—Amaretto Flame (IRE) Terry & Sarah Amos

TWO-YEAR-OLDS

19 REG'S RUBY, b f 15/3 Pursuit of Love—Sweets (IRE) (Persian Heights) R. W. Neale

Other Owners: Mr T. P. Amos, Mrs S. P. Amos, Miss Marie Bridgwater, Mr D. G. Bridgwater, Mr David Ellis, Mrs L. Launchbury.

Jockey (NH): R. Thornton. Conditional: J W Stevenson.

---

65 MR G. F. BRIDGWATER, Claverdon
Postal: The Rowans, 14 Shrewley Common, Shrewley, Warwickshire, CV35 7AP
Contacts: PHONE (01926) 840137 MOBILE (07769) 894400
E-MAIL bridgwater9@aol.com

1 ACKNOWLEDGEMENT, 6, b g Josr Algarhoud (IRE)—On Request (IRE) Mrs G. J. Bridgwater
2 BE MI MAITE, 4, b g Komaite (USA)—Miss Bananas Mr L. Muller
3 CRIMSON FLAME (IRE), 5, b g Celtic Swing—Wish List (IRE) Never Say Never Racing
4 IMPERO, 10, b g Emperor Jones (USA)—Fight Right (FR) See You Later Club
5 TYRANA (GER), 5, ch m Acatenango (GER)—Tascalina (GER) Mrs G. J. Bridgwater
6 VEHARI, 5, ch g Tomba—Nannie Annie Never Say Never Racing

MR G. F. BRIDGWATER—continued

THREE-YEAR-OLDS

7 B f Dilshaan—Haysong (IRE) **Mrs G. J. Bridgwater**

Other Owners: Mr K. W. Bradley, Mr G. F. Rowledge.

66

MR W. M. BRISBOURNE, Nesscliffe
Postal: **Ness Strange Stables, Great Ness, Shrewsbury, Shropshire, SY4 2LE**
Contacts: **PHONE (01743) 741536/741360 FAX (01743) 741285 MOBILE (07803) 019651**

1 ACUZIO, 7, b g Mon Tresor—Veni Vici (IRE) **Derek Hartland & Peter Gradwell**
2 ADOBE, 13, b g Green Desert (USA)—Shamshir **P. R. Kirk**
3 ALMORA GURU, 4, b f Ishiguru (USA)—Princess Almora **J. W. Jenkins**
4 BARBIROLLI, 6, b g Machiavellian (USA)—Blushing Barada (USA) **Mr G. Dewhurst**
5 BECK, 4, ch g Cadeaux Genereux—River Cara (USA) **S. E. Roberts**
6 BILLY THE SHIFTER, 7, b g Aspect (USA)—Birchgrey Lady **Mr S. V. Parry**
7 BUDS DILEMMA, 4, b f Anabaa (USA)—Lady Thynn (FR) **C. G. R. Booth**
8 BUSCADOR (USA), 9, ch g Crafty Prospector (USA)—Fairway Flag (USA) **D. B. Robson**
9 CADI MAY, 4, b f Fasliyev (USA)—Sound of Sleat **Mr W. M. Clare**
10 CHESHIRE PRINCE, 4, b g Desert Prince (IRE)—Bundle Up (USA) **D. C. Rutter & H. Clewlow**
11 CIRCUS POLKA (USA), 4, br c Stravinsky (USA)—Far Wiser (USA) **J. R. Salter**
12 COMPTON DRAGON (USA), 9, ch g Woodman (USA)—Vilikaia (USA) **J. Connor**
13 DESERT HAWK, 7, b g Cape Cross (IRE)—Milling (IRE) **J. Jones Racing Ltd**
14 DESERT LEADER (IRE), 7, b g Green Desert (USA)—Za Aamah (USA) **R. O. Rickett**
15 ENGLISH ARCHER, 5, b g Rock City—Fire Sprite **M. F. Hyman**
16 ENSIGN'S TRICK, 4, b f Cayman Kai (IRE)—River Ensign **Mrs D. M. Brisbourne**
17 GAMESTERS LADY, 5, br m Almushtarak (IRE)—Tycoon Tina **Gamesters Partnership**
18 GRAFTY GREEN (IRE), 5, b g Green Desert (USA)—Banafsajee (USA) **W. M. Brisbourne**
19 GREEN PIRATE, 6, b g Bahamian Bounty—Verdura **Mr J. Babb**
20 HEIGHT OF ESTEEM, 5, b g Mark of Esteem (IRE)—Biscay **A. Pardoe**
21 HILL CLOUD, 6, gr g Cloudings (IRE)—Hill Farm Dancer **Mr M. Hughes Mark Brisbourne**
22 4, Ch c Sir Harry Lewis (USA)—Hill Farm Dancer **Mr M. Hughes**
23 IGNITION, 6, ch m Rock City—Fire Sprite **M. F. Hyman**
24 JUST OSCAR (GER), 4, b g Surako (GER)—Jade Chequer **Mr M. Edwards & Mr D. J. Francis**
25 MACHINATE (USA), 6, b br g Machiavellian (USA)—Dancing Sea (USA) **D. F. Slingsby**
26 MERRYMAKER, 8, b g Machiavellian (USA)—Wild Pavane **The Blacktoffee Partnership**
27 MORBICK, 4, ch g Kyllachy—Direcvil **J. R. Salter**
28 NEW ENGLAND, 6, ch g Bachir (IRE)—West Escape **Mr S. Walker**
29 NEW STAR (UAE), 4, b g Green Desert (USA)—Princess Haifa (USA) **Shropshire Wolves**
30 PRELUDE, 7, b m Danzero (AUS)—Dancing Debut **A. P. Burgoyne**
31 PSYCHO CAT, 5, b g Hunting Lion (IRE)—Canadian Capers **Ben Brisbourne**
32 REGENCY RED (IRE), 10, ch g Dolphin Street (FR)—Future Romance **Hamerton, Twidle**
33 ROCK HAVEN (IRE), 6, b g Danehill Dancer (IRE)—Mahabba (USA)
34 ROMAN MAZE, 8, ch g Lycius (USA)—Maze Garden (USA) **The Jenko & Thomo Partnership**
35 ROYAL ATTRACTION, 7, b g Mon Tresor—Star Gal **Magnet Racing**
36 ROYAL INDULGENCE, 8, b g Royal Applause—Silent Indulgence (USA) **Mr P. G. Evans**
37 SIR SANDICLIFFE (IRE), 4, b g Distant Music (USA)—Desert Rose **The Blacktoffee Partnership**
38 SKIT, 5, b g In The Wings—Skew **A. P. Burgoyne**
39 SQUIRTLE (IRE), 5, ch m In The Wings—Manilia (FR) **J. Jones Racing Ltd**
40 STURGIS (IRE), 5, b g Factual (USA)—Vannuccis Daughter (IRE) **S. Dalton**
41 THE LONDON GANG, 5, b g Mind Games—Nom Francais
42 THORNY MANDATE, 6, b g Diktat—Rosa Canina **R. C. Naylor**
43 TWILIGHT AVENGER (IRE), 5, b g Dr Fong (USA)—Asterita **Miss P. D. Insull**
44 UP DEE CREEK, 6, ch m Tipsy Creek (USA)—Sandra Dee (IRE) **W. M. Brisbourne**
45 VANATINA (IRE), 4, b f Tagula (USA)—Final Trick **Black Diamond Racing**
46 WEET YER TERN (IRE), 6, b g Brave Act—Maxime (IRE) **Ed Weetman (Haulage & Storage) Ltd**
47 YORK CLIFF, 10, b g Marju (IRE)—Azm **Ben Brisbourne**

THREE-YEAR-OLDS

48 Ch f Fleetwood (IRE)—Barden Lady **Mr D. G. Blagden**
49 DANEHILL STORM, b f Statue of Liberty (USA)—Winchcombe **Mr C. Peach**
50 B f Fleetwood (IRE)—Miss Tango **Swanvista**
51 MISTY KIT, b f Umistim—River Ensign **Mrs D. M. Brisbourne**
52 PLAKA (FR), gr f Verglas (IRE)—Top Speed (IRE) **Mr M. A. Holmes**

MR W. M. BRISBOURNE—continued

53 **RAYDAR**, b g Ziggy's Dancer (USA)—Send Me An Angel (IRE) **J. Connor**
54 **RICHARDTHESECOND (IRE)**, b g Acclamation—Tahlil **Mr W. M. Clare**
55 **SECRET ASSET (IRE)**, gr g Clodovil (IRE)—Skerray **Kinsale Racing**
56 **SYBIL'S SURPRISE**, b f Puissance—Fervent Fan (IRE) **Major W. R. Paton-Smith**
57 **THANKFULLY (IRE)**, b f Green Desert (USA)—Your Welcome **Stratford Bards Racing**
58 **THE LAST BOTTLE (IRE)**, ch g Hawk Wing (USA)—Mesmerist (USA) **Shropshire Wolves**
59 **TRIUMPHANT WELCOME**, b g Piccolo—Shoof (USA) **Mr C. Shelton**
60 **TYFOS**, b g Bertolini (USA)—Warminghamsharpish **Mr J. Tomlinson, Mr G. Williams**
61 **WATERWINGS**, b f Clodovil (IRE)—Brise Marine (IRE)

TWO-YEAR-OLDS

62 B f 10/5 Grape Tree Road—Brief Star (IRE) (Brief Truce (USA)) **Mr D. Williams**
63 B g 24/2 Reset (AUS)—Cameo Role (GER) (Acatenango (GER)) (3000)
64 Ch g 29/4 Spartacus (IRE)—Ela Alethia (Kris) (2000)
65 B c 26/4 Kheleyf (USA)—Ezilana (IRE) (Shardari) (4500)
66 **FEET OF FURY**, b f 10/4 Deportivo—Fury Dance (USA) (Cryptoclearance (USA)) (7000) **Stratford Bards Racing**
67 **GAME ROSEANNA**, b f 1/3 Mind Games—Rosy Sunset (IRE) (Red Sunset) **Major W. R. Paton-Smith**
68 **HAAFHDS DELIGHT (IRE)**, br f 24/4 Haafhd—Twitcher's Delight (Polar Falcon (USA)) (3000) **D.R.B. Racing**
69 **K T HAWK**, b f 4/2 Hawk Wing (USA)—Alenushka (Soviet Star (USA)) (2000) **K. Bennett**
70 Ch g 24/1 Reset (AUS)—Lady Soleas (Be My Guest (USA)) (3500)
71 **LAURA LAND**, b f 17/5 Lujain (USA)—Perdicula (IRE) (Persian Heights) (4000) **Law Abiding Citizens**
72 **LILY WATERS**, ch f 24/3 Reset (AUS)—Chilly Waters (Polar Falcon (USA)) **J. E. Oldknow**
73 **MIA SECRET**, b f 26/1 Fraam—Michelle Shift (Night Shift (USA)) (4500) **Kinsale Racing 2**
74 **MUSICAL MAZE (USA)**, b f 17/5 Distant Music (USA)—
                                   Maze Garden (USA) (Riverman (USA)) (2800) **Nelson Pigs Might Fly**
75 B f 26/2 Kheleyf (USA)—Namesake (Nashwan (USA)) (5400)
76 **REDOLINI**, b g 23/4 Bertolini (USA)—Red Cloud (IRE) (Taufan (USA)) (7000) **Mr R. J. Roberts**
77 B f 27/4 Ziggy's Dancer (USA)—Send Me An Angel (IRE) (Lycius (USA)) (1000) **Miss Gill Quincey**
78 **TRANSCENTRAL**, ch f 28/3 Kheleyf (USA)—Khatayif (USA) (Swain (IRE)) (2000) **D.R.B. Racing**
79 **TYLER**, b g 31/3 Bertolini (USA)—Fly Like The Wind (Cyrano de Bergerac) (4000) **Mr W. M. Clare**

Other Owners: A. J. Banton, Mr P. Clare, Mr B. L. Clark, Miss H. Clark, H. Clewlow, Mr S. J. France, P. G. Gradwell, Ms B. L. Hamerton, D. W. Hartland, M. E. Hughes, T. Minnis, M. Murray, Mr S. Petty, Mr M. J. Petty, A. Pitt, J. R. Pugh, N. Ridgway, D. C. Rutter, Mr D. R. Southworth, Exors of the Late D. Sutton, J. F. Thomas, D. Timmis, J. Tomlinson, Mr A. L. Twidle, M. G. West, D. V. Williams, Mr D. G. Williams.

Assistant Trainer: Mrs Pam Brisbourne

Jockey (flat): Liam Jones, T. G. McLaughlin, David Allan, S. W. Kelly. **Amateur:** Mr Ben Brisbourne.

---

67 MR C. E. BRITTAIN, Newmarket
Postal: 'Carlburg', 49 Bury Road, Newmarket, Suffolk, CB8 7BY
Contacts: OFFICE (01638) 664347 HOME (01638) 663739 FAX (01638) 661744
MOBILE (07785) 302121 E-MAIL carlburgst@aol.com

1 **ALBADI**, 7, b g Green Desert (USA)—Lyrist **S. Manana**
2 **BAHAR SHUMAAL**, 6, b h Dubai Millennium—High Spirited **S. Manana**
3 **BAHIANO (IRE)**, 7, ch g Barathea (IRE)—Trystero **C. E. Brittain**
4 **BEST ONE**, 4, ch g Best of The Bests (IRE)—Nasaieb (IRE) **S. Manana**
5 **DUBAI SHADOW (IRE)**, 4, b f Cape Cross (IRE)—Farista **C. E. Brittain**
6 **EXCUSEZ MOI (USA)**, 6, b h Fusaichi Pegasus (USA)—Jiving **Sheikh Hamdan Bin Mohammed Al Maktoum**
7 **HATTAN (IRE)**, 6, ch h Halling (USA)—Luana **S. Manana**
8 **KANDIDATE**, 6, b h Kabool—Valleyrose (IRE) **Exors of the Late A. J. Richards**
9 **LAKE POET (IRE)**, 5, ch h Galileo (USA)—Lyric **Mr M. Rashid**
10 **PARTY BOSS**, 6, gr h Silver Patriarch (IRE)—Third Party **Michael Clarke**
11 **ROYAL CHOIR**, 4, ch f King's Best (USA)—Harmonic Sound (IRE) **C. E. Brittain**
12 **SAHRATI**, 4, ch c In The Wings—Shimna **S. Manana**
13 **YARQUS**, 5, b g Diktat—Will You Dance **S. Manana**

THREE-YEAR-OLDS

14 **AL MUHEER (IRE)**, b c Diktat—Dominion Rose (USA) **S. Manana**
15 **ALBABILIA (IRE)**, b f King's Best (USA)—Sonachan (IRE) **S. Ali**
16 **ALWAYS READY**, ch c Best of The Bests (IRE)—Tahara (IRE) **S. Manana**
17 **ATHEER DUBAI (IRE)**, b c Dubai Destination (USA)—Atheer (USA) **Mr M. Rashid**

MR C. E. BRITTAIN—continued

18 **BAZERGAN (IRE)**, b c Machiavellian (USA)—Lunda (IRE) **S. Manana**
19 **BIG HUG**, b f Diktat—Unconditional Love (IRE) **S. Manana**
20 **CALAKANGA**, ch f Dalakhani (IRE)—Avila **S. Manana**
21 **CUTE**, b f Diktat—Gleam of Light (IRE) **S. Manana**
22 **DARLEY STAR**, gr f King's Best—Amellnaa (IRE) **Mr M. Rashid**
23 **DHAHAB (USA)**, b f Kingmambo (USA)—Lucky Rainbow (USA) **S. Ali**
24 **DHHAMAAN (IRE)**, b c Dilshaan—Safe Care (IRE) **C. E. Brittain**
25 **DUBAI POWER**, b f Cadeaux Genereux—Garmoucheh (USA) **Dr A. Ridha**
26 **DUF'A (USA)**, gr f Diesis—Bridlemere Court (USA) **S. Ali**
27 **EIGHTEEN THOUSAND (IRE)**, b f King's Best—La Dolores (GER) **S. Ali**
28 **EMAIL**, ch f Diesis—Space Time (FR) **S. Manana**
29 **FLY KISS**, b f Arkadian Hero (USA)—Kiss Me Kate **S. Manana**
30 **FORGIVE ME**, ch f Mark of Esteem (IRE)—Francia **S. Manana**
31 **GAABAL (IRE)**, ch f Frenchmans Bay (FR)—Jazz Up **S. Manana**
32 **HEART OF DUBAI (USA)**, b c Outofthebox (USA)—Diablo's Blend (USA) **Mr M. Al Shafar**
33 **HELLO HELLO**, br f Helissio (FR)—Party Charmer **C. E. Brittain**
34 **INTABIH (USA)**, b br c More Than Ready (USA)—Lookaway Dixieland (USA) **S. Manana**
35 **JAYYID (IRE)**, b g Daylami (IRE)—Mellow Jazz **C. E. Brittain**
36 **JEBEL TARA**, b c Diktat—Chantilly (FR) **S. Manana**
37 **KHAZINA (USA)**, b br f Kingmambo (USA)—Easy Now (USA) **S. Manana**
38 **KIPCHAK (IRE)**, b br g Soviet Star (USA)—Khawafi (IRE) **C. E. Brittain**
39 **LIGHT MOON**, b f Oasis Dream—Sismique **S. Manana**
40 **LOVE OF DUBAI (USA)**, b f More Than Ready (USA)—Diamond Kris (USA) **Mr M. Al Shafar**
41 **MA AL SALAMAH (IRE)**, ch f Noverre (USA)—Tres Sage **S. Manana**
42 **MAHADEE (IRE)**, br c Cape Cross (IRE)—Rafiya **S. Manana**
43 **MANSII**, b c Dr Fong (USA)—Enclave (USA) **S. Manana**
44 **MASSIUTA (UAE)**, b f Selkirk (USA)—Forget Me Not (IRE) **S. Manana**
45 **MINJIM**, b c Kyllachy—Sarabah (IRE) **S. Manana**
46 **MUDHISH (IRE)**, b c Lujain (USA)—Silver Satire **C. E. Brittain**
47 **MUHARJAM**, b c Diktat—Elsie Plunkett **S. Manana**
48 B f Cape Cross (IRE)—Mureefa (USA) **Mr M. Rashid**
49 **MUT'AB (USA)**, b c Alhaarth (IRE)—Mistle Song **S. Manana**
50 **NEFAF (IRE)**, b c Cape Cross (IRE)—Iftitan (USA) **Mr M. Rashid**
51 **NICE DREAM**, b f Oasis Dream—Have Fun **S. Ali**
52 **NISBAH**, ch f Kyllachy—Amazing Bay **S. Manana**
53 **QASAYED (IRE)**, b f Diesis—Bright and Cheery (USA) **Sheikh Hamdan Bin Mohammed Al Maktoum**
54 **QUBLA (IRE)**, b f Anabaa (USA)—Al Rajiba (USA) **S. Manana**
55 **RAHAAN (USA)**, b f Forestry (USA)—Jordanesque (USA) **S. Manana**
56 B f Danzig (USA)—Rahy's Darlin (USA) **S. Ali**
57 **REDCHETE**, b f Red Ransom (USA)—Zacheta **S. Ali**
58 **RSMIYA**, b f Diktat—Scenic Venture (IRE) **S. Manana**
59 **SAHARIRI (IRE)**, b f Red Ransom (USA)—Contradictive (USA) **S. Manana**
60 **SARATEE**, b f Mark of Esteem (IRE)—Salalah **S. Manana**
61 **SAYYEDATI SYMPHONY (USA)**, b f Gone West—Sayyedati **M. Obaida**
62 **SWEET SARA**, b f Mark of Esteem (IRE)—Mild Deception (IRE) **Dr A. Ridha**
63 **TAMDIID (USA)**, b f Horse Chestnut (SAF)—Ladue (USA) **S. Manana**
64 **TATHKAAR**, ch f Dr Fong (USA)—Royal Patron **S. Manana**
65 **TRY ME (UAE)**, b br f Singspiel (IRE)—Cunas (USA) **S. Manana**
66 **WADLIA (USA)**, ch f Lemon Drop Kid (USA)—Brusque (USA) **S. Manana**
67 **WARMING UP (IRE)**, b c Kalanisi (IRE)—Sound Asleep (USA) **S. Manana**
68 **WUSUUL**, br f Kyllachy—Cartuccia (IRE) **S. Manana**
69 **YAHRAB (IRE)**, gr c Dalakhani (IRE)—Loire Valley (IRE) **S. Ali**
70 **YASMINE (IRE)**, b br f Rainbow Quest (USA)—Canary Cottage (IRE) **S. Manana**
71 **ZAM ZOOM (IRE)**, gr f Dalakhani (IRE)—Mantesera (IRE) **S. Manana**
72 **ZEERAN**, b c Barathea (IRE)—Mrs Marsh **S. Manana**

TWO-YEAR-OLDS

73 B c 4/4 Theatrical—Abrade (USA) (Mr Prospector (USA)) (58309) **S. Manana**
74 B f 12/4 Kheleyf (USA)—Baalbek (Barathea (IRE)) (36000) **S. Manana**
75 B br f 24/1 Dixieland Band—Be Fair (BRZ) (Fast Gold (USA)) (77745) **S. Manana**
76 B f 25/4 Oasis Dream—Bedazzling (IRE) (Darshaan) (50000) **S. Manana**
77 B br f 18/2 Seeking The Gold (USA)—Cloud Castle (In The Wings) **S. Manana**
78 Ch c 28/4 Diesis—Coolberry (USA) (Rahy) (50000) **S. Manana**
79 Ch c 15/3 Cadeaux Genereux—Crescent Moon (Mr Prospector (USA)) (50000) **S. Ali**
80 B f 7/5 Green Desert (USA)—Darling Flame (USA) (Capote (USA)) (30000) **S. Manana**

MR C. E. BRITTAIN—continued

81 Br f 17/2 Diktat—Enchanted Princess (Royal Applause) (10000) **S. Manana**
82 Ch f 10/5 Nayef (USA)—Ermine (IRE) (Cadeaux Genereux) (40000) **S. Manana**
83 B f 23/1 Fantastic Light (USA)—First Musical (First Trump) (22000) **S. Manana**
84 B f 9/4 Acclamation—Flag (Selkirk (USA)) (40000) **S. Manana**
85 B f 6/2 Elusive City (USA)—Frond (Alzao (USA)) (30000) **S. Manana**
86 B f 21/3 Fasliyev (USA)—Kyda (USA) (Gulch (USA)) (20000) **C. E. Brittain**
87 B f 26/3 Diesis—Lady's Truth (USA) (Riverman (USA)) (42000) **S. Manana**
88 Ch f 24/4 Almutawakel—My American Beauty (Wolfhound (USA)) (32000) **S. Manana**
89 B f 20/4 Dubai Destination (USA)—Nasaieb (IRE) (Fairy King (USA)) (35000) **S. Manana**
90 B f 19/4 Rainbow Quest (USA)—Pagoda (FR) (Sadler's Wells (USA)) (30000) **S. Manana**
91 B f 14/3 Oasis Dream—Presto Vento (Air Express (IRE)) (62000) **S. Manana**
92 B f 4/2 King's Best (USA)—Sadinga (IRE) (Sadler's Wells (USA)) (32000) **S. Manana**
93 B f 31/1 Diktat—Shining Vale (USA) (Twilight Agenda) (42000) **S. Manana**
94 B f 14/4 Needwood Blade—Silent Tribute (IRE) (Lion Cavern (USA)) (27000) **S. Manana**
95 B f 27/1 Tobougg (IRE)—Skew (Niniski (USA)) (32000) **S. Manana**
96 **TOO MANY TEARS (IRE)**, ch f 28/2 Diesis—Westernize (USA) (Gone West (USA)) (40000) **S. Manana**
97 B f 11/2 Fantastic Light (USA)—Zacheta (Polish Precedent (USA)) **S. Ali**

Assistant Trainer: Louise Groom

Apprentice: Charli Leprohon.

---

68 **MR M. A. BRITTAIN, Warthill**
Postal: Northgate Lodge, Warthill, York, YO19 5XR
Contacts: PHONE (01759) 371472 FAX (01759) 372915
E-MAIL email@melbrittain.co.uk WEBSITE www.melbrittain.co.uk

1 **ABOUSTAR**, 8, b g Abou Zouz (USA)—Three Star Rated (IRE) **M. A. Brittain**
2 **BAHAMIAN BAY**, 6, b m Bahamian Bounty—Moly **Northgate Lodge Racing Club**
3 4, B c Zilzal (USA)—Casaque Rose (USA) **Mrs J. Wardman**
4 4, B f Erhaab (USA)—Escalante **Mrs J. Wardman**
5 **ESCALIER**, 5, b g Spectrum (IRE)—Escalante **Mrs J. Wardman**
6 **GUADALOUP**, 6, ch m Loup Sauvage (USA)—Rash **Northgate Red**
7 **LUCKATME**, 4, br f Atraf—Call Me Lucky **Northgate Lodge Racing Club**
8 **MOZAYADA (USA)**, 4, ch f Street Cry (IRE)—Fatina **M. A. Brittain**
9 **NABRA**, 4, b f Kyllachy—Muja Farewell **M. A. Brittain**
10 **QAASI (USA)**, 6, ch g Rahy (USA)—Recording (USA) **Eyes Wide Open Partnership**
11 **SEA ROVER (IRE)**, 4, b c Jade Robbery (USA)—Talah **M. A. Brittain**
12 **SERIAL HABIT (IRE)**, 5, b m Lahib (USA)—Satire **Northgate Lodge Racing Club**
13 5, B g Kayf Tara—Silk Stockings (FR)
14 **STEEL GREY**, 7, gr g Grey Desire—Call Me Lucky **M. A. Brittain**
15 **SUPREME SPEEDSTER**, 4, br c Superior Premium—Effervescent **M. A. Brittain**

THREE-YEAR-OLDS

16 **BAHAMIAN GIFT**, ch f Bahamian Bounty—Desert Nomad **M. A. Brittain**
17 **BIG SLICK (IRE)**, ch c Rossini (USA)—Why Worry Now (IRE) **Northgate Poker**
18 **CAPRIMA (IRE)**, ch f Captain Rio—Titchwell Lass **M. A. Brittain**
19 Ch g Elmaamul (USA)—Casaque Rose (USA) **Mrs J. Wardman**
20 **DISTANT RAINBOW (IRE)**, ch c Distant Music (USA)—Marain (IRE) **Northgate Orange**
21 **FIRST ABODE**, br f First Trump—Villa Del Sol **M. A. Brittain**
22 **FLAXTON (USA)**, b c Halling (USA)—Yasmeen Valley (USA) **M. A. Brittain**
23 **FLOP (IRE)**, b f Fraam—Confidential **Northgate Poker**
24 **FOXY JANE**, b f Lujain (USA)—Foxy Alpha (IRE)
25 **FULFORD**, ch g Elmaamul (USA)—Last Impression **M. A. Brittain**
26 **GREY COMMAND (USA)**, gr c Daylami (IRE)—Shmoose (IRE) **M. A. Brittain**
27 **INDIGO MAIL (IRE)**, b g Modigliani (USA)—Vieux Carre **Holgate Racing Club**
28 **INVINCIBLE ROSE (IRE)**, b f Invincible Spirit (USA)—Yorkshire Rose (IRE) **M. A. Brittain**
29 **KINGSTYLE (IRE)**, b c King Charlemagne (USA)—Stylish Clare (IRE) **M. A. Brittain**
30 **KIWI PRINCESS**, b f Vettori (IRE)—The Kings Daughter **Northgate Green**
31 B f Bahamian Bounty—Lily Missoula (USA)
32 B f Elnadim (USA)—Lions Den (IRE)
33 **LUCKY STREAM**, b f Tamayaz (CAN)—Call Me Lucky **M. A. Brittain**
34 **LUJIANA**, b f Lujain (USA)—Compact Disc (IRE) **M. A. Brittain**
35 **MOTHERWELL**, b f Tamayaz (CAN)—Mother Corrigan (IRE) **M. A. Brittain**

MR M. A. BRITTAIN—continued

36 **MUJADA**, b f Mujahid (USA)—Catriona **M. A. Brittain**
37 **NORTHGATE LODGE (USA)**, ch c Hold That Tiger (USA)—Sabaah Elfull **M. A. Brittain**
38 **PERSONAL CHOICE**, ch f Choisir (AUS)—Bonkers **M. A. Brittain**
39 **PLENILUNE (IRE)**, b c Fantastic Light (USA)—Kathleen's Dream (USA) **M. A. Brittain**
40 **RIVERSIDE**, b c Kyllachy—My Cadeaux **M. A. Brittain**
41 **SANDIES CHOICE**, ch f Tobougg (IRE)—Nijmah **M. A. Brittain**
42 **STEEL MASK (IRE)**, b c Iron Mask (USA)—Thorn Tree **M. A. Brittain**
43 **STRAIGHT (IRE)**, b c King Charlemagne—Fun of The Fair **Northgate Poker**
44 B f Auction House (USA)—Travel Mystery
45 **TURN AND RIVER (IRE)**, b f Viking Ruler (AUS)—Scatter Brain **Northgate Poker**
46 **UPSTANDING**, b f Acclamation—Uplifting **M. A. Brittain**
47 **VARINIA (IRE)**, b f Spartacus (IRE)—Bucaramanga (IRE) **Northgate Black**

TWO-YEAR-OLDS

48 B f 1/4 Lujain (USA)—Ball Gown (Jalmood (USA)) (2000)
49 B c 26/4 Mull of Kintyre (USA)—Brentsville (USA) (Arctic Tern (USA)) (6756)
50 B f 29/3 One Cool Cat (USA)—Caribbean Escape (Pivotal) (6434)
51 B c 12/5 Sesaro (USA)—Daisy Dancer (IRE) (Distinctly North (USA))
52 Ch c 4/3 Bertolini (USA)—Evening Guest (FR) (Be My Guest (USA)) (1500)
53 B f 23/4 Deportivo—Fun Board (FR) (Saumarez)
54 Ch f 25/1 Bahamian Bounty—Golden Fortune (Forzando) (9008) **M. A. Brittain**
55 B c 25/3 Fantastic Light (USA)—Goodnight Kiss (Night Shift (USA)) (4600)
56 B c 27/5 Sakhee (USA)—Hammiya (IRE) (Darshaan) (2251)
57 Ch f 22/3 Falbrav (IRE)—Haniya (IRE) (Caerleon (USA)) (8000)
58 B f 16/4 Dr Fong (USA)—Heavenly Bay (IRE) (Rahy (USA)) (2000)
59 B c 17/4 Reset (AUS)—Honours Even (Highest Honor (FR))
60 Ch c 19/3 Falbrav (IRE)—Irish Light (USA) (Irish River (FR)) (8200) **M. A. Brittain**
61 B f 17/3 Lucky Story (USA)—Ladywell Blaise (IRE) (Turtle Island (IRE)) (2000)
62 Ch c 19/2 Generous (USA)—Love And Kisses (Salse (USA))
63 B c 17/4 Xaar (USA)—Love of Silver (USA) (Arctic Tern (USA)) (3000) **M. A. Brittain**
64 Ch c 13/2 Fantastic Light (USA)—Nebulae (IRE) (Unfuwain (USA)) (2500)
65 B f 15/3 Bertolini (USA)—Nijmah (Halling (USA)) (2200)
66 Ch f 6/4 Shinko Forest (IRE)—Paris Mist (Paris House) (1500)
67 B c 10/4 Mark of Esteem (IRE)—Pompey Blue (Abou Zouz (USA)) (5000)
68 B f 16/2 Polish Precedent (USA)—Purple Tiger (IRE) (Rainbow Quest (USA))
69 B br f 12/2 Xaar (USA)—Saada One (IRE) (Polish Precedent (USA)) (2000)
70 Ch f 8/3 Rossini (USA)—Sabaah Elfull (Kris) (4825)
71 Ch c 27/2 Tobougg (IRE)—Sabrata (IRE) (Zino) (7078) **M. A. Brittain**
72 B c 5/4 Diktat—Shadow Roll (IRE) (Mark of Esteem (IRE)) (2500)
73 Ch c 1/5 Tobougg (IRE)—Snow Shoes (Sri Pekan (USA)) (3200)
74 B f 2/1 One Cool Cat (USA)—Sonatina (Distant Relative) (7400)
75 Ch c 15/4 Spinning World (USA)—Star of Cayman (IRE) (Unfuwain (USA))
76 Ch f 3/4 Spartacus (IRE)—Stormchaser (IRE) (Titus Livius (FR)) (1930)
77 B c 19/3 Spartacus (IRE)—Sylvan Princess (Sylvan Express) (3088)
78 B f 30/3 Xaar—Talah (Danehill (USA)) (3500) **M. A. Brittain**
79 Gr f 23/3 Paris House—Thalya (Crofthall) (2200)
80 B f 5/4 Lucky Story (USA)—Thea (USA) (Marju (IRE)) (2200)
81 B f 6/4 Spartacus (IRE)—Thorn Tree (Zafonic (USA)) (1930) **M. A. Brittain**
82 B c 25/3 Iron Mask (USA)—White Squall (Caerleon (USA)) (1930) **M. A. Brittain**
83 B c 5/4 Spinning World (USA)—Willow Dale (IRE) (Danehill (USA)) (2500)

Other Owners: S. J. Box, Mr P. D. Chambers, Mr C. M. Fryer, J. Jarvis, G. N. Marshall, Mr J. H. Newman, G. D. Pritchard, D. B. White, Mr J. T. Winspear.

Assistant Trainer: Paul Eccles, Head Lad - Neil Jordan

Jockey (flat): M. Lawson, T. Williams. **Apprentice:** A. Carter, G. Edwards.

MR J. E. BROCKBANK, Carlisle
Postal: **Westward Park, Wigton, Cumbria, CA7 8AP**
Contacts: **PHONE (01697) 342391**

1 **LOLIPOP**, 7, ch m Gildoran—Icelandic Poppy **Mrs E. Brockbank**
2 **TOMOPOLLY**, 9, ch g Primitive Rising (USA)—Polly Rickerby **Mrs E. Brockbank**

Assistant Trainer: F. E. Brockbank

Amateur: Mr Luke Morgan, Mr R. Morgan.

70 LADY S. BROOKE, Llandrindod Wells
Postal: **Tyn-y-Berth Farm, Dolau, Llandrindod Wells, Powys, LD1 5TW**
Contacts: **PHONE (01597) 851190 MOBILE (07977) 114834**

1 **ANOTHER FLINT (IRE)**, 8, ch g Accordion—Island Run **Lady S. Brooke**
2 **BALLYLIFFEN BOY (IRE)**, 11, br g Executive Perk—Through The Roof (IRE) **Lady S. Brooke**
3 **DRIVE ON DRIVER (IRE)**, 11, b br m Niels—Gay And Sharp **Lady S. Brooke**
4 **SUPER NOMAD**, 13, b g Nomadic Way (USA)—Super Sue **Lady S. Brooke**
5 **SUPREME MARQUE (IRE)**, 10, b g Supreme Leader—My Motif (IRE) **Lady S. Brooke**

Amateur: Miss Lorna Brooke.

71 MR R. S. BROOKHOUSE, Alcester
Postal: **Moor Hall Farm, Wixford, Alcester, Warwickshire, B49 6DL**
Contacts: **PHONE/FAX (01789) 778244**

1 **LEO'S LUCKYMAN (USA)**, 9, b br g Woodman (USA)—Leo's Lucky Lady (USA) **Mrs S. J. Brookhouse**
2 **LUCK IN RUNNING (USA)**, 5, b br g Running Stag (USA)—Mystery Number (USA) **Mrs S. J. Brookhouse**
3 **ONE NATION (IRE)**, 13, br g Be My Native (USA)—Diklers Run **R. S. Brookhouse**
4 **STAR OF ANGELS**, 4, b g Diktat—City of Angels **R. S. Brookhouse**
5 **STAR OF GERMANY (IRE)**, 8, b g Germany (USA)—Twinkle Bright (USA) **R. S. Brookhouse**
6 **THINK LUCKY**, 5, br g Zafonic (USA)—Hyde Hall **Mrs S. J. Brookhouse**
7 **THREE LIONS**, 11, ch g Jupiter Island—Super Sol **R. S. Brookhouse**

THREE-YEAR-OLDS
8 **DREAM ESTEEM**, b f Mark of Esteem (IRE)—City of Angels **R. S. Brookhouse**

Assistant Trainer: Mr Brian Doran

72 MRS A. E. BROOKS, Towcester
Postal: **Horton House, Alderton, Towcester, Northamptonshire, NN12 7LN**
Contacts: **PHONE (01327) 811354 FAX (01327) 811496 MOBILE (07802) 541294**
E-MAIL onespotracing@hotmail.com

1 **ASAATEEL (IRE)**, 6, br g Unfuwain (USA)—Alabaq (USA) **Robinsons Blick & Brooks**
2 **CARRIG AN UISCE (IRE)**, 7, ch g Portrait Gallery (IRE)—Yarra Glen **Messrs I.J. & R. Kirkham & L. Brooks**
3 **CELTIC SEASON**, 16, b g Vital Season—Welsh Flower **T. L. Brooks**
4 **DEVILS RIVER (IRE)**, 6, b g Anabaa (USA)—Riviere du Diable (USA) **T. L. Brooks**
5 **FRANCO (IRE)**, 10, b g Rashar (USA)—Market Thyne (IRE) **Brooks Haley & Tharratt**
6 **GUNSHIP (IRE)**, 7, b g Needle Gun (IRE)—Teejay's Future (IRE) **I. J. & R. Kirkham & L. & E. Brooks**
7 **HENRY HENBIT**, 13, b br g Henbit (USA)—Turn Mill **Mrs A. E. Brooks**
8 **MINTHARE (IRE)**, 5, br g Bahhare (USA)—Mintaka (IRE) **Shepherd, Ellens & Brooks**
9 **PEARLY STAR**, 7, br g Bob's Return (IRE)—Pearly-B (IRE) **Pricey, Horsey & Brooks**
10 **WINCY SPIDER**, 14, b g Wace (USA)—Sound 'n' Rhythm **T. L. Brooks**

Other Owners: I. Kirkham, Mr R. G. Kirkham, Mr J. Kirkham, Mr J. L. Robinson.

73 MR S. A. BROOKSHAW, Market Drayton
Postal: **Tarri-O, Wollerton, Market Drayton, Shropshire, TF9 3NX**
Contacts: **PHONE/FAX (01630) 685371 MOBILE (07973) 959986**
E-MAIL stevenbrookshaw@hotmail.co.uk

1 **AERONGLAS**, 5, b m Overbury (IRE)—Delilah Blue (NZ) **W. B. R. Davies**
2 **CARRICKMINES (IRE)**, 6, b g Saddlers' Hall (IRE)—Orlas Castle (IRE) **T. G. K. Construction Ltd**
3 **CASSIA HEIGHTS**, 13, b g Montelimar (USA)—Cloncoose (IRE) **D. I. Hewitt**
4 **COORBAWN VIC (IRE)**, 7, ch g Old Vic—Double Harmony (IRE) **T. G. K. Construction Ltd**
5 **GLIMMER OF LIGHT (IRE)**, 8, b g Marju (IRE)—Church Light **Tom Kelly, Ken Edwards & John Edwards**
6 **INCH OVER**, 7, b g Overbury (IRE)—Inch Maid **S. A. Brookshaw**
7 **LORD ADONIS (IRE)**, 5, b g Galileo (IRE)—Flaming June (USA) **T. G. K. Construction Ltd**
8 **POLLENSA BAY**, 9, b g Overbury (IRE)—Cloncoose (IRE) **S. A. Brookshaw**
9 **PORT OF MOGAN (IRE)**, 7, b g Lord Americo—Colleen Donn **T. G. K. Construction Ltd**

MR S. A. BROOKSHAW—continued

10 THE SNEAKSTER (IRE), 10, b m Jurado (USA)—Royal Star (IRE) **S. A. Brookshaw**
11 WELSH WHISPER, 9, b m Overbury (IRE)—Grugiar **S. A. Brookshaw**
12 WILLIAM BUTLER (IRE), 8, b g Safety Catch (USA)—Rosie Josie **T. G. K. Construction Ltd**

Other Owners: K. Edwards, Mr J. H. Edwards.

---

74 MR R. BROTHERTON, Pershore
Postal: **Mill End Racing Stables, Netherton Road, Elmley Castle, Pershore, Worcestershire, WR10 3JF**
Contacts: **PHONE/FAX (01386) 710772 MOBILE (07973) 877280**

1 ARABIAN MOON (IRE), 12, ch g Barathea (IRE)—Excellent Alibi (USA) **Goldliner Racing West Midlands**
2 BLAKESHALL QUEST, 8, b m Piccolo—Corniche Quest (IRE) **Bredon Hill Racing Club**
3 CAPE OF STORMS, 5, b g Cape Cross (IRE)—Lloc **P. S. J. Croft**
4 JACKIE KIELY, 7, ch g Vettori (IRE)—Fudge **P. S. J. Croft**
5 MAKTAVISH, 9, b g Makbul—La Belle Vie **P. S. J. Croft**
6 OAKBRIDGE (IRE), 6, b g Indian Ridge—Chauncy Lane (IRE) **Mrs C. A. Newman**
7 PHONE IN, 5, b g Sinndar (IRE)—Patria (USA) **P. S. J. Croft**
8 WAR OF THE ROSES (IRE), 5, b g Singspiel (IRE)—Calvia Rose **P. S. J. Croft**
9 WILLY (SWE), 6, ch g Heart of Oak (USA)—Kawa-Ib (IRE) **The Joiners Arms Racing Club Quarndon**

THREE-YEAR-OLDS

10 DISTANT NOBLE, b g Carnival Dancer—Fly In Style **P. S. J. Croft**
11 MARYSEDGE, b f Bold Edge—Dekelsmary **T. G. Jones**

Other Owners: Mr D. J. Busby, Mr T. J. Dobson, T. L. Martin, Mrs K. B. Powers, Mr A. M. Wadley, M. J. Whitehall.

Jockey (flat): P. Cosgrave. Apprentice: Liam Jones.

---

75 MR I. A. BROWN, Salton
Postal: **Low Northolme Cottage, Salton, York, North Yorkshire, YO62 6RP**
Contacts: **YARD/HOME (01751) 431066 MOBILE (07840) 842281**

1 FORTUNE'S FOOL, 9, b g Zilzal (USA)—Peryllys **I. A. Brown**
2 MR LEAR (USA), 9, b g Lear Fan (USA)—Majestic Mae (USA) **I. A. Brown**

Amateur: Mrs J. Brown.

---

76 MISS A. E. BROYD, Crickhowell
Postal: **Penrhiw Farm, Llangenny, Crickhowell, Powys, NP8 1HD**
Contacts: **PHONE (01873) 812292 MOBILE (07885) 475492**
E-MAIL alison.broyd@btopenworld.com

1 OLCHONS DEBUT (IRE), 10, ch g Denel (FR)—Buckskins Babe (IRE) **Miss A. E. Broyd**
2 THESEUS (IRE), 12, b g Danehill (USA)—Graecia Magna (USA) **Miss A. E. Broyd**

---

77 MISS M. P. BRYANT, Lewes
Postal: **Bevern Bridge Farm Cottage, South Chailey, Lewes, East Sussex, BN8 4QH**
Contacts: **PHONE/FAX (01273) 400638 MOBILE (07976) 217542**

1 BETTER MOMENT (IRE), 11, b g Turtle Island (IRE)—Snoozeandyoulose (IRE) **Miss M. P. Bryant**
2 FOREVER ROONEY, 11, b g Prince Rooney (IRE)—Forever Blushing **Miss M. P. Bryant**
3 GAMESET'N'MATCH, 7, b g Hector Protector (USA)—Tanasie **Miss M. P. Bryant**
4 HATTERAS (FR), 9, b g Octagonal (NZ)—Hylandra (USA) **Miss M. P. Bryant**
5 HAWK GOLD (IRE), 4, ch g Tendulkar (USA)—Heiress of Meath (IRE) **Miss M. P. Bryant**
6 NDOLA, 9, b g Emperor Jones (USA)—Lykoa **Miss M. P. Bryant**
7 NIGHT GROOVE (IRE), 5, b g Night Shift (USA)—Taysala (IRE) **Miss M. P. Bryant**

Amateur: Miss M. P. Bryant.

78 MR R. H. BUCKLER, Bridport
Postal: Melplash Court Farm, Melplash, Bridport, Dorset, DT6 3UH
Contacts: HOME (01308) 488318 FAX (01308) 488403 MOBILE (07785) 773957

1 **CAMPDEN ANNIE (IRE)**, 6, b m Kayf Tara—Annicombe Run **Golden Cap**
2 **CHARMING OSCAR (IRE)**, 6, b g Oscar Schindler (IRE)—Lady of The West (IRE) **P. Partridge**
3 **CLYFFE HANGER (IRE)**, 8, b g Taipan (IRE)—French Thistle **Mrs C. F. E. Hall**
4 **CRANK HILL**, 6, b g Shambo—Mariner's Air **Strictly Come Racing**
5 **CULLAHILL (IRE)**, 6, b br g Good Thyne (USA)—Rossacrowe Gale (IRE) **N. Elliott**
6 **DOUBLE DIZZY**, 7, b g Double Trigger (IRE)—Miss Diskin (IRE) **M. J. Forrester**
7 **ETHIOPIA**, 5, b g Silver Patriarch (IRE)—Anhaar **N. Elliott**
8 **FIXED INTEREST (IRE)**, 6, b g Taipan (IRE)—Fixed Assets **Mrs D. A. La Trobe**
9 **FREEDOM FRIX**, 6, b g Bandmaster (USA)—Almary **The Freedom Frighters**
10 **HE'S THE BOSS**, 11, b g Supreme Leader—Attykee (IRE) **R. H. Buckler**
11 **HE'S THE GAFFER (IRE)**, 8, b g Oscar (IRE)—Miss Henrietta (IRE) **Mrs D. A. La Trobe**
12 **HENNERS**, 5, b g Exit To Nowhere (USA)—Annicombe Run **Mrs A. Tincknell**
13 **I HEAR THUNDER (IRE)**, 10, b g Montelimar (USA)—Carrigeen Gala **N. Elliott**
14 **KEEPTHEDREAMALIVE**, 10, gr g Roselier (FR)—Nicklup **R. H. Buckler**
15 **LANCASTER SOUND (IRE)**, 6, b g Naheez (USA)—Lovely Affair (IRE) **Mrs A. Tincknell**
16 **LUSTARA**, 5, b m Kayf Tara—Lustrous **T. Fiorillo**
17 **MOSSVILLE (FR)**, 7, b m Villez (USA)—Mosstraye (FR) **Golden Cap**
18 **NICHE MARKET (IRE)**, 7, b g Presenting—Juresse (IRE) **G. J. P. Regan**
19 **ORLYHEART (FR)**, 5, b h Desert Style (IRE)—Blue Burgee (USA) **Barr, Jamieson, Jones**
20 **RIVER INDUS**, 8, b g Rakaposhi King—Flow **Mrs H. R. Dunn**
21 **RIVER REINE (IRE)**, 9, br m Lahib (USA)—Talahari (IRE) **R. H. Buckler**
22 **SADDLER GEORGE (IRE)**, 5, b g Saddlers' Hall (IRE)—Sarasota (FR) **Mrs A. Tincknell**
23 **SMOKE TRAIL (IRE)**, 9, b g Zaffaran (USA)—Ardee Princess **Smoke Trail Partnership**
24 **SO WISE SO YOUNG**, 7, br g Young Ern—Tendresse (IRE) **Woodland Flowers**
25 **TAIPAN'S PROMISE (IRE)**, 6, b g Taipan (IRE)—
                                      She Is Promising (IRE) **Mr Christopher Collier&Mrs Anne Collier**
26 **THE SAWYER (BEL)**, 8, ch g Fleetwood (IRE)—Green Land (BEL) **D. R. Fear**
27 **WE GOT HIM (IRE)**, 8, b br g Taipan (IRE)—Falas Lass **R. H. Buckler**

Other Owners: Mr J. R. Barr, Mr R. H. Buckler, Mr Christopher Collier, Mrs A. Collier, Mr K. J. Crocker, Mr N. F. Crocker, Mrs R. L. Haskins, Mr Ian M. Jamieson, Mr Peter Jones, Mr R. M. Kellow, Mrs C. Lewis, Mr J. S. Murdoch, Mr Kevin Old, Mr Nick Robinson, Mrs H. E. Shane, Mr W. Tincknell.

Assistant Trainer: Giles Scott (Head Lad)

Jockey (NH): Daryl Jacob, William Kennedy. **Conditional:** T. Molloy. **Amateur:** Mr J. Ryan, Miss Carey Buckler.

79 MR M. A. BUCKLEY, Stamford
Postal: Potters Hill Stables, Morkery Lane, Castle Bytham, Stamford, Lincolnshire, NG33 4SP
Contacts: OFFICE (01780) 411158 FAX (01780) 410481 MOBILE (07808) 360488
E-MAIL markbuckley215@btinternet.com

1 **FOOTSTEPSINTHESNOW (IRE)**, 5, b m Medicean—Charlecote (IRE) **Mrs D. J. Buckley**
2 **JAWAAB (IRE)**, 4, ch g King's Best (USA)—Canis Star **C. C. Buckley**
3 **MUMAATHEL (IRE)**, 5, b g Alhaarth (IRE)—Alhufoof (USA) **C. C. Buckley**
4 **VIEWFORTH**, 10, b g Emarati (USA)—Miriam **Mr C. G. Handley**

Other Owners: M. A. Buckley.

80 MR W. D. BURCHELL, Ebbw Vale
Postal: Drysiog Farm, Briery Hill, Ebbw Vale, Gwent, NP23 6BU
Contacts: PHONE (01495) 302551 FAX (01495) 352464 MOBILE (07980) 482860

1 **ASK THE UMPIRE (IRE)**, 13, b g Boyne Valley—Ask Breda **C. A. Davies**
2 **BENEKING**, 8, b br g Wizard King—Gagajulu **B. M. G. Group**
3 **DARK PLANET**, 5, ch g Singspiel (IRE)—Warning Shadows (IRE) **B. J. Williams**
4 **DERE LYN**, 10, b g Awesome—Our Resolution **W. L. Phillips**
5 **EYES TO THE RIGHT (IRE)**, 9, ch g Eagle Eyed (USA)—Capable Kate (IRE) **Don Gould, Wendy Herring**
6 **GREY SHARK (IRE)**, 9, gr g Roselier (FR)—Sharkezan (IRE) **B. J. Williams**
7 **JAUNTY**, 5, ch g Pivotal—Invincible **R. Williams**
8 **PRINCELY TED (IRE)**, 7, b g Princely Heir (IRE)—Just Out (IRE) **M. S. Heath**

MR W. D. BURCHELL—continued

   9 PRINCESS AIMEE, 8, b m Wizard King—Off The Air (IRE) **E. O'Malley**
  10 STAR OF CANTERBURY (IRE), 5, ch g Beckett (IRE)—Villa Nova (IRE) **The Kamil Racing Partnership**
  11 YOUR ADVANTAGE (IRE), 8, b g Septieme Ciel (USA)—Freedom Flame **Mr C. J. Friel**

Other Owners: Mr Dai Burchell, Mr W. R. A. Davies, Mr Don Gould, Miss Wendy Herring, Mr Brian Williams.

Assistant Trainer: Ruth Burchell

Jockey (NH): Christian Williams. **Conditional:** Byron Moorcroft. **Amateur:** Mr R. Hughes, Miss Isabel Tompsett, Mr Nick Williams.

---

81   MR P. V. J. BURGOYNE, Wincanton
Postal: **Knowle Rock, Shepton Montague, Wincanton, Somerset, BA9 8JA**
Contacts: **PHONE (01963) 32138 FAX (01963) 32138 MOBILE (07894) 081008**
E-MAIL knowlesrockracing@hotmail.co.uk WEBSITE www.knowlesrockracing.co.uk

  1 ABTAK (IRE), 8, b m Royal Abjar (USA)—Takhiyra **Mrs C. E. E. Turner**
  2 METROPOLITAN CHIEF, 4, b g Compton Place—Miss Up N Go **L. E. Tomlin**
  3 SIR LOIN, 7, ch g Compton Place—Charnwood Queen **L. E. Tomlin**
  4 TEEN AGER (FR), 4, b g Invincible Spirit (IRE)—Tarwiya (IRE) **Mrs C. E. E. Turner**

Assistant Trainer: Mrs C. Leigh-Turner

Jockey (flat): T. Quinn.

---

82   MR K. J. BURKE, Northleach
Postal: **The Tannery, Northleach, Gloucestershire, GL54 3HT**
Contacts: **PHONE (01451) 824264 MOBILE (07867) 892268**
E-MAIL kahlil@kahlilburkeracing.com WEBSITE www.kahlilburkeracing.com

  1 ASHBY JO (IRE), 7, ch g Flemensfirth (USA)—Ashby Hill (IRE) **Mr G. J. Cossey & Mrs L. E. Cossey**
  2 6, B g Supreme Leader—Beau Belle (IRE)
  3 CALLITWHATYALIKE, 6, b m Tamure (IRE)—Studio Venture **All Things Alpaca**
  4 CRAZY BEAR (IRE), 5, ch m King Charlemagne (USA)—Specifiedrisk (IRE) **Mr J. Bourke**
  5 DIKTATIT, 6, b m Diktat—Mystique Smile **Burns Partnership**
  6 EL SUENO (IRE), 8, b g Anshan—Dont Rough It **Mrs Betty Valentine Ms Sue Milligan**
  7 FISBY, 7, ch g Efisio—Trilby **G. R. P. N. Valentine**
  8 GARDASEE (GER), 6, gr g Dashing Blade—Gladstone Street (IRE) **A. S. Helaissi**
  9 GENERAL ZHANG (IRE), 7, b g Anshan—Calder Rose **De Facto**
  10 GILES (IRE), 8, br g Lahib (USA)—Dromoland **Life Is For Living**
  11 GUILT, 8, b g Mark of Esteem (IRE)—Guillem (USA) **K. J. Burke**
  12 GUNPOINT (IRE), 4, b g Rainbow Quest (USA)—Sharp Point (IRE) **P. Ennis**
  13 INTERSKY SPORTS (USA), 4, gr g Chester House (USA)—Nightlong **Cubic Expression**
  14 LEMON SILK (IRE), 4, ch g Barathea (IRE)—Bois de Citron (USA) **A. S. Helaissi**
  15 MANGE TOUT (IRE), 9, br g Presenting—Nish Bar **Mrs S. Branston**
  16 MURFREESBORO, 5, b h Bahamian Bounty—Merry Rous **Hong Kong Breeders Club**
  17 MYSTIC SPIN (IRE), 4, b c Tendulkar (USA)—Mystical Jumbo **G. R. P. N. Valentine**
  18 NEPTUNE EQUESTER (GB), 5, b h Sovereign Water (FR)—All Things Nice **Andrew Harman**
  19 PORTLAND, 5, b g Zafonic (USA)—Bayswater **Racing For All Club**
  20 QUASIMODO (IRE), 6, b g Night Shift (USA)—Daziyra (IRE) **Mr R. G. Owens**
  21 REGIONAL COUNSEL, 4, b c Medicean—Regency Rose **Hong Kong Breeders Club**
  22 SHEER TENBY (IRE), 11, b h Tenby—Take My Pledge (IRE) **Shanbally More Syndicate**
  23 STAR ANTIQUE (FR), 5, b m Lute Antique (FR)—Lady Start (FR) **Mr & Mrs Redmond**
  24 SYMBIOSIS, 7, b m Bien Bien (USA)—Sound Appeal **One Jump Ahead**
  25 THE ICE BAR (IRE), 7, ch g Carroll House—Polar Crash **Paul Ennis**
  26 THE PREACHER, 5, b g Namaqualand (USA)—Bustling Around **Racing For All Club**
  27 TO ARMS, 6, b g Mujahid (USA)—Toffee **De Facto**
  28 WAVERLEY (IRE), 9, b g Catrail (USA)—Marble Halls (IRE) **K. J. Burke**
  29 WELSH AUCTION, 4, gr g Auction House (USA)—Anneli Rose **Dream Team Racing**
  30 WILLIE WARSON (IRE), 5, gr g Great Palm (USA)—Pimpinella (IRE) **The Ferandlin Peaches**

THREE-YEAR-OLDS

  31 DINARIUS, b c Bertolini (USA)—Ambassadress (USA) **A. S. Helaissi**

MR K. J. BURKE—continued

32 **NAMING PROBLEMS**, ch f Forzando—Basheera **K. J. Burke**
33 **ROUNDEMUPSHEP (IRE)**, ch f Rossini (USA)—Lovat Spring (USA) **Ms Marian Bourke**

TWO-YEAR-OLDS

34 Ch f 14/2 Pursuit of Love—Basheera (Bahhare (USA)) (1238) **Killashee House Stud**

Other Owners: Miss Frances Baker, Mr C. K. Byers, Mr Gordon James Cossey, Mrs L. E. Cossey, Mr Paul Ennis, Mr Timothy L. Greig, Ms R. J. Harris, P. V. Harris, Mr M. P. Kirwan, Mr John McGrath, Mr Keith McKay, Ms Sue Milligan, Mr R. G. Owens, Mrs G. Redmond, Mr W. Redmond, Mrs Betty Valentine, Mr Peter Yip.

Jockey (flat): D. McKeown, N. Callan. **Jockey (NH):** J. W. Farrelly, T. Evans, R. J. Greene. **Conditional:** R. Spate, P. Merrigan. **Amateur:** Mr E. Cookson, Miss I. Tompsett.

---

83 MR K. R. BURKE, Leyburn
Postal: **Spigot Lodge, Middleham, Leyburn, North Yorkshire, DL8 4TL**
Contacts: PHONE (01969) 625088 FAX (01969) 625099 MOBILE (07778) 458777
E-MAIL karl@karlburke.co.uk & kathryn.warnett@virgin.net WEBSITE www.karlburke.co.uk

1 **AAHAYSON**, 4, b c Noverre (USA)—See You Later **Mrs M. P. V. Gittins**
2 **AKAREM**, 7, b g Kingmambo (USA)—Spirit of Tara (IRE) **Mrs M. P. V. Gittins**
3 **ANGEL VOICES (IRE)**, 5, b m Tagula (IRE)—Lithe Spirit (IRE) **Mrs E. M. Burke**
4 **ASHES (IRE)**, 6, b m General Monash (USA)—Wakayi **Bryce, Dower, Morgan**
5 **ATLANTIC GAMBLE (IRE)**, 8, b g Darnay—Full Traceability (IRE) **Mr J. R. Greaney**
6 **BAHAMIAN DUKE**, 5, ch g Bahamian Bounty—Madame Sisu **Mrs E. M. Burke**
7 **BAZART**, 6, b g Highest Honor (FR)—Summer Exhibition **Mrs M. P. V. Gittins**
8 **BLUE SKY THINKING (IRE)**, 9, b g Danehill Dancer (IRE)—Lauretta Blue (IRE) **Mr R. Hoiles**
9 **BOLD MARC (IRE)**, 6, b g Bold Fact (USA)—Zara's Birthday (IRE) **Market Avenue Racing Club Ltd**
10 **CALZAGHE (IRE)**, 4, ch g Galileo (IRE)—Novelette **Mrs M. P. V. Gittins**
11 **DARING AFFAIR**, 7, b m Bien Bien (USA)—Daring Destiny **N. R. Shields**
12 **DICKIE LE DAVOIR**, 4, b g Kyllachy—Downeaster Alexa (USA) **Bigwigs Bloodstock II**
13 **ELECTRIC WARRIOR (IRE)**, 5, b g Bold Fact (USA)—Dungeon Princess (IRE) **Market Avenue Racing Club Ltd**
14 **FURMIGADELAGIUSTA**, 4, ch c Galileo (IRE)—Sispre (FR) **Keep Racing**
15 **MONKEY GLAS (IRE)**, 4, b c Mull of Kintyre (USA)—Maura's Pet (IRE) **Denis Fehan**
16 **MOODY TUNES**, 5, b g Merdon Melody—Lady-Love **G. Hamilton**
17 **NAUGHTY NOD (IRE)**, 5, b g Intikhab (USA)—Quelle Celtique (FR) **Mrs M. P. V. Gittins**
18 **NEW WORLD ORDER (IRE)**, 4, b c Night Shift (USA)—Kama Tashoof **Mrs M. P. V. Gittins**
19 **NOT ANOTHER CAT (USA)**, 4, ch g Hennessy (USA)—Isle Be Loving You (USA) **Mrs M. P. V. Gittins**
20 **PAB SPECIAL (IRE)**, 5, b g City On A Hill (USA)—Tinos Island (IRE) **P. A. Brazier**
21 **PRECOCIOUS STAR (IRE)**, 4, ch f Bold Fact (USA)—Flames **Market Avenue Racing Club Ltd**
22 **PRINCE CHARLEMAGNE (IRE)**, 5, br g King Charlemagne (USA)—Ciubanga (USA) **N. D. Ryan**
23 **RAPTOR (GER)**, 5, b h Auenadler (GER)—Royal Cat **Mr M. Gittins**
24 **SPEEDY SAM**, 5, b h Medicean—Warning Star **Mrs M. P. V. Gittins**
25 **SWIFT PRINCESS (IRE)**, 4, b f Namid—Swift Chorus **Tweenhills Racing**
26 **TRAFALGAR BAY (IRE)**, 5, b g Fruits of Love (USA)—Chatsworth Bay (IRE) **Mrs M. P. V. Gittins**
27 **TYRANNOSAURUS REX (IRE)**, 4, b g Bold Fact (USA)—
                                        Dungeon Princess (IRE) **Market Avenue Racing Club Ltd**
28 **YAZZI (IRE)**, 4, b f Indian Lodge (IRE)—Travel Spot Girl **Mrs E. M. Burke**

THREE-YEAR-OLDS

29 **ANGHARAD**, b f Danehill Dancer (IRE)—Hot Tin Roof (IRE) **Mrs M. P. V. Gittins**
30 **ANNELLIS (UAE)**, b br f Diesis—Japanese Whisper (UAE) **Mrs M. P. V. Gittins**
31 **ARIKINUI**, b f Noverre (USA)—Off The Blocks **Mr P. Richards**
32 **ARKANDO (IRE)**, b f Mull of Kintyre (USA)—Arjan (IRE) **Mrs E. M. Burke**
33 **ATEPHOBIA**, b br c Auction House (USA)—Seren Teg **P. Timmins & A. Rhodes Haulage**
34 **BALDEMAR**, b g Namid—Keen Melody (USA) **A. Rhodes Haulage & Mr P. Timmins**
35 **BARAWIN (IRE)**, ch f Hawk Wing (USA)—Cosabawn (IRE) **M. J. Halligan**
36 **BIGFANOFTHAT (IRE)**, b c Rock of Gibraltar (IRE)—Miss Salsa (USA) **Mrs M. P. V. Gittins**
37 **CABOPINO (IRE)**, ch f Captain Rio—Fey Rouge (IRE) **Mr S. Parkin**
38 **CAFFARI (GER)**, ch f Seattle Dancer (USA)—Calarca (GER) **Mr P. Richards**
39 **CALMDOWNMATE (IRE)**, b g Danehill Dancer (IRE)—Lady Digby (IRE) **Mrs M. P. V. Gittins**
40 **CATHEDRAL WALK (USA)**, ch c Johannesburg (USA)—Hilarity (USA) **Mr C. J. Wall**
41 **CHARLIE ALLNUT**, b g Desert Style (IRE)—Queen of Africa (IRE) **Bigwigs Bloodstock II**
42 **CHERRYTREE ELLA (IRE)**, b f Clodovil (IRE)—Music Khan **Mr & Mrs Halsall**
43 **COMPLETE FRONTLINE (GER)**, ch c Tertullian (USA)—Carola Rouge **Mr M. Roden**

MR K. R. BURKE—continued

44 **CUTE ASS (IRE)**, b f Fath (USA)—John's Ballad (IRE) **Bigwigs Bloodstock II**
45 **DRAMATIC SOLO**, ch f Nayef (USA)—Just Dreams **Joy & Valentine Feerick**
46 **DREAM STREET ROSE (USA)**, b br f Yankee Victor (USA)—Dixie Fine (USA) **Hit The Beach Partnership 1**
47 **GEEZERS COLOURS**, b c Fraam—Konica **C. Waters**
48 **HEAVENLY ENCOUNTER**, b f Lujain (USA)—Inchcoonan **Mrs E. M. Burke**
49 **INONTIME (IRE)**, ch f Golan (IRE)—Phantom Ring **R. Bailey**
50 **IRISH PEARL (IRE)**, b f Statue of Liberty (USA)—Helen Wells (IRE) **M. J. Halligan**
51 **JOHNNY FRIENDLY**, b c Auction House (USA)—Quantum Lady **U. N. Syndicate & Mrs E. Burke**
52 **JUST LOU**, ch f Captain Rio—Bond Royale **Mrs M. P. V. Gittins**
53 **KEEPARRYAPPY (IRE)**, b g Fath (USA)—Coppelia (IRE) **Knightsbridge Partnership**
54 **LESSON IN HUMILITY (IRE)**, b f Mujadil (USA)—Vanity (IRE) **M. Nelmes-Crocker**
55 **LITTONFOUNTAIN (IRE)**, b g Desert Style (IRE)—Idle Chat (USA) **Mr C. J. Wall**
56 **MADAME RIO (IRE)**, b f Captain Rio—Glenviews Purchase (IRE) **A. Jones**
57 **MADDISON COUNTY**, b f Invincible Spirit (IRE)—Topwinder (USA) **Bigwigs Bloodstock XVI**
58 **MERRION TIGER (IRE)**, ch c Choisir (AUS)—Akita (IRE) **Denis Fehan**
59 **NINEFINEIRISHMEN (IRE)**, b br c Statue of Liberty (USA)—Tallassee **Mr C. J. Wall**
60 **PAPILLIO (IRE)**, b c Marju (IRE)—Danish Gem **Clipper Group Holdings Ltd**
61 **PATTHEPAINTER (GER)**, ch c Alhaarth (IRE)—Picturesque **Mrs M. P. V. Gittins**
62 **PELICAN PRINCE**, b c Fraam—Nightingale Song **Market Avenue Racing Club Ltd**
63 **PHILARIO (IRE)**, ch c Captain Rio—Salva **Mr P. Richards**
64 **PLANET QUEEN**, ch f Bahamian Bounty—Ash Moon (USA) **Market Avenue Racing Club Ltd**
65 **ROKER PARK (IRE)**, b g Choisir (AUS)—Joyful (USA) **T. Alderson**
66 **ROUNDTHETWIST (IRE)**, b br g Okawango (USA)—Delta Town (USA) **Mrs E. M. Burke**
67 **RYE ROCKET**, b g Catcher In The Rye (IRE)—Platinum Michelle **Resolute Partnership**
68 **SCANNO (IRE)**, b c Captain Rio—In Denial (IRE) **A. Jones**
69 **SPEEDY SEÑORITA (IRE)**, b f Fayruz—Sinora Wood (IRE) **Market Avenue Racing Club**
70 **SPITFIRE JANE (IRE)**, b f Xaar—Hope of Pekan (IRE) **Bigwigs Bloodstock II**
71 **SWIFT ACCLAIM (IRE)**, b f Acclamation—Swift Chorus **Mr D. Fehan**
72 **THE LITTLE FIZZER (IRE)**, ch f Fayruz—Villaminta (IRE) **Fighttheban Partnership V**
73 **TWILIGHT BELLE (IRE)**, b f Fasliyev (USA)—Pretty Sharp **J. A. Duffy**
74 **WATCH THIS PLACE**, b g Compton Place—Swissmatic **M. Nelmes-Crocker**

TWO-YEAR-OLDS

75 Ch f 22/1 Kyllachy—Ash Moon (IRE) (General Monash (USA)) (10000) **Mrs E. Burke**
76 B c 8/2 Fath (USA)—Barriance (IRE) (Charnwood Forest (IRE)) (7721) **Mr P. Richards**
77 B f 8/5 Acclamation—Bella Vie (IRE) (Sadler's Wells (USA)) (28957) **Mrs M. P. V. Gittins**
78 Ch f 6/4 Bahamian Bounty—Bonkers (Efisio) (16000) **Mrs E. Burke**
79 B f 23/3 Gulch (USA)—Boundless Beauty (USA) (Copelan (USA)) (53449) **Mrs M. P. V. Gittins**
80 B c 29/3 Fasliyev (USA)—Change of Heart (IRE) (Revoque) (30000) **Mrs E. Burke**
81 B c 4/5 Alflora (IRE)—Ella Falls (IRE) (Dancing Dissident) (USA)) **Mr R. Bailey**
82 B f 4/4 Fath (USA)—Ellistown Lady (IRE) (Red Sunset) (19947) **Mrs E. Burke**
83 B br c 11/4 Bold Fact (USA)—Generate (Generous) (USA) **Mrs E. Burke**
84 B br c 30/3 Speightstown (USA)—Green Room (USA) (Theatrical) (53449) **Mrs M. P. V. Gittins**
85 B br f 7/3 Mr Greeley (USA)—I'maknightschoice (USA) (Knights Choice) (213799) **Mrs M. P. V. Gittins**
86 B c 4/4 Peintre Celebre (USA)—Inchberry (Barathea (IRE)) (130000) **Mrs M. P. V. Gittins**
87 B c 14/4 Pyrus (USA)—Italian Affair (Fumo di Londra (IRE)) (2895) **Mr J. Duffy**
88 Ch f 17/2 Piccolo—Key (Midyan (USA)) (14000) **Mrs E. Burke**
89 B c 22/1 Montjeu (IRE)—Lady Lahar (Fraam) (36000) **Mrs M. P. V. Gittins**
90 B c 3/2 Kheleyf (USA)—Lady's Walk (Charnwood Forest (IRE)) (10000) **Mrs E. Burke**
91 Ch c 28/4 Sakhee (USA)—Latin Review (IRE) (Titus Livius (FR)) (54000) **Mr P. Richards**
92 **MAGIC CAT**, b c 27/2 One Cool Cat (USA)—Magic Music (Magic Ring) (160000) **Mr R. Bailey**
93 B c 14/5 Royal Applause—Needwood Epic (Midyan (USA)) (160000) **Mrs M. P. V. Gittins**
94 B br c 23/2 Cherokee Run (USA)—Pertuisane (Zamindar (USA)) (53449) **Market Avenue Racing Club Ltd**
95 B f 28/3 Compton Place—Princess Almora (Pivotal) (20000) **Mrs E. Burke**
96 B f 22/2 Mr Greeley (USA)—Quarrel Over Halo (USA) (Halo (USA)) (51480) **Mrs M. P. V. Gittins**
97 Ch c 11/3 Deportivo—Queens Jubilee (Cayman Kai (IRE)) (20000) **Mrs E. Burke**
98 B c 27/3 High Chaparral (IRE)—Severa (GER) (Acatenango (FR)) (25740) **Mrs M. P. V. Gittins**
99 B f 1/4 Choisir (AUS)—Siem Reap (US) (El Gran Senor) (45044) **Mrs M. P. V. Gittins**
100 B br c 22/3 Mineshaft (USA)—Solar Colony (USA) (Pleasant Colony (USA)) (230806) **Mrs M. P. V. Gittins**
101 **SWEET VIRGINIA (USA)**, b br f 19/4 Arch (USA)—
                              Hey Hey Sunny (Known Fact (USA)) (12000) **Bigwigs Bloodstock**
102 **TEPMOKEA (IRE)**, ch c 29/3 Noverre (USA)—Eroica (GER) (Highest Honor (FR)) (70000) **Keep Racing**
103 B c 26/3 Indian Danehill (USA)—Tiger Wings (IRE) (Thatching) (24000) **Mrs E. Burke**
104 Ch c 20/5 Intikhab (USA)—Trust In Luck (IRE) (Nashwan (USA)) (19304) **Mrs M. P. V. Gittins**

MR K. R. BURKE—continued

Other Owners: A. Rhodes Haulage Ltd, Mr A. Ali, Mr P. Allen, Mr J. Ayre, Mr D. Ball, Mr Bernard Bargh, Mrs M. Bayless, Mr David Blunt, Mr Colin Bryce, K. R. Burke, T. Cockrill, P. Doody, Mrs M. Dower, R. S. Dufficy, Mrs J. F. Feerick, V. Feerick, Mr Tom Gittins, Mrs K. Halsall, Mr S. Halsall, P. Hamilton, R. Hoiles, Mr E. J. Hughes, Mr J. Laughton, Mr P. A. Lewis, Mr D. S. McMahon, Mr David H. Morgan, K. R. Parker, Mr D. Redvers, S. C. B. Limited, A. Taylor, Mr P. Timmins.

Assistant Trainer: Mrs E Burke

Jockey (flat): P. Makin. **Jockey (NH):** B. Keniry. **Apprentice:** A. Elliott, D. Cannon. **Amateur:** Miss K. Burke, Miss L. Burke.

---

84 MR S. BURROUGH, Chard
Postal: **7 Peacocks Close, West Buckland, Wellington, Somerset, TA21 9JY**
Contacts: **PHONE (01823) 660223 MOBILE (07887) 958131**

1 BERENGARIO (IRE), 8, b g Mark of Esteem (IRE)—Ivrea **Mrs D. H. Potter**
2 DEEP QUEST, 9, b g El Conquistador—Ten Deep **Five Deep Partnership**
3 ELUVAPARTY, 8, b g El Conquistador—Ruby Celebration **Westfield Racing**
4 MASTER HALLING, 4, ch g Halling (USA)—Red Empress **Mrs D. H. Potter**
5 SIMPLY BLUE, 4, b g Rainbow High—What A Scene (IRE) **Mrs D. H. Potter**
6 SPARKBRIDGE (IRE), 5, b g Mull of Kintyre (USA)—Persian Velvet (IRE) **H. J. W. Davies**
7 SPITFIRE BOB (USA), 9, b g Mister Baileys—Gulf Cyclone (USA) **Jets**
8 YELLOW JERSEY, 6, b m Mark of Esteem (IRE)—La Bicyclette (FR) **Jets**

Other Owners: Mr S. Burrough, Mrs Maureen Emery, Mr G. W. Giddings, Mrs Jacqueline Smith.

Jockey (NH): R. Greene.

---

85 MR P. BUTLER, Lewes
Postal: **Homewood Gate Racing Stables, Novington Lane, East Chiltington, Lewes, East Sussex, BN7 3AU**
Contacts: **PHONE/FAX (01273) 890124 MOBILE (07973) 873846 E-MAIL homewoodgate@aol.com**

1 CANNI THINKAAR (IRE), 7, b g Alhaarth (IRE)—Cannikin (IRE) **Homewoodgate Racing Club**
2 GEOGRAPHY (IRE), 8, ch g Definite Article—Classic Ring (IRE) **Homewoodgate Racing Club**
3 GHAILL FORCE, 6, b g Piccolo—Coir 'a' Ghaill **J. Richard Wilson**
4 NDOLA, 9, b g Emperor Jones (USA)—Lykoa **Miss M. P. Bryant**
5 NIGHT GROOVE (IRE), 5, b g Night Shift (USA)—Taysala (IRE) **Miss M. P. Bryant**
6 QUALITY STREET, 6, ch m Fraam—Pusey Street Girl **E. H. Whatmough**
7 SWEET DEMERARA, 4, ch f Sugarfoot—Scotland Bay **C. W. Wilson**
8 TIFFANY JONES, 5, b m Kayf Tara—Juleit Jones (IRE) **Mr H. James**
9 WILLOW HALL, 7, b g Saddlers' Hall (IRE)—Willow Gale **P. Butler**
10 WONDERSOBRIGHT (IRE), 9, br b g Magical Wonder (USA)—Brightness **C. W. Wilson**

THREE-YEAR-OLDS

11 MAIREAD'S BOY (IRE), ch c Noverre (USA)—Welltold (IRE) **Mr H. James**

Other Owners: Mrs E. Lucey-Butler.

Assistant Trainer: Mrs E Lucey-Butler

Conditional: R. Lucey-Butler. **Amateur:** Miss Zoe Lilly.

---

86 MR T. BUTT, Jedburgh
Postal: **Cunzierton Farm, Oxnam, Jedburgh, TO8 6BF**
Contacts: **PHONE (01750) 20734 FAX (01750) 722725 MOBILE (07957) 880876 E-MAIL chaser13@tiscali.co.uk**

1 5, B g Flemensfirth (USA)—Baylough Lady (IRE)
2 CLASSIC ACT, 6, b g Classic Cliche (IRE)—Katoski **Miss D. J. Amos**
3 GOOD MUSIC (IRE), 6, b g Good Thyne (USA)—Global Diamond (IRE) **T. Butt**

MR T. BUTT—continued

  4 **LETHEM AIR**, 10, ch g Aragon—Llanddona **T. Butt**
  5 **LETHEM PRESENT (IRE)**, 8, ch m Presenting—Present Tense **T. Butt**
  6 **OH REALLY (IRE)**, 6, b g Anshan—Farojina (IRE) **T. Butt**

Other Owners: Miss D. J. Amos, W. Hamilton, Lethem Racing.

Jockey (NH): Dougie Costello. **Amateur:** Mr Mark Ellwood.

87
MR N. BYCROFT, Malton
Postal: **Cotman Rise, Brandsby, York, YO61 4RN**
Contacts: **PHONE (01347) 888641 MOBILE (07802) 763227**

  1 **AMY'S MERCDES**, 4, ch f Defacto (USA)—Efipetite **Mrs L. Rose**
  2 **DANUM DANCER**, 4, ch c Allied Forces (USA)—Branston Dancer **G.Hart, B.Abbott, R.McGrane, K.Senior**
  3 **DAZZLER MAC**, 7, b g Komaite (USA)—Stilvella
  4 **DIUM MAC**, 7, b g Presidium—Efipetite **J. A. Swinburne**
  5 **EFIDIUM**, 10, ch g Presidium—Efipetite **Hambleton Racing Partnership**
  6 **ELITE LAND**, 5, b g Namaqualand (USA)—Petite Elite **Mrs J. Dickinson**
  7 **ELLIES FAITH**, 4, ch f Sugarfoot—Star Dancer **B. Abbott**
  8 **FIRST VALENTINI**, 4, b f Bertolini (USA)—Oscietra **Mrs J. Dickinson**
  9 **GAME BERTIE**, 5, b g Mind Games—Carol Again **J. G. Lumsden**
10 **PETITE MAC**, 8, b m Timeless Times (USA)—Petite Elite
11 **RED FAMA**, 4, ch g Fraam—Carol Again **B. F. Rayner**
12 **SHOTLEY MAC**, 4, ch g Abou Zouz (USA)—Julie's Gift **J. A. Swinburne**
13 **TOBY MAC**, 6, b g Presidium—Ski Path **N. Bycroft**
14 **TUMP MAC**, 4, ch g Compton Admiral—Petite Elite **N. Bycroft**
15 **UACE MAC**, 4, b f Compton Place—Umbrian Gold (IRE) **N. Bycroft**

THREE-YEAR-OLDS

16 **CARLTON MAC**, ch g Timeless Times (USA)—Julie's Gift **S. D. Rose**
17 **PETIDIUM**, b f Presidium—Efipetite **Hambleton Racing Partnership I**
18 **UMVERTI**, b f Averti (IRE)—Umbrian Gold (IRE) **Mrs C. M. Whatley**

TWO-YEAR-OLDS

19 **ALACITY (IRE)**, b f 26/3 Elusive City (USA)—Minamala (IRE) (Desert King (IRE)) (3000) **Mrs J. Dickinson**
20 **AVEN MAC (IRE)**, ch f 26/4 Indian Haven—Anamara (IRE) (Fairy King (USA)) (2000) **N. Bycroft**
21 **CARHUE PRINCESS (IRE)**, b f 16/3 Desert Prince (IRE)—
                          Carhue Journey (IRE) (Barathea (IRE)) **Mr R. K. Arrowsmith**
22 **INTO MAC**, b c 23/5 Shinko Forest (IRE)—Efipetite (Efisio) **Mr N. Bycroft**
23 **ISHE MAC**, b f 10/4 Ishiguru (USA)—Zacinta (USA) (Hawkster (USA)) (3000) **N. Bycroft**
24 **MAYBEME**, b f 19/2 Lujain (USA)—Malvadilla (IRE) (Doyoun) **Cavalier Racing**
25 **WRENS HOPE**, ch f 4/3 Shinko Forest (IRE)—Star Dancer (Groom Dancer (USA)) (2000) **Mr K. Pennington**

Other Owners: Mr Barrie Abbott, Mr E. D. Atkinson, Mr P. D. Burrow, Mrs H. Cavanagh, Mr R. C. Crawford, Mrs J. Dickinson, Mr G. C. Hart, Mr J. H. Hemy, Mrs E. Hughes, Mr A. Hurd, Mr Raymond McGrane, Mr W. G. Moore, Mr K. Senior, Mrs C. M. Whatley.

Assistant Trainer: Suzzanne France

Jockey (flat): Silvestre De Sousa.

88
MR T. H. CALDWELL, Warrington
Postal: **Burley Heyes Cottage, Arley Road, Appleton, Warrington, Cheshire, WA4 4RR**
Contacts: **PHONE/FAX (01565) 777275 MOBILE (07879) 455767**

  1 **ANCHOR WATCH**, 4, br g Night Shift (USA)—All The Luck (USA) **T. H. Caldwell**
  2 4, B g Lahib (USA)—Cap It If You Can (IRE) **T. H. Caldwell**
  3 **CLEOPATRAS THERAPY (IRE)**, 11, b g Gone Fishin—Nec Precario **T. H. Caldwell**
  4 **DANCING PARTNER (USA)**, 7, b g Distant View (USA)—Bold Ballerina **R. Cabrera-Vargas**
  5 4, B f Sirsan (IRE)—Devtaine (IRE) **R. Cabrera-Vargas**
  6 **INCHMARLOW (IRE)**, 5, b g Cape Cross (IRE)—Glenstal Priory **T. H. Caldwell**
  7 **MASTER MARMALADE**, 7, ch g Trempolino (USA)—Miss Picol **T. H. Caldwell**

MR T. H. CALDWELL—continued

TWO-YEAR-OLDS

8 B c 29/3 Lucky Owners (NZ)—Cap It If You Can (IRE) (Capitano) **T. H. Caldwell**

Assistant Trainer: Mrs P J Wharfe

Jockey (flat): J. Fanning, A. Nicholls, P. Robinson. **Jockey (NH):** A. Dobbin, T. J. Murphy. **Conditional:** B. Wharfe. **Amateur:** Mrs P. Wharfe.

---

89 **MR S. A. CALLAGHAN, Newmarket**
Postal: **Rathmoy Stables, Hamilton Road, Newmarket, Suffolk, CB8 0GU**
Contacts: **PHONE (01638) 664040 FAX (01638) 668446 MOBILE (07909) 924926**

1 **ART GAMBLE (IRE)**, 4, b g Shinko Forest (IRE)—Kiva **Mr R. Lloyd**
2 **EXPENSIVE ART (IRE)**, 4, b f Cape Cross (IRE)—Walnut Lady **M. R. Green**
3 **FINALMENTE**, 6, b g Kahyasi—Sudden Spirit (FR) **E. M. Kirtland**
4 **FROISSEE**, 4, b f Polish Precedent (USA)—Crinkle (IRE) **Mrs T. Foreman**
5 **HAZYTOO**, 4, ch c Sakhee (USA)—Shukran **Mr T Mohan, Mr M Walsh & Allan McNamee**
6 **NANOSECOND (USA)**, 5, ch g Kingmambo (USA)—Easy 'n Gold (USA) **W. Hinge**
7 **SPLINTER GROUP**, 4, ch c Inchinor—Haiyfoona **Mr T. Mohan & Mr Allan McNamee**
8 **SPOOF MASTER (IRE)**, 4, b g Invincible Spirit (IRE)—Talbiya (IRE) **Bill Hinge & Gary Smallbone**

THREE-YEAR-OLDS

9 **BILLION DOLLAR KID**, br c Averti (IRE)—Fredora **Mr M. Sines**
10 **CAPE TYCOON (IRE)**, b g Cape Cross (IRE)—Tycooness (IRE) **Mrs J. R. Ramsden**
11 Br c Kyllachy—Euridice (IRE) **M. Tabor**
12 **EXHIBITION (IRE)**, b c Invincible Spirit (IRE)—Moonbi Ridge (IRE) **Magnier, M Tabor, D Smith & M Green**
13 B g Danehill Dancer (IRE)—Fille de Joie (IRE) **M. Tabor**
14 **GASPAR VAN WITTEL (USA)**, b br c Danehill Dancer (IRE)—Akuna Bay (USA) **M. R. Green**
15 **HIGH STANDING (USA)**, b br g High Yield (USA)—Nena Maka **SP Racing Investments S.A.**
16 **ORPEN'S ART (IRE)**, b c Invincible Spirit (IRE)—Bells of Ireland (UAE) **M. R. Green**
17 **PASTA PRAYER**, br c Bertolini (USA)—Benedicite **Mr J. F. Osborne**
18 **RED ALERT DAY**, b c Diktat—Strike Hard (USA) **Gallagher Equine Ltd**
19 **ROCK ME (IRE)**, ch g Rock of Gibraltar (IRE)—Final Farewell (USA) **T. M. Mohan**
20 **ROSY ALEXANDER**, ch f Spartacus (IRE)—Sweet Angeline **Mrs T. A. Foreman**
21 **SHOOT PONTOON (IRE)**, b c Danehill Dancer (IRE)—Burmese Princess (USA) **The Shoot Pontoon Partnership**
22 **THE YOUNG FELLA**, ch c Compton Place—Centre Court **Mr M. Sines**
23 **VILNA (USA)**, b g Hold That Tiger (USA)—Not to Be Outdone (USA) **M. Tabor**
24 **WYNBERG (IRE)**, b g Danetime (IRE)—Jayzdoll (USA) **Cast Hinge Searchfield & Smallbone 1**

TWO-YEAR-OLDS

25 B c 23/3 Chevalier (IRE)—Cappuchino (IRE) (Roi Danzig (USA)) (26000) **N. A. Callaghan**
26 **CELTIC REBEL (IRE)**, b c 16/4 Bahri—Farjah (IRE) (Charnwood Forest (IRE)) (60000) **P. M. Cunningham**
27 **ECHO DANCER**, br c 29/4 Danehill Dancer (IRE)—Entail (IRE) (Riverman (USA)) (50000) **Mr D. F. O'Rourke**
28 **ELUSIVE RONNIE (IRE)**, b c 6/2 One Cool Cat (USA)—
Elusive Kitty (USA) (Elusive Quality (USA)) **Woodcote Stud Ltd**
29 B c 9/4 One Cool Cat (USA)—Fee Faw Fum (IRE) (Great Commotion (USA)) (100000)
30 Ch f 25/3 Monsieur Bond (IRE)—Feeling Blue (Missed Flight) (40000) **M. R. Green**
31 Ch f 1/2 Johannesburg (USA)—Game Player (USA) (Drumalis) **Mrs E. O'Leary**
32 Gr f 21/4 Verglas (IRE)—Kamalame (USA) (Souvenir Copy (USA)) (25740) **Mr J. Egan**
33 B f 23/1 Medicean—Lady Donatella (Last Tycoon) (42000) **Countrywide Steel & Tubes Ltd**
34 Ch f 28/4 Danehill Dancer (IRE)—Lilissa (IRE) (Doyoun) (210000) **M. Tabor**
35 B f 6/2 Danetime (IRE)—Miss Megs (IRE) (Croco Rouge (IRE)) (28000) **Lord Clinton & Mr M. Green**
36 B f 17/2 Danetime (IRE)—Naraina (IRE) (Desert Story (IRE)) (42000) **Countrywide Steel & Tubes Ltd**
37 B f 14/4 Invincible Spirit (IRE)—Oatey (Master Willie) (130000) **N. A. Callaghan**
38 B c 16/3 Tobougg (IRE)—Panoramic View (Polar Falcon (USA)) (16000) **Mr S. Hope & Mr S. Barrow**
39 B f 11/3 Pivotal—Pietra Dura (Cadeaux Genereux) (380000) **M. Tabor**
40 Ch c 20/2 Auction House (USA)—Pleasant Memories (Danehill (USA)) (7000) **N. A. Callaghan**
41 B f 31/1 Exceed And Excel (AUS)—Quinzey (JPN) (Carnegie (IRE)) (55000) **Sangster Family & M. Green**
42 B f 13/2 Catcher In The Rye (IRE)—Rainbow Java (IRE) (Fairy King (USA)) (35000) **N. A. Callaghan**
43 B c 18/3 War Chant (USA)—Rose of Zollern (IRE) (Seattle Dancer (USA)) (45000) **Mr Y. M. Nasib**
44 B c 22/1 Giant's Causeway (USA)—Spiritual Air (Royal Applause) (250000) **N. A. Callaghan**
45 B c 25/4 Kyllachy—Succumb (Pursuit of Love) (92000) **M. R. Green**
46 B f 9/3 Invincible Spirit (IRE)—To The Woods (IRE) (Woodborough (USA)) (50000) **J. R. Crickmore**

MR S. A. CALLAGHAN—continued

Other Owners: Art Investments International Co S.A., Mr R. G. W. Brown, Mr John Cast, Mrs June Doyle, Mr K. Doyle, Mr M. Fitzpatrick, Mr Bill Hinge, Mrs John Magnier, Mr Allan McNamee, Mr Mark McStay, Mr T. Mohan, Mr B. Morrin, Mr Roger O'Callaghan, Mr R. O'Callaghan, B. V. Sangster, G. E. Sangster, Mr John Searchfield, Mr Gary Smallbone, Mr Derrick Smith, Mr M. Walsh, Mr C. G. P. Wyatt.

Apprentice: Bradley Roper, Kirsty Milczarek.

---

90 MISS J. A CAMACHO, Malton
Postal: **Star Cottage, Welham Road, Norton, Malton, North Yorkshire, YO17 9QE**
Contacts: **PHONE (01653) 696205 FAX (01653) 697533 MOBILE (07779) 318135/(07950) 356440**
E-MAIL jacracing@starcottage.fsbusiness.co.uk

1 BLUSHING HILARY (IRE), 5, ch m City On A Hill (USA)—Trinida **Lee Bolingbroke & Sue Johnson**
2 4, B f Elmaamul (USA)—Calachuchi **Mrs. S. Camacho**
3 CANNY BAY, 5, b g Lahib (USA)—Calachuchi **I. P. Drury**
4 ELKHORN, 6, b g Indian Ridge—Rimba (USA) **Lee Bolingbroke & Partners VI**
5 FALMASSIM, 5, b g Mozart (IRE)—Scostes **L. A. Bolingbroke**
6 FOREIGN EDITION (IRE), 6, b g Anabaa (USA)—Palacegate Episode (IRE) **Lee Bolingbroke & Partners VII**
7 HELLO NOD, 4, b g Polish Precedent (USA)—Nordan Raider **Brian Nordan**
8 LAURO, 8, b m Mukaddamah (USA)—Lapu-Lapu **Miss J. A Camacho**
9 PEGASUS PRINCE (USA), 4, b g Fusaichi Pegasus (USA)—Avian Eden (USA) **D. W. Armstrong**
10 RIO RIVA, 6, b g Pivotal—Dixie Favor (USA) **Rio Riva Partnership**
11 SAUJANA, 4, b g Benny The Dip (USA)—Silky Heights (IRE) **Mrs S. Camacho**
12 SIR NOD, 6, b g Tagula (IRE)—Nordan Raider **Brian Nordan**

THREE-YEAR-OLDS

13 BOUGGLER, b g Tobougg (IRE)—Rush Hour (IRE) **Axom (III)**
14 GAYANULA (USA), b f Yonaguska (USA)—Betamillion Bock (USA) **G. B. Turnbull Ltd**
15 KAI MER (IRE), b f Captain Rio—No Shame **Miss J. A Camacho**
16 LADY IN CHIEF, ch f Fantastic Light (USA)—Risque Lady **Axom V**
17 MOROCCHIUS (USA), b c Black Minnaloushe (USA)—Shakespearean (USA) **L. A. Bolingbroke**
18 NODSERVATORY, ch f Observatory (USA)—Nordan Raider **Brian Nordan**
19 ORKNEY (IRE), b g Trans Island—Bitty Mary **Axom (XIII)**
20 SALSA TIME, b f Hernando (FR)—Kabayil **Elite Racing Club**
21 SHERBET LEMON, b f Nayef (USA)—Travesty (IRE) **Elite Racing Club**
22 YOUNG GLADIATOR (IRE), b c Spartacus (IRE)—Savona (IRE) **L. Bolingbroke**

TWO-YEAR-OLDS

23 Bl gr c 22/5 Paris House—Blue Wraith (Bluegrass Prince (IRE)) (650) **Gail Ruddock**
24 B f 1/3 Red Ransom (USA)—Dixie Favor (USA) (Dixieland Band (USA)) (12000) **Mr. J. Spence**
25 Ch f 26/1 Lomitas—Ecstatic (Nashwan (USA)) (8000) **G. B. Turnbull Ltd.**
26 Ch f 24/3 Medicean—Ivory Dawn (Batshoof) (12000) **D. W. Armstrong**
27 STATE OF GRACE, ch f 26/2 Generous (IRE)—Vent d'aout (IRE) (Imp Society (USA)) **Elite Racing Club**

Other Owners: Axom, Ms M. A. Bramwell, S. Cannon, Mr Dan Downie, G. B. Turnbull Ltd, Mr D. P. Grundy, Mr Tony Hill, Mr Graeme Howard, Ms Sue Johnson, Mr C. J. Murphy, Miss M. Noden, Mr W. Riley.

Assistant Trainer: Mr S Brown

Jockey (flat): T. Eaves. **Apprentice:** Dawn Rankin.

---

91 MR A. M. CAMPION, Malton
Postal: **Whitewell House Stables, Whitewall, Malton, North Yorkshire, YO17 9EH**
Contacts: **PHONE (01653) 692729 FAX (01653) 600066 MOBILE (07973) 178311**
E-MAIL info@markcampion-racing.com WEBSITE www.markcampion-racing.com

1 BARNEYS LYRIC, 8, ch g Hector Protector (USA)—Anchorage (IRE) **Faulkner West & Co Ltd**
2 BUMPER (FR), 7, b br g Cadoudal (FR)—Dame Blonde (FR) **S B P Racing**
3 DESERT NOVA (IRE), 6, ch g Desert King (USA)—Assafiyah (IRE) **Whitewall Racing**
4 JENISE (IRE), 5, b m Orpen (USA)—Griqualand
5 LUCKY ANGLER (IRE), 9, b g Gone Fishin—Lady By Chance (IRE) **A. M. Campion**
6 4, B g Elmaamul (USA)—Newgate Bubbles **W. P. S. Johnson**

MR A. M. CAMPION—continued

7 NEWGATE PARISIEN, 5, b g g Paris House—Gemgem **W. P. S. Johnson**
8 NEWGATE SUDS, 11, b m Kasakov—Newgate Bubbles **W. P. S. Johnson**
9 TUDOR OAK, 6, b g Woods of Windsor (USA)—Tacheo **Wolfracing UK**

Other Owners: Mr A. M. Campion, Mr Barrie Coleman, Mr D. F. Henery, Mr Michael Wheeler, Mr Zig Zwierzewicz.

Conditional: D. Laverty.

92

MS JENNIE CANDLISH, Leek
Postal: **Basford Grange Racing Stables, Basford, Leek, Staffordshire, ST13 7ET**
Contacts: **PHONE (01538) 360324 FAX (01538) 360324**
MOBILE (07779) 042826 or (07826) 848208
E-MAIL jenniecandlish@yahoo.co.uk

1 BARAFUNDLE, 4, ch g Flemensfirth (USA)—Different Dee (IRE) **Mrs J. M. Ratcliff**
2 CASALANI (IRE), 9, br m Fourstars Allstar (USA)—Brandy Hill Girl **A Ram, A Baggie & A Red**
3 CELTS ESPERE, 5, ch g Samraan (USA)—Celtic Dream
4 CREDIT (IRE), 7, b g Intikhab (USA)—Tycooness (IRE) **A Ram, A Baggie & A Red**
5 DECENT LORO, 4, b g Lord of Appeal—Otorum (IRE) **Mrs J. M. Ratcliff**
6 DIKTATORSHIP (IRE), 5, b g Diktat—Polka Dancer **A. J. Baxter**
7 DUKE OF BURGUNDY (FR), 5, b g Danehill (USA)—Valley of Gold (FR) **A. J. Baxter**
8 GLEN OMEN (IRE), 8, b g Flying Legend—Miners Own (IRE) **Mrs J. C. Bamber**
9 HARBOUR BREEZE (IRE), 6, b g Slip Anchor—New Wind (GER) **Mr P. & Mrs G. A. Clarke**
10 JOJESSE, 4, ch g Compton Place—Jodeeka **Ms J. Candlish**
11 LAP OF HONOUR (IRE), 4, b g Danehill Dancer (IRE)—Kingsridge (IRE) **Mr P. & Mrs G. A. Clarke**
12 MINIMIX, 4, gr f Manninamix—Rosilis (FR) **A. J. Baxter**
13 MODERN VERSE (USA), 5, b g Pleasant Tap—Sandalwood (USA) **A. J. Baxter**
14 MONROE GOLD, 8, ch g Pivotal—Golden Daring (IRE) **Ms J. Candlish**
15 NORTH WALK (IRE), 5, b g Monashee Mountain (USA)—Celtic Link (IRE) **A. J. Baxter**
16 OSOLOMIO (IRE), 5, b g Singspiel—Inanna **A. J. Baxter**
17 PAPAJOSH (FR), 5, b g Maresca Sorrento (FR)—Cynthia (FR) **Mr P. & Mrs G. A. Clarke**
18 SEA FROLIC (IRE), 7, b m Shinko Forest (IRE)—Centre Travel **Mrs J. M. Ratcliff**
19 TOMILLIELOU, 7, gr g I'm Supposin (IRE)—Belle Rose (IRE) **A. J. Baxter**

THREE-YEAR-OLDS

20 B f Raintrap—Chausseneige (FR) **Mr P. & Mrs G. A. Clarke**

Other Owners: Mr Peter Clarke, Mrs Gwenda Ann Clarke, Mr Jon Roome, Mr Lee Stewart.

Assistant Trainer: Miss Jenny Carr

Jockey (flat): R. Moore, Hayley Turner. **Jockey (NH):** L. Stephens, A. O'Keeffe, S. Thomas. **Apprentice:** L. Treadwell.
Conditional: L. Treadwell.

93

MR HENRY D. N. B. CANDY, Wantage
Postal: **Kingston Warren, Wantage, Oxfordshire, OX12 9QF**
Contacts: PHONE (01367) 820276/820514 FAX (01367) 820500 MOBILE (07836) 211264
E-MAIL henrycandy@btconnect.com

1 CANDLE, 5, br m Dansili—Celia Brady **Mrs M. J. Blackburn**
2 COLLOQUIAL, 7, b g Classic Cliche (IRE)—Celia Brady **Mrs David Blackburn & Mr M. Blackburn**
3 EFFIGY, 4, b g Efisio—Hymne d'amour (USA) **The Earl Cadogan**
4 GILDED YOUTH, 4, b g Gorse—Nisha **Girsonfield Ltd**
5 GRANARY, 4, b f Singspiel (IRE)—All Grain **Major M. G. Wyatt**
6 KIRK MICHAEL, 4, b g Selkirk (USA)—Pervenche **Girsonfield Ltd**
7 OLDJOESAID, 4, b g Royal Applause—Border Minstral (IRE) **John Joseph Byrne**
8 PRETTY MISS, 4, b f Averti (IRE)—Pretty Poppy **Mrs J. E. L. Wright**
9 RUM JUNGLE, 4, b g Robellino (USA)—Anna Karietta **The Earl Cadogan**
10 SEAMUS SHINDIG, 6, b g Aragon—Sheesha (USA) **Henry D. N. B. Candy**
11 SIGNOR PELTRO, 5, b g Bertolini (USA)—Pewter Lass **First Of Many Partnership**
12 THORNBILL, 5, ch g Gorse—Red Hot Dancer (USA) **Henry D. N. B. Candy**

MR HENRY D. N. B. CANDY—continued

THREE-YEAR-OLDS

13 **AYE AYE DIGBY (IRE)**, b c Captain Rio—Jane Digby (IRE) **Trolley Action**
14 **BIKINI**, b f Trans Island—Chimere (FR) **W. M. Lidsey**
15 **COMPTON ROSE**, ch f Compton Place—Benjarong **Mrs J. E. L. Wright**
16 **CORRYBROUGH**, ch c Kyllachy—Calamanco **Thurloe Thoroughbreds XXI**
17 **CRATAEGUS**, b g Gorse—Dove Tree (FR) **Girsonfield Ltd**
18 **DANAE**, br f Dansili—Pervenche **Girsonfield Ltd**
19 **DUNTULM**, b c Sakhee (USA)—Not Before Time (IRE) **T. Barr**
20 **EXPEDITER**, b f Bahamian Bounty—Iris May **Henry Candy & Partners**
21 **FINNEY HILL**, b f Mark of Esteem (IRE)—Ringing Hill **Major M. G. Wyatt**
22 **FLASHY PHOTON**, b g Compton Place—Showboat (USA) **Trolley Action**
23 **FLYING FLUTE**, b g Piccolo—Fledge **Warren Partnership**
24 **KILLCARA BOY**, b g Tobougg (IRE)—Barakat **Miss J. E. Byrne**
25 **LA FAMIGLIA**, ch f Tobougg (IRE)—Sea Isle **Acloque, Jones & Frost**
26 **MOUSE WHITE**, bl gr g Auction House (USA)—Petinata **Henry D. N. B. Candy**
27 **MR KARTOFFEL (IRE)**, b g Night Shift (USA)—Diamant (IRE) **Henry D. N. B. Candy**
28 **PAPPOOSE**, b f Namid—Bryn **Simon Broke & Partners**
29 **REQUIA**, b f Nayef (USA)—Strelitzia (SAF) **Mrs B. Oppenheimer**
30 **SAINGLEND**, b c Galileo (IRE)—Verbal Intrigue (USA) **Mr W. J. Byrne**
31 **SHANZU**, b f Kyllachy—Limuru **Baraka Partnership**
32 **SOLENT CRYSTAL**, b f Generous (IRE)—Laser Crystal (IRE) **M. D. Poland**
33 **TIMBER CREEK**, b g Tobougg (IRE)—Proserpine **The Earl Cadogan**
34 **TITTLE**, b f Tobougg (IRE)—Poppy's Song **T. A. F. Frost**

TWO-YEAR-OLDS

35 **BENDED KNEE**, b f 16/2 Refuse To Bend (IRE)—Flavian (Catrail) (USA) **Major M. G. Wyatt**
36 B f 27/2 Act One—Bob's Princess (Bob's Return) (IRE) (5000) **Mrs J. E. L. Wright**
37 B f 10/2 Lahib (USA)—Bond Solitaire (Atraf) (15000)
38 B c 11/3 Kyllachy—Cutpurse Moll (Green Desert (USA)) (17000)
39 **FIDLER BAY**, b c 15/2 Falbrav (IRE)—Fiddle-Dee-Dee (IRE) (Mujtahid (USA)) (3000) **Henry D. N. B. Candy**
40 B f 17/4 Domedriver (IRE)—Hymne d'amour (USA) (Dixieland Band) (USA) **The Earl Cadogan**
41 **LADY MASTER**, b f 3/3 Kheleyf (USA)—Syzygy (IRE) (Entrepreneur) (6000) **Fighttheban Partnership VI**
42 Ch c 13/3 Paris House—Miss Prim (Case Law) (1500) **Simon Broke & Partners**
43 **SHANGANI**, b f 23/3 Ishiguru (USA)—Sheesha (Shadeed (USA)) (4000) **Henry D. N. B. Candy**
44 **SPEEDY GURU**, b f 8/3 Ishiguru (USA)—Gowon (Aragon) (4800) **Henry D. N. B. Candy**
45 Ch g 8/3 Forzando—Star of Flanders (Puissance) (4500)
46 B c 25/2 Namid—Syrian Queen (Slip Anchor) (34000) **First of Many Partnership**
47 B c 22/2 Peintre Celebre (USA)—Top Crystal (IRE) (Sadler's Wells) (48000) **M. D. Poland**

Other Owners: Mr Alexander Acloque, Miss H. Acloque, Mrs David Blackburn, Mr Mark Blackburn, Mr Simon Broke, Mr C. J. Burley, Mrs H. Candy, Mr P. J. Carter, Mr S. Clayton, Mr R. E. Crutchley, Mr J. S. Dale, Mr P. A. Deal, Mr A. L. Deal, Mr J. Fitzgerald, Mr Alexander Frost, Mr T. A. F. Frost, T. R. Gittins, Mr John Inverdale, Mr S. Jeffries, Mrs P. Jones, Mrs S. E. Lakin, Mr T. J. Le Blanc-Smith, Mr I. J. Matthews, Sir Arthur Norman, Mr T. Norman, Mr Oliver Pawle, Mr D. Redvers, Mr N. Rustard, Mr Michael Stewart, Mr D. J. Taylor, W. Thornton, Mr M. J. M. Tricks.

Jockey (flat): Dane O'Neill. Apprentice: Amy Scott.

MRS RUTH A. CARR, York
Postal: Mowbray House Farm, Stillington, York, North Yorkshire, YO61 1LT
Contacts: **PHONE** (01347) 821683 **YARD** (01347) 811719 **HOME FAX** (01347) 821683
MOBILE (07721) 926772
E-MAIL ruth@ruthcarrracing.co.uk WEBSITE www.ruthcarrracing.co.uk

1 **AVONTUUR (FR)**, 6, ch g Kabool—Ipoh (FR) **David W. Chapman**
2 **CADOGEN SQUARE**, 6, ch m Takhlid (USA)—Mount Park (IRE) **David W. Chapman**
3 **CHARLIE CHAN**, 7, gr g Paris House—Vindictive Lady (USA) **A. J. Le Blond**
4 **CRYPTIC CLUE (USA)**, 4, b g Cryptoclearance (USA)—Nidd (USA) **Michael Hill**
5 **FAN CLUB**, 4, ch g Zamindar (USA)—Starfan (USA) **J. M. Chapman**
6 **INFLAGRANTEDELICTO (USA)**, 4, ch g Gentlemen (ARG)—Imprudent Love (USA) **David W. Chapman**
7 **JABRAAN (USA)**, 6, b g Aljabr (USA)—Miss Zafonic (FR) **David W. Chapman**
8 **KANISORN (SWE)**, 6, b g Be My Chief (USA)—American Pay Day (USA) **David W. Chapman**
9 **LUNAR STORM (IRE)**, 4, b c Machiavellian (USA)—Moonshell (IRE) **Michael Hill**
10 **MOHEEBB (IRE)**, 4, b g Machiavellian (USA)—Rockerlong **Michael Hill**

MRS RUTH A. CARR—continued

11 NEWGATE (UAE), 4, b c Jade Robbery (USA)—Patruel **Michael Hill**
12 ONLY A SPLASH, 4, b g Primo Valentino (IRE)—Water Well **David W. Chapman**
13 PADDYWACK (IRE), 11, b g Bigstone (IRE)—Millie's Return (IRE) **David W. Chapman**
14 PAWN IN LIFE (IRE), 10, b g Midhish—Lady-Mumtaz **Geraldine Degville & Lawrence Degville**
15 RACCOON (IRE), 8, b g Raphane (USA)—Kunucu (IRE) **P. D. Savill**
16 SPINNING GAME, 4, b f Mind Games—Spindara (IRE) **David W. Chapman**
17 SUNLEY SOVEREIGN, 4, b g Josr Algarhoud (IRE)—Pharsical **David W. Chapman**

THREE-YEAR-OLDS

18 AUTUMN CHARM, ch f Reel Buddy (USA)—Eurolink Cafe **David W. Chapman**
19 NATURAL RHYTHM (IRE), ch c Distant Music (USA)—Nationalartgallery (IRE) **Michael Hill**

Other Owners: Mrs G. J. Degville, L. W. Degville.

Assistant Trainer: David W. Chapman

---

95 **MR A. W. CARROLL**, Cropthorne
Postal: **The Cropthorne Stud, Field Barn Lane, Cropthorne, Pershore, Worcestershire, WR10 3LY**
Contacts: **PHONE** (01386) 861020 **FAX** (01386) 861628 **MOBILE** (07770) 472431
E-MAIL a.w.carroll@btconnect.com **WEBSITE** www.awcarroll.co.uk

1 ALDIRUOS (IRE), 8, ch g Bigstone (IRE)—Ball Cat (FR) **Aramis Racing Syndicate**
2 APACHE CHANT (USA), 4, b g War Chant (USA)—Sterling Pound (USA) **Mr M. S. Cooke**
3 ARCTIC WINGS (IRE), 4, b c In The Wings—Arctic Hunt (IRE) **Mr P. A. Downing**
4 ARTHURS DREAM (IRE), 6, b g Desert Prince (IRE)—Blueprint (USA) **A. W. Carroll**
5 BACKLASH, 7, b m Fraam—Mezza Luna **A. C. Pickford**
6 BECKENHAM'S SECRET, 4, b g Foxhound (USA)—Berliese (IRE) **Allan Jones & Mrs J J G & H Reynolds**
7 CALIBAN (IRE), 10, ch g Rainbows For Life (CAN)—Amour Toujours (IRE) **Mr R. M. Wheelwright**
8 CHATSHOW (USA), 7, b g Distant View (USA)—Galanty Show **One Under Par Racing**
9 CLIFTON, 6, b m Bal Harbour—Contradictory **E. J. Mangan**
10 COUNTBACK (FR), 9, b g Anabaa (USA)—Count Me Out (FR) **Last Day Racing Partnership**
11 DANSE MACABRE (IRE), 9, b g Flemensfirth (USA)—My Romance **Miss V. M. Brown**
12 DARK SOCIETY, 10, b g Imp Society (USA)—No Candles Tonight **Group 1 Racing (1994) Ltd**
13 ERMINE GREY, 7, gr g Wolfhound (USA)—Impulsive Decision (IRE) **L. M. Baker**
14 EVERYMAN, 4, gr g Act One—Maid To Dance **M. Woodall**
15 FANCY YOU (IRE), 5, b m Mull of Kintyre (USA)—Sunset Park (IRE) **Allan Jones & Barry Silkman**
16 FORTUNE POINT (IRE), 10, ch g Cadeaux Genereux—Mountains of Mist (IRE) **The T. J. Racing Partnership**
17 FRANCIS DUNSTAN (IRE), 6, b g Shernazar—Audrey's Turn **Miss V. M. Brown**
18 GOLDEN SQUARE, 6, b g Tomba—Cherish Me **Mr & Mrs J. B.**
19 GOURANGA, 5, b m Robellino (USA)—Hymne d'amour (USA) **Group 1 Racing (1994) Ltd**
20 GREY DASLER (IRE), 5, gr g Saddlers' Hall (IRE)—Glacial Queen (IRE) **Mrs J. Cumiskey Mr T. Joyce**
21 HOLD FIRE, 4, b f Lear Spear (USA)—Kahyasi Moll (IRE) **Marita Bayley & Trevor Turner**
22 IS IT ME (USA), 5, ch g Sky Classic (CAN)—Thea (GER) **J. Billson**
23 JAKE THE SNAKE (IRE), 7, ch g Intikhab (USA)—Tilbrook (IRE) **T. P. Ramsden**
24 JESSICA WIGMO, 5, b m Bahamian Bounty—Queen of Shannon (IRE) **J. Wigmore Racing Partnership**
25 KINKEEL (IRE), 9, b g Hubbly Bubbly (USA)—Bubbly Beau **Group 1 Racing (1994) Ltd**
26 LADY FAS (IRE), 5, b m Fasliyev (USA)—Lady Sheriff **E. J. Mangan**
27 LE CORVEE (IRE), 6, b g Rossini (USA)—Elupa (IRE) **Mr J. G. Boyce**
28 LI LO BOSH (IRE), 6, b g Dr Devious (IRE)—Academic Miss (IRE) **G. J. Roberts**
29 LILY LA BELLE, 4, b f King Charlemagne (USA)—Corniche Quest (IRE) **Lewis Caterers**
30 MANFORALLSEASONS, 5, ch g Gorse—Oleana (IRE) **Seasons Holidays**
31 MEADOW HAWK (USA), 8, b g Spinning World (USA)—Sophonisbe **Mr Malcolm Webb & Mrs Susan Keable**
32 MIDSUMMER BAY, 6, b m Forzando—Sea-Belle (USA) **Miss H. L. James**
33 MOKUM (FR), 7, b g Octagonal (NZ)—Back On Top (FR) **Mr M. S. Cooke**
34 MR FLUFFY, 11, b g Charmer—Hinton Bairn **The Cockpit Crew**
35 MUJAMEAD, 4, b g Mujahid (USA)—Island Mead **J. Billson**
36 NAUTICAL, 10, gr g Lion Cavern (USA)—Russian Royal (USA) **J. Billson**
37 PARISH OAK, 13, b g Rakaposhi King—Poppy's Pride **Mrs M. Mann**
38 PIPS ASSERTIVE WAY, 7, ch m Nomadic Way (USA)—Return to Brighton **Group 1 Racing (1994) Ltd**
39 PRETTILINI, 5, ch m Bertolini (USA)—Pretiosa (IRE) **N. J. Coulson-Stevens**
40 RED RUDY, 6, ch g Pivotal—Piroshka **Winding Wheel Partnership**
41 ROBBIE CAN CAN, 9, b g Robellino (USA)—Can Can Lady **K. F. Coleman**
42 ROBINZAL, 6, b g Zilzal (USA)—Sulitelma (USA) **Mrs J. L. Le Brocq**
43 SALVESTRO, 5, b g Medicean—Katy Nowaitee **Mr J. Rutter**

MR A. W. CARROLL—continued

44 **SHE'S MY OUTSIDER**, 6, b m Docksider (USA)—Solar Flare (IRE) **Lewis Caterers**
45 **SOFINELLA (IRE)**, 5, gr m Titus Livius (FR)—Mystical Jumbo **Mr S. Agodino**
46 **STOOP TO CONQUER**, 8, b g Polar Falcon (USA)—Princess Genista **Seasons Holidays**
47 **SUPER SEASONS (IRE)**, 4, b g Alhaarth (IRE)—Karakorum (IRE) **Seasons Holidays**
48 **THE CARPET MAN**, 4, b g Iron Mask (USA)—Yarrow Bridge **David Shorthouse Nigel Stevens Phil Culliford**
49 **TUDOR PRINCE (IRE)**, 4, b g Cape Cross (IRE)—Savona **Wyck Hall Stud Ltd**
50 **UNDER FIRE (IRE)**, 5, b g Lear Spear (USA)—Kahyasi Moll (IRE) **Marita Bayley & Trevor Turner**
51 **VISCOUNT ROSSINI**, 6, b br g Rossini (USA)—Spain **L. M. Baker**

THREE-YEAR-OLDS

52 **BOLD DIVA**, ch f Bold Edge—Trina's Pet **Mrs Anne Izamis**
53 **GAMBLING JACK**, b g First Trump—Star of Flanders **D. J. Lowe**
54 **HARBOUR BLUES**, ch c Best of The Bests (IRE)—Lady Georgia **Mr D. B. Ward**
55 **ONE CALLED ALICE**, ch gr f Zilzal (USA)—Boadicea The Red (IRE) **J. Billson**

Other Owners: A. Allright, J. T. Bacciochi, Mrs J. M. Bacciochi, Mrs M. Bayley, A. M. Carding, K. E. Collins, Mr P.E. Culliford, Mrs K. T. Cumiskey, Mr K. Edge, W. R. Gibson, I. Gould, R. W. Hills, A. L. Jones, T. F. Joyce, Mrs S. R. Keable, S. C. Lee, R. J. Millen, Mr T. Paphitis, Mrs F. Reynolds, M. Rice, Dr A. D. Rogers, T. J. R. Sanders, Mrs J. Shaw, D. G. Sheldon, D. T. Shorthouse, B. Silkman, R. K. Simmons, A. Sumner, J. H. Treadwell, Mr R. J. Tricker, Mr T. Turner, Mr M. P. Webb, Mrs I. Whitehead, R. F. Whitehouse, J. Wigmore, Mr G. J. Wigmore, Mrs A. D. Williams, D. J. Wood.

Apprentice: Mark Coumbe. **Amateur:** Mr Mark J. J. Smith.

MR D. CARROLL, Sledmere

Postal: **Sledmere House Stables, York Road, Sledmere, East Yorkshire, YO25 3XG**
Contacts: **PHONE** (01377) 236161 **FAX** (01377) 236161 **MOBILE** (07801) 553779
E-MAIL d_carroll66@hotmail.com

1 **AMBER ISLE**, 4, b g Weet-A-Minute (IRE)—Cloudy Reef
2 **ANYTHING ONCE (USA)**, 5, b g Elusive Quality (USA)—Bushy's Pride (USA) **M. Barber**
3 **BIRKSIDE**, 5, ch g Spinning World (USA)—Bright Hope (IRE) **Document Express Ltd**
4 4, B f Warningford—Che Gambe (USA) **Mr Peter Easterby**
5 **CHERRI FOSFATE**, 6, b g Mujahid (USA)—Compradore **Document Express Ltd**
6 **COSTA RUSSI (USA)**, 5, ch g Diesis—Super Supreme (IND) **J. M. Walsh**
7 **COTTAM GRANGE**, 8, b g River Falls—Karminski **Mr Peter Easterby**
8 **FIRST BOY**, 6, b g Polar Prince (IRE)—Seraphim (FR) **Mrs B. Ramsden**
9 **GOLDAN JESS**, 4, b g Golan (IRE)—Bendis (GER) **M. Barber**
10 **HITS ONLY VIC (USA)**, 4, b br g Lemon Drop Kid (USA)—
Royal Family (USA) **Steve Stone, Steve Watson, Clive Whiting**
11 **JAZRAWY**, 6, b g Dansili—Dalila di Mare (IRE) **Mrs B. Ramsden**
12 **JOSEPH JOHN**, 4, ch g Elmaamul (USA)—Kerrich **Miss Jo Stanley**
13 **JOSHUA'S GOLD (IRE)**, 7, b g Sesaro (USA)—Lady of The Night (IRE) **Andy Helm, Simon Bean, David Jones**
14 **KING OF RHYTHM**, 5, b g Imperial Ballet (IRE)—Sharadja (IRE) **Miss J. C. King**
15 **KINGS CONFESSION (IRE)**, 5, b g Danetime (IRE)—Night Rhapsody (IRE) **The Claire King Partnership**
16 **LADY KILLER QUEEN**, b f Killer Instinct—Princess of War **Mr P. W. Piper**
17 **MEETING OF MINDS**, 4, b f Mind Games—Turn Back **J. M. Walsh & R. Glynn**
18 **MIS CHICAF (IRE)**, 7, b m Prince Sabo—Champagne Season (USA) **Mr J. C. James**
19 **NAMROUD (USA)**, 9, b g Irish River (FR)—Top Line (USA) **Mrs B. Ramsden**
20 **NEXT GIRL**, 5, b m Overbury (IRE)—Seraphim (FR) **Mrs B. Ramsden**
21 **NOK TWICE (IRE)**, 7, b g Second Empire (IRE)—Bent Al Fala (USA) **J. M. Walsh**
22 **PILCA (FR)**, 8, ch g Pistolet Bleu (IRE)—Caricoe **Mr & Mrs K.H. Taylor & Mr & Mrs J.Isaacs**
23 **REDDY RONNIE (IRE)**, 8, b g Redback—Daffodil Dale (IRE) **Mr & Mrs K.H. Taylor & Mr & Mrs J.Isaacs**
24 **SAWWAAH (IRE)**, 11, b g Marju (IRE)—Just A Mirage **Document Express**
25 **SHE'S OUR LASS (IRE)**, 7, b m Green Desert (USA)—Sharadja (IRE) **We-Know Partnership**
26 **STEEL CITY BOY (IRE)**, 5, b g Bold Fact (USA)—Balgren (IRE) **We-Know Partnership**
27 **TENDALAY (USA)**, 4, b br c Red Ransom (USA)—Mandalay Point (USA) **Joe O'Leary**
28 **TRAPRAIN (IRE)**, 6, b g Mark of Esteem (IRE)—Nassma (USA) **Mr J. M. Walsh & Mr R. Glynn**

THREE-YEAR-OLDS

29 **DARK QUEEN**, b f Bertolini (USA)—Abstone Queen **Ms G. O'Ferrall**
30 **ENDERBY LIGHT (FR)**, ch g Fantastic Light (USA)—The Best Girl (FR) **J. M. Walsh**
31 **ENDERBY PRINCESS (IRE)**, ch f Storming Home—Zalitzine (USA) **J. M. Walsh**
32 B g Monashee Mountain (USA)—Euro Friendly (IRE) **Dreams**
33 **IMPERIAL DJAY (IRE)**, b g Dilshaan—Slayjay (IRE) **Imperial Racing**

MR D. CARROLL—continued

34 **JUST SAM (IRE)**, b f Mull of Kintyre (USA)—Strawberry Sands **Mr R. Glynn**
35 **OUR NATIONS**, gr c Highest Honor (FR)—Lines of Beauty (USA) **Ninerus**
36 **PORTRUSH STORM**, ch f Observatory (USA)—Overcast (IRE) **M.Symes G.H. & G.J. Briers S & A Franks**
37 **PRECIPICE**, b f Observatory (USA)—On The Brink **Mr J. F. O'Sullivan**
38 **PROUD LINUS (USA)**, b c Proud Citizen (USA)—Radcliffe Yard (USA) **J. M. Walsh**
39 **SCHOLES STREET**, b c Sakhee (USA)—Flamingo Flower (USA) **Glynn Family & Andy Helm**
40 B f Mull of Kintyre (USA)—Stolen Music (IRE) **Dreams**
41 **SYLVIAS GROVE**, b f Royal Applause—Branston Fizz **J. M. Walsh & Ruben Glynn**
42 **TAGULA KING (IRE)**, b c Tagula (IRE)—Isla (IRE) **Mr R. M. Packer**
43 B f Rossini (USA)—The Gibson Girl (IRE) **Dreams**
44 **TOP MAN DAN (IRE)**, b g Danetime (IRE)—Aphra Benn (IRE) **T. W. Heseltine**

TWO-YEAR-OLDS

45 B grc c 4/2 Invincible Spirit (IRE)—Arctic Ice (IRE) (Zafonic (USA)) (34000) **J. M. Walsh**
46 Ch f 12/3 E Dubai (USA)—Blue Stream (USA) (King of Kings (IRE)) (17374) **Mr Ron Hull**
47 B f 7/2 Statue of Liberty (USA)—Bridelina (FR) (Linamix (FR)) (8364) **Gerry Clark**
48 B c 21/2 Mujahid (USA)—Flower Breeze (USA) (Rahy (USA)) **Mr Peter Easterby**
49 **GEORGIE BEE**, b f 4/4 Ishiguru (USA)—Light of Aragon (Aragon) **C. H. Stephenson**
50 Gr f 3/3 Tagula (IRE)—New Deal (Rainbow Quest (USA)) (16730) **Imperial Racing**
51 B f 8/5 Mujahid (USA)—Northern Bird (Interrex (CAN)) **Mr Peter Easterby**

Other Owners: A. Franks, S. Franks, Mr J. R. Isaacs, Mrs P. McDiarmid, R. McDiarmid, J. P. Morris, D. Scott, J. B. Scott, Mrs H. S. Taylor.

Assistant Trainer: Paul Sedgwick

Jockey (flat): Danny Tudhope. **Apprentice:** Jamie Kyne, Paul Pickard. **Amateur:** Miss. D. Allman.

97   MR R. M. CARSON, Lambourn
Postal: **58 Child Street, Lambourn, Hungerford, Berkshire, RG17 8NZ**
Contacts: **PHONE (01488) 72080 MOBILE (07873) 489100**

1 **HAIL THE KING (USA)**, 8, gr g Allied Forces (USA)—Hail Kris (USA) **Mrs P. Carson**

THREE-YEAR-OLDS

2 Ch g King Charlemagne (USA)—Bollicina (USA) **R. M. Carson**

Assistant Trainer: Mrs P Carson

Conditional: J. Kington, R. Lucey-Butler.

98   MR B. I. CASE, Banbury
Postal: **Wardington Gate Farm, Edgcote, Banbury, Oxfordshire, OX17 1AG**
Contacts: **PHONE (01295) 750959 FAX (01295) 758840 MOBILE (07808) 061223**
E-MAIL info@bencaseracing.com WEBSITE www.bencaseracing.com

1 **ANOTHER STORM**, 6, gr m Shambo—Stormswift **Case Racing Partnership**
2 **AQUALUNG (FR)**, 4, b g Port Lyautey (FR)—Verosa (FR)
3 4, B g Darnay—Avro Avian
4 **BEST DEAL**, 7, gr g Presenting—Miss Drury **Case Racing Partnership**
5 **BLUE REBEL (IRE)**, 6, gr g Ala Hounak—Country Melody (IRE) **E Keir D Gee A Case & Nicholson Family**
6 **BUSY BAY**, 6, b m Busy Flight—Killala Bay (IRE) **Case Racing Partnership**
7 **DANCE ISLAND (IRE)**, 5, b g Turtle Island (IRE)—Inse Na Rince (IRE) **Lady Jane Grosvenor**
8 **DEEP REFLECTION**, 8, b g Cloudings (IRE)—Tudor Thyne (IRE) **Mr J. J. M. Bailey**
9 **EARN A BUCK**, 7, b m Young Ern—Buck Comtess (USA) **Denise & Harold Winton**
10 **EDGEFOUR (IRE)**, 4, b f King's Best (USA)—Highshaan **D. C. R. Allen**
11 **ESTRICA (IRE)**, 5, b m Exit To Nowhere (USA)—Mrs Marples (IRE) **D. C. R. Allen**
12 **GOBEJOLLY**, 5, b m Exit To Nowhere (USA)—Ollejess **D. C. R. Allen**
13 **GRAND SYMPHONY**, 4, ch f Zamindar—Gitane (USA) **Mrs S. Case**
14 **HARRY COLLINS**, 10, ch g Sir Harry Lewis (USA)—Run Fast For Gold **Case Racing Partnership**
15 **RING BACK (IRE)**, 7, ch m Bob Back (USA)—Ardrom **D. C. R. Allen**
16 **SUPREME TEAM (IRE)**, 5, b g Supreme Leader—La Gazelle (IRE) **Mr Henry Robinson & Mrs Carol Kelly**
17 **SWEET MATRIARCH**, 6, b m Silver Patriarch (IRE)—Pudding **Paul Rackham**

MR B. I. CASE—continued

18 **THAT'S AN HONOUR (IRE)**, 6, b g City Honours (USA)—Native Brooke (IRE) **The Polk Partnership**
19 **TRUE MARINER (FR)**, 8, b g True Brave (USA)—Miss Above (FR) **D. C. R. Allen**

THREE-YEAR-OLDS

20 **CHIEF ERIC**, gr c Slickly (FR)—Last Romance (IRE) **Itchen Valley Stud**
21 **HANS CRESCENT (FR)**, b c Dansili—Embroider (IRE) **Itchen Valley Stud**
22 **HANSINGER (IRE)**, b g Namid—Whistfilly **Lovely Bubbly Racing**
23 **LEANONLEO (IRE)**, b g Traditionally (USA)—Alinga (IRE)
24 **SUMMER AFFAIR (IRE)**, b g Alhaarth (IRE)—Late Summer (USA)

TWO-YEAR-OLDS

25 B f 31/3 Royal Applause—Boojum (Mujtahid (USA)) (22000) **Itchen Valley Stud**
26 B f 21/4 Lomitas—Chine (Inchinor) (2000)
27 B f 6/5 Old Vic—Dee-One-O-One (Slip Anchor) (27026)
28 B c 27/4 Kalanisi (IRE)—Sadika (IRE) (Bahhare (USA)) (30000) **Itchen Valley Stud**
29 Ch c 20/3 Daggers Drawn (USA)—Sliding (Formidable (USA)) (34000) **Itchen Valley Stud**
30 **WATCH THE MASTER**, b g 22/3 Passing Glance—Fine Arts (Cadeaux Genereux) (4000) **N. Hutley**

Other Owners: D. Annetts, Mr & Mrs D. Baines, J. Balls, Mrs A. D. Bourne, Mrs S. Case, Mrs Robert Case, A. Case, A. Charlton, Mr & Mrs T. Cox, S. Crook, A. Drew, Lord R. Fellowes, Mr H. D. Gee, R. Griffiths, R. Hagen, Mr & Mrs P. Hambly, S. Harrison, D. Holman, Mrs M. Howlett, P. Jackson, A. Jones, Mrs E. Keir, Mrs C. Kelly, Mr A. P. Liggins, P. Lush, Lady S. McCorquodale, Mr Grahame Nicholson, Mr & Mrs C. Nixey, J. Nowell-Smith, Dr M. J. O'Brien, D. Payne, K. Perrem, Mr James Polk, Mr John Polk, S. Powell, Mr H. Robinson, Mr & Mrs G. Rodenhurst, Mr R. Rosenberg, J. Sutton, M. Turner, D. A. Wales, Mr & Mrs J. Way, G. Way, P. Williams, Mr Harold Winton, Mrs D. A. Winton.

Assistant Trainer: Jason Newbold

99

MR H. R. A. CECIL, Newmarket
Postal: **Warren Place, Newmarket, Suffolk, CB8 8QQ**
Contacts: **OFFICE (01638) 662192 FAX (01638) 669005**

1 **AJAAN**, 4, br c Machiavellian (USA)—Alakananda **Exors of the Late S. S. Niarchos**
2 **MANY VOLUMES (USA)**, 4, b c Chester House (USA)—Reams of Verse (USA) **K. Abdulla**
3 **MULTIDIMENSIONAL (IRE)**, 5, b h Danehill (USA)—Sacred Song **Exors of the Late S. S. Niarchos**
4 **PASSAGE OF TIME**, 4, bl f Dansili—Clepsydra **K. Abdulla**
5 **PHOENIX TOWER (USA)**, 4, b c Chester House (USA)—Bionic **K. Abdulla**
6 **SOUND OF NATURE (USA)**, 5, b h Chester House (USA)—Yashmak (USA) **K. Abdulla**
7 **TEMPELSTERN (GER)**, 4, gr c Sternkoenig (IRE)—Temple Esprit **Ennismore Racing I**
8 **TRANQUIL TIGER**, 4, ch c Selkirk (USA)—Serene View (USA) **K. Abdulla**
9 **WALKING TALKING**, 4, b c Rainbow Quest (USA)—Wooden Doll (USA) **K. Abdulla**
10 **WRAITH**, 4, b c Maria's Mon (USA)—Really Polish (USA) **Mr J. I. T. Patel**

THREE-YEAR-OLDS

11 **ANCIENT LIGHTS**, b c High Chaparral (IRE)—Fascinating Hill (FR) **Ennismore Racing II**
12 **ANGEL FOREVER (USA)**, b f Swain (IRE)—Karmifira (FR) **Malih L. Al Basti**
13 **ARABIAN ART (USA)**, br f E Dubai (USA)—Slamya (USA) **Malih L. Al Basti**
14 **AROMATHERAPY**, b f Oasis Dream—Fragrant View (USA) **K. Abdulla**
15 **ATARAXY**, ch f Zamindar (USA)—Bahamian **K. Abdulla**
16 **BATTLE GROUP**, b c Beat Hollow—Cantanta **K. Abdulla**
17 **BORN TOBOUGGIE (GER)**, b f Tobougg (IRE)—Braissim **The Sticky Wicket Syndicate**
18 **BURN THE BREEZE (IRE)**, b f Beat Hollow—Madiyla **Bloomsbury Stud**
19 **CATCHING THE LIGHT (USA)**, b br f Fantastic Light (USA)—Cat Ali (USA) **Lois Hunt & Andrew Sebire**
20 **CHIQUINKIRA (IRE)**, b f Bahri (USA)—Robalana (USA) **F. Hinojosa**
21 **CRYSTANY (IRE)**, b f Green Desert (USA)—Crystal Music (USA) **Ballygallon Stud Limited**
22 **DEA CAELESTIS (FR)**, b f Dream Well (FR)—Gwydion (USA) **Exors of the Late S. S. Niarchos**
23 **DIAMOND YAS (IRE)**, b f Mull of Kintyre (USA)—Balgren (IRE) **Diamond Racing**
24 **EDINBOROUGH (FR)**, b c Helissio (FR)—Eiszeit (GER) **Ammerland Verwaltung GmbH & Co.KG**
25 **ETHEREAL FLAME**, b f Red Ransom (USA)—Running Flame (IND) **Ethereal Racing**
26 **I'M SENSATIONAL**, b f Selkirk (USA)—Ego **Exors of the Late S. S. Niarchos**
27 **JACK DAWKINS (USA)**, b c Fantastic Light (USA)—Do The Mambo (USA) **Mark & Sue Harniman**
28 **JUDPOT (USA)**, ch c A P Indy (USA)—Miesque (USA) **Exors of the Late S. S. Niarchos**
29 **KANDAHAR RUN**, gr c Rock of Gibraltar (IRE)—Kenmist **Ammerland Verwaltung GmbH & Co.KG**
30 **KIMBOLTON**, b f Helissio (FR)—Kyle Rhea **Ennismore Racing II**

MR H. R. A. CECIL—continued

31 **KRITZIA**, gr f Daylami (IRE)—Katrina (IRE) **Lordship Stud**
32 **LADY DARAYNA**, b f Polish Precedent (USA)—Darayna (IRE) **Diamond Racing**
33 **LEMONESSE (USA)**, b f Lemon Drop Kid (USA)—Policy Setter (USA) **Mr J. Singh**
34 B c Swain (IRE)—Magnificent Star (USA) **Malih L. Al Basti**
35 **MARIE LOUISE**, b f Helissio (FR)—Self Esteem **Pierre Van Belle**
36 **MISS OLIVIA**, ch f Dr Fong (USA)—Beleaguer **Diamond Racing**
37 **MONTBRETIA**, b f Montjeu (IRE)—Bayswater **K. Abdulla**
38 **MONTREAL (GER)**, b f Boreal (GER)—Margie's Darling (USA) **Ammerland Verwaltung GmbH & Co.KG**
39 **PORTODORA (USA)**, b f Kingmambo (USA)—High Walden (USA) **K. Abdulla**
40 **RATTAN**, ch c Royal Anthem (USA)—Rouwaki (USA) **K. Abdulla**
41 **REINE DE VIOLETTE**, b f Olden Times—Aissa **Diamond Racing**
42 **SEVENNA (FR)**, b f Galileo (IRE)—Silvassa (IRE) **Ammerland Verwaltung GmbH & Co.KG**
43 **SEVENTH CAVALRY (IRE)**, gr c No Excuse Needed—Mixwayda (FR) **W. H. Ponsonby**
44 **SHECHER PARA**, b f Clodovil (IRE)—Shaken And Stirred **Mr J. McKeon**
45 **SINGLE VOTE**, br f Pivotal—Singleton **K. Abdulla**
46 **SPRING SEASON**, b f Dansili—Midsummer **K. Abdulla**
47 **STEROPE (FR)**, b f Hernando (FR)—Sacred Song (USA) **Exors of the Late S. S. Niarchos**
48 **TIMETABLE**, b c Observatory (USA)—Clepsydra **K. Abdulla**
49 **TOMINTOUL FLYER**, br c Dr Fong (USA)—Miller's Melody **Angus Dundee Distillers Plc**
50 **TWICE OVER**, b c Observatory (USA)—Double Crossed **K. Abdulla**
51 **UNLEASHED (IRE)**, br c Storming Home—Uriah (GER) **Ennismore Racing II**
52 **UNNEFER (IRE)**, b c Danehill Dancer (IRE)—Mimalia (USA) **Exors of the Late S. S. Niarchos**
53 **UPSTART (IRE)**, b g Vettori (IRE)—Foxglove **Dr C. M. H. Wills**
54 **WINGED LEGACY (USA)**, ch c Diesis—Fairy Glade (USA) **K. Abdulla**
55 **WINTER BLOOM (USA)**, b f Aptitude (USA)—Bionic **K. Abdulla**
56 **YEOMANRY**, b g High Chaparral (IRE)—Charming Life (NZ) **Plantation Stud**

TWO-YEAR-OLDS

57 **ALPHA TAURI (USA)**, b c 20/2 Aldebaran (USA)—
Seven Moons (JPN) (Sunday Silence (USA)) **Exors of the Late S. S. Niarchos**
58 B f 19/3 Oasis Dream—Arabesque (Zafonic (USA)) **K. Abdulla**
59 **AT A GREAT RATE (USA)**, b f 5/4 Arch—Glia (A P Indy (USA)) **Exors of the Late S. S. Niarchos**
60 B f 11/3 Halling (USA)—Blue Melody (USA) (Dayjur (USA)) (15000) **The Sticky Wicket Syndicate II**
61 Ch c 6/4 Mr Greeley (USA)—
Blush Damask (USA) (Green Dancer (USA)) **Ammerland Verwaltung GmbH & Co.KG**
62 **BRIBERY (IRE)**, b f 28/4 Bahri (USA)—Foxglove (Hernando (FR)) **Dr C. M. H. Wills**
63 Ch f 18/4 Peintre Celebre (USA)—Brief Escapade (IRE) (Brief Truce (USA)) **Ballygallon Stud Ltd**
64 B c 28/1 Dansili—Clepsydra (Sadler's Wells (USA)) **K. Abdulla**
65 **CONSCIOUSNESS**, ch f 4/3 Pivotal—Sacred Song (USA) (Diesis) **Exors of the Late S. S. Niarchos**
66 B br c 21/4 Storm Cat (USA)—Coup de Genie (USA) (Mr Prospector (USA)) **Exors of the Late S. S. Niarchos**
67 B c 14/3 Montjeu (IRE)—Crystal Gaze (IRE) (Rainbow Quest (USA)) **Ballygallon Stud Ltd**
68 B c 25/1 Xaar—Darabela (IRE) (Desert King (IRE)) (45045) **Ammerland Verwaltung GmbH & Co.KG**
69 **DE LASZLO**, b c 3/4 Rainbow Quest (USA)—Hyde Hall (Barathea (IRE)) **Plantation Stud**
70 **DEMOCRATIC VIEW (IRE)**, b c 26/4 Elnadim (USA)—Radiance (IRE) (Thatching) (9652) **Diamond Racing**
71 B f 15/4 Oasis Dream—Discreet Brief (IRE) (Darshaan) (95000) **Mr G. Schoeningh**
72 B c 5/2 Dansili—Emplane (IRE) (Irish River (FR)) **K. Abdulla**
73 B f 12/4 Cadeaux Genereux—Garmoucheh (USA) (Silver Hawk (USA)) **Malih L. Al Basti**
74 B f 16/2 Sadler's Wells (USA)—Half Glance (Danehill (USA)) **K. Abdulla**
75 B f 10/2 Empire Maker (USA)—Heat Haze (Green Desert (USA)) **K. Abdulla**
76 B c 24/3 Sadler's Wells (USA)—High Praise (USA) (Quest For Fame) **K. Abdulla**
77 **HISARONU (IRE)**, b f 22/4 Stravinsky (USA)—
Journey of Hope (Slew O' Gold (USA)) (10295) **Diamond Racing**
78 B f 26/1 Elusive Quality (USA)—Honest Lady (USA) (Seattle Slew (USA)) **K. Abdulla**
79 **HYADES (IRE)**, b c br c 19/5 Aldebaran (USA)—Lingerie (Shirley Heights) **Exors of the Late S. S. Niarchos**
80 B c 16/3 Empire Maker (USA)—Imroz (USA) (Nureyev (USA)) **K. Abdulla**
81 B f 7/2 Grand Slam (USA)—Katherine Seymour (Green Desert (USA)) (68027) **Mark & Sue Harniman**
82 **KINGS TROOP**, ch c 5/4 Bertolini (USA)—Glorious Colours (Spectrum (IRE)) (25000) **W. H. Ponsonby**
83 **LANGEN VORAUS (GER)**, b f 23/2 Tiger Hill (IRE)—
Luttje Lage (GER) (Acatenango (GER)) (21879) **Ennismore Racing III**
84 Gr f 8/2 Dansili—Lixian (Linamix (FR)) (26000) **Angus Dundee Distillers Plc**
85 B c 19/3 Cape Cross (IRE)—Love Divine (Diesis) **Lordship Stud**
86 B f 13/3 Royal Applause—Maid of Camelot (Caerleon (USA)) (82000) **De La Warr Racing**
87 **MAYOLYNN (USA)**, ch f 13/3 Johannesburg (USA)—Civilynn (USA) (Lost Code (USA)) (121477) **B. Scott**
88 B f 15/2 Loup Solitaire (USA)—Melody Blue (FR) (Poliglote) **Ammerland Verwaltung GmbH & Co.KG**
89 B f 21/3 Oasis Dream—Midsummer (Kingmambo (USA)) **K. Abdulla**

MR H. R. A. CECIL—continued

90 Ch f 15/4 Horse Chestnut (SAF)—Mien (USA) (Nureyev (USA)) (27696) **Malih L. Al Basti**
91 **QUIQUILLO (USA)**, ch f 18/5 Cape Canaveral (USA)—Only Seventeen (USA) (Exploit (USA)) **Diamond Racing**
92 B br f 22/4 Storm Cat (USA)—Rafina (USA) (Mr Prospector (USA)) **Tabor / Magnier / Niarchos**
93 **RAMORA (USA)**, br f 28/1 Monsun (GER)—Madame Cerito (USA) (Diesis) **Plantation Stud**
94 B br f 5/2 Dynaformer (USA)—
　　　　　　　　　　　Randaroo (USA) (Gold Case (USA)) (167310) **Ammerland Verwaltung GmbH & Co.KG**
95 B c 10/5 Oasis Dream—River Fantasy (USA) (Irish River (FR)) (40000) **R. Brown & Partners**
96 Ch c 1/3 Mizzen Mast (USA)—Rouwaki (USA) (Miswaki (USA)) **K. Abdulla**
97 B f 27/4 Giant's Causeway (USA)—Seattle Tac (USA) (Seattle Slew (USA)) (194363) **F. Nass**
98 B c 10/3 Oasis Dream—Set Fair (USA) (Alleged (USA)) **K. Abdulla**
99 B f 11/3 Bernstein (USA)—Shoolha (IRE) (Bluebird (USA)) (180180) **Ammerland Verwaltung GmbH & Co.KG**
100 B c 6/2 Oasis Dream—Singed (Zamindar (USA)) (55000) **J. R. May**
101 Gr f 27/3 Spartacus (IRE)—Siva (FR) (Bellypha) (3860) **Diamond Racing**
102 Ch f 17/1 Dalakhani (IRE)—Slap Shot (IRE) (Lycius (USA)) (150000) **Ammerland Verwaltung GmbH & Co.KG**
103 Ch c 9/4 Lomitas—Special (Polar Falcon (USA)) (20000) **Ennismore Racing III**
104 **UNWAVERING (IRE)**, b c 9/5 Refuse To Bend (IRE)—Archipova (IRE) (Ela-Mana-Mou) **Mr J. McKeon**
105 B f 19/2 Sadler's Wells (USA)—Wemyss Bight (Dancing Brave (USA)) **K. Abdulla**
106 B c 7/2 Bahri (USA)—Woodren (USA) (Woodman (USA)) (35000) **G. Stephenson**
107 **YOUNG STAR GAZER**, ch c 8/5 Observatory (USA)—Ash Glade (Nashwan (USA)) (24000) **Pkd Partnership**
108 ZA ZA, br f 17/4 Barathea (IRE)—Madiya (Darshaan) **Bloomsbury Stud**

Other Owners: M. Harniman, Mrs S. Harniman, T. F. Harris, Mrs E. A. Harris, Henry Cecil & Company Ltd, Mrs L. J. Hunt, Mr K. R. Ives, Ms P. A. Mallalieu, Mr P. B. Moorhead, D. F. O'Rourke, Mrs P. K. O'Rourke, S. Padmanabhan, Mr A. F. Sebire, Mr C. Silverwood, Mrs L. Suresh.

Assistant Trainer: Michael Marshall

Jockey (flat): Ted Durcan, T. Queally, J. Quinn.

---

100 **MR S. G. CHADWICK, Hayton**
Postal: Eskrigg, Hayton, Aspatria, Carlisle, Cumbria, CA7 2PD
Contacts: **PHONE (01697) 321226 MOBILE (07803) 172720**

1 **GIANT'S ROCK (IRE)**, 6, ch g Giant's Causeway (USA)—En Garde (USA) **S. G. Chadwick**
2 **SCURRY DANCER (FR)**, 12, b g Snurge—Fijar Dance (FR) **S. G. Chadwick**

Assistant Trainer: Claire Chadwick

---

101 **MR A. J. CHAMBERLAIN, Swindon**
Postal: North End Farm, Ashton Keynes, Swindon, Wiltshire, SN6 6QR
Contacts: **PHONE (01285) 861347 MOBILE (07941) 829976**
E-MAIL adrianajc@aol.com

1 **ALMAHAZA (IRE)**, 4, b c Alzao (USA)—Morna's Moment (USA) **G. B. Heffaran**
2 **BLAKESHALL HOPE**, 6, ch g Piccolo—Elite Hope (USA) **P. Tarran**
3 **BODGETANDSCARPER**, 4, b g Wizard King—Acorn Catcher **C. Chell**
4 **COASTAL BREEZE**, 5, b g Fasliyev—Classic Design **Exors of the Late Mrs A. G. Sims**
5 **FUN THAI**, 4, ch f Fraam—Thailand **G. B. Heffaran**
6 **IASKOFYOU (IRE)**, 11, br g Jolly Jake (NZ)—Deep Bart **The Runaway Boys**
7 **LUCYS PET**, 7, ch m Oscar Schindler (IRE)—Millmount (IRE) **I. Hutchins**
8 **MR LOIRE**, 4, b g Bertolini (USA)—Miss Sancerre **Miss J. M. Foran**
9 **SPEAGLE (IRE)**, 6, ch g Desert Sun—Pohutakawa (FR) **C. Chell**
10 **STORMBURST (IRE)**, 4, b f Mujadil (USA)—Isca
11 **THE MAGI (IRE)**, 8, b g Rashar (USA)—Superlee (IRE) **A. J. Chamberlain**

THREE-YEAR-OLDS

12 **BLAKESHALL DIAMOND**, gr f Piccolo—Hi Hoh (IRE) **M. P. Bishop**

Other Owners: Mr P. Fiocca, P. A. Green.

Assistant Trainer: M. Bishop

Amateur: Mr D. Alers-Hankey.

102 MR P. R. CHAMINGS, Basingstoke

Postal: **Inhurst Farm Stables, Baughurst, Tadley, Hampshire, RG26 5JS**
Contacts: **PHONE (01189) 814494 FAX (01189) 820454 MOBILE (07831) 360970**
E-MAIL **chamingsracing@talk21.com**

1 5, B g College Chapel—Among Women **R. V. Shaw**
2 BINANTI, 8, b g Bin Ajwaad (IRE)—Princess Rosananti (IRE) **Mrs J. E. L. Wright**
3 FOXHAVEN, 6, ch h Unfuwain (USA)—Dancing Mirage (IRE) **Mrs A. M. Jenkins**
4 GANACHE (IRE), 6, ch g Halling (USA)—Granted (FR) **Inhurst Farm Stables Partnership**
5 HAATMEY, 6, b g Josr Algarhoud (IRE)—Raneen Alwatar **Global Racing**
6 JAMADIEL (IRE), 7, ch g Kadastrof (FR)—Petal Dust (IRE) **R. V. Shaw**
7 LOURDES (IRE), 5, b m Spectrum (IRE)—Loure (USA) **R. V. Shaw**
8 MATUZA (IRE), 5, ch h Cadeaux Genereux—Aoife (IRE) **Act Surprised Partnership**
9 MIDAS WAY, 8, ch g Halling (USA)—Arietta's Way (IRE) **Mrs A. J. Chandris**
10 MILLFIELD (IRE), 5, br g Elnadim (USA)—Eschasse (USA) **Patrick Chamings Sprint Club**
11 OSIRIS WAY, 6, ch g Indian Ridge—Heady **Mrs A. J. Chandris**
12 PACTOLUS WAY, 5, b g Docksider (USA)—Arietta's Way (IRE) **Mrs A. J. Chandris**
13 POWER AGAIN (GER), 7, b m Dashing Blade—Pik Konigin (GER) **Inhurst Farm Stables Partnership**
14 QUAGLINO WAY (GR), 4, b g Mark of Esteem (IRE)—Pringipessa's Way **Mrs A. J. Chandris**
15 REGAL CURTSY, 4, b f Royal Applause—Giant Nipper **Mrs A. M. Jenkins**
16 RICKETY BRIDGE (IRE), 5, ch g Elnadim (USA)—Kriva **Mrs A. M. Jenkins**
17 SURPRISE ACT, 4, gr g Act One—Surprise Surprise **Act Surprised Partnership**
18 WOODCOTE (IRE), 6, b g Monashee Mountain—Tootle **Patrick Chamings Sprint Club**
19 WOODCOTE PLACE, 5, b g Lujain (USA)—Giant Nipper **Edward David Kessly**
20 WRIGHTY ALMIGHTY (IRE), 6, b g Danehill Dancer (IRE)—
   Persian Empress (IRE) **The Boccy Hall Evans Tyrrell Partnership**

THREE-YEAR-OLDS

21 BY WORD OF MOUTH, b g Efisio—Thrasher **Act Surprised Partnership**
22 GIANT ACT, gr g Act One—Giant Nipper **Mrs A. M. Jenkins**
23 B c Zaha (CAN)—Glensara **Basingstoke Commercials**
24 B g Piccolo—Joyful Illusion **Mrs A. M. Jenkins**
25 B c Sakhee (USA)—Leisurely Way **Mrs A. J. Chandris**
26 MISS POPPY, b f Averti (IRE)—Pretty Poppy **The Foxford House Partnership**
27 NYUMBA (IRE), b f High Chaparral (IRE)—Barbizou (FR) **Ballygallon Stud**
28 RAINBOW WAY, b f High Chaparral (IRE)—Dance Lively (USA) **Mrs A. J. Chandris**
29 REGULUS WAY (GR), ch c Harmonic Way—Exotic Way **Mrs A. J. Chandris**
30 ROMIOSINI WAY (GR), gr f Harmonic Way—Omorfita **Mrs A. J. Chandris**
31 RONDEAU (GR), ch g Harmonic Way—Areti (GR) **Mrs A. M. Jenkins**
32 UNCLE FRED, b c Royal Applause—Karla June **Mrs A. M. Jenkins & Mr M. A. Kirby**
33 ZANTIC, ch g Zaha (CAN)—Suta (GER) **Mrs A. M. Jenkins**

TWO-YEAR-OLDS

34 Ch f 20/5 Harmonic Way—Alika's Dance (USA) (Green Dancer (USA)) **Mrs A. J. Chandris**
35 B f 18/2 Royal Applause—Arietta's Way (IRE) (Darshaan) **Mrs A. J. Chandris**
36 Br c 14/2 Diktat—Away To Me (Exit To Nowhere (USA))
37 B f 12/3 Barathea (IRE)—Britannia House (USA) (Diesis) **Mrs A. J. Chandris**
38 Ch c 2/4 Kyllachy—Dance For Fun (Anabaa (USA)) (50000) **Mrs A. M. Jenkins**
39 EAGER TO BOW (IRE), b c 2/4 Acclamation—Tullawadgee (IRE) (Sinndar (IRE)) (46000) **Mrs J. E. L. Wright**
40 B f 14/2 Harmonic Way—Flourishing Way (Sadler's Wells (USA)) (10000) **Mrs A. J. Chandris**
41 B c 16/4 Royal Applause—Heady (Rousillon (USA)) (14000) **Mrs A. J. Chandris**
42 B f 30/3 Guy Butters (GR)—Pringipessa's Way (Machiavellian (USA)) (3809) **Mrs A. J. Chandris**
43 B c 8/4 Bachelor Duke (USA)—Senseansensibility (USA) (Capote (USA)) **Mrs A. J. Chandris**
44 B c 11/5 Beat Hollow—Whitgift Rose (Polar Falcon (USA)) (10000)

Other Owners: Mr D. T. Allen, Mr P. R. Chamings, Mr Tony Colangelo, Dulverton Equine, Mr Bill Evans, Mr Steve Hall, S. J. Howard, Mr F. T. Lee, Mrs R. Lyon, Mr A. P. McCarthy, Miss K. Mundy, A. J. De V. Patrick, Mrs J. V. Patrick, Mr K. W. Tyrrell.

Assistant Trainer: Phillippa Chamings

103 MR N. T. CHANCE, Upper Lambourn

Postal: **Berkeley House Stables, Upper Lambourn, Hungerford, Berkshire, RG17 8QP**
Contacts: **OFFICE (01488) 73436 FAX (01488) 72296 MOBILE (07785) 300168**
E-MAIL **info@noelchanceracing.com** WEBSITE **www.noelchanceracing.com**

1 AUX LE BAHNN (IRE), 7, b g Beneficial—Helvick Lass (IRE) **A. D. Weller**
2 BENNETT, 8, br g Grand Plaisir (IRE)—Ozone River (IRE) **A. D. Weller**

MR N. T. CHANCE—continued

3 **COMMANDER KEV (IRE)**, 7, b g Needle Gun (IRE)—Grange Park (IRE) **Mrs N. Kelly**
4 **COULD BE ALRIGHT (IRE)**, 9, b g Witness Box (USA)—Some Gossip **Simpson & Castledine & Ian Murray**
5 **DERMATOLOGISTE**, 5, b m Kayf Tara—Poor Skin (IRE) **R. N. Frosell**
6 **DIVINE GIFT**, 7, b g Groom Dancer (USA)—Child's Play (USA) **J.Duddy,B.McDonald,A.Heeney,M.McMenamin**
7 **FIRST FEERIE (FR)**, 5, br g Turgeon (USA)—Funny Feerie (FR) **Mr N. M. Watts & Mr N. P. Horsfall**
8 **GOOD LINE (IRE)**, 7, b g Saddlers' Hall (IRE)—Chattering **J. P. McManus**
9 **GOSCAR ROCK (IRE)**, 7, b g Synefos (USA)—Almost Regal (IRE) **P. A. Bancroft**
10 **INISHMOR (IRE)**, 4, gr g Great Palm (USA)—Kampa Island (IRE) **I. R. Murray**
11 **JARDIN DE VIENNE (FR)**, 6, gr g Highest Honor (FR)—Vaguely Money (USA) **Premier Chance Racing**
12 **JETLAG (FR)**, 6, b g Sleeping Car (FR)—Valombrage (FR) **Mrs M. C. Sweeney**
13 **KIMI (IRE)**, 7, b g Presenting—Hatherley **Mrs M. C. Sweeney**
14 **LIT ET MIXE (FR)**, 5, gr g Linamix (FR)—Lit (IRE) **I. R. Murray**
15 **LITTLE BIT OF HUSH (IRE)**, 8, b g Oscar (IRE)—Florenanti **J. P. McManus**
16 **LORD OF BEAUTY (FR)**, 8, ch g Medaaly—Arctic Beauty (USA) **Warren, Upton & Chenkin & Townson**
17 **LORIKEET (IRE)**, 9, b g Rainbow Quest (USA)—Destiny Dance (USA) **The Tribesmen Syndicate**
18 **MENDO**, 8, b g Alderbrook—Ina's Farewell **Mrs M. C. Sweeney**
19 **MINTIVERDI**, 4, br f Kayf Tara—Just Jodi (IRE) **Mrs R. F. Greener**
20 **MISREPRESENTED (IRE)**, 5, b m Presenting—Redstone Lady (IRE) **Warren Upton & Chenkin**
21 **MONCADA WAY (IRE)**, 7, b g Scribano—Ina Moilltear (IRE) **M. F. Browne**
22 **MONGOOSE ALERT (IRE)**, 6, b g Oscar (IRE)—Before (IRE) **Drink Up**
23 4, B f Silver Patriarch (IRE)—Mothers Help **Craughwell & Fairlie**
24 **NIL BLEU (USA)**, 4, b g Swain (USA)—Nany's Affair (USA) **Noel Chance Racing Club**
25 **OBELIX DE LONGECHAUX (FR)**, 6, ch g Bulington (FR)—Psyche II (FR) **Mrs V. Griffiths**
26 **OFFEMONT (FR)**, 7, b br g Bulington (FR)—La Guyonniere (FR) **Miss M. Talbot**
27 **OPEN SEASON (IRE)**, 8, b g Pierre—Poor Man's Rose (IRE) **M. F. Browne**
28 **OPONCE (FR)**, 6, b g Varxi (FR)—Fraxinelle (FR) **Mrs W. Morrell & Mr R. Frossell**
29 **PALM ISLAND (FR)**, 7, b g Priolo (USA)—L'orpheline (FR) **Premier Chance & Ian Preston-Jones**
30 **PASSENGER OMAR (IRE)**, 10, b g Safety Catch (USA)—Princess Douglas **Mrs V. Griffiths**
31 **RED RUFFLES (IRE)**, 9, b g Anshan—Rosie Ruffles (IRE) **T. F. C. Partnership**
32 **RIVER CITY (IRE)**, 11, b g Norwich—Shuil Na Lee (IRE) **Mrs S. Rowley-Williams**
33 **SAINT ERIC (FR)**, 6, b g Lesotho (USA)—Fearnan **Mr I. Preston-Jones**
34 **SIGNS OF LOVE (IRE)**, 5, b g Poliglote—Severina **T. G. Warren**
35 **SINGLE PLAYER (IRE)**, 8, br g Accordion—Alone Party (IRE) **C. C. Shand Kydd**
36 **SLEW CHARM (FR)**, 6, b g Marathon (USA)—Slew Bay (USA) **Premier Chance Racing**
37 **TAKEITEASYJACK (IRE)**, 5, ch g Beneficial—Statoqueen (IRE) **A. D. Weller**
38 **TARAS BULBA (IRE)**, 7, br g Accordion—Mrs Keppel **W. T. Walsh**
39 **TARONGO (FR)**, 10, b g Tel Quel (FR)—Rainbow Rainbow **Mrs L. C. Taylor**
40 **TRUE STAR (IRE)**, 8, ch g Fourstars Allstar (USA)—Scouts Honour (IRE) **T. F. C. Partnership**
41 **TURBULANCE (IRE)**, 6, gr g Snurge—Full Deck (IRE) **A. D. Weller**

THREE-YEAR-OLDS

42 **MISTER NEW YORK (USA)**, b c Forest Wildcat (USA)—Shebane (USA) **Mrs M. Chance**

Other Owners: Mrs Hester Bancroft, Mr Patrick Castledine, Mrs M. Chance, Mr D. Chenkin, Mr J. P. Craughwell, Mr R. Dore, J. Duddy, Mr R. J. Fairlie, Mr K. H. Foster, Mr Robert Frosell, Mr A. Heeney, Mr Bill Hinge, Mr F. Holian, Mr P. Holian, Mr N. P. Horsfall, B. T. McDonald, Mr Ian Preston-Jones, Mr John Searchfield, Mr John Simpson, Mrs L. C. Taylor, Mr K. P. Trowbridge, Mr J. H. P. Upton, Mr T. G. Warren, Mr N. M. Watts.

Assistant Trainer: Eimear Chance

Jockey (flat): Jose De Souza. **Jockey (NH):** W. Kennedy. **Conditional:** J. Jenkinson.

---

104 **MR M. C. CHAPMAN, Market Rasen**
Postal: Woodlands Racing Stables, Woodlands Lane, Willingham Road,
Market Rasen, Lincolnshire, LN8 3RE
Contacts: PHONE/FAX (01673) 843663 MOBILE (07971) 940087
E-MAIL michaelchapman@btconnect.com

1 **ART OF BEING (IRE)**, 4, ch g Selkirk (USA)—Gloriously Bright (USA) **Mrs S. M. Richards**
2 **CHAMPAGNE ROSSINI (IRE)**, 6, b g Rossini (USA)—Alpencrocus (IRE) **R. A. Gadd**
3 **DALRIATH**, 9, b m Fraam—Alsiba **Mrs S. M. Richards**

MR M. C. CHAPMAN—continued

4 EAU GOOD, 4, ch g Cadeaux Genereux—Girl's Best Friend **Sir Clement Freud**
5 FAVOURING (IRE), 6, ch g Fayruz—Peace Dividend (IRE) **Mrs A. J. Firth**
6 FEELING PECKISH (USA), 4, ch g Point Given (USA)—Sunday Bazaar (USA) **J. E. Reed**
7 FINNEGANS RAINBOW, 6, ch g Spectrum (IRE)—Fairy Story (IRE) **J. E. Reed**
8 GAVANELLO, 5, b br g Diktat—Possessive Artiste **Mrs M. M. Chapman**
9 GOVERNMENT (IRE), 7, b g Great Dane (IRE)—Hidden Agenda (FR) **J. F. Gordon-Hall**
10 MINIMUM FUSS (IRE), 4, b f Second Empire (IRE)—Jamis (IRE) **Mrs A. J. Firth**
11 NIGHT REVELLER, 5, b m Night Shift (USA)—Tir-An-Oir (IRE) **J. E. Reed**
12 ORPEN WIDE (IRE), 6, b g Orpen (USA)—Melba (IRE) **Andy & Bev Wright**
13 PEAK SEASONS (IRE), 5, ch g Raise A Grand (IRE)—Teresian Girl (IRE) **J. E. Reed**
14 PRESENT ORIENTED (USA), 7, ch g Southern Halo (USA)—Shy Beauty (CAN) **R. A. Gadd**
15 SIMPLIFIED, 5, b m Lend A Hand—Houston Heiress (USA) **Mr D. A. Wilson**
16 SOUTHERN BAZAAR (USA), 7, ch g Southern Halo (USA)—Sunday Bazaar (USA) **J. C. Greenway / A. Needham**
17 SWALLOW SENORA (IRE), 6, b m Entrepreneur—Sangra (IRE) **P. Tomlinson**
18 WATER PISTOL, 6, b g Double Trigger (IRE)—Water Flower **Mr D. A. Wilson**

THREE-YEAR-OLDS

19 GALLEY SLAVE (IRE), b g Spartacus (IRE)—Cimeterre (IRE) **K. D. Blanch**
20 HOWE'S JACK (IRE), b g Fasliyev (USA)—Berenique (IRE) **Mr Richard Howe & Mr Paul Elsegood**
21 REPRIEVED, ch g Bertolini (USA)—Crystal Seas **K. H. Benson**
22 SO SUBLIME, b g Bertolini (USA)—Petalite **F. A. Dickinson**

Other Owners: Mr P. A. Elsegood, J. C. Greenway, Mr R. W. Howe, A. R. Needham, A. N. Wright, Mrs B. J. Wright.

Jockey (NH): Lee Vickers. Conditional: David Cullinane. Amateur: Miss Sarah Eilbeck.

---

105 MR P. W. CHAPPLE-HYAM, Newmarket
Postal: St Gatien Stables, All Saints Road, Newmarket, Suffolk, CB8 8HJ
Contacts: PHONE (01638) 560827 FAX (01638) 561908
E-MAIL classichorse@chapple-hyam.fsworld.com WEBSITE www.peterchapplehyam.com

1 AL QASI (IRE), 5, b h Elnadim (USA)—Delisha **Z. A. Galadari**
2 DEEP RIVER BAY (USA), 4, b g Dixieland Band (USA)—For All You Do (USA)
3 IDUN, 4, b f Robellino (USA)—I Do **Miss K. Rausing**
4 MORNING FAREWELL, 4, br g Daylami (IRE)—Got To Go **Clark, Darke & Matthews**
5 SANDREY (IRE), 4, b g Noverre (USA)—Boudica (IRE) **Mr N. A. Abuljadayel**
6 STRIVING STORM (USA), 4, b br g Stormin Fever (USA)—
Sugars for Nanny (USA) **Abbey Horse Racing & Breeding Ltd**

THREE-YEAR-OLDS

7 AL BARIZ (USA), b br c Johannesburg (USA)—Circuit City (IRE) **F. Nass**
8 ALCIMEDES, b g Domedriver (IRE)—Allegra **Miss K. Rausing**
9 AMAAKIN (USA), b c Gone West (USA)—Pink Coral (USA) **Saleh Al Homaizi & Imad Al Sagar**
10 ANGEL ROCK (IRE), b c Rock of Gibraltar (USA)—Nomothetis (USA) **Tenuta Dorna Di Montaltuzzo SRL**
11 ART PRIZE (IRE), b g Cadeaux Genereux—Future Flight **M. R. Green**
12 ART TREND (IRE), b c Hawk Wing (USA)—Skiphall **M. R. Green**
13 ART VALUE, ch c Barathea (USA)—Empty Purse **M. R. Green**
14 AZEER (USA), ch c Giant's Causeway (USA)—Touch of Love (USA) **F. Nass**
15 BALLISODARE, b c Elusive Quality (USA)—River Jig (USA) **David & Paul Hearson**
16 BOUGUEREAU, b c Alhaarth (IRE)—Blessed Honour **A. W. Black**
17 CAPE AMBER (IRE), b f Cape Cross (IRE)—Maramba **Five Horses Ltd**
18 DECLARATION OF WAR (IRE), b c Okawango (USA)—Date Mate (USA) **Mrs V. E. Mercer**
19 EMPOWERED (IRE), b c Fasliyev (USA)—Funsie (FR) **Cheveley Park Stud Limited**
20 ETTA PLACE, b f Hawk Wing (USA)—Wavy Up (IRE) **Charnwoodboy & Starpointe Ltd**
21 FAT BOY (IRE), ch c Choisir (AUS)—Gold Shift (USA) **Mr M. Sines**
22 FIRESIDE, b c Dr Fong (USA)—Al Hasnaa **Highclere Thoroughbred Racing (VCI)**
23 GENERAL BLUCHER (IRE), br g Marju (IRE)—Restiv Star (FR) **P. W. Chapple-Hyam**
24 GLORIOUS GIFT (IRE), b c Elnadim (USA)—Queen of Arabia (IRE) **J. Abdullah**
25 JASER, ch c Alhaarth (IRE)—Waafiah **Z. A. Galadari**
26 MARIA DI SCOZIA, ch f Selkirk (USA)—Viva Maria **Miss K. Rausing**
27 MIGHT BE MAGIC, b g Fraam—Modelliste **J. Abdullah**
28 MOKSI, b c Olden Times—Yasalam (IRE) **Saleh Al Homaizi**

MR P. W. CHAPPLE-HYAM—continued

29 **ONCEAPONATIME (IRE)**, b g Invincible Spirit (IRE)—Lake Nyasa (IRE) **Mrs S. M. Roy**
30 **ORIENTALIST ART**, b c Green Desert (USA)—Pink Cristal **M. R. Green**
31 **PLATOCHE (IRE)**, b c Galileo (IRE)—Political Parody (USA)
32 **SEMPRE LIBERA (IRE)**, b f Statue of Liberty (USA)—Lucky Oakwood (USA) **Hintlesham Racing Ltd**
33 **SHALLAL**, b c Cape Cross (IRE)—First Waltz (FR) **Z. A. Galadari**
34 **SPIRIT OF SHARJAH (IRE)**, b c Invincible Spirit (IRE)—Rathbawn Realm **Mr A. Dee**
35 **STRAVELLA (IRE)**, b f Stravinsky (USA)—Princess Ellen **Five Horses Ltd**
36 **TASHEBA**, ch c Dubai Destination (USA)—Tatanka (USA) **T. W. Benson**
37 **TOO RISKY**, b f Fasliyev (USA)—Muwasim (USA) **M. Jaber**
38 **WESTERN ART (USA)**, b br c Hennessy (USA)—Madam West (USA) **Matthew Green & Ben Sangster**
39 B f Montjeu (IRE)—Whassup (FR) **Mr T. Hyde & Mrs P. Shanahan**
40 **WHISTLEDOWNWIND**, b c Danehill Dancer (USA) **Mrs S. M. Roy**
41 **WINKER WATSON**, ch c Piccolo—Bonica **The Comic Strip Heroes & Mrs JD Trotter**
42 **WORLD FAME (IRE)**, b f Spinning World (USA)—Embers of Fame (IRE) **Cheveley Park Stud Limited**
43 **YAHWUDHEE (FR)**, b c Zamindar (USA)—Lady Marshall (FR) **J. Abdullah**

TWO-YEAR-OLDS

44 **ABULHARITH**, b c 15/4 Medicean—Limuru (Salse) (USA) (38000) **Z. A. Galadari**
45 **ACADEMY OF WAR (USA)**, b br c 11/3 Royal Academy (USA)—
Lover Come Back (USA) (Dynaformer (USA)) (55000) **Mrs V. E. Mercer**
46 B f 23/2 Dansili—Achieve (Rainbow Quest (USA)) (300000) **Lady Bamford**
47 Ch c 7/5 Bahamian Bounty—Amaniy (USA) (Dayjur (USA)) (40000) **The Comic Strip Heroes**
48 **ATLANTIC BRAVE**, b c 17/1 Piccolo—Princess Anabaa (FR) (Anabaa (USA)) **J. Abdullah**
49 **AZTEC RULER**, b c 28/1 Galileo (IRE)—Guaranda (Acatenango (GER)) **Plantation Stud**
50 **BAARIQ**, b c 7/3 Royal Applause—Second of May (Lion Cavern (USA)) (56000) **Z. A. Galadari**
51 Ch f 11/4 Rock of Gibraltar (IRE)—Belsay (Belmez (USA)) (57914) **Miss A. Shaykhutdinova**
52 **BOMBINA**, b f 1/2 Lomitas—Firebelly (Nicolotte) **C. G. P. Wyatt**
53 **BURNING FLAME**, ch f 23/1 Pivotal—Red Flame (IRE) (Selkirk (USA)) **Cheveley Park Stud Limited**
54 B f 16/2 Smart Strike (CAN)—Bushra (Danzig (USA)) (34013) **C. G. P. Wyatt**
55 B c 28/2 Clodovil (IRE)—Cape Flattery (IRE) (Cape Cross (IRE)) (32000) **Mr M. Daffey**
56 **CAPTAIN CHURCHILL (IRE)**, ch c 27/4 Captain Rio—
Lafleur (IRE) (Grand Lodge (USA)) (7078) **Diamond Racing Ltd**
57 **CHARGER**, b c 23/3 Rock of Gibraltar (IRE)—
Ruthless Rose (USA) (Conquistador Cielo (USA)) **Cheveley Park Stud Limited**
58 **CRIANZA**, ch f 23/3 Polish Precedent (USA)—Red To Violet (Spectrum (IRE)) (6500)
59 **DIAMOND GIFT (USA)**, ch f 20/4 Johannesburg (USA)—
Granulette (El Gran Senor (USA)) (67000) **Cheveley Park Stud Limited**
60 B c 3/4 Kyllachy—Exhibitor (USA) (Royal Academy (USA)) (26000) **M. R. Green**
61 **GIBB RIVER (IRE)**, ch c 16/3 Mr Greeley (USA)—
Laurentine (USA) (Private Account (USA)) (170000) **Favourites Racing Ltd**
62 Ch c 20/1 Johannesburg (USA)—
Golden Flyer (FR) (Machiavellian (USA)) (100000) **Sangster Family & Matthew Green**
63 B f 2/3 Kyllachy—Halland Park Lass (IRE) (Spectrum (IRE)) (480000) **A. W. Black**
64 B f 22/3 Hawk Wing (USA)—Hampton Lucy (FR) (Anabaa (USA)) (150000) **D. Allan**
65 B c 10/4 Elusive City (USA)—Handy Station (IRE) (Desert Style (IRE)) (23165) **Countrywide Steel & Tubes Ltd**
66 **HYDRANT**, b c 14/5 Haafhd—
Spring (Sadler's Wells (USA)) (125000) **Highclere Thoroughbred Racing(Adm.Rous)**
67 **KIRKSON**, ch c 1/4 Selkirk (USA)—Viva Maria (Hernando (FR)) (10000) **Liggins, Hone & Clark**
68 **MONITOR CLOSELY (IRE)**, b c 13/4 Oasis Dream—Independence (Selkirk (USA)) (140000) **Mr L. J. Inman**
69 B c 20/2 Fasliyev (USA)—Natalie Too (USA) (Irish River (USA)) (52000) **The Comic Strip Heroes**
70 Ch c 4/3 Exceed And Excel (AUS)—Only In Dreams (Polar Falcon (USA)) (40000) **M. R. Green**
71 B c 7/4 One Cool Cat (USA)—Passe Passe (Lear Fan (USA)) (68000) **M. R. Green**
72 B f 12/2 Danehill Dancer (IRE)—
Pink Stone (FR) (Bigstone (IRE)) (82000) **Highclere Thoroughbred Racing (Vc2)**
73 **PRESTIGIOUS BABY (IRE)**, b f 10/5 Storming Home—Min Asl Wafi (IRE) (Octagonal (NZ)) **J. Abdullah**
74 B br c 16/2 Medaglia d'oro (USA)—Ravnina (USA) (Nureyev (USA)) (145772) **Saleh Al Homaizi & Imad Al Sagar**
75 **RAYVIN MAD (IRE)**, b c 21/4 Bahamian Bounty—
Poppy's Song (Owington) (20000) **Mr Ray White & Mr Vincent Walsh**
76 **RIVALRY**, ch f 30/3 Medicean—Fearless Revival (Cozzene) (USA) **Cheveley Park Stud Limited**
77 **ROMANTICIZE**, b f 31/1 Kyllachy—Romancing (Dr Devious (IRE)) **Cheveley Park Stud Limited**
78 **ROYAL EXECUTIONER (USA)**, b c 29/4 Royal Academy (USA)—Guillotine (USA) (Proud Truth (USA)) (14577)
79 **SIZZLING FIRE**, ch c 20/3 Daylami (IRE)—Nasseem Al Zohour (FR) (Grand Lodge (USA)) **J. Abdullah**
80 B c 31/3 Monsieur Bond (IRE)—Song of Skye (Warning) (54000) **S. Harris**
81 B c 22/2 Exceed And Excel (AUS)—Strings (Unfuwain (USA)) (90089) **Miss A. Shaykhutdinova**

MR P. W. CHAPPLE-HYAM—continued

82 SUNSHINE ALWAYS (IRE), b gr c 3/4 Verglas (IRE)—
Easy Sunshine (IRE) (Sadler's Wells (USA)) (80000) **Cheveley Park Stud Limited**
83 TIMELESS DREAM, b f 13/5 Oasis Dream—Simply Times (USA) (Dodge (USA)) **Times Of Wigan Ltd**
84 Br c 31/3 Rock of Gibraltar (IRE)—Twice The Ease (Green Desert (USA)) (130000) **The Comic Strip Heroes**
85 WEST WITH THE WIND (USA), b f 18/2 Gone West (USA)—
Opera Aida (IRE) (Sadler's Wells (USA)) (106899) **Miss K. Rausing**

Other Owners: I. J. Al-Sagar, Mrs C. R. Brosnan, Mrs K. Clark, A. W. Darke, D. N. Hearson, N. P Hearson, The Hon H. M. Herbert, Highclere Thoroughbred Racing Ltd, Dr M. P Hone, T. Hyde, Mr J. A. Liggins, Mrs S. Magnier, T. M. Matthews, D. F. O'Rourke, Mrs P. K. O'Rourke, B. V. Sangster, G. E. Sangster, Mrs L. M. Shanahan, Star Pointe Ltd, Mrs J. E. M. Trotter, V. J. Walsh, Mr R. White, L. Williamson, J. P. Wray.

---

106 **MR G. A. G. CHARLTON, Stocksfield**
Postal: **Mickley Grange Farm, Stocksfield, Northumberland, NE43 7TB**
Contacts: PHONE **(01661) 843247** MOBILE **(07808) 955029**
E-MAIL gcharlton@fsmail.net

1 **BISHOPS PLOY (IRE),** 5, ch g Deploy—Song of The Field (IRE)
2 **BONNIE ROCK (IRE),** 8, b m Oscar (IRE)—A'dhahirah **M. H. Walton**
3 **BYWELL BEAU (IRE),** 9, b g Lord Americo—Early Dalus (IRE) **W. F. Trueman**
4 **CASTLETOWN BOY (IRE),** 6, b g Shernazar—Glenelly Valley (IRE) **Mr & Mrs Raymond Anderson Green**
5 **DANISH REBEL (IRE),** 4, b g Danetime (IRE)—Wheatsheaf Lady (IRE) **J. I. A. Charlton**
6 **DOUBLE GEM (IRE),** 9, ch g Grand Plaisir (IRE)—Thatilldofornow (IRE) **J. I. A. Charlton**
7 **DUKESFIELD (IRE),** 7, b g Pasternak—Tell Mary **G. A. G. Charlton**
8 **FERN BAY (IRE),** 5, ch g Flemensfirth (USA)—Welsh Rhapsody (IRE) **G. A. G. Charlton**
9 **FLIGHTY MIST,** 6, b m Missed Flight—Some Shiela **J. R. Jeffreys**
10 **FLUTINA,** 5, ch m Missed Flight—Some Shiela **J. R. Jeffreys**
11 **HAZELDENE,** 6, ch g Dancing High—Gaelic Charm (IRE) **G. A. G. Charlton**
12 **HEEZ A STEEL (IRE),** 7, b g Naheez (USA)—Ari's Fashion **J. I. A. Charlton**
13 **ICE IMAGE (IRE),** 6, b g Darnay—Ice Trix (IRE) **Sydney Ramsey & Partners**
14 **KNOCKARA BEAU (IRE),** 5, b g Leading Counsel (USA)—Clairabell (IRE) **W. F. Trueman**
15 **KNOCKARA STAR (IRE),** 5, b g Leading Counsel (USA)—Fair Gina (IRE) **J. I. A. Charlton**
16 **LITTLE WIZARD (IRE),** 6, b g Oscar (IRE)—Ruby Lass (IRE) **G. A. G. Charlton**
17 **POLITICAL JADE,** 6, b m Dancing High—Political Diamond **J. W. Robson**
18 **RANDOLF (IRE),** 6, br g Good Thyne (USA)—Lester's Perk **J. I. A. Charlton**
19 **RATHOWEN (IRE),** 9, b g Good Thyne (USA)—Owenageera (IRE) **Mr & Mrs Raymond Anderson Green**
20 **REEL CHARMER,** 8, b m Dancing High—Gaelic Charm (IRE) **G. A. G. Charlton**
21 **ROTHBURY,** 8, b g Overbury (IRE)—The Distaff Spy **J. I. A. Charlton**
22 **SINGHALONGTASVEER,** 6, b g Namaqualand (USA)—Felinwen **Esh Racing**
23 **SNOWY (IRE),** 10, gr g Pierre—Snowy Gunner **Mr & Mrs Raymond Anderson Green**
24 **SPARKY BOY (IRE),** 7, b g Executive Perk—Our Lot (IRE) **G. A. G. Charlton**
25 **TOBESURE (IRE),** 14, b g Asir—Princess Citrus (IRE) **Richard Nixon**

Other Owners: R. A. Green, Mrs A. Green, Mr G. Pickersgill, S. Ramsey, J. T. Stobbs, Mr D. Taylor.

Assistant Trainer: Mr J I A Charlton

Jockey (NH): Jan Faltejsek. **Amateur:** Mr A. J. Findlay.

---

107 **MR ROGER J. CHARLTON, Beckhampton**
Postal: **Beckhampton House, Marlborough, Wilts**
Contacts: OFFICE **(01672) 539533** HOME **(01672) 539330** FAX **(01672) 539456**
MOBILE **(07710) 784511** E-MAIL r.charlton@virgin.net

1 **BLUE MONDAY,** 7, b g Darshaan—Lunda (IRE) **Mountgrange Stud**
2 **CACTUS ROSE,** 4, b g Zamindar (USA)—Bolsena (USA) **Thurloe Thoroughbreds XVIII**
3 **FARLEY STAR,** 4, b f Alzao (USA)—Girl of My Dreams (IRE) **A. Parker**
4 **FIFTY CENTS,** 4, ch g Diesis—Solaia (USA) **Mountgrange Stud Ltd**
5 **GENKI (IRE),** 4, ch g Shinko Forest (IRE)—Emma's Star (ITY) **Ms G. F. Khosla**

MR ROGER J. CHARLTON—continued

6 **LAST SOVEREIGN**, 4, b c Pivotal—Zayala **Mountgrange Stud Ltd**
7 **PRESUMPTIVE (IRE)**, 8, b g Danehill (USA)—Demure **Beckhampton Stables Ltd**
8 **PROPONENT (IRE)**, 4, b g Peintre Celebre (USA)—Pont Audemer (USA) **B. E. Nielsen**
9 **STALKING TIGER (IRE)**, 4, b g King's Best (USA)—Obsessed **Mountgrange Stud Ltd**

THREE-YEAR-OLDS

10 **ALASPIEL (IRE)**, b g Singspiel (IRE)—Alashaan **D. J. Deer**
11 **ASIAN CLASSIC (IRE)**, b g Montjeu (IRE)—Yafoul (USA) **H.R.H. Sultan Ahmad Shah**
12 **ASIAN LADY**, br f Kyllachy—Prancing **H.R.H. Sultan Ahmad Shah**
13 **BARRICADO (FR)**, b c Anabaa (USA)—Aube d'irlande (FR) **M. Pescod**
14 **BELOTTO (IRE)**, b f Peintre Celebre (USA)—Bel **Lady Rothschild**
15 **BENCOOLEN (IRE)**, b c Daylami (IRE)—Jakarta (IRE) **De La Warr Racing**
16 **BRAEMAR GAMES**, b f Montjeu (IRE)—Purple Heather (USA) **Her Majesty The Queen**
17 **CAPRIO (IRE)**, ch c Captain Rio—Disarm (IRE) **Beckhampton Stables Ltd 1**
18 **CARBON PRINT (USA)**, ch c Johannesburg (USA)—Caithness (USA) **K. Abdulla**
19 **CARDINAL**, ch c Pivotal—Fictitious **Her Majesty The Queen**
20 **CARO GEORGE (USA)**, b br f Distant View (USA)—Gossamer (USA) **B. E. Nielsen**
21 **CHORAL SYMPHONY**, ch c Singspiel (IRE)—Celtic Cross **Her Majesty The Queen**
22 **CLOWANCE**, b f Montjeu (IRE)—Freni (GER) **Seasons Holidays**
23 **COLORADO BLUE (IRE)**, ch g Nayef (USA)—Colouring (IRE) **M. Pescod**
24 **CONFEDERATE**, b c Red Ransom (USA)—Grain of Gold **B. E. Nielsen**
25 **CONTRADA**, b c Medicean—Trounce **Mountgrange Stud Ltd**
26 **CUBAN MISSILE**, b g Danehill Dancer (IRE)—Lady Salsa (IRE) **Mountgrange Stud Ltd**
27 **CUBAN RHYTHM (USA)**, b f Kingmambo (USA)—Kournakova (IRE) **Heart Of The South Racing**
28 **DAZZLING LIGHT (UAE)**, b br f Halling (USA)—Crown of Light **B. E. Nielsen**
29 **DEDICATE**, b f Beat Hollow—Total Devotion **K. Abdulla**
30 **FATAL ATTRACTION**, b f Oasis Dream—Millyant **Mountgrange Stud Ltd**
31 **FIFTEEN LOVE (USA)**, b br c Point Given (USA)—Nidd (USA) **K. Abdulla**
32 **FREEDOM SONG**, b f Singspiel (IRE)—Girl of My Dreams (IRE) **A. Parker**
33 **GENERAL TUFTO**, b g Fantastic Light (USA)—Miss Pinkerton **A. E. Oppenheimer**
34 **GLEEFUL**, b f Galileo (IRE)—Kardelle **Beckhampton Stables Ltd**
35 **KING O'THE GYPSIES (IRE)**, b c Sadler's Wells (USA)—Love For Ever (IRE) **B. E. Nielsen**
36 **LADY SELKIRK**, ch f Selkirk (USA)—Hyde Hall **V. Khosla**
37 **LOOK TO THIS DAY**, ch f In The Wings—Yanka (USA) **A. Parker**
38 **MATROSHKA (IRE)**, b f Red Ransom (USA)—Wosaita **B. E. Nielsen**
39 **MELODRAMATIC (IRE)**, b f Sadler's Wells (USA)—My Branch **B. E. Nielsen**
40 **MIDNIGHT FLING**, b f Groom Dancer (USA)—Perfect Night **Mr S. Emmet & Miss R. Emmet**
41 **MOOTED (UAE)**, b g Mtoto—Assraar **Axom (XII)**
42 B f Sadler's Wells (USA)—Mountains of Mist (IRE) **D. J. Deer**
43 **OARSMAN**, ch c Selkirk (USA)—Felucca **K. Abdulla**
44 **PENSION POLICY (USA)**, b br f Danzig (USA)—Domain (USA) **Mr Julian Smith**
45 **PORT PROVIDENCE**, b f Red Ransom (USA)—Rum Cay (USA) **David & Paul Hearson**
46 **PRIME EXHIBIT**, b c Selkirk (USA)—First Exhibit **Mountgrange Stud Ltd**
47 **RUSSIAN MUSIC (USA)**, b g Stravinsky (USA)—Private Seductress **B. E. Nielsen**
48 **SARANDO**, b c Hernando (FR)—Dansara **K. Abdulla**
49 **SARANOME (IRE)**, b c Statue of Liberty (USA)—My Gray (FR) **J. D. Wolfensohn**
50 **SCUFFLE**, gr f Daylami (IRE)—Tantina (USA) **K. Abdulla**
51 **SEA ADMIRAL**, b g Sinndar (IRE)—Overboard (IRE) **Axom (IV)**
52 **SEASONSELITE**, b f Sagamix (FR)—Oleana (IRE) **Seasons Holidays**
53 **SIMONE MARTINI (IRE)**, b g Montjeu (IRE)—Bona Dea (IRE) **Mountgrange Stud Ltd**
54 **SPECIAL INTENTION**, ch f Dalakhani (IRE)—Speciality (IRE) **Mountgrange Stud Ltd**
55 **TARR STEPS (IRE)**, b f Giant's Causeway (USA)—Tamso (USA) **Lady Rothschild**
56 **TOTEM FLOWER (IRE)**, ch f Indian Ridge—Tree Peony **A. E. Oppenheimer**
57 **TRAVELLING LIGHT (USA)**, b f Gone West (USA)—Gaily Tiara (USA) **Sir E. J. Loder**
58 **TRENCHTOWN (IRE)**, b c King's Best (USA)—Barbuda **David & Paul Hearson**
59 **TRIANON**, ch f Nayef (USA)—Trying For Gold (USA) **Her Majesty The Queen**
60 **UNBREAK MY HEART (IRE)**, ch c Bahamian Bounty—Golden Heart **Mountgrange Stud Ltd**

TWO-YEAR-OLDS

61 **ALL ABOUT YOU (IRE)**, b c 23/4 Mind Games—
Expectation (IRE) (Night Shift (USA)) (120000) **Mountgrange Stud Ltd**
62 B f 14/4 Singspiel (IRE)—B Beautiful (IRE) (Be My Guest (USA)) (32000) **Mr Alan Parker**
63 **BADGE**, b c 31/1 Acclamation—Be My Wish (Be My Chief (USA)) (72000) **M. Pescod**
64 **BEATTY**, b c 7/5 Dansili—Seaborne (Slip Anchor) **Lady Rothschild**
65 B f 6/2 Red Ransom (USA)—Bedara (Barathea (IRE)) **The Duchess Of Roxburghe**

MR ROGER J. CHARLTON—continued

66 B c 18/3 Galileo (IRE)—Behera (Mill Reef (USA)) (130000) **Mountgrange Stud Ltd**
67 BORDER PATROL, b c 17/4 Selkirk (USA)—Ffestiniog (IRE) (Efisio) **Elite Racing Club**
68 BROAD CAIRN, b c 28/1 Green Desert (USA)—Celtic Cross (Selkirk (USA)) **Her Majesty The Queen**
69 Ch c 15/3 Galileo (IRE)—Corsican Sunset (USA) (Thunder Gulch (USA)) **Seasons Holidays**
70 Ch c 6/3 Bachelor Duke (USA)—Dawn Chorus (IRE) (Mukaddamah (USA)) (180000) **Ms G. F. Khosla**
71 DEFINIGHTLY, b br c 13/2 Diktat—Perfect Night (Danzig Connection (USA)) **Mr S. Emmet & Miss R. Emmet**
72 B c 27/4 Mizzen Mast (USA)—Euphonize (USA) (Seattle Slew (USA)) **K. Abdulla**
73 FIANCEE (IRE), b f 8/4 Pivotal—Name of Love (IRE) (Petardia) **Lady Rothschild**
74 FIRST SERVICE (IRE), ch c 22/4 Intikhab (USA)—Princess Sceptre (Cadeaux Genereux) (57000) **J. W. Livock**
75 B f 31/3 Hernando (FR)—Freni (GER) (Sternkoenig (IRE)) **Seasons Holidays**
76 GOING FOR GOLD, b f 1/2 Barathea (IRE)—Flash of Gold (Darshaan) **Her Majesty The Queen**
77 B f 21/2 Royal Academy (USA)—Hasardeuse (USA) (Distant View (USA)) **K. Abdulla**
78 B f 3/5 Orientate (USA)—Interval (USA) (Forty Niner) (19436) **K. Abdulla**
79 B f 21/2 Point Given (USA)—Introducing (USA) (Deputy Minister (CAN)) **K. Abdulla**
80 LA TIZONA (IRE), b c 20/5 Alhaarth (IRE)—Rosse (Kris) (36000) **A. E. Oppenheimer**
81 B f 24/2 Marju (IRE)—Lunda (IRE) (Soviet Star (USA)) (110000) **D. G. Hardisty**
82 B f 16/4 High Chaparral (IRE)—Molasses (FR) (Machiavellian (USA)) (60000) **Elite Racing Club**
83 Gr c 22/2 High Chaparral (IRE)—Molly Mello (GER) (Big Shuffle (USA)) **Seasons Holidays**
84 B c 26/3 Zamindar (USA)—Moment (Nashwan (USA)) **K. Abdulla**
85 MORNING CALM, b f 11/2 Montjeu (IRE)—Tempting Prospect (Shirley Heights) **Her Majesty The Queen**
86 B c 22/3 Dansili—Mylania (Midyan (USA)) (140000) **Mountgrange Stud Ltd**
87 B c 20/4 Dansili—New Abbey (Sadler's Wells (USA)) **K. Abdulla**
88 B c 3/4 Tiznow (USA)—Nidd (USA) (Known Fact (USA)) **K. Abdulla**
89 PERCEPTION (IRE), b f 27/4 Hawk Wing (USA)—

Princesse Darsha (GER) (Darshaan) (45045) **De La Warr Racing**
90 Ch c 22/4 Selkirk (USA)—Portelet (Night Shift (USA)) (185000) **Mountgrange Stud Ltd**
91 SALLY FORTH, b f 29/4 Dubai Destination (USA)—Daralbayda (IRE) (Doyoun) **Her Majesty The Queen**
92 B c 4/5 Haafhd—Shanty (Selkirk (USA)) (120000) **Mountgrange Stud Ltd**
93 Ch c 31/3 Falbrav (IRE)—Sharp Terms (Kris) (62000) **Thurloe Thoroughbreds XXII**
94 B c 29/3 Indian Haven—Specifically (USA) (Sky Classic (CAN)) (200000) **J. P. Smith**
95 TAMOSHANTA, b f 4/3 Montjeu (IRE)—Tamso (USA) (Seeking the Gold (USA)) **Lady Rothschild**
96 Gr f 31/1 Daylami (IRE)—Tante Rose (IRE) (Barathea (IRE)) **B. E. Nielsen**
97 B c 6/2 Acclamation—Tasha's Dream (USA) (Woodman (USA)) (160000) **H.R.H. Sultan Ahmad Shah**
98 B c 15/2 Bahamian Bounty—Trundley Wood (Wassl) (48000) **J. W. Livock**
99 B f 27/5 Dynaformer (USA)—Unending Love (USA) (Dixieland Band (USA)) (145772) **Mr Bjorn Nielsen**
100 B f 12/2 Oasis Dream—Valencia (Kenmare (FR)) **K. Abdulla**
101 WATER HEN (IRE), b f 8/2 Diktat—Waterfall One (Nashwan (USA)) **Lady Rothschild**

Other Owners: Axom Ltd, Mr D. Downie, Lt Cdr P. S. Emmet, Miss R. E. Emmet, A. J. Hill, Miss M. Noden, O. J. W. Pawle, J. R. Penny, Mrs C. Penny, Mrs N. H. Stafford.

Assistant Trainer: Tom Grantham

Jockey (flat): Richard Kingscote, S. Drowne.

---

108 **MR R. M. CLARK, West Lothian**
Postal: **Mason Croft, Falla Farm, Carnwath, ML11 8LH**
Contacts: **PHONE (01555) 841775 FAX (01555) 841775 MOBILE (07715) 121387**

1 SCHOOL CLASS, 8, b m Classic Cliche (USA)—School Run **M. Clark**
2 SUNLEY SONG, 5, b m Fleetwood (IRE)—Sunley Sinner **M. Clark**

THREE-YEAR-OLDS

3 RUBY MAY, b f Elmaamul (USA)—Simmie's Special **M. Clark**

---

109 **MR NICOLAS CLEMENT, Chantilly**
Postal: **37, Avenue de Joinville, 60500 Chantilly, France**
Contacts: **PHONE (0033) 3445 75960 FAX (0033) 3445 77084**
E-MAIL **clementoffice@wanadoo.fr** WEBSITE **nicolasclement.com**

1 ANISAKIS (FR), 4, b g Kaldounevees (FR)—Julna (FR)
2 COEUR DE CRISTAL (FR), 4, ch f Limnos (JPN)—Entouka (FR)
3 EIRE (GB), 4, ch f Medicean—Mavourneen (USA)

MR NICOLAS CLEMENT—continued

4 **HOHLETHELONELY**, 4, ch c Medicean—Now And Forever (IRE)
5 **LADY DETTORIA (FR)**, 4, b f Vettori (IRE)—Delimara (IRE)
6 **MACHABA (USA)**, 4, b f Giant's Causeway (USA)—Gracious Living (USA)
7 **PANFILO**, 13, b h Thatching—Reveuse du Soir
8 **PEAK RAIDER (IRE)**, 4, b br c Machiavellian (USA)—Desert Magic (IRE)
9 **REASONS (USA)**, 4, b c Malabar Gold (USA)—Anbella (FR)
10 **ROYALE DANEHILL (IRE)**, 4, b f Danehill (USA)—Royal Ballerina (IRE)
11 **TUMACO (CHI)**, 5, b h Special Quest (FR)—Starwars (CHI)
12 **VALSE MYSTIQUE (FR)**, 4, ch f Grand Lodge (USA)—Vanishing Prairie (USA)
13 **WAITING FOR JOHN (IRE)**, 4, ch f Traditionally (USA)—Magic Feeling (IRE)

THREE-YEAR-OLDS

14 **BANANA TROPIC**, b f Fantastic Light (USA)—Bustling
15 **BRING ON THE STYLE (FR)**, b f Desert Style (IRE)—Tango Two Thousand (IRE)
16 **CHINOISERIE**, b f Rock of Gibraltar (IRE)—Sensitivity (USA)
17 **COOL STAR (FR)**, ch c Starborough—Valverda (USA)
18 **COTTAGE CLUB (USA)**, b f Singspiel (IRE)—Quatre Saisons (FR)
19 **COUNTY KERRY (USA)**, ch f Gone West (USA)—European Rose (USA)
20 **COVARISIERE (FR)**, b f Tobougg (IRE)—Coastline
21 **CURLING (FR)**, b c Highest Honor (FR)—Miss Alleged (USA)
22 **ELEGANT DANCER (FR)**, b c Anabaa (USA)—Sweet Story (IRE)
23 **GREEN DU CIEL (FR)**, gr c Smadoun (FR)—Sucre Blanc (FR)
24 **HALONG BAY (FR)**, b f Montjeu (IRE)—Lorigane (FR)
25 **ICY RIVER (FR)**, gr c Verglas (IRE)—River Sans Retour (FR)
26 **KOENIGSBERG (USA)**, b c Danzig (USA)—Mariensky (USA)
27 **LA YARADA (SWI)**, b f Danehill Dancer (IRE)—La Brise (IRE)
28 **LADY CELINA (USA)**, ch f Carson City (USA)—Spec Account (USA)
29 **MAID FOR WINNING (USA)**, b f Gone West (USA)—Maid For Walking
30 **MERLINA (SWI)**, b f Hawk Wing (USA)—Madame Steinlen
31 **MIDNIGHT'S CHILD (IRE)**, b f Galileo (IRE)—Miscast
32 **MIESQUINA (FR)**, b f Miesque's Son (USA)—Barbarina (FR)
33 **MINZA (FR)**, b f Zamindar (USA)—Domniga (USA)
34 **MISTER DYNAMO (IRE)**, b c Dubai Destination (USA)—Debbie's Next (USA)
35 **MUNDYBASH**, b c Diktat—Cootamundra (FR)
36 **NORTHERN CELEBRE (FR)**, ch c Peintre Celebre (USA)—Corse (IRE)
37 **PEAK RHYTHM (FR)**, b c Daliapour (IRE)—In Tune (USA)
38 **POLITE SOCIETY (IRE)**, b f Seeking The Gold (USA)—Born Something (IRE)
39 **RAFINE**, ch f Peintre Celebre (USA)—La Belga (ARG)
40 **ROSE GRISE (FR)**, gr f Verglas (IRE)—Tempete Tropicale (FR)
41 **SATURNINE (IRE)**, gr f Galileo (USA)—Katchina Quest (FR)
42 **SPEED SKATER (FR)**, gr c Verglas (IRE)—Nidorina (USA)
43 **STUDY (USA)**, b c Deputy Minister (CAN)—Watch The Time (USA)
44 **SUITOR (USA)**, b c Swain (USA)—Eternity
45 **SURVEIL (USA)**, b f Kingmambo (USA)—Watch (USA)
46 **TOUCHING KINGS (FR)**, b c Kutub (IRE)—Touchee d'amour (GER)
47 **TYRANT STAR (FR)**, ro c Chichicastenango (FR)—Hunter of Nowhere (FR)
48 **VASTANYA (USA)**, b f Royal Academy (USA)—Vitola
49 **VERTUEUX (FR)**, gr c Verglas (IRE)—Shahrazad (FR)

TWO-YEAR-OLDS

50 B f 22/3 Elusive City (USA)—Adriana (IRE) (Second Empire (IRE)) (33462)
51 B f 26/4 Lando (GER)—Banakill (FR) (Funambule (USA)) (64350)
52 B c 7/2 Marchand de Sable (USA)—Coastline (Night Shift (USA)) (20592)
53 Ch f 3/4 Mr Greeley (USA)—Consistently (USA) (Storm Boot (USA)) (97181)
54 Ch f 18/3 Starborough—Distant Lover (Distant Relative) (32175)
55 B f 26/3 El Prado (IRE)—Fiscal Year (USA) (Half a Year (USA)) (89893)
56 B f 4/3 Montjeu (IRE)—Fruhling Feuer (FR) (Green Tune (USA)) (57915)
57 **GOOD BYE MY FRIEND (FR)**, b c 18/3 Kendor (FR)—The Wise Lady (FR) (Ganges (USA)) (16087)
58 **GRAND SLAMMER (USA)**, ch c 14/2 Grand Slam (USA)—Blushing Bride (Distant Relative) (29154)
59 B f 17/5 Montjeu (IRE)—Greek Air (IRE) (Ela-Mana-Mou) (51480)
60 **HELIPAD (FR)**, b c 2/3 Green Tune (USA)—High Living (USA) (Diesis) (54697)
61 B c 4/3 Della Francesca (USA)—Jackette (USA) (Mr Greeley (USA)) (23809)
62 B f 15/5 Namid—Kill The Crab (IRE) (Petorius) (19305)
63 **KSHANTI (USA)**, ch f 25/3 Diesis—Oreanda (USA) (Stravinsky (USA))
64 Ch f 20/2 Nayef (USA)—Lia (IRE) (Desert King (IRE))

MR NICOLAS CLEMENT—continued

65 LITIANINNE (FR), b f 1/1 Invincible Spirit (IRE)—Premiere Chance (FR) (Linamix (FR))
66 B c 13/3 Grand Slam (USA)—Miss Firefly (USA) (Salt Lake (USA)) (77745)
67 MORAR, b f 24/3 Kalanisi (IRE)—Moidart (Electric)
68 B f 16/4 Johar (USA)—Queen Douna (FR) (Kaldoun (FR)) (51480)
69 B f 10/5 Brahms (USA)—Sky Bonnet (CAN) (Halo (USA)) (12147)
70 B f 24/3 Desert Style (IRE)—Sprite (Fairy King (USA))
71 Ch f 8/3 Peintre Celebre (USA)—Waldmark (GER) (Mark of Esteem (IRE)) (135135)
72 Bl f 28/4 Pyrus (USA)—Woodland Garden (Godswalk (USA))
73 ZENIT (FR), b c 23/4 Zieten (USA)—Sister Celestine (Bishop of Cashel) (38610)

110 MR P. L. CLINTON, Doveridge
Postal: **Lordlea Farm, Marston Lane, Doveridge, Ashbourne, Derbyshire, DE6 5JS**
Contacts: **PHONE (01889) 566356 MOBILE (07815) 142642**

1 CRAGG VALE LADY, 5, b m Arkadian Hero (USA)—Prinia In The Clear Racing
2 IMPERIAL ROYALE (IRE), 7, ch g Ali-Royal (IRE)—God Speed Her In The Clear Racing

THREE-YEAR-OLDS

3 B f Beat All (USA)—Salska P. L. Clinton

TWO-YEAR-OLDS

4 B c 22/3 Beat All (USA)—Salska (Salse (USA)) In The Clear Racing

Other Owners: Mr P. L. Clinton, Mr G. Worrall.

Assistant Trainer: Phil Bratton

111 MR K. F. CLUTTERBUCK, Newmarket
Postal: **Pond House Stables, Church Lane, Exning, Newmarket, Suffolk, CB8 7HF**
Contacts: **PHONE (01638) 577043 MOBILE (07868) 605995**

1 BALLA D'AIRE (IRE), 13, b br g Balla Cove—Silius K. F. Clutterbuck
2 DISCOMANIA, 6, b g Pursuit of Love—Discomatic (USA) The T Class Partnership
3 JOLLYS JOY, 4, b f Averti (IRE)—Nest Egg Mrs J. K. Hammond
4 MELTONIAN, 11, ch g Past Glories—Meltonby K. F. Clutterbuck
5 RIOLO (IRE), 6, ch g Priolo (USA)—Ostrusa (AUT) K F C Racing
6 VIENNCHEE RUN, 7, b g Commanche Run—Lucky Vienna K F C Racing

Other Owners: Mr K. F. Clutterbuck, Mrs J. Clutterbuck, Mr A. Green, Mr S. Hammond.

Assistant Trainer: Jane Clutterbuck

Conditional: Matt Crawley. **Amateur:** Mr Stewart Best.

112 MR D. J. COAKLEY, West Ilsley
Postal: **Keeper's Stables, West Ilsley, Newbury, Berkshire, RG20 7AH**
Contacts: **PHONE (01635) 281622 FAX (01635) 281624 MOBILE (07768) 658056**
E-MAIL racing@deniscoakley.co.uk WEBSITE www.deniscoakley.co.uk

1 AUNTIE MAME, 4, b f Diktat—Mother Molly (USA) Finders Keepers Partnership
2 KITTO KATSU, 4, b f Ishiguru (USA)—Zacinta (USA) Keepers Racing II
3 POWER PLAYER, 4, br g Diktat—Royal Patron Sir Gordon Brunton
4 STEPPE DANCER (IRE), 5, b h Fasliyev (USA)—Exemina (USA) C. T. Van Hoorn
5 SUBEDAR MAJOR, 4, b g Robellino (USA)—Memsahib Sir Gordon Brunton
6 ZEEUW (IRE), 4, b g Xaar—Lucky Bet (IRE) C. T. Van Hoorn

THREE-YEAR-OLDS

7 AGON EYES (USA), b f Stravinsky (USA)—Dixie Eyes Blazing (USA) Agon Eyes Racing
8 ASMODEA, b f Dr Fong (USA)—Latina (IRE) Dorothy & Ivan Topley
9 BARLIFFEY (IRE), b c Bahri (USA)—Kildare Lady (IRE) Fairfax Racing
10 HOLLANDER (IRE), b c Fasliyev (USA)—Pietra Dura C. T. Van Hoorn

MR D. J. COAKLEY—continued

11 **NOTHING LIKEA DAME**, ch f Bahamian Bounty—Dame Jude **Stableside Racing**
12 **PRECURSOR (IRE)**, ch g Spartacus (IRE)—Secoon (IRE) **P. Rosas**
13 **SCARY MOVIE (IRE)**, b c Daggers Drawn (USA)—Grinning (IRE) **A. Brudenell & J. G. Mountford**

TWO-YEAR-OLDS

14 B f 11/2 One Cool Cat (USA)—Chinon (IRE) (Entrepreneur) (25000) **L. M. A. Hurley**
15 B f 5/3 Bahri (USA)—Daqtora (Dr Devious (IRE)) (20000) **West Ilsley Racing**
16 Ch f 24/2 King's Best (USA)—Rafiya (Halling (USA))
17 B f 31/3 Kyllachy—Sea Music (Inchinor) (10000) **Count Calypso Racing**
18 **VOORTREKKER**, b c 19/3 Imperial Dancer—Sweet Wilhelmina (Indian Ridge) **C. T. Van Hoorn**
19 Ch f 21/3 Rock of Gibraltar (IRE)—Ziya (Lion Cavern (USA)) **M. Kerr-Dineen**

Other Owners: Mr R. J. Bolam, Mrs T. Brudenell, Mr G. Callegari, Mr P. M. Emery, Mrs Lesley Humphries, Mr D. Lancaster-Smith, Mr M. J. Lancaster-Smith, Mr J. G. Mountford, Mr John Ross, Mr D. P. Stottor, Mr I. R. Thomas, Mrs D. Topley, Mr I. Topley, Mr Reg Whitehead.

---

113 **MRS H. J. COBB, Pulborough**
Postal: **Kilbrannan Stud Farm, Gay Street, Pulborough, West Sussex, RH20 2HJ**
Contacts: PHONE **(01798) 812541** FAX **(01798) 817371** MOBILE **(07764) 942854**
E-MAIL **kilbrannanstud@aol.com**

1 **DARCY'S SONG**, 5, gr m Baryshnikov (AUS)—Soldier's Song **Mrs H. J. Cobb**
2 **LANCIER D'ESTRUVAL (FR)**, 9, ch g Epervier Bleu—Pommette III (FR) **Mrs H. J. Cobb**
3 **TRIP TO THE STARS (IRE)**, 8, b m Fourstars Allstar (USA)—Nora Dante (IRE) **Mrs H. J. Cobb**
4 **WINNIE WOOD**, 4, b f Spendent—Effie Wood **Mrs H. J. Cobb**

---

114 **MR P. F. I. COLE, Whatcombe**
Postal: **Whatcombe Estate, Whatcombe, Wantage, Oxfordshire, OX12 9NW**
Contacts: PHONE **(01488) 638433** FAX **(01488) 638609**
E-MAIL **jenny@paulcoleracing.com** WEBSITE **www.paulcoleracing.com**

1 **ANDRONIKOS**, 6, ch h Dr Fong (USA)—Arctic Air **C. Shiacolas**
2 **BENTONG (IRE)**, 5, b g Anabaa (USA)—Miss Party Line (USA) **H.R.H. Sultan Ahmad Shah**
3 **DANETIME PANTHER (IRE)**, 4, b g Danetime (IRE)—Annotate **The Pink Panther Partnership**
4 **DOUBLE BILL (USA)**, 4, b br c Mr Greeley (USA)—Salty Perfume **Mrs S. A. Smith**
5 **EISTEDDFOD**, 7, ch g Cadeaux Genereux—Ffestiniog **Elite Racing Club**
6 **MALTESE FALCON**, 8, b g Mark of Esteem (IRE)—Crime Ofthecentury **C. N. Wright**
7 **NAMID REPROBATE (IRE)**, 5, br g Namid—Morning Surprise **Mrs J. M. Haines**
8 **NEW SEEKER**, 8, b g Green Desert (USA)—Ahbab (IRE) **Elite Racing Club**
9 **PIPPA GREENE**, 4, b c Galileo (IRE)—Funny Girl (IRE) **R. A. H. Evans**
10 **PUTRA SQUARE**, 4, b c Cadeaux Genereux—Razzle (IRE) **H.R.H. Sultan Ahmad Shah**
11 **SRI KUANTAN (IRE)**, 4, ch c Spinning World (USA)—Miss Asia Quest **H.R.H. Sultan Ahmad Shah**
12 **SRI PEKAN TWO**, 4, b g Montjeu (IRE)—Brigadiers Bird (IRE) **H.R.H. Sultan Ahmad Shah**
13 **STRATEGIC MOUNT**, 5, b h Montjeu (IRE)—Danlu (USA) **Ben & Sir Martyn Arbib**
14 **TARKAMARA (IRE)**, 4, ch f Medicean—Tarakana (USA) **A. H. Robinson**
15 **TRANS SIBERIAN**, 4, b c Soviet Star (USA)—Dina Line (USA) **C. Shiacolas**
16 **TREDEGAR**, 4, ch c Inchinor—Ffestiniog (IRE) **Elite Racing Club**

THREE-YEAR-OLDS

17 **ANIMATOR**, b c Act One—Robsart (IRE) **Strategic Thoroughbred Racing**
18 **BAUHAUS BOURBON (USA)**, gr f Behrens (USA)—Southern Tradition (USA) **F. P. Stella**
19 **BEAUTIFUL LADY (IRE)**, b f Peintre Celebre (USA)—Puteri Wentworth **H.R.H. Sultan Ahmad Shah**
20 **BOZEMAN TRAIL**, b c Averti (IRE)—Crystal Power (USA) **W. H. Ponsonby**
21 **CAPEFLY**, b f Cape Cross (IRE)—Patacake Patacake (USA) **Miss A. Shaykhutdinova**
22 **CONTESSINA (IRE)**, ch f Medicean—Queen's Music (USA) **C. Shiacolas**
23 **COTTON REEL**, b c Cape Cross (IRE)—Cotton House (IRE) **J. D. Manley**
24 **DELTA DIVA (USA)**, b f Victory Gallop (CAN)—Tjinouska (USA) **C. N. Wright**
25 **DESERT CLOVER (USA)**, b br c Mutakddim (USA)—Booly (USA) **F. P. Stella**
26 **GENERAL ELIOTT (IRE)**, b c Rock of Gibraltar (IRE)—Marlene-D **Sir George Meyrick**
27 **HARLECH CASTLE**, b c Royal Applause—Ffestiniog (IRE) **Elite Racing Club**
28 **JAMES DEAN (IRE)**, b c Clodovil (IRE)—Karenaragon **P. F. I. Cole Ltd**
29 **JAZZ JAM**, ch f Pivotal—Applaud (USA) **Faisal Salman**
30 **LUCK MONEY (IRE)**, b c Indian Ridge—Dundel (IRE) **Mrs S. A. Smith**

MR P. F. I. COLE—continued

31 **MOYNAHAN (USA)**, ch c Johannesburg (USA)—Lakab (USA) **Mr D. S. Lee**
32 **NIKOLAIEVICH (IRE)**, b c Xaar—Seren Quest **The Fairy Story Partnership**
33 **OASIS WIND**, b c Oasis Dream—Haibah **Miss A. Shaykhutdinova**
34 **OLLIE FLIPTRIK (USA)**, b br c Essence of Dubai (USA)—Etoufee (USA) **The Comic Strip Heroes**
35 **OPENING ACT**, br gr c Daylami (USA)—Bluebelle **Mr Faisal Salman & Kirtlington Stud**
36 **OPTIMUS MAXIMUS (IRE)**, b c Galileo (IRE)—Morning Welcome (IRE) **Mrs S. A. Smith**
37 **PANTHERII (USA)**, ch f Forest Wildcat (USA)—Saraa Ree (USA) **A. H. Robinson**
38 **PIECE OF MY HEART**, b f Fasliyev (USA)—Cultured Pearl (IRE) **Mr & Mrs Christopher Wright**
39 **PRAVDA STREET**, b c Soviet Star (USA)—Sari **R. A. Instone**
40 **RED LEAVES**, b g Rock of Gibraltar (IRE)—Brigadiers Bird (IRE) **Mr & Mrs D. A. Gamble**
41 **RED ROCK PRINCE (IRE)**, b c Rock of Gibraltar (IRE)—Red Bartsia **Mrs L. Spencer**
42 **RIVER PROUD (USA)**, b c Proud Citizen (USA)—Da River Hoss (USA) **Mrs L. Spencer**
43 **STARFALA**, gr f Galileo (IRE)—Farfala (FR) **Ben & Sir Martyn Arbib**
44 **STRATEGIC KNIGHT**, b c Johannesburg (USA)—Western Friend (USA) **H.R.H. Sultan Ahmad Shah**
45 **STRATEGIC MISSION (IRE)**, b c Red Ransom (USA)—North East Bay **H.R.H. Sultan Ahmad Shah**
46 **STRATEGIC MOVER (USA)**, ch c Grand Slam (USA)—Efficient Frontier (USA) **H.R.H. Sultan Ahmad Shah**
47 **THE TWELVE STEPS**, b c Diktat—Polygueza (FR) **D. N. Green**
48 **TITLE ROLE**, b c Mark of Esteem (IRE)—No Comebacks **AXOM (IX)**
49 **TRAPHALGAR (IRE)**, b c Cape Cross (IRE)—Conquestadora **The Fairy Story Partnership**
50 **TRINKILA (USA)**, b f Cat Thief (USA)—Que Belle (CAN) **Mr D. S. Lee**
51 **WHAT KATIE DID (IRE)**, b c Invincible Spirit (IRE)—Chatterberry **B. D. Gover**
52 **YES MEG**, b f Sagamix (FR)—Segsbury Belle **R. A. Instone**

TWO-YEAR-OLDS

53 B c 6/2 Rahy (USA)—Aldiza (USA) (Storm Cat (USA)) (126336) **Mr D. S. Lee**
54 **ALYSTAR (IRE)**, ch f 3/3 Rock of Gibraltar (IRE)—Arpege (IRE) (Sadler's Wells (USA)) (128700) **Mrs S. A. Smith**
55 B f 10/2 One Cool Cat (USA)—Beautiful France (IRE) (Sadler's Wells (USA)) (48261) **Wansdyke Farms**
56 **CLODOLINE**, b f 12/2 Clodovil (IRE)—Esquiline (USA) (Gone West (USA)) (45000) **A. H. Robinson**
57 B f 16/3 Dr Fong (USA)—Darling Harbour (USA) (Candy Stripes (USA)) **Mr C. Wright**
58 **DARWIN'S DRAGON**, ch c 17/3 Royal Dragon (USA)—
                                                            Darwinia (GER) (Acatenango (GER)) (12000) **Mrs E. A. Bass**
59 **DREAM IN WAITING**, b f 16/3 Oasis Dream—Lady In Waiting (Kylian (USA)) **Pegasus Racing Ltd**
60 B c 16/2 Elusive Quality (USA)—Famously (IRE) (Sadler's Wells (USA)) (90000) **Miss A. Shaykhutdinova**
61 **GREAT WESTERN (USA)**, b c 3/2 Gone West (USA)—Pleasant Temper (USA) (Storm Cat (USA)) **J. D. Manley**
62 B f 3/5 Reset (AUS)—In The Groove (Night Shift (USA)) (11000) **Bigwigs Bloodstock**
63 B br c 26/3 Kheleyf (USA)—Karenaragon (Aragon) (38000) **P. F. I. Cole Ltd**
64 **KAYFIAR (USA)**, ch c 21/1 Lion Heart (USA)—Ivor Jewel (USA) (Sir Ivor (USA)) (64349) **Mrs S. A. Smith**
65 **LADY RUSTY (IRE)**, gr f 8/2 Verglas (IRE)—Patteness (FR) (General Holme (USA)) (20591) **Ash Place Stud**
66 Ch c 17/1 Giant's Causeway (USA)—Madeira Mist (IRE) (Grand Lodge (USA)) (128700) **Mrs L. Spencer**
67 **MILIEMIL**, b f 19/1 Acclamation—Lady Betambeau (IRE) (Grand Lodge (USA)) (44000) **Mr D. S. Lee**
68 **NEW ADVENTURE**, b c 14/5 Generous (IRE)—Sari (Faustus (USA)) **R. A. Instone**
69 **NORTHERN TOUR**, b c 28/3 Tobougg (IRE)—
                                                            Swift Spring (FR) (Bluebird (USA)) (20000) **Hunter, Maynard, Ward**
70 **PERCOLATOR**, b f 1/2 Kheleyf (USA)—Coffee Cream (Common Grounds) (2000) **A. H. Robinson**
71 Ch f 31/3 Kingmambo (USA)—Piquetnol (USA) (Private Account) (209137) **Miss A. Shaykhutdinova**
72 **QUEENS FORESTER**, b f 1/3 Needwood Blade—Bonsai (IRE) (Woodman (USA)) (17000) **W. H. Ponsonby**
73 B f 6/5 Mizzen Mast (USA)—Questonia (Rainbow Quest (USA)) (24295) **The Comic Strip Heroes**
74 B c 12/3 Desert Style (IRE)—Sanpala (Sanglamore (USA)) (150000) **H.R.H. Sultan Ahmad Shah**
75 **SHAMPAGNE**, b c 7/3 Orpen (USA)—Arndilly (Robellino) (32000) **Sisters Syndicate**
76 B f 26/3 Distorted Humor (USA)—
                                                            Skygusty (USA) (Skywalker (USA)) (82604) **Mr C.Wright & The Hon Mrs J.M.Corbett**
77 **STELLAR CAUSE (USA)**, ch c 13/3 Giant's Causeway (USA)—
                                                            Stellar (USA) (Grand Slam (USA)) (63168) **Mrs F. H. Hay**
78 **SULTANS WAY (IRE)**, b c 14/5 Indian Ridge—
                                                            Roses From Ridey (IRE) (Petorius) (90089) **H.R.H. Sultan Ahmad Shah**
79 **SUTANIA**, b f 10/2 Nayef (USA)—Suta (GER) (Lomitas) **Mrs E. A. Bass**
80 B c 8/5 Rock of Gibraltar (IRE)—
                                                            Taking Liberties (IRE) (Royal Academy (USA)) (110000) **H.R.H. Sultan Ahmad Shah**
81 Gr ro f 16/4 Smarty Jones (USA)—Terre Haute (USA) (Caro) (48590) **Wansdyke Farms**
82 **TIDAL FORCE (USA)**, ch c 14/4 High Yield (USA)—Shady Waters (CAN) (Rahy (USA)) **Parrish Hill Partnerships**
83 **TRESSWAY (IRE)**, b f 20/4 Giant's Causeway—Chantress (Peintre Celebre (USA)) (85000) **Mr D. S. Lee**
84 B c 5/3 Indian Ridge—Violet Spring (IRE) (Exactly Sharp (USA)) (155000) **Mrs L. Spencer**
85 B c 16/3 Lion Heart (USA)—Waterwild (USA) (River Special (USA)) (36443) **Meyrick & Dunnington-Jefferson**

MR P. F. I. COLE—continued

Other Owners: Mr Ben Arbib, Sir Martyn Arbib, Axom, Mr T. M. Bird, Mr A. Black, Mrs K. F. Bourdon, Mr G. E. Buckham, Mr C. M. Budgett, Mr M. Channon, Mrs P. F. I. Cole, Mr P. F. I. Cole, The Hon Mrs C. Corbett, Mr M. Corcell, Mr S. H. Davies, Mr Dan Downie, Sir Mervyn Dunnington-Jefferson, Mrs Lynne Edwards, Mr R. A. Esau, Mr S. G. Friend, Mrs A. Gamble, D. A. Gamble, Mr E. R. Goodwin, P. E. Hannon, Mr David Herbert, Mr Tony Hill, Mr C. W. Little, Mr J. D. McLaughlin, Miss Daisy Meyrick, Sir George Meyrick, Miss M. Noden, Mr D. C. G. Ollis, P. F. I. Cole Ltd, Mr Faisal Salman, Miss C. S. Scott-Balls, Mr D. M. Thomas, Mr Colin Williams, Mr J. Wray, Mrs Chris Wright.

Assistant Trainer: Oliver Cole

Jockey (flat): Nelson De Souza, Richard Quinn. **Apprentice:** Duilio Da Silva.

---

115 MR ROBERT COLLET, Chantilly
Postal: **32, Avenue Marie Amelie, 60500 Chantilly, France**
Contacts: **PHONE (0033) 3445 70672 FAX (0033) 3445 73225 MOBILE (0033) 6087 89709**
E-MAIL collet-robert@wanadoo.fr

1 **ALLODIAL LAND (USA),** 9, b h Woodman (USA)—Min Elreeh (USA) **Ecurie Vallin**
2 **ATLAS DU BERLAIS (FR),** 4, gr g Saint des Saints (FR)—Phedre Du Berlais (FR) **Mr R. Collet**
3 **BABOUCHE (FR),** 7, b g Desert Prince (IRE)—Les Trois Lamas (FR) **Mr Y. Lamara**
4 **BAKARAT DU BERLAIS (FR),** 4, b g Bonnet Rouge (FR)—Cindy Cad (FR) **Mr R. Collet**
5 **BAMAROK (FR),** 8, b g Loup Solitaire (USA)—Nadelia (FR) **Mrs C. Wingtans**
6 **BELLOZANE (FR),** 4, ro f Enrique—Mazal **Mr Arbib**
7 **BENODET (IRE),** 6, b g King's Best (USA)—Pont-Aven **Ecurie Vallin**
8 **CALASETTA (IRE),** 4, b f Montjeu (IRE)—Mahalia (IRE) **Mr Lucas**
9 **CARLA SONG (FR),** 4, b f Nikos—Carla (FR) **Mr C. Cohen**
10 **DANE DANCER (IRE),** 4, b c Trempolino (USA)—Dawn Dane (FR) **Mr R. Collet**
11 **DE ZEPHYR (FR),** 6, b h Zieten (USA)—Lyceta **B. S. Racing SARL Limited**
12 **DIAMOND SQUARE (FR),** 4, ch f Dyhim Diamond (IRE)—All Square (FR) **Mr Van Dalfsen**
13 **ECLAIR FILANTE,** 4, b c Red Ransom (USA)—Bielska (USA)
14 **ELIXIR DU BERLAIS (FR),** 4, b c Loup Solitaire (USA)—Euil Eagle (FR) **Mr R. Collet**
15 **FABULOUSLY (FR),** 5, b g Antarctique (IRE)—Far Away Girl (FR) **Mr R. Collet**
16 **FAIR ATTITUDE (IRE),** 4, b g King's Theatre (IRE)—No Way (IRE) **Ecurie Vallin**
17 **FAIRY DRESS (IRE),** 4, b f Fasliyev (USA)—Sun Spray (USA) **Miss M. Vidal**
18 **GALMA (FR),** 5, b m Goldneyev—Clarstone (FR) **Mr C. Cohen**
19 **IRIS DU BERLAIS (FR),** 4, b f Bonnet Rouge (FR)—Isis Du Berlais (FR) **Mr Van Dalfsen**
20 **LA BOUM (GER),** 5, b br m Monsun (GER)—La Bouche (GER) **Mr E. Trussardi**
21 **LAC MAJEUR (FR),** 4, b c Daliapour (IRE)—Charming Quest (USA) **Mr A. Azoulay**
22 **MAGIC SARAH (IRE),** 4, ch f Alhaarth (IRE)—Personal Best (IRE) **Mr Valente**
23 **MIKOS (FR),** 8, b g Sicyos (USA)—Sex Pistol (FR) **Mr V. Esposito**
24 **MISTER CHOCOLATE (IRE),** 5, br g Night Shift (USA)—Terracotta Hut **Famille Vidal**
25 **OCEAN DU COCHET (FR),** 6, gr g Grey Risk (FR)—Carentoire (FR) **Mr R. Collet**
26 **OVIDIE (FR),** 6, gr m Gold Away (IRE)—Linaving (FR) **Mr C. Cohen**
27 **PALAFAMIX (FR),** 5, gr g Linamix (FR)—Palafairia (FR) **Ecurie Vallin**
28 **POPULONIA (FR),** 5, b m Polish Precedent (USA)—Sudaka (FR) **Mr C. Cohen**
29 **PSY CHIC (FR),** 4, b c Munir—Psycadelic (FR) **Mrs C. Dubuquoi**
30 **SOFTLANDING (IRE),** 5, b m Nashwan (USA)—Forest Rain (FR) **Haras de la Sas**
31 **SPHINX DU BERLAIS (FR),** 9, b g Nikos—La Taiga (FR) **Miss M. Vidal**
32 **SPRING IS HERE (FR),** 4, ch c King's Best (USA)—Aube d'irlande (FR) **Ecurie Vallin**
33 **TAILSPIN (USA),** 7, ch g Tale of The Cat (USA)—Devil's Nell (USA) **Mr M. Hassan**
34 **TANGO DE L'ORME (FR),** 4, ch g Limnos (JPN)—Yeshaan (FR) **Mr R. Collet**
35 **TEXTOS (FR),** 4, gr f Kaldounevees (FR)—Marie de Pharis (FR) **Mr R. Collet**
36 **TOM'S GIRL FRIEND (FR),** 4, ch f Red Guest (IRE)—L'astree (FR) **Mr R. Collet**
37 **TOO NICE (FR),** 6, gr h Kaldounevees (FR)—Toomixa (FR) **Ecurie Vallin**
38 **TYCOON'S HILL (FR),** 9, b g Danehill (USA)—Tycoon's Drama (IRE) **Miss M. Vidal**
39 **WINGSTAR (IRE),** 4, b f In The Wings—Thirtysomething (USA) **Mr G. Deprez**
40 **WINTER DREAM (IRE),** 4, gr c Act One—Settler **Mr R. Strauss**
41 **ZALIANA (FR),** 4, gr f Daliapour (IRE)—Gandelia (FR) **Miss C. Wingtans**
42 **ZIZANY (IRE),** 5, b h Zafonic (USA)—Zelda (IRE) **Mrs A. Koropoulis**

THREE-YEAR-OLDS

43 **A MAGIC DAY (FR),** b c Miesque's Son (USA)—Kenny Glitters (FR) **Classic Breeding**
44 **ALBISOLA (IRE),** b f Montjeu (IRE)—Mahalia (IRE) **Mr G. Oldham**
45 **ANGEL OF RAIN (IRE),** gr c Dalakhani (IRE)—Mystic Mile (IRE) **Mr R. Collet**

MR ROBERT COLLET—continued

46 **BEAUTY MOON (FR)**, b f Daliapour (IRE)—Moon Shine (FR) **Ne Chee Siong**
47 **BLUE GIN (FR)**, b c Anabaa (USA)—Dancing Rose (FR) **Ecurie Vallin**
48 **DOOKUS (IRE)**, gr f Linamix (FR)—Pharaoh's Delight **Ballylinch Stud**
49 **ECLAIR MAGIQUE (IRE)**, b c Fasliyev (USA)—Miss Satamixa (FR)
50 **FLEURINA (FR)**, b f Le Triton (USA)—Florfilla (FR) **Ecurie Vallin**
51 **ICE CUBES (FR)**, gr f Verglas (IRE)—Charming Quest (USA) **Mr R. Collet**
52 **LA MADONETTA (FR)**, gr f Night Shift (USA)—Venize (IRE) **Mr R. Strauss**
53 **MIESQUINE (FR)**, b f Miesque's Son (USA)—Shatoush (FR) **Mr R. Collet**
54 **MISS DENMARK**, b f Invincible Spirit (IRE)—Hot Coal (USA) **B. S. Racing SARL Limited**
55 **MONT JOKER (FR)**, b c Montjeu (IRE)—Prudence Royale (FR) **Famille Vidal**
56 **NEIGE ETERNEL (FR)**, gr c Verglas (IRE)—Frenchtreska (FR) **Ecurie Vallin**
57 **NEW BOYFRIEND (IRE)**, b c High Chaparral (IRE)—New Story (USA) **Mr R. Strauss**
58 **PELVOUX (FR)**, b c Diktat—Thiva (USA) **Meridian International**
59 **PETILLE (FR)**, b f Indian Rocket—Fancy Lady (FR) **Mr Arbib**
60 **PRESIDENTIABLE (FR)**, b c Anabaa (USA)—Life On The Road (IRE) **B. S. Racing SARL Limited**
61 **PRINCESSE AMANDINE (FR)**, b f King's Theatre (IRE)—Nougatina **Mr R. Collet**
62 **RECAMBE (IRE)**, b f Cape Cross (IRE)—Razana (IRE) **Mr M. Clifford**
63 **REY DAVIS (IRE)**, b c King Charlemagne (USA)—San Luis Rey **Famille Vidal**
64 **RI LE CHARTREUX (FR)**, b c Daliapour (IRE)—Dear Shrimp (FR) **Ng Chee Siong**
65 **ROSCOFF (FR)**, b f Daylami (IRE)—Traou Mad (IRE) **Mr R. Strauss**
66 **RUE ROYALE (IRE)**, b c Anabaa (USA)—Diamond Field (USA) **Famille Vidal**
67 **SAM LION (FR)**, b c Muhtathir—Blue Daisy (USA) **Classic Breeding**
68 **SET ET MATCH (IRE)**, b f Barathea (IRE)—Settler **Mr R. Strauss**
69 **SINGAPORE NICK (FR)**, b c Sagacity (FR)—Lias Creek **Haras De La Sas**
70 **SINGAPORE SPEED (FR)**, b c Mtoto—Madame Est Sortie (FR) **Haras de la Sas**
71 **SINGAPORE TRAMP (FR)**, b c Trempolino (USA)—Singapore Star (FR) **Haras de la Sas**
72 **SUDAMY (FR)**, b c Black Sam Bellamy (IRE)—Sudaka (FR) **Mr C. Cohen**
73 **SWEET AND SOUR (IRE)**, b f Kalanisi (IRE)—Graten (FR) **Mr B. Hayes**
74 **TABOO (GER)**, b f Pivotal—Templerin (GER) **B. S. Racing SARL Limited**
75 **TERIBLE MICHEL (FR)**, gr c Daliapour (IRE)—Khariyada (FR) **Ne Chee Siong**
76 **WAIT AND SEE (FR)**, b f Montjeu (IRE)—Dareen (IRE) **Famille Vidal**

TWO-YEAR-OLDS

77 B c 11/3 Dansili—Aka Lady (FR) (Sanglamore (USA)) (115830) **B. S. Racing SARL Limited**
78 **ARIANE JELOIS (FR)**, b f 9/5 Marchand de Sable (USA)—Vallya Star (FR) (Saumarez) **Mr R. Collet**
79 **BAHALI (FR)**, gr f 12/1 Bahhare (USA)—Linaving (FR) (Linamix (FR)) (30888) **Miss S. Vidal**
80 B f 14/1 Giant's Causeway—Because (IRE) (Sadler's Wells (USA)) (255102) **Mr Scherrer**
81 **BONJOUR L'AFRICAN (FR)**, b c 1/1 Timboroa—Mamana (IRE) (Highest Honor (FR)) **Mr M. Hassan**
82 **BUFERA (IRE)**, b f 14/2 King's Best—Mahalia (IRE) (Danehill (USA)) **Mr G. Oldham**
83 **CHOCK A BLOCK (IRE)**, gr c 17/2 Dalakhani (IRE)—Choc Ice (IRE) (Kahyasi) **Mr R. Strauss**
84 Ch c 11/5 Kendor (FR)—Dareen (IRE) (Rahy (USA)) (41827) **Famille Vidal**
85 **DETACHE MOI (FR)**, b f 4/3 Septieme Ciel—Kal Secret (FR) (Kaldoun (FR)) (3861)
86 **DIKTATING**, b c 10/3 Diktat—Zapping (IRE) (Lycius (USA)) (19305) **Ecurie Skymarc**
87 B f 1/3 Anabaa (USA)—Gontcharova (IRE) (Zafonic (USA)) (96525) **B. S. Racing SARL Limited**
88 Gr c 14/4 Linamix (FR)—Gueridia (IRE) (Night Shift (USA)) (186615) **B. S. Racing SARL Limited**
89 **KAZATCHOK (IRE)**, ch f 26/4 King Charlemagne (USA)—Mawhiba (USA) (Dayjur (USA)) **Mr M. Hassan**
90 B c 2/2 Gone West (USA)—La Promenade (ARG) (Southern Halo (USA)) (102040) **Ecurie Vallin**
91 **LADOUCE (FR)**, b f 14/4 Ski Chief (USA)—Veliana (FR) (Vettori (IRE)) **Ecurie Vallin**
92 B f 29/5 Fasliyev (USA)—Mainmise (USA) (Septieme Ciel (USA)) (25740) **Famille Vidal**
93 **MORNING SMILE (IRE)**, b c 1/2 Haafhd—New Story (USA) (Dynaformer (USA)) (244530) **Mr R. Strauss**
94 B c 14/2 Green Tune (USA)—No Exit (FR) (Exit To Nowhere (USA)) (39897) **Famille Vidal**
95 **PATRON DU LOGIS**, b c 5/3 Exceed And Excel (AUS)—
                              Portella (GER) (Protektor (GER)) (27027) **B. S. Racing SARL Limited**
96 **PORT MANECH (IRE)**, b c 13/2 King's Best (USA)—Lethals Lady (Rudimentary (USA)) **Mr R. Strauss**
97 **QUEEN AMERICA (FR)**, b f 4/4 American Post—Gandelia (FR) (Ganges (USA)) **Mrs C. Wingtans**
98 **REINE DES MERS (IRE)**, br f 24/1 Alhaarth (USA)—Venize (IRE) (Kaldoun (FR)) **Mr R. Strauss**
99 Ch c 1/4 Exceed And Excel (AUS)—Rue Pigalle (IRE) (Bluebird (USA)) (35392)
100 Ch c 26/1 Thunder Gulch (USA)—Scottie (IRE) (Be My Guest) (38610) **Famille Vidal**
101 **SINGAPORE PINK (FR)**, b f 1/1 Sagacity (FR)—Doliouchka (Saumarez) **Haras de la Sas**
102 **SINGAPORE TROY (FR)**, b c 6/4 Sagacity (FR)—Trojan Miss (Troy) **Haras de la Sas**
103 B c 15/5 Sadler's Wells (USA)—Soviet Artic (FR) (Bering) (32175) **Famille Vidal**
104 **THORNS OF LIFE (USA)**, b f 13/3 Fusaichi Pegasus (USA)—
                             After Taxes (USA) (Nureyev (USA)) (87463) **Mr R. Strauss**
105 **TREVIGNANO (IRE)**, b c 18/2 Peintre Celebre (USA)—Perugina (FR) (Highest Honor (FR)) **Mr G. Oldham**

MR ROBERT COLLET—continued

106 B f 7/2 Elusive Quality (USA)—Watership Crystal (IRE) (Sadler's Wells (USA)) (242954) **Mr Scherrer**
107 B f 5/3 Cape Cross (IRE)—Zelding (IRE) (Warning) (501930) **Mr Scherrer**

116 MR H. J. COLLINGRIDGE, Newmarket
Postal: **Harraton Court Stables, Chapel Street, Exning, Newmarket, Suffolk, CB8 7HA**
Contacts: PHONE **(01638) 577288** FAX **(01638) 577952** MOBILE **(07748) 614912**

1 BID FOR GLORY, 4, ch c Auction House (USA)—Woodland Steps **Harraton Court One**
2 BLUE HEDGES, 6, b h Polish Precedent (USA)—Palagene **N. H. Gardner**
3 JOSR'S MAGIC (IRE), 4, b g Josr Algarhoud (IRE)—Just The Trick (USA) **Ken Tyre & Lee Tyre**
4 LORD LAING (USA), 5, b br g Chester House (USA)—Johanna Keene (USA) **Maynard Durrant Partnership II**
5 MOTARJM (USA), 4, br g Elusive Quality (USA)—Agama (USA) **P. D. Band**
6 REGIS FLIGHT, 5, b g Piccolo—Anthem Flight (USA)
7 ROCHESIS, 5, b m Mujahid (USA)—Northern Bird **Rochester Racing**
8 ROYAL PREMIER (IRE), 5, b g King's Theatre (IRE)—Mystic Shadow (IRE) **Maynard Durrant Partnership I**
9 RUBY BLADE, 4, b f Averti (IRE)—Lady of Jakarta (USA) **Miss D. T. Hamblin**
10 SOCIAL RHYTHM, 4, b f Beat All (USA)—Highly Sociable **A. Fairfield**
11 SORREL POINT, 5, b h Bertolini (USA)—Lightning Princess **Mrs D. A. Carter**
12 TAJJREE, 5, b m Lujain (USA)—Rateeba **www.network-racing.com**

THREE-YEAR-OLDS

13 ATHBOY AUCTION, b f Auction House (USA)—Thabeh **J Hancock D McGovern H J Collingridge**
14 BID TO THE BEAT, b c Auction House (USA)—Sophies Symphony **Harraton Court Two**
15 PAINT THE TOWN RED, b c Mujahid (USA)—Onefortheditch (USA) **Miss C. Fordham**
16 TOBALLA, b f Tobougg (IRE)—Ball Gown **Prima Racing Partnership**

Other Owners: Mrs S. Boutflower, Ms Sue Cawthorn, Mr H. J. Collingridge, Mr R. J. Durrant, Miss C. Fordham, Mr John Hancock, Mr C. V. Lines, Mr R. L. Maynard, Mr D. McGovern, Exors of the Late Mr Craig Mitchell, Mrs D. A. Mitchell, Mr S. Morley, Mr M. Roper, Mr K. Tyre, Mr L. Tyre, Mr P. Uniacke, Mr M. J. Wilson.

Jockey (flat): J. Quinn. Amateur: Miss A. L. Hutchinson.

117 MR W. S. COLTHERD, Selkirk
Postal: **Clarilawmuir Farm, Selkirk**
Contacts: PHONE **(01750) 21251** FAX **(01750) 21251** MOBILE **(07801) 398199**
E-MAIL **wscoltherd@clarilawmuir.wanadoo.co.uk**

1 CORBIE LYNN, 11, ch m Jumbo Hirt (USA)—Kilkenny Gorge **J. R. Cheyne**
2 JANAL (IRE), 5, b g Taipan (IRE)—Ben Roseler (IRE) **Alex & Janet Card**
3 MAE MOSS, 7, b m Cayman Kai (IRE)—Miss Brook **Stuart Coltherd, Alex & Janet Card**
4 MERLAWS, 5, ch m Supreme Sound—Colisnova **Mrs I. A. Forrest**
5 MISS PIMPINELLA, 4, b f Bal Harbour—Adjusting (IRE) **Harelaw Racing**
6 POWER STRIKE (USA), 7, b g Coronado's Quest (USA)—Galega **Saltire Racing Club**
7 ROYAL GLEN (IRE), 10, b m Royal Abjar (USA)—Sea Glen (IRE) **W. S. Coltherd**
8 TARTAN SNOW, 8, b g Valseur (USA)—Whitemoss Leader (IRE) **Whitemoss Golf Syndicate**

Other Owners: Mr P. W. Boylett, Mr A. M. Card, Mrs J. A. Card, Mr S. Coltherd, Mrs S. D. B. Lyons, Mr B. F. Lyons, Mr P. H. Pitchford, Mr R. V. Westwood, Mrs Edith Westwood.

Jockey (NH): R. McGrath, P. Aspell, A. Dempsey, B. Harding, G. Lee.

118 LADY CONNELL, Brackley
Postal: **Steane Park, Brackley, Northamptonshire, NN13 6DP**
Contacts: PHONE **(01280) 705899** FAX **(01280) 700873**

1 COURT ADJOURN, 11, b g North Col—Tapalong **Sir Michael Connell**
2 COURT ARISE, 6, b g Classic Cliche (IRE)—Sarah Dream (IRE) **Sir Michael Connell**
3 EXCEPTIONNEL (FR), 9, b g Subotica (FR)—The Exception (FR) **Lady Connell**
4 MAESTRO PLEASE (IRE), 9, b g Old Vic—Greek Melody (IRE) **S. J. Connell**
5 NEEDS TIME (IRE), 7, gr g Lord Americo—Galice Du Soleil (FR) **Lady Connell**

LADY CONNELL—continued

6 **SUNDAY LUNCH (IRE)**, 7, b g Topanoora—Suir Side Lady (IRE) **Sir Michael Connell**
7 **THE FAST FROG (FR)**, 7, b g Kadalko (FR)—Alba Terra (FR) **J. E. Connell**
8 **WHAT ABOUT THIS (IRE)**, 7, b g Fourstars Allstar (USA)—Bint Alsarab **Sir Michael Connell**

Assistant Trainer: Mr Christopher Henn

Amateur: Mr T. Lane, Mr S. Morris.

---

119   MR A. B. COOGAN, Ely
Postal: **31 Hasse Road, Soham, Ely, Cambridgeshire, CB7 5UW**

1 **MATSUNOSUKE**, 6, b g Magic Ring (IRE)—Lon Isa **A. B. Coogan**

THREE-YEAR-OLDS

2 **LADY FLORENCE**, gr f Bollin Eric—Silver Fan **A. B. Coogan**

---

120   MR M. J. COOMBE, Weymouth
Postal: **Sea Barn Farm, Fleet, Weymouth, Dorset, DT3 4ED**
Contacts: **PHONE (01305) 761745 FAX (01305) 775396 MOBILE (07796) 990760**
E-MAIL wib@seabarn.fsnet.co.uk

1 **CHESIL BEACH BOY**, 5, b g Commanche Run—Eatons **C. C. Pugsley**
2 **DALARAM (IRE)**, 8, b g Sadler's Wells (USA)—Dalara (IRE) **J. D. Roberts**
3 **GO ON AHEAD (IRE)**, 8, b g Namaqualand (USA)—Charm The Stars **Mr Richard G. Cuddihy**
4 **SUPPLEMENTARY (IRE)**, 6, b m Rudimentary—Will She What **M. J. Coombe**

Assistant Trainer: Mrs M Roberts

Amateur: Mrs M. Roberts.

---

121   MR L. A. CORCORAN, Kingsbridge
Postal: **Bearscombe Farm Stables, Kingsbridge, Devon, TQ7 2DW**
Contacts: **PHONE (01548) 853614**

1 **AWARD WINNING (IRE)**, 7, b g Oscar (IRE)—Mum's Pride (IRE) **Mrs S. L. Corcoran**
2 **CONVINCING GREY (IRE)**, 6, gr g Convinced—Run Sparky (IRE) **Inter Property Consultancy Ltd**
3 **CREESLOUGH (IRE)**, 4, ch g Riverwise (USA)—Drum Majorette **The A T P Racing Partnership**
4 **FABIAN THE FOX**, 5, b g Parthian Springs—Weldcome **Inter Property Consultancy Ltd**
5 **FEELING (IRE)**, 5, b g Sadler's Wells (USA)—La Pitie (USA) **GD Building & Roofing Contractors Ltd**
6 **JAZZ SCENE (IRE)**, 7, b g Danehill Dancer (IRE)—Dixie Jazz **The A T P Racing Partnership**
7 **LADY OMARA (IRE)**, 5, br m Presenting—Port Queen (IRE) **Inter Property Consultancy Ltd**
8 **MAGICAL LEGEND**, 7, gr m Midnight Legend—Alice's Mirror **R. H. Kerswell**
9 **MAGICAL TREASURE**, 4, gr g Riverwise (USA)—Alice's Mirror **R. H. Kerswell**
10 **MAGICAL WONDERLAND**, 9, gr m Thowra (FR)—Alice's Mirror **R. H. Kerswell**
11 **MARY DUANE**, 4, b f Tragic Role (USA)—Brush Belle **Inter Property Consultancy Ltd**
12 **MR MAXIM**, 6, ch g Lake Coniston (IRE)—White Hare **G. Doel**
13 **NOTHING IS FOREVER (IRE)**, 4, b g Daylami (IRE)—Bequeath (USA) **Mr P. A. Edwards**
14 **PIPER MILLIN**, 5, b g Parthian Springs—Seymour Rambler **Inter Property Consultancy Ltd**
15 **READY RESPONSE (IRE)**, 6, gr g Gothland (FR)—Ballygrangans Lady (IRE) **Inter Property Consultancy Ltd**
16 **ROMANCE DANCE**, 5, b m Terimon—Run On Stirling **Inter Property Consultancy Ltd**
17 **SABY (FR)**, 10, b br g Sassanian (USA)—Valy Flett (FR) **Setsquare Recruitment**
18 **SILVERHAY**, 7, b g Inchinor—Moon Spin **GD Building & Roofing Contractors Ltd**
19 **TALLOW ROAD (IRE)**, 6, br m Anshan—Menedreams (IRE) **Mrs E. M. Worth**
20 **TEL NERO (IRE)**, 5, br g Tel Quel (FR)—Nero's Gem **Inter Property Consultancy Ltd**
21 **WALDO PEPPER (IRE)**, 4, b g Carroll House—Mimosa Rose (IRE) **Inter Property Consultancy Ltd**

Other Owners: Mr A. J. McClafferty, Mr P. J. O'Grady, Mr T. A. Parker, Mr James Parsons.

Assistant Trainer: Mrs S. Corcoran

Jockey (NH): T. J. Murphy. **Conditional:** T. Malone. **Amateur:** Mr L. Adams.

122 **MR J. R. CORNWALL, Melton Mowbray**
Postal: **April Cottage, Pasture Lane, Hose, Melton Mowbray, Leicestershire, LE14 4LB**
Contacts: **PHONE** (01664) 444453 **FAX** (01664) 444754 **MOBILE** (07939) 557091

1 **ART VIRGINIA (FR)**, 9, b g Art Bleu—Sweet Jaune (FR) **J. R. Cornwall**
2 **AVIEMORE**, 6, b g Selkirk (USA)—Film Script **J. R. Cornwall**
3 **CLOCKERS CORNER (IRE)**, 11, b g Eurobus—Pampered Finch VII **J. R. Cornwall**
4 **HE'S MY MAN (IRE)**, 10, b g Be My Native (USA)—That's The Bonus (IRE) **J. R. Cornwall**
5 **LOG ON INTERSKY (IRE)**, 12, ch g Insan (USA)—Arctic Mo (IRE) **J. R. Cornwall**
6 **SUPREME LEISURE (IRE)**, 11, b g Supreme Leader—Maid of Leisure **J. R. Cornwall**

Amateur: Mr Joseph Cornwall.

123 **MR J. F. COUPLAND, Grimsby**
Postal: **College Farm, The Avenue, East Ravendale, Grimsby, South Humberside, DN37 0RX**

1 **APRES SKI (IRE)**, 5, b g Orpen (USA)—Miss Kinabalu **J. F. Coupland**
2 **ERROL**, 9, ch g Dancing Spree (USA)—Primo Panache **J. F. Coupland**
3 **NEVER WITHOUT ME**, 8, ch g Mark of Esteem (IRE)—Festival Sister **J. F. Coupland**
4 **OOPS (IRE)**, 9, b g In The Wings—Atsuko (IRE) **J. F. Coupland**
5 **RAVEN RASCAL**, 4, b f Zaha (CAN)—Eccentric Dancer **J. F. Coupland**
6 **STARCROSS MAID**, 6, ch m Zaha (CAN)—Maculatus (USA) **J. F. Coupland**

THREE-YEAR-OLDS

7 **LITTLE BONES**, ch f Tobougg (IRE)—City Gambler **J. F. Coupland**
8 **SHEIK'N'KNOTSTERD**, ch g Zaha (CAN)—Royal Ivy **J. F. Coupland**
9 **TANLEY**, gr g Compton Admiral—Schatzi **J. F. Coupland**

124 **MR R. M. H. COWELL, Newmarket**
Postal: **Bottisham Heath Stud, Six Mile Bottom, Newmarket, Suffolk, CB8 0TT**
Contacts: **PHONE** (01638) 570330 **FAX** (01638) 570246 **MOBILE** (07785) 512463
E-MAIL cowellracing@aol.com **WEBSITE** www.robertcowellracing.co.uk

1 **BINIOU (IRE)**, 5, b h Mozart (IRE)—Cap Coz (IRE) **Dasmal,Stennett,Rix,Barr,Mrs Penney**
2 **CANADIAN DANEHILL (IRE)**, 6, b h Indian Danehill (IRE)—San Jovita (CAN) **T. W. Morley**
3 **DESERT DUST**, 5, b g Vettori (IRE)—Dust **Bottisham Heath Stud**
4 **FANTASY CRUSADER**, 9, ch g Beveled (USA)—Cranfield Charger **The Fantasy Fellowship**
5 **GO MO (IRE)**, 6, b g Night Shift (USA)—Quiche **Bottisham Heath Stud**
6 **IMMINENT VICTORY**, 5, b g Benny The Dip (USA)—Brave Vanessa (USA) **K. A. Dasmal**
7 **OVERWING (IRE)**, 5, b m Fasliyev (USA)—Sierva (GER) **Keith Robinson & Ian Robinson**
8 **PRIDE OF MINE**, 5, b m Kayf Tara—Triple Zee (USA) **K. A. Dasmal**
9 **SURWAKI (USA)**, 6, b g Miswaki (USA)—Quinella **Tessona Racing Ltd**
10 **TABOOR (IRE)**, 10, b g Mujadil (USA)—Christoph's Girl **T. W. Morley**

THREE-YEAR-OLDS

11 **ACTION GIRL**, gr f Act One—Mohican Girl **Bottisham Heath Stud**
12 **CHANTILLY JEWEL**, b f Century City (IRE)—Betty's Star (USA) **John. J. Greely IV**
13 **HURRICANE HARRIET**, b f Bertolini (USA)—Cold Blow **Mr & Mrs R Foulkes & Mrs Eugenie AbelSmith**
14 **REGAL STEP**, b f Royal Applause—Two Step **Highclere Thoroughbred Racing I**
15 **ROSIE SAYS NO**, b f Catcher In The Rye (IRE)—Curlew Calling (IRE) **The Hercules Horseracing Syndicate**
16 **SUMMER ROSE**, gr f Kyllachy—Roses of Spring **Bottisham Heath Stud**

TWO-YEAR-OLDS

17 **AIR LION (USA)**, b c 7/1 Lion Heart (USA)—
Swigert (USA) (Fusaichi Pegasus (USA)) (30126) **Atlantic Thoroughbreds**
18 B c 8/4 Ishiguru (USA)—Fancier Bit (Lion Cavern (USA)) (3000) **Fantasy Fellowship Partnership**
19 B br f 27/1 Deputy Commander (USA)—Greyciousness (USA) (Miswaki (USA)) (14577) **Prestige Racing**
20 B c 7/2 Doneraile Court (USA)—Incoming Missile (USA) (Touch Gold (USA)) (9718) **Prestige Racing**
21 B c 1/5 Tobougg (IRE)—Millymix (FR) (Linamix (FR)) (3333) **Khalifa Dasmal**
22 Ch c 12/4 Officer (USA)—Protea (USA) (Roanoke (USA)) (26724) **Atlantic Thoroughbreds**
23 B c 15/2 More Than Ready (USA)—Rise and Fall (USA) (Quiet American (USA)) (48590) **Prestige Racing**

MR R. M. H. COWELL—continued

24 B c 11/3 Diktat—Silent Miracle (IRE) (Night Shift (USA)) (761) **Khalifa Dasmal**
25 B c 18/1 Dixieland Band (USA)—

Spanish Harbor (USA) (Corporate Report (USA)) (19436) **Atlantic Thoroughbreds**

Other Owners: Mr F. G. Barr, Mr A. M. Blewitt, Mr Peter Coll, Mrs Eugenie Abel Smith, Mr Khalifa Dasmal, Mr Richard Foulkes, Mrs Richard Foulkes, Ms Susan Gibson, Mr F. Gorman, John Greeley IV, The Hon H. Herbert, Highclere Thoroughbred Racing Ltd, Miss Y. M. G. Jacques, Miss Yvonne Jacques, Mr T. W. Morley, Mrs M. J. Morley, Mrs. J. Morley, Mrs J. M. Penney, Mr Allen Rix, Mr Keith Robinson, Mr Ian J. Robinson, Mr Allan Stennett, J. T. Warner, Mr Terry Warner.

125 MR P. E. COWLEY, Banbury
Postal: **Lodge Farm Barn, Culworth, Banbury, Oxfordshire, OX17 2HL**
Contacts: **PHONE (01295) 768998 MOBILE (07775) 943346**
E-MAIL paulcowleyequine@yahoo.co.uk

1 BILLY MURPHY, 5, gr g Silver Patriarch (IRE)—Sperrin View **The BMWs**
2 KINGFISHER NIAMH, 8, b m Cloudings (IRE)—Legata (IRE) **S. G. West**
3 POLLOVER, 7, b m Overbury (IRE)—Vale of Mowbray **Mrs D. B. Cowley**
4 SUNDARBOB (IRE), 6, bl g Bob Back (USA)—Villian **Coombe Hill Racing**

Other Owners: Mr Richard Batchelor, Mr Bill Booth, Mr Charles Dixey, Mrs Helen Mobley, Mr A. J. Mobley, Mr John Moorhouse, Mrs Katie Sunderland, Mr D. E. Wilson, Miss Elizabeth Wilson.

126 MR C. G. COX, Hungerford
Postal: **Beechdown Farm, Sheepdrove Road, Lambourn, Hungerford, Berkshire, RG17 7UN**
Contacts: **OFFICE (01488) 73072 FAX 01488 73500 MOBILE (07740) 630521**
E-MAIL clive@clivecox.com WEBSITE www.clivecox.com

1 DANCING WIZARD, 4, ch g Dancing Spree (USA)—Magic Legs **R. B. Denny**
2 DANSILI DANCER, 6, b g Dansili—Magic Slipper **The Troupers**
3 DARLING DAISY, 4, ch f Komaite (USA)—Black And Amber **Mrs P. A. Scott-Dunn**
4 DEN'S GIFT (IRE), 4, gr ro g City On A Hill (USA)—Romanylei (IRE) **Mrs O. A. Shaw**
5 DRIFTING GOLD, 4, ch f Bold Edge—Driftholme **Martin C. Oliver**
6 DUNELIGHT (IRE), 5, ch h Desert Sun—Badee'a (IRE) **Mr & Mrs P. Hargreaves**
7 FAREFIELD LODGE (IRE), 4, b g Indian Lodge (IRE)—Fieldfare **The Beechdown Braves**
8 JIMMY STYLES, 4, ch g Inchinor—Inya Lake **Gwyn Powell & Peter Ridgers**
9 KOSTAR, 7, ch g Komaite (USA)—Black And Amber **Mrs P. Scott-Dunn & Mrs F. J. Ryan**
10 LADY SPLODGE, 4, b f Mark of Esteem (IRE)—La Victoria (GER) **Mr N. Agran & Mr R. Bareham**
11 MASON ETTE, 4, br f Grand Lodge (USA)—Karlaska **Brighthelm Racing**
12 ONE TO FOLLOW, 4, b g Mtoto—Becalmed **Pat & Brian Makepeace & Stephen Barrow**
13 OUT AFTER DARK, 7, b g Cadeaux Genereux—Midnight Shift (IRE) **The Night Owls**
14 PEARLY WEY, 5, b g Lujain (USA)—Dunkellin (USA) **D. Shaw**
15 PERFECT PRACTICE, 4, ch f Medicean—Giusina Mia (USA) **The Perfect Partnership II**
16 PERFECT STAR, 4, b f Act One—Granted (FR) **Dr Bridget Drew & Mr E E Dedman**

THREE-YEAR-OLDS

17 AMYLEE (IRE), b f Danehill Dancer (IRE)—Igreja (ARG) **D. Shaw**
18 BEACON LODGE (IRE), b c Clodovil (IRE)—Royal House (FR) **Mr & Mrs P. Hargreaves**
19 BREXCA (IRE), b g Diktat—Hemaca **P. G. Jacobs & Partners**
20 B f Mtoto—Cavina **P G Jacobs & A Signy**
21 CHELSEA GIRL, b f Kyllachy—Ghassanah **A. D. Spence**
22 CONQUISTO, ch g Hernando (FR)—Seal Indigo (IRE) **Reid's Racers**
23 DON'T FORGET FAITH (USA), b f Victory Gallop (CAN)—Contredance (USA) **Mr S. R. Hope & Mr S. W. Barrow**
24 DUNN'O (IRE), b g Cape Cross (IRE)—Indian Express **D. Shaw**
25 EASY STREET, b c Compton Place—Tart And A Half **Lady Whent**
26 ELECTROLYSER (IRE), gr c Daylami (IRE)—Iviza (IRE) **Mr & Mrs P. Hargreaves**
27 FANCY FOOTSTEPS (IRE), gr f Noverre (USA)—Fancy Intense **John & Anne Soul**
28 HIGHLAND DAUGHTER (IRE), b f Kyllachy—Raysiza (IRE) **Highland Thoroughbred Ltd**
29 Ch g Medicean—In Luck **Mr P J Skinner**
30 ISITANYWONDER, b g Anabaa (USA)—Woodwin (USA) **Richard & Daryl Bowden & Stephen Barrow**
31 LADY SPECIAL, b f Namid—Crevelli (IRE) **L. Buckley**
32 LITTLE TOTO, b c Mtoto—Moonlight Seas **Mr John Mason & Mr Philip Mason**
33 MEKONG MELODY (IRE), b f Cape Cross (IRE)—Nini Princesse (IRE) **Miss B. Egan**
34 MIRACLE SEEKER, br f Rainbow Quest (USA)—Miracle **D. J. Burke**

MR C. G. COX—continued

35 Ch g Zaha (CAN)—Mo Stopher **Canisbay Bloodstock**
36 **PERFECT ACT,** b f Act One—Markova's Dance **Dr Bridget Drew & Mr E E Dedman**
37 **PERFECT SILENCE,** b f Dansili—Perfect Echo **R. J. Vines**
38 **RED MERLIN (IRE),** ch g Soviet Star (USA)—Truly Bewitched (USA) **Reid's Allstars**
39 **SECRET GEM (IRE),** b f Cape Cross (IRE)—Orlena (USA) **Carmel Stud**

TWO-YEAR-OLDS

40 B f 14/4 Singspiel (IRE)—B Beautiful (IRE) (Be My Guest) (32000) **Mr A. Parker**
41 B f 21/3 Needwood Blade—Bollin Victoria (Jalmood (USA)) (5000) **L. Buckley**
42 **BOUGGIE DAIZE,** b f 15/2 Tobougg (IRE)—Milly's Lass (Mind Games) (1333) **Ken Lock Racing Ltd**
43 **BROOKLYN SPIRIT,** ch c 28/2 Cadeaux Genereux—
Serengeti Bride (USA) (Lion Cavern (USA)) (32000) **Gwyn Powell & Peter Ridgers**
44 **DAYANARA (USA),** b br f 31/3 Action This Day (USA)—
Dana Did It (USA) (Wagon Limit (USA)) (24295) **M. T. Watts**
45 **DECISION,** b c 11/2 Royal Applause—Corinium (IRE) (Turtle Island (IRE)) (52000) **A. D. Spence**
46 Ch c 27/3 Hold That Tiger (USA)—Fairy Dancer (Nijinsky (CAN)) (48590) **D. Shaw**
47 Ch f 26/1 Dixieland Band (USA)—Fran's Flash (USA) (Star de Naskra (USA)) (30126) **Highland Thoroughbred Ltd**
48 **GILT EDGE GIRL,** ch f 2/4 Monsieur Bond (IRE)—
Tahara (IRE) (Caerleon (USA)) (17000) **Wood Street Syndicate V & Mr C. J. Harper**
49 B f 2/3 Forest Wildcat (USA)—Kisses To Yall (USA) (Copelan (USA)) (26724)
50 Ch f 30/1 Desert Sun—Lindoras Glory (Gone West (USA)) (30000) **D. Shaw**
51 **LOUISE BONNE (USA),** b br f 11/4 Yes It's True (USA)—
Blushing Issue (Blushing John (USA)) (19436) **Old Peartree Stud**
52 **MORNING QUEEN,** b f 5/3 Night Shift (USA)—Woodland Glade (Mark of Esteem (IRE)) **Mr J. T. Thomas**
53 **NO MEAN TRICK (USA),** b c 14/4 Grand Slam (USA)—
Ruby's Reception (USA) (Rubiano (USA)) (48590) **Mr & Mrs P. Hargreaves**
54 B br f 20/3 Chapel Royal (USA)—Padrao Global (USA) (Storm Bird (CAN)) (43731) **S. R. Hope & Mrs S. Barrow**
55 **PERFECT CLASS,** b f 4/2 Cape Cross (IRE)—Liberty (Singspiel (IRE)) (27000) **Mr J. Drew & Dr B. Drew**
56 **POLLY'S MARK (IRE),** b f 2/4 Mark of Esteem (IRE)—Kotdiji (Mtoto) **Mr M. Flitton**
57 B br f 4/4 Grand Slam (USA)—Setting (USA) (Exclusive Native (USA)) (24295) **S. R. Hope & S. Barrow**
58 **SILKEN SANDS (IRE),** b f 3/1 Green Desert (USA)—Arctic Silk (Selkirk (USA)) (30000) **John & Anne Soul**
59 B c 16/4 Kyllachy—St James's Antigua (IRE) (Law Society (USA)) (16000) **Mr J. H. Wilkinson**
60 B c 14/3 Tobougg (IRE)—Surrealist (ITY) (Night Shift (USA)) (24000) **Mr D. Jones**
61 **TASTE THE WINE,** gr c 5/2 Verglas (IRE)—Àzia (IRE) (Desert Story (IRE)) (53000) **Jimmy & Susie Wenman**
62 B f 27/4 Hernando (FR)—Victoire Finale (Peintre Celebre (USA)) **Mr S. A. Stuckey**
63 **WHISKY GALORE,** ch c 2/5 Kyllachy—
Owdbetts (IRE) (High Estate) (45044) **Mr & Mrs P. Hargreaves & Mr A. D. Spence**

Other Owners: Mr N. Agran, Mr R. Bareham, Mr Stephen W. Barrow, Mr R. Bowden, Mr Daryl Bowden, Mr Tony Briam, Mrs L. Chandler, Mr G. W. Chandler, Mrs Jan Corden, Mrs T. L. Cox, Mr E. Dedman, Mr Dan Downie, Mr John Drew, Miss G. B. Drew, G. W. Elphick, Mr Jim Glasgow, Mrs A. M. Goor, Mr G. J. Hamer, Mr R. J. Hargreaves, Mr P. K. Hargreaves, Mr J. Hetherington, Lady Ruby Evelyn Hill, Mr Paul G. Jacobs, Mr Luke Lillingston, Mr B. D. Makepeace, Mrs P. Makepeace, Mr Philip Mason, Mr John Mason, Mr J. G. Moore, Mr Peter Morgan, Mrs Michelle Morgan, Miss M. Noden, Mr J. Osborne, Mr Gwyn Powell, Mr B. D. H. Preston, Mr R. J. H. Preston, Mr J. A. Reid, Mr Peter Ridgers, K. G. Rowley, Mrs F. J. Ryan, Mr Adam Signy, Mrs A. Sloyan, Mr J. Soul, Mrs A. Soul, J. Wenman, Mrs S. Wenman.

Assistant Trainer: Andrew Llewellyn

Jockey (flat): Richard Thomas, Adam Kirby, Philip Robinson. **Amateur:** Miss J. Ferguson.

127 **MR R. CRAGGS, Sedgefield**
Postal: **East Close Farm, Sedgefield, Stockton-On-Tees, Cleveland, TS21 3HW**
Contacts: **PHONE (01740) 620239 FAX (01740) 623476**

1 **SHAPE UP (IRE),** 8, b g Octagonal (NZ)—Bint Kaldoun (IRE) **R. Craggs**
2 **TOUR D'AMOUR (IRE),** 5, b m Fruits of Love (USA)—Touraneena **R. Craggs**
3 **WATERLOO CORNER,** 6, b g Cayman Kai (IRE)—Rasin Luck **R. Craggs**
4 **WITCHELLE,** 7, br m Wizard King—Tachelle (IRE) **R. Craggs**

Assistant Trainer: Miss J N Craggs

Amateur: Miss Nicola Craggs.

128 MR E. J. CREIGHTON, Hungerford
Postal: **Mabberleys Stables, Front Street, East Garston, Hungerford, Berkshire, RG17 7EU**
Contacts: **PHONE (01488) 648179 FAX (01488) 648179**
E-MAIL edwardcreighton@btinternet.com

1 **ALISAR (IRE)**, 8, b g Entrepreneur—Aliya (IRE) **The Vixens**
2 **CLIPPERDOWN (IRE)**, 7, b g Green Desert (USA)—Maroussie (FR) **Travel Spot LLP**
3 **DALCASSIAN (IRE)**, 8, b h Sadler's Wells (USA)—Twyla **The Vixens**
4 **FLAME CREEK (IRE)**, 12, b g Shardari—Sheila's Pet (IRE) **E. J. Creighton**
5 **GERTIE (IRE)**, 4, b f Redback—Rosalia (USA) **E. J. Creighton**
6 **JETHRO WHEELER**, 5, b g Marju (IRE)—Panorama **The Vixens**
7 **MAEVE (IRE)**, 4, b f Tomba—Boozy **E. J. Creighton**
8 **MEJHAR (IRE)**, 8, b g Desert Prince (USA)—Factice (USA) **The Vixens**
9 **MILLENIUM SUN (IRE)**, 4, b g Tendulkar (USA)—Millenium Love (IRE) **Se A Haon Syndicate**
10 **PERSEVERANCE (IRE)**, 8, ch g Van Der Linden (FR)—Glenair Melody (IRE) **The T. T. Syndicate**
11 **SCAR TISSUE**, 4, ch f Medicean—Possessive Lady **The Vixens**
12 **SEKULA PATA (NZ)**, 9, b g Pompeii Court (USA)—Torquay (NZ) **The Vixens**
13 **TAMWORTH (IRE)**, 6, b g Perugino (USA)—Faiblesse **E. J. Creighton**
14 **WELL BLESSED**, 5, b m Petoski—Danny Rhy **V. R. Bedley**
15 **ZAAFIRA (SPA)**, 4, b f Limpid—Hot Doris (IRE) **The Vixens**

Other Owners: Mr P. Coady, Ms T. Cornwell, Mrs C. Creighton, Mr P. Fox, Mr P. I. Harper, C. J. James, Mr A. Kirwan, Mr T. Lynam, Con Smyth, Mr C. H. Sterling.

Jockey (flat): Edward Creighton. **Apprentice:** Shane Creighton, Alan Creighton.

129 MR A. CROOK, Leyburn
Postal: **Lilac Cottage, Harmby, Leyburn, North Yorkshire, DL8 5PD**
Contacts: **PHONE (01969) 640302 (01969) 623096 FAX (01969) 640303 MOBILE (07764) 158899**
E-MAIL andycrookracing@fsmail.net WEBSITE www.andrewcrookracing.co.uk

1 **AMMEYRR**, 4, b g Mark of Esteem (IRE)—Walimu (IRE) **Mr C. Walker**
2 **CUTE N YOU KNOW IT**, 5, b m Tamure (IRE)—Clodaigh Gale **C Walker,A Gillway,J Saxby & Partnership**
3 **ESQUILLON**, 6, b m High Estate—Our Aisling
4 **JONTYS'LASS**, 7, b m Tamure (IRE)—Gay Muse **Minster Commercial Leasing**
5 **MATMATA DE TENDRON (FR)**, 8, gr g Badolato (USA)—Cora des Tamarix (FR) **Lucky Catch Partnership**
6 **MISTER MAQ**, 5, b g Namaqualand (USA)—Nordico Princess **Mr G. Gunn**
7 5, B g Presenting—Native Wood (USA) **R. P. E. Berry**
8 **NIZA D'ALM (FR)**, 7, b br m Passing Sale (FR)—Bekaa II (FR) **Lerigo Family**
9 5, B m Alflora (IRE)—Oriel Dream **Leeds Plywood & Doors Ltd**
10 **SPLENDIDIO**, 4, b f Zamindar (USA)—Diddymu (IRE) **Lucky Catch Partnership**
11 **STOLEN LIGHT (IRE)**, 7, ch g Grand Lodge (USA)—Spring To Light (USA) **Mrs H. Sinclair**
12 **STRATHAIRD (IRE)**, 4, b g Medicean—Heed My Warning (IRE) **John Sinclair (Haulage) Ltd**
13 **TIME FOR TARA**, 5, b m Kayf Tara—Keldholme **Minster Commercial Leasing**
14 **VICIOUS PRINCE (IRE)**, 9, b g Sadler's Wells (USA)—Sunny Flower (FR) **J. W. Coates**

THREE-YEAR-OLDS

15 B f Tamayaz (CAN)—Paper Flight **David Ward**
16 **TIEGAN AN JOSH**, b f Lahib (USA)—Poungada (FR) **Mr & Mrs Calderbank**

Other Owners: Mr J. Calderbank, Mrs J. Calderbank, Mr J. W. Coates, Mr A. Crook, Mr Alan Gillway, Mr Jim Gordon, Mrs S. Hollingsworth, Mr E. W. Lerigo, Mr Jim Lerigo, Mr Gordon Lerigo, Mrs Debra Lerigo, Mr J. Saxby, Mrs E. A. Webster, H. Young.

130 MISS J. P. CROWLEY, Whitcombe
Postal: **Whitcombe Moneymusk Racing Stables, Whitcombe, Dorchester, Dorset, DT2 8NY**
Contacts: **PHONE (01305) 265300 FAX (01305) 265499 MOBILE (07918) 735219**
E-MAIL jocrowley6@hotmail.co.uk

1 **ART MARKET (CAN)**, 5, ch g Giant's Causeway (USA)—Fantasy Lake (USA) **Mrs E. A. M. Nelson**
2 **BASRA (IRE)**, 5, b g Soviet Star (USA)—Azra (IRE) **Mrs E. A. M. Nelson**
3 **LEND A GRAND (IRE)**, 4, br g Lend A Hand—Grand Madam **Mrs E. A. M. Nelson**
4 **PATAVIUM PRINCE (IRE)**, 5, ch g Titus Livius (FR)—
Hoyland Common (IRE) **Mr B. Cains Mr C. Purnell Mr Clements**
5 **RYDAL (USA)**, 7, ch g Gilded Time (USA)—Tennis Partner (USA) **Mrs E. A. M. Nelson**

MISS J. P. CROWLEY—continued

6 **STARRY GIRL (IRE)**, 4, b f Fourstars Allstar (USA)—Yiayia's Girl **Mrs E. A. M. Nelson**
7 **TRIFTI**, 7, b g Vettori (IRE)—Time For Tea (IRE) **Mrs E. A. M. Nelson**

THREE-YEAR-OLDS

8 **LADY SANDICLIFFE (IRE)**, b f Noverre (USA)—Tigava (USA) **Mrs E. A. M. Nelson**
9 **SILVER HARRIET (IRE)**, gr f King Charlemagne (USA)—Silver Moon **Mrs E. A. M. Nelson**
10 **STRAIGHT AND LEVEL (CAN)**, gr c Buddha (USA)—Azusa (USA) **Mrs E. A. M. Nelson**

TWO-YEAR-OLDS

11 **CHAMPAGNE FIZZ (IRE)**, gr f 12/2 King Charlemagne (USA)—
Silver Moon (Environment Friend) **Mrs E. A. M. Nelson**
12 **IVORY'S ICON (IRE)**, gr c 25/1 Catcher In The Rye (IRE)—Ivory's Promise (Pursuit of Love) **Mrs E. A. M. Nelson**

Other Owners: Mr B. Cains, M. A. Clements, C. A. Lennan-Purnell.

Assistant Trainer: Paul Phillips

Jockey (flat): N. Callan, C. Catlin.

131
MR L. M. CUMANI, Newmarket
Postal: **Bedford House Stables, Bury Road, Newmarket, Suffolk, CB8 7BX**
Contacts: **PHONE (01638) 665432 FAX (01638) 667160 MOBILE (07801) 225300**
E-MAIL luca@lucacumani.com WEBSITE www.lucacumani.com

1 **AXIOM**, 4, ch c Pivotal—Exhibitor (USA) **DIC Racing Syndicate**
2 **BALTHAZAAR'S GIFT (IRE)**, 5, b h Xaar—Thats Your Opinion **Ms Nicola Mahoney & De La Warr Racing**
3 **BANKABLE (IRE)**, 4, b c Medicean—Dance To The Top **JMC Breed & Race Limited**
4 **BAUER (IRE)**, 5, gr h Halling (USA)—Dali's Grey **Aston House Stud**
5 **BOZ**, 4, gr c Grand Lodge (USA)—Dali's Grey **Aston House Stud**
6 **COSMODROME (USA)**, 4, b f Bahri (USA)—Space Time (FR) **Fittocks Stud**
7 **GHOST DANCER**, 4, ch c Danehill Dancer (IRE)—Reservation (IRE) **Kevin Bailey & Philip Booth**
8 **KAHARA**, 4, b f Sadler's Wells (USA)—Kithanga (IRE) **Fittocks Stud & Mrs John Magnier**
9 **LADIES BEST**, 4, b c King's Best (USA)—Lady of the Lake **R. C. Thompson**
10 **LEPIDO (ITY)**, 4, b g Montjeu (IRE)—Luv Is For Sharing (USA) **P. Makin**
11 **LIBOR (IRE)**, 5, b h Lend A Hand—America Lontana (FR) **Mrs A. S. Silver**
12 **LION SANDS**, 4, b c Montjeu (IRE)—Puce **The Alpen House ULC**
13 **MAD RUSH (USA)**, 4, b c Lemon Drop Kid (USA)—Revonda (IRE) **E. I. Mack**
14 **MILITARY CROSS**, 5, b g Cape Cross (IRE)—Tipsy **Mr R Thompson & Mr A Bengough**
15 **MONTE ALTO (IRE)**, 4, b c Danehill Dancer (IRE)—Peruvian Witch (IRE) **Mr T. M. Steel**
16 **PENTATONIC**, 5, b m Giant's Causeway (USA)—Fascinating Rhythm **Helena Springfield Ltd**
17 **PRESVIS**, 4, b g Sakhee (USA)—Forest Fire (SWE) **L. Marinopoulos**
18 **PURPLE MOON (IRE)**, 5, ch g Galileo (IRE)—Vanishing Prairie (USA) **C. Bennett**
19 **RIGGINS (IRE)**, 4, b c Cape Cross (IRE)—Rentless **Scuderia Rencati Srl**
20 **SAMIRA GOLD (FR)**, 4, ch f Gold Away (IRE)—Capework (USA) **J. Abdullah**
21 **SANBUCH**, 4, b c Tobougg (IRE)—Monte Calvo **Scuderia Rencati Srl**
22 **SPEED GIFTED**, 4, b c Montjeu (IRE)—Good Standing (USA) **JMC Breed & Race Limited**
23 **SPEED TICKET**, 4, b c Galileo (IRE)—Kassiyra (IRE) **JMC Breed & Race Limited**
24 **SWOP**, 5, b g Shinko Forest (IRE)—Changing Partners **Mrs A. S. Silver**
25 **WATCHFUL (IRE)**, 4, b f Galileo (IRE)—Sharakawa (IRE) **De La Warr Racing**
26 **WING EXPRESS (IRE)**, 4, b c Montjeu (IRE)—Eurobird **JMC Breed & Race Limited**

THREE-YEAR-OLDS

27 **ACROSTIC**, ch g Tobougg (IRE)—Royal Dream **L. Marinopoulos**
28 **ANNABELLE'S CHARM (IRE)**, ch f Indian Ridge—Kylemore (IRE) **Merry Fox Stud Limited**
29 **ATEESH**, ch c Medicean—Diana Panagaea **Sheikh Mohammed Obaid Al Maktoum**
30 **AWALEY (IRE)**, ch c Dr Fong (USA)—Hejraan Two (IRE) **Sheikh Mohammed Obaid Al Maktoum**
31 **BULLET MAN (USA)**, br c Mr Greeley (USA)—Silk Tapestry (USA) **Kevin Bailey & Ms Nicola Mahoney**
32 **CAPSTAN**, ch c Lomitas—Reamur **Aston House Stud**
33 **CELT**, b c Selkirk (USA)—Puce **Fittocks Stud**
34 **CREDIT SWAP**, b c Diktat—Locharia **Mrs A. S. Silver**
35 **CRUSOE'S RETURN**, b c Selkirk (USA)—Colorsnap **Castle Down Racing**
36 **CURTAIN CALL (FR)**, b c Sadler's Wells (USA)—Apsara (FR) **Mrs P. K. Cooper**
37 **FALCATIV**, b c Falbrav (IRE)—Frottola **Scuderia Rencati Srl**

MR L. M. CUMANI—continued

38 **FILUN**, b c Montjeu (IRE)—Sispre (FR) **Scuderia Rencati Srl**
39 **GINGHAM**, b gr f Barathea (IRE)—Sianema **Mrs James Wigan**
40 **HUZANA**, b f Pivotal—Hasta (USA) **JMC Breed & Race Limited**
41 **KIDLAD**, b c Cape Cross (IRE)—Arruhan (IRE) **Sheikh Mohammed Obaid Al Maktoum**
42 **KOSSACK**, b c Sadler's Wells (USA)—Kithanga (IRE) **Fittocks Stud & Mrs John Magnier**
43 **LEE MILLER (IRE)**, ch f Danehill Dancer (USA)—Brianza (USA) **Scuderia Rencati Srl**
44 **MAZARIS (IRE)**, b c Mull of Kintyre (USA)—Kingdom Pearl **L. Marinopoulos**
45 **MINSHAR**, ch f Noverre (USA)—Reine de Neige **J. Abdullah**
46 **MOTIVATED CHOICE**, b f Compton Place—Makhsusah (IRE) **Allevamento Gialloblu**
47 **MOUJ BAHRI**, b c Fasliyev (USA)—Hiddnah (USA) **J. Abdullah**
48 **MUBROOK (USA)**, b c Alhaarth (IRE)—Zomaradah **Sheikh Mohammed Obaid Al Maktoum**
49 **MUHAJAAR (IRE)**, b c Cape Cross (IRE)—Ya Hajar **J. Abdullah**
50 **ORDONEY**, b c Intikhab (USA)—Mitawa (USA) **Sheikh Mohammed Obaid Al Maktoum**
51 **PIVOTAL QUEEN**, ch f Pivotal—Queen of Norway (USA) **Tsega Horses Company Ltd**
52 **RAVILIOUS**, b c Selkirk (USA)—Risen Raven (USA) **Aston House Stud**
53 **SAVARAIN**, b c Rainbow Quest (USA)—Frangy **JMC Breed & Race Limited**
54 **SCHOPENHAUER (USA)**, b br c Giant's Causeway (USA)—Fine Jade (USA) **E. I. Mack**
55 **SHABEE AL REEM (IRE)**, ch f Daylami (USA)—Nasseem Al Zohour (IRE) **Mr A. Jaber**
56 **SIREN PARTY**, br f Pivotal—Ludynosa (USA) **Equibreed S.R.L.**
57 **SKY DIVE**, ch c Dr Fong (USA)—Free Flying **Fittocks Stud**
58 **SPIRIT OF ST LOUIS (USA)**, b br c Giant's Causeway (USA)—Isle Go West (USA) **E. I. Mack**
59 **TEDDY BEARS PICNIC**, b f Oasis Dream—Jackie's Opera (FR) **C. N. Wright**
60 **TEENAGE KICKS (IRE)**, ch c Giant's Causeway (USA)—Ruissec (USA) **R. J. Baines**
61 **TEPEE**, ch f Halling (USA)—Tentpole (USA) **Fittocks Stud**
62 **THUMBS UP**, gr c Intikhab (USA)—Exclusive Approval (USA) **Team Spirit**
63 **TIME CONTROL**, b f Sadler's Wells (USA)—Time Away (IRE) **Merry Fox Stud Limited**

TWO-YEAR-OLDS

64 Ch c 19/2 Nayef (USA)—Alligram (USA) (Alysheba (USA)) **Castle Down Racing**
65 **AUSONIUS**, b c 30/3 Kyllachy—Baileys Silver (USA) (Marlin (USA)) (80000) **Robert Tullett & Partners**
66 **BARTER**, ch f 7/5 Daylami (IRE)—Souk (IRE) (Ahonoora) **Fittocks Stud**
67 B f 27/4 Cadeaux Genereux—Bianca Nera (Salse (USA)) (180000) **Helena Springfield Ltd**
68 **BOURNE**, gr c 29/3 Linamix (FR)—L'affaire Monique (Machiavellian (USA)) (60000) **Aston House Stud**
69 **BURMA ROCK (IRE)**, b c 14/4 Danehill Dancer (IRE)—
                                   Burmese Princess (USA) (King of Kings (IRE)) (68000) **Drones Racing**
70 **CASTER SUGAR (USA)**, b f 5/3 Cozzene (USA)—Only Royale (IRE) (Caerleon (USA)) **Mrs James Wigan**
71 B c 13/3 Captain Rio—Choral Sundown (Night Shift (USA)) (32000) **L. Marinopoulos**
72 B c 6/5 Haafhd—Colorvista (Shirley Heights) **Castle Down Racing**
73 B c 14/3 With Approval (CAN)—Crisp and Cool (Oygyian (USA)) (10500) **J. Abdullah**
74 **CYGNET**, b c 9/2 Dansili—
                                   Ballet Princess (Muhtarram (USA)) (150000) **Lady Milford Haven & The Hon Mrs Steel**
75 **DANNIOS**, b c 25/2 Tobougg (IRE)—Fleuve d'or (IRE) (Last Tycoon) (42000) **Mr P. Booth & Mr D. Boorer**
76 **DICE (IRE)**, b c 4/5 Kalanisi (IRE)—Rain Dancer (IRE) (Sadler's Wells (USA)) (35000) **DIC Racing Syndicate**
77 B c 2/3 Falbrav (IRE)—Eurolink Raindance (IRE) (Alzao (USA)) **Antoniades Family**
78 **FANTASIA**, b f 10/2 Sadler's Wells (USA)—Blue Symphony (Darshaan) **Fittocks Stud & Mr A. Bengough**
79 **FIRST QUEEN**, b f 14/2 Rock of Gibraltar (IRE)—Orange Blossom (IRE) (Sadler's Wells (USA)) **J. Abdullah**
80 **FORTE DEI MARMI**, b c 30/3 Selkirk (USA)—Frangy (Sadler's Wells (USA)) **Fittocks Stud**
81 **FREE FALLING**, ch f 10/2 Selkirk (USA)—Free Flying (Groom Dancer (USA)) **Fittocks Stud**
82 **FURIUS**, b c 15/1 Montjeu (IRE)—Frottola (Muhtarram (USA)) **Scuderia Rencati Srl**
83 **I SEE NICE SEA**, b f 16/2 Miesque's Son (USA)—North Sea (IRE) (Selkirk (USA)) **J. Abdullah**
84 **IANTHI (GR)**, b f 20/2 Catcher In The Rye (IRE)—Askri (Lion Cavern (USA)) **Mrs M. Marinopoulos**
85 **IASOS (GR)**, b c 10/3 Filandros (GR)—Courtesy (USA) (Diesis) **Mrs M. Marinopoulos**
86 Br c 8/5 Monsun (GER)—Ice Dream (GER) (Mondrian (GER)) (55000) **L. Marinopoulos**
87 **IKADIOS (GR)**, b c 30/3 Filandros (GR)—Melissanthe (IRE) (Elmaamul (USA)) **Mrs M. Marinopoulos**
88 **ISSA (GR)**, gr f 10/2 Filandros (GR)—Eriza (Distant Relative) **Mrs M. Marinopoulos**
89 Ch f 12/3 Malibu Moon (USA)—Jealous Forum (USA) (Open Forum (USA)) **C. N. Wright**
90 B c 12/2 Rainbow Quest (USA)—Kasota (IRE) (Alzao (USA)) (125000) **B. Corman**
91 B f 25/4 Royal Applause—Kissing Time (Lugana Beach) **J. Abdullah**
92 B f 26/3 Montjeu (IRE)—Leaping Water (Sure Blade (USA)) (85000) **Mr S. A. Stuckey**
93 **LIFFEY DANCER (IRE)**, b f 21/3 Sadler's Wells (USA)—
                                   Brigid (USA) (Irish River (FR)) (2500000) **Merry Fox Stud**
94 **MABAIT**, b c 1/3 Kyllachy—
                                   Czarna Roza (Polish Precedent (USA)) (70000) **Sheikh Mohammed Obaid Al Maktoum**
95 **MAGALING (IRE)**, ch c 15/3 Medicean—
                                   Fling (Pursuit of Love) (110000) **Sheikh Mohammed Obaid Al Maktoum**

MR L. M. CUMANI—continued

96 MASWERTE (IRE), b c 24/2 Fraam—Rose Chime (IRE) (Tirol) (48000) **Sheikh Mohammed Obaid Al Maktoum**
97 B c 17/3 Danehill Dancer (IRE)—
   Model Queen (Kingmambo (USA)) (350000) **Lady C. Warren & The Hon Mrs H. Herbert**
98 MONACO (GER), b c 6/3 Monsun (GER)—
   Miss Holsten (USA) (Diesis) (50000) **Mr Andy Macdonald & Mr Chris Wright**
99 MUNJUM, b c 30/3 Sakhee (USA)—
   Ann Veronica (IRE) (Sadler's Wells (USA)) (55000) **Sheikh Mohammed Obaid Al Maktoum**
100 B c 20/2 Kyllachy—Nationality (Nashwan (USA)) (25740) **Mrs A. Silver**
101 PAISLEY, ch f 21/2 Pivotal—Pongee (Barathea (IRE)) **Fittocks Stud**
102 POSTER (IRE), b c 18/4 Johannesburg (USA)—
   Whipped Queen (USA) (Kingmambo (USA)) (22000) **Scuderia Archi Romani**
103 PRIVATE FUNDS, b c 7/3 Medicean—Syringa (Lure (USA)) (22000) **DIC Racing Syndicate**
104 B c 14/5 Danehill Dancer (IRE)—
   Puck's Castle (Shirley Heights) (64349) **Mr Chris Wright & Mr Andy Macdonald**
105 B f 4/3 Xaar—Queen Chief (IRE) (Grand Lodge (USA)) **J. Abdullah**
106 RAGLAN (IRE), ch c 3/5 Night Shift (USA)—Intellectuelle (Caerleon (USA)) (52000) **L. Marinopoulos**
107 SCENE TWO, gr c 29/3 Act One—Gleaming Water (Kalaglow) (35000) **Team Spirit 2**
108 B c 9/5 Xaar—She Looks On High (USA) (Secreto (USA)) (9652) **Mr R. Levi & Mr S. Roden**
109 Ch f 11/3 Barathea (IRE)—Shesadelight (Shirley Heights) (160875) **Scuderia Rencati Srl**
110 Ch c 26/3 Pivotal—Sispre (FR) (Master Willie) **Scuderia Rencati Srl**
111 SPENDASCIUN, b c 10/3 Falbrav (IRE)—Corndavon (USA) (Sheikh Albadou) (30000) **Scuderia Rencati Srl**
112 SPLASHDOWN, ch f 25/2 Falbrav (IRE)—Space Time (FR) (Bering) **Fittocks Stud**
113 Ch c 29/4 Kyllachy—Starfleet (Inchinor) (95000) **S. Suhail**
114 Ch c 24/4 Intikhab (USA)—Terre Vierge (FR) (Common Grounds) (12870)
115 THREE DUCKS, b f 30/3 Diktat—Three Terns (USA) (Arctic Tern (USA)) **Mrs James Wigan**
116 TOO TALL, b c 28/4 Medicean—Embark (Soviet Star (USA)) (145000) **S. C. B. Limited**
117 VENTURE CAPITALIST, b c 19/2 Diktat—Ventura Highway (Machiavellian (USA)) (45000) **Castle Down Racing**
118 B c 14/2 Cape Cross (IRE)—
   Viola da Braccio (IRE) (Vettori (IRE)) (140000) **Sheikh Mohammed Obaid Al Maktoum**

Other Owners: P. Agostini, Mrs E. Agostini, S. Alansari, Mrs Carolyn Antoniades, Miss E. C. Antoniades, Miss A. C. Antoniades, Mr P. C. Barnett, D. Boorer, Mr W. F. Charnley, The Hon Mrs C. Corbett, Mrs Luca Cumani, Mr L. J. Dowley, Mrs H. S. Ellingsen, Mr B. Grizzetti, The Hon H. M. Herbert, M. Kerr-Dineen, Mr A. T. Macdonald, The Marquess Of G. I. L. Milford Haven, R. H. W. Morecombe, M. Pescod, Mr G. G. Peterson, SP Racing Investments S.A., Mr Paul G. S. Silver, Mr R. P. Tullett, Lady Carolyn Warren, M. Weinfeld, Mr A. R. Wright.

Assistant Trainer: Charles Henson, Edward Walker

Jockey (flat): N. Mackay. **Apprentice:** A. Hamblett, H. McGee. **Amateur:** Mrs S. Cumani, Miss F. Cumani.

---

132 MR P. D. CUNDELL, Compton
Postal: **Roden House, Wallingford Road, Compton, Newbury, Berkshire, RG20 6QR**
Contacts: **PHONE** (01635) 578267 **FAX** (01635) 578267 **MOBILE** (07967) 227346
E-MAIL peter.cundell@googlemail.com

1 ALNWICK, 4, b g Kylian (USA)—Cebwob **Entre Nous & P. D. Cundell**
2 COLOSO, 4, ch g Compton Place—Nashville Blues (IRE) **P. Rosas**
3 HAVING A BALL, 4, b g Mark of Esteem (IRE)—All Smiles **Miss M. C. Fraser**
4 MCNAIROBI, 5, b m Josr Algarhoud (IRE)—Bonita Bee **I. M. Brown**
5 NAWOW, 8, b g Blushing Flame (USA)—Fair Test **I. M. Brown**
6 SQUIFFY, 5, br g Kylian (USA)—Cebwob **N. Johnson-Hill**
7 TAKITWO, 5, b g Delta Dancer—Tiama (IRE) **Miss M. C. Fraser**

THREE-YEAR-OLDS

8 PARSON'S PUNCH, b g Beat Hollow—Ordained **N. Johnson-Hill**
9 RUBY DELTA, b g Delta Dancer—Picolette **Ruby Delta Partnership**

TWO-YEAR-OLDS

10 B f 12/3 Bertolini (USA)—Bonita Bee (King of Spain) **I. M. Brown**
11 Br g 5/3 Delta Dancer—Cebwob (Rock City) **P. D. Cundell**
12 DIKIKA, b br f 17/2 Diktat—Lady McNair (Sheikh Albadou) **I. M. Brown**

MR P. D. CUNDELL—continued

Other Owners: Mr P. D. Cundell, Mr John Davies (Stonehill), Mr W. M. Dobson, Mr M. R. Kent, Mr John B. Sunley.

Assistant Trainer: Miss L. E. Newberry

---

133 **MR M. CUNNINGHAM, Navan**
Postal: **Gormanstown Stables, Kildalkey, Navan, Co.Meath, Ireland**
Contacts: **PHONE (00353) 4694 31672 FAX (00353) 4694 31467 MOBILE (00353) 8625 93962**

1 **ALL DIAMONDS (IRE)**, 7, ch h Priolo (USA)—Afisiak **Ms Heather Topping**
2 **BELANAK (IRE)**, 5, b h Sinndar (IRE)—Balanka (IRE) **Ms Heather Topping**
3 4, B c Barathea (IRE)—Bold Lillian (IRE) **Herb M. Stanley**
4 **IFYOUCOULDSEEMENOW (IRE)**, 6, b m Saddlers' Hall (IRE)—Sallie's Girl (IRE) **Mr P. J. Magnier**
5 **LAURELDEAN (IRE)**, 10, b g Shernazar—Power Run **Mr M. Cunningham**
6 **LEADING DIAMONDS (IRE)**, 6, b g Leading Counsel (USA)—Noeleen's Delight (IRE) **Ms Heather Topping**
7 **MHILU (IRE)**, 6, b g Rock Hopper—Moohono (IRE) **Dream On Boys Syndicate**
8 **MOVING DIAMONDS**, 5, b m Lomitas—Euro Empire (USA) **Ms Heather Topping**
9 **RAVEN'S RUN (IRE)**, 6, b g Sea Raven (IRE)—Sandy Run (IRE) **Michael J. Heaslip**
10 **ROCK DIPLOMAT (IRE)**, 8, b g Oscar (IRE)—Pre-Let (IRE) **Mr P. G. Molony & Mr C. O'Reilly-Hyland**
11 **SHAREKAN (IRE)**, 5, ch h Sinndar (IRE)—Sharemata (IRE) **Canal Racing Syndicate**

TWO-YEAR-OLDS

12 B f 25/3 Dr Fong (USA)—Reprise (Darshaan) **Mrs Paul Shanahan & Mrs Michael Cunningham**

Assistant Trainer: Tara Cunningham

---

134 **MR J. M. S. CURRAN, Faringdon**
Postal: **Grey Fox Stables, Hatford, Nr Faringdon, Oxfordshire**
Contacts: **PHONE (01367) 718708 FAX (01993) 825928 MOBILE (07774) 146169**
E-MAIL Greyfoxracing@btconnect.com WEBSITE www.greyfoxracing.co.uk

1 **AMARILLO SLIM (IRE)**, 4, b g Danehill Dancer (IRE)—Jungle Story (IRE) **L. M. Power**
2 5, B h Arctic Owl—Be My Sweetheart (IRE) **G. Nolan & D. Conroy**
3 **BERNABEU (IRE)**, 6, b g Mark of Esteem (IRE)—Snow Ballet (IRE) **G. D. Peck**
4 **DAME DE BALME (FR)**, 6, b m Phantom Breeze—Dame Fontenail (FR) **L. M. Power**
5 **EL BATAL (IRE)**, 7, b g Oscar (IRE)—Native Sunset (IRE) **Mr T. A. Killoran**
6 **EXPLOSIVE FOX (IRE)**, 7, gr g Foxhound (USA)—Grise Mine (FR) **L. M. Power**
7 **IRIS DE BALME (FR)**, 8, ch g Phantom Breeze—Fleur d'ecajeul (FR) **L. M. Power**
8 **JALANDY (IRE)**, 5, b m Desert Millennium (IRE)—Jaldini (IRE) **G. D. Peck**
9 **L'APPRENTI SORCIER (FR)**, 5, b g Phantom Breeze—Flower Of Dream (FR) **D. Clayton**
10 **LE CHIFFRE (IRE)**, 6, br g Celtic Swing—Implicit View **L. M. Power**
11 **MUSIC CELEBRE (IRE)**, 8, b g Peintre Celebre (USA)—Marwell **L. M. Power**
12 **NORTHERN DESERT (IRE)**, 9, b g Desert Style (IRE)—Rosie's Guest (IRE) **Miss N. S. Henton**
13 **PEYEKASHE (FR)**, 5, b g Scribe (IRE)—Ukashe (FR)
14 6, B h Rock Hopper—Pollys Leader (IRE)
15 **PROPHETE DE GUYE (FR)**, 5, b g Apple Tree (FR)—Kasibelle de Guye (FR) **Mrs J. M. Hobson**
16 **QUITE A SPLASH (USA)**, 4, b g Smart Strike (CAN)—Easy Sunshine (IRE) **Mr P. Jewell**
17 **SAGUNT (GER)**, 5, ch g Tertullian (USA)—Suva (GER) **Miss N. S. Henton**
18 **TINSTRE (IRE)**, 10, ch g Dolphin Street (FR)—Satin Poppy **M. Wennington**
19 **TOLEDO SUN**, 8, b g Zamindar (USA)—Shafir (IRE) **L. M. Power**
20 **USHNU (USA)**, 5, ch g Giant's Causeway (USA)—Serape (USA) **Ken Washbourne, Tony Regan, Tom Ford**
21 **VACATION (IRE)**, 5, b h King Charlemagne (USA)—Lady Peculiar (CAN) **D. Clayton**
22 4, Ch c Emperor Fountain—Vera's First (IRE)
23 **ZIZOU (IRE)**, 5, b g Fantastic Light (USA)—Search Committee (USA) **I. Hutchinson**

THREE-YEAR-OLDS

24 **FREUDIAN SLIP**, b f Ishiguru—Perle d'azur **L. M. Power**
25 **JANET'S DELIGHT**, b f Erhaab (USA)—Ishona **Terry & Jan**
26 **LA BELLE JOANNIE**, b f Lujain (USA)—Sea Clover (IRE) **L. M. Power**

Other Owners: Mr Terry Brock, Mr Tom Ford, Ms Janet Gazey, Mr A. W. Regan, Mr Ken Washbourne.

135 MR R. CURTIS, Lambourn
Postal: **Delamere Stables, Baydon Road, Lambourn, Hungerford, Berkshire, RG17 8NT**
Contacts: PHONE **(01488) 73007** FAX **(01488) 73909** MOBILE **(07836) 320690**
E-MAIL **rcurtislambourn@aol.com** WEBSITE **www.rogercurtis.com**

1 ALDERBROOK GIRL (IRE), 8, b b m Alderbrook—Trassey Bridge **IPO Racing Partnership**
2 4, B g Rossini (USA)—Belmont Princess (IRE)
3 6, B m Taipan (IRE)—Calamaire **The J'Adore Partnership**
4 COPPERMALT (USA), 10, b g Affirmed (USA)—Poppy Carew (IRE) **Collective Dreamers**
5 J'ADORE (GER), 6, b g Chato (USA)—Josa (GER) **The J'Adore Partnership**
6 LADY KORRIANDA, 7, ch m Dr Fong (USA)—Prima Verde **Collective Dreamers**
7 MADAM CLICHE, 6, b m Classic Cliche (IRE)—Mirador **The Madam Cliche Partnership**
8 MADERSON BLUE (IRE), 6, b g Pistolet Bleu (IRE)—Not A Bid (IRE)
9 MANCEBO (GER), 5, b g Acambaro (GER)—Marsxia (FR) **The Tech Eagle Partnership**
10 MUCHO LOCO (IRE), 5, ch g Tagula (IRE)—Mousseux (IRE) **Guildings Racing Club**
11 NEAR GERMANY (IRE), 8, b g Germany (USA)—Night Year (IRE) **Miss M. D. Evans**
12 PAULA LANE, 8, b m Factual (USA)—Colfax Classic **Mrs R. A. Smith**
13 ROMNEY MARSH, 7, br m Glacial Storm (USA)—Mirador **The Romney Marsh Partnership**
14 TECH EAGLE, 8, b h Eagle Eyed (USA)—Technik (GER) **The Tech Eagle Partnership**

Other Owners: R. Adair, Miss Andrea Atkin, Ms L. M. Barton, R. Bedford, H. Beynon, Mrs A. Beynon, P. Burns, G. Carson, P. Carter, P. Clayton, Mrs S. Conway, R. Cook, Mrs B. Cox, T. Coyle, R. Crow, Mr Roger Curtis, C. Dick, M. Dodd, R. Dyett, A. Fenn, A. Fletcher, Mr C. H. Foster, Mrs Dawn Gibbs, J. Gray, R. Grey, W. Hayler, J. Hewish, R. Horne, N. Howe, T. Huchinson, M. King, J. King, Mrs R. Lakin, R. Last, C. Line, Mrs P. McCluskey, S. McInnes, A. Morris, D. Morris, Dr E. Moses, Mr B. D. Newman, W. Nutley, A. Rawlinson, Mrs V. Roach, Mr P. A. Sells, Mr Peter A. Smith, Prof. S. Smith, Mrs P. Snook, S. Stockdale, Mrs A. Styles, J. Sweet, R. Taylor, Dr Patrick Walker, T. Weller, Alex Wilson, Christopher Winn, T. Wynne.

Assistant Trainer: Dawn Gibbs

Jockey (NH): J. Davies.

136 MR T. A. K. CUTHBERT, Carlisle
Postal: **26 Eden Grange, Little Corby, Carlisle, Cumbria, CA4 8QW**
Contacts: PHONE **(01228) 560822** STABLES **(01228) 561328** FAX **(01228) 560822**
MOBILE **(07747) 843344**

1 BRAMANTINO (IRE), 8, b g Perugino (USA)—Headrest **W. O. Hurst**
2 HEBENUS, 9, b g Hamas (IRE)—Stinging Nettle **Mrs J. Cuthbert**
3 QUICKS THE WORD, 9, b g Sri Pekan (USA)—Fast Tempo (IRE) **W. O. Hurst**
4 SECOND REEF, 6, b g Second Empire (IRE)—Vax Lady **Mrs J. Cuthbert**
5 SKYLARKER (USA), 10, b g Sky Classic (CAN)—O My Darling (USA) **Mrs J. Cuthbert**

Amateur: Miss H. Cuthbert.

137 MR P. W. D'ARCY, Newmarket
Postal: **Charnwood Stables, Hamilton Road, Newmarket, Suffolk, CB8 7JQ**
Contacts: PHONE **(01638) 662000** FAX **(01638) 661100** MOBILE **(07768) 807653**
E-MAIL **pauldarcy@fsmail.net** WEBSITE **www.pauldarcyracing.com**

1 BUGSY'S BOY, 4, b g Double Trigger (IRE)—Bugsy's Sister **Seaton Stud Limited**
2 INVASIAN (IRE), 7, ch g Desert Prince (IRE)—Jarrayan **Dr K. Sanderson**
3 SIR DUKE (IRE), 4, b g Danehill (USA)—Dimanche **Mrs J. Harris**
4 VALLEMELDEE (IRE), 4, b f Bering—Vassiana (FR) **Mrs D. Burlton**
5 WHAT A BUZZ, 6, ch g Zaha (CAN)—G'ima Buzz **D. M. Beresford**

THREE-YEAR-OLDS

6 ASTANIA, b f Shahrastani (USA)—So Ambitious **Skeltools Ltd**
7 AUGMENTATION, br c Dansili—Moulin Rouge **Dr K. Sanderson**
8 BOSUN BREESE, b g Bahamian Bounty—Nellie Melba **Lodge Hyson Delnevo & Breese Racing**
9 KYLAYNE, b f Kyllachy—Penmayne **Mrs J. Harris**
10 RAMPANT RONNIE (USA), b r Honor Glide (USA)—Jalfrezi **Mr R. J. Delnevo**
11 SUZI'S DECISION, gr f Act One—Funny Girl (IRE) **Greenstead Hall Racing Ltd**

MR P. W. D'ARCY—continued

TWO-YEAR-OLDS

12 **CALAHONDA**, ch f 31/3 Haafhd—Californie (IRE) (Rainbow Quest (USA)) (6000) **Gongolphin & Racing**
13 **CHARISMATIC CHARLI (IRE)**, b c 13/3 King Charlemagne (USA)—
        Emly Express (IRE) (High Estate) (10500) **Mrs S. J. Bailey**
14 Ch c 29/3 Sulamani (IRE)—Denica (IRE) (Night Shift (USA)) **Skeltools Ltd**
15 **DESERT FAIRY**, b f 18/3 Tobougg (IRE)—Regal Fairy (IRE) (Desert King (IRE)) **A. H. Bennett**
16 B c 6/3 Namid—Funny Girl (IRE) (Darshaan) (15000) **Mr D. R. Lodge**
17 B f 5/5 Fasliyev (USA)—Kelpie (IRE) (Kahyasi) (15000) **Mrs D. Burlton**
18 Ch c 30/3 Generous (IRE)—Polish Sprite (Danzig Connection (USA)) **Skeltools Ltd**
19 B br c 19/5 Arch (USA)—Raven Quiver (USA) (Old Trieste (USA)) (23000) **Mrs J. Harris**
20 Ch f 6/4 Fantastic Light (USA)—Resourceful (IRE) (Entrepreneur) (16000) **Mrs J. Harris**
21 Ch c 8/5 Generous (USA)—So Ambitious (Teenoso) (USA)) **Skeltools Ltd**
22 B c 13/5 Falbrav (IRE)—Wavy Up (IRE) (Brustolon) (8000) **P. Lupson**

Other Owners: Mr D. A. Breese, P. W. D'Arcy, Mrs S. I. D'Arcy, Mr M. J. Hyson.

Assistant Trainer: Sue D'Arcy

---

138 **MR L. A. DACE, Billingshurst**
Postal: **Copped Hall Farm, Okehurst Lane, Billingshurst, West Sussex, RH14 9HR**
Contacts: **OFFICE (01403) 780889 FAX (01403) 780889 MOBILE (07949) 401085**
E-MAIL lukedace@yahoo.co.uk WEBSITE www.lukedace.co.uk

1 **BARNBROOK EMPIRE (IRE)**, 6, b m Second Empire (IRE)—Home Comforts **Let's Have Fun Syndicate**
2 **BELLESTANI**, 4, b g Shahrastani (USA)—Saved By The Belle **Mr & Mrs L. P. Dace**
3 **BREAK THE ICE**, 7, b m North Col—Frozen Pipe **A. P. Brewer**
4 **FREEZE THE DREAM**, 6, b m North Col—Frozen Pipe **Let's Have Fun Syndicate**
5 **OPTIMUM ASSET (IRE)**, 5, ch g Rudimentary (USA)—Barthez (IRE) **Collacott, Sells, Tustin, Barber**
6 **PUBLIC EYE**, 7, b g Zafonic (USA)—Stardom **Let's Have Fun Syndicate**
7 **STAND IN BLACK (NZ)**, 4, br g Istidaad (USA)—Aprikot (NZ) **Mrs A. Miller**
8 **TABARAN (FR)**, 5, ch g Polish Precedent (USA)—Tabariya (FR) **Mr G. Collacott**
9 **WEE ALFIE (IRE)**, 6, b g Supreme Leader—Rose Wee (IRE) **Auld Firm Partnership**

TWO-YEAR-OLDS

10 B f 3/2 Lujain (USA)—Alzianah (Alzao (USA)) (10000) **Let's Have Fun Syndicate**

Other Owners: Mr Tony Barber, Mr Luke Dace, Mrs L. J. Dace, Mr D. McPherson, Mr J. D. Sells, Mr K. W. Touhey, Mr G. Tustin.

Assistant Trainer: Mrs L Dace

Amateur: Mrs L. Dace.

---

139 **MS H. DALTON, Shifnal**
Postal: **Helshaw Grange, Warrant Road, Tern Hill, Nr Market Drayton, Shropshire, TF9 2JP**
Contacts: **PHONE (01630) 637120 FAX (01630) 637141 MOBILE (07785) 972131**
E-MAIL heatherdalton@hotmail.co.uk WEBSITE www.heatherdaltonracing.co.uk

1 **ANOTHER PRESENT (IRE)**, 6, b m Presenting—Bell Walks Run (IRE) **Helshaw Grange Stud**
2 **ARPEGGIO MAJOR (IRE)**, 6, b g Beauchamp King—Bucks Slave **Mr S. J. Bushell & Mr T. J. Bushell**
3 **BEFORE DARK (IRE)**, 10, b g Phardante (FR)—Menebeans (IRE) **C. B. Compton**
4 **BREIZ DREAM'S (FR)**, 6, ch g East of Heaven (IRE)—Impish (FR) **Mr D. R. Williams & Mrs J. McHale**
5 **CAHEERLOCH (IRE)**, 6, b g Sinndar (IRE)—Pharmacist (IRE) **Ms H. Dalton**
6 **CELTICELLO (IRE)**, 6, b br g Celtic Swing—Viola Royale (IRE) **Mr R. Edwards & Steve Hughes**
7 **DANMEGELLA**, 5, b g Overbury (IRE)—Dublin Ferry **Mr D. R. Williams**
8 **DONASTRELA (IRE)**, 7, b m Tagula (IRE)—David's Star **Ms H. Dalton**
9 **DRAWBACK (IRE)**, 5, b g Daggers Drawn (USA)—Sacred Heart (IRE) **Ms H. Dalton**
10 4, B g King's Theatre (IRE)—Gavotte du Cochet (FR) **Miss L. J. Hales**
11 6, B g Commanche Run—Glentanna Girl **Mrs A. Constantine & Mr L. G. Litchfield**
12 **GO WEST (IRE)**, 7, b g Flemensfirth (USA)—Roaming (IRE) **The Socialspitfires Partnership**
13 **GYPSY BOB (IRE)**, 5, b g Bob's Return (IRE)—Be My Gypsy (IRE) **J. Mcgrath**
14 **HATTON ROCK (IRE)**, 6, ch g Rock Hopper—Lady de Hatton (IRE) **Mr D. R. Williams**

MS H. DALTON—continued

15 **HENRI PRENDS GARDE (FR)**, 6, b g Enrique—Marie Prends Garde (FR) **Mr D. R. Williams**
16 **HUCKLEBERRY (IRE)**, 6, b g Hubbly Bubbly (USA)—
    Laur's Melody (IRE) **Racing Shrews Syndicate Bayston Hill**
17 **LONGWOOD LAW (IRE)**, 6, b g Key of Luck (USA)—Lady Bodmin (IRE) **Penketh & Sankey Jech Racing Club**
18 **LUCY'S TURN (IRE)**, 5, b m Luso—Noble Turn (IRE) **D. R. T. Gibbons**
19 **MAGGIE BOON (IRE)**, 6, br m Glacial Storm (USA)—Lizzie Boon **Helshaw Grange Stud**
20 **MALMO BOY (IRE)**, 9, gr g Roselier (FR)—Charming Mo (IRE) **M. B. Jones**
21 **MARUFO (IRE)**, 6, b g Presenting—Bucks Cregg (IRE) **Miss L. J. Hales**
22 **MEANT TO BEE (IRE)**, 5, b m Saddlers' Hall (IRE)—Maid of Honey (IRE) **Helshaw Grange Stud**
23 **MORENITO (FR)**, 5, b g Nononito (FR)—Cohiba (FR) **Mr C. B. Compton & Mr B. J. Johnston**
24 **MOUNT COOK (FR)**, 8, b g Gold and Steel (FR)—Debandade (FR) **Miss L. J. Hales**
25 **NITE FOX (IRE)**, 9, ch m Anshan—New Talent **Mrs A Beard Miss M Knapper & Mr J Dalton**
26 **PRIVATE AYE (IRE)**, 6, ch g Rudimentary (USA)—I Say Aye (IRE) **Penketh & Sankey Jech Racing Club**
27 **RASHARTIC (IRE)**, 6, ch g Rashar (USA)—Gothic Ash (IRE) **Ashleybank Investments Limited**
28 **REBUS (IRE)**, 4, b g Witness Box (USA)—Blackwater Babe **Miss L. J. Hales**
29 **ROCK ALLIANCE (IRE)**, 5, b g Rock Hopper—Lost Coin **Mr W. Ferrier**
30 **ROVING BOB (IRE)**, 6, b g Bob's Return (IRE)—Dunnoholm **Salopian Racing**
31 **RUDINERO (IRE)**, 6, gr g Rudimentary (USA)—Cash Chase (IRE) **D. R. T. Gibbons**
32 **SAMADHI STYLE (IRE)**, 7, ch g Shernazar—Noble Turn (IRE) **D. R. T. Gibbons**
33 **SHROPSHIRE GIRL**, 7, b m Cloudings (IRE)—Rosie O'keeffe (IRE) **Mrs C. L. Shaw**
34 **SUMNER (IRE)**, 4, b g Xaar—Black Jack Girl (IRE) **Miss L. J. Hales**
35 **SWORDS**, 6, b g Vettori (IRE)—Pomorie (IRE)
36 **TEST OF FRIENDSHIP**, 11, br g Roselier (FR)—Grease Pot **Severn River Racing**
37 **THE GOOD DOCTOR (IRE)**, 6, b g Dr Massini (IRE)—Farran Garrett (IRE) **Mr W. Ferrier**
38 **VICTOR DALY (IRE)**, 7, b g Old Vic—Murphy's Lady (IRE) **C. B. Compton**
39 **YORKSHIRE OWL**, 7, b br g Marju (IRE)—Rosa Canina **David Croft & Steve Lane**
40 **ZONIC BOOM (IRE)**, 8, b br g Zafonic (USA)—Rosi Zambotti (IRE) **Mr C. Fletcher**

Other Owners: Mrs Angela Beard, Ms Heather Dalton.

Assistant Trainer: Susan Fairweather

Jockey (NH): S. J. Craine, A. Hawkins. **Amateur:** Mr Matthew Sollitt.

140 **MR P. T. DALTON, Burton-on-Trent**
Postal: Dovecote Cottage, Bretby Park, Bretby, Burton-On-Trent, Staffordshire, DE15 0RB
Contacts: HOME/OFFICE (01283) 221922 FAX (01283) 229657 MOBILE (07774) 240753
E-MAIL daltonpauldalton@aol.co.uk

1 **BLAZING HILLS**, 12, ch g Shaab—Cottage Blaze **Mrs J. M. T. Martin**
2 **CLOUDINA**, 7, b m Cloudings (IRE)—Lucia Forte **Mrs L. Farmer**
3 **OUT OF INDIA**, 6, b m Marju (IRE)—Tide of Fortune **Mrs J. M. T. Martin**
4 **WILLIAM THE BLOODY**, 7, b g Bob's Return (IRE)—Society News **Mrs J. M. T. Martin**

Other Owners: D. R. Martin.

Assistant Trainer: Susan Dalton

141 **MR H. D. J. DALY, Ludlow**
Postal: Downton Hall Stables, Ludlow, Shropshire, SY8 3DX
Contacts: OFFICE (01584) 873688 FAX (01584) 873525 MOBILE (07720) 074544
E-MAIL henry@henrydaly.co.uk

1 **ALDERBURN**, 9, b g Alderbrook—Threewaygirl **Mrs D. P. G. Flory**
2 **BEHERAYN**, 5, b g Dansili—Behera **The Behrajan Partnership**
3 **BILLYVODDAN (IRE)**, 9, b g Accordion—Derryclare **T. J. Hemmings**
4 **BOOMERANG (IRE)**, 6, b g Needle Gun (IRE)—Garden County **Mrs F. Nesbitt**
5 **BRIERY FOX (IRE)**, 10, ch g Phardante (FR)—Briery Gale **Vicky Reed Helen Plumbly Jane Trafford**
6 **CHARINGWORTH (IRE)**, 5, b g Supreme Leader—Quinnsboro Guest (IRE) **T. J. Hemmings**
7 **COLD HARBOUR**, 4, b g Classic Cliche (IRE)—Anchorage (IRE) **Mrs F. Nesbitt**
8 **DOWN'S FOLLY (IRE)**, 8, b g Darnay—Pils Invader (IRE) **Strachan,Gabb,Clarke,Griffith & Barlow**
9 **FERIMON**, 9, gr g Rhyming Moppet **Strachan Myddelton Gabb Stoddart Lawson**
10 **FLUTTER BYE (IRE)**, 4, b f Alflora (IRE)—Nova Rose **Mrs Juliet Minton & Mrs Henry Daly**
11 **GLENARY (IRE)**, 6, ch g Presenting—My Native Glen (IRE) **T. J. Hemmings**

MR H. D. J. DALY—continued

12 HOPKINS (IRE), 7, ch g Topanoora—Derryclare **T. J. Hemmings**
13 IN ACCORD, 9, ch g Accordion—Henry's True Love **T. F. F. Nixon**
14 JAUNTY TIMES, 8, b g Luso—Jaunty June **J. B. Sumner**
15 JUDY THE DRINKER, 9, b m Snurge—Mardessa **A. J. Haden**
16 KACK HANDED, 5, b g Terimoon—Hand Inn Glove **Patrick Burling Developments Ltd**
17 KAYCEECEE (IRE), 7, b g Mister Mat (FR)—Maid of Glenduragh (IRE) **M. Lowe**
18 KEDGEREE, 6, b g Fleetwood (IRE)—Coh Sho No **Strachan,Griffith,Shakerley & Parkinson**
19 MAGE D'ESTRUVAL (FR), 8, b g Sheyrann—Ivresse d'estruval (FR) **R. M. Kirkland**
20 MAJOR SUSPECT, 5, ch g Hernando (FR)—Angel Chimes **D. Sandells**
21 MARTHA'S KINSMAN (IRE), 9, b g Petoski—Martha's Daughter **Barlow, Hartley & Brereton**
22 MASTER SOMERVILLE, 6, b g Aïflora (IRE)—Lucy Glitters **Mrs A. Churton**
23 MY MOMENT (IRE), 5, ch g Presenting—Golden Moment (IRE) **T. J. Hemmings**
24 NAKOMA (IRE), 6, b m Bahhare (USA)—Indian Imp **Ludlow Racing Partnership**
25 NATOUMBA (FR), 7, ch g Hawker's News (IRE)—Vanella (FR) **John Hanley John Brindley**
26 OBAKI DE GRISSAY (FR), 6, b g Robin des Pres—Topeka (FR) **M. Lowe**
27 OPERA DE COEUR (FR), 6, b g East of Heaven (IRE)—Eden de Coeur (FR) **The Hon Mrs M. J. Heber-Percy**
28 ORDRE DE BATAILLE (FR), 6, gr g Ungaro (GER)—Hache de Guerre (FR) **Mrs A. W. Timpson**
29 OXLEY (FR), 6, b g Assessor (IRE)—Tartifume II (FR) **The Earl Cadogan**
30 PALARSHAN (FR), 10, b br g Darshaan—Palavera (FR) **Sumner Wellesley**
31 PANTALAIMON, 7, b g Classic Cliche (IRE)—Threewaygirl **Mrs D. P. G. Flory**
32 PARSOU (FR), 5, gr g April Night (FR)—Parcelle Coloree (FR) **Million in Mind Partnership**
33 PICKAMUS (FR), 5, gr g April Night (FR)—Duchesse du Cochet (FR) **Mr N. J. Statham**
34 POP (FR), 5, b g Cricket Ball (USA)—Senzi (FR) **R. M. Kirkland**
35 POSH DUDE (IRE), 7, ch g Presenting—Briery Gale **Mrs H. Plumbly**
36 PRINCESS ANGELIQUE (FR), 4, br f Sagacity (FR)—Princesse Mimi (FR) **P. E. Truscott**
37 PRINCIPE AZZURRO (FR), 7, b g Pistolet Bleu (IRE)—Massalia (GER) **W. J. Tolhurst**
38 PROF DE L'ISLE (FR), 5, b g Kadalko (FR)—
                                     Gratiene de L'isle (FR) **Mrs Strachan,Thompson,Wood & Lady Inkin**
39 RAKALACKEY, 10, br g Rakaposhi King—Celtic Slave **B. G. Hellyer**
40 ROYAL KICKS (FR), 7, b g Garde Royale—Al Kicks (FR) **Strachan Gabb Griffith Harford Graham**
41 SEA EAGLE (IRE), 6, b g Sea Raven (IRE)—Roseocean (IRE) **Viscountess Knutsford**
42 SHERWOODS FOLLY, 6, b g Classic Cliche (IRE)—Action de Balle (FR) **T. J. Hemmings**
43 SIR PETER (IRE), 6, b g City Honours (USA)—Any Offers **Mrs M. L. Stevenson**
44 SPEED BONNIE BOAT, 5, ch m Aïflora (IRE)—Sail By The Stars **Mrs M. C. Humphries-Cuff**
45 STUMPED, 5, b g Bertolini (USA)—So Saucy **Gibson, Goddard, Hamer & Hawkes**
46 SUNSETTEN (IRE), 4, b g Tendulkar (USA)—Rosy Affair **M. C. Stoddart**
47 TAMBOURINE RIDGE (IRE), 6, br m Tamure (IRE)—Rhyming Moppet **E. R. Hanbury**
48 THIEVERY, 7, gr g Terimoon—Piracy **Mrs A. W. Timpson**
49 TIMPO (FR), 5, ch g Baby Turk—Faensa (FR) **Mrs A. W. Timpson**
50 TOBY BELCH (IRE), 5, ch g Presenting—Peptic Lady **Strachan,Griffith,Gabb,Lewis & Lawson**

Other Owners: Susan Lady Barlow, Mr R. J. Brereton, Mr John Brindley, Mr A. R. Bromley, Mrs S. T. Clarke, Mrs Henry Daly, Lord Daresbury, Lady Forester, Mrs Roger Gabb, Mr B. Gibson, Mr Arthur Goddard, Mr Graham Goode, Mrs Douglas Graham, Mrs J. G. Griffith, Mr D. Griffith, Mr C. M. Hamer, Mr John Hanley, Mr H. Harford, Mr R. L. C. Hartley, Mr M. Hawkes, Mrs A. Hellyer, Mr Tony Hill, Lady Inkin, Mrs A. S. Lawson, Mrs David Lewis, Mr Simon Marsh, Mr D. Minton, Mrs Juliet Minton, Mr G. C. Myddelton, Mrs D. Nicholson, Mr T. F. F. Nixon, Miss M. Noden, Mr Michael Opperman, Mrs C. L. Parkinson, Mrs Helen Plumbly, Mrs V. J. Reed, Mr Michael Stoddart, Mrs Richard Strachan, Mr J. B. Sumner, Mrs L. C. Thompson, Mrs Jane Trafford, Exors of the Late Major P. G. Verdin, Mr J. R. Weatherby, Lady Richard Wellesley, Mrs E. Wood.

Assistant Trainer: Tom Gretton

Jockey (NH): M. Bradburne, R. Johnson. **Conditional:** P. Callaghan.

---

142 **MR V. R. A. DARTNALL, Barnstaple**
Postal: Higher Shutscombe Farm, Charles, Brayford, Barnstaple, Devon, EX32 7PU
Contacts: PHONE (01598) 710280 FAX (01598) 710708 MOBILE (07974) 374272
E-MAIL victor@victordartnallracing.com WEBSITE www.victordartnallracing.com

1 ASPARAGUS WINGNUT (IRE), 6, ch g In The Wings—Damiana (IRE)
2 BENETWOOD (IRE), 7, br g Beneficial—Donegal Thyne (IRE) **J. P. McManus**
3 BOREHILL JOKER, 12, ch g Pure Melody (USA)—Queen Matilda **Devonshire Jokers**
4 BRAYFORD LAD (IRE), 5, b g Oscar (IRE)—Pallastown Breeze **G. D. Hake**
5 BROOMHILL FLYER (IRE), 6, b g Heron Island (IRE)—Electric Smiles (IRE) **A Maddox, N Thorn, M Southcott**
6 BUSINESSMONEY JADE, 4, b f Dolpour—Cloverjay **Businessmoney Ltd**
7 DANCING DASI (IRE), 9, b m Supreme Leader—Little Dasi (IRE) **F. D. A. Snowden**

MR V. R. A. DARTNALL—continued

8 DANCING MIST (IRE), 5, gr g Shernazar—Daddy's Girl (IRE) **Willis, Rich & Russian Partners**
9 DANESBROOK, 8, b g New Reputation—Wood Heath **Devonshire Partners**
10 DARSTARDLY DICK (IRE), 5, b g Oscar—Fiery Belle (IRE) **Cheltenham Or Bust**
11 DIP ANCHOR, 5, b g Slip Anchor—Streccia **Mr F. Rogers**
12 DOUBLE HEADER (IRE), 9, b g Old Vic—Ballybeggan Lady (IRE) **F. R. Williamson**
13 DOUBLE INTRUDER (IRE), 7, ch g Alderbrook—Aunty Dawn (IRE) **Hinge, Searchfield & Tamburro**
14 EXMOOR RANGER (IRE), 6, ch g Grand Plaisir (IRE)—Slygulf Torus (IRE) **The Rangers Partnership**
15 FRENCH LEAVE (IRE), 6, ch g Gunner B—La Kabyle (FR) **F. R. Williamson**
16 GOLD AGAIN (IRE), 10, b g Old Vic—Thomastown Girl **The Hon Mrs A. M. Cookson**
17 4, B f Oscar (IRE)—Greybrook Lass (IRE) **Mrs L. M. Northover**
18 HERE'S JOHNNY (IRE), 9, ch g Presenting—Treble Basc (IRE) **The Big Boys Toys Partnership**
19 JOKERS LEGACY (IRE), 6, b g Fourstars Allstar (USA)—
Sweet Charm (IRE) **The Wife Thinks I'm Working Partnership**
20 KARANJA, 9, b g Karinga Bay—Proverbial Rose **D. G. Staddon**
21 LE BRIAR SOUL (IRE), 8, b g Luso—El Moss (IRE) **Cape Codders**
22 LODGE LANE (IRE), 7, b g Norwich—Garrenroe **Mr O. C. R. Wynne & Mrs S. J. Wynne**
23 6, Ch g Presenting—Mandys Gale (IRE) **Drink Up**
24 MOLE'S CHAMBER (IRE), 7, b g Saddlers' Hall (IRE)—Magic Gale (IRE) **Robin & Chris Barber**
25 MOLESKIN (IRE), 5, b g Saddlers' Hall (IRE)—Magic Gale (IRE) **Robin & Chris Barber**
26 NORTON SAPPHIRE, 9, ch m Karinga Bay—Sea of Pearls (IRE) **Miracle In Mind Partnership**
27 POLISHED, 9, ch g Danzig Connection (USA)—Glitter (FR) **Cape Codders**
28 RICHARD'S SUNDANCE (IRE), 6, b g Saddlers' Hall (IRE)—
Celestial Rose (IRE) **Elizabeth Masterman & Sara Vernon**
29 ROGANSTOWN (IRE), 5, b g Lahib (USA)—Nickys Peril **Stewart Andrew & Jim Shaw**
30 RUSSIAN TRIGGER, 6, b g Double Trigger (IRE)—Cobusino
31 4, B g Flemensfirth (USA)—Shean Hill (IRE)
32 SILKWOOD TOP (IRE), 9, b g Norwich—Brave Mum **Mr O. C. R. Wynne & Mrs S. J. Wynne**
33 SIR REMBRANDT (IRE), 12, b g Mandalus—Sue's A Lady **A. Hordle**
34 SIR WINSTON (IRE), 6, b g Supreme Leader—Aliandbet Jewel (IRE) **D. G. Staddon**
35 SPORTING REBEL (IRE), 8, b g Zaffaran (USA)—High Church Annie (IRE) **W. Hinge**
36 STRIKING VIKING, 5, ch g Sula Bula—Quiet Confusion (IRE) **Viking Partnership**
37 THE APPRENTICE (IRE), 6, b g Shernazar—Kate Farly (IRE) **R. Sinclair**
38 THE VENETIAN (IRE), 7, b g Presenting—Dashing March **A. Hordle**
39 TINTINHULL (IRE), 6, b g Presenting—Persian Avenue (IRE) **Robin & Chris Barber**
40 YOUNG DANCER (IRE), 10, b g Eurobus—Misquested **V. R. A. Dartnall**

Other Owners: Mr K. Adams, Mr B. Alder, S. Andrew, R. D. Barber, Mrs C. M. Barber, Mr E. N. L. Boyce, Mr M. W Caswell, Mr T.G. Cowell, S. Harris, A. J. Hartnoll, Higos Insurance Services Ltd, Mr J. W. Johns, Mr R. M. Leatherdale, Mr J. L. Lightfoot, Mr A. P. Maddox, Mrs E. Masterman, Mr G. R. Mcbride, Mr M. A. G. Nicholson, N. M. S. Rich, Mr P. A. Roberts, Mr J. R. Searchfield, R. R. Shand, J. Shaw, M. C. Smith, Mr M. J. Southcott, M. S. Tamburro, Mr N. J. Thorne, Mrs S. B. Vernon, Mr R. I. Walker, Mr R. Watts, Mr D. C. Willis, Mrs S. J. Wynne, O. C. R. Wynne.

Assistant Trainer: G A Dartnall

Conditional: James White, Jack Doyle. **Amateur:** Mr E. Glassonbury.

---

143 **MR T. G. DASCOMBE, Lambourn**
Postal: Oneway, Folly Road, Lambourn, Berkshire, RG17 3QE
Contacts: PHONE (01488) 71839 FAX (01488) 71839 MOBILE (07973) 511664
E-MAIL tomdascombe@onewayracing.co.uk WEBSITE www.onewayracing.co.uk

1 SAVILE'S DELIGHT (IRE), 9, b g Cadeaux Genereux—Across The Ice (USA) **ONEWAY Partners**
2 SAWWAAH (IRE), 11, b g Marju (IRE)—Just A Mirage **A. D. Solomon**

THREE-YEAR-OLDS

3 CLIFTON DANCER, b f Fraam—Crofters Ceilidh **Clifton Partners**
4 B f Dansili—Cup Of Kindness (USA) **Mr Adrian Smith**
5 DOCTOR ROBERT, b g Sakhee (USA)—Please **The Friends Partnership**
6 DRUMHALLAGH (IRE), b g Barathea (IRE)—Nashua Song (IRE) **R. George & J. Brown**
7 GROSS PROPHET, b g Lujain (USA)—Done And Dusted (IRE) **A. D. Solomon**
8 MAX ONE TWO THREE (IRE), b f Princely Heir (IRE)—Dakota Sioux (IRE) **A. W. Black**
9 B g Mujahid (USA)—Munakashah (IRE) **P. A. Deal**
10 ONEMOREANDSTAY, ch f Dr Fong (USA)—Subito **Grant Thornton Racing Club**
11 PARISIAN GIFT (IRE), b g Statue of Liberty (USA)—My Micheline **The P. G. Tipsters**

MR T. G. DASCOMBE—continued

12 **PRINCE DESIRE (IRE)**, b c Fasliyev (USA)—No Quest (IRE) **De La Warr Racing**
13 **SECRET FINISH**, b f Mujahid (USA)—Les Hurlants (IRE) **Sideways Racing**
14 **TRUE AND FAIR (IRE)**, b f Xaar—Quintellina **Grant Thornton Racing Club**
15 **WHAT'S FOR TEA**, b f Beat All (USA)—Come To Tea (IRE) **A. D. Solomon**
16 **ZASKAR**, b f Anabaa (USA)—Bezzaaf **P. A. Deal & M. J. Silver**

TWO-YEAR-OLDS

17 **DIAPASON (IRE)**, b f 30/4 Mull of Kintyre (USA)—Suaad (IRE) (Fools Holme (USA)) (20591) **Mr John Brown**
18 B c 20/2 Zieten (USA)—Emergency Exit (FR) (Exit To Nowhere (USA)) (17000) **Mr Michael Watt**
19 B c 4/3 Mull of Kintyre (USA)—Free To Trade (IRE) (Royal Academy (USA)) (7078)
20 **HAAFHD TIME (IRE)**, b f 4/2 Haafhd—Amusing Time (IRE) (Sadler's Wells (USA)) (8364) **Mrs Maureen Coxon**
21 B f 6/4 Lend A Hand—Just Magic (Beveled (USA)) (761) **Mr Michael Arum**
22 B g 22/5 Cyrano de Bergerac—Kairine (IRE) (Kahyasi) (2500) **Mr Adrian Smith**
23 **KALOOKI LADY**, b f 6/5 Bertolini (USA)—Bezzaaf (Machiavellian (USA)) (10000) **P. A. Deal & M. J. Silver**
24 Ch f 8/3 Bahamian Bounty—Mana Pools (IRE) (Brief Truce (USA)) (9000) **Miss Caroline George**
25 B br f 2/4 Diktat—Mexican Hawk (USA) (Silver Hawk (USA)) (9000) **W R B Racing**
26 B c 28/2 Halling (USA)—Mystery Play (IRE) (Sadler's Wells (USA)) (25000) **Mrs Caroline Sanderson**
27 **PURPLE SUN**, b c 10/3 Desert Sun—
　　　　　　　Palisandra (USA) (Chief's Crown (USA)) (4500) **Messrs Basing Bellman Blakemore Eastment**
28 B c 7/3 Daggers Drawn (USA)—Queen Bodicea (IRE) (Revoque (IRE)) (12225)
29 B c 26/1 Auction House (USA)—Queen of Scotland (IRE) (Mujadil (USA)) (20000) **123 Racing Partnership**
30 B f 16/4 One Cool Cat (USA)—San Luis Rey (Zieten (USA)) (28957) **Mr Martin Stillwell**
31 **SHIVA ADIVA**, gr f 15/4 Needwood Blade—Eastern Lyric (Petong) (1523) **Mr Stephen Bayliss**
32 B c 17/3 Pursuit of Love—Starboard Tack (FR) (Saddlers' Hall (IRE)) (1523) **Mr A. D. Solomon**
33 B f 19/4 Bachelor Duke (USA)—Suzuran (Generous (IRE)) (6434)
34 Ch c 28/3 Hawk Wing (USA)—Talbiya (IRE) (Mujtahid (USA)) (10000) **Mr Chris McHale**
35 B f 30/3 Elusive City (USA)—Virgin Stanza (USA) (Opening Verse (USA)) (12869)
36 B c 30/3 Traditionally (USA)—Wish List (IRE) (Mujadil (USA)) (5000) **Mr Dan Perchard**

Other Owners: Mr S. A. Cochrane, Mr G. J. Dascombe, Mr T. Dascombe, Mr P.S. Dove, Mr P.T. Fenwick, Mr Allan Galley, Mrs Caroline Ingram, Mr Stephen Arthur Jones, Mr S. M. Little, Mr N. J. McKibbin, Mr Stuart McPhee, Mr Geoff Neville, Mr C. D. Pritchard, Mr D. Redvers, Mr M. Sowerby, Mr M. Stone, Mr Evan M. Sutherland, The Holmes Office, Mr Jim White, Mr Matty Williams.

Assistant Trainer: Miss Michaela Sowerby

Jockey (flat): Richard Kingscote. **Amateur:** Miss Michaela Sowerby, Mr Nuno Santos.

---

144 MR J. D. J. DAVIES, Ammanford
Postal: Haul Y Bryn, Garnswllt, Ammanford, South Wales

1 **GRAND DREAM (IRE)**, 4, ch g Grand Lodge (USA)—Tamaya (IRE) **Mrs M. H. Davies**

---

145 MR J. J. DAVIES, Darlington
Postal: Denton Grange, Piercebridge, Darlington, Co. Durham
Contacts: PHONE (01325) 374366 MOBILE (07746) 292782

1 **HABANUS LIVIUS (IRE)**, 5, ch g Titus Livius (FR)—Wheatsheaf Lady (IRE) **J. J. Davies**
2 **MISCHIEF NIGHT**, 6, ch g Lake Coniston (IRE)—On Till Morning (IRE) **J. J. Davies**
3 **SEADIP**, 5, b m Sea Raven (IRE)—Dipador (IRE) **J. J. Davies**

Jockey (NH): M. H. Naughton.

146 MISS J. S. DAVIS, East Garston

Postal: **Parsonage Farm Racing Stables, Newbury Road, East Garston, Hungerford, Berkshire, RG17 7ER**
Contacts: **PHONE (01488) 649977 FAX (01488) 649977 MOBILE (07879) 811535**
E-MAIL davisjo_007@hotmail.com WEBSITE www.jodavisracing.co.uk

1 **BITE UN FIGHT,** 5, ch m Classic Cliche (IRE)—Ginger Rogers **Lockstone Business Services & D. Febry**
2 **CORREY,** 4, ch f Tobougg (IRE)—Numerate **P. J. Ponting**
3 **CROFT (IRE),** 5, b g Mull of Kintyre (USA)—Home Comforts **Lockstone Business Services Ltd**
4 **GLOWING DAWN (IRE),** 6, b m Definite Article—Alizee (IRE) **Open Brook Racing**
5 **KING'S SPEAR (IRE),** 5, b g Lear Spear (USA)—First Veil
6 **LOCKSTONE LAD (USA),** 5, gr g Mazel Trick (USA)—Humble (USA) **Lockstone Business Services Ltd**
7 **LOWE GO,** 8, b g First Trump—Hotel California (IRE) **Lockstone Business Services Ltd**
8 **MY BEAUTAFUL,** 4, ch f Classic Cliche (IRE)—Ginger Rogers **Mr P. Ponting**
9 **PUKKA TIQUE,** 5, b g Groom Dancer (USA)—Surf Bird **J. L. Marriott**
10 **SALIM,** 11, b g Salse (USA)—Moviegoer **Lockstone Business Services Ltd**
11 **SECRET GLEN (IRE),** 9, b g Un Desperado (FR)—Bornacurra Ella **Mr P. Ponting & Mr R. Butterworth**
12 **SPROWLER,** 4, b g Peintre Celebre (USA)—Enlisted (IRE) **Lockstone Business Services Ltd**
13 **THESEAINTTOYS (IRE),** 5, ch g Quws—Three In A Twist (IRE) **The Toyboys**
14 **TINA'S RIDGE (IRE),** 4, ch g Indian Ridge—Phantom Waters **J. L. Marriott**
15 **WAIFER'S LAD,** 5, gr g Double Trigger (IRE)—Belmore Cloud **John & Liz de Lotz**

THREE-YEAR-OLDS

16 **FESTIVAL DREAMS,** ch g Largesse—Bright Spangle (IRE) **The Three B's**
17 B f Zindabad (FR)—Ginger Rogers **Mr P. Ponting**

TWO-YEAR-OLDS

18 B c 6/5 Thowra (FR)—Bright Spangle (IRE) (General Monash (USA))
19 Ch f 1/3 Dr Fong (USA)—Clipper (Salse (USA)) (6000) **Mr & Mrs D. Bennyworth**

Other Owners: Mr M. P. Boorman, Mr William Terence Brown, D. R. Febry, Mr Albert L. Marriott, Mr G. Yexley, Mr J. R. de Lotz, Mrs E. A. de Lotz.

Conditional: Marc Goldstein.

147 MISS L. V. DAVIS, Stafford

Postal: **The Stables, Hillcrest, Bradley Lane, Levedale, Stafford**
Contacts: **PHONE (01543) 424697 MOBILE (07722) 004304**
E-MAIL vky1971@yahoo.co.uk

1 **ATAHUELPA,** 8, b g Hernando (FR)—Certain Story **Miss L. V. Davis**
2 **EASTERN DAGGER,** 8, b g Kris—Shehana (USA) **Miss L. V. Davis**
3 **SUPERSHOT (IRE),** 10, b g Son of Sharp Shot (IRE)—One To Two (IRE) **Miss L. V. Davis**
4 **TRUST RULE,** 8, b g Selkirk (USA)—Hagwah (USA) **Miss L. V. Davis**
5 **VESTA FLAME,** 7, b m Vettori (IRE)—Ciel de Feu (IRE) **Miss L. V. Davis**

Jockey (NH): Adam Hawkins.

148 MISS Z. C. DAVISON, East Grinstead

Postal: **Shovelstrode Racing Stables, Shovelstrode Lane, Ashurstwood, East Grinstead, West Sussex, RH19 3PN**
Contacts: **PHONE (01342) 323153 FAX (01342) 323153 MOBILE (07970) 839357**

1 **ASHMOLIAN (IRE),** 5, b g Grand Lodge (USA)—Animatrice (USA) **The Secret Circle**
2 **BALLYGOREY,** 7, b g Komaite (USA)—Chasmarella **Exors of the Late Mrs G. A. Davison**
3 **CALL ME DAVE,** 7, b g Bin Ajwaad (IRE)—Heckle **Exors of the Late Mrs G. A. Davison**
4 **CERTIFIABLE,** 7, b g Deploy—Gentle Irony **Mrs S. E. Colville**
5 **CHARLIE BEAR,** 7, ch h Bahamian Bounty—Abi **M. P. Merwood**
6 **CODE (IRE),** 7, b g Danehill (USA)—Hidden Meaning (USA) **Rags To Riches**
7 **DAMASCUS GOLD,** 4, b c Thowra (FR)—Damasquiner **Miss P. I. Westbrook**
8 5, B g Midnight Legend—Dark Romance (IRE) **Alan Goldson**
9 **JUST BEWARE,** 6, b m Makbul—Bewails (IRE) **The Secret Circle**
10 **KORIKANCHA (IRE),** 5, b m Fasliyev (USA)—Amravati (IRE) **The Secret Circle**
11 **LAP OF THE GODS,** 4, b g Fleetwood (IRE)—Casarabonela **A. J. Irvine**

MISS Z. C. DAVISON—continued

12 PATH TO GLORY, 4, b c Makbul—Just Glory David J. Bearman
13 REIGNING MONARCH (USA), 5, b g Fusaichi Pegasus (USA)—Torros Straits (USA) J. E. Belsey
14 SHERJAWY (IRE), 4, b g Diktat—Arruhan (IRE) J. E. Belsey
15 SPIDER BOY, 11, b g Jupiter Island—Great Dilemma B. Ward
16 WINNING SPIRIT (IRE), 4, b g Invincible Spirit—Taisho (IRE) A. J. Irvine

TWO-YEAR-OLDS

17 Br c 27/3 Makbul—Havantadoubt (IRE) (Desert King (IRE)) Secret Circle

Other Owners: Miss Z. C. Davison, Mr J. Green, Mrs J. Irvine, Mr G. Morley, Mr Antony Waters.

Assistant Trainer: A Irvine

Jockey (flat): Sam Hitchcott, Adrian McCarthy. **Amateur:** Mr H. G. Miller, Miss G. D. Gracey-Davison.

---

149 MR N. J. DAWE, Bridgwater
Postal: **Chantry Cottage, Sea Lane, Kilve, Bridgwater, Somerset, TA5 1EG**
Contacts: **PHONE (01278) 741457 MOBILE (07766) 150656**
E-MAIL chantry_cottage@hotmail.com

1 PROUD PEER (IRE), 10, ch g Mister Lord (USA)—Raffeen Pride Mrs J. Dawe

Assistant Trainer: Mrs J. C. Dawe

---

150 MR W. DE BEST-TURNER, Calne
Postal: **North Farm Stables, West Overton, Marlborough, Wiltshire, SN8 1QE**
Contacts: **PHONE (01249) 811944 HOME (07977) 910779 FAX (01249) 811955**
E-MAIL william@debestracing.fsnet.co.uk

1 BEAU JAZZ, 7, br g Merdon Melody—Ichor W. de Best-Turner
2 BELTANE, 10, b g Magic Ring (IRE)—Sally's Trust (IRE) Mrs G. R. Swanton
3 SAGASSA, 4, b f Largesse—Sally's Trust (IRE) Mrs G. R. Swanton
4 SEA COOKIE, 4, b f Largesse—Maylan (IRE) W. de Best-Turner
5 STERLING MOLL, 5, gr m Lord of Men—Princess Maud (USA) De Best Racing

THREE-YEAR-OLDS

6 SHISHIO, b c Largesse—Sachiko W. de Best-Turner

TWO-YEAR-OLDS

7 LORD OF THE FLAME, br c 28/2 Largesse—Maylan (IRE) (Lashkari) W. de Best-Turner
8 B f 3/3 Largesse—Sally's Trust (IRE) (Classic Secret (USA)) Mrs G. R. Swanton

Other Owners: Miss S J Slade, Mr R. T. Swanton.

Assistant Trainer: Gillian Swanton

---

151 MR B. DE HAAN, Lambourn
Postal: **Fair View, Long Hedge, Lambourn, Newbury, Berkshire, RG17 8NA**
Contacts: **PHONE (01488) 72163 FAX (01488) 71306 MOBILE (07831) 104574**
E-MAIL bendehaanracing@aol.com WEBSITE www.bendehaan.net

1 BENGO (IRE), 8, b g Beneficial—Goforroad (IRE) Willsford Racing Ltd
2 CLASSIC GOLD (GER), 7, br g Gold And Ivory (USA)—Classic Woman (IRE) W. A. Tyrer
3 DEVENISH LAD (IRE), 6, b g Anshan—Roseowen Mrs D Vaughan & Ms Pat Treacy
4 FIDELIS (IRE), 4, gr g Great Palm (USA)—Americo Rescue (IRE) Mr & Mrs Nicholas Tatman
5 HEEZAZARI (IRE), 7, b g Darazari (IRE)—Golden Fashion (IRE)
6 HILLRIDGE, 5, ch g Fumo di Londra (IRE)—Josifina J. Simms
7 JAVA VICTORY (IRE), 6, b g Old Vic—Damile (IRE) Java Racing
8 JOHN CHARLES (IRE), 6, b g Fraam—Norwegian Queen (IRE) MTT/Consulting Limited
9 JUST TALKING (IRE), 6, br g Windsor Castle—Fam-E Fam-E (IRE) JT Syndicate
10 MATUHI, 5, b g Dansili—Montserrat Willsford Racing Ltd

MR B. DE HAAN—continued

11 **MEALAGH VALLEY (IRE)**, 7, b g Darazari (IRE)—Sister Dympna **Mrs J. A. Phillips**
12 **MONKEY MASSINI (IRE)**, 6, b g Dr Massini (IRE)—Madam's Monkey **Mr D. A. Stalder**
13 **NOM DE GUERRE (IRE)**, 6, b g Presenting—Asklynn (IRE) **Mr & Mrs Nicholas Tatman**
14 **ORIGINAL THOUGHT (IRE)**, 8, b g Entrepreneur—Troyanos **W. A. Tyrer**
15 **SCARAMOUCHE**, 8, b g Busy Flight—Laura Lye (IRE) **B. D. Heath**
16 5, B g Oscar (IRE)—Suka (IRE) **Mrs C. Walwyn, Lady Aitken, Mr S. Johnson**
17 **TEACH TO PREACH (USA)**, 5, ch g Pulpit (USA)—Chateaubaby (USA) **Mrs D. Vaughan**
18 **TRAVELLING FOX**, 5, b g Slip Anchor—Lola Mora **Peter Fenwick Partnership**
19 **UFFA FOX (IRE)**, 5, b g Bravefoot—Ocean Mist (IRE) **Lady V Aitken, Mrs F Walwyn, Mr D Heath**

THREE-YEAR-OLDS

20 **AVA GEE**, br f Averti (IRE)—Spring Sunrise **Mrs D. Vaughan**
21 **BRAVE KNAVE (IRE)**, b c Averti (IRE)—Recall (IRE) **Mrs D. Vaughan**
22 **CAPTAIN KIR (IRE)**, ch c Captain Rio—A Lot of Kir (IRE) **Mrs D. Vaughan**
23 **KOUTOUBIA (IRE)**, b f Daylami (IRE)—Aqaba **J. P. Repard**
24 **LENOUSKA (IRE)**, b f Montjeu (IRE)—Crystal City **Mr M. Hoodless**
25 **WHATALOTOFBUTS**, ch c Kirkwall—Wontcostalotbut **Wontcostalot Partnership**

TWO-YEAR-OLDS

26 **GOOD QUEEN BEST**, b f 22/2 Best of The Bests (IRE)—Spring Sunrise (Robellino (USA) **Mrs D. Vaughan**
27 B f 24/1 Selkirk (USA)—Song of Hope (Chief Singer) (16000) **Looks A Bright Prospect Racing**

Other Owners: Lady Aitken, Mr J. Andrews, Mr J. F. Ansell, Mrs D. P. Ansell, Mr P. V. Burnand, Mr A. A. Clifford, Mr R. L. Clifford, Mr P. T. Fenwick, Mr Duncan Heath, Mr B. R. Jervis, Mr Nicholas Tatman, Mrs Elizabeth Tatman, Ms Pat Treacy, Mrs D. Vaughan, Mrs F. Walwyn.

Jockey (flat): A. Kirby. **Jockey (NH):** N. Fehily. **Conditional:** A. Yoxall.

152 **MR A. J. DEAKIN, Cannock**
Postal: **7 Hornbeam Crescent, Hazel Slade, Cannock, Staffordshire, WS12 5SU**
Contacts: **PHONE (01543) 424262 MOBILE (07880) 666986**
E-MAIL tonydeakin1@hotmail.co.uk

1 **ANCIENT SITE (USA)**, 4, ch g Distant View (USA)—Victorian Style **A. J. Deakin**

Jockey (NH): P. J. Brennan.

153 **MR R. DICKIN, Stratford-upon-Avon**
Postal: **Alscot Racing Stables, Alscot Park, Atherston On Stour, Stratford-upon-Avon, Warwickshire, CV37 8BL**
Contacts: **PHONE (01789) 450052 FAX (01789) 450053 MOBILE (07979) 518593 / (07979) 518594**
E-MAIL robin@robindickinracing.org.uk

1 **ARCTIC SHADOW**, 6, b g Bonny Scot (IRE)—Dickies Girl **The Magnificent Seven**
2 **ARCTIC SPIRIT**, 13, b g Arctic Lord—Dickies Girl **The Lordy Racing Partnership**
3 **ATHERSTONE HILL**, 6, b g Presenting—Mystic Madam (IRE) **Nigel Austin**
4 **GUNS OF LOVE**, 6, b g Lord of Appeal—Golden Seekers **Whoops 72!**
5 **HANBRIN BHOY (IRE)**, 4, b g Cape Cross (IRE)—Sea of Stone (USA) **John Hanley John Brindley**
6 **ILONGUE (FR)**, 7, b m Nononito (FR)—Marie De Geneve (FR) **Steve Webb & Gerry Parker**
7 **JACARADO (IRE)**, 10, b g Jurado (USA)—Lady Mearba (IRE) **R. G. & R. A. Whitehead**
8 **JACK OF SPADES (IRE)**, 12, b g Mister Lord (USA)—Dooney's Daughter **E. R. C. Beech & B. Wilkinson**
9 **JESNIC (IRE)**, 8, b g Kahyasi—Fur Hat **J. Hanna**
10 **JOSE BOVE**, 6, ch g So Factual (USA)—Dark Sirona **Miss C. A. B. Allsopp**
11 **KHADIJA**, 7, ch m Kadastrof (FR)—Dark Sirona **Miss C. A. B. Allsopp**
12 **LUCOZADE**, 7, b g Sir Harry Lewis (USA)—Brioletta **Robin's Rebels**
13 **MADAM HARRIET**, 6, b m Sir Harry Lewis (USA)—Norska **The Apostles**
14 **MISS LADYBIRD (USA)**, 7, b br m Labeeb—Bird Dance (USA) **W. J. Wyatt**
15 **MISS PEBBLES (IRE)**, 8, ch m Lake Coniston (IRE)—Sea of Stone (USA) **The Alscot Blue Group**
16 **MISTER TRICKSTER (IRE)**, 7, b g Woodborough (USA)—Tinos Island (IRE) **The Tricksters**
17 **MY BEAUTIFUL LOSER (IRE)**, 6, gr m Silver Patriarch (IRE)—Miss Diakin (IRE) **Mr J. C. Clemmow**
18 **NAUTIC (FR)**, 7, b g Apple Tree (FR)—Bella Dicta (FR) **Scrumpy Jacks**
19 **NEWICK PARK**, 13, gr g Chilibang—Quilpee Mai **Mrs C. M. Dickin**
20 **RAZZAMATAZZ**, 10, b g Alhijaz—Salvezza (IRE) **Mrs M. A. Cooper**

MR R. DICKIN—continued

21 **REGAL TERM (IRE)**, 10, b g Welsh Term—Regal Hostess **Seckington Whitehead**
22 **RHUBY RIVER (IRE)**, 6, b m Bahhare (USA)—Westside Flyer **C. J. Dickin**
23 **ROMANY DREAM**, 10, b m Nomadic Way (USA)—Half Asleep **The Snoozy Partnership**
24 **ROTHRES (FR)**, 4, b f Lavirco (GER)—Academic Dance (FR) **Stratford Members Club**
25 **SIMPLE GLORY (IRE)**, 9, br m Simply Great (FR)—Cabin Glory **Mr E. R. C. Beech**
26 5, Gr g Jimble (FR)—Something Fun (FR) **C. J. Dickin**
27 **TUDOR BUCK (IRE)**, 8, b br g Luso—Tudor Doe (IRE) **Robin's Rebels**
28 4, Ch c Kadastrof (FR)—Vent Vert (IRE) **Mrs M. A. Cooper**

THREE-YEAR-OLDS

29 Ch f Kadastrof (FR)—Whistling Song **Mrs C. M. Dickin**

Other Owners: Mr M. S. Anderson, Mr N. Austin, Mr E. R. Clifford Beech, Mr John Brindley, Mr Andrew Bull, Mr C. N. Butters, Ms Joanne Clark, Mr R. A. Cockrell, Mr J. R. Cooper, Mrs G. A. Day, Mrs C. M. Dickin, Mr C. J. Dickin, Mr P. A. J. Doyle, Mr John Hanley, Mr D. Hern, Dr N. W. Imlah, Ms S. Johnson, Mr D. C. Marten, Mr Gerry Parker, Mrs M. Payne, Mr Alan Varey, Mr P. Venvell, Mr J. R. Walker, Mr Steve Webb, Mr R. G. Whitehead, Mrs R. A. Whitehead, Mr B. Wilkinson, Mr Brian Wilson, Mrs J. Wood, Miss E. J. Wright.

Assistant Trainer: Claire Dickin

Jockey (flat): Royston Ffrench, Mickey Fenton. **Jockey (NH):** Rodi Greene, Josh Byrne, Henry Oliver, D. R. Dennis. **Conditional:** Phillip Thomas, Charlie Poste, Lee Edwards. **Amateur:** Mr Jamie Goss.

---

154 MR A. DICKMAN, Sandhutton
Postal: **Breckenbrough House (2nd Yard), Sandhutton, Thirsk, North Yorkshire, YO7 4EL**
Contacts: **HOME (01845) 587432 FAX (01845) 587432 MOBILE (07977) 694777**

1 **INTER VISION (USA)**, 8, b g Cryptoclearance (USA)—Fateful (USA) **Mrs D. Hodgkinson**
2 **ISHETOO**, 4, b g Ishiguru (USA)—Ticcatoo (IRE) **J. H. Sissons**
3 **RED CONTACT (USA)**, 7, b g Sahm (USA)—Basma (USA) **Miss S. Lehkonen**
4 **THE HONEST FIDDLER**, 5, b g Kayf Tara—Zihuatanejo **The Sting Partnership**
5 **WHOZART (IRE)**, 5, b g Mozart (IRE)—Hertford Castle **The Marooned Crew**

THREE-YEAR-OLDS

6 **TROJAN HERO (IRE)**, b g Royal Applause—Anne Boleyn **The Future Generation**

TWO-YEAR-OLDS

7 **BELLA FIGHETTA**, b f 9/3 Bertolini (USA)—My Girl (Mon Tresor) (7500)
8 **CONSEQUENCE**, br gr c 10/3 Paris House—Scrutinize (IRE) (Selkirk (USA))
9 **DARK MOMENT**, gr c 7/2 Spartacus (IRE)—Dim Ofan (Petong) (16000) **Construction Crew Racing Partnership**
10 **FUTURE GEM**, b f 10/2 Bertolini (USA)—Georgianna (IRE) (Petardia) (4000)
11 **REAL DIAMOND**, b f 26/3 Bertolini (USA)—Miss Fit (IRE) (Hamas (IRE)) (10000)
12 **SLEEPY VALLEY (IRE)**, b f 27/5 Clodovil (IRE)—Kilkee Bay (IRE) (Case Law) (8500)
13 **WITHOUT EQUAL**, ch f 5/4 Tobougg (IRE)—Sans Egale (FR) (Lashkari) (10000)

Other Owners: Mr Andrew Dickman, Mr L. L. Dickman, Mr D. J. Hardy, Mr Dick Janney, Mr T. Park, Mr T. Robinson, Mr John Sissons, Mr Gerald Slack, Mr Brian White.

Assistant Trainer: B Bennett

Jockey (flat): R Winston, D. Tudhope, P. Hanagan. **Jockey (NH):** D. Cullinane, J. McCarthy.

---

155 MR J. E. DIXON, Carlisle
Postal: **Moorend, Thursby, Carlisle, Cumbria, CA5 6QP**
Contacts: **PHONE (01228) 711019**

1 **CROFTON ARCH**, 8, b g Jumbo Hirt (USA)—Joyful Imp **Mrs E. M. Dixon**
2 **DANIEL'S DREAM**, 8, b g Prince Daniel (USA)—Amber Holly **Mrs E. M. Dixon**

156 MR M. J. K. DODS, Darlington

Postal: Denton Hall Farm, Piercebridge, Darlington, Co. Durham, DL2 3TY
Contacts: PHONE (01325) 374270 FAX (01325) 374020 MOBILE (07860) 411590/(07773) 290830
E-MAIL dods@teesdale-online.co.uk WEBSITE www.michaeldodsracing.co.uk

1 APACHE NATION (IRE), 5, b g Fruits of Love (USA)—Rachel Green (IRE) D. R. Graham
2 BALAKIREF, 9, b g Royal Applause—Pluck Septimus Racing Group
3 BARNEY MCGREW (IRE), 5, b g Mark of Esteem (IRE)—Success Story Mr W. A. Tinkler
4 BEST PROSPECT (IRE), 6, b g Orpen (USA)—Bright Prospect (USA) D. Neale
5 BURNING INCENSE (IRE), 5, b g Namid—Night Scent (IRE) Mr W. A. Tinkler
6 CELTIC CHANGE (IRE), 4, br g Celtic Swing—Changi (IRE) Mr P. Taylor
7 CHARLES PARNELL (IRE), 5, b g Elnadim—Titania C. A. Lynch
8 DISTANT PLEASURE, 4, b f Diktat—Our Pleasure (IRE) Pontefract Racecourse Racing Syndicate
9 DIVINE SPIRIT, 7, b g Foxhound—Vocation (IRE) The Newcastle Racing Club
10 DUCAL PIP SQUEAK, 4, b f Bertolini (USA)—Creeking Ducal Racing
11 FIVE WISHES, 4, b f Bahamian Bounty—Due West Exors of the Late M. Swift
12 GLASSHOUGHTON, 5, b g Dansili—Roseum J. N. Blackburn
13 HICCUPS, 8, b g Polar Prince (IRE)—Simmie's Special Mr W. A. Tinkler
14 HONORABLE LOVE, 4, ch f Highest Honor (FR)—Everlasting Love Mr P. Taylor
15 HULA BALLEW, 8, ch m Weldnaas (USA)—Ballon Mrs J. W. Hutchinson & Mrs P. A. Knox
16 LADY VALENTINO, 4, b f Primo Valentino (IRE)—Mystery Night (USA) Mrs J. W. Hutchinson & Mrs P. A. Knox
17 MAGIC ECHO, 4, br g Wizard King—Sunday News'n'echo (USA) D. C. Batey
18 MAJESTIC ISSUE (IRE), 4, ch g Fruits of Love (USA)—Queen's Share Pratt, Henderson & Partners
19 MAJOR MAGPIE (IRE), 6, b g Rossini (USA)—Picnic Basket Mrs P. Monk
20 MISPHIRE, 5, b m Mister Baileys—Bombay Sapphire The Cresswell Partnership
21 OSTEOPATHIC REMEDY (IRE), 4, ch g Inchinor—Dolce Vita (IRE) K. Kirkup
22 POLISH CORRIDOR, 9, b g Danzig Connection (USA)—Possibility R. D. Mould
23 PRINCE EGOR (IRE), 5, b g Imperial Ballet (IRE)—Harifana (FR) Harris Racing Partnership
24 RONNIE HOWE, 4, b g Hunting Lion (IRE)—Arasong Mrs C. E. Dods
25 ROTUMA (IRE), 9, b g Tagula (IRE)—Cross Question (USA) Denton Hall Racing Ltd
26 SOCIETY MUSIC (IRE), 6, b m Almutawakel—Society Fair (FR) H. Hewitson
27 STILL DREAMING, 4, ch f Singspiel (IRE)—Three Green Leaves (IRE) J. A. Wynn-Williams
28 THE OSTEOPATH (IRE), 5, ch g Danehill Dancer (IRE)—Miss Margate K. Kirkup
29 TOY TOP (USA), 5, gr ro m Tactical Cat (USA)—I'll Flutter By (USA) D. V. Roper

THREE-YEAR-OLDS

30 ACTABOU, b g Tobougg (IRE)—Carreamia J. Ellis
31 ANOTHER DECREE, b g Diktat—Akhira Mrs K. S. Pratt
32 BLINDSPIN, b g Intikhab (USA)—Blinding (IRE) A. Mallen
33 DREAM EXPRESS (IRE), b g Fasliyev (USA)—Lothlorien (USA) Mr J A Wynn-Williams Mr Les Waugh
34 KIOWA PRINCESS, ch f Compton Place—Sunley Stars D. R. Graham
35 KIWI BAY, b g Mujahid (USA)—Bay of Plenty (FR) Kiwi Racing
36 MARVELLOUS VALUE (IRE), b g Danetime (IRE)—Despondent (IRE) A. J. Henderson
37 PHANTOM SERENADE (IRE), b g Orpen (USA)—Phantom Rain North Briton Racing
38 Ch c Mark of Esteem (IRE)—Rose Bounty The Bounty Hunters
39 RUBIROSA (IRE), b g Acclamation—Bendis (GER) P. Rosas
40 SCRUFFY SKIP (IRE), b g Diktat—Capoeira (USA) Moneyleague Ltd
41 THE OIL MAGNATE, ch g Dr Fong (USA)—Bob's Princess Smith & Allan Racing
42 TOP EDGE, b f Intikhab (USA)—Chine Dick Dennis & Partners
43 WOODLAND MIST, b f Tobougg (IRE)—Aker Wood N. A. Riddell

TWO-YEAR-OLDS

44 B g 9/2 Trans Island—Cappuccino (IRE) (Mujadil (USA)) (23000) J. A. Wynn-Williams
45 Ch c 21/4 Compton Place—Coffee Time (IRE) (Efisio) (25000) Septimus Racing Group
46 Ch c 5/5 Beat Hollow—Dan's Delight (Machiavellian (USA)) (27000) D. V. Roper
47 Ch c 3/5 Exit To Nowhere (USA)—Dance A Dream (Sadler's Wells (USA)) (32000) Mould Partnership
48 EDEN PARK, ch f 22/2 Tobougg (IRE)—Aegean Flame (Anshan) (16000) Mr J. M. & Mrs E. E. Ranson
49 B c 3/2 Storming Home—Ipsa Loquitur (Unfuwain (USA)) (15000) D. R. Graham
50 JIMWIL (IRE), b c 4/2 One Cool Cat (USA)—
         Vulnerable (Hector Protector (USA)) (35000) Bill Nelson & Jim Mahony
51 Ch c 21/3 Green Tune (USA)—Lomapamar (Nashwan (USA)) (35000) Mr W. A. Tinkler
52 Ch g 30/3 Haafhd—Mall Queen (Sheikh Albadou) (18000) D. Neale
53 B g 30/4 Chevalier (IRE)—Miss Barcelona (IRE) (Mac's Imp (USA)) (7721) N. A. Riddell
54 B c 27/3 Tobougg (IRE)—Natalie Jay (Ballacashtal (CAN)) (22000) Just Five Racing Partners
55 Ch f 25/3 Orpen (USA)—Paula's Pride (Pivotal) (7078) Mrs B. Riddell
56 Ch c 14/3 Noverre (USA)—Psychic (IRE) (Alhaarth (IRE)) (50000) Mr W. A. Tinkler

MR M. J. K. DODS—continued

57 Ch g 1/4 Daggers Drawn (USA)—Quizzical Lady (Mind Games) (16086) **D. Neale**
58 B c 10/4 Acclamation—Razor Sharp (Bering) (45000) **Mr A. Dick**
59 Br c 23/2 Namid—Red Leggings (Shareef Dancer (USA)) (12000) **C. C. S. MacMillan**
60 B f 13/3 Tobougg (IRE)—Seeking Utopia (Wolfhound (USA)) (5000) **Denton Hall Racing Ltd**
61 Ch c 7/3 Monsieur Bond (IRE)—Sheen Falls (IRE) (Prince Rupert (FR)) (30887) **Mr W. A. Tinkler**
62 B f 20/4 Overbury (IRE)—Sunday News'n'echo (USA) (Trempolino (USA)) **D. C. Batey**
63 B c 27/2 Tobougg (IRE)—Thrasher (Hector Protector (USA)) (5500) **M. Dods**
64 B g 8/3 Olmodavor (USA)—Wildsplash (USA) (Deputy Minister (CAN)) (7000) **Just Five Racing Partners**
65 B g 30/1 Key of Luck (USA)—Zingari (Groom Dancer (USA)) (10295) **C. A. Lynch**
66 B c 18/3 Alhaarth (IRE)—Zobaida (IRE) (Green Desert (USA)) (32000) **Partnership**

Other Owners: Mrs Stella Barclay, Mr J. N. Blackburn, Mr S. A. Breakwell, Mr R. Brown (Co. Durham), Mr J. J. Brummitt, Mr P. J. Carr, Mr Paul Clarkson, Mr P. E. Cranston, Mr M. J. K. Dods, Mrs C. E. Dods, Mr J. Ellis, Mr K. J. Green, Mr H. R. Harris, Mr A. J. Henderson, Mrs J. W. Hutchinson, Mr Maurice Hutchinson, Mrs Alison Iles, Mr D. Kirsopp, Mrs P. A. Knox, Mr K. Knox, Mr J. J. J. Mahony, Mr A. Mallen, Mrs Patsy Monk, Mr C. W. Nelson, Mrs Karen S. Pratt, Mr J. M. Ranson, Mrs E. E. Ranson, Mr Roger Stokell, Mr D. J. Stokell, Mr Foster Watson, Mr David Watts, Mr Les Waugh, Mr J. R. Wharton, Mr Paul Wyatt, Mr B. Yeadon.

Assistant Trainer: C Dods, Eddie Jones

---

157 MR FRANCOIS DOUMEN, Bouce
Postal: **Le Gue, 61570 Bouce, France**
Contacts: **PHONE (0033) 2332 69146 (0033) 2336 71159 FAX (0033) 2336 78237**
MOBILE (0033) 6074 23358 E-MAIL doumenecouves@orange.fr

1 **ARBOR VITAE (FR)**, 10, b g Double Bed (FR)—Gloire de Rose
2 **BASTRINGUE (FR)**, 5, b h Double Bed (FR)—Cabaret Club (FR)
3 **DANAW (FR)**, 7, b g Lomitas—Damanka (IRE)
4 **DESERT JIM (FR)**, 6, ch g Desert King (IRE)—Jimshine (FR)
5 **DISTALINO (FR)**, 5, b g Poliglote—Distale (FR)
6 **DOUBLE TONIC (FR)**, 9, br g Double Bed (FR)—Jimka (FR)
7 **FAST LANE LILI**, 5, b m Fasliyev (USA)—Mercedes (GER)
8 **FOOLISH EGO (FR)**, 4, b c Hernando (FR)—L'annee Folle (FR)
9 **GOT STAR (FR)**, 4, ch c Starborough—Aphrodisias (FR)
10 **GRAND BLEU (IRE)**, 5, b g Great Palm (USA)—Blue Pool
11 **GRAND SCHLEM (FR)**, 4, b c Astarabad (USA)—Forty Love (FR)
12 **KASBAH BLISS (FR)**, 6, b g Kahyasi—Marital Bliss (FR)
13 **KELAMI (FR)**, 10, ch g Lute Antique (FR)—Voltige De Nievre (FR)
14 **KILOMETRE NEUF (FR)**, 5, b h Double Bed (FR)—Mary Astor (FR)
15 **L'AMI (FR)**, 9, ch g Lute Antique (FR)—Voltige De Nievre (FR)
16 **LUDRE (FR)**, 9, gr g True Brave (USA)—Ahhotep (FR)
17 **LUISANT (FR)**, 5, ch h Pivotal—La Legere (USA)
18 **MA BELLE EMMA (FR)**, 4, b f Hamas (IRE)—Landed (USA)
19 **MAJIMOURIEN (FR)**, 5, b m Majorien—Jolie Jim (FR)
20 **MILLENIUM ROYAL (FR)**, 8, ch g Mansonnien (FR)—Pink Champagne (FR)
21 **MOULIN RICHE (FR)**, 8, b g Video Rock (FR)—Gintonique (FR)
22 **NEVADA (FR)**, 7, ch g Ragmar (FR)—Attualita (FR)
23 **NITRAT (FR)**, 7, b g Brier Creek (USA)—Evane (FR)
24 **OMMEGA (FR)**, 6, gr g Ragmar (FR)—Cathou (FR)
25 **ONNIX (FR)**, 6, ch g Funny Baby (FR)—Elza III (FR)
26 **PARPAILLOT (FR)**, 5, b g Subotica (FR)—Voilette (FR)
27 **PARRAIN (FR)**, 5, b g Brier Creek (USA)—Grenelle II (FR)
28 **POMMEROL (FR)**, 5, b g Subotica (FR)—Irish Cofee (FR)
29 **POWERFUL (IRE)**, 4, b g Mr Combustible (IRE)—Perfect Colour (IRE)
30 **QOMIX (FR)**, 4, b g Fragrant Mix (IRE)—Hyrondelle II (FR)
31 **QOMPRESOR (FR)**, 4, b g Subotica (FR)—Elza III (FR)
32 **QONQUERANT (FR)**, 4, b g Video Rock (FR)—Devise II (FR)
33 **QUASPIA (FR)**, 4, b f Fragrant Mix (IRE)—Jonquiere (FR)
34 **QUEL SAINT (FR)**, 4, b g Saint des Saints (FR)—Ahhotep (FR)
35 **QUIBBLE (FR)**, 4, b f Jimble (FR)—French Kiss Iv (FR)
36 **QUOLIBET (FR)**, 4, gr g Fragrant Mix (IRE)—Goguette II (FR)
37 **STANDING START (FR)**, 4, b c Indian Danehill (IRE)—Startup (IRE)
38 **STEED (FR)**, 6, b h Double Bed (FR)—River Tweed
39 **SUNRISE SPIRIT (FR)**, 7, b g Double Bed (FR)—Belle Chaumiere
40 **SUNRISE SUNRISE (FR)**, 4, ch c Double Bed (FR)—Belle Chaumiere

MR FRANCOIS DOUMEN—continued

41 **TROQUE (FR)**, 4, b c Enrique—The Trollop (FR)
42 **TURFONTEIN (FR)**, 4, b f Kahyasi—Gigawatt (FR)

THREE-YEAR-OLDS

43 **BEDARUN (FR)**, b f Bedawin (FR)—Coureuse (FR)
44 **BEDASTORM (FR)**, b c Bedawin (FR)—Mary Astor (FR)
45 **BRONCOLI (FR)**, b c Observatory (USA)—Balouchina (IRE)
46 **CABARETUNE (FR)**, b c Green Tune (USA)—Cabaret Club (FR)
47 **CAPTAINE COURAGE (IRE)**, ch c Bering—Four Green (FR)
48 **CHI WARA SHEBA (FR)**, ch f High Yield (USA)—Lisheba (USA)
49 **CITY LOOK**, b f Vettori (IRE)—Cover Look (SAF)
50 **GIGANA (FR)**, b br f Anabaa Blue—Gigawatt (FR)
51 **ICE AND SHINY (FR)**, b c Verglas (IRE)—Jimshine (FR)
52 **JIMANGO (FR)**, b c Chichicastenango (FR)—Jolie Jim (FR)
53 **LANDINE (FR)**, b f Bedawin (FR)—Landed (USA)
54 **MARYLINE**, b f Bertolini (USA)—Mary Sea (FR)
55 **MENESTREL (FR)**, b c Cadoudal (FR)—Madame Baccarat (FR)
56 **MOONLIGHT DANCEUSE (IRE)**, ch f Bering—Stage Struck (IRE)
57 **NEXT SUNRISE (FR)**, ch f Nikos—Belle Chaumiere
58 **ORPEN VIEW (IRE)**, b f Orpen (USA)—Model View (USA)
59 **POUR CHANGER (FR)**, b c Daliapour (IRE)—Chop And Change (FR)
60 **PUBLIC RANSOM (IRE)**, b f Red Ransom (USA)—En Public (FR)
61 **QUEEN OF THE BONGO**, b f Beat Hollow—Harbour Queen (IRE)
62 **RAMADAN (FR)**, b c Bedawin (FR)—Ma'am (FR)
63 **RAMSES D'ARON (FR)**, b g Network (GER)—Heureka (FR)
64 **ROBUSTE (FR)**, gr c April Night (FR)—Elione (FR)
65 **ROCK D'ARON (FR)**, b g Video Rock (FR)—Fleche Noir II (FR)
66 **ROSE BIRD (FR)**, ch f Bering—Rose d'or (IRE)
67 **ROUMAIN (FR)**, b g Network (GER)—Douce Nuit II (FR)
68 **ROX (FR)**, b g Subotica (FR)—Jaxelle (FR)
69 **ROYAL BERE (FR)**, gr c Verglas (IRE)—Honeymoon Suite (FR)
70 **SAINTE RUSSY (FR)**, b f Saint des Saints (FR)—Lattaquie (FR)
71 **SYLVERTUNE (FR)**, b f Green Tune (USA)—Syvanie (FR)
72 **TOP NUMBERS (IRE)**, b c Numerous (USA)—Tipsy Topsy
73 **TRUE BLUE SAGA (FR)**, b c Anabaa Blue—Saiga (FR)
74 **VICTOR VICTORIA (FR)**, ch g bedawin (fr)—victoria regia (ire)

TWO-YEAR-OLDS

75 **BATTY CIRCUS (FR)**, ch f 9/4 Bedawin (FR)—Coureuse (FR) (Jeune Homme (USA))
76 **BENGUERRA (FR)**, b f 19/5 Beat Hollow—Gigawatt (FR) (Double Bed (FR))
77 **CARD IN HAND (FR)**, b f 15/4 Hernando (FR)—Carte Blanche (FR) (Highest Honor (FR))
78 **CHASSE CROISE (FR)**, gr c 13/3 Kendor (FR)—Veiled Wings (FR) (Priolo (USA)) (41827)
79 **DIABLE DE JIM (FR)**, b c 20/5 Diableneyev (USA)—Jolie Jim (FR) (Double Bed (FR))
80 **DIAMOND BOY (FR)**, b c 28/4 Mansonnien (FR)—Gold Or Silver (FR) (Glint of Gold) (54697)
81 Ch c 29/4 Monsun (GER)—Distant Horizon (USA) (Diesis) (51480)
82 B f 19/3 Royal Applause—Everlasting Love (Pursuit of Love) (54697)
83 **FOLLE DINGUE (FR)**, b f 8/4 Golan (FR)—L'annee Folle (FR) (Double Bed (FR))
84 **GOLD EXCHANGE (FR)**, ch c 6/4 Gold Away (IRE)—Chop And Change (FR) (Double Bed (FR))
85 **GOOD LORD (FR)**, b c 7/3 Lord of Men—The Trollop (FR) (Double Bed (FR))
86 **GREEN BANANAS (FR)**, b f 22/4 Green Tune (USA)—Anabaa Republic (FR) (Anabaa (USA))
87 **HIS TWEEDS (FR)**, ch c 31/5 Hernando (FR)—River Tweed (Selkirk (USA))
88 Gr f 11/3 Hernando (FR)—La Josselinaise (FR) (Balleroy (USA)) (45045)
89 **LA TENDRE GUERRE (FR)**, b f 1/5 Sendawar (IRE)—Cabaret Club (FR) (Top Ville)
90 **MEZZA LUNA (FR)**, gr c 14/5 Laveron—Quiquijana (FR) (Smadoun (FR))
91 **MIXT BEHAVIOUR (FR)**, gr f 10/3 Sagamix (FR)—Miss Behaviour (FR) (Dolpour)
92 **RACHMANINOV (FR)**, ch c 8/2 Verglas (IRE)—Restless Rixa (FR) (Linamix (FR)) (61132)
93 **ROSIER D'ASIE (FR)**, b c 17/4 Kahyasi—Super Rose (FR) (Darshaan)
94 **RUMINA (FR)**, ch f 15/5 Dashing Blade—Razida (IRE) (Last Tycoon)
95 **SPIV (FR)**, b c 13/3 Bedawin (FR)—French Kiss lv (FR) (Art Francais (USA))
96 **SPUNK (FR)**, b c 10/6 Laveron—Ma'am (FR) (Garde Royale)
97 **SYMPHONIE BERE (FR)**, b f 3/4 Della Francesca (USA)—Ajab Alzamaan (Rainbow Quest (USA)) (25740)
98 **WICCA (FR)**, b f 26/2 Invincible Spirit (IRE)—Guest Place (FR) (Be My Guest (USA)) (77220)

MR FRANCOIS DOUMEN—continued

Owners: Mr Herve d'Armaille, Comtesse Armand, Mr Gerard Augustin Normand, Mr Fritz Von Ballmoos, Mr Michel Bessis, Mr Claude Botton, Baron Louis de Bourgoing, Baron Philippe de Bourgoing, Mr Richard Britten-Long, Mr Dermot Cantillon, Mr Bruno Catoire, Mrs Bernard Destrenau, Mr Dominique Dormeuil, Forenaghts Stud, Mr Jean-Rene de Fraguier, Mr Francois Guyot de Villeneuve, Halewood International Limited, Haras d'Ecouves, Haras d'Etreham, Mr William Jeffcock, Mr Robert Jeffcock, Mr Patrice Laporte, Mr Jean Laurent-Bellue, Comte Etienne de Maupeou, Mr J. A. McCarthy, Mr John P McManus, Conte Henri de Pracomtal, Mr Eric Puerari, Mrs Diana Roth, Mr Gautier de la Selle, Mr Jean-Claude Seroul, Mr Anthony Smurfit, Sir Michael Smurfit, Mr Michael Somerset-Leeke, Mr Hubert Tassin, Uplifting Bloodstock Ltd, Mr Joerg Vasicek, Mr Hans Peter Vogt, Comtesse De Vogue, Mr Graf Von Westphalen, Mrs Deborah Williams.

Jockey (NH): Christophe Pieux. **Amateur:** Mr E. Montfort.

---

158   **MR S. L. DOW, Epsom**
Postal: **Clear Height Stables, Derby Stables Road, Epsom, Surrey, KT18 5LB**
Contacts: **PHONE (01372) 721490 FAX (01372) 748099 MOBILE (07860) 800109**
E-MAIL **simon@simondow.co.uk** Office: **mary@simondow.co.uk** WEBSITE **www.simondow.co.uk**

1 BIRKSPIEL (GER), 7, b g Singspiel (IRE)—Beaute (GER) **Miss H. Chamberlain**
2 CHINA CHERUB, 5, ch m Inchinor—Ashlinn (IRE)
3 EMERGING MARKET, 6, ch g Mark of Esteem (IRE)—Aurora Bay (IRE) **Aldis, Caunce & Dow**
4 IRISH BALLAD, 6, b g Singspiel (IRE)—Auenlust (GER) **Chua, White, Moore & Jurd**
5 MERLIN'S DANCER, 8, b g Magic Ring (IRE)—La Piaf (FR) **Miss Helen Chamberlain & Mr Tom Parker**
6 NAPOLETANO (GER), 7, b g Soviet Star (USA)—Noble House (GER) **Miss H. Chamberlain**
7 NORTHERN SPY (USA), 4, b c War Chant (USA)—Sunray Superstar **J. R. May**
8 PICKLED AGAIN, 4, br f Piccolo—Queen of Tides (IRE) **T. G. Parker**
9 QUANTUM LEAP, 11, b g Efisio—Prejudice **Mrs M. E. O'Shea**
10 RAFFERTY (IRE), 9, ch g Lion Cavern (USA)—Badawi (USA) **S. L. Dow**
11 RECALCITRANT, 5, b g Josr Algarhoud (IRE)—Lady Isabell **T. Staplehurst**
12 VENGEANCE, 8, b g Fleetwood (IRE)—Lady Isabell **T. Staplehurst**

THREE-YEAR-OLDS

13 DEEP WATERS (IRE), b g Bahri (USA)—Keithara (IRE) **T. G. Parker**
14 FLIPACOIN, b f Josr Algarhoud (IRE)—Eclectic **T. G. Parker**
15 HERRBEE (IRE), b g Mark of Esteem (IRE)—Reematna **T. G. Parker**
16 I CERTAINLY MAY, b g Royal Applause—Deep Ravine (USA) **S. L. Dow**
17 MAYBE I WILL (IRE), b f Hawk Wing (USA)—Canterbury Lace (USA) **Mrs A. Aldis**
18 MY SHADOW, b c Zamindar (USA)—Reflections **T. G. Parker**
19 QUEEN'S TREASURE (IRE), b f Bahamian Bounty—Daltak **Miss W Smith, N Scandrett & W J Taylor**
20 SARAH'S BOY, ch g Nayef (USA)—Bella Bianca (IRE) **Ms S. Hayes**
21 SEASONAL CROSS, b f Cape Cross (IRE)—Seasonal Blossom (IRE) **Mrs A. Aldis**
22 TOTALLY FOCUSSED (IRE), gr ro g Trans Island—Premier Place (USA) **The St Cloud Partnership**
23 UBIQUITOUS, b f Erhaab (USA)—Lady Isabell **T. Staplehurst**
24 YAMANMICKMCCANN, b c Desert Style (IRE)—Cashel Kiss **J. R. May**

Other Owners: R. E. Anderson, S. A. Caunce, C. G. J. Chua, D. G. Churston, Mr R. Moore, N. S. Scandrett, Mrs L. M. Shepherd, Ms W. J. Smith, Mr W. J. Taylor, Lord Wolverton.

Apprentice: T. Bubb. **Amateur:** Mr Peter Jones.

---

159   **MR C. J. DOWN, Cullompton**
Postal: **Upton, Cullompton, Devon, EX15 1RA**
Contacts: **PHONE (01884) 33097 FAX (01884) 33097 MOBILE (07828) 021232**

1 APRIL ATTRACTION (FR), 6, b m Mark of Esteem (IRE)—April Lee (USA) **Mrs J. Scrivens**
2 ASPRA (FR), 8, b m Green Tune (USA)—Ambri Piotta (FR) **P. D. Holland & C. Hackett**
3 BROWN FOX (FR), 7, b g Polar Falcon (USA)—Garneria (FR) **Mr M. D. Rusden**
4 5, Ch m Roi de Rome (USA)—Copper Valley **Mrs F. Down**
5 CORNISH JESTER, 9, b g Slip Anchor—Fortune's Girl **C. J. Down**
6 DARN HOT, 4, b f Sir Harry Lewis (USA)—Hot Classic **No Illusions Partnership**
7 DEVON BLUE (IRE), 9, ch m Hubbly Bubbly (USA)—Tuney Blade **Rodney Peacock Mrs JM Greed Mrs F Down**
8 DOUBLEEXCEL, 5, b m Roi de Rome (USA)—Tinoforty (FR)
9 ELBDOUBLEU, 8, ch m Classic Cliche (IRE)—Bowling Fort **Mrs F. Down, Mrs S. Norman, Mr J. A. Norman**
10 FARMER BRENT (IRE), 8, b br g Lord Americo—Highland Party **G. R. Waterman**

MR C. J. DOWN—continued

11 **FLEMENS RIVER (IRE)**, 7, b g Flemensfirth (USA)—Miss River (IRE) **G. R. Waterman**
12 **FLYING GREY (IRE)**, 4, gr g Desert Prince (IRE)—Grey Goddess **Quarter Past Three**
13 **GREY BROTHER**, 10, gr g Morpeth—Pigeon Loft (IRE) **Pot Black Racing**
14 **JOSEAR**, 6, b g Josr Algarhoud (IRE)—Real Popcorn (IRE) **Mrs L. M. Edwards**
15 **LINE ARTIC (FR)**, 4, b f Freedom Cry—Si Jamais (FR) **W. Bromley, A. Bromley, D. Minton**
16 **MY DEVON GIRL**, 6, ch m Double Trigger (IRE)—My Native Girl (IRE) **Mr P. McClave**
17 **NEARLY A BREEZE**, 5, b m Thowra (FR)—Nearly At Sea **Mrs F. Down**
18 **NEW RACKHEATH (IRE)**, 5, gr g Norwich—Bonne Sante (IRE) **Miss S. J. Lock**
20 **PIPPLING**, 6, b g Bandmaster (USA)—Sailors Moon **H. J. Patrick**
20 **POPCORN ROSIE**, 5, b m Diktat—Real Popcorn (IRE) **Mrs L. M. Edwards**
21 **POSH PENNY**, 6, b m Classic Cliche (IRE)—Myblackthorn (IRE) **Mrs F. Down**
22 **ROAMING WEST (IRE)**, 5, br m Roi de Rome (USA)—Key West (FR)
23 **SEA YOU MADAME**, 9, b m Sea Raven (IRE)—Mildame **Mrs F. Down**
24 **SHADES OF BLUE**, 5, b m Bandmaster (USA)—Just Sidium **Mr D. N. Gladwin**
25 **SIR HARRY ORMESHER**, 5, b g Sir Harry Lewis (USA)—Glamour Game **W. A. Bromley**
26 **STAGEHAND (IRE)**, 4, b g Lend A Hand—Ridotto **G. R. Waterman**
27 **SUPREME CARA**, 8, b m Morpeth—Supreme Daughter **Pot Black Racing**
28 **TEAM SECRET**, 7, b m Teamster—Silly Sausage **P. J. Hickman**
29 **THEBELLOFTHEBALL**, 5, ch m Classic Cliche (IRE)—
                                     Juste Belle (FR) **P.Holland,M.Lavis,G.Waterman,R.Turvey.**
30 **THUMBPRINT (IRE)**, 8, b g Aahsaylad—Tinerana Girl (IRE) **Mrs L. M. Edwards**
31 **WASTE NOT WANT NOT**, 4, b f Roi de Rome (USA)—Glamour Game **No Illusions Partnership**
32 **WRAGS TO RICHES (IRE)**, 11, b g Tremblant—Clonea Lady (IRE) **No Illusions Partnership**

THREE-YEAR-OLDS

33 **IAMAGREY (IRE)**, gr f Clodovil (IRE)—Xania
34 **OCHENVAY**, gr f Tobougg (IRE)—Bogus Mix (IRE)

Other Owners: Mr W. A. Bromley, Mr A. R. Bromley, Mrs J. M. Greed, Mr C. Hackett, Mrs David Hancock, Mr P. Holland, Mr M. R. Lavis, Mr A. Loze, Mrs C. Loze, Mr D. Minton, Mr Michael C. Morris, Mr Rodney Peacock, Mrs D. M. Philpott, Mr M. J. Philpott, Mr R. G. Turvey, Mr G. Waterman.

Assistant Trainer: Richard Down

Jockey (NH): O. Nelmes, C. Honour, J.A. McCarthy. **Conditional:** D. O'Dwyer. **Amateur:** Mr D. Burton.

---

160 **MS J. S. DOYLE, Hungerford**
Postal: **Anniversary Cottage, Eastbury, Hungerford, Berks, RG17 7JG**
Contacts: **HOUSE (01488) 72222 MOBILE (07831) 880678**
E-MAIL doyleracing@yahoo.co.uk

1 **BAYLINI**, 4, gr f Bertolini (USA)—Bay of Plenty (FR) **Mr J. P. Doyle**
2 **DREAM MOUNTAIN**, 5, b g Mozart (IRE)—Statua (IRE) **Ms J. S. Doyle**
3 **HAXTON**, 8, b g Sadler's Way—Ember **The Ember Partnership**
4 **MISTER COMPLETELY (IRE)**, 7, b g Princely Heir (IRE)—Blue Goose **James Doyle**
5 **REDFLO**, 4, b f Redback—Button Hole Flower (IRE) **Ms J. S. Doyle**
6 **TRIVIA (IRE)**, 4, br f Marju (IRE)—Lehua (IRE) **W. A. Wood**
7 **ZANAY**, 12, b g Forzando—Nineteenth of May **Ms J. S. Doyle**

THREE-YEAR-OLDS

8 **ROSY DAWN**, ch f Bertolini (USA)—Blushing Sunrise (USA) **W. A. Wood**

Other Owners: Mr M. A. King.

Jockey (flat): James Doyle. **Jockey (NH):** James Doyle. **Apprentice:** Sophie Doyle.

161 MR C. DREW, Rampton
Postal: **Fox End Stables, 83 King Street, Rampton, Cambridgeshire, CB24 8QD**
Contacts: PHONE/FAX (01954) 250772 MOBILE (07917) 718127

1 SMILE FOR US, 5, b g Whittingham (IRE)—Don't Smile **C. Drew**

TWO-YEAR-OLDS

2 Ch f 2/3 Zaha (CAN)—Chatter's Princess (Cadeaux Genereux) **C. Drew**
3 B f 6/4 Rambling Bear—La Noisette (Rock Hopper) (1600) **A. D. Plumb**
4 B f 9/5 Needwood Blade—Rewardia (IRE) (Petardia) (1800) **A. D. Plumb**
5 B f 21/4 Zaha (CAN)—Silent Scream (IRE) (Lahib (USA)) **C. Drew**

Assistant Trainer: Miss Polly Drew

162 MR C. J. DREWE, Didcot
Postal: **Lower Cross Farm, Blewbury Road, East Hagbourne, Didcot, Oxfordshire, OX11 9ND**
Contacts: PHONE (01235) 813124 MOBILE (07787) 503709

1 GREYFIN, 4, gr f Terimon—Wild Happening (GER) **W. P. Long**
2 5, Ch g Alderbrook—Sallo Tune (IRE) **C. J. Drewe**
3 SOLEIL D'HIVER, 7, b m Bahamian Bounty—Catriona **C. J. Drewe**

Assistant Trainer: Lorraine Drewe

163 MRS A. DUFFIELD, Leyburn
Postal: **Sun Hill Racing Stables, Sun Hill Farm, Constable Burton, Leyburn, North Yorkshire, DL8 5RL**
Contacts: PHONE (01677) 450303 FAX (01677) 450993 MOBILE (07802) 496332
E-MAIL ann@annduffield.co.uk WEBSITE www.annduffield.co.uk

1 ALUGAT (IRE), 5, b g Tagula (IRE)—Notley Park **Mr Ian West & Partners**
2 ELOQUENT ROSE (IRE), 4, b f Elnadim (USA)—Quintellina **Mrs D. Addison & Mr & Mrs P. Addison**
3 FALCON'S FIRE (IRE), 4, b g Orpen (USA)—Tres Chic (USA) **BDC Racing Club**
4 FINLAND (UAE), 6, b g Timber Country (USA)—Najm Al Bahar (FR) **S. Adamson**
5 HENRY HOTSPUR, 4, b g Defacto (USA)—Mirror Four Sport **Major G. W. Thompson**
6 JOSEPHINE MALINES, 4, b f Inchinor—Alrisha (IRE) **Middleham Park Racing IX**
7 JUST LILLE (IRE), 5, b m Mull of Kintyre (USA)—Tamasriya (IRE) **Miss H. Wynne**
8 MURACO, 4, b g Bertolini (USA)—Miss Honeypenny (IRE) **Middleham Park Racing I**
9 PAUVIC (IRE), 5, b g Fayruz—Turntable (IRE) **Middleham Park Racing XLV**
10 PRINCE NAMID, 6, b g Namid—Fen Princess (IRE) **S. Adamson**
11 SANTERA (IRE), 4, br f Gold Away (IRE)—Sainte Gig (FR) **P. Rosas**
12 SHANDELIGHT (IRE), 4, b f Dilshaan—By Candlelight (IRE) **Lee Bolingbroke David Andrew Rod Jordan**
13 TELLING, 4, b g Josr Algarhoud—Crystal Canyon **Mr A. Owen**
14 TOBOGGAN LADY, 4, b f Tobougg (IRE)—Northbend **Mr T. P. McMahon & Mr D. McMahon**

THREE-YEAR-OLDS

15 BAVARIAN NORDIC (USA), b c Barathea (IRE)—Dubai Diamond **Six Iron Partnership**
16 BLAZING MASK (IRE), b f Barathea (IRE)—Alphilda **Mr T. P. McMahon & Mr D. McMahon**
17 BONJOUR ALLURE (IRE), b f Hawk Wing (USA)—Exact Replica **Middleham Park Racing XLVIII**
18 BOURBON BALISTIC, ch c Piccolo—Last Ambition (IRE) **Mr J. W. Woodhead**
19 BRANDANE (IRE), br g Danehill Dancer (IRE)—Oumaldaaya (USA) **Mrs H. Steel**
20 ELOQUENT ISLE (IRE), b f Mull of Kintyre (USA)—County Girl (IRE) **Mrs D. Addison**
21 FAIRWAY DANCER (IRE), b f Danetime (IRE)—Rappide **Cameron & Smith**
22 JENDAS JEM, b f Josr Algarhoud (IRE)—Miss Hit **Mr D. C. Betts**
23 JETTA JOY (IRE), b f Hawk Wing (USA)—Woopi Gold **Six Iron Partnership**
24 JUST PICKLES, b g Piccolo—Tenderetta
25 LADY RANGALI (IRE), b f Danehill Dancer (IRE)—Promising Lady **Mrs S. E. Woodhead**
26 LANTERNS OF GOLD, b f Fantastic Light (USA)—Reason To Dance **A. Mordain**
27 MAJESTIC MOVER (IRE), b f Noverre (USA)—Cappella (IRE) **Mrs H. Steel**
28 MARQUIS DE LOUVOIS (IRE), b g Iron Mask (USA)—Sweet Compliance **Middleham Park Racing XXVI**
29 RIVER KENT, b g Fantastic Light (USA)—Ciboure **Mr & Mrs G. Middlebrook**
30 SALEROSA (IRE), b f Monashee Mountain (USA)—Sainte Gig (FR) **P. Rosas**
31 SAN SILVESTRO (IRE), b c Fayruz—Skehana (IRE) **Middleham Park Racing XIV**
32 SETA PURA, b f Domedriver (IRE)—Sulitelma (USA) **Miss K. Rausing**

MRS A. DUFFIELD—continued

33 **SILKEN SPELL,** b f Tobougg (IRE)—Walsham Witch **Mr L Shears Mr S Watson & Mrs A Duffield**
34 **SPRINGFIELD LASS,** b f Compton Place—Mouchez Le Nez (IRE) **Mr T. & Mrs P. Wilson**
35 **THE REAL GURU,** b c Ishiguru (USA)—Aloma's Reality (USA) **Adrian & Alison Parry**
36 **VISCAYA (IRE),** b f Xaar—Fearfully Grand **Mr & Mrs I. Beckett,Dr Gawthorpe,P. White**

TWO-YEAR-OLDS

37 B f 19/1 Ishiguru (USA)—Aloma's Reality (USA) (Proper Reality (USA)) **Adrian & Alison Parry**
38 **BOGULA (IRE),** b f 27/4 Tagula (IRE)—Bobbydazzle (Rock Hopper) (9973) **Mrs Ann Starkie**
39 **CAMELOT COMMUNION (IRE),** b f 9/1 Elusive City (USA)—
                                              Second Prayer (Singspiel (IRE)) (41826) **Middleham Park Racing XXIV**
40 Ch f 27/3 Fraam—Carradale (Pursuit of Love) **Evelyn Duchess of Sutherland**
41 B f 10/2 Catcher In The Rye (IRE)—Celtic Guest (IRE) (Be My Guest (USA)) (13000)
42 B f 3/2 Acclamation—Cliveden Gail (IRE) (Law Society (USA)) (22000) **Miss H. Wynne**
43 **COUNTRYWIDE ASH,** b c 8/3 Bahamian Bounty—
                                     Bobby's Dream (Reference Point) (11500) **Countrywide Steel & Tubes Ltd**
44 B c 22/3 Barathea (IRE)—Darayna (IRE) (Shernazar) (13000)
45 **DAWN SUNSHINE,** b f 11/4 Alhaarth (IRE)—Katrina (IRE) (Ela-Mana-Mou) (11000) **Middleham Park Racing LIV**
46 B f 13/3 Reel Buddy (USA)—Day Star (Dayjur (USA)) (12000) **Mr T. Holdcroft & Mrs G. Garrity**
47 **DEE FLAWLESS BOY,** ch c 6/2 Piccolo—
                                Radiant Sky (IRE) (Spectrum (IRE)) (19000) **John & David Birtles & William Allan**
48 **DOTTY'S BROTHER,** ch g 24/1 Forzando—
                        Colonel's Daughter (Colonel Collins (USA)) (8000) **Middleham Park Racing LIV**
49 **FIREBET (IRE),** b c 2/4 Dubai Destination (USA)—
                                  Dancing Prize (IRE) (Sadler's Wells (USA)) (32174) **Mrs H. Steel**
50 B c 17/2 Lujain (USA)—Fred's Dream (Cadeaux Genereux) (8000)
51 **GO SUNSHINE (IRE),** b c 1/3 Tagula (IRE)—Taoveret (IRE) (Flash of Steel) (7000) **W. N. Smith**
52 **HEL'S ANGEL (IRE),** b f 3/4 Pyrus (USA)—Any Dream (IRE) (Shernazar) (3539) **Mrs H. L. Baines**
53 Ch c 28/2 Medicean—Helen Sharp (Pivotal) (45000) **Middleham Park Racing XXVIII**
54 **HIGHLY ACCLAIMED,** b f 3/2 Acclamation—Ebba (Elmaamul (USA)) (11000) **Middleham Park Racing V**
55 **INDIGO BELLE (IRE),** b f 6/2 Mull of Kintyre (USA)—
                                Frances Canty (USA) (Lear Fan (USA)) (12000) **Mr D. K. Barker & Mrs C. McMahon**
56 **LADY FANTASIE,** b f 20/3 Fasliyev (USA)—Andilisa (Danehill (USA)) (7000) **Mr I. J. Farrington**
57 **LADY LUACHMHAR (IRE),** b f 13/4 Galileo (IRE)—Radhwa (FR) (Shining Steel) (141569) **Mrs H. Steel**
58 Ch c 13/2 Selkirk (USA)—Louve Sereine (FR) (Sadler's Wells (USA)) (10000) **M. R. Johnson**
59 **MARILLOS PROTERRAS,** b f 24/1 Fraam—Legend of Aragon (Aragon) (10000) **Mr S. P. Everatt**
60 **MARY MASON,** b f 18/5 Hunting Lion (IRE)—Kalarram (Muhtarram (USA)) **R. R. Whitton**
61 **NO QUARTER GIVEN (IRE),** b c 14/4 Elusive City (USA)—Tides (Bahamian Bounty) (17000) **W. Maguire**
62 **PACIFIC BAY (IRE),** b f 3/2 Diktat—Wild Clover (Lomitas) (32174) **Mrs H. Steel**
63 **SARDAN DANSAR (IRE),** b f 11/2 Alhaarth (IRE)—Peruvian Witch (IRE) (Perugino (USA)) (14000) **Mr S. I. Dalziel**
64 Ch c 14/5 Dr Fong (USA)—Sayuri (USA) (Sadler's Wells (USA)) (18000) **Mr M. R. Johnson**
65 **SCARLET BLADE,** b c 7/2 Needwood Blade—Red Typhoon (Belfort (FR)) (8000) **J. Carter**
66 **SMOKE ME A KIPPER,** gr f 20/1 Verglas (IRE)—
                            Anoukit (Green Desert (USA)) (10000) **Reavey Gough Racing Partnership**
67 **STAR OF SOPHIA (IRE),** b f 12/3 Hawk Wing (USA)—
                         Sofia Aurora (USA) (Chief Honcho (USA)) (21235) **Middleham Park Racing XVII**
68 **STREVELYN,** br c 19/2 Namid—Kali (Linamix (FR)) (18500) **Mr C. L. Stirling**
69 **VENETIAN LADY,** b f 10/2 Tobougg (IRE)—Perfect Partner (Be My Chief (USA)) (20000) **Mr S. I. Dalziel**
70 B f 9/3 Noverre (USA)—Wonders Gift (Dr Devious (IRE)) **Mr Michael Magill**

Other Owners: Mrs D. Addison, Mr P. Addison, Mrs S. Addison, Mr David Andrew, Mr Anthony Bamford, D. K. Barker, Mrs J. A. Beckett, Mr I. Beckett, Mr Andrew Bird, Mr Lee Bolingbroke, Mr K. M. Brown, Mr James D. Cameron, Mrs Corinne Crowley, Mr J. P. Dunne, Mr S. Grundy, Mr Rod Jordan, Miss C. P. Laffin, Mr Keith Lindsay, Mr D. McMahon, Mr T. P. McMahon, Mrs C. A. McMahon, Mr G. Middlebrook, Mrs L. Middlebrook, Mr T. S. Palin, Mr Adrian Parry, Mrs Alison Parry, Mr M. Prince, Mr Gerald Sanderson, Mr L. Shears, Ms Wendy Smith, Mr Steven Watson, Mr Ian West, Mr Phil White, Mr Trevor Wilson, Mrs P. Wilson.

Assistant Trainer: G Duffield

Jockey (flat): Royston Ffrench. **Apprentice:** A. Mullen.

164 MR B. W. DUKE, Lambourn
Postal: **Coppington Stables, Greenways, Lambourn, Berkshire, RG17 7LG**
Contacts: PHONE **(01488) 71888** FAX **(01488) 71888** MOBILE **(07792) 532388**

1 **GOOD TO BE GREY**, 6, gr g Environment Friend—Jarin Rose (IRE) **Miss S. E. Smith**
2 **HAYWARD'S HEATH**, 4, ch f Allied Forces (USA)—Penny Gold (IRE) **Brendan W. Duke Racing**
3 **LADY MALOUSA**, 5, ch m Alflora (IRE)—Miss Wyandotte **Mr N. P. Horan**
4 **MISTER BENEDICTINE**, 5, b g Mister Baileys—Cultural Role **Mr N. P. Horan**
5 **OPENIDE**, 7, b g Key of Luck (USA)—Eyelet (IRE) **Brendan W. Duke Racing**
6 **STRUT THE STAGE (IRE)**, 4, b g Lil's Boy (USA)—Eva Luna (IRE) **Northern Lights Racing**
7 **ZAFONICAL STORM (USA)**, 4, ch c Aljabr (USA)—Fonage **Briton International**

THREE-YEAR-OLDS

8 **AUSSIE BATTLER (IRE)**, b c Noverre (USA)—Dancerette **Miss A. C. Telling**
9 **BLACK TOR FIGARRO (IRE)**, b c Rock of Gibraltar (IRE)—
  Will Be Blue (IRE) **Miss A. Telling, Ms R. Tupper, Mr T. Fletcher**
10 B c Alhaarth (IRE)—Glamorous Girl (IRE) **Briton International**
11 **HEADACHE**, b c Cape Cross (IRE)—Romantic Myth **J. McCarthy**
12 **MALT EMPRESS (IRE)**, b f Second Empire (IRE)—Sunset Malt (IRE) **Brendan W. Duke Racing**
13 **MISTER CAFNEX (IRE)**, b c Royal Applause—Makelovelast (IRE) **Mr N. P. Horan**
14 **OSTINATA (IRE)**, ch f Spartacus (IRE)—Poly Dancer **Tom & Evelyn Yates**
15 **SAMMY THE SNAKE (IRE)**, b c Diktat—Love Emerald (USA) **J. Duke**

TWO-YEAR-OLDS

16 Ch c 27/3 Titus Livius (FR)—Flattering News (USA) (Pleasant Colony (USA)) (8364) **Brendan W. Duke Racing**
17 B c 19/3 Xaar—Miss Bellbird (IRE) (Danehill (USA)) (19304) **J. Duke**
18 B c 11/2 Barathea (IRE)—Silver Hut (USA) (Silver Hawk (USA)) (10295) **Brendan W. Duke Racing**

Other Owners: Mr R. Clarke, B. W. Duke, Mr T. H. Fletcher, B. H. Goldswain, Mrs J. B. H. Goldswain, K. Saunders, Ms R. E. Tupper, Mr T. D. S. Yates, Mrs E. Yates.

Assistant Trainer: A C Telling

Jockey (flat): Wanderson D'Avila. **Jockey (NH):** N. Fehily, D. Jacob. **Apprentice:** K. Gundowry.

165 MR E. A. L. DUNLOP, Newmarket
Postal: **Gainsborough Stables, Hamilton Road, Newmarket, Suffolk, CB8 0TE**
Contacts: PHONE **(01638) 661998** FAX **(01638) 667394** MOBILE **(07785) 328537**
E-MAIL edunlop@eddunlopracing.co.uk WEBSITE www.edunlop.com

1 **AL KHALEEJ (IRE)**, 4, b g Sakhee (USA)—Mood Swings (IRE) **M. Sultan**
2 **BROOMIELAW**, 4, ch c Rock of Gibraltar (IRE)—Peony **Lady C. R. Ferguson**
3 **CHANTILLY TIFFANY**, 4, ch f Pivotal—Gaily Royal (IRE) **Ballygallon Stud Limited**
4 **COEUR DE LIONNE (IRE)**, 4, b g Invincible Spirit (IRE)—Lionne **The Lamprell Partnership**
5 **DEAR MAURICE**, 4, b c Indian Ridge—Shamaiel (IRE) **A. R. Al Khalifa**
6 **EKTIMAAL**, 5, ch g Bahamian Bounty—Secret Circle **The Serendipity Partnership**
7 **JEER (IRE)**, 4, ch g Selkirk (USA)—Purring (USA) **M. Jaber**
8 **KING CHARLES**, 4, b g King's Best (USA)—Charlecote (IRE) **K. Sultan**
9 **ROYAL JASRA**, 4, b c Royal Applause—Lake Pleasant (IRE) **A. R. Al Khalifa**
10 **SILAAH**, 4, b c Mind Games—Ocean Grove (IRE) **Hamdan Al Maktoum**
11 **TREAT**, 4, b f Barathea (IRE)—Cream Tease **Highclere Thoroughbred Racing XXXVI**

THREE-YEAR-OLDS

12 **ALZAROOF (USA)**, b f Kingmambo (USA)—Ranin **Hamdan Al Maktoum**
13 **AMERICAN OPERA (IRE)**, ch g Singspiel (IRE)—Groom Order **Ballygallon Stud Limited**
14 **ARABIAN SPIRIT**, b c Oasis Dream—Royal Flame (IRE) **P A Deal A L Deal & G Holland-Bosworth**
15 **CANARY ISLANDS**, br c El Prado (IRE)—Dubai Spirit (USA) **Gainsborough**
16 **CHEEKY DOWNLOAD (IRE)**, b f Fasliyev (USA)—Glam Rock **Lord A. Lloyd-Webber**
17 **CLASS DISS MISS**, b f Lujain (USA)—Never Diss Miss **T. H. Fenner**
18 **CLEARING HOUSE**, ch c Zamindar (USA)—Easy Option (IRE) **Gainsborough**
19 **COIN OF THE REALM (IRE)**, b c Galileo (IRE)—Common Knowledge **R. F. Barnes**
20 **DANCER'S LEGACY**, ch c Nayef (USA)—Blond Moment **Miltil Consortium**
21 **DANSE THE BLUES**, br f Dansili—Dixie d'oats **Downlands Racing**
22 **DIAMOND ROYAL (IRE)**, b f Red Ransom (USA)—Gaily Royal (IRE) **Ballygallon Stud Limited**

MR E. A. L. DUNLOP—continued

23 **DREAM BEE**, b f Oasis Dream—Chief Bee **Mrs Mark Burrell & Mr Anthony Burrell**
24 **ELSAFEER (IRE)**, b g Sakhee (USA)—Nabadhaat (USA) **Hamdan Al Maktoum**
25 **ELZEEZA (USA)**, b br f Stravinsky (USA)—Khibrah (IRE) **Hamdan Al Maktoum**
26 **EUREKA MOMENT**, b f Alhaarth (IRE)—Burn Baby Burn (IRE) **St Albans Bloodstock LLP**
27 **EVER RIGG**, b f Dubai Destination (USA)—Bianca Nera **St Albans Bloodstock LLP**
28 **FORMATION (USA)**, ch g Van Nistelrooy (USA)—
                                Miss Valedictorian (USA) **Highclere Thoroughbred Racing (Tamarisk)**
29 **GIRL OF PANGAEA (GER)**, b f Soviet Star (USA)—Genevra (IRE) **Mrs G. A. Rupert**
30 **HASTY RETREAT**, b g King's Best (USA)—Madame Maxine (USA) **Mrs S. M. Roy**
31 **HIGH STEPPING (USA)**, ch c High Yield (USA)—Dance Colony (USA) **Hesmonds Stud Ltd**
32 **HIP**, b f Pivotal—Hypnotize **Cheveley Park Stud Limited**
33 **IZZIBIZZI**, b f Medicean—Sleave Silk (IRE) **J. Weatherby, Champneys**
34 **LAST THREE MINUTES (IRE)**, b c Val Royal (FR)—Circe's Isle **The Right Angle Club**
35 **LAUREL**, b f Royal Applause—Bayleaf **Highclere Thoroughbred Racing(Petrushka)**
36 **MALIBU GIRL (USA)**, b f Malibu Moon (USA)—Gale The Queen (USA) **Hesmonds Stud Ltd**
37 **MIGHTY ALFRED (IRE)**, gr c Kendor (FR)—Night Shifter (USA) **Mr P. Lassen**
38 **MIGNONETTE (IRE)**, b f Fasliyev (USA)—Labrusca **Hesmonds Stud Ltd**
39 **MISCHIEF LADY**, b f Cape Cross (IRE)—Cruinn A Bhord **Triermore Stud & Lord Derby**
40 **MISCHIEF MAKING (USA)**, b br f Lemon Drop Kid (USA)—Fraulein **Cliveden Stud Ltd**
41 **MOOARABA**, ch f Pivotal—Ta Rib (USA) **Hamdan Al Maktoum**
42 **MOON CRYSTAL**, b f Fasliyev (USA)—Sabreon **Eurostrait Ltd**
43 **MUJAADEL (USA)**, ch c Street Cry (IRE)—Quiet Rumour (USA) **Hamdan Al Maktoum**
44 **NORDIC COMMANDER (IRE)**, b c Viking Ruler (AUS)—Rising Lady **The Serendipity Partnership**
45 **PARADISE ISLAND (IRE)**, b f Green Desert (USA)—Meadow Pipit (CAN) **Gainsborough**
46 **PHARAOHS QUEEN (IRE)**, b f Bahri (USA)—Medway (IRE) **Mrs J. M. Quy**
47 **PINKINDIE (USA)**, ch c Smart Strike (CAN)—Only Princesses (USA) **Mr C. Cornes**
48 **QEYAADA (USA)**, b f Elusive Quality (USA)—Al Desima **Hamdan Al Maktoum**
49 **RIQAAB (IRE)**, b c Peintre Celebre (USA)—Jeed (IRE) **Hamdan Al Maktoum**
50 **SALLYGRAIN (USA)**, b f Dynaformer (USA)—Jig (IRE) **St Albans Bloodstock LLP**
51 **SARAH'S FIRST**, ch f Cadeaux Genereux—Band (USA) **Mr Andy Macdonald & Mrs Sarah Wigley**
52 **SATWA KNIGHT (USA)**, b br c Mr Greeley (USA)—Meadow Mystic (USA) **The Lamprell Partnership**
53 **SIDDARTHA**, b br f Pivotal—Sita (IRE) **The Earl Of Derby**
54 **SIRYENA**, b f Oasis Dream—Ard Na Sighe (IRE) **Mr Patrick Milmo & Itchen Valley Stud**
55 **STOCK MARKET (USA)**, ch c Rahy (USA)—Two Marks (USA) **Gainsborough**
56 **STONE OF SCONE**, b c Pivotal—Independence **Cliveden Stud Ltd**
57 **TASHAABOH (IRE)**, br g Xaar—Prepare For War (IRE) **Hamdan Al Maktoum**
58 **TEMPLE OF THEBES (IRE)**, b f Bahri (USA)—Franglais (GER) **Cliveden Stud Ltd**
59 **TESTIMONIAL**, b f Singspiel (IRE)—Endorsement **Cliveden Stud Ltd**
60 **TRULY DIVINE**, b c Invincible Spirit (IRE)—Shabarana (FR) **Mrs S. M. Roy**
61 **VALVIGNERES (IRE)**, gr g Dalakhani (IRE)—Albacora (IRE) **Miltil Consortium**
62 **WANNAROCK (IRE)**, b br g Rock of Gibraltar (USA)—Propensity **R. J. Arculli & B. Vuchot**
63 **WASAN**, ch c Pivotal—Solaia (USA) **Hamdan Al Maktoum**
64 **ZERKY (USA)**, b f Kingmambo (USA)—Penny's Valentine (USA) **Hamdan Al Maktoum**

TWO-YEAR-OLDS

65 Ch f 30/3 Giant's Causeway (USA)—
                  Akuna Bay (USA) (Mr Prospector (USA)) (130000) **Highclere Thoroughbred Racing (Eclipse)**
66 B c 8/4 Red Ransom (USA)—Albaiyda (IRE) (Brief Truce (USA)) (25000) **Byculla Thoroughbreds**
67 **ALKHAFIF**, b c 8/3 Royal Applause—My First Romance (Danehill (USA)) (180000) **Hamdan Al Maktoum**
68 **ANDHAAR**, b br c 27/1 Bahri (USA)—Deraasaat (Nashwan (USA)) **Hamdan Al Maktoum**
69 **AQWAAL (IRE)**, b c 3/2 Red Ransom (USA)—Mubkera (IRE) (Nashwan (USA)) **Hamdan Al Maktoum**
70 Ch c 6/3 Cadeaux Genereux—Artisia (IRE) (Peintre Celebre (USA)) (55000) **R. J. Arculli**
71 **AZWA**, b f 17/2 Haafhd—Shahaamah (IRE) (Red Ransom (USA)) **Hamdan Al Maktoum**
72 B f 22/4 Medicean—Bandit Queen (Desert Prince (IRE)) (25000) **M. Jaber**
73 Ch f 21/3 Night Shift (USA)—Barbizou (FR) (Selkirk (USA)) **Ballygallon Stud Limited**
74 B c 12/4 Montjeu (IRE)—Bayberry (UAE) (Bering) **Ballygallon Stud Limited**
75 **CANDY RIDE (IRE)**, ch f 12/2 Pivotal—Mia Mambo (USA) (Affirmed (USA)) **R. F. Barnes**
76 B f 24/2 Haafhd—Celestial Choir (Celestial Storm (USA)) (32000) **M. Jaber**
77 B c 27/4 Efisio—Celt Song (IRE) (Unfuwain (USA)) (12500) **Pims Partnership**
78 **CHAMPAGNE LOVER**, ch f 30/4 Singspiel (IRE)—
                  Total Love (Cadeaux Genereux) (15000) **John Brown & Megan Dennis**
79 B gr f 18/1 Fantastic Light (USA)—Citrine Spirit (USA) (Soviet Star (USA)) **S. Suhail**
80 Br f 31/1 Galileo (IRE)—Common Knowledge (Rainbow Quest (USA)) (145000) **St Albans Bloodstock LLP**
81 B c 27/2 Royal Applause—Crown of Spring (USA) (Chief's Crown (USA)) **The Lamprell Partnership**
82 **DERBAAS (USA)**, b c 26/2 Seeking The Gold (USA)—Sultana (USA) (Storm Cat (USA)) **Hamdan Al Maktoum**

MR E. A. L. DUNLOP—continued

83 B f 5/3 Royal Applause—Desert Royalty (IRE) (Alhaarth (IRE)) (48000)
84 FAREER, ch c 29/4 Bahamian Bounty—Songsheet (Dominion) (160000) **Hamdan Al Maktoum**
85 B c 3/2 Piccolo—Fleeting Moon (Fleetwood (IRE)) (40000) **Old Road Securities Plc**
86 GTAAB, b c 11/4 Cape Cross (IRE)—Nabadhaat (USA) (Mr Prospector (USA)) **Hamdan Al Maktoum**
87 Ch f 26/2 Bertolini (USA)—Holgera (GER) (Winged Love (IRE)) (12869) **J. Weatherby, Champneys**
88 HUKBA (IRE), b f 21/2 Anabaa (USA)—Banaadir (USA) (Diesis) **Hamdan Al Maktoum**
89 IMPLICATION, b f 6/4 Pivotal—Insinuation (IRE) (Danehill (USA)) **Cheveley Park Stud Limited**
90 JOHNNY ROOK (GER), b c 4/2 Dashing Blade—Just Zoud (Ezzoud (IRE)) (37323) **The Serendipity Partnership**
91 B f 22/2 Rock of Gibraltar (IRE)—Lady Scarlett (Woodman (USA)) (90000) **Thurloe Thoroughbreds XXIII**
92 LITTLE CALLA (IRE), ch f 1/4 Indian Ridge—
             Queen of Palms (IRE) (Desert Prince (IRE)) (93306) **St Albans Bloodstock LLP**
93 MASAMAH (IRE), gr c 19/3 Exceed And Excel (AUS)—Bethesda (Distant Relative) (60000) **Hamdan Al Maktoum**
94 MEFRAAS (IRE), b c 25/4 King's Best (USA)—Khaizarana (Alhaarth (IRE)) **Hamdan Al Maktoum**
95 MOOJEH (IRE), ch f 15/4 King's Best (USA)—Bahareeya (USA) (Riverman (USA)) **Hamdan Al Maktoum**
96 MOONBURST, ch ro f 10/3 Dalakhani (IRE)—Moon Goddess (Rainbow Quest (USA)) **Cheveley Park Stud Limited**
97 NASEMAH (IRE), ch f 12/5 Sakhee (USA)—Nafhaat (USA) (Roberto (USA)) **Hamdan Al Maktoum**
98 Ch c 3/4 Rahy (USA)—No More Ironing (USA) (Slew O' Gold (USA)) (210000) **The Lamprell Partnership**
99 NORTHERN HERO (IRE), b c 21/1 Hawk Wing (USA)—Bona Dea (IRE) (Danehill (USA)) (75000)
100 B f 13/4 Galileo (IRE)—Palacoona (FR) (Last Tycoon) (220000) **St Albans Bloodstock LLP**
101 PAN TADEUS, b f 20/5 Kyllachy—Polish Romance (USA) (Danzig (USA)) **Cheveley Park Stud Limited**
102 PARTNER SHIFT (IRE), b c 22/2 Night Shift (USA)—
             What A Picture (FR) (Peintre Celebre (USA)) (64350) **Mr P. Lassen**
103 PASSAGGIO, b f 19/1 Pivotal—Place de L'opera (Sadler's Wells (USA)) **Cliveden Stud Ltd**
104 B br f 23/3 War Chant (USA)—Polar Bird (Thatching) (52000) **Sangster Family**
105 B c 28/3 Johannesburg (USA)—Policy Setter (USA) (Deputy Minister (CAN)) (150000) **The Lamprell Partnership**
106 PROWL, b f 7/3 One Cool Cat (USA)—
             Go Supersonic (Zafonic (USA)) (38000) **Highclere Thoroughbred Racing (St Simon)**
107 RAPID LIGHT, ch f 5/2 Tobougg (IRE)—La Coqueta (Ger) (Kris) (26000) **Cheveley Park Stud Limited**
108 B c 28/3 King's Best (USA)—Sheppard's Watch (Night Shift (USA)) (30000) **The Lamprell Partnership**
109 SILK COTTON (USA), b f 2/4 Giant's Causeway (USA)—
             Calico Moon (USA) (Seeking The Gold (USA)) (60000) **R. F. Barnes**
110 TOLL ROAD, b f 10/5 Dubai Destination (USA)—Endorsement (Warning) **Cliveden Stud Ltd**
111 B c 1/2 Storming Home—Tropical Breeze (IRE) (Kris) (16086) **S. Suhail**
112 Br gr f 31/1 Daylami (IRE)—Wosaita (Generous (IRE)) **Eurostrait Ltd**
113 B f 26/2 Dr Fong (USA)—Yavari (IRE) (Alzao (USA)) **Mrs S. M. Roy**
114 ZAFFAAN, ch c 18/2 Efisio—Danceabout (Shareef Dancer (USA)) **Hamdan Al Maktoum**

Other Owners: Mr R. J. Arculli, Mrs A. D. Bourne, Mr R. G. W. Brown, Mr J. M. Brown, Mrs M. Burrell, A. M. Burrell, Mr G. A. Campbell, Mr N. Cooper, Mr P. A. Deal, Mr A. L. Deal, Mrs Megan Dennis, Mrs Edward Dunlop, Sir Alex Ferguson, Mr Tom Goff, Mrs B. A. Hanbury, The Hon H. Herbert, Mr S. Herbert, Highclere Thoroughbred Racing Ltd, Mr G. Holland-Bosworth, Mrs A. Horrell, Mr S. Lamprell, Mrs G. Lamprell, Mr I. Lawrence, Mr A. P. Liggins, Mr A. T. Macdonald, Sheikh Ahmed Al Maktoum, Mr Patrick Milmo, Sheikh Mohammed, Mr Peter G. Morgan, Mr P. O'Sullivan, Mr Oliver Pawle, Mr M. Pepper, Mr K. B. Purcell, Mr S. J. Purdew, Mr I. Quy, Mr George Ramsay, Mr J. B. Stafford, Mr Andrew Stone, Mrs M. F. Stone, Mrs A. M. Sturges, Mr S. A. Tilling, Mr Benjamin Vuchot, Lady Amelia Ward, Mr J. R. Weatherby, Mrs S. J. Wigley.

---

166 MR H. J. L. DUNLOP, Lambourn
Postal: **Windsor House Stables, Crowle Road, Lambourn, Hungerford, Berkshire, RG17 8NR**
Contacts: PHONE (01488) 73584 FAX (01488) 674172 MOBILE (07880) 791895
E-MAIL info@harrydunloperacing.com WEBSITE www.harrydunloperacing.com

1 GO BUT GO, 4, b g Tobougg (IRE)—Faraway Lass **Mrs C. M. Hardman**
2 JUST A THOUGHT (IRE), 5, b g Orpen (USA)—Gold Fly (IRE) **Mr Sam Swallow & Mrs H. Dunlop**
3 ORSUS (FR), 6, ch g Baloo Du Camp (FR)—Belle de Bauregard (FR) **Phil & Sam Swallow**
4 THE THUNDERER, 9, gr g Terimon—By Line **Mr Tom Wilson**
5 WANDERING MINSTRAL, 5, br g Accordion—Vagrancy **See You Then Partnership**

THREE-YEAR-OLDS

6 AIR CHIEF, ch g Dr Fong (USA)—Fly For Fame **Chris Craig-Wood & Tina Blockley**
7 BAHAMIAN BLUE (IRE), ch g Touch of The Blues (FR)—Cattiva (ITY) **Hart Royal Partnership**
8 BETTER IN HEAVEN, b c Zamindar (USA)—Peace **Hesmonds Stud Ltd**
9 BRAVE BOOGIE, ch f Tobougg (IRE)—Be Brave (FR) **Lord MacLaurin**
10 CLASSIC REMARK (IRE), b f Dr Fong (USA)—Claxon **Hesmonds Stud Ltd**
11 DANCING SWORD, b g Groom Dancer (USA)—Kristina **Julian & Bobby Richmond-Watson**
12 DARK CAMELLIA, b f Olden Times—Miss Mirror **Edward & Joanna Russell & Templeton Stud**

MR H. J. L. DUNLOP—continued

13 **DESERT THISTLE (IRE)**, b c Tamarisk (IRE)—Taajreh (IRE) **Harry Dunlop Racing Partnership**
14 **DR BRASS**, b c Dr Fong (USA)—Tropical Heights (FR) **Normandie Stud Ltd**
15 **FESTOSO (IRE)**, b f Diesis—Garah **Prince A. A. Faisal**
16 **LADY DOCKER (IRE)**, ch f Docksider (USA)—Copper Creek **Mrs S. J. Dunlop**
17 **LADY PETRUS**, b f Oasis Dream—Odalisque (IRE) **Mrs E. C. Roberts**
18 **LAST OF THE LINE**, b c Efisio—Dance By Night **Woodcote Stud Ltd**
19 **NEXT ACT**, b g Act One—Brocheta **David & Jennifer Sieff & Bloomsbury Stud**
20 **RED AMARYLLIS**, ch f Piccolo—Passiflora **Mrs H. Dunlop**
21 **RHODE ISLAND RED (USA)**, ch f Tale of The Cat (USA)—Miss Sobriety (CAN) **Heart Of The South Racing**
22 **ROSENTRAUB**, b c Dansili—Ambrosine **Normandie Stud Ltd**
23 **TEA CAKE (IRE)**, b f Compton Place—Griddle Cake (IRE) **Mrs C. A. Waters & Tessona Racing**

TWO-YEAR-OLDS

24 Ch c 25/2 Fraam—Anapola (GER) (Polish Precedent (USA)) (13500)
25 **ARRIVEDERLA (IRE)**, b f 14/3 Acclamation—Alwiyda (USA) (Trempolino (USA)) (45044) **W. J. Armitage**
26 **BAGBER**, b c 26/2 Diktat—Torcross (Vettori (IRE)) (13000) **R. J. McCreery & Major & Mrs R. B. Kennard**
27 B f 10/3 Diktat—Bayleaf (Efisio) (5000) **J. F. Jarvis**
28 B f 21/2 One Cool Cat—Bolivia (USA) (Distant View (USA)) (23000) **Eurostrait Ltd & Templeton Stud**
29 **BORN ROMANTIC**, b f 7/5 High Chaparral (IRE)—Maid For Romance (Pursuit of Love) **Normandie Stud Ltd**
30 **BRAVE BEAT**, b c 18/4 Beat Hollow—Be Brave (FR) (Green Forest (USA)) **Lord MacLaurin**
31 **BY PRECEDENCE (USA)**, b br c 4/4 Johannesburg (USA)—
                              Episode (USA) (Kris S (USA)) (100000) **Prince A. A. Faisal**
32 **CAT PATROL**, b f 2/4 One Cool Cat (USA)—Ambrosine (Nashwan (USA)) **Normandie Stud Ltd**
33 **FONDANT FANCY**, b f 2/5 Falbrav (IRE)—Foodbroker Fancy (IRE) (Halling (USA)) **Normandie Stud Ltd**
34 **FORGOTTEN DREAMS (IRE)**, b f 23/2 Olden Times—
                              Jawaher (IRE) (Dancing Brave (USA)) (45000) **Prince A. A. Faisal**
35 **KEY TO LOVE (IRE)**, b f 27/3 Key of Luck (USA)—Ski For Me (IRE) (Barathea (IRE)) **Anamoine Ltd**
36 B c 26/4 Spartacus (IRE)—My First Paige (IRE) (Runnett) (15500) **Harry Dunlop Racing Partnership**
37 **ORDER ORDER**, br f 14/3 Diktat—Brocheta (Hector Protector (USA)) (9000) **David & Jennifer Sieff**
38 **PETER GRIMES (IRE)**, ch c 28/3 Alhaarth (IRE)—Aldburgh (Bluebird (USA)) (18000) **Be Hopeful Partnership**
39 **THREE MOONS (IRE)**, b f 22/1 Montjeu (IRE)—Three Owls (IRE) (Warning) **Mrs Ben Goldsmith**
40 **WIGHTGOLD**, ch f 29/3 Golden Snake (USA)—Main Brand (Main Reef) **Mrs P. M. Ignarski**

Other Owners: Mr G. Bishop, Miss Eloise Penny, Mr Ronnie Beevor, Bloomsbury Stud, Mr Martin Broughton, Mr John Darby, Mr Harry Dunlop, Mr A. Grazebrook, Miss C. A. Green, Mrs Nicholas Jones, Mrs R. A. Lomax, Mr Barry Marsden, Mr D. Moore, Mr John Penny, Mrs Caroline Penny, Mrs S. M. Rogers, Mr John Scott.

Apprentice: V. Santos.

---

167 ## MR J. L. DUNLOP, Arundel
Postal: **Castle Stables, Arundel, West Sussex, BN18 9AB**
Contacts: PHONE **(01903) 882194** FAX **(01903) 884173** MOBILE **(07860) 339805**
E-MAIL **jldunlop@jldunlop.co.uk** WEBSITE **www.jldunlop.co.uk**

1 **AJEEL (IRE)**, 9, b g Green Desert (USA)—Samheh (USA) **Hamdan Al Maktoum**
2 **BALNAGORE**, 4, b br c Tobougg (IRE)—Bogus Mix (IRE) **Mrs J. P. R. Boscawen**
3 **BOLD BOBBY BE (IRE)**, 4, br g Bob Back (USA)—Fantasy Girl (IRE) **Windflower Overseas Holdings Inc**
4 **DOUBLE BANDED (IRE)**, 4, b g Mark of Esteem (IRE)—Bronzewing **Sir Thomas Pilkington**
5 **EGLEVSKI (IRE)**, 4, b g Danehill Dancer (IRE)—Ski For Gold **Windflower Overseas Holdings Inc**
6 **FREE OFFER**, 4, b f Generous (IRE)—Proserpine **The Earl Cadogan**
7 **JEDBURGH**, 7, b h Selkirk (USA)—Conspiracy **The Earl Cadogan**
8 **MAID TO BELIEVE**, 4, b f Galileo (IRE)—Maid For The Hills **Normandie Stud Ltd**
9 **MUNSEF**, 6, b g Zafonic (USA)—Mazaya (IRE) **Hamdan Al Maktoum**
10 **PER INCANTO (USA)**, 4, b br c Street Cry (IRE)—Pappa Reale **Hamdan Al Maktoum**
11 **SAMUEL**, 4, ch c Sakhee (USA)—Dolores **Normandie Stud Ltd**
12 **SPANISH HIDALGO (IRE)**, 4, b c Night Shift (USA)—Spanish Lady (IRE) **Windflower Overseas Holdings Inc**
13 **SWAN QUEEN**, 5, b m In The Wings—Bronzewing **Sir Thomas Pilkington**
14 **TELL**, 5, b h Green Desert (USA)—Cephalonie (USA) **Prince A. A. Faisal**
15 **VELVET HEIGHTS**, 6, b h Barathea (IRE)—Height of Fantasy (IRE) **Windflower Overseas Holdings Inc**

THREE-YEAR-OLDS

16 **ACQUIFER**, b f Oasis Dream—Llyn Gwynant **Capt J. Macdonald-Buchanan**
17 **AL AZY (IRE)**, b c Nayef (USA)—Nasheed (USA) **Hamdan Al Maktoum**
18 **ALSADEEK (IRE)**, b c Fasliyev (USA)—Khulan (USA) **Hamdan Al Maktoum**

MR J. L. DUNLOP—continued

19 **ALWAABEL**, b c Green Desert (USA)—Etizaaz (USA) **Hamdan Al Maktoum**
20 **BADWEIA (USA)**, b f Kingmambo (USA)—Alshadiyah (USA) **Hamdan Al Maktoum**
21 **BARAARI (USA)**, b br f Nayef (USA)—Reem Al Barari (USA) **Hamdan Al Maktoum**
22 **BENHAVIS**, b c Lomitas—Northern Goddess **Mrs J. M. Khan**
23 **BY COMMAND**, b c Red Ransom (USA)—Rafha **Prince A. A. Faisal**
24 **CHIOROSCURO**, gr g Act One—Colorspin (FR) **J. L. Dunlop**
25 **DALHAAN (USA)**, b c Fusaichi Pegasus (USA)—Khazayin (USA) **Hamdan Al Maktoum**
26 **DANCE EASILY**, b f Dansili—Crystal Flite (IRE) **G. N. Clark**
27 **DONA ALBA (IRE)**, b f Peintre Celebre (USA)—Fantastic Fantasy (IRE) **Windflower Overseas Holdings Inc**
28 **DOWNHILLER (IRE)**, ch c Alhaarth (IRE)—Ski For Gold **Windflower Overseas Holdings Inc**
29 **DUNCAN**, b c Dalakhani (IRE)—Dolores **Normandie Stud Ltd**
30 **DUSK**, b g Fantastic Light (USA)—Dark Veil (USA) **Gail Brown Racing Partnership**
31 **ELMALEEHA**, b f Galileo (IRE)—Winsa **Hamdan Al Maktoum**
32 **EQBAAL**, gr c Linamix (FR)—Calling Card **Hamdan Al Maktoum**
33 **FAIRY WOOD (IRE)**, b f Fasliyev (USA)—Fantasy Wood (IRE) **Windflower Overseas Holdings Inc**
34 **FEARLESS WARRIOR**, br g Erhaab (USA)—Princess Genista **Mrs J. Stewart-Brown**
35 **FERAA**, b f Sakhee (USA)—Ayun (USA) **Hamdan Al Maktoum**
36 **FESTIVALE (IRE)**, b f Invincible Spirit (IRE)—Cephalonie (USA) **Prince A. A. Faisal**
37 **GOODWOOD STARLIGHT (IRE)**, br c Mtoto—Starring (FR) **Goodwood Racehorse Owners Group Fourteen Ltd**
38 **HARLESTONE GOLD**, b g Golden Snake (USA)—Harlestone Lady **J. L. Dunlop**
39 **IO (IRE)**, b f King's Best (USA)—Callisto (USA) **Mr Ian de Wesselow (Susan Abbott Racing)**
40 **KALOKAIRI (IRE)**, b f Galileo (IRE)—Naziriya (FR) **B. Andersson**
41 **KASHOOF**, b f Green Desert (USA)—Khulood (USA) **Hamdan Al Maktoum**
42 **KELOWNA (IRE)**, ch f Pivotal—Kootenay (IRE) **Capt J. Macdonald-Buchanan**
43 **KRASAVITSA**, b f Fasliyev (USA)—Desert Alchemy (IRE) **Mrs Philippa Cooper**
44 **KRISTAL GLORY (IRE)**, ch c Night Shift (USA)—Kristal's Paradise (IRE) **Windflower Overseas Holdings Inc**
45 **LEITMOTIF (USA)**, gr ro c Linamix (FR)—First Melody **Robin F. Scully**
46 **LOOTER (FR)**, b g Red Ransom (USA)—Water Echo (USA) **Eurostrait Ltd**
47 **MANERE BAY**, b f Olden Times—Madurai **J. L. Dunlop**
48 **MAZARA (IRE)**, ch g Alhaarth (IRE)—Azdihaar (USA) **Hamdan Al Maktoum**
49 **MON PLAISIR (USA)**, b br c Pleasant Tap (USA)—Coquine (USA) **Robin F. Scully**
50 **MOUNTAIN PRIDE (IRE)**, b c High Chaparral (IRE)—Lioness **Ian Cameron**
51 **MUTHABARA (IRE)**, b f Red Ransom (USA)—Hureya (USA) **Hamdan Al Maktoum**
52 **NIGHT SKIER (IRE)**, ch f Night Shift (USA)—Ski For Me (IRE) **Windflower Overseas Holdings Inc**
53 **NISAAL (IRE)**, b c Indian Ridge—Kahalah (IRE) **Hamdan Al Maktoum**
54 **PERKS (IRE)**, b g Selkirk (USA)—Green Charter **B. Andersson**
55 **PIMENTO (IRE)**, b g Red Ransom (USA)—Souffle **Mrs H. I. Slade**
56 **PRESBYTERIAN NUN (IRE)**, b f Daylami (IRE)—Conspiracy **The Earl Cadogan**
57 **PURE SONG**, b f Singspiel (IRE)—Pure Grain **R. Barnett**
58 **SAYEDATI ELHASNA (IRE)**, b f Alhaarth (IRE)—Sayedati Eljamilah (USA) **Hamdan Al Maktoum**
59 **STAR OF GIBRALTAR**, b f Rock of Gibraltar (IRE)—Fallen Star **Normandie Stud Ltd**
60 **SWINGKEEL (IRE)**, ch g Singspiel (IRE)—Anniversary **Mrs H. I. Slade**
61 **TAARESH (IRE)**, b c Sakhee (USA)—Tanaghum **Hamdan Al Maktoum**
62 **TARQEYA**, b f Nayef (USA)—Weqaar (USA) **Hamdan Al Maktoum**
63 **TASEEL (USA)**, b f Danzig (USA)—Alabaq (USA) **Hamdan Al Maktoum**
64 **THE HOOFER (IRE)**, b f Vision of Night—Dance In The Sun **J. L. Dunlop**
65 **TRIPLE DREAM**, ch g Vision of Night—Triple Joy **Hesmonds Stud Ltd**
66 **UNBIASED (IRE)**, b c Olden Times—Sharp Mode (USA) **Prince A. A. Faisal**
67 **YATHREB (USA)**, b br c Kingmambo (USA)—Thawakib (IRE) **Hamdan Al Maktoum**
68 **ZIA ZABEL (IRE)**, b f Rock of Gibraltar (IRE)—Blu Meltemi (ITY) **A. Pettinari**

TWO-YEAR-OLDS

69 **AKMAL**, ch c 31/1 Selkirk (USA)—Ayun (USA) (Swain (IRE)) **Hamdan Al Maktoum**
70 **AL TAMOOH (IRE)**, b f 9/4 Dalakhani (IRE)—Claxon (Caerleon (USA)) (260000) **Hamdan Al Maktoum**
71 **ALBAHER**, b c 30/3 Oasis Dream—
                        Dance Sequence (USA) (Mr Prospector (USA)) (150000) **Hamdan Al Maktoum**
72 **ALHUDHUD (USA)**, b c 11/3 Swain (IRE)—Wasnah (USA) (Nijinsky (CAN)) (150000) **Hamdan Al Maktoum**
73 **ALMAZAR**, b c 26/4 Green Desert (USA)—Zaqrah (USA) (Silver Hawk (USA)) **Hamdan Al Maktoum**
74 **ANAASHEED**, b f 12/2 Cape Cross (IRE)—Kahalah (IRE) (Darshaan) **Hamdan Al Maktoum**
75 **ASWAAQ (IRE)**, b f 10/3 Peintre Celebre (USA)—Hureya (USA) (Woodman (USA)) **Hamdan Al Maktoum**
76 **BOBBIE SOXER (IRE)**, br f 26/3 Pivotal—Fantasy Girl (IRE) (Marju (IRE)) **Windflower Overseas Holdings Inc**
77 B c 25/4 Polish Precedent—Brooklyn's Sky (Septieme Ciel (USA)) (18000) **The Hon. Sir David Sieff**
78 **COMPRIMARIO (IRE)**, b c 29/4 Montjeu (IRE)—Soubrette (USA) (Opening Verse (USA)) (70000) **Mrs H. I. Slade**
79 **DARK QUEST**, b f 28/2 Rainbow Quest (USA)—Pure Grain (Polish Precedent (USA)) **R. Barnett**
80 **DEVIL TO PAY**, b c 2/4 Red Ransom (USA)—My Way (IRE) (Marju (IRE)) (35000) **Sir Philip Wroughton**

MR J. L. DUNLOP—continued

81 FALLEN IN LOVE, b f 8/3 Galileo (IRE)—Fallen Star (Brief Truce (USA)) **Normandie Stud Ltd**
82 FLEURISSIMO, ch f 4/2 Dr Fong (USA)—Agnus (IRE) (In The Wings) **Normandie Stud Ltd**
83 GOLDEN GAMES (IRE), b f 4/4 Montjeu (IRE)—
      Ski For Gold (Shirley Heights) **Windflower Overseas Holdings Inc**
84 GOOD FOR HER, b f 26/2 Rock of Gibraltar (IRE)—Tyranny (Machiavellian (USA)) **Normandie Stud Ltd**
85 GOODWOOD CHIMES (IRE), b c 14/3 Elnadim (USA)—
      Cloche Du Roi (FR) (Fairy King (USA)) (28000) **Goodwood Racehorse Owners Group (Fifteen)**
86 GYR (IRE), ch c 2/3 Pivotal—Rafha (Kris) (180000) **Prince A. A. Faisal**
87 HARLESTONE SNAKE, b g 17/2 Golden Snake (USA)—Harlestone Lady (Shaamit (IRE)) **J. L. Dunlop**
88 HOBOOB (USA), b c f 6/4 Seeking The Gold (USA)—Bint Salsabil (USA) (Nashwan (USA)) **Hamdan Al Maktoum**
89 HOWARD, ch c 10/3 Haafhd—Dolores (Danehill (USA)) **Normandie Stud Ltd**
90 IMAAM, ch c 30/1 Pivotal—Khulood (Storm Cat (USA)) **Hamdan Al Maktoum**
91 IN SECRET, b f 8/3 Dalakhani (IRE)—Conspiracy (Rudimentary (USA)) **The Earl Cadogan**
92 ITLAAQ, b c 25/3 Alhaarth (IRE)—Hathrah (IRE) (Linamix (FR)) **Hamdan Al Maktoum**
93 JUMAANA (IRE), b f 12/2 Selkirk (USA)—Weqaar (USA) (Red Ransom (USA)) **Hamdan Al Maktoum**
94 KING OF WANDS, b c 7/2 Galileo (IRE)—Maid To Treasure (IRE) (Rainbow Quest (USA)) **Normandie Stud Ltd**
95 KYLE OF BUTE, ch c 8/3 Kyllachy—Blinding Mission (Marju (IRE)) (32000) **Mrs H. I. Slade**
96 B f 5/5 Dr Fong (USA)—Lady of The Lake (Caerleon (USA)) **Capt J. Macdonald-Buchanan**
97 LAST SYLLABLE (USA), ch f 3/4 Pleasantly Perfect (USA)—Coquine (USA) (Gone West (USA)) **Robin F. Scully**
98 MAWJAAT (IRE), b f 23/1 Sakhee (USA)—Al Durrah (USA) (Darshaan) **Hamdan Al Maktoum**
99 MEJALA (IRE), b f 12/2 Red Ransom (USA)—Wissal (USA) (Woodman (USA)) **Hamdan Al Maktoum**
100 MERDAAM, ch c 2/2 Dubai Destination (USA)—Faydah (Bahri (USA)) **Hamdan Al Maktoum**
101 NAIZAK, ch f 24/2 Medicean—Sunny Davis (USA) (Alydar (USA)) (110000) **Hamdan Al Maktoum**
102 PALAVICINI (USA), b c 2/2 Giant's Causeway (USA)—
      Cara Fantasy (IRE) (Sadler's Wells (USA)) **Windflower Overseas Holdings Inc**
103 PERFECT SHOT (IRE), b c 21/3 High Chaparral (IRE)—
      Zoom Lens (IRE) (Caerleon (USA)) (20000) **Sir Philip Wroughton**
104 PERSIAN MEMORIES (IRE), br f 2/2 Indian Ridge—
      Persian Fantasy (Persian Bold) **Windflower Overseas Holdings Inc**
105 B g 10/5 Olden Times—Princess Genista (Ile de Bourbon (USA)) **Mrs J. Stewart-Brown**
106 RED ROBERT, b c 29/3 Dr Fong (USA)—Red Bug (Cadeaux Genereux) (5000) **Susan Abbott Racing**
107 ROCKY HEIGHTS (IRE), b f 23/2 Rock of Gibraltar (IRE)—
      Height of Fantasy (IRE) (Shirley Heights) **Windflower Overseas Holdings Inc**
108 RUBAA (IRE), ch c 1/5 King's Best (USA)—Shuruk (Cadeaux Genereux) **Hamdan Al Maktoum**
109 SAMAKAAT (IRE), b br f 1/5 Marju (IRE)—Sayedati Eljamilah (USA) (Mr Prospector (USA)) **Hamdan Al Maktoum**
110 SALOMO (GER), b c 5/3 Monsun (GER)—Salka (GER) (Doyoun) (276705) **Hamdan Al Maktoum**
111 SHAWQ, b f 28/4 Noverre (USA)—Ashwaaq (USA) (Gone West (USA)) **Hamdan Al Maktoum**
112 SICILIAN PINK, b f 8/2 Beat Hollow—Sweet Pea (Persian Bold) **N. M. H. Jones**
113 SOLAR GRAPHITE (IRE), b c 8/4 Rock of Gibraltar (IRE)—
      Solar Crystal (IRE) (Alzao (USA)) (45000) **Gail Brown Racing Partnership**
114 TACTIC, b c 16/5 Sadler's Wells (USA)—Tanaghum (Darshaan) **Hamdan Al Maktoum**
115 TINKERBELLE (IRE), br f 8/2 Marju (IRE)—Pershaan (IRE) (Darshaan) **Windflower Overseas Holdings Inc**
116 WAAHEJ, bc 23/1 Haafhd—Madam Ninette (Mark of Esteem) (130000) **Hamdan Al Maktoum**
117 WAHEEBA, b f 17/4 Pivotal—Winsa (USA) (Riverman (USA)) **Hamdan Al Maktoum**
118 ZAAQYA, b f 13/2 Nayef (USA)—Classical Dancer (Dr Fong) (300000) **Hamdan Al Maktoum**

Other Owners: Mr Peter Allen, M. C. C. Armitage, Mr Peter Bailey, Mr James Barber, Mr John Bingley, Mrs Antony Croker Poole, Mr George Galazka, Mr Adrian Grazebrook, Mr Simon Johnson, Sir Nevil Macready, M. J. Meacock, Sir Philip Payne-Gallwey, I. A. D. Pilkington, Mr Laurence Reed, Lady Ricketts, Mr A. J. Struthers, Tessona Racing, Mr David Thorpe.

Assistant Trainer: David Menuisier

---

168   **MRS C. A. DUNNETT, Norwich**
Postal: **College Farm, Hingham, Norwich, Norfolk, NR9 4PP**
Contacts: PHONE (01953) 850596 FAX (01953) 851364 MOBILE (07775) 793523
E-MAIL christine.dunnett@lineone.net WEBSITE www.christinedunnett.com

1 GONE'N'DUNNETT (IRE), 9, b g Petardia—Skerries Bell **Christine Dunnett Racing**
2 KENNINGTON, 8, ch g Compton Place—Mim **Christine Dunnett Racing**
3 LAWYER TO WORLD, 4, gr c Marju (IRE)—Legal Steps (IRE) **Annwell Inn Syndicate**
4 LIFE'S A WHIRL, 6, b m Machiavellian (USA)—Spinning Top **Life's a Whirl Partnership**
5 MONEY HILLS, 3, b g Vettori (IRE)—Starfida **Mrs C. A. Dunnett**
6 NORCROFT, 6, b g Fasliyev (USA)—Norcroft Joy **G. R. Price**
7 POLAR FORCE, 8, ch g Polar Falcon (USA)—Irish Light (USA) **Mrs C. A. Dunnett**
8 QUEEN TARA, 6, b m Kayf Tara—Lucy Tufty **F. Butler**

MRS C. A. DUNNETT—continued

9 **REGISTRAR**, 6, ch g Machiavellian (USA)—Confidante (USA) **The Smart Syndicate**
10 **RUSSIAN ROCKET (IRE)**, 6, b g Indian Rocket—Soviet Girl (IRE) **Mrs C. A. Dunnett**
11 **SOUTHBURGH (IRE)**, 7, b g Spectrum (IRE)—College Night (IRE) **Mrs C. A. Dunnett**

THREE-YEAR-OLDS

12 **DORSO ROSSO (IRE)**, b g Redback—Baraloti (IRE) **The Star Seekers**
13 **FABER HALL FLYER**, b g Danetime (IRE)—Pinini **Mrs C. A. Dunnett**
14 **MISS MEDUSA**, b f Medicean—College Night (IRE) **Mrs S. E. A. Burton**
15 **PALMER'S GREEN**, b g Mujahid (USA)—Moss **Mr S. C. Palmer**
16 **SIENA**, b f Lomitas—Sea Lane
17 **SOUTHWARK NEWSBOY (IRE)**, b g Chevalier (IRE)—Canoe Cove (IRE) **Southwark News Racing Club**
18 **STAR OF TOMORROW**, b f Best of The Bests (IRE)—Starfida **Miss Alice Dunnett**
19 **WHERE TO NOW**, b f Where Or When (IRE)—Starminda **Mr A. S. Machin**
20 **WHODOUTHINKUR (IRE)**, b g Beckett (IRE)—Scarletta (USA) **Mr G. Gilks**
21 **YIPPYIAYIPPYIO**, ch f Fraam—Sandy Lady (IRE) **J. Purcell**

TWO-YEAR-OLDS

22 B f 21/3 Choisir (AUS)—Capstick (JPN) (Machiavellian (USA))
23 B c 14/4 Mujahid (USA)—Girl Next Door (Local Suitor (USA))
24 B c 14/4 Mujahid (USA)—Pinini (Pivotal)
25 Br f 1/4 Lucky Story (USA)—Sea Lane (Zafonic (USA))
26 B c 19/3 Mujahid (USA)—Starminda (Zamindar (USA))

Other Owners: Mrs Liz Allen, Mr Michael Benton, Mr Mike Bringloe, Mr G. Bromley, Mr M. L. Clements, Mrs Christine Dunnett, Miss Karen Everitt, Mr Graham Everitt, Mr B. Green, Mr A. K. Lennox, Mr O. Nugent, Mr J. D. Sheehan, Mr G. W. Smart, Mrs J. C. Turner, Mr R. R. Wright.

---

169 **MRS P. N. DUTFIELD, Seaton**
Postal: **Crabhayne Farm, Axmouth, Seaton, Devon, EX12 4BW**
Contacts: PHONE **(01297) 553560** FAX **(01297) 551185**
E-MAIL **nerys.dutfield@tiscali.co.uk** WEBSITE **www.nerysdutfield.com**

1 **BOLD ARGUMENT (IRE)**, 5, ch g Shinko Forest (IRE)—Ivory Bride **S. J. Dutfield**
2 **COLONEL FLAY**, 4, ch g Danehill Dancer (IRE)—Bobbie Dee **John Boswell**
3 **IN DEEP**, 7, b m Deploy—Bobbie Dee **T. J. Hawkins**
4 **IS IT TIME (IRE)**, 4, b f Danetime (IRE)—Ishaam **G. G. Payne**
5 **MAN OF LEISURE**, 4, b g Karinga Bay—Girl of Pleasure (IRE) **Mrs P. N. Dutfield**
6 **RAISE AGAIN (IRE)**, 5, b g Raise A Grand (IRE)—Paryiana (IRE) **S. J. Dutfield**
7 **ROYAL AXMINSTER**, 13, b g Alzao (USA)—Number One Spot **Axminster Carpets Ltd**
8 **SHOULDNTBETHERE (IRE)**, 4, ch g Soviet Star (USA)—Octomone (USA) **Mrs K. A. Stuart**
9 **SURFACE TO AIR**, 7, b g Samraan (USA)—Travelling Lady **T. Urry**
10 **VOIR DIRE**, 6, b g Vettori (IRE)—Bobbie Dee **Mrs P. N. Dutfield**

THREE-YEAR-OLDS

11 **ALANNAH (IRE)**, b f Alhaarth (IRE)—Aljeeza **Mrs P. N. Dutfield**
12 **CHARLIE BE (IRE)**, ch g King Charlemagne (USA)—Miriana (IRE) **Mrs P. N. Dutfield**
13 **LA VARROSA**, b f Josr Algarhoud (IRE)—Ebony Anne (IRE) **M. A. J. Daly**
14 **MR FUNSHINE**, b c Namid—Sunrise Girl **Unity Farm Holiday Centre Ltd**
15 **SHYBUTWILLING (IRE)**, ch f Best of The Bests (IRE)—Reticent Bride (IRE) **Mrs C. J. Walsh**

Other Owners: Mrs Nerys Dutfield, Mr P. G. Gibbins, Mr P. J. Quinn, Mrs Linda Salter, Mr A. J. White.

Apprentice: N. Bazeley.

---

170 **MR C. DWYER, Newmarket**
Postal: **Ravens Barn, Bradley Road, Burrough Green, Newmarket, Suffolk, CB8 9NH**
Contacts: FAX **(01638) 507033** MOBILE **(07831) 579844**
E-MAIL **getadwyer@aol.com**

1 **MIA'S BOY**, 4, b c Pivotal—Bint Zamayem (IRE) **I. Parvizi**
2 **WIND FLOW**, 4, b g Dr Fong (USA)—Spring **David L. Bowkett**

MR C. DWYER—continued

THREE-YEAR-OLDS

3 **RACIE GRACIE**, gr f Dr Fong (USA)—Maxizone (FR) **Super Six Partnership**
4 **YOUNG IVANHOE**, b g Oasis Dream—Cybinka **S B Components (International) Ltd**

TWO-YEAR-OLDS

5 Ch f 16/4 Cayman Kai (IRE)—Badger Bay (IRE) (Salt Dome (USA)) **Mr G. Middlemiss**
6 Ch g 24/5 Bertolini (USA)—High Stepping (IRE) (Taufan (USA)) **Mrs S. A. Dwyer & Mrs J. A. Chapman**
7 B f 26/4 Cayman Kai (IRE)—Sassy Lady (IRE) (Brief Truce (USA)) **Mr G. Middlemiss**

Other Owners: Mrs S. Dwyer.

Assistant Trainer: Shelley Dwyer

Jockey (flat): J Quinn, John Egan, A. McCarthy, F. Norton. **Apprentice:** James O'Reilly. **Amateur:** Mr C Wallis.

---

171 MISS C. DYSON, Bromsgrove
Postal: **Froglands Stud Farm, Froglands Lane, Cleeve Prior, Evesham, Worcestershire, WR11 8LB**
Contacts: **FAX** (01527) 821493 **MOBILE** (07803) 720183

1 4, B c Commanche Run—Double Chimes **Miss C. Dyson**
2 **HARBOURS ROSE**, 5, gr m Silver Patriarch (IRE)—Baroness Rose **Mrs Diane Brown**
3 **LA LUNE BLEU (FR)**, 6, gr m Cyborg (FR)—Cle de Lune (FR) **J. S. Allen**
4 **LORIKO D'AIRY (FR)**, 9, b g Oblat (FR)—Ursali d'airy (FR) **Miss C. Dyson**
5 **MARGHUB (IRE)**, 9, b g Darshaan—Arctique Royale **Miss C. Evans**
6 5, B g Shahrastani (USA)—Nordic Crown (IRE) **J. S. Allen**
7 4, Gr c Executive Perk—Scallymill **Miss C. Dyson**
8 **SUPREME PIPER (IRE)**, 10, b g Supreme Leader—Whistling Doe **Miss C. Dyson**
9 **TANNER TOWERS**, 6, b g I'm Supposin (IRE)—Foxgrove **Miss C. Dyson**
10 **TANNERS COURT**, 11, b g Framlington Court—True Nell **Miss C. Dyson**
11 **TANNERS DEN**, 8, b g Abzu—Equilibrium **Miss C. Dyson**
12 **TANNERS ROCK**, 5, b g Samraan (USA)—Whittle Rock **Miss C. Dyson**
13 **WEN'S DREAM**, 5, b m Roi de Rome (USA)—Solo Girl (IRE) **Exhall Dodgers**

THREE-YEAR-OLDS

14 **RIORUN (IRE)**, b g Captain Rio—Sulaka **Miss C. Evans**

Other Owners: C. Oscroft, Mr R. G. Owens, Mrs S. A. Vaughan.

Assistant Trainer: John Dyson

Jockey (flat): Vince Slattery. **Jockey (NH):** T J Phelan. **Amateur:** Miss C. Evans, Miss C. Dyson.

---

172 MR M. W. EASTERBY, Sheriff Hutton
Postal: **New House Farm, Sheriff Hutton, York, North Yorkshire, YO60 6TN**
Contacts: **PHONE** (01347) 878368 **FAX** (01347) 878204 **MOBILE** (07831) 347481

1 **AHLAWY (IRE)**, 5, gr g Green Desert (USA)—On Call **Mr K. Hodgson & Mrs J. Hodgson**
2 **ANCIENT CROSS**, 4, b g Machiavellian (USA)—Magna Graecia (IRE)
3 **APOLLO SATURN FIVE**, 6, b g Overbury (IRE)—Kadari **Mr C Walker & Lord Daresbury**
4 **ATLANTIC STORY (USA)**, 6, b br g Stormy Atlantic (USA)—Story Book Girl (USA) **M. R. Green**
5 **BAL BIRNIE**, 5, ch g Bal Harbour—Kalymnia (GER) **J. Connor**
6 **BALTIMORE JACK (IRE)**, 4, b g Night Shift (USA)—Itsibitsi (IRE) **Mr D. Swales**
7 **BANCHORY TWO (IRE)**, 8, b g Un Desperado (FR)—Theyllallwin (IRE) **Lord Daresbury**
8 **BANG AND BLAME (IRE)**, 12, b g Be My Native (USA)—Miss Lucille **E. C. Wilkin**
9 **BLUE BUSTER**, 8, b g Young Buster (IRE)—Lazybird Blue (IRE) **J. Connor**
10 **BLUE SPINNAKER (IRE)**, 9, b g Bluebird (USA)—Suedoise **G. Sparkes, G. Hart, S Curtis & T Dewhirst**
11 **BRIGHT SPARKY (GER)**, 5, ch g Dashing Blade—Braissim
12 **CAULKLEYS BANK**, 8, b g Slip Anchor—Mayroni **Lord Daresbury**
13 **CHEER US ON**, 6, b g Bahhare (USA)—Markapen (IRE) **J. Connor**
14 **DESERT VISION**, 4, b g Alhaarth (IRE)—Fragrant Oasis **A Black,R Edmonds,J Holdroyd,J Quickfall**
15 **DIAVOLERIA**, 5, b m Slip Anchor—Markapen (IRE) **Lord Daresbury**
16 **EMPEROR'S WELL**, 9, ch g First Trump—Catherines Well **M. W. Easterby**

MR M. W. EASTERBY—continued

17 **FENNERS (USA)**, 5, ch g Pleasant Tap (USA)—Legal Opinion (IRE) **K. Wreglesworth**
18 **FEVER**, 4, b g Dr Fong (USA)—Follow Flanders **M. W. Easterby**
19 **FORT AMHURST (IRE)**, 4, ch g Halling (USA)—Soft Breeze **Lord Daresbury**
20 **GALA SUNDAY (USA)**, 8, b g Lear Fan (USA)—Sunday Bazaar (USA) **S. Hull**
21 **GASTORNIS**, 10, ch g Primitive Rising (USA)—Meggies Dene **Lord Daresbury**
22 **GENTLEMAN'S DEAL (IRE)**, 7, b h Danehill (USA)—Sleepytime (IRE) **S. J. Curtis**
23 **GINGER'S LAD**, 4, ch g Elmaamul (USA)—Chadwick's Ginger **Mr M. H. Tinning & Mrs J. A. Tinning**
24 **GRAMM**, 5, b g Fraam—Beacon Silver **Mr D. Pearson**
25 **HIGH COMMAND**, 5, b g Galileo (IRE)—Final Shot **Mr A. Saha**
26 **HURLINGHAM**, 4, b c Halling (USA)—Society (IRE) **A. G. Black**
27 **INSIDE STORY (IRE)**, 6, b g Rossini (USA)—Sliding **M. R. Green**
28 **INTENSE SUSPENSE (IRE)**, 5, ch g Bob's Return (IRE)—In Sin (IRE) **Mr S. P. Roberts**
29 **IT'S A DREAM (FR)**, 5, b g Kaldounevees (FR)—Bahia Mar (USA) **M. R. Green**
30 **JOSEPH**, 5, b g Josr Algarhoud (IRE)—Kisty (IRE) **Mrs Caroline MacEchern & Lady Daresbury**
31 **JUST DUST**, 4, b g Makbul—Dusty Bankes **M. R. Green**
32 **KALASAM**, 4, ch g Noverre (USA)—Spring Sixpence **A. J. De V. Patrick & M. J. Caddy**
33 **KYOTO SUMMIT**, 5, ch g Lomitas—Alligram (USA) **The Woodford Group Plc**
34 **LAKE CHINI (IRE)**, 6, b g Raise A Grand (IRE)—Where's The Money **Mrs L. J. Turpin**
35 **LAMBRINI LEGEND (IRE)**, 6, br g Bob's Return (IRE)—Spur of The Moment **Halewood International Ltd**
36 **LONGSPUR**, br c Singspiel (IRE)—Bunting
37 **LORD RASPBERRY**, 4, br g Vettori (IRE)—Arminda **Mr Rye Braune & Lord Daresbury**
38 **MAJURO (IRE)**, 4, b c Danetime (IRE)—First Fling **The Woodford Group PLC**
39 **MEZUZAH**, 8, b g Barathea (IRE)—Mezzogiorno **The Woodford Group PLC**
40 **MISCHIEF MAN**, 6, b g Afflora (IRE)—Rascally **Lady Henrietta Spencer-Churchill**
41 **MISTTORI BELLE**, 5, b m Vettori (IRE)—Misbelief **Mrs S. C. Goodall**
42 **MOON PHASE (USA)**, 4, b g Rahy (USA)—Noctilucent (JPN) **Mr C Walker & Lord Daresbury**
43 **MORMEATMIC**, 5, b g Orpen (USA)—Mimining **Mr M. Broad & Mrs M. E. Attwood**
44 **MUHANNAK (IRE)**, 6, b g Chester House (USA)—Opera **The Woodford Group Plc**
45 **NORTHERN BOY (USA)**, 5, ch g Lure (USA)—Catala (USA) **East Riding Horse Racing Syndicate**
46 **NORTONTHORPE LAD (IRE)**, 6, b g Charnwood Forest (IRE)—
                         Tisima (FR) **Mr Gavin MacEchern & Lord Daresbury** 1
47 **OLD ROMNEY**, 4, br c Halling (USA)—Zaeema **J. R. Crickmore**
48 **ONE MORE GYPSY**, 4, br f Warningford—Gypsy Race (IRE) **M. C. Stoddart**
49 **PEE JAY'S DREAM**, 6, ch g Vettori (IRE)—Langtry Lady **Mr P. Bown & Mr R. Edmonds**
50 **PERTEMPS NETWORKS**, 4, b g Golden Snake (USA)—Society Girl **D. Pearson**
51 **PROVOST**, 4, ch g Danehill Dancer (USA)—Dixielake (IRE) **Mr D. Pearson**
52 **REALISM (FR)**, 8, b g Machiavellian (USA)—Kissing Cousin (IRE) **The Woodford Group Plc**
53 **ROCKING ROD (IRE)**, 4, b g Dilshaan—Tavildara (IRE) **Mr N. Bannister**
54 **SEA SENOR**, 6, b g Sea Freedom—Portonia **J. Connor**
55 **SHARADIYN**, 5, b g Generous (IRE)—Sharadiya (IRE) **Mr N. Bannister**
56 **SOTO**, 5, b g Averti (IRE)—Belle of The Blues (IRE) **W. H. & Mrs J. A. Tinning**
57 **SPENCE'S CHOICE (IRE)**, 4, b g Desert Sun—Late Night Lady (IRE) **E. A. Brook**
58 **SPORTING GESTURE**, 11, ch g Safawan—Polly Packer **S. Hull**
59 **SPRING MARGOT (FR)**, 12, b g Kadalko (FR)—La Brunante (FR) **Gavin MacEchern & Lord Daresbury**
60 **TAMATAVE (IRE)**, 6, b g Darshaan—Manuetti (IRE) **D. Pearson**
61 **THE GLEANER**, 6, b g Kayf Tara—Handmaiden **Mrs M. E. Curtis**
62 **THE NOMAD**, 12, b g Nomadic Way (USA)—Bubbling **S. H. J. Brewer**
63 **THE SNURGLAR (IRE)**, 6, b g Snurge—Burksie (IRE) **The Hon A. G. Vestey**
64 **TRACER**, 4, br g Kyllachy—Western Sal **Mrs L. J. Turpin**
65 **TREEFELLA (IRE)**, 7, b g Woods of Windsor—Divine Dancer (IRE) **Lord Daresbury**
66 **TROUBLE MOUNTAIN (USA)**, 11, br g Mt Livermore (USA)—Trouble Free (USA) **Mrs L. J. Turpin**
67 **VICE ADMIRAL**, 5, ch g Vettori (IRE)—Queen of Scotland (IRE) **A. C. R. Stubbs**
68 **WORD PERFECT**, 6, b m Diktat—Better Still (IRE) **Mrs L. J. Turpin**

THREE-YEAR-OLDS

69 **BERRYMEAD**, br f Killer Instinct—Mill End Quest **W. T. Allgood**
70 **CLIMAXTACKLEDOTCOM**, b g Bahri (USA)—La Danseuse **Climax Fishing Tackle & Miss J Flint**
71 **EIGHTY TWENTY**, b f Diktat—Stonegrave **Bamford Trading S.Hull D.Buchanan A.Brewer**
72 **FU WA (USA)**, ch f Distant View (USA)—Fire And Shade (USA) **Mr J. T. Brown**
73 **HEROLDS BAY**, br f Bertolini (USA)—Prime Property (IRE) **A. G. Black**
74 **INDECISION**, b f Muhtarram (USA)—Emma Amour **K. Wreglesworth**
75 **JEMIMA'S ART**, b br f Fantastic Light (USA)—Subya **M. R. Green**
76 **LADY GRANTLEY**, ch f Bertolini (USA)—South Shore **Mrs K. L. Pearson**
77 **MAJIGAL**, b f High Estate—Face The Judge (USA) **D. A. Drake**
78 **NOTE PERFECT**, b f Diktat—Better Still (IRE) **Mrs L. J. Turpin**

MR M. W. EASTERBY—continued

79 **PREDICTABLE (IRE)**, b f Traditionally (USA)—Presumed (USA) **Mr K. Hodgson & Mrs J. Hodgson**
80 **PURE SCANDAL**, b g Barathea (IRE)—Sharena (IRE) **R. M. Braune**
81 **SNICKERS FIRST**, ch f Presidium—Mirror Four Sport **Clark Industrial Services Partnership**
82 **UTRILLO'S ART (IRE)**, ch f Medecis—Theory of Law **M. R. Green**

TWO-YEAR-OLDS

83 B f 6/4 Halling (USA)—Alpenglow (Ezzoud (IRE)) **Mr A. G. Black**
84 B f 18/2 Mind Games—Alustar (Emarati (USA)) (18000) **Mr B. Bargh**
85 B c 4/5 Mujahid (USA)—Anelyn's Gift (Namid) **The Woodford Group Plc**
86 B f 11/4 Sulamani (USA)—Bahirah (Ashkalani (IRE)) (9500) **Mr D. Swales & Mr S. Hull**
87 Gr c 12/5 Mujahid (USA)—Beat Time (Lion Cavern (USA)) (8000) **Mr R. Braune**
88 **BILL ON THE HILL**, b g 26/3 Makbul—Mill End Quest (King's Signet (USA)) **Mr B. Bargh**
89 B c 1/4 Erhaab (USA)—Boulevard Rouge (USA) (Red Ransom (USA)) **Mr K. & Mrs J. Hodgson**
90 Br c 12/5 Lend A Hand—Bow Peep (IRE) (Shalford (IRE)) **Mrs A. Jarvis**
91 **CURTAIN UP**, b g 23/4 Act One—Better Still (IRE) (Glenstal (USA)) **Mrs L. J. Turpin**
92 Br f 7/4 Makbul—Emma Amour (Emarati (USA)) (3000) **Mr K. Wreglesworth**
93 **FIRST HAND**, b f 3/4 Act One—Strong Hand (First Trump) **Mrs L. J. Turpin**
94 B f 9/5 Sakhee (USA)—Flower O'cannie (IRE) (Mujadil (USA))
95 Ch c 7/4 Nayef (USA)—Fragrant Oasis (Rahy (USA)) (5500) **Mr John Connor**
96 **GA GA**, b f 29/3 Baryshnikov (AUS)—Spring Dew (FR) (Starborough) (666) **Mr J. T. Brown**
97 Br f 1/4 Compton Place—Harambee (IRE) (Robellino (USA)) (9000) **Mrs A. Blanchard**
98 B c 18/5 Mujahid (USA)—High Petergate (IRE) (Mujadil (USA)) (800) **Mr S. Hull**
99 B c 20/4 Orpen (USA)—Kiss Me Kate (Aragon) (20000)
100 B c 12/3 Mujahid (USA)—Loch Maree (Primo Dominie)
101 B f 14/3 Nayef (USA)—Mount Hillaby (IRE) (Mujadil (USA)) **Mr John Southway**
102 Ch f 30/1 Halling (USA)—Roseate (USA) (Mt Livermore (USA)) **Mr A. G. Black**
103 Br c 11/5 Sakhee (USA)—Royal Distant (USA) (Distant View (USA)) **T. Dewhurst, R. Moore, G. Sparkes**
104 B f 27/4 Orpen (USA)—Spanish Serenade (Nashwan (USA)) (6000) **Mr Matthew Green**
105 B c 7/3 Hawk Wing (USA)—Stardance (USA) (Rahy (USA)) **Mr Forbes Connor**

Other Owners: Mrs M. E. Attwood, Bamford Trading Ltd, Mr A. G. Black, Mr Richard Blanchard, Mr P. J. Bown, Mr A. J. Brewer, Mr M. E. Broad, Mr E. A. Brook, Mr D. Buchanan, M. J. Caddy, Mr Jim Clark, Mr A. W. Clark, Mr Stephen J. Curtis, Lord Daresbury, Mr P. A. Davies, Mr M. E. T. Davies, Mr Peter Davies, Mr T. C. Dewhirst, Mr D. R. C. Elsworth, Mr A. Flint, Sir Roger G. Gibbs, Mr G. C. Hart, Mr K. Hodgson, Mrs J. H. Hodgson, Mr John L. Holdroyd, Mr Steve Hull, Mr Gavin MacEchern, A. J. De V. Patrick, Mr J. E. H. Quickfall, Mr G. H. Sparkes, Mr D. F. Spence, Mrs J. A. Tinning, Mr W. H. Tinning, Mr Christopher Walker, Mrs E. Wright.

Assistant Trainer: D. M. Easterby

Jockey (flat): Dale Gibson, P. Mulrennan. **Apprentice:** Nicky Lawes. **Amateur:** Mr T. Greenall, Mr O. Greenall.

---

173 **MR B. J. ECKLEY, Brecon**
Postal: **Closcedi Farm, Llanspyddid, Brecon, Powys, LD3 8NS**
Contacts: **PHONE (01874) 622422 MOBILE (07891) 445409**

1 4, Gr f Cloudings (IRE)—Alice Smith **B. J. Eckley**
2 4, B f Overbury (IRE)—Jaunty June **B. J. Eckley**
3 4, B f Witness Box (USA)—Little Time **B. J. Eckley**
4 **POPPY SMITH**, 6, ch m Busy Flight—Alice Smith **B. J. Eckley**

---

174 **MR P. J. J. EDDERY, Nether Winchendon**
Postal: **Musk Hill Stud, Nether Winchendon, Aylesbury, Buckinghamshire, HP18 0EB**
Contacts: **RACING OFFICE: (01844) 296153 FAX (01844) 290282 MOBILE (07880) 746781**
E-MAIL **info@patedderyracing.com** WEBSITE **www.patedderyracing.com**

1 **ACCOLATION**, 4, b g Royal Applause—Jasmine Breeze **Pat Eddery Racing (Law Society)**
2 **ASCALON**, 4, ch c Galileo (IRE)—Leaping Flame (USA) **P. J. J. Eddery, Mrs John Magnier, M. Tabor**
3 **COMPULSION**, 5, br m Bertolini (USA)—Comme Ca **P. J. J. Eddery**
4 **EDEN ROCK (IRE)**, 7, b g Danehill (USA)—Marlene-D **Mrs G. K. Smith**
5 **LAPINA (IRE)**, 4, ch f Fath (USA)—Alpina (USA) **Aitken & Phillips**
6 **LAWYERS CHOICE**, 4, b f Namid—Finger of Light **R. C. Tooth**
7 **NEW AMBITIONS (IRE)**, 5, br g Definite Article—My Darling Dodo (IRE) **P. J. J. Eddery**

MR P. J. J. EDDERY—continued

8 SLEEPY MOUNTAIN, 4, ch g Beat Hollow—La Sorrela (IRE) **P. J. J. Eddery**
9 SPIRIT OF ADJISA (IRE), 4, br g Invincible Spirit (IRE)—Adjisa (IRE) **Darr, Johnson, Weston & Whitaker**

THREE-YEAR-OLDS

10 ACQUIRED TASTE (IRE), b c Namid—Sheila Blige
11 BUDDY HOLLY, b c Reel Buddy (USA)—Night Symphonie **Hayman, Pearson, Phillips & McGuinness**
12 CASTLES IN THE AIR, b c Oasis Dream—Dance Parade (USA) **Reg Griffin & Jim McGrath**
13 CHOISEAU (IRE), b c Choisir—Little Linnet **Pat Eddery Racing (Danehill Dancer)**
14 FARAAMI (IRE), ch f Fraam—Maraami **Pat Eddery Racing (Marling)**
15 GIFTED LEADER (USA), b c Diesis—Zaghruta (USA) **K. Abdulla**
16 KORALEVA TECTONA (IRE), b f Fasliyev—Miss Teak (USA) **Pat Eddery Racing (Ramruma)**
17 MORE APPLAUSE, b f Royal Applause—Three More (USA) **K. Abdulla**
18 PENCHESCO (IRE), b c Orpen—Francesca (IRE) **Pat Eddery Racing (Sanglamore)**
19 REPLICATOR, b c Mujahid (USA)—Valldemosa **Pat Eddery Racing (Cadeaux Genereux)**
20 RESENTFUL ANGEL, b f Danehill Dancer (IRE)—Leaping Flame (USA) **P. J. J. Eddery**
21 SUEDE, b f Zamindar (USA)—Blue Gentian (USA) **K. Abdulla**

TWO-YEAR-OLDS

22 B c 1/3 Captain Rio—Alice Blackthorn (Forzando) (19000) **Pat Eddery Racing (Qtr 6)**
23 B c 1/4 Diktat—Cape Cod (IRE) (Unfuwain (USA)) (17000) **Pat Eddery Racing (Toulon)**
24 B c 9/2 Redback—La Mata (IRE) (Danehill Dancer (IRE)) (18000) **Pat Eddery Racing (Sharpo)**
25 Ch f 1/4 Lear Spear (USA)—Milladella (Nureyev (USA)) (380) **R. C. Tooth**
26 B f 18/2 Dansili—Musical Key (Key of Luck (USA)) (100000) **F. C. T. Wilson**
27 OUTRAGEOUS REQUEST, ch c 28/3 Rainbow Quest (USA)—La Sorrela (IRE) (Cadeaux Genereux) **P. J. J. Eddery**
28 B f 3/5 Exceed And Excel (AUS)—Panglossian (IRE) (Barathea (IRE)) (115000) **F. C. T. Wilson**
29 B c 1/5 Prince Sabo—Pieta (IRE) (Perugino (USA)) (13000)
30 Br f 23/2 One Cool Cat (USA)—Shinkoh Rose (FR) (Warning) (22000) **Pat Eddery Racing (Scintillate)**
31 B c 11/2 Beat Hollow—Three More (USA) (Sanglamore) (USA) **K. Abdulla**
32 Br f 10/3 Captain Rio—Trillie (Never So Bold) (8000)
33 B c 7/4 Captain Rio—Victoria's Secret (Law Society (USA)) (30000) **Pat Eddery Racing (Lomond)**
34 Ch c 18/3 Choisir (AUS)—Widescreen (USA) (Distant View (USA)) **K. Abdulla**
35 B f 23/3 Diesis—Zaghruta (USA) (Gone West (USA)) **K. Abdulla**

Other Owners: Mrs Pam Aitken, Mr Reg Griffin, Ms S. Johnson, Mrs John Magnier, Mr Jim McGrath, Pat Eddery Racing Limited, Mr Edwin S. Phillips, Mr M. Tabor.

Assistant Trainer: Carolyn Eddery

---

175 MR G. F. EDWARDS, Minehead
Postal: Summering, Wheddon Cross, Minehead, Somerset, TA24 7AT
Contacts: PHONE (01643) 831549 FAX (01643) 831549 MOBILE (07970) 059297
E-MAIL dazjock001@hotmail.com

1 ACKHURST (IRE), 9, br g Anshan—Sassy Sally (IRE) **G. F. Edwards**
2 DELAYDEE VIC (IRE), 5, ch m Old Vic—Moonshee (IRE) **G. F. Edwards**
3 DEVITO (FR), 7, ch g Trempolino (USA)—Snowy **G. F. Edwards**
4 KNIGHTSBRIDGE HILL (IRE), 6, b g Raise A Grand (IRE)—Desert Gem **G. F. Edwards**

Amateur: Mr D. Edwards.

---

176 MR C. R. EGERTON, Chaddleworth
Postal: Heads Farm Stables, Chaddleworth, Newbury, Berkshire, RG20 7EU
Contacts: OFFICE (01488) 638771 HOME (01488) 638454 FAX (01488) 638832
MOBILE (07795) 220630
E-MAIL charles@charlesegerton.co.uk

1 BURNSWOOD (IRE), 4, b g Monsun (GER)—Banaja (IRE) **W. J. Byrne**
2 CANALTURN (IRE), 6, b g Assessor (IRE)—Caline de Froment (FR) **The Dover Street Boys**
3 CAPETONIAN (FR), 5, ch g Mansonnien (FR)—Chanson du Chenet (FR) **Lady M. C. Laidlaw**
4 DUTY FREE (IRE), 4, b g Rock of Gibraltar (IRE)—Photographie (USA) **Lady M. C. Laidlaw**
5 FIFTY SHEETS, 5, b g Spadoun (FR)—Kandis **Byrne Bros (Formwork) Limited**
6 HIGH TECH MADE (FR), 8, b g Nononito (FR)—Home Made (FR) **R. F. Bailey**
7 HILAL, 6, gr g Linamix (FR)—Magnificent Star (USA) **Vineste**

MR C. R. EGERTON—continued

8 **HOBBS HILL**, 9, b g Alflora (IRE)—Rim of Pearl **Mrs Orton & the Exors of the Late P. Orton**
9 **HUMUNGOUS (IRE)**, 5, ch g Giant's Causeway (USA)—Doula (USA) **Exors of the Late Mrs E. A. Hankinson**
10 **KRUGUYROVA (FR)**, 5, ch m Muhtathir—Kruguy **R. A. Brimacombe**
11 **MIGHTY BOLD**, 5, b g Alflora (IRE)—Grignette (FR) **E. R. Hanbury**
12 **MISSISIPI ASSASSIN (IRE)**, 7, b g Safety Catch (USA)—America River (IRE) **G. Nock**
13 **RISK (IRE)**, 5, ch g Acatenango (GER)—Belua (GER) **The Picnic Party**
14 **RUSSIAN SYMPHONY (USA)**, 7, ch g Stravinsky (USA)—
Backwoods Teacher (USA) **Exors of the Late Mrs E. A. Hankinson**
15 **SMOKE AND MIRRORS**, 4, b g Mujahid (USA)—Fayrooz (USA) **Bernard Gover Bloodstock Trading Ltd**
16 **THE ENTOMOLOGIST (IRE)**, 7, b g Saddlers' Hall (IRE)—Winter Ground (IRE) **R. A. Brimacombe**
17 **THE LOCAL**, 8, b g Selkirk (USA)—Finger of Light **B. R. Marsden**
18 **VINANDO**, 7, ch g Hernando (FR)—Sirena (GER) **Exors of the Late Mrs E. A. Hankinson**
19 **VINCENZIO (IRE)**, 4, b g Galileo (IRE)—Mystic Lure **Exors of the Late Mrs E. A. Hankinson**
20 **WAR ANTHEM**, 4, br g Vettori (IRE)—Lucy Boo **J. A. E. O'Malley**
21 **WILLIE PEP (IRE)**, 7, b g Saddlers' Hall (IRE)—Favorable Exchange (USA) **The Egerton Partnership**

THREE-YEAR-OLDS

22 **DANCING MARABOUT (IRE)**, ch g Danehill Dancer (IRE)—
Bluebell Wood (IRE) **Allsopp, Astor, Broughton & Drummond I**
23 **DR LIVINGSTONE (IRE)**, b g Dr Fong (USA)—Radwha (FR) **Exors of the Late Mrs E. A. Hankinson**
24 **HIGH LADY**, b f Pivotal—Ballerina Suprema (IRE) **Exors of the Late Mrs E. A. Hankinson**
25 **HIGHLAND LADDIE**, ch g Lomitas—Sirena (GER) **Lady M. C. Laidlaw**
26 **MYSTIC ART (IRE)**, b g Peintre Celebre (USA)—Mystic Lure **Exors of the Late Mrs E. A. Hankinson**
27 **NEW HAVENS**, b f Indian Ridge—Lady High Havens (IRE) **Exors of the Late Mrs E. A. Hankinson**
28 **NINO COCHISE (IRE)**, b g High Chaparral (IRE)—Lady Scarlett **Vineste**
29 **SMOOTH AS SILK (IRE)**, b f Danehill Dancer (IRE)—Doula (USA) **Exors of the Late Mrs E. A. Hankinson**
30 **SOLAR MAX (IRE)**, b g Galileo (IRE)—Vanishing River (USA) **Exors of the Late Mrs E. A. Hankinson**
31 **SPECIAL BRANCH AMI (IRE)**, ch g Galileo (IRE)—Helena's Paris (IRE) **Ronald Brimacombe & Pav Sanghera**
32 **SPECIAL FEATURE (IRE)**, b g Montjeu (IRE)—Starring Role (IRE) **Exors of the Late Mrs E. A. Hankinson**

TWO-YEAR-OLDS

33 **CALALOO (IRE)**, b c 4/3 Dansili—Maraami (Selkirk (USA)) (115000) **The Manton Thoroughbred Partnership**
34 B c 17/4 King's Theatre (IRE)—Guest of Anchor (Slip Anchor) (27670) **Mrs Paul Shanahan**
35 **HIGHLAND FLASH**, b c 23/4 Halling (IRE)—Silk (IRE) (Machiavellian (USA)) (200000) **Lady M. C. Laidlaw**
36 B f 13/3 Oasis Dream—Miss Party Line (USA) (Phone Trick (USA)) (180000) **P. A. Byrne**
37 **NOORDHOEK KID**, b c 23/2 Dansili—Angood (IRE) (Elmaamul (USA)) (150000) **Lady M. C. Laidlaw**

Other Owners: Rick Allen, Jonny Allison, Austin Allison, James Allison, James Allsopp, Lee Amaitis, The Hon William Astor, Charles Balfour, James Blackshaw, D. Bradshaw, Mrs Fiona Brannon, Andrew Brannon, The Hon Henry Broughton, R. K. Carvill, J. P Cavanagh, James Collister, Lord Daresbury, Lady Daresbury, M. E. T. Davies, Bill Delaney, A. Drummond, Mrs Anne Fulton, Sir Roger G. Gibbs, T. Hoare, Philip Holden, P. McNally, Bob Michaelson, Martin Mitchell, Henry Philips, G. Rickman, Julian Rogers-Coltman, Michael Stoddart, Swettenham Stud, Graham Triefus, Mrs P. T. Walwyn, J. R. Weatherby, Mrs Alison Weatherby, Sir Brian Williamson.

Assistant Trainer: David Plunkett - Mobile - (07778) 379341, Home - (01488) 638998

Jockey (NH): A. P. McCoy, P. J. Brennan, J.A. McCarthy.

---

177 | MR BRIAN ELLISON, Malton
Postal: **Spring Cottage Stables, Langton Road, Norton, Malton, North Yorkshire, YO17 9PY**
Contacts: **OFFICE** (01653) 690004 **HOME** (01653) 690005 **FAX** (01653) 690008
MOBILE (07785) 747426
E-MAIL ellisonracing@aol.com WEBSITE www.brianellisonracing.co.uk

1 **AUREATE**, 4, ch c Jade Robbery (USA)—Anne d'autriche (IRE) **The Seasiders Again**
2 **BARKASS (UAE)**, 4, b g Halling (USA)—Areydha **Jelly Fish**
3 **BRUTUS MAXIMUS**, 5, b h Sir Harry Lewis (USA)—Horton Lady **R. E. Cook**
4 **CORONADO'S GOLD (USA)**, 7, ch g Coronado's Quest (USA)—Debit My Account (USA) **S. Hawe**
5 **COURT OF APPEAL**, 11, ch g Bering—Hiawatha's Song (USA) **Spring Cottage Syndicate No 2**
6 **DAAWEITZA**, 5, ch g Daawe (USA)—Chichen Itza **Mrs A. M. Mallinson**
7 **FORT CHURCHILL (IRE)**, 7, b g Barathea (IRE)—Brisighella (IRE) **Mr L.D.Gamble & Mr & Mrs J.H.Mathias**
8 **GHAFEER (USA)**, 4, b g War Chant (USA)—Hasheema (IRE)
9 **GREAT AS GOLD (IRE)**, 9, b g Goldmark (USA)—Great Land (USA) **K. Middleton**
10 **GREY GURKHA**, 7, gr h Kasakov—Royal Rebeka **R. E. Cook**

MR BRIAN ELLISON—continued

11 **HUE**, 7, ch g Peintre Celebre (USA)—Quandary (USA) **M. C. Ashton**
12 **JOHN FORBES**, 6, b g High Estate—Mavourneen (USA) **Raymond Wagner**
13 **JUN FAN (USA)**, 6, br g Artax (USA)—Ringside Lady (NZ) **The Lucky Magpies**
14 4, B g Daawe (USA)—Kandymal (IRE)
15 **KEISHA KAYLEIGH (IRE)**, 5, b m Almutawakel—Awtaar (USA) **C. E. Sherry**
16 **MALINSA BLUE (IRE)**, 6, b m Desert Style (IRE)—Talina's Law (IRE) **Mrs A. Mallinson**
17 **MARCH MATE**, 4, b g Warningford—Daira **R. McCulloch**
18 **MISS DAAWE**, 4, b f Daawe (USA)—Feiticeira (USA) **A. Mallinson**
19 **MISTER ARJAY (USA)**, 8, b g Mister Baileys—Crystal Stepper (USA) **K. Middleton**
20 **SEA LAND (FR)**, 4, ch g King's Best (USA)—Green Bonnet (IRE) **Good Little Workers**
21 **SIMONSIDE**, 5, b g Shahrastani (USA)—Only So Far **Racing Management & Training Ltd**
22 **SIR ARTHUR (IRE)**, 5, ch g Desert Prince (IRE)—Park Express **Raymond Wagner**
23 **SWIPER HILL (IRE)**, 5, b g City On A Hill (USA)—Alkariyh (USA) **Swiper Hill**
24 **TILT**, 6, b g Daylami (IRE)—Tromond **The Seasiders**
25 **TIZZY MAY (FR)**, 8, ch g Highest Honor (FR)—Forentia **S. Hawe**
26 **TRANSIT**, 9, b g Lion Cavern (USA)—Black Fighter (USA) **The Lucky Magpies**

Other Owners: Mr Azad Amin, Ms G. Brydon, Mr Ashley Carr, Mr T. Cosgrove, Mr D. Cowley, Mr Brian Ellison, Mrs Claire Ellison, Mr David Foster, Mr L. D. Gamble, Miss K. J. Gamble, Mr Wayne Hawkes, Mr M. A. Howitt, Mr H. J. Lynn, Mr C. P. Malkin, Mr A. Marucci, Mr J. H. Mathias, J. A. Milburn, Mr Paul Sargent, Mr J. K. Thompson, Mr Gus Williamson.

Assistant Trainer: Lorraine Ellison, Mobile (07968) 353417

Jockey (flat): T. Eaves. **Amateur:** Miss L. Ellison.

---

178 MR D. R. C. ELSWORTH, Newmarket
Postal: **Egerton House Stables, Cambridge Road, Newmarket, Suffolk, CB8 0TH**
Contacts: **PHONE** (01638) 665511 **FAX** (01638) 665310 **MOBILE** (07771) 804828
E-MAIL david.elsworth@virgin.net

1 **AGGRAVATION**, 6, b g Sure Blade (USA)—Confection **Perry, Vivian & Elsworth**
2 **BALKAN KNIGHT**, 8, b g Selkirk (USA)—Crown of Light **R. C. Tooth**
3 **BARRY ISLAND**, 9, b g Turtle Island (IRE)—Pine Ridge **D. R. C. Elsworth**
4 **BARSHIBA (IRE)**, 4, ch f Barathea (IRE)—Dashiba **J. C. Smith**
5 **CLASSIC PUNCH (IRE)**, 5, b g Mozart (IRE)—Rum Cay (USA) **J. C. Smith**
6 **CYBORG**, 4, ch g Halling (USA)—Ciboure **J. C. Smith**
7 **GOWER SONG**, 5, b m Singspiel (IRE)—Gleaming Water **Usk Valley Stud**
8 **HIGHLAND HARVEST**, 4, b c Averti (IRE)—Bee One (IRE) **J. Wotherspoon**
9 **HORSEFORD HILL**, 4, b g In The Wings—Love of Silver (USA) **R. C. Tooth**
10 **KNOW THE LAW**, 4, b g Danehill Dancer (IRE)—Mackenzie's Friend **Mr Raymond Tooth & Mr Steve Gilbey**
11 **LEPTIS MAGNA**, 4, ch g Danehill Dancer (IRE)—Dark Eyed Lady (IRE) **C. Green**
12 **MAY WEST**, 4, ch f Act One—Mill On The Floss **M. R. Green**
13 **NATIONAL DAY (IRE)**, 4, b f Barathea (IRE)—Rise And Fall **Egerton House Racing**
14 **PATHOS (GER)**, 4, b g Danehill Dancer (IRE)—Panthere (GER) **Richard Green & Matthew Green**
15 **SATIN BRAID**, 4, b f Diktat—Beading **Wyck Hall Stud Ltd**
16 **SAVIOUR SAND (IRE)**, 4, b g Desert Sun—Teacher Preacher (IRE) **The Save Your Sand Partnership**
17 **SILVER SUITOR (IRE)**, 4, gr g Swain (USA)—Taatof (IRE) **J. C. Smith**
18 **SUMMER DANCER (IRE)**, 4, br g Fasliyev (USA)—Summer Style (IRE) **The Sunday Lunch Partnership**
19 **SUNLEY PEACE**, 4, ch g Lomitas—Messala Rose **Davies, Sunley, Coombs & Cox**
20 **THE LITTLE MASTER (IRE)**, 4, b br g Tendulkar (USA)—Minatina (IRE) **The Howarting's Partnership**
21 **UPSTAIRS**, 4, ch g Sugarfoot—Laena **D. R. C. Elsworth**
22 **VITAL STATISTICS**, 4, br f Indian Ridge—Emerald Peace (IRE)
23 **VIVA VETTORI**, 4, ch c Vettori (IRE)—Cruinn A Bhord **Mr M. Watson**

THREE-YEAR-OLDS

24 **AFFIRMATIVELY**, b f Diktat—Circlet **Wyck Hall Stud Ltd**
25 **ART PROFIT (IRE)**, b c Viking Ruler (AUS)—Princess Mood (GER) **M. R. Green**
26 **CARAMEL CREME**, ch f Cadeaux Genereux—Foodbroker Fancy (IRE) **Normandie Stud Ltd**
27 **CHAMPION BREEZE**, b c Xaar—Glorious **G. W. Y. Li**
28 **CLASSIC FORTUNE (IRE)**, b c Royal Applause—Injaaz **Mr F. L. Li**
29 **EXCAPE (IRE)**, b c Cape Cross (IRE)—Viscaria (IRE) **R. C. Tooth**
30 **FAIRFIELD FLAME (GER)**, b f Oasis Dream—Fantastic Flame (IRE) **Mrs A. M. Coughlan**
31 **FRENCH ART**, ch c Peintre Celebre (USA)—Orange Sunset (IRE) **M. R. Green**
32 **GAINSBOROUGH'S ART (IRE)**, ch g Desert Prince (IRE)—Cathy Garcia (IRE) **M. R. Green**

MR D. R. C. ELSWORTH—continued

33 **GALLIC CHARM (IRE)**, b f Key of Luck (USA)—Kimash (IRE) **The Bramfield Racing Syndicate**
34 **HIGHLAND VENTURE (IRE)**, b f Averti (IRE)—Bee One (IRE) **J. Wotherspoon**
35 **IGOTATIGABYTHETAIL**, b g Tiger Hill (IRE)—Goldkatze (GER)
36 **JAMES POLLARD (IRE)**, ch c Indian Ridge—Manuetti (IRE) **Dwyer, Ramsden, Green & Elsworth**
37 **LAZY DAYS**, ch g Bahamian Bounty—Vivianna **Lordship Stud 3**
38 Ch f Horse Chestnut (SAF)—Lolita's Gold (USA) **Mr & Mrs W. J. Williams**
39 **LUCKY DANCER**, ch g Selkirk (USA)—Spot Prize (USA) **J. C. Smith**
40 **MARTHA (IRE)**, ch f Alhaarth (IRE)—Dominio (IRE) **N. E. Poole**
41 **MISS EMMA MAY (IRE)**, b f Hawk Wing (USA)—For Example (USA) **G. B. Partnership**
42 B f Averti (IRE)—Rivermead (USA) **Mr & Mrs W. J. Williams**
43 **SACRILEGE**, ch g Sakhee (USA)—Idolize **The National Stud 1**
44 **SEATTLE STORM (IRE)**, b c Robellino (USA)—Seattle Ribbon (USA) **J. C. Smith**
45 **SHEER BLUFF (IRE)**, b g Indian Ridge—Sheer Bliss (IRE) **Mr M. C. Morris & Partners**
46 **SILVER WATERS**, gr c Fantastic Light (USA)—Silent Waters **D. R. C. Elsworth**
47 **SQUIRE BOLDWOOD (IRE)**, b c Nayef (USA)—Lanelle (USA) **The Madding Crowd**
48 **STUBBS ART (IRE)**, ch c Hawk Wing (USA)—Rich Dancer **M. R. Green**
49 **STYLE ICON**, ch c Mark of Esteem (IRE)—Break Point **Mr Brian Cooper & Miss Elaine Reffo**
50 **SUNLEY SMILES**, ch f Arkadian Hero (USA)—Sunley Scent **John B. Sunley**
51 **SWISS FRANC**, br c Mr Greeley (USA)—Swiss Lake (USA) **Lordship Stud**
52 **WARDEN FIZZ**, b c Efisio—Miss Rimex (IRE) **Park Farm Racing**
53 **WIN ON RED (IRE)**, b f Red Ransom (USA)—Premier Prize **J. C. Smith**

TWO-YEAR-OLDS

54 B c 18/4 Indian Creek—Bee One (IRE) (Catrail (USA)) **J. Wotherspoon**
55 Ch f 1/5 Intikhab—Blazing Glory (IRE) (Glow (USA)) (28957) **Oak Lodge Stud**
56 B c 7/3 Elusive City (USA)—Certainly Brave (Indian Ridge) (60000) **Mr R. Tooth**
57 Ch c 17/2 Medicean—Faraway Waters (Pharly (FR)) (75000) **M. R. Green**
58 **FLEURON**, b br f 20/3 Diktat—Forthwith (Midyan (USA)) (58000) **Wyck Hall Stud Ltd**
59 Ch f 26/3 Rock of Gibraltar (IRE)—Gold Flair (Tap On Wood) (11582)
60 **IZZI HILL (USA)**, gr ro f 12/4 Lemon Drop Kid (USA)—Lets Get Cozzy (USA) (Cozzene (USA)) (37000)
61 Gr f 6/5 Indian Creek—Jilly Woo (Environment Friend) **J. Wotherspoon**
62 B f 27/3 Celtic Swing—Juvenilia (IRE) (Masterclass (USA)) **G. B. Partnership**
63 Ch c 11/2 Halling (USA)—Melisendra (FR) (Highest Honor (FR)) (32000) **The Howartings Partnership**
64 Ch f 4/2 Selkirk (USA)—Millay (Polish Precedent (USA)) (28957)
65 Ch c 14/2 Compton Place—Miss Rimex (IRE) (Ezzoud (IRE)) (65000) **M. R. Green**
66 **NORMANDIE ART**, b f 16/3 Rainbow Quest (USA)—
                                    Light Wind (Unfuwain (USA)) (125000) **Normandie Stud & Matthew Green**
67 B c 18/2 Lomitas—Odabella's Charm (Cadeaux Genereux) (55000) **Mr R. Tooth**
68 B f 21/4 Fasliyev (USA)—Premier Prize (Selkirk (USA)) **J. C. Smith**
69 B c 30/4 Elusive City (USA)—Quintellina (Robellino (USA)) (5000)
70 B f 19/3 Dalakhani (IRE)—Red Bartsia (Barathea (IRE)) (24000) **Huggins, McGrath & Elsworth**
71 **SALFORD SPIRIT**, b c 10/4 Desert Sun—Cribella (USA) (Robellino (USA)) (145000) **Mr A. J. Thompson**
72 Gr c 23/1 Alhaarth (USA)—Santa Sophia (IRE) (Linamix (FR)) (35000) **M. R. Green**
73 B f 24/2 Indian Haven—Sarah-Clare (Reach)
74 B f 7/2 Montjeu (IRE)—Seattle Ribbon (USA) (Seattle Dancer (USA)) **J. C. Smith**
75 B c 31/3 Singspiel (IRE)—Spot Prize (USA) (Seattle Dancer (USA)) **J. C. Smith**
76 B c 4/3 Desert Sun—Sunley Scent (Wolfhound (USA)) (34000)
77 **SWISS DIVA**, br f 4/2 Pivotal—Swiss Lake (USA) (Indian Ridge) **Lordship Stud**
78 B c 14/1 Lomitas—Zacchera (Zamindar (USA)) (25000) **G. W. Y. Li**

Other Owners: Mr Mike Balcomb, Mrs J. A. Ballamy, Mr Keith Childs, Mr Paul Clifton, Mr A. Coombs, B. A. Cooper, Mr N. Cox, Mr A. Cruickshank, Mr John Davies (Stonehill), Mr A. C. Deville, Mr John Dwyer, Mr D. R. C. Elsworth, Mr R. L. W. Frisby, Mr Steve Gilbey, Mr R. A. Green, Mr T. F. Harris, Mrs E. A. Harris, Mr M. G. H. Heald, Mr A. M. H. Heald, Mr Alastair Hodge, Mrs H. J. Lewis, McDowell Racing, Mr K. J. Mercer, Mrs S. Mercer, Mr M. C. Morris, Mr A. R. Parrish, Mr W. I. M. Perry, Mrs J. R. Ramsden, Ms E. M. B. A. Reffo, Mr R. Standring, Mr John B. Sunley, Mr D. D. Sutherland, Mr Raymond Tooth, Mrs Rose Vivian, Mr Mike Watson, Mrs Jacqueline Williams, Mrs M. Williams, Mr W. J. Williams.

Assistant Trainer: Mrs Jeannie Brown

MR A. M. ENNIS, Dorking
Postal: Henfold House Stables, Henfold Lane, Beare Green, Dorking, Surrey, RH5 4RW
Contacts: HOME/OFFICE/FAX (01306) 631529 MOBILE (07970) 424017
E-MAIL albert@henfoldstables.co.uk WEBSITE www.henfoldstables.co.uk

1 4, B g Beneficial—As Tu As (USA) **A. T. A. Wates**
2 **BLACK CLOUD**, 5, gr g Cloudings (IRE)—Dutch Czarina **Mrs Kate Lyons & Mrs Myra Jean Fuller**

MR A. M. ENNIS—continued

3 **CASTLECOMER (IRE)**, 7, ch g Presenting—Miss Mylette (IRE) **A. T. A. Wates**
4 **CASTLEMAINE VIC (IRE)**, 5, b g Old Vic—Dusky Walk (IRE) **The A T P Racing Partnership**
5 **GUNNER'S VIEW**, 4, ch c Medicean—Stark Ballet (IRE) **Fred Camis Martin Langley Darran Redman**
6 **HOMESPUN MAGIC**, 4, b f Fleetwood (IRE)—Bewails (IRE) **The Henfold Partnership**
7 **NAGAM (FR)**, 7, b g Denham Red (FR)—Gamaytoise (FR) **A. T. A. Wates**
8 **RODDY THE VET (IRE)**, 10, ch g Be My Native (USA)—Caronia (IRE) **A. T. A. Wates**
9 4, B g Presenting—Shipping News (IRE) **A. T. A. Wates**
10 **SPENDENT SPREE**, 5, b m Spendent—Posh Spice (IRE) **A. C. Ayres**
11 **SYKALINO (FR)**, 5, b g Robin des Champs (FR)—Et Que Ca Saute (FR) **A. T. A. Wates**
12 **THE CHISHOLM (IRE)**, 6, b g Oscar (IRE)—Dipped In Silver (IRE)
13 **ULTIMATE LIMIT**, 8, b g Bonny Scot (IRE)—Second Call **A. T. A. Wates**
14 4, B g Moscow Society (USA)—Who Tells Jan **A. T. A. Wates**

Other Owners: Mr Fred Camis, Mr R. Farmer, Mrs M. J. Fuller, Mr James Hartigan, Mr Martin Langley, Mrs Kate Lyons, Mr A. J. McClafferty, Mr P. J. O'Grady, Mr T. A. Parker, Mr Darran Redman.

---

180 MR G. P. ENRIGHT, Lewes
Postal: **The Oaks, Old Lewes Racecourse, Lewes, East Sussex, BN7 1UR**
Contacts: PHONE/FAX **(01273) 479183** MOBILE **(07922) 085875**
E-MAIL **enright@btinternet.com**

1 **BRASILIA PRINCE**, 9, ch g Karinga Bay—Cappuccino Girl **Mrs E. M. J Gray**
2 **CARLY BAY**, 10, b m Carlton (GER)—Polly Minor **A. O. Ashford**
3 **CLOUDY SUNSET**, 4, b g Cloudings (IRE)—Dutch Czarina **The Cloudy Club**
4 **COMMANCHE DAWN**, 6, b m Commanche Run—Charlycia **A. O. Ashford**
5 **HIGH POINT (IRE)**, 10, b g Ela-Mana-Mou—Top Lady (IRE) **The Aedean Partnership**
6 **PHARLY GREEN**, 6, ch m Pharly (FR)—Pastures Green **Homebred Racing**
7 **WELSH ASSEMBLY**, 12, ch g Presidium—Celtic Chimes **G. P. Enright**
8 **WELSH GUARD (USA)**, 5, ch g Silver Hawk (USA)—Royal Devotion (USA) **Racehill Partners**
9 **WHITESMITH BELLE**, 4, ch f Fleetwood (IRE)—Phil's Folly **Whitesmith Farm Stud**

TWO-YEAR-OLDS

10 **JENNIE WREN**, b f 6/2 Tobougg (IRE)—Dowhatjen (Desert Style) (IRE) (4000) **The Jennie Wren Partnership**
11 B c 4/4 Josr Algarhoud (IRE)—Polly Minor (Sunley Builds) **A. O. Ashford**

Other Owners: Mrs M. Enright, Mr G. P. Enright, Mrs A. Enright, Mrs Madeleine E. Etheridge, Mr Anthony A. Etheridge, Mr R. Gurney, G. R. Macdonald, Miss P. A. Ross, Mr Russell Stevenson, Mrs J. L. Stevenson, Mrs Michelle Stevenson, C. M. Wall, Mrs S. Wall.

Assistant Trainer: Mrs M Enright

Jockey (NH): R. Thornton.

---

181 MR J. M. P. EUSTACE, Newmarket
Postal: **Park Lodge Stables, Park Lane, Newmarket, Suffolk, CB8 8AX**
Contacts: PHONE **(01638) 664277** FAX **(01638) 664156** MOBILE **(07802) 243764**
E-MAIL **james@parklodgestables.demon.co.uk** WEBSITE **www.jameseustace.com**

1 **AT THE MONEY**, 5, b g Robellino (USA)—Coh Sho No **H. D. Nass**
2 **CAVENDISH**, 4, b g Pursuit of Love—Bathwick Babe (IRE) **The Cavendish Partnership**
3 **COLTON**, 5, b g Zilzal (USA)—Picot **Park Lodge Racing**
4 **POCHARD**, 5, br m Inchinor—Pomorie (IRE) **Mrs J. J. Shaw**
5 **WAR ARTIST (AUS)**, 5, b g Orpen (USA)—Royal Solitaire (AUS) **Vintage Thoroughbreds**
6 **WESTER LODGE (IRE)**, 6, ch g Fraam—Reamzafonic **Mrs R. A. Moszkowicz**
7 **WESTER ROSS (IRE)**, 4, b g Fruits of Love (USA)—Diabaig **P. J. Hillman**

THREE-YEAR-OLDS

8 **DOUBLE ON RED**, br f Red Ransom (USA)—Rosy Outlook (USA) **J. C. Smith**
9 **FARSIGHTED**, b f Where Or When (IRE)—Classic Vision **Blue Peter Racing 7**
10 **FLASH OF FIRE (USA)**, b g Fantastic Light (USA)—Mistle Thrush (USA) **J. C. Smith**
11 **ICE BELLINI**, ch f Erhaab (USA)—Peach Sorbet (IRE) **JCS Partnership**
12 **LADY AVENGER (IRE)**, ch f Namid—Shioda (USA) **J. C. Smith**
13 **SECOND OPINION (IRE)**, ch f Dr Fong (USA)—Second To Go (USA) **Major M. G. Wyatt**

MR J. M. P. EUSTACE—continued

14 **SUNNY SPRITE**, b g Lujain (USA)—Dragon Star **T. H. Barma**
15 **SZABA**, ch f Tipsy Creek (USA)—Compton Alice **Mrs P. Akhurst**
16 **TOO HOT TO HANDLE (IRE)**, br f Elnadim (USA)—Tropical Zone **J. C. Smith**

TWO-YEAR-OLDS

17 B c 11/3 Intikhab (USA)—Alegria (Night Shift (USA)) **J. C. Smith**
18 **BLUE ARCTIC**, b f 3/2 Bertolini (USA)—Bogus Mix (IRE) (Linamix (FR)) (8000) **Blue Peter Racing 8**
19 B c 1/3 Alhaarth (IRE)—Feel Free (IRE) (Generous (IRE)) **J. C. Smith**
20 **GENERAL ZHUKOV**, b c 1/3 Largesse—Hickleton Lady (IRE) (Kala Shikari) (6000) **Mrs R. A. Moszkowicz**
21 B c 1/1 One Cool Cat (USA)—Genevra (IRE) (Danehill (USA)) **J. C. Smith**
22 **JOE CASTER**, b c 26/4 Makbul—Oedipus Regina (Fraam) **The Greek Myths**
23 **LUJADE**, b f 23/1 Lujain (USA)—Sea Jade (IRE) (Mujadil (USA)) **T. H. Barma**
24 Ch c 11/2 Indian Haven—Maine Lobster (USA) (Woodman (USA))
25 B f 5/2 Bertolini (USA)—Malabarista (FR) (Assert) (17000) **Mr Y. Gelgin**
26 **MISTER STANDFAST**, b c 22/4 Haafhd—Off The Blocks (Salse (USA)) (30000) **The MacDougall Partnership**
27 **ON CUE (IRE)**, ch f 11/3 Indian Haven—On Time Arrival (Devil's Bag (USA)) (6500) **P. J. Hillman**
28 **PENPERTH**, b f 7/4 Xaar—Penelewey (Groom Dancer (USA)) **Major M. G. Wyatt**

Other Owners: Mr J. L. Atkinson, Mr D. F. Ballheimer, C. Z. Curtis, Mrs G. R. Eustace, S. J. Gibson, Dr R. D. Hinshelwood, T. V. Jones, Mrs L. R. Lawson, R. M. Levitt, Mrs K. A. McGladdery, H. R. Moszkowicz, Mr N. J. Percival, Mr M. Percival, Mr S. W. J. Rose, D. A. Rosenbaum, Ms G. P. Walker.

Amateur: Mr D. J. Eustace.

---

182 **MR H. J. EVANS, Honeybourne**
Postal: **Poden Farm, Mickleton Road, Honeybourne, Evesham, Worcestershire, WR11 7PS**
Contacts: **PHONE (01386) 438241 FAX (01386) 430268 MOBILE (07813) 166430**
E-MAIL herbie_evans@hotmail.com

1 **COCKSPUR (IRE)**, 7, b g Darazari (IRE)—Melarka **Treglown, Nettles, Peace, Evans**
2 **GENERAL SMITH**, 9, b g Greensmith—Second Call **Mrs J. Evans**
3 **GRANNY DUFFY**, 6, ch m Gildoran—Friendly Fairy **ownaracehorse.co.uk (Honeybourne)**
4 **MISSY MOSCOW (IRE)**, 10, b m Moscow Society (USA)—
                                Bright Shares (IRE) **ownaracehorse.co.uk (Honeybourne)**
5 **PETRUS DE SORMAIN (FR)**, 5, b g Milford Track (USA)—Bialystok (FR) **ownaracehorse.co.uk (Honeybourne)**
6 **SECRET CAVERN (USA)**, 6, b g Lion Cavern (USA)—River Dyna **M. S. Fentiman**
7 **SHARBASIA (IRE)**, 5, b m King's Best (USA)—Sharbata (IRE) **ownaracehorse.co.uk (Bidford)**
8 **SHAVA**, 8, b g Atraf—Anita Marie **Mrs J. Evans, Mr D. Stockton**
9 **SMART CASSIE**, 5, ch m Allied Forces (USA)—Katy-Q (IRE) **Mr & Mrs D. J. Smart**
10 **SMART JOHN**, 8, b g Bin Ajwaad (IRE)—Katy-Q (IRE) **Mr & Mrs D. J. Smart**

THREE-YEAR-OLDS

11 **SHAKESPEARE'S SON**, b g Mind Games—Eastern Blue (IRE) **ownaracehorse.co.uk (Shakespeare)**
12 **SMART TAZZ**, b g Mujahid (USA)—Katy-Q (IRE) **Mr & Mrs D. J. Smart**

Other Owners: Mrs J. Evans, Mr Tim Lively, Mrs Cathy Nettles, Ownaracehorse Ltd (ownaracehorse.co.uk), Mrs Susan Peace, Mr D. J. Smart, Mrs K. D. Smart, Mrs Sara Treglown.

Assistant Trainer: Mrs Jane Evans

Amateur: Mr J. Goss.

---

183 **MRS N. S. EVANS, Abergavenny**
Postal: **Penbiddle Farm, Penbidwal, Pandy, Abergavenny, Gwent, NP7 8EA**
Contacts: **PHONE/FAX (01873) 890957 MOBILE (07977) 753437**
E-MAIL nikki@penbiddle.fsnet.co.uk WEBSITE www.penbiddleracing.com

1 **ANOTHER WINNIE**, 5, b g Parthian Springs—Another Kav (IRE) **Mayhem Racing**
2 **ARABELLAS HOMER**, 4, b f Mark of Esteem (IRE)—Rush Hour (IRE) **Mayhem Racing**
3 **AYMARD DES FIEFFES (FR)**, 6, ch g Lute Antique (FR)—Margot des Fieffes (FR) **Mr M. Llewellyn**
4 **BOLD TRUMP**, 7, b g First Trump—Blue Nile (IRE) **G. Statham**
5 **IT'S NO PROBLEM (IRE)**, 4, b f Averti (IRE)—Polar Rock **Mrs N. Evans**
6 6, Ch g Classic Cliche (IRE)—McMahon's River **J. V. C. Davenport**

MRS N. S. EVANS—continued

7 4, B g Roi de Rome (USA)—McMahon's River **J. V. C. Davenport**
8 **QUICKBUCK**, 7, b g Desert Story (IRE)—Ahohoney **P. T. Evans**
9 **REVELINO (IRE)**, 9, b g Revouge (IRE)—Forelino (USA) **The Illiney Group**
10 **ROYALE RAG (IRE)**, 7, b g Garde Royale—Scarlet Rag (IRE) **E. A. McGuinness**
11 **TRACE ELEMENTS (IRE)**, 5, ch g Accordion—Buttermilk Square (IRE) **T. I. Thomas**
12 **VENEER (IRE)**, 6, b g Woodborough—Sweet Lass **Mrs E. C. Kidd**

Other Owners: Mr J. V. C. Davenport, Mr P. T. Evans, Mr David Howie, Mr H. J. Lewis, Mr E. A. McGuinness, Mr J. Rawlings, Mr David P. Stanton, Mr K. E. Watkins, Mr Sonny West.

Assistant Trainer: Mr P. T. Evans

Jockey (NH): J. Mogford.

---

184 MR P. D. EVANS, Abergavenny
Postal: **Ty Derlwyn Farm, Pandy, Abergavenny, Monmouthshire, NP7 8DR**
Contacts: **PHONE** (01873) 890837 (07834) 834775 E. Folkes **FAX** (01873) 890837
MOBILE (07860) 668499
E-MAIL pdevansracing@aol.com WEBSITE www.pdevansracing.co.uk

1 **BAZROY (IRE)**, 4, b g Soviet Star (USA)—Kunucu (IRE) **Mr B. McCabe**
2 **BUZZIN'BOYZEE (IRE)**, 5, ch m Monashee Mountain (USA)—Las Bela **Mrs I. M. Folkes**
3 **CAPANIA (IRE)**, 4, br f Cape Cross (IRE)—Gentle Papoose **Mr R. Edwards & Mr J. Swinnerton**
4 **CARCINETTO (IRE)**, 6, b m Danetime (IRE)—Dolphin Stamp (IRE) **Mrs S. E. Edwards**
5 **CASABLANCA MINX (IRE)**, 5, br m Desert Story (IRE)—Conspire (IRE) **J. E. Abbey**
6 **COVERT MISSION**, 5, b m Overbury (IRE)—Peg's Permission **Lost Souls Racing**
7 **DEMATRAF (IRE)**, 6, gr m Atraf—Demolition Jo **T. V. Cullen**
8 **ELLA Y ROSSA**, ch f Bertolini (USA)—Meandering Rose (USA) **Miss D L Wisbey & Mr R J Viney**
9 **GLOBAL TRAFFIC**, 4, br c Generous (IRE)—Eyes Wide Open **Mrs Folkes, Mrs Madden & Mrs Prendergast**
10 **GOODBYE CASH (IRE)**, 4, b f Danetime (IRE)—Jellybeen (IRE) **D. Healy**
11 **GRENANE (IRE)**, 5, b h Princely Heir (IRE)—Another Rainbow (IRE) **T. H. Gallienne**
12 **HOMECROFT BOY**, 4, ch g Kyllachy—Quiz Time **Mrs I. M. Folkes**
13 **INDIAN STAR (GER)**, 10, br g Sternkoenig (IRE)—Indian Night (GER) **M. D. Jones**
14 **KENSINGTON (IRE)**, 7, b g Cape Cross (IRE)—March Star (IRE) **D. J. Buckley**
15 **LYSTER (IRE)**, 9, bg Oscar (IRE)—Sea Skin **M. D. Jones**
16 **MAN OF GWENT (UAE)**, 4, b g In The Wings—Welsh Valley (USA) **K. J. Mercer**
17 **MEMPHIS MAN**, 5, b g Bertolini (USA)—Something Blue **M. D. Jones**
18 **MONDIAL JACK (FR)**, 9, ch g Apple Tree (FR)—Cackle (USA) **M. D. Jones**
19 **OBE ROYAL**, 4, b g Wizard King—Gagajulu **Mrs I. M. Folkes**
20 **PRET A PORTER (UAE)**, 4, br f Jade Robbery (USA)—Velour **J. P. Jones**
21 **RAINBOW BAY**, 5, b g Komaite (USA)—Bollin Victoria **Dusktilldawn Racing I**
22 **RONSARD (IRE)**, 6, b g Spectrum (IRE)—Touche-A-Tout (IRE) **Mrs I. M. Folkes**
23 **THE KIDDYKID (IRE)**, 8, b g Danetime (IRE)—Mezzanine **Mrs C. Massey**
24 **TIBINTA**, 4, b f Averti—Bint Albadou (IRE) **J. P. Jones**
25 **WATERLINE TWENTY (IRE)**, 5, b m Indian Danehill (IRE)—Taisho (IRE) **Waterline Racing Club**
26 **WIZBY**, 5, m Wizard King—Diamond Vanessa (IRE) **Miss D L Wisbey & Mr R J Viney**

THREE-YEAR-OLDS

27 **BAZGUY**, br ro g Josr Algarhoud (IRE)—Ewenny **Mr B. McCabe & Mr K. J. Mercer**
28 **BERE DAVIS (FR)**, gr g Verglas (IRE)—Zerelda **Mr Hilary John Sweeney**
29 **BEWDLEY**, b f Best of The Bests (IRE)—Garota De Ipanema (FR) **N. Shutts**
30 **CARRY ON CLEO**, ch f First Trump—Classy Cleo **J. E. Abbey**
31 **JUST JIMMY (IRE)**, b g Ashkalani (IRE)—Berkeley Hall **Mr Richard Edwards Mr Gwynne Williams**
32 **LADY AMBERLINI**, ch f Bertolini (USA)—Deco Lady **Miss Deborah Wisbey**
33 **LITTLE SARK (IRE)**, b c Singspiel (IRE)—Notenqueen (GER) **Mr T. Gallienne**
34 **MISTER GOLD**, ch c Lomitas—Sur Le Fil (IRE) **Mrs C. Massey**
35 **NIGHT ROBE**, b f Robellino (USA)—Camp Fire (IRE) **G. E. Amey**
36 **NO NUKES**, b g Where Or When (IRE)—Intellibet One **G. E. Amey**
37 **POLISH PRIORY (IRE)**, b f Polish Precedent (USA)—Glenstal Priory **Mr J. Ennis**
38 **VHUJON (IRE)**, b c Mujadil (USA)—Livius Lady (IRE) **N. Shutts**

TWO-YEAR-OLDS

39 B g 31/1 Forzando—Aunt Susan (Distant Relative) (8000) **Crewe & Nantwich Racing**
40 B g 29/4 Noverre (USA)—Berenica (IRE) (College Chapel) (11582) **Mr P. D. Evans**

MR P. D. EVANS—continued

41 BUCKERS BEAUTY (IRE), b f 28/4 Viking Ruler (AUS)—Kingpin Delight (Emarati (USA)) (3539) **Mr D. Buckley**
42 Gr f 10/3 Verglas (IRE)—Clochette (IRE) (Namaqualand (USA)) (18017) **Mr P. D. Evans**
43 COME ON BUCKERS (IRE), ch g 7/4 Fath (USA)—Deerussa (IRE) (Jareer (USA)) (5147) **Mr D. Buckley**
44 B f 17/4 Night Shift (USA)—Ivy Queen (IRE) (Green Desert (USA)) (16730) **Mr P. D. Evans**
45 B f 25/1 Tagula (IRE)—Luisa Demon (IRE) (Barathea (IRE)) (16730) **Mr P. D. Evans**
46 Ch g 22/2 Sandmason—Miss Margate (IRE) (Don't Forget Me) (3860) **Mr P. D. Evans**
47 Ch g 19/4 Needwood Blade—My Bonus (Cyrano de Bergerac) (12000) **Mr P. D. Evans**
48 B gr f 14/4 Xaar—Perugia (IRE) (Perugino (USA)) (15443) **Mr P. D. Evans**
49 B f 5/4 Red Ransom (USA)—Pondicherry (USA) (Sir Wimborne (USA)) **Mr P. D. Evans**
50 B f 17/4 Bahamian Bounty—Shaieef (IRE) (Shareef Dancer (USA)) (20000) **Mr P. D. Evans**
51 B f 17/4 Reel Buddy (USA)—So Discreet (Tragic Role (USA)) (5000) **Mr P. D. Evans**
52 B f 14/2 Beat Hollow—Three Greens (Niniski (USA)) **Mr P. D. Evans**

Other Owners: Mr J. E. Abbey, Mr J. Babb, Mr P.E. Davies, Mr Richard Edwards, Mr James Ennis, Mrs I. M. Folkes, Mr Don Gould, Mr David Harding, Mr M. D. Jones, Mr M. W. Lawrence, Mrs J. Madden, Mr Barry McCabe, Mr G. M. McGuinness, Mrs S. Mercer, Mr Mike Nolan, Mr Mervyn Phillips, Mrs H. F. Prendergast, Mr R. J. Viney, Mr Norman E. Webb, J. G. K. White, Mr Gwynne Williams (Powys), Mrs Margaret Williams, Miss D. L. Wisbey.

Assistant Trainer: Miss E. Folkes

Jockey (NH): Antony Evans. **Apprentice:** Richard Evans, Miss Bernadette Quinn. **Amateur:** Miss E. Folkes.

185

MR J. EWART, Langholm
Postal: **James Ewart Racing Ltd, Burn Cottage, Westerkirk, Langholm, Dumfriesshire, DG13 0NZ**
Contacts: **PHONE (01387) 370274 FAX (01387) 370720 MOBILE (07770) 937232**
E-MAIL jamesewartracing@fsmail.net WEBSITE www.jamesewartracing.co.uk

1 AMBER MAY, 5, b m Mark of Esteem (IRE)—June Brilly (IRE) **David & Nicola Leggate**
2 CLASSIC CUT, 4, b g Classic Cliche (IRE)—Leading Line **J. D. Gordon**
3 DEVIL WATER, 5, br g Maresca Sorrento (FR)—Craig Burn **N. M. L. Ewart**
4 FRONTIER BOY (IRE), 4, b g New Frontier (IRE)—Mary Bridie (IRE) **D. A. Norris**
5 LA TROUSSARDIERE (FR), 5, b m Maresca Sorrento (FR)—Sainte Lea (FR) **The Monkey Syndicate**
6 NASRHA (FR), 7, bl m Princeton (FR)—Contessina (FR) **N. M. L. Ewart**
7 OCARINA (FR), 6, b g Bulington (FR)—Alconea (FR) **Mrs H. Calder**
8 OPEN DE L'ISLE (FR), 6, b g Funny Baby (FR)—Gratiene de L'isle (FR) **The Open De L'Isle Partnership**
9 P'TIT VOUSTER (FR), 5, b g Grand Tresor (FR)—Abalary (FR) **Stobart, Ritson, Conneely, Cassie, Lever**
10 QUICK WILL (FR), 4, b g Dark Moondancer—Beautiful Lady (FR) **Mr W. H. Whitley, Mr C. Davidson**
11 RAINING HORSE (FR), 6, b g Rainbow Reef—Gabatine (FR) **KessonStobartLockhartSmithReidsHumbert**

THREE-YEAR-OLDS

12 BISHOPS HEIR, b g Turbo Speed—Linns Heir **C. Davidson, G.Reid, M.Lindley, J.Waugh**
13 MOCHA (FR), b f Mansonnien (FR)—Pocahontas (FR) **J. Ewart**
14 SI BIEN (FR), b g Solon (GER)—Secret Gold (GER) **J. Ewart**
15 TURBO ISLAND, b g Turbo Speed—Island Path (IRE)
16 ZAUREL (FR), b br f Mansonnien (FR)—Zianini (FR) **J. Ewart**

Other Owners: Mr Billy Berridge, Mr Jim Blackbale, Mr Nick Burnett, Mrs Lynn Burnett, Mr Edward Cassie, Mr B. Conneely, Mr J. D. Cotton, Mrs B. Cotton, Mr John Crichton, Mr Rob Dalgleish, Mr C. Davidson, Mr Gerry Davidson, Mr N. M. L. Ewart, Mr Arthur Humbert, Dr Colin Kesson, Mr David S. Leggate, Mrs Nicola Leggate, Mrs L. Lever, Mr M. Lindley, Mrs P. Lockhart Smith, Mr L. Marshall, Mrs Janie Reid, Mr Graeme Reid, Capt T. W. Ritson, Mrs R. Stobart, The Whistlejack Partnership, Mr J. Waugh, Mr John Waugh, Mr D. Waugh, Mr W. H. Whitley, Mr David Woodhouse.

Assistant Trainer: Mr I. Jardine

Jockey (NH): T. Dreaper. **Conditional:** G. Berridge.

186

MR R. A. FAHEY, Malton
Postal: RF Racing Ltd, Mews House, Musley Bank, Malton, North Yorkshire, YO17 6TD
Contacts: PHONE (01653) 698915 FAX (01653) 699735 MOBILE (07713) 478079
E-MAIL enquiries@richardfahey.com WEBSITE www.richardfahey.com

1 AMANDA CARTER, 4, b f Tobougg (IRE)—Al Guswa **Mrs J. M. MacPherson**
2 ANNA PAVLOVA, 5, b m Danehill Dancer (IRE)—Wheeler's Wonder (IRE) **Galaxy Racing**

MR R. A. FAHEY—continued

3 **BENANDONNER (USA)**, 5, ch g Giant's Causeway (USA)—Cape Verdi (IRE) **J. C. Parsons & Sinead Parsons**
4 **BILLY DANE (IRE)**, 4, b g Fayruz—Lomalou (IRE) **Mr K. Lee & Mr I. Davies**
5 **BO MCGINTY (IRE)**, 7, ch g Fayruz—Georges Park Lady (IRE) **Paddy McGinty & Bo Turnbull**
6 **BOLODENKA (IRE)**, 6, b g Soviet Star (USA)—My-Lorraine (IRE) **Mr Enda Hunston**
7 **BOLTON HALL (IRE)**, 6, b g Imperial Ballet (IRE)—Muneera (USA) **J. J. Staunton**
8 **BOPPYS PRIDE**, 5, ch h Clan of Roses—Joara (FR) **Mrs S. Bond**
9 **CHARLIE TOKYO (IRE)**, 5, b g Trans Island—Ellistown Lady (IRE) **Mr S. W. S. Yu**
10 **COLLETTE'S CHOICE**, 5, b m Royal Applause—Brilliance **P. D. Smith Holdings Ltd**
11 **COMMANDER HAWK**, 4, b g Indian Lodge (IRE)—Karisal (IRE) **J. E. M. Hawkins Ltd**
12 **DANCING LYRA**, 7, b g Alzao (USA)—Badaayer (USA) **Aidan J Ryan Racing**
13 **DARK CHARM (FR)**, 9, b g Anabaa (USA)—Wardara **R. A. Fahey**
14 **DENVER GOLD**, 5, b g Terimon—Jindabyne **J. D. Clark & Partners I**
15 **ELUSIVE WARRIOR (USA)**, 5, b g Elusive Quality (USA)—
                                       Love To Fight (CAN) **Northumbria Leisure Ltd & Mr B. Morton**
16 **FISHFORCOMPLIMENTS**, 4, b c Royal Applause—Flyfisher (USA) **Mr Mel Roberts & Ms Nicola Meese**
17 **FLYING BANTAM (IRE)**, 7, b g Fayruz—Natural Pearl **The Matthewman Partnership**
18 **FLYING CLARETS (IRE)**, 5, b m Titus Livius (FR)—Sheryl Lynn **The Matthewman Partnership**
19 **FONTHILL ROAD (IRE)**, 8, ch g Royal Abjar (USA)—Hannah Huxtable (IRE) **Mrs U. Towell**
20 **FORTUNATE ISLE (USA)**, 6, ch g Swain (USA)—Isla Del Rey (USA) **The First Team**
21 **FREELOADER (IRE)**, 8, b g Revoque (IRE)—Indian Sand **Mr Enda Hunston**
22 **GAP PRINCESS (IRE)**, 4, b f Noverre (USA)—Safe Care (IRE) **Dr W. D. Ashworth**
23 **GEORGE'S FLYER (IRE)**, 5, b g Daggers Drawn (USA)—Winged Victory (IRE) **P. D. Smith Holdings Ltd**
24 **GREEN PARK (IRE)**, 5, b g Shinko Forest (IRE)—Danccini (IRE) **G. A. Fixings Ltd**
25 **GREENWICH MEANTIME**, 8, b g Royal Academy (USA)—
                                       Shirley Valentine **K Lee D Barlow B Crumbley & L Rutherford**
26 **HALLA SAN**, 6, b g Halling (USA)—St Radegund **Mrs C. E. Reynard**
27 **HANDSOME FALCON**, 4, b g Kyllachy—Bonne Etoile **Bernard Shaw**
28 **INSTRUCTOR**, 7, ch g Groom Dancer (USA)—Doctor's Glory (USA) **Yorkshire Racing Club Owners Group 1990**
29 **KINDKINTYRE (IRE)**, 4, b g Mull of Kintyre (USA)—Sweet Nature (IRE) **G. J. Paver**
30 **KINGS COLLEGE BOY**, 8, b g College Chapel—The Kings Daughter **The Cosmic Cases**
31 **KNOT IN WOOD (IRE)**, 6, b g Shinko Forest—Notley Park **Rhodes, Kenyon & Gill**
32 **LITTLE JIMBOB**, 7, b g Desert Story (IRE)—Artistic Licence **Dale Scaffolding Co Ltd**
33 **MEGALO MANIAC**, 5, b g Efisio—Sharanella **A. Long**
34 **MISS RESPECT**, 4, b f Mark of Esteem (IRE)—Lady Zonda **Mrs E. A. Murray**
35 **MISSUS MOLLY BROWN**, 4, b f Mind Games—Prim N Proper **J. E. M. Hawkins Ltd**
36 **MONET'S LADY (IRE)**, 4, gr f Daylami (USA)—Wide Range (IRE) **Mrs U. Towell**
37 **MUTAWAFFER**, 7, b g Marju (IRE)—Absaar (USA) **P. D. Smith Holdings Ltd**
38 **MY SARA**, 4, b f Mujahid (USA)—Ancestry **Mrs D. M. Swinburn**
39 **NEVER PANIC (IRE)**, 4, ch f Indian Lodge (IRE)—Lucky Lilly (IRE) **L. Mulryan**
40 **OCHRE (IRE)**, 4, br f Diktat—Cox Orange (USA) **D. Brennan**
41 **ORANMORE CASTLE (IRE)**, 6, b g Giant's Causeway (USA)—Twice The Ease **The Knavesmire Alliance**
42 **PAINTED SKY**, 5, ch g Rainbow Quest (USA)—Emplane (USA) **J P M Syndicate**
43 **PERUVIAN PRINCE (USA)**, 6, b g Silver Hawk (USA)—Inca Dove (USA) **R. G. Leatham**
44 **PHILHARMONIC**, 7, b g Victory Note (USA)—Lambast **R. Cowie**
45 **PLAYTOTHEAUDIENCE**, 5, b g Royal Applause—Flyfisher (USA) **Mr David M. Knaggs & Mel Roberts**
46 **PRINCESS COCOA (IRE)**, 5, b m Desert Sun—Daily Double (FR) **Mr P. Ashton**
47 **RAINBOW FOX**, 4, b g Foxhound (USA)—Bollin Victoria **Kevin Lee & David Barlow**
48 **SADLER'S KINGDOM (IRE)**, 4, b c Sadler's Wells (USA)—Artful Pleasure (USA) **J. J. Staunton**
49 **SEA SALT**, 5, b g Titus Livius (FR)—Carati **J. H. Tattersall**
50 **SHAYDREAMBELIEVER**, 5, ch g Daggers Drawn (USA)—Aunt Sadie **The Matthewman Partnership**
51 **SIN CITY**, 5, b g Sinndar (IRE)—Turn of A Century **M. A. Leatham**
52 **SKI JUMP (USA)**, 8, gr g El Prado (IRE)—Skiable (IRE) **P. D. Smith Holdings Ltd**
53 **SMART INSTINCT (USA)**, 4, ch g Smart Strike (CAN)—Smile n Molly (USA) **David & Jackie Knaggs**
54 **SMOOTHLY DOES IT**, 7, b g Efisio—Exotic Forest **The Ipso Facto Syndicate**
55 **ST SAVARIN (FR)**, 7, ch g Highest Honor (FR)—Sacara (GER) **J. H. Tattersall**
56 **STEELCUT**, 8, b g Iron Mask (USA)—Apple Sauce **A. Rhodes Haulage & Mr P. Timmins**
57 **STONECRABSTOMORROW (IRE)**, 5, b g Fasliyev (USA)—Tordasia (USA) **Miss S. K. Bowles**
58 **STRATHMORE (IRE)**, 4, gr g Fath (USA)—In The Highlands **J. Gill**
59 **SUMI GIRL (IRE)**, 4, b f Tiger Hill (IRE)—Allonia (GER) **A. J. Ryan**
60 **SUNNYSIDE TOM (IRE)**, 4, b g Danetime (IRE)—So Kind **The Sunnyside Racing Partnership**
61 **SUPERIOR STAR**, 5, b g Superior Premium—Lindfield Belle (IRE) **J. C. Parsons**
62 **SWINBROOK (USA)**, 7, ch g Stravinsky (USA)—Dance Diane (USA) **R. A. Fahey**
63 **TAGULA SUNRISE (IRE)**, 6, ch m Tagula (IRE)—Lady From Limerick (IRE) **Mr David M. Knaggs & Mel Roberts**
64 **TROJAN FLIGHT**, 7, ch g Hector Protector (USA)—Fairywings **T. J. O'Gram**
65 **TRULY FRUITFUL (IRE)**, 5, ch g Fruits of Love (USA)—Truly Flattering **A. J. Ryan**
66 **TUATARA BAY (IRE)**, 8, b g Luso—Timely Reminder (IRE) **Mrs P A Morrison & Mr P S Cresswell**

MR R. A. FAHEY—continued

67 **UTMOST RESPECT,** 4, b g Danetime (IRE)—Utmost (IRE) **The Rumpole Partnership**
68 **VALLEY OF THE MOON (IRE),** 4, b f Monashee Mountain (USA)—Unaria **T.Elsey,S.A.Elsey,R.Mustill,J.Tunstall**
69 **WOQOODD,** 4, b g Royal Applause—Intervene **G. Houghton**
70 **WYATT EARP (IRE),** 7, b g Piccolo—Tribal Lady **Los Bandidos Racing**

THREE-YEAR-OLDS

71 **ANGLE OF ATTACK (IRE),** b g Acclamation—Travel Spot Girl **E. Tynan**
72 **ANNALIESSE (IRE),** ch f Rock of Gibraltar (IRE)—Oh So Well (IRE) **Dr A. J. F. Gillespie**
73 **CAT WHISTLE,** b f Dansili—Mighty Flyer (IRE) **R. A. Fahey**
74 **CUNNING CLARETS (IRE),** ch g Trans Island—Ellistown Lady (IRE) **The Matthewman One Partnership**
75 **DARK TARA,** br f Diktat—Karisal (IRE) **J. E. M. Hawkins Ltd**
76 **DIAMOND LASS (IRE),** b f Rock of Gibraltar (IRE)—Keralba (USA) **Mr Mel Roberts & Ms Nicola Meese**
77 **DUNMORE DODGER (IRE),** b c Tagula (IRE)—Decrescendo (IRE) **J. A. Rattigan**
78 **FANTASTIC LASS,** b f Fantastic Light (USA)—Shaanara (IRE) **Mr Mel Roberts & Ms Nicola Meese**
79 **FUJIN DANCER (FR),** ch c Storming Home—Badaayer (USA) **Aidan J Ryan Racing**
80 **GALA CASINO STAR (IRE),** ch c Dr Fong (USA)—Abir **The Friar Tuck Racing Club**
81 **GRACEFUL DESCENT (FR),** b f Hawk Wing (USA)—Itab (USA) **Miss S. K. Bowles**
82 **GUNNER FLY (IRE),** b c Noverre (USA)—Anne-Lise **The Matthewman One Partnership**
83 **HARRISON GEORGE (IRE),** b c Danetime (IRE)—Dry Lightning **P. D. Smith Holdings Ltd**
84 **HURSTPIERPOINT (IRE),** b f Night Shift (USA)—Double Gamble **Miss S. K. Bowles**
85 **LAURELDEAN BREEZE (USA),** ch f Good And Tough (USA)—Cozwhy (USA) **D. Brennan**
86 **LECANVEY,** b c Where Or When (IRE)—Catch The Flame (USA) **J. J. Staunton**
87 **MAAHE (IRE),** b f Namid—Almond Flower (IRE) **Miss S. K. Bowles**
88 **MARIE CAMARGO,** b f Kyllachy—Wheeler's Wonder (IRE) **Galaxy Racing**
89 **MISTER HARDY,** b c Kyllachy—Balladonia **The Cosmic Cases**
90 **PRINCESS ALIUSKA,** b f Domedriver (IRE)—Aliuska (IRE) **Mr R. M. Jeffs, Mr J. Potter & Mr W. Walker**
91 **PRINCESS MARIA (USA),** b f Giant's Causeway (USA)—Passive Action (USA) **Mr Enda Hunston**
92 **RED DELIGHT (IRE),** b f Redback—Lindas Delight **The Dandy Dons Partnership**
93 **RESOUNDING GLORY (USA),** b c Honour And Glory (USA)—Resounding Grace (USA) **Mr M. Wynne**
94 **ROSE SIOG,** ch f Bahamian Bounty—Madame Sisu **The Mick Sweeney Syndicate**
95 **ROSSINI'S DANCER,** b c Rossini (USA)—Bint Alhabib **Lets Go Racing 1**
96 **SCIENTIFIC,** b g Fraam—Lady Butler (IRE) **Galaxy Racing**
97 **SMARTERTHANUTHINK (USA),** b c Smart Strike (CAN)—Dance Gaily (USA) **David & Jackie Knaggs**
98 **STATESIDE (CAN),** b f El Corredor (USA)—Double Trick (USA) **P. Timmins**
99 **SWEET MIND,** b f Mind Games—Cape Charlotte **I. T. S. Racing**
100 **TRIP THE LIGHT,** b g Fantastic Light (USA)—Jumaireyah **The Matthewman One Partnership**

Other Owners: A. Rhodes Haulage Ltd, Dr W. D. Ashworth, Mr J. R. Atkins, Mr David Barlow, Mr Jim Blair, Mr Stuart Brown, Mr I. T. Buchanan, Mr S. Burnley, Mr John D. Clark, Mrs Eileen Collier, Mr Paul James Colwood, Mr Richard Connaughton, Mr R. Cowie, Mr P. S. Cresswell, Mr B. A. Crumbley, Mr I. L. Davies, Mr Steve Durkin, Mr Samuel Ellis, Mr Terence Elsey, Mrs Sheila Elsey, Mr R. A. Fahey, Mr John Finegan, Miss C. Foster, Mr Jonathan Gill, Mr J. J. Gilmartin, Mr Brett T. Graham, Mr I. Hartley, Mr R. M. Jeffs, Mr Philip J. Jones, Mrs M. W. Kenyon, Mr D. M. Knaggs, Mrs Jackie Knaggs, Mr Mark A. Leatham, Mr G. H. Leatham, Mr K. Lee, Mr Eric Lumley, Mr P. McGinty, Mr P. McGrane, Ms Nicola Meese, Mrs P. A. Morrison, Mr Brian Morton, Mr Richard Mustill, Northumbria Leisure Ltd, Mr E. O'Sullivan, Mr J. C. Parsons, Mr J. Potter, Mr Arthur Rhodes, Mr Mel Roberts, Mr Mark S. Russell, Mr L. M. Rutherford, Mr Aidan J. Ryan, Mr M. A. Scaife, Mr A. W. Sheret, Mr Mark Smith, Mr J. J. Staunton, Mr M. Sweeney, Mrs Doreen M. Swinburn, Mr A. Tattersall, Mr T. Threlfall, Mr P. Timmins, Mr Jim Tunstall, Mr Bo Turnbull, Mr L. Vettraino, Mr S. L. Walker, Mr G. H. M. Walker, Mr Bill Walker, Mr M. Wassall, Mrs E. A. Webster, Mr John Wicks, Yorkshire Racing Club Owners Group 1990, Mr H. Young.

Assistant Trainer: Robin O'Ryan

Jockey (flat): T. Hamilton, P. Hanagan. **Apprentice:** Barry McHugh, Jamie Moriarty, James Rogers.
Amateur: Miss V. Tunnicliffe.

---

187 **MR C. W. FAIRHURST, Middleham**
Postal: Glasgow House, Middleham, Leyburn, North Yorkshire, DL8 4QG
Contacts: **PHONE/FAX** (01969) 622039 **MOBILE** (07889) 410840
E-MAIL cfairhurst@tiscali.co.uk **WEBSITE** www.chrisfairhurstracing.com

1 **BURNT OAK (UAE),** 6, b g Timber Country (USA)—Anaam **Glasgow House Racing Syndicate**
2 **CHA CHA CHA DANCER,** 8, ch g Groom Dancer (USA)—Amber Fizz (USA) **Scotnorth Racing Ltd**
3 **FALIMAR,** 4, b f Fasliyev (USA)—Mar Blue (FR) **J. G. Gibb**
4 **FIRESTORM (IRE),** 4, b g Celtic Swing—National Ballet **Mrs C. Arnold**
5 **LADY ANNE NEVILL,** 4, b f Nomadic Way (USA)—Prudent Pet **Mrs C. Arnold**

MR C. W. FAIRHURST—continued

6 **LOVES LIFE,** 4, b f Pursuit of Love—Reine de Thebes (FR) **G. H. & S. Leggott**
7 **PASSION FRUIT,** 7, b m Pursuit of Love—Reine de Thebes (FR) **G. H. & S. Leggott**
8 **PRINCESS SHIRL,** 4, b f Shahrastani (USA)—Shirl **Roseland Racing Partnership**
9 **THE THRIFTY BEAR,** 5, ch g Rambling Bear—Prudent Pet **Mrs C. Arnold**
10 **YORKE'S FOLLY (USA),** 7, b m Stravinsky (USA)—Tommelise (USA) **Mrs A. M. Leggett**

THREE-YEAR-OLDS

11 **ONE TOU MANY,** b f Tobougg (IRE)—Reine de Thebes (FR) **G. H. & S. Leggott**
12 **PEQUENO DINERO (IRE),** b f Iron Mask (USA)—Mrs Kanning **The PQD Partnership**
13 **RED RIVER BOY,** ch g Bahamian Bounty—Riviere Rouge **J. G. Gibb**

Other Owners: Mrs B. Boocock, Mrs S. France, Mr W. Hill, North Cheshire Trading & Storage Ltd.

---

188   MR J. R. FANSHAWE, Newmarket

Postal: **Pegasus Stables, Snailwell Road, Newmarket, Suffolk, CB8 7DJ**
Contacts: **PHONE (01638) 664525/660153 FAX (01638) 664523**
E-MAIL james@jamesfanshawe.com

1 **APHORISM,** 5, b m Halling (USA)—Applecross **Dr C. M. H. Wills**
2 **ARTIMINO,** 4, b c Medicean—Palatial **Cheveley Park Stud Limited**
3 **ATHENIAN WAY (IRE),** 4, b f Barathea (IRE)—Grecian Bride (IRE) **Mrs C. C. Regalado-Gonzalez**
4 **BRIGYDON (IRE),** 5, b g Fasliyev (USA)—Creme Caramel **G. S. C. Gibson**
5 **BUSTER HYVONEN (IRE),** 6, b g Dansili—Serotina (IRE) **G. S. C. Gibson**
6 **CESARE,** 7, b g Machiavellian (USA)—Tromond **Cheveley Park Stud Limited**
7 **CONKERING (USA),** 5, ch g Horse Chestnut (SAF)—Nunbridled (USA) **J. P. McManus**
8 **DART,** 4, br f Diktat—Eilean Shona **Dr C. M. H. Wills**
9 **DAWNHILL (GER),** 4, b g Tiger Hill (IRE)—Dateline (GER) **Mrs V. M. Shelton**
10 **FONDLED,** 4, b f Selkirk (USA)—Embraced **Cheveley Park Stud Limited**
11 **KINGSCAPE (IRE),** 5, br g King Charlemagne (USA)—Cape Clear **J. P. McManus**
12 **LIMBO KING,** 4, b g Barathea (IRE)—Ermine (IRE) **N. Brunskill**
13 **NUTKIN,** 4, gr f Act One—Cashew **Lord Vestey**
14 **OMMADAWN (IRE),** 4, b f Montjeu (IRE)—Lyphard's Delta **Mr & Mrs R. Scott**
15 **RATIO,** 10, ch g Pivotal—Owdbetts (IRE) **Mrs John Davall & Mr R. W. Armstrong**
16 **REBALLO (IRE),** 5, b g King's Best (USA)—Lyrical Dance (USA) **Clipper Group Holdings Ltd**
17 **REVEILLEZ,** 9, gr g First Trump—Amalancher (USA) **J. P. McManus**
18 **ROYAL ENCORE,** 4, b f Royal Applause—Footlight Fantasy **Helena Springfield Ltd**
19 **ROYAL FANTASY (IRE),** 5, b br m King's Best (USA)—Dreams **Nigel & Carolyn Elwes**
20 **SCORCHED (IRE),** 4, ch f Desert Sun—Kappa Signey (USA) **Scorched Partnership**
21 **SHELA HOUSE,** 4, ch g Selkirk (USA)—Villa Carlotta **J. H. Richmond-Watson**
22 **SIGN OF THE CROSS,** 4, b g Mark of Esteem (IRE)—Thea **T. R. G. Vestey**
23 **SISTER ACT,** 4, b f Marju (IRE)—Kalinka (IRE) **Elite Racing Club**
24 **SONG OF SONGS,** 6, b g Singspiel (IRE)—Thea (USA) **J. P. McManus**
25 **SPRING JIM,** 7, br g First Trump—Spring Sixpence **Andrew & Julia Turner**
26 **WYETH,** 4, ch g Grand Lodge (USA)—Bordighera (USA) **Lael Stable**
27 **ZIDANE,** 6, b g Danzero (AUS)—Juliet Bravo **Jan & Peter Hopper**

THREE-YEAR-OLDS

28 Ch f Galileo (IRE)—Alikhlas **Miss A. H. Marshall**
29 **ALSACE LORRAINE (IRE),** b f Giant's Causeway (USA)—Mer de Corail (IRE) **Merry Fox Stud Limited**
30 **ALVEE (IRE),** br f Key of Luck (USA)—Alleluia **Merry Fox Stud Limited**
31 **BIANCA CAPELLO,** b f Medicean—Totom **C. T. Van Hoorn & Mrs J. Fanshawe**
32 **BRIGADIER MARK (IRE),** b g Marju (IRE)—Goldilocks (IRE) **Miss R. Galligan**
33 **BROKEN MOON,** gr f Galileo (IRE)—Bedazzling (IRE) **B. J. McAllister**
34 **CASHPOINT,** b g Fantastic Light (USA)—Cashew **Lady Vestey**
35 **DAN CHILLINGWORTH (IRE),** b c Indian Ridge—Shizao (IRE) **R. C. Thompson**
36 **DEAR WILL,** br g Mark of Esteem (IRE)—Sweet Wilhelmina **C. T. Van Hoorn**
37 **DOLCETTO (IRE),** b f Danehill Dancer (IRE)—Rutledge (IRE) **Mrs L. H. Field**
38 **FALCOLNRY (IRE),** b f Hawk Wing (USA)—Fear And Greed (IRE) **Mr & Mrs Duncan Davidson**
39 **FINMORE QUEEN (USA),** ch f Grand Slam (USA)—Slew City Slicker (USA) **Mrs C. C. Regalado-Gonzalez**
40 **FLAM,** b f Singspiel—Delauncy **Wood Hall Stud Limited**
41 **FLYING FREE,** b g Bertolini (USA)—Fly Like The Wind **Mr G. B. Norman & Mr C. B. Norman**
42 **FOREIGN AGENT (USA),** b br c Deputy Minister (CAN)—Wandering Star (USA) **J. Allen**
43 **GAME PARK (USA),** ch g Elusive Quality (USA)—
Carefree Cheetah (USA) **Mrs Andrew Crawshaw & Mr Duncan Davidson**

MR J. R. FANSHAWE—continued

44 **HARALD BLUETOOTH (IRE),** b c Danetime (IRE)—Goldthroat (IRE) **Mr & Mrs Duncan Davidson**
45 **HEPBURN BELL (IRE),** ch f Intikhab (USA)—Borsalino (USA) **Mr & Mrs Duncan Davidson**
46 **HOLLY CLEUGH,** ch f Compton Place—True Precision **Mr & Mrs Duncan Davidson**
47 **INDY DRIVER,** ch c Domedriver (IRE)—Condoleezza (USA) **Mrs C. C. Regalado-Gonzalez**
48 **INTERCHANGE (IRE),** b f Montjeu (IRE)—Key Change (IRE) **Lady Clague**
49 **ISABELLA'S FANCY,** br f Captain Rio—Princess of Spain **Mrs Nicholas Kairis**
50 **LA SARRAZINE (FR),** b f Medicean—Fulcrum **Mr & Mrs Duncan Davidson**
51 **LADY ROSE ANNE (IRE),** b f Red Ransom—Surval **Miss R. Galligan**
52 Gr ro f Quiet American (USA)—Laiyl (IRE) **Miss A. H. Marshall**
53 **LILBURN (IRE),** b g Statue of Liberty (USA)—Vahine (USA) **Mr & Mrs Duncan Davidson**
54 B g Fantastic Light (USA)—Littlepacepaddocks (IRE) **Mrs Joan Keaney**
55 **LONG DISTANCE (FR),** b br g Storming Home—Lovers Luck (IRE) **Mr Simon Gibson**
56 **MARGALIT,** b f Rainbow Quest (USA)—Darmagi (IRE) **Wood Hall Stud Limited**
57 **OPERA DE LUNA,** ch f Singspiel (IRE)—Villa Carlotta **J. H. Richmond-Watson**
58 **ORLANDO'S TALE (USA),** ch c Tale of The Cat (USA)—Tell Seattle (USA) **Mr & Mrs Duncan Davidson**
59 **PEAS IN A POD,** ch g Kyllachy—Entwine **A. J. Perkins**
60 **PEDIMENT,** b f Desert Prince (IRE)—White Palace **Cheveley Park Stud Limited**
61 **PREVAILING WIND,** b c Gone West (USA)—Royal Alchemist (USA) **Mr & Mrs Duncan Davidson**
62 **QUI MOI (CAN),** b br f Swain (IRE)—Qui Bid (USA) **Mrs C. C. Regalado - Gonzalez**
63 **RED LILY (IRE),** b f Red Ransom (USA)—Panna **The Earl Of Halifax**
64 **ROYAL BLOOM (IRE),** b f Royal Applause—Bethesda **Mrs V. M. Shelton**
65 **SECRET DANCER (IRE),** b g Sadler's Wells—Discreet Brief (IRE) **Mr & Mrs Duncan Davidson**
66 **SIR GERRY (USA),** ch c Carson City (USA)—Incredulous (FR) **Mrs Gerry Galligan**
67 **SPACIOUS,** b f Nayef (USA)—Palatial **Cheveley Park Stud Limited**
68 **SPHERE (IRE),** b f Daylami (IRE)—Apple Town **Dr C. M. H. Wills**
69 **STREET STAR (USA),** b f Street Cry (IRE)—Domludge (USA) **Mrs C. C. Regalado-Gonzalez**
70 **TAKEN (IRE),** b g Red Ransom (USA)—Heart's Harmony **Mrs D. M. Haynes**
71 **TRENCHANT,** b g Medicean—Tromond **Cheveley Park Stud Limited**
72 **VIENNA AFFAIR,** b f Red Ransom (USA)—Wiener Wald (USA) **The Eclipse Partnership**
73 **WATER VIOLET,** b f Dubai Destination (USA)—Spring **The Earl Of Halifax**
74 **YETHOLM (USA),** gr ro c Dynaformer (USA)—Gypsy (USA) **Mr & Mrs Duncan Davidson**

TWO-YEAR-OLDS

75 **ANNA IVANOVNA,** ch f 31/1 Selkirk (USA)—Ice Palace (Polar Falcon (USA)) **Cheveley Park Stud Limited**
76 **CACTUS CURTSEY,** b f 3/3 Royal Applause—Prairie Flower (IRE) (Zieten (USA)) **Cheveley Park Stud Limited**
77 **CLUNY,** b f 19/2 Celtic Swing—Muschana (Deploy) **Nigel & Carolyn Elwes**
78 **CONGENIAL,** b f 16/2 Kyllachy—Peace (Sadler's Wells (USA)) **Cheveley Park Stud Limited**
79 **DOUBLE DAD (IRE),** b c 19/2 Bahamian Bounty—Machudi (Bluebird (USA)) (32000) **A. J. Perkins**
80 **ELIZA DOOLITTLE,** b f 16/5 Royal Applause—
                    Green Supreme (Primo Dominie) (140000) **Mrs C. C. Regalado-Gonzalez**
81 **FLAME OF HESTIA (IRE),** ch f 14/5 Giant's Causeway (USA)—
                    Ellen (IRE) (Machiavellian (USA)) (1000000) **Miss A. Condon**
82 **FLANNEL (IRE),** gr c 20/3 Clodovil (IRE)—La Captive (IRE) (Selkirk (USA)) (65000) **C. T. Van Hoorn**
83 **FRANCIS WALSINGHAM (IRE),** b c 27/3 Invincible Spirit (IRE)—
                    Web of Intrigue (Machiavellian (USA)) **Mr & Mrs Duncan Davidson**
84 Ch c 21/4 Dr Fong (USA)—Genoa (Zafonic (USA)) (35000) **Axom (XV)**
85 **INCENDO,** ch c 27/3 King's Best (USA)—Kindle (Selkirk (USA)) (30000) **Andrew & Julia Turner**
86 **KATYA KABANOVA,** b f 24/1 Sadler's Wells (USA)—Kiftsgate Rose (FR) (Nashwan (USA)) **Miss K. Rausing**
87 **KNOTGARDEN (IRE),** b f 7/5 Dr Fong (USA)—Eilean Shona (Suave Dancer (USA)) **Dr C. M. H. Wills**
88 **LADY TRISH,** b f 28/2 Red Ransom (USA)—Artifice (Green Desert (USA)) (70000) **Mrs T. Galligan**
89 **MARGARITA (IRE),** b f 5/5 Marju (IRE)—Kalinka (IRE) (Soviet Star (USA)) **Elite Racing Club**
90 **PEACE CORPS,** ch c 27/4 Medicean—Tromond (Lomond (USA)) **Cheveley Park Stud Limited**
91 **PRIMAEVAL,** ch c 21/4 Pivotal—Langoustine (AUS) (Danehill (USA)) **Lord Vestey**
92 **PROFUSE,** b f 22/4 Falbrav (IRE)—Abundant (Zafonic (USA)) **Cheveley Park Stud Limited**
93 **RED SALVIA,** b f 16/2 Selkirk (USA)—Red Camellia (Polar Falcon (USA)) **Cheveley Park Stud Limited**
94 **ROTUNDA,** b f 21/4 Pivotal—Palatial (Green Desert (USA)) **Cheveley Park Stud Limited**
95 **SITWELL,** b c 18/1 Dr Fong (USA)—
                    First Fantasy (Be My Chief (USA)) (22000) **Rupert Hambro & Nigel & Carolyn Elwes**
96 **SIXTY SIX SHIRTS (IRE),** b c 7/5 Mujadil (USA)—
                    Persian Sally (IRE) (Persian Bold) (50000) **Mrs Hannele Morgan**
97 **STYLISH DREAM (USA),** b br f 16/1 Elusive Quality (USA)—
                    Stylelistick (Storm Cat (USA)) (364431) **F. Nass**
98 B f 27/2 Marju (IRE)—Szabo (IRE) (Anabaa (USA)) (150000) **Lael Stable**
99 **XPRESSO,** b f 4/2 Xaar—Morning After (Emperor Jones (USA)) **The Nightcaps**

MR J. R. FANSHAWE—continued

Other Owners: R. W. Armstrong, G. A. Bathurst Norman, C. C. Bathurst Norman, Mrs A. J. Brudenell, Mrs T. Brudenell, Mrs Andrew Crawshaw, Mr D. Davidson, Mrs D. Davidson, D. W. Dennis, Mrs H. S. Ellingsen, Mr Nigel Elwes, Mrs Carolyn Elwes, Mrs J. M. J. Fanshawe, N. J. Forman Hardy, Mrs Elizabeth Grundy, R. N. Hambro, Mr Tony Hill, Mrs Jan Hopper, Mr Peter Hopper, Mr R. Jackson, Mrs G. S. Jackson, Mr Michael Kerr-Dineen, D. M. Kerr, Mr Donald M. Kerr, M. Kerr-Dineen, Mrs Pamela Morrell, Miss M. Noden, Mr Robert Scott, Mrs P. M. Scott, Mrs Gilly Thompson, A. R. Turner, Mrs J. J. Turner, M. Weinfeld, Mrs Sue Willson.

Assistant Trainer: Emma Candy

---

189 **MR R. A. FARRANT, Upper Lambourn**
Postal: Frenchmans Stables, Upper Lambourn, Hungerford, Berkshire, RG17 8QT
Contacts: PHONE (01488) 72736 FAX (01488) 670357 MOBILE (07771) 682045

1 AZIONE, 5, b m Exit To Nowhere (USA)—Little Feat **Friends of Saunton Sands**
2 COAST OF MALABAR (IRE), 6, b g Luso—Sparky Mary (IRE) **C. B. S.**
3 EDGE END, 4, ch g Bold Edge—Rag Time Belle **R. H. Hughes**
4 FULL VICTORY (IRE), 6, b g Imperial Ballet (IRE)—Full Traceability (IRE) **Friends of Saunton Sands**
5 4, B g Rashar (USA)—Hill Supreme (IRE) **Syndicate**
6 ROYAL FLYER (IRE), 4, b g Winged Love (IRE)—Saronicos King (IRE) **Winged Love Syndicate**
7 SWETE DEVA, 8, b g El Conquistador—Swete Fudge **Mrs A. Curtis**
8 WEST END FINAL, 5, b g Kayf Tara—Fine Fettle **The Fine Gild Racing Partnership**

THREE-YEAR-OLDS

9 Ch f Compton Place—Fine Fettle **The Fine Line Racing Partnership**
10 LITTLE PETE (IRE), ch g City On A Hill (USA)—Full Traceability (IRE) **P. Brend**

Other Owners: Mr P. A. Brend, Mr R. A. Farrant, Mr G. P. Golbey, Dr L. A. Hatter, P. Hibbard, Mr A. J. Kingdon.

---

190 **MS L. M. FEATHERSTONE, Ashbourne**
Postal: Closes Farm, Atlow, Ashbourne, Derbyshire, DE6 1PZ
Contacts: PHONE (01335) 372108 MOBILE (07977) 930801

1 4, Ch c And Beyond (IRE)—Argostoli
2 CARSINGTON, 4, ch f And Beyond (IRE)—Nutmeg Point **J. D. Roundtree**
3 COMMANDER WISH, 5, ch g Arkadian Hero (USA)—Flighty Dancer **J. D. Roundtree & E. A. Buckley**
4 JENNY SOBA, 5, b m Observatory (USA)—Majalis **J. D. Roundtree**
5 MOONLIGHT FANTASY (IRE), 5, b g Night Shift (USA)—County Girl (IRE) **J. D. Roundtree**
6 ONEFOURSEVEN, 15, b g Jumbo Hirt (USA)—Dominance **J. D. Roundtree**
7 RESTART (IRE), 7, b g Revoque (IRE)—Stargard **J. D. Roundtree**
8 ROMAN CANDLE (IRE), 12, b g Sabrehill (USA)—Penny Banger (IRE) **Ms L. M. Featherstone**
9 SNOWBERRY HILL (USA), 5, b g Woodman (USA)—Class Skipper (USA) **J. D. Roundtree**

THREE-YEAR-OLDS

10 Ch g And Beyond (IRE)—Argostoli
11 Ch f First Trump—Flighty Dancer

TWO-YEAR-OLDS

12 B f 21/2 And Beyond (IRE)—Richenda (Mister Baileys)
13 Br c 25/2 And Beyond (IRE)—Silent Angel (Petong)

Other Owners: Mr E. A. Buckley, P. A. Green, Heart Of England Racing, The Hon Cherry King, Reg Parnham, Mr J. Roundtree.

Assistant Trainer: J. P. Featherstone

Jockey (flat): N. Chalmers, T. G. McLaughlin. **Jockey (NH):** Liam Treadwell. **Amateur:** Mr J. P. Featherstone.

191 MISS J. D. FEILDEN, Newmarket
Postal: **Harraton Stud, Laceys Lane, Exning, Newmarket, Suffolk, CB8 7HW**
Contacts: **PHONE (01638) 577470 FAX (01638) 578628 MOBILE (07974) 817694**
E-MAIL hoofbeatstours@aol.com

1 **BAARRIJ**, 4, ch f Tobougg (IRE)—Bint Albaadiya (USA) **G. Wilson**
2 **BAVARICA**, 6, b m Danisli—Blue Gentian (USA) **Hoofbeats Racing Club**
3 **CAPTAIN SMOOTHY**, 8, b g Charmer—The Lady Captain
4 **DANCEWITHTHESTARS (USA)**, 4, b f Cryptoclearance (USA)—Sir Harry's Waltz (IRE) **Miss J. D. Feilden**
5 **NEW PERK (IRE)**, 10, b g Executive Perk—New Chello (IRE) **A. J. White**
6 **NIGHT ORBIT**, 4, b c Observatory (USA)—Dansara
7 **POP MUSIC (IRE)**, 5, b g Tagula (IRE)—Easy Pop (IRE) **Mr M. B. Jenner**
8 **RAPID CITY**, 5, b g Danisli—West Dakota (USA)
9 **RUFFIE (IRE)**, 5, b m Medicean—Darling Lover (USA)
10 **SAND REPEAL (IRE)**, 6, b g Revoque (IRE)—Columbian Sand (IRE) **The Sultans of Speed**
11 **SEATTLE SPY (USA)**, 5, b br g Catienus (USA)—Theyrplayinoursong (USA) **G. Wilson**

THREE-YEAR-OLDS
12 **BUSHY DELL (IRE)**, br f King Charlemagne (USA)—Nisibis **R. J. Creese**
13 **DIRECTOR'S CHAIR**, b c Catcher In The Rye (IRE)—Capegulch (USA) **Ocean Trailers Ltd**
14 Ch c Tumbleweed Ridge—Genteel (IRE)
15 **KING COLUMBO (IRE)**, ch c King Charlemagne (USA)—Columbian Sand (IRE) **Columbian Kings**
16 **MR FANTOZZI (IRE)**, br c Statue of Liberty (USA)—Indian Sand **Mrs R. Cioffi**
17 **OCEAN LEGEND (IRE)**, b c Night Shift (USA)—Rose of Mooncoin (IRE) **Ocean Trailers Ltd**
18 **PEPPER'S GHOST**, gr c Act One—Mill On The Floss **Carol Bushnell & Partners**
19 **ROMFORD CAR TWO**, b c Josr Algarhoud (IRE)—Film Buff **Romford Mini Cabs**

TWO-YEAR-OLDS
20 Ch f 20/2 Beat Hollow—Blue Gentian (USA) (Known Fact) (USA) (4000)
21 **CHADWELL SPRING (IRE)**, b f 6/3 Statue of Liberty (USA)—Cresalin (Coquelin (USA)) (20000)
22 **CRAZY GRACIE (IRE)**, b f 14/3 Beckett (IRE)—Miss Hoofbeats (Unfuwain (USA))
23 B c 11/4 Traditionally (USA)—Lilli Marlane (Sri Pekan (USA)) (16000) **P. P. Mclaughlin**
24 **LILY EVA**, ch f 18/2 Definite Article—Avanindra (Zamindar (USA))
25 B f 30/3 Bertolini (USA)—Najaaba (Bahhare (USA)) (4500)
26 B c 21/2 Statue of Liberty (USA)—Nisibis (In The Wings) (40000)
27 **OCEAN COUNTESS (IRE)**, b f 23/2 Storming Home—Pennycairn (Last Tycoon)
28 Gr c 11/5 One Cool Cat (USA)—Persian Mistress (IRE) (Persian Bold) (16000)

Other Owners: J. Birkett, Mrs C. T. Bushnell, Mr A. Dee, Miss J Feilden, Mr Chris Page, Miss S. L. White.

Assistant Trainer: John Birkett

Apprentice: Amy Baker. **Amateur:** Mr R. Birkett.

192 MR P. S. FELGATE, Melton Mowbray
Postal: **Grimston Stud, Grimston, Melton Mowbray, Leicestershire, LE14 3BZ**
Contacts: **PHONE (01664) 812019**

1 **BOISDALE (IRE)**, 10, b g Common Grounds—Alstomeria **Ms S. Gray & Mr M. F. Galvin**
2 **HOME COMING**, 10, br g Primo Dominie—Carolside **P. S. Felgate**
3 **PRIME RECREATION**, 11, b g Primo Dominie—Night Transaction **M. Heywood**
4 **SOTONIAN (HOL)**, 15, br g Statoblest—Visage **A. F. S. Dean**
5 **TANNE BLIXEN**, 7, b m Great Dane (IRE)—Night Transaction **P. S. Felgate**
6 **THREE NO TRUMPS**, 4, ch f First Trump—Renaissance Lady (IRE) **Mrs T. E. Fitsall**

Other Owners: Mr M. F. Galvin, Ms S. A. Gray.

193 MR D. J. S. FFRENCH DAVIS, Lambourn
Postal: **Windy Hollow Stables, Sheepdrove, Lambourn, Hungerford, Berkshire, RG17 7XA**
Contacts: **YARD (01488) 73675 HOME (01793) 780257 FAX (01488) 73675**
MOBILE (07831) 118764
E-MAIL ffrenchdavis@btinternet.com WEBSITE www.ffrenchdavis.com

1 **ATH TIOMAIN (IRE)**, 5, b g Night Shift (USA)—Broken Spirit (IRE) **Marchwood Aggregates**
2 **BLESSED PLACE**, 8, ch g Compton Place—Cathedra **S. J. Edwards**

MR D. J. S. FFRENCH DAVIS—continued

3 BLUECROP BOY, 4, b g Zaha (CAN)—Pearl Dawn (IRE) **Mrs J. E. Taylor**
4 BRANDYWELL BOY (IRE), 5, b g Danetime (IRE)—Alexander Eliott (IRE) **P. B. Gallagher**
5 JUSTCALLMEHANDSOME, 6, ch g Handsome Ridge—Pearl Dawn (IRE) **Mrs J. E. Taylor**
6 LILAC WINE, 5, ch m Dancing Spree (USA)—Stay With Me Baby **G. H. Black**
7 PALANOVERRE (IRE), 4, ch f Noverre (USA)—Palavera (FR) **Miss Alison Jones**
8 THENFORD FLYER (IRE), 8, b g Oscar (IRE)—Broadway Baby **Fools With Horses**
9 TIPSY LAD, 9, b g Tipsy Creek (USA)—Perfidy (FR) **S. J. Edwards**

THREE-YEAR-OLDS

10 AVRIL VALLEY, b f Averti (IRE)—Shamrock Fair (IRE) **C. R. Cox**
11 CHAMPAGNE DANCER, ch g Lomitas—Rosewood Belle (USA) **Fools With Horses**
12 FANTADOT, b g Fantastic Light (USA)—Bardot **Mr B. W. Taylor**
13 YAKAMA (IRE), b c Indian Danehill (IRE)—Working Progress (IRE) **The Three Dogs**

TWO-YEAR-OLDS

14 Ch c 25/4 Captain Rio—Alicedale (USA) (Trempolino (USA)) (8500) **Hargood Limited**
15 B f 17/2 Namid—Attymon Lill (IRE) (Marju (IRE)) **Miss A. Jones**

Other Owners: Mr D. J. Blanchard, Mr J. C. Collingbourne, Mr A. D. Crook, Mr M. Duthie, Mr D. J. Ffrench Davis, Mr A. Hesketh, Ms P. Hinde, Mr L. Johnsey, Mr P. Pagliaroli, Mr D. T. Stockton.

Assistant Trainer: Avery Ffrench Davis

Jockey (flat): T. Quinn, R. Thomas. **Jockey (NH):** M. Bradburne. **Apprentice:** Billy Cray.

---

194 MR R. FIELDER, Godalming
Postal: **Little Burgate Farm, Markwick Lane, Loxhill, Godalming, Surrey, GU8 4BD**
Contacts: **PHONE (01483) 208353 MOBILE (07920) 185959**
E-MAIL valerie.h.fielder@talk21.com

1 ELECTRIC BALOO, 6, b h Morpeth—Sky Baloo **FA EvansInternationalRacing Mrs JHemmens**
2 LARRYS HALL, 8, b g Saddlers' Hall—Larry's Law (IRE)
3 LILLIE LOU, 5, b m Tomba—Tread Carefully **R. Fielder**
4 LINLITHGOW LAD, 8, br g Terimon—Nessfield **Miss K. Roberts**
5 MY RETREAT (USA), 11, b g Hermitage (USA)—My Jessica Ann (USA) **R. Fielder**
6 TANKTASTIC, 6, b g Chaddleworth (IRE)—Honeybed Wood **The Hillands Partnership**

Other Owners: Mrs J. Allison, Miss F. A. Evans, Miss S. Garry, Mr A. Hamilton-Bird, Mrs J. M. Hemmens, Mr P. D. Hemmens, C. J. Silverthorne.

Amateur: Mr P. York.

---

195 MR G. FIERRO, Hednesford
Postal: **"Woodview", Hazel Slade Racing Stables, Rugeley Road, Hazel Slade, Hednesford, Staffordshire, WS12 5PH**
Contacts: **HOME/YARD (01543) 879611 MOBILE (07976) 321468**

1 GO ON JACK, 10, ch g Saint Keyne—Swift Messenger **G. Fierro**
2 JUST BETH, 12, ch m Carlingford Castle—One For The Road **G. Fierro**
3 JUST CHRISSIE, 4, b f Classic Cliche (IRE)—Marsh Marigold **G. Fierro**
4 JUST OLIVE, 7, ch m Double Trigger—My Home **G. Fierro**
5 PASQUALINA MIA, 5, b m Classic Cliche (IRE)—Anchor Express **G. Fierro**
6 YES SES LES, 9, b g El Conquistador—Kellsboro Queen **G. Fierro**

Assistant Trainer: M Fierro

---

196 MR R. F. FISHER, Ulverston
Postal: **Great Head House, Priory Road, Ulverston, Cumbria, LA12 9RX**
Contacts: **PHONE (01229) 585664 FAX (01229) 585079 MOBILE (07779) 609068**
E-MAIL roger.fisher@homecall.co.uk WEBSITE www.roger-fisher.com

1 BECKERMET (IRE), 6, b g Second Empire (IRE)—Razida (IRE) **Great Head House Taylor Nash Edwards**
2 CINAMAN (IRE), 4, b g Key of Luck (USA)—Madame Nureyev (USA) **Sporting Occasions 12**

MR R. F. FISHER—continued

   3 GRIZEBECK (IRE), 6, b g Trans Island—Premier Amour **Sporting Occasions**
   4 HIGHLAND SONG (IRE), 5, ch g Fayruz—Rose 'n Reason (IRE) **Mr A. M. Kerr**
   5 MARIESCHI (USA), 4, b g Maria's Mon (USA)—Pennygown **Great Head House Estates Ltd**
   6 MEATHOP (IRE), 4, b g Imperial Ballet (IRE)—Jacobina **Great Head House Estates Ltd**
   7 MUNCASTER CASTLE (IRE), 4, b g Johannesburg (USA)—Eubee (FR) **Sporting Occasions 7**
   8 MYSTIFIED (IRE), 5, b g Raise A Grand (IRE)—Sunrise (IRE) **S. P. Marsh**
   9 PROCRASTINATE (IRE), 6, ch g Rossini (USA)—May Hinton **Sporting Occasions Racing No 4**
10 RARE COINCIDENCE, 7, ch g Atraf—Green Seed (IRE) **Mr A. M. Kerr**
11 STOIC LEADER, 8, b g Danehill Dancer (IRE)—Starlust **A. Willoughby**
12 VERSTONE (IRE), 6, b m Brave Act—Golden Charm (IRE) **Carr Family Racing**

THREE-YEAR-OLDS

13 LAVEMILL (IRE), ch f City On A Hill (USA)—Mackem Beat **Mr L. B. Kerr**

Other Owners: Mr Mel Catlow, Mrs D. Catlow, Mr Robert Edwards, Great Head House Estates Limited, Mr K. Holmes, Mr L. E. Nash, Mr Matthew Taylor.

Jockey (flat): C. Catlin, P. Hanagan, R. Ffrench. **Jockey (NH):** K. Mercer, D. Elsworth, R. McGrath. **Apprentice:** K. Ghunowa. **Amateur:** Mr G. Gilbertson.

---

197   MR T. J. FITZGERALD, Malton
Postal: **Norton Grange, Norton, Malton, North Yorkshire, YO17 9EA**
Contacts: **OFFICE (01653) 692718 FAX (01653) 600214 MOBILE (07950) 356437**
E-MAIL fitzgeraldracing@aol.com

   1 4, Ch g Elmaamul (USA)—Campaspe
   2 CAPTAIN LING, 4, ch g Presidium—Giffoine **T. J. Fitzgerald**
   3 5, B m Deploy—Dublivia
   4 INCHNADAMPH, 8, b g Inchinor—Pelf (USA) **R. N. Cardwell**
   5 LAWFUL PLEASURES (IRE), 4, b g Josr Algarhoud (IRE)—Fullfilling (IRE) **T. J. Fitzgerald**
   6 MEDIC (IRE), 7, b g Dr Fong (USA)—Elupa (IRE) **J. S. Murdoch**
   7 MOMENT OF MADNESS (IRE), 10, ch g Treasure Hunter—Sip of Orange **Mrs R. Haggie**
   8 NAVELINA, 8, b m Presidium—Orange Imp **Mrs R. Haggie**
   9 OH MISTER PINCEAU (FR), 6, bl g Cupidon (FR)—Altesse D'o (FR) **Mrs R. Haggie**
10 OUR MAN IN BANGKOK, 8, b g Defacto (USA)—Ninety-Five **N. H. T. Wrigley**
11 RIVER DANUBE, 5, b g Dansili—Campaspe **Mr A. Huddlestone**
12 4, B g King's Theatre (IRE)—Smile Awhile (USA) **Regalmist**
13 5, Ch g Distant Music (USA)—Sunny Slope
14 4, B g Kayf Tara—Velcro Girl (IRE)
15 VICENTIO, 9, br g Vettori—Smah **Shaw Thing Partnership**

THREE-YEAR-OLDS

16 B g Beat Hollow—Campaspe
17 HARDANGER (IRE), b c Halling (USA)—Naughty Nell **R. N. Cardwell**
18 KING OF SPARTA (USA), b c Van Nistelrooy (USA)—Selling Sunshine (USA) **N F L Racing**
19 SWEET ANDROMEDA, ch f Observatory (USA)—Smooth Princess (IRE) **T. J. Fitzgerald**

Other Owners: Mr Alan Beenshill, Mr M. Collins, Mrs Peter Corbett, Mrs E. A. Fitzgerald, Mr M. Fowler, Mrs William Hall, Mr D. Jenkinson, Mr Rob Mason, Mr J. S. Murdoch.

---

198   MR J. L. FLINT, Bridgend
Postal: **Cherry Tree, 71 Woodlands Park, Kenfig Hill, Bridgend, Mid-Glamorgan, CF33 6EB**
Contacts: **PHONE (01656) 744347 MOBILE (07713) 053626 or MOBILE (07968) 044487 (Mrs Martine Flint)** E-MAIL john.flint@tesco.net

   1 COUNTRYWIDE BELLE, 5, b m Josr Algarhoud (IRE)—Dancing Bluebell (IRE) **J. L. Flint**
   2 LUCKY ERIC, 4, bl c Key of Luck (USA)—Ellopassoff
   3 MANGO MASHER (IRE), 4, ch g Danehill Dancer (USA)—Shariyfa (FR) **M. I. Thomas**
   4 PRIMESHADE PROMISE, 7, ch m Opening Verse (USA)—Bonnie Lassie **Meelin Racing Syndicate**
   5 RAQUEL WHITE, 4, b f Robellino (USA)—Spinella **N. Poacher**
   6 RIGHT OPTION (IRE), 4, b g Daylami (IRE)—Option (IRE) **Mr R. E. Mathias**
   7 SKYLER, 7, b g Dr Massini (IRE)—Commanche Token (IRE)

MR J. L. FLINT—continued

THREE-YEAR-OLDS

8 B f Ishiguru (USA)—Ellopassoff

Other Owners: Mr Ben Collins, Mr T. R. Fooks, Mr Carl Kerrigan, Mr Eric Griffiths.

Assistant Trainer: Mrs Martine Louise Flint

Amateur: Mr. Rhys Flint.

---

199   MR F. FLOOD, Grangecon
Postal: Ballynure, Grangecon, Co. Wicklow, Ireland
Contacts: PHONE (00353) 4540 3136 (00353) 8349 777 FAX (00353) 4540 3214
MOBILE (00353) 8725 90919
E-MAIL fjflood1@eircom.net

1 **AIMEES MARK (IRE)**, 12, br g Jolly Jake (NZ)—Wee Mite **Mr R. McConn**
2 **ARTIC WEB (IRE)**, 8, b g Arctic Lord—Balela Maid **The Webs Syndicate**
3 **BALLYSHANNON LADY (IRE)**, 5, b m Flemensfirth (USA)—Miss Eurolink **Suncroft Syndicate**
4 **BE MY LEADER (IRE)**, 9, b m Supreme Leader—Try Your Case **Mr P. Ryan**
5 **BEAU FLEUR (IRE)**, 6, b m Beau Sher—Souled Out (IRE) **Robert Hall**
6 **BIZET (IRE)**, 12, b g Zaffaran (USA)—Annie Sue VI **Mr A. Foley**
7 **BLANCHFIELD (IRE)**, 8, b m Luso—Peace Time Girl **Mrs F.J. O'Reilly**
8 **BLUE STEEL BOY (IRE)**, 6, gr g Pistolet Bleu (IRE)—Steel Grey Lady (IRE) **P. Young**
9 **BOBSTHEWIZARD (IRE)**, 6, b g Bob Back (USA)—Dun Belle (IRE) **P. Joseph Kelly**
10 **BRONX BOY (IRE)**, 5, b g Snurge—Young Preacher **Thomas Nestor**
11 **BRONX GIRL (IRE)**, 6, ch m Quws—Mill Lane Lady (IRE) **Thomas Nestor**
12 **COLDWELLS (IRE)**, 8, b m Presenting—Coolmoonan **Thomas McParland**
13 **DOCK STREET (IRE)**, 4, b g Old Vic—Annadot (IRE) **L. Kelly**
14 **FOLDUF (IRE)**, 5, b g Presenting—Danny's Charm **A. Foley**
15 **FRIENDSOFMINE (IRE)**, 5, ch m Carroll House—The Bratpack (IRE) **D. O'Brien**
16 **G V A IRELAND (IRE)**, 10, br g Beneficial—Dippers Daughter **Mr D. O'Buachalla**
17 **GIOLLA DE (IRE)**, 9, b g Glacial Storm (USA)—Deep Inagh **Mr C. Falls**
18 **IMAALHALL (IRE)**, 5, b g King's Theatre (IRE)—Graffogue (IRE) **Thomas McParland**
19 **KNOCKNADRUCE (IRE)**, 9, b g Oscar (IRE)—Winter Run **Mr T. Owens**
20 **LADY USK (IRE)**, 8, b m Broken Hearted—Toretta **Mr T O'Gorman**
21 **LEPOUSHKA KING (IRE)**, 7, b g Desert King (IRE)—Singing Filly **Kildare Racing Club**
22 **MR AUSSIE (AUS)**, 9, b g Runyon (IRE)—Bright (NZ) **Kildare Racing Club**
23 **MYSHERAMOUR (IRE)**, 5, b m Beau Sher—Busters Lodge **Kildare Racing Club**
24 **OSCAR CEOL (IRE)**, 7, b g Oscar (IRE)—Ceolbridgequeen (IRE) **Grangemore Syndicate**
25 **P'TIT FUTE (FR)**, 5, b g Roakarad—Centadj (FR) **J. R. M. Racing Syndicate**
26 **POM FLYER (FR)**, 8, b g Broadway Flyer (USA)—Pomme D'emeraude (FR) **Madfish Syndicate**
27 **PRINCE MASSINI (IRE)**, 7, b g Dr Massini (IRE)—Persian Desert (IRE) **Cathal McCarthy**
28 **REAL OVERDRIVE (USA)**, 7, b g Real Quiet (USA)—Third Party (FR) **Mrs M. Hackett**
29 **REYKJAVIK (IRE)**, 4, b g Alflora (IRE)—Returning **R. P. Behan**
30 **RUSSELLSTOWN BOY (IRE)**, 8, b br g Arctic Lord—Lough Borough (IRE) **Mrs Tanya Deane**
31 **SATOHA (IRE)**, 10, b g Zaffaran (USA)—Whackers World **Never Despair Syndicate**
32 **SHOT OF THE DAY (IRE)**, 6, b g Saddlers' Hall (IRE)—Fast Adventure **John P. McManus**
33 **SLIEVECORRAGH (IRE)**, 4, b g Celtic Swing—Graffogue (IRE) **Thomas McParland**
34 **TEARS OF JADE (IRE)**, 7, b br m Presenting—Orient Nickel (IRE) **Alice Reeves-Smyth**
35 **THE PENITENT MAN (IRE)**, 10, b g Corrouge (USA)—Swift Glider (IRE) **Mr M. Holly**
36 **VAN WYCK**, 4, b g Flemensfirth (USA)—Caitlin Rose (IRE) **Thomas Nestor**
37 **WHITEHILLS (IRE)**, 7, b g Oscar (IRE)—Carrigpreme (IRE) **Mr T. McParland**
38 **WILL SHE SMILE (IRE)**, 6, b m Rudimentary (USA)—Laugh Away **Ms Jean Corrigan**
39 **ZIZOU GIRL (FR)**, 6, b m Broadway Flyer (USA)—Kimouna (FR) **Kildare Racing Club**

Assistant Trainer: F. J. Flood

Jockey (NH): M. Walsh. **Conditional:** S. J. Hassett. **Amateur:** Mr A. Conlon, Mr S. O'Rourke.

200 MR R. FORD, Tarporley

Postal: **Folly Farm, Forest Road, Little Budworth, Tarporley, Cheshire, CW6 9ES**
Contacts: PHONE **(01829) 760095** FAX **(01829) 760895** MOBILE **(07976) 522768**
E-MAIL **richardford.racing@virgin.net** WEBSITE **www.richardfordracing.co.uk**

1 **ADLESTROP**, 8, ch m Alderbrook—Lady Buck **D. W. Watson**
2 **AL MOULATHAM**, 9, b g Rainbow Quest (USA)—High Standard **Tarporley Turf Club & Keith Hesketh**
3 **BATTLE STATIONS**, 7, ch g Classic Cliche (IRE)—Lady Padivor (IRE) **Miss R. Williams**
4 **BEAUTY ONE**, 5, b g Josr Algarhoud (IRE)—Beauty (IRE) **Mr Jeff Nield & Mrs C Barclay**
5 5, B gr g Most Welcome—Blossomville **Forge Bloodstock**
6 **BOLD PIONEER (USA)**, 5, b g Pioneering (USA)—Uber Alyce (USA) **Mr & Mrs G. E. Pickering**
7 **CARROLL'S O'TULLY (IRE)**, 8, b m Carroll House—Miss O'tully (IRE) **A. Eyres & D. F. Price**
8 **CHABRIMAL MINSTER**, 11, b g Minster Son—Bromley Rose **B. Mills, C. Roberts, M & M Burrows**
9 **ESPRIT SAINT (FR)**, 7, b g Mansonnien (FR)—Escopette (FR) **Mr P. & Mrs G. A. Clarke**
10 **FOREST SPRINGS**, 5, b g Parthian Springs—Shoreham Lady **Mr J. Gilsenan**
11 **GENERAL ALARM**, 11, b g Warning—Reprocolor **Tarporley Turf Club**
12 **GOOD SPIRIT (FR)**, 6, b g Smadoun (FR)—Haute Tension (FR) **Mr P. & Mrs G. A. Clarke**
13 **HARLEQUIN HUGO**, 5, b g Polar Prince (IRE)—Ecaterina (NZ) **Acton Stud**
14 **INSPIRINA (IRE)**, 4, b c Invincible Spirit (IRE)—La Stellina (IRE) **Miss G. Quincey**
15 **INSTANT SHOT (IRE)**, 5, b g Definite Article—Mistress Mine (IRE) **J. Connor**
16 **KATESVILLE (IRE)**, 4, b f King's Theatre (IRE)—Great Days (IRE) **R. S. Blandford**
17 **KEELUNG (USA)**, 7, b g Lear Fan (USA)—Miss Universal (IRE) **D. W. Watson**
18 **KING VERTI**, 4, b g Averti (IRE)—Proudfoot (IRE) **Mrs C. Barclay**
19 **LAST PIONEER (IRE)**, 6, b g New Frontier (IRE)—Toordillon (IRE) **R. S. Blandford**
20 **LEBANON (IRE)**, 8, b g Zaffaran (USA)—Millhaven Princess **BellHouseRacing.com**
21 **MEDIANOCHE (IRE)**, 8, b g Spanish Place (USA)—Midnights Daughter (USA) **Miss M. Burrows**
22 **NOLWENN (FR)**, 7, b m Lute Antique (FR)—Asterie L'ermitage (FR) **Mrs S. H. Shirley-Beavan**
23 **OPTIMISTIC HARRY**, 9, b g Sir Harry Lewis (USA)—Miss Optimist **Bell House Racing Limited**
24 **RIVERBANK RAINBOW**, 7, b m Overbury (IRE)—Riverbank Rainbow **The Gary Wheildon Syndicate**
25 **SADDLERS' GAIT (IRE)**, 6, b m Saddlers' Hall (IRE)—Snow Bank (IRE) **C. Jones T. Hocking & Friends**
26 **SHEIKHMAN (IRE)**, 7, b g Sadler's Wells (USA)—Maria Isabella (USA) **R. S. Blandford**
27 **SHORT STRAW (IRE)**, 5, b g Lord Americo—Marita Ann **Mr M. A. Proudfoot**
28 **SMOKE IT (IRE)**, 5, b g Carrowkeel (IRE)—Deerussa (IRE) **G. Williams**
29 5, B g Classic Cliche (IRE)—Tactix **Mr Dave Teasdale**
30 **TAYLOR'S TAILOR**, 5, b g Mister Mat (FR)—Waffling **Miss N. C. Taylor**
31 **THE GREEN HAT (IRE)**, 8, b br g Mister Lord (USA)—Dark Native (IRE) **Mrs C. J. Walsh**
32 **TOPINAMBOUR (FR)**, 8, gr g Turgeon (USA)—La Deviniere (IRE) **D. W. Watson**
33 **TRAGIC OHIO**, 9, b g Tragic Role (USA)—Kiniohio (IRE) **Sandicroft Stud**
34 **UNOWATIMEEN (IRE)**, 8, b g Supreme Leader—Collinstown Queen (IRE) **Sandicroft Stud**
35 **WARRIOR KING**, 4, b g Arkadian Hero (USA)—Lyna **Mrs C. Barclay, Mr J. Nield**
36 **WOODVIEW (IRE)**, 9, ch g Flemensfirth (USA)—Marys Bard **Mrs J. E. Gordon**

THREE-YEAR-OLDS

37 B gr g Terimon—Mugnano **Mr Reg Blandford**

Other Owners: Mrs C. Barclay, Miss K. S. Buckley, M. R. Burrows, Mr Peter Clarke, Mrs Gwenda Ann Clarke, Mr A. Eyres, Mr Richard Ford, Mr I. L. Goldberg, Mr K. Hesketh, T. Hocking, C. P. Jones, Mr S. Ledbrooke, Mr D. W. Lyon, Mrs P. O. Lyon, Mr J. S. Middleton, B. C. Mills, Mr Jeff Nield, Mrs Pearl Pickering, Mr George Pickering, Mr D. F. Price, C. A. Roberts, Mr S. A. Stokes, Mr G. J. Wheildon, Mrs M. R. Wheildon, Mr C. G. Wilson.

Assistant Trainer: Carrie Ford

Jockey (NH): G. Lee, R. McGrath. **Conditional:** Tom Greenway. **Amateur:** Miss Caroline Hurley, Mr Harry Challoner.

201 MISS S. E. FORSTER, Kelso

Postal: **Halterburn Head, Yetholm, Kelso, Roxburghshire, TD5 8PP**
Contacts: PHONE/FAX **(01573) 420615** FAX **(01573) 420615**
MOBILE **(07880) 727877 or (07976) 587315** E-MAIL **clivestorey@btinternet.com**

1 **ASTYANAX (IRE)**, 8, b g Hector Protector (USA)—Craigmill **C. Storey**
2 **BROMLEY BAY**, 5, ch m Karinga Bay—Little Bromley **Mrs H. N. Eubank**
3 **CHARLIE TANGO (IRE)**, 7, b g Desert Prince (IRE)—Precedence (IRE) **C. Storey**
4 **DESCRIPTION (IRE)**, 6, b g Humbel (USA)—Magic User **J. W. Stephenson**
5 **JUSTWHATEVERULIKE (IRE)**, 7, b g Courtship—Rose of Summer (IRE) **P. D. Innes**
6 **ONE BLACK CAT**, 5, b m Wizard King—Princess Topaz

MISS S. E. FORSTER—continued

7 **PRINCE ADJAL (IRE)**, 8, b g Desert Prince (IRE)—Adjalisa (IRE) **C. Storey**
8 **RADAR (IRE)**, 13, b g Petardia—Soignee **C. Storey**
9 **SKENFRITH**, 9, b g Atraf—Hobbs Choice **J M & Miss H M Crichton, Miss S Forster**
10 **SOUL ANGEL**, 4, ch g Tipsy Creek (USA)—Over Keen **Soul Searchers**
11 **STORYMAKER**, 7, b g Midnight Legend—Amys Delight **J M & Miss H M Crichton, Miss S Forster**
12 **THENFORD SIR (IRE)**, 7, b g General Monash (USA)—Alpencrocus (IRE) **C. Storey**
13 **TREASURED MEMORIES**, 8, b m Cloudings (IRE)—Glen Morvern **J M & Miss H M Crichton, Miss S Forster**
14 **WELSH DREAM**, 11, b g Mtoto—Morgannwg (IRE) **C. Storey**

Other Owners: Mr F. Berry, Miss Hazel Crichton, Mr J. M. Crichton, Miss Sandra Forster, Mr D. Skeldon.

Assistant Trainer: C Storey

Jockey (NH): N. Mulholland. **Conditional:** T. Messenger. **Amateur:** Mr C. Storey, Mr. A. Merriam.

---

202 MR A. G. FOSTER, Cousland
Postal: **Ashgrove Racing Stables, Cousland, Midlothian**
Contacts: **MOBILE (07855) 374346**

1 **ASHGROVE DIAMOND (IRE)**, 4, b f Desert Sun—Nurses Run (IRE) **Lothian Recycling Limited**
2 **BEAUMONT BOY**, 4, b g Foxhound (USA)—Play The Game **Lothian Recycling Limited**
3 **HURRICANE WARNING (IRE)**, 4, b g Warningford—All Our Blessings (IRE) **Tip Top Bloodstock**
4 **KING OF LEGEND (IRE)**, 4, b c King Charlemagne (USA)—Last Quarry **Mr J. M. Snellings**
5 **MALGURU**, 4, b g Ishiguru (USA)—Vento Del Oreno (FR) **Lothian Recycling Limited**
6 **MOSCOW ALI (IRE)**, 8, ch g Moscow Society (USA)—Down The Bog (IRE) **Lothian Recycling Limited**
7 **OLD TRAFFORD (IRE)**, 5, b g Shinko Forest (IRE)—
                                  Creese (USA) **A. K. Collins, Sangster Family, Lothian Recycling Ltd**
8 6, Ch g Karinga Bay—Twenty Winks
9 **WEE SEAN (IRE)**, 8, b g Rashar (USA)—Mrs Blobby (IRE) **Lothian Recycling Limited**
10 **WOODSLEY HOUSE (IRE)**, 6, b g Orpen (USA)—Flame And Shadow (IRE) **Mrs V. L. Davis**

THREE-YEAR-OLDS

11 B f Mtoto—Armada Grove **Lothian Recycling Limited**
12 **DANCE CARD**, b f Cape Cross (IRE)—Dance On **Crazy Ladies**
13 **NOTFORLOVEORMONEY**, br f Kyllachy—Greenfly **Mr J. M. Snellings**
14 B f King Charlemagne (USA)—Rosie (FR) **Lothian Recycling Limited**

TWO-YEAR-OLDS

15 B f 23/4 Reset (AUS)—Appelone (Emperor Jones (USA)) (2500) **Lothian Recycling Limited**
16 Ch c 12/4 Bertolini (USA)—Armada Grove (Fleetwood (IRE)) **Lothian Recycling Limited & Mr John Guthrie**
17 B f 20/4 Fayruz—Courtisane (Persepolis (FR)) **Lothian Recycling Limited**
18 B f 4/4 Lend A Hand—Rhiann (Anshan) (2800) **Lothian Recycling Limited**

Other Owners: Mr D. Shaw, Mrs C. T. Woodley.

Conditional: Ryan Mania.

---

203 MISS J. E. FOSTER, Ilkley
Postal: **Brookleigh Farm, Menston, Ilkley, West Yorkshire, LS29 6NS**
Contacts: **PHONE (01943) 874266 FAX (01943) 874266 MOBILE (07980) 301808**
E-MAIL yorkspt2ptclub@tiscoli.co.uk WEBSITE www.jofosterracing.co.uk

1 **AIRES ROCK (IRE)**, 8, b g Courtship—Newgate Music (IRE) **P. Grindrod**
2 **BY STORM**, 5, b m Largesse—Polar Storm (IRE) **P. Foster**
3 **FUN TO DREAM**, 7, ch m Primitive Rising (USA)—Ethel's Dream **Mr N. Pilling**
4 **NOUNOU**, 7, b g Starborough—Watheeqah (USA) **The Smash Block Partnership**
5 **PHINERINE**, 5, ch g Bahamian Bounty—Golden Panda **P. Grindrod**
6 **PROPER ARTICLE (IRE)**, 6, b g Definite Article—Feather 'n Lace (USA) **Mr N. Pilling**
7 **RAINBOW FLAME**, 4, b g Alhaarth (IRE)—Rainbow d'beaute **The Trinity Girls**
8 **THE REAL ALYDALY (IRE)**, 6, br g Poltarf (USA)—Real Town (IRE) **R. Naylor**
9 **WOODWISH (FR)**, 6, ch g Lyphard's Wish (FR)—Woodstock (FR) **Mr S. Breakspeare**
10 **ZENNERMAN (IRE)**, 5, b g Observatory (USA)—Precocious Miss (USA) **P. Foster**

MISS J. E. FOSTER—continued

Other Owners: Mr P. J. Deakin, Miss J. E. Foster, Mrs D. M. Shaw.
Assistant Trainer: Mr Paul Grindrod
Jockey (flat): Paul Mulrennan. Jockey (NH): Dominic Elsworth. Conditional: Philip Kinsella. Amateur: Miss J. Foster.

---

204 MR J. R. H. FOWLER, Summerhill
Postal: Rahinston, Summerhill, Co. Meath, Ireland
Contacts: PHONE (00353) 4695 57014 FAX (00353) 4695 57537

1 BLACKSON ZULU (IRE), 7, b g Supreme Leader—Janet Lindup **J. R. H. Fowler**
2 BRACKNEY HALL (IRE), 5, b m Saddlers' Hall (IRE)—Locksley Native (IRE) **R. J. Wilson**
3 CORBETSTOWN QUEEN (IRE), 6, b m Oscar (IRE)—Mary Kate Finn **M. G. Daly**
4 DARK SMILE (IRE), 8, b m Kahyasi—Ebony And Ivory (IRE) **Lady J. Fowler**
5 FREEMANTLE DOCTOR (IRE), 8, b m Luso—Lottobuck **March Hares Syndicate**
6 HEARTBREAK HILL (IRE), 9, b m Synefos (USA)—Knockea Hill **Lady J. Fowler**
7 HONEYBROOK (IRE), 7, br m Alderbrook—Hi Honey (IRE) **M. G. Daly**
8 JUST JANE (IRE), 7, b m Shernazar—Yashgans Vision (IRE) **Brian Robinson**
9 LA MARIANNE, 8, b m Supreme Leader—Belle Magello (FR) **Mrs R. Chugg & Lady J. Fowler**
10 MARMALADE SKY (IRE), 10, ch g Be My Native (USA)—Armagale (IRE) **Miss D. Duggan**
11 MAY'S MAGIC (IRE), 6, b m Bob's Return (IRE)—Northwood May **M. G. Daly**
12 5, Br m Anshan—Northwood May **M. G. Daly**
13 5, B m Bob Back (USA)—One Swoop (IRE) **M. G. Daly**
14 READING GAOL (IRE), 5, b g Oscar (IRE)—Fast Adventure **Lady J. Fowler**
15 RUN TO THE SEA (IRE), 5, b g Turtle Island (IRE)—Sweet Run **Lady J. Fowler**
16 SAY GRACE (IRE), 6, b m Saddlers' Hall (IRE)—Shining Willow **Simon Tindall**
17 SCHOLAR GEORGE (IRE), 6, ch g Classic Cliche (IRE)—Princess Florine (USA) **Simon Tindall**
18 SELOUS SCOUT (IRE), 11, ch g Be My Native (USA)—Lady Leona **Lady J. Fowler**
19 SILENT WHISPER (IRE), 6, b m Presenting—Loud Whisper (IRE) **T. A. Bruton**
20 SUPREME SURPRISE (IRE), 6, b m Presenting—Liskilnewabbey (IRE) **J. R. H. Fowler & Mrs A. Byrne**
21 SUPREMITY (IRE), 7, b m Supreme Leader—Pharetta (IRE) **J. R. H. Fowler**
22 THE ILLALA (IRE), 5, b g Great Palm (USA)—Mahaasin **Lady J. Fowler**

Jockey (NH): R. Geraghty. Conditional: A. P. Fagan. Amateur: Mr R. H. Fowler.

---

205 MR J. C. FOX, Marlborough
Postal: Highlands Farm Stables, Herridge, Collingbourne Ducis, Marlborough, Wiltshire, SN8 3EG
Contacts: PHONE (01264) 850218 MOBILE (07702) 880010

1 A NOD AND A WINK (IRE), 4, b f Raise A Grand (IRE)—Earth Charter **Mrs M. C. Thomas**
2 CHAMPAGNE FLOOZIE, 5, ch m Fleetwood (IRE)—On Request (IRE) **Miss S. J. Durman**
3 CHRISTALINI, 4, b g Bertolini (USA)—Jay Tee (IRE) **Miss H. J. Flower**
4 COLERIDGE (AUS), 9, ch g Yeats (USA)—Coco Cheval (AUS) **Mrs M. C. Thomas**
5 COLTSCROFT, 8, b g Teenoso (USA)—Marquesa Juana **Mrs M. Morrow**
6 GLORIOUS CASTLEBAR, 7, b g Carlingford Castle—Glorious Day **Mrs A. Doyle**
7 HAYLEY'S FLOWER (IRE), 4, b f Night Shift (USA)—Plastiqueuse (USA) **Miss H. J. Flower**
8 INN FOR THE DANCER, 6, b g Groom Dancer (USA)—Lady Joyce (FR) **Miss S. J. Durman**
9 IRISH HONOURS (IRE), 4, b f City Honours (USA)—Back To Black (IRE) **Miss S. J. Durman**
10 KILMEENA MAGIC, 6, b m Fumo di Londra (IRE)—Kilmeena Lady **Mrs J. A. Cleary**
11 MAGIC WARRIOR, 8, b g Magic Ring—Clarista (USA) **Miss H. J. Flower**
12 MUSICAL LOCKET, 4, b f Distant Music (USA)—My Lucy Locket (IRE) **Mrs M. C. Thomas**
13 MY JEANIE (IRE), 4, ch f King Charlemagne (USA)—Home Comforts **Rob Hurst & Rick Kavanagh**
14 O'SO NEET, 10, b br g Teenoso (USA)—Unveiled
15 OAKLEY ABSOLUTE, 6, ch g Bluegrass Prince (IRE)—Susie Oakley VII **B. C. Oakley**
16 TAGULA SANDS (IRE), 4, b g Tagula (IRE)—Pomme Pomme (USA) **R. E. Kavanagh**
17 VEVERKA, 7, b m King's Theatre (IRE)—Once Smitten (IRE) **Mrs A. Doyle**
18 WILD LASS, 7, ch m Bluegrass Prince (IRE)—Pink Pumpkin **Mrs J. A. Cleary**

THREE-YEAR-OLDS

19 ANNES ROCKET (IRE), b c Fasliyev (USA)—Aguilas Perla (IRE) **Mrs A. M. Coughlan**

Other Owners: Mr Rob Hurst, Mr R. E. Kavanagh.

Assistant Trainer: Sarah-Jane Durman

Jockey (flat): Pat Dobbs. Jockey (NH): S. Curran, S. Fox. Conditional: Wayne Burton. Amateur: Miss Sarah-Jane Durman.

206 MR M. FRANCIS, Lambourn
Postal: **Folly House, Upper Lambourn Road, Lambourn, Hungerford, Berkshire, RG17 8QG**
Contacts: **PHONE (01488) 71700 FAX (01488) 73208 MOBILE (07836) 244988**
E-MAIL Merrick@lrtltd.demon.co.uk

1 ICE CREAM (FR), 7, ch m Cyborg (FR)—Icone (FR) **Mrs A. M. Francis**

207 MR J. D. FROST, Buckfastleigh
Postal: **Hawson Stables, Buckfastleigh, Devon, TQ11 0HP**
Contacts: **YARD (01364) 642267 HOME (01364) 642332 FAX (01364) 643182**
MOBILE (07860) 220229

1 BEYOND MOONBEAMS, 4, b g Morpeth—Workamiracle **J. D. Frost**
2 CAPTAIN BECKET, 5, b g Access Ski—Sporting Annie **N. W. Lake**
3 CORNISH FLAME, 8, b g Thowra (FR)—Regal Flame **P. A. Tylor**
4 CRITICAL STAGE (IRE), 9, b g King's Theatre (IRE)—Zandaka (FR) **Le Rochjobi Partnership**
5 DEFINITE LYNN (IRE), 5, bl m Definite Article—Gavotte du Cochet (FR) **Mrs S. I. Haywood**
6 DIK DIK, 5, b g Diktat—Totom **W. N. Peto**
7 DUNKERRON, 11, b g Pursuit of Love—Top Berry **Dr D. Edwards**
8 FLY DIRECT (IRE), 5, b g Dr Massini (IRE)—Hurst Flyer **Mrs J. Bury**
9 KOSCIUSKO, 7, b m Sea Raven (IRE)—Impetuous Lady (USA) **P. A. Tylor**
10 LONGBOW WARRIOR, 6, b g Tout Ensemble—D'nial **Mr N. J. Wall & Miss S. J. Hartley**
11 MARKER, 8, ch g Pivotal—Palace Street (USA) **Miss W. J. Edmonds**
12 MASTER WELLS (IRE), 7, b g Sadler's Wells (USA)—Eljazzi **Cloud Nine-Premier Six**
13 NINETY NINE LOOKS (IRE), 6, ch g Old Vic—Oranrose (IRE) **G. D. Thompson**
14 OSCAR BAY (IRE), 6, b br g Oscar (IRE)—Rabbit Sand (IRE) **G. D. Thompson**
15 SEA SAFFRON, 7, b g Sea Raven (IRE)—Saffron Lake **G. N. Noye**
16 SHARE MY DREAM (IRE), 9, b m Shernazar—Nature's Best **Ms H. M. Vernon-Jones**
17 SHARP TUNE (USA), 6, ch g Diesis—Moonflute (USA) **J. D. Frost**
18 SILENT CITY, 8, ch m Karinga Bay—Gordons Girl (IRE) **Mr N. J. Wall & Miss S. J. Hartley**
19 SILVER SISTER, 7, gr m Morpeth—Pigeon Loft (IRE) **The Silver Stars**
20 SOUTHWAY QUEEN, 4, b f Morpeth—Nearly A Score **T. R. Watts**
21 TEMPER LAD (USA), 13, b g Riverman (USA)—Dokki (USA) **R. C. Burridge**
22 THE FLYING PHENOM, 5, gr g Paris House—Miss Flossa **P. M. Tosh**
23 WHATCANISAY, 9, b g Morpeth—Supreme Daughter **Mr N. M. Rooke**

Other Owners: G. B. Balding, J. E. Blake, Mrs B. M. Blake, Mr R. P. K. Clarkson, Mr C. V. Coward, Miss S. Hartley, Mrs R. M. Lane, Mr J. F. Lanigan, Mrs M. Mitchell, Mr N. Wall, Mrs J. A. Williams, Miss Elaine D. Williams.

Assistant Trainer: G Frost

Jockey (NH): T. O'Connor. **Conditional:** Byron Moorcroft. **Amateur:** Miss S. Gaisford.

208 MR JOHN GALLAGHER, Moreton-in-Marsh
Postal: **Grove Farm, Chastleton, Moreton-In-Marsh, Gloucestershire, GL56 0SZ**
Contacts: **PHONE/FAX (01608) 674492 MOBILE (07780) 972663**
E-MAIL gallagher.racing@virgin.net WEBSITE www.gallagherracing.com

1 BERTIE SWIFT, 4, b g Bertolini (USA)—Hollybell **C. R. Marks (Banbury)**
2 CHAMPAGNE STAR, 4, ch f Midnight Legend—Nicky's Choice **Mr I. Forde**
3 HARVEST JOY (IRE), 4, b f Daggers Drawn (USA)—Windomen (IRE) **R. Jeffery**
4 MAC GILLE EOIN, 4, b c Bertolini (USA)—Peruvian Jade **M. C. S. D. Racing Partnership**
5 MAKE MY DREAM, 5, b g My Best Valentine—Sandkatoon (IRE) **Mrs I. L. Clifford**
6 PETER ISLAND (FR), 5, b g Dansili—Catania **C. R. Marks (Banbury)**
7 PUSEY STREET GIRL, 4, b f Averti (IRE)—Pusey Street Girl **C. R. Marks (Banbury)**
8 SHAHEER (IRE), 6, b g Shahrastani (USA)—Atmospheric Blues (IRE) **Colin Rashbrook & John Gallagher**
9 SNAKE SKIN, 5, ch m Golden Snake (USA)—Silken Dalliance **Adweb Ltd**

THREE-YEAR-OLDS

10 DOUBLOON, b g Umistim—Glistening Silver **Colin Rashbrook & John Gallagher**
11 PERCYSLAVENDERBLUE, gr f Orpen—Peacock Blue (IRE) **Coombeshead Racing**
12 POWER OF SPEECH, b c Advise (FR)—Marsara
13 SHAMROCK LADY (IRE), b f Orpen (USA)—Shashi (IRE) **Mrs I. Clifford**

MR JOHN GALLAGHER—continued

14 **SOFTLY KILLING ME**, b f Umistim—Slims Lady **S. R. Prior**
15 **SOUNDBYTE**, b g Beat All (USA)—Gloaming **Mr O. M. Parsons**

TWO-YEAR-OLDS

16 **EVERY LITTLE HELPS**, b f 21/2 Fraam—Riyma (IRE) (Dr Fong (USA)) (6800) **Coombeshead Racing**
17 B c 26/3 Umistim—Glistening Silver (Puissance) (1333) **J. Gallagher**
18 **MISS HOLLYBELL**, b f 31/3 Umistim—Hollybell (Beveled (USA)) (8500) **J. Gallagher & Mrs D. Yeats Brown**
19 Ch f 29/4 Compton Place—Pusey Street Girl (Gildoran) **J. Gallagher**
20 **TALLULAH'S SECRET**, b f 21/3 Bertolini (USA)—Ascend (IRE) (Glint of Gold) **Mr J. Gaze**

Other Owners: Mr Tony Bricknell-Webb, Mrs T. Bricknell-Webb, Mrs A. J. Forde, Mr J. Gaze, Mr J. F. Long, Mrs B. A. Long, Mr S. C. Matthews, Mr B. J. McClean, Mrs M. B. McClean, Mr R. A. Newman, Mrs T. Newman, Mr D. T. Nicholls, Mr Colin Rashbrook, Mrs D. A. Yeats Brown.

Jockey (flat): J. Crowley, N. Callan, J. Spencer. **Jockey (NH):** M. Batchelor, R. Johnson. **Apprentice:** Sinead Logush.

---

209 **MR D. R. GANDOLFO, Somerton**
Postal: **Footsteps, High Street, Charlton Adam, Somerton, Somerset, TA11 7AR**
Contacts: **PHONE (01458) 224110 FAX (01458) 224111 MOBILE (07836) 208010**
E-MAIL dgandolfo@btconnect.com

1 **ALAMKHAN (IRE)**, 6, ch g Ashkalani (IRE)—Alaiyda (USA) **D. R. Gandolfo Ltd**
2 **BESSIE SMITH (IRE)**, 5, ch m Almutawakel—Rajaura (IRE) **D. R. Gandolfo Ltd**
3 **DARWAZ (IRE)**, 6, ch g Grand Lodge (USA)—Dawala (IRE) **Mrs P. H. Frost**
4 **FLEURETTE**, 8, b m Alflora (IRE)—Miss Wrensborough **Starlight Racing**
5 **GALOSHES**, 6, b g Kayf Tara—Seymourswift **Starlight Racing**
6 **GLENGARRA (IRE)**, 11, ch g Phardante (FR)—Glengarra Princess **Starlight Racing**
7 **GRAY'S EULOGY**, 10, ch g Presenting—Gray's Ellergy **M. A. Dore**
8 **MIGHTYMULLER (IRE)**, 6, b g Montjeu (IRE)—Anazara (USA) **A. E. Frost**
9 **PHOENIX HILL (IRE)**, 5, b g Montjeu (IRE)—Cielo Vodkamartini (USA) **Starlight Racing**
10 **QUATRAIN (IRE)**, 8, ch g Anshan—Gray's Ellergy **Starlight Racing**
11 **QUICKSILVERED**, 5, b m Silver Patriarch (IRE)—Seymourswift **Starlight Racing**
12 **RAYDAN (IRE)**, 6, b g Danehill (USA)—Rayseka (IRE) **B. R. K. Pain**
13 **RINGO CODY (IRE)**, 7, b g Dushyantor (USA)—Just A Second **Starlight Racing**
14 **ROOSTER'S REUNION (IRE)**, 9, gr g Presenting—Court Town **Mrs John Lee**
15 **ROYAL EVENT**, 17, ch g Rakaposhi King—Upham Reunion **D. R. Gandolfo Ltd**
16 **SHIRAZI**, 10, b g Mtoto—Al Shadeedah (USA) **D. R. Gandolfo Ltd**
17 **SILBERHORN EXPRESS**, 5, gr g Silver Patriarch (IRE)—Lotschberg Express **A. W. F. Clapperton**

Other Owners: Mr James Blackshaw, Mrs J. Bradley, Mr J. P. Carrington, Mr G. Clarke, Mr M. L. Fisher, Mr G. C. Hartigan, Mrs L. Melotti, Mr D. Payne, Mr O. Pierce, Mr P. Renahan, Mr C. Ritchie, Mr P. Slade, Mrs J. Snell, Mr V. Vyner Brooks, Mr J. Webb, Mr H. J. M. Webb, Mr T. J. Whitley.

---

210 **MRS S. GARDNER, Longdown**
Postal: **Woodhayes Farm, Longdown, Exeter, EX6 7SB**
Contacts: **PHONE/FAX (01392) 811213 MOBILE (07971) 097936**
E-MAIL woodhayesstudfarm@bt.com

1 **CALL ME SIR (IRE)**, 6, br g Lord Americo—Crash Call **J. Sluggett J. Lightfoot D. V. Gardner**
2 **CREDIT CRISIS**, 4, b f Relief Pitcher—B For Business **Mrs R. T. Cook**
3 **GEMGABALLOU (IRE)**, 5, b m Luso—Time To Kill (IRE) **D. V. Gardner**
4 **KRACKATARA**, 6, b g Kayf Tara—Kolyas Girl (IRE) **Mr & Mrs Searle**
5 **MUMS CHATTERBOX (IRE)**, 6, b m Accordion—Mum Said (IRE) **Mr J. L. Lightfoot**
6 **ORION EXPRESS**, 7, b g Bahhare (USA)—Kaprisky (IRE) **The Barley Mow Syndicate**
7 **TARA WHALE**, 5, b m Kayf Tara—Baby Whale (IRE) **F. D. A. Snowden**

Other Owners: G. D. L. Gray, Mr D. J. Hodge, M. A. F. Searle, Mrs B. M. Searle, M. J. Sluggett.

Assistant Trainer: D V Gardner

Jockey (NH): R. Lucey-Butler. **Amateur:** Miss L. Gardner.

211 MR J. R. GASK, Warminster

Postal: Horses First Racing Ltd, Sutton Veny, Warminster, Wiltshire, BA12 7BY
Contacts: PHONE (01985) 841166 FAX (01985) 840474 MOBILE (07507) 555303
E-MAIL info@horsesfirstracing.com WEBSITE www.horsesfirstracing.com

1 **BERGO (GER)**, 5, b g Silvano (GER)—Bella Figura (GER) **Horses First Racing Ltd**
2 **CHEONMADO (USA)**, 4, ch g Miswaki (USA)—Academie Royale (IRE) **J. Hawkins**
3 **CHIEF EXEC**, 6, br g Zafonic (USA)—Shot At Love (IRE) **Horses First Racing Ltd**
4 **COUNT TREVISIO (IRE)**, 5, b g Danehill (USA)—Stylish **Horses First Racing Ltd**
5 **EL DIEGO (IRE)**, 4, b g Sadler's Wells (USA)—Goncharova (USA) **Horses First Racing Ltd**
6 **ELEANOR ELOISE (USA)**, 4, b f Minardi (USA)—Javana (USA) **J. Hawkins**
7 **ESCOLHIDA (IRE)**, 4, b f Montjeu (IRE)—Caladira (IRE) **Horses First Racing Ltd**
8 **HASSAAD**, 5, b g Danehill (USA)—Ghazal (USA) **Horses First Racing Ltd**
9 **HOLD'S NIK (FR)**, 4, ch g Nikos—Hold Her (FR) **Horses First Racing Ltd**
10 **JAHASH**, 10, ch g Hernando (FR)—Jalsun **Mrs C. Hawkins**
11 **KLASSEN (USA)**, 5, b br g Pine Bluff (USA)—One Great Lady (USA) **J. Hawkins**
12 4, B g Flemensfirth (USA)—Leteminletemout (USA) **Horses First Racing Ltd**
13 **MAIDANNI (USA)**, 6, b br g Private Terms (USA)—Carley's Birthday (USA) **Resurrection Partners**
14 **MICKY COLE (IRE)**, 8, b g Luso—Simple Mind **Mrs M. Findlay**
15 **MONTICELLI (GER)**, 8, b g Pelder (IRE)—Marcelia (GER) **Horses First Racing Ltd**
16 **MOWADEH (IRE)**, 4, ch g In The Wings—Jazmeer **Horses First Racing Ltd**
17 **MUTUAL RESPECT (IRE)**, 6, b g Moscow Society (USA)—Deepest Thoughts (IRE) **Horses First Racing Ltd**
18 **NOBELIX (IRE)**, 6, gr g Linamix (FR)—Nataliana **Horses First Racing Ltd**
19 **NORTHERN DESTINY**, 4, b f Terimon—Northern Jinks **Mrs E. R. Smith**
20 **NORTHERN ENDEAVOUR**, 9, b g Alflora (IRE)—Northern Jinks **Mrs E. R. Smith**
21 **NORTHERN SEREN**, 7, b m Bob's Return (IRE)—Northern Jinks **Mrs E. R. Smith**
22 **OUNINPOHJA (IRE)**, 7, b g Imperial Ballet (IRE)—Daziyra (IRE) **Horses First Racing Ltd**
23 **PARADIGM SHIFT**, 5, ch g Night Shift (USA)—Demeter (USA) **Horses First Racing Ltd**
24 **QUEDILLAC (FR)**, 4, b g Clerkenwell (USA)—Esmidanne (FR) **Horses First Racing Ltd**
25 **REMEMBER RAMON (USA)**, 5, ch g Diesis—Future Act (USA) **Horses First Racing Ltd**
26 **SAUCY NIGHT**, 12, ch g Anshan—Kiss In The Dark **Horses First Racing Ltd**
27 **SERIBASE (FR)**, 6, b g Dear Doctor (FR)—Reine de Thou (FR) **Horses First Racing Ltd**
28 **SILENT DREAM**, 10, br g Alflora (IRE)—Silent Surrender **Horses First Racing Ltd**
29 **SOWDREY**, 4, b g In The Wings—Baaderah (IRE) **Horses First Racing Ltd**
30 **STAMFORD STREET (IRE)**, 5, ch g Distant Music (USA)—Exemplaire (FR) **Horses First Racing Ltd**
31 **THE EMPTY TIN (IRE)**, 7, b g Topanoora—Paean Express (IRE) **Horses First Racing Ltd**

THREE-YEAR-OLDS

32 **STREET POWER (USA)**, b br c Street Cry (IRE)—Javana (USA) **Horses First Racing Ltd**
33 **TAINE (IRE)**, b c Invincible Spirit (IRE)—Farjah (IRE) **Horses First Racing Ltd**
34 **YVONNE EVELYN (USA)**, gr ro f Cozzene (USA)—One Great Lady (USA) **J. Hawkins**

TWO-YEAR-OLDS

35 B c 2/4 Tobougg (IRE)—Alexander Ballet (Mind Games) (50000) **Horses First Racing Ltd**
36 Ch c 6/4 Haafhd—Decision Maid (USA) (Diesis) (50000) **Horses First Racing Ltd**
37 B c 27/2 Barathea (IRE)—Future Flight (Polar Falcon (USA)) (45000) **Horses First Racing Ltd**
38 **HANTA YO (IRE)**, ch c 31/3 Alhaarth (IRE)—Tekindia (FR) (Indian Ridge) (105000) **Horses First Racing Ltd**
39 B f 6/2 Bahamian Bounty—Locharia (Wolfhound (USA)) (11000) **Horses First Racing Ltd**
40 **MEDICEAN MAN**, ch c 31/3 Medicean—Kalindi (Efisio) (80000) **Horses First Racing Ltd**
41 **NUMBER NINE DREAM (USA)**, ch c 11/4 Buckhar (USA)—
      Let's Dance (USA) (Thorn Dance (USA)) **Horses First Racing Ltd**
42 Ch f 25/4 King's Best (USA)—Pretty Sharp (Interrex (CAN)) (50000) **Horses First Racing Ltd**
43 **SUTTON VENY (IRE)**, b f 14/3 Acclamation—Carabine (Dehere (USA)) (52000) **Horses First Racing Ltd**
44 B c 28/4 Danetime (IRE)—Tumbleweed Pearl (Aragon) (62000) **Horses First Racing Ltd**

Other Owners: R. L. Page.

Conditional: Luke Kilgarriff.

212 MR J. GEAKE, Andover

Postal: Kimpton Down Stables, Kimpton Farm, Andover, Hampshire, SP11 8PQ
Contacts: PHONE (01264) 772278/771815 FAX (01264) 771221 MOBILE (07768) 350738
E-MAIL serena@baldingstraining.fsnet.co.uk & lesley@kimptonstables.com
WEBSITE www.jonathangeake.co.uk

1 **ABSOLUT POWER (GER)**, 7, ch g Acatenango (GER)—All Our Dreams **Dr G. Madan Mohan**
2 **APRIL FOOL**, 4, ch g Pivotal—Palace Affair **Miss B. E. Swire**

MR J. GEAKE—continued

3 **ASK OSCAR (IRE)**, 7, b g Oscar (IRE)—Fishers Lady (IRE) **Argent Racing**
4 **BALLYFIN (IRE)**, 10, b g Lord Americo—Scar Stream **Double Kings Partnership**
5 **BALLYMAN (IRE)**, 7, gr g Accordion—Sliabhin Rose **Dr & Mrs Peter Leftley**
6 **BENEDICT BAY**, 6, b g In The Wings—Persia (IRE) **Dr & Mrs Peter Leftley**
7 **BEWARE CHALK PIT (IRE)**, 4, b g Anshan—Rakiura (IRE) **Dr & Mrs Peter Leftley**
8 **BLACK HILLS**, 9, b g Dilum (USA)—Dakota Girl **The Kingfisher Partnership**
9 5, Ch g Alderbrook—Bone of Contention (IRE) **Baldings (Training) Ltd**
10 **BREEZER**, 8, b g Forzando—Lady Lacey **Kimpton Down Racing Club**
11 **CARDENAS (GER)**, 9, b g Acatenango (GER)—Cocorna **Dr G. Madan Mohan**
12 **CHANGIZ**, 5, b g Foxhound—Persia (IRE) **Dr & Mrs Peter Leftley**
13 **COLLATERAL**, 5, ch m Groom Dancer (USA)—Cugina **Miss B. E. Swire**
14 **COSIMO PRIMO**, 4, b g Medicean—Cugina **Miss B. E. Swire**
15 **DANCING MELODY**, 5, b m Dr Fong (USA)—Spring Mood (FR) **Double Kings Partnership**
16 **DECISION DAY**, 4, b f Groom Dancer (USA)—Indubitable **Miss B. E. Swire**
17 **DESAILLY**, 14, ch g Teamster—G W Superstar **J. Geake**
18 6, B m Luso—Eadestown **Baldings (Training) Ltd**
19 **FINAL PROMISE**, 6, b g Lujain (USA)—Unerring **Sideways Racing**
20 **FOREVER THINE**, 5, ch m Groom Dancer (USA)—Indubitable **Miss B. E. Swire**
21 **FOXY BOB (IRE)**, 6, b g Bob's Return (USA)—Mullabawn (IRE) **Q. J. Jones**
22 **GOLD RING**, 8, ch g Groom Dancer (USA)—Indubitable **Miss B. E. Swire**
23 **HISTORIC PLACE (USA)**, 8, b g Dynaformer (USA)—Captive Island **Keay, Geake & Balding**
24 **HONDALIA (IRE)**, 6, b g City Honours (USA)—Rodalia (IRE) **Supreme Team**
25 **KELTIC CLICHE**, 5, br m Classic Cliche (IRE)—Goldenswift (IRE) **Mr T. Geake & Mr D. J. Erwin**
26 **KELTIC ROCK**, 9, ch g Bigstone (IRE)—Sibley **Keltic Rockers**
27 **KICK AND PRANCE**, 5, ch g Groom Dancer (USA)—Unerring **Sideways Racing III**
28 **KIMPTON CARER**, 4, b g Groom Dancer (USA)—So True **Miss B. E. Swire**
29 **KING'S CAPRICE**, 7, ch g Pursuit of Love—Palace Street (USA) **Miss B. E. Swire**
30 4, Ch f Nikos—Kris Mundi **Baldings (Training) Ltd**
31 **M'LORD**, 10, b g Mister Lord (USA)—Dishcloth **Dr G. Madan Mohan**
32 **MAREE HALL (IRE)**, 7, b g Saddlers' Hall (IRE)—My Sunny South **B. J. Keay**
33 **MEERSBROOK (USA)**, 7, b g Kingmambo (USA)—Karakorum (IRE) **The Team**
34 **MIRACLE BABY**, 6, b m Atraf—Musica **Kimpton Down Racing Club**
35 6, B g Rainbow Quest (USA)—Miss Arizona (IRE) **Baldings (Training) Ltd**
36 **MISTER TIBUS (FR)**, 7, b g Signe Divin—Ferlia (FR) **Peter Collier & Miss Melanie Parkinson**
37 **MISTER TROUBRIDGE**, 6, ch g Mister Baileys—So True **Miss B. E. Swire**
38 **PALAIS POLAIRE**, 6, ch m Polar Falcon (USA)—Palace Street (USA) **Miss B. E. Swire**
39 **PARNASSIAN**, 8, ch g Sabrehill (USA)—Delphic Way **Miss B. E. Swire**
40 **PARTHENOPE**, 5, gr m Namid—Twosixtythreewest (FR) **Dr & Mrs John Merrington**
41 **PEVERIL PANDORA**, 5, b m Kayf Tara—Spellbinder (IRE) **Baldings (Training) Ltd**
42 **PEVERIL PRIDE**, 10, b g Past Glories—Peveril Princess **Mrs E. A. Haycock**
43 **POLDEN FORCE**, 9, b g Forzando—Maid of Mischief **Mrs P. R. Barnett & Mr G. B. Balding**
44 **RED RAPTOR**, 7, ch g Polar Falcon (USA)—Star Precision **Miss B. E. Swire**
45 **RHAPSILIAN**, 4, br f Dansili—Rivers Rhapsody **Mr Rex Mead & Mr David Mead**
46 **RIPPLES MAID**, 5, b m Dansili—Rivers Rhapsody **Mr Rex Mead & Mr David Mead**
47 **RUMBLED**, 4, b f Halling (USA)—Tatanka (IRE) **The Rumble Racing Club**
48 **SPARTAN DANCE**, 4, ch g Groom Dancer (USA)—Delphic Way **Miss B. E. Swire**
49 4, Ch g Double Trigger (IRE)—Spellbinder (IRE) **Baldings (Training) Ltd**
50 **SPIDERS NEPHEW**, 4, b g Alflora (IRE)—Copper Rose Hill **H. M. F. McCall**
51 **STARLIGHT GAZER**, 5, b g Observatory (USA)—Dancing Fire (USA) **The Burning Stars**
52 **SUPREME TADGH (IRE)**, 11, b g Supreme Leader—Mariaetta (IRE) **Dr & Mrs Peter Leftley**
53 **TAGULA SONG (IRE)**, 4, b f Tagula (IRE)—Bouffant **Baldings (Training) Ltd**

THREE-YEAR-OLDS

54 **COUP D'OEIL**, b g Observatory (USA)—Cugina **Miss B. E. Swire**
55 **IN DECORUM**, gr f Averti (IRE)—Decorous (IRE) **William Stewart Partnership**
56 **MAELSTROM SEA**, b g Sea Freedom—Maedance **The Dancing Partners**
57 B c Superior Premium—Maid of Mischief **Mrs P. R. Barnett & Mr G. B. Balding**
58 **ORIENTAL GIRL**, b f Dr Fong (USA)—Zacchera **Kimpton Down Partnership**
59 **PROMISED GOLD**, ch c Bahamian Bounty—Delphic Way **Miss B. E. Swire**
60 **SIR KYFFIN'S FOLLY**, b f Dansili—Persia (IRE) **Dr & Mrs Peter Leftley**

TWO-YEAR-OLDS

61 **ARTFUL ALFIE**, b c 5/3 Medicean—Diliza (Dilum (USA)) (20000) **Redenham Racing Group**
62 **FIRE KING**, b c 15/5 Falbrav (IRE)—Dancing Fire (USA) (Dayjur (USA)) (16000) **Redenham Racing Group**
63 **LOUIE'S LAD**, ch gr g 15/2 Compton Place—Silver Louie (IRE) (Titus Livius (FR)) **Mr & Mrs K. Finch**

MR J. GEAKE—continued

64 **PLATINUM BOUNTY,** ch f 18/3 Bahamian Bounty—Maxizone (FR) (Linamix (FR)) **Mrs Lisa Bloxsome**
65 B f 27/2 Royal Applause—Rivers Rhapsody (Dominion) **Mr Rex Mead & Mr David Mead**

Other Owners: Mrs C. Bailey, Mrs G. Bailey, Mr B. Blundell, Mr S. Cooke, Mr M. Cuddigan, Mr J. Curnow, Mrs G. Dawson, Mr N. Debenham, Mr P S. Dove, Miss P Downing, Mr P Duffy, Mr J. Ellison, Mrs E. Estall, Mr M. Evans, Mrs A. Gale, Mrs M. Geake, Mrs S. A. Geake, Mr R. George, Mr T. Gordon, Mrs S. Grant, Mr P R. Greeves, Mrs P D. Gulliver, Mr W. Hackney, Mr M. Halloran, Mrs J. Hanslip, Mr B. Harding, Mr G. Harrison, Mrs C. Hobbs, Mrs J. Hopkins, Mrs J. Humby, Mr M. Humby, Mr D. Humphreys, Mr A. Johnson, Dr J. Leigh, Mr S. M. Little, Mrs J. Manger, Sir Brian McGrath, Mr Mark Nicholson, Mr Mark Nicholson, Mr J. Nolan, Mrs H. Padfield, Mr M. Painter, Mrs J. Palmer, Mrs C. Parry, Mr M. Perkins, Mrs K. L. Perrin, Mr M. Polding, Mrs M. Puddick, Mrs L. Ricci, Mrs S. Sheperd, Mr R. Smith, Mr R. J. Spencer, Mrs M. Stokes, Mr P Sutton, Mr M. Toone, Mrs C. Toplis, Mrs J. Townend, Mr R. Unwin, Mr T. Waddington, Mrs F. Wilson, Mr N. Yeatman.

Assistant Trainer: Mr G B Balding

Jockey (flat): Richard Thomas. **Jockey (NH):** M. Bradburne, J. A. McCarthy, S. Elliott.

---

213 MR T. R. GEORGE, Slad
Postal: **Down Farm, Slad, Stroud, Gloucestershire, GL6 7QE**
Contacts: **PHONE** (01452) 814267 **FAX** (01452) 814246 **MOBILE** (07850) 793483
E-MAIL tom@trgeorge.com **WEBSITE** www.tomgeorgeracing.co.uk

1 **BALLYFOY (IRE),** 7, b br g Alderbrook—Okanagan Valley (IRE) **M. K. George**
2 **BLOSSOM KING (FR),** 4, b g King's Best (USA)—Red Blossom (USA) **Silkword Racing Partnership**
3 4, B g Runyon (IRE)—Bucks Slave
4 **CARTHYS CROSS (IRE),** 9, ch g Moscow Society (USA)—Sweet Tarquin **L. H. Ballinger**
5 **DILLAY BROOK (IRE),** 8, b m Supreme Leader—Anns Run **Cheltenham Racing Ltd**
6 **DOUBLE SHOT,** 6, b g Double Trigger (USA)—Topsy Bee **Mrs S. C. Nelson**
7 **FIRE WITHIN,** 5, b g Saddlers' Hall (IRE)—Mystere (IRE) **Mrs S. C. Nelson**
8 **GOOD CITIZEN (IRE),** 8, b g Good Thyne (USA)—Citizen Levee **Miss J. A. Hoskins**
9 **HONOUR'S DREAM (FR),** 5, ch h Acatenango (GER)—
                                                The Last Dream (FR) **Power Panels Electrical Systems Ltd**
10 **ISLAND FLYER (IRE),** 6, b g Heron Island (IRE)—Lindas Statement (IRE) **Thoroughbred Ladies**
11 **JOE MANGO,** 6, b m Alflora (IRE)—Slipstream Star **Mrs S. I. Tainton**
12 **KATHLEENS PRIDE (IRE),** 8, b g Broken Hearted—Cyprus Hill (IRE) **Solihull Syndicate**
13 **KAYF LADY,** 5, b m Kayf Tara—Girlzone **Richard Davies & Dick Hibberd**
14 **KILBEGGAN BLADE,** 9, b g Sure Blade (USA)—Moheli **Mr K. Doocey & Mrs A. Doocey**
15 **KITTY WONG (IRE),** 6, b m Supreme Leader—Parson River (IRE) **Thoroughbred Ladies**
16 **LORD RYEFORD (IRE),** 8, br g Arctic Lord—Killoskehan Queen **Five Valleys Racing Partnership**
17 **LOSE THE ATTITUDE (IRE),** 8, br g Alphabatim (USA)—Legal Minstrel (IRE) **Thoroughbred Ladies**
18 **MAJAALES (USA),** 5, b g Diesis—Roseate Tern **S Nelson, J Bowen-Rees, D O'Donohoe**
19 **MEWSTONE,** 5, b m Supreme Leader—Carmel's Joy (IRE) **Mr & Mrs D. A. Gamble**
20 **MIDNIGHT RUBY,** 4, b f Midnight Legend—Miss Crusty **L. H. Ballinger**
21 **MOMENT OF MAGIC (IRE),** 5, b g Alderbrook—Pankhurst (IRE) **R & L Channing & S & F Roberts**
22 **MOUNTAIN OSCAR (IRE),** 7, b g Oscar (IRE)—Mountain Beauty (IRE) **Power Panels Electrical Systems Ltd**
23 **NACARAT (FR),** 7, gr g Smadoun (FR)—Gerbora (FR) **Mr S. W. Clarke**
24 **NO COMPLAINT (IRE),** 8, b g Acting Brave—Carolin Lass (IRE) **R. P. Foden**
25 **OH BRAGA (FR),** 6, b g April Night (FR)—Braga (FR) **Jayne Roberts Amanda Horst**
26 **OSSMANN (IRE),** 8, b g Luso—Bit of A Chance **Silkword Racing Partnership**
27 **QUICOLAI (FR),** 4, ch g Ragmar (FR)—Alene (FR) **Slad Valley Racing Partnership**
28 **RING BO REE (IRE),** 9, ch g Topanoora—La Ronde (FR) **Miss J. D. Wilson**
29 **RIVER RIPPLES (IRE),** 9, ch g Over The River (FR)—Aelia Paetina **B Corrigan J French S Nelson J Newiss**
30 6, B g Alflora (IRE)—Sabeel **T. R. George**
31 5, Ch g Alflora (IRE)—Sabeel **T. R. George**
32 **SAPHIRE NIGHT,** 7, b m Sir Harry Lewis (USA)—Tyrilda (FR) **Simon W. Clarke & David Zeffman**
33 **SAUCY BINGO (IRE),** 6, gr g Supreme Leader—Tante Marie **R & L Channing & A & P Hurley**
34 **SHAKE THE BARLEY (IRE),** 5, ch g Marignan (USA)—Glengarra Princess **Slad Valley Racing Partnership**
35 **SOMERSET ROSE,** 4, ch f Silver Patriarch (IRE)—What A Gem **The Brendon Toffs**
36 **SOVEREIGN'S JOY,** 8, b g Sovereign Water (FR)—Carmel's Joy (IRE) **Mr & Mrs D. A. Gamble**
37 **TANK TOP,** 7, b g Sovereign Water (FR)—Sabeel **R & L Channing & A & P Hurley**
38 **TED MOSS,** 7, b g Supreme Leader—Carlingford Gale (IRE) **Mr & Mrs D. A. Gamble**
39 **THE BIG I AM,** 5, ch g Shahrastani (USA)—Gaygo Lady **Mrs S. C. Nelson**
40 **THEMANFROMMAYO,** 6, gr g Cloudings (IRE)—Moheli **The Doocey Family**
41 **THENAMEESCAPESME,** 8, b g Alderbrook—Gaygo Lady **Mrs T. D. Yeomans**
42 **TOULOUSE-LAUTREC (IRE),** 12, ch g Toulon—Bucks Slave **J. A. R. R. French**
43 **TRAVELLI (POL),** 4, gr g Freedom's Choice (USA)—Transylwania (POL) **Mrs S. C. Nelson**

MR T. R. GEORGE—continued

44 **WHAT A SCIENTIST (IRE)**, 8, b g Karinga Bay—Half Irish **Mr & Mrs Gordon Pink**
45 **WHITE GATE (IRE)**, 6, br g Bob Back (USA)—Mount Sackville **Mrs M. J. George**
46 **ZAAD (IRE)**, 4, b g Muhtarram (USA)—Mahasin (USA) **Mrs T. D. Yeomans**
47 **ZANIR (FR)**, 4, b g Munir—Shahmy (USA) **Power Panels Electrical Systems Ltd**

THREE-YEAR-OLDS

48 **CESIUM (FR)**, b g Green Tune (USA)—Tantatura (FR) **Mr. & Mrs. D. A. Gamble.**
49 **MONSIEUR CADOU (FR)**, b g Cadoudal (FR)—Dame De Trefles (FR)
50 **THECIRCLEOFTRUST (FR)**, ch g Gold Away (IRE)—Dash (FR)

Other Owners: Mrs C. D. Chamberlain, Mrs Lisa Channing, B. C. Corrigan, Mrs J. Cumiskey, Mr R. Davies, Mrs A. M. Doocey, Mr Kevin Doocey, Mrs Sarah Fox, Mrs Alison Gamble, Mr D. A. Gamble, Mrs S. P. George, Mr T. R. George, Prof John Hermon-Taylor, Mr Dick Hibberd, Ms Amanda Horst, Mr A. D. Hurley, Mr T. Joyce, Mr John B. Lawson, Mr Malcolm Morgan, Mrs Sharon C. Nelson, Mr J. R. S. Newiss, Mr D. J. O'Donohoe, Mr P. T. Petrie, Mr G. K. G. Pink, Mrs K. M. Pink, Mrs Jayne Roberts, Mr Simon Roberts, Mr Carl Slowley, Mr R. F. Tromans, Mr Michael Watkins, Mr David Zeffman.

Conditional: Willie McCarthy. **Amateur:** Mr Charlie Dailly.

---

214 **MISS J. R. GIBNEY, Shenley**
Postal: Wood Hall Stud, Wood Hall Lane, Shenley, Hertfordshire, WD7 9AX
Contacts: PHONE (01923) 289999 FAX (01923) 289988 MOBILE (07990) 520706
E-MAIL jrg@woodhall.com

THREE-YEAR-OLDS

1 **BEN AMI**, ch g Pivotal—Darya (USA) **Wood Hall Stud Limited**
2 **TZORA**, b g Sakhee (USA)—Lucky Arrow **Wood Hall Stud Limited**

TWO-YEAR-OLDS

3 **COBOS**, b f 21/4 Royal Applause—Darya (USA) (Gulch (USA)) **Wood Hall Stud Limited**
4 B f 10/4 Fasliyev (USA)—Screaming Eagle (IRE) (Sadler's Wells (USA)) **Wood Hall Stud Limited**
5 Ch c 3/4 Highest Honor (FR)—Tycoon's Dolce (IRE) (Rainbows For Life (CAN)) (38610) **Wood Hall Stud Limited**
6 **VAL DE FLORES**, b f 6/5 Oasis Dream—My Lass (Elmaamul (USA)) (45000) **Wood Hall Stud Limited**

---

215 **MR RICHARD GIBSON, Lamorlaye**
Postal: 3, chemin du Mont de Po, 60260 Lamorlaye, France
Contacts: PHONE (0033) 3445 75300 FAX (0033) 3445 81548 MOBILE (0033) 6086 15788
E-MAIL richard.gibson@wanadoo.fr WEBSITE www.richardgibsonracing.com

1 **BLUE ROCKIES**, 4, b c Rock of Gibraltar (IRE)—Blue Fern (USA) **Mr E. Mordukhovitch, Mr V. Bukhtoyarov**
2 **CANONGATE**, 4, gr c Highest Honor (FR)—Tremiere (FR) **Lady Bland**
3 **DOCTOR DINO (FR)**, 6, ch h Muhtathir—Logica (IRE) **Mr J. Martinez Salmean**
4 **ILIE NASTASE (FR)**, 4, b c Royal Applause—Flying Diva **Mr J. Livock**
5 **LOUP BRETON (IRE)**, 4, b c Anabaa (USA)—Louve (USA) **Ecurie Wildenstein**
6 **LUMIERE NOIRE (FR)**, 4, ch f Dashing Blade—Lumiere Rouge (FR) **Famille de Moussac**
7 **MESHUGAH (IRE)**, 4, ch c Grand Lodge (USA)—Posta Vecchia (USA) **Mr E. Mordukhovitch, Mr V. Bukhtoyarov**
8 **MIXEDUP**, 4, b c Ocean of Wisdom (USA)—Muramixa (FR) **Mr R. Stephenson**
9 **RICHHILL LADY**, 4, gr f Mark of Esteem (IRE)—Mix Me Up (FR) **Mr W. Baumann, Mr G. H. Duke**

THREE-YEAR-OLDS

10 **ALAPOUR (IRE)**, ch c Pivotal—Alasha (IRE) **S. A. Aga Khan**
11 **ALTAN (IRE)**, ch c Rock of Gibraltar (IRE)—Blushing Away (USA) **Mr E. Mordukhovitch, Mr V. Bukhtoyarov**
12 **BITHIA (IRE)**, b f Vettori—Mistra (USA) **Mr G. A. Oldham**
13 **BRISE OCEANNE (FR)**, b f Kendor (FR)—Veiled Wings (FR) **Mme. G. Forien**
14 **CARNET DES NUITS (FR)**, gr f Highest Honor (FR)—Marie Laurencin **Mr A. E. Oppenheimer**
15 **CARVED EMERALD**, b f Pivotal—Emerald Peace (IRE) **Ecurie Skymarc Farm, Castlemartin Stud**
16 **CAT OF CATS**, b br f More Than Ready (USA)—Ready Cat (USA) **Mr D. Stein**
17 **CHASING MOONBEAMS (IRE)**, b f Fasliyev (USA)—Chabada (IRE) **Ecurie Skymarc Farm**
18 **ELOUGES (IRE)**, b f Dalakhani (IRE)—Morina (USA) **Mme A. Kavanagh**
19 **FANCY STONE (IRE)**, ch f Rainbow Quest (USA)—Mountain Spirit (IRE) **Mr Al Maddah**
20 **FINDHORN FLYER**, b c Kyllachy—Ozi Dream (FR) **Mr J. Wallinger, Mr D. D'Ambrumenil**
21 **GIVRE (FR)**, gr c Verglas (IRE)—Ghostly Quiet **Mme A. Gibson**

MR RICHARD GIBSON—continued

22 **GOLDEN DESERT (FR)**, b c Green Desert (USA)—Here On Earth (USA) **Mr E. Soderberg**
23 **GREEN ASCOT (IRE)**, b c Barathea (IRE)—Dirigeante (IRE) **Mr E. Soderberg**
24 **HEX (IRE)**, gr c Linamix (FR)—Amen (USA) **H. H. Aga Khan**
25 **MAJOR WING (IRE)**, b c Hawk Wing (USA)—Majinskaya (USA) **Mr E. Soderberg**
26 **MOLNIJA (FR)**, b f Medicean—La Peregrina **Mr E. Mordukhovitch, Mr V. Bukhtoyarov**
27 **NINKA (FR)**, gr f Linamix (FR)—Ashaninka (USA) **H. H. Aga Khan**
28 **PRESTANCE (IRE)**, b f Catcher In The Rye (IRE)—Pop Alliance (IRE) **Ecurie des Monceaux**
29 **RED CATTIVA (IRE)**, b f Red Ransom (USA)—Signorina Cattiva (USA) **6 C Racing Ltd**
30 **RIOKA (IRE)**, b f Captain Rio—Karlinaxa **Mme M. Shenkman**
31 **SESTET**, b f Golden Snake (USA)—Sestina (USA) **Mme K. Blance**
32 **SOTTOVOCE (FR)**, b f Xaar—Sweet Opera (FR) **H. H. Aga Khan**
33 **SRHISTORIC (GER)**, b c Red Ransom (USA)—Santenay (IRE) **Mr Al Maddah**
34 **SUMMER LEMONS (USA)**, b f Lemon Drop Kid (USA)—Sahara Sun (USA) **Ecurie Skymarc Farm**
35 **TIBERINA (IRE)**, b f Hawk Wing (USA)—Perugina (FR) **Mr G. A. Oldham**
36 **TIGNELLO (IRE)**, b c Kendor (FR)—La Genereuse **Mme Campbell Andenaes**
37 **VERBA (FR)**, gr f Anabaa (USA)—Tambura (FR) **Mr E. Mordukhovitch, Mr V. Bukhtoyarov**
38 **ZANNKIYA**, b f Sendawar (IRE)—Zanakiya (IRE) **H. H. Aga Khan**

TWO-YEAR-OLDS

39 Gr c 1/1 Linamix (FR)—Brusca (USA) (Grindstone (USA)) **H. H. Aga Khan**
40 B f 19/2 Xaar—Chabada (IRE) (Barathea (IRE)) **Ecurie Skymarc Farm**
41 **HURRY BASIL (IRE)**, b c 19/1 Barathea (IRE)—
                      Elle S'voyait Deja (USA) (Carson City (USA)) (38610) **Mr E. Soderberg**
42 **KEKOVA**, b f 22/5 Montjeu (IRE)—Koniya (IRE) (Doyoun) **Mme Jamison**
43 **MAFRA (IRE)**, b f 17/4 Kalanisi (IRE)—Sovana (IRE) (Desert King (IRE)) **Mme A. Kavanagh**
44 B f 1/1 Oasis Dream—Maid of Dawkins (IRE) (Kendor (FR)) **Mme G. Forien**
45 B c 29/1 Green Tune (USA)—Matin de Tempete (FR) (Cardoun (FR)) (70785) **Thurloe France**
46 B f 8/3 Mark of Esteem (IRE)—Missy Dancer (Shareef Dancer (USA)) (48000) **Mr James Rowsell**
47 **PROMESSE D'OR (FR)**, ch f 11/3 Divine Light (JPN)—
                      Love Love Kate (FR) (Saint Andrews (FR)) (22522) **Mr A. Pettinari**
48 B f 23/3 Lord of Men—Zigalixa (FR) (Linamix (FR)) (7078) **Mr A. Berghgracht**

Assistant Trainer: Eric Gandon

Jockey (flat): T. Thulliez, O. Peslier. **Apprentice:** T. Richer.

---

216   MR N. GIFFORD, Findon
Postal: **The Downs, Stable Lane, Findon, West Sussex, BN14 0RR**
Contacts: **OFFICE** (01903) 872226 **FAX** (01903) 877232 **MOBILE** (07940) 518077
E-MAIL downs.stables@btconnect.com

1 **ALDERLUCK (IRE)**, 5, ch g Alderbrook—Cecelia's Charm (IRE) **Mrs C. J. Rayner**
2 **ASHLEYS LAD (IRE)**, 4, ch g Ashley Park (IRE)—Scarlet Poppy **Mrs T. J. Stone-Brown**
3 **ASHLEYS PETALE (IRE)**, 5, br m Ashley Park (IRE)—Petale de Rose (IRE) **Mrs T. J. Stone-Brown**
4 **ASHLEYS POPPY (IRE)**, 5, b m Ashley Park (IRE)—Scarlet Poppy **Mrs T. J. Stone-Brown**
5 **BETTER TOGETHER**, 6, ch g Spadoun (FR)—Persian Jewel **Core Strength**
6 **BIG PADDY (IRE)**, 6, b g Priolo (USA)—Dark Hyacinth (IRE) **Core Strength**
7 **BOY'S HURRAH (IRE)**, 12, b g Phardante (FR)—Gorryelm **Woolpack Farm Partnership**
8 **BRUFF ACADEMY (IRE)**, 5, ch g Beneficial—Galballygirl (IRE) **S. N. Embiricos**
9 **BY GEORGE (IRE)**, 6, b g New Frontier (IRE)—Ann's Fort **Pell-mell Partners**
10 **CATHEDRAL ROCK (IRE)**, 6, b g New Frontier (IRE)—Cathadubh (IRE) **Mrs S. N. J. Embiricos**
11 **DARKSIDEOFTHEMOON (IRE)**, 6, b g Accordion—Supreme Valentine (IRE) **D. Dunsdon**
12 **DEE EE WILLIAMS (IRE)**, 5, b g Dushyantor (USA)—Fainne Oir (IRE) **Tullamore Dew**
13 **DIAMOND DAFFODIL (IRE)**, 5, b g Clerkenwell (USA)—Miss Red Devil (IRE) **Burnt Toast Ltd**
14 **DIGGER GETS LUCKY (IRE)**, 6, b g Lord Americo—Exclusive View (IRE) **The Chanctonbury Ring**
15 **DUSKY LORD**, 9, b g Lord Americo—Red Dusk **The American Dream**
16 **FOLLOW YOUR HEART (IRE)**, 8, b br g Broken Hearted—Souled Out (IRE) **J. P. McManus**
17 **GENTLE CARIBOU (IRE)**, 4, b f Dushyantor (USA)—Attention (IRE)
18 **GIVE ME A DIME (IRE)**, 6, b g Beneficial—Miss Di (IRE) **Mrs S. N. J. Embiricos**
19 **GLANDORE MOON**, 9, br g Presenting—My Gonny (IRE) **Mr C. Keeley**
20 **GOFLO (IRE)**, 4, ch f Alflora (IRE)—Helens Last (IRE) **Mrs M. C. Sweeney**
21 **HIMBA**, 5, b g Vettori (IRE)—Be My Wish **Martin & Valerie Slade**
22 **JECZMIEN (POL)**, 5, b h Fourth of June (USA)—Jetka (POL) **Sir Christopher Wates**
23 **KELTIC MOON (IRE)**, 7, b g Posidonas—Birthday Honours (IRE) **Mr C. Keeley**

MR N. GIFFORD—continued

24 KING OF MUSIC (USA), 7, ch g Jade Hunter (USA)—Hail Roberta (USA) **T & Z Racing Club**
25 MOONHAMMER, 9, ch g Karinga Bay—Binny Grove **Mr C. Keeley**
26 NEIL HARVEY (IRE), 5, b g Winged Love (IRE)—At Dawn (IRE) **P. W. Beck**
27 NOMECHEKI (FR), 6, b g Kalmoss (FR)—Kan A Dare (FR) **The Stewart Family**
28 OURS (FR), 6, b g Discover d'auteuil (FR)—Geographie (FR) **Core Strength**
29 PASCHA BERE (FR), 5, gr g Verglas (IRE)—Ephelide (FR) **Mr M. Tracey**
30 PETIT TURK (FR), 7, b g Baby Turk—Petite Mer (FR) **P. W. Beck**
31 PUSH THE PORT (IRE), 6, b b g Dushyantor (USA)—Port Queen (IRE) **The Pink Soc**
32 ROYAL WEDDING, 6, b g King's Best (USA)—Liaison (USA) **D. G. Trangmar**
33 RUSSIAN AROUND (IRE), 7, ch g Moscow Society (USA)—Irish Pride (IRE) **R. F. Eliot**
34 SOBERS (IRE), 7, b g Epervier Bleu—Falcon Crest (FR) **P. W. Beck**
35 SOCIAL EVENT (IRE), 6, b g Luso—Desperate Marble (IRE) **Pell-mell Partners**
36 SOLEIL FIX (FR), 7, b g Mansonnien (FR)—Ifaty (FR) **D. Dunsdon**
37 SONNING STAR (IRE), 4, b g Desert Prince (IRE)—Fantazia **Mrs C. L. Kyle**
38 SPARTAN PLACE, 8, b g Overbury (IRE)—Pennethorne Place **Sir Christopher Wates**
39 STRAW BEAR (USA), 7, ch g Diesis—Highland Ceilidh (IRE) **J. P. McManus**
40 THEOPHRASTUS (IRE), 6, b g Overbury (IRE)—Over The Glen (IRE) **Core Strength**
41 TULLAMORE DEW (IRE), 6, ch g Pistolet Bleu (IRE)—Heather Point **Tullamore Dew**
42 WEE ROBBIE, 8, b g Bob Back (USA)—Blast Freeze (IRE) **P. H. Betts (Holdings) Ltd**
43 WITNESS RUN (IRE), 8, b g Witness Box (USA)—Early Run **Thurloe KTH**

Other Owners: G. H. L. Bird, A. W. Black, D. H. C. Booth, Mr A. Bradley, J. Chromiak, Mr N. H. Fairbrother, Miss Z. Fakirmohamed, R. Gilder, Mrs A. Gurney, R. Gurney, Mr L. Horvath, Mr C. J. Hughes, T. Keogh, H. P J. Lowe, R. J. Markwick, O. J. W. Pawle, D. M. Slade, Mrs V. J. M. Slade, Mr A. Stewart, Mrs J. A. Stewart, Mr J. A. Talbot, Mr T. White.

Conditional: J. Pemberton. **Amateur:** Mr S. Hanson, Mr D. H. Dunsdon.

---

217 MR M. A. GILLARD, Sherborne
Postal: **Elm Tree Stud, Holwell, Sherborne, Dorset, DT9 5LL**
Contacts: **PHONE (01963) 23026 FAX (01963) 23297 MOBILE (07970) 700605**
E-MAIL Mark@thegillards.co.uk

1 CAPE THEA, 4, b f Cape Cross (IRE)—Pasithea (IRE) **Miss K. Russell**
2 CELLARMASTER, 7, ch g Alhaarth (IRE)—Cheeky Weeky **Pippa Grace**
3 GANYMEDE, 7, gr g Daylami (IRE)—Germane **T. J. C. Seegar - Kay Stone**
4 HALF A TSAR (IRE), 4, b g Soviet Star (USA)—Villarica (IRE) **Mrs L. M. Clarke**
5 LITTLETON ALDOR (IRE), 8, b g Pennekamp (USA)—Belle Etoile (FR) **T. J. C. Seegar**
6 PAUNTLEY GOFA, 12, b g Afzal—Gotageton **T. J. C. Seegar**
7 THE IRON GIANT (IRE), 6, b g Giant's Causeway (USA)—Shalimar (IRE) **Kay Stone**

TWO-YEAR-OLDS

8 B c 28/3 Lucky Owners (NZ)—Catmint (Piccolo) (2200) **M. C. Denning**
9 B f 14/2 Lucky Owners (NZ)—Into Orbit (Safawan) **Pippa Grace**
10 B c 20/2 Where Or When (IRE)—Snaefell Heights (Suave Dancer (USA)) **Pippa Grace**

Assistant Trainer: Pippa Grace

Jockey (NH): T. Phelan. **Apprentice:** Jack Dean, Tolley Dean.

---

218 MR S. J. GILMORE, Banbury
Postal: **1 Spinners Cottages, Magpie Road, Sulgrave, Banbury**
Contacts: **PHONE (01295) 768384 MOBILE (07786) 586418**

1 CLANDE BOYE (IRE), 7, b g Lord Americo—Over The Sands (IRE) **S. J. Gilmore**
2 MAJOR EURO (IRE), 11, b g Lord Americo—Gold Bank **Miss J. A. Frost**
3 SYLVAN SHACK (IRE), 10, b br g Grand Plaisir (IRE)—Caddy Shack **The Wellies**
4 UNCLE LIONEL, 6, b g Sylvan Express—La Carlotta **Miss D. J. Day**

Other Owners: Mrs Jill Cartwright, Miss Jumbo Frost, Mr S. J. Gilmore, Mr R. A. Jeffery, Mr M. J. Swain.

219 MR M. J. GINGELL, Kings Lynn

Postal: **Runcton Hall Centre, North Runcton, Kings Lynn, Norfolk, PE33 0RB**
Contacts: HOME **(01553) 842420** FAX **(01553) 842420** MOBILE **(07831) 623624 / (07770) 533488**
E-MAIL **gingell@ukonline.co.uk** WEBSITE **www.mattgingell.com**

1 **ALPHA JULIET (IRE)**, 7, b m Victory Note (USA)—Zara's Birthday (IRE) **Wordingham Plant Hire**
2 **BOOSTER DIVIN (FR)**, 6, b g Signe Divin (USA)—Shenedova (FR) **W. Stanger, P. Whittall & G. Plastow**
3 **BOSCALL HILL (IRE)**, 9, ch g Teamster—Annabella **Two's Up Partnership**
4 **CAVALLO DI FERRO (IRE)**, 4, b g Iron Mask (USA)—Lacinia **P. Chakko & M. J. Gingell**
5 **CLEVERMANSAM**, 6, b g Tragic Role (USA)—Flower of Tintern **Win-A-Lot Syndicate**
6 **ELIZABETH GARRETT**, 4, b f Dr Fong (USA)—Eleonor Sympson **M. J. Gingell**
7 **ENTRELECHAMBRE**, 6, b g Entrepreneur—Cambronne **The No Lies Partnership**
8 **ETOILE D'OR (IRE)**, 4, ch f Soviet Star (USA)—Christeningpresent (IRE) **P. F. Chakko**
9 **FIRST FROST**, 4, ch f Atraf—Bless **The Real Tadzio Partnership**
10 **FLOWER HAVEN**, 6, b m Dr Fong (USA)—Daisy May **Gentlemen Don't Work on Mondays**
11 **GLOBAL ACHIEVER**, 7, b g Key of Luck (USA)—Inflation **Runcton Hall Racing**
12 **KANONKOP**, 4, b f Observatory (USA)—Camcorder **The Fenlands Eight Plus Four's**
13 **KASSUTA**, 4, b f Kyllachy—Happy Omen **Mr J. Sargeant**
14 **LAWAAHEB (IRE)**, 7, b g Alhaarth (IRE)—Ajayib (USA) **Penrose Jones Partnership**
15 **LITTLE HOTPOTCH**, 4, b f Erhaab (USA)—Berzoud **M. J. Gingell**
16 **PRESENT**, 4, ch f Generous (IRE)—Miss Picol **Mr M. R. Hole**
17 **RAINBOW PRINCE**, 5, b g Desert Prince (IRE)—Eve **S. J. Kidd**
18 **SILVER RING**, 5, b g Silver Patriarch (IRE)—Direct Hit **Silver Ring Partnership**
19 **SMILING TIGER**, 4, b g Contract Law (USA)—Nouvelle Cuisine **S. J. Kidd**
20 **TIP TOES (IRE)**, 6, b m Bianconi (USA)—Tip Tap Toe (USA) **Going Grey Partnership**
21 **TIRAILLEUR (IRE)**, 8, b m Eagle Eyed (USA)—Tiralle (IRE) **The Real Tadzio Partnership**
22 **WICKEDISH**, 4, b f Medicean—Sleave Silk (IRE) **Wordingham Plant Hire**
23 **WORDY'S GIRL**, 5, b m Little Jim—Wordy's Wonder **Wordingham Plant Hire**

Other Owners: Dr Tom Alexander, Mr M. Bevington, Mr Philip Chakko, Mr B. Dowling, Mr T. Evans, Mr M. J. Gingell, Mrs A. Gingell, Mr N. P Haley, Mr K. J. Hewitt, Mr N. Jones, Mr P.C. Meadows, Mr G. Penrose, Dr G. S. Plastow, Miss J. Seaman, Mrs Wendy Stanger, Mr P. G. Stockdale, Mr Pete Whittall, Mr L. Wordingham, Mr P. L. Wordingham, Mrs P. A. Wordingham.

Assistant Trainer: Mrs A Gingell

Jockey (NH): Derek Laverty, **Conditional:** Adam Pogson.

220 MR JAMES GIVEN, Willoughton

Postal: **Mount House Stables, Long Lane, Willoughton, Gainsborough, Lincolnshire, DN21 5SQ**
Contacts: PHONE **(01427) 667618** FAX **(01427) 667734** MOBILE **(07801) 100496**
E-MAIL **james.given@bigfoot.com** WEBSITE **www.jamesgivenracing.com**

1 **BAILEYS OUTSHINE**, 4, ch f Inchinor—Red Ryding Hood **G. R. Bailey Ltd**
2 **BRIGADORE**, 9, b g Magic Ring (IRE)—Music Mistress (IRE) **White Rose Poultry Ltd**
3 **CALL ME ROSY (IRE)**, 4, ch f Shinko Forest (IRE)—Fanciful (IRE) **Mrs Patricia Brown**
4 **DREAM LODGE (IRE)**, 4, ch c Grand Lodge (USA)—Secret Dream (IRE) **The G-Guck Group**
5 **FEELIN FOXY**, 4, b f Foxhound (USA)—Charlie Girl **Danethorpe Racing Partnership**
6 **FREGATE ISLAND (IRE)**, 5, gr g Daylami (IRE)—Briery (IRE) **Mr & Mrs G. Middlebrook**
7 **GIVEN A CHOICE (IRE)**, 6, b g Trans Island—Miss Audimar (USA) **M. J. Beadle**
8 **GLENRIDDING**, 4, b g Averti (IRE)—Appelone **Tremousser Partnership**
9 **GREEN LAGONDA (AUS)**, 6, gr g Crown Jester (AUS)—
                                        Fidelis (AUS) **Mr P. J. & Mrs Y. Brain & Mr R. S. G. Jones**
10 **KENMORE**, 4, b g Compton Place—Watheeqah (USA) **Paul Moulton**
11 **KIMONO MY HOUSE**, 4, ch f Dr Fong (USA)—Roselyn **Tremousser Partnership**
12 **LADY GLORIA**, 4, b f Diktat—Tara Moon **Mr M. H. Tourle**
13 **MAMBO SPIRIT (IRE)**, 4, b g Invincible Spirit (IRE)—Mambodorga (USA) **Jones, Jones, Clarke & O'Sullivan**
14 4, Ch g Arkadian Hero (USA)—Miss Ritz
15 **MORINQUA (IRE)**, 4, b f Cadeaux Genereux—Victoria Regia (IRE) **Mrs S. O'Sullivan & Mr D. Mac A'Bhaird**
16 **OFF THE RECORD**, 4, b c Desert Style (IRE)—Record Time **Mr Peter Onslow & Mr Ian Henderson**
17 **RILEY BOYS (IRE)**, 7, ch g Most Welcome—Scarlett Holly **Mr Paul Riley**
18 **TODWICK OWL**, 4, b g Namid—Blinding Mission (IRE) **Tremousser Partnership**
19 **ZAIN (IRE)**, 4, b g Alhaarth (IRE)—Karenaragon **Mrs G. A. Jennings**
20 4, B g Dansili—Zapatista

MR JAMES GIVEN—continued

THREE-YEAR-OLDS

21 **ABITOFAFATH (IRE)**, b g Fath (USA)—Queen's Victory **Twojam Racing Partnership**
22 **BABILU**, ch f Lomitas—Creeking **Paul Moulton**
23 **BAILEYS BENCHMARK**, ch f Mark of Esteem (IRE)—Estrelinha **G. R. Bailey Ltd**
24 **BOHOBE (IRE)**, b f Noverre (USA)—Green Life **P. A. Horton, Mr M. J. Beadle & Mr I. Booth**
25 **CAN CAN DANCER**, b f Fantastic Light (USA)—Bitwa (USA) **A. W. & Ian Robinson**
26 **DEFIES LOGIC**, ch g Domedriver (IRE)—Khandarat **J. Ellis**
27 **FITS OF GIGGLES (IRE)**, b f Cape Cross (IRE)—Itsibitsi (IRE) **D. Eiffe**
28 **GAELIC DANCER (IRE)**, b c Fasliyev (USA)—Touch And Love (IRE) **Axom (XI)**
29 **IN WITH A SHOUT**, b f Choisir (AUS)—Shouting The Odds (IRE) **Mr Peter Onslow & Mr Ian Henderson**
30 **INCARNATION**, b f Samum (GER)—River Patrol **Paul Moulton**
31 **INDIAN DAYS**, ch c Daylami (IRE)—Cap Coz (IRE) **Mr D. J. Fish**
32 **LA CHICALUNA**, ch f Cadeaux Genereux—Crescent Moon **The Living Legend Racing Partnership II**
33 **LINNET PARK**, b f Compton Place—Shifty Mouse **R. Walker**
34 **MADAM CARWELL**, b f King's Best (USA)—Delirious Moment (IRE) **Irene White & Diana Jones**
35 **MISTRESS RIO (IRE)**, ch f Captain Rio—Bu Hagab (IRE) **Mr and Mrs M. Bradshaw**
36 B c No Excuse Needed—On Tiptoes **Limestone Stud**
37 **PENTANDRA (IRE)**, b f Bahri (USA)—Miss Willow Bend (USA) **Mrs Y. Allan**
38 **PICK OF THE DAY (IRE)**, ch g Choisir (AUS)—Reveuse de Jour (IRE) **Tremousser Partnership**
39 **QUICK OFF THE MARK**, b f Dr Fong (USA)—Equity Princess **Mr Peter Onslow & Mr Ian Henderson**
40 **SLIM JIM PHANTOM**, b g Compton Place—Lyna **A. Clarke**
41 **SUPER TUSCAN (IRE)**, b c Fath (USA)—Ornellaia (IRE) **Hintlesham Racing**
42 **THREE GOLD LEAVES**, ch c Zaha (CAN)—Tab's Gift **R. N. Pennell**
43 **WARSAW WALTZ**, b f Polish Precedent (USA)—Generous Diana **Elite Racing Club**

TWO-YEAR-OLDS

44 B f 27/1 Noverre (USA)—Abington Angel (Machiavellian (USA) (24000) **Mr R. S. G. Jones & Mr B. Coulthard**
45 Br c 2/4 Dr Fong (USA)—Bimbola (FR) (Bikala) (23000) **Mr R. S. G. Jones & Mr B. Coulthard**
46 Br c 8/2 Diktat—Chanterelle (IRE) (Indian Ridge) (12000) **Mr M. J. Beadle & Mr I. Booth**
47 B f 6/5 Josr Algarhoud (IRE)—Charlie Girl (Puissance) (17000) **Danethorpe Racing Partnership**
48 B f 5/3 Desert Style (IRE)—Cover Girl (IRE) (Common Grounds) (35000) **Mr N. Collins**
49 Ch c 11/3 Pursuit of Love—Ellovamul (Elmaamul (USA)) **Mr Joe Horgan**
50 B f 24/3 Royal Applause—First Degree (Sabrehill) (USA) (23165) **The Living Legend Racing Partnership**
51 B f 17/4 Zamindar (USA)—Hamsah (IRE) (Green Desert (USA)) (20000) **G. R. Bailey Ltd**
52 **HIGHLAND STORM**, b c 3/3 Storming Home—Real Emotion (USA) (El Prado (IRE)) (55000) **Mr D. J. Fish**
53 Ch c 11/3 Mark of Esteem (IRE)—Lake Diva (Docksider (USA)) (9000) **Mr P. B. Doyle**
54 **LOOKAFTERNUMBERONE (IRE)**, gr c 27/2 Verglas (IRE)—
          Septieme Face (USA) (Lit de Justice (USA)) (32000) **Cavan Pickering & Stewart Whitehead**
55 B c 16/3 Alhaarth (IRE)—Mythical Girl (USA) (Gone West (USA)) (12000)
56 **NAIRANA**, b f 11/4 Lend A Hand—Flukes (Distant Relative) **Wolsey Stud**
57 B c 11/4 Mujadil (USA)—Nashwan Star (IRE) (Nashwan (USA)) (35392) **Mr R. S. G. Jones & Mr B. Coulthard**
58 Ch f 16/2 American Post—Navarazi (Arazi (USA)) **A. Clarke**
59 B f 9/4 Daylami (IRE)—Panna (Polish Precedent (USA)) **Lord Halifax**
60 **PUNCH DRUNK**, b f 26/4 Beat Hollow—Bebe de Cham (Tragic Role) (USA) (7500) **Lovely Bubbly Racing**
61 **REAL DANDY**, b c 1/3 Bahamian Bounty—
          You Make Me Real (USA) (Give Me Strength) (USA) (26000) **Mr Peter Onslow & Mr Ian Henderson**
62 B c 14/2 Diktat—Red Ryding Hood (Wolfhound (USA)) **G. R. Bailey Ltd**
63 **ROYAL TROOPER (IRE)**, b c 22/2 Hawk Wing (USA)—
          Strawberry Roan (IRE) (Sadler's Wells (USA)) (64349) **Mr J. A. Barson**
64 **SHE'S IN THE MONEY**, b f 18/2 High Chaparral (IRE)—
          Luminda (IRE) (Danehill) (USA) (30000) **Cavan Pickering & Stewart Whitehead**
65 B f 21/2 Diktat—Shifty Mouse (Night Shift (USA)) (4000) **R. Walker**
66 B c 27/3 Fath (USA)—Solas Abu (IRE) (Red Sunset) (20000) **The One Stop Partnership**
67 B f 7/4 Beat Hollow—Supersonic (Shirley Heights) (5000) **Limestone Stud**
68 B f 27/2 Marju (IRE)—The Stick (Singspiel (IRE)) (17000) **Danethorpe Racing Partnership**
69 B f 31/3 Sakhee (USA)—Thracian (Green Desert (USA)) (5500) **Moonfleet Racing**
70 **TRICKY SITUATION**, b f 22/2 Mark of Esteem (IRE)—
          Trick of Ace (USA) (Clever Trick) (USA) (26000) **Mr Peter Onslow & Mr Ian Henderson**
71 B c 2/2 Noverre (USA)—Waroonga (IRE) (Brief Truce (USA)) (32000) **Danethorpe Racing Partnership**
72 Ch f 16/5 Rock of Gibraltar (IRE)—Woodyousmileforme (USA) (Woodman (USA)) (51480) **Brighton Farm Ltd**

Other Owners: D. Allan, Axom Ltd, I. Booth, Mrs M. H. Bradshaw, Mr M. M. Bradshaw, N. Collins, Mr D. Downie, N. P. Hardy, I. Henderson, A. J. Hill, Mr P. A. Horton, R. H. Jennings, R. S. G. Jones, D. G. Jones, Mr J. Lamb, D. J. P. McWilliams, G. Middlebrook, Mrs L. A. Middlebrook, Miss M. Noden, Mrs J. A. Pennell, Mr C. Pickering, Mr S. J. Shaughnessy, P Swann, Mr S. Taplin, Mrs G. O. Tourle, D. F. White, White Rose Poultry Ltd, Mr S. Whitehead, Mrs B. E. Wilkinson, Mr J. Womersley.

221 MR J. S. GOLDIE, Glasgow

Postal: **Libo Hill Farm, Uplawmoor, Glasgow, Lanarkshire, G78 4BA**
Contacts: **PHONE (01505) 850212 MOBILE (07778) 241522**
WEBSITE **www.jimgoldieracingclub.co.uk**

1 **ALMOST MARRIED (IRE)**, 4, b g Indian Ridge—Shining Hour (USA) **M. J. Dawson**
2 **BENE LAD (IRE)**, 6, b br g Beneficial—Sandwell Old Rose (IRE) **Mr & Mrs Raymond Anderson Green**
3 **BLAZING HEIGHTS**, 5, b g Compton Place—Harrken Heights (IRE) **Jim Goldie Racing Club**
4 **CHIN WAG (IRE)**, 4, b g Iron Mask (USA)—Sweet Chat (IRE) **Mr A. McWilliam**
5 **COLLEGE MAID (IRE)**, 11, b m College Chapel—Maid of Mourne **S. Bruce**
6 **DARFOUR**, 4, b g Inchinor—Gai Bulga **J. S. Morrison**
7 **DESTINY HILL**, 7, b m Destroyer—Harrken Heights (IRE) **Jim Goldie Racing Club**
8 **DHAULAR DHAR (IRE)**, 6, b h Indian Ridge—Pescara (IRE) **The Vital Sparks**
9 **ENDLESS POWER (IRE)**, 8, b g Perugino (USA)—Charroux (IRE) **Fyffees**
10 **ESOTERICA (IRE)**, 5, b g Bluebird (USA)—Mysterious Plans (IRE) **Mrs S. E. Bruce**
11 **FRANK CROW**, 5, b g Josr Algarhoud (IRE)—Belle de Nuit (IRE) **Mrs J. M. MacPherson**
12 **GEOJIMALI**, 6, ch g Compton Place—Harrken Heights (IRE) **Fyffees 2**
13 **GIANT STAR (USA)**, 5, b g Giant's Causeway (USA)—Vogue Star (ARG) **The Reluctant Suitor's**
14 **GRAND DIAMOND (IRE)**, 4, b g Grand Lodge (USA)—Winona (IRE) **Mrs M. Craig**
15 **GRANDAD BILL (IRE)**, 5, ch g Intikhab (USA)—Matikanehanafubuki (IRE) **Tough Construction Ltd**
16 **HO PANG YAU**, 10, b g Pivotal—La Cabrilla **A. G. Guthrie**
17 **INCH HIGH**, 10, ch g Inchinor—Harrken Heights (IRE) **Jim Goldie Racing Club**
18 **JANE OF ARC (FR)**, 4, ch f Trempolino (USA)—Aerleon Jane **Cressington Park Farms**
19 **JOHN KEATS**, 5, b g Bertolini (USA)—Nightingale **Tough Construction Ltd**
20 **KISS CHASE (IRE)**, 4, br g Val Royal (FR)—Zurarah **J. S. Goldie**
21 **KYBER**, 7, ch g First Trump—Mahbob Dancer (FR) **Great Northern Partnership**
22 **LAMBENCY (IRE)**, 5, b m Daylami (IRE)—Triomphale (USA) **The Reluctant Suitor's**
23 **LAMPION DU BOST (FR)**, 9, b g Mont Basile (FR)—Ballerine du Bost (FR) **The Dodoz Partnership**
24 **MIDDLEMARCH (IRE)**, 8, ch g Grand Lodge (USA)—Blanche Dubois **W. M. Johnstone**
25 **PAPA'S PRINCESS**, 4, b f Mujadil (USA)—Desert Flower **Mrs J. M. MacPherson**
26 **REGENT'S SECRET (USA)**, 8, br g Cryptoclearance (USA)—Misty Regent (CAN) **Mrs M. Craig**
27 **RING FORNANDO**, 4, ch g Forzando—Magic Hanne **J. S. Goldie**
28 **RIVER FALCON**, 8, b g Pivotal—Pearly River **S. Bruce**
29 **ROTHESAY DANCER**, 5, b m Lujain (USA)—Rhinefield Beauty (IRE) **Highland Racing**
30 **SOMETHING SILVER**, 7, gr g Silver Patriarch (IRE)—Phantom Singer **Happy Sundays Racing Club**
31 **STELLITE**, 8, ch g Pivotal—Donation **S. Bruce**
32 **STRAVAIGIN**, 8, ch m Primitive Rising (USA)—Countryside First **A. J. R. Russell**
33 **WIND SHUFFLE (GER)**, 5, b g Big Shuffle (USA)—Wiesensturmerin (GER) **Mrs S. E. Bruce**
34 **YORKSHIRE BLUE**, 9, b g Atraf—Something Blue **Great Northern Partnership 1**
35 **ZA BEAU (IRE)**, 7, b m Beneficial—Shuil Na Gale **Mrs S. Horne**

THREE-YEAR-OLDS

36 **GLENLUJI**, b g Lujain (USA)—Glenhurich (IRE) **Jim Goldie Racing Club**
37 **KEEP SHINING**, b f Tomba—Turf Moor (IRE) **Valley Paddocks Racing Limited**
38 **KILLER CLASS**, ch f Kyllachy—Class Wan **F. Brady**
39 **MISS SUNSHINE**, b f Piccolo—Rhinefield Beauty (IRE) **F. Brady**
40 **PRIMO HEIGHTS**, b f Primo Valentino (IRE)—Harrken Heights (IRE) **The Vital Sparks**
41 **WILLYN (IRE)**, b f Lujain (USA)—Lamasat (USA) **The Vital Sparks**

Other Owners: Mrs C. Biggs, Mr E. Bruce, Mr Billy Dodds, Mr J. Fyffe, Mr S. Fyffe, Mrs D. I. Goldie, G. D. Goldie, James Goldie, Mr Raymond Anderson Green, Mrs Anita Green, Mr A. L. Gregg, Mrs E. M. Horne, Mr G. Illingworth, Mr Keen-Shing Law, Mr F. Mallon, Mr Craig Moore, W. Powrie, Mr N. Saltrese, Mr Stuart Scott, Mr A. H. Slone.

Assistant Trainer: James And George Goldie

Jockey (flat): D. Tudhope, F. Lynch. **Jockey (NH):** G. Lee, R. McGrath, K. Renwick. **Apprentice:** G. Bartley. **Amateur:** Mrs Carol Bartley, Mrs I. Goldie, Mr G. Goldie.

222 MR R. H. GOLDIE, Kilmarnock

Postal: **Harpercroft, Old Loans Road, Dundonald, Kilmarnock, Ayrshire, KA2 9DD**
Contacts: **PHONE (01292) 317222 FAX (01292) 313585 MOBILE (07801) 922552**

1 **ALEXANDER OATS**, 5, b g Insan (USA)—Easter Oats **R. H. Goldie**
2 **BATTLE OF SONG (IRE)**, 8, b g Warcraft (USA)—Waajib's Song (IRE) **R. H. Goldie**
3 **EASTER VIC**, 7, b m Old Vic—Easter Oats **R. H. Goldie**

MR R. H. GOLDIE—continued

   4 5, B m Alflora (IRE)—Ice Bavard **R. H. Goldie**
   5 **PEPE GALVEZ (SWE)**, 11, br g Mango Express—Mango Sampaquita (SWE) **R. H. Goldie**

Assistant Trainer: Mrs R H Goldie

Amateur: Mr. David Halley.

---

223 **MR K. GOLDSWORTHY, Kilgetty**
Postal: **Grumbly Bush Farm, Yerbeston, Kilgetty, Pembrokeshire, SA68 0NS**
Contacts: **PHONE/FAX (01834) 891343 MOBILE (07796) 497733**
E-MAIL grumbly@supanet.com WEBSITE www.keithgoldsworthyracing.com

  1 **CHARANGO STAR**, 10, b g Petoski—Pejawi **Mr C. R. Johnson**
  2 **CHASING MEMORIES (IRE)**, 4, b f Pursuit of Love—Resemblance **K. Goldsworthy**
  3 **DEREKS (IRE)**, 6, b g Dr Massini (IRE)—Top Drawer (IRE) **Miss J. Dollan**
  4 **DEW DROP INN (IRE)**, 5, b m Saddlers' Hall (IRE)—Share A Tale (IRE) **Miss J. Dollan**
  5 **HILLS OF ARAN**, 6, b g Sadler's Wells (USA)—Danefair **David Hughes Mike Evans & Partners**
  6 **HOLD EM (USA)**, 6, b g Moscow Society (USA)—One To Two (IRE) **David Hughes Mike Evans & Partners**
  7 **KING OF THE BEERS (USA)**, 4, gr ro c Silver Deputy (CAN)—Pracer (USA) **Dr S. Clarke**
  8 **MR DOW JONES (IRE)**, 16, b g The Bart (USA)—Roseowen **Mrs L. A. Goldsworthy**
  9 **PICABO KID (USA)**, 5, b g Lemon Drop Kid (USA)—Picabo Street (USA) **Ms Diane Morgan**
10 **RAJAM**, 10, b g Sadler's Wells (USA)—Rafif (USA) **Miss J. Dollan**
11 **RAPPAREE DRIVE (IRE)**, 6, br g Anshan—Real Decent (IRE) **David Hughes Mike Evans & Partners**

Other Owners: Mr M. Evans, Greenacre Racing Partnership Ltd, R. Higgins, D. B. T. Hughes, Mr W. B. H. Scale.

Assistant Trainer: Mrs L A Goldsworthy

---

224 **MR C. E. GORDON, Winchester**
Postal: **Morestead Farm Stables, Morestead, Winchester, Hampshire, SO21 1JD**
Contacts: **PHONE (01962) 712774 MOBILE (07713) 082392**
E-MAIL chrisgordon68@hotmail.co.uk

  1 **ABSOLUTE SHAMBLES**, 4, b g Shambo—Brass Castle (IRE) **Mrs C. M. Grant**
  2 **AFECTIONATESQUEEZE (IRE)**, 4, b g Sunshine Street (USA)—Middleofthenight (IRE) **Mr M. J. Holliday**
  3 **BRUSHFORD (IRE)**, 4, b g High Roller (IRE)—Vesper Time **Mrs D. M. Lawes**
  4 **FORFEITER (USA)**, 6, ch g Petionville (USA)—Picabo (USA) **Mrs K. Digweed**
  5 **GLIDE**, 7, ch g In The Wings—Ash Glade **Miss S. C. Holliday**
  6 **JACK HARBOUR (IRE)**, 4, b g Presenting—Mr K's Winterblues (IRE) **Mrs I. D. Colderick**
  7 **KING EDMUND**, 5, b g Roi de Rome (USA)—Cadbury Castle **S. P. Tindall**
  8 **MONZON (FR)**, 8, b g Kadalko (FR)—Queenly (FR) **Mr A. J. O' Gorman**
  9 **NAPOLITO (FR)**, 7, b g Ragmar (FR)—Clairette III (FR) **Mr G. D. V. Anderson**
10 **OUR FUGITIVE (IRE)**, 6, gr g Titus Livius (FR)—Mystical Jumbo **Mrs K. Digweed**
11 **QUARRYMOUNT**, 7, b g Polar Falcon (USA)—Quilt **E. J. Farrant**
12 **SEARCH ME**, 6, ch g Danzig Connection (USA)—Elusive
13 **SEBBER BRIDGE (IRE)**, 7, b m Mister Lord (USA)—Artic Squaw (IRE) **Miss S. C. Holliday**
14 **SIR HARRY COOL**, 5, b g Sir Harry Lewis (USA)—Cool Merenda (IRE) **I. W. Moss**
15 **SLO MO SHUN**, 4, b f Polish Precedent (USA)—Malvadilla (IRE) **Gordon Racing**
16 **SOVEREIGN SPIRIT (IRE)**, 6, b g Desert Prince (IRE)—Sheer Spirit (IRE) **L. Gilbert**
17 **TANTERARI (IRE)**, 10, b g Safety Catch (USA)—Cobblers Crest (IRE) **S. C. Robinson**
18 **TIN TRADER (IRE)**, 8, b g Mister Lord (USA)—Ross Rag **P. A. Bonner**
19 **TWINKLING STAR**, 6, b m King of Kings (IRE)—Miss Twinkletoes (IRE) **S. P. Tindall**
20 **UPHAM ATOM**, 5, b g Silver Patriarch (USA)—Upham Lady **Mr M. J. Le May**

Other Owners: C. E. Gordon, Mrs J. L. Gordon, A. C. Ward-Thomas.

Assistant Trainer: Jenny Gordon

Jockey (NH): Colin Bolger.

225 MR J. H. M. GOSDEN, Newmarket

Postal: Clarehaven Stables, Bury Road, Newmarket, Suffolk, CB8 7BY
Contacts: PHONE (01638) 565400 FAX (01638) 565401
E-MAIL jhmg@johngosden.com

1 BATTLE PAINT (USA), 4, b c Tale of The Cat (USA)—Black Speck (USA)
2 CAPE COBRA, 4, ch g Inchinor—Cape Merino
3 ESCAPE ROUTE (USA), 4, b g Elusive Quality (USA)—Away (USA)
4 LUCARNO (USA), 4, b c Dynaformer (USA)—Vignette (USA)
5 NOVIKOV, 4, ch g Danehill Dancer (IRE)—Ardisia (USA)
6 PIPEDREAMER, 4, b c Selkirk (USA)—Follow A Dream (USA)
7 RACER FOREVER (USA), 5, b g Rahy (USA)—Ras Shaikh (USA)
8 RAINCOAT, 4, b c Barathea (IRE)—Love The Rain
9 ROYAL OATH (USA), 5, b h Kingmambo (USA)—Sherkiya (IRE)
10 TAZEEZ (USA), 4, b br g Silver Hawk (USA)—Soiree Russe (USA)
11 TRANSCEND, 4, ch g Beat Hollow—Pleasuring

THREE-YEAR-OLDS

12 ABORIGINIE (USA), ch c Street Cry (IRE)—Native Roots (IRE)
13 ADAB (IRE), b c Invincible Spirit (IRE)—Acate (IRE)
14 ANNE OF KIEV (IRE), b f Oasis Dream—Top Flight Queen
15 BABY HOUSEMAN, b f Oasis Dream—Photogenic
16 BASTAKIYA (IRE), ch f Dubai Destination (USA)—Ting A Folie (ARG)
17 BELORUSSIAN (USA), b c Danzig (USA)—Attach (USA)
18 BESTOWED, b c Kyllachy—Granted (FR)
19 BRONZE CANNON (USA), b br c Lemon Drop Kid (USA)—Victoria Cross (IRE)
20 CADRE (IRE), b c King's Best (USA)—Desert Frolic (IRE)
21 CAPUCCI, b c King's Best (USA)—Design Perfection (USA)
22 CENTENNIAL (IRE), gr c Dalakhani (IRE)—Lurina (IRE)
23 CHARM SCHOOL, b c Dubai Destination (USA)—Eve
24 CITRON PRESSE (USA), b br f Lemon Drop Kid (USA)—Cozy Maria (USA)
25 CITY BONUS (IRE), b c Cadeaux Genereux—Ellebanna
26 COSMOPOLITAN, ch f Cadeaux Genereux—Parisian Elegance
27 CULLODEN (UAE), ch c Selkirk (USA)—Last Resort
28 DAR RE MI, b f Singspiel (IRE)—Darara
29 DE FACTO, ch c Medicean—Ascendancy
30 DISTINCTIVE IMAGE (USA), b c Mineshaft (USA)—Dock Leaf (USA)
31 DUNEDIN STAR, b f Cape Cross (IRE)—Midnight Line (USA)
32 EJEED (USA), b c Rahy (USA)—Lahan
33 ENLIGHTENED, b f Bahamian Bounty—Lady Roxanne
34 FRABJOUS, b f Pivotal—Minute Waltz
35 FRIVOLOUS (IRE), b f Green Desert (USA)—Sweet Folly (IRE)
36 GAME HUNT, b c Oasis Dream—Moment
37 HAMSAT ELQAMAR, b f Nayef (USA)—Moon's Whisper (USA)
38 ILLUSION, b f Anabaa (USA)—Fantasize
39 INFALLIBLE, b f Pivotal—Irresistible
40 ISTIQDAAM, b c Pivotal—Auspicious
41 LA TROUPE (IRE), b f King's Best (USA)—Passe Passe (USA)
42 LAKE WINDERMERE (IRE), b f Oasis Dream—Spinnette (IRE)
43 LEGAL EAGLE (IRE), b c Invincible Spirit (IRE)—Lupulina (CAN)
44 LEGISLATION, b c Oasis Dream—Kite Mark
45 LIGHT BOX, ch f Medicean—Lightsabre
46 LYME REGIS, b c Lemon Drop Kid (USA)—Alyssum (USA)
47 MADE TO RANSOM, b c Red Ransom (USA)—Maid For The Hills
48 MALTA, b f Gone West (USA)—Kithira
49 MASTER SPY, br c Cape Cross (IRE)—Secret Seeker (USA)
50 METTERNICH (USA), b br c Seeking The Gold (USA)—Valentine Waltz (IRE)
51 MICHITA (USA), b br f Dynaformer (USA)—Thunder Kitten (USA)
52 MIDNIGHT RANSOM, b f Red Ransom (USA)—Midnight Air (USA)
53 MOHATHAB (IRE), b c Cadeaux Genereux—Zeiting (IRE)
54 MOONQUAKE (USA), b br c Mr Greeley—Beaming Meteor (USA)
55 MUKHBER, br g Anabaa (USA)—Tarbiyah
56 NILE CRUISE (USA), b c Danzig (USA)—Zenda
57 ORANGE RIVER (IRE), b f Cape Cross (IRE)—Simla Bibi
58 PAMPAS CAT (USA), b c Seeking The Gold (USA)—Golden Cat (USA)
59 PARCEL, ch f Beat Hollow—Aquamarine

MR J. H. M. GOSDEN—continued

60 **PARTY FROCK,** b f Oasis Dream—Dance Dress (USA)
61 **PIXIE'S BLUE (IRE),** br f Hawk Wing—Isle of Flame
62 **PROFITABILITY (USA),** b f Cherokee Run (USA)—Lucrative (USA)
63 **PROHIBIT,** b c Oasis Dream—Well Warned
64 **QUEEN OF NAPLES,** b f Singspiel (IRE)—Napoleon's Sister (IRE)
65 **QUEEN'S SPEECH (IRE),** b f Medicean—Jazan (IRE)
66 **QUIRINA,** b f Red Ransom (USA)—Qirmazi (USA)
67 **RAKEEKAH,** b f Bahri (USA)—Amanah (USA)
68 **RAVEN'S PASS (USA),** ch c Elusive Quality (USA)—Ascutney (USA)
69 **RED JADE,** ch c Dubai Destination (USA)—Red Slippers (USA)
70 **REVIVALISM,** b c Where Or When (IRE)—Revival
71 **RHADEGUNDA,** b f Pivotal—St Radegund
72 **RIDGE DANCE,** b c Selkirk (USA)—Pearl Dance (USA)
73 **ROBERT BURNS (IRE),** b c Invincible Spirit (IRE)—Double Red (IRE)
74 **ROCHEFORT (IRE),** b c Red Ransom (USA)—Sombreffe
75 **SENSE OF JOY,** b f Dansili—Bonash
76 **SERIOUS IMPACT (USA),** b c Empire Maker (USA)—Diese (USA)
77 **SHABHAANA (USA),** ch f Diesis—Jawla
78 **SHAKTI,** ch f Indian Ridge—Sundari (IRE)
79 **SHARKI,** ch f Indian Ridge—Blue Sirocco
80 **STAR PATTERN (USA),** ch c Seeking The Gold (USA)—Starlore (USA)
81 **STAR ROCKER,** ch c Galileo (IRE)—Rockerlong
82 **STORMY VIEW (USA),** b br f Cozzene (USA)—Another Storm (USA)
83 **SURREALISM,** gr f Pivotal—Dali's Grey
84 **THEORY,** b f Oasis Dream—Insinuate (USA)
85 **UPTON GREY (IRE),** gr c Dalakhani (IRE)—Rosse
86 **VIRTUAL,** b c Pivotal—Virtuous
87 **WOODCUTTER (IRE),** gr c Daylami (IRE)—Cinnamon Rose (USA)
88 **WORLD TIME,** ch c Dalakhani (IRE)—Time Ahead

TWO-YEAR-OLDS

89 B c 13/5 Spartacus (IRE)—Alexia Reveuse (IRE) (Dr Devious (IRE)) (40000)
90 B c 16/2 Barathea (IRE)—Almanza (IRE) (Dr Devious (IRE)) (30000)
91 **BAWAARDI (IRE),** b c 26/1 Acclamation—Global Trend (Bluebird (USA)) (130000)
92 **BISHAARA (IRE),** b f 29/4 Alhaarth (IRE)—Majmu (USA) (Al Nasr (FR))
93 Ch c 3/3 Dr Fong (USA)—Carambola (IRE) (Danehill (USA)) (110000)
94 **DEBUSSY (IRE),** b c 26/2 Diesis—Opera Comique (FR) (Singspiel (IRE))
95 B f 12/4 Stormy Atlantic (USA)—Dock Leaf (USA) (Woodman (USA))
96 **DREAMCOAT,** ch c 25/4 Pivotal—Follow A Dream (USA) (Gone West (USA)) (120000)
97 B br c 29/4 Dynaformer (USA)—Fit For A Queen (USA) (Fit To Fight (USA)) (242954)
98 **FLINTLOCK (IRE),** b c 21/3 Oasis Dream—Finity (USA) (Diesis) (62000)
99 **FLOODLIT,** b f 8/3 Fantastic Light (USA)—Westerly Air (USA) (Gone West (USA))
100 Ch c 7/4 Bertolini (USA)—Follow Flanders (Pursuit of Love) (85000)
101 **FROSTED,** ch f 15/5 Dr Fong (USA)—Arctic Air (Polar Falcon (USA)) (170000)
102 **GREEN BERET (IRE),** b c 16/2 Fayruz—Grandel (Owington) (120000)
103 **HALLIWELL HOUSE,** ch f 10/2 Selkirk (USA)—Dusty Answer (Zafonic (USA)) (105000)
104 B c 20/1 Cape Cross (IRE)—Have Faith (IRE) (Machiavellian (USA))
105 **HOMETOWN,** b f 14/3 Storming Home—Nazoo (IRE) (Nijinsky (CAN))
106 B c 3/3 Nayef (USA)—Hyperspectra (Rainbow Quest (USA)) (230000)
107 B f 6/3 Montjeu (IRE)—Insinuate (USA) (Mr Prospector (USA))
108 Ch c 27/3 Elusive Quality (USA)—Journalist (IRE) (Night Shift (USA))
109 **KANSAI SPIRIT (IRE),** ch c 24/3 Sinndar (IRE)—Daanat Nawal (Machiavellian (USA)) (30000)
110 B c 15/3 Oasis Dream—Krisia (Kris)
111 B c 27/3 Danetime (IRE)—Lady Ingabelle (IRE) (Catrail (USA)) (130000)
112 Ch f 14/1 Selkirk (USA)—Land of Dreams (Cadeaux Genereux) (95000)
113 B c 26/3 Red Ransom (USA)—Lane County (USA) (Rahy (USA))
114 **MAFAAZ,** ch c 10/1 Medicean—Complimentary Pass (Danehill (USA)) (400000)
115 **MANDHOOMA,** b f 20/1 Oasis Dream—Shatarah (Gulch (USA))
116 **MAYAALAH,** b f 29/3 Cape Cross (IRE)—Chater (Alhaarth (IRE))
117 Ch gr c 2/3 Cadeaux Genereux—Miss Universe (IRE) (Warning) (120000)
118 **MOOAKADA (IRE),** gr f 18/4 Montjeu (IRE)—Sulaalah (Darshaan)
119 **MURAWEG (IRE),** b c 14/4 Kheleyf (USA)—Lady Moranbon (Trempolino (USA)) (90000)
120 Ch c 29/4 Indian Ridge—Mystic Tempo (El Gran Senor (USA)) (140000)
121 **NEHAAM,** b c 10/3 Nayef (USA)—Charm The Stars (Roi Danzig (USA)) (200000)
122 B c 2/2 Falbrav (IRE)—On The Tide (Slip Anchor) (60000)

MR J. H. M. GOSDEN—continued

123 B c 22/4 Dalakhani (IRE)—Pinaflore (FR) (Formidable (USA)) (130000)
124 B c 11/5 Royal Applause—Pizzicato (Statoblest) (42000)
125 PURITY, ch f 7/5 Pivotal—Virtuous (Exit To Nowhere (USA))
126 B br f 23/1 El Corredor (USA)—Red Dot (USA) (Diesis) (70000)
127 RUN FOR THE HILLS, b c 13/4 Oasis Dream—Maid For The Hills (Indian Ridge)
128 SABI STAR, b c 5/5 Green Desert (USA)—Balisada (Kris) (140000)
129 SANCTUM, b f 23/4 Medicean—Auspicious (Shirley Heights)
130 Ch c 6/3 Indian Ridge—Scruple (IRE) (Catrail (USA)) (150000)
131 SEAWAY, b c 18/2 Dr Fong (USA)—Atlantic Destiny (IRE) (Royal Academy (USA)) (160000)
132 B c 24/1 Gone West (USA)—Shoogle (USA) (A P Indy (USA))
133 Ch f 5/5 Danehill Dancer (IRE)—Stage Presence (IRE) (Selkirk (USA)) (375000)
134 STAR APPROVAL (IRE), b f 26/3 Hawk Wing (USA)—Mail Boat (Formidable (USA)) (95000)
135 B f 29/1 Falbrav (IRE)—Strike Lightly (Rainbow Quest (USA))
136 B c 10/3 Exceed And Excel (AUS)—Strutting (IRE) (Ela-Mana-Mou) (60000)
137 B f 3/2 Seeking The Gold (USA)—Sunray Superstar (Nashwan (USA))
138 B c 24/3 Pivotal—Tolyatti (Green Desert (USA)) (95000)
139 Ch f 20/3 Halling—Tolzey (USA) (Rahy (USA))
140 TWISTED, ch c 14/1 Selkirk (USA)—Winding (USA) (Irish River (FR)) (155000)
141 VAGLEFIELD, b c 19/4 Montjeu (IRE)—Photogenic (Midyan (USA))
142 B f 10/5 Cape Cross (IRE)—Vituisa (Bering)
143 B f 31/3 Green Desert (USA)—Viz (USA) (Kris S (USA))
144 WAJAHA (IRE), ch f 22/4 Haafhd—Amanah (USA) (Mr Prospector (USA))
145 B c 27/1 More Than Ready (USA)—You Again (USA) (Wild Again (USA)) (210000)
146 B f 18/2 Storm Cat (USA)—Zenda (Zamindar (USA))

Jockey (flat): J. Fortune, R. Havlin, D. Kinsella.

226	**MRS H. O. GRAHAM, Jedburgh** Postal: **Brundeanlaws Cottage, Camptown, Jedburgh, Roxburghshire, TD8 6NW** Contacts: **PHONE (01835) 840354 MOBILE (07843) 380401** E-MAIL hgrahamracing@aol.com WEBSITE www.harrietgrahamracing.co.uk

1 5, B m Deploy—Bucks Slave **Mrs H. O. Graham**
2 BUCKSTRUTHER (IRE), 6, ch g Anshan—Immediate Action **A. R. Bell**
3 4, Gr f Loup Sauvage (USA)—Casino Nell **Mrs H. O. Graham**
4 HOOKY'S HOPE, 5, b m Endoli (USA)—Hooky's Treat **Mrs H. O. Graham**
5 HOOKY'S QUEST, 6, br m Environment Friend—Hooky's Treat **Mrs H. O. Graham**
6 INNISFREE (IRE), 10, ch g Presenting—Sweet Peach (IRE) **The Brave Lads Racing Syndicate**
7 LOFTY LEADER (IRE), 9, b g Norwich—Slaney Jazz **L. H. Gilmurray**
8 MARINGO (FR), 8, b g Kadalko (FR)—Tacoma II (FR) **Camptown Racers**
9 MAYLEE (IRE), 6, br m Good Thyne (USA)—Ganpati (IRE) **A. R. Bell**
10 ROSALYONS (IRE), 14, gr g Roselier (FR)—Coffee Shop **Mrs H. O. Graham**
11 RUSSIAN SKY, 9, gr g Endoli (USA)—Anzarna **H G Racing**
12 SCARVAGH SOLITAIRE (IRE), 6, b br m Beauchamp King—Zaffaran Blends (IRE) **M S Borders Racing Club**
13 4, Ch f Loup Sauvage (USA)—The Ultimate Buzz (IRE) **Mrs H. O. Graham**

Other Owners: Mr P. Andries, Mrs R. Bell, Mrs R. L. Elliot, Mrs H. O. Graham, Mr R. D. Graham, Mr Andrew Hamilton, Mr J. A. Mabon, Mr J. W. Purdie.

Assistant Trainer: R D Graham

Jockey (NH): O. Nelmes, M. Bradburne. **Conditional:** T. Messenger. **Amateur:** Miss R. Davidson, Mr S. Turnbull.

227	**MR C. GRANT, Billingham** Postal: **Low Burntoft Farm, Wolviston, Billingham, Cleveland, TS22 5PD** Contacts: **PHONE/FAX (01740) 644054 MOBILE (07860) 577998** E-MAIL chris@chrisgrantracing.fsnet.co.uk WEBSITE www.chrisgrantracing.co.uk

1 CHARLES STREET, 6, gr g Cois Na Tine (IRE)—Yemaail (IRE) **Mr A. Dawson & Mrs K. Campbell**
2 CRUISE LEADER (IRE), 13, b g Supreme Leader—Ormskirk Mover **C. Grant**
3 DOUBLE VODKA (IRE), 7, b br g Russian Revival (USA)—Silius **Mr S. Wilson**

MR C. GRANT—continued

4 EMERALD DESTINY (IRE), 6, b g Key of Luck (USA)—Green Belt (FR) **WRB Racing 53 (wrbracing.com)**
5 GOOD EVENING (IRE), 6, b g Even Top (IRE)—Our Next Rose (IRE) **T. J. Hemmings**
6 LAERTES, 7, gr g Theatrical Charmer—Handmaiden **Panther Racing Limited**
7 LAZY DARREN, 4, b g Largesse—Palmstead Belle (IRE) **Woodgate Family**
8 MEY CLOUDS (IRE), 6, b g Cloudings (IRE)—Lady of Mey (IRE) **T. J. Hemmings**
9 MINSTER SHADOW, 9, b g Minster Son—Polar Belle **Anne Cairns & Partners**
10 NEVINSTOWN (IRE), 8, b g Lahib (USA)—Moon Tango (IRE) **C. Grant**
11 NINJA (IRE), 5, b g Turtle Island (IRE)—Billeragh Thyne (IRE) **R. G. Bonson**
12 NOW THEN BASIL, 5, b g JB Quick—Shadi Lady (IRE) **C. Grant**
13 PAST GAMBLES (IRE), 6, b br g Pasternak—Most Effective (IRE) **C. Grant**
14 RHINE REWLER, 6, b g Rasanto (GER)—Woodside Rewlette **D. M. P. R. Racing**
15 RURAL PRIDE (IRE), 5, b g Luso—Nearly Decent **T. J. Hemmings**
16 STAR PLAYER (IRE), 6, ch g Accordion—Folle Idee De Luz (FR) **S. Wilson,G. & J. Bonson,K. Waddup**
17 SUN QUEST, 4, b g Groom Dancer (USA)—Icaressa **Panther Racing Limited**
18 THEATRE BELLE, 7, b m King's Theatre (IRE)—Cumbrian Rhapsody **Division Bell Partnership**
19 TROYS STEPS, 4, b f Cloudings (IRE)—Troys Guest (IRE) **T. J. Hemmings**
20 TURBO SHANDY, 5, b g Piccolo—Carn Maire **Panther Racing Limited**

Other Owners: A. W. A. Bates, Mrs J. M. Bonson, A. Cairns, Mrs A. Cairns, Mrs K. Campbell, Lord Daresbury, A. Dawson, J. Ennis, Mr D. A. Lofthouse, A. Meale, Mrs M. Nicholas, W. Raw, Mr K. C. Waddup, Wetherby Racing Bureau Ltd, Mr J. Woodgate, Mr A. W. Woodgate.

Assistant Trainer: Mrs S Grant

Jockey (NH): R. McGrath. **Amateur:** Mr T. Greenall.

---

228 MR L. P. GRASSICK, Cheltenham
Postal: **Postlip Racing Stables, Winchcombe, Cheltenham, Gloucestershire, GL54 5AQ**
Contacts: PHONE (01242) 603124 YARD (01242) 603919 FAX (01242) 603602
MOBILE (07816) 930423 E-MAIL billy.grassick@btopenworld.com

1 BIT OF A MONKEY, 4, b g Superior Premium—Rita's Rock Ape **Baskerville Racing Club**
2 BOBBIE'S QUEST (IRE), 6, b m Bob's Return (IRE)—Lauristown Cross (IRE) **Baskerville Racing Club**
3 FATHER PAT, 5, br g Chaddleworth (IRE)—Lady Crusty **L. P. Grassick**
4 MIKE SIMMONS, 12, b g Ballacashtal (CAN)—Lady Crusty **L. P. Grassick**
5 MUIR COTTAGE, 7, br g Chaddleworth (IRE)—Lady Crusty **L. P. Grassick**
6 ROYAL RENEGADE, 5, b m Bettergeton—Impromptu Melody (IRE)
7 SANDYWELL GEORGE, 13, ch g Zambrano—Farmcote Air **David Lloyd & Mrs Carole Lloyd**
8 SUN BIAN, 6, br g Makbul—Silken Dalliance **N Goodger, S Crawley, L Grassick**

THREE-YEAR-OLDS

9 ROSE DE RITA, br f Superior Premium—Rita's Rock Ape **Mrs J. Pearce & Mr K. Carpenter**

Other Owners: Mr K. T. Carpenter, Mrs S. Crawley, Mr Nigel Goodger, Mr L. P. Grassick, Mr D. V. Lloyd, Mrs C. J. Lloyd, Mrs J. A. Pearce.

Jockey (flat): V. Slattery. **Jockey (NH):** D. Laverty. **Amateur:** Mr Joe Herbert.

---

229 MR M. J. GRASSICK, Curragh
Postal: **Fenpark Stables, Pollardstown, Curragh, Co. Kildare, Ireland**
Contacts: PHONE (00353) 4543 4483 (00353) 4543 6956 FAX (00353) 4543 7895
MOBILE (00353) 8724 31923
E-MAIL mjgrassick2@eircom.net

1 ALICE STRAND (IRE), 4, b f Indian Danehill (IRE)—Miami Sands (IRE) **Mrs S. Grassick**
2 BEECH GARDENS, 4, b f Sadler's Wells (USA)—Hatton Gardens **J. Higgins**
3 BIDALIA (IRE), 4, ch f Danehill Dancer (IRE)—Stately Bid (USA) **A. Finney**
4 BOCACCIO (IRE), 10, b g Brief Truce (USA)—Idara **Mrs C. Grassick**
5 CLASSICAL SWING (IRE), 4, b br f Celtic Swing—Classical Flair (USA) **O. Murphy**
6 CORAL CREEK (IRE), 4, b f Invincible Spirit (IRE)—Antapoura (IRE) **M.C. Grassick**
7 ETERNAL SPIRIT (IRE), 4, b g Invincible Spirit (IRE)—Here To Eternity (FR) **Mrs D. Finegan**
8 HARD ROCK CITY (USA), 8, b g Danzig (USA)—All The Moves (USA) **J. Dolan**

MR M. J. GRASSICK—continued

9 **LITTLE NYMPH**, 6, ch m Emperor Fountain—Light On Her Toes **S. Fox**
10 **LUCKY CLIO (IRE)**, 4, gr f Key of Luck (USA)—Special Lady (FR) **C. Faeste**
11 **MOORE'S LAW (USA)**, 10, b g Technology (USA)—Brass Needles (USA) **Mrs S. Grassick**
12 **PARADISE ROYALE (USA)**, 4, b f Royal Applause—Kissing Gate (USA) **Mr K. Campbell**
13 **PASSARELLE (USA)**, 4, b f In The Wings—Kitza (IRE) **M. O'Flynn**
14 **PRINCESS NICOLE (IRE)**, 5, ch m Alhaarth (IRE)—Tycooness (IRE) **Mr K. Campbell**
15 **RED CHERUB**, 4, ch f Arkadian Hero (USA)—Redgrave Devil **A. Bish**
16 **ROCK OF TARIK (IRE)**, 4, ch c Rock of Gibraltar (IRE)—Molasses (FR) **Miss P. O'Kelly**
17 **SHEER DANCE (IRE)**, 5, ch m Namid—Sheer Dane (IRE) **K. Griffin**
18 **SILVER TIDE (USA)**, 4, ch f Silver Hawk (USA)—Soaring Bay (USA) **O. Murphy**
19 **THOMAS SADLER (IRE)**, 4, b g Sadler's Wells (USA)—Nuts In May (USA) **M. O'Flynn**
20 **TRIKIRK (IRE)**, 7, b g Selkirk (USA)—Shastri (USA) **K. Smith**
21 **TULIPA NEGRA (USA)**, 5, b m Bahri (USA)—Tulipe Noire (USA) **S. Corbett, T. Dwyer**
22 **WINDBENEATHMYWINGS (IRE)**, 4, b f In The Wings—Moneefa **M. Duffy**

THREE-YEAR-OLDS

23 **ACCLAIMED PIPER (IRE)**, b g Acclamation—Piping Pearl (IRE) **O. Murphy**
24 **BETT'S SPIRIT (IRE)**, b f Invincible Spirit (IRE)—Hi Bettina **Miss P. F. O'Kelly**
25 **CEDROS BAY (IRE)**, ch c Frenchmans Bay (FR)—Second Dream (IRE) **J. Dolan**
26 **DALAVAL (IRE)**, b c Dalakhani (IRE)—Mayenne (USA) **Miss P. F. O'Kelly**
27 **DAYLITE ROBBERY (IRE)**, b g Statue of Liberty (USA)—Fey Lady (IRE) **J. Yarr**
28 Br f Rock of Gibraltar (IRE)—Dearest (USA) **Miss P. F. O'Kelly**
29 **DISTANT ROCK**, b f Distant Music (USA)—Chaffinch (USA) **J. Dolan**
30 **DIVINITUS**, b c Medicean—Diuinia Mia **Mrs S. Grassick**
31 **ESSENTIAL ELEMENT (IRE)**, ch c Cadeaux Genereux—Kincob (USA) **S. Rogers**
32 **FIVE SATINS (IRE)**, b f Invincible Spirit (IRE)—Manarah **M. J. Grassick**
33 **KAYFOUR (IRE)**, b f Raise A Grand (IRE)—Sunrise (IRE) **A. Moore**
34 **LAUREL CREEK (IRE)**, b c Sakura Laurel (JPN)—Eastern Sky (AUS) **Mr Nakao**
35 **OASIS GOLD (IRE)**, b f Oasis Dream—Fernanda **J. Higgins**
36 **PROMISE OF LOVE**, b f Royal Applause—Beloved Visitor (USA) **K. Campbell**
37 **QUEEN OF TARA (IRE)**, b f Sadler's Wells (USA)—Welsh Love **Miss P. F. O'Kelly**
38 **REALIGNMENT (IRE)**, b g Celtic Swing—Sharera (IRE) **K. Smith**
39 **SECULAR (IRE)**, b c Orpen (USA)—Ya Ya (IRE) **O. Murphy**
40 **SHAKOKO (IRE)**, b f Choisir (AUS)—Kayoko (IRE) **J. Dolan**
41 **SHEKARRY (IRE)**, ch f Kris Kin (USA)—Singing Millie **S. Von. Schilcher**
42 B f Emperor Jones (USA)—Storm And Sunshine (USA) **MBD Partnership**
43 **TORINA**, ch f Golan (IRE)—Tordasia (IRE) **M. C. Grassick**
44 B f Cape Cross (IRE)—Treacle (USA) **K. Campbell**
45 **VESTAVIA (IRE)**, b br f Alhaarth (IRE)—Tilbrook (IRE) **M. C. Grassick**
46 **WHISPER DANCE (USA)**, b f Stravinsky (USA)—My Cherie (USA) **J. Higgins**

TWO-YEAR-OLDS

47 B c 18/5 Clodovil (IRE)—Aglaia (SWI) (Aguarico (GER)) **R. Weiss**
48 B f 12/3 High Chaparral (IRE)—Blue Mary (FR) (Fabulous Dancer (USA)) (19304)
49 **CACACE (IRE)**, b f 30/4 Medecis—Jenbro (IRE) (Petorius) (771) **M. C. Grassick**
50 B c 15/5 One Cool Cat (USA)—Chia Laguna (IRE) (Ela-Mana-Mou) (13513) **R. Weiss**
51 B c 14/4 Cape Cross (IRE)—Dame Alicia (IRE) (Sadler's Wells) **Miss P. F. O'Kelly**
52 B c 5/5 Soviet Star (USA)—Evictress (IRE) (Sharp Victor (USA)) (41826) **J. Keeling**
53 B f 29/1 Montjeu (IRE)—Gamra (IRE) (Green Desert (USA)) **K. Campbell**
54 B f 8/4 Fasliyev (USA)—Grenouillere (USA) (Alysheba (USA))
55 B f 18/3 Speightstown (USA)—Ivy Leaf (IRE) (Nureyev (USA)) (85034) **M. O'Flynn**
56 Gr f 9/3 Verglas (IRE)—La Tintoretta (IRE) (Desert Prince (IRE)) (16086) **Mrs S. Grassick**
57 **LITTLE PRUDENCE**, ch f 4/3 Generous (IRE)—Redgrave Devil (Tug of War) **S. Fox**
58 Ch f 29/3 Pivotal—Lurina (IRE) (Lure (USA))
59 Gr c 29/3 Slickly (FR)—Mono Star (IRE) (Soviet Star (USA)) (7721) **J. Dolan**
60 Ch f 2/2 King's Best (USA)—Naazeq (Nashwan (USA)) **Mrs S. Grassick**
61 B f 15/3 Bertolini (USA)—Nirvana (USA) (Green Dancer (USA)) (48261)
62 B f 30/3 Rock of Gibraltar (USA)—Quiet Mouse (USA) (Quiet American (USA)) (173744) **M. O'Flynn**
63 Ch c 13/5 Distant Music (USA)—Tertia (IRE) (Polish Patriot (USA)) (2059) **S. Von Schilcher**

Assistant Trainer: Mr M. C. Grassick

Apprentice: D. Sweeney. **Amateur:** Mr M. C. Grassick.

230 MR C. J. GRAY, Bridgwater
Postal: **Horlake, Moorland, Bridgwater, Somerset, TA7 0AT**
Contacts: **HOME (01278) 691359 MOBILE (07989) 768163**

1 BRIGHT GREEN, 9, b g Green Desert (USA)—Shining High **Riverdance Consortium I**
2 LE FOREZIEN (FR), 9, b g Gunboat Diplomacy (FR)—Diane du Forez (FR) **S. C. Botham**
3 MAYEUL (FR), 8, ch g Luchiroverte (IRE)—Elbe (FR) **Riverdance Consortium 2**
4 MON CHEVALIER (IRE), 5, b h Montjeu (IRE)—Kumta (IRE) **S. C. Botham**
5 NOMAD (FR), 7, b g Brier Creek (USA)—Fortune V (FR) **A. P. Helliar**
6 RIFF RAFF, 5, b m Daylami (IRE)—Rafiya **Mr R. G. Botham**

Other Owners: Mr M. J. Colenutt, Mr Richard Flenk, Mrs Christine Gray, Mr A. P. Hayne.

Assistant Trainer: Mrs C. M. L. Gray

Conditional: B. Wharfe

231 MR P. M. GRAYSON, Formby
Postal: **South Moss Stud, Pasture Lane, Formby, Merseyside, L37 0AP**
Contacts: **PHONE (01704) 830668 FAX (01704) 830668**
E-MAIL info@pgr.uk.com WEBSITE www.pgr.uk.com

1 AUTOGRAPH HUNTER, 4, b g Tobougg (IRE)—Kalindi **G. Ferrigno**
2 AVA'S WORLD (IRE), 4, b f Desert Prince (IRE)—Taibhseach (USA) **Peter Grayson Racing Clubs Limited**
3 BOLD ALASKA (IRE), 5, b g Cape Cross (IRE)—Dramatic Entry (IRE) **Mr R. Teatum & Mr S. Kamis**
4 CALYPSO KING, 5, b g Agnes World (USA)—T G's Girl **R. S. Teatum**
5 EGYPTIAN LORD, 5, ch g Bold Edge—Calypso Lady (IRE) **D & R Rhodes & Mrs S. Grayson**
6 FISH CALLED JOHNNY, 4, b g Kyllachy—Clare Celeste **The Touche Boys**
7 FLASHIN AMBER, 4, ch g Kyllachy—Shebasis (USA) **Mr A. Williams**
8 GIFTED GAMBLE, 6, b g Mind Games—Its Another Gift **Peter Grayson Racing Clubs Limited**
9 GRANGE LILI (IRE), 4, b f Daggers Drawn (USA)—Lili Cup (FR) **R. S. Teatum**
10 HEPHAESTUS, 4, b g Piccolo—Fragrant Cloud **Peter Grayson Racing Clubs Limited**
11 JAMES STREET (IRE), 5, b g Fruits of Love (USA)—Humble Mission **Mr K. Hill**
12 KILVICKEON (IRE), 4, b g Daggers Drawn (USA)—Queen of Sweden (IRE) **The Horse Power Partnership**
13 LADY BAHIA (IRE), 7, b m Orpen (USA)—Do The Right Thing **Peter Grayson Racing Clubs Limited**
14 LADY HOPEFUL (IRE), 6, b m Lend A Hand—Treble Term **Peter Grayson Racing Clubs Limited**
15 MAGIC GLADE, 9, b g Magic Ring (IRE)—Ash Glade **Mrs S. L. Grayson**
16 NOVA TOR (IRE), 6, b m Trans Island—Nordic Living (IRE) **Mr R. Teatum & Mrs S. Grayson**
17 NUSOOR (IRE), 5, b g Fasliyev (USA)—Zulfaa (USA) **Mr R. Teatum & Mrs S. Grayson**
18 OLD ETONIAN (UAE), 4, ch g Jade Robbery (USA)—Favoured **R. S. Teatum**
19 PRINCESS OF AENEAS (IRE), 5, b m Beckett (USA)—Romangoddess (IRE) **Mrs E. D. Hozack**
20 REGAL ROYALE, 5, b g Medicean—Regal Rose **Mr S. Kamis & Mrs S. Grayson**
21 RIGHTCAR BEVERLEY (IRE), 4, b g Kalanisi (IRE)—Do The Right Thing **Mr S. Kamis & Mr R. Teatum**
22 SAINT REMUS (IRE), 4, b g Diktat—Fur Will Fly **S. A. Kamis**
23 SILENT STORM, 8, ch g Zafonic (USA)—Nanda **R. S. Teatum**
24 SOLDIERS QUEST, 4, b c Rainbow Quest (USA)—Janaat **Peter Grayson Racing Clubs Limited**
25 STONEACRE BOY (IRE), 5, ch g City On A Hill (USA)—Sans Ceriph (IRE) **R. S. Teatum**
26 STONEACRE DONNY (IRE), 4, br c Lend A Hand—Election Special **R. S. Teatum**
27 STONEACRE GARETH (IRE), 4, b g Grand Lodge (USA)—Tidal Reach (USA) **Mr R. Teatum & Mrs S. Grayson**
28 STONEACRE LAD (IRE), 5, b h Bluebird (USA)—Jay And-A (IRE) **R. S. Teatum**
29 TOUS LES DEUX, 5, b g Efisio—Caerosa **Boys In Blue**
30 WIBBADUNE (IRE), 4, ch f Daggers Drawn (USA)—Becada (GER) **Peter Grayson Racing Clubs Limited**

THREE-YEAR-OLDS

31 GELERT (IRE), b c Acclamation—Game Leader (IRE) **T. W. Blane**
32 KAY TEE JO (IRE), br f High Chaparral (IRE)—Kariyh (USA) **A. P. Shandley**
33 MAYOMAN (IRE), b c Namid—America Lontana (FR) **Mr T. J. Tuohy**
34 OCEAN GLORY (IRE), b g Redback—Finty (IRE) **Lloyd Partnership**
35 RIGHTCAR DOMINIC, b c Kyllachy—Vallauris **Mr S. Kamis & Mrs S. Grayson**
36 RIGHTCAR ELLIE (IRE), b f Namid—Maid To Order (IRE) **Mr S. Kamis & Mrs S. Grayson**
37 RIGHTCAR HULL (IRE), b f Fantastic Light (USA)—Verbania (IRE) **Mr S. Kamis & Mrs S. Grayson**
38 RIGHTCAR LEWIS, ch f Noverre (USA)—Abeyr **Mr S. Kamis & Mrs S. Grayson**
39 RIO TAFFETA, b g Diktat—Taffeta (IRE) **R. S. Teatum**
40 SEVENOVUS (IRE), ch c Observatory (USA)—Flaming Salsa (FR) **Mees Demolition Partnership**
41 SINEAD OF AGLISH (IRE), ch f Captain Rio—Final Favour (IRE) **Men At Work Racing**

MR P. M. GRAYSON—continued

42 **STAR IN THE EAST**, ch f Observatory (USA)—Snipe Hall **R. S. Teatum**
43 **STONEACRE BABY (USA)**, ch f Stravinsky (USA)—Katiba (USA) **R. S. Teatum**
44 **STONEACRE CHRIS (USA)**, ch f Belong To Me (USA)—Fonage **Mr R. Teatum & Mrs S. Grayson**
45 **STONEACRE MA**, b f Dubai Destination (USA)—Silent Tribute (IRE) **Mr R. Teatum & Mrs S. Grayson**
46 **STONEACRE PADDY (IRE)**, ch c Golan (IRE)—Nocturnal (FR) **Mr R. Teatum & Mrs S. Grayson**
47 **STONEACRE PAT (IRE)**, b c Iron Mask (USA)—Sans Ceriph (IRE)
48 **STONEACRE SARAH**, b f Cadeaux Genereux—Tropical **Mr R. Teatum & Mrs S. Grayson**
49 **SUNSET RESORT (IRE)**, b c King's Best (USA)—Summer Dreams (IRE) **T. W. Blane**
50 Ch f Fath (USA)—The Poachers Lady (IRE)
51 **TILLY ANN (IRE)**, b f Turtle Island (IRE)—Buckland Filleigh (IRE) **Mrs T. Harding**
52 **WHERE'S KILLORAN**, b f Iron Mask (USA)—Calypso Lady (IRE) **W. K. Syndicate**

TWO-YEAR-OLDS

53 Ch f 10/2 Monsieur Bond (IRE)—Antonia's Folly (Music Boy) (4500)
54 B f 16/4 Statue of Liberty (USA)—Baltic Beach (IRE) (Polish Precedent (USA))
55 B c 20/2 Elusive City (USA)—Cannikin (IRE) (Lahib (USA))
56 Ch f 20/4 Bold Edge—Houdini Bay (IRE) (Indian Lodge (IRE))
57 B f 14/3 Galileo (IRE)—Lilly Gee (IRE) (Ashkalani (IRE))
58 Ch c 16/4 Falbrav (IRE)—Marrakech (IRE) (Barathea (IRE)) (13000)
59 Br f 14/2 Captain Rio (USA)—Oh So Rosie (IRE) (Danehill Dancer (IRE)) (5000)
60 Ch c 4/4 Primo Valentino (IRE)—Pearls (Mon Tresor) (4200)
61 B f 23/1 Namid—Rihana (IRE) (Priolo (USA)) (8000)
62 **USUAL SUSPECTS**, b f 12/2 Royal Applause—Soft Breeze (Zafonic (USA)) (30000)
63 B f 20/3 Bahri (USA)—Vampire Queen (IRE) (General Monash (USA))
64 Ch c 20/4 Bold Edge—Wendy's Girl (IRE) (Ashkalani (IRE))
65 B f 14/5 Needwood Blade—Yabint El Sham (Sizzling Melody) (20000)
66 Bl f 6/3 Needwood Blade—Zamyatina (IRE) (Danehill Dancer (IRE)) (8000)

Other Owners: Mr S. Forde, Mrs Sarah Grayson, Mr P Grayson, Mr S. A. Kamis, Killoran Civil Engineering Ltd, Mr J. R. Lloyd, Mrs Helen Jane Lloyd, Mr J. P. McGing, Mr Danny O'Neill, D. L. Rhodes, Mr A. Stubbs, Mr Richard Teatum, Mr Matt Thompson.

Assistant Trainer: Mrs S. Grayson

Apprentice: Liam Keniry. **Apprentice:** Ryan Hill. **Amateur:** Mr C. Ellingham.

---

232 MR P. GREEN, Lydiate
Postal: Oak Lea, Southport Road, Lydiate, Liverpool, Merseyside, L31 4HH
Contacts: PHONE (0151) 526 0093 FAX (0151) 520 0299 MOBILE (07748) 630685
E-MAIL paulgreen@mitchell-james.com

1 **BUNGIE**, 4, gr g Forzando—Sweet Whisper **Mr M. J. McHugh**
2 **CANINA**, 5, b m Foxhound (USA)—Fizzy Fiona **The Three Degrees**
3 **CELEB STYLE (IRE)**, 4, b f Tagula (IRE)—Lovely Me (IRE) **Celeb Style Racing**
4 **INVINCIBLE FORCE (IRE)**, 4, b g Invincible Spirit (IRE)—Highly Respected (IRE) **Mr T. P. Cummins**
5 **JILLY WHY (IRE)**, 7, b m Mujadil (USA)—Ruwy **Oaklea Racing**
6 **PUNTA GALERA (IRE)**, 5, br g Zafonic (USA)—Kobalt Sea (FR) **Mr D. A. Howard**
7 **RIGHT YOU ARE (IRE)**, 8, ch g Right Win (IRE)—Ancadia **P. Green**

THREE-YEAR-OLDS

8 **CHARLIE GREEN (IRE)**, b g Traditionally (USA)—Saninka (IRE) **Oaklea Racing**
9 **FEELING FRESH (IRE)**, b c Xaar—Oh'cecilia (IRE) **Mr M. H. Kay**
10 **SATURDAY BOY**, b c Josr Algarhoud (IRE)—Prideway (IRE) **P. Boyers**
11 **SUDDEN IMPACT (IRE)**, b br f Modigliani—Suddenly **Mr T. P. Cummins**

TWO-YEAR-OLDS

12 B c 19/1 Kyllachy—Latina (IRE) (King's Theatre (IRE)) (40000) **Mr M. H. Kay**
13 B f 18/5 Saffron Walden (FR)—Locorotondo (IRE) (Broken Hearted) (5791) **P. Green**
14 **LUCKY DAN (IRE)**, b c 26/3 Danetime (IRE)—
          Katherine Gorge (USA) (Hansel (USA)) (7078) **Daniel Britton & Luke Cummins**
15 Br c 18/3 Invincible Spirit (IRE)—Mughetta (Prince Sabo) (25740) **Mr M. H. Kay**
16 **NEO'S MATE (IRE)**, br f 2/4 Modigliani (USA)—Gute (IRE) (Petardia) (5147) **Mr D. A. Howard**
17 B c 26/3 Modigliani—Woodenitbenice (USA) (Nasty And Bold (USA)) (19304) **P. Green**

Other Owners: Mr P. A. Baines, Mr L. Barton, Mr D. Britton, Mr L. Cummins, D. J. Jones, I. P. Mason, D. Nicholls.

Assistant Trainer: Fiona Ford

233 MR V. G. GREENWAY, Taunton
Postal: **Manor Farm House, Fitzhead, Taunton, Somerset, TA4 3JZ**
Contacts: **PHONE (01823) 400091 MOBILE (07854) 626928**

1 EL HOMBRE DEL RIO (IRE), 11, ch g Over The River (FR)—Hug In A Fog (IRE) **V. G. Greenway**
2 JOIZEL (FR), 11, b g Fill My Hopes (FR)—Anne de Boizel (FR) **V. G. Greenway**

Other Owners: Mrs M. Greenway.

234 MR S. G. GRIFFITHS, Carmarthen
Postal: **Rwyth Farm, Nantgaredig, Carmarthen, Dyfed, SA32 7LG**
Contacts: **PHONE (01267) 290321/290120**

1 ICE RAIN (IRE), 8, gr g Zaffaran (USA)—Turbet Lass (IRE) **S. G. Griffiths**
2 JIMMY BEDNEY (IRE), 7, b br g Simply Great (FR)—Double Token **S. G. Griffiths**
3 MARTLE KING, 5, ch g Peacock Jewel—Redoran **S. G. Griffiths**

Assistant Trainer: Martyn Roger Griffiths

235 MR D. M. GRISSELL, Brightling
Postal: **Brightling Park, Robertsbridge, East Sussex, TN32 5HH**
Contacts: **PHONE (01424) 838241 MOBILE (07787) 843277**
E-MAIL ggrissell@aol.com

1 BUCKLAND GOLD (IRE), 8, b g Lord Americo—Beann Ard (IRE) **Mrs R. M. Hepburn**
2 CORKER, 6, ch g Grand Lodge (USA)—Immortelle **Bernard & Jan Wolford**
3 GREEN GAMBLE, 8, gr g Environment Friend—Gemma's Wager (IRE) **Mr Barry & Baroness Noakes**
4 HERCULES MORSE (IRE), 12, b g Spanish Place (USA)—Pragownia **A. W. K. Merriam**
5 ISLE DE MAURICE, 6, b g Sinndar (IRE)—Circe's Isle **Chegwidden Systems Ltd**
6 LEADAWAY, 9, b g Supreme Leader—Annicombe Run **Chegwidden Systems Ltd**
7 PERANGE (FR), 12, ch g Perrault—La Mesange (FR) **Mrs A. T. Merriam**
8 SADDLERS MOT, 4, b f Saddlers' Hall (IRE)—Be My Mot (IRE) **R. Winchester & Son**

Other Owners: Baroness Noakes, Mr C. B. Noakes, Mr B. Wolford, Mrs J. Wolford.

236 MR J. B. GROUCOTT, Much Wenlock
Postal: **11 Bourton, Much Wenlock, Shropshire, TF13 6QF**
Contacts: **PHONE (01746) 785603 FAX (01746) 785603 MOBILE (07866) 480830**
E-MAIL lisajmwillis@aol.com

1 GATSBY (IRE), 12, gr g Roselier (FR)—Burren Gale (IRE) **Ms L. J. M. Willis**
2 IKEMBA (IRE), 11, b g Executive Perk—Ardglass Pride **Ms L. J. M. Willis**
3 MAKING OVERTURES, 6, b m Overbury (IRE)—Random Romance **Mrs A. V. Winwood**
4 PRET A THOU (FR), 5, ch g Funny Baby (FR)—Va Thou Line (FR) **C. J. Tipton**

237 MR BRIAN GUBBY, Bagshot
Postal: **Dukes Wood, Bracknell Road, Bagshot, Surrey, GU19 5HX**
Contacts: **OFFICE (01276) 850513 FAX (01276) 479859 MOBILE (07768) 867368**

1 DAWSON CREEK (IRE), 4, ch g Titus Livius (FR)—Particular Friend **Brian Gubby**
2 JEBEL ALI (IRE), 5, b g Fruits of Love (USA)—Assertive Lass (USA) **Brian Gubby**

THREE-YEAR-OLDS

3 AL AQABAH (IRE), ch f Redback—Snow Eagle (IRE) **Brian Gubby**
4 EVENSTORM, ch f Stephen Got Even (USA)—Summer Wind Storm (USA) **Brian Gubby**

TWO-YEAR-OLDS

5 RICHARDLIONHEART (USA), ch c 21/1 Lion Heart (USA)—
Cleito (USA) (Unbridled's Song (USA)) (22837) **Brian Gubby**
6 SON OF THE CAT (USA), b c 24/3 Tale of The Cat (USA)—
Dixieland Gal (USA) (Dixieland Band (USA)) (48590) **Brian Gubby**

238 **MR R. GUEST, Newmarket**
Postal: **Chestnut Tree Stables, Hamilton Road, Newmarket, Suffolk, CB8 0NY**
Contacts: PHONE (01638) 661508 FAX (01638) 667317 MOBILE (07711) 301095
E-MAIL raeguest@raeguest.com WEBSITE www.raeguest.com

1 AFTER THE SHOW, 7, b g Royal Applause—Tango Teaser **Miss L. Thompson**
2 BAHIA BREEZE, 6, b m Mister Baileys—Ring of Love **Mr S. Balfour**
3 CRYSTAL BALL, 4, b f Diktat—First Sapphire **Mr & Mrs B. Cooper**
4 DANCING JEST (IRE), 4, b f Averti (IRE)—Mezzanine **Mrs J. E. Lury & Mr O. T. Lury**
5 DAWN MYSTERY, 4, gr f Daylami (IRE)—Frustration **Mrs J. E. Lury & Mr O. T. Lury**
6 LADY'S LAW, 5, b m Diktat—Snugfit Annie **Miss E. Jenkins**
7 LAURENTIAN LAD, 4, ch c Medicean—Cup Of Kindness (USA) **Adrian Smith**
8 MAGDALENE, 4, ch f Act One—Three Terns (USA) **Mrs P. Smith**
9 WORLD SPIRIT, 4, ch f Agnes World—Belle Esprit **R. J. Searle**

THREE-YEAR-OLDS

10 AMICABLE TERMS, b f Royal Applause—
    Friendly Finance **D. G. A. W. Woods, Mr & Mrs T. Barnett & Storm Again Syndicate**
11 CLASSIC LASS, b f Dr Fong (USA)—Cool Storm (IRE) **Mr & Mrs B. Cooper**
12 B f Bertolini (USA)—Cosmic Countess (IRE) **Mr R. V. Young**
13 FILLIGREE (IRE), b f Kyllachy—Clunie **The Filligree Partnership**
14 MIDNIGHT OASIS, b f Oasis Dream—Midnight Shift (IRE) **Mrs L. J. Mills**
15 B f Royal Applause—Miss Anabaa **C. J. Mills**
16 PRETTY OFFICER (USA), b f Deputy Commander (USA)—La Samanna (USA) **ROA Racing Partnership VIII**
17 ROSA GRACE, ro f Lomitas—Night Haven **E. P. Duggan**
18 SI BELLE (IRE), gr f Dalakhani (IRE)—Stunning (USA) **Miss K. Rausing**
19 SYVILLA, b f Nayef (USA)—Dance Steppe **T. J. Cooper**
20 TEYATEYANENG (IRE), b f Hawk Wing (USA)—Shir Dar (FR) **Mrs J. A. M. Poulter**
21 THANKFUL, b f Diesis—La Martina **T. J. Cooper**

TWO-YEAR-OLDS

22 Ch f 25/2 Haafhd—Broken Romance (IRE) (Ela-Mana-Mou) (50000) **E. P. Duggan**
23 Ch f 2/3 King Charlemagne (USA)—Clunie (Inchinor) (4000) **Mr Tony Hirschfeld**
24 DIKTAT QUEEN, b f 12/2 Diktat—Sakura Queen (IRE) (Woodman) (3400) **Jennifer & Barry Stewart**
25 FIERY (IRE), b f 13/3 Lujain (USA)—Fifth Edition (Rock Hopper) **Rachel Flynn & Rae Guest**
26 Gr f 10/2 Linamix (FR)—
    Hymenee (USA) (Chief's Crown (USA)) (32000) **Storm Again Syndicate & Dwayne Woods**
27 Ch f 11/2 Rahy (USA)—Khazayin (Bahri) (22837) **Mrs P. Smith & Mr Rae Guest**
28 B f 15/3 Oasis Dream—Midnight Shift (IRE) (Night Shift (USA)) **C. J. Mills**
29 B c 29/3 Royal Applause—Millyant (Primo Dominie) **C. J. Mills**
30 Ch f 24/3 Exceed And Excel (AUS)—Sedna (FR) (Bering) (20000) **Beadle, Booth, Davies & Jennings**
31 B br f 22/2 Singspiel (IRE)—Sicily (USA) (Kris S (USA)) (5000)
32 B f 15/4 King Charlemagne (USA)—Teller (ARG) (Southern Halo (USA)) (24000) **Mr Tony Hirschfeld**
33 B f 10/3 Red Ransom (USA)—The Blade (GER) (Sure Blade (USA)) (10000)
34 B f 30/4 Toccet (USA)—Vingt Et Une (FR) (Sadler's Wells) (46161) **Mrs P. Smith & Mr Rae Guest**
35 Ch c 18/2 Bertolini (USA)—Windmill Princess (Gorytus (USA)) (12000) **R. V. Young**
36 B f 23/3 Mtoto—Zameyla (IRE) (Cape Cross (IRE)) (7500) **Purple & Yellow Partnership & Mr Rae Guest**

Other Owners: Miss D. A. Avery, M. J. Beadle, B. A. Cooper, Mr T. A. Daniels, A. P. Davies, Mr R. Davis, Ms L. M. Dorling, Mr B. J. Flahive, T. R. Gittins, Mr Rae Guest, T. Hirschfeld, R. H. Jennings, Mrs J. E. Lury, Mr O. T. Lury, Mrs B. Penrose, Mr Kevin Reddington, Ms E. M. B. A. Reffo, Mr S. D. Russell, L. J. M. J. Vaessen, M. K. Willis.

Amateur: Ms Rachel Flynn.

239 **MR W. J. HAGGAS, Newmarket**
Postal: **Somerville Lodge, Fordham Road, Newmarket, Suffolk, CB8 7AA**
Contacts: PHONE (01638) 667013 FAX (01638) 660534
E-MAIL william@somerville-lodge.co.uk

1 ABANDON (USA), 5, ch m Rahy (USA)—Caerless (IRE) **Cheveley Park Stud Limited**
2 CANDIDATO ROY (ARG), 7, ch g Roy (USA)—Candila (ARG) **Robert Muir & Des Scott**
3 CONQUEST (IRE), 4, b g Invincible Spirit (IRE)—Aguinaga (IRE) **Highclere Thoroughbred Racing XXXVIII**
4 CRETE (IRE), 6, b g Montjeu (IRE)—Paesanella **Highclere Thoroughbred Racing (Crete)**
5 DEL MAR SUNSET, 9, b g Unfuwain (USA)—City of Angels **R. A. Dawson**
6 ENTICING (IRE), 4, b f Pivotal—Superstar Leo (IRE) **Lael Stables Partnership**

MR W. J. HAGGAS—continued

7 **FYODOR (IRE)**, 7, b g Fasliyev (USA)—Royale Figurine (IRE) **The Fyodor Partnership**
8 **HEAVEN KNOWS**, 5, ch g Halling (USA)—Rambling Rose **Hamdan Al Maktoum**
9 **KAATEB (IRE)**, 5, b g Alhaarth (IRE)—Muhaba (USA) **Hamdan Al Maktoum**
10 **LADY GRACE (IRE)**, 4, b f Orpen (USA)—Lady Taufan (IRE) **F. C. T. Wilson**
11 **MUSAALEM (USA)**, 4, gr g Aljabr (USA)—Atyab (USA) **Hamdan Al Maktoum**
12 **MUTAJARRED**, 4, ch g Alhaarth (IRE)—Bedara **Hamdan Al Maktoum**
13 **STARGAZER JIM (FR)**, 6, br g Fly To The Stars—L'americaine (USA) **N. J. Hughes**
14 **TIFERNATI**, 4, b g Dansili—Pain Perdu (IRE) **Mr J. Townsend**
15 **VERY WISE**, 6, b g Pursuit of Love—With Care **J. M. Greetham**

THREE-YEAR-OLDS

16 **ALFATHAA**, b c Nayef (USA)—Arctic Char **Hamdan Al Maktoum**
17 **AQLAAM**, b c Oasis Dream—Bourbonella **Hamdan Al Maktoum**
18 **BASQUE BEAUTY**, b f Nayef (USA)—River Cara (USA) **Mr & Mrs Neil Weekes**
19 **BELLOMI (IRE)**, br gr g Lemon Drop Kid (USA)—Reina Blanca **Hit The Beach Partnership**
20 **BRILLIANT RESULT (IRE)**, b f Barathea (IRE)—Marjie (IRE) **B. N. Wallace**
21 **CANDELA BAY (IRE)**, b f Captain Rio—Incendio **Mrs A. Goddard & Mr M. Hawkes**
22 **CARPE DIEM**, b g Stravinsky (USA)—Spare That Tree (USA) **Joseph Ogden, J. Hanson, John Ogden**
23 **COLLECTION (IRE)**, b c Peintre Celebre (USA)—
    Lasting Chance (USA) **Highclere Thoroughbred Racing (Brunel)**
24 **ELEONORA (FR)**, b f Fasliyev (USA)—Josey Wood (SAF) **D. I. Scott**
25 **ENSNARE**, b c Pivotal—Entrap **Cheveley Park Stud Limited**
26 **FLOWER**, ch f Zamindar (USA)—Time For Tea (IRE) **Mrs C. A. Cyzer**
27 **HAYDENS MARK**, b g Efisio—Lady In Colour (IRE) **Mrs J. J. Dye**
28 **INSAAF**, b f Averti (IRE)—Molly Brown **Hamdan Al Maktoum**
29 **MAGHYA (IRE)**, b f Mujahid (USA)—Khaizarana **Hamdan Al Maktoum**
30 **MAGNITUDE**, ch c Pivotal—Miswaki Belle (USA) **Cheveley Park Stud Limited**
31 **MAID OF AILSA (USA)**, ch f Pivotal—Chiquita (IRE) **B. N. Wallace**
32 **MAIMOONA (IRE)**, ch f Pivotal—Shuruk **Hamdan Al Maktoum**
33 **MAJEEN**, ch c Rock of Gibraltar (IRE)—Guilty Secret **A. Al Khalifa**
34 **MANDELIEU (IRE)**, b g Acclamation—Notley Park **L Palmer/ B Smith/ W Haggas**
35 **MARDOOD**, b g Oasis Dream—Gaelic Swan (IRE) **Hamdan Al Maktoum**
36 **MONAADEMA (IRE)**, b f Elnadim (USA)—Suhaad **Hamdan Al Maktoum**
37 **MONT CERVIN**, b g Sakhee (USA)—Daylight Dreams **Mrs C. A. Cyzer**
38 **NABEEH (IRE)**, b g Storming Home—Budoor **K. Alsayegh**
39 **PRITI FABULOUS (IRE)**, b f Invincible Spirit (IRE)—Flying Diva **K. A. Murphy**
40 **RAMAAD**, ch g Dr Fong (USA)—Artifice **Hamdan Al Maktoum**
41 **ROARING FORTE (IRE)**, b c Cape Cross (IRE)—Descant (USA) **Flying Tiger Partnership**
42 **ROMANTIC VERSE**, b f Kyllachy—Romancing **Romantic Verse Partnership**
43 **ROWAN RIO**, ch g Lomitas—Lemon Tree (USA) **Rowan Stud Partnership 1**
44 **SABANCAYA**, b f Nayef (USA)—Serra Negra **Mrs M. Slack**
45 **SHAMALI**, ch c Selkirk (USA)—Shamaiel (IRE) **A. Al Khalifa**
46 **SILVANUS (IRE)**, b g Danehill Dancer (USA)—Mala Mala (IRE) **Norman Lee**
47 **SINGE**, ch f Pivotal—Red Flame (IRE) **Cheveley Park Stud Limited**
48 **SNOWDROP PRINCESS**, b f Vettori (IRE)—Princess Louise **Snowdrop Stud Company Ltd**
49 **SPEED SONG**, b f Fasliyev (USA)—Superstar Leo (IRE) **Lael Stable**
50 **STORYLAND (USA)**, b f Menifee (USA)—Auspice (USA) **Mr & Mrs R. Scott**
51 **TANTO FAZ (IRE)**, b c Rock of Gibraltar (IRE)—Sharakawa (IRE) **Tanto Faz Partnership**
52 **TIGER MIST (IRE)**, ch f Galileo (IRE)—Arlesiana (USA) **M S Bloodstock Ltd**
53 **VINEYARD**, b g Alhaarth (IRE)—Abime (USA) **Highclere Thoroughbred Racing (VCI)**
54 **VITAL LINK (IRE)**, gr g Pivotal—Attachment (USA) **Flying Tiger Partnership**
55 **WAARID**, b g Alhaarth (IRE)—Nibbs Point (IRE) **Hamdan Al Maktoum**
56 **WINE 'N DINE**, b c Rainbow Quest (USA)—Seasonal Splendour (IRE) **Mrs C. A. Cyzer**
57 **WISE HAWK**, b g Hawk Wing (USA)—Dombeya (IRE) **Wise Move UK Limited**
58 **WISE LEE**, b g Zilzal (USA)—Ayunli **Wise Move UK Limited**
59 **WISE MELODY**, b f Zamindar (USA)—Swellegant **Wise Move UK Limited**

TWO-YEAR-OLDS

60 **ADORING (IRE)**, b f 14/4 One Cool Cat (USA)—
    Refined (IRE) (Statoblest) (70000) **Highclere Thoroughbred Racing (Gimcrack)**
61 **ATHAAKEEL (IRE)**, b f 18/5 Almutawakel—Asaafeer (USA) (Dayjur (USA)) **Hamdan Al Maktoum**
62 **AWFEYAA (IRE)**, ch f 26/1 Haafhd—Aspen Leaves (USA) (Woodman (USA)) **Hamdan Al Maktoum**
63 **CHORAL SERVICE**, ch c 10/5 Pivotal—Choir Mistress (Chief Singer) **Cheveley Park Stud Limited**
64 **B** f 7/5 Tobougg (IRE)—Composition (Wolfhound (USA)) **The Tricky Bloke Partnership**
65 **COSTEBELLE (IRE)**, b c 4/2 Cape Cross (IRE)—Steel Princess (IRE) (Danehill (USA)) (58000) **J. Hanson**

MR W. J. HAGGAS—continued

66 B f 26/5 Efisio—Council Rock (General Assembly (USA)) **Mr A. Hirschfield & Partners**
67 **COUNTENANCE**, ch c 27/1 Medicean—
      Glamorous (Sanglamore (USA)) (90000) **Highclere Thoroughbred Racing (Ormonde)**
68 B c 3/5 Danehill Dancer (IRE)—Crumpetsfortea (IRE) (Henbit (USA)) (215000) **Mrs Nicola Mahoney**
69 Ch f 6/4 Elusive Quality (USA)—Dabaweyaa (Shareef Dancer (USA)) **M. Obaida**
70 **DANEHILL DESTINY**, b f 25/2 Danehill Dancer (IRE)—
      Comeraincomeshine (IRE) (Night Shift (USA)) (120000) **Cheveley Park Stud Limited**
71 **DEMAND**, b f 12/2 Red Ransom (USA)—Coy (IRE) (Danehill (USA)) **Cheveley Park Stud Limited**
72 **DIDDUMS**, b c 15/4 Royal Applause—Sahara Shade (USA) (Shadeed (USA)) (8000) **B. Haggas**
73 **DREAM DATE (IRE)**, b f 15/2 Oasis Dream—Femme Fatale (Fairy King (USA)) (90000) **F. C. T. Wilson**
74 **FUSSY**, ch f 18/1 Dr Fong (USA)—Blue Dream (IRE) (Cadeaux Genereux) **B. Haggas**
75 **GASSAL**, b f 24/1 Oasis Dream—Hasten (USA) (Lear Fan (USA)) **Hamdan Al Maktoum**
76 B f 14/3 Captain Rio—Good Health (Magic Ring (USA)) (18000) **Scotney, Asplin, Symonds Partnership**
77 B br f 27/2 Hawk Wing (USA)—Hawala (IRE) (Warning) (115000) **Mr F. C. T. Wilson**
78 **JACHOL (IRE)**, b c 13/5 Bachelor Duke (USA)—
      Restiv Star (FR) (Soviet Star (USA)) (32174) **Ian & Christine Beard**
79 B c 18/1 Elusive Quality (USA)—June Moon (IRE) (Sadler's Wells (USA)) **B. Kantor**
80 B c 10/3 Montjeu (IRE)—Late Summer (USA) (Gone West (USA)) (20000) **B. Kantor**
81 **MASTOORA**, b f 16/3 Acclamation—Sacred Love (IRE) (Barathea (IRE)) (110000) **Hamdan Al Maktoum**
82 **MOOTRIBA**, ch f 19/3 Nayef (USA)—Tarbiyah (Singspiel (IRE)) **Hamdan Al Maktoum**
83 **MUTAMAASHI**, b c 11/2 Sakhee (USA)—Almahab (USA) (Danzig (USA)) **Hamdan Al Maktoum**
84 **MUTAWARATH**, b c 9/3 Marju (IRE)—Castlerahan (IRE) (Thatching) **Hamdan Al Maktoum**
85 **NEMOROSA**, b f 5/3 Pivotal—Anthos (GER) (Big Shuffle (USA)) **Cheveley Park Stud Limited**
86 **PENITENT**, b c 3/2 Kyllachy—Pious (Bishop of Cashel) **Cheveley Park Stud Limited**
87 **PURE PERFECTION (IRE)**, b f 26/2 Hawk Wing (USA)—Politesse (USA) (Barathea (IRE)) **B. Kantor**
88 **QUASH**, b c 20/2 Marju (IRE)—Blue Crush (IRE) (Entrepreneur) (32000) **Gibson, Goddard, Hamer & Hawkes**
89 **RAWAADAH**, ch f 29/1 Monsieur Bond—Amazed (Clantime) (154440) **Hamdan Al Maktoum**
90 **REJECT**, b c 8/3 Green Desert (USA)—Wardat Allayl (IRE) (Mtoto) (78000) **J. B. Haggas**
91 **RESPITE**, b f 11/5 Pivotal—Truce (Nashwan (USA)) **Cheveley Park Stud Limited**
92 **RIMTHAH (IRE)**, b f 5/1 Redback—Midnight Special (IRE) (Danetime (IRE)) (52000) **Hamdan Al Maktoum**
93 **RISAALA**, b f 23/2 Alhaarth (IRE)—Perfect Plum (Darshaan) **Hamdan Al Maktoum**
94 **SHAJEE (IRE)**, b c 18/3 Elusive City (USA)—Nagida (Skyliner) (42000) **Hamdan Al Maktoum**
95 **SIR ISAAC**, b c 27/1 Key of Luck (USA)—Rainbow Queen (FR) (Spectrum (IRE)) (25000) **Mr & Mrs R. Scott**
96 **SOUTH EASTER (IRE)**, ch c 14/5 Galileo (IRE)—Dance Treat (USA) (Nureyev (USA)) (210000) **B. Kantor**
97 B f 29/3 Storming Home—Sueboog (IRE) (Darshaan) **M. Obaida**
98 **TAGSEED (IRE)**, b c 8/2 Elusive City (USA)—Allegorica (IRE) (Alzao (USA)) (100000) **Hamdan Al Maktoum**
99 **WEDDING LIST**, ch f 15/5 Pivotal—Confetti (Groom Dancer (USA)) **Cheveley Park Stud Limited**
100 **WHERE YOU WILL**, ch f 17/1 Where Or When (IRE)—Red Duchess (Halling (USA)) **Cheveley Park Stud Limited**
101 B f 23/2 Kheleyf (USA)—
      Winter Tern (USA) (Arctic Tern (USA)) (28000) **B. Smith, A. Duke, J. Netherthorpe, G. Goddard**
102 B c 15/2 Dubai Destination (USA)—
      Zephirine Drouhin (Desert Style (IRE)) (50000) **Mr Ricky Wong & Sentinel Bloodstock**

Other Owners: Mr I. Beard, Mrs C. Beard, Mr W. Bottriell, Mr Ian Brown, R. L. Burton, C. F. Deuters, Mr B. Gibson, Mr Arthur
Goddard, Mrs T. Goddard, Mr F. M. Green, Mr C. M. Hamer, Mr J. Hanson, Mr M. Hawkes, The Hon H. Herbert, Highclere
Thoroughbred Racing Ltd, Mr Tony Hirschfeld, Mr R. Jackson, Mrs G. S. Jackson, W. P. Jenks, L. K. Piggott Ltd, Mr G.
Middlebrook, Mrs L. Middlebrook, Mr Robert C. Muir, Mr Joseph Ogden, Mr John Ogden, Mr Lee Palmer, Mrs Rosalind Ridout,
Mr J. S. Ridout, Mr G. A. Roberts, Mr D. I. Scott, Mrs P M. Scott, R. Scott, Mr Bob W. Smith, The Hon Mrs Stanley, Tessona
Racing Ltd, Mr Brian Wallace, Mrs R. Weekes, Mr N. Weekes, Mr E. B. Whittal-Williams, Mr Adrian Wright.

| **240** | **MISS V. HAIGH, Wiseton**
Postal: Studgroom House, Wiseton Hall Stables, Wiseton, Nr Doncaster, South Yorkshire, DN10 5AE
Contacts: PHONE (01777) 818200 FAX (01777) 818856 MOBILE (07816) 772451
E-MAIL enquiries@wisetonstables.co.uk WEBSITE www.wisetonstables.co.uk |

1 **LAITH (IRE)**, 5, b g Royal Applause—Dania (GER) **R. J. Budge**
2 **MUSICAL BEAT**, 4, ch f Beat Hollow—Warbler **R. J. Budge**

THREE-YEAR-OLDS

3 **AMAZING SPIRIT**, ch f Hawk Wing (USA)—Free Spirit (IRE) **R. J. Budge**
4 **EXTREME NORTH (USA)**, b g Stravinsky (USA)—North Dream (USA) **R. J. Budge**
5 **HONEY MONSTER (IRE)**, ch g Choisir (AUS)—Caribbean Escape **J. T. C. Longley**
6 **LANDED GENT (IRE)**, b g Kyllachy—Land Ahead (USA) **R. J. Budge**
7 **LITTLE ANGEL (IRE)**, br f Auction House (USA)—Green Sea **Miss V. Haigh**

MISS V. HAIGH—continued

8 **MODERN PRACTICE (IRE)**, br g Modigliani (USA)—Practice (USA) **R. J. Budge**
9 **MOLLYATTI**, b f Medicean—Tolyatti **R. J. Budge**
10 **TACTICAL MOVE**, b g Diktat—My Mariam **Mr R. Smith & R. J. Budge**
11 **THOMAS MALORY (IRE)**, b g Mujadil (USA)—Isca **R. J. Budge**
12 **ZAKYNTHOS (USA)**, ch g Singspiel (IRE)—Calista **R. J. Budge**

TWO-YEAR-OLDS

13 Br f 9/4 Celtic Swing—Golconda (IRE) (Lahib (USA)) (6434)
14 B f 2/4 Intikhab (USA)—Happy Story (IRE) (Bigstone (IRE)) (5147)
15 Ch f 5/5 Touch of The Blues (FR)—Hierarchy (Sabrehill (USA)) (1930)
16 B f 30/4 Exceed And Excel (AUS)—Kalwada (Roberto (USA)) (1608) **R. J. Budge**
17 B c 4/4 Fath (USA)—Majesty's Dancer (IRE) (Danehill Dancer (IRE)) (2573)
18 B f 3/4 Elusive City (USA)—Sagaing (Machiavellian (USA)) (4181)
19 B f 17/2 Kheleyf (USA)—Star Lodge (Grand Lodge (USA)) (1286)
20 B f 14/5 Acclamation—Thornby Park (Unfuwain (USA)) (3539) **Aiden & Carey Walsh**
21 Ch f 7/2 No Excuse Needed—Tilbrook (IRE) (Don't Forget Me) (2830)

Other Owners: Mr R. J. Budge.

Jockey (flat): Edward Creighton. **Apprentice:** Shane Creighton. **Amateur:** Miss V. Haigh.

MR J. S. HALDANE, Mindrum
Postal: The Yard Cottage, Mindrum, Northumberland, TD12 4QN
Contacts: PHONE (01890) 850382

1 **BILLSGREY (IRE)**, 6, gr g Pistolet Bleu (IRE)—Grouse-N-Heather **John & Mary Stenhouse**
2 **BILLSLEGACY (IRE)**, 6, ch g Commanche Run—Nickys Peril **John & Mary Stenhouse**
3 **BORDER SOVEREIGN**, 8, b g Sovereign Water (FR)—Skelton **Mrs Hugh Fraser**
4 **BOWERHOPE**, 8, b m Teenoso (USA)—Miss Aylesbury (IRE) **J. S. Haldane**
5 **FLORIDA VALLEY (IRE)**, 9, b m Florida Son—La Lucilla (IRE) **J. S. Haldane**
6 **HIGH EXPECTATIONS (IRE)**, 13, ch g Over The River (FR)—Andy's Fancy (IRE) **John & Mary Stenhouse**
7 **MR GILBERT**, 6, br g Overbury (IRE)—Brownhill Lass **J. S. Haldane**
8 **PACKAGE HOLIDAY (IRE)**, 8, ch g Florida Son—Wraparound Sue **Mrs Hugh Fraser**
9 **RAVENSBILL (IRE)**, 6, b g Sea Raven (IRE)—Two Hills Folly **John & Mary Stenhouse**
10 **SCOTTISH SPIRIT (IRE)**, 4, b g Invincible Spirit (IRE)—Triphibious **J. S. Haldane**
11 **THEATRE RIGHTS (IRE)**, 8, ch g Old Vic—Deep Perk (IRE) **John & Mary Stenhouse**

Other Owners: Mr J. M. Stenhouse, Mrs M. Stenhouse.

MR A. M. HALES, Daventry
Postal: Grange Farm, Preston Capes, Daventry, Northamptonshire, NN11 3TQ
Contacts: PHONE OFFICE (01296) 655255 (01327) 360919 FAX (01327) 361822
MOBILE (07771) 511652
E-MAIL alex@alexhalesracing.co.uk WEBSITE www.alexhalesracing.co.uk

1 **ABRAHAM SMITH**, 8, b g Lord Americo—Alice Smith **Call Me Dan**
2 **AMERICAN CRICKET (IRE)**, 7, b g Lord Americo—
Dixons Dutchess (IRE) **Mr A. Cohen & Glenmore Investments Ltd**
3 **ARYSHVIC**, 4, gr f Baryshnikov (AUS)—Cadal Queen (FR) **Brick Farm Racing**
4 **BALLYROBERT (IRE)**, 11, b br g Bob's Return (IRE)—Line Abreast **The Patient Partnership**
5 **BATCHWORTH BEAU**, 7, ch g Bluegrass Prince (IRE)—Batchworth Belle **Brick Farm Racing**
6 **CHERISHED NUMBER**, 9, b g King's Signet (USA)—Pretty Average **J. A. Findlay**
7 **CHILLY MILLY**, 7, b m Shambo—Phrase'n Cold (IRE) **Gumbrills Racing Partnership**
8 **DAKOTA BOY (IRE)**, 6, ch g Flying Legend (USA)—Lisaleen River **M. J. Tuckey**
9 **ENDLESS NIGHT**, 5, ch g Dracula (AUS)—La Notte **Brick Farm Racing**
10 **EXECUTIVE PADDY (IRE)**, 9, b g Executive Perk—Illbethereforyou (IRE) **Pennywise Racing**
11 **FANTASY LEGEND (IRE)**, 5, ch g Beckett (IRE)—Sianiski **Brick Farm Racing**
12 **FRIENDS OF TINA (IRE)**, 5, ch m Environment Friend—Runaway Tina (IRE) **The New Nemesis Partnership**
13 **FULL ON**, 11, b g Le Moss—Flighty Dove **The Mossy Partnership**
14 **HALFWAY CUT**, 6, b g Definite Article—Forest of Arden **The Patient Partnership**
15 **HELLO YOU**, 6, b g Pharly (FR)—Mardessa **Yeah or Neigh Racing Partnership**
16 **HIAWATHA (IRE)**, 9, b g Danehill (USA)—Hi Bettina **Pennywise Racing**
17 **ICONOCLAST (IRE)**, 7, b br g Topanoora—La Cigale (IRE) **John & Lorraine Barlow & Nick Hewinson**

MR A. M. HALES—continued

18 **JAGO (SWI)**, 5, b g Brief Truce (USA)—Jariyah (USA) **Four Counties Partnership**
19 **KHARAK (FR)**, 9, gr g Danehill (USA)—Khariyda (FR) **It's All About A Grey Partnership**
20 **KILMISTON SATURN**, 4, ch g Trifolio—Sunley Solaire **Pennywise Racing**
21 **KITE RUNNER (GER)**, 6, b g Winged Love (IRE)—Kayama (GER) **Hyzakite Racing**
22 **LAUGHING GAME**, 4, b f Classic Cliche (IRE)—Ground Game **Mr M Watt & Mrs P Fenwick**
23 **MARAAKEZ**, 5, b g Kalanisi (IRE)—Questabelle **A. M. Hales**
24 **MISS MIMM (IRE)**, 6, b m Ajraas (USA)—Salcantay **M. J. Tuckey**
25 **POLITICAL DISSENT**, 6, b m Commanche Run—Ranahinch (IRE) **D. M. Huglin**
26 **PONGO'S NEPHEW**, 7, b g Executive Perk—Major Hoolihan **Brick Farm Racing**
27 **RAZZANO (IRE)**, 4, b f Fasliyev (USA)—Shewillifshewants (IRE) **Brick Farm Racing**
28 **REGAL RAIDER (IRE)**, 5, b g King's Best (USA)—Alegranza (IRE) **Brick Farm Racing**
29 **ROCK SALMON**, 5, ch g Silver Patriarch (IRE)—The Lady Scores (IRE) **Mr A. F. Lousada**
30 **SALTANGO (GER)**, 9, b g Acatenango (GER)—Salde (GER) **CohenClearyKaplanMinnsPayneWatsonWilson**
31 **SECRET PACT (IRE)**, 6, br g Lend A Hand—Schust Madame (IRE) **The Secret Pact Partnership**
32 **SHARP RIGGING (IRE)**, 8, b g Son of Sharp Shot (IRE)—In The Rigging (USA) **The Sharpshooters**
33 **SHE KNOWS TOO MUCH**, 4, ch f Tobougg (IRE)—How Do I Know **Brick Farm Racing**
34 **SPECIAL RATE (IRE)**, 11, br g Grand Plaisir (IRE)—
                                                    Clerical Artist (IRE) **The Brown Family, Deeley, Faccenda, Bunter**
35 **SUPERIOR WISDOM (IRE)**, 8, b g Pierre—Viva Las Vegas (IRE) **Mr A. Cohen & Glenmore Investments Ltd**
36 **TETRAGON (IRE)**, 8, b g Octagonal (NZ)—Viva Verdi (IRE) **Brick Farm Racing**
37 **THE NEW NEMESIS (IRE)**, 5, b g Shadeed (USA)—Frivolous Fan (USA) **The New Nemesis Partnership**
38 **TUPPACE A BAG (IRE)**, 7, ch m Ajraas (USA)—Lisaleen River **Hyzakite Racing**
39 **WHAT DO YOU KNOW**, 5, b g Compton Place—How Do I Know **Brick Farm Racing**

THREE-YEAR-OLDS

40 **CRIMSONWING (IRE)**, b f Vettori (IRE)—Crimson Topaz **Brick Farm Racing**
41 **FONGSTER**, b g Dr Fong (USA)—First Lite of Dawn **Broadway Sky Partnership**
42 **STEALTH PROJECT**, b c Elmaamul (USA)—Guardee **D. M. Huglin**

Other Owners: Mrs L. Barlow, Mr J. W. Bettles, G. Bridgford, Exors of the Late Mrs S. R. Brown, Mrs P. S. Bunter, Miss S. Burnell, Mr J. Cleary, A. L. Cohen, Mr G. Connor, M. R. Deeley, Mr N. Doughty, Mrs S. Faccenda, Mrs D. J. R. Fenwick, J. S. C. Fry, Mrs K. A. Fry, Glenmore Investments Ltd, Mrs C. Haggar, Mr P. V. Haggar, D. A. Hibbert, Mrs J. Honess, Alan Kaplan, A. S. Lancaster, Mrs S. E. Lindley, G. P. Martin, P. J. Minns, R. E. Morris-Adams, J. E. Payne, Mr S. Pearman, G. R. Poole, Mr T. C. Steele, I. R. Taylor, Mrs J. C. Walker, G. M. Watson, M. Watt, Mrs J. E. Wilson, Mr N. J. Witts-Hewinson.

Jockey (NH): W. T. Kennedy.

---

243 MISS S. E. HALL, Middleham
Postal: **Brecongill, Coverham, Leyburn, North Yorkshire, DL8 4TJ**
Contacts: PHONE **(01969) 640223** FAX **(08450) 091223**
E-MAIL sally@brecongill.co.uk

1 **BLUE OPAL**, 6, b m Bold Edge—Second Affair (IRE) **Colin Platts**
2 **BOLD HAZE**, 6, ch g Bold Edge—Melody Park **Mrs J. Hodgson**
3 **HUNTING HAZE**, 5, b g Foxhound (USA)—Second Affair (IRE) **Colin Platts**
4 **LUCINDA LAMB**, 6, b m Kayf Tara—Caroline Lamb **Miss S. E. Hall**
5 **PIGMENT**, 4, ch f Zamindar (USA)—Lady Mayor **Miss S. E. Hall**
6 **SOUND OF SILVER**, 5, b g Supreme Sound—Silver's Girl **Mr & Mrs W. H. Woods**

THREE-YEAR-OLDS

7 B g Vettori (IRE)—Second Affair (IRE) **Miss S. E. Hall**

TWO-YEAR-OLDS

8 **MAGIC HAZE**, b g 3/5 Makbul—Turn Back (Pivotal) **Mrs J. Hodgson**
9 **MARKADAM**, b g 22/2 Mark of Esteem (IRE)—Elucidate (Elmaamul (USA)) (10000) **Mrs J. Hodgson**

Other Owners: Miss S. E. Hall, Mr W. H. Woods, Mrs G. H. Woods.

Assistant Trainer: Colin Platts

Jockey (NH): R. Johnson. **Amateur:** Mrs D. S. Wilkinson.

244 **MR S. W. HALL, Ipswich**
Postal: **Claydon Hall, Claydon, Ipswich, Suffolk, IP6 OEL**
Contacts: **PHONE (01473) 831183 MOBILE (07738) 128957**
E-MAIL taroc4@hotmail.com

1 BOOK OF FACTS (FR), 4, ch g Machiavellian (USA)—Historian (IRE) **Bournston Equestrian**
2 LITTLEMISSDYNAMITE, 5, b m Observatory (USA)—Once In My Life (IRE) **Claydon Hall Stud Partnership No 1**
3 RED BARNET, 4, ch g Tipsy Creek (USA)—Heather Valley **Miss V. Pratt**

THREE-YEAR-OLDS

4 CAROLE OS (IRE), b f Catcher In The Rye (IRE)—
Kuda Chantik (IRE) **John Howard, Jeremy Goddard Russell Holden**
5 COBBOLD POINT, b g Tipsy Creek (USA)—Mofeyda (IRE) **Miss V. Pratt**
6 EAST COAST GIRL (IRE), ch f Captain Rio—Toledana (IRE) **Just Good Friends Partnership**
7 MADAME MONTOM (USA), b f French Envoy (USA)—Sticky Fingers (USA) **Witnesham Ventures Limited**
8 TREASURE ISLANDS (IRE), b f Trans Island—Gold Prospector (IRE) **Mrs Jane Howard & Mr D J Kavanagh**

Other Owners: Mr E. J. Barham, Mr J. W. Goddard, Mr R. Holden, J. S. Howard, Mrs J. C. Howard, Mr D. J. Kavanagh.

Assistant Trainer: Mr P. Kerr

245 **MR G. A. HAM, Axbridge**
Postal: **Rose Farm, Rooksbridge, Axbridge, Somerset, BS26 2TH**
Contacts: **HOME (01934) 750331 FAX (01934) 751341 MOBILE (07732) 979962**
E-MAIL info@rosefarm.biz

1 CASPAR OF TARSUS (IRE), 5, ch g Moonax (IRE)—Another Thurn (IRE) **The Holmes Office Limited**
2 DIRTY' ARRY, 6, b h Fumo di Londra (IRE)—Midnight Romance **Mrs K. Hitchins**
3 FREDDY'S STAR (IRE), 6, ch g Kris—Kutaisi (IRE) **F. A. Clegg**
4 KAZARUS (FR), 4, b g Poplar Bluff—Miss Gee-Ell **Mr N. G. Ahier**
5 KRISMICK (IRE), 4, b f Orpen (USA)—Untold **Ashton Racing Club**
6 LANSDOWNE PRINCESS, 6, b m Cloudings (IRE)—Premier Princess **The Lansdowners**
7 MILK AND SULTANA, 8, b m Millkom—Premier Princess **Rose Farm Developments (UK) Ltd**
8 MR EXCEL (IRE), 5, b g Orpen (USA)—Collected (IRE) **Mrs K. Hitchins**
9 NOT TOO TAXING, 4, b g Forzando—Areish (IRE) **Mrs K. Hitchins**
10 REELINGA, 9, b m Karinga Bay—Reeling **The Lansdowners**
11 SABRE'S EDGE (IRE), 7, b g Sadler's Wells (USA)—Brave Kris (IRE) **Mrs D. S. Brown**
12 SNINFIA (IRE), 8, b m Hector Protector (USA)—Christmas Kiss **Rose Farm Developments (UK) Ltd**
13 THISTLE, 7, ch g Selkirk (USA)—Ardisia (USA) **F. A. Clegg**
14 TRAVELLO (GER), 8, b g Bakharoff (USA)—Travista (GER) **G. A. Ham**
15 WATCH OUT, 4, b g Observatory (USA)—Ballet Fame (USA) **G. A. Ham**
16 WORLD SUPREMACY (IRE), 5, b g Spinning World (USA)—Cream Jug (IRE) **Miss A. Bourne**

THREE-YEAR-OLDS

17 AGE OF MIRACLES (IRE), b g Carrowkeel (IRE)—Busking **The Holmes Office Limited**

Other Owners: Mr J. F. Baldwin, Mr P. Green, Mr T. Hosier, Mr R. T. Wilkins.

Assistant Trainer: Jonathan Ham

Jockey (flat): S. Drowne, J. Quinn. Jockey (NH): Rodi Greene. Conditional: E. Dehdashti, Bernie Wharfe.

246 **MRS M. C. HAMBRO, Cheltenham**
Postal: **Cotswold Stud, Sezincote, Moreton-In-Marsh, Gloucestershire, GL56 9TB**
Contacts: **PHONE (01386) 700700 FAX (01386) 700701 MOBILE (07860) 632990**
E-MAIL maryhambro@mac.com

1 BECKY'S HILL, 6, b m Mtoto—Neptunalia **Richard A. Hambro**
2 DEBDENE BANK (IRE), 5, b m Pivotal—Nedaarah **Richard A. Hambro**
3 DOVER'S HILL, 6, b g Pistolet Bleu (IRE)—Classic Beauty (IRE) **Richard A. Hambro**
4 KITEBROOK, 7, b m Saddlers' Hall (IRE)—Neptunalia **Richard A. Hambro**
5 ROSE ROW, 4, gr f Act One—D'azy **Richard A. Hambro**

MRS M. C. HAMBRO—continued

THREE-YEAR-OLDS

6 WARREN BANK, b g Nayef (USA)—Neptunalia **Mrs M. C. Hambro**

Jockey (flat): Vince Slattery.

---

247 **MRS A. HAMILTON, Newcastle Upon Tyne**
Postal: Claywalls Farm, Capheaton, Newcastle Upon Tyne
Contacts: PHONE (01830) 530219
E-MAIL annhamilton1952@hotmail.com

1 DOMESTIC FLIGHT, 5, b m Missed Flight—Lady Manello **I. Hamilton**
2 FRED BOJANGALS (IRE), 6, b g Scribano—Southern Princess **I. Hamilton**
3 HEDCHESTER, 7, b g Missed Flight—Lady Manello **I. Hamilton**
4 NILE MOON (IRE), 7, b g Simply Great (FR)—Reasonable Time (IRE) **I. Hamilton**
5 ROLECARR (IRE), 5, b g Tragic Role (USA)—Nuit d'ete (USA) **I. Hamilton**
6 SILVER SEDGE (IRE), 9, gr g Aristocracy—Pollyfaster **I. Hamilton**

THREE-YEAR-OLDS

7 B f Karinga Bay—Deb's Ball **I. Hamilton**

TWO-YEAR-OLDS

8 B g 4/6 And Beyond (IRE)—Lady Manello (Mandrake Major) **I. Hamilton**

Assistant Trainer: Ian Hamilton

---

248 **MRS A. C. HAMILTON, Hawick**
Postal: Old Orchard Cottage, Cavers, Hawick
Contacts: PHONE (01450) 376399 MOBILE (07886) 084844

1 MY FINAL BID (IRE), 9, b g Supreme Leader—Mini Minor (IRE) **J. P. G. Hamilton**

THREE-YEAR-OLDS

2 Ch c Karinga Bay—Princess Topaz **Mr & Mrs J. P. G. Hamilton**

Assistant Trainer: Mr G Hamilton

---

249 **MOUSE HAMILTON-FAIRLEY, Hook**
Postal: Moor Place, Plough Lane, Bramshill, Hook, Hampshire, RG27 0RF
Contacts: PHONE (0118) 932 6269 FAX (0118) 932 6085 MOBILE (07798) 577761
E-MAIL mouse@hamilton-fairley.co.uk WEBSITE www.mousehamilton-fairley.co.uk

1 ACT THREE, 4, br f Beat Hollow—Rada's Daughter **Anric Racing**
2 ALLEZ MELINA, 7, b m Cloudings (IRE)—Theme Arena **Hamilton-Fairley Racing**
3 HATCH A PLAN (IRE), 7, b g Vettori (IRE)—Fast Chick **Hamilton-Fairley Racing**
4 LADY DIKTAT, 6, b m Diktat—Scared **Runs In The Family**
5 MOUNT BENGER, 8, ch g Selkirk (USA)—Vice Vixen (CAN) **Hamilton-Fairley Racing**
6 MUSICAL SCRIPT (USA), 5, b g Stravinsky (USA)—Cyrillic (USA) **The Composers**
7 PHONE CALL, 5, b m Anabaa (USA)—Phone West (USA) **Fairley Risky**
8 THEATRE ROYAL, 5, b m Royal Applause—Rada's Daughter **Runs In The Family**

THREE-YEAR-OLDS

9 ENCORE BELLE, b f Beat Hollow—Rada's Daughter **Rectory Racing**
10 HOLDEN CAULFIELD (IRE), b g Catcher In The Rye (IRE)—God Speed Her **Fairley Risky**
11 THUNDER GORGE (USA), b c Thunder Gulch (USA)—Renaissance Fair (USA) **Bramshill Racing**

TWO-YEAR-OLDS

12 LUCKY SCORE (IRE), b f 7/3 Lucky Story (USA)—
                        Musical Score (Blushing Flame (USA)) (29000) **Mrs Richard Plummer & Partners**

MOUSE HAMILTON-FAIRLEY—continued

Other Owners: P. J. Box, Mr Timothy Bunting, Ms Sarah Bunting, Mrs Charles Donald, J. A. Fergusson, Mrs C. M. Foster, Mouse Hamilton-Fairley, Mr Geoffrey Hamilton-Fairley, Mrs Nigel Hurst-Brown, Mrs E. A. Ireland, Sir Nevil Macready, Mrs Satu Marks, Mrs Richard Plummer, Mr Richard Plummer, Mr Christopher Symons.

Assistant Trainer: Larry Mancini

Jockey (NH): P. Hide. **Conditional:** S. Jones. **Apprentice:** T. Block.

---

250   MR M. D. HAMMOND, Middleham
Postal: **Oakwood Stables, East Witton Road, Middleham, Leyburn, North Yorkshire, DL8 4PT**
Contacts: **PHONE** (01969) 625223 **FAX** (01969) 625224 **MOBILE** (07808) 572777
E-MAIL mdhammondracing@tiscali.co.uk

1 ARCTIC COVE, 7, b g Vettori (IRE)—Sundae Girl (USA) **Oakwood Racing Partnership**
2 ASTON LAD, 7, b g Bijou d'inde—Fishki **S. T. Brankin**
3 BIG BERTHA, 10, ch m Dancing Spree (USA)—Bertrade **Mike & Eileen Newbould**
4 CALFRAZ, 6, b br g Tamure (IRE)—Pas de Chat **Mr J. McAllister**
5 CAMPLI (IRE), 6, b g Zafonic (USA)—Sept A Neuf **Racing Management & Training Ltd**
6 CHARLOTTE VALE, 7, ch m Pivotal—Drying Grass Moon **P. J. Davies**
7 CHATEAU ROUGE (IRE), 7, b g Tiraaz (USA)—Carolina Rua (USA) **The Vin Rouge Partnership**
8 CHERNIK (IRE), 7, b g Norwich—Sue Pickering (IRE) **M. D. Hammond**
9 DAWN RIDE (IRE), 7, b g New Frontier (IRE)—Atlantic Dawn (IRE) **Belarus Partnership**
10 DESERT HUNTER (IRE), 5, b g Desert Story (IRE)—She-Wolff (IRE)
11 DESERT RAT (IRE), 4, b g Desert Sun—Virtue Rewarded (USA) **Mr N. Rust**
12 DIVEX (IRE), 7, b g Taipan (IRE)—Ebony Countess (IRE) **The County Set (Two)**
13 FAIR SPIN, 8, ch g Pivotal—Frankie Fair **Ms J. Monaghan**
14 FARNE ISLAND, 5, ch g Arkadian Hero (USA)—Holy Island **J. Buzzeo**
15 GEORGE THE BEST (IRE), 7, b g Imperial Ballet (IRE)—En Retard (IRE) **Stefanos Stefanou**
16 HELVETIO, 6, b g Theatrical—Personal Love (USA) **Stefanos Stefanou**
17 HIGH COUNTRY (IRE), 8, b g Danehill (USA)—Dance Date (IRE) **Mr D. & Mrs C. Green**
18 HOLLIS, 4, b g Lost Soldier (USA)—Cutting Reef (USA) **Mr R. Bickenson**
19 INDUSTRIAL STAR (IRE), 7, ch g Singspiel (IRE)—Faribole (IRE) **Racing Management & Training Ltd.**
20 INGLEBY HILL (IRE), 4, b g Averti (IRE)—Living Daylights (IRE) **Mr E. Whalley**
21 KERRY'S BLADE (IRE), 6, ch g Daggers Drawn (USA)—Treasure (IRE) **Mr T. Matthews**
22 LA PANTERA ROSA (IRE), 5, br g Tragic Role (USA)—Fortune Cookie **N. J. Rust**
23 LORD COLLINGWOOD (IRE), 7, ch g Accordion—Cracker Dawn (IRE) **Mike & Eileen Newbould**
24 LUSENTO (IRE), 5, b g Luso—Richmond Breeze **Hope Springs Eternal**
25 MANBOW (IRE), 10, b g Mandalus—Treble Base (IRE) **Hope Springs Eternal**
26 MOTAFARRED (IRE), 6, ch g Machiavellian (USA)—Thurayya **Mr R. Bickenson**
27 MR CRYSTAL (FR), 4, ch g Trempolino (USA)—Iyrbila (FR) **Mr S. Henderson**
28 PADDYMCGINTYSGOAT (IRE), 5, b g Saddlers' Hall (IRE)—One More Dash (IRE) **Cocker Doody Do**
29 RIMSKY KORSAKOV (IRE), 4, b g Sadler's Wells (USA)—Tedarshana
30 SALUTE THE GENERAL, 5, ch g Mark of Esteem (IRE)—Oiselina (FR) **Oakwood Racing Partnership**
31 SAN DENG, 6, gr g Averti (IRE)—Miss Mirror **Oakwood Racing Partnership**
32 SNOW'S RIDE, 8, gr g Hernando (FR)—Crodelle (IRE) **Belarus Partnership**
33 SWAINS BRIDGE (USA), 6, b g Swain (IRE)—Saraa Ree (USA) **F. Hanson**
34 TERENZIUM (IRE), 6, br g Cape Cross (IRE)—Tatanka (ITY) **O'Sunburn Partnership**
35 TIDY (IRE), 8, b g Mujadil (USA)—Neat Shilling (IRE) **Yorkshire Jolly Boys Partnership**
36 TITINIUS (IRE), 8, ch g Titus Livius (FR)—Maiyria (IRE) **Paul & Anne Sellars**
37 TRAFALGAR MAN (IRE), 7, b br g Scribano—Call Over **Mike & Eileen Newbould**
38 TRANOS (USA), 5, b g Bahri—Balancoire (USA) **J. Buzzeo**
39 TUCKER, 6, b g Inchinor—Tender Moment (IRE) **F. Hanson**

THREE-YEAR-OLDS

40 RING BERTIE, b g Bertolini (USA)—Ring Side (IRE) **Mr G. Shiel**

TWO-YEAR-OLDS

41 GOSWICK, ch f 17/3 Bertolini (USA)—Holy Island (Deploy) **Mr G. Shiel**
42 Ch c 15/3 Where Or When (IRE)—Star Entry (In The Wings) (4500)
43 Gr ro c 12/4 Monsieur Bond (IRE)—Top (Shirley Heights) (17000)

Other Owners: Mr Bobby Anderson, Mr D. Bamlett, Mr P. H. Bell, Mr John Bell, Mrs E. Bryant, Mr S. R. Caley, Mr Ian Clarkson, Mr T. Cockrill, Mr Patrick Doody, Mr P. B. Finnegan, Mr George Godsman, Mr Douglas Godsman, Mr D. Green, Mrs C. Green, Mr E. D. Haggart, Mr Nik. H. B. Ingham, Mrs G. Mackintosh, Mr J. M. Mcintyre, Mr Mike Newbould, Mrs E. E. Newbould, Mr H. G. Owen, Mr B. Raper, Mr Paul Sellars, Mrs Anne Sellars, Mr A. W. Sinclair, Mr O. R. Weeks.

251 MR M. P. HAMMOND, Lower Broadheath
Postal: The Stables, Frenchlands Lane, Lower Broadheath, Worcestershire, WR2 6QU
Contacts: PHONE (01905) 641421 MOBILE 07894 050183
E-MAIL mphatwellcottage@aol.com WEBSITE hammondracing.co.uk

1 AMBER LOVE, 5, b m Exit To Nowhere (USA)—Rossmore Girl (IRE) **Mrs S. I. Tainton**
2 ELGAR, 11, ch g Alflora (IRE)—School Run **Mrs S. I. Tainton**
3 GAYE DREAM, 10, b g Gildoran—Gaye Fame **Mrs S. I. Tainton**
4 JIVER (IRE), 9, b g Flemensfirth (USA)—Choice Brush (IRE) **Mrs S. I. Tainton**
5 MARTLE KING, 5, ch g Peacock Jewel—Redoran **S. G. Griffiths**
6 SHAAMIT THE VAAMIT (IRE), 8, b g Shaamit (IRE)—Shocker (IRE) **Mrs S. I. Tainton**
7 5, Ch m Karinga Bay—Third Time (IRE) **M. S. Poste**
8 TOOTSIE TOO, 6, b m Overbury (IRE)—Tap On Tootsie **D. P. Constable**
9 WORKING LATE, 6, b g Night Shift (USA)—All The Luck (USA) **Mr D. E. Portman**
10 ZAFFARANI'S STAR, 7, b g Zaffaran (USA)—Slipstream Star **Mrs S. I. Tainton**
11 ZAFFARANS SCENE, 7, b g Zaffaran (USA)—Rossmore Girl (IRE) **Mrs S. I. Tainton**

Assistant Trainer: Zoe Hammond

252 MRS S. E. HANDLEY, Market Drayton
Postal: Moreton Wood Forge, Moreton Wood, Market Drayton, Shropshire, TF9 3SF
Contacts: PHONE (01948) 890301 MOBILE (07932) 140668
E-MAIL sue@forgemaster.demon.co.uk

1 ANACRUSIS, 7, b g Yaheeb (USA)—Ellerbeck **P. C. & S. E. Handley**
2 ASK SCOTTY, 5, b g Kayf Tara—Minnie Bloo Min (IRE) **P. C. & S. E. Handley**
3 NOT NEAR WYSE (IRE), 6, b g Perpendicular—Ballinliss Lady **P. C. & S. E. Handley**
4 SIZZLING SHIZZY, 6, b m Spadoun (FR)—Loch Irish (IRE) **P. C. & S. E. Handley**
5 SNARGATE, 8, b g Double Eclipse (IRE)—Loch Irish (IRE) **P. C. & S. E. Handley**
6 YOUNG CUTHBERT, 10, b g Homo Sapien—Deirdres Dream **P. C. & S. E. Handley**

Other Owners: Mr P. C. Handley, Mrs S. E. Handley.

253 MR R. HANNON, Marlborough
Postal: East Everleigh Stables, Everleigh, Marlborough, Wiltshire, SN8 3EY
Contacts: PHONE (01264) 850 254 FAX (01264) 850 820

1 ASSERTIVE, 5, ch h Bold Edge—Tart And A Half **Lady Whent**
2 CAPE HAWK (IRE), 4, b g Cape Cross (IRE)—Hawksbill Special (IRE) **Thurloe Thoroughbreds XVII**
3 CRYSTAL GAZER (FR), 4, b f Elnadim (USA)—Chrysalu **A. F. J. Merritt**
4 DANEHILLSUNDANCE (IRE), 4, b c Danehill Dancer (IRE)—Rosie's Guest (IRE) **J. P. Hardiman**
5 EDGE CLOSER, 4, b c Bold Edge—Blue Goddess (IRE) **Lady Whent & Friends**
6 GALEOTA (IRE), 6, b g Mujadil (USA)—Refined (IRE) **Mr R. J. Blunt**
7 GONNASHINE, 4, ch f Muhtarram (USA)—Gulshan **Mrs J. K. Powell**
8 GRANDE CAIMAN (IRE), 4, ch c Grand Lodge (USA)—Sweet Retreat **I. A. N. Wight**
9 KYLE (IRE), 4, ch g Kyllachy—Staylily (IRE) **Noodles Racing**
10 MAJOR CADEAUX, 4, ch c Cadeaux Genereux—
                     Maine Lobster (USA) **N A Woodcock, A C Pickford & David Mort**
11 MALT OR MASH (USA), 4, gr c Black Minnaloushe (USA)—Southern Tradition (USA) **A. P. Patey**
12 MR AVIATOR (USA), 4, b br c Lear Fan (USA)—In Bloom (USA) **Mrs S. A. F. Brendish**
13 OAKLEY HEFFERT (IRE), 4, b g Titus Livius (FR)—Daftiyna (IRE) **B. C. Oakley**
14 ORCHARD SUPREME, 5, ch g Titus Livius (FR)—Bogus Penny (IRE) **B. C. Oakley**
15 PLUM PUDDING (IRE), 5, b g Elnadim (USA)—Karayb (IRE) **Hyde Sporting Promotions Ltd**
16 PRINCE SABAAH (IRE), 4, b c Spectrum (IRE)—Princess Sabaah (IRE) **D. Boocock**
17 SELINKA, 4, b f Selkirk (USA)—Lady Links **R. Barnett**
18 SONNY RED (IRE), 4, b c Redback—Magic Melody **Mr Michael Pescod & Mr J.A.Leek**
19 TINNARINKA, 4, ch f Observatory (USA)—Dancing Fire (USA) **D. J. Barry**
20 VITZNAU (IRE), 4, b c Val Royal (FR)—Neat Dish (CAN) **L. S. A. Stalder**

THREE-YEAR-OLDS

21 AVERTITOP, b c Averti (IRE)—Lucayan Belle **The Hill Top Partnership**
22 BERBICE (IRE), gr c Acclamation—Pearl Bright (FR) **J. McCarthy**
23 BLUES MINOR (IRE), b c Acclamation—Narbayda (IRE) **M. Pescod**
24 BLUR, b f Oasis Dream—Easy To Love (USA) **R. H. W. Morecombe**

MR R. HANNON—continued

25 **BON TON ROULET**, ch f Hawk Wing (USA)—Evangeline **G. Howard-Spink**
26 **BORDER OWL (IRE)**, b g Selkirk (USA)—Nightbird (IRE) **K. T. Ivory**
27 **CAKE (IRE)**, b f Acclamation—Carpet Lady (IRE) **Mr D. J. Anderson**
28 **CAPE COLONY**, gr c Cape Town (IRE)—Lucky Princess **A. F. J. Merritt**
29 **CHARTIST**, ch c Choisir (AUS)—Sareb (FR) **J A Leek & Michael Pescod**
30 **CITY OF THE KINGS (IRE)**, b c Cape Cross (IRE)—Prima Volta **T. Hyde**
31 **CLIFTON FOUR (USA)**, b f Forest Wildcat (USA)—Black Truffle (USA) **Mr A. T. J. Russell**
32 **COMMANDER CAVE (USA)**, b br c Tale of The Cat (USA)—Royal Shyness **Sir C. D. Seale**
33 **CORDELL (IRE)**, b c Fasliyev (USA)—Urgele (FR) **Mrs J. Wood**
34 **DESIDERIO**, b c Oasis Dream—Pleasuring **Exors of the Late Cathal M. Ryan**
35 **DREAM DAY**, b f Oasis Dream—Capistrano Day (USA) **R. Barnett**
36 **EASTERN GIFT**, ch c Cadeaux Genereux—Dahshah **J. A. Lazzari**
37 **ELIZABETH SWANN**, ch f Bahamian Bounty—Last Exhibit **R. H. W. Morecombe**
38 **FARTHERMOST (IRE)**, ch c Fath (USA)—Matila (IRE) **Mill House Partnership**
39 **FIRESTREAK**, b g Green Desert (USA)—Flash of Gold **Her Majesty The Queen**
40 **FIUME**, ch c Medicean—River Abouali **Lord Donoughmore & Mr T. Hely-Hutchinson**
41 **FLY IN JOHNNY (IRE)**, b g Fasliyev (USA)—Goodness Gracious (IRE) **The Ninth Pheasant Inn Partnership**
42 **FORGET IT**, b c Galileo (IRE)—Queens Way (FR) **Jim Horgan & Partners II**
43 **HADRON COLLIDER (FR)**, ch c Dubai Destination (USA)—Liver De Saron (USA) **Mrs J. Wood**
44 **HIGH PLAINS (FR)**, ch c Golan (IRE)—Perusha (USA) **M. Pescod**
45 **HIT THE ROOF**, b c Auction House (USA)—Rave On (ITY) **A. F. M. (Holdings) Ltd**
46 **HOLD THAT CALL (USA)**, ch g Hold That Tiger (USA)
          Rainbow Master (USA) **J B R Leisure Ltd & Fairway Racing**
47 **HUSTLE (IRE)**, ch c Choisir (AUS)—Granny Kelly (USA) **Highclere Thoroughbred Racing (Tamarisk)**
48 **IRISH ARTIST (FR)**, b c Orpen (USA)—Anchusa **M. R. Green**
49 **ISLE OF CAPRI**, b f Cape Cross (IRE)—Zenith **Her Majesty The Queen**
50 **KING SUPREME (IRE)**, b c King's Best (USA)—Oregon Trail (USA) **B. C. Oakley**
51 **KYRIE ELEISON (IRE)**, b c Kalanisi (IRE)—Peratus (IRE) **Mrs J. Wood**
52 **LA COLUMBINA**, ch f Carnival Dancer—Darshay (FR) **R. C. Tooth**
53 **LATIN LAD**, b c Hernando (FR)—Decision Maid (USA) **Noodles Racing**
54 **LUSH (IRE)**, b f Fasliyev (USA)—Our Hope **Mrs R. Ablett**
55 **MARTYR**, b c Cape Cross (IRE)—Sudeley **Highclere Thoroughbred Racing (Delilah)**
56 **MAY DAY QUEEN (IRE)**, b f Danetime (IRE)—Birthday Present **J. R. May**
57 **MELT (IRE)**, b f Intikhab—Kindle **J. Wigan**
58 **MILEAMINUTEMURPHY**, b g Fasliyev (USA)—Shining Hour (USA) **J. D. Manley**
59 **MONTEVETRO**, b c Galileo (IRE)—Three Piece **J. D. Manley**
60 **MYMUMSAYSIMTHEBEST**, b c Reel Buddy (USA)—Night Gypsy **Mrs M. J. George**
61 **NIGHT PREMIERE (IRE)**, b f Night Shift (USA)—Star Studded **Star Thoroughbreds**
62 **ORANGE SQUARE (IRE)**, br c King Charlemagne (USA)—Unaria **N A Woodcock,D Pody, M McGee & J Ball**
63 **PACO BOY (IRE)**, b c Desert Style (IRE)—Tappen Zee **The Calvera Partnership No. 2**
64 **PALMERIN**, b c Oasis Dream—Armorique (IRE) **Mrs N. F. Lee**
65 **PASSIONFORFASHION (IRE)**, b f Fasliyev (USA)—Jiving **Plantation Stud**
66 **PAY THE GREY**, gr f Daylami (IRE)—Dance Clear (IRE) **The Mystery Partnership**
67 **POLITEIA (USA)**, b br f Mr Greeley (USA)—Ujane (USA) **Justin Dowley & Michael Pescod**
68 **PROUD MARY (IRE)**, b f Acclamation—La Doyenne (IRE) **The Major Shear**
69 **REDESIGNATION (IRE)**, b c Key of Luck (USA)—Disregard That (IRE) **F. Jones**
70 **REDOLENT (IRE)**, ch c Redback—Esterlina (IRE) **De La Warr Racing**
71 **REEL GIFT**, b f Reel Buddy (USA)—Its Another Gift **Mr G. Battocchi & Mrs Anna Doyle**
72 **RESCUE ME**, b f Red Ransom (USA)—Duchcov **A. F. J. Merritt**
73 **RINTERVAL (IRE)**, ch c Desert Prince (USA)—Interpose **F. Jones**
74 **ROMANY PRINCESS (IRE)**, b f Viking Ruler (AUS)—Fag End (IRE) **M. R. Green**
75 **ROYAL INTRUDER**, b c Royal Applause—Surprise Visitor (IRE) **Thurloe Thoroughbreds XX**
76 **SAHAADI**, b f Dansili—Shardette (IRE) **Mrs A. Wigan**
77 **SCINTILLO**, ch c Fantastic Light (USA)—Danseuse du Soir (IRE) **White Beech Farm**
78 **SHELLY'S RULE**, ch f Viking Ruler (AUS)—Child's Play (USA) **I. A. N. Wight**
79 **SILVER RIME (FR)**, gr c Verglas (IRE)—Severina **Fieldspring Racing**
80 **SPECIAL RESERVE (IRE)**, b c Sadler's Wells (USA)—Ionian Sea **Mrs J. Wood**
81 **SWANKY LADY**, b f Cape Cross (IRE)—Lady Links **W. Durkan**
82 **TALK OF SAAFEND (IRE)**, b c Barathea (IRE)—Sopran Marida (IRE) **J. B. R. Leisure Ltd**
83 **TIGER'S ROCKET (IRE)**, b c Monashee Mountain (USA)—Brown Foam **M. Mulholland**
84 **VICTORIA REEL**, ch f Danehill Dancer (USA)—New Assembly (IRE) **Her Majesty The Queen**
85 **YAMANMICKMCCANN**, b c Desert Style (IRE)—Cashel Kiss **J. R. May**

TWO-YEAR-OLDS

86 **ACQUIESCED (IRE)**, b f 23/1 Refuse To Bend (IRE)—
      North East Bay (USA) (Prospect Bay (CAN)) (96525) **Mrs J. Wood**

MR R. HANNON—continued

87 ALWAYS THERE (IRE), b f 3/3 Bachelor Duke (USA)—
Ansariya (USA) (Shahrastani (USA)) (119047) **Mrs J. Wood**
88 ANACAONA (IRE), ch f 24/1 Distant Music (USA)—Tarrara (UAE) (Lammtarra (USA)) (7000) **J. A. Lazzari**
89 APPRAISAL, ch c 6/5 Mark of Esteem (IRE)—Anytime Baby (Bairn (USA)) (52000) **Waney Racing Group Inc**
90 AURORIAN (IRE), b c 12/2 Fantastic Light (USA)—Aurelia (Rainbow Quest (USA)) (27000) **Mr M. J. Mitchell**
91 B f 11/3 Invincible Spirit (IRE)—Baileys Cream (Mister Baileys) (102960) W. Durkan
92 BALLYALLA, b f 2/4 Mind Games—Molly Brown (Rudimentary (USA)) (65000) **D. J. Barry**
93 B c 22/4 Lucky Story—Beechnut (IRE) (Mujadil (USA)) (35000) Rory Donohue
94 BLACK NUN, b f 5/1 Fasliyev (USA)—Roxy (Rock City) **B. Bull**
95 BLACK SKIRT, b f 11/2 Kyllachy—Prends Ca (IRE) (Reprimand) (5000) **B. Bull**
96 CAPITELLI (IRE), b f 14/3 Cape Cross (IRE)—
Dear Girl (IRE) (Fairy King (USA)) (60000) **The Royal Ascot Racing Club**
97 CARESSING, b f 12/5 Kyllachy—Ella Lamees (Statoblest) (14000) **Mrs J. Wood**
98 B c 9/2 Fantastic Light (USA)—Comme Ca (Cyrano de Bergerac) (25000) I. A. N. Wight
99 B c 14/4 One Cool Cat (USA)—Congress (IRE) (Dancing Brave (USA)) (57914) Thurloe Finsbury II
100 B c 7/2 Kyllachy—Cutting Reef (IRE) (Kris) (66000) A. J. Ilsley
101 DAILY DOUBLE, gr c 11/2 Needwood Blade—Coffee To Go (Environment Friend) (36000) **K. T. Ivory**
102 DANE'S WORLD (IRE), b f 7/5 Danehill Dancer (USA)—Khamseh (Thatching) (75000) **R. C. Tooth**
103 B c 17/4 Fasliyev (USA)—Danseuse du Bois (USA) (Woodman (USA)) (25000) Mr H. R. Heffer
104 Ch f 5/3 Namid—Dundel (IRE) (Machiavellian (USA)) (110000) P. A. Byrne
105 DUSTRY (IRE), b c 19/3 Chevalier (IRE)—Church Mice (IRE) (Petardia) (7000) **D. J. Walker**
106 B c 4/3 Choisir (AUS)—Eastern Ember (Indian King (USA)) (85000) M. R. Green
107 ELNAWIN, b c 13/4 Elnadim (USA)—Acicula (Night Shift (USA)) (28000) **Noodles Lodge**
108 EVALUATION, gr f 4/5 El Prado (IRE)—Day of Reckoning (Daylami (IRE)) **Her Majesty The Queen**
109 B f 8/2 Exceed And Excel (AUS)—Evangeline (Sadler's Wells (USA)) (9000) G. Howard-Spink
110 B br c 2/5 Hawk Wing (USA)—Fabulous Pet (Somethingfabulous (USA)) J. P. Hardiman
111 B c 28/4 Captain Rio—Fairy Free (Rousillon (USA)) (8042) L. S. A. Stalder
112 FANDITHA (IRE), ch f 6/5 Danehill Dancer (IRE)—Splendid (IRE) (Mujtahid (USA)) (90089) **A. P. Patey**
113 FORMULA (USA), b br c 19/4 Stormin Fever (USA)—
Misty Gallop (Victory Gallop (CAN)) (90000) **Highclere Thoroughbred Racing-SunChariot**
114 FREE AGENT, b c 13/5 Dr Fong (USA)—Film Script (Unfuwain (USA)) **Her Majesty The Queen**
115 FULL TOSS, b c 8/2 Nayef (USA)—Spinning Top (Alzao (USA)) **Her Majesty The Queen**
116 B c 17/3 Trans Island—Gold Blended (IRE) (Goldmark (USA)) (25000) Raymond Keogh
117 GRANSKI (IRE), b c 10/3 Alhaarth (IRE)—Purple Haze (IRE) (Spectrum (IRE)) (90089) **Mrs A. Williams**
118 B gr c 18/3 Mull of Kintyre (USA)—Grey Again (Unfuwain (USA)) (37000) Joe Connolly
119 HAWKSPUR (IRE), b c 17/1 Hawk Wing (USA)—
Lyric Fantasy (IRE) (Tate Gallery (USA)) (50000) **Royal Ascot Racing Club**
120 HEADS WILL TURN, b f 24/1 Royal Applause—
Half Past Twelve (USA) (Cozzene (USA)) (90000) **R. H. W. Morecombe**
121 HELIODOR (USA), b c 12/4 Scrimshaw (USA)—
Playing Footsie (USA) (Valiant Nature (USA)) (35000) **Mrs J. Wood**
122 ICESOLATOR (IRE), b c 10/3 One Cool Cat (USA)—Zinnia (Zilzal (USA)) (41826) **B. Bull**
123 B f 6/5 Exceed And Excel (AUS)—Inforapenny (Deploy) (37000) F. Jones
124 INSTALMENT, b c 18/3 Cape Cross (IRE)—New Assembly (IRE) (Machiavellian (USA)) **Her Majesty The Queen**
125 JAZZ POLICE, b c 6/4 Beat Hollow—Tease (IRE) (Green Desert (USA)) (26000) **M. Pescod**
126 Ch c 28/4 Redback—La Paola (IRE) (Common Grounds) (19000) Coriolan Partnership V
127 B f 28/2 Trans Island—Lady Corduff (IRE) (Titus Livius (FR)) (10000) Tony Allan
128 LETHAL GLAZE (IRE), gr c 24/4 Verglas (IRE)—Sticky Green (Lion Cavern (USA)) (30000) **N. H. Morris**
129 LIKE FOR LIKE (IRE), ch f 29/4 Kheleyf (USA)—
Just Like Annie (Mujadil (USA)) (16000) **S. French, R. Morecombe & J. Perryman**
130 LITTLE BLACKNUMBER, b f 1/2 Superior Premium—
The Synergist (Botanic (USA)) (57000) **Mrs S. A. F. Brendish**
131 LUCKY REDBACK (IRE), b c 11/4 Redback—Bayletta (IRE) (Woodborough (USA)) (21000) **Bruce Coulthard**
132 LUVMEDO (IRE), b f 4/2 One Cool Cat (USA)—Dress Code (IRE) (Barathea (IRE)) (80437) **Mr M. G. J. Dolan**
133 LUXURIA (IRE), b f 7/3 Kheleyf (USA)—Dust Flicker (Suave Dancer (USA)) **Mrs J. Wood**
134 MARRAKECH EXPRESS, b c 11/3 Elusive City (USA)—Savage (IRE) (Polish Patriot (USA)) (56627)
135 MEASUREMENT (IRE), b c 23/1 Viking Ruler (AUS)—El-Libaab (Unfuwain (USA)) (17000) **B. Bull**
136 MIDNIGHT CRUISER (IRE), ch c 24/2 Captain Rio—Kriva (Reference Point) (65000) **M. Pescod**
137 MINOR VAMP (IRE), b f 9/4 Hawk Wing (USA)—
Miss Champagne (FR) (Bering) (28957) **Mr Michael Pescod & Mr Justin Dowley**
138 MISS FRITTON (IRE), b f 1/3 Refuse To Bend (IRE)—
Golly Gosh (IRE) (Danehill (USA)) (76000) **Justin Dowley & Michael Pescod**
139 B c 5/2 Tagula (IRE)—More Risk (IRE) (Fayruz) (35000) J. McCarthy
140 B f 20/4 Elusive City (USA)—Multicolour Wave (IRE) (Rainbow Quest (USA)) (12869) Mr A. T. J. Russell
141 Ch c 6/2 Bold Edge—My Dancer (IRE) (Alhaarth (IRE)) (16000) The Fifth Pheasant Inn Partnership

MR R. HANNON—continued

142 MY DIXIE DARLING (USA), b f 13/5 Bernstein (USA)—
Dixie Eyes Blazing (USA) (Gone West (USA)) (7500) **G. Howard-Spink**
143 B f 11/3 Dr Fong (USA)—Mystify (Batshoof) (45000) **J. R. May**
144 Gr ro f 17/3 Smoke Glacken (USA)—Newhall Road (USA) (Dixieland Band (USA)) (32174) **F. Jones**
145 B c 23/2 Marju (IRE)—Night Owl (Night Shift (USA)) (65000) **Mr A. T. J. Russell**
146 B f 11/2 Exceed And Excel (AUS)—Night Scent (IRE) (Scenic) (33461) **Mr A. T. J. Russell**
147 NOBLE JACK (IRE), b c 16/2 Elusive City (USA)—Begine (IRE) (Germany (USA)) (55000) **M. K. George**
148 ORATORY (IRE), b c 22/2 Danehill Dancer (IRE)—
Gentle Night (Zafonic (USA)) (57914) **Highclere Thoroughbred Racing (Munnings)**
149 OUR DAY WILL COME, b f 10/1 Red Ransom (USA)—
Dawnus (IRE) (Night Shift (USA)) (23000) **Derek & Jean Clee**
150 PENNY'S GIFT, b f 15/2 Tobougg (IRE)—Happy Lady (FR) (Cadeaux Genereux) (10000) **Malcolm Brown**
151 B f 13/4 Indian Ridge—Phantom Waters (Pharly (FR)) (42000) **C. F. Harrington**
152 POLLY'S CHOICE (IRE), ch f 9/3 Hawk Wing (USA)—Scanno's Choice (IRE) (Pennine Walk) **Martin Flitton**
153 PRINCESS CAGLIARI, b f 1/2 Efisio—Queenie (Indian Ridge) (45000) **R. H. W. Morecombe**
154 PRINCESS HANNAH, b f 26/2 Royal Applause—
Helloimustbegoing (USA) (Red Ransom (USA)) (37000) **A. P. Patey**
155 B c 6/4 Fantastic Light (USA)—Princess Minnie (Mistertopogigo (IRE)) (40000) **The Early Bath Partnership**
156 Ch c 23/1 Cozzene (USA)—Promptly (IRE) (Lead On Time (USA)) (90000) **Mr H. R. Heffer**
157 PURE POETRY (IRE), b c 31/3 Tagula (IRE)—Express Logic (Air Express (IRE)) (40000) **Mrs J. Wood**
158 B f 30/4 Acclamation—Pure Speculation (Salse (USA)) (16000) **S. Leech**
159 B f 6/3 King's Best (USA)—Raindancing (IRE) (Tirol) (48000) **Knockainey Stud Limited**
160 REBECCA DE WINTER, b f 17/2 Kyllachy—Miss Adelaide (IRE) (Alzao (USA)) (20000) **Mrs J. Wood**
161 RED ROSSINI (IRE), b c 17/2 Rossini (USA)—La Scala (USA) (Theatrical) (65000) **Terry Neill**
162 REDHEAD (IRE), ch f 2/4 Redback—Rinneen (IRE) (Bien Bien (USA)) (80000) **Mrs J. Wood**
163 RETRO (IRE), b c 5/5 Tagula (IRE)—Cabcharge Princess (IRE) (Rambo Dancer (CAN)) (68000) **Mrs J. Wood**
164 RIO DEL ORO (USA), b c 25/1 Touch Gold (USA)—
Diablo's Girl (Diablo (USA)) (88000) **Waney Racing Group Inc**
165 RIVER RYE (IRE), b f 1/2 Acclamation—Rye (IRE) (Charnwood Forest (IRE)) (36000) **Bruce Coulthard**
166 B c 28/4 Invincible Spirit (IRE)—Rosie's Guest (IRE) (Be My Guest (USA)) **J. P. Hardiman**
167 SAINTS BAY (IRE), b f 15/1 Redback—Alexander Eliott (IRE) (Night Shift (USA)) (28000) **N. A. Woodcock**
168 Ch c 18/2 Intikhab (USA)—Scottish Exile (IRE) (Ashkalani (IRE)) (46000) **Thurloe Thoroughbreds XXII**
169 SECURITY JOAN (IRE), ch f 28/4 Dubai Destination (USA)—
Divine Quest (Kris) (30000) **Mr Michael Pescod & Mr Justin Dowley**
170 SHARPENER (IRE), b f 27/3 Invincible Spirit (IRE)—Daily Double (FR) (Unfuwain (USA)) (75000) **Mrs J. Wood**
171 SHOOTING PARTY (IRE), b c 14/4 Noverre (USA)—L-Way First (IRE) (Vision (USA)) (84000) **Mrs R. Ablett**
172 SOHCAHTOA (IRE), b c 19/3 Val Royal (FR)—
Stroke of Six (IRE) (Woodborough (USA)) (65000) **Mrs S. A. F. Brendish**
173 SOUTER'S SISTER (IRE), b f 6/3 Desert Style (IRE)—Hemaca (Distinctly North (USA)) (9000) **A. F. J. Merritt**
174 STRAITJACKET, b f 8/3 Refuse To Bend (IRE)—Thara'a (IRE) (Desert Prince (IRE)) (68000) **R. C. Tooth**
175 SUN SHIP (IRE), b c 14/1 Xaar—Silky Dawn (IRE) (Night Shift (USA)) (58000) **M. Pescod**
176 B c 24/4 Invincible Spirit (IRE)—
Tappen Zee (Sandhurst Prince) (51480) **McKendrick, Mahal, Morecombe, Anderson**
177 TARQUA (IRE), b f 4/5 King Charlemagne (USA)—Shining Creek (CAN) (Bering) (23165) **Earl of Carnarvon**
178 THE MINIVER ROSE (IRE), b f 2/2 High Chaparral (IRE)—
Bloemfontain (IRE) (Cape Cross (IRE)) (100000) **Mrs J. Wood**
179 TISHTAR, br c 27/3 Kyllachy—Xtrasensory (Royal Applause) **Waney Racing Group Inc**
180 B c 2/5 Lucky Story (USA)—Tranquillity (Night Shift (USA)) (33000) **White Beech Farm**
181 B f 14/4 Tobougg (IRE)—Truly Madly Deeply (Most Welcome) (6000) **A. J. Ilsley**
182 Ch c 4/3 Bahamian Bounty—Tuppenny Blue (Pennekamp (USA)) **A. J. Ilsley**
183 VERLEGEN (IRE), b f 13/3 Royal Applause—Petite Epaulette (Night Shift (USA)) (68000) **Mr J. N. Reus**
184 MYTSHKI (IRE), gr c 17/3 Verglas (FR)—Mythie (Octagonal (NZ)) (64350) **J. A. Lazzari**

Other Owners: Mr J. P. Ball, G. P. Battocchi, Mr P. H. Brown, Mr M. J. Brown, Mrs P. A. Brown, P. Burgoyne, D. D. Clee, Mrs J. P. Clee, Mrs J. Coolledge, B. Coulthard, Lord De La Warr, Countess De La Warr, The Earl Of Donoughmore, Mr L. J. Dowley, Mrs A. M. Doyle, J. G. Ferrand, Mr E. P. Finlason, J. K. Grimes, Mr J. Hall, Mrs F. M. Hallett, R. Hannon, R. Hannon Jnr, T. M. Hely-Hutchinson, The Hon H. M. Herbert, Highclere Thoroughbred Racing Ltd, James Horgan, Wing Comdr A. Howie, N. J. Hughes, T. Jackson, J. F. Jarvis, Mr Desmond Kavanagh, J. A. Leek, A. F. Leighton, D. M. J. Lloyd, Ms K. Lowe, D. A. Lucie-Smith, Mr M. T. McGee, M. J. Morrison, D. M. D. Mort, D. F. O'Rourke, Mrs P. K. O'Rourke, O. J. W. Pawle, A. C. Pickford, Mr D. A. Pody, Sir William Purves, N. M. S. Rich, Mrs N. H. Stafford, D. J. Taylor, J. S. Threadwell, G. P. Triefus, Mrs A. Turner, Major-Gen G. H. Watkins, G. A. Wilson, Mrs C. R. D. Wilson, N. A. Woodcock.

Assistant Trainer: Richard Hannon Jnr

Jockey (flat): P. Dobbs, R. Hughes, Ryan Moore, Dane O'Neill, R. Smith. **Conditional:** Hadden Frost. **Apprentice:** Charles Eddery, Patrick Hills, Hadden Frost.

254 MR G. A. HARKER, Thirsk
Postal: Stockhill Green, York Rd, Thirkleby, Thirsk, North Yorkshire, YO7 3AS
Contacts: PHONE (01845) 501117 FAX (01845) 501614 MOBILE (07803) 116412/(07930) 125544
E-MAIL gandjhome@aol.com

1 AMHAIRGHIN (IRE), 8, ch g Accordion—North Gale **A. S. Ward**
2 APERITIF, 7, ch g Pivotal—Art Deco Lady **Good Breed Ltd**
3 ARCTIC ROCK, 5, ch g Prince Daniel (USA)—Celtic Tern **C. F. H. Cook**
4 BAIE DES FLAMANDS (USA), 6, b g Kingmambo—Isle de France (USA) **John Pointon & Sons**
5 BALAMORY DAN (IRE), 7, b g Fort Morgan (USA)—Musical Horn **Desmond Woods**
6 BOING BOING (IRE), 8, b g King's Theatre (IRE)—Limerick Princess (IRE) **A. S. Ward**
7 CHIGORIN, 7, b g Pivotal—Belle Vue **John Pointon & Sons**
8 CUSTOM DESIGN, 7, ch g Minster Son—Scotto's Regret **A S Ward & A Cooper**
9 CYBORG DE SOU (FR), 10, b g Cyborg (FR)—Moomaw **J. J. Maguire**
10 EIJAAZ (IRE), 7, b g Green Desert (USA)—Kismah **A. S. Ward**
11 FAIRY SKIN MAKER (IRE), 10, ch g Nomadic Way (USA)—Malvern Madam **Mrs J. L. Harker**
12 FARNE ISLE, 9, ch m Midnight Legend—Biloela **Steer Arms Belton Racing Club**
13 JETHRO TULL (IRE), 9, b g Witness Box (USA)—Country Project (IRE) **J. J. Maguire**
14 KWAMI GUN, 5, b m Double Trigger (IRE)—Delvecchia **Mrs J. M. Phillips**
15 MISS SHRED EASY, 8, ch m Gunner B—D C Flyer **Shred Easy**
16 MR EX (ARG), 7, b g Numerous (USA)—Express Toss (ARG) **P. I. Harker**
17 NOTAPROBLEM (IRE), 9, b g Oscar (IRE)—Smashed Free (IRE) **Mrs J. L. Harker**
18 NUIT SOMBRE (IRE), 8, b g Night Shift (USA)—Belair Princess (USA) **P. I. Harker**
19 OAKAPPLE DIAMOND (IRE), 5, b m Bob's Return (IRE)—Royal Nora (IRE) **Mr P. Taylor**
20 OAKAPPLE EXPRESS, 8, b g Alflora (IRE)—Royal Scarlet **M.Barnes T.Cartner M.Black M.Cooper**
21 OAKAPPLE PRINCESS (IRE), 7, b m Alderbrook—Timeless Rose **Mr P. Taylor**
22 PUMBOO (FR), 5, gr g Dadarissime (FR)—Contessina (FR) **J. J. Maguire**
23 QUE CALOR LA VIDA (FR), 4, b f Lavirco (GER)—Hasta Manana (FR) **Mr A. Thomson & Mr S. Peel**
24 RUBY QUEEN (IRE), 6, b br m King's Theatre (IRE)—Ardrina **Roger Eddleston & David Cunningham**
25 SERAPHIN (FR), 5, b g Muhtathir—Lirfa (USA) **Mr M. Clementson**
26 SKYE BUT N BEN, 4, b g Auction House (USA)—Island Colony (USA) **J. J. Maguire**
27 ZAFFIE PARSON (IRE), 7, b m Zaffaran (USA)—Katie Parson **Mr David Adair**

THREE-YEAR-OLDS

28 B g Cois Na Tine (IRE)—Champagne N Dreams **Mrs J. L. Harker**
29 ROYAL ACCLAMATION (IRE), b c Acclamation—Lady Abigail (IRE) **Good Breed Limited**

Other Owners: Mr Mark Barnes, Mr M. Black, Mr T. Cartner, Mr M. Cooper, Mr A. Cooper, Mr S. Costello, D. C. Cunningham, R. T. Eddleston, Mr J. G. Knibb, Mr D. Nicholls, Mr T. S. Palin, Mr M. Prince, Mr A. S. Ward.

Assistant Trainer: Jenny Harker

Jockey (NH): W. T. Kennedy.

255 MRS P. E. HARKIN, Daventry
Postal: Westlands, Long Buckby Road, Daventry, Northamptonshire, NN11 5LT
Contacts: PHONE (01327) 704223 FAX (01327) 872927 MOBILE (07970) 770236
E-MAIL sales@velvetenergy.com WEBSITE www.velvetenergy.com

1 VELVET BLU, 6, gr m Environment Friend—Bit of A Bird **Mrs P. E. Harkin**
2 VELVET DREAM, 5, b m Alflora (IRE)—Supreme Dream (IRE) **Mrs P. E. Harkin**
3 VELVET RED, 6, ch m Classic Cliche (IRE)—Careful Dove **Mrs P. E. Harkin**
4 VELVET SKYE, 8, gr m Terimon—Mermaid Bay **Mrs P. E. Harkin**

Assistant Trainer: Doug Harkin

256 MR R. C. HARPER, Banbury
Postal: Home Farm, Kings Sutton, Banbury, Oxfordshire, OX17 3RS
Contacts: PHONE (01295) 810997 FAX (01295) 812787 MOBILE (07970) 223481
E-MAIL rharper@freeuk.com

1 CASH 'N CARROTS, 9, b g Missed Flight—Rhiannon **R. C. Harper**
2 MASTERPOINT, 8, ch g Mark of Esteem (IRE)—Baize **R. C. Harper**
3 TRAWBREAGA BAY, 8, ch g Bijou d'inde—Give Me A Day **R. C. Harper**

Conditional: M. Nicholls.

257 MRS JESSICA HARRINGTON, Kildare

Postal: **Commonstown Stables, Moone, Co. Kildare, Ireland**
Contacts: PHONE **(00353) 5986 24153** FAX **(00353) 5986 24292** MOBILE **(00353) 8725 66129**
E-MAIL **jessicaharrington@eircom.net**

1 AFASHEEN (IRE), 5, b m Presenting—Afarka (IRE) **P. Myerscough**
2 ALBANOV (IRE), 8, b g Sadler's Wells (USA)—Love For Ever (IRE) **Ronnie Scott Four Syndicate**
3 5, B br m Presenting—Ali's Dipper (IRE) **Gerry Leahy**
4 ALPINE EAGLE (IRE), 4, b c Golan (IRE)—Alpine Symphony **J. P. McManus**
5 ANDREWS PET (IRE), 5, ch m Presenting—Serengeti Plains (IRE) **Brendan Scully, Stephen Foughner**
6 ANNESTOWN (IRE), 5, b m Bob's Return (IRE)—Seat of Learning **Peter Queally & John Harrington**
7 BAD DAY BAD DAY, 6, b g Silver Patriarch (IRE)—Cromarty **Mighty Mac's Syndicate**
8 BADGERLAW (IRE), 8, b g Accordion—Beglawella **Lynn Wilson**
9 5, B m Alflora (IRE)—Be My Rainbow (IRE) **Brendan Fitzpatrick**
10 BECOLARK (IRE), 7, b g City Honours (USA)—Sainte Jocelyne (FR) **A Four Syndicate**
11 BOOTSANDSLIPPERS (IRE), 6, b m Even Top (IRE)—Paris Biv (IRE) **Four M's Syndicate**
12 BORYENKA, 4, b g Soviet Star (USA)—Exultate Jubilate (USA) **Spooner, Weaves, Jamie, Dukey**
13 BOUCHARD, 4, ch g Kyllachy—Lucky Arrow **Joe O'Flaherty**
14 CALA LEVANTE (IRE), 7, gr g Supreme Leader—Mondeo Rose (IRE) **Crispin Wall & John Harrington**
15 CAMAN SWINGER (IRE), 6, b g Key of Luck (USA)—Over Swing (FR) **Big Hurlers Syndicate**
16 CAPE ALLSTAR (IRE), 5, b m Fourstars Allstar (USA)—Stuarts Point (IRE) **Mighty Mac's Syndicate**
17 CAPO DI CAPI (IRE), 6, b g In The Wings—Sea Spray (IRE) **Joe O'Flaherty**
18 CARPENTER (IRE), 6, b g Definite Article—Ladies Gallery (IRE) **Joe O'Flaherty**
19 CELTIC FINN (IRE), 4, b g Celtic Swing—Marguerite Bay (IRE) **Kristina O'Toole**
20 CHAPMANS PEAK (IRE), 5, b g Beneficial—Archetype **David Attwood & Sally Simpson**
21 CHASING CARS (IRE), 6, b g Supreme Leader—Great Outlook (IRE) **Howard Spooner**
22 CITY MEANING (USA), 4, ch g Johannesburg (USA)—Substance (USA) **Whathappenedtomurphy Syndicate**
23 CLASSIC VIC (IRE), 8, ch g Old Vic—Grangeclare Rose (IRE) **Malcolm Graham**
24 COME ON BOB (IRE), 6, b g Bob Back (USA)—Irene Good-Night (IRE) **Lakeside Racing Syndicate**
25 CORK ALL STAR (IRE), 6, b g Fasliyev (USA)—Lucky State (USA) **Executors of the Late Cathal M. Ryan**
26 DAYTONA LILY (IRE), 6, b m Beneficial—Balda Girl (IRE) **Gill Browne**
27 DESERT ABBEY (IRE), 6, b m Presenting—Scientia (USA) **Joe O'Flaherty**
28 DINGLE BELLE (IRE), 5, b m Celtic Swing—Laurentia (USA) **Tommy Sheehy**
29 DIRECT EXIT (IRE), 5, b h Exit To Nowhere (USA)—Corculinnus Lass (IRE) **Mighty Mac's Synicate**
30 DJANGO, 9, ch g Glacial Storm—Rathtrim **K K Construction**
31 DOUBLE EAGLE (FR), 5, b h Anabaa (USA)—Style For Life (IRE) **Rick Barnes**
32 DREAMY GENT (IRE), 6, b g Trans Island—Calamity Kate (IRE) **Say Nothing Syndicate**
33 EASTERN CANAL (IRE), 7, b h Son of Sharp Shot (IRE)—Suez Canal (FR) **Joe O'Flaherty**
34 EXIT CLOSED (IRE), 5, b g Exit To Nowhere (USA)—Bramble Fair (IRE) **Liam Quinn**
35 EXOTIC MARINER (IRE), 5, b g Anabaa (USA)—Sea Spray (USA) **Ballymacoll Stud Farm Ltd**
36 FAHRQUAR, 5, ch h Fahris (IRE)—Tsarevna (IRE) **Lady Virginia Petersham**
37 FALSE EVIDENCE (IRE), 6, b g Witness Box (USA)—
                                                Merrys Delight (IRE) **D Reid Scott, Dermot Cox, James Osbourne**
38 FANTOCHE (BRZ), 6, ch h Roi Normand (USA)—Diet Lark (BRZ) **Cova Syndicate**
39 FARINELLI, 5, br g Selkirk (USA)—Melodica **Byerley Thoroughbred Racing Syndicate**
40 FIONN TRA (IRE), 4, b g Definite Article—Shawiya (IRE) **Joe O'Flaherty**
41 FIONN UISCE (IRE), 6, b m Luso—Princess Seal **Joe O'Flaherty**
42 FOLION (IRE), 5, b g Needle Gun (IRE)—Lady For Life (IRE) **Right G Syndicate**
43 FONTAINE HALL (IRE), 7, b m Saddlers' Hall—Millie Fontaine (IRE) **Siobhan Rice**
44 FRAGINEER, 7, b g Grand Plaisir (IRE)—Arnestown Host (IRE) **Maynooth Racing Syndicate**
45 FRANC VILLEZ (FR), 6, ch g Villez (USA)—Nekhtabet (FR) **Martin Lynch**
46 GALLANT LIGHT, 4, b g Golan (IRE)—Light Ballet **Joe O'Flaherty**
47 GAZZA'S GIRL (IRE), 8, b br m Norwich—Miss Ranova **Arthur McCooey**
48 GEMINI LUCY (IRE), 8, ch m Glacial Storm (USA)—Jodi (IRE) **Queens Price Syndicate**
49 GIVE IT TIME, 5, b m Kayf Tara—Startino **John Harrington**
50 GLENROCK LEADER (IRE), 6, b g Supreme Leader—Never At Home (IRE) **Tom Curran**
51 GOT ATTITUDE (IRE), 5, ch g Beneficial—Ilderton Road **D Reid Scott, Dermot Cox, James Osbourne**
52 5, B g Supreme Leader—Great Outlook (IRE) **John Harrington**
53 GUITAR RORY (IRE), 6, b g Presenting—Prolific Scot **Cova Syndicate**
54 HARNIKOS (FR), 4, ch f Nikos—Harpves (FR) **Thomas Markham**
55 HEIGHT OF FURY (IRE), 5, b g Sadler's Wells (USA)—Height of Fantasy (IRE) **Anamoine Ltd**
56 HELVIC HEAD (IRE), 6, b g Anshan—Glenpatrick Peach (IRE) **Peter Queally & John Harrington**
57 HORNER WOODS (IRE), 6, br g Presenting—Horner Water (IRE) **Howard Spooner**
58 I'LL CALL YOU BACK (IRE), 9, b h Zaffaran (USA)—Ben Tack **Mighty Mac's Syndicate**
59 JOHN'S ELIZA (IRE), 6, b m Dr Massini (IRE)—Clashwilliam Girl (IRE) **Joe Patterson**
60 JUMBAJUKIBA, 5, b h Barathea (IRE)—Danseuse du Soir (IRE) **Joe O'Flaherty**
61 KERRY ALLSTAR (IRE), 6, b m Oscar (IRE)—Lady Ivers (IRE) **Michael O'Sullivan**

MRS JESSICA HARRINGTON—continued

62 **KING RALPH (IRE)**, 5, b g Moscow Society (USA)—Glenpatrick Peach (IRE) **John Harrington**
63 **KNIGHT LEGEND (IRE)**, 9, b g Flying Legend (USA)—Well Trucked (IRE) **Martin St. Quinton & Lynn Wilson**
64 **KNOCKATUBBER (IRE)**, 5, b g Clerkenwell (USA)—Arch Your Back (IRE) **Setting Sun Syndicate**
65 **LOUGH CUAN (IRE)**, 6, b m Zaffaran (USA)—Wilmott's Fancy **John Peutherer**
66 **LUKIE VICTOR (IRE)**, 7, ch g Old Vic—Chapanga (IRE) **Old Hogan Stand Racing Syndicate**
67 **LUTEUR COLLONGES (FR)**, 9, br g Kadalko (FR)—Amazone Collonges (FR) **Philip Scouller**
68 **MAGNESIUM (USA)**, 8, ch g Kris S (USA)—Proflare (USA) **Con Harrington**
69 **MARYBORO LAD (IRE)**, 6, b g Fourstars Allstar (USA)—Rachael's Dawn **Sport Racing**
70 **MERVEILLES**, 5, b g Vettori (IRE)—Finlaggan **BB Horse Racing Club**
71 **MIDNIGHT RAMBLE (IRE)**, 5, b g Presenting—Liskilnewabbey (IRE) **Gina Galvin**
72 **MINTMARSH (IRE)**, 6, b m Charnwood Forest (IRE)—Bella **M. Hamilton, F. Eastwood & Partners**
73 **MONACO FLYER (IRE)**, 5, ch g Flemensfirth (USA)—Willmakemoney (IRE) **Martin Landau**
74 **MOSCOW DYNAMO (IRE)**, 4, b g Moscow Society (USA)—Bulgaden Gypsy **Brian Kearney**
75 **MR MCGONAGLE (IRE)**, 6, ch g Snurge—Rumi **Gerry Byrne**
76 **NELL'S OSCAR (IRE)**, 7, b m Oscar (IRE)—Dantes Term (USA) **Michael Murphy**
77 **NOBETTER BUACHAILL (IRE)**, 6, ch g Carroll House—

Current Liability **Brendan Fitzpatrick & Michael Sammon**
78 **OSCAR HONEY (IRE)**, 7, b g Oscar Schindler (IRE)—Tanhoney (IRE) **Mr & Mrs Duncan Davidson**
79 **PARADIS DE THAIX (FR)**, 5, ch g April Night (FR)—Etoile de Thaix (FR) **Hard To Get Ten Syndicate**
80 **PARZANNI (IRE)**, 6, ch h Arzanni—Sylvia Beach **Harry Graham**
81 **PASSION'S QUEST (IRE)**, 4, b f Traditionally (USA)—Quest of Passion (FR) **John Power**
82 **PEBBLE REACH (IRE)**, 5, b br m Orbis (USA)—Scree (IRE) **Star Syndicate**
83 **PERSONAL COLUMN**, 4, ch g Pursuit of Love—Tromond **Howard Spooner & Peter Askew**
84 **PHANTOM LAD (IRE)**, 5, b g Desert Prince (IRE)—Phantom Waters **Con Harrington**
85 **QUARTINO**, 7, b g Dynaformer (USA)—Qirmazi (USA) **Midas Syndicate**
86 **RATHGANLEY LASS (IRE)**, 8, b br m Taipan (IRE)—Cotton Call (IRE) **Mick Pender**
87 **REALT NA CARRAIGE (IRE)**, 5, gr m Moscow Society (USA)—Edward Street (IRE) **AAMM Syndicate**
88 **RIDGE BOY (IRE)**, 7, b h Indian Ridge—Bold Tina (IRE) **C. F. Harrington**
89 **ROAD HOME**, 5, ch g Grand Lodge (USA)—Lady In Waiting **Mr H. Q. Spooner**
90 **ROMANCE OF STEEL (FR)**, 5, gr m Highest Honor (FR)—On The Razz (USA) **Paul Howard**
91 **SAN JOSE (IRE)**, 5, b g Frimaire—Leinster Lady (IRE) **Joe O'Flaherty**
92 **SANDYMOUNT EARL (IRE)**, 5, ch g Hernando (FR)—Joleah (IRE) **Ron Wood**
93 5, B m Anshan—Scientia (IRE) **John Harrington**
94 **SLIEVE ROCKET (IRE)**, 5, b m Close Conflict (USA)—Shou Naya (IRE) **The Cross Country Syndicate**
95 **SPIRIT RUN (IRE)**, 6, b m Luso—Satula **Frank Burke**
96 **STUDMASTER**, 8, ch g Snurge—Danlu (USA) **Mothership Racing Club**
97 **TARAVADA**, 5, b g Kayf Tara—Prevada **L. Doyle**
98 **THE GROVE (IRE)**, 5, b g Supreme Leader—Bint Alsarab **Brian Kearney**
99 **THE LAST HURRAH (IRE)**, 8, b h In The Wings—Last Exit **Mrs A. Gurney**
100 5, Ch g Sonus (IRE)—The Mighty Midge **Howard Spooner**
101 **TOP OF THE ROCK (IRE)**, 5, ch g Beneficial—One Last Cut (IRE) **Joe O'Flaherty**
102 **TURTLE TIME LUCKY (IRE)**, 5, b g Turtle Island (IRE)—Homersware (IRE) **Mothership Racing Club**
103 **UNDER OFFER (IRE)**, 5, b g Little Bighorn—Tender Ann (IRE) **Dermot Cox, Paddy Jordan, John Harrington**
104 **VALLEY OF GIANTS (IRE)**, 6, ch h Giant's Causeway—Karri Valley (USA) **Macs J Syndicate**
105 **VAQUERAS (FR)**, 5, b g Pennekamp (USA)—Las Americas (FR) **H. Spooner**
106 **WAIT FOR GREEN (IRE)**, 5, b g Supreme Leader—Celia's Pet (IRE) **Stephen Faughnan & Brendan Scully**
107 **WAR PILOT**, 5, b g Classic Cliche (IRE)—Coole Pilate **Richard Doyle**
108 **WESTERN GALE (IRE)**, 5, br g Presenting—Kate Gale (IRE) **Tom Curran**
109 **WOODHOUSE (IRE)**, 9, b g Glacial Storm (USA)—Alices Run **Alexandra Noone**
110 **ZARINAVA (IRE)**, 4, gr f Daylami (IRE)—Zariliya (IRE) **Des Donegan**

THREE-YEAR-OLDS

111 **AUBUSSON (IRE)**, b f Montjeu (IRE)—Stitching (IRE) **Ben Jellet**
112 **COSY ONE**, b f Domedriver (IRE)—Kiruna **John Harrington**
113 **LITTLE MISS DIVA (IRE)**, b f Diktat—Anchorage (IRE) **John Harrington**
114 **MANOR PARK (IRE)**, b c Hernando (FR)—Campiglia (IRE) **Patrick Cooper & Adam Gurney**
115 **NO ONE TELLS ME**, ch f Dr Fong (USA)—Bajan Blue **John Harrington**
116 **PAPADOPOLI (USA)**, ch f Van Nistelrooy (USA)—Soundproof (USA) **D. Reid Scott, K. Doyle, J. Ryan, A. Nicholl**
117 **WHERE'S MY SLAVE (IRE)**, b f Daylami (IRE)—Greek Princess (IRE) **John Harrington**

TWO-YEAR-OLDS

118 B c 16/2 Sadler's Wells (USA)—No Review (USA) (Nodouble (USA)) (39896) **John Hennessey & John Wholey**

MRS JESSICA HARRINGTON—continued

Other Owners: A. J. Duke, J. E. Mulhern, Eimear Mulhern, Lord James Netherthorpe, I. L. Weaver.

Jockey (NH): Barry Geraghty, Robert Power, T.P Treacy, A.D. Leigh. **Conditional:** Mark Bolger. **Amateur:** Mr M. Fahey, Mr S. Byrne, Miss K. Harrington.

---

258 MR J. A. HARRIS, Melton Mowbray
Postal: **Eastwell Hall Stables, Eastwell, Melton Mowbray, Leicestershire, LE14 4EE**
Contacts: **YARD/FAX (01949) 860671 HOME (01400) 282819 MOBILE (07989) 947712**

1 ADJAMI (IRE), 7, b g Entrepreneur—Adjriyna **Truframe Limited**
2 BARATI (IRE), 7, b g Sadler's Wells (USA)—Oriane **Five Naybors**
3 BOGSIDE DANCER, 6, b g Groom Dancer (USA)—Madame Crecy (USA) **Mrs A. E. Harris**
4 BOWDLANE BARB, 7, b m Commanche Run—Foxs Shadow **R. H. Fox**
5 CITY FOR CONQUEST (IRE), 5, b m City On A Hill (USA)—Northern Life (IRE) **M. F. Schofield & Mick Casey**
6 CRAFTY FOX, 5, b g Foxhound (USA)—Surrealist (ITY) **Mrs A. E. Harris**
7 CREDENTIAL, 6, b h Dansili—Sabria (USA) **A. J. McLaren**
8 HIGHAM, 6, b g Silver Patriarch (IRE)—Myumi **J. L. Burt**
9 KAPAROLO (USA), 9, ch g El Prado (IRE)—Parliament House (USA) **J. South**
10 LONG GONE, 5, b m Mtoto—Absentee **J. H. Henderson**
11 LOUISIADE (IRE), 7, b g Tagula (IRE)—Titchwell Lass **Mrs A. E. Harris**
12 MISS ZIGZAG, 6, b m Desert Story (IRE)—Watership Glass **Cleartherm Glass Sealed Units Ltd**
13 MUNTAMI (IRE), 7, gr g Daylami (IRE)—Bashashah (IRE) **Mr Chris Owens & Mrs A. E. Harris**
14 NAUGHTY GIRL (IRE), 8, b m Dr Devious (IRE)—Mary Magdalene **Mrs A. E. Harris**
15 OURS (IRE), 5, b g Mark of Esteem (IRE)—Ellebanna **Mr D. A. Spencer**
16 RUSSIAN CONSORT (IRE), 6, ch g Groom Dancer (USA)—Ukraine Venture **M. F. Schofield**
17 SATINDRA (IRE), 4, b g Lil's Boy (USA)—Voronova (IRE) **Miss L. J. Morgan**
18 SION HILL, 7, b g Desert Prince (IRE)—Mobilia **P. Taylor**
19 T'AI CHI, 7, b m Pursuit of Love—Trojan Desert **P. E. Barrett**
20 TAG TEAM (IRE), 7, ch g Tagula (IRE)—Okay Baby **Cleartherm Glass Sealed Units Ltd**
21 TIVERS SONG (IRE), 4, gr c Buddha (USA)—Rousing **J. South**
22 UNION JACK JACKSON (IRE), 6, b g Daggers Drawn (USA)—Beechwood Quest (IRE) **Shaun Taylor**
23 ZABEEL HOUSE, 5, b g Anabaa (USA)—Divine Quest **Cricklewood Timber & Building Supplies Ltd**

THREE-YEAR-OLDS

24 AMAZING DAY, b g Averti (IRE)—Daynabee

Other Owners: Mr M. Casey, Mr Chris Owens.

Assistant Trainer: Miss Vicki M Harris, Mrs A E Harris

Jockey (flat): Dean McKeown, S. Sanders.

---

259 MR M. HARRIS, Banbury
Postal: **Trafford Bridge Stables, Edgcote, Banbury, Oxfordshire, OX17 1AG**
Contacts: **PHONE (01295) 660713 FAX (01295) 660767 MOBILE (07879) 634308**
E-MAIL **info@miltonharrisracing.com** WEBSITE **www.miltonharrisracing.com**

1 ALFADORA, 8, ch g Alflora (IRE)—Dorazine **The Virtual Partnership**
2 BE BE KING (IRE), 9, br g Bob Back (USA)—Trimar Gold **J. D. Macgregor**
3 CHANINBAR (FR), 5, b g Milford Track (IRE)—Logicia (FR) **Milton Harris Racing Club**
4 CRAVEN (IRE), 8, b g Accordion—Glen Dieu **Racing Roses Partnership**
5 CREINCH, 7, b g Overbury (IRE)—Kingsfold Blaze **Pet Necessities Partnership**
6 DAR ES SALAAM, 4, ch g King's Best (USA)—Place de L'opera **J. D. Macgregor**
7 FEDERSTAR (GER), 6, b g In A Tiff (IRE)—Federspeil **The Piranha Partnership**
8 FLINDERS BAY (IRE), 8, b br g Luso—McMufins Princess **Mr A. J. Rawlings**
9 GRACIALINA (GER), 5, ch m Kornado—Giovanella (IRE) **M. Harris**
10 HERECOMESTANLEY, 9, b g Missed Flight—Moonspell **Christopher Shankland & Barbara Woodcock**
11 HOT 'N' HOLY, 9, b g Supreme Leader—Clonmello **A. J. Duffield**
12 LEOPOLD (SLO), 7, b g Solarstern (FR)—Lucera (GER) **A. J. Duffield**
13 MADE IN MONTOT (FR), 8, b g Video Rock (FR)—Deep Turple (FR) **J. S. Tackley**
14 MAGIC SKY (FR), 8, b g Simon du Desert (FR)—Kailasa (FR) **thehorseracingclub.com partnership**
15 MOONFLEET (IRE), 6, b m Entrepreneur—Lunasa (IRE) **Moonfleet Racing**
16 MUDAWIN (IRE), 7, b g Intikhab (USA)—Fida (IRE) **J. D. Macgregor**

MR M. HARRIS—continued

17 **PAXFORD JACK**, 12, ch g Afflora (IRE)—Rakajack **Mrs R. E. Nelmes**
18 **PSEUDONYM (IRE)**, 6, ch g Daylami (IRE)—Stage Struck (IRE) **Mrs S. E. Brown**
19 **ROSIE'S GLORY (USA)**, 4, b br f More Than Ready (USA)—Cukee (USA) **M. Harris**
20 **SAINT GODEGRAND (FR)**, 6, gr g Saint Preuil (FR)—
      Sa Majeste (FR) **Coutts Construction, R Nelmes, D Dewbery**
21 **SALINAS (GER)**, 9, b g Macanal (USA)—Santa Ana (GER) **Prevention & Detection (Holdings) Limited**
22 **SILVO (NZ)**, 9, gr g Lowell (USA)—Silvadella (NZ) **Milton Harris Racing Club**
23 **SISTER AGNES (IRE)**, 4, ch f Dr Fong (USA)—Nibbs Point (IRE) **Franconson Partners**
24 **SITE SENTRY (IRE)**, 5, ch h Nashwan (USA)—Balwa (USA) **Prevention & Detection (Holdings) Limited**
25 **SNAKE CHARMER**, 5, b g Golden Snake (USA)—Moly **Racing Roses Partnership**
26 **SPEEDY DIRECTA (GER)**, 5, b g Areion (GER)—Sourour (IRE) **Speedy Director Partnership**
27 **TALCEN GWYN (IRE)**, 6, b g Fayruz—Cheerful Knight (IRE) **Mr D. K. Watkins**
28 **VICTORY MILE (USA)**, 4, b c Victory Gallop (CAN)—Viva Girl (USA) **Mrs Ruth Nelmes & Mrs Diane Dewbery**
29 **WESTSTERN (GER)**, 5, b h Dashing Blade—Westafrika (GER) **Partners In Crime**

Other Owners: Mr S. A. Albiston, Mr C. W. Arrand, Mr S. J. Corcoran, Mrs N. Corcoran, Coutts Construction Limited, Mrs D. Curran, D. Curran, Mrs D. Dewbery, Mrs A. Frampton, Mr W. G. Graham, R. Hart, T. Hart, Mr G. R. Laycock, Mr E. M. Leighton, Mr R. A. McNeish, Mr A. Miles, Mr J. Naylor, Mr J. Peavoy, M. S. Poste, Miss N. C. Preston, C. H. Shankland, Mr M. Stratford, Mr R. C. Tozer, Ms B. Woodcock.

Assistant Trainer: Sam Geffray

Conditional: C. Poste.

---

260 **MR R. A. HARRIS, Chepstow**
Postal: **Ridge House Stables, Earlswood, Chepstow, Monmouthshire, NP16 6AN**
Contacts: PHONE **(01291) 641689** FAX **(01291) 641258** MOBILE **(07831) 770899**
E-MAIL ridgehousestables.ltd@btinternet.com WEBSITE www.ronharrisracing.co.uk

1 **ARTURIUS (IRE)**, 6, b h Anabaa (USA)—Steeple **Mr N. O'Farrell**
2 **DARING AFFAIR**, 7, b m Bien Bien (USA)—Daring Destiny **The Yes No Wait Sorries**
3 **FAR SEEKING**, 4, b c Distant Music (USA)—House Hunting **S. & A. Mares**
4 **FLYING GOOSE (IRE)**, 4, ch c Danehill Dancer (USA)—Top of The Form (IRE) **Leeway Group Limited**
5 **GOLDEN SPECTRUM (IRE)**, 9, ch g Spectrum (IRE)—Plessaya (USA) **Peter A. Price**
6 **HART OF GOLD**, 4, b g Foxhound (USA)—Bullion **The Yes No Wait Sorries**
7 **HELLO ROBERTO**, 7, b m Up And At 'em—Hello Hobson's (IRE) **Peter A. Price**
8 **IMPOSTOR (IRE)**, 5, b g In The Wings—Princess Caraboo (IRE) **The Yes No Wait Sorries**
9 **JUDGE 'N JURY**, 4, ch g Pivotal—Cyclone Connie **Mrs R. M. Serrell**
10 **MARKO JADEO (IRE)**, 10, b g Eagle Eyed (USA)—Fleeting Quest **Ron Harris & David Thornton**
11 **MISARO (GER)**, 7, b g Acambaro (GER)—Misniniski **Messrs Criddle Davies Dawson & Villa**
12 **MONTANA SKY (IRE)**, 5, b g Peintre Celebre (USA)—Catch The Lights **Johnsey Estates (1990) Ltd**
13 **NIGHT PROSPECTOR**, 8, b g Night Shift (USA)—Pride of My Heart **Leeway Group Limited**
14 **PASSATO (GER)**, 4, b c Lando (GER)—Passata (FR) **Mrs J. Bloomfield**
15 **PERSONIFY**, 6, ch g Zafonic (USA)—Dignify (IRE) **Leeway Group Limited**
16 **PETROVICH (USA)**, 5, ch h Giant's Causeway (USA)—Pharma (USA) **Peter A. Price**
17 **RED CURRENT**, 4, b f Soviet Star (USA)—Fleet Amour (USA) **Leeway Group Limited**
18 **SIR DOUGLAS**, 5, ch h Desert Sun—Daintree (IRE) **Leeway Group Limited**
19 **THE GAIKWAR (IRE)**, 9, b g Indian Ridge—Broadmara (IRE) **Leeway Group Limited**
20 **TOMS LAUGHTER**, 4, ch g Mamalik (USA)—Time Clash **Five To Follow**
21 **TRINCULO (IRE)**, 11, b g Anita's Prince—Fandangerina (USA) **Peter A. Price**
22 **WINGED FARASI**, 4, b c Desert Style (USA)—Clara Vale (IRE) **Uk Mortgages Abroad Ltd**
23 **ZAYYIR (IRE)**, 4, b c Indian Ridge—Lurina (IRE) **Leeway Group Limited**

THREE-YEAR-OLDS

24 **BAHAMARAMA (IRE)**, ch f Bahamian Bounty—Cole Slaw **Mrs R. M. Serrell**
25 **CARNIVAL DREAM**, b f Carnival Dancer—Reach The Wind (USA) **Mrs J. Bloomfield**
26 **HOLLOW DREAM (IRE)**, b f Beat Hollow—Sarah's Dream (IRE) **Johnsey Estates (1990) Ltd**
27 **JAL MUSIC**, ch g Ishiguru—Musica **Mrs R. M. Serrell**
28 **SPIC 'N SPAN**, b g Piccolo—Sally Slade **Mrs R. M. Serrell**
29 **TEN POLE TUDOR**, b g Royal Applause—Amaniy (USA) **Mrs J. E. F. Adams**
30 **VEGAS LIGHTS (IRE)**, b f Beat Hollow—Catch The Lights **Johnsey Estates (1990) Ltd**

TWO-YEAR-OLDS

31 B c 4/5 Fraam—Amazing Bay (Mazilier (USA)) (8500) **E. Poynter**
32 B f 7/3 Bertolini (USA)—Real Popcorn (IRE) (Jareer (USA)) (2000) **Peter A. Price**

MR R. A. HARRIS—continued

33 B c 2/2 Tobougg (IRE)—Relativity (IRE) (Distant Relative) **Leeway Group Limited**
34 B c 20/3 Systematic—Royal Recreation (USA) (His Majesty (USA)) (3000)
35 B c 18/3 Orpen (USA)—Silent Star (IRE) (Ali-Royal (IRE)) (12500)
36 **SPIRITUAL BOND**, b f 9/3 Monsieur Bond (IRE)—
Country Spirit (Sayf El Arab (USA)) (2500) **Leeway Group Limited**
37 B c 10/4 Mujahid (USA)—Sweet Angeline (Deploy) (4000)

Other Owners: C. S. J. Coley, Jason Criddle, Mr M. T. Davies, R. A. Harris, Mrs D. J. Hughes, D. M. Hussey, Mr S. Mares, Mrs A. Mares, N. Phillips, D. M. Thornton.

Amateur: Mr Josh Harris.

---

261 MR PATRICK HASLAM, Middleham
Postal: **Manor House Stables, Middleham, Leyburn, North Yorkshire, DL8 4QL**
Contacts: **PHONE (01969) 624351 FAX (01969) 624463 MOBILE (07702) 449607**
E-MAIL haslamracing@rapidial.co.uk WEBSITE www.patrickhaslamracing.com

1 **ACAIRDE (IRE)**, 7, b g Supreme Leader—Arctic Snow Cat **J. P. McManus**
2 **ALTO VERTIGO**, 5, b g Averti (IRE)—Singer On The Roof **Middleham Park Racing XXXI**
3 **BEDOUIN BLUE (IRE)**, 5, b g Desert Style (IRE)—Society Fair (FR) **Blue Lion Racing VII**
4 **BLUTO**, 4, b g Mtoto—Low Line **Blue Lion Racing VII**
5 **DREAMAKER (IRE)**, 7, b g Saddlers' Hall (IRE)—Hi' Upham **J. P. McManus**
6 **ESQUILLON**, 6, b m High Estate—Our Aisling **Blue Lion Racing VII**
7 **ETOILE RUSSE (IRE)**, 6, b g Soviet Star (USA)—To The Skies (USA) **M. C. Mason**
8 **FIRE IN CAIRO (IRE)**, 4, b f Barathea (IRE)—Ibiza (GER) **Middleham Park Racing XXVII**
9 **GREEN DAY PACKER (IRE)**, 4, br g Daylami (IRE)—Durrah Green **Middleham Park Racing XXX & C. Denton**
10 **HERALDRY**, 8, b g Mark of Esteem (IRE)—Sorb Apple (IRE) **Mrs A. M. O'Sullivan**
11 **HI DANCER**, 5, b g Medicean—Sea Music **Middleham Park Racing & R. Tocher**
12 **IMPECCABLE GUEST (IRE)**, 5, b m Orpen (USA)—Perfect Guest **Middleham Park Racing XXXII**
13 **JOHN DILLON (IRE)**, 4, ch g Traditionally (USA)—
Matikanehanafubuki (IRE) **Mr Michael Ryan & Mr John Maguire**
14 **KING REVO (IRE)**, 8, b g Revoque (IRE)—Tycoon Aly (IRE) **J. P. McManus**
15 **LORD ON THE RUN (IRE)**, 9, b g Lord Americo—Polar Crash **Mrs A. M. O'Sullivan**
16 **MONSIEUR (FR)**, 3, b g Cyborg (FR)—Quintessence III (FR) **J. P. McManus**
17 **PARK'S PRODIGY**, 4, b g Desert Prince (IRE)—Up And About **Middleham Park Racing XLIII**
18 **PATXARAN (IRE)**, 6, b m Revoque (IRE)—Stargard **Mrs M. Robson**
19 **RIGUEZ DANCER**, 4, b g Dansili—Tricoteuse **Middleham Park Racing XII**
20 **ROCK DIVA (IRE)**, 4, ch f Rock of Gibraltar (IRE)—Merlannah (IRE) **Middleham Park Racing IV**
21 **SCUTCH MILL (IRE)**, 6, ch g Alhaarth (IRE)—Bumble **Kary-On Racing**
22 **VIRTUE**, 6, ch m Vettori—Zenith **J. P. McManus**

THREE-YEAR-OLDS

23 **BESPOKE BOY**, b g Acclamation—Milly Fleur **Mrs W. E. Lucas**
24 **BOURBON HIGHBALL (IRE)**, b g Catcher In The Rye (IRE)—Be Exciting (IRE) **Middleham Park Racing XXXIV**
25 **CHOOSE YOUR MOMENT**, b c Choisir (AUS)—Time Will Show (IRE) **Mr & Mrs Duncan Davidson**
26 **DUKE OF TOURAINE (IRE)**, gr g Linamix (FR)—Miss Mission (IRE) **S. A. B. Dinsmore**
27 **LADY BENJAMIN**, b f Spinning World (USA)—Fresh Look (IRE) **Mr G. Lampard**
28 **MISS SOLO**, b br f Intikhab (USA)—American Rouge (IRE) **Middleham Park Racing II & Dick Renwick**
29 **MISSION IMPOSSIBLE**, gr g Kyllachy—Eastern Lyric **Vyas Ltd & M. T. Buckley**
30 **REALLY RANSOM**, b f Red Ransom (USA)—Really Polish (USA) **Mrs R. J. Jacobs**
31 **RIVER ARDECHE**, b g Elnadim (USA)—Overcome **S. A. B. Dinsmore**
32 **SHEER FANTASTIC**, b g Fantastic Light (USA)—Sheer Bliss (USA) **Middleham Park Racing XVIII**
33 **SHOT THROUGH (USA)**, b g Golden Missile (USA)—Halo's Gleam (USA) **Blue Lion Racing VII**
34 **SOSOSTRIS PITCH (FR)**, b g Pivotal—Sonja's Faith (IRE) **Mrs R. J. Jacobs**
35 **THE MIGHTY ONE**, b g Mujadil (USA)—Presently **Middleham Park Racing VI**
36 **THOMPSONS WALLS (IRE)**, b g Trans Island—Nordic Living (IRE) **Middleham Park Racing**
37 **VOLVORETAS RAINBOW**, ch f Rainbow Quest—Volvoreta **Mrs R. J. Jacobs**

TWO-YEAR-OLDS

38 B f 29/4 Pyrus (USA)—Amoras (IRE) (Hamas (IRE)) (6000) **Miss Karen Theobald**
39 **ARES CHOIX**, b f 12/2 Choisir (AUS)—Ares Vallis (IRE) (Caerleon (USA)) (32000) **Mrs R. J. Jacobs**
40 **ASIAN TALE (IRE)**, b f 18/2 Namid—Literary (Woodman) (USA) (8000) **Middleham Park Racing XXXIX**
41 **BACHELOR DAYS (IRE)**, b g 21/4 Bachelor Duke (USA)—
Anchorage (IRE) (Slip Anchor) (42000) **Middleham Park Racing LI**

MR PATRICK HASLAM—continued

42 **BLUE DAGGER (IRE)**, ch c 6/3 Daggers Drawn (USA)—
                              Sports Post Lady (IRE) (M Double M (USA)) (20000) **Blue Lion Racing VII**
43 **FARAWAY SOUND (IRE)**, b c 11/2 Distant Music (USA)—
                              Queen Consort (Diesis) **Middleham Park Racing XXXIX**
44 **INCA SLEW (IRE)**, ch g 8/2 City On A Hill (USA)—
                              Con Dancer (Shareef Dancer (USA)) (6500) **Middleham Park Racing XXXIX**
45 B f 22/3 Bahamian Bounty—Marionetta (Nijinsky (CAN)) **P. D. Player**
46 **MONACO MISTRESS (IRE)**, b f 24/3 Acclamation—
                              Bendis (GER) (Danehill (USA)) (57000) **Team Fashion Rocks**
47 Ch c 17/3 Lomitas—Nellie Melba (Hurricane Sky (AUS)) **Lady Lonsdale**
48 B f 23/3 Makbul—Parkside Prospect (Piccolo) (3200) **Middleham Park Racing XXXIX**
49 Ch f 16/3 Compton Place—Petarga (Petong) (8000) **Tally Ho Stud**
50 **QUEEN OF DALYAN (IRE)**, ch f 23/4 Redback—
                              Face The Storm (IRE) (Barathea (IRE)) (6000) **Middleham Park Racing XXXIX**
51 **RIOJA RUBY (IRE)**, b f 29/4 Redback—
                              Bacchanalia (IRE) (Blues Traveller (IRE)) (6200) **Middleham Park Racing XXXIX**
52 B f 6/4 Pyrus (USA)—Riskie Things (Risk Me (FR)) **Miss Karen Theobald**
53 **RON'S PRINCESS (IRE)**, b f 7/3 Fantastic Light (USA)—
                              Persea (IRE) (Fasliyev (USA)) (3000) **Middleham Park Racing LII**
54 Br f 27/3 Captain Rio—Saibhreas (IRE) (Last Tycoon) (12869) **Mrs A. M. O'Sullivan**
55 Ch g 24/3 Loup Sauvage (USA)—Sea Idol (IRE) (Astronef) **Miss Karen Theobald**

Other Owners: Mr J. D. Briscoe, Mr M. T. Buckley, Mr P. J. Curson, Mr D. Davidson, Mrs D. Davidson, Mr P. Drinkall, Mrs A. Duffield, Mr P. C. Haslam, C. R. Jackson, Mr John J. Maguire, D. Nicholls, Mr T. S. Palin, Mr M. Prince, Mr Dick Renwick, Mr Michael Ryan (Bradford), D. R. Tucker, Vyas Ltd, Mr R. Young.

Assistant Trainer: Ben Haslam

Jockey (NH): A. P. McCoy, F. Keniry. **Conditional:** Warren Cafferty. **Apprentice:** Leanne Kershaw.

---

262 **MR N. J. HAWKE, Woolminstone**
Postal: Blackmore Farm, Woolminstone, Crewkerne, Somerset, TA18 8QP
Contacts: **PHONE (01635) 578101 MOBILE (07899) 922827**

1 **BRAVE JO (FR)**, 7, ch g Villez (USA)—Eau de Nuit **D. R. Mead**
2 **FRIENDLY REQUEST**, 9, b br m Environment Friend—Who Tells Jan **W. E. Donohue**
3 **HAZELBURY**, 7, b m Overbury (IRE)—Mira Lady **Mrs J. McDermid**
4 **HOW REALEE (IRE)**, 5, b g Kotashaan (FR)—Lucky Diverse (IRE) **Mrs D. A. Wetherall**
5 **ITSTOOEARLY**, 5, b m Overbury (IRE)—Deb's Ball **Mrs A. L. Heayns**
6 **JUNCTIONTWENTYFOUR**, 7, b g Gildoran—Layston Pinzal **D. R. Mead**
7 **KINETIC POWER (IRE)**, 5, gr g Alhaarth (IRE)—Nichodoula **G. D. Taylor**
8 **LORD LIEUTENANT (FR)**, 5, gr g Kaldounevees (FR)—Lady Lieutenant (IRE) **H. R. Gibbs**
9 **LOULOU NIVERNAIS (FR)**, 9, b g Lights Out (FR)—Clemence (FR)
10 **MAGIC CLICHE**, 5, gr m Classic Cliche (IRE)—Redlands Magic **Mr G. Deren**
11 **MERRIOTT'S OSCAR (IRE)**, 8, b g Oscar Schindler (IRE)—Killone Lady (IRE) **G. D. Taylor**
12 **MISTER WISEMAN**, 6, gr g Bal Harbour—Genie Spirit **D. R. Mead**
13 **MONTROLIN**, 8, ch g Classic Cliche (IRE)—Charmed I'm Sure **Miss J. Gregory**
14 **NEVER RED (IRE)**, 5, ch m Flemensfirth (USA)—Latin Mistress **Set To Stun Partnership**
15 **OPPORTUNITY KNOCKS**, 8, gr g Wace (USA)—Madame Ruby (FR) **Mrs D. A. Wetherall**
16 **PAUL SUPERSTAR (FR)**, 6, gr g Kaldounevees (FR)—Lady Lieutenant (IRE) **Mrs J. McDermid**
17 **PEEL HOUSE**, 5, ch g Grand Lodge (USA)—Ice House **D. R. Mead**
18 **PERSIAN WARRIOR (IRE)**, 5, b g Desert Prince (IRE)—Viscaria (IRE) **Mr C. Hansford**
19 **PLUMTREE LASS**, 4, b f Tomba—My Poppet **G. C. Fox**
20 **RUNNING HOT**, 10, b g Sunley Builds—Running Cool **C. G. Newman**
21 **SPEEDY CAR (FR)**, 4, b g Sleeping Car (FR)—Katchassa (FR) **Mr G. Deren**
22 **SULTAN FONTENAILLE (FR)**, 6, b h Kaldounevees (FR)—Diane Fontenaille (FR) **D & P Mead**
23 **TOM FONTENAILLES (FR)**, 5, b g Kaldounevees (FR)—Miss Fontenailles (FR) **The South West Wind**
24 **TRIPLE BLUFF**, 5, b g Medicean—Trinity Reef **Mr T. J. G. Martin**
25 **USHIRO EMERY (FR)**, 4, b g Saint des Saints (FR)—Mountain Stage (IRE) **Mr G. Deren**
26 **VINTAGE FABRIC (USA)**, 6, b g Royal Anthem (USA)—Sandalwood (USA) **N. J. McMullan & S. H. Bryant**
27 **WORTHA LILY**, 5, b m Thowra (USA)—Urban Lily **Mrs A. Cole**
28 **XILA FONTENAILLES (FR)**, 7, gr m Turgeon (USA)—
                              Miss Fontenailles (FR) **Pearce Bros & Thresher Partnership**
29 **ZIMBABWE (FR)**, 8, b g Turgeon (USA)—Razzamatazz (FR) **R. J. & Mrs J. A. Peake**

MR N. J. HAWKE—continued

Other Owners: Mrs Kate Brain, S. H. Bryant, N. Cox, J. Davies, Mrs J. Gibbs, Mr S. M. Lambert, N. J. McMullan, Mrs P. J. Mead, Mr J. Newton-Sharp, Mr Russell J. Peake, Mrs J. A. Peake, Mr Steve Pearce, Mr K. Scutt.

Assistant Trainer: Mrs S Hawke

Amateur: Miss T. Newman.

---

263 **MR JOHN C HAYDEN, Kildare**
Postal: **Castlemartin Abbey House Stables, Kilcullen, Co. Kildare, Ireland**
Contacts: PHONE (00353) 4548 1598 FAX (00353) 4548 1598 MOBILE (00353) 8682 26717
E-MAIL hayden_jj@yahoo.com WEBSITE www.jchayden.com

1 ALONE HE STANDS (IRE), 8, b g Flying Spur (AUS)—Millennium Tale (FR)
2 EMILY BLAKE (IRE), 4, b f Lend A Hand (IRE)—Kirri (IRE)
3 GREENHILLS KING (IRE), 5, b h Distant Music (USA)—Kirri (IRE)
4 6, Ch m Lahib (USA)—Island Goddess

THREE-YEAR-OLDS

5 SINE QUA NON, ch f Pivotal—Red May (IRE)

TWO-YEAR-OLDS

6 B f 15/3 Invincible Spirit (IRE)—Caraiyma (IRE) (Shahrastani (USA))
7 Gr c 20/2 Verglas (IRE)—Mubadalah (USA) (Dumaani (USA)) (23809)

Other Owners: F. Campbell, Castlemartin Racing Club, Mr J. Hardiman, Mr S. Hayden, Mr G. Hayden, Mr J. Keeling, Mr E. McAllister, Sir A. J. O'Reilly, Lady O'Reilly, Mr F. J. O'Toole.

Assistant Trainer: J J Hayden

Jockey (flat): J. P. Murtagh, J. P. Spencer. **Jockey (NH):** D. J. Casey. **Apprentice:** P. Townend. **Amateur:** Mr M. Hayden.

---

264 **MR D. HAYDN JONES, Pontypridd**
Postal: **Garth Paddocks, Efail Isaf, Pontypridd, Mid-Glamorgan, CF38 1SN**
Contacts: PHONE (01443) 202515 FAX (01443) 201877 MOBILE (07967) 680012

1 CHIA (IRE), 5, ch m Ashkalani (IRE)—Motley **G. I. D. Llewellyn**
2 ENCIRCLED, 4, b f In The Wings—Ring of Esteem **Mrs M L Parry & Mr P Steele-Mortimer**
3 GWILYM (GER), 5, b h Agnes World (USA)—Glady Rose (GER) **S. Kon, D. Llewelyn & J. Runeckles**
4 KATIE LAWSON (IRE), 5, b m Xaar—Idle Chat (USA) **Monolithic Refractories Ltd**
5 MEGA DAME (IRE), 4, b f Iron Mask (USA)—Easter Girl **W. G. Weeks**
6 MONTEMAYORPRINCESS (IRE), 4, b f Fath (USA)—Blonde Goddess (IRE) **Mr R. Phillips**
7 PASS THE PORT, 7, ch g Docksider (USA)—One of The Family **The Porters**
8 ROYAL ORISSA, 6, b g Royal Applause—Ling Lane **Llewellyn, Runeckles**
9 SILVABELLA (IRE), 5, gr m Monashee Mountain (USA)—Siva (FR) **K. Kynaston**
10 SOLICITUDE, 5, ch m Bertolini (USA)—Sibilant **David Llewelyn Partnership**

THREE-YEAR-OLDS

11 MONTE MAYOR BIRDIE (IRE), b f Captain Rio—Ascoli **Mr R. Phillips**
12 RATHMOLYON, ch f Bahamian Bounty—Feather Circle (IRE) **Miss G. M. Byrne**
13 SUNSHINE LADY (IRE), b f Captain Rio—Damezao **B. Sheppard**
14 WESTWOOD, ch g Captain Rio—Consignia (IRE) **Merry Llewelyn & Runeckles**

TWO-YEAR-OLDS

15 DIVINATORE, b c 11/4 Sakhee (USA)—Divina Mia (Dowsing (USA)) (75000) **The Preseli Partnership**
16 Ch f 24/4 Captain Rio—Ink Pot (USA) (Green Dancer (USA)) (5469) **Miss G. M. Byrne**
17 PEPIN (IRE), ch c 11/3 King Charlemagne (USA)—
                                  Consignia (IRE) (Definite Article) **Merry Llewelyn & Runeckles**
18 B f 7/2 Captain Rio—Sea of Serenity (USA) (Conquistador Cielo (USA)) (19000) **J. E. Keeling**
19 TINSHU (IRE), ch f 30/3 Fantastic Light (USA)—
                                  Ring of Esteem (Mark of Esteem (IRE)) (10000) **Llewellyn, Runeckles**

MR D. HAYDN JONES—continued

Other Owners: Mr R. T. Drage, Mr J. P. Foley, Mrs E. M. Haydn Jones, Mr Stephen Kon, Mr Steve Merry, Mrs M. L. Parry, Mr J. Runeckles, Mr Brian Sheppard, Mr P. Steele-Mortimer.

Assistant Trainer: Mrs E. M. Haydn Jones

Apprentice: L. Brewer.

---

265 **MR A. B. HAYNES, Limpley Stoke**
Postal: **A. H. Racing Ltd, Conkwell Grange Stables, Limpley Stoke, Bath, Somerset, BA2 7FD**
Contacts: **PHONE (01225) 723248 FAX (01225) 720356 MOBILE (07811) 102171**
E-MAIL info@ah-horseracing.co.uk WEBSITE www.ah-horseracing.co.uk

1 BATHWICK PENNY, 4, b f Peintre Celebre (USA)—La Riveraine (USA) **H. M. W. Clifford**
2 BLACK MOMA (IRE), 4, b f Averti (IRE)—Sareb (FR) **A. W. Moore**
3 BORDER CASTLE, 7, b g Grand Lodge (USA)—Tempting Prospect **Staverton Owners Group**
4 BRAVE FACE, 6, b g Commanche Run—Miss Piera **Staverton Owners Group**
5 CALL ME MYRTLE (IRE), 4, b f Turtle Island (IRE)—Carols Cracker (IRE) **I. M. McGready**
6 CASTLEMORE (IRE), 10, b g Be My Native (USA)—Parsonetta **Staverton Owners Group**
7 DESPERATE DAN, 7, b g Danzero (AUS)—Alzianah **J. P. McCarthy**
8 EVER CHEERFUL, 7, b g Atraf—Big Story **Abacus Employment Services Ltd**
9 FRANK'S QUEST (IRE), 8, b g Mujadil (USA)—Questuary (IRE) **Ms C. Berry**
10 FUN IN THE SUN, 4, b g Piccolo—Caught In The Rain **H. M. W. Clifford**
11 GENEROUS LAD (IRE), 5, b g Generous (IRE)—Tudor Loom **M. Bowden**
12 KILROGAN (IRE), 9, b g Shernazar—Beauty's Pride (IRE) **Mrs V. A. Butcher**
13 KINGS TOPIC (IRE), 8, ch g Kingmambo (USA)—Topicount (USA) **Ms C. Berry**
14 LITTLE MISS TARA (IRE), 4, b f Namid—Circled (USA) **Mrs S.Maine,K.Wills,D.Fuller,L.Bloxsome**
15 LOOKS COULD KILL (USA), 6, b br g Red Ransom (USA)—Mingling Glances (USA) **Ms C. Berry**
16 LORD NELLSSON, 12, b g Arctic Lord—Miss Petronella **Dajam Ltd**
17 MAFAHEEM, 6, b g Mujahid (USA)—Legend of Aragon **H. M. W. Clifford**
18 NOBLE MOUNT, 7, b g Muhtarram (USA)—Our Poppet (IRE) **Ms C. Berry**
19 PICCOSTAR, 5, b m Piccolo—Anneliina **Ms C. Berry**
20 POPPETS SWEETLOVE, 4, b f Foxhound (USA)—Our Poppet (IRE) **G. S. Robinson**
21 PURE MAGIC (FR), 7, b g Lake Coniston (IRE)—La Le Lu (FR) **West Country Racing - Winter Warmer**
22 SENESCHAL, 7, b g Polar Falcon (USA)—Broughton Singer (IRE) **P. Cook**
23 STAR OF POMPEY, 4, b f Hernando (FR)—Discerning **Double-R-Racing**
24 4, B g Tipsy Creek (USA)—Sulapuff **Dajam Ltd**

THREE-YEAR-OLDS

25 ADAM ETERNO (IRE), ch g Spartacus (IRE)—Mermaid Melody **J. M. Sancaster**
26 ATTRIBUTION, b c Royal Applause—Thrilling Day **P. Cook**
27 BATHWICK ICON (IRE), b f Xaar—Greek Icon **H. M. W. Clifford**
28 BATHWICK MINSTREL, br f Singspiel—Polenta (IRE) **H. M. W. Clifford**
29 BOSAMCLIFF (IRE), b f Daylami (IRE)—L'animee **T. Samuel, D. Burns & W. Clifford**
30 DEFNIKOV, gr g Baryshnikov (AUS)—By Definition (IRE) **Paul & Ann de Weck**
31 DOUBLE R, b f Fraam—Bint Albadou (IRE) **Double-R-Racing**
32 HAS TO BE ABACUS (IRE), br c Indian Lodge (IRE)—No Way (IRE) **Abacus Employment Services Ltd**
33 HEROIC LAD, ch g Arkadian Hero (USA)—Erith's Chill Wind **Alison Mallia Lisa Clarke**
34 LANCASTER LAD, b c Piccolo—Ruby Julie **Mrs S. M. Maine**
35 MIDNITE BLEWS (IRE), gr g Trans Island—Felicita (IRE) **Mr A. Moore & Mr P. Brett**
36 MISS BOOTYLISHES, b f Mujahid (USA)—Moxby **Mrs H. Adams**
37 NESTOR PROTECTOR (IRE), b g Bold Fact (USA)—Irma La Douce (IRE) **Abacus Employment Services Ltd**
38 STATION PLACE, b f Bahamian Bounty—Twin Time **Dajam Ltd**
39 SWINDON TOWN FLYER (IRE), b g Captain Rio—Baltic Breeze (USA) **WCR IV The County Ground Syndicate**
40 VALENTINE BLUE, ch g Tobougg (IRE)—Blue Topaz (IRE) **West Country Racing III**
41 Br c Val Royal (FR)—Welsh Harp

TWO-YEAR-OLDS

42 B c 18/3 Bertolini (USA)—Adamas (IRE) (Fairy King (USA)) **Mrs A. De Weck & Mr P. De Weck**
43 Br f 11/3 First Trump—Angel Maid (Forzando) (1000)
44 Ch c 4/4 Hawkeye (IRE)—Appalachia (IRE) (Imperial Frontier (USA)) **Mrs H. Adams**
45 B f 25/2 Tagula (IRE)—Baby Loves (Sadler's Wells (USA)) (5500) **Mrs S. Clifford**
46 B c 27/3 Deportivo—Blossoming (Vague Shot) (800) **H. M. W. Clifford**
47 B f 9/3 Kyllachy—Broughton Singer (IRE) (Common Grounds) (8000) **P. Cook**

MR A. B. HAYNES—continued

48 Ch f 26/3 Baryshnikov (AUS)—By Definition (IRE) (Definite Article) **Paul & Ann de Weck**
49 **CALL ME COURAGEOUS (IRE)**, ch c 27/2 Captain Rio—
              Golden Concorde (Super Concorde (USA)) **Mr D. O'Neil & Mr C. Kelly**
50 Br f 1/2 One Cool Cat (USA)—Cosabawn (IRE) (Barathea (IRE)) (15000)
51 B f 31/3 Monsieur Bond (IRE)—Delicious (Dominion) (800)
52 DUCAL DAISEY, b f 18/2 Shahrastani (USA)—
              Jimgareen (IRE) (Lahib (USA)) (2000) **Abacus Employment Services Ltd**
53 **HASSADIN**, ch c 27/1 Reset (AUS)—Crocolat (Croco Rouge (IRE)) (20000) **Ms J. Loylert**
54 B f 27/3 Barathea (IRE)—La Riveraine (USA) (Riverman (USA)) (2500) **Mrs S. Clifford**
55 B f 24/3 Reset (AUS) Moxby (Efisio)
56 Ch c 10/4 Reel Buddy (USA)—Musical Day (Singspiel (IRE)) (3000)
57 **PICCASO'S SKY**, b c 30/3 Piccolo—Skylark (Polar Falcon (USA)) (7200) **Mr K. Corke**
58 **POPPET'S LOVEIN**, b f 27/3 Lomitas—Our Poppet (IRE) (Warning)
59 B c 28/4 Night Shift (USA)—Scared (Royal Academy (USA)) (7200) **H. M. W. Clifford**
60 Ch c 30/1 Monsieur Bond (IRE)—Splicing (Sharpo) **J. P. McCarthy**
61 Ch c 6/3 Primo Valentino (IRE)—Yanomami (USA) (Slew O' Gold (USA)) (5500) **J. P. McCarthy**

Other Owners: M. J. Blake, Mrs S. E. Blake, Mrs L. H. Bloxsome, P. W. Brett, Ms D. Burns, Mrs L. M. Clarke, Mrs A. De Weck, D. G. J. Fuller, Mr S. R. J. Heaney, Mr C. P. Kelly, Mrs A. D. Mallia, Miss F. Matthewman, Mr B. McCabe, Mr D. O'Neill, Mrs D. Robinson, Mr T. Samuel, N. E. Webb, K. R. Wills, P. L. de Weck.

Apprentice: Paul Nolan, Gemma Elford.

MR H. E. HAYNES, Highworth
Postal: **Red Down Farm, Highworth, Wiltshire, SN6 7SH**
Contacts: **PHONE/FAX** (01793) 762437 **FAX** (01793) 762437
MOBILE (07704) 707728/(07711) 488341
E-MAIL reddownracing@aol.com

1 **FINE EDGE**, 7, ch m Keen—Cap That **H. E. Haynes**
2 **FIZZY LIZZY**, 8, b m Cool Jazz—Formidable Liz **Mrs F. Haynes**
3 **FLY FROM BASRA**, 5, br g Petrizzo—Fly Home **Miss S. R. Haynes**
4 **GRACIE BEACH**, 6, b m Alflora (IRE)—
              Ur Only Young Once **Reddown High Explosive Partnership, H. E. Haynes**
5 **JAMAICA STORM**, 5, b m Kayf Tara—Stormworthy Miss (IRE) **Miss S. R. Haynes**
6 5, Ch g Sure Blade (USA)—Locket **H. E. Haynes**
7 **MR MOTORMOUTH**, 5, b g Manhal—Viola **Reddown High Explosive Partnership, H. E. Haynes**
8 5, B m Petrizzo—Rupert's Princess (IRE) **Miss S. R. Haynes**
9 **WORTH A GAMBLE**, 10, ch g So Factual (USA)—The Strid (IRE) **Miss S. R. Haynes**

THREE-YEAR-OLDS

10 B c Sir Harry Lewis (USA)—Fly Home **Miss S. R. Haynes**
11 B f Kayf Tara—Rupert's Princess (IRE) **Miss S. R. Haynes**
12 **STORMWOOD**, b c Fleetwood (IRE)—Stormworthy Miss (IRE) **Miss S. R. Haynes**

Other Owners: Patrick Beach (Jnr), Mr Rex Trotman.

Assistant Trainer: Sally R Haynes

Jockey (flat): R Winston. **Amateur:** Miss F. Haynes.

MR J. C. HAYNES, Brampton
Postal: **Cleugh Head, Low Row, Brampton, Cumbria, CA8 2JB**
Contacts: **PHONE** (01697) 746253 **MOBILE** (07771) 511471

1 **MISS PORTSIDE**, 5, b m Mull of Kintyre (USA)—Collision **J. C. Haynes**
2 **PANTHERS RUN**, 8, b g Jendali (USA)—Dorado Beach **J. C. Haynes**
3 **SILVER DAGGER**, 10, gr g Dr Devious (IRE)—La Belle Affair (USA) **J. C. Haynes**

Jockey (NH): F. Keniry. **Conditional:** Michael McAlister.

268 MRS C. HEAD, Chantilly

Postal: **32 Avenue du General Leclerc, 60500 Chantilly, France**
Contacts: **PHONE (0033) 3445 70101 FAX (0033) 3445 85333 MOBILE (0033) 6073 10505**
E-MAIL christiane.head@wanadoo.fr

1 **GARDA (USA)**, 4, b c Lemon Drop Kid (USA)—Gilded Leaf (USA) **R. Scully**
2 **GRASS COURT (USA)**, 4, b c Lemon Drop Kid (USA)—Pleine Lune (IRE) **C. Head**
3 **HELLO MY LORD (FR)**, 4, gr c Anabaa Blue—Hello Molly (FR) **Mrs Leurson**
4 **MALABA (FR)**, 4, b f Anabaa—Malaisie **Mrs Alec Head**
5 **MALIENNE (FR)**, 4, b f Numerous—Matanilla **Mrs Alec Head**
6 **MYLIE (FR)**, 4, b f Numerous—Moly (FR) **Mrs Alec Head**
7 **PALLADIEN (FR)**, 4, b br c Anabaa (USA)—Passionnee (USA) **Wertheimer et Frere, Mr Alec Head**
8 **PARETO (FR)**, 5, ch h Bering—Padina (GER) **Hildegard Focke**
9 **PASSAGER (FR)**, 5, b h Anabaa (USA)—Passionnee (USA) **Christiane Head**
10 **SILVERY BAY (FR)**, 4, b f Numerous—Silvermine **Mrs Alec Head**
11 **SKYTEAM (FR)**, 4, b c Anabaa (USA)—Spenderella (FR) **Mr Alec Head**

THREE-YEAR-OLDS

12 **ADDITIONAL**, ch f Zamindar (USA)—Dawna **Prince Khalid Abdullah**
13 **AFRICAN ROSE**, ch f Observatory (USA)—New Orchid (USA) **Prince Khalid Abdullah**
14 **ARCTIC SYMPHONY (FR)**, ch f Distant Music—Artic Blue **Mrs Leurson**
15 **BLUSH TONE**, b f Xaar—Stay Behind **Prince Khalid Abdullah**
16 **CAFE LASSERE (USA)**, b f Giant's Causeway—Net Worth (USA) **Dr T. A. Ryan**
17 **CHASING STARS**, ch f Observatory (USA)—Post Modern (USA) **Prince Khalid Abdullah**
18 **DAILY HELP**, b f Dalakhani (IRE)—Houseproud (USA) **Prince Khalid Abdullah**
19 **DUNKERQUE (FR)**, b c Highest Honor (FR)—Dissertation (FR) **Mr Alec Head**
20 **FLAG**, b c Numerous—Special Gallery **Martine Head**
21 **FULL OF GOLD (FR)**, ch c Gold Away (IRE)—Funny Feerie (FR) **Mr Alec Head**
22 **HEAD ON (FR)**, ch f Smart Strike (CAN)—Heritiere (AUS) **Mrs Alec Head**
23 **HELLO MORNING (FR)**, gr c Poliglote—Hello Molly (FR) **Mrs Leurson**
24 **KANGAROO JACK (IRE)**, b c Poliglote—Galitizine (USA) **P. Savill**
25 **KARMA LINA**, b f King's Best (USA)—Armilina (FR) **Kilboy Estate**
26 **LA BOUDEUSE (FR)**, b f Bering—Shark Bay **Mr Meyrat**
27 **LOST IN THOUGHT**, ch f Selkirk (USA)—Well Away (IRE) **Prince Khalid Abdullah**
28 **MAKOKO (FR)**, gr c Anabaa (USA)—Mamamia (FR) **Mr Alec Head**
29 **MARYMOUNT (FR)**, b f Numerous—Malaisie (USA) **Mrs Alec Head**
30 **NEVERTHELESS**, b c Bering—Seven Sing (USA) **Prince Khalid Abdullah**
31 **OCEAN LADY (FR)**, ch f Urban Ocean (FR)—Lonely Lady (FR) **C. Head**
32 **OUT VOTED**, b gr c Linamix (FR)—Minority **Prince Khalid Abdullah**
33 **PENNY (FR)**, bl c Anabaa (USA)—Passonaria (FR) **Mr Alec Head**
34 **PORGY**, b c Dansili—Light Ballet **Prince Khalid Abdullah**
35 **PREMIERE PARTIE (FR)**, b f Numerous—Porretta (IRE) **Mrs Alec Head**
36 **PUTNEY BRIDGE**, b c Mizzen Mast (USA)—Valentine Band (USA) **Prince Khalid Abdullah**
37 **RED TULIP**, c f Bering—Silver Tulip (USA) **Martine Head**
38 **ROCK HARMONIE (FR)**, b f Rock of Gibraltar (IRE)—Rigoureuse (USA) **Mrs Leurson**
39 **ROYALE LIFE (FR)**, bl f Anabaa (USA)—Royale Highnest (FR) **Mrs Alec Head**
40 **ROYALEMIXA (FR)**, b f Linamix (FR)—Riziere (FR) **Mrs Alec Head**
41 **SENDAWALIS (FR)**, b c Sendawar (IRE)—Isola D'elba (USA) **G. Maarek**
42 **SICILE (FR)**, b f Anabaa (USA)—Spenderella (FR) **Mrs Alec Head**
43 **SMALL GREY (FR)**, gr f Verglas (USA)—Small Partie (FR) **Mrs Leurson**
44 **SWEET SIXTEEN (FR)**, ch f Numerous—Silverware **G. Maarek**
45 **TAKING PART**, b c Diesis—Arewehavingfunyet (USA) **Prince Khalid Abdullah**
46 **TRYANA (FR)**, b f Anabaa (USA)—Tresoriere (USA) **Mrs Alec Head**
47 **VASSINELLA (FR)**, b f Anabaa (USA)—Vassia (USA) **Mrs Alec Head**

TWO-YEAR-OLDS

48 B c 29/3 Okawango (USA)—Apparrement (IRE) (Anabaa (USA)) (10939) **G. Maarek**
49 B c 9/5 Smart Strike (CAN)—Call Account (USA) (Private Account (USA)) **Prince Khalid Abdullah**
50 B c 18/3 Bering—Flamenco Red (Warning) **Prince Khalid Abdullah**
51 **HEART OF AMERICA (FR)**, bl f 14/4 American Post—Hierarchie (FR) (Sillery (USA)) **C. Head**
52 Ch f 11/3 American Post—High Summer (USA) (Nureyev (USA)) **Prince Khalid Abdullah**
53 **L'IMPRESARIO (USA)**, b c 1/1 Bernstein (USA)—Catchascatchcan (Pursuit of Love) **Dr T. A. Ryan**
54 B f 15/4 American Post—Loyola (FR) (Sicyos (USA)) (17374) **G. Maarek**
55 B f 7/3 Beat Hollow—Minority (Generous (IRE)) **Prince Khalid Abdullah**
56 **MIRIFIC (FR)**, gr c 2/3 Linamix (FR)—Matanilla (Anabaa (USA)) **Alec Head**
57 **PERSE (FR)**, ch f 13/3 Divine Light (JPN)—Primrail (FR) (Catrail (USA)) **C. Head**

MRS C. HEAD—continued

58 B f 21/1 Zamindar (USA)—Posteritas (USA) (Lear Fan (USA)) **Prince Khalid Abdullah**
59 Ch f 6/2 Peintre Celebre (USA)—Singleton (Singspiel (IRE)) **Prince Khallid Abdullah**
60 **STRICKE (FR),** b c 7/5 Della Francesca (USA)—Salvia (FR) (Septieme Ciel (USA)) (10296) **G. Maarek**
61 **SWEET SEVENTEEN (FR),** b f 15/2 Green Tune (USA)—Silverware (FR) (Polish Precedent (USA)) **G. Maarek**
62 B c 13/2 Maria's Mon (USA)—Valentine Band (USA) (Dixieland Band (USA)) **Prince Khalid Abdullah**

Assistant Trainer: Charley Rossi

---

269 **MR N. J. HENDERSON, Lambourn**
Postal: **Seven Barrows, Lambourn, Hungerford, Berkshire, RG17 8UH**
Contacts: **PHONE (01488) 72259 FAX (01488) 72596**

1 **ADDICTED (IRE),** 5, b g Machiavellian (USA)—Peneia (USA) **Mrs T. Styles**
2 **AFRAD (FR),** 7, gr g Linamix (FR)—Afragha (IRE) **The Not Afraid Partnership**
3 **AFSOUN (FR),** 6, b g Kahyasi—Afragha (IRE) **T. J. Hemmings**
4 **AIGLE D'OR,** 5, b g Halling (USA)—Epistole (IRE) **J. P. McManus**
5 **ALL STAR (GER),** 8, b g Lomitas—Alte Garde (FR) **Lynn Wilson, Nick Wilson, Martin Landau**
6 **AMARETTO ROSE,** 7, b m Alflora (IRE)—Teenero **Shade Oak Stud**
7 **AU COURANT (IRE),** 8, b g Zaffaran (USA)—Thatsthefashion (IRE) **M. A. C. Buckley**
8 **BACK TO THE WIND (IRE),** 6, ch g Bob Back (USA)—Saucy Gale (IRE) **The Not Afraid Partnership**
9 **BAHIA BLANCA (FR),** 4, b br f Astarabad (USA)—Guerville (FR) **W. H. Ponsonby**
10 **BARBERS SHOP,** 6, b g Saddlers' Hall (IRE)—Close Harmony **Her Majesty The Queen**
11 **BINOCULAR (FR),** 4, b g Enrique—Bleu Ciel Et Blanc (FR) **J. P. McManus**
12 **BLUE SHARK (FR),** 6, b br g Cadoudal (FR)—Sweet Beauty **T. J. Hemmings**
13 **BONCHESTER BRIDGE,** 7, b m Shambo—Cabriole Legs **W. H. Ponsonby**
14 **BONIKOS (FR),** 4, b g Bonnet Rouge (FR)—Baby Sitter (FR) **The Salmon Racing Partnership**
15 **BOOMSHAKALAKA (IRE),** 8, ch g Anshan—Fairy Gale (IRE) **The Cigar Bar Partnership**
16 **BRIERY STAR,** 5, b m Overbury (IRE)—Briery Ann **J. Finch**
17 **BRILLIANT CUT,** 8, b gr g Terimon—Always Shining **W. H. Ponsonby**
18 **CAMPANNELLO,** 7, b m Saddlers' Hall (IRE)—Soundsgoodtome **R. D. Chugg**
19 **CAPITANA (GER),** 7, ch m Lando (GER)—Capitolina (GER) **P. J. D. Pottinger**
20 **CARACCIOLA (GER),** 11, b g Lando (GER)—Capitolina (FR) **P. J. D. Pottinger**
21 **CAROLE'S LEGACY,** 4, ch f Sir Harry Lewis (USA)—Carole's Crusader **P. Murphy**
22 **CHANTACO (USA),** 6, b g Bahri (USA)—Dominant Dancer **R. Tooth**
23 **CHOMBA WOMBA (IRE),** 7, b m Fourstars Allstar (USA)—Miss Muppet (IRE) **Mr & Mrs R. Kelvin-Hughes**
24 **CHOUXDAMOUR (FR),** 5, ch g Murmure (FR)—Choucouli (FR) **Mrs J Reed Lady Kiszely Miss S Henderson**
25 **CLASSIC FIDDLE,** 6, ch m Classic Cliche (IRE)—Fiddling The Facts (IRE) **Mrs E. C. Roberts**
26 **CLAY HOLLISTER,** 5, ch g Monsun (GER)—Polish Palace (IRE) **Mrs S. Magnier**
27 **COMKILRED CHAMP (IRE),** 6, b br g Zaffaran (USA)—Comkilred (IRE) **M. R. Landau**
28 4, B br g Anshan—Cool Thistle **N. J. Henderson**
29 **COPSALE LAD,** 11, ch g Karinga Bay—Squeaky Cottage **Swallow Partnership**
30 **CROZAN (FR),** 8, b g Sassanian (USA)—La Guyonniere (FR) **T. J. Hemmings**
31 **DARAYBAD (FR),** 6, b g Octagonal (NZ)—Daraydala (IRE) **J. P. McManus**
32 **DAVE'S DREAM (IRE),** 5, b g Anshan—Native Success (IRE) **Mr D. Murdoch**
33 **DEBUT (IRE),** 6, br m Presenting—Kings Rose (IRE) **B. T. Stewart-Brown Esq**
34 4, B g King's Theatre (IRE)—Disallowed (IRE) **N. J. Henderson**
35 **DUC DE REGNIERE (FR),** 6, b g Rajpoute (FR)—Gladys De Richerie (FR) **Sir Peter & Lady Gibbings**
36 **EARTH CRYSTAL (IRE),** 6, b g Bob's Return (IRE)—Crystal Mover (IRE) **M. A. C. Buckley**
37 **FIDDLING AGAIN,** 5, b m Hernando—Fiddling The Facts (IRE) **Mrs E. C. Roberts**
38 **FIFTYONEFIFTYONE (IRE),** 4, b g Oscar (IRE)—Great Dante (IRE) **A. Taylor**
39 **FIRST POINT (GER),** 5, b g Trempolino (USA)—First Smile
40 **FLEET STREET,** 9, ch g Wolfhound (USA)—Farmer's Pet **W. H. Ponsonby**
41 **FRENCH OPERA,** 5, b g Bering—On Fair Stage (IRE) **Lynn Wilson & Martin Landau**
42 **GALIENT (FR),** 5, b g Galileo (USA)—Endorsement **Mr & Mrs Kevan Watts**
43 **GENEVA BAY,** 5, b g Alflora (IRE)—Lady Geneva **Newbury Racehorse Owners Group**
44 **GOLD AWARD,** 5, b g Daylami (IRE)—Trying For Gold (USA) **Her Majesty The Queen**
45 **GREAT REASON,** 4, br g Alflora (IRE)—Grignette (FR) **E. R. Hanbury**
46 **GREENHOPE (IRE),** 10, b g Definite Article—
Unbidden Melody (USA) **Lynn Wilson Giles Wilson Martin Landau**
47 **INGRATITUDE (IRE),** 5, ch g Inchinor—Merci (IRE) **Club ISM & JSC Sport**
48 **ITS A DREAM (IRE),** 8, b g Oscar (IRE)—Gra-Bri (IRE) **Mrs R. Murdoch & David Murdoch**
49 **JACK THE GIANT (IRE),** 6, b g Giant's Causeway (USA)—State Crystal (IRE) **Hanbury Syndicate**
50 **JACOB RUISDAEL (IRE),** 6, b g Supreme Leader—South Quay **Lady R. Green**
51 **JEAN LE POISSON (FR),** 6, b g Villez (USA)—Baladinine (FR) **The Fourth Pheasant Inn Partnership**
52 **JUVEIGNEUR (FR),** 11, ch g Funny Baby (FR)—Azurea (FR) **T. J. Hemmings**

MR N. J. HENDERSON—continued

53 KENZO III (FR), 10, ch g Agent Bleu (FR)—Kelinda (FR) Killinghurst Park Stud
54 KHYBER KIM, 6, b g Mujahid (USA)—Jungle Rose Mrs C. M. Mould
55 KINHARVIE, 5, b m Alflora (IRE)—Dalbeattie Mr & Mrs Duncan Davidson
56 LA DAME BRUNE (FR), 6, b m Mansonnien (FR)—Madame Extra (FR) Mr & Mrs J. D. Cotton
57 LESTER LEAPS IN (USA), 5, b or g Red Ransom (USA)—Rose Aurora (USA) The Zeus Racing Partnership
58 LINDEMAN (IRE), 5, b m Presenting—Southcoast Gale Mr & Mrs R. Kelvin-Hughes
59 LORD BOSIE (IRE), 4, b g Oscar (IRE)—Carrigbuck (IRE) Mr R. Kelvin-Hughes
60 MAD MAX (IRE), 6, b g Kayf Tara—Carole's Crusader Carole Skipworth & Paul Murphy
61 MAHARBAL (FR), 8, b g Assessor (IRE)—Cynthia (FR) The Pheasant Inn Partnership
62 MAJOR MILLER, 7, b g Opera Ghost—Millers Action W. H. Ponsonby
63 MARVELLOUS DREAM (FR), 6, ch m Muhtathir—Abstraite Brian J Griffiths & John Nicholson
64 MENCHIKOV (FR), 8, br g Garde Royale—Caucasie (FR) Sir Robert Ogden C.B.E., LLD
65 MIDSUMMER MAGIC, 4, b f Muhtarram (USA)—Romantic Dream Her Majesty The Queen
66 MODEL GIRL, 5, b m Classic Cliche (IRE)—Wedge Musical T. J. Hemmings
67 MONFILS MONFILS (USA), 6, b g Sahm (USA)—Sorpresa (USA) Thurloe 50
68 MONTANA GOLD (IRE), 7, b g Bob Back (USA)—Tell A Tale P. J. Orme
69 MOONLIT PATH, 5, b m Shambo—Lunabelle Her Majesty The Queen
70 MY PETRA, 5, b m Midnight Legend—Lac Marmot (FR) Mr & Mrs R. Kelvin-Hughes
71 NO REGRETS (FR), 7, b g Nononito (FR)—Betty Royale (FR) Mr & Mrs J. D. Cotton
72 OEDIPE (FR), 6, ch g Chamberlin (FR)—Massada (FR) W. J. Brown
73 OSBALDESTON (IRE), 5, b g Oscar (IRE)—Sharonamar (IRE) Mr & Mrs Duncan Davidson
74 OSTROGOTH (FR), 6, b g Ungaro (GER)—Holding (FR) Mr & Mrs John Poynton
75 OVERTLY BLUE (FR), 6, b g Epervier Bleu—Ipsala (FR) L. A. Wilson
76 PAMAK D'AIRY (FR), 5, b g Cadoubel (FR)—Gamaska d'airy (FR) M. R. Green
77 PAPINI (IRE), 7, ch g Lomitas—Pariana (USA) Newbury Racehorse Owners Group
78 PETIT ROBIN (FR), 5, b g Robin des Pres (FR)—Joie de Cotte (FR) Mr & Mrs John Poynton
79 PHARANTO (IRE), 6, b g Dushyantor (USA)—Pharavo (IRE) B K M Partnership
80 PIPE BANNER, 4, b g Silver Patriarch (IRE)—Bella Macrae Her Majesty The Queen
81 POLYFAST (FR), 5, b g Start Fast (FR)—Ephese V (FR) W. J. Brown
82 PRINCE DU BEURY (FR), 5, ch g Epaphos (GER)—Hirondelle des Bois (FR) W. H. Ponsonby
83 PROCAS DE THAIX (FR), 5, ch g Ragmar (FR)—
                    Isca de Thaix (FR) Richard Green Matthew Green NJ Henderson
84 PROUD PRESENCE (IRE), 5, b br g Presenting—Pride of St Gallen (IRE) Mr W. J. Brown & Mrs T. Brown
85 PUNJABI, 5, b g Komaite (USA)—Competa R. C. Tooth
86 QUARL EGO (FR), 4, b g Ungaro (GER)—Jourenuit (FR) A. Cohen
87 RAVELLO BAY, 5, b m Supreme Leader—Clonmello Turf Club 2006
88 RESTLESS D'ARTAIX (FR), 6, b g Restless Carl (IRE)—Akente (FR) L. Wilson
89 RIVER BEAUTY, 4, ch f Exit To Nowhere (USA)—Just Beautiful (FR) Trevor & Linda Marlow
90 ROI DE L'ODET (FR), 8, b g Grape Tree Road—Fanfare du Roi Elite Racing Club
91 ROYALEETY (FR), 9, b g Garde Royale—La Grive (FR) Mr & Mrs John Poynton
92 ROYALS DARLING (GER), 6, ch g Kallisto (GER)—Royal Rivalry (USA) P. C. Green
93 RUN FOR MOOR (IRE), 7, b g Accordion—Run For Shelter R. G. Kelvin-Hughes
94 RUSTLER, 6, b g Green Desert (USA)—Borgia P. C. Green
95 SCHIEHALLION (IRE), 6, b g Pistolet Bleu (IRE)—Lessons Lass (IRE) Mr & Mrs Sandy Orr
96 SCOTS DRAGOON, 6, gr g Silver Patriarch (IRE)—Misowni W. H. Ponsonby
97 SHATABDI (IRE), 6, b br m Mtoto—Violet Express (FR) R. B. Waley-Cohen
98 SHIP'S HILL (IRE), 7, b g Oscar (IRE)—Ballykea (IRE) A. Taylor
99 SIMILAR FASHION, 6, ch m Alflora (IRE)—Like Manner Weatherbys Racing Club
100 SIR JIMMY SHAND (IRE), 7, b br g Accordion—Morganone (IRE) W. H. Ponsonby
101 TANIKOS (FR), 9, b g Nikos—Tamana (USA) Studwell Two Partnership
102 TARANIS, 5, b g Lomitas—Woodbuck ROA Racing Partnership V
103 TARLAC (GER), 7, ch g Dashing Blade—Tintina (USA) J. P. McManus
104 TASH MCGARRY (IRE), 6, b m Publisher (USA)—Moss Abbey The Caledonian Club
105 TEMOIN, 8, b g Groom Dancer (USA)—Kowtow (USA) The Unemployables
106 TESSANOORA, 7, b m Topanoora—Club Sandwich Miss T. J. Henderson
107 THE MARKET MAN (NZ), 8, ch g Grosvenor (NZ)—Eastern Bazzaar (IRE) Sir Robert Ogden C.B.E., LLD
108 THE MIGHTY BARD (IRE), 5, b g Old Vic—Out of Danger (IRE) Mr & Mrs Sandy Orr
109 THE POLOMOCHE (IRE), 5, b g Beneficial—Lessons Lass (IRE) Anthony Speelman
110 THE SPIELER (IRE), 9, b br g In Desperado (FR)—Mettle Kettle The Terrible Business Partnership
111 THEFT, 5, b m Silver Patriarch (IRE)—Piracy The Eighth Pheasant Inn Partnership
112 TICKLE MY FANCY, 6, b m Terimon—Tickle The Tiller (IRE) Guys & Dolls
113 TINAGOODNIGHT (FR), 4, b f Sleeping Car (FR)—Tinarctica (FR) Mr & Mrs R. Kelvin-Hughes
114 TISSEMAN (IRE), 6, ch g Bob Back (USA)—Native Sunset (IRE) Mrs B. A. Hanbury
115 TOLEDE (FR), 7, ch g Nikos—Calligraphie (FR) P. J. D. Pottinger
116 TRABOLGAN (IRE), 10, b g King's Ride—Derrella T. J. Hemmings
117 TREASURY COUNSEL (IRE), 6, br g Leading Counsel (USA)—Dunacarney The Not Afraid Partnership

MR N. J. HENDERSON—continued

118 TROMPETTE (USA), 6, b m Bahri (USA)—Bold Bold (IRE) **Elite Racing Club**
119 TURFSHUFFLE (GER), 5, b g Big Shuffle (USA)—Turfquelle (IRE) **Million in Mind Partnership**
120 VON GALEN (IRE), 7, b g Germany (USA)—Castle Carrig (IRE) **Mr & Mrs Duncan Davidson**
121 WANTAGE ROAD (IRE), 6, br g Pistolet Bleu (IRE)—Glowing Lines (IRE) **L. A. Wilson**
122 WHIZZ BACK (IRE), 4, b f Bob Back (USA)—Whizz **D. Sumpter**
123 WOGAN, 8, b g Presenting—Fall About **P. A. Deal**
124 WORKING TITLE (IRE), 6, b g Oscar (IRE)—Dantes Term (IRE) **Auld Hayes & Murphy**
125 YOU'RE THE TOP (FR), 4, b g Poliglote—Lolly Lodge (FR) **M. Buckley**
126 ZEBRA CROSSING (SAF), 7, ch g Jallad (USA)—Teclafields (SAF) **P. Deal & M. St Quinton**

Other Owners: Mr D. Allatt, Mr Ray Antell, Mr Charles Auld, Mr Barry Baggott, Mr Barry J. Bailey, Mr P. A. G. Banes-Walker, Mr David Bannon, Mr M. Bassington, Mrs V. J. Baxter, Mr Peter Bentley, Mr D. Benwell, Mr Gerald Blackwell, P. J. Box, Mr Liam Breslin, Mrs D. C. Broad, A. R. Bromley, Mr B. G. Brown, Mr Tom Brown, Mr W. J. Brown, Mr Geoffrey Bruce, Mr K. D. Bruckshaw, Mr Michael Buckley, Mr Eddie Burke, Mr Edward Cassie, Mr R. D. Chugg, Mrs Nicholas Clark, Mr Robert Cochrane, Mr Mark Coley, Mr Pat Cornell, Mr J. D. Cotton, Mrs B. Cotton, Mr J. Craft, Mr George Cross, Mr J. M. Curtis, Mrs Alexina Curtis, Lord Daresbury, Mr D. Davidson, Mrs D. Davidson, Mr P. A. Deal, B. P. Dickson, Mrs Clare Diplock, Mr P. N. Dodding, Mr A. T. Eggleton, Mrs Judy England, Miss S. Esmond Rees, Mr J. G. Ferrand, Mr John H. W. Finch, Mr Tony Fox, Mr F. R. Fox, Mr Alan R. Fraser, Mr Bill Gavan, Sir Peter Gibbings, Lady Gibbings, Mr Aidan James Gilroy, Mr Tom Gittins, G. F. Goode, Mrs A. H. Goulandris, Mrs N. J. G. Green, Mr R. A. Green, Mr Matthew Green, Mr Brian J. Griffiths, Mrs Sue Griffiths, Mr Brian Hague, Major Christopher Hanbury, Mrs Christopher Hanbury, Mr Ray Harding, Mr Eugene Hayes, Mr N. J. Henderson, Miss Sarah L. Henderson, Mr Tony Hill, Mrs Emma Hockenhull, Mr P. D. Hockenhull, J. Hornsey, Mr E. J. Hounslow, Mr D. Howard, Mr David Howse, Mr Jon Hughes, Mr Richard Hurst, Mr G. Ireland, Mr John F. Jarvis, Mr Peter F. Jordan, Mrs R. Kelvin-Hughes, Mr R. Kelvin-Hughes, Mr M. B. J. Kimmins, Lady Kiszely, Miss E. A. Lake, Mr Patrick Lambert, Mr Martin R. Landau, Mr Tony Lapping, Mr J-P Lim, Mr John Lomas, Mr M. J. Lowry, Mrs Francis Lukas, Mr C. Mackenzie, Mr Trevor Marlow, Mrs Linda Marlow, Mrs Christian Marner, Mr Ed McCormack, Mr J. D. McLaughlin, Mr B. McGee, Mr D. R. Midwood, Mr Ian D. Miller, Mr D. Minton, Mr P. A. Moss, Mrs T. A. Mulligan, Mrs R. Murdoch, Mr David Murdoch, Mr Paul Murphy, Mr J. M. Nicholson, Mrs D. C. Nicholson, Miss M. Noden, Mrs Sandy Orr, Mr Sandy Orr, Mr D. R. Painter, Mr B. F. Painter, Mr A. C. Parker, Mr D. Parsons, Mr Oliver Pawle, Mr G. W. Pilkington, Mrs Helen Plumbly, Mr Stephen Pollard, Mr John Poynton, Mrs Anne Poynton, Mr S. Prior, Mrs Johnny Reed, Mr A. Reid, Mr Paul Robson, Mrs F. C. Saint Jean, Mr W. Shand Kydd, Mr W. G. Shaw, Prof D. B. A. Silk, Mrs C. Skipworth, Mr John Robert Smith, Mr J. Spence, Mr M. G. St Quinton, Mr C. F. D. Staddon, Mr G. C. Stevens, Mr R. D. W. Stokes, Mrs T. Brown, Mr Ron Stuart, Mr John Studd, Mrs B. M. Studd, Mr R. T. Styles, D. F. Sumpter, Mr P. W. Talbot-Ponsonby, Ms Davina Tanner, Mr A. Taylor, Mr Roy Tofts, Mr Matt Tombs, Mr Peter Truman, Mr M. K. B. Turner, Mr D. G. Usher, Mr Peter Verity, Mr Marcus Waley-Cohen, Mr Kevan Watts, Mrs Prudence Watts, Mr J. R. Weatherby, Mr R. N. Weatherby, Mr Lee Westwood, Miss S. Wilde, Mr Colin Williams, Mr Lynn Wilson, Mr N. C. Wilson, Mr M. J. F. T. Wilson, Mr Giles Wilson, Mr D. J. Wray.

Jockey (NH): M. A. Fitzgerald, M. Foley, A. Tinkler. **Conditional:** F. De Giles.

---

270 **MR P. F. HENDERSON, Fordingbridge**
Postal: 4 Down Farm Cottage, Rockbourne, Fordingbridge, Hampshire, SP6 3NX
Contacts: PHONE (01725) 518113 MOBILE (07958) 482213
E-MAIL Farrier@phenperson3.freeserve.co.uk

1 HOOF IT HARRY (IRE), 7, ch g City Honours (USA)—Miss Boots (IRE) **P. F. Henderson**
2 LIDJO DE ROUGE (FR), 9, b g Murmure (FR)—Delijoe (FR) **P. F. Henderson**
3 SCHEMER FAGAN (IRE), 8, ch g Nucleon (USA)—Less Hassle (IRE) **P. F. Henderson**

---

271 **LADY HERRIES, Littlehampton**
Postal: Angmering Park, Littlehampton, West Sussex, BN16 4EX
Contacts: YARD (01903) 871460 HOME (01903) 871421 FAX (01903) 871609
MOBILE (07785) 282996 E-MAIL www.angparkstables@btconnect.com

1 AUTHORITY (IRE), 8, b g Bluebird (USA)—Persian Tapestry **Lady Herries**
2 BELL ISLAND, 4, b c Dansili—Thermal Spring **L. G. Lazarus**
3 CLEAVER, 7, ch g Kris—Much Too Risky **Lady Herries**
4 GOLDEN FOLLY, 4, ch g Polish Precedent (USA)—Height of Folly **Lady Herries & Friends**
5 HENCHMAN, 5, b g Anabaa (USA)—Gay Heroine **Lady Herries**
6 HONOUR HIGH, 6, gr g Cloudings (IRE)—Meant To Be **Lady Mary Mumford & Sir Roger Gibbs**
7 ILE MICHEL, 11, b g Machiavellian (USA)—Circe's Isle **Lady Herries**
8 KIBOKO, 4, b g Generous (IRE)—Shirley Collins **Lady S. Clutton**
9 KIPSIGIS (IRE), 7, b g Octagonal (NZ)—Kisumu **Lady S. Clutton**
10 KOKKOKILA, 4, b f Robellino (USA)—Meant To Be **Lady Mary Mumford MrJWoodcock & Mr J Cowdrey**
11 MUTAMAASEK (USA), 6, b br g Swain (IRE)—Tamgeed (USA) **Lady Herries**
12 THERMIDOR (USA), 5, ch g Giant's Causeway (USA)—Langoustine (AUS) **Seymour Bloodstock (UK) Ltd**

LADY HERRIES—continued

13 **WAQAARR**, 4, b g Tobougg (IRE)—Seeking Utopia **The Waqaarr Partnership**
14 **WARNINGCAMP (GER)**, 7, b g Lando (GER)—Wilette (GER) **Lady S. Clutton**
15 **ZONERGEM**, 10, ch g Zafonic (USA)—Anasazi (IRE) **Lady Herries & Friends**

THREE-YEAR-OLDS

16 **CABOCHON**, b f Erhaab (USA)—Shamrock **Lady Herries**
17 B f Silver Patriarch (IRE)—Meant To Be **Lady Mary Mumford**

TWO-YEAR-OLDS

18 B c 2/4 Grape Tree Road—Meant To Be (Morston (FR) **Lady Mary Mumford**
19 **SIR FREDDIE**, b c 15/3 Fraam—Height of Folly (Shirley Heights) **Lady Herries**

Other Owners: Mr James D. Cameron, Mr J. C. Cowdrey, Sir Roger G. Gibbs, Lady Herries, Mr Michael Melluish, Lady Mary Mumford, Seymour Bloodstock (UK) Ltd, Mr R. Turner, Mr John Woodcock.

---

272 MR R. J. HEWITT, Anglesey
Postal: **Benllech Farm, Tyn Y Gongl, Anglesey**
Contacts: **MOBILE (07831) 281442**

1 **ANOTHER BARGAIN (IRE)**, 9, b g Mister Lord (USA)—Flashy Treasure **R. J. Hewitt**
2 **CLODAGH VALLEY (IRE)**, 13, b g Doubletour (USA)—Raise A Princess (USA) **R. J. Hewitt**
3 **COLDITZ (IRE)**, 4, ch g Noverre (USA)—West Escape **R. J. Hewitt**
4 **CURLY SPENCER (IRE)**, 14, br g Yashgan—Tim's Brief **R. J. Hewitt**
5 **DELAWARE TRAIL**, 9, b g Catrail (USA)—Dilwara (IRE) **R. J. Hewitt**
6 **EURODEAL (IRE)**, 10, b g Eurobus—Cailin Labhras **R. J. Hewitt**
7 **FERRYPORT HOUSE (IRE)**, 11, b br g Over The River (FR)—Tusker Lady **R. J. Hewitt**
8 **HUGS DEALER**, 6, gr g Environment Friend—Lexham Belle **R. J. Hewitt**
9 **INCHING CLOSER**, 11, b g Inchinor—Maiyaasah **R. J. Hewitt**
10 **LE SEYCHELLOIS (FR)**, 8, ch g Mansonnien (FR)—Adjirah (FR) **R. J. Hewitt**
11 **MAJESTIC (IRE)**, 13, b g Belmez (USA)—Noble Lily (USA) **R. J. Hewitt**
12 **NOBEL BLEU DE KERPAUL (FR)**, 7, b g Pistolet Bleu (IRE)—Gecika de Kerpaul (FR) **R. J. Hewitt**
13 **RICKY B**, 12, b g Rakaposhi King—Fililode **R. J. Hewitt**
14 **SCOTT**, 7, gr g Polar Falcon (USA)—Circled (USA) **R. J. Hewitt**

Assistant Trainer: Rachel Jones

---

273 MR P. W. HIATT, Banbury
Postal: **Six Ash Farm, Hook Norton, Banbury, Oxfordshire, OX15 5DB**
Contacts: **PHONE (01608) 737255 FAX (01608) 730641 MOBILE (07973) 751115**

1 **ALQAAYID**, 7, b g Machiavellian (USA)—One So Wonderful **S. F. Holder**
2 **BELSAY CASTLE**, 5, b g Lugana Beach—Folk Dance (USA) **P. W. Hiatt**
3 **BEN BACCHUS (IRE)**, 6, b g Bahhare—Bodfaridistinction (IRE) **J. W. Hedges**
4 **BLUE HILLS**, 7, br g Vettori (IRE)—Slow Jazz (USA) **Mr T. J. Pratt**
5 **FAIRLY HONEST**, 4, b g Alhaarth (IRE)—Miller's Melody **P. W. Hiatt**
6 **ISA'AF (IRE)**, 9, b g Darshaan—Shauna's Honey (IRE) **P. Kelly**
7 **LYGON LEGEND**, 5, b g Midnight Legend—Gold Nite **I. G. Potter**
8 **MASLAK (IRE)**, 4, b g In The Wings—Jeed (IRE) **C. C. H. Roberts**
9 **MOONSHINE BEACH**, 10, b g Lugana Beach—Monongelia **Mrs K. D. Lewis**
10 **MULBERRY LAD (IRE)**, 6, b g Entrepreneur—Taisho (IRE) **P. W. Hiatt**
11 **RAWAABET (IRE)**, 6, b g Bahhare (USA)—Haddeyah (USA) **P. J. Morgan**
12 **REBELLIOUS SPIRIT**, 5, b g Mark of Esteem (IRE)—Robellino Miss (USA) **Mrs Lucia Stockley & Ken Read**
13 **ROYAL RAINBOW**, 4, ch g Rainbow Quest (USA)—Royal Future (IRE) **C. C. H. Roberts**
14 **TEN TO THE DOZEN**, 5, b g Royal Applause—Almost Amber (USA) **Clive Roberts Vince Walsh**
15 **THEY ALL LAUGHED**, 5, ch g Zafonic (USA)—Royal Future (IRE) **C. C. H. Roberts**
16 **TIEGS (IRE)**, 6, ch m Desert Prince (IRE)—Helianthus **The Fox Inn Partnership**
17 **VERY WELL RED**, 5, b m First Trump—Little Scarlett **P. Kelly**
18 **WALTON WAY**, 8, b g Charmer—Needwood Poppy **Walton Way Partnership**

THREE-YEAR-OLDS

19 **CORAL SHORES**, b f Carnival Dancer—Leading Role **P. W. Hiatt**
20 **TUXEDO**, ch g Cadeaux Genereux—Serengeti Bride (USA) **P. Kelly**

MR P. W. HIATT—continued

Other Owners: Mr J. L. Aizpuru, Mr Phillip Coton, Mr G. Daniell, Mr P. W. Hiatt, Mrs K. Morgan, Mr Paul Porter, Mr Ken Read, Mr Clive Roberts, Mr J. R. Smith, Mrs Lucia Stockley, Mr V. J. Walsh.

Assistant Trainer: Mrs E Hiatt

Jockey (flat): Darren Williams. **Apprentice:** T. Dean. **Amateur:** Miss Dawn Bridgewater, Mrs Marie King.

---

274 **MR M. E. HILL, Totnes**
Postal: **The Barn, Knaves Ash Stables, Nr Redpost, Littlehempston, Totnes, Devon, TQ9 6NG**
Contacts: **PHONE (01803) 813102 MOBILE (07980) 490220**
E-MAIL knavesashracing@itq9.com

1 **BEAT THE SYSTEM**, 5, b g Beat All (USA)—Ardentinny **Fun In The Sun Partnership**
2 **DRUM DANCE (IRE)**, 6, b g Namid—Socialite (IRE) **Fun In The Sun Partnership**
3 **FIRST FRIEND (IRE)**, 7, b g Mark of Esteem (IRE)—Bustira **M. E. Hill**
4 **HORNPIPE**, 6, b g Danehill—Dance Sequence (USA) **M. E. Hill**
5 4, B f Bandmaster (USA)—Kingston Black **M. E. Hill**
6 **MAN OF LETTERS (UAE)**, 7, b g Belong To Me (USA)—Personal Business (USA) **M. E. Hill**
7 **MONDA**, 6, b m Danzig Connection (USA)—Fairey Firefly **Fun In The Sun Partnership**
8 **MUSICAL GIFT**, 8, ch g Cadeaux Genereux—Kazoo **Fun In The Sun Partnership**
9 **RYEDALE OVATION (IRE)**, 5, b g Royal Applause—Passe Passe (USA) **M. E. Hill**

Other Owners: J. S. Hearne.

Jockey (NH): Tom O'Connor. **Apprentice:** Hadden Frost. **Amateur:** Mr W. Puddifer.

---

275 **MRS T. J. HILL, Aston Rowant**
Postal: **Woodway Farm, Aston Rowant, Watlington, Oxford**
Contacts: **PHONE (01844) 353051 FAX (01844) 354751 MOBILE (07769) 862648**
E-MAIL lawney@lawneyhill.co.uk

1 **BALLYBOUGH JACK (IRE)**, 8, b g Shernazar—Lunar Approach (IRE) **McNeill Racing**
2 **HANDY CROSS**, 5, gr m Petoski—Blakelin **Mrs T. J. Hill**
3 5, B m Makbul—Home From The Hill (IRE) **A. Hill**
4 **IN EXTRA TIME (IRE)**, 9, b br g Topanoora—Overtime (IRE) **A. Hill**
5 **JACKELLA (IRE)**, 7, b g Accordion—First Session (IRE) **McNeill Racing**
6 **RELATIVE HERO (IRE)**, 8, ch g Entrepreneur—Aunty (FR) **The Sunday Night Partnership**

Other Owners: Mrs T. Hill, Mr Alan Hill, Mr M. McNeill, Mrs P. McNeill.

Jockey (NH): R. Thornton, A. Thornton. **Conditional:** S. Walsh. **Amateur:** Mr James Tudor.

---

276 **MR B. W. HILLS, Lambourn**
Postal: **Wetherdown House, Lambourn, Hungerford, Berkshire, RG17 8UB**
Contacts: **OFFICE (01488) 71548 FAX (01488) 72823**
E-MAIL info@barryhills.com WEBSITE www.barryhills.com

1 **BONNIE PRINCE BLUE**, 5, ch g Tipsy Creek (USA)—Heart So Blue **G. J. Hicks**
2 **CAPTAIN MARVELOUS (IRE)**, 4, b c Invincible Spirit (IRE)—Shesasmartlady (IRE) **R. J. Arculli**
3 **DABBERS RIDGE (IRE)**, 6, b h Indian Ridge—Much Commended **Mr Maurice Mogg**
4 **GIGANTICUS (USA)**, 5, ch g Giant's Causeway (USA)—
    Shy Princess (USA) **DM James,Cavendish Inv Ltd,Matthew Green**
5 **PRIME DEFENDER**, 4, ch c Bertolini (USA)—Arian Da **S. Falle, M. Franklin, J. Sumsion**
6 **SPECIAL DAY**, 4, b f Fasliyev (USA)—Mustique Dream **Suzanne & Nigel Williams**
7 **TASTAHIL (IRE)**, 4, ch c Singspiel (IRE)—Luana **Hamdan Al Maktoum**
8 **THE LAST DROP (IRE)**, 5, b h Galileo (IRE)—Epping **J Hanson, Cavendish Inv.Ltd, A Patrick**
9 **ZAAHID (IRE)**, 4, ch c Sakhee (USA)—Murjana (IRE) **Hamdan Al Maktoum**

THREE-YEAR-OLDS

10 **ALLIUM (IRE)**, ch f Namid—Top of The Form (IRE) **B. W. Hills**
11 **ALMOUTAZ (USA)**, b br c Kingmambo (USA)—Dessert (USA) **Hamdan Al Maktoum**
12 **AMBER QUEEN (IRE)**, ch f Cadeaux Genereux—Our Queen of Kings **Lady Richard Wellesley**

MR B. W. HILLS—continued

13 **AMERICAN ART (IRE)**, b g Statue of Liberty (USA)—Peshawar **Mr Matthew Green & Mr T Hyde**
14 **BALLOCHROY (IRE)**, b c Mull of Kintyre (USA)—Shonara's Way **The Mystic Mogg Partnership**
15 **BASANTI (USA)**, ch f Galileo (IRE)—Ozone Friendly (USA) **Lady Bamford**
16 **BOBS SURPRISE**, ch c Bertolini (USA)—Flourish **A. L. R. Morton**
17 **CENTENEROLA (USA)**, b f Century City (IRE)—Lady Angharad (IRE) **Paul Moulton**
18 **CIGALAS**, ch g Selkirk (USA)—Langoustine (AUS) **Mrs A Gurney, Lord Vestey, Cavendish Inv**
19 **CRAZY ABOUT YOU (IRE)**, b f Montjeu (USA)—Touch of Magic (IRE) **David Reid Scott & Mr A V Nicoll**
20 **CRUEL SEA (USA)**, gr f Mizzen Mast (USA)—Storm Dove (USA) **K. Abdulla**
21 **CRYSTAL ROCK (IRE)**, br g Rock of Gibraltar (IRE)—State Crystal (IRE) **Triermore Stud**
22 **DARAAHEM (USA)**, ch c Act One—Shamah **Hamdan Al Maktoum**
23 **DAY OF DESTINY (IRE)**, gr c Clodovil (IRE)—El Corazon (IRE) **Suzanne & Nigel Williams**
24 **DEIRA DUBAI**, b f Green Desert (USA)—Aspen Leaves (USA) **Hamdan Al Maktoum**
25 **DUBAI'S WONDER (IRE)**, b c Galileo (IRE)—Sena Desert **Mohamed Obaida**
26 **EFFINGHAM (IRE)**, br c Celtic Swing—Deemeh (IRE) **Mr A. Black**
27 **EFFORTLESS**, ch f Beat Hollow—Xaymara (USA) **K. Abdulla**
28 **ESEEJ (USA)**, ch g Aljabr (USA)—Jinaan (USA) **Hamdan Al Maktoum**
29 **FEARED IN FLIGHT (IRE)**, b c Hawk Wing (USA)—Solar Crystal (IRE) **J Hanson, Cavendish Inv.Ltd, A Patrick**
30 **GOOD GORSOON (USA)**, b c Stravinsky (USA)—Alwaysinbloom (USA) **Triermore Stud & Partner**
31 **GULF STREAM LADY (IRE)**, ch f Cadeaux Genereux—Aoife (IRE) **Mr Martin S. Schwartz**
32 **HAMALKA (IRE)**, br f Alhaarth (IRE)—Night Owl **Mr E. D. Kessly**
33 **HAWAANA (IRE)**, b c Bahri (USA)—Congress (IRE) **Hamdan Al Maktoum**
34 **HAWK HOUSE**, gr g Alhaarth (IRE)—Arinaga **A. L. R. Morton**
35 **HUNT THE BOTTLE (IRE)**, b c Bertolini (USA)—Zanoubia (USA) **Jack Hanson & Sir Alex Ferguson**
36 **HUZZAH (IRE)**, b c Acclamation—Borders Belle (IRE) **J Gale,J Finch,D Cole,R Dollar,D Powell**
37 **JABAL TARIQ**, ch c Rock of Gibraltar (IRE)—Sueboog (IRE) **Mohamed Obaida**
38 **JANINA**, b f Namid—Lady Dominatrix (IRE) **Hamdan Al Maktoum**
39 **JUST A DANCER (IRE)**, b f Choisir (AUS)—New Foundation (USA) **Mr John C. Grant**
40 **KATIMONT (IRE)**, b f Montjeu (USA)—Katiyfa **Mr Martin S. Schwartz**
41 **KAY ES JAY (FR)**, b f Xaar—Angel Rose (IRE) **Mr & Mrs Steven Jenkins**
42 **KING'S KAZEEM**, b f King's Best (USA)—Kazeem **D. J. Deer**
43 **KINNEGO BAY (IRE)**, ch c Hennessy (USA)—New Music (USA) **Mr John C. Grant & Mr R. J. Arculli**
44 **LORD SANDICLIFFE (IRE)**, ch c Spartacus (USA)—Devious Miss (IRE) **Mr Henry Barton**
45 **LUCKY DREAM**, b f Oasis Dream—All The Luck (USA) **K. Abdulla**
46 **LULLABY LADY**, b f Piccolo—Musetta (IRE) **Cavendish Investing Ltd**
47 **MANHATTAN DREAM (USA)**, b f Statue of Liberty (USA)—Vallee des Reves (USA) **Lady Richard Wellesley**
48 **MARIE TEMPEST**, b f Act One—Hakkaniyah **B. W. Hills**
49 **MONAAZALAH (IRE)**, b f Green Desert (USA)—Karamah **Hamdan Al Maktoum**
50 **MOOKHLESA**, b br f Marju (IRE)—Ikhlas (IRE) **Hamdan Al Maktoum**
51 **MOTIF**, b f Observatory (USA)—Bolas **K. Abdulla**
52 **MOVILLE (IRE)**, b g Alhaarth (IRE)—No Sugar Baby (FR) **Mr John C. Grant**
53 **MUSIC IN EXILE (USA)**, ch f Diesis—Royal Occasion (USA) **Sangster Family**
54 **MUSICAL BAR (IRE)**, b f Barathea (IRE)—Musical Treat (IRE) **Mr Martin S. Schwartz**
55 **NACHO LIBRE**, b c Kyllachy—Expectation (IRE) **Mr R. J. Arculli & John C. Grant**
56 **PIANO SONATA**, b f Observatory (USA)—Matinee **K. Abdulla**
57 **PORTHOLE (USA)**, gr ro c Mizzen Mast (USA)—Privity (USA) **K. Abdulla**
58 **PRIME FACTOR**, b g Bertolini (USA)—Medina de Rioseco (IRE) **Mrs W. Falle & Mr M. Franklin**
59 **PROMISE MAKER (USA)**, b c Empire Maker (USA)—Sunday Bazaar (USA) **K. Abdulla**
60 **PROVENCE**, b f Averti (IRE)—Prowse **D. J. Deer**
61 **ROCKELLIO (IRE)**, b f Rock of Gibraltar (IRE)—Lillibits (USA) **Joseph Ogden, J. Hanson, John Ogden**
62 **ROYAL CONFIDENCE**, b f Royal Applause—Never A Doubt **Mr D. M. James**
63 **SEPIA**, b f Dansili—Spanish Sun (USA) **K. Abdulla**
64 **SHAMAYEL**, b f Pivotal—Mauri Moon **Hamdan Al Maktoum**
65 **SHAMTARI (IRE)**, b f Alhaarth (IRE)—Al Bahathri (USA) **Hamdan Al Maktoum**
66 **SLAM**, b c Beat Hollow—House Hunting **K. Abdulla**
67 **SLUGGER O'TOOLE**, br g Intikhab (USA)—Haddeyah (USA) **Mr R. J. Crothers, Phil Cunningham**
68 **SPINNING LUCY (IRE)**, ch f Spinning World (USA)—Dolara (IRE) **Mr Steve Jenkins**
69 **SPIRITONTHEMOUNT (USA)**, b br c Pulpit (USA)—
                                   Stirling Bridge (USA) **Mr RJ Arculli & Cavendish Investing Ltd**
70 **STRIKING SPIRIT**, b c Oasis Dream—Aspiring Diva (USA) **K. Abdulla**
71 **SUGAR MINT (IRE)**, b f High Chaparral (IRE)—Anna Karenina (USA) **Mr Rick Barnes**
72 **TAJDEEF (USA)**, gr c Aljabr (USA)—Tabheej (IRE) **Hamdan Al Maktoum**
73 **TASLEYA**, b c Oasis Dream—Princess Athena **Hamdan Al Maktoum**
74 **THANNAAN (USA)**, gr c Elusive Quality (USA)—Lady Aloma (CAN) **Hamdan Al Maktoum**
75 **THARAWAAT (IRE)**, b c Alhaarth (IRE)—Sevi's Choice (USA) **Hamdan Al Maktoum**
76 **THE JOSTLER**, b f Dansili—The Jotter **Burton Agnes Bloodstock**
77 **TOURIST**, b c Oasis Dream—West Devon (USA) **K. Abdulla**

MR B. W. HILLS—continued

78 **WELSH ROCK**, b g Rock of Gibraltar (IRE)—Opari (IRE) **Mr Steve Jenkins**
79 **YANKADI (USA)**, b c Johannesburg (USA)—Clog Dance **K. Abdulla**

TWO-YEAR-OLDS

80 **ABOVE AVERAGE (IRE)**, b c 31/3 High Chaparral (IRE)—Crystal Valkyrie (IRE) (Danehill (USA)) (45044)
81 **AIM TO ACHIEVE (IRE)**, b f 13/2 Galileo (IRE)—Sabander Bay (USA) (Lear Fan (USA)) (122264)
82 **ALGAAWIA (USA)**, b f 28/3 Giant's Causeway (USA)—Sarayir (USA) (Mr Prospector (USA))
83 **ALYARF (USA)**, b c 22/4 Dixie Union (USA)—Tabheej (IRE) (Mujtahid (USA))
84 B br c 25/3 Elusive City (USA)—Arctic Flight (Polar Falcon (USA)) (46000)
85 Ch f 11/4 Bertolini (USA)—Arian Da (Superlative) (100000)
86 B c 29/1 High Chaparral (IRE)—Arum Lily (Woodman (USA))
87 **ASATEER (IRE)**, b c 21/2 Alhaarth (IRE)—Catatonic (Zafonic (USA)) (220000)
88 **CAPTAIN DANCER (IRE)**, ch c 12/4 Danehill Dancer (IRE)—Rain Flower (IRE) (Indian Ridge) (112612)
89 **CHAPTER AND VERSE (IRE)**, gr c 23/3 One Cool Cat (USA)—Beautiful Hill (IRE) (Danehill (USA)) (90089)
90 **CHERISH THE MOMENT (IRE)**, b c 20/3 Galileo (IRE)—Belleclaire (IRE) (Bigstone (IRE)) (96524)
91 Ch f 31/3 Danehill Dancer (IRE)—Crystal Curling (IRE) (Peintre Celebre (USA))
92 **DABBERS CHIEF (USA)**, b c 13/2 Broken Vow (USA)—Grey Matter (USA) (Housebuster (USA)) (77220)
93 **DAMIEN (IRE)**, gr c 20/4 Namid—Miss Shaan (FR) (Darshaan) (32000)
94 **DAY OF DECISION (IRE)**, b c 1/4 Gold Away (FR)—Golden Land (FR) (Octagonal (NZ))
95 **DESERT FEVER**, b c 23/4 Dubai Destination (USA)—Gaijin (Caerleon (USA)) (26000)
96 **DEVOTION TO DUTY (IRE)**, b c 8/4 Montjeu (IRE)—Charmante (USA) (Alydar (USA)) (96524)
97 **EVELYN MAY (IRE)**, b f 8/3 Acclamation—Lady Eberspacher (IRE) (Royal Abjar (USA)) (9500)
98 **FEATHERWEIGHT (IRE)**, ch f 9/4 Fantastic Light (USA)—Dancing Feather (Suave Dancer (USA)) (27000)
99 **FISADARA**, b f 22/2 Nayef (USA)—Success Story (Sharrood (USA))
100 **FORTUNATE BID (IRE)**, ch c 7/3 Modigliani (USA)—Mystery Bid (Auction Ring (USA)) (30000)
101 **GLEN MOLLY (IRE)**, b f 25/1 Danetime (IRE)—Sonorous (IRE) (Ashkalani (IRE)) (70784)
102 **GOLDEN ROSIE (IRE)**, ch f 16/4 Exceed And Excel (AUS)—Kelsey Rose (Most Welcome) (55000)
103 Ch f 20/2 Namid—Goldilocks (IRE) (Caerleon (USA)) (41826)
104 B f 4/4 Royal Applause—Harda Arda (USA) (Nureyev (USA)) (80000)
105 **HEAVEN KNOWS WHEN (IRE)**, b f 6/2 Dansili—Change Partners (IRE) (Hernando (FR))
106 **HENRI CLEWS (IRE)**, b c 22/4 Sadler's Wells (USA)—Adjalisa (IRE) (Darshaan) (35392)
107 **HIGH TWELVE (USA)**, b c 13/1 Giant's Causeway (USA)—Saree (Barathea (IRE)) (375000)
108 **INFIRAAD**, ch c 8/3 Haafhd—Razzle (IRE) (Green Desert (USA)) (160000)
109 B f 27/1 Royal Applause—Kiris World (Distant Relative) (26000)
110 B f 23/2 Danehill Dancer (IRE)—Kylemore (IRE) (Sadler's Wells (USA)) (99741)
111 **KYLLORIEN**, b f 26/1 Kyllachy—Lorien Hill (IRE) (Danehill (USA))
112 B f 26/4 Montjeu (IRE)—L'amour (USA) (Gone West (USA))
113 **LA DE TWO (IRE)**, ch c 9/5 Galileo (IRE)—Firecrest (USA) (Darshaan) (115000)
114 **LADY DRAC (IRE)**, gr f 4/3 Hawk Wing (USA)—Cause Celebre (IRE) (Peintre Celebre (USA))
115 **LASSARINA (IRE)**, b f 8/5 Sakhee (USA)—Kalanda (Desert King (USA)) (37000)
116 B c 15/4 Noverre (USA)—Love In The Mist (USA) (Silver Hawk (USA)) (45044)
117 **MAKAAMEN**, ch c 25/1 Selkirk (USA)—Bird Key (Cadeaux Genereux)
118 **MAKHAALEB (IRE)**, b c 30/1 Haafhd—Summerhill Parkes (Zafonic (USA))
119 **MASSILAH**, b f 21/3 Namid—Loveleaves (Polar Falcon (USA)) (90000)
120 **MASTER FONG (IRE)**, b c 28/2 Dr Fong (USA)—Last Cry (FR) (Peintre Celebre (USA)) (35000)
121 B f 2/1 Royal Applause—McQueenie (IRE) (Danehill (USA)) (50000)
122 **MEYYAL (USA)**, b c 1/1 War Chant (USA)—Tamgeed (USA) (Woodman (USA))
123 **MISDAQEYA**, br f 21/3 Red Ransom (USA)—Crystal Power (USA) (Pleasant Colony (USA)) (65000)
124 **MISTER DEE BEE (IRE)**, b c 24/2 Orpen (USA)—Acidanthera (Alzao (USA)) (32000)
125 **MR MELODIOUS**, ch c 24/2 Green Tune (USA)—Moly (FR) (Anabaa (USA)) (30000)
126 **MR PROLIFIC**, b c 20/3 Haafhd—Rumpipumpy (Shirley Heights) (44000)
127 **MUSTAQER (IRE)**, b c 16/2 Dalakhani (IRE)—Al Ihtithar (IRE) (Barathea (IRE))
128 B c 28/2 Nayef (USA)—My Funny Valentine (USA) (Mukaddamah (USA)) (70784)
129 **NIGHT DANCER (IRE)**, b f 26/2 Night Shift (USA)—Graten (IRE) (Zieten (USA)) (12869)
130 B f 31/3 Marju (IRE)—Night Eyes (FR) (Night Shift (USA)) (64349)
131 B f 20/3 Fasliyev (USA)—Octagleam (Octagonal (NZ)) (77220)
132 **OUQBA**, b c 18/4 Red Ransom (USA)—Dancing Mirage (IRE) (Machiavellian (USA)) (140000)
133 **PARK LANE (IRE)**, b c 12/3 Royal Applause—Kazeem (Darshaan) (55000)
134 B c 24/2 Danetime (IRE)—Play A Tune (USA) (Fayruz) (15000)
135 B f 12/3 Oasis Dream—Prophecy (IRE) (Warning)
136 Ch f 25/1 Officer (USA)—Rhumb Line (USA) (Mr Greeley) (62000)
137 **ROCKSON (IRE)**, b br f 25/2 Rock of Gibraltar (IRE)—Opera Star (IRE) (Sadler's Wells (USA))
138 **RULER OF ALL (IRE)**, b c 11/4 Sadler's Wells (USA)—Shabby Chic (Red Ransom (USA)) (340000)
139 Ch f 25/3 Medicean—Saturnalia (Cadeaux Genereux) (50000)
140 **SAYYAAF**, ch c 26/4 Alhaarth (IRE)—Almurooj (Zafonic (USA))

MR B. W. HILLS—continued

141 **SEEK N' DESTROY (IRE)**, b c 4/4 Exceed And Excel (AUS)—Very Nice (Daylami (IRE)) (60000)
142 **SERVOCA (CAN)**, b c 8/3 El Prado (USA)—Cinderellaslipper (USA) (Touch Gold (USA)) (83654)
143 **SHABIB (USA)**, b c 19/3 Intidab (USA)—Muklah (USA) (Singspiel (IRE))
144 B c 11/3 Dansili—Shining Water (Kalaglow)
145 B f 14/3 Distant View (USA)—Silver Star (Zafonic (USA))
146 B c 24/3 Oasis Dream—Stormy Channel (USA) (Storm Cat (USA))
147 B c 17/5 Strong Hope (USA)—Sunday Bazaar (USA) (Nureyev (USA))
148 B f 30/4 Dynaformer (USA)—Super Staff (USA) (Secretariat (USA))
149 B f 19/2 Exceed And Excel (AUS)—Tallahassee Spirit (THA) (Presidential (USA)) (15000)
150 **TAQARUB (IRE)**, b f 24/5 Marju (IRE)—Maraatib (IRE) (Green Desert (USA))
151 B f 1/2 Xaar—Taroudannt (IRE) (Danehill (USA)) (70784)
152 **THREE STEPS TO HEAVEN**, b c 15/3 Haafhd—Bella Bianca (IRE) (Barathea (IRE)) (60000)
153 B c 8/4 Acclamation—Tribal Rite (Be My Native (USA)) (25740)
154 B f 24/4 High Chaparral (IRE)—Uncharted Haven (Turtle Island (IRE)) (70784)
155 **WEST LEAKE (IRE)**, b c 19/4 Acclamation—Kilshanny (Groom Dancer (USA)) (42000)
156 **WHEN DOVES CRY**, b f 13/2 Grandera (IRE)—Deeply (IRE) (Darshaan (USA)) (12869)
157 B f 10/3 Xaar—Xaymara (USA) (Sanglamore (USA))
158 Gr ro f 25/4 Mizzen Mast (USA)—Zante (Zafonic (USA))

Other Owners: Mr Thomas Barr, Mr N. N. Browne, C. J. O'Shea & Co Ltd., Cavendish Investing Ltd., Mrs J. Clarke, Mr R. J. Crothers, The Hon Mrs E. S. Cunliffe-Lister, Mr T. S. M. Cunningham, Mrs T. S. M. Cunningham, Mr G. M. Cunningham, Mr D. J. Deer, Mr Robin Gruber, F. Guerrini-Maraldi, Mr Jeremy Gumpertz, Mrs C. E. Gurney, Major Christopher Hanbury, Mrs Christopher Hanbury, Mrs Barbara James, Mrs K. S. Jenkins, Mr Simon Keswick, Mrs Flora Lane, Mrs John Magnier, Mr Paul McNamara, Mr Patrick Milmo, Mr Rhydian Morgan-Jones, Mr H. R. Mould, Mr A. V. Nicoll, Sir Robert Ogden, Mrs S. E. Ramsay, Mr Steve Richards, Mr Urs E. Schwarzenbach, Mrs Paul Shanahan, Mr John Sillett, Raymond Tooth, Lord Vestey, Viscountess Whitelaw, N. Williams.

Assistant Trainer: K. Mooney, C. Hills

Apprentice: Ashton Byles, Chris Glenister.

---

277 **MR J. W. HILLS, Lambourn**
Postal: The Croft, Upper Lambourn, Newbury, Berkshire, RG17 8QH
Contacts: PHONE (01488) 73144 FAX (01488) 73099 MOBILE (07836) 283091
E-MAIL john@johnhills.com WEBSITE www.johnhills.com

1 **AMBITIOUS GENES (IRE)**, 4, ch f Grand Lodge (USA)—Doula (USA) **J. Jamgotchian**
2 **BABY PRINCESS (BRZ)**, 4, b f Crimson Tide (IRE)—Shareef Princess **Nick Hubbard & Ross Hunter**
3 **BOMBER COMMAND (USA)**, 5, b g Stravinsky (USA)—Parish Manor (USA) **Gary & Linnet Woodward (2)**
4 **CAPE VELVET (IRE)**, 4, b f Cape Cross (IRE)—Material Lady (IRE) **Mrs Kingham Amity Ltd Mr Ellis Mrs Moore**
5 **COPPER KING**, 4, ch g Ishiguru (USA)—Dorissio (IRE) **J. Davies**
6 **DARK ISLANDER (IRE)**, 5, b h Singspiel (USA)—Lamanka Lass (USA) **D. M. Kerr**
7 **FAIR SAILING (IRE)**, 4, ch f Docksider (USA)—Fair of The Furze **Mrs S. M. Rogers**
8 **FOLLOW THE COLOURS (IRE)**, 5, b g Rainbow Quest (USA)—Gardenia (IRE) **Mrs P. de W. Johnson**
9 **GOLDEN PROSPECT**, 4, b g Lujain (USA)—Petonellajill **Michael Wauchope & Partners**
10 **LADY FRIEND**, 6, gr m Environment Friend (USA)—Lady Prunella (IRE) **Mrs P. de W. Johnson**
11 **LANDUCCI**, 7, b g Averti (IRE)—Divina Luna **R. J. Tufft**
12 **MARSH COURT**, 5, b m Overbury (IRE)—Lady Prunella (IRE) **Mrs P. de W. Johnson**
13 **POTENTIALE (IRE)**, 4, ch g Singspiel (IRE)—No Frills **J. W. Hills**
14 **PRIDE OF NATION (IRE)**, 6, b h Danehill Dancer (IRE)—Anita Via (IRE) **G. Woodward**
15 **PUTRA LAJU (IRE)**, 4, b c Trans Island—El Corazon (IRE) **Mr F. Lee**
16 **STANLEY GOODSPEED**, 5, ch g Inchinor—Flying Carpet **R. J. Tufft**
17 **TRANSVESTITE (IRE)**, 6, b g Trans Island—Christoph's Girl **Tony Waspe Partnership**

THREE-YEAR-OLDS

18 **AUTUMN BLADES (IRE)**, ch c Daggers Drawn (USA)—September Tide (IRE) **The Phantom Partnership**
19 **CRAFTY DEALER (IRE)**, b c Intikhab (USA)—Lizanne (USA) **The Champagne Elite Partnership**
20 **DANSEUSE VOLANTE (IRE)**, ch f Danehill Dancer (IRE)—Termania (USA) **Mrs F. Hills**
21 **DON'T STOP ME NOW (IRE)**, b f Catcher In The Rye (IRE)—Persian Flower **Mrs L. M. Shanahan**
22 **DREAM TOWER (IRE)**, b f Mull of Kintyre (USA)—Yavarro **J. W. Hills**
23 **DUBAI SAMURAI**, b c Dubai Destination (USA)—Eishin Eleuthera (IRE) **Amity Finance Tom Kelly Miss W Hall**
24 **FIRST TRACKS (IRE)**, b c Oasis Dream—Housekeeper (IRE) **Gary & Linnet Woodward**
25 **GOLDEN SEVEN (FR)**, b c Septieme Ciel (USA)—Golden Fortuna **G. Tong**
26 **JELLY MO**, b f Royal Applause—Flawless **'Over The Moon Racing'**

MR J. W. HILLS—continued

27 **KARMEI**, b c Royal Applause—Lafite **Wood Hall Stud Limited**
28 **KIBITZER**, b c Diesis—Kitza (IRE) **Mountgrange Stud Ltd**
29 **KRYPTONITE (IRE)**, b c Kris Kin (USA)—Brockton Saga (IRE) **R. J. Tufft**
30 **LEDGERWOOD**, b g Royal Applause—Skies Are Blue **Gary & Linnet Woodward and Neil Ledger**
31 **LEKEZIA (IRE)**, b f Fasliyev (USA)—Etaaq (IRE) **Mrs C. M. Smith**
32 **MELLIFLUOUS (IRE)**, b f Noverre—Danestar **Mrs P. de W. Johnson**
33 **MILITARY POWER**, b c Dubai Destination (USA)—Susun Kelapa (USA) **H. R. H. Princess Haya of Jordan**
34 **MISSELLIEBEE**, b f Polish Precedent (USA)—Pursuit of Peace (IRE) **Mrs M. Borsberry**
35 **SINBAD THE SAILOR**, b c Cape Cross (IRE)—Sinead (USA) **Wauchope Cottam Sir S Dunning Mrs Caroe**
36 **SPARKLING MONTJEU (IRE)**, b f Montjeu (IRE)—Dart Board (IRE) **J. Jamgotchian**
37 **SPEYSIDE (IRE)**, b g Orpen (USA)—Dandaka **The Champagne Elite Partnership**
38 **TEEN SPIRIT (IRE)**, b g Sinndar (IRE)—Whitefoot **Gary & Linnet Woodward**
39 **TRI NATIONS (UAE)**, ch g Halling (USA)—Six Nations (USA) **D. M. Kerr**
40 **XTRAVAGANZA (IRE)**, b f Xaar—Royal Jubilee (IRE) **Mrs P. de W. Johnson**
41 **YES EIGHTEEN (IRE)**, b c Diktat—Siskin (IRE) **Yes Eighteen**

TWO-YEAR-OLDS

42 B f 10/3 Royal Applause—Alyousufeya (IRE) (Kingmambo (USA)) (32000)
43 **ASHRAM (IRE)**, ch c 25/3 Indian Haven—Tara's Girl (IRE) (Fayruz) (70000) **Mountgrange Stud Ltd**
44 Br f 21/3 Singspiel (IRE)—Big Pink (Bigstone (IRE)) (32000)
45 B c 22/1 War Chant (USA)—Biretta (USA) (Rahy USA)
46 Ch f 28/4 Newfoundland (USA)—Bloomin Thunder (USA) (Thunder Gulch (USA)) (2000) **J. Jamgotchian**
47 B c 10/4 Monsieur Bond (IRE)—Blue Indigo (FR) (Pistolet Bleu (IRE)) (26000) **Gary & Linnet Woodward**
48 Ch c 16/2 Hawk Wing (USA)—Cassilis (IRE) (Persian Bold) (25740)
49 Ch c 18/3 Halling (USA)—Charlock (Nureyev (USA)) (32174) **R. J. Tufft**
50 B br f 26/1 Street Cry (IRE)—Cycle of Life (USA) (Spinning World (USA)) **J. Jamgotchian**
51 B f 22/1 Acclamation—Different Story (Stravinsky (USA)) (2000)
52 **FLAPPER (IRE)**, b f 16/3 Selkirk (USA)—Pure Spin (USA) (Machiavellian (USA))
53 Br c 21/2 Dansili—Halcyon Daze (Halling (USA)) **C. N. Wright**
54 Ch f 26/4 Spinning World (USA)—Hishmah (Nashwan (USA))
55 Ch f 22/1 Acclamation—Irish Moss (USA) (Irish River (FR)) (20591)
56 B c 6/3 Giant's Causeway (USA)—Lady Carla (Caerleon (USA)) (48000) **E. H. Jones (Paints) Ltd**
57 Ch f 21/3 Lucky Story (USA)—Lamanka Lass (USA) (Woodman (USA))
58 B br f 18/3 Arch (USA)—Maisonette (USA) (Pulpit (USA)) **J. Jamgotchian**
59 B c 15/3 Xaar—Mas A Fuera (IRE) (Alzao (USA)) (16086)
60 B f 14/4 Gulch (USA)—Need More Business (IRE) (Alzao (USA)) (5000) **J. Jamgotchian**
61 **OMNIUM DUKE (IRE)**, ch c 15/3 Indian Haven—Please Be Good (IRE) (Prince of Birds (USA)) (25740)
62 B br f 23/4 War Chant (USA)—Orissa (USA) (Devil's Bag (USA)) (5000) **J. Jamgotchian**
63 B c 23/2 Dubai Destination (USA)—Possessive Artiste (Shareef Dancer (USA)) (21000) **J. W. Hills**
64 B c 19/2 Invincible Spirit (IRE)—Princess Caraboo (IRE) (Alzao (USA)) (28000)
65 B c 14/3 High Chaparral (IRE)—Queens Wharf (IRE) (Ela-Mana-Mou) (32174) **J. W. Hills**
66 **QUINSMAN**, b c 5/3 Singspiel (IRE)—Penny Cross (Efisio) (50000) **D. M. Kerr**
67 B c 18/4 Diesis—Seeking the Jewel (USA) (Seeking The Gold (USA)) (19436) **Mountgrange Stud Ltd**
68 Ch c 27/1 Barathea (IRE)—Shakalaka Baby (Nashwan (USA))
69 **SWISS LAKE SWEETIE (USA)**, ch f 8/3 Across This Day (USA)—
                                                Almost Blue (USA) (Mr Greeley (USA)) (25000) **J. Jamgotchian**
70 B br c 2/3 Sky Mesa (USA)—Thunder Warmth (USA) (Thunder Gulch (USA)) (30000) **J. Jamgotchian**
71 Ch f 23/4 Refuse To Bend (IRE)—Wondrous Joy (Machiavellian (USA)) (25740)

Other Owners: Mr Tony C. Allan, Amity Finance Ltd, Mr Nigel Barnes, Mrs Nicky Barnes, Mr A. H. Bartlett, Mr R. J. Bolam, Mr C. M. Budgett, Mr Duncan Carmichael-Jack, Mrs Peter Caroe, Mr Robert Cottam, Sir Simon Dunning, Mr William Eason, Mr D. J. Ellis, Mr Roy Faichney, Mr Tom Gaffney, Mr Peter Gleeson, Miss W. D. Hall, Mr N. B. F. Hubbard, Mr R. Hunter, Mr T. Kelly, Mr Michael Kerr-Dineen, Mrs Brian Kingham, Mr Neil Ledger, Mrs John Magnier, Mrs Lynne P Meagher, Mrs M. A. Moore, Mr M. J. Pallett, Mr G. C. Rothwell, Mr R. Siu, Mr Julian Smith, Mr M. A. Styles, Mr D. J. Taplin, Mr E. Tsui, Mr R. P. Tullett, Mr Michael Wauchope, Mr Gary Woodward, Mrs Linnet Woodward, Mr D. Yuen.

Assistant Trainer: Colin Gorman

Jockey (flat): E. Ahern, R. Hills, M. Hills. **Apprentice:** P. Hills.

---

278 **MR M. R. HOAD, Lewes**
Postal: **Windmill Lodge Stables, Spital Road, Lewes, East Sussex, BN7 1LS**
Contacts: **PHONE (01273) 477124/(01273) 480691 FAX (01273) 477124 MOBILE (07742) 446168**
E-MAIL markhoad@aol.com

1 **BEAUCHAMP TWIST**, 6, b m Pharly (FR)—Beauchamp Cactus **Mrs J. E. Taylor**
2 **CHRISTMAS TRUCE (IRE)**, 9, b g Brief Truce (USA)—Superflash **Mr M. J. Huxley**

MR M. R. HOAD—continued

3 HUNGRY FOR MORE, 4, b g Silver Patriarch (IRE)—Plaything I.R. Headington
4 MAFEKING (UAE), 4, b g Jade Robbery (USA)—Melisendra (FR) Mrs J. E. Taylor
5 MAKAI, 5, ch g Cayman Kai (IRE)—Young Sue Double-R-Racing
6 NECKER (FR), 7, b g Useful (IRE)—Babouche (FR) T. Locke
7 PRINCE DES NEIGES (FR), 5, b g Milford Track (IRE)—Miss Smith (FR) Brick Farm Racing
8 PRIVATE BENJAMIN, 8, gr g Ridgewood Ben—Jilly Woo

Other Owners: Mr Gary P. Martin, Mrs J. C. Walker.

---

279 MR P. J. HOBBS, Minehead

Postal: Sandhill Racing Stables, Bilbrook, Minehead, Somerset, TA24 6HA
Contacts: PHONE (01984) 640366 FAX (01984) 641124 MOBILE (07860) 729795
E-MAIL pjhobbs@pjhobbs.com WEBSITE www.pjhobbs.com

1 ADARE PRINCE (IRE), 7, b g Supreme Leader—Legal Challenge (IRE) J. P. McManus
2 BALLYDUB (IRE), 5, b g Presenting—Sovereign Leader (IRE) H. R. Gibbs
3 BAODAI (FR), 6, b g Cadoudal (FR)—Royale Aube (FR) Louisville Syndicate II
4 BASEBALL TED (IRE), 6, b g Beneficial—Lishpower A. E. Peterson
5 BEST OF THREE (IRE), 7, ch g Flemensfirth (USA)—Carlingford Run J. E. Mutch
6 BETAVIX, 5, br g Cloudings (IRE)—Lay It Off (IRE) M. J. Tuckey
7 BLUE HURRICANE (IRE), 6, b g Pistolet Bleu (IRE)—Rainy Way (IRE) Mrs K. V. Vann
8 BLUEGUN (IRE), 6, b g Pistolet Bleu (IRE)—Supreme Spice (IRE) Mrs D. L. Whateley
9 BON VIVEUR, 5, b g Mozart (IRE)—Fantazia R. W. Devlin
10 BOYCHUK (IRE), 7, b g Insan (USA)—Golden Flower (GER) Mrs D. L. Whateley
11 BREMEN, 5, br g Sadler's Wells (USA)—Anka Germania Brian Walsh,John Costello, Paul Tarpey
12 BUREAUCRAT, 6, b g Machiavellian (USA)—Lajna Peter Luff
13 BUSY ISIT, 8, br g Busy Flight—Eatons Busy Isit Partnership
14 CALUSA CRYSTAL (FR), 5, b m Double Bed (FR)—Mahogany River Peter Luff
15 CAOBA, 4, b f Hernando (FR)—Seeker Exe Valley Racing
16 CAPTAIN CORELLI, 11, b g Weld—Deaconess P. A. Bancroft
17 CHANCE DU ROY (FR), 4, ch g Morespeed—La Chance Au Roy (FR) Miss I. D. Du Pre
18 CHIARO (FR), 6, b g Hamas (IRE)—Link Diamond (FR) A. L. Cohen
19 CHITA'S FLIGHT, 8, gr m Busy Flight—Chita's Cone I. M. Ham
20 COCKNEY TRUCKER (IRE), 6, b g Presenting—Kiltiernan Easter (IRE) Mrs K. V. Vann
21 COEUR D'ALENE, 7, gr g Hernando—Chambre Separee (USA) Dr V. M. G. Ferguson
22 COOLDINE BOY (IRE), 7, b g Oscar (IRE)—Roouan Girl (IRE) Mrs D. L. Whateley
23 COPPER BLEU (IRE), 6, b g Pistolet Bleu (IRE)—Copper Supreme (IRE) A. E. Peterson
24 COUNTY ZEN (FR), 5, b br g Lost World (IRE)—Fair County (FR) A. L. Cohen
25 COUSIN NICKY, 7, ch g Bob Back (USA)—Little Red Spider Mr P. Beach
26 CRYPTIC, 6, b g Kayf Tara—Persian Symphony (IRE) Mrs D. L. Whateley
27 5, b g Old Vic—Current Liability M. J. P. Fordham
28 CUTTING CREW (USA), 7, ch g Diesis—Poppy Carew (IRE) Mrs P. W. Harris
29 DALYAN DANCER, 6, b g Alflora (IRE)—Mrs Moneypenny Mrs D. L. Whateley
30 DANCING ROCK, 10, b g Dancing High—Liblet D. C. R. Allen
31 DANGER ZONE, 6, b g Danzero (AUS)—Red Tulle (USA) Mr R. T. Kanter & Mr A. J. Scrimgeour
32 DESERT STORM (DEN), 6, br g Desert Prince (IRE)—Boss Lady (IRE) R. Green
33 DIAMANT ROSE (FR), 4, gr g Testa Rossa (AUS)—Restless Mixa (IRE) Mrs K. V. Vann
34 DREAM ALLIANCE, 7, ch g Bien Bien (USA)—Rewbell The Alliance Partnership
35 DRUMBEATER (IRE), 8, b g Supreme Leader—Ballydrummund (IRE) D. C. R. Allen
36 ELTON, 5, ch g Classic Cliche (IRE)—Happy Go Lucky Chickerellites
37 EQUITY RELEASE (IRE), 8, b g Supreme Leader—Loshian (IRE) B. Walsh
38 ESPRIT DE CORPS, 6, b g Hernando (FR)—Entente Cordiale (USA) Mrs M. Findlay
39 EVELITH ABBEY (IRE), 6, br m Presenting—Papoose (IRE) A. Stennett
40 FAIR ALONG (GER), 6, b g Alkalde (GER)—Fairy Tango (FR) A. E. Peterson
41 FAIROAK HAITCH (IRE), 5, b g Norwich—Strong Opinion A. E. Peterson
42 FAIROAK LAD (IRE), 5, br g Tiraaz (USA)—Flair Dante A. E. Peterson
43 FIGHTING CHANCE (IRE), 8, b g Germany (USA)—Una Juna (IRE) P. A. Bonner
44 FOXSPUR (IRE), 5, b g Flemensfirth (USA)—Ellway Lady R Triple H
45 FRENCH SAULAIE (FR), 7, b g French Glory—Parade Royale (FR) Mrs C. Skan
46 GENTLE JOHN (FR), 5, b g Le Balafre (FR)—Perky (FR) Martin St Quinton & Others
47 GERSHWIN (IRE), 5, gr g Alhaarth (IRE)—Galletina (IRE) Favourites Racing XI
48 GHALLAB, 5, b g Alhaarth (IRE)—Ta Rib (USA) Capt E. J. Edwards-Heathcote
49 GOLD MEDALLIST, 8, ch g Zilzal (USA)—Spot Prize (USA) Mrs D. L. Whateley
50 GUYMUR (FR), 8, ch g Murmure (FR)—Meggy (FR) C. de P. Berry & C. Moore
51 HIBIKI (IRE), 4, b c Montjeu (IRE)—White Queen (IRE) R. Green

MR P. J. HOBBS—continued

52 **HOT DIAMOND**, 4, b g Desert Prince (IRE)—Panna **Louisville Syndicate**
53 **HUGUENOT (IRE)**, 5, b g King's Best (USA)—Kingsridge (IRE) **Mr M. C. Sargent**
54 **I HEAR A SYMPHONY (IRE)**, 6, b g Accordion—Annilogs Daughter (IRE) **A. E. Peterson**
55 **I PREDICT A RIOT (IRE)**, 4, b g Danehill Dancer (IRE)—Manon's Song (IRE) **Mrs A. Tincknell**
56 **I'M SUPREME (IRE)**, 6, b g Supreme Leader—Imtheone (IRE) **D. R. Peppiatt**
57 **JIM EDWARDS (IRE)**, 7, ch g Bob Back (USA)—G W Superstar **Mrs D. L. Whateley**
58 **KALCA MOME (FR)**, 10, b g En Calcat (FR)—Belle Mome (FR) **Miss I. D. Du Pre**
59 **KEKI BUKU (FR)**, 5, b g Kadalko (FR)—Bigouden **Mrs D. L. Whateley**
60 **KHASAB (IRE)**, 7, b g Supreme Leader—Tower Princess (IRE) **Mrs C. Skan**
61 **KORNATI KID**, 6, b g Kayf Tara—Hiltonstown Lass (IRE) **Mrs D. L. Whateley**
62 **LACDOUDAL (FR)**, 9, gr g Cadoudal (FR)—Belfaster (FR) **Mrs C. Skan**
63 **LADY PURTON**, 7, b m I'm Supposin (IRE)—Sharp Vixen **G. K. Probert**
64 **LEAD ON (IRE)**, 7, b g Supreme Leader—Dressed In Style (IRE) **B. K. Peppiatt**
65 **LIBERATE**, 5, ch g Lomitas—Eversince (USA) **Mrs D. L. Whateley**
66 **LIKE A HURRICANE (IRE)**, 5, b g Simply Great (IRE)—Legal Challenge (IRE) **M. J. P. Fordham**
67 **LINCOLN'S INN (IRE)**, 6, b g Old Vic—Eurodawn (IRE) **Mrs L. H. Field**
68 **LOITA HILLS (IRE)**, 8, b g Norwich—Gleann Oisin (IRE) **Mr R. T. Kanter & Mr A. J. Scrimgeour**
69 **LORD CREWE (IRE)**, 5, b g Sinndar (IRE)—Eurobird **The Country Side**
70 **LORD HENRY (IRE)**, 9, b g Lord Americo—Auntie Honnie (IRE) **Mrs K. V. Vann**
71 **LORD LESCRIBAA (FR)**, 5, b g Ungaro (GER)—Manon Lescribaa (FR) **Elizabeth & Michael Krysztofiak Racing**
72 **MANHATTAN BOY (GER)**, 6, ch g Monsun (GER)—Manhattan Girl (USA) **Big Apples**
73 **MARCHAND D'ARGENT (FR)**, 5, b h Marchand de Sable (USA)—Masslama (FR) **P. J. Hobbs**
74 **MARK THE BOOK (IRE)**, 7, b g Mister Lord (USA)—Boardroom Belle (IRE) **D. C. R. Allen**
75 **MASSINI'S MAGUIRE (IRE)**, 7, b g Dr Massini (IRE)—Molly Maguire (IRE) **A. E. Peterson**
76 **MASTER WOLFE (IRE)**, 6, b g Saddlers' Hall (IRE)—Queen of Wolves **The Country Side**
77 **MERLIN'S MAGIC (FR)**, 6, gr g Marathon (USA)—Dompteuse (FR) **Mrs E. A. Prowting**
78 **MINELLA TIPPERARY (IRE)**, 7, b g Saddlers' Hall (IRE)—Graiguehashia (IRE) **J & B Gibbs & Sons Ltd**
79 **MISSIS POTTS**, 7, b m Overbury (IRE)—Potter's Gale (IRE) **James & Jean Potter**
80 **MISTER CHATTERBOX (IRE)**, 7, b g Presenting—Lotta Talk (IRE) **The Royal Oak Syndicate**
81 **MISTER GLOSS (IRE)**, 7, b g Mister Mat (FR)—Princess Megan (IRE) **J & B Gibbs & Sons Ltd**
82 **MONKERHOSTIN (FR)**, 11, b g Shining Steel—Ladoun (FR) **M. G. St Quinton**
83 **NAWAADI**, 5, b g Intikhab (USA)—Elhilmeya (IRE) **P. A. Deal**
84 **NOBLE REQUEST (FR)**, 7, gr g Highest Honor (FR)—Restless Mixa (FR) **Mrs K. V. Vann**
85 **NOTABOTHERONME (IRE)**, 6, b br g Religiously (USA)—Kylogue's Delight **J. E. Mutch**
86 **O'TOOLE (IRE)**, 9, b g Toulon—Leps Burke (IRE) **Mrs L. R. Lovell**
87 **OCEANOS DES OBEAUX (FR)**, 6, b g April Night (FR)—Gypsie d'artois (FR) **M. J. Tuckey**
88 **ODAL D'AIRY (FR)**, 6, b g Cadoubel (FR)—Dalina d'airy (FR) **Mrs K. V. Vann**
89 **OISEAU DE NUIT (FR)**, 6, b g Evening World (FR)—Idylle du Marais (FR) **J. T. Warner**
90 **OLDRIK (GER)**, 5, b g Tannenkonig (IRE)—Onestep (GER) **D. J. Jones**
91 **OR BLEU (FR)**, 6, ch g Discover d'auteuil (FR)—Kidibleue (FR) **The Kingpins**
92 **OSCATELLO (USA)**, 8, b br g Woodman (USA)—Galea des Bois (FR) **R. M. Braune**
93 **OUT THE BLACK (IRE)**, 10, b br g Presenting—Executive Wonder (IRE) **The Hon J. R. Drummond**
94 **PANCAKE (FR)**, 5, ch g Cyborg (FR)—Six Fois Sept (FR) **A. L. Cohen**
95 **PARSONS LEGACY (IRE)**, 10, b g Leading Counsel (USA)—The Parson's Girl (IRE) **R. A. S. Offer**
96 **PAVILLON BLEU (FR)**, 5, b g Vaguely Pleasant (FR)—Isaure de Bussy (FR) **Mrs A. M. Taylor**
97 **PEARL KING (FR)**, 6, gr g Daylami (IRE)—Regal Opinion (USA) **J. P. McManus**
98 **PENN DA BENN (FR)**, 5, b g Passing Sale (FR)—Gwen Ha Du (FR) **J. T. Warner**
99 **PERFECT LINE**, 4, gr g Highest Honor (FR)—Quandary (USA) **A. L. Cohen**
100 **PISTOLJEAN**, 8, ch g Garde Royale—Sainte Etoile (FR) **Three Line Whip**
101 **PISTOLET DOVE (IRE)**, 6, br g Pistolet Bleu (IRE)—Emerald Dove **J. P. McManus**
102 **PLANET OF SOUND**, 6, b g Kayf Tara—Herald The Dawn **C. G. M. Lloyd-Baker**
103 **PRESENTING COPPER (IRE)**, 7, b m Presenting—Copper Supreme (IRE) **A. E. Peterson**
104 **PRESIDENT ROYAL (FR)**, 5, b g Video Rock (FR)—Etoile du Pontet (FR) **J. T. Warner**
105 **PRINCE TAIME (FR)**, 5, b g Astarabad (USA)—Maite (FR) **Mrs D. L. Whateley**
106 **PRIVATE BE**, 9, b g Gunner B—Foxgrove **David & Daphne Walsh**
107 **PYLEIGH LADY**, 7, b m Zaffaran (USA)—Lady Callernish **F. D. Popham**
108 **QROKTOU (FR)**, 4, b g Fragrant Mix (USA)—Cathou (FR) **P. A. Bonner**
109 **QUEEN FELLOW (FR)**, 4, b g Passing Sale (FR)—All Mighty Fellow (FR) **Mrs K. V. Vann**
110 **RING THE BOSS (IRE)**, 7, b g Kahyasi—Fortune's Girl **A. E. Peterson**
111 **SAUNDERS ROAD (IRE)**, 7, b g King's Theatre (IRE)—Shaunies Lady (IRE) **J. P. McManus**
112 5, b g Presenting—Scented Night (IRE) **P. J. Hobbs**
113 **SHANAHAN (IRE)**, 7, b g Little Bighorn—Thomastown Girl **Mr A. R. E. Ash**
114 **SHANXI GIRL**, 5, br m Overbury (IRE)—Celtic Native (IRE) **Mrs A. Tincknell**
115 **SIR RIQUE (FR)**, 5, b g Enrique—Fontaine Guerard (FR) **Ash Place Stud**
116 **SNAP TIE (IRE)**, 6, b g Pistolet Bleu (IRE)—Aries Girl **Mrs D. L. Whateley**
117 **SNOW PATROL**, 7, gr g Linamix (FR)—Overcast (IRE) **Michael H. Watt & Dr David Harris**

MR P. J. HOBBS—continued

118 **SPUD**, 6, b g Spadoun (FR)—Parslin **Mrs M. Findlay**
119 **STORM OF APPLAUSE (IRE)**, 7, b g Accordion—Dolce Notte (IRE) **RP Racing**
120 **SUPREME DUKE (IRE)**, 6, br g Supreme Leader—Shelikesitstraight (IRE) **Mrs K. V. Vann**
121 **SUPREME PRINCE (IRE)**, 11, b g Supreme Leader—Strong Serenade (IRE) **Mrs K. V. Vann**
122 **TAGO MAGO (IRE)**, 5, b g Oscar (IRE)—Manta Vision (IRE) **Mrs D. L. Whateley**
123 **TAMADOT (IRE)**, 6, b g Supreme Leader—Barenises Rose (IRE) **Mrs D. L. Whateley**
124 **TAMANGO (IRE)**, 11, gr g Klimt (FR)—Tipmosa (FR) **The Brushmakers**
125 **TARTAN ARTICLE (IRE)**, 5, b m Definite Article—Knocktartan (IRE) **Racegoers Club Owners Group**
126 **TEMPLER (IRE)**, 7, ch g Charmer—Ballinamona Lady (IRE) **A. P. Staple**
127 **THE BOAT (IRE)**, 6, b g Anshan—Sallowglen Gale (IRE) **Mrs L. R. Lovell**
128 **THE GREY BERRY**, 4, gr g Observatory—Elderberry **Mrs D. L. Whateley**
129 **TOM SAYERS (IRE)**, 10, b g Toulon—Jillie James **Capt E. J. Edwards-Heathcote**
130 **TRIBAL VENTURE (FR)**, 10, gr g Dom Alco (FR)—Babacha (FR) **H. A. Murphy**
131 5, B br g Presenting—Velsheda (IRE) **Mrs D. L. Whateley**
132 **WAKEFUL**, 5, b m Kayf Tara—Herald The Dawn **C. G. M. Lloyd-Baker**
133 **WARSAW PACT (IRE)**, 5, b g Polish Precedent (USA)—Always Friendly **Mrs D. L. Whateley**
134 **WHISTLE DIXIE**, 7, ch g Double Trigger (IRE)—Sendai **C L T**
135 **YABOYA (IRE)**, 9, b g King's Theatre (IRE)—Oh Jemima **J. P. McManus**

Other Owners: Mrs H. Bancroft, Claude Berry, C. J. Butler, Mrs C. E. Caddick, M. A. Clark, Mr J. P. Cooper, P. A. Corrigan, Mr J. Costello, Mr D. E. Crouch, H. B. Davies, Mr J. R. Eburne, Mrs J. N. Edwards-Heathcote, G. N. Faber, Mrs S. M. Francis, Mr K. French, B. J. Greening, T. M. Hailstone, J. R. Hall, Dr D. Harris, C. G. Hellyer, J. R. Holmes, Mr B. R. Ingram, R. T. Kanter, Mr M. Krysztofiak, Mrs E. D. Krysztofiak, C. Moore, Mr R. Mowlam, Mrs L. H. Oakley, N. D. Peppiatt, J. E. Potter, Mrs M. J. Potter, D. A. Rees, M. B. Roberts, M. J. Rowe, Exors of the Late Mr I. Russell, Mrs A. M. F. Russell, N. C. Savery, A. J. Scrimgeour, P. B. Shaw, M. Short, Mr G. H. Skeats, G. F. Steel, M. A. Strong, Mrs M. H. Sutcliffe, Mr P. Tarpey, W. C. Tincknell, Mrs S. M. Trump, C. J. M. Walker, Mr A. J. A. Waller, D. R. Walsh, Mrs D M Walsh, M. H. Watt, M. J. Weeden, T. C. Wheeler, Mrs T. S. Wheeler.

Assistant Trainer: Richard White & Tim Dennis

Jockey (NH): R. Johnson, Tom O'Brien. **Conditional:** Tom Molloy, D O'Dwyer. **Amateur:** Mr Sam Allwood, Mr Josh Guerriero, Mr Shaun Parish, Mr Ian Popham.

---

280 MR R. J. HODGES, Somerton
Postal: **Bull Brook Stables, West Charlton, Charlton Mackrell, Somerton, Somerset, TA11 7AL**
Contacts: **PHONE (01458) 223922 FAX (01458) 223969 MOBILE (07770) 625846**

1 **ARCHIE GUNN**, 6, b g Silver Patriarch (IRE)—Persistent Gunner **Miss R. J. Dobson**
2 **BARODINE**, 5, ch g Barathea (IRE)—Granted (FR) **The Gardens Entertainments Ltd**
3 **CANTABILLY (IRE)**, 5, b g Distant Music (USA)—Cantaloupe **Mrs S. G. Clapp**
4 **CHARLTON KINGS (IRE)**, 10, b g King's Ride—Grove Gale (IRE) **Fieldspring Racing**
5 **COMPTON STAR**, 8, ch g Compton Place—Darakah **A. M. Midgley**
6 **DREAM FALCON**, 8, b g Polar Falcon (USA)—Pip's Dream **P. E. Axon**
7 **FLASHING WILD (IRE)**, 7, b g Clerkenwell (USA)—Supreme Cloud **Hunt & Co (Bournemouth) Ltd**
8 **GOOSE GREEN (IRE)**, 4, b g Invincible Spirit (IRE)—Narbayda (IRE) **Mrs S. G. Clapp**
9 **GRACECHURCH (IRE)**, 5, b g Marju (IRE)—Saffron Crocus **Mrs S. G. Clapp**
10 **IMPERIAL SUN (IRE)**, 9, b g Un Desperado (FR)—Ashley's Princess (FR) **Fieldspring Racing**
11 **JOLI CLASSICAL (IRE)**, 6, b m Classic Cliche (IRE)—Mesp (IRE) **Joli Racing**
12 **JOMELAMIN**, 6, gr m Silver Patriarch (IRE)—Jomel Amou (IRE) **R. J. Hodges**
13 **JUPON VERT (FR)**, 11, b g Lights Out (FR)—Danse Verte (FR) **Mr E Jenkins Mr T Jenkins Miss R Jenkins**
14 **LEGAL GLORY (IRE)**, 8, b g Bob Back (USA)—Native Shore (IRE) **J. W. Mursell**
15 **LITTLE EDWARD**, 10, gr g King's Signet (USA)—Cedar Lady **J. W. Mursell**
16 **MAGROOM**, 4, b g Compton Place—Fudge **Mrs A. Hart Mrs A. Hodges Mrs C. Penny**
17 **MARLOWE (IRE)**, 6, b h Sadler's Wells (USA)—Minnie Habit **Fieldspring Racing**
18 **MASTER BELL**, 6, b g Bandmaster (USA)—Parklands Belle **Nineways**
19 **MASTER MAHOGANY**, 7, b g Bandmaster (USA)—Impropriety **Villagers Five**
20 **MISS MIDNIGHT**, 7, b m Midnight Legend—Miss Marigold **John & Greer Norman**
21 **MURPHY'S MATE**, 4, b g Alflora (IRE)—Be My Babe **J. M. Dare**
22 **POSH EMILY**, 5, b m Rakaposhi King—Persistent Gunner **Racing Demons Partnership**
23 **PREACHER BOY**, 9, b g Classic Cliche (IRE)—Gospel (IRE) **Hunt & Co (Bournemouth) Ltd**
24 **RED SOMERSET (USA)**, 5, b g Red Ransom (USA)—Bielska (USA) **Fieldspring Racing**
25 **ROYAL PRODIGY (USA)**, 9, ch g Royal Academy (USA)—
Prospector's Queen (USA) **The Gardens Entertainments Ltd**
26 **SALLY ARMY**, 7, b m Silver Patriarch (IRE)—Persistent Gunner **Miss R. J. Dobson**
27 **TUNE UP THE BAND**, 4, b c Bandmaster (USA)—Name That Tune **Beckington Racing**

MR R. J. HODGES—continued

28 **WHOS COUNTING**, 4, ch f Woodborough (USA)—Hard To Follow **J. W. Mursell**
29 **WIZARD OF EDGE**, 8, b g Wizard King—Forever Shineing **Mrs C. Taylor & K. Small**

THREE-YEAR-OLDS

30 **CHEMISE (IRE)**, b f Chevalier (IRE)—Louvolite (IRE) **Miss R. J. Dobson**
31 **CLEAR CALL**, b f Bandmaster (USA)—Distant Call **Miss R. J. Dobson**

Other Owners: Mr C. Bowen, Mr Chris J. Buckerfield, Mr K. J. Corcoran, Mr Graham Craig, Mrs Anna Doyle, Mr Peter Doyle, Mrs Angela Hart, Mr R. J. Hodges, Mrs A. S. Hodges, Mr G. B. J. Humphries, Mr E. E. B. Jenkins, Mr T. C. A. Jenkins, Miss R. H. O. Jenkins, Mr Andrew Midgley, Mr R. G. Morgan, Miss J. E. Murray-Playfair, Mr J. Newsome, Mr John Norman, Mrs G. O. Norman, Mrs Catherine Penny, Mr M. Peters, Mr K. Small, Mr R. V. Taylor, Mrs Carol Taylor, Mrs P. J. Taylor, Mr C. E. Weare.

---

281 MR M. J. HOGAN, Findon
Postal: 2 New Cottages, Gallops Farm, Findon, West Sussex, BN14 0RQ
Contacts: PHONE (01903) 873348 MOBILE (07850) 441891

1 **BEARE NECESSITIES (IRE)**, 9, ch g Presenting—Lady Laburnum **Mrs B. E. Hogan**
2 **KINGS SIGNAL (USA)**, 10, b g Red Ransom (USA)—Star of Albion **Mrs B. E. Hogan**
3 **MYSTICAL STAR (FR)**, 11, b g Nicolotte—Addaya (IRE) **Mrs B. E. Hogan**

Assistant Trainer: Mrs Barbara Hogan

---

282 MR TOM HOGAN, Nenagh
Postal: Fattheen House Stables, Nenagh, Co. Tipperary, Ireland
Contacts: PHONE (00353) 674 6080 FAX (00353) 673 3989 MOBILE (00353) 8723 32111
E-MAIL thracing@indigo.ie

1 **ALBRIGHTON**, 13, b g Terimon—Bright-One **J. Gurhy**
2 **ALMANSHOOD (USA)**, 6, b br g Bahri (USA)—Lahan **Mrs M. Roche**
3 **ANAMUNDI**, 4, b f Rock of Gibraltar (IRE)—Sardonic **T. Hogan & M. Costello**
4 **ARPINO (GER)**, 5, b g Protektor (GER)—Arbarine (GER) **Mr M. Burke**
5 **BLUEBYYOU (IRE)**, 7, b g Lake Coniston (IRE)—Stony View (IRE) **Mrs N. P. Conneely**
6 **BOHERBUEE (IRE)**, 6, b g Shernazar—Polar Charm (IRE) **Temptation Syndicate**
7 4, B f Nikos—Cadourova (FR) **S. Harris**
8 **CAROLINES DREAM (IRE)**, 5, b g Carrowkeel (IRE)—Fuchsia Belle **N. Harten**
9 **CLASSIC CROCO (GER)**, 7, gr g Croco Rouge (IRE)—Classic Light (IRE) **Chilled Out Syndicate**
10 **COMERAGH STAR (IRE)**, 5, b h Monashee Mountain (USA)—Nocturnal (FR) **Top of The World Syndicate**
11 **EASTER FOLLY (IRE)**, 5, b m Broken Hearted—Corston Dancer (IRE) **Mrs N. Riggsmiller**
12 **EDUCATED THIEF (IRE)**, 4, b g Orpen (USA)—Verette **Ballintlea Syndicate**
13 **EMPIRE THEATRE (IRE)**, 4, b c King's Theatre (IRE)—Foreign Estates (IRE) **Mrs B. M. McKinney**
14 **EXTENSION OF TIME (IRE)**, 4, b c Orpen (USA)—Super Times **Mr B. Adheson**
15 **FLARE STAR**, 5, ch m Nashwan (USA)—Flame Cutter (USA) **Priory Syndicate**
16 **FRUTTI TUTTI (IRE)**, 4, b f Fruits of Love (USA)—Irish Lover (USA) **Vincent McKey & Partners**
17 **INHERITRESS (IRE)**, 4, b f Broadway Flyer (USA)—Heiress (IRE) **M. Bowe / M. Roche / M. Burke**
18 **KALDERON (GER)**, 8, br g Big Shuffle (USA)—Kreuzdame (GER) **Miss M. Masterson**
19 **KING BREX (DEN)**, 5, b g Primatico (USA)—Moon Shine (DEN) **Mr N. Armstrong & Partners**
20 **KING OF THE TITANS (IRE)**, 5, b g Titus Livius (FR)—She's The Tops **Mrs M. Roche**
21 **KIRBYBROGUELANTERN (IRE)**, 7, br g Tidaro (USA)—Karline Ka (FR) **Brogue Lanterns Syndicate**
22 6, B g Bachir (IRE)—La Fenice (IRE) **M. Bowe**
23 **LUKE'S BENEFIT (IRE)**, 6, gr g Beneficial—St Anne's Lady (IRE) **M. & T. O'Brien**
24 **MALIN MIST (USA)**, 4, ro f Mizzen Mast (USA)—Barrister Kathleen (USA) **Western Alliance Syndicate**
25 **MIDNIGHT MINNIE**, 6, b m Saddlers' Hall (IRE)—Midnight Light (IRE) **Mrs J. Hogan**
26 **MISTY HEATHER (IRE)**, 5, b m Oscar (IRE)—Stony View (IRE) **Mr J. O'Dwyer**
27 **MOLTON ROCK (IRE)**, 5, b g Brave Act—Silver Prairie (USA) **Super Six Syndicate**
28 4, B g Subtle Power (IRE)—Most Stylish **Mr T. Hogan**
29 5, B g Marignan (USA)—Native Country (IRE) **The Cool Out Syndicate**
30 **NATIVE ROYAL (IRE)**, 6, ch m Zaffaran (USA)—Native Sound (IRE) **South Syndicate**
31 **NEEDLE FLYER (IRE)**, 6, b m Needle Gun (IRE)—Dandy Mandy (USA) **Fourways Syndicate**
32 **OUT IN THE OPEN (IRE)**, 7, br g Orpen (USA)—Out In The Sun (USA) **Michael D. Mee**
33 **PASS THE VODKA (IRE)**, 7, b g Pasternak—Best Served Cherry (IRE) **Pass The Vodka Syndicate**
34 **PLEASE THE KING (IRE)**, 4, b c King Charlemagne (USA)—Placate **T. Hogan & Peter McCutcheon**
35 **RACKANS RAMBLER (IRE)**, 7, b m Zaffaran (USA)—Swan Bridge (IRE) **Vincent Duignan**
36 **SAVOURY GEM (IRE)**, 4, b f Mull of Kintyre (USA)—El-Libaad **Max Bar Syndicate**

MR TOM HOGAN—continued

37 **SHANNON WEIR (IRE)**, 6, br g Norwich—Go Meekly (IRE) **Supreme Corner Gang**
38 **SILVER JARO (FR)**, 5, ch g Muhtathir—John Quatz (FR) **Miss M. Masterson**
39 **SONNYANJOE (IRE)**, 10, b g Roselier (FR)—Carrabawn **Anthony Byrne**
40 4, B g Florida Son—Sounds Grand (IRE) **The South Syndicate**
41 **SPANISH BLUE (IRE)**, 5, b g Bluebird (USA)—Spanish Sal (IRE) **Stand Syndicate**
42 **THAOMIDA (IRE)**, 5, ch g Titus Livius (FR)—Cashel Ridge **Byrnes Bar Syndicate**
43 **TOD SLOAN (IRE)**, 6, ch g Titus Livius (FR)—Poscimur (IRE) **Tod Sloan Syndicate**
44 **VALTORA**, 5, b m Vettori (IRE)—Shaieef (IRE) **P. Curran**
45 **WEST DANCE (IRE)**, 6, ch g Pistolet Bleu (IRE)—Lady of Grange (IRE) **Mr E. Casey**
46 **WOULD YOU (IRE)**, 5, b g Shinko Forest (IRE)—Hakone (IRE) **Mrs Josephine Hogan**

THREE-YEAR-OLDS

47 **AMENDED**, ch f Beat Hollow—Daki (USA) **Mr P. McCutcheon**
48 **BEST PLEASED**, b c Rossini (USA)—Placate **Peter McCutcheon & T. Hogan**
49 **CASBET**, br f Golan (IRE)—Niseem (USA) **Derbar Racing Partnership**
50 **CATCH KELLY**, b f Kalanisi (IRE)—Catcher Applause **Mrs J. Hogan**
51 **CHEVI**, b c Chevalier (IRE)—Omanah (USA) **Mr R. Young**
52 **DR ZING**, ch f Dr Fong (USA)—Zingari **Mr D. Kelly**
53 B f Monashee Mountain (USA)—Exquisite Sal (IRE) **M. Sprice**
54 **FLYING ROUVRES (IRE)**, B f Rouvres (FR)—Mazalunna (FR) **D. Lenihan**
55 **JINXY JILL**, b f Royal Applause—Forever Fine (USA) **Mrs B. M. McKinney**
56 **KARMA LINA**, b f King's Best (USA)—Armilina (FR) **Kilboy Estate**
57 **MISS MARKHAM (IRE)**, ch f Soviet Star (USA)—Dynamo Minsk (IRE) **J. Freeman**
58 **REGAL OBLIGATION**, ch f Generous (IRE)—Duty Bound **Plantation Stud**
59 B f Monashee Mountain (USA)—Spanish Sal (IRE) **M. Sprice**
60 **SPILLETTA (IRE)**, bl f Rouvres (FR)—Heiress (IRE) **M. Bowe / M. Roche / M. Burke**

Other Owners: N. R. Elwes, Mrs C. P. Elwes.

Jockey (flat): F. Berry, R. M. Burke. **Conditional:** S.F. Ryder, A. Clifford. **Apprentice:** A. Clifford, E. McNamara. **Amateur:** Mr C. Sharkey, Mr A. J. Hogan.

---

283   MR H. P. HOGARTH, Stillington
Postal: **New Grange Farm, Stillington, York**
Contacts: **PHONE (01347) 811168 FAX (01347) 811168 MOBILE (07788) 777044**

1 **AITCH DOUBLEYOU (IRE)**, 8, ch g Classic Memory—Bucksreward (IRE) **Hogarth Racing**
2 **APACHE BRAVE (IRE)**, 5, ch g Kahtan—Glenstal Forest (IRE) **Hogarth Racing**
3 **CEDAR RAPIDS (IRE)**, 8, b br g Lord Americo—Amys Girl (IRE) **Hogarth Racing**
4 **DAY OF CLAIES (FR)**, 7, b g Passing Sale (FR)—Dayoula **Hogarth Racing**
5 **KING KILLONE (IRE)**, 8, b g Moonax (IRE)—Killone Brae **Hogarth Racing**
6 **MASTER PAPA (IRE)**, 9, bl g Key of Luck (USA)—Beguine (USA) **Hogarth Racing**
7 **MYSTERIOUS WORLD (IRE)**, 4, ch g Desert Prince—Salligram **Hogarth Racing**
8 **NORTHERN QUEST (IRE)**, 7, ch g Un Desperado (FR)—Strong Heather (IRE) **Hogarth Racing**
9 **NORTHERN VIC (IRE)**, 7, ch g Old Vic—Myra Gaye **Hogarth Racing**
10 **PARADIGM INVESTOR (IRE)**, 5, b g Great Palm (USA)—Cruby Hill (IRE) **Hogarth Racing**
11 **SHE'S THE BIZZ (IRE)**, 6, b m Mister Lord (USA)—Mens Business (IRE) **Hogarth Racing**
12 **SHREWD INVESTOR (IRE)**, 8, ch g Mister Lord (USA)—Mens Business (IRE) **Hogarth Racing**

Other Owners: H. P. Hogarth, P. H. Hogarth, J. Hogarth, J. L. Hogarth.

Assistant Trainer: Jennie Butler

Jockey (NH): D. O'Meara. **Conditional:** P. Kinsella.

---

284   MR A. F. HOLLINGSWORTH, Feckenham
Postal: **Lanket House, Crofts Lane, Feckenham, Redditch, Worcestershire, B96 6PU**
Contacts: **PHONE (01527) 68644/892054 FAX (01527) 60310 MOBILE (07775) 670644**

1 5, B m Aflora (IRE)—An Bothar Dubh **P. Adams**
2 **BLACKANBLUE**, 9, b g Alflora (IRE)—Emmabella **A. F. Hollingsworth**
3 5, Ch g Alflora (IRE)—Celtic Tore (IRE) **A. F. Hollingsworth**
4 **CENTREFOLD**, 8, b g Sea Raven (IRE)—Gemmabel **A. F. Hollingsworth**

MR A. F. HOLLINGSWORTH—continued

5 CRUELLA, 5, gr m Terimon—Gemmabel **A. F. Hollingsworth**
6 EXACTLY, 5, br g Terimon—Emmabella **A. F. Hollingsworth**
7 GALLIK DAWN, 10, ch g Anshan—Sticky Money **P. Adams**
8 MAKE IT PLAIN, 9, b m Alflora (IRE)—Gemmabel **A. F. Hollingsworth**
9 REWIND, 8, br g Rakaposhi King—Celtic Tore (IRE) **A. F. Hollingsworth**
10 5, B m Alflora (IRE)—Shadowgraff **A. F. Hollingsworth**

Assistant Trainer: Sharon Smith

Jockey (NH): R. Walsh, M. A. Fitzgerald, A. Thornton. **Amateur:** Mr G. Hanmer, Mr T. Stephenson.

---

285 | **MR R. HOLLINSHEAD, Upper Longdon**
Postal: **Lodge Farm, Upper Longdon, Rugeley, Staffordshire, WS15 1QF**
Contacts: PHONE (01543) 490298 FAX (01543) 490490

1 ALL YOU NEED (IRE), 4, b g Iron Mask (USA)—Choice Pickings (IRE) **N. Chapman**
2 AMRON HILL, 5, b g Polar Prince (IRE)—Maradata (IRE) **Mr G. Lloyd**
3 BRASTAR JELOIS (FR), 5, b m True Brave (USA)—Star Angels (FR) **Mr P. Pye**
4 CAP ST JEAN (IRE), 4, b g Cape Cross (IRE)—Karminiya (IRE) **Edenbrook Partnership**
5 CLEVELAND, 6, b g Pennekamp (USA)—Clerio **Mrs S. M. H. Haslehurst**
6 DANCING DEANO (IRE), 6, b g Second Empire (IRE)—Ultimate Beat (IRE) **Mr R. Wood**
7 DAVID'S CAVALIER, 4, b g Beat All (USA)—Foxtrot Pie **The Three R's**
8 DRAWN GOLD, 4, b g Daggers Drawn (USA)—Gold Belt (IRE) **E. T. D. Leadbeater**
9 GARLOGS, 5, b g Hunting Lion (IRE)—Fading **P. G. Freeman**
10 GIDDYWELL, 4, b f Ishiguru (USA)—Understudy **The Giddy Gang**
11 GILDED COVE, 8, b h Polar Prince (IRE)—Cloudy Reef **M. A. N. Johnson**
12 HEATHYARDS PRIDE, 8, b g Polar Prince (IRE)—Heathyards Lady (USA) **L. A. Morgan**
13 HEATHYARDS RED, 5, ch m Roi de Rome (USA)—Heathyards Lady (USA) **L. A. Morgan**
14 HOH WOTANITE, 5, ch h Stravinsky (USA)—West One **The Three R's**
15 ISHISMART, 4, ch f Ishiguru (USA)—Smartie Lee **Mrs N. S. Harris**
16 KEON (IRE), 6, b g Rossini (USA)—Lonely Brook (USA) **Chasetown Civil Engineering Ltd**
17 LEGAL LOVER (IRE), 6, b g Woodborough (USA)—Victoria's Secret (IRE) **E. T. D. Leadbeater**
18 MAKFLY, 5, b g Makbul—Flying Flip **E. T. D. Leadbeater**
19 METAL GURU, 4, ch f Ishiguru (USA)—Gemtastic **Moores Metals Ltd**
20 NORMA HILL, 7, ch m Polar Prince (IRE)—Smartie Lee **Mr G. Lloyd**
21 OCHRE BAY, 5, b h Polar Prince (IRE)—Cloudy Reef **M. A. N. Johnson**
22 OPERA WRITER (IRE), 5, b g Rossini (USA)—Miss Flite (IRE) **J. L. Marriott**
23 PAULINE'S PRINCE, 6, b h Polar Prince (IRE)—Etma Rose (IRE) **N. Chapman**
24 PURE BRIEF (IRE), 11, b g Brief Truce (USA)—Epure **Mrs V. D. Gandola-Gray**
25 STRAVARA, 5, b b g Kayf Tara—Stravsea **E. Bennion**
26 STRAVITA, 4, b f Weet-A-Minute (IRE)—Stravsea **E. Bennion**
27 TINA'S RIDGE, 4, ch g Indian Ridge—Phantom Waters **J. L. Marriott**
28 TORA PETCHA (IRE), 5, b g Bahhare (USA)—Magdalene (FR) **J. L. Marriott**
29 TREETOPS HOTEL (IRE), 9, ch g Grand Lodge (USA)—Rousinette **R. Robinson**
30 TRI CHARA (IRE), 4, ch c Grand Slam (USA)—Lamzena (IRE) **The Tri Chara Partnership**
31 VIPER, 6, b g Polar Prince (IRE)—Maradata (IRE) **Mr G. Lloyd**

THREE-YEAR-OLDS

32 BAHAMIAN KID, b c Bahamian Bounty—Barachois Princess (USA) **J. D. Graham**
33 BAHAMIAN LAD, b c Bahamian Bounty—Danehill Princess (IRE) **J. D. Graham**
34 BAHAMIAN PRINCESS, ch f Bahamian Bounty—Cutlass Princess (USA) **J. D. Graham**
35 CARMINE ROCK, ch f Arkadian Hero (USA)—Cloudy Reef **M. A. N. Johnson**
36 FLOWING CAPE (IRE), b c Cape Cross (IRE)—Jet Lock (USA) **J. L. Marriott**
37 HELPING HAND (IRE), b c Lend A Hand—Cardinal Press **N. Chapman**
38 MISS BRONTE, b f Ishiguru (USA)—Gemtastic **Mrs J. Hughes**
39 MY MATE MAX, b g Fraam—Victory Flip (IRE) **E. T. D. Leadbeater**
40 STARLIGHT PRINCE, b g Forzando—Inchtina **Mrs C. A. Stevenson**
41 WEET A SURPRISE, b f Bertolini (USA)—Ticcatoo (IRE) **Ed Weetman (Haulage & Storage) Ltd**
42 WEET BY FAR, b f Bertolini (USA)—Shaiybara (IRE) **T. E. Weetman**
43 WEETFROMTHECHAFF, gr g Weet-A-Minute (IRE)—Weet Ees Girl (IRE) **Ed Weetman (Haulage & Storage) Ltd**

TWO-YEAR-OLDS

44 B c 4/4 Mark of Esteem (IRE)—Barachois Princess (USA) (Barachois (CAN)) **J. D. Graham**
45 B f 8/2 Deportivo—Carati (Selkirk (USA)) (7000) **R. Hollinshead**

MR R. HOLLINSHEAD—continued

46 **CHARLIETOO,** b c 9/5 King Charlemagne (USA)—Ticcatoo (IRE) (Dolphin Street (FR)) (8500) **J. L. Marriott**
47 Ch f 3/5 Mark of Esteem (IRE)—Cutlass Princess (USA) (Cutlass (USA)) **J. D. Graham**
48 B f 6/4 Mark of Esteem (IRE)—Danehill Princess (IRE) (Danehill (USA)) **J. D. Graham**
49 B c 28/4 Bold Edge—Gemtastic (Tagula (IRE)) **R. Hollinshead**
50 F 9/2 Beckett (IRE)—Lady Charlotte (Night Shift (USA)) (5500) **R. Hollinshead**
51 B c 18/4 Captain Rio—Persian Fortune (Forzando) (12000) **Ed Weetman (Haulage & Storage) Ltd**
52 **RED ROSANNA,** b f 11/3 Bertolini (USA)—Lamarita (Emarati (USA)) (10500) **Mrs D. A. Hodson**
53 **TILLERS SATISFIED (IRE),** b f 27/3 Tillerman—Lady of Pleasure (IRE) (Marju (IRE)) (4500) **Mr M. D. Wootton**

Other Owners: Mrs H. Bellingham, Mr S. G. Brook, D. Coppenhall, Mrs P. A. Eden, Mrs M. E. Hill, Miss S. A. Hollinshead, D. R. Horne, A. Lawrence, A. L. Marriott, Mr N. S. Sweeney.

Assistant Trainer: A N Hollinshead

Apprentice: R. Kennemore. **Amateur:** Mr S. Harrison.

---

286   MR J. R. HOLT, Peckleton
Postal: **Hall Farm, Church Road, Peckleton, Leicester**
Contacts: **PHONE/FAX (01455) 821972 MOBILE (07850) 321059**
E-MAIL hallfarmracing@btconnect.com WEBSITE www.hallfarmracing.co.uk

1 **COLEORTON DAGGER,** 4, ch f Daggers Drawn—Tayovullin (IRE) **Coleorton Moor Racing**
2 **DIRECT ACCESS (IRE),** 13, ch g Roselier (FR)—Spanish Flame (IRE) **J. R. Holt**
3 **EL COTO,** 8, b g Forzando—Thatcherella **J. P. Hames**
4 **EL POTRO,** 6, b g Forzando—Gaelic Air **Mr D. J. Facer-Harrison**
5 **HOT LIPS PAGE (FR),** 7, b m Hamas (IRE)—Salt Peanuts (IRE) **Elliott & Brown Racing**
6 **HOWZAT HARRY,** 5, b g Shahrastani (USA)—Princess Lieven **Mr P. V. Thomas**
7 **KINGS ROCK,** 7, ch g Kris—Both Sides Now (USA) **J. Billson**
8 **PRIMITIVE ACADEMY,** 6, b h Primitive Rising (USA)—Royal Fontaine (IRE) **M. Massarella**
9 **RIVERWELD,** 6, ch g Weldnaas (USA)—Riverain **J. R. Holt**
10 **TERMON BOY,** 4, b c Rainbow High—Killmacrennan Lady (IRE)
11 **THE GRAIG,** 4, b g Josr Algarhoud (IRE)—Souadah (USA) **P. J. Nicholls**
12 **TICKERS WAY,** 7, gr g Cloudings (IRE)—Zany Lady **P. J. Nicholls**
13 **TUCKERS MIST,** 6, b br m Samraan (USA)—Mainvalley Queen (IRE) **Mr K. & Mr A. K. Smith**

THREE-YEAR-OLDS

14 **AMYANN (IRE),** b f Indian Lodge (IRE)—Moral Certainty (USA) **Louella Racing**
15 **BANDORAN,** ch g Band On The Run—Breezy Day **Mr D. J. Facer-Harrison**
16 **GREAT FUTURE,** ch f Fantastic Light (USA)—Silvernus **Louella Racing**

TWO-YEAR-OLDS

17 B f 6/5 Hamas (IRE)—Funky (Classic Music (USA)) **The Higham Partnership**
18 **JOANS GEM,** b c 4/3 Piccolo—Blonde En Blonde (IRE) (Hamas (IRE)) **Elliott & Brown Racing**

Other Owners: Mr M. W. Elliott, Exors of the Late Ms J. Brown, A. C. Henson, M. P. Higson, A. Holmes, L. Massarella, G. Pickering, R J H Limited, Mr K. Smith, A. K. Smith.

Assistant Trainer: Ellen Holt

---

287   MR A. HONEYBALL, Beaminster
Postal: **The Flat, Manor Farm, Seaborough, Beaminster, Dorset, DT8 3QY**
Contacts: **PHONE (01823) 451106 MOBILE (07815) 898569**
E-MAIL aannjames@aol.com

1 **BRIGHT QUEST,** 6, b m El Conquistador—Bright Lady **M. S. Green**
2 **CHERRY FLORA,** 5, b m Afflora (IRE)—Triggered **Broomfield Racing**
3 **CLASSIC FAIR,** 7, b m Classic Cliche (IRE)—Bay Fair **Apple Pie Partnership**
4 **FOUNTAIN HILL (IRE),** 9, b g King's Theatre (IRE)—Highest Land (FR) **The Fountains Partnership**
5 **FOUNTAINS FLYPAST,** 4, b g Broadway Flyer (USA)—Miss Flower Girl **The Fountains Partnership**
6 **NOBLE ACTION,** 9, ch g Mister Lord (USA)—Triggered **Mrs S. Chown**

Other Owners: G. T. Birks, Mrs A. P. Bone, Mrs M. H. Bowden, A. R. Franklin, Mr M. N. Franklin.

Amateur: Miss R. A. Green.

288 MR CON HORGAN, Ogbourne Maizey
Postal: **Pond Cottage, Uffcott, Swindon, Wiltshire, SN4 9NB**
Contacts: **OFFICE (01793) 731676 FAX (01793) 731889 MOBILE (07850) 365459**
E-MAIL conhorganpondc@aol.com

1 ARTZOLA (IRE), 8, b m Alzao (USA)—Polistatic **Mrs B. Sumner**
2 BLUE QUIVER (IRE), 8, b g Bluebird (USA)—Paradise Forum **Con Horgan**
3 DIAMOND WORLD, 5, b m Agnes World (USA)—In A Twinkling (IRE) **Mrs B. Woodford, Mr & Mrs David Tapper**
4 FUTURE DEAL, 7, b m First Trump—Katyushka (IRE) **Mrs B. Woodford**
5 HALLINGS OVERTURE (USA), 9, b g Halling (USA)—Sonata **Mrs B. Sumner**
6 OCEAN AVENUE (IRE), 9, b g Dolphin Street (FR)—Trinity Hall **Mr & Mrs D. Tapper & Mr C. Horgan**
7 OCEAN ROCK, 7, b g Perugino (USA)—Polistatic **Mrs B. Sumner**
8 PEARL FARM, 7, b m Foxhound (USA)—Trinity Hall **Mrs B. Woodford**
9 RANGALI BELLE, 4, b f Diktat—Dalaauna **Mrs B. Sumner**
10 ROYAL SENGA, 5, b m Agnes World (USA)—Katyushka (IRE) **Mrs B. Woodford**

THREE-YEAR-OLDS

11 CAPE ROCK, b g Cape Cross (IRE)—Wildwood Flower **Mrs B. Sumner**
12 WARRIOR CONQUEST, b g Alhaarth (IRE)—Eilean Shona **Mrs B. Sumner**

TWO-YEAR-OLDS

13 B g 19/1 Tillerman—Northern Tara (IRE) (Fayruz) (20000) **Mrs B. Sumner**
14 B c 8/5 Verglas (IRE)—Yellow Trumpet (Petong) (62000) **Mrs B. Sumner**

Other Owners: D. Tapper.

289 MR M. HOURIGAN, Limerick
Postal: **Lissaleen, Patrickswell, Limerick, Ireland**
Contacts: **PHONE (00353) 6139 6603 FAX (00353) 6139 6812 MOBILE (00353) 8682 26655**
E-MAIL info@mhourigan.ie WEBSITE www.mhourigan.ie

1 A NEW STORY (IRE), 10, b g Fourstars Allstar (USA)—Diyala (FR) **Storys Over Syndicate**
2 ADAIR MOHR (IRE), 8, gr g Luso—Cullenstown Lady (IRE)
3 ALMIER (IRE), 10, gr g Phardante (FR)—Stepfaster **C. Maune**
4 AMICUS CURIAE (IRE), 6, ch g Snurge—Mill Dancer (IRE) **Happy Ever After Syndicate**
5 ARTEEA (IRE), 9, b g Oscar (IRE)—Merric **M. O'Flaherty**
6 BEEF OR SALMON (IRE), 12, ch g Cajetano (USA)—Farinella (IRE) **B. J. Craig**
7 BORN HIGH (IRE), 4, br c Key of Luck (USA)—Alaynia (IRE) **Dr. Ronan Lambe**
8 CHEVAUX LOCO (IRE), 9, br g Jolly Jake (NZ)—Kilbane Lass (IRE) **Carwash Syndicate**
9 CHURCH ISLAND (IRE), 9, ch g Erins Isle—Just Possible **B. J. Craig**
10 CLANCY (IRE), 7, b m Oscar (IRE)—Reign of Terror (IRE) **M. O'Flaherty**
11 CLUAIN ARRA (IRE), 10, b m Supreme Leader—Shuil Alanna **Miss Tracey Hennessy**
12 COOLCOMIN (IRE), 6, ch g Moscow Society (USA)—Rosy Affair (IRE) **C. Maune**
13 CULLYS WOOD (IRE), 7, b g Shardari—Maeve's Magic (IRE) **Mr M. McDonagh**
14 DANCING TORNADO (IRE), 7, ch g Golden Tornado (IRE)—Lady Dante (IRE) **J. P. McManus**
15 DEAD OR ALIVE (IRE), 5, b g Exit To Nowhere (USA)—Avro Avian **Gigginstown House Stud**
16 DOC REASON (IRE), 5, b g Dr Massini (IRE)—Name A Reason (IRE) **Aficionados Syndicate**
17 DOODLE EILE (IRE), 5, br g Humbel (USA)—Galtee Lady (IRE) **Mrs M. Hourigan**
18 EASYFIX (IRE), 5, ch g Naheez (USA)—Eurolucy (IRE) **Mr M. Earls**
19 EIGHT FIFTY SIX (IRE), 7, gr g General Monash (USA)—Mignonnette (FR) **Laragh Two Syndicate**
20 EL JO (IRE), 7, b g Oscar (IRE)—Gayla Orchestra **John Carey**
21 EXCELSIOR (IRE), 8, b g Luso—Sorimak Gale (IRE) **Gigginstown House Stud**
22 FIELD COMMANDER (IRE), 6, b g Blue Ocean (USA)—Fern Fields (IRE) **Gigginstown House Stud**
23 FINAL ADVENTURE (IRE), 6, b g Fahris—Corrie Lough (IRE) **Four Borders Syndicate**
24 FLYING DIPPY (IRE), 5, b g Flying Legend—Trillick (IRE) **Blackwood Racing Syndicate**
25 FLYING JOHNNY M (IRE), 8, ch g Flying Legend—How Doudo **Miss L. A. Hourigan**
26 GUTS FOR GARTERS (IRE), 5, br g Presenting—Asklynn (IRE) **Gigginstown House Stud**
27 HARDTOTAKE (IRE), 8, ch g Arctic Cider (USA)—Hard Enough (IRE) **J. P. McManus**
28 HI CLOY (IRE), 11, b g Be My Native (USA)—Thomastown Girl **Mrs S. McCloy**
29 HOGAN KNOWS BEST (IRE), 7, b g Humbel (USA)—Lyphards Anemone **Mrs M. Hourigan**
30 IHEARYOUCALLINGME (IRE), 5, br m Exit To Nowhere (USA)—Bewildered (IRE) **John McLaman**
31 JOHNJOES CROSS (IRE), 7, b m Rock Hopper—Palatine Lady **J. & J. Syndicate**
32 JUNIOR BOSS (IRE), 5, ch g All My Dreams (IRE)—Bowland Park **Mr M. Earls**
33 JUST (IRE), 9, ch g Great Marquess—Gerdando Lady (IRE) **J & N Syndicate**
34 L'ALSACIEN (FR), 7, b g Phantom Breeze—Yvelines (FR) **Miss M. Hourigan**

MR M. HOURIGAN—continued

35 **LADY MOON (IRE)**, 6, b m Moonax (IRE)—Ahawilk Anna (IRE) **Mr M. Walsh**
36 **LESCERS BOY**, 6, ch g Keen—Grange Gracie **Mr T. Sheehan**
37 **MARY FITZ (IRE)**, 5, b m Muharib (USA)—Flying Forward (IRE) **Woodlands House Hotel Syndicate**
38 **MISS BEIJING (IRE)**, 5, b br m Orpen (USA)—Over Swing (FR) **Irememberitwell Syndicate**
39 **MISS SAAFEND PLAZA (IRE)**, 4, b f Danetime (IRE)—Coup de Coeur (IRE) **Fools on Stools Syndicate**
40 **MOSCOW MO CHUISLE (IRE)**, 7, b m Moscow Society (USA)—Vesper Time **T. Noland**
41 **MOSSBANK (IRE)**, 8, b g Kadeed (IRE)—Miromaid **Gigginstown House Stud**
42 **MYSTICAL BREEZE (IRE)**, 8, b g Mujadil (USA)—Follow The Wind **Mr J. McLarnon / Mr B. J. Craig**
43 **NO INVITATIONS**, 6, b g Wizard King—Deirdres Dream **Themond Racing Syndicate**
44 **ONE CHAPTER ONE (IRE)**, 5, b g Old Vic—Kickalong **Height Syndicate**
45 **OSCARS BREEZE (IRE)**, 6, b g Oscar (IRE)—Kilcrea Breeze (IRE) **John Carey**
46 **SALLY'S DREAM (IRE)**, 6, b m Key of Luck (USA)—Winning Sally (IRE) **D. J. Reddan**
47 **SHAVHALE (IRE)**, 6, br m Zaffaran (USA)—Bewildered (USA) **Miss L. A. Hourigan**
48 **SLY TOUCH (IRE)**, 5, b m Exit To Nowhere (USA)—Imperial Touch (IRE) **P. Trant**
49 **SOME CRAIC (IRE)**, 8, b g Presenting—The Branner (IRE) **The Laune Syndicate**
50 **SPACEMAN**, 5, b g In The Wings—Souk (IRE) **John Carey**
51 **SUPERIOR GUEST (IRE)**, 5, b g Superior Premium—Autumn Guest (CZE) **Mrs M. Hourigan**
52 **TEADA (IRE)**, 5, b br m Presenting—Deise Cailin (IRE) **G. Cummins**
53 **TEN TO TWELVE (IRE)**, 6, b m Flemensfirth (USA)—Rainardia (IRE) **S. Lucey, P. Ryan**
54 **THE PARISHIONER (IRE)**, 10, ch m Glacial Storm (USA)—Phairy Miracles (IRE) **Fergus Syndicate**
55 **THE UNDER ACHIEVER (IRE)**, 8, b g Luso—Kemaldor **P. A. Byrne**
56 **TOM DOODLE (IRE)**, 7, b g Old Vic—Hiltons Executive (IRE) **Miss Mairead O'Carroll**
57 **TUBBER GAEL HOLLY (IRE)**, 8, ch m Arctic Cider (USA)—Joy's Toy **Tuffy Ten Syndicate**

Other Owners: London Leisure Services Limited.

Assistant Trainer: Kay Hourigan

Jockey (NH): A. J. McNamara, T. Doyle, M. Darcy. **Conditional:** S. J. Gray. **Apprentice:** S. J. Gray. **Amateur:** Miss L. A. Hourigan, Mr J. C. Barry, Mr M. J. Davidson.

---

290 MR H. S. HOWE, Tiverton
Postal: **Ringstone Stables, Oakford, Tiverton, Devon, EX16 9EU**
Contacts: PHONE (01398) 351224 FAX (01398) 351153 MOBILE (07802) 506344
E-MAIL hshowe@stuarthoweracing.co.uk

1 **BOBSLEIGH**, 9, b g Robellino (USA)—Do Run Run **Mrs V. W. Jones**
2 **BOOGIE DANCER**, 4, b f Tobougg (IRE)—Bolero **Brian,Gwen,Terri & Kelly Griffiths**
3 **DAMHSOIR (IRE)**, 4, b f Invincible Spirit (IRE)—Ceide Dancer (IRE) **Mr R. Roper**
4 **DOUBLE'S DAUGHTER**, 6, b m Double Trigger (IRE)—Flexwing **Horses Away Ltd**
5 **LADY OF LORNE (IRE)**, 4, b f Mull of Kintyre (USA)—Harvest Gold (IRE) **H. S. Howe**
6 **OUR TIME (IRE)**, 5, b m Danetime (IRE)—Tolomena **Horses Away Ltd**
7 **PARTY PALACE**, 4, b f Auction House (USA)—Lady-Love **Horses Away Ltd**
8 **POLISH PROSPECT (IRE)**, 4, ch f Elnadim (USA)—Always True (USA) **R. J. Parish**
9 **SILVER CHARMER**, 9, b m Charmer—Sea Dart **Brian,Gwen,Terri & Kelly Griffiths**
10 **SILVER DREAMER (IRE)**, 6, b m Brave Act—Heads We Called (IRE) **Miss K. J. Spurway**
11 **UIG**, 7, ch m Bien Bien (USA)—Madam Zando **B. P. Jones**

THREE-YEAR-OLDS

12 B g Lend A Hand—Dorian
13 **HONEYPOT SPLENDA**, sk f Stetsen—Balfour Lady
14 **LES ALLUES (IRE)**, b f Chevalier (IRE)—Cwm Deri (IRE) **Kate Lindsay-Flynn**

TWO-YEAR-OLDS

15 **BLUSHING MAID**, br f 3/3 Namid—Music Maid (IRE) (Inzar (USA)) (7000) **Mr R. Roper**
16 B f 17/2 Tillerman—Everlasting (Desert King (IRE)) **B. P. Jones**
17 Ch f 26/2 Compton Place—Scylla (Rock City) **Mr R. Roper**
18 Gr f 12/5 Lucky Story (USA)—Smooth Princess (IRE) (Roi Danzig (USA)) (3000) **Mrs V. W. Jones**
19 Ch f 3/3 Tobougg (IRE)—Stealthy (Kind of Hush) (4200)
20 B f 25/4 Tillerman—Zafine (Zafonic (USA)) **B. P. Jones**

Jockey (flat): Dane O'Neill, A. McCarthy, S. Drowne. **Jockey (NH):** R. Greene.

291 MR P. HOWLING, Newmarket
Postal: The Bungalow, Warren Place, Newmarket, Suffolk, CB8 8QQ
Contacts: PHONE (01638) 668503 MOBILE (07866) 674469
E-MAIL billichang@aol.com WEBSITE www.paulhowlingracing.co.uk

1 **A TEEN**, 10, ch g Presidium—Very Good **P. Howling**
2 **CHRISTIAN BENDIX**, 6, ch g Presidium—Very Good **Mrs A. K. Petersen**
3 **COOL ISLE**, 5, b m Polar Prince (IRE)—Fisher Island (IRE) **R. Murphy**
4 **DVINSKY (USA)**, 7, b g Stravinsky (USA)—Festive Season (USA) **R. P. Berenson**
5 **ELMS SCHOOLBOY**, 6, ch g Komaite (USA)—Elms Schoolgirl **P. Howling**
6 **FIGARO FLYER (IRE)**, 5, b g Mozart (IRE)—Ellway Star (IRE) **S. J. Hammond**
7 **GUILDENSTERN (IRE)**, 6, b g Danetime (IRE)—Lyphard Abu (IRE) **D. Brown**
8 **ICENI PRINCESS**, 4, b f Victory Note (USA)—Swing Job **M. A. Shipman**
9 **MIGHTY KITCHENER (USA)**, 5, br g Mighty (USA)—Libeccio (NZ) **S. J. Hammond**
10 **OUR KES (IRE)**, 6, gr m Revoque (IRE)—Gracious Gretclo **S. J. Hammond**
11 **RESPLENDENT ACE (IRE)**, 4, b c Trans Island—Persian Polly **Resplendent Racing Limited**
12 **RESPLENDENT ALPHA**, 4, ch g Best of The Bests (IRE)—Sunley Scent **Resplendent Racing Limited**
13 **RESPLENDENT NOVA**, 6, b g Pivotal—Santiburi Girl **Resplendent Racing Limited**
14 **TABULATE**, 5, b m Dansili—Let Alone **R. P. Berenson**
15 **TAMINO (IRE)**, 5, b g Mozart (IRE)—Stop Out **Resplendent Racing Limited**

THREE-YEAR-OLDS
16 **BONZO**, b g Where Or When—Making Memories (IRE) **M. A. Shipman**
17 **COUNTRYWIDE COMET (IRE)**, b g Desert Style—Darzao (IRE) **Mrs J. P. Howling**
18 **FORTUNELLA**, b f Polish Precedent (USA)—Hazy Heights **Wyck Hall Stud Ltd**
19 **GENEROUS THOUGHT**, b c Cadeaux Genereux—Rosie's Posy (IRE) **L. Sheridan**
20 **HISS AND BOO**, ch g Starborough—Royal Lady (IRE) **The Royal Oak Southwark Syndicate**
21 **LIZ LONG**, b f Reel Buddy (USA)—Surrealist (ITY) **Mrs J. P. Howling**
22 **SHABNAAM**, b f Diktat—Noble View (USA) **Theobalds Stud**
23 **WHISTFUL MISS**, b f First Trump—Mise En Scene **Mr G. W. Lawlan**

TWO-YEAR-OLDS
24 B c 5/4 Diktat—Bella Bellisimo (IRE) (Alzao (USA)) **Mr P. Howling**
25 Ch c 24/3 Pursuit of Love—Eglantine (IRE) (Royal Academy (USA)) (2000) **P. Holmes**
26 **GRAND HONOUR (IRE)**, gr c 28/3 Verglas (IRE)—Rosy Dudley (IRE) (Grand Lodge (USA)) (16000) **Mr A. Ahmed**
27 B c 30/4 Superior Premium—Lady Sabina (Bairn (USA)) (2000) **P. Howling**
28 **LYRICAL INTENT**, ch g 8/3 Imperial Dancer—Magical Flute (Piccolo) (12000) **Mr A. Ahmed**
29 B f 31/1 Deportivo—Swing Job (Ezzoud (IRE)) (800) **M. Shipman**

Other Owners: Mr P. Cook, Mr E. W. Gordon, Mr Paul Howling, Mr Brian Johnson, Mr D. C. Patrick, Mr J. A. Porteous, Mr P. Woodward, Mr C. N. Wright.

Assistant Trainer: Mrs J Howling

Jockey (flat): J. Quinn, Shane Kelly. **Jockey (NH):** Jamie Moore.

292 MR D. T. HUGHES, Kildare
Postal: Osborne Lodge, Kildare, Co. Kildare, Ireland
Contacts: PHONE (00353) 4552 1490 FAX (00353) 4552 1643 MOBILE (00353) 8625 34098

1 5, Ch g Lord of Appeal—Arabella Bee **Clashbeg Syndicate**
2 5, B g Old Vic—Arlington Dancer (IRE) **H. A. Campbell**
3 **AUGHACASHEL (IRE)**, 6, b g Entrepreneur—Castlerahan (IRE) **Mrs M. Brady**
4 **BACK IS BACK (IRE)**, 4, b g Bob Back (USA)—Kings Gap (IRE) **Old Moss Farm**
5 **BALLYFINNEY (IRE)**, 7, ch g Good Thyne (USA)—Sounds Confident **Mr C. P. O'Brien**
6 **BEN MORE ASSYNT (IRE)**, 5, b g Supreme Leader—Mightyatom **B. C. Marshall**
7 **BEN VRACKIE (IRE)**, 7, b g Saddlers' Hall (IRE)—Marie's Pride **B. C. Marshall**
8 **BISHOPSTOWN BOY (IRE)**, 5, ch g Accordion—Muxlowhill (IRE) **R. Humphreys**
9 **BLACK APALACHI (IRE)**, 9, b g Old Vic—Hattons Dream (IRE) **G. Burke**
10 5, B g Bob Back (USA)—Bramdean **K. F. McNulty**
11 **CAPPACURRY DAWN (IRE)**, 7, br g Anshan—Kept In The Dark **P. Ward**
12 **CASTLEDOCKRELL (IRE)**, 5, b g Luso—Myaree (IRE) **Mrs N. Doyle**
13 **CENTRAL HOUSE (IRE)**, 11, b g Alflora (IRE)—Fantasy World **John F. Kenny**
14 **CHALK EYE (IRE)**, 6, b g Presenting—Wayward Words **Mrs K. Leech**
15 5, B g Muroto—Clashbeg (IRE) **Clashbeg Syndicate**

MR D. T. HUGHES—continued

16 **COLLEGE DAISY (IRE)**, 5, b br m City Honours (USA)—Royal Rosmoylan (IRE) **J. Rogers**
17 **CRY PRESTO (USA)**, 4, b g Street Cry (IRE)—Sabaah Elfull **J. P. Prunty**
18 **DAN GEORGE (IRE)**, 8, b g Taipan (IRE)—Mosephine (IRE) **D. King**
19 **DANIEL DELANY (IRE)**, 5, b g Bishop of Cashel—Snipe Hunt (IRE) **Slaneyville Syndicate**
20 **DEAL DONE (FR)**, 4, b g Vertical Speed (FR)—Five Rivers (FR) **Mrs A. N. Durkan**
21 **DEAL MAKER (FR)**, 5, b g Vertical Speed (FR)—Five Rivers (FR) **Mrs A. N. Durkan**
22 **DEFYING GRAVITY (IRE)**, 5, b g Old Vic—Night Escape (IRE) **G. Burke**
23 **DICERA (IRE)**, 6, b m Flemensfirth (USA)—Alice's Perk (IRE) **AMPC Syndicate**
24 **DOSCO (IRE)**, 9, b br g Oscar (IRE)—Broken Rein (IRE) **J. Rogers**
25 **DUBLIN HUNTER (IRE)**, 12, br g Treasure Hunter—Cutty Sark **Woodlawn Racing Syndicate**
26 **DUE RESPECT (IRE)**, 8, b g Danehill (USA)—Stylish **P. Brady**
27 **EMPIRE MAGIC (IRE)**, 5, b g Second Empire (IRE)—Mileeha (USA) **W. Thompson**
28 **ERRITT LODGE (IRE)**, 5, b g Overbury (IRE)—Bean Alainn **K. F. McNulty**
29 5, B g Alderbrook—Fabulous Evening **T. Mulhern**
30 4, B g Saddlers' Hall (IRE)—Fairly Deep **G. Morrin**
31 **FIFTY YEARSON (IRE)**, 7, br g Alderbrook—Amari Queen **R. T. Guilford**
32 **FOND OF A DROP**, 7, br g Overbury (IRE)—Pearl's Choice (IRE) **Mr J. M. Doyle**
33 **FOREST LEAVES (IRE)**, 8, bl g Charnwood Forest (IRE)—Premier Code (IRE) **Legal Access Syndicate**
34 **GETTING BACK (IRE)**, 6, b g Bob Back (USA)—Tourist Attraction (IRE) **J. P. McManus**
35 **GLAVEY (IRE)**, 6, b g Old Vic—Milford Run **K. F. McNulty**
36 **GLENBARROW (IRE)**, 4, b g Old Vic—Cry In The Dark **Anne-Marie Ryan**
37 **GOOD CONTROL (IRE)**, 7, b g Oscar (IRE)—Garryduff Supreme (IRE) **L. Fitzpatrick**
38 **GRANGECLARE GOLD (IRE)**, 5, ch m Old Vic—Grangeclare Dancer (IRE) **T. Hendy**
39 **GRANGECLARE LARK (IRE)**, 7, b m Old Vic—Grangeclare Rose (IRE) **Thomas Hendy**
40 4, B g Lord Americo—Grangeclare Rose (IRE) **D A Southside Syndicate**
41 **HARDY EUSTACE (IRE)**, 11, b g Archway—Sterna Star **L. Byrne**
42 **HATTERS CROSS (IRE)**, 6, b g Brave Act—Red River Rose (IRE) **Punta Group Syndicate**
43 **HOWS TRIX (IRE)**, 8, b g Lord Americo—Bannow Drive (IRE) **R D Racing Syndicate**
44 **IRISH STREAM (USA)**, 10, ch h Irish River (FR)—Euphonic (USA) **James T. Barton**
45 **JIMMY BER (IRE)**, 6, b g Supreme Leader—Hail To You (USA) **L. Byrne**
46 **JOHNNY TWO KEYS (IRE)**, 5, ch g Florida Son—Ice Pearl **B. C. Marshall**
47 **JUSTPOURIT (IRE)**, 9, b g Glacial Storm (USA)—Gale Choice (IRE) **Hanged Man's Five Sndicate**
48 **KILKENNY ALL STAR (IRE)**, 7, b g Alderbrook—Borris Bounty (IRE) **Exors of the late C. M. Ryan**
49 **KING OF THE OPERA (IRE)**, 6, ch g Snurge—Top Step (IRE) **Mind The Step Syndicate**
50 **KRIEGSPIEL**, 6, b br g Singspiel (IRE)—Karlaya (IRE) **G. Burke**
51 **LAURA'S LIGHT (IRE)**, 6, b g Turtle Island (IRE)—Conditional Sale (IRE) **Francis G. Kenny**
52 **LENABANE (IRE)**, 6, b g Luso—Meelick Lady (IRE) **K. F. McNulty**
53 **LEON OG (IRE)**, 5, b g Oscar (IRE)—Arctic Chatter **Horseplay Syndicate**
54 **LOUTH (IRE)**, 7, b g Alderbrook—Sesheta **Exors of the late C. M. Ryan**
55 **LURGAN (IRE)**, 6, b g Taipan (IRE)—Clashbeg (IRE) **Clashbeg Syndicate**
56 **LYCEUM (GER)**, 6, ch g Trempolino (USA)—Liza (IRE) **D A Southside Syndicate**
57 **MISTER TIBBS (IRE)**, 5, b br g Rashar (USA)—Native Craft (IRE) **C. Ryan**
58 **MOFFIRR**, 4, b g Tobougg (IRE)—Galatrix **P. J. Fahy**
59 **MR DUFFY (IRE)**, 8, b g Presenting—Senorita Bonita (IRE) **Mr Kevin McNulty**
60 **MUTINEER (IRE)**, 9, gr h Highest Honor (FR)—Miss Amy R (USA) **Seven To Eleven Syndicate**
61 4, Ch g Oscar Schindler (IRE)—My Alanna **N. Power**
62 **NOBLE PRIZE (GER)**, 6, ch g Acatenango (GER)—Noble Pearl (GER) **Mr Michael Moore**
63 **OLD SI (IRE)**, 5, b g Saddlers' Hall (IRE)—Shaping **H. A. Campbell**
64 **OSCAR TANGO (IRE)**, 7, b g Oscar (IRE)—Park Jewel (IRE) **L. Kinsella**
65 **OULART**, 9, ch g Sabrehill (USA)—Gaye Fame **Mr G. Pierse**
66 **PADDY CURRY (IRE)**, 6, b br g Pistolet Bleu (IRE)—Sterna Star **L. Byrne**
67 **PERSAN BLEU (FR)**, 5, b g Epervier Bleu—Dear Blue (IRE) **Gigginstown House Stud**
68 **PISTOL JACK (IRE)**, 6, b br g Pistolet Bleu (IRE)—Burren Gale (IRE) **Mr D. King**
69 **PLUNGE (IRE)**, 6, b g Luso—Afrostar (IRE) **Gigginstown House Stud**
70 4, B f Turtle Island (IRE)—Prudent Rose (IRE) **F. Fagan**
71 5, B g Luso—Quick Pick (IRE) **G. Burke**
72 **QUISCAL (FR)**, 4, b br g Sleeping Car (FR)—Jonque (FR) **G. T. Pierse**
73 **RACKHAM (FR)**, 6, ch g Villez (USA)—Teardrops Fall (FR) **Rackham Syndicate**
74 **RARE ARTICLE (IRE)**, 5, b m Definite Article—Czarina's Sister **Papin Syndicate (SvB)**
75 **RARE BOB (IRE)**, 6, b br g Bob Back (USA)—Cut Ahead **D. A. Syndicate**
76 **REBEL FIGHTER (IRE)**, 7, b g Mister Mat (FR)—Wigwam Mam (IRE) **Gigginstown House Stud**
77 **SALTINO (IRE)**, 6, b g Daylami (IRE)—Mahalia (IRE) **Mrs J. Nicholson**
78 **SARTEANO (FR)**, 5, gr g Kaldounevees (FR)—Sovereign Touch (IRE)
79 **SCHINDLERS HUNT (IRE)**, 8, ch g Oscar Schindler (IRE)—Snipe Hunt (IRE) **Slaneyville Syndicate**
80 **SEA DIVA (IRE)**, 8, b m Old Vic—Upsail **C. J. O'Reilly**
81 **SECRET ADMIRER (IRE)**, 5, b m Definite Article—Mis Fortune (IRE) **J. M. Doyle**

MR D. T. HUGHES—continued

82 **SHEPHERD MOON (IRE)**, 6, b g Taipan (IRE)—Bluebird Lane (IRE) **P. Furey**
83 **SIEGEMASTER (IRE)**, 7, b g Lord Americo—Shabra Princess **Gigginstown House Stud**
84 **SLANEYBROOK (IRE)**, 4, b g Presenting—What A Topper (IRE) **Hoding Syndicate**
85 **SPIRIT OF DUBLIN (IRE)**, 7, b g Old Vic—Royal Encounter (IRE) **B. Barrable**
86 **STRONG FLOW (IRE)**, 11, br g Over The River (FR)—Stormy Skies **B. C. Marshall**
87 **STUNT MAN (IRE)**, 6, br g Overbury (IRE)—Fionnuala **D. T. Hughes**
88 5, B g Saddlers' Hall (IRE)—Sullane River (IRE) **G. Burke**
89 **SUPERIOR BEN (IRE)**, 5, b g Beneficial—Mother Superior (IRE) **T. Curran**
90 **TANGO LINE (IRE)**, 6, b g Lord of Appeal—Winds Light **Austin Delaney**
91 **TEN FIRES (GER)**, 6, b br g Acambaro (GER)—Tosca Dona (GER) **B. Connell**
92 **THE RALL (IRE)**, 6, b g Old Vic—Arlington Dancer (IRE) **H. A. Campbell**
93 **TRIMBELLINA (IRE)**, 5, b m Presenting—Magneeto (IRE) **G. Burke**
94 **VIEL GLUCK (IRE)**, 5, b g Supreme Leader—Discerning Air **P. J. Fahy**
95 **WALKIN AISY**, 8, b g Rudimentary (USA)—Lady Shipley **B. C. Marshall**
96 **WELL OILED (IRE)**, 7, b g Supreme Leader—Mightyatom **B. Connaughton**
97 **WHATYOURACKING**, 4, b br g Mtoto—Kelimutu **K. Judge**
98 **ZAFFRAN LADY (IRE)**, 9, b m Zaffaran (USA)—Windmill Star (IRE) **J. P. Farrell**

THREE-YEAR-OLDS

99 **FLAG OF HONOUR (IRE)**, b c Alhaarth (IRE)—Polyandry (IRE) **G. T. Pierse**
100 B f Definite Article—Le Sueur (IRE)
101 B c Tiger Hill (IRE)—Wells Whisper (FR)

TWO-YEAR-OLDS

102 B c 5/2 Domedriver (IRE)—All Is Fair (Selkirk (USA)) (21878)
103 B f 27/3 Oscar (IRE)—Le Sueur (IRE) (Shernazar)
104 B c 24/4 Alhaarth (IRE)—Piacenza (IRE) (Darshaan) (16086)

Jockey (NH): R. Loughran. **Conditional:** N. J. O'Shea, I. McCarthy, C. D. Maxwell. **Amateur:** Mr Robert Hennessy.

293

MR S. A. HUGHES, Gilfach Goch
Postal: **Dusty Forge, Oak Street, Gilfach Goch, Porth, Mid-Glamorgan, CF39 8UG**
Contacts: **PHONE (07823) 334300 (01443) 672110 FAX (01443) 672110 MOBILE (07823) 334282**
E-MAIL dustyforge@aol.com

1 **COLORADO STORM**, 5, b m Weld—Beinn Mohr **S. A. Hughes**
2 **GALLANT HERO**, 9, b g Rainbow Quest (USA)—Gay Gallanta (USA) **S. A. Hughes**
3 **SHE'S LITTLE DON**, 8, b m Gran Alba (USA)—Doubting Donna **S. A. Hughes**
4 **WHITE TIE**, 5, ch g Commanche Run—Glen Nova **S. A. Hughes**

Assistant Trainer: Maggie Kidner Hughes

294

MS N. M. HUGO, Malpas
Postal: **Yew Tree House, 1 Brasseys Contract Road, Edge, Malpas, Cheshire, SY14 8LB**
Contacts: **PHONE (01829) 782020 (01948) 820649 FAX (01829) 782020 MOBILE (07736) 360550**
E-MAIL nicky.hugo@btconnect.com

1 6, Ch g Defacto (USA)—Mrs Mills **Ms N. M. Hugo**
2 **PRINCE OF GOLD**, 8, b g Polar Prince (IRE)—Gold Belt (IRE) **Barton Partnership**
3 **YOUNG BRAVE**, 7, b g Commanche Run—Double Chimes **Ms N. M. Hugo**

Other Owners: H. W. M. Houlbrook, K. Rowlands.

295

MRS S. J. HUMPHREY, West Wratting
Postal: **Yen Hall Farm, West Wratting, Cambridge, Cambridgeshire, CB21 5LP**
Contacts: **PHONE (01223) 291445 FAX (01223) 291451 MOBILE (07798) 702484**
E-MAIL sarah.yenhallfarm@btinternet.com

1 **BALLAD MAKER (IRE)**, 4, b g Marju (IRE)—Cappella (IRE) **Mrs S. J. Humphrey**
2 **PAPILLON DE IENA (FR)**, 8, ch g Varese (FR)—Belle Du Chesne (FR) **Mrs S. J. Humphrey**
3 **PENTASILEA**, 5, b m Nashwan (USA)—Isabella Gonzaga **Mrs S. J. Humphrey**

MRS S. J. HUMPHREY—continued

4 TASHKANDI (IRE), 8, gr g Polish Precedent (USA)—Tashiriya (IRE) Mrs S. J. Humphrey
5 ZUMRAH (IRE), 7, b g Machiavellian (USA)—The Perfect Life (IRE) Mrs S. J. Humphrey

Assistant Trainer: Mr A. Humphrey

Amateur: Mr Matthew Smith.

---

296 MRS C. J. IKIN, Sutton In The Elms
Postal: Walton Lodge Farm, Sutton In The Elms, Leicestershire, LE9 6RB
Contacts: PHONE (01455) 282321 MOBILE (07850) 278491
E-MAIL nevagree@yahoo.co.uk WEBSITE www.equinespa.co.uk

1 HOLLYWOOD, 7, b m Bin Ajwaad (IRE)—Raaha Mrs C. J. Ikin
2 PARK QUEST (IRE), 10, br g Jolly Jake (NZ)—Ann's Fort Mrs C. J. Ikin
3 SHINJIRU (USA), 8, b g Broad Brush (USA)—Kalwada (USA) Mrs C. J. Ikin

Assistant Trainer: Mr P. J. Ikin.

Amateur: Mr James Hooper.

---

297 MR R. INGRAM, Epsom
Postal: Wendover Stables, Burgh Heath Road, Epsom, Surrey, KT17 4LX
Contacts: PHONE (01372) 748505 or (01372) 749157 MOBILE (0777) 3665980
E-MAIL roger.ingram.racing@virgin.net WEBSITE www.rogeringramracing.com

1 BUXTON, 4, b g Auction House (USA)—Dam Certain (IRE) Mr P. J. Burton
2 DOUBLE VALENTINE, 5, ch m Primo Valentino (IRE)—Charlottevalentina (IRE) Ellangowan Racing Partners
3 LANCASTER'S QUEST, 4, ch g Auction House (USA)—Gabibti (IRE) Mrs E. N. Nield
4 LOVES BIDDING, 4, b g Auction House (USA)—Charlottevalentina (IRE) Ellangowan Racing & Cricketers Club
5 LYSANDER'S QUEST (IRE), 10, br g King's Theatre (IRE)—Haramayda (FR) Mrs E. N. Nield
6 MONDAY SURPRISE, 4, b f Silver Wizard (USA)—Its All Too Much Mr P. Coley
7 NAN JAN, 6, b m Komaite (USA)—Dam Certain (IRE) The Waltons
8 POSTMASTER, 6, b g Dansili—Post Modern (USA) Cricketers Club Racing Group
9 RIDGEWAY STAR, 4, b g Tumbleweed Ridge—Princess Starla Ridgeway Star Partnership
10 WHAXAAR (IRE), 4, b g Xaar—Sheriyna (FR) G. F. Chesneaux

THREE-YEAR-OLDS

11 B f Imperial Ballet (IRE)—Anne-Sophie Roger Ingram Racing Ltd
12 B g Auction House (USA)—Dam Certain (IRE) Roger Ingram Racing Ltd
13 Ch f Tumbleweed Ridge—Its All Too Much Coyne O'Connell, Ploughman
14 KALLIGAL, br f Kyllachy—Anytime Baby Mrs C. E. Hallam
15 LORD'S BIDDING, b c Auction House (USA)—Lady Ploy Cricketers Club Racing Group
16 MAGGIE KATE, b f Auction House (USA)—Perecapa (IRE) Mr T. Tighe

TWO-YEAR-OLDS

17 Ch c 1/1 Auction House (USA)—Charlottevalentina (IRE) (Perugino (USA)) Ellangowen Racing Partners
18 B c 7/4 Auction House (USA)—Figura (Rudimentary (USA)) Mr M. Joy

Other Owners: Cricketers Club Racing Group, Mr R. A. Hooker, Mr E. McCardle, Mr K. H. Walton, Mrs J. R. Walton, Mrs Linda Wright, Mr Adrian Wright.

Assistant Trainer: Sharon Ingram

Amateur: Miss Sarah Sawyer.

---

298 MR D. K. IVORY, Radlett
Postal: Harper Lodge Farm, Harper Lane, Radlett, Hertfordshire, WD7 7HU
Contacts: PHONE (01923) 855337 FAX (01923) 852470 MOBILE (07785) 118658
E-MAIL dean.ivory@virgin.net WEBSITE www.deanivoryracing.co.uk

1 BENS GEORGIE (IRE), 6, ch m Opening Verse (USA)—Peperonata (IRE) Marcoe Electrical
2 BERTOLIVER, 4, b g Bertolini (USA)—Calcavella Mrs M. Shone

MR D. K. IVORY—continued

3 **BIG RALPH**, 5, ch g Mark of Esteem (IRE)—Wish Me Luck (IRE) **R. Barton, G. Molen, T. Exall**
4 **BOBBY ROSE**, 5, b g Sanglamore (USA)—Grown At Rowan **T. G. N. Burrage**
5 **CAMISSA**, 4, b f Averti (IRE)—Ambitious **K. T. Ivory**
6 **FROMSONG (IRE)**, 10, b g Fayruz—Lindas Delight **D. K. Ivory**
7 **GLENDALE**, 7, ch g Opening Verse (USA)—Kayartis **Mrs J. A. Cornwell**
8 **GOOD ARTICLE (IRE)**, 7, b g Definite Article—Good News (IRE) **T. G. N. Burrage**
9 **HEREFORD BOY**, 4, ch g Tomba—Grown At Rowan **T. G. N. Burrage**
10 **JOOLS**, 10, b g Cadeaux Genereux—Madame Crecy (USA) **D. K. Ivory**
11 **MARLYN RIDGE**, 4, b g Tumbleweed Ridge—Kayartis **John G. Smith & Alan D. Pryer**
12 **SAILOR KING (IRE)**, 6, b g King's Best (USA)—Manureva (USA) **Mr J. F. Stocker**
13 **SILVER PRELUDE**, 7, gr g Prince Sabo—Silver Blessings **Mrs M. Shone**
14 **SOVEREIGNTY (JPN)**, 6, b g King's Best (USA)—Calando (USA) **Radlett Racing**

THREE-YEAR-OLDS

15 **A DREAM COME TRUE**, b f Where Or When (IRE)—Katy Ivory (IRE) **D. K. Ivory**
16 **A WISH FOR YOU**, ch f Tumbleweed Ridge—Peperonata (IRE) **Lesley Ivory & Cynthia Smith**
17 **AMICUS**, br f Xaar—Kartuzy (JPN) **Mrs L. A. Ivory**
18 **AMPHIBALUS (IRE)**, gr g Daylami (IRE)—Dramatically (USA) **Mr J. F. Stocker**
19 **BALLYHEALY LADY**, b f Tobougg (IRE)—Amal **Mr J. F. Connolly**
20 **ELLEMUJIE**, b g Mujahid (USA)—Jennelle **Mrs J. A. Cornwell & Mr John G. Smith**
21 **GOOD NEWS TOO**, ch f Tomba—Think It Over **T. G. N. Burrage**
22 **IVORY SILK**, b f Diktat—Ivory's Joy **K. T. Ivory**
23 **KAYSTAR RIDGE**, b c Tumbleweed Ridge—Kayartis **Mrs J A Cornwell & David G Owen**
24 **LANDIKHAYA (IRE)**, ch c Kris Kin (USA)—Montana Lady (IRE) **K. T. Ivory**
25 **REEL MAN**, ch g Reel Buddy—Yanomami (USA) **Radlett Racing**
26 **WHERE'S SUSIE**, ch f Where Or When (IRE)—Linda's Schoolgirl (IRE) **T. G. N. Burrage**

TWO-YEAR-OLDS

27 Ch c 4/2 Primo Valentino (IRE)—Ambitious (Ardkinglass) **D. K. Ivory**
28 Ch f 22/2 Primo Valentino (IRE)—Blue Topaz (IRE) (Bluebird (USA)) **Mr D. J Macham**
29 Br gr f 24/2 One Cool Cat (USA)—Cloridja (Indian Ridge) (11500) **D. K. Ivory**
30 **DAY IN DUBAI**, b f 18/2 Dubai Destination (USA)—Pazzazz (IRE) (Green Desert (USA)) (2200) **K. T. Ivory**
31 **LUJEANIE**, br c 28/2 Lujain (USA)—Ivory's Joy (Tina's Pet) **K. T. Ivory**
32 **MENHIR BAY**, b c 21/3 Sure Blade (USA)—Turkish Delight (Prince Sabo) (5000) **J. A. Khan**
33 B c 30/3 Fraam—Prancing (Prince Sabo) (3500) **Linda Hipkiss**
34 Ch f 15/3 Ishiguru (USA)—Sandblaster (Most Welcome) (2000) **D. K. Ivory**
35 **SURVIVOR'S SONG**, b c 15/3 Falbrav (IRE)—Linda's Schoolgirl (IRE) (Grand Lodge (USA)) **T. G. N. Burrage**

Other Owners: Mrs J. A. Cornwell, Mr M. S. Crilley, Dean Ivory Racing Ltd, Mrs K. Exall, Mrs L. A. Ivory, Mr David G. Owen, Mr A. D. Pryer, Mrs Cynthia Smith, Mr John G. Smith, Mr R. E. Webb.

Assistant Trainer: Chris Scally

Apprentice: James Millman, Jamie Jones.

---

299 **MR S. M. JACOBS, Laugharne**
Postal: Glancorran Farm, Horsepool Road, Laugharne, Carmarthenshire, SA33 4QL
Contacts: PHONE (01994) 427754 MOBILE (07975) 974044

1 **CELTIC STARLIGHT**, 9, gr m Arzanni—Celtic Berry **Mrs C. A. Jacobs**
2 **GLENKILL (IRE)**, 10, b m Beneficial—Parsons Choice (IRE) **Mrs C. A. Jacobs**
3 **TIGGER**, 5, b g Kayf Tara—Time Clash **Mrs C. A. Jacobs**

---

300 **MR L. R. JAMES, Malton**
Postal: Cheesecake Hill Stables, Beverley Road, Norton, Malton, North Yorkshire, YO17 9PJ
Contacts: PHONE (01653) 699466 FAX (01653) 691455 MOBILE (07984) 328821

1 **ASHSTANZA**, 7, gr g Ashkalani (IRE)—Poetry In Motion (IRE) **Mrs J. Pestryy**
2 **ATTACK MINDED**, 7, ch g Timeless Times (USA)—French Ginger **L. R. James Limited**
3 **BELLA MARIE**, 5, b m Kasakov—Onemoretime **Mrs M. Lingwood**
4 6, Ch m Timeless Times (USA)—French Ginger **L. R. James Limited**
5 4, B g Defacto (USA)—French Ginger **L. R. James Limited**
6 **PRE EMINANCE (IRE)**, 7, b g Peintre Celebre (USA)—Sorb Apple (IRE) **C. E. Raine**

MR L. R. JAMES—continued

7 **REVOLVING WORLD (IRE)**, 5, b g Spinning World (USA)—Mannakea (USA) **L. R. James Limited**
8 **SHE WHO DARES WINS**, 8, b m Atraf—Mirani (IRE) **L. R. James Limited**
9 **TIOGA GOLD (IRE)**, 9, b g Goldmark (USA)—Coffee Bean **L. R. James Limited**
10 **TOFTA TILLY**, 8, ch m Muhtarram (USA)—Budding Prospect **L. R. James Limited**

THREE-YEAR-OLDS

11 B f Sugarfoot—Giffoine **L. R. James Limited**

Assistant Trainer: Carol James

Amateur: Mr K. James.

---

301 MR A. P. JARVIS, Twyford

Postal: **Twyford Mill, Mill Lane, Twyford, Buckinghamshire, MK18 4HA**
Contacts: **PHONE (01296) 730707 FAX (01296) 733572 MOBILE (07770) 785551**
E-MAIL alan@alanjarvis.co.uk WEBSITE www.alanjarvis.co.uk

1 **AWATUKI (IRE)**, 5, b g Distant Music (USA)—Itkan (IRE) **A. B. Pope**
2 **BED FELLOW (IRE)**, 4, b g Trans Island—Moonlight Partner (IRE) **Geoffrey Bishop & Ann Jarvis**
3 **CROSS THE LINE (IRE)**, 6, b g Cape Cross (IRE)—Baalbek **Eurostrait Ltd**
4 **FOLLOW ON**, 6, b h Barathea (IRE)—Handora (IRE) **Morton Bamford Bishop & Jarvis Partners**
5 **GLEAMING SPIRIT (IRE)**, 4, b g Mujadil (USA)—Gleam **Geoffrey Bishop & Ann Jarvis**
6 **LOVE ON SIGHT**, 4, b f Beat Hollow—Greek Dream (USA) **Mrs Ann Jarvis**
7 **OUR BLESSING (IRE)**, 4, b g Lujain—Berenice (ITY) **Geoffrey Bishop & Ann Jarvis**
8 **SMART CAT (IRE)**, 5, ch m Barathea (IRE)—Lioness **Jarvis Associates**
9 **SPRING GODDESS (IRE)**, 7, b m Daggers Drawn (USA)—Easter Girl **Grant & Bowman Limited**
10 **SWEET WORLD**, 4, b g Agnes World (USA)—Douce Maison (IRE) **Geoffrey Bishop & Ann Jarvis**
11 **SWIFT CUT (IRE)**, 4, ch g Daggers Drawn (USA)—Jugendliebe (IRE) **Geoffrey Bishop & Ann Jarvis**
12 **TAKE TO THE SKIES (IRE)**, 4, b c Lujain—To The Skies (USA) **Geoffrey Bishop & Ann Jarvis**
13 **TITLE DEED (USA)**, 4, b g Belong To Me (USA)—Said Privately (USA) **Geoffrey Bishop & Ann Jarvis**
14 **TRANS SONIC**, 5, ch g Trans Island—Sankaty Light (USA) **Eurostrait Ltd**
15 **UP THE CHIMNEY**, 4, gr g Kyllachy—Simply Sooty **Geoffrey Bishop & Ann Jarvis**
16 **WISE DENNIS**, 6, b g Polar Falcon (USA)—Bowden Rose **Allen B. Pope, Andrew J. King**

THREE-YEAR-OLDS

17 B g Captain Rio—Amoras (IRE) **Mrs Ann Jarvis**
18 **EMPERORS JADE**, b c Averti (IRE)—Bliss (IRE) **Eurostrait Ltd**
19 **IRISH MUSIC (IRE)**, b c Namid—Kelly's Tune **Mrs Ann Jarvis**
20 **LADY SORCERER**, b f Diktat—Silk Law (IRE) **The Aston Partnership**
21 **RICH HARVEST (USA)**, b br c High Yield (USA)—Mangano (USA) **Eurostrait Ltd**
22 **RIVER BOUNTY**, b f Bahamian Bounty—Artistic Merit **Mrs Ann Jarvis**
23 **RIVER GLEAM (IRE)**, b f Trans Island—Gleam **Graeme Renton Partnership**
24 **SUE'S HAWK (IRE)**, ch f Hawk Wing (USA)—Desert Blues (IRE) **A. L. R. Morton**
25 **SUN IN SPLENDOUR (USA)**, ch c Hold That Tiger (USA)—Fit To Win (USA) **Eurostrait Ltd**

TWO-YEAR-OLDS

26 Ch f 28/1 Exceed And Excel (AUS)—Amount (Salse (USA)) (16086) **Mrs Ann Jarvis**
27 B f 22/4 Belong To Me (USA)—Bingo Meeting (USA) (General Meeting (USA)) (19304)
28 B f 5/5 Lujain (USA)—Blushing Belle (Local Suitor (USA)) **C. H. Shankland**
29 B f 24/3 Lujain (USA)—Bon Marche (Definite Article) **C. H. Shankland**
30 B f 3/3 Desert Style (USA)—Charlene Lacy (IRE) (Pips Pride) (5147)
31 Ch c 3/5 Where Or When (IRE)—Chelsea (USA) (Miswaki (USA)) (5000)
32 B f 25/4 Refuse To Bend (IRE)—Deadly Buzz (IRE) (Darshaan) (17374)
33 Br c 6/2 Statue of Liberty (USA)—For Freedom (IRE) (King of Kings (IRE)) (11582)
34 B c 3/4 King's Best (USA)—Full Cream (USA) (Hennessy (USA)) (28957) **Mrs Ann Jarvis**
35 **HIGHLAND MAGIC (IRE)**, ch c 29/1 Rainbow Quest (USA)—
Adultress (IRE) (Ela-Mana-Mou) (22521) **Mr P. Milburn**
36 B f 1/3 Hawk Wing (USA)—Kissin A Lot (USA) (Kissin Kris (USA)) (7500)
37 Ch c 13/5 Spinning World (USA)—Mad Annie (USA) (Anabaa (USA)) **Mrs Ann Jarvis**
38 B c 17/3 Fasliyev—Monalee Lass (IRE) (Mujtahid (USA)) (11000)
39 B f 17/4 Acclamation—Nice Spice (IRE) (Common Grounds) (10295)
40 Ch f 20/3 Deportivo—Prowse (USA) (King of Kings (IRE)) (20000)
41 B c 10/4 Dixie Union (USA)—Redeem (USA) (Devil's Bag (USA)) (32174)

MR A. P. JARVIS—continued

42 B f 9/2 Aptitude (USA)—Second Wind (USA) (Hennessy (USA)) (28957)
43 B c 7/5 Trans Island—Spinsky (USA) (Spinning World (USA)) (6434)
44 Ch f 27/4 Fath (USA)—Xania (Mujtahid (USA)) (5000)

Other Owners: Mr G. S. Bishop, A. P Jarvis, A. J. King, G. Renton.

Assistant Trainer: M A Jarvis, S E Simmons

Jockey (flat): Seb Sanders, Jamie Spencer, Neil Pollard.

---

302 MR M. A. JARVIS, Newmarket
Postal: **Kremlin House Stables, Fordham Road, Newmarket, Suffolk, CB8 7AQ**
Contacts: **OFFICE** (01638) 661702 **HOME** (01638) 662519 **FAX** (01638) 667018
MOBILE (07836) 649280 **E-MAIL** majarvis@hotmail.com

1 BLACK ROCK (IRE), 4, ch c Rock of Gibraltar (IRE)—Biraya **A. D. Spence**
2 BUKIT TINGGI (IRE), 4, b g Peintre Celebre (USA)—Puteri Wentworth **H.R.H. Sultan Ahmad Shah**
3 DAWN SKY, 4, b c Fantastic Light (USA)—Zacheta **S. Ali**
4 DICHOH, 5, b g Diktat—Hoh Dancer **T. G. Warner**
5 FRAGRANCY (IRE), 4, ch f Singspiel (IRE)—Zibet **M. Al Nabouda**
6 HANNICEAN, 4, ch c Medicean—Hannah's Music **Magno-Pulse Ltd**
7 IRISH QUEST (IRE), 4, b c Galileo (IRE)—No Quest (IRE) **A. D. Spence**
8 MILLVILLE, 8, ch g Millkom—Miss Top Ville (FR) **T. G. Warner**
9 PHILATELIST (USA), 4, b c Rahy (USA)—Polent **G. A. Tanaka**
10 PRESSING (IRE), 5, b br h Soviet Star (USA)—Rafif (USA) **G. A. Tanaka**
11 PRINCE FOREVER (IRE), 4, b c Giant's Causeway (USA)—Routilante (IRE) **H.R.H. Sultan Ahmad Shah**
12 ROSE STREET (IRE), 4, b f Noverre (USA)—Archipova (IRE) **Mr & Mrs Raymond Anderson Green**
13 ROYAL AND REGAL (IRE), 4, b c Sadler's Wells (USA)—Smart 'n Noble (USA) **P. D. Savill**
14 RUSSIAN EPIC, 4, b g Diktat—Russian Rhapsody **Magno-Pulse Ltd**
15 ST ANDREWS (IRE), 8, b g Celtic Swing—Viola Royale (IRE) **M. A. Jarvis**
16 WE'LL COME, 4, b g Elnadim (USA)—Off The Blocks **S. Dartnell**

THREE-YEAR-OLDS

17 AL COBRA (IRE), b f Sadler's Wells (USA)—Marienbad (FR) **S. Ali**
18 ALBAROUCHE, b f Sadler's Wells (USA)—Alakananda **Mrs Barbara Facchino**
19 ALL THE ACES (IRE), b c Spartacus (IRE)—Lili Cup (FR) **A. D. Spence**
20 ALMOUTEZAH (USA), b f Storm Cat (USA)—Probable Colony (USA) **Hamdan Al Maktoum**
21 ALMUSHKHAS (USA), b c Rahy (USA)—Elrafa Ah (USA) **Hamdan Al Maktoum**
22 AMERIGO (IRE), gr g Daylami (IRE)—Geminiani (IRE) **B. E. Nielsen**
23 ANCIEN REGIME (IRE), b c King's Best (USA)—Sadalsud (IRE) **Sheikh Ahmed Al Maktoum**
24 ARMURE, gr f Dalakhani (IRE)—Bombazine (IRE) **Sarah J. Leigh & Robin S. Leigh**
25 BANDERAZ, b g Hernando (FR)—Language of Love **Mrs P. Good**
26 BEFORTYFOUR, b g Kyllachy—Ivania **M. Bailey**
27 BOLD CHOICE (IRE), b c Dubai Destination (USA)—Sheer Spirit (IRE) **B. E. Nielsen**
28 BRAVE HAWK, b c Hawk Wing (USA)—Triomphale **Mr & Mrs K Watts & Mr & Mrs S Bamber**
29 CAPE EXPRESS (IRE), b c Cape Cross (IRE)—Lilissa (IRE) **A. D. Spence**
30 CARIBANA, ch f Hernando (FR)—Carenage (IRE) **Miss K. Rausing**
31 COOL JUDGEMENT (IRE), b c Peintre Celebre (USA)—Sadinga (IRE) **H.R.H. Sultan Ahmad Shah**
32 DARK PROSPECT, b c Nayef (USA)—Miss Mirasol **Mr T. G. & Mrs M. E. Holdcroft**
33 DIXEY, br f Diktat—Hoh Dancer **T. G. Warner**
34 EBN MALK (IRE), ch c King's Best (USA)—Auntie Maureen (IRE) **Sheikh Ahmed Al Maktoum**
35 ELYSEE PALACE (IRE), b f King's Best (USA)—Noble Rose (IRE) **Sheikh Ahmed Al Maktoum**
36 ETERNAL LUCK (IRE), b g Tagula (IRE)—Erne Project (IRE) **H.R.H. Sultan Ahmad Shah**
37 FIRST AVENUE, b c Montjeu (IRE)—Marciala (USA) **M. Tabor**
38 FRAAEDD (USA), b c Empire Maker (USA)—Agama (USA) **Sheikh Ahmed Al Maktoum**
39 GHAIDAA (IRE), b f Cape Cross (IRE)—Midway Lady (USA) **Hamdan Al Maktoum**
40 GRAND STRATEGY (IRE), b br c Singspiel (IRE)—Game Plan **Sheikh Ahmed Al Maktoum**
41 INCHWOOD (IRE), b f Dubai Destination (USA)—Inchiri **Sheikh Ahmed Al Maktoum**
42 ISLAND VISTA, b f Montjeu (IRE)—Colorvista **Helena Springfield Ltd**
43 KAL BARG, b c Medicean—Persian Air **Sheikh Ahmed Al Maktoum**
44 KEY NEWS (IRE), br f Halling (USA)—Belle Argentine (FR) **Sheikh Ahmed Al Maktoum**
45 KHATEEB (IRE), b c King's Best (USA)—Choc Ice (IRE) **Hamdan Al Maktoum**
46 KING OLAV (UAE), ch c Halling (USA)—Karamzin (USA) **Sheikh Ahmed Al Maktoum**
47 LAA BAAS (IRE), b f Green Desert (USA)—Baaderah (IRE) **Sheikh Ahmed Al Maktoum**

MR M. A. JARVIS—continued

48 LAZEYMA, b f Fantastic Light (USA)—Zahrat Dubai **Sheikh Ahmed Al Maktoum**
49 MAADRAA (IRE), br c Josr Algarhoud (IRE)—Del Deya (IRE) **Sheikh Ahmed Al Maktoum**
50 MAGISTRATE (IRE), b gr c Nayef (USA)—Alabastrine **Highclere Thoroughbred Racing(Petrushka)**
51 MAKAASEB (USA), b f Pulpit (USA)—Turn and Sparkle **Hamdan Al Maktoum**
52 MARAASED, b c Alhaarth (IRE)—Fleeting Rainbow **Hamdan Al Maktoum**
53 MASLAHA, b f Selkirk (USA)—Mingora (USA) **Sheikh Ahmed Al Maktoum**
54 MESHTRI (IRE), ch c Dalakhani (IRE)—Arctic Hunt (IRE) **Sheikh Ahmed Al Maktoum**
55 MISS JOLYON (USA), b f Johannesburg (USA)—Konvincha (USA) **A. A. Lyons**
56 MONAADI (IRE), b c Singspiel (IRE)—Bint Albaadiya (USA) **Sheikh Ahmed Al Maktoum**
57 MUSHTAAQ (USA), b c Dynaformer (USA)—Siyadah (USA) **Hamdan Al Maktoum**
58 NASTJIR, b c Nayef (USA)—Success Story **Sheikh Ahmed Al Maktoum**
59 OTAARED, b br c Storm Cat (USA)—Society Lady (USA) **Sheikh Ahmed Al Maktoum**
60 PACIFISM (UAE), ch g Halling (USA)—African Peace (USA) **Hamdan Al Maktoum**
61 PERSIAN SEA (UAE), b f Dubai Destination (USA)—Polska (USA) **Sheikh Ahmed Al Maktoum**
62 RED DUNE (IRE), b f Red Ransom (USA)—Desert Beauty (IRE) **Sheikh Ahmed Al Maktoum**
63 REEFALJAMAL (USA), b br f Dixieland Band (USA)—Hasnaael Reef (USA) **Hamdan Al Maktoum**
64 ROBAABB (IRE), b f Dubai Destination (USA)—Brocatelle **Sheikh Ahmed Al Maktoum**
65 ROCK QUEEN (IRE), b f Rock of Gibraltar (IRE)—Biraya **A. D. Spence**
66 ROYALIST (IRE), b c King's Best (USA)—Nebraas **Sheikh Ahmed Al Maktoum**
67 SHEER ELEGANCE (IRE), b f Pivotal—Shabby Chic (USA) **P. D. Savill**
68 SKI SUNDAY, b c King's Best (USA)—Lille Hammer **Sheikh Ahmed Al Maktoum**
69 SORTITA (GER), b c Monsun (GER)—Sacarina **Hamdan Al Maktoum**
70 SPEEDY DOLLAR (USA), b c Dixie Union (USA)—Kelli's Ransom (USA) **S. Dartnell**
71 SRI PUTRA (IRE), b c Invincible Spirit (IRE)—You Rang Here (USA) **H.R.H. Sultan Ahmad Shah**
72 SUMMERSTRAND (IRE), b f Cape Cross (IRE)—Flamelet (USA) **Sheikh Ahmed Al Maktoum**
73 TASDEER (USA), b c Rahy (USA)—Mehthaaf (USA) **Hamdan Al Maktoum**
74 TATBEEQ (IRE), b f Invincible Spirit (USA)—Announcing Peace **Hamdan Al Maktoum**
75 TAWAASH (USA), b br c Storm Cat (USA)—Victory Ride (USA) **Hamdan Al Maktoum**
76 TIGHNABRUAICH (IRE), b c Rainbow Quest (USA)—Miss Mistletoes (IRE) **T. Barr**
77 TORPHICHEN, ch c Alhaarth (IRE)—Genoa **T. Barr**
78 TWO PASS (IRE), b f Mtoto—Pass The Peace **Sheikh Ahmed Al Maktoum**
79 WHERRY (USA), b f Cherokee Run (USA)—Whist **Sheikh Ahmed Al Maktoum**
80 YADDREE, ch c Singspiel (IRE)—Jathaabeh **Sheikh Ahmed Al Maktoum**

TWO-YEAR-OLDS

81 AAKEF (IRE), b c 31/1 Exceed And Excel (AUS)—Bush Baby (Zamindar (USA)) (210000) **Hamdan Al Maktoum**
82 Ch c 11/3 Rahy (USA)—Al Theraab (USA) (Roberto (USA)) (242954) **B. E. Nielsen**
83 ALAFOOR (FR), gr c 19/2 Linamix (FR)—
           Green Delight (IRE) (Green Desert (USA)) (193050) **Hamdan Al Maktoum**
84 ALAINMAAR (FR), b c 6/5 Johar (USA)—
           Lady Elgar (IRE) (Sadler's Wells (USA)) (154440) **Hamdan Al Maktoum**
85 ALAZEYAB (USA), b c 2/3 El Prado (IRE)—Itnab (Green Desert (USA)) **Hamdan Al Maktoum**
86 ALL GUNS FIRING (IRE), b c 17/4 High Chaparral (IRE)—
           Lili Cup (FR) (Fabulous Dancer (USA)) (77220) **A. D. Spence**
87 ALMIQDAAD, b c 1/2 Haafhd—Etizaaz (USA) (Diesis) **Hamdan Al Maktoum**
88 AMSAAR, b br c 5/2 Kyllachy—Selkirk Rose (USA) (Pips Pride) (150000) **Hamdan Al Maktoum**
89 BENMALK (IRE), b c 8/3 King's Best (USA)—Arhaaft (IRE) (Danehill (USA)) (55000) **Sheikh Ahmed Al Maktoum**
90 BERAIMI (IRE), b c 18/4 Alhaarth (IRE)—Akrmina (Zafonic (USA)) **Sheikh Ahmed Al Maktoum**
91 B f 6/3 Red Ransom (USA)—Beraysim (Lion Cavern (USA)) **Sheikh Ahmed Al Maktoum**
92 Ch c 21/5 Monsun (GER)—Calypso Grant (IRE) (Danehill (USA)) (80437) **Thurloe Thoroughbreds XXII**
93 CARTOON, br f 27/3 Danehill Dancer (IRE)—
           Elfin Laughter (Alzao (USA)) (110000) **Highclere Thoroughbred Racing-SunChariot**
94 CUT AND THRUST (IRE), b c 6/4 Haafhd—Ego (Green Desert (USA)) (85000) **A. D. Spence**
95 B f 9/3 Acclamation—Danish Pan (IRE) (Danehill (USA)) (38610) **Hamdan Al Maktoum**
96 B f 25/2 Alhaarth (IRE)—Dayville (USA) (Dayjur (USA)) (42000) **M. A. Jarvis**
97 Ch c 20/2 Kyllachy—Duena (Grand Lodge (USA)) (40000) **Barnett, Manasseh & Partners**
98 EBIAYN (IRE), b c 16/2 Monsun (GER)—Drei (USA) (Lyphard (USA)) **Hamdan Al Maktoum**
99 Br f 22/3 Johannesburg (USA)—Grable (USA) (Sadler's Wells (USA)) (148004) **Mrs C. C. Regalado-Gonzalez**
100 B f 20/1 Acclamation—Green Life (Green Desert (USA)) (90000) **S. Dartnell**
101 HARRY PATCH, b c 18/3 Lujain (USA)—Hoh Dancer (Indian Ridge) (6500) **Mrs G. A. S. Jarvis**
102 HAWDAJ, b f 4/3 Nayef (USA)—Najayeb (USA) (Silver Hawk (USA)) **Hamdan Al Maktoum**
103 HAZAYNA, b f 27/3 Barathea (IRE)—Hazaradjat (IRE) (Darshaan) (280000) **Lordship Stud**
104 JABROOT (IRE), ch f 26/5 Alhaarth (IRE)—Walesiana (IRE) (Star Appeal) **Sheikh Ahmed Al Maktoum**
105 B c 18/3 Dubai Destination (USA)—Jalousie (IRE) (Barathea (IRE)) (55000) **Mr D. A. Yardy**
106 KAMMAAN, b f 6/2 Diktat—Qasirah (IRE) (Machiavellian (USA)) **Sheikh Ahmed Al Maktoum**

MR M. A. JARVIS—continued

107 B c 27/4 Refuse To Bend (IRE)—Kardashina (FR) (Darshaan) (128700) **A. D. Spence**
108 B c 26/4 Galileo (IRE)—Kite Mark (Mark of Esteem (IRE)) (270000) **T. Barr**
109 **LAAHEB,** b c 25/2 Cape Cross (IRE)—Maskunah (IRE) (Sadler's Wells (USA)) (200000) **Hamdan Al Maktoum**
110 **LACROSSE,** b c 31/3 Cape Cross (IRE)—La Sky (IRE) (Law Society (USA)) (150000) **Lordship Stud**
111 **LADY OF INTRIGUE (IRE),** b f 8/1 Sadler's Wells (USA)—
                           Dedicated Lady (Pennine Walk) (540000) **Merry Fox Stud Limited**
112 B c 2/2 Tobougg (IRE)—Margaret's Gift (Beveled (USA)) (85000) **T. Barr**
113 **MYSHKIN,** b c 14/2 Refuse To Bend (IRE)—
                         Marmaga (IRE) (Shernazar) (62000) **D Spratt, M Rutherford & A Wilson**
114 **OSTAADI,** b c 17/2 Nayef (USA)—Blodwen (USA) (Mister Baileys) (280000) **Sheikh Ahmed Al Maktoum**
115 B c 7/4 Oasis Dream—Royal Passion (Ahonoora) **Mrs P. Good**
116 **RUSSIAN JAR (IRE),** b c 22/2 Xaar—Lady Windermere (IRE) (Lake Coniston (IRE)) (80000) **J A R Partnership**
117 **SAIFAAN,** b c 14/5 Needwood Blade—Gagajulu (Al Hareb (USA)) (85000) **Sheikh Ahmed Al Maktoum**
118 **SANA ABEL (IRE),** b f 22/5 Alhaarth (IRE)—Midway Lady (USA) (Alleged (USA)) **Hamdan Al Maktoum**
119 Ch c 10/2 Lomitas—Seyooll (IRE) (Danehill) (USA) **Sheikh Ahmed Al Maktoum**
120 **SHEMOLI,** ch c 22/2 Singspiel (IRE)—Felawnah (USA) (Mr Prospector (USA)) **Sheikh Ahmed Al Maktoum**
121 B c 7/5 Danehill Dancer (IRE)—Veronica Cooper (IRE) (Kahyasi) (135134) **H.R.H. Sultan Ahmad Shah**
122 B c 6/2 Tale of the Cat (USA)—
                         Vole Vole Monamour (USA) (Woodman) (USA) (72886) **H.R.H. Sultan Ahmad Shah**
123 **WARDATI,** ch f 21/3 Sulamani (IRE)—Jathaabeh (Nashwan (USA)) **Sheikh Ahmed Al Maktoum**
124 B c 19/3 Oasis Dream—Wendylina (IRE) (In The Wings) (240000) **H.R.H. Sultan Ahmad Shah**

Other Owners: Mr K. Allen, Mr S. P. Bamber, Mrs E. Bamber, Mr J. Barnett, Mr A. Cole, Mrs H. S. Ellingsen, R. A. Green, Mrs A. Green, T. F. Harris, Mrs E. A. Harris, Mrs L. B. Hart, The Hon H. M. Herbert, Highclere Thoroughbred Racing Ltd, Mr L. King, Miss S. J. E. Leigh, R. S. Leigh, Mr D. C. Manasseh, O. J. W. Pawle, Mrs E. E. Roseby, Mr M. A. Rutherford, Mr D. T. Spratt, Mrs N. H. Stafford, Mr K. Watts, Mrs P. M. L. Watts, M. Weinfeld, Mr A. Wilson.

Assistant Trainer: Roger Varian

Jockey (flat): P. Robinson, N. Callan. **Apprentice:** M. Guest.

---

303   **MR W. JARVIS, Newmarket**
Postal: **Phantom House Stables, Fordham Road, Newmarket, Suffolk, CB8 7AA**
Contacts: **OFFICE** (01638) 669873 **HOME** (01638) 662677 **FAX** (01638) 667328
E-MAIL mail@williamjarvis.com WEBSITE www.williamjarvis.com

1 **DISPATCH BOX,** 4, b c Dansili—Division Bell **Canisbay Bloodstock**
2 **INSTANTLY (IRE),** 4, b f Dansili—Wigging **The Bigmore Partnership**
3 **JUST TWO NUMBERS,** 4, b g Bahamian Bounty—Khadino **Camsey, Folan, Lees & Heath**
4 **KILLENA BOY (IRE),** 6, b g Imperial Ballet (IRE)—Habaza **Capel (CS) Ltd**
5 **LATANAZUL,** 4, b f Sakhee (USA)—Karamah **G. B. Turnbull Ltd**
6 **MATARAM (USA),** 5, b g Matty G (USA)—Kalinka (USA) **Sales Race 2001 Syndicate**
7 **MUMBLESWERVE (IRE),** 4, b c City On A Hill (USA)—Dolcezza (FR) **The XPY Partnership**
8 **NATURAL ACTION,** 4, b g Diktat—Naskhi **H. J. W. Steckmest & Partners**
9 **OI VAY JOE (IRE),** 4, b g Namid—Nuit des Temps **The Oi Vay Joe Partnership**
10 **ROLLIN 'N TUMBLIN,** 4, ch c Zaha (CAN)—Steppin Out **Canisbay Bloodstock**
11 **SHOGUN PRINCE (IRE),** 5, b g Shinko Forest (IRE)—Lady of Dreams (IRE) **M. C. Banks**
12 **SPICE GARDENS,** 4, ch f Indian Ridge—Lime Gardens **Mrs S. J. Davis**
13 **TROUBADOUR (IRE),** 7, b g Danehill (USA)—Taking Liberties (IRE) **Dr J. Walker**

THREE-YEAR-OLDS

14 **ADMIRAL DUNDAS (IRE),** b c Noverre (USA)—Brandish **Dr J. Walker**
15 B g Desert Prince (IRE)—Blushing Gleam **G. Middlebrook**
16 **BRAVE MAVE,** gr f Daylami (IRE)—Baalbek **J. W. Munroe Construction Ltd**
17 **BRUNTON BLUE,** b f Compton Place—Persian Blue **G. S. Shropshire**
18 **COLORADO SPRINGS,** b f Olden Times—Engulfed (USA) **Mr T. M. Hedin**
19 **EL DUENDE (USA),** b br c Elusive Quality (USA)—Brianda (USA) **A. Foster**
20 **GRAVITATION,** b f Galileo (IRE)—Guaranda **Lady G. De Walden**
21 **HIDDEN DOOR (IRE),** b f Montjeu (IRE)—Yaselda **Mr H. Q. Spooner**
22 **JUST SORT IT,** b g Averti (IRE)—Lady Kris (IRE) **Mr R. J. Harriss**
23 **KING OF DUBAI (IRE),** b g Dubai Destination (USA)—Pearl Barley (IRE) **The King Of Dubai Partnership**
24 **LONGEVITY,** b c Olden Times—Gevity **Lady G. De Walden**
25 **MEGA WATT (IRE),** b c Acclamation—Kilshanny **The Mega Watt Partnership**
26 **MEXICAN VENTURE,** b c Tobougg (IRE)—Nacho Venture (FR) **The Mexican Venture Partnership**

MR W. JARVIS—continued

27 **MOON SISTER (IRE)**, b f Cadeaux Genereux—Tanz (IRE) **A. S. Belhab**
28 **NEVER ENDING TALE**, ch c Singspiel (IRE)—Bright Finish (USA) **A. Saeed**
29 **NOTEPAD**, b f King's Best (USA)—Petite Epaulette **J. A. Reed**
30 **PEREZ PRADO (USA)**, b c Kingmambo (USA)—Marisa (USA) **A. Foster**
31 **PHANTOM FLYER**, b c Royal Applause—Australian Dreams **S. C. B. Limited**
32 **SCARLET JUNE**, b f Mujahid (USA)—Scarlet Veil **Mr P. J. McCalmont**
33 **SILVER DIAMOND**, b f Josr Algarhoud (IRE)—Silvermour **Harca Race Horses**
34 **SPIDER SILK**, b g Lomitas—Silken Brief (IRE) **J. Kelsey-Fry**
35 **TEAGAN (IRE)**, b c Dubai Destination (USA)—Tegwen (USA) **A. S. Belhab**
36 **TO BE OR NOT TO BE**, b f Tobougg (IRE)—Lady Mayor **J. M. Greetham**
37 **TRIMONTIUM WAY (IRE)**, b c Spectrum (IRE)—Kilbarchan **Dr J. Walker**

TWO-YEAR-OLDS

38 **AGE OF COUTURE**, ch f 18/3 Hold That Tiger (USA)—
Three Wishes (Sadler's Wells (USA)) (50000) **D. F. O'Rourke**
39 **ARCHIE RICE (USA)**, b c 8/3 Arch (USA)—Gold Bowl (USA) (Seeking The Gold (USA)) (55879) **A. Foster**
40 **CLERK'S CHOICE (IRE)**, b c 19/3 Bachelor Duke (USA)—
Credit Crunch (IRE) (Caerleon (USA)) (18000) **M. C. Banks**
41 **DANCE CLUB (IRE)**, b f 1/3 Fasliyev (USA)—Two Clubs (First Trump) (75000) **Dr John Fike**
42 B c 8/4 Mark of Esteem (IRE)—Engulfed (USA) (Gulch (USA)) **Mr T. M. Hedin**
43 Ch f 23/2 Hawk Wing (USA)—Grecian Glory (IRE) (Zafonic (USA)) (32174) **Mr Paul Shanahan**
44 B c 8/5 Danehill Dancer (IRE)—Kingsridge (IRE) (King's Theatre (IRE)) (38000)
45 B f 21/3 Tobougg (IRE)—Miss Arizona (IRE) (Sure Blade (USA)) (6000)
46 **MONACO DREAM (IRE)**, b f 1/2 Hawk Wing (USA)—
Parvenue (FR) (Ezzoud (IRE)) (51480) **Monaco Dream Partnership**
47 **PAPYRIAN**, b c 8/3 Oasis Dream—La Papagena (Habitat) **Lady G. De Walden**
48 **PRIVATE EQUITY (IRE)**, b f 28/4 Haafhd—Profit Alert (IRE) (Alzao (USA)) (30000) **Mrs S. J. Davis**
49 **ROYAL WILLY (IRE)**, b c 2/5 Val Royal (FR)—Neat Dish (CAN) (Stalwart (USA)) (50000)
50 **SMOKEY STORM**, b br c 19/2 One Cool Cat (USA)—Marisa (GER) (Desert Sun) (22000) **The BK Partnership**
51 **THE MUMBO**, b f 27/2 Bahamian Bounty—Mandolin (IRE) (Sabrehill (USA)) (11000) **Peter & Willie Robertson**
52 B f 8/2 Tiger Hill (IRE)—Wellspring (IRE) (Caerleon (USA)) (30000) **A Partnership**
53 **WEST KIRK**, b c 21/2 Alhaarth (IRE)—Naughty Crown (USA) (Chief's Crown (USA)) (67000) **Dr J. Walker**

Other Owners: Matthew Bassett, Miss Natalie Beckitt, Steve Bennett, A. Besgin-McCarthy, Mr J. P. Bigmore, Mrs Holly Bigmore, Mr James Bowditch, A. Briam, Mr J. Camsey, Kevin Cohen, Pete Czernin, Neil Davey, Nigel Dawes, John Dowman, Stephen Duckworth, J. R. B. George, Keith Goodwin, Steve Graham, Peter Gram, Eigil Grimstueat, Mr A. C. Grundy, Mr G. J. Harca, Mr J. Harca, Robert Hawkins, Mr D. Heath, Barry Hogg, Mr R. F. Kilby, Bob King, Mr R. I. H. Lees, P. H. Marsh, Henry Marsh, Tim Marshall, Kevin McDermott, Richard McDonnell, Mike Menard, Mr David Murrell, Mr Mick Narcross, Mr D. Nicholls, Paul O'Meara, Michael Orr, Michael Payton, Mr A. A. Polydor, Jamie Pullen, Mrs J. R. Ramsden, Mr E. Randall, Ian Robertson, Mr Nicholas Ruddell, Tim Santry, Mr Phil Spencer, Mr H. Steckmest, Miss Maureen Stopher, Mr Chris Summers, Dominic Vail, Mr Tony Verrier, Mr Jim Wilkes, Mr Mark Yexley.

Assistant Trainer: Mrs J Cecil

Jockey (flat): Alan Munro.

---

304 MR J. M. JEFFERSON, Malton
Postal: **Newstead Cottage Stables, Norton, Malton, North Yorkshire, YO17 9PJ**
Contacts: **PHONE (01653) 697225 FAX (01653) 697225 MOBILE (07710) 502044**
E-MAIL newsteadracing@btconnect.com

1 **ACCORDING TO PETE**, 7, b g Accordion—Magic Bloom **P. Nelson**
2 4, B gr g Kayf Tara—Altogether Now (IRE) **M. K. Lee**
3 **ANNIE'S GIFT (IRE)**, 4, br f Presenting—Magic Bloom **P. Nelson**
4 **ANOTHER JAMESON (IRE)**, 8, b m Good Thyne (USA)—
Another Grouse **Mrs K. S. Gaffney & Mrs Alix Stevenson**
5 **BALLURE BAY (IRE)**, 6, b g Presenting—Cadisa **T. J. Hemmings**
6 **BRECKS LANE**, 4, b g Kayf Tara—Magic Bloom **P. Nelson**
7 **BROOKLYN BROWNIE (IRE)**, 9, b g Presenting—In The Brownies (IRE) **P. Gaffney & J. N. Stevenson**
8 **CADOUDALAS (FR)**, 5, b g Cadoudal (FR)—Popie D'ecorcei (FR) **T. J. Hemmings**
9 **CALATAGAN (FR)**, 9, ch g Danzig Connection (USA)—Calachuchi **Mr & Mrs J. M. Davenport**
10 **CAPE TRIBULATION**, 4, b g Hernando (FR)—Gay Fantastic **J. D. Abell**
11 **CLASSIC CAPERS**, 9, ch g Classic Cliche (IRE)—Jobiska **R. Collins**
12 **CUMBRIAN KNIGHT (IRE)**, 10, b g Presenting—Crashrun **J. M. Jefferson**

MR J. M. JEFFERSON—continued

13 **DAD'S ARMY (IRE)**, 7, b g Saddlers' Hall (IRE)—Corston Dancer (IRE) **A. S. Lyburn**
14 **DOUBLE ELLS**, 6, b m Yaheeb (USA)—Knayton Lass **Mr & Mrs J. M. Davenport**
15 **ELVIS RETURNS**, 10, b g Alhaatmi—Buckmist Blue (IRE) **J. M. Cleeve**
16 **GREAT GRIMSBY (IRE)**, 6, b g Presenting—Proud Polly **J. W. Hardy**
17 **I'LL DO IT TODAY**, 7, b g Mtoto—Knayton Lass **Mr & Mrs J. M. Davenport**
18 **INSPECTOR FROST**, 5, gr g Terimon—Den Is Over (IRE) **Mrs T. H. Barclay/Mrs F. D. McInnes Skinner**
19 **ISSAQUAH (IRE)**, 6, b m Supreme Leader—Our Sioux (IRE) **Mr & Mrs J. M. Davenport**
20 **JUSTTHEONEFORYOU**, 6, ch g Classic Cliche (IRE)—Cerise Bleue (FR) **Mrs M. E. Dixon**
21 **LORD LARSSON**, 5, b g Kayf Tara—Shuildante (IRE) **Mrs K. S. Gaffney & Mrs Alix Stevenson**
22 **MASSAPOAG (IRE)**, 5, b g Bob Back (USA)—Mondeo Rose (IRE) **Dean Bostock & Raymond Bostock**
23 **MCMURROUGH (IRE)**, 4, b c Spectrum (IRE)—Sensitive (IRE) **M. K. Lee**
24 **MISS VIVACIOUS**, 4, b f Robertico—Anabranch **K. Lee & L. M. Rutherford**
25 **MY BOBBY**, 5, b g Supreme Sound—Derwent River **Miss H. Wilson**
26 5, B g Saddlers' Hall (IRE)—Nanavits (IRE) **J. M. Jefferson**
27 **OSCAR THE BOXER (IRE)**, 9, b g Oscar (IRE)—Here She Comes **Boundary Garage (Bury) Limited**
28 **OUR SEB (IRE)**, 6, b g Supreme Leader—Ramble Along (IRE) **T. J. Hemmings**
29 **OVERBRANCH**, 5, b br m Overbury (IRE)—Anabranch **Mrs M. Barker**
30 **PISCATAQUA**, 6, b g Kayf Tara—Flitcham **Dean Bostock & Raymond Bostock**
31 **POKANOKET (IRE)**, 5, b m Accordion—Our Sioux (IRE) **Mrs M. J. Hales**
32 **POLAR GUNNER**, 11, b g Gunner B—Polar Belle **Mrs M. E. Dixon**
33 **PORTAVADIE**, 9, b g Rakaposhi King—Woodland Flower **Ashleybank Investments Limited**
34 **QUANNAPOWITT (IRE)**, 4, b g Bob's Return (IRE)—
                                        Autumn Sunset (IRE) **R.Gordon Marshall,Dean & Raymond Bostock**
35 **ROMAN ARK**, 10, gr g Terimon—Larksmore **R. Collins**
36 **RUBIPRESENT (IRE)**, 4, b g Presenting—Azaban (IRE) **Mr J. H. Wilson**
37 **SCHINKEN OTTO (IRE)**, 7, ch g Shinko Forest (IRE)—Athassel Rose (IRE) **J. Donald**
38 **SEATTLE SOUND**, 5, b m Kayf Tara—Primitive Gift **Mr H. Young**
39 **SILVER BOW**, 7, b m Silver Patriarch (IRE)—Isabeau **Terry Pryke, John Cleeve & Peter Birch**
40 **STICK TOGETHER**, 5, gr m Kayf Tara—Altogether Now (IRE) **J. M. Jefferson**
41 **THAMES (IRE)**, 10, b g Over The River (FR)—Aon Dochas (IRE) **T. J. Hemmings**
42 **THE PANAMA KID (IRE)**, 4, b g Presenting—Mrs Jodi **Mr & Mrs J. M. Davenport**
43 **THE PORTONION (IRE)**, 4, b g Accordion—Mazza **R.Gordon Marshall,Dean & Raymond Bostock**
44 **TOM'S TOYBOX**, 6, b g Classic Cliche (IRE)—Jobiska **R. Collins**
45 **TOT O'WHISKEY**, 7, b g Saddlers' Hall (IRE)—Whatagale **Boundary Garage (Bury) Limited**
46 **WILHEWISPA**, 6, b g Winning Gallery—More To Life **D. T. Todd**
47 **ZOENICIBEL**, 4, b f Kayf Tara—Romany Hill **Capt M. S. Bagley**

THREE-YEAR-OLDS

48 **ALTAN KHAN**, b g Kayf Tara—Anabranch **Mrs M. Barker**
49 **BETTERTHANLIKELY**, b g Presenting—Mrs Jodi **Mr & Mrs J. M. Davenport**

Other Owners: Mrs T. H. Barclay, P. F. Birch, Mr J. R. Bostock, Mr Dean Graham Bostock, Mr J. M. Davenport, Mrs J. M. Davenport, Mr P Gaffney, Mrs K. S. Gaffney, Mr K. Lee, Mr R. G. Marshall, Mrs F. D. McInnes Skinner, T. R. Pryke, Mr L. M. Rutherford, Mr J. N. Stevenson, Mrs Alix Stevenson, Mrs E. A. Webster, H. Young.

Jockey (NH): F. King, G. Lee. **Conditional:** J. Halliday, T. Dreaper. **Apprentice:** P. Pickard. **Amateur:** Miss N. Jefferson, Mr O. Williams.

---

305 **MR J. R. W. JENKINS, Royston**
Postal: **Kings Ride, Baldock Road, Royston, Hertfordshire, SG8 9NN**
Contacts: PHONE (01763) 241141 HOME (01763) 246611 FAX (01763) 248223
MOBILE (07802) 750855
E-MAIL john@johnjenkinsracing.co.uk WEBSITE www.johnjenkinsracing.co.uk

1 **AMWELL BRAVE**, 7, b g Pyramus (USA)—Passage Creeping (IRE) **Amwell Racing**
2 **ANFIELD DREAM**, 6, b g Lujain—Fifth Emerald **The Saints Partnership**
3 **ASHWELL ROSE**, 6, b m Anabaa (USA)—Finicia (USA) **Mr & Mrs C. Schwick**
4 **BALI BELONY**, 4, b f Erhaab (USA)—Daarat Alayaam (IRE) **Michael Ng**
5 **BILLY RED**, 4, ch g Dr Fong (USA)—Liberty Bound **Mrs I. C. Hampson**
6 **BOOKIESINDEX BOY**, 4, b br g Piccolo—United Passion **Mr R. Stevens**
7 **CLASSIC LEA**, 4, b c Classic Cliche (IRE)—Double Spice **Mrs C. Davis**
8 **COCO L'ESCARGOT**, 4, b f Slip Anchor—Dafne **N. R. Hodge**
9 **DAVIDS MARK**, 8, b g Polar Prince (IRE)—Star of Flanders **Mrs W. A. Jenkins**
10 **DOMENICO (IRE)**, 10, b g Sadler's Wells (USA)—Russian Ballet (USA) **Skullduggery**

MR J. R. W. JENKINS—continued

11 **ERNMOOR**, 6, b g Young Ern—Linpac North Moor **If Only Partnership**
12 **GO AMWELL**, 5, b g Kayf Tara—Daarat Alayaam (IRE) **Mr R. Stevens**
13 **HAASEM (USA)**, 5, b h Seeking The Gold (USA)—Thawakib (IRE) **Robin Stevens & Stephen Bullock**
14 **HOLLOW JO**, 8, b g Most Welcome—Sir Hollow (USA) **J. McCarthy**
15 **JOLLIE ABILOLA**, 5, gr m Shahrastani (USA)—Bonita Blakeney **Mr & Mrs Leon Shack**
16 **MAGIC AMIGO**, 7, ch g Zilzal—Emaline (IRE) **Mrs W. A. Jenkins**
17 **MID VALLEY**, 5, ch g Zilzal (USA)—Isabella d'este (IRE) **Michael Ng**
18 **MISS IPPOLITA**, 4, b f Diktat—Isabella d'este (IRE) **D. J. P. Bryans**
19 **MOON EMPEROR**, 11, b g Emperor Jones (USA)—Sir Hollow (USA) **R. M. Ellis**
20 **MOON MIX (FR)**, 5, gr g Linamix (FR)—Cherry Moon (USA) **N. Trevithick**
21 **MR CELLOPHANE**, 5, ch g Pursuit of Love—Fresh Fruit Daily **R. B. Hill**
22 **MY SPRING ROSE**, 4, b f Lake Coniston (IRE)—Diamond Jayne (IRE) **Mr P. Ward**
23 **PROUD KILLER**, 5, b g Killer Instinct—Thewarri (USA) **Nolan's Bar Racing Syndicate**
24 **ROYAL GUEST**, 4, b g Royal Applause—Bajan Blue **Mr & Mrs Leon Shack**
25 **SIR HAYDN**, 8, ch g Definite Article—Snowscape **Mr A. Sowle**
26 **SIR LEONARD (IRE)**, 7, b g Aahsaylad—Miss Paleface **Mrs W. A. Jenkins**
27 **SMASH N'GRAB (IRE)**, 4, ch f Jade Robbery (USA)—Sallwa (IRE) **Bookmakers Index Ltd**
28 **TILSWORTH CHARLIE**, 5, br m Dansili—Glossary **Michael Ng**
29 **TRACHONITIS (IRE)**, 4, b c Dansili—Hasina (IRE) **J. McCarthy**
30 **TRIGGER LEA**, 5, b m Double Trigger (IRE)—Double Spice **Mrs C. Davis**

THREE-YEAR-OLDS

31 **AIM**, b c Weetman's Weigh (IRE)—Ballet On Ice (FR) **Sheikh M. Al Sabah**
32 **ALABJAR**, b c High Estate—Princess Lieven **Mr A. M. A. Al Mowed**
33 **AMWELL HOUSE**, gr g Auction House (USA)—Amwell Star (USA) **Amwell Racing**
34 **JARRAH**, b c Cool Jazz—Churchtown Spirit **Sheikh M. Al Sabah**
35 **LANGHAM HOUSE**, ch g Best of The Bests—Dafne **N. R. Hodge**
36 **LIGHTNING LAD**, b c Cool Jazz—Cappucino Lady **Sheikh M. Al Sabah**
37 **MY FLAME**, b c Cool Jazz—Suselja (IRE) **Sheikh M. Al Sabah**
38 **PEBBLE ROCK (IRE)**, b g Sadler's Wells (USA)—Soviet Artic (FR) **J. McCarthy**
39 **SAKHACITY**, b f Sakhee (USA)—Subtle One (IRE) **D. J. P. Bryans**
40 **SPITFIRE**, b g Mujahid (USA)—Fresh Fruit Daily **The Spitfire Partnership**

TWO-YEAR-OLDS

41 Ch c 12/4 Tobougg (IRE)—
Bijan (IRE) (Mukaddamah (USA)) (22000) **Irene Hampson, Carol Davis, David Bryans**
42 Ch f 4/2 Tobougg (IRE)—Isabella d'este (IRE) (Irish River (FR)) (20000) **Michael Ng**
43 **LOVE YOU LOUIS**, b c 30/3 Mark of Esteem (IRE)—Maddie's A Jem (Emperor Jones (USA)) (6500) **J. Pepper**
44 B f 23/4 Tobougg (IRE)—Once Removed (Distant Relative) (8000)
45 B f 28/3 Central Park (USA)—Waterline Dancer (IRE) (Danehill Dancer (IRE)) (1200) **Gareth Dickson, Ryan Kadiri**

Other Owners: Mr D. C. Bandey, Miss S. Bather, Mr D. Bryans, Mr Stephen Bullock, Miss P. Casey, Mr W. E. Cockman, Mrs J. Devereaux Loska, Mr M. Francis, Mr R. B. Hill, Mr P. J. Kirkpatrick, Mr Stephen Kramer, Mr M. Ng, Mr T. G. Nolan, Mr C. Schwick, Mrs C. Schwick, Mr L. Shack, Mrs S. Shack, Mr Robin Stevens, Mr G. Strang, Mr D. J. Tattersall, Mr H. Thomas.

306 MR A. E. M. JESSOP, Chelmsford
Postal: **Flemings Farm, Warren Road, South Hanningfield, Chelmsford, Essex, CM3 8HU**
Contacts: **PHONE (01268) 710210 MOBILE (07718) 736482**

1 **BELVILLEZ**, 5, b g Villez (USA)—Bellidium **Mrs G. Jessop**
2 **CNIDOS**, 4, b g Nikos—Flemings Delight **Mrs G. Jessop**
3 **ELLIE LOU**, 7, b m Lord Americo—Flemings Delight **Mrs G. Jessop**
4 **MAJY D'AUTEUIL (FR)**, 6, b g Discover d'auteuil (FR)—Majestic Dancer (FR) **Mrs G. Jessop**
5 **MISS COLMESNIL (FR)**, 8, b m Dear Doctor (FR)—Princesse Dolly (FR) **Mrs G. Jessop**

307 MR F. JESTIN, Wigton
Postal: **Hilltop, Brocklebank, Wigton, Cumbria, CA7 8DL**
Contacts: **PHONE (01697) 478439**

1 **BEAUCHAMP VALLEY (IRE)**, 7, b g Beauchamp King—Valley of Time (FR) **F. Jestin**
2 **DAFFI (IRE)**, 8, b m Zaffaran (USA)—Bdoore (IRE) **F. Jestin**
3 **HAPTHOR**, 9, ch m Zaffaran (USA)—My Goddess **F. Jestin**
4 **RAHOOD (IRE)**, 6, b g Afif—Cawkwell Patricia **F. Jestin**

MR F. JESTIN—continued

TWO-YEAR-OLDS

5 Ch c 14/2 Daylami (IRE)—Toffee Nosed (Selkirk (USA)) **F. & E. Jestin**

---

308 | **MRS L. C. JEWELL, Sutton Valence**
Postal: **Southfield Stables, South Lane, Sutton Valence, Maidstone, Kent, ME17 3AZ**
Contacts: PHONE **(01622) 842788** FAX **(01622) 842943** MOBILE **(07856) 686657**
E-MAIL **lindajewell@hotmail.com** WEBSITE **www.lindajewellracing.co.uk**

1 BALLYRAINEY (IRE), 9, b br g Carroll House—Foxborough Lady **K. Johnson, K. Jessup**
2 CAPTAIN WILLOUGHBY (IRE), 7, b g Good Thyne (USA)—Wadablast (IRE) **D. Fisher**
3 CAPTIVATE, 5, ch m Hernando (FR)—Catch (USA) **D. Fisher**
4 CONTENTED (IRE), 6, b g Orpen (USA)—Joyfullness (USA) **Mr O. J. C. Shannon Mrs Linda Beasley**
5 CUPID'S GLORY, 6, b g Pursuit of Love—Doctor's Glory (USA) **K. Johnson, K. Jessup**
6 EDDYSTONE (IRE), 4, ch g Fantastic Light (USA)—Far Reaching (USA) **Six Aces**
7 HEREDITARY, 6, ch g Hernando (FR)—Eversince (USA) **P. A. Oppenheimer**
8 JOE RICH, 4, b g Piccolo—Lady Lacey **Marbary Partnership**
9 KAZAKSTAN, 4, b g Kyllachy—Niseem (USA) **J. P. Jones**
10 KNOCK BOY (IRE), 6, b g Pistolet Bleu (IRE)—Past Times (IRE) **Wild Card**
11 4, B g Vettori (IRE)—Libretta **Mrs L. C. Jewell**
12 LORD OF ADVENTURE (IRE), 6, b g Inzar (USA)—Highly Fashionable (IRE) **Barrie & Shirley Sancto**
13 ONE STEP CLOSER (IRE), 8, b m Broken Hearted—Toghermore Lass **Barvin Partnership**
14 PANADIN (IRE), 6, b g Desert King (IRE)—Strident Note **Capt N. M. Davies**
15 RED ENSIGN, 11, ch g Lancastrian—Medway Queen **Mrs S.Stanier,Mrs C.Diplock,Mr R.Young**
16 ROWE PARK, 5, b g Dancing Spree—Magic Legs **Mrs Sue Ashdown & Mrs Lesley Hammond**
17 SETT ASIDE, 10, b g Set Adrift—Fields of Fortune **Field Of Fortune**
18 SHE'S HUMBLE (IRE), 6, ch m Humbel (USA)—She's No Tourist (IRE) **J. P. Jones**
19 SILISTRA, 9, gr g Sadler's Wells (USA)—Dundel (IRE) **Miss K. Jewell**
20 SIRONI (IRE), 8, b br g Erins Isle—Nordic Cousin (IRE) **P. A. Oppenheimer**
21 STEELY DAN, 9, b g Danzig Connection (USA)—No Comebacks **Mrs L. C. Jewell**
22 SURELY KEEN, 8, ch g Keen—Katie Jo **R. B. Morton**
23 THE SLIDER, 4, b f Erhaab (USA)—Cottage Maid **Mr R. I. B. Young & Mrs F. J. Meekins**
24 TOWER HILL (IRE), 5, b g Grand Lodge (USA)—Champaka (IRE) **Marbary Partnership**
25 TRAVELING MAN, 6, b g Nomadic Way (USA)—Wilomeno **Mr K. E. Hay**

THREE-YEAR-OLDS

26 CH g King's Best (USA)—Across The Ice (USA) **J. P. Jones**
27 HONEST VALUE (IRE), b g Chevalier (IRE)—Sensimelia (IRE) **Mr K. C. Bennett**
28 HONEST YANKEE (USA), ch c Yankee Gentleman (USA)—Tresor (USA) **Mr K. C. Bennett**
29 JANE'S PAYOFF (IRE), b f Danetime (IRE)—Alimony (IRE) **Mr K. C. Bennett**

Other Owners: Mrs S. M. Ashdown, Mrs Linda J. Beasley, Mrs Clare Diplock, Mrs A. Emanuel, Mr G. Gordon, Mrs L. M. Hammond, Mr K. Jessup, Mrs Linda Jewell, Mr K. Johnson, Mrs F. J. Meekins, Mr K. O'Sullivan, Mrs J. E. Omer, B. D. Sancto, Mrs S. A. Sancto, Mr O. J. C. Shannon, Mrs S. Stanier, Mr Barry Yates, Mrs Margaret Yates, Mr R. I. B. Young.

Assistant Trainer: Karen Jewell

Amateur: Mr Craig Messenger.

---

309 | **MR B. R. JOHNSON, Epsom**
Postal: **Little Woodruffe Racing Stables, Headley Road, Epsom, Surrey, KT18 6BH**
Contacts: YARD **(01372) 270199** MOBILE **(07768) 697141**
E-MAIL **vanessabuckman@hotmail.com**

1 COMMANCHE DREAM, 5, b g Commanche Run—Busy Girl **The Twenty Five Club**
2 EAGLE NEBULA, 4, ch g Observatory (USA)—Tarocchi (USA) **Tann Racing**
3 EVIDENT PRIDE (USA), 5, b g Chester House (USA)—Proud Fact (USA) **C. Lefevre**
4 FLANAGANS CHOICE (IRE), 6, b m Lord of Appeal—Rivers Town Rosie (IRE) **Miss E. Mulvaney**
5 KATIYPOUR (IRE), 11, ch g Be My Guest (USA)—Katiyfa **P. D. Crate**
6 PAB SPECIAL (IRE), 5, b g City On A Hill (USA)—Tinos Island (IRE) **Miss T. R. Hale**
7 ROCKER, 4, b g Rock of Gibraltar (IRE)—Jessica's Dream (IRE) **Sir Eric Parker**
8 ST SAVARIN (FR), 7, ch g Highest Honor (FR)—Sacara (GER) **A. A. Lyons**

MR B. R. JOHNSON—continued

THREE-YEAR-OLDS

9 **BYE BABY BUNTING**, ch f Bahamian Bounty—Cuore di Aliante **Mrs A. M. Upsdell**
10 **FAREEHA**, b f King's Best (USA)—Shatarah **Miss T. R. Hale**
11 **ILE ROYALE**, b f Royal Applause—Island Destiny **Mrs A. M. Upsdell**
12 **SHAYERA**, b f Hawk Wing (USA)—Trick (IRE) **C. Lefevre**
13 **VALTAT**, b g Fasliyev (USA)—Wooden Doll **Tann Racing**

Other Owners: P. Grimes, P. Morley, G. Tann, Mrs E. Tann.

Assistant Trainer: Vanessa Buckman

---

310 MISS E. A. JOHNSON HOUGHTON, Blewbury
Postal: Woodway, Blewbury, Didcot, Oxfordshire, OX11 9EZ
Contacts: **PHONE** (01235) 850480 **FAX** (01235) 851045 **MOBILE** (07721) 622700
E-MAIL Eve@johnsonhoughton.com **WEBSITE** www.johnsonhoughton.com

1 **BEAVER PATROL (IRE)**, 6, ch g Tagula (IRE)—Erne Project (IRE) **G. C. Stevens**
2 **CINNAMON HILL**, 4, ch f Compton Place—Cajole (IRE) **Mrs C. J. Hue Williams**
3 **FLEURET**, 4, b br f Diktat—Forthwith **Wyck Hall Stud Ltd**
4 **JUDD STREET**, 6, b g Compton Place—Pudding Lane (IRE) **R. F. Johnson Houghton**
5 **LOOKING GREAT (USA)**, 6, b g Gulch (USA)—Shoofha (IRE) **R. F. Johnson Houghton**
6 **MUJOOD**, 5, b g Mujahid (USA)—Waqood (USA) **Eden Racing**
7 **PHLUKE**, 7, b g Most Welcome—Phlirty **Mrs F. M. Johnson Houghton**
8 **PUNCHING**, 4, b g Kyllachy—Candescent **Anthony Pye-Jeary & Mel Smith**
9 **ROODOLPH**, 4, ch g Primo Valentino (IRE)—Roo **Eden Racing (II)**
10 **ROSIE CROSS (IRE)**, 4, b f Cape Cross (IRE)—Professional Mom (USA) **Betfair Club ROA**
11 **SHAKE ON IT**, 4, b g Lomitas—Decision Maid (USA) **Eden Racing (III)**
12 **SUPPORT FUND (IRE)**, 4, ch f Intikhab (USA)—Almost A Lady (IRE)

THREE-YEAR-OLDS

13 **BOFFIN**, b c Kalanisi (IRE)—Phi Beta Kappa (USA) **Mrs F. M. Johnson Houghton**
14 **BOMBARDIER WELLS**, b c Red Ransom (USA)—Bow River Gold **G. C. Stevens**
15 **FUTURITY**, ch f Lomitas—Forthwith **Wyck Hall Stud Ltd**
16 **HOBSON**, b g Choisir (AUS)—Educating Rita **Anthony Pye-Jeary & Mel Smith**
17 **HOLY STORM (IRE)**, b g Mujahid (USA)—Slupia (IRE) **Richard Maynard & Partners**
18 **KIHO**, b c Dashing Blade—Krim (GER) **R. F. Johnson Houghton**
19 **SYDNEYSIDER**, b g Averti (IRE)—Cajole (IRE) **Mrs C. J. Hue Williams**

TWO-YEAR-OLDS

20 **AUTUMN MORNING (IRE)**, b f 26/4 Danetime (IRE)—
Soviet Maid (IRE) (Soviet Star (USA)) (15500) **Fighttheban Partnership II**
21 **BAD BARON (IRE)**, ch c 4/3 Lomitas—Dyna Flyer (USA) (Marquetry (USA)) (7000) **Mrs F. M. Johnson Houghton**
22 **DAVIDS MATADOR**, b c 6/2 Dansili—Mousseline (USA) (Barathea (IRE)) (50000) **Mr D. T. Herbert**
23 **DEUCE**, ch f 5/4 Where Or When (IRE)—Justbetweenfriends (USA) (Diesis) (48000) **P. H. Marsh**
24 **FLAVOUR**, b f 21/3 Lujain (USA)—Forum (Lion Cavern (USA)) **Wyck Hall Stud Ltd**
25 B f 8/2 Reset (AUS)—Golubitsa (IRE) (Bluebird (USA)) (6000) **Fyfield Racing**
26 **GREEN POPPY**, b f 23/4 Green Desert (USA)—Vimy Ridge (FR) (Indian Ridge) (26000) **Mr J. R. Hobby**
27 **HAY FEVER (IRE)**, b c 22/1 Namid—Allergy (Alzao (USA)) (11582) **Eden Racing IV**
28 **JEWELLED REEF (IRE)**, b f 9/3 Marju (USA)—Aqaba (Lake Coniston (IRE)) (30000) **Wood Street Syndicate V**
29 B c 31/3 Monsieur Bond (IRE)—May Light (Midyan (USA)) (40000) **Dr J. A. E. Hobby**
30 B c 5/5 King's Best (USA)—One of The Family (Alzao (USA)) (35000) **Miss E. A. Johnson Houghton**
31 Ch c 17/2 Fraam—Pudding Lane (IRE) (College Chapel) (16000) **R. F. Johnson Houghton**
32 B f 28/3 Bertolini (USA)—Queen Linear (USA) (Polish Navy (USA)) (10000) **Miss E. A. Johnson Houghton**
33 **SLANT (IRE)**, b br f 2/2 Spinning World (USA)—
Sweet Honesty (IRE) (Charnwood Forest (IRE)) (9652) **Miss E. A. Johnson Houghton**
34 B c 2/3 Xaar—Veiled Beauty (USA) (Royal Academy (USA)) (58000) **Anthony Pye-Jeary & Mel Smith**

Other Owners: C. R. A. Ferguson, T. R. Gittins, R. L. Maynard, A. J. Pye-Jeary, Mr D. Redvers, J. P. Repard, Mrs S. Ryan, Mr A. J. Sinfield, M. K. Smith, G. H. Summers.

Assistant Trainer: R. F. Johnson Houghton

Jockey (flat): S. Carson.

311 MR J. H. JOHNSON, Crook

Postal: White Lea Farm, Crook, Co. Durham, DL15 9QN
Contacts: PHONE (01388) 762113 CAR (07914) 691017 FAX (01388) 768278
MOBILE (07714) 691016/691017
E-MAIL lucy@directroute1.co.uk

1 **ABSTINENCE (IRE)**, 5, b g Spectrum (IRE)—Ballerina Gold (USA) **Andrea & Graham Wylie**
2 **ACT SIRIUS (IRE)**, 4, ch g Grand Lodge (USA)—Folgore (USA) **Andrea & Graham Wylie**
3 **ACTION STRASSE (IRE)**, 6, b g Old Vic—Platin Run (IRE) **Andrea & Graham Wylie**
4 **ADIEU MARI (FR)**, 5, gr g Adieu Au Roi (IRE)—Mariwonder (FR) **Andrea & Graham Wylie**
5 **AKILAK (IRE)**, 7, br g Charnwood Forest (IRE)—Akilara (IRE) **ADA Partnership**
6 **ALBANY (IRE)**, 8, ch g Alhaarth (IRE)—Tochar Ban (USA) **Gordon Brown, Bert Watson & J H Johnson**
7 **ALLOVERAGAIN (IRE)**, 6, b g Pistolet Bleu (IRE)—Askasilla (IRE) **J. H. Johnson**
8 **ANAY CAR (FR)**, 4, b g Sleeping Car (FR)—Anayette (FR) **Andrea & Graham Wylie**
9 **ANDY ANSHAN (IRE)**, 7, b br g Anshan—Donegal Grey (IRE) **Lord Daresbury, M. Green & J. H. Johnson**
10 **ARCALIS**, 8, gr g Lear Fan (USA)—Aristocratique **Andrea & Graham Wylie**
11 **ARTLESS (USA)**, 5, b m Aptitude—Eternity **Andrea & Graham Wylie**
12 **ASTARADOR (FR)**, 6, b g Astarabad (USA)—Touques (FR) **Alderclad Roofing Ltd & S V Rutter**
13 **ASTRONOMIC**, 8, b g Zafonic (USA)—Sky Love (USA) **Andrea & Graham Wylie**
14 **BACKBEAT (IRE)**, 11, ch g Bob Back (USA)—Pinata **Andrea & Graham Wylie**
15 **BAFANA BOY**, 8, br g Presenting—Lorna's Choice **Andrea & Graham Wylie**
16 **BALYAN (IRE)**, 7, b g Bahhare (USA)—Balaniya (USA) **Andrea & Graham Wylie**
17 **BASODA**, 7, b g Karinga Bay—Another Wag **Andrea & Graham Wylie**
18 **BAYONYX (IRE)**, 4, b c Montjeu (IRE)—Dafariyna (IRE) **Andrea & Graham Wylie**
19 **BERGONZI (IRE)**, 4, ch g Indian Ridge—Lady Windley **Andrea & Graham Wylie**
20 **BEST ACCOLADE**, 9, b g Oscar (IRE)—Made of Talent **Andrea & Graham Wylie**
21 **BESTOFTHEBROWNIES (IRE)**, 7, b g Bob Back (USA)—Just A Brownie (IRE) **Andrea & Graham Wylie**
22 **BEWLEYS BERRY (IRE)**, 10, ch g Shernazar—Approach The Dawn (IRE) **Andrea & Graham Wylie**
23 **BLEAK HOUSE (IRE)**, 6, b g Rudimentary (USA)—Dannkalia (IRE) **Andrea & Graham Wylie**
24 **BLEU POIS (IRE)**, 6, ch g Pistolet Bleu (IRE)—Peas (IRE) **R J Partnership**
25 **BOBTANTE (IRE)**, 4, ch g Bob Back (USA)—Erintante (IRE) **Gordon Brown, Bert Watson & J H Johnson**
26 **CALIN ROYAL (FR)**, 7, ch g Garde Royale—Caline de Froment (FR) **Andrea & Graham Wylie**
27 **CANADA STREET (IRE)**, 7, b g Old Vic—Saucy Sprite **Andrea & Graham Wylie**
28 **CAST IRON CASEY (IRE)**, 6, ch g Carroll House—Ashie's Friend (IRE) **Alderclad Roofing Ltd**
29 **CEDRUS LIBANI (IRE)**, 7, b g Beneficial—Cedar Castle (IRE) **Mr Matthew Green & Mr J H Johnson**
30 4, B g Oscar (IRE)—Celestial Dance **Andrea & Graham Wylie**
31 **CHAPEL HOUSE**, 5, b g Beneficial—My Moona **J. H. Johnson**
32 **CHECKERBOARD (IRE)**, 5, b g Alderbrook—Jamie's Lady **Andrea & Graham Wylie**
33 **CIRCASSIAN (IRE)**, 7, b g Groom Dancer (USA)—Daraliya (IRE) **Andrea & Graham Wylie**
34 **COAT OF HONOUR (USA)**, 8, gr g Mark of Esteem (IRE)—Ballymac Girl **Andrea & Graham Wylie**
35 **COMPANERO (IRE)**, 8, b g Supreme Leader—Smart Decision (IRE) **J. H. Johnson**
36 **COMPROMIZNOTENSION (IRE)**, 5, br g Key of Luck (USA)—Music Khan **Andrea & Graham Wylie**
37 **COOL OPERATOR**, 5, b g Kahyasi—Gardana (FR) **Andrea & Graham Wylie**
38 **COOLDINE LAD (IRE)**, 8, b g Flemensfirth (USA)—Lotto Lady **J. H. Johnson**
39 **CRAIGLANDS (IRE)**, 6, b g Dushyantor (USA)—Fernhill (IRE) **J. H. Johnson**
40 **CROCODILE DUNDEE (IRE)**, 7, b g Croco Rouge (IRE)—Miss Salsa Dancer **Andrea & Graham Wylie**
41 **DARK DESTINY (IRE)**, 4, b g Beneficial—Platin Run (IRE) **Andrea & Graham Wylie**
42 **DEGAS ART (IRE)**, 5, b g Danehill Dancer (IRE)—Answer **Andrea & Graham Wylie**
43 **DIAMOND FRONTIER (IRE)**, 5, gr g Sadler's Wells (USA)—Diamond Line (FR) **Andrea & Graham Wylie**
44 **DIGITAL MEDIA (IRE)**, 6, b g Taipan (IRE)—Cats Concert (IRE) **Andrea & Graham Wylie**
45 **DIKTATORIAL**, 6, br g Diktat—Reason To Dance **Andrea & Graham Wylie**
46 **DOODLEBOP (IRE)**, 5, ch g Carroll House—Polar Mistress (IRE) **J. H. Johnson**
47 **DORAFLORA**, 4, b f Alflora (IRE)—Gretton **J. H. Johnson**
48 **DREVER ROUTE (IRE)**, 5, b g Flemensfirth (USA)—I Remember It Well (IRE) **Andrea & Graham Wylie**
49 **EL VAQUERO (IRE)**, 10, ch g Un Desperado (FR)—Marble Fontaine **Andrea & Graham Wylie**
50 **ELLERSLIE GEORGE (IRE)**, 8, br g Presenting—Proud Polly (IRE) **Andrea & Graham Wylie**
51 **EMMENSO (IRE)**, 6, ch g Flemensfirth (USA)—Pops Princess (IRE) **Andrea & Graham Wylie**
52 **FALPIASE (IRE)**, 6, b g Montjeu (IRE)—Gift of The Night (USA) **Andrea & Graham Wylie**
53 **FRANKIE FIGG (IRE)**, 6, b g Portrait Gallery (IRE)—Ardnataggle (IRE) **Andrea & Graham Wylie**
54 **FUSHE JO**, 4, gr g Act One—Aristocratique **Shearer Fulton & Johnson**
55 **GALAXY SPIRIT (IRE)**, 4, b g Presenting—Mine Rock Native (IRE) **Andrea & Graham Wylie**
56 **GALERO**, 9, b g Overbury (IRE)—Rare Luck **J. H. Johnson**
57 **GENERAL LEDGER (IRE)**, 6, b g Alderbrook—Las-Cancellas **Andrea & Graham Wylie**
58 **GLENGAP (IRE)**, 5, br g Needle Gun (IRE)—Miss Betsy (IRE) **Andrea & Graham Wylie**
59 **GOLD THREAD (IRE)**, 7, b g Oscar (IRE)—Queen Boadicea (IRE) **Andrea & Graham Wylie**
60 **GRAND ART (IRE)**, 4, b g Raise A Grand (IRE)—Mulberry River (IRE) **Mr M. Green & Mr J. H. Johnson**
61 **GRAND OPERA (IRE)**, 5, b g City On A Hill (USA)—Victoria's Secret (IRE) **Transcend Bloodstock LLP**

MR J. H. JOHNSON—continued

62 **GRATTAN LODGE (IRE)**, 11, gr g Roselier (FR)—Shallow Run **W. M. G. Black**
63 **GRINGO**, 6, gr g Alzao (USA)—Glen Falls **Andrea & Graham Wylie**
64 **GUNNER ROYAL**, 10, b g Gunner B—Loadplan Lass **Mrs E Dunn & Mr J Howard Johnson**
65 **GUPPY (IRE)**, 4, b g Darnay—Arushofgold (IRE) **J. H. Johnson**
66 **HARD ACT TO FOLLOW (IRE)**, 9, ch g Shernazar—Lauren's Gem **Andrea & Graham Wylie**
67 **HE'S THE BUSINESS**, 4, b g Exit To Nowhere (USA)—Spindle's **Sutton Business Centre**
68 **HERBIE (IRE)**, 6, b g Good Thyne (USA)—Hamshire Gale (IRE) **Mr P. J. Harle & J. H. Johnson**
69 **HEUREUX (USA)**, 5, b h Stravinsky (USA)—Storm West (USA) **Transcend Bloodstock LLP**
70 **HOCKENHEIM (FR)**, 7, b g Kadalko (FR)—L'inka (FR) **Andrea & Graham Wylie**
71 **INGLIS DREVER (IRE)**, 8, b g In The Wings—Cormorant Creek **Andrea & Graham Wylie**
72 **ISAN (IRE)**, 6, b g Insan (USA)—Legal Action (IRE) **Andrea & Graham Wylie**
73 5, B g Bob Back (USA)—Isotonia **J. H. Johnson**
74 **JACK THE BLASTER**, 8, b g Afflora (IRE)—Marsden Rock **R J Partnership & J Howard Johnson**
75 **JOHNNY ROCHE (IRE)**, 6, b g Oscar (IRE)—Ou La La (IRE) **Andrea & Graham Wylie**
76 **JULIUS CAESAR**, 8, b g Sadler's Wells (USA)—Stiletta **Jack Coupe & John Thompson**
77 4, B g Dushyantor (USA)—June's Bride (IRE) **J. H. Johnson**
78 **KANDELIN (IRE)**, 5, b g Beneficial—Bright Moonbeam (IRE) **Andrea & Graham Wylie**
79 **KEALSHORE BOY**, 5, br g Overbury (IRE)—Rippling Brook **Andrea & Graham Wylie**
80 **KEY TIME (IRE)**, 6, b g Darshaan—Kasota (IRE) **Andrea & Graham Wylie**
81 **KNIGHT VALLIANT**, 5, bl g Dansili—Aristocratique **Andrea & Graham Wylie**
82 **KNOCKAVILLA (IRE)**, 5, b g Saddlers' Hall (IRE)—Native Singer (IRE) **Andrea & Graham Wylie**
83 **LABOREC (IRE)**, 5, gr g Oscar (IRE)—Bere Science (IRE) **Andrea & Graham Wylie**
84 **LEMON DRIZZLE (IRE)**, 4, ch f Old Vic—Decent Shower **J. H. Johnson**
85 **LENNON (IRE)**, 8, b br g Beneficial—Stradbally Bay **Andrea & Graham Wylie**
86 **LETTERPRESS (IRE)**, 4, b g King's Theatre (IRE)—Empress of Light **Andrea & Graham Wylie**
87 **LOCKSMITH**, 8, gr g Linamix (FR)—Zenith **Andrea & Graham Wylie**
88 **LOCKSTOWN**, 5, ch g Exit To Nowhere (USA)—Slaney Rose (IRE) **J. H. Johnson**
89 **LOGANS RUN (IRE)**, 5, b g Shernazar—Toposki (FR) **Andrea & Graham Wylie**
90 **MARLEYBOW (IRE)**, 5, br g Presenting—Gaye Artiste (IRE) **Andrea & Graham Wylie**
91 **MASAFI (IRE)**, 7, b g Desert King (IRE)—Mrs Fisher (IRE) **Andrea & Graham Wylie**
92 **MEPHISTO (IRE)**, 9, b g Machiavellian (USA)—Cunning **Andrea & Graham Wylie**
93 4, Ch g Flemensfirth (USA)—Miss Murtle (IRE) **Andrea & Graham Wylie**
94 **MOONHAWK**, 5, b g Montjeu (USA)—Enclave (USA) **Transcend Bloodstock LLP**
95 **MOTIVE (FR)**, 7, ch g Machiavellian (USA)—Mistle Song **Andrea & Graham Wylie**
96 **NIGHT FORCE**, 5, br g Sovereign Water (FR)—Oatis Rose **Andrea & Graham Wylie**
97 **NO REFUGE (IRE)**, 8, ch g Hernando (FR)—Shamarra (IRE) **Andrea & Graham Wylie**
98 **NOSFERATU (IRE)**, 5, b g In The Wings—Gothic Dream (IRE) **Andrea & Graham Wylie**
99 **ODD SOCKS (IRE)**, 5, ch g Zaffaran (USA)—Mrs Marples (IRE) **Mr W. M. G. Black & Mrs S. Johnson**
100 **OH PICKLES (IRE)**, 6, b g Needle Gun (IRE)—Tartan Trouble **W. M. G. Black**
101 **OSCAR GOGO (IRE)**, 6, b g Oscar (IRE)—Ceolbridgequeen (IRE) **Mrs A. M. Rutter**
102 **OSWIE (IRE)**, 5, b g Sonus (IRE)—Meldrum Park (IRE) **J. H. Johnson**
103 **PANTHERA LEO (IRE)**, 5, b g Beneficial—Katie Fairy (IRE) **Andrea & Graham Wylie**
104 **PERCUSSIONIST (IRE)**, 7, b g Sadler's Wells (USA)—Magnificent Style (USA) **Andrea & Graham Wylie**
105 **PLAYER (FR)**, 5, ch g Apple Tree (FR)—Fleur des Marais II (FR) **Andrea & Graham Wylie**
106 **PRINCE CAR (FR)**, 5, br g Sleeping Car (FR)—Angelina (FR) **Andrea & Graham Wylie**
107 **PROFESSOR HIGGINS (IRE)**, 5, ch g Flemensfirth (USA)—Shuil Iontach (IRE) **Andrea & Graham Wylie**
108 **QDOS (IRE)**, 6, br g Presenting—Emma's Way (IRE) **J. H. Johnson**
109 **RIVERHILL (IRE)**, 5, b g Mull of Kintyre (USA)—Thrill Seeker (IRE) **Andrea & Graham Wylie**
110 **ROYAL ROSA (FR)**, 9, ch g Garde Royale—Crystalza (FR) **Andrea & Graham Wylie**
111 **SAN PEIRE (FR)**, 11, b g Cyborg (FR)—Shakapoura (FR) **Ellenvalley Optimists & J Howard Johnson**
112 **SCOTMAIL (IRE)**, 7, b g Old Vic—Snipe Singer **J. H. Johnson**
113 **SCRIPTWRITER (IRE)**, 6, b g Sadler's Wells (USA)—Dayanata **Andrea & Graham Wylie**
114 **SCULASTIC**, 5, b g Galileo (IRE)—Mutual Consent (IRE) **Andrea & Graham Wylie**
115 **SOME TOUCH (IRE)**, 8, b g Scribano—Sarahs Touch (IRE) **Andrea & Graham Wylie**
116 **SONARA (IRE)**, 4, b g Peintre Celebre (USA)—Fay (IRE) **Andrea & Graham Wylie**
117 **SPELLCHECKER (IRE)**, 4, ch g Alderbrook—Auntie Sally (IRE) **Andrea & Graham Wylie**
118 **ST WILFRID**, 6, ch g Loup Sauvage (USA)—Fairy Flax (IRE) **Andrea & Graham Wylie**
119 **STONEHAUGH (IRE)**, 5, b g King Charlemagne (USA)—Canary Bird (IRE) **Transcend Bloodstock LLP**
120 **STRIKING ARTICLE (IRE)**, 6, ch g Definite Article—Sindabezi (IRE) **Andrea & Graham Wylie**
121 4, B g Presenting—Talk To The Missus (IRE) **Andrea & Graham Wylie**
122 **TARRABURN (USA)**, 4, ch g Eltish (USA)—Rahy's Wish (USA) **Transcend Bloodstock LLP**
123 **TEENAGE IDOL (IRE)**, 4, b br g Sadler's Wells (USA)—Kaaba (IRE) **Andrea & Graham Wylie**
124 **THE REVEREND (IRE)**, 8, b br g Taipan (IRE)—Sounds Classical (IRE) **Andrea & Graham Wylie**
125 **THEATRE KNIGHT (IRE)**, 10, b g Old Vic—Musical View (IRE) **Andrea & Graham Wylie**
126 **TIDAL BAY (IRE)**, 7, b g Flemensfirth (USA)—June's Bride (IRE) **Andrea & Graham Wylie**
127 **TIGERIFIC (IRE)**, 5, gr m Beneficial—Grey Mo (IRE) **J. H. Johnson**

MR J. H. JOHNSON—continued

128 TOMBI (USA), 4, b g Johannesburg (USA)—Tune in to the Cat (USA) **Transcend Bloodstock LLP**
129 TOP DRESSING (IRE), 7, br g Rashar (USA)—Ross Gale **Andrea & Graham Wylie**
130 TOY GUN (IRE), 6, b g Pistolet Bleu (IRE)—Di's Wag **Ellenvalley Optimists**
131 TREACLE MOON, 5, b m Kayf Tara—Monica's Story **P. J. Harle**
132 TREEHOUSE, 5, b g Nomadic Way (USA)—Swift Reward **J. H. Johnson**
133 TSAROXY (IRE), 6, b g Xaar—Belsay **Andrea & Graham Wylie**
134 VECCHIO SENSO (IRE), 6, b g Old Vic—Ravens Way **W. M. G. Black**
135 VULCAN PILOT, 5, br g Overbury (IRE)—Snitton Lane **Group Capt J. A. Prideaux**
136 WATERLOO ROAD (IRE), 5, b g Old Vic—Struell Lady (IRE) **Andrea & Graham Wylie**
137 WEE BERTIE (IRE), 6, b g Sea Raven (IRE)—Commanche Glen (IRE) **Mrs A. H. Watson**
138 WEE FORBEES (IRE), 6, b g Shernazar—Gender Gap **Mr Matthew Green & Mr J H Johnson**
139 WHISKY MAGIC (FR), 4, b g Maresca Sorrento (FR)—Winska Girl (FR) **Andrea & Graham Wylie**
140 WHISPERING DEATH, 6, br g Pivotal—Lucky Arrow **Andrea & Graham Wylie**

THREE-YEAR-OLDS

141 ABBALEEN (IRE), b g Traditionally (USA)—Savieres (IRE) **Transcend Bloodstock LLP**
142 APOLLO SHARK (IRE), ch g Spartacus (IRE)—Shot of Redemption **Transcend Bloodstock LLP**
143 BARASHI, b g King's Best (USA)—Maid To Dance **Transcend Bloodstock LLP**
144 ETON RIFLES (IRE), b g Pivotal—Maritsa (IRE) **Transcend Bloodstock LLP**
145 INDIAN GROOM (IRE), gr g High Chaparral (IRE)—Taatof (IRE) **Transcend Bloodstock LLP**
146 MADISON HEIGHTS (IRE), ch g Monashee Mountain (USA)—Stormchaser (IRE) **Transcend Bloodstock LLP**
147 MANUKA BEE, b g Xaar—Legend **J. H. Johnson**
148 MINTAKA PASS (IRE), b g Danehill Dancer (IRE)—Mahrah (USA) **Transcend Bloodstock LLP**
149 MONTAQUILA, b g Hawk Wing (USA)—Intellectuelle **Transcend Bloodstock LLP**
150 NINE STORIES (IRE), b g Catcher In The Rye (IRE)—Irinatinvidio **Transcend Bloodstock LLP**
151 PANAMAR BESAR (IRE), b g Bahri (USA)—Paradise Blue (IRE) **Transcend Bloodstock LLP**
152 PEMBERTON, ch g Lomitas—Whitehaven **Transcend Bloodstock LLP**
153 PINTANO, ch g Dr Fong (USA)—Heckle **Transcend Bloodstock LLP**
154 RESOLUTE DEFENDER (IRE), b g Namid—Snowspin **Transcend Bloodstock LLP**
155 RIO NOVO, b g Nayef (USA)—Dead Certain **Transcend Bloodstock LLP**
156 ROCHEPORT, ch g Reel Buddy (USA)—Just A Gem **Transcend Bloodstock LLP**
157 ROYAL SOVEREIGN (IRE), b g Invincible Spirit (IRE)—Ombry Girl (IRE) **Transcend Bloodstock LLP**
158 SILK DRUM (IRE), gr g Intikhab (USA)—Aneydia (IRE) **Transcend Bloodstock LLP**
159 TERRASINI (FR), gr g Linamix (FR)—Trazando **Transcend Bloodstock LLP**
160 WOODY WALLER, ch g Lomitas—Reamzafonic **J. H. Johnson**

TWO-YEAR-OLDS

161 B g 14/5 Hawk Wing (USA)—Montmartre (IRE) (Grand Lodge (USA)) **Transcend Bloodstock LLP**

Other Owners: Alderclad Roofing Ltd, Mr R. J. Betteridge, Mr W. M. G. Black, Mr Gordon Brown, Mr Ron Brown, Mr Jim Buchanan, Mrs F. Buchanan, Mr J. Coupe, Lord Daresbury, Mrs Enid M. Dunn, Mr David M. Fulton, Mr Matthew Green, Mr P. J. Harle, Mrs S. Johnson, Mr S. V. Rutter, Mr A. Shearer, Mr A. Shield, Mr J. Thompson (Prudhoe), Mr Robert Watson, Mr Graham Wylie, Mrs Andrea Wylie.

Jockey (flat): R. Winston, Tom Eaves. Jockey (NH): Denis O'Regan. Conditional: Liam Berridge, J. P. O'Farrell. Amateur: Mr Richard Smith.

---

312 **MR ROBERT W. JOHNSON, Newcastle Upon Tyne**
Postal: **Grange Farm, Newburn, Newcastle Upon Tyne**
Contacts: PHONE **(01912) 674464** MOBILE **(07774) 131133**

1 COMPTON ECLAIRE (IRE), 8, ch m Lycius (USA)—Baylands Sunshine (IRE) **S. V. Rutter**
2 DECHIPER (IRE), 6, b br g Almutawakel—Safiya (USA) **J. L. Armstrong**
3 DISPOL PETO, 8, gr g Petong—Plie **T. Forbes**
4 LA VECCHIA SCUOLA (IRE), 4, b f Mull of Kintyre (USA)—Force Divine (FR) **G. Brown**
5 MOYNE PLEASURE (IRE), 10, b g Exit To Nowhere (USA)—Ilanga (IRE) **R. C. Whitelock**
6 PENDLE FOREST (IRE), 8, gr m Charnwood Forest (IRE)—Pride of Pendle **Mrs L. Miller**
7 SANDS RISING, 11, b g Primitive Rising (USA)—Celtic Sands **T. L. A. Robson**
8 STONEFERRY, 8, b g Hatim (USA)—Richards Kate **J. B. Wharf**
9 STORMY BEECH, 12, b g Glacial Storm (USA)—Cheeny's Brig **Robert W. Johnson**
10 TIPP MID WEST (IRE), 6, b m Close Conflict (USA)—Delightful Choice (IRE) **Robert W. Johnson**

MR ROBERT W. JOHNSON—continued

11 **TOULOUSE EXPRESS (IRE)**, 9, b g Toulon—Miss Ivy (IRE) **T. Forbes**
12 **UNCLE MICHAEL**, 7, b g Mon Tresor—De Valera **Mr P. Quinn**

Other Owners: Mr J. Blythe, Mr Robert Johnson.

Jockey (NH): K. Johnson. **Amateur:** Mr P. Johnson.

---

313 **MRS S. M. JOHNSON, Madley**
Postal: **Carwardine Farm, Madley, Hereford**
Contacts: **PHONE (01981) 250214 FAX (01981) 251538**

1 **AGOODUN**, 7, b g Parthian Springs—God Is Good **Mrs C. L. Goodinson**
2 **MRS BRIDGE**, 6, gr m Environment Friend—Celtic Bridge **I. K. Johnson**
3 **RADNOR LAD**, 8, ch g Double Trigger (IRE)—Gabibti (IRE) **The Ever Hopeful Partnership**
4 **SPIKE JONES (NZ)**, 10, br g Colonel Collins (USA)—Gloss (NZ) **I. K. Johnson**

Other Owners: R. A. Davies, Mr R. T. R. Price.

Jockey (NH): R. Johnson. **Amateur:** Mr R Hughes.

---

314 **MR A. E. JONES, Newport**
Postal: **Cefn Llogell Racing Stables, Coed Kernew, Newport, Gwent, NP10 8UD**
Contacts: **FAX (01633) 680232 MOBILE (07901) 505064**
E-MAIL aejonesracing@btconnect.com

1 **BISCAR TWO (IRE)**, 7, b g Daggers Drawn (USA)—Thoughtful Kate **J. Spence**
2 **HIDDENSEE (USA)**, 6, b g Cozzene (USA)—Zarani Sidi Anna (USA) **J. Spence**
3 **LETS GET CRACKING (FR)**, 4, b c Anabaa Blue—Queenhood (FR) **J. Spence**
4 **MANATHON (FR)**, 5, b g Marathon (USA)—Fleurissante (FR) **N. F. Glynn**
5 **NEAT 'N TIDY**, 4, b f Josr Algarhoud (IRE)—Raspberry Sauce **J. Spence**
6 **NOBLE BILY (FR)**, 7, b g Signe Divin (USA)—Vaillante Bily (FR) **G. Molen**
7 **NORISAN**, 4, ch c Inchinor—Dream On Deya (IRE) **J. Spence**
8 **PARTICIPATION**, 5, b g Dansili—Andaleeb (USA) **J. Spence**
9 **PENNYROCK (IRE)**, 4, b c Rock of Gibraltar (IRE)—Inforapenny **J. Spence**
10 **TAPIMIX (FR)**, 5, gr h Linamix (FR)—Secretariat's Tap (USA) **J. Spence**

Assistant Trainer: Miss A Bartelink

Jockey (NH): C. Williams, M. Foley. **Conditional:** D. Laverty, L. Heard.

---

315 **MR G. ELWYN JONES, Lampeter**
Postal: **Lluestnewydd, Bettws, Lampeter, Dyfed, SA48 8PB**
Contacts: **PHONE (01570) 493261 MOBILE (07817) 885504**

1 **DESERT SPA (USA)**, 13, b g Sheikh Albadou—Healing Waters (USA) **G. Elwyn Jones**
2 **ORREZZO (GER)**, 8, br g Zinaad—Ordessa (GER) **G. Elwyn Jones**

Amateur: Mr T. O'Brien, Miss I. G. Tompsett.

---

316 **MR P. J. JONES, Marlborough**
Postal: **Fox Twitchen, East Kennett, Marlborough, Wiltshire, SN8 4EY**
Contacts: **PHONE (01672) 861427 FAX (01672) 861147**

1 **FILLYOFTHEVALLEY**, 5, b m Wizard King—Slipmatic **P. J. Jones**
2 **GEORGES BOY (IRE)**, 10, b g Toulon—Glebelands Girl **P. J. Jones**
3 **LADY BLING BLING**, 7, b m Midnight Legend—Slipmatic **P. J. Jones**
4 **STRIPE ME BLUE**, 6, b g Miner's Lamp—Slipmatic **Mrs A. H. Jones**

317 MR T. M. JONES, Guildford
Postal: **Brook Farm, Albury, Guildford, Surrey, GU5 9DJ**
Contacts: PHONE **(01483) 202604** FAX **(01483) 202604** MOBILE **(07929) 024680**
E-MAIL **buck@brookfarmracing.com** WEBSITE **www.brookfarmracing.com**

1 ICANNSHIFT (IRE), 8, b g Night Shift (USA)—Cannikin (IRE) **T. M. Jones**
2 SHE WONT WAIT, 4, b f Piccolo—Who Goes There **Miss K. Windsor-Luck**

THREE-YEAR-OLDS

3 ROME ANTIQUE, ch g Presidium—Inonder **P. W. Saunders**

TWO-YEAR-OLDS

4 MISS BELLE EVE, b f 20/4 Josr Algarhoud (IRE)—Waraqa (USA) (Red Ransom (USA)) (1142) **M. C. Lane**

Other Owners: Mrs P. A. Palmer.

Assistant Trainer: Miss K. Windsor-Luck

318 MR F. T. J. JORDAN, Towcester
Postal: **Highfields Stables, Adstone, Towcester, Northamptonshire, NN12 8DS**
Contacts: OFFICE **(01327) 861162** HOME **(01327) 861162** FAX **(01327) 861162**
MOBILE **(07831) 101632** E-MAIL **jordyracer29@hotmail.co.uk**

1 BEECH GAMES, 4, b g Mind Games—Dane Dancing (IRE) **P. Ratcliffe**
2 CEARAN (CZE), 5, b g Rainbows For Life (CAN)—Ceara (CZE) **P. Ratcliffe**
3 FANTASTIC MORNING, 4, ch g Fantastic Light (USA)—Gombay Girl (USA) **F. T. J. Jordan**
4 FORMEDABLE (IRE), 6, ch g Moonax (IRE)—Castle Flame (IRE)
5 HOT CHOCOLAT, 8, b g Parthian Springs—Bally Muire **D. Pugh**
6 JERRY LEE (IRE), 5, b g Orpen (USA)—Vinicky (USA) **F. T. J. Jordan**
7 KILLFINNAN CASTLE (IRE), 5, br g Arctic Lord—Golden Seekers **Chris & Sallie Swan**
8 KING DIAMOND (FR), 7, b g Exit To Nowhere (USA)—Diamona (FR) **F. T. J. Jordan**
9 LIBRE, 8, b g Bahamian Bounty—Premier Blues (FR) **On The Up Partnership**
10 MEDKHAN (IRE), 11, ch g Lahib (USA)—Safayn (USA) **Miss L. M. Rochford**
11 MILLENIUM MAG (FR), 8, b g Cyborg (FR)—Feat (FR) **Mrs L. O. Ballard**
12 MONSIEUR GEORGES (FR), 8, b g Kadalko (FR)—Djoumi (FR) **Near & Far Racing**
13 MUSICAL AFFAIR, 4, b f Alflora (IRE)—Song For Jess (IRE) **F. T. J. Jordan**
14 SAFIN (GER), 4, b g Pennekamp (USA)—Sankt Johanna (GER) **Supercraft Structures Limited**
15 SUMMER BOUNTY, 12, b g Lugana Beach—Tender Moment (IRE) **Mr T. Powell**

Other Owners: Mr R. K. Betts, Mr Tim Powell, Mr J. Sleightholme, Mrs Sallie Swan, Mr Chris Swan, Mr David M. Thornton.

Assistant Trainer: Mrs G. Williams

Jockey (flat): E. Ahern, G. Baker, J Fortune. **Jockey (NH):** Tony McCoy, L. Aspell.

319 MR A. G. JUCKES, Abberley
Postal: **Cherry Ash, Worsley Farm, Abberley, Worcester**
Contacts: PHONE **(01299) 896471** FAX **(01299) 890114** MOBILE **(07970) 141246**

1 BIRTHDAY STAR (IRE), 6, b g Desert King (IRE)—White Paper (IRE) **Mr P. M. Cooper**
2 GIVE ME LOVE (FR), 8, ch g Bering—Cout Contact (USA) **B. J. Hine**
3 PERSIAN FOX (IRE), 4, b g King Charlemagne (USA)—Persian Mistress (IRE) **Whispering Winds**
4 ZAFFEU, 7, ch g Zafonic (USA)—Leaping Flame (USA) **Whispering Winds**

Other Owners: Mrs D. J. Bond, N. I. P. Brown, A. G. Juckes.

Assistant Trainer: R T Juckes

Jockey (flat): N. Callan, A. Kirby. **Conditional:** C. Poste, L. Heard, R. Spate.

320 MR D. P. KEANE, Shaftesbury
Postal: **Larkinglass Farm, Motcombe, Shaftesbury, Dorset, SP7 9HY**
Contacts: PHONE **(01747) 854666** FAX **(01747) 851112** MOBILE **(07764) 200012**
E-MAIL **paul@paulkeaneracing.com** WEBSITE **www.paulkeaneracing.com**

1 ALFATRIX (IRE), 5, b g Alflora (IRE)—Dutch Majesty **Jackie Abbott & Peter Gray**
2 ALFRED'S TOWER, 6, b g Alflora (IRE)—Dutch Majesty **Proverbial Optimists**
3 ALL IN THE STARS (IRE), 10, ch g Fourstars Allstar (USA)—Luton Flyer **Mrs H. R. Cross**
4 ALLUMEE, 9, ch g Alflora (IRE)—Coire Vannich **Mrs J. M. Abbott**
5 ANNOUNCING ALICE (IRE), 7, ch m Presenting—Alice Brennan (IRE) **Burnt Toast Ltd**
6 4, Br f Alflora (IRE)—Barton Dante **Lady H. J. Clarke**
7 BARTON FLOWER, 7, br m Danzero (AUS)—Iota **Lady H. J. Clarke**
8 CHARLIE POOLE (IRE), 6, b g Shambo—Country Store **Mrs A. Walker Mrs M. Poole**
9 COLONIAL JIM (IRE), 5, b g Rudimentary (USA)—Jenny May **Colony Stable LLC**
10 FAIRLIGHT SHADOW (IRE), 7, b g Good Thyne (USA)—Marble Fontaine **Mr M. G. Cahill**
11 4, B g Alflora (IRE)—Home From The Hill **Lady H. J. Clarke**
12 I'M A LEGEND, 6, b g Midnight Legend—I'm Maggy (NZ) **Wincanton Race Club**
13 ISLAND OF MEMORIES, 8, ch m Beneficial—Coronea Sea Queen (IRE) **P. C. Tory**
14 LORD LINGTON (FR), 9, b g Bulington (FR)—Tosca de Bussy (FR) **D. J. Bridger**
15 MAORI LEGEND, 7, b m Midnight Legend—Hinemoa (IRE) **Mrs H. R. Cross**
16 MIDNIGHT CHASE, 6, b g Midnight Legend—Yamrah **Lady H. J. Clarke**
17 MR DASS (IRE), 6, ch g Bob's Return (IRE)—Belle Babillard (IRE) **Dr E. Colhoun**
18 NATIONAL DIPLOMA (IRE), 8, b g Warcraft (USA)—Lady of Spain **Lady H. J. Clarke**
19 NORMANDY LANDINGS, 5, gr h Alflora (IRE)—Hinemoa (IRE) **Mrs H. R. Cross**
20 POPPY MAROON, 10, b m Supreme Leader—Maries Party **Mrs M. R. Dangerfield**
21 REBEL ROCK (IRE), 6, b g Rock Hopper—Penstal Lady (IRE) **Mr D. Casey**
22 RINNWOOD LASS (IRE), 7, b m Courtship—Classic Difference (IRE) **Mrs U. Brady**
23 ROOFING SPIRIT (IRE), 10, b g Beneficial—Vulcash (IRE) **F. J. Matthews**
24 SOUTHFIELD HALL (IRE), 4, b g Saddlers' Hall (IRE)—Bonny Lass **Angela Yeoman**
25 SPIRITUAL SOCIETY (IRE), 8, b g Moscow Society (USA)—Sniggy **Mr L J Marsh & Mr C D Ridgway**
26 SULA'S LEGEND, 7, ch g Midnight Legend—Sulapuff **Dajam Ltd**
27 THE LAYING HEN (IRE), 8, ch m Anshan—Glacial Run (IRE) **Strawberry Field Catering**
28 TOPLESS (IRE), 7, gr m Presenting—Tara The Grey (IRE) **J & S Baigent**
29 TOSULA, 5, b m Syrtos—Sulapuff **Dajam Ltd**
30 WINSLEY HILL, 6, b m Midnight Legend—Hinemoa (IRE) **Mrs H. R. Cross**
31 YOU KNOW BRIDIE (IRE), 6, b m Rudimentary (USA)—Lock The Bar **The Don't Tell Daddy Partnership**
32 ZAFFARELLA (IRE), 7, b m Zaffaran (USA)—Bay Gale (USA) **Miss J. A. Buchanan**

Other Owners: Mrs J. A. V. Allen, Avon Thoroughbreds Ltd, Mr J. R. Baigent, Mrs S. J. Baigent, Mr. P Barratt, Mr. I. Barton, Mrs P. A. Brewer, Mr Paul Brewer, Mrs M. A. Clark, Major R. C. D. Dangerfield, Mrs C. Lewis, Mr L. J. Marsh, Mrs M. F. Poole, Mr C. D. Ridgway, Mr Nick Robinson, Mrs A. G. L. Walker.

Jockey (NH): N. Mullholland.

321 MR T. KEDDY, Newmarket
Postal: **Heyward Place, Hamilton Road, Newmarket, Suffolk, CB8 7JQ**
Contacts: PHONE **(01638) 561498** FAX **(01638) 561498** MOBILE **(07804) 953420**
E-MAIL **tkracing@aol.com**

1 ABBEYGATE, 7, b g Unfuwain (USA)—Ayunli **Mrs H. Keddy**
2 APACHE FORT, 5, b g Desert Prince (IRE)—Apogee **A. J. Duffield**
3 BANJO PATTERSON, 6, b h Green Desert (USA)—Rumpipumpy **T. P. Ramsden**
4 BARLEY MOON, 4, b f Vettori (IRE)—Trojan Desert **P. E. Barrett**
5 BLACK WADI (IRE), 6, br m Desert King (IRE)—Tamelia **Lemberg Stables**
6 CLASSIC HALL (IRE), 5, b m Saddlers' Hall (IRE)—Classic Mix (IRE) **OK Partnership**
7 DHURWAH (IRE), 5, b m Green Desert (USA)—Bintalbawadi (IRE) **A. J. Duffield**
8 DINNER DATE, 6, ch g Groom Dancer (USA)—Misleading Lady **Mrs H. Keddy**
9 FIDDLERS FORD (IRE), 7, b g Sadler's Wells (USA)—Old Domesday Book **J. H. Fielding**
10 JAKE THE SNAKE (IRE), 7, ch g Intikhab (USA)—Tilbrook **T. P. Ramsden**
11 PEAS 'N BEANS (IRE), 5, ch g Medicean—No Sugar Baby (FR) **P. E. Barrett**
12 SA NAU, 5, b g Generous (USA)—Trellis Bay **J. H. Fielding**
13 TICKING, 5, ch g Barathea (IRE)—Tuning **J. H. Fielding**
14 WOMANISER (IRE), 4, br g Rock of Gibraltar (IRE)—Top Table **M. Keddy**

MR T. KEDDY—continued

THREE-YEAR-OLDS

15 **PISCEAN (USA)**, b br c Stravinsky (USA)—Navasha (USA) **A. J. Duffield**
16 **ROCKETRY**, ch c Desert Prince (IRE)—Moon Search **J. H. Fielding**
17 **WRENINGHAM**, br g Diktat—Slave To The Rythm (IRE) **M. L. Ayers**

TWO-YEAR-OLDS

18 Br c 6/3 Trans Island—Heike (Glenstal (USA)) (30000) **G. Huffer**
19 B f 1/4 Refuse To Bend (IRE)—Lady Digby (IRE) (Petorius) (41826) **A. J. Duffield**
20 B f 3/3 Mark of Esteem (IRE)—Mommkin (Royal Academy (USA)) (25740) **A. J. Duffield**
21 Ch f 13/1 Lomitas—Mountain Stream (FR) (Vettori (IRE)) (2000) **E. Buddle**

Other Owners: Mr P. Karanjia, Mr Peter Newman.

Assistant Trainer: Hayley Keddy

---

322 MRS C. KEEVIL, Blagdon
Postal: **Limekiln Stables, Charterhouse-on-Mendip, Blagdon, Bristol, BS40 7XW**
Contacts: **PHONE (07768) 867424 FAX (01761) 463927 MOBILE (07768) 867424**
E-MAIL **carolinekeevil@yahoo.co.uk**

1 **A PROPER CHARLIE**, 12, b g Cashwyn—Kate's Girl **Mrs J. Menzies & Mr H. Morris**
2 **ARCTIC FLOW**, 4, b f Alflora (IRE)—Flow **Mrs C. J. Dunn**
3 **BALLYVADEN (IRE)**, 8, b g Mister Lord (USA)—Anner Lodge (IRE) **M. J. O'Connor**
4 **CARAPAX (IRE)**, 4, b g Turtle Island (IRE)—Kate Air (IRE) **The Hon J. R. Drummond**
5 **DANDIVITO**, 5, b g Danzig Connection (USA)—Welsh Lustre (IRE) **Mrs L. R. Lovell**
6 **DAWN SILK (IRE)**, 8, b g Zaffaran (USA)—Dark Deep Dawn **Shortwood Family**
7 **DEEP POCKETS (IRE)**, 9, b g Fourstars Allstar (USA)—Pocket Price (IRE) **The Deep Pockets Partnership**
8 4, Gr f Silver Patriarch (IRE)—Flamebird (IRE) **Mrs L. R. Lovell**
9 5, B m Alflora (IRE)—Marzia (IRE) **Mrs J. Menzies & Mr H. Morris**
10 **MATAKO (FR)**, 5, b g Nikos—Verabatim (FR) **P. L. Hart**
11 **MINELLA LODGE**, 8, b g Environment Friend—Flakey Dove **M. J. O'Connor**
12 **THE WELL OF DREAMS (IRE)**, 7, ch g Presenting—Caribbean Rose (IRE) **The Hon J. R. Drummond**
13 4, B f Double Trigger (IRE)—Via Del Quatro (IRE) **M. J. O'Connor**

Other Owners: Mr W. R. Bougourd, Mr P. M. Bryant, Mrs Mary Dowds, Capt G. Dowds, Mrs Caroline Keevil, Mr H. F. Morris.

Amateur: Mr J. Snowden, Mr. I. Popham.

---

323 MRS F. J. KEHOE, Leighton Buzzard
Postal: **The Croft Farm, Wing Road, Stewkley, Leighton Buzzard, Bedfordshire, LU7 0JB**
Contacts: **PHONE (01525) 240749 FAX (01525) 240749 MOBILE (07795) 096908**
E-MAIL **f.kehoe@btinternet.com**

1 **LORD BROWNLOW**, 4, b g Best of The Bests (IRE)—Catriona **M. Kehoe**
2 **TICKFORD ABBEY**, 6, br g Emperor Fountain—Flash-By **M. Kehoe**

---

324 MR M. H. KEIGHLEY, Cheltenham
Postal: **2 Station Cottages, Toddington, Cheltenham, Gloucestershire, GL54 5DT**
Contacts: **PHONE (01242) 621479 MOBILE (07767) 472547**
E-MAIL **info@martinkeighleyracing.com WEBSITE www.martinkeighleyracing.com**

1 **BADLY BRUISED (IRE)**, 7, b g Tiraaz (USA)—Krissykiss **The Plough Inn At Ford Partnership**
2 **HAREEM (IRE)**, 4, b g King's Best (USA)—Knight's Place (IRE) **J. Finch**
3 **KING OZZY (IRE)**, 4, b g King Charlemagne (USA)—Kingpin Delight **The Black Pearl**
4 **MIC AUBIN (FR)**, 5, b g Broadway Flyer (USA)—Patney **C. M. Clarke**
5 **OCARITO (GER)**, 7, b g Auenadler (GER)—Okkasion **Mr K. Flook**
6 **PALMERS PEAK (IRE)**, 9, b g Arctic Lord—Shahraza **J. F. R. Stainer**
7 **PRESIDENT HILL (IRE)**, 10, b g Roselier (FR)—Bid For Fun (IRE) **All The President's Men**
8 **PRINCE DUNDEE (FR)**, 13, ch g Ecossais (FR)—Princesse Normande (FR) **M Keighley, D W Phipps & D E Cull**
9 **RODRIGO GONZALES (IRE)**, 6, b g Accordion—Newgate Beauty (IRE) **Nicholson Racing Syndicates**
10 **SARROCOCCA (IRE)**, 9, b g Supreme Leader—What's The Story **J. C. G. Williams**

MR M. H. KEIGHLEY—continued

11 **SHERMAN'S NEESE (IRE)**, 7, br m Presenting—Pallastown Gale (IRE) **Mrs J. F. Holloway**
12 **SKY CALLING**, 5, b m Bal Harbour—Curlew Calling (IRE) **Miss S. J. Sandes**
13 **STOCKTON FLYER**, 7, b g m Supposin (IRE)—Orange Alert **Mrs D. A. Butler**
14 4, B f Classic Cliche (IRE)—Vado Via

Other Owners: Mr M. J. Allen, Mr. S. Aspinall, Mr. J. E. Baylis, Mr C. Brown, Mr. T. Chanin, Ms. B. Chanin, Mr D. E. Cull, Ms. L. Deacon, Mr John H. W. Finch, Mr G. A. Hollick, Mr. Graham Hollick, Mr M. Keighley, Mrs V. Kinch, Mr. J. McConkey, Mr Bradley Moore, Mrs S. J. Mulraine, Mr. P. Murphy, Mrs D. Nicholson, Mr. J. O'Toole, Mr D. W. Phipps, Mr Jo Stainer, Mr H. R. Taylor, Ms. M. Turner.

Assistant Trainer: Mrs Belinda Keighley

Jockey (NH): Warren Marston, Tom Siddall. **Conditional:** Gerard Tumelty. **Amateur:** Mr Richard Burton.

---

325 MR C. N. KELLETT, Burton-on-Trent
Postal: **Stoneyford Croft, Barton-under-Needwood, Burton-on-Trent, Staffordshire, DE13 8BW**
Contacts: **PHONE (01283) 575646 FAX (01283) 575646 MOBILE (07966) 097989**
E-MAIL christopherkellett@btinternet.com WEBSITE www.chriskelletttracing.co.uk

1 **BAHHMIRAGE (IRE)**, 5, ch m Bahhare (USA)—Border Mirage **Miss S. L. Walley**
2 **BARTON BELLE**, 6, b m Barathea (USA)—Veronica **Mr N. Turnbull**
3 **BEE MAGIC**, 5, ch g Magic Ring (IRE)—Miss Bananas **G. C. Chipman**
4 **BLUECOAT (USA)**, 8, b g Majestic Twoeleven (USA)—
                       Elusive Peace (USA) **D. H. Muir & Exors of the Late Mrs R. E. Muir**
5 **DAWESVILLE**, 7, ch g Karinga Bay—Le Belle Avril (IRE) **J. E. Titley**
6 **FABREZAN (FR)**, 9, b g Nikos—Fabulous Secret (FR) **Keith O. Warner**
7 **FIGARO'S QUEST (IRE)**, 6, b g Singspiel (IRE)—Seren Quest **Keith O. Warner**
8 **FIGHT THE FEELING**, 10, ch g Beveled—Alvecote Lady **T. Morning**
9 **LADY LUCINDA**, 7, b m Muhtarram (USA)—Lady Phyl **Mr W. A. Gonsalves**
10 4, B g Best of The Bests (IRE)—Monte Mayor Lady (IRE) **D. H. Muir & Exors of the Late Mrs R. E. Muir**
11 **RICCARDO (IRE)**, 7, b g Arctic Lord—Another Kitty **J. E. Titley**
12 **ROOKERY LAD**, 10, b g Makbul—Wayzgoose (USA) **Mr S. Kitching & Mrs K. Taylor**
13 **TARA SLANE**, 5, ch g Kayf Tara—Quibbling **Slane Construction**

THREE-YEAR-OLDS

14 **ADMIRALS WAY**, ch c Observatory (USA)—Dockage (CAN) **J. E. Titley**

Other Owners: Miss K. E. Jones, S. Kearns, J. Kearns, Mr S. Kitching, Mr Drew Muir, Exors of the late Mrs R. E. Muir, Mrs K. Taylor.

Amateur: Miss Susannah Wileman.

---

326 MISS G. M. KELLEWAY, Newmarket
Postal: **Queen Alexandra Stables, 2 Chapel Street, Exning, Newmarket, Suffolk, CB8 7HA**
Contacts: **PHONE (01638) 577778 FAX (01638) 577778 MOBILE (07974) 948768**
E-MAIL gay@gaykelleway.co.uk WEBSITE www.gaykelleway.co.uk

1 **ARCTIC DESERT**, 8, b g Desert Prince—Thamud (IRE) **Miss G. M. Kelleway**
2 **BALLINTENI**, 6, b g Machiavellian (USA)—Silabteni (USA) **D. Cohen**
3 **BIENHEUREUX**, 7, b g Bien Bien (USA)—Rochea **Mr & Mrs I. Henderson**
4 **BOUNDLESS PROSPECT (USA)**, 9, b g Boundary (USA)—Cape (USA) **Mr M M Foulger Mr A Maclennan**
5 **COW GIRL (IRE)**, 4, b f King's Best (USA)—Reveuse de Jour (IRE) **Winterbeck Manor Stud Ltd**
6 **ESTURGEON DU RANCH (FR)**, 7, b g Turgeon (USA)—Belle Louloute (FR) **A. C. Maylam**
7 **FAJR (IRE)**, 6, b g Green Desert (USA)—Ta Rib (USA) **The New Dawn Partnership**
8 **MR LAMBROS**, 7, ch g Pivotal—Magical Veil **Winterbeck Manor Stud Ltd**
9 **MUSANGO**, 5, b g Night Shift (USA)—Imbabala **T & Z Racing Club**
10 **MUSIC NOTE (IRE)**, 5, b g Indian Ridge—Samara Middle East (FR) **Countrywide Classics Ltd**
11 **RASMANI**, 4, ch f Medicean—Rasmalai **Winterbeck Manor Stud Ltd**
12 **RED SUN**, 11, b g Foxhound (USA)—Superetta **A. C. Maylam**
13 **RUN TO ME**, 6, b m Commanche Run—Uninvited **Countrywide Classics Ltd**
14 **STAR STRIDER**, 4, gr g Royal Applause—Onefortheditch (USA) **Holistic Racing Ltd**
15 **STRINGSOFMYHEART**, 4, b f Halling (USA)—Heart's Harmony **Worldwide Jobs Ltd T/A Betting Jobs.Com**
16 **VORTEX**, 9, b g Danehill (USA)—Roupala (USA) **Coriolis Partnership**

MISS G. M. KELLEWAY—continued

THREE-YEAR-OLDS

17 **ASHTON HEIGHTS**, b c Kyllachy—Silver Elite **Mr A. P. Griffin**
18 **BRIDGE OF FERMOY (IRE)**, b c Danetime (IRE)—Banco Solo **T & Z Racing Club**
19 **BURY TREASURE (IRE)**, ch c Choisir (AUS)—Future Treasure **MM Foulger P Andrews Deauville Daze Pship**
20 **GRAIL KNIGHT**, ch g Carnival Dancer—Nashkova **Mr & Mrs P. Reynolds**

Other Owners: Mr P. Andrews, R. J. Brennan, R. Davies, T. A. Edwards, P. H. Ewing, Miss Z. Fakirmohamed, M. M. Foulger, I. Henderson, Exors of the Late A. J. Henderson, Mr M. V. Hill, Mr A. G. MacLennan, A. H. Nicholas, Mr P. B. Reynolds, Mrs H. Reynolds, Mr T. White, Mrs A. P. Wilkinson, C. J. Wilkinson, T. D. Williams.

Assistant Trainer: Miss Olivia Maylam
Amateur: Miss Olivia Maylam.

---

327 **MR G. P. KELLY, Sheriff Hutton**
Postal: **3 Church End Cottages, Sheriff Hutton, North Yorkshire, YO60 6SY**
Contacts: **HOME (01347) 878770/878994 MOBILE (07866) 285187**

1 **HIGH WINDOW (IRE)**, 8, b g King's Theatre (IRE)—Kayradja (IRE) **A. C. Barrett**
2 **LITTLE PANDORA**, 4, b f Komaite (USA)—Little Talitha **C. I. Ratcliffe**
3 4, B g Gods Solution—Morcat **C. I. Ratcliffe**
4 **SHERIFF STAR**, 5, b m Killer Instinct—Westcourt Ruby **A. C. Barrett**
5 **SPENCE'S CHOICE (IRE)**, 4, b g Desert Sun—Late Night Lady (IRE) **G. P. Kelly**
6 **YVOIRE**, 5, ch m Sugarfoot—Crambella (IRE) **C. I. Ratcliffe**

Other Owners: S. Fox, Mr G. P. Kelly, Mr M. Punchard.

Assistant Trainer: Ian Ratcliffe
Jockey (flat): Paul Mulrennan. **Amateur:** Miss S. Brotherton, Mr T. Greenall, Mr C. Mulhall, Mr M. Walford.

---

328 **MR P. KELSALL, Ledbury**
Postal: **Linwell House, Hope End, Ledbury, Herefordshire, HR8 1JQ**
Contacts: **PHONE (01531) 631128 FAX (01531) 631128 MOBILE (07802) 160584**

1 **ALL SONSILVER (FR)**, 11, b g Son of Silver—All Licette (FR) **P. Kelsall**
2 **AR AN SHRON**, 8, b g Alderbrook—Charlotte's Festival **P. Kelsall**
3 **DECREE NISI**, 5, ch g Compton Place—Palisandra (USA) **P. Kelsall**
4 **KIMONO ROYAL (FR)**, 10, b br g Garde Royale—Alizane (FR) **P. Kelsall**
5 **MOBASHER (IRE)**, 9, b g Spectrum (IRE)—Danse Royale (IRE) **P. Kelsall**
6 **MONETS MASTERPIECE (USA)**, 5, b g Quiet American (USA)—Math (USA) **P. Kelsall**
Assistant Trainer: Miss J Kelsall

---

329 **MRS C. J. KERR, Aberfeldy**
Postal: **Balnacraig Farm, Fortingall, Aberfeldy, Perthshire, PH15 2LJ**
Contacts: **PHONE (01887) 830354 MOBILE (07768) 682841**

1 **ATHOLLBROSE (USA)**, 7, b g Mister Baileys—Knightly Cut Up (USA) **Mrs C. J. Kerr**
2 **FISHER STREET**, 13, gr g Tigani—Pricket Walk **Mrs C. J. Kerr**
3 **LOST PROPERTY (IRE)**, 10, b g Phardante (FR)—Icy Rock **Mrs C. J. Kerr**
4 **PHARAGON (IRE)**, 10, b g Phardante (FR)—Hogan (IRE) **Mrs C. J. Kerr**
Assistant Trainer: David Dasilva

---

330 **MISS K. KEY, Knaresborough**
Postal: **Merryvale Stud, Cass Lane, Forest Moor Road, Knaresborough, North Yorkshire, HG5 8JZ**
Contacts: **PHONE (01423) 297971 MOBILE (07504) 241853**

1 **MERRYVALE MAN**, 11, b g Rudimentary (USA)—Salu **Kariana Key**
2 **MISS TIDDLYPUSH**, 7, gr m Defacto (USA)—Misty Rocket **Mainframe Management Limited**
3 **MISTER MOUSSAC**, 9, b g Kasakov—Salu **Kariana Key**

MISS K. KEY—continued

THREE-YEAR-OLDS

4 DARCY'S DARLING, b br f Kasakov—Salu **Kariana Key**

---

331 **MRS A. L. M. KING, Stratford-upon-Avon**
Postal: Ridgeway House, Moor Farm, Wilmcote, Stratford-upon-Avon, Warwickshire, CV37 9XG
Contacts: OFFICE (01789) 205087 HOME (01789) 298346 FAX (01789) 263260
E-MAIL anabelking.racing@virgin.net

1 ARFINNIT (IRE), 7, b g College Chapel—Tidal Reach (USA) **All The Kings Horses**
2 BURNLEY (IRE), 5, b g Distant Music—Dance Ahead **H. A. Murphy**
3 CHAPTER (IRE), 6, ch g Sinndar (IRE)—Web of Intrigue **Mrs A. L. M. King**
4 COME ON EDDIE, 5, b g Deploy—Arusha **A. R. Mapp**
5 DANIEL THOMAS (IRE), 6, b g Dansili—Last Look **Mr G. Martin**
6 DROMDERRIG (IRE), 6, b g Fourstars Allstar (USA)—Lucky River (IRE) **H. A. Murphy**
7 FINTAN, 5, ch g Generous (IRE)—Seeker **H. A. Murphy**
8 GREAT VIEW (IRE), 9, b g Great Commotion (USA)—Tara View (IRE) **All The Kings Horses**
9 INDIAN LADY (IRE), 5, b m Namid—Lady Eberspacher (IRE) **H. A. Murphy**
10 IZITA STAR, 5, b m Lomitas—Shaanara (IRE) **Mrs D. L. Whateley**
11 4, B f Kayf Tara—May Queen Megan **Mr T. P. Hilliam**
12 VERY GREEN (FR), 6, b g Barathea (IRE)—Green Bend (USA) **H. A. Murphy**
13 WISTERIA LANE (IRE), 5, b g In The Wings—Web of Intrigue **H. A. Murphy**

THREE-YEAR-OLDS

14 REDEFINE, ch f Bertolini (USA)—Azur (IRE) **Mrs L. H. Field**

TWO-YEAR-OLDS

15 BETOULA, ch f 10/2 Bertolini (USA)—Pab's Choice (Telsmoss) **C. Papaioannou**

Amateur: Mr O. J. Murphy.

---

332 **MR ALAN KING, Barbury Castle**
Postal: Barbury Castle Stables, Wroughton, Wiltshire, SN4 0QZ
Contacts: PHONE (01793) 815009 FAX (01793) 845080 MOBILE (07973) 461233
E-MAIL alanking.racing@virgin.net WEBSITE www.alankingracing.co.uk

1 ADORABELLA (IRE), 5, b m Revoque (IRE)—Febrile (USA) **Mrs C. Hawkins**
2 AL TAYYARA, 6, b m Alflora (IRE)—Quiet Dawn **Mrs B. J. Booty**
3 ALFASONIC, 8, b g Alflora (IRE)—Lady Solstice **Mrs S. Warren**
4 ARCHDUKE FERDINAND (FR), 10, ch g Dernier Empereur (USA)—Lady Norcliffe (USA) **Mr D. J. S. Sewell**
5 ATOMIC WINNER (IRE), 4, b f Poliglote—Freedom Flame **Elite Racing Club**
6 AWESOME GEORGE, 4, b g Exit To Nowhere (USA)—Awesome Aunt (IRE) **Mrs G. Meacham & Alan Briscoe**
7 AYPEEYES (IRE), 4, b g King Charlemagne (USA)—Habaza (USA) **D. A. Wallace**
8 BAKBENSCHER, 9, gr g Bob Back (USA)—Jessolle **Three Line Whip**
9 BALLAMUSIC (IRE), 6, b g Accordion—Hazy Fiddler (IRE) **T. J. Hemmings**
10 BEVERLY HILL BILLY, 4, b g Primo Valentino (IRE)—Miss Beverley **B. Winfield & A. King**
11 BLAZING BAILEY, 6, b g Mister Baileys—Wannaplantatree **Three Line Whip**
12 BLISTERING (IRE), 5, ch g Insan (USA)—Broken Boots (IRE) **The Laodiceans**
13 BLUE DARK (FR), 4, ch g Dark Moondancer—Windsor Blue (FR) **D. M. Mason**
14 BORMO (FR), 4, b g Marathon (USA)—Borane (FR) **M 2 C Racing Partnership**
15 BORN LEADER (IRE), 10, b g Supreme Leader—Real Lace **Nigel Bunter & Jules Sigler**
16 BUDDYS LOOKOUT (IRE), 6, ch g Buddy's Friend—Grey Lookout (IRE) **Dr & Mrs Why**
17 CALAFICIAL (IRE), 5, br g Beneficial—Calamaire **T. J. Hemmings**
18 CALL ME A LEGEND, 4, ch f Midnight Legend—Second Call **Mrs K. Holmes**
19 CEE CEE RIDER, 6, b m Classic Cliche (IRE)—Rachel C (IRE) **The Laodiceans**
20 CHARMAINE WOOD, 5, b m Double Trigger (IRE)—Forest Pride (IRE) **Let's Live Racing**
21 CILLA BLACK, 6, br m Overbury (IRE)—Camillas Legacy **F.O.T.O Finish Partnership**
22 COLOUR FOOTAGE (IRE), 6, b m Supreme Leader—Lipstick Lady (IRE) **Killinghurst Park Stud**
23 COPPER BAY (IRE), 6, b g Revoque (IRE)—Bahia Laura (FR) **The Copper Bay Partnership**
24 CRYSTAL D'AINAY (FR), 9, b g Saint Preuil (FR)—Guendale (FR) **Mr Tony Fisher & Mrs Jeni Fisher**
25 D'ARGENT (IRE), 11, gr g Roselier (FR)—Money Galore **N. S. G. Bunter**
26 DAN BUOY (FR), 5, b g Slip Anchor—Bramosia **N. S. G. Bunter**
27 DANCINGWITHBUBBLES (IRE), 5, b m Supreme Leader—Kates Charm (IRE) **C. B. Brookes**

MR ALAN KING—continued

28 4, B f King's Theatre (IRE)—Daprika (FR) **Netherfield House Stud**
29 DARYAL (IRE), 7, b g Night Shift (USA)—Darata (IRE) **Let's Live Racing**
30 DAY'S OVER, 6, br m Overbury (IRE)—Red Dusk **Ms J. H. Menzies**
31 DIVALI PRINCESS, 4, b f Muhtarram (USA)—Diva **Mrs Joy Fenton & Partners**
32 DRAGON EYE (IRE), 6, b g Saddlers' Hall (IRE)—Bint Alsarab **Mrs A. M. Brodie**
33 ELLEN TILLEY, 4, b f Overbury (IRE)—Fortunes Course **J. E. Garrett**
34 EMERALD WILDERNESS (IRE), 4, b g Green Desert (USA)—Simla Bibi **Terry Warner & David Sewell**
35 EVELITH ECHO, 5, b g Overbury (IRE)—Sunday News'n'echo (USA) **A. Stennett**
36 FIVE COLOURS (IRE), 8, b br g Lord Americo—Thousand Springs **J. Sigler**
37 FLEETWOOD FOREST, 8, b g Fleetwood (IRE)—Louise Moillon **Mr Tony Fisher & Mrs Jeni Fisher**
38 FRANCHOEK (IRE), 4, ch g Trempolino (USA)—Snow House (IRE) **J. P. McManus**
39 GAYE STARLET (IRE), 5, b m Soviet Star (USA)—Gaye Humour (IRE) **Racegoers Club Owners Group**
40 GENTLEMAN JIMMY, 8, br g Alderbrook—Irish Orchid **Burridge,Burridge,Pilkington & Rutland**
41 GEORGIAN KING, 5, b g Overbury (IRE)—Roslin **R. Allsop**
42 GOLD REEF, 5, ch m Double Trigger (IRE)—
                                      Realms of Gold (USA) **Mr & Mrs Welch, King, Phillipson & Rowland**
43 GREENBRIDGE (IRE), 6, b g Luso—Green Divot **T. J. Hemmings**
44 GREMLIN, 4, b g Mujahid (USA)—Fairy Free **Mrs J. K. Powell**
45 GROUP CAPTAIN, 6, b g Dr Fong (USA)—Alusha **P. Webb**
46 HALCON GENELARDAIS (IRE), 8, ch g Halcon—Francetphile (FR) **Ian Payne & Kim Franklin**
47 HALDIBARI (IRE), 4, b g Kahyasi—Haladiya (IRE) **Mr P. Harding & Mr S. Williams**
48 HEARTSANDDIAMONDS, 4, ch f First Trump—La Volta **Mr and Mrs Tom W. H. Dancer**
49 HIGH LIFE, 6, br m Kayf Tara—By Line **Cheltenham Racing Ltd**
50 HIGHLAND CHIEF (IRE), 8, b br g Taipan (IRE)—Catatonia (IRE) **P. J. Dunkley & D. F. Reilly**
51 HILLS OF HOME (IRE), 7, b g Pasternak—Carrick Shannon **Killinghurst Park Stud**
52 HOWLE HILL (IRE), 8, b g Ali-Royal (IRE)—
                                      Grandeur And Grace (USA) **The Brown Family, R. Benton & R. Lucas**
53 HUGO WOLF (IRE), 6, b g Mtoto—Instabene **P. E. Atkinson**
54 IL DUCE (IRE), 8, br g Anshan—Glory-Glory (IRE) **Mrs E. A. Prowting**
55 IN VINO, 4, b g Kayf Tara—Carousel Music **Ms L. V. Agran**
56 INDICIBLE (FR), 4, ch g Dyhim Diamond (IRE)—Caslon (FR) **Million in Mind Partnership**
57 ITSA LEGEND, 9, b g Midnight Legend—Onawing Andaprayer **The We're A Legend Partnership**
58 KAHRAYN, 5, ch g Generous (IRE)—Kadassa (IRE) **R. & P. Scott & I. Payne & K. Franklin**
59 KANDJAR D'ALLIER (FR), 10, gr g Royal Charter (FR)—Miss Akarad (FR) **Let's Live Racing**
60 KARABAK (FR), 5, b g Kahyasi—Mosstraye (FR) **D. M. Mason**
61 KATCHIT (IRE), 5, b g Kalanisi (IRE)—Miracle **D S J P Syndicate**
62 KATESS (IRE), 5, b m Spectrum—Esclava (USA) **Mrs M. C. Sweeney**
63 KAUTO THE ROC (FR), 4, ch g With The Flow (USA)—Kauto of Realm (FR) **Mrs R. J. King**
64 KELREV (FR), 10, ch g Video Rock (FR)—Bellie II (FR) **Flintham, King & Roberts**
65 KIKOS (FR), 6, ch g Nikos—Balgarde (FR) **Sir Robert Ogden C.B.E., LLD**
66 KING'S REVENGE, 5, br g Wizard King—Retaliator **IanKirkham JonnyKirkham RichardKirkham**
67 4, B g Beat All (USA)—Kingsfold Blaze **A. Stennett**
68 KNIGHTON LAD (IRE), 8, b g Supreme Leader—Tarqueen (IRE) **Mrs M. M. Stobart**
69 KNIGHTSBRIDGELIVES (IRE), 5, b g Taipan (IRE)—Shean Rose (IRE) **Nigel Bunter & Jules Sigler**
70 LA GRANDE VILLEZ (FR), 6, b m Villez (USA)—Grande Sultane (FR) **The Copper Bay Partnership**
71 LADY OF RATHCANNON (IRE), 6, b m Anshan—Miss Fern **Mrs P. Andrews**
72 LAKE LEGEND, 4, b g Midnight Legend—Lac Marmot (FR) **J. Wright,P. Wilson,F. J. Allen & R. Preston**
73 LEVERA, 5, b g Groom Dancer (USA)—Prancing **Four Mile Racing**
74 LONG HOP (IRE), 5, b g City Honours (USA)—Dangan River (IRE) **Mr D. J. S. Sewell**
75 MAD JACK DUNCAN (IRE), 6, br g Presenting—My Native Gesture **Favourites Racing IX**
76 MADNESS (IRE), 5, b g King's Theatre (IRE)—Chez Georges **Extraman Ltd, Tony Chard, Martin Lyes**
77 MAJOR RUMBLE, 5, b g Classic Cliche (IRE)—Fall About **Let's Get Ready To Rumble Partnership**
78 MARSHALLS RUN (IRE), 8, b g Accordion—Lady's Bridge (USA) **T. J. Hemmings**
79 MASKED MAN (IRE), 5, ch g Alhaarth (IRE)—Misbegotten (IRE) **N. D. Bruce Copp**
80 MEXICAN BOB, 5, b g Atraf—Eskimo Nel (IRE) **First Chance Racing**
81 MEXICAN PETE, 8, b g Atraf—Eskimo Nel (IRE) **First Chance Racing**
82 MIDNIGHT SAIL, 5, b g Midnight Legend—Mayina **M 2 C Racing Partnership**
83 MILL FOLLY, 5, b g Simply Great (FR)—Mill Afrique **Mrs D. Shutes**
84 MILLE ET UNE (FR), 5, b m Trempolino (USA)—Musareva (FR) **Netherfield House Stud**
85 MISS CARROLL, 5, b m Carroll House—Miss Fern **Mrs P. Andrews**
86 MUGHAS (IRE), 9, b g Sadler's Wells (USA)—Quest of Passion (USA) **B. Winfield, C. Fenton & A. Longman**
87 MY WAY DE SOLZEN (FR), 8, b g Assessor (FR)—
                             Agathe de Solzen (FR) **B. Winfield,A. Longman,J. Wright & C. Fenton**
88 NENUPHAR COLLONGES (FR), 7, b g Video Rock (FR)—Diane Collonges (FR) **Top Brass Partnership**
89 NORMAN THE GREAT, 4, b g Night Shift (USA)—Encore du Cristal (USA) **McNeill Racing**
90 NOTICEABLE (IRE), 4, b c Night Shift (USA)—Nawaji (USA) **The Hairy Lemon Partnership**

MR ALAN KING—continued

91 **NULATO (IRE)**, 5, b g Turtle Island (IRE)—Newtown Wonder (IRE) **Ian Payne & Kim Franklin**
92 **NYKEL (FR)**, 7, ch g Brier Creek (USA)—Une Du Chatelier (FR) **The Unlucky For Some Partnership**
93 **NYRCHE (FR)**, 8, b g Medaaly—Thoiry (USA) **Mr Tony Fisher & Mrs Jeni Fisher**
94 **OH CRICK (FR)**, 5, ch g Nikos—Other Crik (FR) **Mr D. J. S. Sewell**
95 **OLD BENNY**, 7, b g Saddlers' Hall (IRE)—Jack's The Girl (IRE) **T. J. Hemmings**
96 **ONIPHLAURE (FR)**, 6, b g Turgeon (USA)—Flaurella (FR) **Mr & Mrs F. C. Welch**
97 **ONYX BRUERE (FR)**, 6, gr g Mansonnien (FR)—Hervine Bruere (FR) **Mr & Mrs R. Scott**
98 **ORION D'OUDAIRIES (FR)**, 6, b g Grand Tresor (FR)—Quelinda (FR) **Tim & Sarah Ingram Hill**
99 **OTARIE (FR)**, 6, b m Lute Antique (FR)—Birdie IV (FR) **Mr E. J. M. Spurrier**
100 **OUZBECK (FR)**, 6, b g Denham Red (FR)—Volodia (FR) **Axom VII**
101 **OVER SIXTY**, 5, b m Overbury (IRE)—Free Travel **Mr & Mrs Christopher Harris**
102 **PAGANO (IRE)**, 5, b g Night Shift (USA)—Frippet (IRE) **Mr & Mrs F. D. Bell**
103 **PAKTOLOS (FR)**, 5, b g Dansili—Pithara (GR) **Mr P. Finnegan**
104 **PANGBOURNE (FR)**, 7, b g Double Bed (FR)—Valgrija (FR) **T. J. Hemmings**
105 **PARADISE REGAINED (FR)**, 5, b g Lost World (IRE)—Bajabala (FR) **Mrs P. Andrews**
106 **PATTON (FR)**, 5, b g Bonnet Rouge (FR)—Gesse Parade (FR) **G. C. Mordaunt**
107 **PENNEK (FR)**, 5, b g Grand Tresor (FR)—Annabelle Treveene (FR) **Mr H. D. Read**
108 **PENNY ISLAND (IRE)**, 6, b g Trans Island—Sparklingsovereign **Alan King**
109 **PENZANCE**, 7, ch g Pennekamp (USA)—Kalinka (IRE) **Elite Racing Club**
110 **POLIGLOTTI (FR)**, 6, b g Poliglote—Loretta Gianni (FR) **Westcote Inn Partnership**
111 **POLLY POTTER**, 5, b m Kayf Tara—Potter's Gale (IRE) **J. E. Potter**
112 **PORTERS WAR (IRE)**, 8, ch g Flemensfirth (USA)—Grainne Geal **Sarah Waugh & Paul Porter**
113 **POUVOIR (FR)**, 5, gr g Verglas (IRE)—Policia (FR) **Mr & Mrs R. Scott**
114 **PRETTY STAR (FR)**, 8, b g Lando (GER)—Pretty Ballerina **Mrs Lottie Hayman-Joyce & H J Racing**
115 **PRIDEUS (IRE)**, 4, gr g Atticus (USA)—Pride Of Baino (USA) **The Tin Bar Syndicate**
116 **PRINCE BROC (FR)**, 5, gr g Madoun (FR)—Elseural (FR) **McNeill Racing**
117 **PRINCE BUSTER (FR)**, 5, b g Sinjar (FR)—Eliflo (FR) **The Unusual Racegoers Partnership**
118 **PRINCE DU SEUIL (FR)**, 5, b g Lucky Dream (FR)—Hermione III (FR) **Mrs E. A. Prowting**
119 **PUR DE SIVOLA (FR)**, 5, b g Robin des Champs (FR)—Gamine d'ici (FR) **Thurloe 50**
120 **QUATRO PIERJI (FR)**, 4, br g Robin des Champs (FR)—Bebenefertiti (FR) **Sir Robert Ogden C.B.E., LLD**
121 **QUELCLASSE (FR)**, 4, b g Ultimately Lucky (IRE)—Huronne (FR) **Martin St Quinton & Friends**
122 **QUIET BOB (IRE)**, 5, b g Bob Back (USA)—Quit The Noise (IRE) **T. J. Hemmings**
123 4, B f Alflora (IRE)—Quistaquay **A. Stennett**
124 **QUIZZENE (USA)**, 6, gr g Cozzene (USA)—Company Binness (USA) **Favourites Racing VII**
125 **RISK RUNNER (IRE)**, 5, b g Mull of Kintyre (USA)—Fizzygig **The Norf 'N' Sarf Partnership**
126 **RODNEY'S PILLAR**, 5, ch g Karinga Bay—Killatty Player (IRE) **I. Anderson, G. Phillipson & C. Rowland**
127 **ROOD GIRL**, 5, ch m Alflora (IRE)—Quiet Dawn **Mrs B. J. Booty**
128 **ROOD REPORT**, 8, ch g Gunner B—Quiet Dawn **Mrs B. J. Booty**
129 **ROWLEY HILL**, 10, b g Karinga Bay—Scarlet Dymond **The Brown Family & Mrs S. Faccenda**
130 **RUSSIAN INVADER (IRE)**, 4, ch g Acatenango (GER)—Ukraine Venture **N. S. G. Bunter**
131 **RUSTARIX (FR)**, 7, b g Housamix (FR)—Star of Russia (FR) **Mrs C. Skan**
132 **SAM LORD**, 4, ch g Observatory (USA)—My Mariam **Winter Madness**
133 **SANTIA**, 5, b m Kahyasi—Santana Lady (IRE) **The Meadow Men**
134 **SASSANIAS (FR)**, 4, b g Sassanian (USA)—Dindouna (FR) **Sir Robert Ogden C.B.E., LLD**
135 **SEA THE LIGHT**, 8, b g Blue Ocean (USA)—Lamper's Light **Mr & Mrs F. C. Welch**
136 **SELF RESPECT (USA)**, 6, b g Lear Fan (USA)—Cap of Dignity **Sir Robert Ogden C.B.E., LLD**
137 **SHA BIHAN (FR)**, 7, b g Villez (USA)—Shadrou (FR) **Elite Racing Club**
138 **SHABENITO (IRE)**, 4, b g Anshan—Glory-Glory (IRE) **Mr Tony Fisher & Mrs Jeni Fisher**
139 **SHALONE**, 4, ch g Tobougg (IRE)—Let Alone **Mr Tony Fisher & Mrs Jeni Fisher**
140 **SHARAJAN (IRE)**, 8, b g Desert King (IRE)—Balakera (IRE) **Mr Tony Fisher & Mrs Jeni Fisher**
141 **SHIPMASTER**, 5, b g Slip Anchor—Cover Look (SAF) **N. S. G. Bunter**
142 **SILENCIO (IRE)**, 7, b g Sillery (USA)—Flabbergasted (IRE) **Let's Live Racing**
143 **SILVER SPINNER**, 5, gr m Silver Patriarch (IRE)—Mrs Jennifer Mickleton Racing Club
144 **SIMBA SUN (IRE)**, 4, b g Intikhab (USA)—Lions Den (IRE) **The Calvera Partnership**
145 **SINDANNA**, 4, ch f Sinndar (IRE)—Esclava (USA) **Mrs M. C. Sweeney**
146 **SIR HARRY ORMESHER**, 5, b g Sir Harry Lewis (USA)—Glamour Game **Mr D. J. S. Sewell**
147 **SONGMASTER**, 5, b g Singspiel (IRE)—One Beautiful Lady (IRE) **Mr & Mrs R. Scott**
148 **SOUTHERN REGENT (IND)**, 7, b g Razeen (USA)—Allinda (IND) **A. Stennett**
149 **SOVEREIGN KING**, 6, b g Sovereign Water (FR)—Bedwyn Bridge **Miss J. M. Bodycote**
150 **SPARE CASH (IRE)**, 6, ch g Zaffaran (USA)—Money Galore (IRE) **Blackwell, Bunter & Thomas**
151 **SPIRITED SPOUSE (IRE)**, 5, ch g Exit To Nowhere (USA)—Fiancee (FR) **Burnt Toast Ltd**
152 **SPRING DREAM (IRE)**, 5, gr m Kalanisi (IRE)—Zest (USA) **W. H. Ponsonby**
153 **SQUADRON**, 8, b g Sakhee (USA)—Machaera **Mr Tony Fisher & Mrs Jeni Fisher**
154 **STARBURST DIAMOND (IRE)**, 6, ro g Old Vic—Camlin Rose (IRE) **Anne Reilly & Denise Dunkley**
155 **STERNENZELT (GER)**, 5, gr g Silvano (GER)—Sterlina (GER) **Mrs C. Skan**
156 **STOLEN MOMENTS (FR)**, 7, gr g Villez (USA)—Brave Lola (FR) **The Poppet Partnership**

MR ALAN KING—continued

157 **STONEY'S TREASURE**, 4, ch g Silver Patriarch (IRE)—Stoney Path **Mrs S. C. Welch**
158 **STOWAY (FR)**, 6, b g Broadway Flyer (USA)—Stowe (FR) **Mr Tony Fisher & Mrs Jeni Fisher**
159 **SUMMER OF LOVE (IRE)**, 4, b f Fasliyev (USA)—Overboard (IRE) **A. Sheppard, A. Windle & K. Hix**
160 **SWIFT SAILOR**, 7, gr g Slip Anchor—New Wind (GER) **Mike Charlton & Rodger Sargent**
161 **SYLVAN WINGS**, 5, gr m Silver Patriarch (IRE)—Wing On **Mrs A. E. R. Goodwin**
162 **TAKOTNA (IRE)**, 6, b m Bering—Another Legend (USA) **Ian Payne & Kim Franklin**
163 **THE HAIRY LEMON**, 8, b g Eagle Eyed (USA)—Angie's Darling **The Hairy Lemon Partnership**
164 **THEATRE GIRL**, 5, b m King's Theatre (IRE)—Fortune's Girl **Let's Live Racing**
165 **THENFORD STAR (IRE)**, 7, b m Zaffaran (USA)—Limavady Lady (IRE) **The Armchair Jockeys**
166 **TIMAQUAN WARRIOR**, 5, gr g Exit To Nowhere (USA)—Siroyalta (FR) **N. G. Bunter**
167 **TRIGGER THE LIGHT**, 7, ch g Double Trigger (IRE)—Lamper's Light **Mr & Mrs F. C. Welch & Mrs A. A. Shutes**
168 **TROUBLE AT BAY (IRE)**, 8, b g Slip Anchor—Fight Right (FR) **N. S. G. Bunter**
169 **UNANSWERED**, 4, b c Double Trigger (IRE)—Kassala (FR) **J. Sigler**
170 **VALLEYOFTHEDOLLS**, 4, b f King's Theatre (IRE)—Fortune's Girl **Let's Live Racing**
171 **VOY POR USTEDES (FR)**, 7, b g Villez (USA)—Nuit D'ecajeul (FR) **Sir Robert Ogden C.B.E., LLD**
172 **WEST END ROCKER (IRE)**, 6, b br g Grand Plaisir (IRE)—Slyguff Lord (IRE) **Mr B. Winfield & Mr A. Longman**
173 **YARDBIRD (IRE)**, 9, b g Moonax (IRE)—Princess Lizzie (IRE) **Gilco**
174 **YOUR AMOUNT (IRE)**, 5, b g Beckett (IRE)—Sin Lucha (USA) **The Norf 'N' Sarf Partnership**
175 **ZAMBOOZLE (IRE)**, 6, ch g Halling (USA)—Blue Sirocco **R. C. Tooth**
176 **ZILCASH**, 5, b g Mujahid (USA)—Empty Purse **Mr David Bellamy & Mr Stephen Williams**
177 **ZIRKEL (IRE)**, 5, br g Highest Honor (FR)—Mythical Creek (USA) **Mrs L. H. Field**

THREE-YEAR-OLDS

178 **ALL LIT UP**, b g Fantastic Light (USA)—Maiden Aunt (IRE) **Four Mile Racing**
179 **BLACK JACARI (IRE)**, b g Black Sam Bellamy (IRE)—Amalia (IRE) **David Bellamy & Alan King**
180 **COSMEA**, b f Compton Place—St James's Analogy (IRE) **Four Mile Racing**
181 **FLOWER SONG**, b f Act One—Sweet Pea **Coln Valley Syndicate**
182 **FLYING APPLAUSE**, b g Royal Applause—Mrs Gray **Four Mile Racing**
183 **IT'S A DATE**, b c Kyllachy—By Arrangement (IRE) **Four Mile Racing**
184 **LATIN SCHOLAR (IRE)**, ch g Titus Livius (FR)—Crimada (IRE) **Four Mile Racing**
185 **MADAME BOUNTIFUL**, ch f Bahamian Bounty—Madame Crecy (USA) **Mrs M. T. Stopford-Sackville**
186 **MANYRIVERSTOCROSS (IRE)**, bc Cape Cross (IRE)—Alexandra S (IRE) **Mrs M. C. Sweeney**
187 **POTEMKIN (USA)**, b br g Van Nistelrooy (USA)—Bolshoia (USA) **Mr & Mrs David Thornhill**
188 **TUTTO BENE (IRE)**, ch c Modigliani (USA)—Butterwick (USA) **Mr John Vinden & Mr Andy Longman**

Other Owners: Mr C. Adams, Mr D. Allatt, F. J. Allen, I. F. Anderson, A. M. Armitage, Axom Ltd, M. Ball, Mr P. J. Barrett, Mrs H. L. Bell, Mr F. D. Bell, D. Bellamy, R. J. Benton, Mrs A. Blackwell, Mr A. F. Briscoe, A. R. Bromley, Exors of the Late Mrs S. R. Brown, C. G. Brown, Mrs M. V. Bruce Copp, J. G. St. Paul Burridge, S. St. P Burridge, Mrs C. E. Caddick, Mrs L. K. S. Campbell, R. G. Carter, A. M. Chard, M. R. Charlton, Mr G. J. Clark, J. L. Clarke, Mr D. E. Collier, Mr T. Collins, C. Conroy, T. W. H. Dancer, Mrs R. Dancer, G. F. Davies, Mrs A. L. Davies, Mrs M. C. Diplock, Mr D. Downie, P. J. Dunkley, Mrs D. Dunkley, Mr J. R. Eburne, Extraman Ltd, Mrs S. Faccenda, N. Farrell, A. G. Fear, C. F. Fenton, Mrs I. J. Fenton, Mr J. J. Fildes, A. D. Fisher, Mrs J. A. Fisher, L. R. Frampton, Miss K. M. Franklin, S. G. Friend, G. B. Turnbull Ltd, N. A. Gill, T. R. Gittins, G. F. Goode, Mr J. J. Gouder, A. P Gregory, B. F. Gregory, J. D. Groves, P. M. Harding, Mr C. I. K. Harris, Mrs C. A. Harris, Mrs C. A. M. Hayman-Joyce, Mr J. L. Hayman-Joyce, Mr D. A. Heffer, P. Hickey, A. J. Hill, D. F. Hill, Mrs K. E. Hix, J. Holmes, D. W. Holpin, Mr T. Ingram-Hill, Mrs S. P Ingram-Hill, N. M. H. Jones, Mr J. D. King, I. Kirkham, Mr R. G. Kirkham, Mr J. Kirkham, C. D. Leach, Mr W. P Ledward, M. W. Lightbody, Mr R. M. Lightbody, Mrs J. G. Lightbody, T. A. Lloyd, A. Longman, R. A. Lucas, D. A. Lucie-Smith, Mr M. A. J. Lyes, Mr A. R. W. Marsh, J. G. Mason, W. McGregor, M. S. McNeill, Mrs P R. McNeill, Mrs G. Meacham, Miss V. Medwell, W. D. C. Minton, Mr H. F. Morris, Mr J. J. Murray, Mrs D. C. Nicholson, Miss M. Noden, J. O'Grady, Mrs L. H. Oakley, Mr A. Oaten, Mr S. J. Oaten, O. J. W. Pawle, Mr I. T. Payne, Mr F. Peppiatt, Mr G. B. Phillipson, G. K. Pilkington, P. Porter, G. M. Powell, R. J. Preston, Mr R. Purcell, D. F. Reilly, Mrs A. S. Reilly, John P. L. Reynolds, Mr H. Ringwood, Mr A. J. Roberts, Ms C. C. Rowland, L. M. Rutherford, Exors of the Late H. J. S. Rutland, R. D. Sargent, R. F. Sayer, R. Scott, Mrs P. M. Scott, Mr A. N. Sheppard, H. R. Siegle, Mr G. H. Skeats, S. Smith, Mr S. St Quinton, J. S. Sterry, M. A. Strong, J. Studd, Mrs B. A. M. Studd, B. G. Swallow, M. Taylor, Mr N. A. Thomas, Mr D. Thornhill, Mrs C. Thornhill, Mr A. P. Tucker, Mrs K. J. Tudor, A. J. Viall, Mr J. F. Vinden, J. T. Warner, Miss S. M. Waugh, F. C. Welch, Dr H. J. F. Why, Mrs J. A. Why, S. P. Williams, Mr P. Wilson, Mr A. J. Windle, B. Winfield, J. Wright.

Assistant Trainer: Noel Williams

Jockey (NH): W. Hutchinson, R. Thornton, **Conditional:** G. Tumelty.

---

333 **MR N. KING, Newmarket**
Postal: St Gatien Cottage, Vicarage Road, Newmarket, Suffolk, CB8 8HP
Contacts: PHONE/FAX (01638) 666150 FAX (01638) 666150 MOBILE (07880) 702325
E-MAIL neil@neil-king.co.uk WEBSITE www.neil-king.co.uk

1 **BALLYBOLEY (IRE)**, 10, b g Roselier (FR)—Benbradagh Vard (IRE) **N. Catterwell C. Flinton R. Swinfen C. Appleton**
2 **BIJOU LOVE (IRE)**, 4, br f Winged Love (IRE)—Bukowina (GER) **Mr N. Catterwell**

MR N. KING—continued

3 **CELIAN (FR)**, 5, b g Indian River (FR)—Celinda (FR) **N. J. Catterwell & B. M. V. Williams**
4 **CHALICE WELCOME**, 5, b g Most Welcome—Blue Peru (IRE) **The Dyball Partnership**
5 **DIAMOND DESTINY (IRE)**, 5, ch m Carrowkeel (IRE)—Papal **Diamond Racing Ltd**
6 **DONT TELL JILL (IRE)**, 5, ch m Clerkenwell (USA)—Elly Fleetfoot (IRE) **M. C. Whatley**
7 **EL ZORRO**, 7, b g El Conquistador—Miss Wrensborough **G. C. Hartigan**
8 **FESTIVE CHIMES (IRE)**, 7, b m Efisio—Delightful Chime (IRE) **Mr Nolan Catterwell & Mr W. Persse**
9 **GALLILEO FIGARO (IRE)**, 5, b g Galileo (IRE)—Temperence Gift (USA) **The Not Over Big Partnership**
10 **JUMPTHEQUW (IRE)**, 5, ch g Quws—Papinette (IRE) **Mr I. R. Thurtle**
11 **ORCHARD KING (IRE)**, 7, ch g Beneficial—Evelyn Anthony (IRE) **Blue Tiger Partnership**
12 **PROSPECTS LADY (IRE)**, 6, ch m Presenting—Mullaghmore House **M. & M. Gavin**
13 **RAMVASWANI (IRE)**, 5, b g Spectrum (IRE)—Caesarea (GER) **Mr Nolan Catterwell & Partners**
14 **SERHAAPHIM**, 4, gr f Erhaab—Salinova (FR) **Mr R. S. Keeley**
15 **TANCREDI (SWE)**, 6, b g Rossini (USA)—Begine (USA) **Mr R. S. Keeley**
16 **THE RED LAIRD**, 5, b g Kayf Tara—Sekhmet **The Red Laird Partnership**
17 **THEHONOURABLELADY**, 7, b m Prince Daniel (USA)—Sapling **Miss S. Wilson**
18 **TONI ALCALA**, 9, b g Ezzoud (IRE)—Etourdie (USA) **Mr B. Williams & The Chuckleberries**
19 **ZAHRA'S PLACE**, 5, ch m Zaha (CAN)—La Piazza (IRE) **The Porcia Partnership**

THREE-YEAR-OLDS

20 Ch f Zaha (CAN)—La Piazza (IRE)

Other Owners: Mr C. T. Appleton, Mrs P. B. E. Beaton, Mr I. J. Beaton, Mr M. Bloor, Mr T. S. Clifford, Mr A. R. Day, D. J. S. Dyball, C. A. Dyball, Mr P. J. Edwards, C. Flinton, G. J. Foster, Mr M. J. Gavin, Mr M. G. Gavin, Mrs J. Haverson, Mr R. Hunter, Mr I. Jones, R. O. Oliver-Smith, Mr W. W. Persse, P. J. H. Rowe, Mr R. H. Swinfen, R. M. Venn, Mr A. A. Whyte, Mr B. M. V. Williams.

Assistant Trainer: Oliver Marsh

Jockey (flat): Jerry O'Dwyer. **Jockey (NH):** Owyn Nelmes, R. Johnson. **Conditional:** Chris Honour. **Amateur:** Mr Alex Merriam, Miss Zoe Lilly, Mr J. Owen.

---

334 **MR F. KIRBY, Northallerton**
Postal: **High Whinholme Farm, Danby Wiske, Northallerton, North Yorkshire, DL7 0AS**
Contacts: **PHONE/FAX (01325) 378213 MOBILE (07891) 858088**

1 **JUST MATTY**, 5, b g Bertolini (USA)—Frisson **F. Kirby**
2 **MAGIC BENGIE**, 9, b g Magic Ring (IRE)—Lady Rachel (IRE) **F. Kirby**
3 **NAVAL ATTACHE**, 6, b g Slip Anchor—Cayla **F. Kirby**
4 **SOUND OF CHEERS**, 11, br g Zilzal (USA)—Martha Stevens (USA) **F. Kirby**

Assistant Trainer: N. A. Kirby

Jockey (NH): K. Johnson.

---

335 **MR S. A. KIRK, Upper Lambourn**
Postal: **Cedar Lodge Stables, Upper Lambourn, Hungerford, Berkshire, RG17 8QT**
Contacts: **PHONE (01488) 73215 FAX (01488) 73826 MOBILE (07768) 855261**

1 **BLUE CHARM**, 4, b g Averti (IRE)—Exotic Forest **A. W. Nielsen**
2 **CALDRA (IRE)**, 4, b g Elnadim (USA)—Lady Rachel (IRE) **Mr N. Ormiston**
3 **ELHAMRI**, 4, b br g Noverre (USA)—Seamstress (IRE) **Mr N. Ormiston**
4 **GREENMEADOW**, 6, b m Sure Blade (USA)—Pea Green **Miss A. J. Rawding**
5 **OUR FAYE**, 5, b m College Chapel—Tamara **J. B. J. Richards**
6 **SRI DIAMOND**, 8, b g Sri Pekan (USA)—Hana Marie **Ascot Brew Racing**

THREE-YEAR-OLDS

7 **ADDIKT (IRE)**, b c Diktat—Frond **The Par 6**
8 **BAINISTEOIR**, b g Tobougg (IRE)—Peruvian Jade **Martin White & Partners**
9 B g Zaha (CAN)—Cabaret Artiste **E. McCay**
10 **CASELA PARK (IRE)**, ch g Elnadim (USA)—Taormina (IRE) **Mr N. Ormiston**
11 **COMEBACK QUEEN**, b gr f Nayef (USA)—Miss Universe (IRE) **Mr & Mrs Christopher Wright**
12 **DAISY NOOK**, b f Domedriver (IRE)—Kilbride **Mr N. Ormiston**
13 **DAUBERVAL (IRE)**, b g Noverre (USA)—Just In Love (FR) **Mr N. Ormiston**

MR S. A. KIRK—continued

14 **DUTY DOCTOR,** ch f Dr Fong (USA)—Duty Paid (IRE) **J. C. Smith**
15 **ESPY,** b c Piccolo—Running Glimpse (IRE) **A. F. Merritt J. Davies T. Sharman**
16 **FAIR GALE,** b g Storming Home—Triple Green **Mr N. Ormiston**
17 **FATHSTA (IRE),** b c Fath (USA)—Kilbride Lass (IRE) **Speedlith Group**
18 **HANDBAGS AT DAWN (IRE),** b f Clodovil (IRE)—Questing Star **Mr Liam Braslin**
19 **HAVANAVICH,** b c Xaar—Queen of Havana (USA) **M. Nicolson, G. Doran, A. Wilson**
20 **LIBERTY VALANCE (IRE),** b g Statue of Liberty (USA)—Tabdea (USA) **J. C. Smith**
21 **LIBERTYTYNE,** br f Statue of Liberty (USA)—Coffee Time (IRE) **Mrs E. A. Kelvin-Hughes**
22 **LOYAL KNIGHT (IRE),** ch g Choisir (AUS)—Always True (USA) **Pillar To Post Racing (IV)**
23 **MISS PHOEBE (IRE),** b f Catcher In The Rye (IRE)—Stroke of Six (IRE) **Hedsor Stud Associates**
24 **MOMENT'S NOTICE,** ch g Beat Hollow—Figlette **Mr C. Wright & The Hon Mrs J. M. Corbett**
25 **NICE WEE GIRL (IRE),** b f Clodovil (IRE)—
                                      Neat Dish (CAN) **Family Amusements Ltd, D. Kavanagh & J. Horgan**
26 **OPERA PRINCE,** b g Kyllachy—Optaria **J. C. Smith**
27 **PAPUAN PRINCE (IRE),** b g Tagula (IRE)—Pussie Willow (IRE) **Wood Street Syndicate**
28 **RAMONA CHASE,** b g High Chaparral (IRE)—Audacieuse **Mr N. Ormiston**
29 **TALAMAHANA,** b f Kyllachy—Bahawir Pour (USA) **M. Nicolson, G. Doran, A. Wilson**
30 **THEMWERETHEDAYS,** b c Olden Times—Zither **Mike & Maureen Browne**
31 **VIGANO (IRE),** b g Noverre (USA)—Perugia (IRE) **Mr N. Ormiston**
32 **WEE BUNS,** b g Piccolo—Gigetta (IRE) **Club Ism & Mr S. Kirk**
33 **YATTENDON,** ch g Compton Place—Arian Da **S. A. Kirk**

TWO-YEAR-OLDS

34 Ch f 6/4 King Charlemagne (USA)—Amiela (FR) (Mujtahid (USA)) **R. J. Brennan & D. Boocock**
35 **BARWELL BRIDGE,** b c 26/1 Red Ransom (USA)—Sentimental Value (USA) (Diesis) (35000) **N. Pickett**
36 B c 13/2 Captain Rio—Belle Etoile (FR) (Lead On Time (USA)) **J. C. Smith**
37 **CABO POLONIO (IRE),** ch f 31/3 Captain Rio—Sibilant (Selkirk (USA)) (16730) **A. W. Nielsen**
38 B c 29/4 Danetime (IRE)—Ceannanas (IRE) (Magical Wonder (USA)) (12000) **S. A. Kirk**
39 **COUSIN CHARLIE,** b c 26/3 Choisir (AUS)—Michelle Ma Belle (IRE) (Shareef Dancer (USA))
40 Ch c 3/2 Efisio—Duty Paid (USA) (Barathea (IRE)) **J. C. Smith**
41 B f 12/4 Monsieur Bond (IRE)—Ferrybridge (IRE) (Mister Baileys) (8000) **Mr N. Ormiston**
42 B f 13/2 Montjeu (IRE)—Figlette (Darshaan) (26000) **C. N. Wright**
43 **FLEUR DE'LION (IRE),** ch f 10/4 Lion Heart (USA)—
                                      Viburnum (USA) (El Gran Senor (USA)) (20000) **Mrs N. F. Lee**
44 Ch c 29/3 Hawkeye (IRE)—Green Crystal (Green Dancer (USA)) (2000)
45 **HARRY RAFFLE,** b br c 2/3 Observatory—Encore My Love (Royal Applause) (22000)
46 B f 15/3 King Charlemagne (USA)—Harry's Irish Rose (USA) (Sir Harry Lewis (USA)) **J. C. Smith**
47 **HELLBENDER (IRE),** ch c 30/1 Exceed And Excel (AUS)—
                                      Desert Rose (Green Desert (USA)) (65000) **Mr N. Ormiston**
48 B f 25/4 Celtic Swing—Khwezi (Bering) **Bell House Racing Limited**
49 B f 15/2 Fasliyev (USA)—Lolita's Gold (USA) (Royal Academy (USA)) (18000) **S. A. Kirk**
50 **LUCKIER (IRE),** gr f 28/2 Key of Luck (USA)—
                                      Ibiza (GER) (Linamix (FR)) (19304) **The Hon Mrs J. M. Corbett & Mr C. Wright**
51 **NOWORNEVA,** ch c 9/4 Where Or When (IRE)—Azula (Bluebird (USA)) (5000)
52 **ORCHESTRAL GOLD,** ch f 3/3 Piccolo—All My Gold (GER) (Deploy) (5238) **J. B. J. Richards**
53 Ch c 21/4 Captain Rio—Pardoned (IRE) (Mujadil (USA)) (10295)
54 Ch c 9/3 Dr Fong (USA)—Red Roses Story (FR) (Pink (FR)) **J. C. Smith**
55 B c 18/3 Compton Place—Rush Hour (IRE) (Night Shift (USA)) (65000) **Brannon Dennis Dick Holden**
56 B c 27/1 Fantastic Light (USA)—Seamstress (IRE) (Barathea (IRE)) (75000) **Mr N. Ormiston**
57 B f 17/4 Fasliyev (USA)—Soltura (IRE) (Sadler's Wells (USA)) (25740) **S. A. Kirk**
58 B c 10/4 Rock of Gibraltar (IRE)—Tammany Hall (IRE) (Petorius) (57914) **Mr N. Ormiston**
59 **TRUE BRITANNIA,** b c 22/2 Lujain (USA)—Surf Bird (Shareef Dancer (USA)) **Mr T. R. Lock**
60 **TRUE DECISION,** b c 21/4 Reset (AUS)—True Precision (Presidium) (8000)
61 Gr c 22/2 Desert Style (IRE)—Vax Star (Petong) (14000) **S. A. Kirk**
62 B c 10/2 Statue of Liberty (USA)—Velvet Slipper (Muhtafal (USA)) **R. J. Brennan & D. Boocock**
63 B f 4/5 Danehill Dancer (IRE)—Windmill (Ezzoud (IRE)) (62000) **S. A. Kirk**
64 B g 26/2 Mujahid (USA)—With Distinction (Zafonic (USA)) (16000) **Deauville Daze Partnership**
65 B br f 2/3 Choisir (AUS)—Zwadi (IRE) (Docksider (USA)) (15443) **S. A. Kirk**

Other Owners: Mrs S. Z. Bates, D. Boocock, R. J. Brennan, Mr Mike Browne, Mrs Maureen Browne, The Hon Mrs C. Corbett, A. J. Cousins, Mrs D. Crow, J. Davies, M. N. Dennis, Mr A. Dick, Ms Gill Doran, J. Dwight, Mr M. V. Hill, R. T. Horrell, Mr W. K. Jones, Mrs M. Jones, Mr R. Kelvin-Hughes, Mr A. F. Merritt, Mr D. Minton, Mr M. Nicolson, Mr R. X. O'Rahilly, J. P. Repard, Mr John A. Sanders, Mr Trevor Sharman, Mr Lee Westwood, M. G. White, R. E. Williams, Mr Alasdair Wilson, Mrs J. A. Wright.

Assistant Trainer: Fanny Kirk
Apprentice: Matthew Birch.

336 MR W. S. KITTOW, Cullompton
Postal: **Haynefield Farm, Blackborough, Cullompton, Devon, EX15 2JD**
Contacts: **HOME (01823) 680183 FAX (01823) 680601 MOBILE (07714) 218921**
E-MAIL stuartkittowracing@hotmail.com

1 **ARCTIC MAGIC (IRE)**, 8, b m Saddlers' Hall (IRE)—Arctic Verb **Midd Shire Racing**
2 **BOLUISCE (IRE)**, 5, ch m Zilzal (USA)—No Islands **Mr S. M. King**
3 **CARSON'S SPIRIT (USA)**, 4, ch g Carson City (USA)—Pascarina (FR) **Mr K. B. Hodges**
4 **DANCING STORM**, 5, b m Trans Island—Stormswell **The Quintet Partnership**
5 **DOVE COTTAGE (IRE)**, 6, b g Great Commotion (USA)—Pooka **R. S. E. Gifford**
6 **FOOLISH CLICHE**, 5, b m Classic Cliche (IRE)—Hopperdane (IRE) **L. D. Cornall**
7 **GUILDED WARRIOR**, 5, b g Mujahid (USA)—Pearly River **The Racing Guild**
8 **HAWRIDGE KING**, 6, b g Erhaab (USA)—Sadaka (USA) **E. J. S. Gadsden**
9 **HAWRIDGE STAR (IRE)**, 6, b g Alzao (USA)—Serenity **E. J. S. Gadsden**
10 **JOY IN THE GUILD (IRE)**, 5, b m Mull of Kintyre (USA)—About Face **The Racing Guild**
11 **KEN'S GIRL**, 4, ch f Ishiguru (USA)—There's Two (IRE) **Midd Shire Racing**
12 **MISS NIGHTSHADE**, 4, b f Alflora (IRE)—Black Secret
13 **MUNLOCHY BAY**, 4, b f Karinga Bay—Meghdoot **John & Val Urquhart**
14 **ONLY FOR SUE**, 9, ch g Pivotal—Barbary Court **Mrs S. G. Arnesen**
15 **RYDAL MOUNT (IRE)**, 5, b m Cape Cross (IRE)—Pooka **R. S. E. Gifford**
16 **TAKAFU (USA)**, 6, b g Lemon Drop Kid (USA)—Proper Protocol (USA) **Midd Shire Racing**
17 **TROUBLESOME GERRI**, 6, b m Thowra (FR)—Sid's Pretence **L. D. Cornall**

THREE-YEAR-OLDS

18 **ACCLIMATE**, b f Acclamation—Chispa **John Boswell**
19 **DESERT PRIDE**, b g Desert Style (IRE)—Dalu (IRE) **M. E. Harris**
20 Gr f Baryshnikov (AUS)—Guarded Expression
21 **ORBITAL ORCHID**, b f Mujahid (USA)—Carati **Chris & David Stam**
22 **OUR PICCADILLY (IRE)**, b f Piccolo—Dilys **J. Hopkins, S. Kittow, R. Perry**
23 **RASH JUDGEMENT**, b c Mark of Esteem (IRE)—Let Alone **R. S. E. Gifford**
24 **SIR IKE (IRE)**, b c Xaar—Iktidar **Mrs S. G. Arnesen**
25 **SUESACOMIN**, b f Teofilio (IRE)—Suantley
26 **TOMBA'S LASS**, ch f Tomba—Charleigh Keary

TWO-YEAR-OLDS

27 B f 29/2 Piccolo—Baileys Applause (Royal Applause) (3500) **Mr K. B. Hodges**
28 B f 4/4 Hello Mister—Branston Lucy (Prince Sabo)
29 **FLUTE MAGIC**, b c 27/4 Piccolo—Overcome (Belmez (USA)) **Midd Shire Racing**
30 **LEVITATION (IRE)**, b f 27/3 Vettori (IRE)—Uplifting (Magic Ring (IRE))
31 **MACDILLON**, b c 1/4 Acclamation—Dilys (Efisio) **The MacDillon Partnership**
32 **MARJU KING (IRE)**, b c 6/3 Marju (IRE)—Blue Reema (IRE) (Bluebird (USA)) (40000) **Chris & David Stam**
33 **ROSIE TWO**, b f 27/2 Acclamation—Just A Glimmer (Bishop of Cashel) (50000) **P. A. & M. J. Reditt**
34 B c 8/4 Almutawakel—Shamah (Unfuwain (USA)) (13000) **Dr G. S. Plastow**
35 B g 2/4 Reset (AUS)—Sleepless (Night Shift (USA)) (12000)

Other Owners: D. W. Arnesen, Mr L. R. Browning, Mr D. Evans, Mrs J. C. Hopkins, W. S. Kittow, Mrs J. F. Maitland-Jones, B. G. Middleton, Mrs R. J. M. Perry, Mrs P. A. Reditt, M. J. Reditt, A. J. Shire, Mr D. B. Stam, Mrs C. Stam, Ms W. A. Stoker, R. A. Stoker, Mr J. R. Urquhart, Mrs V. A. Urquhart.

Assistant Trainer: Mrs Judy Kittow

Jockey (flat): D. Sweeney. **Jockey (NH):** T. Scudamore. **Apprentice:** Timothy Meadows.

337 MISS H. C. KNIGHT, Wantage
Postal: **West Lockinge Farm, Wantage, Oxfordshire, OX12 8QF**
Contacts: **PHONE (01235) 833535 CAR (07808) 290898 FAX (01235) 820110**
MOBILE (07860) 110153
E-MAIL hen@westlockinge.co.uk

1 **ALTOLUSSO (IRE)**, 5, b g Luso—Over The Reef (IRE) **Mr L. D. Mumford**
2 **ATHALIAH**, 6, ch m Primitive Rising (USA)—Sharp Move **Miss C. A. Spurrier**
3 **AZTEC WARRIOR (IRE)**, 7, b g Taipan (IRE)—Eurocurrency (IRE) **Mrs C. M. Radford**
4 **BALLY CONN (IRE)**, 6, br g Supreme Leader—Gladtogetit **The Bally Conn Partnership**
5 **BENMORE BOY (IRE)**, 5, b g Old Vic—Proudstown Lady (IRE) **Mrs C. M. Radford**
6 **BLUE TEAL (IRE)**, 6, b g Pistolet Bleu (IRE)—Boreen Brook (IRE) **Lady Vestey & Barry Brazier**

MISS H. C. KNIGHT—continued

7 **BRIGHT SPIRIT,** 7, b g Petoski—Lunabelle **Her Majesty The Queen**
8 **BUTTERFLY ROSE,** 7, b m Tragic Role (USA)—Rosemoss **M. D. C. Jenks**
9 **BYNACK MHOR (IRE),** 7, b g Taipan (IRE)—Pride of Poznan (IRE) **Mrs David Gardiner & Family**
10 **CALGARY BAY (IRE),** 5, b g Taipan (IRE)—Dante's Thatch (IRE) **Mrs C. M. Radford**
11 **CAVE HILL (IRE),** 6, b g Dr Massini (IRE)—Eurogal (IRE) **T. J. Hemmings**
12 **CHARLOTTES WEBB (IRE),** 6, b m Luso—Kilcrea Deer (IRE) **Johnny Eddis Susan Kottler Emma Buchanan**
13 **COMBER (IRE),** 6, b g Luso—Charleys Lane (IRE) **Mrs M. A. Humphries**
14 **CRUISING RIVER (IRE),** 9, b g Over The River (FR)—Jellaride (IRE) **Four Stablemates**
15 **DESERT STAR,** 8, b g Green Desert (USA)—Phantom Gold **Her Majesty The Queen**
16 **DOTTIE,** 4, b f Rainbow High—Murchan Tyne (IRE) **Hilton & Lyn Ramseyer**
17 **EASTER PRESENT (IRE),** 9, br g Presenting—Spring Fiddler (IRE) **Mrs M. A. Humphries**
18 **ERMINE SEA,** 5, b g Rainbow Quest (USA)—Bint Pasha (USA) **Lady Bamford & Alice Bamford**
19 **ETON BLUE,** 5, b g Classic Cliche (IRE)—Owena Deep **Eton Blue Partnership**
20 **EXUBERANCE (IRE),** 6, b g Exit To Nowhere (USA)—Hook's Close **Exuberance Racing**
21 **FAL AGH BAGH (IRE),** 5, b g Luso—Tikigold (FR) **Executive Racing**
22 **GLASKER MILL (IRE),** 8, b g Old Vic—Lucey Allen **T. J. Hemmings**
23 **HARRINGAY,** 8, b m Sir Harry Lewis (USA)—Tamergale (IRE) **Mrs R. I. Vaughan**
24 **HARRIS BAY,** 9, b g Karinga Bay—Harristown Lady **Mrs G. M. Sturges & H. Stephen Smith**
25 **HOWRWENOW (IRE),** 10, b g Commanche Run—Maythefifth **T. Cole**
26 **ICE BUCKET (IRE),** 8, ch g Glacial Storm—Tranbu (IRE) **Mrs A. J. Jamieson**
27 **INDIGO SKY (IRE),** 7, gr g Adieu Au Roi (IRE)—Urban Sky (FR) **Hilton & Lyn Ramseyer**
28 **JOHN DIAMOND (IRE),** 7, b g Un Desperado (FR)—Lessons Lass (IRE) **Mrs D. A. Winton**
29 **KATALINA,** 5, b m Hernando (FR)—Queen of Spades (IRE) **Mrs R. I. Vaughan**
30 **LITTLE EAGLET (IRE),** 4, br g Dushyantor (USA)—Bagatelle (IRE) **Lady Bamford & Alice Bamford**
31 **MARKILA (FR),** 5, b m Mark of Esteem (IRE)—Ile Mamou (IRE) **Lord Vestey**
32 **MILLER'S DAWN,** 4, ch g Karinga Bay—Dawn Gait **Carfield Partners**
33 **MOUS OF MEN (FR),** 5, b g Lord of Men—Mousmee (FR) **D. A. Johnson**
34 **MUHTENBAR,** 8, b g Muhtarram (USA)—Ardenbar **T. J. Wyatt**
35 **MUSICAL CHAIRS (IRE),** 6, b g Musical Pursuit—Kings Pearl (IRE) **H. Stephen Smith & Partners**
36 **MY SKIPPER (IRE),** 7, b g Old Vic—Nil Faic (IRE) **Peter & Janet Borst**
37 **OLMETO COLLONGES (FR),** 6, br g Brier Creek (USA)—Castille Collonges (FR) **Mr T. Cole & Mr A. Finney**
38 **OPENDITCH (FR),** 6, b g Video Rock (FR)—Enita (FR) **D. A. Johnson**
39 **ORFEO CONTI (FR),** 6, ch g Bulington (FR)—Gazelle Lulu (FR) **Martin Broughton & Friends 1**
40 **PLUME D'OUDAIRIES (FR),** 5, b m Grand Seigneur (FR)—Harmat (FR) **H. S. Winton**
41 **QUARRY TOWN (IRE),** 6, b g Pistolet Bleu (IRE)—Dano Doo (IRE) **D. A. Johnson**
42 **RACING DEMON (IRE),** 8, b g Old Vic—All Set (IRE) **Mrs C. M. Radford**
43 **RATHMULEN (IRE),** 5, b br g Tel Quel (FR)—Northcha Lady (IRE) **Mrs C. M. Radford**
44 **RED RATTLE (IRE),** 6, ch g Old Vic—Only Her Way (IRE) **Red Rattle Partnership**
45 **RINGAROSES,** 7, b g Karinga Bay—Rose Ravine **Mrs Nicholas Jones/Martin Broughton**
46 **SILVER BALLERINA,** 8, ch m Silver Patriarch (IRE)—Balancing Act **Mrs C. Shand Kydd**
47 **SOIXANTE (IRE),** 5, b g Old Vic—Dantes Serenade (IRE) **Martin, Jocelyn & Steve Broughton**
48 **SOMERSBY (IRE),** 4, b g Second Empire (IRE)—Back To Roost (IRE) **Mrs T. Radford**
49 **SOUTH BANK (IRE),** 6, b g Old Vic—Cluain-Ard (IRE) **Four Stablemates**
50 **STORM SURGE (IRE),** 5, gr g Great Palm (USA)—Ashfield Rosie (IRE) **The Tyser Family**
51 **SWING BILL (FR),** 7, gr g Grey Risk (FR)—Melodie Royale (FR) **D. A. Johnson**
52 **TEDDY'S REFLECTION (IRE),** 5, b g Beneficial—Regal Pursuit (IRE) **The Bailey Family**
53 **THE VICAR (IRE),** 5, b g Bob Back (USA)—Moon Storm (IRE) **T. J. Hemmings**
54 **VAL DU CIRON (FR),** 5, b g True Brave (USA)—Dix Huit Brumaire (FR) **The Hon Mrs V. M. A. Tower**
55 **WAR FOOTING,** 5, b g Cadoudal (FR)—Sans Regrets (FR) **Mrs S. L. Tyser**
56 **WEST END KING (IRE),** 6, b g Old Vic—Last Princess **M. F. Broughton & Partners**
57 **WINDS AND DRAGONS (IRE),** 8, b g Taipan (IRE)—Windy Bop (IRE) **Executive Racing III**

Other Owners: Mrs Christine Ashford, Mrs C. Bailey, Mr E. J. T. Bailey, Mr J. J. M. Bailey, Lady Bamford, Miss Alice Bamford, Mr B. M. Barrett, Mrs Judith Anne Battey, Mr Kit Bell, Mr Peter Borst, Mrs J. N. Borst, Mr Barry Brazier, Mr Martin Broughton, Mr S. W. Broughton, Mrs E. S. Buchanan, Mr G. M. Carty, Mr Simon W. Clarke, Mr N. M. P Clarke, Mr Toby Cole, Mr D. J. Coles, Mrs Rowena Cotton, Mr E. J. Dolan-Abrahams, J. L. Eddis, Mr R. F. Fay, Mr Alex J. Finney, Mrs David Gardiner, Mrs N. E. S. Gardiner, Mr A. B. Greenfield, Mrs Sue Griffiths, Mr I. Gurel, Mr Brian M. Hartigan, Viscount Head, Mr J. Hyde, Mrs N. Jones, Mrs S. E. Kottler, Mr A. M. McKeever, Mr Stephen Perry, Mrs L. Ramseyer, Mr H. Ramseyer, Mr Ian Rees, Mr H. Stephen Smith, Dr M. A. Sparrow, Mrs G. M. Sturges, Mr G. A. Thomas, Mrs J. A. Thomas, Mr G. J. Thomas, The Hon Mrs Townshend, The Hon Mrs Susan Tyser, Mr Harry Tyser, Lady Vestey, Mrs R. B. Weaver, T. C. Wilson, Mr M. Winter, Mr David Zeffman.

338 MR W. J. KNIGHT, Angmering

Postal: **Lower Coombe Racing Stables, Angmering Park, Littlehampton, West Sussex, BN16 4EX**
Contacts: PHONE **(01903) 871188** FAX **(01903) 871184** MOBILE **(07770) 720828**
E-MAIL william@wknightracing.co.uk WEBSITE www.wknightracing.co.uk

1 ASHDOWN EXPRESS (IRE), 9, ch g Ashkalani (IRE)—Indian Express **W. J. P. Jackson**
2 BOLD BOBBY, 4, b f Pivotal—Mrs P **Mrs R. Cohen**
3 GREENWICH VILLAGE, 5, b g Mtoto—D'azy **R. A. B. Duff**
4 ILLUSTRIOUS BLUE, 5, b br h Dansili—Gipsy Moth **Mr & Mrs I. Bendelow**
5 KING OF DIXIE (USA), 4, ch c Kingmambo (USA)—Dixie Accent (USA) **Hesmonds Stud Ltd**
6 POWER BALLAD, 4, ch f Titus Livius (FR)—Sea Music **Mrs E. C. Roberts**
7 SHIMONI, 4, b f Mark of Esteem (IRE)—Limuru **The Welldiggers Partnership**
8 SPRING WARRIOR, 4, b f Mujahid (USA)—Spring Mood (FR) **D. R. L. Evans**
9 TITAN TRIUMPH, 4, b c Zamindar (USA)—Triple Green **Canisbay Bloodstock**

THREE-YEAR-OLDS

10 AFRAM BLUE, b g Fraam—Tup Tim **Mr & Mrs I. Bendelow**
11 CASILDA (IRE), b f Cape Cross (IRE)—Koniya (IRE) **Mrs P. G. M. Jamison**
12 DUSTY MOON, ch f Dr Fong (USA)—Dust Dancer **Hesmonds Stud Ltd**
13 EVENTIDE, ch f Where Or When (IRE)—Evening Guest (FR) **Mrs A. R. Ruggles**
14 EXTREME PLEASURE (IRE), b f High Chaparral (IRE)—Height of Passion **Mrs P. G. M. Jamison**
15 KANNON, b f Kyllachy—Violet (IRE) **Mrs S. A. M. Fleming**
16 KEEN EYE, b f Nayef (USA)—Mexican Hawk (USA) **Hesmonds Stud Ltd**
17 PHA MAI BLUE, b c Acclamation—Queen of Silk (IRE) **Mr & Mrs I. Bendelow**
18 QUINZEY'S BEST (IRE), ch f King's Best (USA)—Quinzey (JPN) **The Big Boys**
19 RAGAMUFFIN MAN (IRE), gr c Dalakhani (IRE)—Chamela Bay (IRE) **Hardisty, Hutton & Spiers**
20 TURFANI (IRE), b f Danetime (IRE)—Tuhfah **The Pheasant Rew Partnership**
21 WELL STYLED, b c Oasis Dream—Summer Fashion **The George Partnership**

TWO-YEAR-OLDS

22 DALRADIAN (IRE), b c 3/5 Dansili—Aethra (USA) (Trempolino (USA)) **Hesmonds Stud Ltd**
23 DECEMBER DRAW (IRE), br c 14/4 Medecis—New York (IRE) (Danzero (AUS)) (25000) **Brook House**
24 DESERT ICON (IRE), b c 6/3 Desert Style (IRE)—
    Gilded Vanity (IRE) (Indian Ridge) (36000) **Mr B. & Mrs D. Willis, Mr B. & Mrs M. Pullin**
25 DOME ROCKET, b c 5/3 Domedriver (IRE)—Sea Ridge (Slip Anchor) **Hesmonds Stud Ltd**
26 B c 4/2 Cape Cross (IRE)—Fantasize (Groom Dancer) (USA) **Mrs G. M. Cotton**
27 GIFT OF TIME, b f 28/3 Cadeaux Genereux—
    Watchkeeper (Rudimentary (USA)) (32000) **Hesmonds Stud Ltd**
28 MACKTEN, b c 10/4 Makbul—Tender (IRE) (Zieten (USA)) **Mrs F. Ashfield**
29 B f 7/4 Xaar—Mildred (IRE) (Peintre Celebre (USA)) (20000)
30 MISS SOPHISTICAT, b f 5/3 Alhaarth (IRE)—She's Classy (Boundary (USA)) (75000) **Mrs S. M. Mitchell**
31 PENZENA, ch f 6/2 Tobougg (IRE)—Penmayne (Inchinor) (45000) **Spiers, Taylor, Taylor**
32 PRIMO DILETTANTE, b c 20/4 Primo Valentino (IRE)—Jezadil (IRE) (Mujadil (USA)) **O. J. Williams**
33 Br f 4/2 King's Best (USA)—Qui Liz (USA) (Benny The Dip (USA)) **D. G. Hardisty**
34 ROYAL TOERAG, b c 7/3 Bertolini (USA)—Yesterday's Song (Shirley Heights) **Bryan Fry & The Toerags**
35 STARLARKS (IRE), b f 7/3 Mujahid (USA)—Violet (IRE) (Mukaddamah (USA)) (22000) **Mrs S. A. M. Fleming**
36 STRAIGHT LACED, b f 10/2 Refuse To Bend (IRE)—Gaelic Swan (IRE) (Nashwan (USA)) **Mrs P. A. Cooke**
37 TAKE THE MICKY, b c 12/2 Beat Hollow—
    Ailincala (IRE) (Pursuit of Love) (13000) **Botham, Dale, Nunns & Shopland**
38 TRANSFORMER (IRE), b c 14/2 Trans Island—Lady At War (Warning) **Miss S. K. Bowles**
39 B f 1/5 Falbrav (IRE)—Zarma (FR) (Machiavellian (USA)) (16000) **Miss S. K. Bowles**

Other Owners: I. H. Bendelow, Mrs P. Bendelow, P. J. W. Botham, R. G. W. Brown, Mr W. R. Dale, Dr D. B. Davis, W. W.
Fleming, B. Fry, M. Goodrum, M. J. Hutton, R. F. Kilby, W. J. Knight, Mrs S. E. Lakin, Mr J. Makin, Mr P. J. Moss, Mr D. D.
Mountney, Mr S. T. Nunns, Mr B. O'Brien, Mr B. T. Pullin, Mrs M. J. Pullin, Mr T. G. Roddick, Mr N. J. Shopland, Mr B. P. J.
Spiers, Miss M. E. Stopher, D. Sutherland, Mrs N. Sutherland, Mr L. A. Taylor, Mr M. J. Taylor, W. Thornton, Mrs D. A. Willis,
Mr B. J. C. Willis, Miss C. J. Wills.

Assistant Trainer: Matthew Darling

Jockey (flat): Paul Doe. **Amateur:** Mrs E. Knight.

339 MR R. F. KNIPE, Allensmore

Postal: **Cobhall Court Stud, Millennium House, Allensmore, Herefordshire, HR2 9BE**
Contacts: PHONE **(01432) 277245** MOBILE **(07774) 866547**

1 CRACKING CLICHE, 6, ch m Classic Cliche (IRE)—Calametta **Mrs. R. F. Knipe**
Assistant Trainer: Mrs S. D. Knipe

340 MR C. LAFFON-PARIAS, Chantilly
Postal: 38, Avenue du General Leclerc, 60500 Chantilly, France
Contacts: **PHONE** (0033) 3445 75375 **FAX** (0033) 3445 75243
E-MAIL ecuries.laffon.parias@wanadoo.fr

1 **ASCLIPIOS (FR)**, 4, b c Kendor (FR)—Loxandra **Stilvi Compania Financiera**
2 **BALDORIA (IRE)**, 5, b m In The Wings—Prickly Pearl (IRE) **Felix Sanz Blanco**
3 **BALIUS (IRE)**, 5, b h Mujahid (USA)—Akhla (USA) **Stilvi Compania Financiera**
4 **GAVRIOTIS (IRE)**, 4, b c Sendawar (IRE)—Pithara (GR) **Stilvi Compania Financiera**
5 **GWENSEB (FR)**, 5, ch m Green Tune (USA)—La Popesse (USA) **Wertheimer et Frere**
6 **KANDARI (FR)**, 4, b c Kahyasi—Nee Brune (FR) **Stilvi Compania Financiera**
7 **KRATAIOS (FR)**, 8, b g Sabrehill (USA)—Loxandra **Stilvi Compania Financiera**
8 **LIGHT IMPACT (IRE)**, 4, b f Fantastic Light (USA)—Ganga (IRE) **Mrs A. Cuadra-Lores**
9 **SILVER POINT (FR)**, 5, b br h Commands (AUS)—Silver Fame (USA) **Alec Head**
10 **TITREE**, 4, b f Highest Honor (FR)—Timber Nymph (USA) **Alec Head**
11 **WELMARK**, 4, b gr c Mark of Esteem (IRE)—Welimina (IRE) **Wertheimer et Frere**

THREE-YEAR-OLDS

12 **ALHAURIN (USA)**, b c Gone West (USA)—Ronda **S. L. Darpat**
13 **ALKIVIA (FR)**, ch f Peintre Celebre (USA)—Storm Card **Stilvi Compania Financiera**
14 **ARGOMILLA (FR)**, b f Dansili—Motzki (FR) **Mrs G. Cabrero**
15 **ARRAYAN**, b c Catcher In The Rye (IRE)—Ganga (IRE) **Mrs A. Cuadra-Lores**
16 **ASKANIOS (IRE)**, b c Montjeu (USA)—Askri **Stilvi Compania Financiera**
17 **AUDAZ**, b br f Oasis Dream—Albahaca (USA) **Mrs A. Cuadra-Lores**
18 **BETILLA (IRE)**, b f Bering—Ecoutila (USA) **Felipe Hinojosa**
19 **BIG DAY TODAY (FR)**, gr f Linamix (FR)—Reine de La Ciel (USA) **John-Henry Metzger**
20 **BRUNETE (FR)**, b c Numerous (USA)—Aranda **S. L. Darpat**
21 **CARPO (FR)**, b c Trempolino (USA)—Carole Dream (FR) **Stilvi Compania Financiera**
22 **CARRATRACA**, ch f Highest Honor (FR)—Pharatta (IRE) **S. L. Darpat**
23 **CHINCHON (IRE)**, b c Marju (IRE)—Jarama (IRE) **S. L. Darpat**
24 **CHURRIANA (IRE)**, gr f Anabaa (USA)—Souvenir Souvenir **S. L. Darpat**
25 **CRAZY MASK (IRE)**, b f Iron Mask (USA)—Daftiyna (IRE) **Wertheimer et Frere**
26 **DECOUVERTE (IRE)**, b f Rainbow Quest (USA)—Russyskia (USA) **Wertheimer et Frere**
27 **DELFINIA (FR)**, ch f Drastikos (GR)—Akhla (USA) **Stilvi Compania Financiera**
28 **DIAVOLIKOS**, b c Tobougg (IRE)—Trefoil (FR) **Stilvi Compania Financiera**
29 **DON RAMIRO (FR)**, b c Dyhim Diamond (IRE)—Dayka (USA) **J. Gonzalez**
30 **DREAMKING (USA)**, b c Kingmambo (USA)—Quiet Dream (USA) **Wertheimer et Frere**
31 **DUST IN THE WING (FR)**, ch f Highest Honor (FR)—Gentilesse **C. Laffon Parias**
32 **EL FONTAN (FR)**, gr c Verglas (IRE)—Valeriane (FR) **J. Gonzalez**
33 **FALCO (USA)**, b c Pivotal—Icelips (USA) **Wertheimer et Frere**
34 **FREEMIX (FR)**, gr c Linamix (FR)—Freezing (USA) **Wertheimer et Frere**
35 **FRUELA (FR)**, b c Fasliyev (USA)—Gold Dodger (USA) **Felipe Hinojosa**
36 **FRYNIA (USA)**, b br f Cat Thief (USA)—Wayward Bound (USA) **Stilvi Compania Financiera**
37 **GALAKTEA (IRE)**, br f Statue of Liberty (USA)—Granadilla **Stilvi Compania Financiera**
38 **GAYALA (IRE)**, b f Iron Mask (USA)—Balliamo (IRE) **Wertheimer et Frere**
39 **HIGH FUN (USA)**, gr ro f High Yield (USA)—Blame Itonmidnight (USA) **Wertheimer et Frere**
40 **HONNEUR BLEU (FR)**, ch f Anabaa Blue—Bering Honneur (USA) **Stilvi Compania Financiera**
41 **HURRICANE DRIVE (USA)**, ch c Belong To Me (USA)—Rababah **Miss A. Shaykhutdinova**
42 **IXALOS (IRE)**, b c Hawk Wing (USA)—Ziria (IRE) **Stilvi Compania Financiera**
43 **JAVATO (IRE)**, b c Mark of Esteem (IRE)—Taysala (IRE) **C. Laffon Parias**
44 **KAYABA**, b f Anabaa (USA)—Senkaya (FR) **Wertheimer et Frere**
45 **KIRKINOLA**, b f Selkirk (USA)—Spinola (FR) **Felipe Hinojosa**
46 **KOROVOS (FR)**, bl c Act One—Arikaria (IRE) **Stilvi Compania Financiera**
47 **KYRNOS (IRE)**, b c Peintre Celebre (USA)—Diotima **Stilvi Compania Financiera**
48 **LASOS (FR)**, b c Miesque's Son (USA)—Erivia (FR) **Stilvi Compania Financiera**
49 **LOTHARIOS (FR)**, b c Hawk Wing (USA)—Eden (IRE) **Stilvi Compania Financiera**
50 **LYKARIA**, b f Fantastic Light (USA)—Wendylina (USA) **Stilvi Compania Financiera**
51 **MADAWAY**, ch f Machiavellian (USA)—Danzigaway (USA) **Wertheimer et Frere**
52 **NEGULESCA (USA)**, b br f Distant View (USA)—Noblissima (IRE) **I. Ferrer**
53 **NOTIA (IRE)**, b f Numerous (USA)—Tritonia (GR) **Stilvi Compania Financiera**
54 **NUMIDOCO (IRE)**, b c Peintre Celebre (USA)—Witch of Fate (USA) **Felipe Hinojosa**
55 **OKALEA (IRE)**, ch f Dalakhani (IRE)—Solosole (USA) **Stilvi Compania Financiera**
56 **ORGANISATEUR (FR)**, b c Highest Honor (FR)—Willamina (IRE) **Wertheimer et Frere**
57 **OTROSI (USA)**, b c Langfuhr (CAN)—Siempre Asi (USA) **Mrs A. Cuadra-Lores**
58 **PALATINO (IRE)**, ch c Peintre Celebre (USA)—Plastiqueuse (USA) **Felipe Hinojosa**
59 **PATANEGRA (IRE)**, b f Barathea (IRE)—Pelagic **Haras D'Etreham**

MR C. LAFFON-PARIAS—continued

60 **PEARL EARRINE (FR)**, gr f Kaldounevees (FR)—Girl of France **Stilvi Compania Financiera**
61 **PERIANA (FR)**, ch f Dubai Destination (USA)—Cazorla (IRE) **S. L. Darpat**
62 **POLIGOLD (IRE)**, b c Poliglote—Soft Gold (USA) **Wertheimer et Frere**
63 **POMPEYANO (IRE)**, b c Rainbow Quest (USA)—Lady Lodger **Felipe Hinojosa**
64 **PRAXITHEA (FR)**, b f Galileo (IRE)—Esperis (IRE) **Stilvi Compania Financiera**
65 **REY SILO (FR)**, ch c Highest Honor (FR)—Smiling Eyes **Jose Gonzalez**
66 **ROSE ROSE (USA)**, ch f Cozzene (USA)—Seeking the Roses (USA) **Alec Head**
67 **SAINTINA**, gr f Royal Academy (USA)—Kistena (FR) **Wertheimer et Frere**
68 **SALAMANDRA (FR)**, b f Numerous (USA)—Soierie (FR) **Alec Head**
69 **SAVOYA (FR)**, b f Anabaa (USA)—Silver Fame (USA) **Alec Head**
70 **SEA LIFE (FR)**, b f Anabaa (USA)—Seacleef (FR) **Alec Head**
71 **SEEKING THE FUN (USA)**, b f Alhaarth (IRE)—Golden Party (USA) **Wertheimer et Frere**
72 **SIRHAM (IRE)**, b c Sadler's Wells (USA)—Velvet Moon (IRE) **Felipe Hinojosa**
73 **SONGSONG (USA)**, b c Rahy (USA)—Moiava (FR) **Wertheimer et Frere**
74 **SPARKLE GREEN (FR)**, ch f Green Tune (USA)—Giola (USA) **J. Gonzalez**
75 **SPRING TOUCH (USA)**, b f Elusive Quality (USA)—Spring Star (FR) **Wertheimer et Frere**
76 **TARTESOS**, b c In The Wings—Bimbola (FR) **Felipe Hinojosa**
77 **TITO BUSTILLO (FR)**, b c Kahyasi—Litani Queen **J. Gonzalez**
78 **VINICIO (IRE)**, b c Montjeu (IRE)—Tadris (USA) **Felipe Hinojosa**
79 **VRAIMENT ROUGE (FR)**, b f Red Ransom (USA)—Red Stella (FR) **Wertheimer et Frere**
80 **WIFI (GER)**, b c Pivotal—Welimina (IRE) **Wertheimer et Frere**
81 **WILD DESERT (FR)**, b c Desert Prince (IRE)—Sallivera (IRE) **Wertheimer et Frere**
82 **YDILIQUE (IRE)**, b f Sadler's Wells (USA)—Angelic Song (CAN) **Wertheimer et Frere**
83 **YUSUF (IRE)**, b c High Chaparral (IRE)—La Rosetta (IRE) **Felipe Hinojosa**

TWO-YEAR-OLDS

84 B c 19/3 Barathea (IRE)—Albacora (IRE) (Fairy King (USA)) (20000) **Stilvi Compania Financiera**
85 **ALLYBAR (IRE)**, ch c 24/3 King's Best (USA)—Irika (USA) (Irish River (FR)) **Wertheimer et Frere**
86 **ALYDIX**, b gr c 24/2 Anabaa (USA)—Beautimix (FR) (Linamix (FR)) **Wertheimer et Frere**
87 **AMABILITE**, b f 1/4 Selkirk (USA)—Sweet Name (USA) (Danzig (USA)) **Wertheimer et Frere**
88 B c 23/3 Anabaa (USA)—Arazena (USA) (Woodman (USA)) (57915) **S. L. Darpat**
89 B f 11/4 Anabaa (USA)—Asi (USA) (El Prado (IRE)) (48262) **Mrs A. Cuadra-Lores**
90 **BLOWAWAY (FR)**, gr f 1/1 Linamix (FR)—Soft Pleasure (USA) (Diesis) **Wertheimer et Frere**
91 **CELEBRA (FR)**, ch f 1/1 Peintre Celebre (USA)—Thearena (USA) (Seattle Slew (USA)) **Wertheimer et Frere**
92 **COUNTERBID (IRE)**, b c 22/2 Rainbow Quest (USA)—
    Brooklyn Gleam (FR) (Caerleon (USA)) **Wertheimer et Frere**
93 **DAFNEA (FR)**, b f 1/1 Hawk Wing (USA)—Vivacity (Trempolino (USA)) **Stilvi Compania Financiera**
94 **DIODOROS (FR)**, b c 1/1 High Chaparral (IRE)—
    Light Quest (USA) (Quest For Fame) **Stilvi Compania Financiera**
95 B c 28/2 Galileo (IRE)—Diotima (High Estate) **Stilvi Compania Financiera**
96 B c 22/3 Loxias (FR)—Erivia (FR) (Kendor (FR)) **Stilvi Compania Financiera**
97 **HIGHMIX**, gr c 15/4 Singspiel (IRE)—Goldamix (IRE) (Linamix (FR)) **Wertheimer et Frere**
98 **KALIMINA (FR)**, gr f 1/1 Monsun (GER)—Welimina (IRE) (Sadler's Wells (USA)) **Wertheimer et Frere**
99 **KARMI (FR)**, ch f 20/5 Green Tune (USA)—
    Karlabrunum (IRE) (Spectrum (IRE)) (19305) **Stilvi Compania Financiera**
100 B c 4/3 Tiger Hill (IRE)—Manhattan Sunset (USA) (El Gran Senor (USA)) (12000) **Stilvi Compania Financiera**
101 **MONETAIRE (FR)**, b c 1/1 Anabaa (USA)—Monitrice (FR) (Groom Dancer (USA)) **Alec Head**
102 **PERSPECTIVE NEVSKI**, b f 7/3 Montjeu (IRE)—Real Secret (IRE) (Danehill (USA)) (96525) **J-C. Seroul**
103 Ch c 3/3 Traditionally—Pyramid Painter (IRE) (Peintre Celebre (USA)) (27027) **J. Gonzalez**
104 B f 21/4 Elusive Quality (USA)—Ronda (Bluebird (USA)) **S. L. Darpat**
105 **SHINAWAY (FR)**, b f 1/1 Gold Away (IRE)—Brilliante (Sillery (USA)) **Wertheimer et Frere**
106 B f 8/2 Montjeu (IRE)—Suite Royale (USA) (Diesis) (41827) **Stilvi Compania Financiera**
107 **SUPERIEUR (FR)**, b c 1/1 Highest Honor (FR)—
    Fabulous Hostess (USA) (Fabulous Dancer (USA)) **Wertheimer et Frere**
108 B c 1/3 Marju (IRE)—Tijuana Tango (CAN) (Tejano (USA)) (28000) **S. L. Darpat**
109 B f 22/3 Nayef (USA)—Triple Green (Green Desert (USA)) (36000) **Stilvi Compania Financiera**
110 B f 31/5 Johannesburg (USA)—Tuviah (USA) (Eastern Echo (USA)) (24295) **S. L. Darpat**
111 **VRILISSOS (FR)**, b c 1/1 Xaar—Storm Card (Zalazl (USA)) **Stilvi Compania Financiera**
112 **WAROLINO (FR)**, b c 28/5 War Chant (USA)—Zaragoza Girl (BRZ) (Trempolino (USA)) **Wertheimer et Frere**
113 **WILD BRIDE (IRE)**, b c 28/1 Daylami (IRE)—Gold Round (IRE) (Caerleon (USA)) **Wertheimer et Frere**

Assistant Trainer: Charles Peck

Jockey (flat): Miguel Blancpain, O. Peslier.

341 MRS S. LAMYMAN, Louth
Postal: **Ruckland Manor, Louth, Lincolnshire, LN11 8RQ**
Contacts: **PHONE (01507) 533260 FAX (01507) 534236 MOBILE (07733) 165721**
E-MAIL peter.lenoard@bt.com

1 **GOOD CAUSE (IRE)**, 7, b g Simply Great (FR)—Smashing Pet **Mr P. E. L. Lamyman**
2 **GOOD ETIQUETTE**, 4, b g Tipsy Creek (USA)—Aliuska (IRE) **Mr S. A. Nicholson**
3 **JAMAICAN FLIGHT (USA)**, 15, b h Sunshine Forever (USA)—Kalamona (USA) **Mr P. E. L. Lamyman**
4 **KEEN WARRIOR**, 8, gr g Keen—Briden **R.Hill,D.Ellis,B.Kemp**
5 **MATINEE IDOL**, 5, ch m In The Wings—Bibliotheque (USA) **Mr P. E. L. Lamyman**
6 **NEW BEGINNING (IRE)**, 4, b g Keltos (FR)—Goldthroat (USA) **Mr P. E. L. Lamyman**
7 **SPARES AND REPAIRS**, 5, b g Robellino (USA)—Lady Blackfoot **Mr P. E. L. Lamyman**
8 **TRUE (IRE)**, 7, ch m Barathea (IRE)—Bibliotheque (USA) **The Underlaws**
9 **VICTORY QUEST (IRE)**, 8, b g Victory Note (USA)—Marade (USA) **Mr P. E. L. Lamyman**

TWO-YEAR-OLDS

10 B f 18/4 Christophene (USA)—Lotus Flower (IRE) (Grand Lodge (USA)) (800) **Mr P. E. L. Lamyman**
11 B f 6/5 Sesaro (USA)—Mickey Towbar (IRE) (Mujadil (USA)) (800) **Mr P. E. L. Lamyman**
12 B c 12/4 Lujain (USA)—Mitsuki (Puissance) (2000) **Mr P. E. L. Lamyman**

Other Owners: Mr Don Ellis, Mr Rowland Hill, Mr B. C. S. Kemp, Mrs S. Lamyman, Mr P. Lamyman, Sotby Farming Company Limited, Mrs Sarah Underwood, Mr Nigel Underwood.

Assistant Trainer: P. Lamyman

342 MR D. R. LANIGAN, Newmarket
Postal: **Revida Place, Hamilton Road, Newmarket, Suffolk, CB8 7JQ**
Contacts: **PHONE (01638) 662313 FAX (01638) 661652**

1 **BEN CHORLEY**, 4, gr g Inchinor—Arantxa

THREE-YEAR-OLDS

2 **CONFERENCE (IRE)**, b f Montjeu (IRE)—Desert Bluebell

TWO-YEAR-OLDS

3 B c 20/2 Redback—Banco Solo (Distant Relative) (21000)
4 **CONVITEZZA**, b f 13/2 Domedriver (IRE)—Condoleezza (USA) (Cozzene (USA))
5 B c 28/4 Aldebaran (USA)—Cuanto Es (USA) (Exbourne (USA))
6 B f 16/4 Galileo (IRE)—Desert Bluebell (Kalaglow) (51480)
7 **DITTO DITTO**, b c 23/2 Mark of Esteem (IRE)—City Gambler (Rock City) (6000)
8 B c 25/3 Rahy (USA)—Grand Ogygia (USA) (Ogygian (USA)) (133624)
9 B c 5/4 Rainbow Quest (USA)—Kartuzy (JPN) (Polish Precedent (USA)) (20000)
10 B c 15/2 Domedriver (IRE)—Kilbride (Selkirk (USA)) (3000)
11 B f 13/5 Cape Cross (IRE)—Marienbad (FR) (Darshaan) (100000)
12 B c 6/5 Theatrical—Miasma (USA) (Lear Fan (USA)) (63168)
13 B f 29/1 Galileo (IRE)—Ninth Wonder (USA) (Forty Niner (USA)) (51480)
14 B f 8/2 Dubai Destination (USA)—Noble Lily (USA) (Vaguely Noble) (40000)
15 **NOT SO INNOCENT**, b f 26/2 Fusaichi Pegasus (USA)—Little Firefly (IRE) (Danehill (USA))
16 **OTTOMAN EMPIRE (FR)**, ch c 7/5 Pivotal—Chesnut Bird (IRE) (Storm Bird (CAN)) (231660)
17 B f 22/1 Oasis Dream—Pilgrim Spirit (USA) (Saint Ballado (CAN)) (30000)
18 Ch f 1/4 Dr Fong (USA)—Quiet Counsel (IRE) (Law Society (USA)) (18000)
19 Gr f 7/2 El Prado (IRE)—Sauterne (Rainbow Quest (USA)) (75000)
20 B c 26/4 Barathea (IRE)—Sheer Spirit (IRE) (Caerleon (USA)) (32000)
21 **SIR BERE (FR)**, b c 8/3 Della Francesca (USA)—Known Alibi (USA) (Known Fact (USA)) (19305)
22 B f 24/3 Refuse To Bend (IRE)—Star Studded (Cadeaux Genereux) (90000)
23 B f 18/2 Danehill Dancer (IRE)—Streak of Silver (USA) (Dynaformer (USA)) (72886)
24 B br f 1/5 Dynaformer (USA)—Tuscoga (USA) (Theatrical) (315840)
25 B c 11/4 King's Best (USA)—Wannabe Grand (IRE) (Danehill (USA)) (75000)

Other Owners: Mr Paul Brosnan, Mr Paul Darling, Mr Paul Dean, Diamond Racing, Mr Bob Lanigan, Lord & Lady Lloyd-Webber, Mrs John Magnier, Miss Nicola Mahony, Mr Julian May, Mr & Mrs Dermot O'Rourke, Rabbah Bloodstock, Miss Kirsten Rausing, The Niarchos Family.

343 MISS E. C. LAVELLE, Andover

Postal: **Cottage Stables, Hatherden, Andover, Hampshire, SP11 0HY**
Contacts: **PHONE** (01264) 735509 **OFFICE** (01264) 735412 **FAX** (01264) 735529
MOBILE (07774) 993998
E-MAIL emma@elavelle.freeserve.co.uk **WEBSITE** www.emmalavelle.co.uk

1 ALAGHIRAAR (IRE), 4, b g Act One—Tarsheeh (USA) **Paul G. Jacobs & Richard B. Denny**
2 AMBROSIANO, 4, b g Averti (IRE)—Secret Circle **P. G. Jacobs**
3 ASAGAI, 6, b g Tragic Role (USA)—Mia Xandra **Mrs S. Hamilton**
4 BETWEEN DREAMS, 5, br m Silver Wizard (USA)—I Have A Dream (SWE) **J. A. Dewhurst**
5 BISHOP'S BRIDGE (IRE), 10, b g Norwich—River Swell (IRE) **S. Kimber**
6 BLACK ON BLACK (FR), 4, b g Nikos—Cadougia (FR) **R. Grenville-Webb**
7 BLAEBERRY, 7, b m Kirkwall—Top Berry **Lady Bland**
8 BRACKENRIDGE, 4, b g Tumbleweed Ridge—I Have A Dream (SWE) **Diane & John Dewhurst**
9 CHUQUICAMATA, 6, ch g Classic Cliche (IRE)—River Bay (IRE) **Mr M. E. Thompson**
10 CRACK AWAY JACK, 4, ch g Gold Away (IRE)—Jolly Harbour **GDM Partnership**
11 DALTABAN (FR), 4, ch g Rainbow Quest (USA)—Daltaiyma (IRE) **D. A. Johnson**
12 DE WELSH WIZZARD, 5, b g Karinga Bay—Valls d'andorra **N. Mustoe**
13 DOUBLE LAW, 8, ch g Double Trigger (IRE)—Sister-In-Law **Mrs P. A. Scott-Dunn**
14 EASTER LEGEND, 4, ch f Midnight Legend—Easter Comet **Mr S. C. Willes**
15 ET MAINTENANT (FR), 6, ch g Johann Quatz (FR)—Dunlora **Axom (II)**
16 FIELDSOFCLOVER (IRE), 11, br g Montelimar (USA)—Power Point **Seven Plus One Syndicate**
17 FIRE AND RAIN (FR), 5, b g Galileo (USA)—Quatre Saisons (FR) **Fraser Miller Racing**
18 FOLIE DANCER, 5, b m Exit To Nowhere (USA)—Kirov Royale **J. R. Lavelle & Dr Mark Scott**
19 FOR HIS SINS (IRE), 5, b g Dr Massini (IRE)—Thistle Chat **N. Mustoe**
20 GANDY DANCER (IRE), 8, b m Dr Massini (IRE)—Muckride Lady **Mrs S. V. M. Stevens**
21 INVENTION (USA), 5, b g Lear Fan (USA)—Carya (USA) **Fraser Miller Racing**
22 KADOUCHSKI (FR), 4, b g Ski Chief (USA)—Douchka (FR) **GDM Partnership**
23 KITTE OU DOUBLE (FR), 10, b g Agent Bleu (FR)—Briffault (FR) **GDM Partnership**
24 LABELTHOU (FR), 9, b m Saint Preuil (FR)—Suzy de Thou (FR) **GDM Partnership**
25 LAGAVULIN (IRE), 4, b c Marju (IRE)—Anna Kareena (IRE) **D. M. Bell**
26 LE COMMENCEMENT (IRE), 6, b g Beneficial—Ballyduggan Queen (IRE) **Frisky Fillies 4**
27 MARCUS, 7, gr g Silver Patriarch (IRE)—Loving Around (FR) **Bloomsbury Stud**
28 MIGWELL (FR), 8, b g Assessor (IRE)—Uguette IV (FR) **GDM Partnership**
29 NAJCA DE THAIX (FR), 7, b br g Marmato—Isca de Thaix (FR) **Les Trois Amis**
30 NYBORG MADRIK (FR), 7, b g Cyborg (FR)—Little Blue (FR) **D. A. Johnson**
31 OPUS CAFE (FR), 6, b g Panoramic—Cafefleur (FR) **N. Mustoe**
32 OTANTIQUE (FR), 6, b g Lute Antique (FR)—Gracieuse Antique (FR) **The Antique Partnership**
33 PALUA, 11, b g Sri Pekan (USA)—Reticent Bride (USA) **R. J. Lavelle**
34 PHAR AGAIN (IRE), 5, b g Beneficial—Phar From Men (IRE) **Favourites Racing XII**
35 PREMIER HOPE (IRE), 7, b m Second Empire (IRE)—Our Hope **Fortnum Racing**
36 PRESENCE OF MIND (IRE), 10, ch g Presenting—Blue Rose (IRE) **M. L. Coghlan**
37 PRESENTING EXPRESS (IRE), 9, b g Presenting—Glenbane Express (IRE) **N. Mustoe**
38 PRINCE VILLEVERT (FR), 5, b g Goldneyev (USA)—Jubilation (FR) **Stan Adams & Robert Kirkland**
39 PRIORS DALE, 8, br g Lahib (USA)—Mathaayl (USA) **Mrs L. M. Alexander**
40 PROPHETS HONOR (FR), 5, b m Highest Honor (FR)—Lovely Noor (USA) **N. Mustoe**
41 RAKAMAN, 7, b g Rakaposhi King—Manettia (IRE) **Hellyer Prior Syder Few Brown**
42 REGAL QUOTE (IRE), 5, b g Classic Cliche (IRE)—Glen Princess (IRE) **R. J. Lavelle**
43 RIO DE JANEIRO (IRE), 7, b g Sadler's Wells—Alleged Devotion (USA) **Fraser Miller Racing**
44 SEYMAR LAD (IRE), 8, b g Oscar (IRE)—Far And Deep (IRE) **Mr A. A. Gemmell**
45 SIR LAUGHALOT, 8, b g Alzao (USA)—Funny Hilarious (USA) **S. Hepworth, M. Webster, E. Lavelle**
46 STADIUM ARCADIUM (IRE), 5, ch g Clerkenwell (USA)—Miles **Top Of The Market Syndicate**
47 SUNTINI (GER), 6, b g Platini (GER)—Sunita (GER) **Favourites Racing XX**
48 SUPREME COPPER (IRE), 8, br g Supreme Leader—Black Wind (IRE) **N. Collison**
49 TALENTI (IRE), 5, b g Sadler's Wells (USA)—Sumoto **Fraser Miller Racing**
50 TANA RIVER (IRE), 12, b g Over The River (FR)—Home In The Glen **The Frisky Fillies**
51 THE BANDIT (IRE), 11, b g Un Desperado (FR)—Sweet Friendship **R. J. Lavelle**
52 THE JOLLY SPOOFER (IRE), 6, b g Luso—Some News (IRE) **The Hawkhurst Spoofers**
53 THE KING AND I (IRE), 4, b g Monashee Mountain (USA)—Scrimshaw **The Villains**
54 —, 4, b g Golan (IRE)—The Merry Widow (IRE) **E. C. Lavelle**
55 TOMINA, 8, b g Deploy—Cavina **P. G. Jacobs**
56 TOWEROFCHARLEMAGNE (IRE), 5, ch g King Charlemagne (USA)—Nozet **R. Grenville-Webb**
57 TRITONVILLE LODGE (IRE), 6, b g Grand Lodge—Olean **Frisky Fillies 3**
58 TWEED RIVER (USA), 4, b c Royal Academy (USA)—Gotablush **D. M. Bell**
59 UMBRELLA MAN (IRE), 12, ch g Insan (USA)—Askasilla (USA) **Mrs J. Dollar & Mrs M. Hall**
60 VAGRANT EMPEROR (IRE), 5, b g Oscar (IRE)—Dragonmist (IRE) **N. Mustoe**
61 ZERO (IRE), 5, b h Halling (USA)—Zonda **Mr G. P. MacIntosh**

MISS E. C. LAVELLE—continued

Other Owners: S. P. Adams, K. A. Alexander, Axom Ltd, Mr L. F. Carney, G. Charlesworth, D. Charlesworth, Mrs H. Charlet, Mr M. Cutler, Mrs A. L. Davies, Mrs P. A. Deal, R. B. Denny, Mrs D. S. Dewhurst, Mrs J. A. Dollar, Mr D. Downie, Mr J. R. Eburne, Mr S. A. Fahy, Mrs J. R. Foster, Mrs M. Hall, C. G. Hellyer, Mrs S. C. Hepworth, A. J. Hill, R. W. Jones, P. H. Jones, R. M. Kirkland, Mrs A. C. Lavelle, J. R. Lavelle, J. M. Layton, R. M. Levitt, P. B. Mitford-Slade, Mr S. A. J. Penny, Mrs S. K. Prior, K. P. Ryan, Dr M. J. Scott, Sir David Sieff, Lady J. R. Sieff, Mr G. H. Skeats, B. G. Slade, Mr M. Smith, R. W. Smith, D. F. Sumpter, Mrs R. D. Sumpter, Mr T. J. Swift, Mrs A. W. Timpson, L. R. Turland, M. A. Webster, Mrs P. H. Williams.

Jockey (NH): B. Fenton.

---

344 **MR B. L. LAY, Chipping Norton**
Postal: Rest Hill Farm, Over Worton, Chipping Norton, Oxfordshire, OX7 7EW
Contacts: PHONE (01608) 683608
E-MAIL lawrence.lay@zoom.co.uk

1 TEARS, 6, b g Manhal—Secret Stolen (USA) **B. L. Lay**
2 THENFORD TROUT (IRE), 7, b g Midhish—Monteanna (IRE) **B. L. Lay**
3 WORTON BOY, 7, ch g Manhal—Taffidale **B. L. Lay**

Assistant Trainer: L. Lay

Amateur: Mr L. Lay.

---

345 **MRS J. L. LE BROCQ, Jersey**
Postal: St Etienne, Rue D'Elysee, St Peters, Jersey, JE3 7DT
Contacts: PHONE/FAX (01534) 481461 MOBILE (07797) 750823

1 BOLLIN FERGUS, 4, br c Vettori (IRE)—Bollin Harriet **Mrs J. Le Brocq**
2 CARR HALL (IRE), 5, b g Rossini (USA)—Pidgeon Bay (IRE) **Mrs J. Le Brocq, C. Benest, N. Blake**
3 CERISE EN BLEU (FR), 4, ch g Goldneyev (USA)—Wild Rita **Mrs J. Le Brocq**
4 DIDOE, 9, br m Son Pardo—My Diamond Ring **Mrs M. E. Wickham**
5 FLAXBY, 6, b g Mister Baileys—Harryana **Mrs J. Le Brocq**
6 FLIGHTY FELLOW (IRE), 8, ch g Flying Spur (AUS)—Al Theraab (USA) **Mrs J. Le Brocq**
7 HIGH VOLTAGE, 7, ch g Wolfhound (USA)—Real Emotion (USA) **Mrs J. Le Brocq**
8 I'M AIMEE, 6, ch m Timeless Times (USA)—Marfen **Myami Racing**
9 LAST CHAPTER (IRE), 6, b g Desert Story (IRE)—Dutosky **Mrs J. Le Brocq**
10 MARTIN'S SUNSET, 10, ch g Royal Academy (USA)—Mainly Sunset **Mrs J. Le Brocq**
11 SECRET ASSASSIN (IRE), 5, b g Daggers Drawn (USA)—Lypharden (IRE) **The Names's Bond Partnership**
12 WALL STREET RUNNER, 7, ch m Kirkwall—Running Tycoon (IRE) **Lavender Racing Club**

THREE-YEAR-OLDS

13 LORD OF THE WING, b c Daggers Drawn (USA)—Brangane (IRE) **Frank & Annette Brady**
14 ROPE BRIDGE (IRE), b c Orpen (USA)—Carhue Journey (IRE) **Mrs J. Le Brocq**

Other Owners: D. Barrons, Mrs J. Bentley, Mr Allan Butler, Mr & Mrs Colin Casey, J. Davies, Seamus Gallagher, Advocate R. Michel, Caroline Michel, Mike Quenault, Joe Quinn, G. Vibert.

Assistant Trainer: Edward Hanmer

Jockey (flat): Dean Gallagher, Amy Baker, V. Slattery. Jockey (NH): P. Holley, Dean Gallagher, V. Slattery. Amateur: Mr M. Brint, Mr N. Cook.

---

346 **MR RICHARD LEE, Presteigne**
Postal: The Bell House, Byton, Presteigne
Contacts: PHONE (01544) 267672 FAX (01544) 260247 MOBILE (07836) 537145
E-MAIL info@rleeracing.com WEBSITE www.rleeracing.com

1 ALMAYDAN, 10, b g Marju (IRE)—Cunning **George Brookes & Family**
2 BATTLEFIELD, 8, b g Overbury (IRE)—Tapua Taranata (IRE) **Brereton Jackson & Compton**
3 BORORA, 9, gr g Shareef Dancer (USA)—Bustling Nelly **Mrs E. M. Clarke**
4 COTTINGHAM (IRE), 7, b g Perugino (USA)—Stately Princess **Glass Half Full**
5 CURSUM PERFICIO, 6, b g Tagula (IRE)—Simply Sooty **Mrs C. Lee**
6 DANTE'S DIAMOND (IRE), 6, b g Orpen (USA)—Flower From Heaven **Glass Half Full**

MR RICHARD LEE—continued

7 **EXTRA BOLD**, 6, b g Overbury (IRE)—Tellicherry **Exors of the Late R. J. Jenks**
8 **GOFORTHEGAP (IRE)**, 9, ch g Broken Hearted—Gender Gap (USA) **Lord Daresbury & Tom Lee**
9 **HONOR AND GLORY**, 8, br g Past Glories—Scalby Anna **A. & B. Beard**
10 **IFFY**, 7, b g Orpen (USA)—Hopesay **Six To Five Against**
11 **ILE DE PARIS (FR)**, 9, b g Cadoudal (FR)—Sweet Beauty (FR) **George Brookes & Family & Lord Daresbury**
12 **ISTRON BAY**, 6, b g Petoski—Annie Buckers (IRE) **A. M. Grazebrook, Dr Du Croz & C. R. J. Fleming**
13 **JOLEJOKER**, 10, b g Alflora (IRE)—Jolejester **D. E. Edwards**
14 **LAGO**, 10, b g Maelstrom Lake—Jugendliebe (IRE) **B. Bargh, J. Hamer, Des Cound, Kevin Ackerman**
15 **MARKED MAN (IRE)**, 12, b g Grand Plaisir (IRE)—Teazle **Mr & Mrs C. R. Elliott**
16 **MISTER POTTER**, 8, b g Classic Cliche (IRE)—Potter's Gale (IRE) **James & Jean Potter**
17 **PEDROS BRIEF (IRE)**, 10, b br g Leading Counsel (USA)—Pedros Pet (IRE) **Gale Force Five**
18 **POTTS OF MAGIC**, 9, b g Classic Cliche (IRE)—Potter's Gale (IRE) **James & Jean Potter**
19 **RAPIDE PLAISIR (IRE)**, 10, b g Grand Plaisir (IRE)—Royal Well **The Another Comedy Partnership**
20 **RIFLEMAN (IRE)**, 8, ch g Starborough—En Garde (USA) **J. Jackson & M. Bevan**
21 **SILIVRI**, 6, gr m Silver Patriarch (IRE)—Riviere **Dr R. G. Fairs**
22 **SOLARIAS QUEST**, 6, b g Pursuit of Love—Persuasion **A. Longman**
23 **SURE FLAME (IRE)**, 6, b g Needle Gun (IRE)—Gallic Flame **The Hopkins Trower Partnership**
24 **THE GLEN**, 10, gr g Mtoto—Silver Singer **The Monarchs Of The Glen**

Other Owners: Mr N. Abbott, K. Ackerman, Mrs S. Archdale, Mr Bernard Bargh, Mr M. Bevan, Mr Henry Boss, Mr R. J. Brereton, Mr George Brookes, Mr P. Browning, Mr Anthony J. Compton, Mr Des Cound, Mr Tony Gale, Mr J. Hamer, Mr David N. Harris, Mr R. L. C. Hartley, Mr John M. Jackson, Mr Richard Lee, Mr Tom Lee, Dr Darien Lott, Mr Des Murray, Mr Rex Norton, Lady Susan Ripley, Mr Will Roseff, Mr J. G. Storey, Mr James Whittle.

Assistant Trainer: Kerry Lee

Jockey (NH): R. Johnson, R. Thornton. **Conditional:** C. Poste. **Amateur:** Mr T. Greenall, Mr Ashley Bird.

---

347   MRS S. V. O. LEECH, Didcot
Postal: **Whiteshoot Stables, Blewbury, Didcot**
Contacts: **PHONE (01235) 851988 FAX (01235) 851988 MOBILE (07775) 874630**
E-MAIL info@leechracing.co.uk WEBSITE ww.leechracing.co.uk

1 **AMAZING REQUEST**, 4, b c Rainbow Quest (USA)—Maze Garden (USA) **Mr C. R. Leech**
2 **CHAMACCO (FR)**, 8, b g Cadoudal (FR)—Awentina (FR) **C. J. Leech**
3 **CROC AN OIR (IRE)**, 11, ch g Treasure Hunter—Cool Mary **I. Thompson, O. O'Reilly, Leech Racing**
4 **EL ALAMEIN (IRE)**, 5, ch g Nashwan (USA)—El Rabab (USA)
5 **KINGS STORY (IRE)**, 4, b c Royal Applause—Poppy Carew (IRE) **M. Boyers, W. Hobson, J. Adams**
6 **LUSTRE LAD**, 7, b g Overbury (IRE)—Welsh Lustre (IRE) **C. J. Leech**
7 **SILMI**, 4, gr c Daylami (IRE)—Intimaa (IRE) **It All Started At Newmarket**
8 **WAIT FOR THE LIGHT**, 4, b g Fantastic Light (USA)—Lady In Waiting **I. J. Turner & M. A. Gray**

Other Owners: J. M. Adams, Mr M. H. Boyers, Mr M. A. Gray, William (Bill) Hobson, Mr O. O'Reilly, Mr I. C. Thompson, Mr I. J. Turner.

Assistant Trainer: Christian Leech

---

348   MR ELIE LELLOUCHE, Lamorlaye
Postal: **23 Rue Charles Pratt, 60260 Lamorlaye, France**
Contacts: **PHONE (0033) 3442 19916 FAX (0033) 3442 14614**

1 **GLOBAL HERO (GER)**, 6, b h Big Shuffle (USA)—Goonda **F. Teboul**
2 **PERFECT MURDER (IRE)**, 6, ch h Desert King (IRE)—Pine Chip (USA) **Ecurie Wildenstein**
3 **PETROGRAD (FR)**, 7, b h Peintre Celebre (USA)—Palmeraie (USA) **Ecurie Wildenstein**
4 **POINTILLISTE (USA)**, 5, ch h Giant's Causeway (USA)—Peinture Bleue (USA) **Ecurie Wildenstein**
5 **STARAMIX (FR)**, 7, gr h Linamix (FR)—Sectarine (FR) **Daniel Malingue**
6 **SUPERIOR OFFICER (FR)**, 6, b h Anabaa (USA)—Supergirl (USA) **Ecurie Wildenstein**
7 **SUREYYA (GER)**, 5, b m Monsun (GER)—Sankt Johanna (GER) **Ecurie Wildenstein**
8 **VASSILIEVSKY (IRE)**, 7, ch h Peintre Celebre (USA)—Verveine (USA) **Ecurie Wildenstein**
9 **VENDANGEUR (IRE)**, 5, b h Galileo (IRE)—Vahine (USA) **Ecurie Wildenstein**

THREE-YEAR-OLDS

10 **ALBERT HALL (USA)**, b c Stravinsky (USA)—Albertine (FR) **Ecurie Wildenstein**
11 **ART HISTORIAN (GER)**, b c Red Ransom (USA)—Arlesienne (IRE) **Ecurie Wildenstein**

MR ELIE LELLOUCHE—continued

12 **AURORE (IRE)**, b f Fasliyev (USA)—Agathe (USA) **Ecurie Wildenstein**
13 **LANZO (FR)**, b c Gold Away (IRE)—Bleu Ciel Et Blanc (FR) **E. Lellouche**
14 **MAGADAN (IRE)**, b c High Chaparral (IRE)—Molasses (FR) **Ecurie Wildenstein**
15 **MISS STREAM (FR)**, ch f Trempolino (USA)—Tonic Stream (FR) **Etoiles Du Galop**
16 **MISSION SECRETE (IRE)**, b br f Galileo (IRE)—Miss Tahiti (IRE) **Ecurie Wildenstein**
17 **ORPHEE (IRE)**, ch f Peintre Celebre (USA)—Odessa (IRE) **Ecurie Wildenstein**
18 **PANTAGRUEL (IRE)**, b c Peintre Celebre (USA)—Parisienne (IRE) **Ecurie Wildenstein**
19 **POUVOIR ABSOLU**, b c Sadler's Wells (USA)—Pine Chip (USA) **Ecurie Wildenstein**
20 **RASPOUTINE (USA)**, b br c Seeking The Gold (USA)—Rolly Polly (IRE) **Ecurie Wildenstein**
21 **VICHY (IRE)**, ch f Hawk Wing (USA)—Veleni (IRE) **Ecurie Wildenstein**

Jockey (flat): O. Peslier, G. Faucon.

---

349 **MISS H. LEWIS, Lisvane**
Postal: **The Hollies Stables, Rudry Road, Lisvane, Cardiff, South Glamorgan, CF14 0SN**
Contacts: **PHONE (02920) 764856 FAX (02920) 764856 MOBILE (07730) 387991**
E-MAIL hlewis7@hotmail.co.uk

1 4, Ch g Bach (IRE)—Aillwee Dawn **Walters Plant Hire Ltd**
2 **CELTIC BOY (IRE)**, 10, b g Arctic Lord—Laugh Away **Walters Plant Hire Ltd, Egan Waste Ltd**
3 **CELTIC MAJOR (IRE)**, 10, gr g Roselier (FR)—Dun Oengus (IRE) **Walters Plant Hire Ltd**
4 **DAIS RETURN (IRE)**, 4, b g Lahib (USA)—Bayazida **West Coast Haulage Limited**
5 4, B g Presenting—Dante's Skip (IRE) **Walters Plant Hire Ltd**
6 **GO ON GEORGE (IRE)**, 6, gr g Pasternak—Rosy Posy (IRE) **Walters Plant Hire Ltd**
7 **GRAND SLAM HERO (IRE)**, 7, ch g Anshan—Tidal Princess (IRE) **Walters Plant Hire Ltd**
8 **HELENS VISION**, 5, b m Alflora (IRE)—Kinlet Vision **Mr W. D. Morris**
9 **LORD GENEROUS**, 4, ch g Generous (IRE)—Lady Rebecca **Walters Plant Hire Ltd**
10 **MANJAM (IRE)**, 4, b g Almutawakel—Mubkera (IRE) **Walters Plant Hire Ltd**
11 **NATIONAL TRUST**, 6, b g Sadler's Wells (USA)—National Treasure **Walters Plant Hire Ltd**
12 **NAYODABAYO (IRE)**, 8, b g Definite Article—Babushka (IRE) **Walters Plant Hire Ltd**
13 **POWER KING (IRE)**, 6, b g Supreme Leader—Quennie Mo Ghra (IRE) **Walters Plant Hire Ltd**
14 **PUTNEY BRIDGE**, 6, b g Slip Anchor—Mayroni
15 **SHANNONS BOY (IRE)**, 6, b g Anshan—Dusky Lady **Walters Plant Hire Ltd**
16 **SHUIL AN BURREN (IRE)**, 7, b g Luso—National Stoirmeach (IRE) **Mr R. J. Williams**
17 **SKY MACK (IRE)**, 7, ch g Anshan—Ramona Style (IRE) **Walters Plant Hire Ltd**
18 **TIGU (IRE)**, 7, b g Tiraaz (USA)—Christy's Girl (IRE) **C. G. Bolton**
19 **TRIPLE SEVEN (IRE)**, 7, b br g Rashar (USA)—Hill of Bargy **Walters Plant Hire Ltd**
20 4, B g Lahib (USA)—Viking Dream (IRE) **Walters Plant Hire Ltd**
21 **WILD TONTO (IRE)**, 5, b g Saddlers' Hall (IRE)—Shipping News (IRE) **Walters Plant Hire Ltd**

Other Owners: Mr C. G. Bolton, Egan Waste Services Ltd, Mr W. D. Morris, W D Lewis Holdings Ltd, Walters Plant Hire Ltd, West Coast Haulage LTD, Mr R. J. Williams.

Jockey (NH): M. Fitzgerald, R. Johnson, P. J. Brennan. **Conditional:** Liam Treadwell, Paddy Merrigan.

---

350 **MR R. W. LEWIS, Newport, Gwent**
Postal: **Court Farm, Llanmartin, Newport, Gwent, NP18 2EB**
Contacts: **PHONE (01633) 412344**

1 **FREELINE FURY**, 8, b g Sir Harry Lewis (USA)—Queen's Favourite **Guy Lewis Racing**
2 **KADAM (IRE)**, 8, b g Night Shift (USA)—Kadassa (IRE) **Guy Lewis Racing**

Other Owners: Mr G. M. Lewis, R. W. Lewis.
Assistant Trainer: Guy Lewis

---

351 **MR A. J. D. LIDDERDALE, Hungerford**
Postal: **T/A Lidderdale Racing, Eastbury Cottage Stables, Eastbury, Hungerford, Berkshire, RG17 7JJ**
Contacts: **PHONE (01488) 73694 FAX (01488) 670443 MOBILE (07785) 785375**
E-MAIL alastairlidderdale@btinternet.com WEBSITE www.lidderdaleracing.co.uk

1 **CEMGRAFT**, 7, b m In The Wings—Soviet Maid (IRE) **The Clover Leaf Consortium**

MR A. J. D. LIDDERDALE—continued

2 CLAWS, 5, b m Marju (IRE)—Paws (IRE) **Orbit Performance**
3 KILBURN, 4, b g Grand Lodge (USA)—Lady Lahar
4 MISTRESS NELL, 8, b m Thethingaboutitis (USA)—Neladar **A. J. H. Hallows**
5 MR BELVEDERE, 7, b g Royal Applause—Alarming Motown **Entertainments Committee**
6 POLIA (FR), 5, b m Grand Tresor (FR)—Donapolia (FR) **The KMC Partnership**
7 REGGAE RHYTHM (IRE), 14, b g Be My Native (USA)—Invery Lady **Mrs A. Lidderdale**
8 TAKE IT THERE, 6, ch m Cadeaux Genereux—Feel Free (IRE) **Entertainments Committee**

TWO-YEAR-OLDS

9 BELVIDERA, b f 9/4 Golden Snake (USA)—Satiric (IRE) (Doyoun) (800) **Patrick Brain**
10 B f 26/3 Trans Island—Common Cause (Polish Patriot (USA)) (9000) **AC Lighting**
11 IT'S DUBAI DOLLY, ch f 13/2 Dubai Destination (USA)—
Betrothal (IRE) (Groom Dancer (USA)) (3000) **Mrs Mervin Cox**

Other Owners: Mr L. Garside-Beattie, Ms N. C. Heath, Mrs A. Lidderdale, Mr David Lidderdale, Mr M. S. Lilly.

Amateur: Miss Zoe Lilly.

352 MRS S. A. LIDDIARD, Great Shefford
Postal: **Shefford Valley Stud, Great Shefford, Hungerford, Berkshire, RG17 7EF**
Contacts: **FAX** (01488) 648939 **MOBILE** (07887) 991292
E-MAIL stef@svstud.co.uk WEBSITE www.stef-liddiard.co.uk

1 CALLOFF THE SEARCH, 4, b g Piccolo—Unchain My Heart **Lobster & The Wizrat Busters**
2 CERTAIN JUSTICE, 10, gr g Lit de Justice (USA)—Pure Misk **Mrs S. A. Liddiard**
3 COUNCELLOR (FR), 6, b g Gilded Time (USA)—Sudden Storm Bird (USA) **ownaracehorse.co.uk**
4 EARL COMPTON (IRE), 4, b g Compton Place—Noble Story **Mrs S. A. Liddiard**
5 FINANCIAL TIMES (USA), 6, b g Awesome Again (CAN)—Investabull (USA) **Mrs S. A. Liddiard**
6 MAIDEN INVESTOR, 5, b m Orpen (USA)—Actress **R. A. Webb**
7 NICADA (IRE), 4, ch g Titus Livius (FR)—Rhapsani (IRE) **Mr S. P. Cook & Miss Michelle Button**
8 SIENA STAR (IRE), 10, b g Brief Truce (USA)—Gooseberry Pie **Ownaracehorse.co.uk (Shefford)**
9 TREASON TRIAL, 7, b g Peintre Celebre (USA)—Pampabella (IRE) **Mrs S. A. Liddiard**
10 TYZACK (IRE), 7, b g Fasliyev (USA)—Rabea (USA) **Mrs S. J. Roberts**

THREE-YEAR-OLDS

11 TEN SPOT (IRE), b f Intikhab (USA)—Allergy **Mrs F. Ashfield**
12 THE MAGIC BLANKET (IRE), b g Bahamian Bounty—Zietunzeen (IRE) **D. M. J. Gilbert**
13 VICTORIAN BOUNTY, b c Bahamian Bounty—Baby Bunting **D. M. J. Gilbert**

TWO-YEAR-OLDS

14 RIO RAPIDO (GB), b c 11/3 Diktat—
Araguaia (IRE) (Zafonic (USA)) (5000) **Mr G. E. Griffiths & Mr C. M. Bennett**

Other Owners: Mr C. M. Bennett, Miss M. Button, Mr S. P. Cook, G. E. Griffiths, Mr G. S. Jehu, ownaracehorse Ltd.

Jockey (flat): M. Fenton.

353 MR N. P. LITTMODEN, Newmarket
Postal: **Southgate, Hamilton Road, Newmarket, Suffolk, CB8 0WY**
Contacts: **PHONE** (01638) 663375 **FAX** (01638) 661948 **MOBILE** (07770) 964865
E-MAIL nicklittmoden@btinternet.com WEBSITE www.nicklittmoden.com

1 COUNTRYWIDE MAGIC, 5, b g Royal Applause—Elsie Plunkett **Countrywide Steel & Tubes Ltd**
2 FUSILI (IRE), 5, ch m Silvano (GER)—Flunder **N. R. Shields**
3 JIMMY THE GUESSER, 5, ch g Piccolo—Brush Away **Miss V. A. Church**
4 KINDLELIGHT BLUE (IRE), 4, gr g Golan (IRE)—Kalimar (IRE) **Kindlelight Ltd**
5 LORD THEO, 4, b g Averti (IRE)—Love You Too **R. D. Hartshorn**
6 MOAYED, 9, b g Selkirk (USA)—Song of Years (IRE) **N. R. Shields**
7 MUTARED (IRE), 10, b g Marju (IRE)—Shahaada (USA) **Mrs E. P. Littmoden**
8 NINTH HOUSE (USA), 6, b h Chester House (USA)—Ninette (USA) **N. R. Shields**
9 ORPSIE BOY (IRE), 5, b g Orpen (USA)—Nordicolini (IRE) **Miss V. A. Church**
10 QADAR (IRE), 6, b g Xaar—Iktidar **N. R. Shields**

MR N. P. LITTMODEN—continued

11 **SMOKIN BEAU**, 11, b g Cigar—Beau Dada (IRE) **Miss V. A. Church**
12 **SPELLMAN**, 4, ch g Dr Fong (USA)—Justbetweenfriends (USA) **Berry Racing**
13 **SUN OF THE SEA**, 4, b g Best of The Bests (IRE)—Gem **Miss V. A. Church**
14 **WAVERTREE WARRIOR (IRE)**, 6, br g Indian Lodge (IRE)—Karamana **Wavertree Racing Partnership C**

THREE-YEAR-OLDS

15 **BEST OF THE WEST**, ch g Best of The Bests (IRE)—Palisandra (USA) **N. P. Littmoden**
16 **CAPTAIN MAINWARING**, b g Auction House (USA)—Shalyah (IRE) **Mr J. B. Waterfall**
17 **HAWA KHANA (IRE)**, br f Indian Danehill (IRE)—Anearlybird (USA) **Miss V. A. Church**
18 **HERON (IRE)**, b g Invincible Spirit (IRE)—Alexander Express (IRE) **The Six Shooters**
19 **LADY CHARLEMAGNE**, b f King Charlemagne (USA)—Prospering **N. P. Littmoden**
20 **MISS DEEDS (IRE)**, b f Invincible Spirit (IRE)—Aseelah **Southgate Racing**
21 **TOWNKAB (IRE)**, b g Intikhab (USA)—Town Girl (IRE) **Trojan Racing**
22 **UNIQUE (IRE)**, b c Invincible Spirit (IRE)—Licorne **The Six Shooters**
23 **WAVERTREE PRINCESS (IRE)**, gr f Invincible Spirit (IRE)—Blushing Queen (IRE) **Wavertree Racing Partnership D**

TWO-YEAR-OLDS

24 Ch f 16/4 Needwood Blade—Shalyah (IRE) (Shalford (IRE)) **N. P. Littmoden**
25 B f 8/4 Piccolo—Tallulah Belle (Crowning Honors (CAN)) (4000) **Mr B. Lever**
26 **VALKYRIE (IRE)**, b f 25/1 Danehill Dancer (IRE)—Ridotto (Salse (USA)) (35000) **V. & J. Properties**

Other Owners: Mr Toby Brereton, Mr J. Caplan, Ms A. Dawson, Mr A. A. Goodman, Mrs K. B. Graham, Mrs K. Graham, Mr A. Highfield, Mr Robert Levitt, Mr D. Palmer, Mr K. R. Parker, T. R. Pritchard, Mrs S. M. Pritchard, Mr M. D. H. West, Mr J. L. Whitten, Mrs Ann Whitten.

Amateur: Mrs Emma Littmoden.

---

354 MR B. LLEWELLYN, Swansea
Postal: **Abergelli Farm, Felindre, Swansea, West Glamorgan, SA5 7NN**
Contacts: **PHONE (01792) 776174**

1 **CLOONAVERY (IRE)**, 6, b g Xaar—Hero's Pride (FR) **Mrs M. Llewellyn**
2 **TEDSDALE MAC**, 9, ch g Presidium—Stilvella **Mrs M. Llewellyn**

---

355 MR B. J. LLEWELLYN, Bargoed
Postal: **Ffynonau Duon Farm, Pentwyn, Fochriw, Bargoed, Mid-Glamorgan, CF81 9NP**
Contacts: PHONE **(01685) 841259** FAX **(01685) 843838** MOBILE **(07971) 233473/(07971) 283262**
E-MAIL **bernard.llewellyn@btopenworld.com**

1 **BALLYBUNION (IRE)**, 9, ch g Entrepreneur—Clarentia **The Over The Bridge Partnership**
2 **BENAYOUN**, 4, b c Inchinor—Sosumi **G. Mills**
3 **CAVA BIEN**, 6, b g Bien Bien (USA)—Bebe de Cham **Mr C. R. Howell**
4 **FLEXIBLE FRIEND (IRE)**, 4, b c Danehill (USA)—Ripple of Pride (IRE) **B. J. Llewellyn**
5 **GREAT COMPTON**, 8, b g Compton Place—Thundercloud **Monnington Leisure Limited**
6 **HIDDEN TALENTS (IRE)**, 8, b g Arctic Lord—Cherry Avenue **B. J. Llewellyn**
7 **LEPRECHAUN'S GOLD (IRE)**, 4, ch g Spectrum (IRE)—Ashirah **B. J. Llewellyn**
8 **LIGHTNING FIRE (IRE)**, 6, b g Woodborough (USA)—Glowlamp (IRE) **A. J. Williams**
9 **LYRICAL LILY**, 10, b m Alflora (IRE)—Music Interpreter **G. Mills**
10 **MASTER D'OR (FR)**, 8, b g Cyborg (FR)—Une Pomme d'or (FR) **J. T. Warner**
11 **MOUNTAIN PASS (USA)**, 6, b g Stravinsky (USA)—Ribbony (USA) **B. J. Llewellyn**
12 **RAISE THE HEIGHTS (IRE)**, 5, b g Orpen (USA)—Blue Heights (IRE) **B. J. Llewellyn**
13 **SIR PANDY (IRE)**, 8, b g Taipan (IRE)—Miss Pitpan **G. Mills**
14 **SONNENGOLD (GER)**, 7, b br m Java Gold (USA)—Standing Ovation (ITY) **B. J. Llewellyn**
15 **STAR STRUCTURE (IRE)**, 4, b g Sadler's Wells (USA)—Above Water (IRE) **B. J. Llewellyn**
16 **WINGED D'ARGENT (IRE)**, 7, b br g In The Wings—Petite-D-Argent **J. T. Warner & B. J. Llewellyn**

Other Owners: Mr B. J. Llewellyn.

Assistant Trainer: J. L. Llewellyn

Jockey (flat): R. Havlin. **Jockey (NH):** C. Williams. **Apprentice:** David Probert. **Amateur:** Miss I. Thompsett, Mr J. L. Llewellyn.

356 MR C. LLEWELLYN, Upper Lambourn

Postal: Weathercock House, Upper Lambourn, Hungerford, Berkshire, RG17 8QT
Contacts: PHONE (01488) 73311 FAX (01488) 71065 MOBILE (07836) 783223
E-MAIL carl@carlracing.co.uk WEBSITE www.carlracing.co.uk

1 AMMUNITION (IRE), 8, b g Needle Gun (IRE)—Flapping Freda (IRE) Mrs E. Pearce
2 ANGE OU DEMON (IRE), 4, ch c Exit To Nowhere (USA)—Andromeda (IRE) Sir Robert Ogden C.B.E., LLD
3 4, Ch g Anabaa Blue—Ariadne (GER) M. C. Denmark
4 ASHLEYS ROSE (IRE), 4, gr f Ashley Park (IRE)—Petale de Rose (IRE) Mrs T. J. Stone-Brown
5 ASK THE GATHERER (IRE), 10, b g Be My Native (USA)—Shean Bracken (IRE) R. Pitman
6 BEST ACTOR (IRE), 9, b g Oscar (IRE)—Supreme Princess (IRE) M. C. Denmark
7 BLUE MONTY (IRE), 7, b g Supreme Leader—Choice of Kings (IRE) Mrs A. Tincknell
8 BUALA BOS (IRE), 7, b g Oscar (IRE)—Cathy Dee (IRE) Mrs T. J. Stone-Brown
9 CAN'T BUY A THRILL (IRE), 7, ch g Accordion—Gaye Humour (IRE) M. C. Denmark
10 CARRICK OSCAR (IRE), 8, b g Oscar (IRE)—Regents Prancer J L N
11 CELTIC HEATHER (IRE), 7, b m Darazari (IRE)—Kirsten (IRE) Mrs D. Romanes
12 CROUCH END FLYER, 6, b m Overbury (IRE)—Edithmead (IRE) Blane Nairn Racing
13 DEBAUCHERY (IRE), 6, b g Old Vic—Bring It With You M. C. Denmark
14 DEN OF INIQUITY, 7, b g Supreme Leader—Divine Comedy (IRE) M. C. Denmark
15 FOR ALL MANKIND, 7, b g Zaffaran (USA)—Gilston Lass M. C. Denmark
16 FREDENSBORG (NZ), 7, b g Danske (NZ)—Showplace (AUS) Sir Robert Ogden C.B.E., LLD
17 FREE WORLD (IRE), 6, b g Luso—Paddy's Dancer M. C. Denmark
18 GENIES LAMP (IRE), 4, ch f Snurge—Kyle Lamp (IRE) Mrs T. J. Stone-Brown
19 GLENDA HODDLE, 6, b m Kayf Tara—Mrs Bossy Boots Mr J. Goodman
20 HARRYCONE LEWIS, 10, b g Sir Harry Lewis (USA)—Rosie Cone The Craftsmen
21 HAVE YOU SEEN ME?, 5, b g Beneficial—Silent Supreme (IRE) The Maple Hurst Partnership
22 HELLFIRE CLUB, 5, br g Overbury (IRE)—Tapua Taranata (IRE) M. C. Denmark
23 HENNESSY (IRE), 7, b g Presenting—Steel Grey Lady M. C. Denmark
24 JOYRYDER, 7, gr g Cloudings (IRE)—Knight Ryde M. C. Denmark
25 JUMP JET (IRE), 6, ch g Beneficial—Cherry In A Hurry R. C. Thesiger
26 KID CHARLEMAGNE (IRE), 5, b g King Charlemagne (USA)—Albertville (GER) M. C. Denmark
27 KING FASLIEV (IRE), 5, b g Fasliyev (USA)—Open Air (GER) Sir Robert Ogden C.B.E., LLD
28 KING OF THE JUNGLE (IRE), 7, ch g Accordion—What It Takes (IRE) Mrs E. Pearce
29 KINGSTON LANE (IRE), 6, b g Sassanian (USA)—Two Roads M. C. Denmark
30 LADY OF THE MOOR, 7, b m Fraam—Sobranie S. D. Hemstock
31 LETALUS (GER), 7, b g Tannenkonig (GER)—Lerida (GER) Mrs Jill Eynon & Mr Robin Eynon
32 LIMITED EDITION (IRE), 10, b g Parthian Springs—Rosemount Rose M. C. Denmark
33 LORDY (NZ), 6, b g Senor Pete (USA)—Lydney (USA) The High Altitude Partnership
34 MASTER CHARM (FR), 4, b g Smadoun (FR)—Kandania (FR) Sir Robert Ogden C.B.E., LLD
35 MONSIGNORITA (IRE), 6, b m Classic Cliche (IRE)—Black Spring (IRE) M. C. Denmark
36 MURPHY (IRE), 6, b g Lord Americo—Kyle Cailin Mrs T. J. Stone-Brown
37 OSCAR GOLD (IRE), 4, b g Oscar (IRE)—Ballinaroone Girl A. Stennett
38 PADRE (IRE), 9, b g Mister Lord (USA)—Lee Valley Lady (IRE) M. C. Denmark
39 PRINCE TOM, 4, br g King's Theatre (IRE)—Cresswell Native (IRE) Mrs A. Tincknell
40 QUARTANO, 5, ch g Platini (GER)—Queen's Diamond (GER) M. C. Denmark
41 QUELQU'UN COMME TOI (FR), 4, b br g Evening World (FR)—Urta (FR) Pokerholics Racing
42 QUICK SHOT (FR), 4, b g Sassanian (USA)—Byrsa (FR) Mrs Jill Eynon & Mr Robin Eynon
43 R'CAM (IRE), 6, br g Glacial Storm (USA)—Beann Ard (IRE) The High Altitude Partnership
44 RETURN TO SENDER (IRE), 4, b g Beneficial—Silent Supreme (IRE) S. D. Hemstock
45 ROCKY RIVER (IRE), 5, b g High Roller (IRE)—Wall-Nut Grove (IRE) Mr B. A. Body
46 ROLL ALONG (IRE), 8, b g Carroll House—Callmartel (IRE) Bryan & Philippa Burrough
47 SABREFLIGHT, 8, ch m Sabrehill (USA)—Little Redwing D. S. Coates
48 SEEKING THE BUCK (USA), 4, b c Seeking The Gold (USA)—Cuanto Es (USA) M. C. Denmark
49 SELF DEFENSE, 11, b g Warning—Dansara Fraser Miller Racing
50 SHREWD DUDE, 4, b br c Val Royal (FR)—Lily Dale (IRE) G. Pascoe, S. Brewer, K. Wood
51 STEIG (IRE), 5, b g Xaar—Ring of Kerry (IRE) Something In The City 2
52 STRATEGIC APPROACH (IRE), 6, ch g Bob Back (USA)—Merrill Gaye (IRE) M. C. Denmark
53 SUPER MARTINA (IRE), 6, b m Flemensfirth (USA)—Runaway Tina (IRE) Lawson Group & Cliff Puffett
54 SYDNEY (IRE), 8, b g Saddlers' Hall (IRE)—Magic Gale (IRE) M. C. Denmark
55 TARA QUEEN, 5, b m Kayf Tara—Kaydee Queen (IRE) Mrs D. Romanes
56 TAYMAN (IRE), 6, b br g Sinndar (IRE)—Sweet Emotion (IRE) Pokerholics Racing
57 THE OLD PRETENDER (IRE), 5, ch g Old Vic—Cluain-Ard (IRE) Bryan & Philippa Burrough
58 TIZZY BLUE (IRE), 6, b m Oscar (IRE)—Satellite Dancer S. D. Hemstock
59 TOO FORWARD (IRE), 12, ch g Toulon—One Back (IRE) Mr T. L. Gibson & Mr D. Mathias
60 TREAT EM MEAN, 7, gr g Keen—Knowing M. C. Denmark
61 URBAN TIGER (GER), 5, b g Marju (IRE)—Ukraine Venture Club ISM

MR C. LLEWELLYN—continued

62 **VOICE OF REASON (IRE)**, 6, ch g Accordion—Ginger Bar (IRE) **M. C. Denmark**
63 **WALDENSTROEM (GER)**, 5, gr g Silver Patriarch (IRE)—Weissglut (GER) **M. C. Denmark**
64 **WIND INSTRUMENT (IRE)**, 7, ch g Accordion—Windy Bee (IRE) **Mrs E. Pearce**
65 **WITHOUT A DOUBT**, 9, b g Singspiel (IRE)—El Rabab (USA) **M. C. Denmark**

Other Owners: Mr Robert Benton, Mr Mike Blane, Lady Blyth, Ms Karen Bourdon, Mr S. J. Brewer, Mr L. Brien, Mr N. A. Brimble, Mr B. R. H. Burrough, Mrs Philippa Burrough, Mrs Liz Dalby, Mr Charidimos Demetriou, Mr P. J. Dixon, Mrs J. M. Eynon, Mr R. A. F. Eynon, Mr N. Finn, Mrs J. R. Foster, Mr John Gale, Mr T. L. Gibson, Wing Comdr A. Howie, Mr T. E. Kerfoot, Mr J. Lambe, Lawson Group Ltd, Mr D. Mathias, Mr J. J. McNeile, Mr D. Minton, Mr Andy Nairn, Mr G. J. Pascoe, Mr C. J. Puffett, D. J. Robertson, Mr A. Robinson, Mrs Nicky Rushman, Mr N. Scanlan, Mr B. G. Slade, Mr Andrew Stewart, Mrs J. Stewart, Mr W. Tincknell, Mr Daniel Watkins, Mr P. R. Weston, Mr A. G. Weston, Mr Lee Westwood, Mr A. J. Wheeler, Lady Whent, Mr Godfrey Wilson, Mrs Caroline Wilson, Mr Kevin Wood.

Assistant Trainer: Paul Price

Jockey (flat): G. Baker, H. Turner. **Jockey (NH):** N. Fehily, P Moloney, T. Murphy. **Conditional:** Jonathan Milczarek, Robert L. Rutler. **Amateur:** Mr Sam Painting, Miss Zoe Lilly.

357
MR A. J. LOCKWOOD, Malton
Postal: Fleet Cross Farm, Brawby, Malton, North Yorkshire, YO17 6QA
Contacts: **PHONE (01751) 431796 MOBILE (07747) 002535**

1 **BOLLIN FREDDIE**, 4, ch g Golden Snake (USA)—Bollin Roberta **Highgreen Partnership**
2 **FRANKINCENSE (IRE)**, 12, gr g Paris House—Mistral Wood (USA) **A. L. Bosomworth**
3 **JAMES BAY (IRE)**, 7, b g Bob Back (USA)—Slave Gale (IRE) **J. L. Holdroyd**
4 **ONLY WORDS (USA)**, 11, ch g Shuailaan (USA)—Conversation Piece (USA) **Mrs L. Lumley**
5 **PARCHMENT (IRE)**, 6, ch g Singspiel (IRE)—Hannalou (FR) **A. J. Lockwood**

Other Owners: Mr J. Richardson, Mr Derek Wilson.

358
MR J. E. LONG, Woldingham
Postal: Main Yard, Tillingdowns, Woldingham, Caterham, Surrey, CR3 7JA
Contacts: **PHONE (01883) 340730 MOBILE (07958) 296945/(07815) 186085**
E-MAIL winalot@aol.com

1 **BAKERS BOY**, 4, ch g Tipsy Creek (USA)—Unparalleled **Mr Raymond Gross, Ms Adrienne Gross**
2 **BOLLIN FRANNY**, 4, br c Bertolini—Bollin Ann **Mr P. R. Saxon**
3 **BRIANNSTA (IRE)**, 6, b g Bluebird (USA)—Nacote (USA) **Mr P. R. Saxon**
4 **CATIVO CAVALLINO**, 5, ch g Bertolini (USA)—Sea Isle **Mr P. R. Saxon**
5 **CHALENTINA**, 5, b m Primo Valentino (IRE)—Chantilly Myth **T. H. Bambridge**
6 **CULMINATE**, 11, ch g Afzal—Straw Blade **J. King**
7 **EFISIO PRINCESS**, 5, br m Efisio—Hardiprincess **Miss M. B. Fernandes**
8 **FOR LIFE (IRE)**, 6, b g Bachir (IRE)—Zest (USA) **T. H. Bambridge**
9 **KEAGLES (ITY)**, 5, b m Indian Danehill (IRE)—Athens Belle (IRE) **Essex Racing Club**
10 **OUR GLENARD**, 9, b g Royal Applause—Loucoum (FR) **Mr P. R. Saxon**

THREE-YEAR-OLDS

11 **GUAPISIMA**, b f Tamayaz (CAN)—Miss Verity **Amaroni**
12 **KAROSHDEE**, ch f Fantastic Light (USA)—Larousse **Amaroni**
13 **LA PRECIOSA**, b f Arrasas (USA)—Morning Star **Amaroni**
14 **MUMTAZ BEGUM**, ch f Kyllachy—Indian Gift **Amaroni**
15 **PARISIAN PEARL**, gr f Paris House—Stand By **Mr R. D. John**

Other Owners: Mr A. Conroy, Mr R. Duff, Mr Raymond Gross, Ms Adrienne Gross, Mr R. D. John, Mr R. Khemlani, Mr Brian C. Oakley, Mr A. Penny, Mr Barry Root, Mrs Joan Root, Mrs Sue Simmonds.

Assistant Trainer: Miss S. Cassidy

Jockey (flat): Natalia Gemelova, Richard Thomas. **Amateur:** Miss S. Cassidy.

359 MR C. LONGSDON, Moreton-in-Marsh
Postal: Coronation Lodge, Cotswold Stud, Sezincote, Moreton-in-Marsh, Gloucestershire, GL56 9TB
Contacts: PHONE (08450) 525264 FAX (08450) 525265 MOBILE (07775) 993263
E-MAIL charlie@charlielongsdonracing.com WEBSITE www.charlielongsdonracing.com

1 A TOI A MOI (FR), 8, ch g Cyborg (FR)—Peperonelle (FR) T. England
2 ABOUKIR BAY (IRE), 4, b g Desert Sun—Tamarsiya (USA) C. Longsdon
3 DIVERS (FR), 4, gr g Highest Honor (FR)—Divination (FR) Million in Mind Partnership
4 DOCTOR COLLINS, 5, b g Terimon—Larksmore Pershore Pessimists
5 FAR MORE SERIOUS (IRE), 8, b br g Needle Gun (IRE)—Womans Heart (IRE) Neysauteur Partnership
6 GREAT TSAR (IRE), 5, b g Moscow Society (USA)—Simply Slippy (IRE) The Plundering Cow
7 IN MEDIA RES (FR), 7, b g Dushyantor (USA)—Colour Scheme (FR) Killinghurst Park Stud
8 IRIS ROYAL (FR), 12, b g Garde Royale—Tchela (FR) Sir Robert Ogden C.B.E., LLD
9 IWILLREMEMBERYOU (IRE), 8, b br g Lord Americo—Endless Patience (IRE) Tunnel Vision
10 JOE BROWN, 8, b g Overbury (IRE)—Miss Roscoe Miss C. A. Owen
11 MALKO DE BEAUMONT (FR), 8, b br g Gold and Steel (FR)—Givry (FR) D. A. Halsall
12 MIGHTY MATTERS (IRE), 9, b g Muroto—Hasaway (IRE) Mrs L. Suenson-Taylor
13 OLYMPIAN (FR), 6, b g Video Rock (FR)—Attualita (FR) Sir Robert Ogden C.B.E., LLD
14 OMEGA KING (FR), 6, b m Rajpoute (FR)—Eden King (FR) R. D. J. Swinburne
15 ONEFOURFUN (IRE), 6, b g Taipan (IRE)—One For Millennium (IRE) Hopeful Half Dozen
16 ORPHELIN COLLONGES (FR), 6, b g Video Rock (FR)—Altesse Collonges (FR) Sir Robert Ogden C.B.E., LLD
17 ORTEGA (FR), 6, b g Useful (FR)—Madame Dabrovine (FR) Hunting United
18 OTAGE DE BRION (FR), 6, b g Rajpoute (FR)—Gesse Parade (FR) Sir Robert Ogden C.B.E., LLD
19 REVE D'AMI, 6, b g Environment Friend—Reve En Rose M. D. McMillan
20 SIR IAN (IRE), 5, b g Turtle Island (IRE)—Bobby Hays (IRE) Mrs M. L. Stevenson
21 SONGE (FR), 4, b c Hernando (FR)—Sierra (FR) D. A. Halsall
22 STRATEGIC PLAN (FR), 5, ch g Pivotal—Peony Girl (FR) C. Longsdon
23 THE PARTING GLASS (FR), 6, b g Anshan—Ardfallon (IRE) Hunting United
24 TOP BRASS (IRE), 7, ch g Night Shift (USA)—Opus One Hunting United
25 WHITE DOVE (FR), 10, b m Beaudelaire (USA)—Hermine And Pearls (FR) Creme de la Creme

Other Owners: Mr R. P. Blake, A. R. Bromley, Mr J. P. Byrne, R. J. Clarke, G. J. Clinton, Mrs J. E. Clinton, A. Connor, Mrs S. Debenham, H. J. Fentum, T. R. Gittins, G. F. Goode, Mrs N. Knott, Mr R. M. S. Longsdon, W. D. C. Minton, Mrs D. C. Nicholson, Mrs J. Pauling, Miss L. R. Rivers Bulkeley, Mr E. A. E. Roberts, J. Studd, Mrs B. A. M. Studd.

Assistant Trainer: Sarah Rippon

360 MR L. LUNGO, Carrutherstown
Postal: Hetland Hill Farm, Carrutherstown, Dumfriesshire, DG1 4JX
Contacts: PHONE (01387) 840691 FAX (01387) 840323 MOBILE (07850) 711438
E-MAIL office@lenlungo.com WEBSITE www.lenlungo.com

1 ALL OUT FOR SEVEN (IRE), 6, b g Simply Great (FR)—Sunset Linda (IRE) Mr C. Woodward
2 ARGENTINE (IRE), 4, b g Fasliyev (USA)—Teller (ARG) SW Group Logistics Ltd & Mr Colin Woodward
3 ARMAGUEDON (FR), 10, b g Garde Royale—Miss Dundee (FR) Ashleybank Investments Limited
4 BANOGE (IRE), 6, b g Flemensfirth (USA)—Prove It (IRE) The Hookers
5 4, B g Kayf Tara—Be My Bird Len Lungo Racing Limited
6 BERWICK LAW (IRE), 6, ch g Snurge—Cruby Hill (IRE) Mr & Mrs Raymond Anderson Green
7 BORDER FOX, 5, b g Foxhound (USA)—Vado Via Heli-Beds Racing
8 BRANDY WINE (IRE), 10, b g Roselier (FR)—Sakonnet (USA) Ashleybank Investments Limited
9 BRIAN'S JOURNEY, 6, b g Benny The Dip (USA)—Soviet Cry G. Hamilton
10 BRIARHILL BOY (IRE), 4, br g Oscar (IRE)—Raise A Melody (IRE) L. Mulryan
11 BRIARHILL LAD (IRE), 5, b g Supreme Leader—Lady Rag L. Mulryan
12 BROOKLYN BREEZE (IRE), 11, b br g Be My Native (USA)—Moss Gale Ashleybank Investments Limited
13 CHEF DE COUR (FR), 7, b g Pistolet Bleu (FR)—Cour de Rome (FR) Ashleybank Investments Limited
14 CLOUDMOR (IRE), 7, b g Cloudings (IRE)—Glen Morvern J. Harrison
15 4, B g Bob's Return (IRE)—Condonstown (IRE) Len Lungo Racing Limited
16 CORRIB LAD (IRE), 10, b g Supreme Leader—Nun So Game L. Mulryan
17 COTE D'ARGENT, 5, b g Lujain (USA)—In The Groove Len Lungo Racing Limited
18 7, Ch g Carroll House—Dark Deep Dawn Len Lungo Racing Limited
19 DELIGHTFULLY (FR), 4, b rf Sagacity (FR)—Green House (FR) Elite Racing Club
20 FIND ME (USA), 4, ch g Point Given (USA)—Island Jamboree (USA) Mr & Mrs Raymond Anderson Green
21 FLAMED AMAZEMENT, 4, b g Hernando (FR)—Alligram (USA) Mr & Mrs Raymond Anderson Green
22 5, B g Beat All (USA)—Forever Shineing Len Lungo Racing Limited
23 FREETOWN (IRE), 12, b g Shirley Heights—Pageantry Miss S. Blumberg & Mr R. Nairn
24 GREY LIGHT (IRE), 4, b g Namid—Flying Clouds L. Mulryan

MR L. LUNGO—continued

25 **HEART O' THE WEST (IRE)**, 4, b g Tamayaz (CAN)—She's All Heart **K. Milligan Partnership**
26 **IDARAH (USA)**, 5, gr g Aljabr (USA)—Fatina **L. Mulryan**
27 **JENNY POTTS**, 4, b f Robellino (USA)—Fleeting Vision (IRE) **Len Lungo Racing Limited**
28 **LAOUEN (FR)**, 10, br g Funny Baby (FR)—Olive Noire (FR) **Ashley Bank Investments & Dr K.Fraser**
29 **MALT DE VERGY (FR)**, 8, br g Sleeping Car (FR)—Intense (FR) **Ashleybank Investments Limited**
30 **MAMBA (GER)**, 6, b m Tannenkonig (IRE)—Mostly Sure (IRE) **Len Lungo Racing Limited**
31 **MENSIO (IRE)**, 6, ch g Anshan—Rosie Fort (IRE) **R. A. Bartlett**
32 **MIRJAN (IRE)**, 12, b g Tenby—Mirana (IRE) **Len Lungo Racing Limited**
33 **MONOLITH**, 10, b g Bigstone (IRE)—Ancara **Elite Racing Club**
34 **MR GUPPY (IRE)**, 7, b g Clerkenwell (USA)—Gene of The Glen (IRE) **S W Group Logistics Limited**
35 4, B g Arctic Lord—Polls Joy **R. A. Green**
36 **REHEARSAL**, 7, b g Singspiel (IRE)—Daralaka (IRE) **Elite Racing Club**
37 **SOUTHERNESS**, 4, ch g Halling (USA)—Teresa Balbi **Len Lungo Racing Limited**
38 **THE BAJAN BANDIT (IRE)**, 13, b g Commanche Run—Sunrise Highway VII **Mrs L. A. Stevenson**
39 **THE PIOUS PRINCE (IRE)**, 7, ch g Shahrastani (USA)—Ara Blend (IRE) **T. Barr**
40 **TRIGGERMAN**, 6, b g Double Trigger (IRE)—Carrikins **Len Lungo Racing Limited**
41 **TROLL (FR)**, 7, b g Cadoudal (FR)—Miss Dundee (FR) **Ashleybank Investments Limited**
42 **TWILIGHT DAWN**, 4, ch f Muhtarram (USA)—Indigo Dawn **Len Lungo Racing Limited**
43 **VILLON (IRE)**, 9, b g Topanoora—Deep Adventure **R. A. Bartlett**
44 **WILD CANE RIDGE (IRE)**, 9, gr g Roselier (FR)—Shuil Na Lee (IRE) **Ashleybank Investments Limited**

THREE-YEAR-OLDS

45 **LEGION D'HONNEUR (UAE)**, b g Halling (USA)—Renowned (IRE) **Len Lungo Racing Limited**
46 **MITHIAN**, b g Alflora (IRE)—Vent d'aout (IRE) **Elite Racing Club**

Other Owners: Miss S. Blumberg, R. Colvin, Mrs C. M. T. Cunningham-Jardine, Lady Duncan, Dr K. S. Fraser, Mrs A. Green, T. D. Griffiths, A. J. Hill, Miss G. Hives, Mr I. C. Marr, K. J. Milligan, R. Nairn, Miss M. Noden, Mr D. G. Tate.

Jockey (NH): K. Mercer, G. Berridge. **Conditional:** M. Turnbull.

---

361 **MR M. J. LURCOCK, Ilfracombe**
Postal: The Woodlands, Torrs Park, Ilfracombe, Devon, EX34 8AZ
Contacts: **PHONE** (01271) 863098 **MOBILE** (07973) 418257
E-MAIL mike@cityracingclub.com **WEBSITE** www.cityracingclub.com

1 **CAPTAIN CAN CAN (IRE)**, 8, b g Hernando (FR)—Can Can Lady **M. J. Lurcock**
2 **FAST LANE (IRE)**, 9, ch g Hamas (IRE)—Rainstone **M. J. Lurcock**
3 **LEVANTINE (IRE)**, 11, b g Sadler's Wells (USA)—Spain Lane (USA) **M. J. Lurcock**
4 **REDHOT FILLYPEPPER**, 9, b m Lancastrian—Millennium Classic **M. J. Lurcock**
5 **SOX IN THE CITY**, 4, b g Silver Patriarch (IRE)—Mezzo Princess **M. J. Lurcock**

THREE-YEAR-OLDS

6 **DASHING PATRIARCH**, b c Silver Patriarch (IRE)—Mezzo Princess **M. J. Lurcock**

Conditional: John Moorman. **Amateur:** Mr Mike Lurcock.

---

362 **MR S. LYCETT, Bourton-On-The-Water**
Postal: 3 Broadmoor Cottage, Nr Clapton-On-The-Hill, Bourton-On-The-Water,
Gloucestershire, GL54 2LQ
Contacts: **MOBILE** (07788) 100894
E-MAIL bourotoracing@aol.com

1 **AMOUR MULTIPLE (IRE)**, 9, b g Poliglote—Onereuse **Mr S. A. Young**
2 **FADE TO GREY (IRE)**, 4, gr g Aljabr (USA)—Aly McBear (USA) **Bill Hinge & Gary Smallbone**
3 **IRIS MARY (IRE)**, 7, ch m Flemensfirth (USA)—Here To-Day **N. E. Powell**
4 **JAMAAHIR (USA)**, 5, b g Bahri (USA)—Elrehaan **The Futures Bright Partnership**
5 **KING ROCKY**, 7, b g Rakaposhi King—Jims Sister **The Atkin Partnership**
6 **MARQUE DEPOSEE (FR)**, 8, br m Cadoudal (FR)—Unextase (FR) **The Berryman Lycett Experience**
7 **RASHIDA**, 6, b m King's Best (USA)—Nimble Lady (AUS) **O. F. Ryan**
8 **RICARDO'S CHANCE**, 9, b g Alflora (IRE)—Jims Sister **The Atkin Partnership**
9 **ROAD TO RECOVERY**, 4, b g Mujahid (USA)—Legend of Aragon **Mr D. L. Gill**
10 **SHERGILL (IRE)**, 7, b br g Weld—Gaelic Holly (IRE) **Mrs R. Gill-Bahia**
11 **SPIRITWIND (IRE)**, 5, ch g In The Wings—Tallahassee Spirit (THA) **Cotswold Racing Club (CRC)**

MR S. LYCETT—continued

12 **TWIST BOOKIE (IRE)**, 8, br g Perugino (USA)—Twist Scarlett (GER) **F. W. Dronzek**
13 **WASHANGO (IRE)**, 6, b m Presenting—Peptic Lady (IRE) **The Berryman Lycett Experience**

Other Owners: J. A. Atkin, T. J. Atkin, P. P. Berryman, S. D. A. Berryman, J. D. Berryman, Mr G. Bryan, Mr C. R. Cook, Mr C. N. M. Hanks, W. Hinge, S. Lycett, G. D. Smallbone, Mr W. H. G. Spiers.

---

363 MR GER LYONS, Dunsany
Postal: Glenburnie Stables, Dunsany, Co. Meath, Ireland
Contacts: **PHONE** (00353) 4690 25666 **FAX** (00353) 4690 26364 **MOBILE** (00353) 8685 02439
E-MAIL gerlyons@iol.ie **WEBSITE** www.gerlyons.ie

1 **AN TADH (IRE)**, 5, b g Halling (USA)—Tithcar **Vincent Gaul**
2 **APOLLO RUN (IRE)**, 5, ch g Namid—She's Our Lady (IRE) **John Burke**
3 **BENWILT BREEZE (IRE)**, 6, b g Mujadil (USA)—Image of Truce (IRE) **Mr S. Shields**
4 **DYNAMO DANCER (IRE)**, 5, ch g Danehill Dancer (IRE)—Imperial Graf (USA) **Third Avenue Syndicate**
5 **IN THEORY**, 9, b g Ezzoud (IRE)—Little Black Dress (USA) **G S Racing Club**
6 **LITTLE WHITE LIE (IRE)**, 4, b g Orpen (USA)—Miss Informed (IRE) **Laura De Haast & Luc Hemeruck**
7 **NORTBURN**, 4, b g Tobougg (IRE)—Duxyana (IRE) **Francis Hughes**
8 **OKALYDOKELY (IRE)**, 4, b g Shinko Forest (IRE)—Delirious Tantrum (IRE) **Mrs Lynne Lyons**
9 **ROCKAZAR**, 7, b g Opening Verse (USA)—Final Rush **Derbar Racing Partnership**
10 **ROMEO'S ON FIRE (IRE)**, 4, b g Danehill (USA)—Fighting Countess (USA) **Glenview House Stud**
11 **SUMMIT SURGE (IRE)**, 4, b g Noverre (USA)—Lady Peculiar (CAN) **Mr W. Bellew**
12 **THAT'S HOT (IRE)**, 5, b m Namid—Smoke Lady (USA) **John Burke**
13 **VINCENZIO GALILEI (USA)**, 4, ch g Galileo (IRE)—Sometime (USA) **Glenview House Stud**

THREE-YEAR-OLDS

14 **ARCHMANI (USA)**, b f Arch (USA)—Latifah (USA) **F. O'Byrne**
15 **ASHKA (IRE)**, b f Catcher In The Rye (IRE)—Road Harbour (USA) **Charlie Harvey**
16 **BE FANTASTIC (IRE)**, ch g Fantastic Light (USA)—Be Decisive **Byerley Racing Limited**
17 **BLUE TURK**, b g Where Or When (IRE)—Pearly River **Byerley Racing Limited**
18 **BOBBY JANE**, br f Diktat—Twilight Sonnet **R. Fagan**
19 **BOOT BOY (IRE)**, b g Xaar—Khawater (USA) **Sean Jones**
20 **CHASING CLOUDS (IRE)**, b f Acclamation—Flying Clouds **Byerley Racing Limited**
21 **DOHASA (IRE)**, b g Bold Fact (USA)—Zara's Birthday (IRE) **Sean Jones**
22 **ELLETELLE (IRE)**, b f Elnadim (USA)—Flamanda **Jesse Club Syndicate**
23 **EPIC ODYSSEY**, ch g Dubai Destination (USA)—Royal Gift **Mrs G. Hourigan**
24 **FIERY LAD (IRE)**, b g Mull of Kintyre (USA)—Forget Paris (IRE) **Mr W. Bellew**
25 **FORCE AND MOTION (IRE)**, b g Acclamation—In Time **Mr W. Bellew**
26 **GROVE VIEW STAR**, ch g Auction House (USA)—Gracious Imp (USA) **W. J. Hamilton**
27 **HE'S COOL (IRE)**, b g Viking Ruler (AUS)—Miss Progressive (IRE) **Matt Mullen**
28 **HOMEBREW (IRE)**, br g Celtic Swing—Irish Ensign (SAF) **Mike Finn**
29 **INVINCIBLE JOE (IRE)**, b g Invincible Spirit (IRE)—Abbey Park (USA) **Glenview House Stud**
30 **LEANDROS (FR)**, br c Invincible Spirit (IRE)—Logjam (IRE) **Tenela Investments Limited**
31 **REMIND ME MONDAY (IRE)**, b g Spartacus (IRE)—Phoenix Venture (IRE) **Glenview House Stud**
32 **ROYAL ENTOURAGE**, b g Royal Applause—Trempkate (USA) **Vincent Gaul**
33 **SHAQ ATTACK (IRE)**, ch g Traditionally (USA)—Smoke Lady (USA) **John Burke**
34 **SLAM DUNK (USA)**, b c Grand Slam (USA)—Deep In My Heart (USA) **Glenview House Stud**
35 **TURK (IRE)**, ch g Dr Fong (USA)—Input **Tenela Investments Ltd**
36 **YOUNG JEMMY (IRE)**, b g Tagula (IRE)—Baileys First (IRE) **Sean Jones**

TWO-YEAR-OLDS

37 B c 19/4 Rock of Gibraltar (IRE)—Alluring Park (IRE) (Green Desert (USA)) (100000) **Mrs Seamus Burns**
38 **BIG JOE (ITY)**, b c 30/4 Colossus (IRE)—Jovian (Petong) (10296)
39 B c 28/2 Rock of Gibraltar (IRE)—Blue Cloud (IRE) (Nashwan (USA)) (14156)
40 B c 22/4 Sakhee (USA)—Canterloupe (IRE) (Wolfhound (USA)) (54697)
41 **COOL STAR (IRE)**, b c 13/3 One Cool Cat (USA)—Pack Ice (USA) (Wekiva Springs (USA)) (33000) **G. M. Lyons**
42 B c 22/4 Beat Hollow—Crimson Shower (Dowsing (USA)) (31000)
43 B f 25/1 Noverre (USA)—Crohal di San Jore (Saddlers' Hall (IRE)) (28957)
44 B c 21/3 Oasis Dream—Forever Phoenix (Shareef Dancer (USA)) (32174)
45 B c 16/4 Bertolini (USA)—Genny Lim (IRE) (Barathea (IRE)) (40000)
46 B f 3/4 Statue of Liberty (USA)—Gerobies Girl (USA) (Deposit Ticket (USA))
47 B f 9/2 Elnadim (USA)—Give A Whistle (IRE) (Mujadil (USA)) (16086)
48 B f 18/2 Dalakhani (IRE)—Green Lassy (FR) (Green Tune (USA)) (51480)
49 **KALACAN (IRE)**, br c 10/3 Kalanisi (IRE)—Lovelyst (IRE) (Machiavellian (USA)) (19947)

MR GER LYONS—continued

50 Br c 21/1 Celtic Swing—La Catalane (IRE) (Marju (IRE)) (75000)
51 B f 4/3 Danehill Dancer (IRE)—Lac Dessert (USA) (Lac Ouimet (USA)) (54697)
52 Ch c 26/3 Kyllachy—Louhossoa (USA) (Trempolino (USA)) (35392)
53 B f 7/4 Soviet Star (USA)—Love Sonnet (Singspiel (IRE)) (21235)
54 LOVERS QUEST (IRE), b f 1/2 Pyrus—Amorous Pursuits (Pursuit of Love) (16086)
55 B f 1/3 Key of Luck (USA)—Manuscript (Machiavellian (USA)) (38609)
56 Ch c 16/4 Haafhd—Megdale (IRE) (Waajib) (42000)
57 B c 21/2 Daggers Drawn (USA)—Motocross (IRE) (Cape Cross (IRE)) (6434)
58 B f 2/5 Refuse To Bend (IRE)—Rainbow Dream (Rainbow Quest (USA)) (12869)
59 B c 12/2 Haafhd—Regrette Rien (USA) (Unbridled's Song (USA)) (75000)
60 B f 27/1 Danehill Dancer (IRE)—Russian Muse (FR) (Machiavellian (USA)) (41826)
61 SHE'S SO SPIRIT (IRE), b c 1/3 Invincible Spirit (IRE)—She's So Lovely (Distant Relative) (51480)
62 B c 18/1 One Cool Cat (USA)—Soft (USA) (Lear Fan (USA)) (38000)
63 TARRSILLE (IRE), b c 17/2 Dansili—Tara Gold (IRE) (Royal Academy (USA))
64 THE ROSSMEISTER (IRE), b c 12/4 Celtic Swing—Evelyn One (Alhaarth (IRE)) (8500)

Jockey (flat): Johnny Murtagh. Amateur: Miss Nina Carberry, Mr Andrew Duff.

---

364 **MR G. MACAIRE, Les Mathes**
Postal: Hippodrome de la Palmyre, 17570 Les Mathes, France
Contacts: PHONE (0033) 5462 36254/225 855 FAX (0033) 5462 25438 MOBILE (0033) 6076 54992
E-MAIL entrainement-g.macaire@wanadoo.fr WEBSITE guillaumemacaire.com

1 AL RECIBIR (FR), 5, ch g Evening World (FR)—Darlin (FR) Mr Roger-Yves Simon
2 ALIFIERI (GER), 5, b h Surako (GER)—Anjou (GER) Mr F. Fernandez
3 ASKLEPION (GER), 4, ch c Acatenango (GER)—Aerope Mr T. Amos
4 BEN VETO (FR), 7, ch g Perrault—Sainte Lea (FR) Mme M. Bryant
5 BET ON ME (GER), 5, b h Second Set (IRE)—Bella Vista (GER) Mr T. Amos
6 CALIDEO (FR), 6, b g Video Rock (FR)—Dona Cali (FR) Mr O. Delegue
7 CARLYSSAR (FR), 7, b m Bricassar (USA)—Carlynie (FR) Mrs A. M. Roux
8 CARSON (FR), 6, b g Sleeping Car (FR)—Sunmania (FR) Mr R. Fougedoire
9 CHANTEGRIL (FR), 8, b h Hasa (FR)—Mazzina (FR) Mr J. M. Reillier
10 CHERCHEUR D'OR (FR), 4, b c Robin des Champs (FR)—Miss Noir Et Or (FR) Mr R. Fougedoire
11 CONCETTA (GER), 5, b m Winged Love (IRE)—Courtly Times Mr B. Glitsch
12 CYRIEN DEUX MILLE (FR), 8, b g Saint Cyrien (FR)—Top Chiz (FR) Mme M. Bryant
13 DARAE (FR), 4, b f Robin des Champs (FR)—Nuit D'ecajeul (FR) Mr F. Picoulet
14 DENT SUCREE (FR), 6, gr m Turgeon (USA)—Sweet Racine (FR) Mrs H. Devin
15 GOLDEN FLIGHT (FR), 9, b g Saint Cyrien (FR)—Sunday Flight (FR) Mr J. Cotton
16 GOLDEN MELODY (GER), 4, b f Kornado—Goldsamt (GER) Mr J. M. Reillier
17 GORGIBUS (FR), 5, b g Bonnet Rouge (FR)—Goburge (FR) Mr R. Fougedoire
18 GOTHIKA (FR), 4, b f Lost World (IRE)—Viva Cupid (FR) Mr J-P Girot
19 HARTANY (GER), 7, b h Lavirco (GER)—Harasava (FR) Mrs F. Montauban
20 JOE JEAN (FR), 7, b g Saumarez—Shabby Bleue (FR) Ecurie Rib
21 KAMI DES OBEAUX (FR), 10, b g Saint Preuil (FR)—Ulisa II (FR) Mme P. Papot
22 KAP ROCK (FR), 4, b c Video Rock (FR)—Kaprika (FR) Mr R. W. Denechere
23 KATRIA (GER), 5, ch m Protektor (GER)—Kelly's Diamond (FR) Mr J. M. Robin
24 KELLYE (FR), 4, b f Mansonnien (FR)—Minouche (FR) Mr F. Videaud
25 KICK BACK (GER), 4, b f Royal Dragon (USA)—Kimberley Kate (GER) Mr O. Perroton
26 KIRO DE LA PREE (FR), 4, b g Robin des Pres (FR)—Kica (FR) Mr M. Foissard
27 L'AS DE PEMBO (FR), 9, b g Panoramic—Lumiere Du Porh (FR) Mr A. Faucheux
28 LA BAZEUGE (FR), 4, b f Nikos—La Bazine (FR) Mr M. Carteaud
29 LA MORINE (FR), 4, b f Bonnet Rouge (FR)—Juventa (FR) Mr P. de Maleissye
30 LADIES CHOICE (FR), 6, b m Turgeon (USA)—Ladies View (FR) Mrs H. Devin
31 LE BAZIN (FR), 5, b g Turgeon (USA)—La Bazine (FR) Mr R. Fougedoire
32 LE PERO (FR), 10, b g Perrault—Nuit D'ecajeul (FR) Mme M. Bryant
33 LE RIBARDON (FR), 8, b g Freedom Cry—Shabby Bleue (FR) Ecurie Rib
34 LEADER DU COCHET (FR), 9, b g Byzantium (FR)—Voiture Du Cochet (FR) Mrs F. Montauban
35 LITTLE BRUERE (FR), 9, b g Villez (FR)—Divine Bruere (FR) Mr R. Fougedoire
36 LOUMTA (FR), 5, gr g Mansonnien (FR)—Fadinette (FR) Mr F. Picoulet
37 MADISON ROAD (FR), 4, b f Hernando (FR)—Abstraite Mr E. Simian
38 MARSELIN (FR), 5, b g April Night (FR)—Princesse de Mars (FR) Mr R. Fougedoire
39 MAXEDY (FR), 4, b c Roli Abi (FR)—Night Of Honor (FR) Mr D. Le Breton
40 MEISIR DU LUC (FR), 8, b h Chamberlin (FR)—Acca Du luc (FR) Mr C. Dumeau
41 MESSAGE PERSONNEL (FR), 4, gr f Mansonnien (FR)—Moulouya (FR) Mr R. Green
42 MIA LESCRIBAA (FR), 4, b f Saint des Saints (FR)—Mona Lisa (FR) Mme M. Bryant

MR G. MACAIRE—continued

43 **MICADOU (FR)**, 8, b g Cadoudal (FR)—Minouche (FR) **Mr F. Videaud**
44 **MINUTIEUX (FR)**, 4, b g Maille Pistol (FR)—Rouge Folie (FR) **Mr R. Fougedoire**
45 **MISTRAL BOY (FR)**, 8, b g Port Lyautey (FR)—Une de Mai IV (FR) **Mrs A. Mahe**
46 **MISTRIAL (FR)**, 4, b g Comte du Bourg (FR)—Miss World (FR) **Mrs H. Devin**
47 **MOKA DE L'ISLE (FR)**, 8, ch g Video Rock (FR)—Ceres de L'isle (FR) **Mrs S. A. Bramall**
48 **MONT MISERE (FR)**, 12, b g Mont Basile (FR)—Pique Flamme (FR) **Mr A. Chiche**
49 **MOON SIR (GER)**, 6, b h Surako (GER)—Moonlit Water **Mr R. Fougedoire**
50 **MOUILLEURDEPONGES (FR)**, 7, b g Saumarez—Royale Flamby (FR) **Mr R. Fougedoire**
51 **NEW ROCK (FR)**, 7, ch g Video Rock (FR)—Agathe de Beard (FR) **Mme B. Gabeur**
52 **NOEUD PAPILLLON (FR)**, 7, b g Video Rock (FR)—Samara IV (FR) **Mr R. Fougedoire**
53 **NOPLEASARO (GER)**, 4, ch c Vaguely Pleasant (FR)—Not To Beat (GER) **Mr Orillac**
54 **NUAGE DE COTTE (FR)**, 7, b g Sleeping Car (FR)—Kariantique (FR) **Mr R. Fougedoire**
55 **OEIL POUR OEIL (FR)**, 6, b g Take Risks (FR)—Ribalina (FR) **Mr R. Fougedoire**
56 **ONE TO CATCH (FR)**, 6, b m Video Rock (FR)—Biblos (FR) **Mr F. Lazar**
57 **ORPHICA DE THAIX (FR)**, 6, b g Video Rock (FR)—Jessica de Thaix (FR) **Mr R. Fougedoire**
58 **OUI (FR)**, 6, b m Saint Preuil (FR)—Friandise II (FR)
59 **OWARD (FR)**, 6, b h Mansonnien (FR)—Violette D'avril (FR) **Mme B. Gabeur**
60 **PAQUET CADEAU (FR)**, 5, b g Robin des Champs (FR)—Chantalouette (FR) **Mr R. Fougedoire**
61 **PENVERN (FR)**, 5, b h Nononito (FR)—Fest Noz (FR) **Mme M. Bryant**
62 **PEPSYROCK (FR)**, 5, b h Video Rock (FR)—La Baine (FR) **Mr J. Cotton**
63 **PERPETUAL MOBILE (IRE)**, 4, b g Acatenango (GER)—Pariana (USA) **Mr P. Fellous**
64 **PHAKOS (FR)**, 5, b g Robin des Champs (FR)—Tipperary (FR) **Mr J. Detre**
65 **POLY FLIGHT (FR)**, 4, b c Poliglote—Sunday Flight (FR) **Mr J. Cotton**
66 **PORT GAUGAIN (FR)**, 5, ch h Port Lyautey (FR)—Jobereine (FR) **Mr A. Faucheux**
67 **PRAHDA (FR)**, 4, b g Start Fast (FR)—Praha (FR) **Mr D. Lemesle**
68 **PRALIN DE l'ISLE (FR)**, 5, b g Sleeping Car (FR)—Hotesse de L'isle (FR) **Mr M. Bessis**
69 **PRETTY BRUERE (FR)**, 5, ch m Villez (USA)—Hervine Bruere (FR) **Mme M. Bryant**
70 **PRINCE OF SURINAM (FR)**, 4, bl g Surako (GER)—Possibility (GER) **Mme M. Bryant**
71 **PROJET D'AVENIR (FR)**, 5, b g Mansonnien (FR)—Ribalina (FR) **Mr J. Detre**
72 **PROSPER DES PLACES (FR)**, 5, b g Iris Noir (FR)—Bakougine (FR) **Mr J. Detre**
73 **PUR ET DUR (FR)**, 5, b g Sleeping Car (FR)—Kunkia (FR) **Mr R. Fougedoire**
74 **QOSMOS DES MOTTES (FR)**, 4, b c Maresca Sorrento (FR)—Anareta des Mottes (FR) **C. Cohen**
75 **QUAIOU (FR)**, 4, b g Robin des Pins (USA)—Ella Pampa (FR) **Mrs B. Gabeur**
76 **QUANTIQUE DE COTTE (FR)**, 4, ch g Agent Bleu (FR)—Kariantique (FR) **Mr R. Fougedoire**
77 **QUARTE (FR)**, 4, gr f Dark Moondancer—Formosa (FR) **Mr F. Rimaud**
78 **QUARTZ DE COTTE (FR)**, 4, b g Ragmar (FR)—Kadalka de Cotte (FR) **Mr R. Fougedoire**
79 **QUASTING (FR)**, 4, b g Passing Sale (FR)—Beatty's (FR) **Mme P. Papot**
80 **QUATRE TEMPS (FR)**, 4, b g Video Rock (FR)—Dame Grisbi (FR) **Haras de Saint Voir**
81 **QUE DIRE DE PLUS (FR)**, 4, ch c Mansonnien (FR)—Tourbrune (FR) **Mr R. Fougedoire**
82 **QUEEN BRUERE (FR)**, 4, b f Mansonnien (FR)—Divine Bruere (FR) **Mme M. Bryant**
83 **QUEIROS (FR)**, 4, ch g Rifapour (IRE)—Fetuque de Moulin (FR) **Mr R. Fougedoire**
84 **QUEL BRUERE (FR)**, 4, gr g Sassanian (USA)—Housseliere (FR) **Mr R. Fougedoire**
85 **QUELCA DE THAIX (FR)**, 4, ch g Dom Alco (FR)—Fonseca de Thaix (FR) **Mr R. Fougedoire**
86 **QUETOUT (FR)**, 4, ch g Sheyrann—Grace de Vonnas (FR) **Mr R. Fougedoire**
87 **QUI L'EUT CRÛ (FR)**, 4, b f Lavirco (GER)—First Wool (FR) **Mr R. Fougedoire**
88 **QUICODY (FR)**, 4, b g Dom Alco (FR)—Idy (FR) **Mr P. Joubert**
89 **QUIDAM D'OUDAIRIES (FR)**, 4, b g Princeton (FR)—Java d'oudairies (FR) **Mr R. Fougedoire**
90 **QUIDITCH D'OUXY (FR)**, 4, b g Dark Moondancer—Jaca de Bissy (FR) **Mr P. Joubert**
91 **QUORA VALLIS (FR)**, 4, b f Mansonnien (FR)—Bora Vallis (FR) **Mrs A. Dutertre**
92 **QURONOS DE VAUZELLE (FR)**, 4, b g Ragmar (FR)—Athena de l'isle (FR) **Mr R. Fougedoire**
93 **REXLOR (FR)**, 7, b g Port Lyautey (FR)—Isle du Tresor (FR) **Mr R. Fougedoire**
94 **RIGOUREUX (FR)**, 8, b g Villez (USA)—Rouge Folie (FR) **Mr R. Fougedoire**
95 **SAINT FONTENAILLES (FR)**, 4, ch g Kaldounevees (FR)—Sissi Fontenailles (FR) **Mme H. Devin**
96 **SAINTE NONO (FR)**, 5, b m Nononito (FR)—Sainte Astrid (FR) **Mrs P. Papot**
97 **SAINTE SCOLASSE (FR)**, 4, b f Saint des Saints (FR)—Surfing France (FR) **Mme I. Garcon**
98 **SAINTENITOUCHE (FR)**, 4, b f Saint des Saints (FR)—White Consel (FR) **Mr Garcon**
99 **SAINTETE (FR)**, 4, b f Saint des Saints (FR)—Ribalina (FR) **Mr R. Fougedoire**
100 **SANTA BAMBA (FR)**, 4, b f Saint des Saints (FR)—Bumble (FR) **Mr J. Detre**
101 **SHANNON FALLS (FR)**, 4, b f Turgeon (USA)—Shannon River (FR) **Mrs H. Devin**
102 **SIRE DES IFS (FR)**, 4, ch g Robin des Champs (FR)—Brodie Flor (FR) **Mr R. Fougedoire**
103 **SIX DES CHAMPS (FR)**, 4, b f Robin des Champs (FR)—Balle Six (FR) **Mr J. Detre**
104 **SOURI DES CHAMPS (FR)**, 5, b m Robin des Champs (FR)—Guendale (FR) **Mr R. Fougedoire**
105 **SPIWING (FR)**, 5, ch g Evening World (FR)—Spinage (FR) **Mr D. Bonnaudet**
106 **STAR OF MEMORY (FR)**, 4, b g Starborough—Desert Memory (FR) **Mr T. Amos**
107 **SYNAPTIQUE (FR)**, 4, b c Saint des Saints (FR)—Gavotte de Brejoux (FR) **Mr J Detre**
108 **TEMPO D'OR (FR)**, 10, b g Esprit du Nord (USA)—Peau d'or (FR) **Mrs F. Montauban**

MR G. MACAIRE—continued

109 **THE KALDOW (FR)**, 5, b h The Shadow (FR)—La Calotterie (FR) **Mme M. Bryant**
110 **TIRO BLUFF (FR)**, 4, b g Poplar Bluff—Tirolean Belle (FR) **Mr O. Perroton**
111 **TITITONI (FR)**, 6, b h Nikos—Fassonwest (FR) **Mme B. Gabeur**
112 **TURKISH SURPRISE (FR)**, 5, b g Baby Turk—Madame Extra (FR) **J. D. Cotton**
113 **UN NONONITO (FR)**, 6, b g Nononito (FR)—Basket Girande (FR) **Mme P. Papot**
114 **VILLENTIN (FR)**, 6, b h Villez (USA)—Cadence Vite (FR) **Mr J. Detre**
115 **VIRGINIA DESIR (FR)**, 4, b c Discover d'auteuil (FR)—Sweet Jaune (FR) **Mr R. Fougedoire**
116 **WESTONNE (FR)**, 4, b f Mansonnien (FR)—Fassonwest (FR) **Mme M. Bryant**
117 **WINEGLASS BAY (FR)**, 4, b c Maille Pistol (FR)—Geografia Loca (FR) **Mr J. Beres**
118 **YAMSEC (FR)**, 4, b c Lavirco (GER)—Castada (FR) **Mr M. Bessis**
119 **YUDA FU (FR)**, 4, b g Maresca Sorrento (FR)—Sainte Lea (FR) **Mr T. Amos**
120 **ZENTAURUS (GER)**, 4, b c Law Society (USA)—Zypern (GER) **Mr F. Lazar**
121 **ZESTE DE LUNE (FR)**, 5, b g Cadoudal (FR)—Tikidoun (FR) **Mr F. Picoulet**

THREE-YEAR-OLDS

122 **ANGE DU SOIR (FR)**, b c Saint des Saints (FR)—Soiree Mondaine (FR) **Mr T. Amos**
123 **BE ABLE (FR)**, b c Lavirco (GER)—Bibelle (FR) **Mme P. Papot**
124 **BOUVINE (FR)**, ch c Khalkevi (IRE)—Palmeria (FR) **Mr J. Detre**
125 **CHIHUAHUA (FR)**, b f April Night (FR)—Sainte Lea (FR) **Mr P. de Maleissye**
126 **CHITA MAGNETIC (IRE)**, ch f Mansonnien (FR)—Chicita du Berlais (FR) **Mr E. Simian**
127 **D'ACCORD (GER)**, ch c Aeskulap (GER)—Daisy Dance (FR) **Mr T. Nivel**
128 **FABANNSO (FR)**, b f Dream Well (FR)—Rose Beryl (FR) **Mr D. Le Breton**
129 **FOLIE LOINTAINE (FR)**, b f Poliglote—Far Away Girl (FR) **Mr J-P. Dubois**
130 **GARDECIEL (FR)**, b c Kapgarde (FR)—Sky River (FR) **Mr F. Remy**
131 **LADY AN CO (FR)**, b f Lavirco (GER)—Lady Start (FR) **Mme B. Gabeur**
132 **LE PRINTEMPS (FR)**, b c Kapgarde (FR)—Free Demo (FR) **Mr M. Froissard**
133 **LES PETITS CARRES (FR)**, b c Mansonnien (FR)—Fleur d'ajonc (FR) **Mr S. Benaroche**
134 **LONG RUN (FR)**, b g Cadoudal (FR)—Libertina (FR) **Mme B. Gabeur**
135 **MAJESTIE WING (FR)**, b c Hawk Wing (USA)—Silver Cobra (USA) **Mr T. Nivel**
136 **NICTORY VOTE (FR)**, b c Victory Note (USA)—Nabita (FR) **Mr D. Galt**
137 **NOBLE BEAUTY**, b f Laveron—Niveole (IRE) **Mr B. Glutsch**
138 **NOKIS (FR)**, b c Nikos—Kiss Maite (FR) **Mme P. Papot**
139 **OBUNTO (FR)**, ch c Nikos—Haute Tension (FR) **Mr J-C. Audry**
140 **PLUS OR LESS (FR)**, b f Sleeping Car (FR)—Feuillee (FR) **Mr P. de Maleissye**
141 **PORDIOSERO (FR)**, b c Bering—Hollywood Girl **Mr G. Macaire**
142 **RETOUR DE NUIT (FR)**, ch g Kapgarde (FR)—Je Te Donne (FR) **Mr A. Chiche**
143 **ROMANTIQUE COTTE (FR)**, b f Robin des Champs (FR)—Kariantique (FR) **Mr T. Amos**
144 **ROSA MILL (GER)**, b c Pentire—Rosarium (GER) **Mr J-C. Audry**
145 **ROUBLARD (FR)**, ch g Volochine (IRE)—Algarabia (FR) **Mr J. Detre**
146 **ROYALE MAJESTY (FR)**, b f Nikos—Royale The Best (FR) **Mme I. Garcon**
147 **RYME BERE (FR)**, b f Until Sundown (USA)—Hornblower Girl **Mme P. Papot**
148 **SIR DAL (FR)**, b c Cadoudal (FR)—Energia (FR) **Mme M. Bryant**
149 **SPEED ROSE (FR)**, b g Passing Sale (FR)—Rose Angevine (FR) **Mr D. Le Breton**
150 **SWING MAMBO (FR)**, b c Enrique—Almadina (FR) **Mme P. Papot**
151 **SYNEFOR (FR)**, b g Bonnet Rouge (FR)—Karenzed (FR) **Mr J-M. Robin**
152 **TOP ALEX (FR)**, b c Mansonnien (FR)—Topkar (FR) **Mr D. Le Breton**
153 **WALKYRIE (FR)**, b f Sleeping Car (FR)—Temara (FR) **Mr P. de Maleissye**
154 **WAVY (FR)**, b f Lavirco (GER)—Short Wave (FR) **Mme P. Papot**

Jockey (NH): Francois Pamart, B. Gicquel, Jacques Ricou, Lenie Suzineau. **Amateur:** Mr John-Lee Monk.

---

365 | **MR W. J. W. MACKIE, Church Broughton**
Postal: The Bungalow, Barton Blount, Church Broughton, Derby
Contacts: PHONE (01283) 585604/585603 FAX (01283) 585603 MOBILE (07799) 145283
E-MAIL jmackie@bartonblount.freeserve.co.uk WEBSITE www.johnmackieracing.co.uk

1 **ASHOVER ROCK (IRE)**, 4, b g Danetime (IRE)—Ascoli **J. Woodward**
2 **BONNET O'BONNIE**, 4, br f Makbul—Parkside Prospect **J. M. Graham**
3 **CAME BACK (IRE)**, 5, ch h Bertolini (USA)—Distant Decree (USA) **W. I. Bloomfield**
4 **CORDIER**, 6, b g Desert Style (IRE)—Slipper **Mr F. E. & Mrs J. J. Brindley**
5 **FAVERSHAM**, 5, b g Halling (USA)—Barger (USA) **P. Riley**
6 **FLAMENCO BAY (IRE)**, 6, b g Flemensfirth (USA)—Beanco Bay (IRE) **The Whistling Dixie Partnership**
7 **FOURSQUARE FLYER (IRE)**, 6, ch g Tagula (IRE)—Isla (IRE) **T. Kelly**
8 **FRESH WINTER**, 6, br g Overbury (IRE)—Olnistar (FR) **A. J. Winterton**

MR W. J. W. MACKIE—continued

9 **GIDAM GIDAM (IRE)**, 6, b g King's Best (USA)—Flamands (IRE) **Jennifer Woodward & Caroline Lawson**
10 **HADITOVSKI**, 12, b g Hatim (USA)—Grand Occasion **Mrs S. P. Adams**
11 **JAYNE'S CRUSADER**, 5, b g Lord Americo—Carole's Crusader **P. Murphy**
12 **KANSAS GOLD**, 5, b g Alhaarth (IRE)—Star Tulip **A. J. Winterton**
13 **KILDARE SUN (IRE)**, 6, b g Desert Sun—Megan's Dream (IRE) **Mrs B. Woodworth**
14 **KINGDOM OF DREAMS (IRE)**, 6, b g Sadler's Wells (USA)—Regal Portrait (IRE) **Living the Dream Partnership**
15 **MABEL (IRE)**, 5, b m In The Wings—Ma N'ieme Biche (USA) **G. A. Greaves**
16 **MULAAZEM**, 5, b g King's Best (USA)—Harayir (USA) **Jennifer Woodward & Caroline Lawson**
17 **PAGAN RULES (IRE)**, 4, b g Desert Prince (IRE)—Fernanda **Derbyshire Racing**
18 **SPEED VENTURE**, 11, b g Owington—Jade Venture **Wall Racing Partners**
19 **STORM MISSION (USA)**, 4, b br g Storm Creek (USA)—Bemissed (USA) **W. I. Bloomfield**
20 **SUNBOLT (IRE)**, 5, b g Barathea (IRE)—Sunset (IRE) **Derbyshire Racing II**
21 **SUNISA (IRE)**, 7, b m Daggers Drawn (USA)—Winged Victory (IRE) **G. A. Greaves**
22 **TRAVELLING BAND (IRE)**, 10, b g Blues Traveller—Kind of Cute **T. Kelly**
23 **VITELLI**, 8, b g Vettori (IRE)—Mourne Trix **R. S. Blurton**
24 **YEOMAN SPIRIT (IRE)**, 5, ch g Soviet Star (USA)—Hollywood Pearl (USA) **Mrs S. P. Adams**

Other Owners: Mr S. P. Adams, Mr M. A. Bates, Mr F. E. Brindley, Mrs J. J. Brindley, Mr P. Joynson, Mr John Lomas, Mr David Penman, Mrs Jillian Reason, Sotby Farming Company Limited, Mr A. J. Wall, Mr C. J. Wall, Mr R. T. Wall, Mrs Jennifer Woodward, Mr Philip Youngson.

366
MR A. B. MACTAGGART, Hawick
Postal: Greendale, Hawick, Roxburghshire, TD9 7LH
Contacts: PHONE/FAX (01450) 372086 MOBILE (07764) 159852/(07718) 920072
E-MAIL brucemct@btinternet.co.uk

1 **BUFFY**, 8, b m Classic Cliche (IRE)—Annie Kelly **Harlequin Racing**
2 **CASSIUS (IRE)**, 6, b g Pistolet Bleu (IRE)—L'enfant Unique (IRE) **JohnElgin DouglasRenton HilaryMactaggart**
3 5, Ch m Karinga Bay—Cavalry
4 **CORBURY**, 4, b f Overbury (IRE)—Corbie's Glen **R. K. Bruce**
5 5, Br g Anshan—Craic Go Leor
6 **DANTE'S BROOK (IRE)**, 14, ch g Phardante (FR)—Arborfield Brook
7 5, Ch g Karinga Bay—Dreamy Desire
8 **EXECUTIVE XPRESS**, 6, b g Executive Perk—Furryvale **J. B. Jeffrey**
9 **HANSOMIS (IRE)**, 4, b f Titus Livius (FR)—Handsome Anna (IRE) **Corsby Racing**
10 **MISS KIMBERLIE**, 8, b m Balnibarbi—Speculate
11 4, B g Arctic Lord—Perspex Queen **W. B. Mactaggart**
12 5, B m Namaqualand (USA)—Richards Kate **Barrie Wharf**
13 **SHE'S ON HER TOES**, 4, b f Winged Love (IRE)—Hannah Park (IRE) **Potassium Partnership**
14 **STEEL MAN (IRE)**, 6, b g Anshan—One Edge (IRE) **Kelso Members Lowflyers Club**

THREE-YEAR-OLDS

15 B g Winged Love (IRE)—Cavalry **B. Mactaggart**

TWO-YEAR-OLDS

16 B c 2/3 Exit To Nowhere (USA)—Friendly Craic (IRE) (Mister Lord (USA)) **W. B. Mactaggart**
17 B g 23/3 Kayf Tara—Hannah Park (IRE) (Lycius (USA)) **Potassium Partnership**
18 B f 14/4 Classic Cliche (IRE)—Water Stratford (IRE) (Jurado (USA)) **W. B. Mactaggart**

Other Owners: Miss Susie Bruce, Mr J. R. Elgin, Mr Jim Jeffrey, R. N. Ker-Ramsay, Mrs Hilary Mactaggart, Mr. K. Rennie, Mr Douglas Renton, Mr D. Revel, Mr B. Wharf, J. R. Williams, Mr R. Woods.

Assistant Trainer: Mrs H. Mactaggart

Jockey (NH): G. Lee.

367
MR A. H. MACTAGGART, Hawick
Postal: Wells, Denholm, Hawick, Roxburghshire, TD9 8TD
Contacts: PHONE (01450) 870060 MOBILE (07711) 200445

1 **CUPID'S MISSION (IRE)**, 8, b m Alflora (IRE)—Poppea (IRE) **Mrs A. H. Mactaggart**
2 5, B g Beat All (USA)—Hobbs Choice

MR A. H. MACTAGGART—continued

  3 4, B g Overbury (IRE)—Kadari
  4 ROYAL MACKINTOSH, 7, b g Sovereign Water (FR)—Quick Quote **A. H. Mactaggart**

Other Owners: Mr A. H. Mactaggart.

Assistant Trainer: Mrs M. A. Mactaggart

---

368 MR P. MADDISON, Skewsby
Postal: **5 West End Cottages, Skewsby, York, YO61 4SG**
Contacts: **PHONE (01347) 888385**

  1 LOTHIAN FALCON, 9, b g Relief Pitcher—Lothian Rose **P. Maddison**
  2 SOLEMN VOW, 7, b m Zaffaran (USA)—Quick Quick Sloe **P. Maddison**

Jockey (NH): Robert Walford.

---

369 MR M. J. MADGWICK, Denmead
Postal: **Forest Farm, Forest Road, Denmead, Waterlooville, Hampshire, PO7 6UA**
Contacts: **PHONE/FAX (02392) 258313 MOBILE (07835) 964969**

  1 BANDITS PISTOL (NZ), 8, gr g Foxbay (NZ)—Copasetic (NZ) **DDB Racing**
  2 BLUE LINE, 6, gr m Bluegrass Prince (IRE)—Out Line **Miss E. M. L. Coller**
  3 DE PORT HEIGHTS (IRE), 4, bl g Redback—Raise-A-Secret (IRE) **W. E. Baird**
  4 EDWARD (IRE), 6, b g Namid—Daltak **Mr J. J. Swallow**
  5 HARCOURT (USA), 8, b g Cozzene (USA)—Ballinamallard (USA) **DDB Racing**
  6 JADES DOUBLE, 7, b m Double Trigger (IRE)—Jaydeebee **J. D. Brownrigg**
  7 SUMDANCER (NZ), 6, b g Summer Suspicion (JPN)—Epic Dancer (NZ) **DDB Racing**

THREE-YEAR-OLDS

  8 RAY DIAMOND, ch g Medicean—Musical Twist (USA) **Miss K. A. Garraway**

TWO-YEAR-OLDS

  9 LEAF HOLLOW, ch f 22/3 Beat Hollow—Lauren (GER) (Lightning (FR)) (8000) **Miss E. M. L. Coller**

Other Owners: Miss E. Hicks-Little, Mr M. Madgwick, Mr D. J. Willis.

Assistant Trainer: David Madgwick

Jockey (flat): G. Baker. **Jockey (NH):** Jamie Moore. **Conditional:** Marc Goldstein.

---

370 MR M. A. MAGNUSSON, Upper Lambourn
Postal: **The Old Manor, Upper Lambourn, Hungerford, Berkshire, RG17 8RG**
Contacts: **OFFICE (01488) 73966 FAX (01488) 71702 MOBILE (07775) 556306**
E-MAIL mikeal.magnusson@virgin.net

  1 FAITHFUL RULER (USA), 4, b br g Elusive Quality (USA)—
                                 Fancy Ruler (USA) **Eastwind Racing Ltd & Martha Trussell**
  2 PROUD SCHOLAR (USA), 6, b m Royal Academy (USA)—Proud Fact (USA) **East Wind Racing Ltd**
  3 SMART ENOUGH, 5, gr h Cadeaux Genereux—Good Enough (FR) **East Wind Racing Ltd**
  4 SPINDOR (USA), 9, ch g Spinning World (USA)—Doree (USA) **East Wind Racing Ltd**

THREE-YEAR-OLDS

  5 EDIE SUPERSTAR (USA), b f Forestry (USA)—Just Out (USA) **Eastwind Racing & Mountgrange Stud**
  6 KING OF CADEAUX (IRE), br g Cadeaux Genereux—Purple Haze (IRE) **East Wind Racing Ltd**
  7 MIDDLE OF NOWHERE (USA), b c Carson City (USA)—Ivy Leaf (IRE) **Eastwind Racing Ltd & Martha Trussell**
  8 REGAL BIRD (USA), b br f Grand Slam (USA)—Storm Ring (USA) **Eastwind Racing Ltd & Martha Trussell**
  9 THRONE OF POWER (USA), b br c Pulpit (USA)—Lakabi (USA) **Eastwind Racing Ltd & Martha Trussell**

TWO-YEAR-OLDS

  10 B br c 19/5 Giant's Causeway (USA)—
                        Lady Doc (USA) (Doc's Leader (USA)) (121477) **Eastwind Racing Ltd & Martha Trussell**

MR M. A. MAGNUSSON—continued

11 B c 8/3 Indian Charlie (USA)—
      Out Too Late (USA) (Future Storm (USA)) (24295) **Eastwind Racing Ltd & Martha Trussell**
12 **QUEEN MARTHA (USA),** b f 19/5 Rahy (USA)—
      Cryptoqueen (USA) (Cryptoclearance (USA)) (48590) **Eastwind Racing Ltd & Martha Trussell**
13 B c 28/3 Songandaprayer (USA)—
      Ra Hydee (USA) (Rahy (USA)) (10689) **Eastwind Racing Ltd & Martha Trussell**
14 **SOUTH AFRICAN (USA),** gr ro f 3/5 Johannesburg (USA)—
      River Cache (USA) (Unbridled (USA)) (72886) **Eastwind Racing Ltd & Martha Trussell**
15 **SPIRITUAL TREASURE (USA),** b br c 22/4 Perfect Soul (IRE)—
      Storm Runner (USA) (Miswaki (USA)) (82604) **Eastwind Racing Ltd & Martha Trussell**
16 **SPRING OF FAME (USA),** b c 21/4 Grand Slam (USA)—
      Bloomy (USA) (Polish Numbers (USA)) (82604) **Eastwind Racing Ltd & Martha Trussell**

Other Owners: East Wind Racing Ltd, Mountgrange Stud, Mrs Robert B. Trussell.

---

371   MR P. J. MAKIN, Marlborough
Postal: **Bonita Racing Stables, Ogbourne Maisey, Marlborough, Wiltshire, SN8 1RY**
Contacts: **PHONE** (01672) 512973 **FAX** (01672) 514166
E-MAIL hq@petermakin-racing.com

1 **BLUE SPACE,** 4, b f Mtoto—La Tour de Blay (USA) **Dr John Wilson & Partners**
2 **BODY GOLD (ARG),** 5, b h Body Glove (ARG)—Aurifera (ARG) **Mr Sandy Harper, J. P. Carrington**
3 **DANSKI,** 5, b h Dansili—Manila Selection (USA) **Camamile Hessert Scott Partnership**
4 **EMPEROR COURT (IRE),** 4, ch c Singspiel (IRE)—Tarquina (USA) **Four Seasons Racing Ltd**
5 **FIRST TO CALL,** 4, ch c First Trump—Scarlett Holly **Dr John Wilson & Partners**
6 **HARVEST QUEEN (IRE),** 5, ch m Spinning World (USA)—Royal Bounty (IRE) **Bakewell Bloodstock Ltd**
7 **HEAVENS WALK,** 7, ch h Compton Place—Ghost Dancing **Mrs P. J. Makin**
8 **KINRANDE (IRE),** 6, b g Sri Pekan (USA)—Pipers Pool (IRE) **G & R Marchant Ahier Carrington & Moore**
9 **LOUPHOLE,** 6, ch g Loup Sauvage (USA)—Goodwood Lass (IRE) **Ten Of Hearts**
10 **PIVOTAL POINT,** 8, b g Pivotal—True Precision **John Perry**
11 **SHARPAZMAX (IRE),** 4, b c Daggers Drawn (USA)—Amour Toujours (IRE) **Weldspec Glasgow Limited**
12 **SHUSTRAYA,** 4, b f Dansili—Nimble Fan (USA) **Four Leaf Clover**
13 **SOTIK STAR (IRE),** 5, b g Elnadim (USA)—Crystal Springs (IRE) **D.Ladhams M.Holland J.Ritchie G.Marchant**
14 **TUBBY ISAACS,** 4, b g Cyrano de Bergerac—Opuntia **John Khan & Arnold Bros.**
15 **WATAMU (IRE),** 7, b g Groom Dancer (USA)—Miss Golden Sands **R. A. Henley**

THREE-YEAR-OLDS

16 **CLASSIC DESCENT,** b c Auction House (USA)—Polish Descent (IRE) **Mr J. Joyce**
17 B g Quiet American (USA)—Do The Hustle (USA) **Mrs J. Carrington**
18 **EL FUSER,** ch g Zamindar (USA)—Nimble Fan (USA) **G M D Racing**
19 **FABREZE,** ch c Choisir (AUS)—Impulsive Decision (IRE) **Weldspec Glasgow Limited**
20 B g Tobougg (IRE)—Goldfill **P. J. Makin**
21 **GREEN VELVET,** b f Iron Mask (USA)—Scarlett Ribbon **Mrs P. J. Makin**
22 **HEAVEN,** ch g Reel Buddy (USA)—Wedgewood Star **Wedgewood Estates**
23 **JOSS STICK,** b g Josr Algarhoud (IRE)—Queen's College (IRE) **Lady Davis, J. P. Carrington, D. M. Ahier**
24 **LUNAR LIMELIGHT,** b c Royal Applause—Moon Magic **Mrs J. McColl**
25 B c Orpen (USA)—Manuka Too (IRE) **P. J. Makin**
26 **QUEENS MANTLE,** b f Bold Edge—Queen Shirley (IRE) **P. Wightman, R. Marchant, Lady Whent, J. Berwald**
27 **SAMURAI WARRIOR,** br g Beat All (USA)—Ma Vie **Countess Of Lonsdale & R. P. Marchant**
28 **SILKY STEPS (IRE),** gr f Nayef (USA)—Legal Steps (IRE) **Thurloe Thoroughbreds XXI**
29 **SOLO RIVER,** b f Averti (IRE)—Surakarta **Ten Of Hearts II**

TWO-YEAR-OLDS

30 **BANDA SEA (IRE),** b c 16/3 Tagula (IRE)—
      Non Ultra (USA) (Peintre Celebre (USA)) (15000) **J. Gale, M. H. Holland, D. Powell, R. C. Dollar**
31 **CARBON HOOFPRINT,** b c 9/5 Green Tune (USA)—Salome's Attack (Anabaa (USA)) (15000) **The Billinomas**
32 **COOL HAND JAKE,** b c 3/2 Storming Home—Monawara (IRE) (Namaqualand (USA)) **Wedgewood Estates**
33 Ch c 21/4 Fantastic Light (USA)—Crystal Star (Mark of Esteem (IRE)) (26000) **Keith & Brian Brackpool**
34 Ch f 22/3 Captain Rio—Dear Catch (IRE) (Bluebird (USA)) (5000) **Golden Keys, M. H. Holland**
35 B f 22/2 Lend A Hand—Eljariha (Unfuwain (USA)) (10000)
36 B c 25/3 Lujain (USA)—Gem (Most Welcome) (10000) **D. Poole**
37 B c 16/4 Efisio—Impulsive Decision (USA) (Nomination) (36000) **Weldspec Glasgow Limited**
38 **KUANYAO (IRE),** b c 24/2 American Post—
      Nullarbor (Green Desert (USA)) (37000) **D. M. Ahier, R. P. Marchant, J. P. Carrington**

MR P. J. MAKIN—continued

39 **MABUYA (UAE)**, b c 13/3 Halling (USA)—City of Gold (IRE) (Sadler's Wells (USA)) (52000) **R. A. Henley**
40 B f 7/2 Barathea (IRE)—Nishan (Nashwan (USA)) (50000) **The Countess Of Lonsdale**
41 Br c 25/4 Efisio—Peyto Princess (Bold Arrangement) (16000) **M. H. Holland, R. P. Marchant**
42 Ch c 30/1 Kris Kin (USA)—Polmara (IRE) (Polish Precedent) (20000)
43 Ch c 23/1 Central Park (IRE)—Retaliator (Rudimentary (USA)) (16000)
44 B c 18/4 Lend A Hand—Scarlett Holly (Red Sunset) **Ten Horsepower**
45 Ch c 2/2 Polish Precedent (USA)—Wou Oodd (Barathea (IRE)) (10000)

Other Owners: D. Allen, Mr Stephen Arnold, Mr A. E. Arnold, Mr G. F. Bear, Mr John Berwald, Mr K. Brackpool, Mr David Brocklehurst, J. C. F. Burke, John Burke, Mr R. Byron-Scott, R. Byron-Scott, Mr J. P Carrington, Mr H. J. W. Davies, Lady Davis, Mr R. C. Dollar, Andy Ellis, Mr & Mrs F. Everleigh, Mr S. Harper, D. J. Holding, Mr David Holding, Mr S. James, Mr R. Kent, Mr John Khan, Mr D. Kilcoyne, Mr David Ladhams, Mrs N. E. Lyon, Mr Mike Maher, Mrs Greta Sarfaty Marchant, S. J. Messer, Mrs M. A. Moore, Mr Paul Murphy, Mr K. M. Nee, Mr Michael O'Hagan, Mr B. P O'Hagan, Mr L. O'Neill, Mr L. O'Neill, Mr Oliver Pawle, Mr E. John Perry, M. T. Perry, Mr D. A. Poole, Mr D. Powell, Mrs J. S. G. Ritchie, Mr D. S. Ritchie, Mr J. A. B. Stafford, Mr D. J. Taylor, Mr Paul Tusen, Mr P A. E. Tuson, Mr T. W. Wellard, Lady Whent, Mr P J. Wightman, Dr John Wilson (Beaconsfield).

Jockey (flat): S. Sanders, D. Sweeney. **Amateur:** Mr S. Walker.

---

372 **MR R. MALETROIT, St Peter, Jersey**
Postal: Flat 5, Clos des Charmes, La Rue de L'Eglise, St. Peter, Jersey, JE3 7JU
Contacts: **PHONE (01469) 589419 FAX (01469) 589419 MOBILE (07855) 065589**

1 **EMERALD GREEN (GER)**, 9, br g Goofalik (USA)—Elaine (GER) **Mr R. Maletroit**
2 **MAN OF KENT**, 8, b g Paris House—Club Elite **Mr R. Maletroit**
3 **RED RIVER ROCK (IRE)**, 6, b g Spectrum (IRE)—Ann's Annie (IRE) **Mr R. Maletroit**
4 **SABO PRINCE**, 6, ch g Atraf—Moving Princess **Mr R. Maletroit**
5 **VALENTINES VISION**, 11, b g Distinctly North (USA)—Sharp Anne **Mr R. Maletroit**

Other Owners: A. Beenshill, J. M. Bradley, Mrs J. K. Bradley, R. Mason.
Jockey (flat): V. Slattery. **Jockey (NH):** T. Siddall.

---

373 **MRS ALYSON MALZARD, Jersey**
Postal: Les Etabl'yes, Grosnez Farm, St Ouen, Jersey, JE3 2AD
Contacts: **PHONE (01534) 483773 MOBILE (07797) 738128**
E-MAIL themalzards@localdial.com

1 **CADOCHERDO (FR)**, 7, ch g Johann Quatz (FR)—Danse Bretonne (FR) **Mrs A. Malzard**
2 **CRONKYVODDY**, 7, b g Groom Dancer (USA)—Miss Pout **Mr J. Mercier & Miss J. Edear**
3 **KAZARUS (FR)**, 4, b g Poplar Bluff—Miss Gee-Ell **N. Ahier**
4 **KHUZDAR (IRE)**, 9, ch g Definite Article—
Mariyda (IRE) **Mrs Y. Burnett, Mr D. Le Poidevin & Mr H. Le Poidevin**
5 **KOKA FAST (FR)**, 6, ch g Start Fast (FR)—Kaly Flight (FR) **The Executor of the late Mr Phil Benest**
6 **KRISTINOR (FR)**, 6, ch g Inchinor—Kristina **Jim Jamouneau**
7 **MOBUS WAN (FR)**, 5, b g Le Triton (USA)—Brustanette (FR) **The Mobus Syndicate**
8 **NOBLE REEF**, 11, b g Deploy—Penny Mint **Mrs A. Malzard**
9 **PERFECT PORTRAIT**, 8, ch g Selkirk (USA)—Flawless Image (USA) **Mrs P. Somers**
10 **REGAL ALI (IRE)**, 9, ch g Ali-Royal (IRE)—Depeche (FR) **N. Ahier**
11 **SANS SA DAME (FR)**, 5, ch g Wathik (USA)—
Danemara (FR) **Mr G. Amy, Mrs S. Amy, Ms J. Amy & Ms Y. Stead**
12 **SIAKIRA**, 5, ch m Golden Snake (USA)—Minette **Mrs P. Somers**

Assistant Trainer: Mrs Grace Poingdestre

Jockey (flat): Adam Jones, Emmett Stack. **Jockey (NH):** Adam Jones. **Amateur:** Mr D. Cuthbert, Mrs G. Poingdestre.

---

374 **MR JAMES J. MANGAN, Mallow**
Postal: Curraheen, Conna, Co. Cork, Ireland
Contacts: **PHONE (00353) 0585 9116 FAX (00353) 0585 9116 MOBILE (00353) 8726 84611**
E-MAIL connastud@gmail.ie

1 **ALPINE GLADE (IRE)**, 6, b m Oscar (IRE)—Stony View (IRE) **Mr John Coffey**
2 **ASHSTORM (IRE)**, 12, ch g Glacial Storm (USA)—Sandy Ash (IRE) **Mrs M. Mangan**

MR JAMES J. MANGAN—continued

3 **CONNA CASTLE (IRE)**, 9, b g Germany (USA)—Mrs Hegarty **The Kings Syndicate**
4 **ECHO FALLS (IRE)**, 6, b m Glacial Storm (USA)—Laboc **Mrs M. Mangan**
5 **KILCREA ASLA (IRE)**, 7, b g Oscar (IRE)—Alottalady (IRE) **Mr M. O'Driscoll**
6 **LOUGHANELTEEN (IRE)**, 10, b g Satco (FR)—Ruths Rhapsody (IRE) **Mr. Justin Burke**
7 **MISS CLAIR (IRE)**, 6, b m Supreme Leader—Shunnagh Two (IRE) **Mr Enda Hall**
8 **PERKS OF WINTER (IRE)**, 7, br m Executive Perk—Mr K's Winterblues (IRE) **Mrs T. C. Kouwemberg**
9 **PORTACARRON BAY (IRE)**, 6, b g Rudimentary (USA)—Lady Bar **Mr M. I. Dixon**
10 **RIVER SHANAKILL (IRE)**, 5, b m Flemensfirth (USA)—Shanakill River (IRE) **Mrs M. Mangan**
11 **TOP TWIG (IRE)**, 9, b g Flemensfirth (USA)—Lovely Tyrone **Mrs M. Mangan**

Assistant Trainer: Mary Mangan

---

375 MR C. J. MANN, Upper Lambourn
Postal: **Whitcoombe House Stables, Maddle Road, Upper Lambourn, Hungerford, Berkshire, RG17 8RA**
Contacts: PHONE **(01488) 71717/73118** FAX **(01488) 73223** MOBILE **(07721) 888333**
E-MAIL **charlie@charliemann.org** WEBSITE **www.charliemann.com**

1 **AIR FORCE ONE (GER)**, 6, ch h Lando (GER)—Ame Soeur (FR) **B. Walsh**
2 **ALPHABETICAL (IRE)**, 9, br g Alphabatim (USA)—Sheeghee (USA) **H. E. C. Villiers**
3 **ALROYAL (GER)**, 9, ch g Royal Solo (IRE)—Alamel (USA) **P. Cook**
4 **BAGAN (FR)**, 9, b br g Rainbow Quest (USA)—Maid of Erin (USA) **The Centaur Group Partnership VII**
5 **BARTERCARD (USA)**, 7, b g Sir Cat (USA)—Pure Misk **E. Good, I. Kirkham, J. Kirkham & R. Kirkham**
6 **BLAZING DIVA (IRE)**, 5, gr m Blueprint (IRE)—Irene's Call (IRE) **Mrs L. C. Taylor & Miss M. Talbot**
7 **BORERO (FR)**, 5, ch g Discover d'auteuil (FR)—Harmonique (FR) **N. W. A. Bannister**
8 **CAGED TIGER**, 9, b g Classic Cliche (IRE)—Run Tiger (IRE) **Mrs D. L. Mosley**
9 **CHASE THE DAWN**, 6, gr g Silver Patriarch (IRE)—Marquesa Juana **Bryan & Philippa Burrough**
10 **CORTINAS (IRE)**, 6, b g Lomitas—Cocorna **W. Brindle, B. Fulton, T. Hayward & A. Merritt**
11 **DONATESSA (GER)**, 5, b m Sternkoenig (IRE)—Donadea (GER) **The Grosvenor Square Partnership**
12 **FAIR POINT (IRE)**, 6, ch g Moonax (USA)—Pampered Molly (USA) **Mr Jared Sullivan & Mr R.P.B. Michaelson**
13 **FANDANI (GER)**, 8, b g Lomitas—Fainting Spell (FR) **Mr N. Kempner & Mr W. J. Smith**
14 **FIGURITA**, 5, br m Acatenango (GER)—Frille (FR) **B. Walsh**
15 **FLIGHT COMMAND**, 10, ch g Gunner B—Wing On **Whitcoombe House Partnership**
16 **FLOREANA (GER)**, 4, b m Acatenango (GER)—Frille (FR) **Mr M. Lynch**
17 **GAORA LANE (IRE)**, 7, ch g Anshan—Lisfuncheon Adage **S. Beccle,Lady Hart,M. Webster,R. Hunter**
18 **GAUVAIN (GER)**, 6, b g Sternkoenig (IRE)—Gamina (GER) **Mr J. H. McDougall**
19 **GWYNIE**, 4, b f King's Theatre (IRE)—Gaye Mercy **Normandie Stud Ltd**
20 **HAGGLE TWINS (IRE)**, 8, b g Thowra (FR)—Orwell Gaye (IRE) **A. F. Merritt, D. Burgess & P. Cook**
21 **HER TURN NOW**, 4, gr f Act One—Wishful (IRE) **C. J. Mann**
22 **HOH VISS**, 8, b g Rudimentary (USA)—Now And Forever (IRE) **Mr & Mrs N. Kempner**
23 **HOW'S BUSINESS**, 4, b f Josr Algarhoud (IRE)—Love And Kisses **C. J. Mann**
24 **ITS ALL CHAT**, 7, b g Cloudings (IRE)—Chat In The Box (IRE) **Nick Quesnel & Mark Hunter**
25 **JAZZ DANCE (IRE)**, 8, b g Arctic Lord—Nut Eile (IRE) **C. J. Mann**
26 **JOE McHUGH (IRE)**, 9, ch g Topanoora—Run For Shelter **Sally Morgan & Richard Prince**
27 **KANAD**, 6, b g Bold Edge—Multi-Softt **P. M. Warren**
28 **LAREDO SOUND (IRE)**, 6, ch g Singspiel (IRE)—Lanelly (GER) **Mr Jared Sullivan & Mr Robert Tompkins**
29 **MACS GOOSE**, 6, b m Kayf Tara—Zaffaran Run (IRE)
30 **MELFORD (IRE)**, 10, br g Presenting—Echo Creek (IRE) **Mrs J. M. Mayo**
31 **MOON OVER MIAMI (GER)**, 7, b g Dashing Blade—Miss Esther (GER) **Mrs A. E. Fulton & Mr M. T. Lynch**
32 **MY TURN NOW (IRE)**, 6, ch g In The Wings—Wishful (IRE) **Mountgrange Brindle Kempner & Merritt**
33 **NADOVER (IRE)**, 7, br g Cyborg (FR)—Djerissa (FR) **Tony Hayward & Barry Fulton**
34 **OUR CHOICE (IRE)**, 6, b g Indian Danehill (IRE)—Spring Daffodil **John Southway & Andrew Hughes**
35 **PATRIOT (IRE)**, 4, b c Sadler's Wells (USA)—Sweeten Up **C. J. Mann**
36 **PEINTRE DU ROI (USA)**, 4, ch g El Prado (IRE)—Peinture Bleue (USA) **C. J. Mann**
37 **PRINCESS YASMIN**, 4, b f Double Trigger (IRE)—Beamo **Group Clean Ltd**
38 **QUILVER TATOU (FR)**, 4, b g Silver Rainbow—Canlastou (FR) **Martin Myers**
39 **REBEL MELODY (IRE)**, 7, b g Houmayoun (FR)—Queenford Melody (IRE) **Mrs J. F. Maynard**
40 **SAYAGO (GER)**, 6, b g Lavirco (GER)—Sweet Virtue (USA) **The Safest Syndicate 2**
41 **SHINING GALE (IRE)**, 6, b g Glacial Storm (USA)—
                                             The Shining Force (IRE) **J. Sullivan S. Brown & Group Clean Ltd**
42 **STELLENBOSCH (USA)**, 5, b g Cape Town (USA)—
                                             New Account (USA) **Mrs Judy Maynard & Mr John McDougall**
43 **SULLUMO (GER)**, 5, b h Acatenango (GER)—Secret of Salome (IRE) **Mr & Mrs D. A. Gamble**
44 **SUPER MAXAMILLION**, 5, ch g Emperor Fountain—Speckyfoureyes **Group Clean Ltd**

MR C. J. MANN—continued

45 **TEAMGEIST (IRE)**, 7, b g Taipan (IRE)—Stage Debut **Realty Racing II**
46 **WILLIAM BONNEY (IRE)**, 8, br g Oscar (IRE)—Beaudel **The Safest Syndicate 2**

Other Owners: Mr Bryan Beacham, Mr S. Beccle, Mr W. Brindle, Mr S. J. Brown, Mr D. Burgess, Mr B. R. H. Burrough, Mrs Philippa Burrough, Mr P. Cook, Mr A. J. Cork, Mr R. T. Hunter, Ms Felicity Devonshire, Mrs A. E. Fulton, Mr B. N. Fulton, Mrs Alison Gamble, Mr D. A. Gamble, Mr R. E. Good, Group Clean Ltd, Lady Hart, Mr K. R. W. Hawkins, Mr Tony Hayward, Mr Andrew Hughes, Mr Mark Hunter, Mr N. J. Kempner, Mrs Rosalind Kempner, Mr Ian Kirkham, Mr Jonny Kirkham, Mr R. G. Kirkham, Mr Michael T. Lynch, Mrs C. J. Mann, Mrs Judy Maynard, Mr J. H. McDougall, Mr A. F. Merritt, Mr R. P. B. Michaelson, Mrs Sally Morgan, Mr Richard J. Prince, Mr Nick Quesnel, Mr William J. Smith, Mr K. Sobey, Mr John Southway, Mr Jared Sullivan, Miss M. Talbot, Mrs L. C. Taylor, Mr R. J. Tompkins, Mr M. A. Webster.

Assistant Trainer: Richard Morgan-Evans

Jockey (NH): D. Crosse, Noel Fehily. **Conditional:** K. Tobin. **Amateur:** Mr B. Garner.

376

MRS J. M. E. MANN, Leamington Spa
Postal: **Hill Farm, Ufton, Leamington Spa, Warwickshire, CV33 9PP**
Contacts: **PHONE (01926) 612208**
E-MAIL goldlinestud@btconnect.com

1 **FLAX HILL**, 7, ch m Zaffaran (USA)—Annicombe Run **Mrs J. M. E. Mann**
2 **JUST MALT**, 5, b g Sir Harry Lewis (USA)—G-And-T **Mrs J. M. E. Mann**
3 **KILLARNEY PRINCE (IRE)**, 9, b g Lord Americo—Henry Woman (IRE) **Mrs J. M. E. Mann**
4 **MUNRO (IRE)**, 5, b g Houmayoun (FR)—Boolavogue (IRE) **Mrs J. M. E. Mann**
5 **SHOWMAN (IRE)**, 5, ch g Carroll House—Bettys The Act (IRE) **Mrs J. M. E. Mann**

Amateur: Mr Peter Mann.

377

MR H. J. MANNERS, Swindon
Postal: **Common Farm, Highworth, Swindon, Wilts**
Contacts: **PHONE (01793) 762232 FAX 01793 861781 MOBILE (07753) 638858**
E-MAIL commonfarm@btconnect.com

1 **AITCHJAYEM**, 8, b g Rakaposhi King—G W Supermare **H. J. Manners**
2 **FARMER JOHN**, 8, ch g Petrizzo—Luvankiss **H. J. Manners**
3 **FOX JOHN**, 9, b g Ballet Royal (USA)—Muskerry Miss (IRE) **H. J. Manners**
4 **FRISKY JOHN**, 5, gr g My Best Valentine—Risky Girl **H. J. Manners**
5 **HUNTING LODGE (IRE)**, 7, ch g Grand Lodge (USA)—Vijaya (USA) **H. J. Manners**
6 **KEESILUV**, 7, ch m Petrizzo—Luvankiss **H. J. Manners**
7 **MAN FROM HIGHWORTH**, 9, b g Ballet Royal (USA)—Cavisoir **H. J. Manners**
8 **MANNERS (IRE)**, 10, b g Topanoora—Maneree **H. J. Manners**
9 **NO JOHN NO**, 6, b g Petrizzo—Margaret Modes **H. J. Manners**
10 **RUNNING TIMES (USA)**, 11, b g Brocco (USA)—Concert Peace (USA) **H. J. Manners**
11 **RUSTIC JOHN**, 8, ch g Afzal—Spartiquick **H. J. Manners**
12 **SHEKNOWSYOUKNOW**, 7, b m Petrizzo—Margaret Modes **H. J. Manners**
13 **SPARKES**, 10, b g Ballet Royal (USA)—Saxon Lass **H. J. Manners**
14 **SUPERFLING**, 7, ch g Superpower—Jobiska **H. J. Manners**
15 **TIFFIN DEANO (IRE)**, 6, b g Mujadil (USA)—Xania **H. J. Manners**
16 **TRIZZY**, 8, b m Petrizzo—Cavisoir **H. J. Manners**

Assistant Trainer: Mrs H. J. Manners

Amateur: Miss Kirsty Whitbread, Mr William Telfer, **Conditional:** Felix De Giles.

378

MR G. G. MARGARSON, Newmarket
Postal: **Graham Lodge, Birdcage Walk, Newmarket, Suffolk, CB8 0NE**
Contacts: **HOME/FAX (01638) 668043 MOBILE (07860) 198303**
E-MAIL george@georgemargarson.co.uk WEBSITE www.georgemargarson.co.uk

1 **ATAVUS**, 11, b g Distant Relative—Elysian **G. G. Margarson**
2 **GENEROUS JEM**, 5, b m Generous (IRE)—Top Jem **Norcroft Park Stud**
3 **GINGER POP**, 4, ch g Mark of Esteem (IRE)—Norcroft Lady **League Of Mentalmen**
4 **JOLIS TARA**, 5, b m Kayf Tara—Jolis Absent **Norcroft Park Stud**

MR G. G. MARGARSON—continued

5 **MICK IS BACK**, 4, b g Diktat—Classy Cleo (IRE) **Wendy Smith & Michael Jenner**
6 **NORTHERN JEM**, 4, b g Mark of Esteem (IRE)—Top Jem **Norcroft Park Stud**
7 **POLISH RED**, 4, b g Polish Precedent (USA)—Norcroft Joy **Norcroft Park Stud**
8 **WOOLFALL BLUE (IRE)**, 5, gr h Bluebird (USA)—Diamond Waltz (IRE) **J. F. Bower**
9 **WOOLFALL ROSE**, 4, b f Generous—Rose Noble (USA) **J. F. Bower**
10 **YOUNG MICK**, 6, br g King's Theatre (IRE)—Just Warning **M. F. Kentish**

THREE-YEAR-OLDS

11 **BEST DANCER**, b f King's Best (USA)—Fresher **Norcroft Park Stud**
12 **DANAMIGHT (IRE)**, gr f Danetime (IRE)—Nuit Chaud (USA)
13 B c Lomitas—Distant Diva
14 **DRY SPEEDFIT (IRE)**, b g Desert Style (IRE)—Annmary Girl **J. D. Guest**
15 B f High Chaparral (IRE)—House In Wood (FR)
16 **MAGICAL SPEEDFIT (IRE)**, ch g Bold Fact (USA)—Magical Peace (IRE) **J. D. Guest**
17 **NOUVELLE NOVA (IRE)**, b f Noverre (USA)—Uhud (IRE) **Stevens, Stemp & Clarke**
18 **TOTOMAN**, b c Mtoto—Norcroft Lady **Norcroft Park Stud**
19 **WOOLFALL TREASURE**, gr c Daylami (IRE)—Treasure Trove (USA) **J. F. Bower**

TWO-YEAR-OLDS

20 Ch c 3/5 Fantastic Light (USA)—Countess Guest (IRE) (Spectrum (IRE)) (13000) **J. D. Guest**
21 B f 7/2 Lend A Hand—Distant Diva (Distant Relative)
22 B f 17/2 Tillerman—Emaura (Dominion) (3500)
23 B c 17/2 Fantastic Light (USA)—Enchanted (Magic Ring (IRE))
24 B f 26/4 Grape Tree Road—Glorious Aragon (Aragon) (600)
25 B f 20/3 Primo Valentino (IRE)—Just Warning (Warning)
26 Ch f 15/4 Mark of Esteem (IRE)—Kalamansi (IRE) (Sadler's Wells (USA))
27 B c 21/2 Noverre (USA)—Mandragore (USA) (Slew O' Gold (USA)) (45000)
28 Ch c 7/2 Lomitas—Norcroft Joy (Rock Hopper)
29 Ch f 15/2 Bertolini—Norcroft Lady (Mujtahid (USA))
30 B f 27/4 Needwood Blade—Plentitude (FR) (Ela-Mana-Mou) (3500)
31 Ch c 19/2 Imperial Dancer—Princess Speedfit (FR) (Desert Prince (IRE)) (20000) **J. D. Guest**
32 B f 27/1 Diktat—Star of Normandie (USA) (Gulch (USA))
33 B c 29/4 Hawk Wing (USA)—Yakutia (IRE) (Polish Precedent (USA)) (30000)

Other Owners: Mr A. L. Baisden, Mr G. M. Clarke, A. J. Hollis, M. D. Hollis, Mr Michael Jenner, Peter McCutcheon, Ms Wendy Smith, Mr P Spires, Mr E. S. Stemp, Mr M. J. G. Stevens.

Amateur: Miss Katie Margarson.

---

379   MR S. J. MARSHALL, Morpeth
Postal: **West Moneylaws Farm, Cornhill-on-Tweed, Northumberland, TD12 4QD**
Contacts: PHONE (01890) 850673 MOBILE (07971) 541365
E-MAIL lizannett@hotmail.com

1 **CROSS THE PALM (IRE)**, 5, gr m Great Palm (USA)—Smooth Leader (IRE) **Mrs E. Annett**
2 **MISS MATTIE ROSS**, 12, b m Milieu—Mother Machree **S. J. Marshall**
3 **MONEYLAWS (IRE)**, 7, b m Zaffaran (USA)—Winter Sunset **Mrs E. Annett**
4 **SHE'S A RAINBOW (IRE)**, 8, b m Glacial Storm—Roselle **Mrs E. Annett**

THREE-YEAR-OLDS

5 B f Turtle Island (IRE)—Aon Suil Amhain (IRE) **Mrs E. Annett & S. J. Marshall**
6 B f Milan—The Purple Penguin **Mrs E. Annett & S. J. Marshall**

TWO-YEAR-OLDS

7 B f 26/4 Milieu—Croaghnacree (IRE) (Mister Lord (USA)) **Mrs E. Annett & S. J. Marshall**

Assistant Trainer: Liz Annett

---

380   MR S. T. MASON, Lanchester
Postal: **Low Meadows Farm, Lanchester, Co. Durham, DH2 1TH**
Contacts: PHONE (01207) 529629 (01914) 920529 FAX (01207) 529629 MOBILE (07789) 511144
E-MAIL info@mason-racing.com WEBSITE www.mason-racing.com

1 **BEAMSLEY BEACON**, 7, ch g Wolfhound (USA)—Petindia **K. Kirkup**
2 **BLACKHEATH (IRE)**, 12, ch g Common Grounds—Queen Caroline (USA) **Middleham Park Racing XX**

MR S. T. MASON—continued

3 **GENERAL FEELING (IRE)**, 7, b g General Monash (USA)—Kamadara (IRE) **The Mason Racing Partnership I**
4 **HAWAII PRINCE**, 4, b g Primo Valentino (IRE)—Bollin Rita **Dream On**
5 **MR MINSTER MOSS**, 6, b g Minster Son—Ciara's Gale (IRE)
6 **SHE'S OUR BEAUTY (IRE)**, 5, b m Imperial Ballet (IRE)—Eleonora d'arborea **Tarn Lads Syndicate**
7 **SUSIEDIL (IRE)**, 7, b m Mujadil (USA)—Don't Take Me (IRE) **Dream On & Mrs Gillian Mason**
8 **SUSPENDER (IRE)**, 4, b f Distant Music (USA)—Feather 'n Lace (IRE) **Mr R. Mason & Mr J. A. Welsh**

Other Owners: P.J. Doyle, Mr K. Hodgson, M. J. Holley, Mrs G. Mason, S. T. Mason, Mr R. Mason, T. S. Palin, M. Prince, Mr R. Riches, Mr G. V. Stelfox, Mr R. Tocher, Mr J. A. Welsh, J. White.

Jockey (flat): Adrian Nicholls, Silvestre De Sousa. **Conditional:** Brian Hughes. **Apprentice:** Duran Fentiman.

---

381 **MR R. MATHEW, Burford**
Postal: **Church Farm, Little Barrington, Burford, Oxfordshire, OX18 4TE**
Contacts: **PHONE (01451) 844311 FAX (01451) 844768**

1 **CUNNING PURSUIT**, 7, b g Pursuit of Love—Mistitled (USA) **R. Mathew**
2 **HEARTACHE**, 11, b g Jurado (USA)—Heresy (IRE) **R. Mathew**
3 **HUM THE TUNE**, 4, b c Beat Hollow—Waki Music (USA) **R. Mathew**
4 **WHAM BANG**, 4, b g Double Trigger (IRE)—Idiot's Lady **R. Mathew**

Jockey (NH): W. Hutchinson.

---

382 **MR A. J. MCCABE, Retford**
Postal: **The Lodge, Babworth, Retford, Nottinghamshire, DN22 8ES**
Contacts: **PHONE (01777) 869300 FAX (01777) 869326 MOBILE (07766) 302092**
E-MAIL **ajmacc@tiscali.co.uk**

1 **ACTIVE ASSET (IRE)**, 6, ch g Sinndar (IRE)—Sacristy **B. Morton**
2 **ARDENT PRINCE**, 5, b g Polar Prince (IRE)—Anthem Flight (USA) **B. M. Fletcher**
3 **CAPITAL LASS**, 5, b m Forzando—Fair Test **P. J. Dixon**
4 **CAPRICORN RUN (USA)**, 5, b br g Elusive Quality (USA)—Cercida (USA) **Paul J. Dixon & Placida Racing**
5 **CEREBUS**, 6, b m Wolfhound (USA)—Bring On The Choir **P. J. Dixon**
6 **CORNUS**, 6, ch g Inchinor—Demerger (USA) **Betfair Club ROA**
7 **DASHEENA**, 5, b m Magic Ring (IRE)—Sweet And Lucky **P. J. Dixon**
8 **DIDACTIC**, 4, b g Diktat—Scene (IRE) **P. J. Dixon**
9 **GAELIC PRESENT (IRE)**, 6, ch g Presenting—Dark Gale (IRE) **Mr Michael F. Maguire**
10 **HOLIDAY ROCK**, 4, b g Rock City—Angie Gold **A Good Day Out Partnership**
11 **INVERTED**, 4, b g Averti (IRE)—Indian Silk (IRE) **Paul J Dixon,Keith Barratt,Raymond Fagan**
12 **JORD (IRE)**, 4, b f Trans Island—Arcevia (IRE) **P. J. Dixon & The Chrystal Maze Partnership**
13 **KABEER**, 10, ch g Unfuwain (USA)—Ta Rib (USA) **Placida Racing**
14 **LUSCIVIOUS**, 4, ch g Kyllachy—Lloc **Paul J. Dixon & Keith Barratt**
15 **NEARDOWN BEAUTY (IRE)**, 5, br m Bahhare (USA)—Habla Me (IRE) **Mr Brian Morton**
16 **NEW YORK OSCAR (IRE)**, 4, b g Tobougg (IRE)—Special Dissident **Mr Paul J Dixon & Mr James Kennerley**
17 **NO TIME (IRE)**, 8, b h Danetime (IRE)—Muckross Park **P. J. Dixon**
18 **PAPPAS IMAGE**, 4, b g Arkadian Hero (USA)—Fair Attempt (IRE) **P. J. Dixon**
19 **PICCLEYES**, 7, b g Piccolo—Dark Eyed Lady (IRE) **P. J. Dixon**
20 **RED WINE**, 9, b g Hamas (IRE)—Red Bouquet **P. J. Dixon**
21 **SUMMER LODGE**, 5, b g Indian Lodge—Summer Siren (FR) **P. J. Dixon**
22 **TENANCY (IRE)**, 4, b g Rock of Gibraltar (IRE)—Brush Strokes **P. J. Dixon**
23 **THEORETICAL**, 4, b f Marju (IRE)—Relativity (IRE) **Paul J. Dixon & Michael F. Maguire**
24 **THUNDEROUSAPPLAUSE**, 4, b f Royal Applause—Trustthunder **P. J. Dixon**

THREE-YEAR-OLDS

25 **BARBOSSA**, ch g Bahamian Bounty—Marjurita (IRE) **Paul J. Dixon & D. Sharp**
26 **BLACK DAHLIA**, br f Dansili—South Rock **Paul J. Dixon & D. Sharp**
27 **BONA FIDELIS (IRE)**, b f Namid—Sacred Love (IRE) **Paul J. Dixon & D. Sharp**
28 **CHRYSTAL VENTURE (IRE)**, ch f Barathea (IRE)—Ukraine Venture **Paul J Dixon & The Chrystal Maze Ptn**
29 **FRAMMENTI**, br f Fraam—Blushing Victoria **P. J. Dixon**
30 **INCOMPARABLE**, ch c Compton Place—Indian Silk (IRE) **Paul J. Dixon & Michael F. Maguire**
31 **INSURED**, ch g Intikhab (USA)—Self Assured (IRE) **Paul J. Dixon & Andrew Timms**
32 **LOOSE CABOOSE (IRE)**, b f Tagula (IRE)—Tama (IRE) **Paul J. Dixon & Greg McCabe**
33 **MAC DALIA**, b f Namid—Maugwenna **P. J. Dixon**

MR A. J. MCCABE—continued

34 B c Josr Algarhoud (IRE)—Scene (IRE) **P. J. Dixon**
35 **VALIDITY**, ch f Forzando—Wittily **Paul J. Dixon & Mrs J. Griffin**

TWO-YEAR-OLDS

36 B c 26/2 Ishiguru (USA)—Blushing Victoria (Weldnaas (USA)) **P. J. Dixon**
37 **COMMON DIVA**, ch f 15/4 Auction House (USA)—
    Vida (IRE) (Wolfhound (USA)) (1200) **Alotincommon Partnership**
38 Ch f 22/4 Tobougg (IRE)—Marjurita (IRE) (Marju (IRE)) **P. J. Dixon**
39 B f 30/3 Josr Algarhoud (IRE)—Promised (IRE) (Petardia) **P. J. Dixon**
40 **SIR GEOFFREY**, b c 7/3 Captain Rio—Disarm (IRE) (Bahamian Bounty) (7000) **Paul J. Dixon & Mr Brian Morton**
41 Ch c 19/3 Haafhd—Trustthunder (Selkirk (USA)) **Paul J. Dixon & Mr Brian Morton**
42 B brf 25/1 And Beyond (USA)—Yeveed (IRE) (Wassl)

Other Owners: Mr Keith Barratt, Mrs J. Buckley, Mr M. Buckley, Mr R. J. Fagan, Mr Tom Gittins, General Sir Geoffrey Howlett, Mr James S. Kennerley, Mr G. A. Lucas, Mr Michael F. Maguire, Mrs M. J. McCabe, Mr A. C. McCabe, Mr Greg McCabe, Mr J. McCabe, Mr F. McCabe, Mr K. J. Newsome, Mrs Sadie Ryan, Mrs D. E. Sharp, Mr A. C. Timms, Mr Alan Wilson, Mr Lee Wilson.

Assistant Trainer: Scott Dixon

Jockey (flat): Natalia Gemelova, Patrick Mathers, Seb Sanders. **Jockey (NH):** J. P Byrne. **Conditional:** Jonathan Moorman.
Amateur: Miss Jane Dunton, Mr James Owen.

---

383 MR D. R. MCCAIN, Cholmondeley
Postal: **Bankhouse, Cholmondeley, Malpas, Cheshire, SY14 8AL**
Contacts: **PHONE** (01829) 720352 **FAX** (01829) 720475 **MOBILE** (07903) 066194

1 **BALLABRIGGS (IRE)**, 7, b g Presenting—Papoose (IRE) **T. J. Hemmings**
2 **BALLABROOK (IRE)**, 6, b g Alderbrook—Summer Holiday (IRE) **T. J. Hemmings**
3 **BALLYNALTY EXPRESS (IRE)**, 6, b br g Tiraaz (USA)—Regal Hostess **The Vyner-Brooks Family**
4 **BANNISTER LANE**, 8, b g Overbury (IRE)—Miss Club Royal **Shaw Hill Golf Club(Sage Cott Props Ltd)**
5 5, B m Kayf Tara—Barton Gale (IRE)
6 **BE TRUE (IRE)**, 4, b g Strategic Choice (USA)—Miss Perky (IRE)
7 **BEAUTIFUL NIGHT (FR)**, 6, b m Sleeping Car (FR)—Doll Night (FR) **David Reynolds & Edward Spellman**
8 **BLESSED FOREVER (IRE)**, 5, b g Rudimentary (USA)—Josh's Fancy (IRE) **R. A. George**
9 **BOUNCING KING**, 6, b g Kayf Tara—Springfield Gail **Sandicroft Stud**
10 **BRING ON THE BLING (IRE)**, 5, b m Fruits of Love (USA)—Genetta **Gingers Whingers**
11 **CAMELIA WALK**, b m Sir Harry Lewis (USA)—Castle Rouge **D. McCain**
12 **CANDY'S ROOM (IRE)**, 4, b f Alderbrook—Summer Holiday (IRE) **Jon Glews & Peter Knight**
13 5, Ch h Flemensfirth (USA)—Chancy Gal
14 **CHICKAPEAKRAY**, 7, b m Overbury (IRE)—Nevermind Hey **R. Pattison**
15 **CHORD**, 4, ch g Pivotal—Choirgirl **Jon Glews & Peter Knight**
16 **CLOUDY LANE**, 8, b g Cloudings (IRE)—Celtic Cygnet **T. J. Hemmings**
17 **COFFIN DODGER**, 5, ch m Dracula (AUS)—Karakul (IRE)
18 **COLONEL POTTER**, 7, ch g Pursuit of Love—Constant Delight **T. J. Crehan**
19 **COMHLA RI COIG**, 7, b g Sir Harry Lewis (USA)—Analogical **Gingers Whingers**
20 **CORLANDE (IRE)**, 8, br g Teamster—Vaguely Deesse (USA) **Crow Partnership**
21 **CROMWELL COURT**, 7, b g Overbury (IRE)—Slip A Coin **Mr D. A. Price**
22 5, Ch g Fourstars Allstar (USA)—Curahard Again (IRE)
23 **DEPRAUX (IRE)**, 5, br g Generous (IRE)—Happy Memories (IRE) **Mrs P. Davies**
24 **DEVILS AND DUST (IRE)**, 7, b g Needle Gun (IRE)—Tartan Trouble **Mr J. M. Glews**
25 **DICKIE LEWIS**, 10, b g Well Beloved—Moneyacre **Mr & Mrs Peter James Douglas**
26 **DOUBLE EAGLE**, 6, b g Silver Patriarch (IRE)—Grayrose Double **Dr G. M. Thelwall Jones**
27 **EMPTY SKY**, 4, b g Machiavellian (USA)—Zafadola (IRE) **Glews & Knight**
28 **FIRST FOUGHT (IRE)**, 6, b g Germany (USA)—Royal Flame (IRE) **G. & P. Barker Ltd**
29 **GILSLAND (IRE)**, 5, b g Alderbrook—Credit Transfer (IRE)
30 **GLENWOOD KNIGHT (IRE)**, 5, ch g Presenting—Glens Lady (IRE) **Peter Knight & Jon Glews**
31 **GRASSCUTTER (IRE)**, 4, b g Presenting—Cherry Black (IRE) **The Trevor-McDonald Partnership**
32 **HARRY WOOD (FR)**, 6, b g Cyborg (FR)—Madame Fifi (FR) **J. K. Shaw**
33 4, B g Snurge—Haveafewmanners (IRE)
34 5, B h Beat All (USA)—Heathyards Gem
35 4, B c Beat All (USA)—Heathyards Gem
36 **HELLO IT'S ME**, 7, ch g Deploy—Evening Charm (IRE) **Mrs P. A. L. Butler**
37 **HERNANDO CORTES**, 4, b c Sadler's Wells (USA)—Houseproud (USA) **The Haydock Club**
38 **ICE TEA (IRE)**, 8, ch g Glacial Storm (USA)—Kakemona **Sandicroft Stud**

MR D. R. MCCAIN—continued

39 **IDLE TALK (IRE)**, 9, br g Hubbly Bubbly (USA)—Belon Breeze (IRE) **T. J. Hemmings**
40 **IMPRESS**, 5, ch g Fantastic Light (USA)—Kissogram **Gingers Whingers**
41 **INVESTMENT AFFAIR (IRE)**, 8, b g Sesaro (USA)—Superb Investment (IRE) **R. N. Fuller**
42 **ISAAC NEWTON (IRE)**, 4, b c Fantastic Light (USA)—For Example (USA) **Mr J. M. Glews**
43 **IT'S A DISCOVERY (IRE)**, 7, b m Grand Plaisir (IRE)—Kilnock Lass **The Vyner-Brooks Family**
44 **JIMMY THE SAINT (IRE)**, 5, b g Flemensfirth—Sheknowso **Jon Glews & Peter Knight**
45 **JUNGLELAND (IRE)**, 6, b g Flemensfirth (USA)—Lady Chauffer (IRE) **Mr J. M. Glews**
46 **JUST SMOKIE**, 6, gr m Cloudings (IRE)—Rakajack **Essential Racing 1**
47 **KEALSHORE LAD**, 7, b g Supreme Leader—Our Aisling **T. J. Hemmings**
48 **KHACHATURIAN (IRE)**, 5, b g Spectrum (IRE)—On Air (FR) **Brendan Richardson & Jon Glews**
49 **LA PIROGUE (IRE)**, 5, b m Simply Great (FR)—Pollyputthekettleon (IRE) **G. A. Greaves**
50 **MARJU'S GOLD**, 4, b c Marju (IRE)—Dubious **Bluecoat Partnership**
51 **MAURICE (FR)**, 8, ch g Video Rock (FR)—Beveland (FR) **T. J. Hemmings**
52 **MILLBILL MOSS**, 5, b g King Charlemagne (USA)—Carina Clare **David Hughes & Phil Moss**
53 **MITRASH**, 8, b g Darshaan—L'ideale (USA) **D. R. McCain**
54 **MOHAYER (IRE)**, 6, gr g Giant's Causeway (USA)—Karlafsha **G. & P. Barker Ltd**
55 **MORNING SUNSHINE (IRE)**, 5, b g Presenting—Culfadda Girl (IRE) **Jon Glews & Peter Knight**
56 **MRS O'MALLEY**, 8, b m Overbury (IRE)—Chapel Hill (IRE) **The Cant Kent Partnership**
57 **MY CONDOR (IRE)**, 7, b g Beneficial—Margellen's Castle (IRE) **Mr E. Chapman**
58 **NEVADA RED**, 7, ch g Classic Cliche (IRE)—Sovereign Belle **Proactive Racing**
59 **NEVER ASK (IRE)**, 5, b h Spectrum (IRE)—Royal Flame (IRE) **Mr E. Chapman**
60 6, B g Classic Cliche (IRE)—Nevermind Hey **Champ Chicken Co Ltd**
61 5, B g Sir Harry Lewis (USA)—Nevermind Hey **J. Singleton**
62 **NOTRE CYBORG (FR)**, 7, ch g Cyborg (FR)—Cate Bleue (FR) **G. & P. Barker Ltd**
63 4, B f Alflora (IRE)—Ollejess
64 **ORIGINAL FLY (FR)**, 6, b g Chef de Clan II (FR)—
                          Ultim de Plaisance (FR) **Chadwick Pattison Chapman Partnership**
65 **OUR JASPER**, 8, gr g Tina's Pet—Dawn's Della **K. Benson**
66 **OUR JIM**, 6, ch g Sir Harry Lewis (USA)—Dawn's Della **Mrs E. Benson**
67 **PACK DRILL**, 7, b g Zaffaran (USA)—Quinag **D. McCain**
68 **PENCIL HOUSE (IRE)**, 8, ch g Carroll House—Pencil **Sandicroft Stud**
69 **PETERS STAR (IRE)**, 6, b g Fourstars Allstar—
                          Supreme View **Peter & Richard Foden Racing Partnership**
70 6, B h Overbury (IRE)—Potter's Gale (IRE) **Mrs M. J. Potter**
71 **RED NOT BLUE (IRE)**, 5, b g Blueprint (IRE)—Silent Valley **Mrs S. J. Meehan**
72 **RED O'DONNELL (IRE)**, 5, ch g Presenting—Madam Chloe **Mr D. J. Costello**
73 **REGAL HEIGHTS (IRE)**, 7, b g Grand Plaisir (IRE)—Regal Hostess **Mrs J. Heler**
74 **RIGHTWAY STAR (IRE)**, 5, b g Stowaway—Decent Shower **D. M. Proos**
75 **ROMPING HOME (IRE)**, 5, b m Rock Hopper—Euro Joy (IRE) **24 - 7 / Gappersonnel**
76 **ROSIE ALL OVER**, 6, br m Overbury (IRE)—Hallo Rosie (IRE) **T. J. Crehan**
77 **SISTERHOOD (IRE)**, 4, b f Mtoto—Kymin (IRE) **Gilbert/Pattison Partnership**
78 **SLEEPERS HILL (IRE)**, 5, b g Luso—Astral Way **Mr P. & Mrs M. Moss**
79 **SO CLOUDY**, 7, gr m Cloudings (IRE)—Sotattie **Tim & Miranda Johnson Partnership**
80 **SON OF FLICKA**, 4, b g Groom Dancer (USA)—Calendula **Mr P. Williams-Twenty Four Seven**
81 **SPRING DREAMER**, 6, gr m Environment Friend—Spring Wheat **D. McCain**
82 **SUNDAY CITY (JPN)**, 7, ch g Sunday Silence (USA)—Diamond City (USA) **C. E. R. Greenway**
83 **SWORD OF DAMASCUS (IRE)**, 6, b g Darshaan—Damascene (IRE) **Mr J. M. Glews**
84 **TASTES LIKE MORE (IRE)**, 6, b m Close Conflict (USA)—Fly Your Kite **Mr J. M. Glews**
85 **TELEGONUS**, 5, b g Fantastic Light (USA)—Circe's Isle **Penketh & Sankey Jech Racing Club**
86 **TEMPLE PLACE (IRE)**, 7, b g Sadler's Wells—Puzzled Look (USA) **Brendan Richardson & Jon Glews**
87 **THE ROCKING DOCK (IRE)**, 7, gr g Dr Massini (IRE)—Ackle Backle **Team Staffordshire**
88 **TOUT OR ET BLEUE**, 5, b m Beat All (USA)—Cerise Bleue (FR) **W. A. Bromley**
89 **TRAGIC OHIO**, 9, B G Tragic Role (USA)—Kiniohio (FR)
90 **TRIPLE MINT (IRE)**, 7, b g Flemensfirth (USA)—Bucktina **Mrs J. Heler**
91 **UNOWATIMEEN (IRE)**, 8, B G Supreme Leader—Collinstown Queen (IRE)
92 **VICARIO**, 7, gr g Vettori (IRE)—Arantxa **Mr J. M. Glews**
93 **WHISTLE BLOWING (IRE)**, 6, b g Forzando—Philgwyn **R. N. Fuller**
94 **WHITEOAK (IRE)**, 5, b m Oscar (IRE)—Gayla Orchestra **B. J. Richardson**
95 **WIZARDS DUST (IRE)**, 6, gr g Environment Friend—Linoats **Tim & Miranda Johnson Partnership**
96 **WOOD FERN (UAE)**, 8, b g Green Desert (USA)—Woodsia **The Generals Men Racing Club**
97 **WOODCRAFT**, 4, ch c Observatory (USA)—Woodwardia (USA) **X8 Racing**
98 **YOUNGSTOWN (IRE)**, 5, b g Luso—Blue Approach (IRE) **Jon Glews & Peter Knight**

MR D. R. MCCAIN—continued

Other Owners: Mrs S. E. Barclay, Mr Dave Barlow, Mr Daren Brown, Miss K. S. Buckley, Mr Mick Burrowes, Mr G. Caine, B. W. Callinan, Mr Bob Cant, Mr Alf Chadwick, P. M. Clarkson, Mr Gary Dewhurst, Mr Peter J. Douglas, Mrs L. Douglas, Mr W. A. Eastup, Mr J. K. Ebbrell, Mr Dave Ellis, J. C. Evans, Mr E. P. Foden, Mr R. P. Foden, Mrs Wendy Gilbert, Mr Jon Glews, Mrs Amanda Grandison, Mr R. G. Griffiths, Mr David M. Hughes, Mr Tim Johnson, Mrs Miranda Johnson, Mr G. L. Joynson, Mr S. A. Kaznowski, Mr R. Kent, Mr P. A. Knight, D. J. Lockwood, Mr P. S. Lowrey, Mr D. McCain, Mr Stewart McDonald, Mr J. S. Middleton, Mr P. Moss, Mrs M. Moss, Mrs Julie Nolan, Mr Ray Pattison, Mr Dave Pearson, Mr David Reynolds, Mr Brendan Richardson, Mr R. J. Rossiter, Mr Ian T. Smethurst, Mr Edward Spellman, Mr S. Trevor, Mr V. R. Vyner-Brooks, Mrs G. E. Vyner-Brooks, Mr C. S. Vyner-Brooks, Mr P. J. Williams, M. A. Woodward.

Assistant Trainer: William Kinsey

Jockey (NH): Jason Maguire. **Conditional:** Paul Benson. **Amateur:** Mr. W. Kinsey, Mr. T. Garner.

---

384 MR N. P. MCCORMACK, Rowlands Gill
Postal: **The Cottage, Southfield Farm, Hamsterley Mill, Rowlands Gill, Tyne and Wear, NE39 1NQ**
Contacts: **HOME (01207) 549700 MOBILE (07961) 540173**

1 **DON FREDERIKO (FR)**, 7, gr g Monsun (GER)—Donna Ines (IRE) **Mrs D. McCormack**
2 **SECRET DRINKER (IRE)**, 12, b g Husyan (USA)—Try Le Reste (IRE) **Mrs D. McCormack**

Assistant Trainer: Mrs D. McCormack

---

385 MR M. MCGRATH, Maidstone
Postal: **Spicketts House, Kiln Barn Road, East Malling, Kent, ME19 6BJ**
Contacts: **FAX (01732) 873774**

1 **CORLOUGH MOUNTAIN**, 4, ch g Inchinor—Two Step **Gallagher O'Rourke**
2 **ENHANCER**, 10, b g Zafonic (USA)—Ypha (USA) **Gallagher Equine Ltd**
3 **SADLER'S HILL (IRE)**, 4, b g Sadler's Wells (USA)—Dedicated Lady (IRE) **Gallagher Equine Ltd**
4 **SHABAHAR (IRE)**, 4, b g Hernando (FR)—Shara (IRE) **Gallagher Equine Ltd**

THREE-YEAR-OLDS

5 **JENNY'S GOLD**, b f Dolpour—Zaffre Bleu (IRE) **Mrs D. A. T. Salmon**

TWO-YEAR-OLDS

6 B c 21/4 Oasis Dream—Danella (FR) (Highest Honor (FR)) (75000) **Gallagher Equine Ltd**
7 B c 3/3 Elusive City (USA)—Seguro (IRE) (Indian Ridge) (46000) **Gallagher Equine Ltd**

Other Owners: D. O'Rourke.

---

386 MRS J. C. MCGREGOR, Milnathort
Postal: **Tillyrie House, Milnathort, Kinross**
Contacts: **PHONE (01577) 865071 (01577) 863418 FAX (01577) 863418 MOBILE (07764) 464299**
E-MAIL john-lawrie@btconnect.com

1 **ANTHEMION (IRE)**, 11, ch g Night Shift (USA)—New Sensitive **Tillyrie Racing Club**
2 **DALAWAN**, 9, b g Nashwan (USA)—Magdala (IRE) **Discounted Cashflow**
3 **EVEN SMARTER**, 6, b g Entrepreneur—College Night (IRE) **Mrs Jean McGregor**
4 **GOODBADINDIFERENT (IRE)**, 12, b br g Mandalus—Stay As You Are **The Good To Soft Firm**
5 **KING'S ENVOY (USA)**, 9, b g Royal Academy (USA)—Island of Silver (USA) **Off & Running**
6 **MASTERS HOUSE (IRE)**, 5, b g Indian Lodge (IRE)—Aster Aweke (IRE) **Mrs J. C. McGregor**
7 **MORE SHENNANIGANS**, 7, ch g Rock City—Blooming Spring (IRE) **J. Thomson**
8 **TEENYBASH**, 6, b m Overbury (IRE)—Ayeknowso **Mr S. Taylor**
9 **WATERSKI**, 7, b g Petoski—Celtic Waters **The Trail Blazers**
10 **WHAT'S AHEAD**, 8, ch m Emperor Fountain—Our Wilma **Mrs J. C. McGregor**
11 **WILMINGTON**, 4, ch g Compton Place—Bahawir Pour (USA) **Allan Brown Partnership**

THREE-YEAR-OLDS

12 B c Cois Na Tine (IRE)—More Champagne
13 B f Tipsy Creek (USA)—Silver Wedding
14 B c Tipsy Creek (USA)—Tudorealm (USA)

MRS J. C. MCGREGOR—continued

Other Owners: W. S. Allan, Mr W. Allen, I. S. F. Brown, Mr & Mrs I. Brown, Mr Paul Byrne, Mrs C. Harper Gow, Mr J. Ivory, Mrs F. Ivory, Mrs Jean McGregor, Mr & Mrs Newstead, Mr M. O'Connor, Mr S. Taylor, Mrs Dorothy Thomson, Mr J. Thomson, Mr K. Trail, Mrs R. Trail.

Jockey (NH): P. Aspell, K. Mercer, B. Harding, G. Lee. **Conditional:** T. Dreaper, P. Kinsella. **Apprentice:** A. Mullen. **Amateur:** Mr S. Byrne.

---

387   MR I. W. MCINNES, Catwick
Postal: Riston Whins Farm, Rise Lane, Catwick, Beverley, North Humberside, HU17 5PN
Contacts: HOME/FAX (01964) 542115 FAX (01964) 542115 MOBILE (07720) 451233

1 **ANOTHER GENEPI (USA)**, 5, b m Stravinsky (USA)—Dawn Aurora (USA)
2 **BAYLAW STAR**, 7, b g Case Law—Caisson **S. P. Hackney**
3 **BODDEN BAY**, 6, b g Cayman Kai (IRE)—Badger Bay (IRE) **Wold Construction Company**
4 **BRUTUS MAXIMUS**, 5, b h Sir Harry Lewis (USA)—Horton Lady **R. E. & Mrs G. M. Cook**
5 **COMMANDO SCOTT (IRE)**, 7, b g Danetime (IRE)—Faye **Mrs A. Morris**
6 **DESERT LIGHTNING (IRE)**, 6, ch g Desert Prince (IRE)—Saibhreas (IRE) **C. G. R. Booth**
7 **EMPIRE DANCER (IRE)**, 5, b g Second Empire (IRE)—Dance To The Beat **M. S. Whitehead**
8 **FIEFDOM (IRE)**, 6, br g Singspiel (IRE)—Chiquita Linda (IRE) **S. P. Hackney**
9 **FORTUITOUS (IRE)**, 4, ch g Tobougg (IRE)—Shallop **C. G. R. Booth**
10 **FRANKSALOT (IRE)**, 8, ch g Desert Story (IRE)—Rosie's Guest (IRE) **S. P. Hackney**
11 **GREY CAVALIER**, 6, gr g Presidium—Royal Rebeka **R. E. & Mrs G. M. Cook**
12 **GREY GURKHA**, 7, gr h Kasakov—Royal Rebeka **R. E. & Mrs G. M. Cook**
13 **GREY SAMURAI**, 8, gr g Gothenberg (IRE)—Royal Rebeka **R. E. & Mrs G. M. Cook**
14 **H HARRISON (IRE)**, 8, b g Eagle Eyed (USA)—Penrose (IRE) **Mr D. A. Lees**
15 **JARVO**, 7, b g Pursuit of Love—Pinkie Rose (FR) **F. S. W. Partnership**
16 **KINGSHOLM**, 6, ch g Selkirk (USA)—Putuna **Riverside Racing**
17 **LOADERFUN (IRE)**, 6, br g Danehill Dancer (IRE)—Sideloader Special **Paul & Linda Dixon**
18 **LOBENGULA (IRE)**, 6, b g Spectrum (IRE)—Playwaki **C. G. R. Booth**
19 **MISTER ALWAYS**, 4, b g Titus Livius (FR)—Pieta (IRE) **B. Kirby**
20 **MOTU (IRE)**, 7, b g Desert Style (IRE)—Pink Cashmere (IRE) **G. Parkinson**
21 **PAPARAAZI (IRE)**, 6, b g Victory Note (USA)—Raazi **Horses 4 Courses**
22 **POPPY'S ROSE**, 4, b f Diktat—Perfect Peach **Mrs A. Morris**
23 **PROFESSOR TWINKLE**, 4, ch c Dr Fong (USA)—Shining High **The Pinkoes Partnership**
24 **ROYAL CHALLENGE**, 7, b g Royal Applause—Anotheranniversary **Truck Export**
25 **RULE FOR EVER**, 6, br g Diktat—Tous Les Jours (USA) **J. A. Milburn**
26 **SANDS OF BARRA (IRE)**, 5, gr g Marju (IRE)—Purple Risks (FR) **Wold Construction Company**
27 **TIME TO REGRET**, 8, b g Presidium—Scoffera **Horses 4 Courses**
28 **WOTAVADUN (IRE)**, 5, ch g King of Kings (IRE)—Blush With Love (USA) **B. Kirby**

THREE-YEAR-OLDS

29 **FOXHOLES LODGE**, b f Nasheyt—Duxford Lodge **Mr G. Scruton**
30 **FREDDIES FONG**, ch c Dr Fong (USA)—Perfect Peach **Mrs A. Morris**

Other Owners: Mrs R. Auchterlounie, Mr Wayne Bavill, Mr A. Bethell, Mr P. J. Cowing, Mr Paul W. H. Dixon, Mrs L. J. Dixon, Mr Terence Elsey, Mr A. Firman, Mr R. N. Forman, Mr Michael Holmes, Mr A. J. McClymont, Mr Richard Mustill, Mr A. P. Newell, Mr C. C. Straw, R. M. Sutton, Mr I. D. Woolfitt.

Assistant Trainer: Mr Ian McInnes (Senior)

Jockey (flat): A. Elliott, R. Ffrench, D. Tudhope. **Amateur:** S. Dobson.

---

388   MS K. J. MCLINTOCK, Newcastle-Upon-Tyne
Postal: The Byerley Stud, Ingoe, Newcastle-Upon-Tyne
Contacts: PHONE (01661) 886356 FAX (01661) 886356 MOBILE (07966) 776710
E-MAIL byerleystudingoe@aol.com

1 **CALCUTTA CUP (UAE)**, 5, br g Jade Robbery (USA)—Six Nations (USA) **Mr M. W. Joyce**
2 **DONNA'S DOUBLE**, 13, ch g Weldnaas (USA)—Shadha **J. R. Adams (Newcastle) Limited**
3 **DUNASKIN (IRE)**, 8, b g Bahhare (USA)—Mirwara (IRE) **Equiname Ltd**
4 **FAIR SHAKE (IRE)**, 8, b g Sheikh Albadou—Shamrock Fair (IRE) **I. R. Clements**
5 **FOUR KINGS**, 7, b g Forzando—High Cut **Mr G. Marshall**
6 **MR VIAILLIE (IRE)**, 6, b g Kayf Tara—Formidable Task **Violet Payne & Edith-Marthe Kitching**
7 **NOBLE EDGE**, 5, ch g Bold Edge—Noble Soul **Ms D. E. Young**

MS K. J. MCLINTOCK—continued

  8 **NODFORM WILLIAM,** 6, b g Prince Sabo—Periwinkle (FR) **Ms K J McLintock**
  9 **RUN FOREST RUN (IRE),** 4, b g Anshan—Lucky Supreme (IRE) **Mr A. C. Lamont**
10 **THE DARK HORSE,** 4, b g Grand Lodge (USA)—Ares Vallis (IRE) **Mr A. C. Lamont**

TWO-YEAR-OLDS

11 B f 6/3 Xaar—Blue Mantle (IRE) (Barathea (IRE)) (2500) **J R Adams Ltd**

Other Owners: Mrs E. Kitching, Mr K. C. Martindale, Mrs V. Payne.

Assistant Trainer: Donald Eddy

---

389   MR E. S. A. MCMAHON, Lichfield
Postal: **Horsley Brook Farm, Tamworth Road, Lichfield, Staffordshire, WS14 9PT**
Contacts: PHONE/FAX (01543) 481224 MOBILE (07787) 951630
E-MAIL comeracing@horsleybrook.fsnet.co.uk

  1 **CARTIMANDUA,** 4, b f Medicean—Agrippina **Mrs F. S. Williams**
  2 **ELIZABETH SPIRIT (IRE),** 4, b f Invincible Spirit (IRE)—Generate **Mrs J. McMahon**
  3 **JAKEINI (IRE),** 5, b g Rossini (USA)—Talita Kumi (IRE) **Mr M. W. Crane**
  4 **MURDOCH,** 4, b g Mutamarkiz (IRE)—Miss Pharly **M. N. Jenkins**
  5 **NIGELLA,** 5, b m Band On The Run—Yabint El Sham **C. G. Conway**
  6 **PIVOTAL FLAME,** 6, b h Pivotal—Reddening **R. L. Bedding**
  7 **RAINBOW MIRAGE (IRE),** 4, b g Spectrum (IRE)—Embers of Fame (IRE) **R. L. Bedding**
  8 **SIR DON (IRE),** 9, b g Lake Coniston (IRE)—New Sensitive **Mrs D. Plant**
  9 **SMIRFYS SYSTEMS,** 9, b g Safawan—Saint Systems **Mrs D. Plant**
10 **TENDER PROCESS (IRE),** 5, b g Monashee Mountain (USA)—Appledorn **J. J. Staunton**

THREE-YEAR-OLDS

11 **ANOTHER SOCKET,** b f Overbury (IRE)—Elsocko **Mrs J. McMahon**
12 **CHAIN OF GOLD,** ch c Bahamian Bounty—Beading **J. C. Fretwell**
13 **DANEHILL RHAPSODY,** ch c Danehill Dancer (IRE)—Mandolin (IRE) **R. L. Bedding**
14 **FOCAIL EILE,** b g Noverre (USA)—Glittering Image (IRE) **Mr C. Fegan**
15 **HYDE LEA FLYER,** b c Hernando (FR)—Sea Ridge **Kemmel Partnership**
16 **INTO THE LIGHT,** b c Fantastic Light (USA)—Boadicea's Chariot **Mr P. A. Wilkins**
17 **ORPEN FIRE (IRE),** b f Orpen (USA)—Feet of Flame (USA) **Facts & Figures**
18 **SEMAH HAROLD,** b g Beat All (USA)—Semah's Dream **J. P. Hames**
19 **SILVER SPRUCE,** gr c First Trump—Red Typhoon **Mrs J. McMahon**
20 **SUPERMASSIVE MUSE (IRE),** br g Captain Rio—Cautionary (USA) **Mr N. J. Hughes**
21 **SUPPORTING ROLE (IRE),** b c Marju—Intercession **J. C. Fretwell**

TWO-YEAR-OLDS

22 Ch f 26/1 Bahamian Bounty—Artistry (Night Shift (USA)) (5000) **J. C. Fretwell**
23 B f 21/3 Refuse To Bend (IRE)—Be Decisive (Diesis) (17000) **J. C. Fretwell**
24 Ch c 13/2 Fantastic Light (USA)—Beading (Polish Precedent (USA)) (14000) **J. C. Fretwell**
25 Ch f 3/3 Monsieur Bond (IRE)—Birthday Belle (Lycius (USA)) (8000) **J. C. Fretwell**
26 **BLADES PRINCESS,** ch f 23/5 Needwood Blade—Breezy Palms (Tragic Role (USA)) (9500) **R. L. Bedding**
27 Ch c 4/3 Bahamian Bounty—Dancing Spirit (IRE) (Ahonoora) (10000) **J. C. Fretwell**
28 B f 2/3 Dubai Destination (USA)—Green Tambourine (Green Desert (USA)) (25000) **J. C. Fretwell**
29 Ch f 15/2 Monsieur Bond (IRE)—Harryana (Efisio) (34000) **J. C. Fretwell**
30 **LIVELY BLADE,** ch c 30/5 Needwood Blade—Breezy Day (Day Is Done) (40000) **R. L. Bedding**
31 **MOONLIGHT AFFAIR (IRE),** b f 19/4 Distant Music (USA)—
                         Petite Maxine (Sharpo) (10000) **D. J. Allen, S. E. Allen, G. A. Weetman**
32 B f 9/4 Danehill Dancer (IRE)—Mother of Pearl (IRE) (Sadler's Wells (USA)) **P. Murphy**
33 **NOBLE STORM (USA),** b c 31/3 Yankee Gentleman (USA)—
                         Changed Tune (USA) (Tunerup (USA)) (10500) **R. L. Bedding**
34 **NORWEGIAN DANCER (UAE),** b c 8/3 Halling (USA)—
                         Time Changes (USA) (Danzig (USA)) (15000) **Mr P. A. Wilkins**
35 B c 24/3 Kyllachy—Pendulum (Pursuit of Love) (38000) **J. C. Fretwell**
36 B c 26/1 Alhaarth (IRE)—Polish Lake (Polish Precedent (USA)) (7000) **Mrs J. McMahon**
37 **SMIRFYS ERIC (IRE),** b c 24/3 Bollin Eric—Smirfys Dance Hall (IRE) (Halling (USA)) **Mrs D. Plant**

Other Owners: D. J. Allen, Mrs S. E. Allen, Mr P. Mcvay, Mr C. Mullin, G. Pickering, Mrs G. A. Weetman.

Assistant Trainer: Bryan Arthur McMahon

Jockey (flat): G. Gibbons. **Amateur:** Miss E. George.

390 MR B. J. MCMATH, Newmarket
Postal: **Stockbridge Stables, High Street, Newmarket, Suffolk**
Contacts: **PHONE (01638) 660706 FAX (01638) 660706**
E-MAIL **brian.mcmath@tesco.net**

1 BLUE EYED ELOISE, 6, b m Overbury (IRE)—Galix (FR) **Miss M. E. Steele**
2 BROUHAHA, 4, b g Bahhare (USA)—Top of The Morning **G. D. Newton**
3 CYBER SPACE, 4, b g Medicean—Coyaima (GER) **Cyber Space Partnership**
4 FIRST COMING, 4, ch g Best of The Bests (IRE)—Arriving **N. Mustoe, T. Lewis, V. Dunn**
5 KARRUMBA (IRE), 4, ch f Desert Prince (IRE)—Royal Bossi (IRE) **Mr R. B. Rowley**
6 MARY DUNSMORE, 4, b f Mujahid (USA)—Piroshka **Mrs B. Sidgewick**
7 PERSONA (IRE), 6, b m Night Shift (USA)—Alonsa (IRE) **B. Belchem, B. J. McMath**
8 THE FOX'S DECREE, 4, br g Diktat—Foxie Lady **Miss M. E. Steele**
9 WOKSAPA, 5, b m Mujahid (USA)—Into Orbit **Miss A. L. Donkin**

THREE-YEAR-OLDS

10 CULZEAN BAY, b f Mind Games—Florie Nightingale **Mr G. Newton**
11 HARRYANA TO, ch f Compton Place—Harryana **S. Kimberley**
12 I AM THE MAN, b g Auction House (USA)—Sally Gardens **Mr S. Elsum**
13 MR SKIPITON (IRE), b c Statue of Liberty (USA)—Salty Air (IRE) **Steve & Ros Chaplin-Brown**
14 PRINCESS GEE, b f Reel Buddy (USA)—Queen G (USA) **The S. & N. Partnership**

TWO-YEAR-OLDS

15 B f 26/2 Bertolini (USA)—Alizar (IRE) (Rahy (USA)) (2000) **Rectory House Stud**

Other Owners: Mr J. Asbridge, Mr B. Belchem, Mr Steve Brown, Ms Ros Chaplin, Miss V. C. Dunn, R. G. Levin, T. J. B. Lewis, Mr Kevin Moorcroft, N. Mustoe.

Amateur: Miss A. Donkin.

391 MR I. MCMATH, Carlisle
Postal: **Thornedge, Station Road, Cumwhinton, Carlisle, Cumbria, CA4 8DJ**
Contacts: **PHONE (01228) 560007 FAX (01228) 560053**
E-MAIL **ianmcmath@aol.com**

1 BANANA GROVE (IRE), 7, b g Sesaro (USA)—Megan's Dream (IRE) **Mr J. Horsfall Mrs A. McMath**
2 BENEFICIAL GUEST (IRE), 7, b g Beneficial—Kyle Lark **Mr F. Lowe Mrs A. McMath**
3 CUCCINELLO (IRE), 5, b m Makbul—Costa Verde **Auldyn Stud Limited**
4 ELSIES NOOK, 4, b f Foxhound (USA)—Pearls **Mr G. Wilkinson**
5 FOR NO ONE (IRE), 5, b g Mozart (USA)—Dame Laura **Mrs A. J. McMath**
6 FOV (IRE), 4, ch g Traditionally (USA)—Granza (FR) **Mr J. Kershaw, Mr Phil Kershaw, Mrs A. McMath**
7 GALLOWAY MAC, 8, ch g Environment Friend—Docklands **The Pink Guys**
8 GLEN TANAR (IRE), 7, ch g Zaffaran (USA)—Mandyslady (IRE) **Mrs A. J. McMath**
9 HIGH STAND LAD, 6, gr g Rock City—Snowys Pet **D Graves A McMath G Mitchell D Gillespie**
10 INGLEWOOD LAD (IRE), 6, gr g Environment Friend—
Pretty Obvious **D Graves A McMath G Mitchell D Gillespie**
11 LOOKIN DAGGERS (IRE), 4, ch g Daggers Drawn (USA)—Shefoog **W. E. B. Racing**
12 MIGHTY MAGNUS (IRE), 5, ch g Night Shift (USA)—Arbaletta (GER) **Pentakan Ltd**
13 NICOZETTO (FR), 8, b g Nicolotte—Arcizette (FR) **M. Wilson**
14 PATRIOT (IRE), 4, b c Sadler's Wells (USA)—Sweeten Up **Pentakan Ltd**
15 PRIORYJO, 5, b m Foxhound (USA)—Milliscent **Mr D. Graves Mr P. Brown Mrs A. McMath**
16 REMAINDER, 5, ch g Mark of Esteem (IRE)—
Stay Behind **Mrs A. McMath, Mrs V. Short, Mr R. Irving, Mr D. Graves**
17 SONEVA GILI (IRE), 4, ch c Sakhee (USA)—
Navajo Love Song (IRE) **W.E.B. Racing Mr M. Wilson Mrs A. McMath**
18 SWEET MEMORIES (IRE), 7, b g Houmayoun (FR)—Lady's Dream **Mr F. Lowe Mrs A. McMath**
19 TIN HEALY'S PASS, 8, b g Puissance—Shaa Spin **Brampton 7's**
20 TURTLE BAY, 6, ch m Dr Fong (USA)—My Valentina **S. A. McGimpsey**
21 WENSLEYDALE WEB, 6, b m Kayf Tara—Little Red Spider **Javas Charvers**
22 WINDS OF KILDARE, 5, br g Shaddad (USA)—Asturiana **Mrs A. J. McMath**
23 WIREFOX, 4, b g Foxhound (USA)—Shaa Spin **The Social Clubbers**
24 ZANJEER, 8, b g Averti (IRE)—Cloudslea (USA) **Mr M. Wilson Mr K. Twentyman**

Other Owners: Mr K. Barker, Mr R. Broatch, Mr R. H. Brown, Mr P. S. Brown, Mr Gary Etheridge, Mr D. Gillespie, Mr J. D. Graves, Mr J. Horsfall, Mr A. D. Huck, Mr R. Irving, Mr J. Kershaw, Mr P. Kershaw, Mr C. Lee, Mr F. Lowe, G. W. Mitchell, Mr A. M. Moscrop, A. T. Pimbley, Mrs V. M. Short, Mr J. I. A. Spedding, Mr K. Twentyman.

Assistant Trainer: Miss Lynsey Kendall

Amateur: Miss L. Kendall.

392 **MR M. D. MCMILLAN, Cheltenham**
Postal: **Pindrup Moor, Fossebridge, Cheltenham, Gloucestershire, GL54 3JR**
Contacts: PHONE **(01285) 721050** MOBILE **(07973) 543272**
E-MAIL **md.mcm@btinternet.com**

1 TENKO, 9, ch m Environment Friend—Taco **M. D. McMillan**

393 **MR G. P. MCPHERSON, Stow-On-The-Wold**
Postal: **Martins Hill, Bledington Road, Stow-on-the-Wold, Gloucestershire, GL54 1JH**
Contacts: PHONE **(01451) 830715** MOBILE **(07815) 887360**
WEBSITE **www.martinshillracing.co.uk**

1 THE RIVER JOKER (IRE), 12, ch g Over The River (FR)—Augustaeliza (IRE) **G. P. McPherson**
2 WILLIE JOHN DALY (IRE), 11, b g Mister Lord (USA)—Murphy's Lady (IRE) **G. P. McPherson**

Assistant Trainer: Liam Payter

Amateur: Mr Liam Payter.

394 **MR B. J. MEEHAN, Manton**
Postal: **Manton Stables, Manton House Estate, Manton, Marlborough, SN8 1PN**
Contacts: PHONE **(01672) 517191** FAX **(01672) 517192** MOBILE **(07836) 754254**
E-MAIL **info@brianmeehan.com** WEBSITE **www.brianmeehan.com**

1 AMERICAN SPIN, 4, ch c Groom Dancer (USA)—Sea Vixen **M. Watt**
2 CHARLIE FARNSBARNS (IRE), 4, b c Cape Cross (IRE)—Lafleur (IRE) **The English Girls**
3 CINQUANTE CINQ (IRE), 4, b f Danehill (USA)—Castilian Queen (USA) **Sangster Family**
4 DAY BY DAY, 4, ch f Kyllachy—Dayville (USA) **Mr T. G. & Mrs M. E. Holdcroft**
5 DIAMOND TYCOON (USA), 4, b c Johannesburg (USA)—Palacoona (FR) **Mrs S. J. McKeever**
6 FASCINATIN RHYTHM, 4, br f Fantastic Light (USA)—Marguerite de Vine **W. Harrison-Allen**
7 FREDERICK OZANAM (IRE), 4, b g Traditionally (USA)—Sudden Hope (FR) **S. Dartnell**
8 HUMBLE OPINION, 6, br g Singspiel (IRE)—For More (FR) **Paul & Jenny Green**
9 JACK JUNIOR (USA), 4, b br c Songandaprayer (USA)—Ra Hydee (USA) **Roldvale Ltd**
10 JUNIOR, 5, ch g Singspiel (IRE)—For More (FR) **P. C. Green**
11 KHUN JOHN (IRE), 5, ch Marju (IRE)—Kathy Caerleon (IRE) **The Strawberries To A Donkey Partnership**
12 MONTROSE MAN, 4, ch g Foxhound (USA)—Don't Jump (IRE) **Vino Veritas**
13 ONCE UPON A GRACE (IRE), 4, b f Spinning World (USA)—Adamparis **J. Paul Reddam**
14 PERMANENT WAY (IRE), 5, b g Fantastic Light (USA)—Itab (USA) **Exors of the Late Dr T. A. Ryan**
15 PUGILIST, 6, b g Fraam—Travel Mystery **Rascals Racing**
16 RED ROCKS (IRE), 5, b br h Galileo (IRE)—Pharmacist (IRE) **J. Paul Reddam**
17 SUPERSONIC DAVE (USA), 4, b br c Swain (IRE)—Vickey's Echo (CAN) **Roldvale Ltd**

THREE-YEAR-OLDS

18 ARNIECOCO, b c Dr Fong (USA)—Groovy **Willsford Racing Ltd / Wood Hall Stud**
19 AUSTINTATIOUS (USA), ch c Distorted Humor (USA)—Fancy Ruler (USA) **Mr A. Rosen**
20 BAILEY (IRE), ch g Captain Rio—Baileys Cream **J. L. Allbritton**
21 B f Galileo (IRE)—Beat It (USA) **Mr A. Rosen**
22 BOUNTIFUL BAY, b f Bahamian Bounty—My Preference **J. Widdows**
23 BRAKEY HILL (USA), gr c Forest Wildcat (USA)—Divine Angel (USA) **Gold Group International Ltd**
24 Gr c Spartacus (IRE)—Bridelina (FR) **W. Harrison-Allen**
25 BYBLOS, ch g Tobougg (IRE)—My Girl **M. C. Denmark**
26 B c Tobougg (IRE)—Cape Siren **Park Racing**
27 CARELESS FREEDOM, ch f Bertolini (USA)—Humble Pie **T. D. Holland-Martin**
28 CAT JUNIOR (USA), b br c Storm Cat (USA)—Luna Wells (IRE) **Roldvale Ltd**
29 Gr ro c Pleasant Tap (USA)—Celestial Bliss (USA) **Mrs W. O'Leary**
30 CHANGING SKIES, b f Sadler's Wells (USA)—Magnificient Style (USA) **Sangster Family**
31 CHARMING TALE (USA), b f Kingmambo—Crystal Crossing (IRE) **Sangster Family & Ben Sangster**
32 CHEVIOT RED, b f Red Ransom (USA)—Cheviot Hills (USA) **Miss J. Semple**
33 CITY LEADER (IRE), gr c Fasliyev (USA)—Kanmary (FR) **Sangster Family**
34 CLASSIC LEGEND, b f Galileo (IRE)—Lady Lahar **Mrs M. T. McNamara**
35 COSSACK PRINCE, b g Dubai Destination—Danemere (IRE) **Wyck Hall Stud Ltd**
36 DAY TRIP (IRE), gr c Daylami (IRE)—Mount Street (IRE) **Ballymacoll Stud Farm Ltd**
37 DEO VALENTE (IRE), b c Dubai Destination (USA)—Pack Ice (USA) **Mr J. S. Threadwell & Mr W. O'Donnell**
38 DOUBLE DUTY, b f Danehill Dancer (IRE)—Taking Liberties (IRE) **Sangster Family**

MR B. J. MEEHAN—continued

39 **DYNAMO DAVE (USA)**, b c Distorted Humor (USA)—Nothing Special (CAN) **Roldvale Ltd**
40 **ELNA BRIGHT**, b c Elnadim (USA)—Acicula (IRE) **D. M. D. Mort**
41 **EMERALD CRYSTAL (IRE)**, b c Green Desert (USA)—Crystal Spray **Lord A. Lloyd-Webber**
42 **EMPIRE SEEKER (USA)**, br c Seeking The Gold (USA)—Lady From Shanghai (USA) **Wetumpka Racing**
43 **EXCLAMATION**, br c Acclamation—Summer Siren (FR) **R. C. Tooth**
44 **FILM MAKER (IRE)**, b c Danetime (IRE)—Alexander Anapolis (IRE) **Bayardo**
45 **FIRST TRIM (IRE)**, b g Acclamation—Spanker **Kennet Valley Thoroughbreds II**
46 **FOOL'S WILDCAT (USA)**, b br c Forest Wildcat (USA)—Nine Flags (USA) **Favourites Racing XV**
47 **GARABELLE (IRE)**, ch f Galileo (IRE)—Panache Arabelle **T. W. Bloodstock Ltd**
48 **HILBRE COURT (IRE)**, br c Doneraile Court (USA)—Glasgow's Gold (USA) **E. H. Jones (Paints) Ltd**
49 **HUMBLE SPIRIT (USA)**, b br f Kingmambo—Saintly Speech (USA) **Sangster Family**
50 **HURRICANE HYMNBOOK (USA)**, b c Pulpit (USA)—April Squall (USA) **Bill Hinge & John Searchfield**
51 **ICON PROJECT (USA)**, b br f Empire Maker (USA)—La Gueriere (USA) **Mr A. Rosen**
52 **INVENTOR (IRE)**, b c Alzao (USA)—Magnificent Bell (IRE) **Highclere Thoroughbred Racing (Lake Con)**
53 **IRISH MAYHEM (USA)**, b c br c Woodman (USA)—Adventurous Di (USA) **Mr D. R. Fleming**
54 **JEMILIAH**, b f Dubai Destination (USA)—Cape Cod (IRE) **N. Stafford**
55 **JENNIE JEROME (IRE)**, br f Pivotal—Colourfast (IRE) **E. I. Mack**
56 **LA COVETA (IRE)**, b f Marju (IRE)—Colourful Cast (IRE) **Mrs W. M. English**
57 **LA VOILE ROUGE**, ch g Daggers Drawn (USA)—At Amal (IRE) **M. C. Denmark**
58 **LADY AQUITAINE (USA)**, gr f El Prado (IRE)—Chalamont (IRE) **Sangster Family**
59 B c Makbul—Lake Melody **Park Racing**
60 **LIBERALLY (IRE)**, b f Statue of Liberty (USA)—Specifically (USA) **Mr A. Rosen**
61 **LIBERTY ISLAND (IRE)**, b c Statue of Liberty (USA)—Birthday (IRE) **Iona Equine**
62 B c Peintre Celebre—Lipica (USA) **Paul & Jenny Green**
63 **LODI (IRE)**, ch g Bertolini (USA)—Lady of Leisure (USA) **6C Racing & Attenborough,Mann & Maynard**
64 **MAJOR EAZY (IRE)**, b c Fasliyev (USA)—Castilian Queen (USA) **The Comic Strip Heroes**
65 **MAN APPEAL**, ch f Mark of Esteem (IRE)—Emma Peel **A. E. Smith & Co**
66 **MANASSAS (IRE)**, b c Cape Cross (IRE)—Monnavanna (IRE) **Mrs R. Philipps**
67 **MASADA (IRE)**, br f Key of Luck (USA)—Desert Bloom (IRE) **Ballymacoll Stud Farm Ltd**
68 **MEDICI GOLD**, ch f Medicean—Silence Is Golden **Miss J. Semple**
69 **MISS PELLING (IRE)**, b f Danehill Dancer (USA)—Morningsurprice (USA) **Kennet Valley Thoroughbreds III**
70 **MONSIEUR REYNARD**, ch g Compton Place—Tell Tale Fox **Mrs S. Briddon**
71 **MOOSLEY (IRE)**, b c Marju (IRE)—Shauna's Honey (IRE) **I. Parvizi**
72 B br f Mr Greeley (USA)—Mutton Maniac (USA) **Sangster Family & Andrew Rosen**
73 **NAVAJO JOE (IRE)**, ch c Indian Ridge—Maid of Killeen (IRE) **J. L. Allbritton**
74 **NEZAMI (IRE)**, b g Elnadim (USA)—Stands To Reason (USA) **E. McCormack**
75 **NORTH PARADE**, b c Nayef (USA)—Queen Sceptre (IRE) **E. H. Jones (Paints) Ltd**
76 **OPENING HAND**, b g Observatory—Belle Ile (USA) **B. J. Meehan**
77 **ORDINATION (IRE)**, ch c Fantastic Light (USA)—Seek Easy (USA) **Mr Catesby W. Clay**
78 **POLMAILY**, b c Hawk Wing (USA)—Hampton Lucy (IRE) **Mrs S. M. Roy**
79 **REDEEMED**, b f Red Ransom (USA)—Pastel **Wyck Hall Stud Ltd**
80 **ROSALEEN (IRE)**, b f Cadeaux Genereux—Dark Rosaleen (IRE) **F. C. T. Wilson**
81 **SAAFEND GEEZER**, ch g Kyllachy—Kindred Spirit (USA) **J. B. R. Leisure Ltd**
82 **SACRED FLAME (USA)**, b f Rahy (USA)—Ashraakat (USA) **Middleham Park Racing XLI**
83 **SARAH PARK (IRE)**, ch f Redback—Brillano (FR) **Park Racing**
84 **SEVEN STARS**, b c Dubai Destination (USA)—Galette **Mrs L. Freedman**
85 **SHARP NEPHEW**, ch c Dr Fong (USA)—Snap Crackle Pop (IRE) **Saleh Al Homeizi & Imad Al Sagar**
86 **SKADRAK (USA)**, ch c Forest Camp (USA)—Occhi Verdi (IRE) **I. Parvizi**
87 B f Selkirk (USA)—Ski Run **T. Holland-Martin**
88 **SOPHIE'S GIRL**, b f Bahamian Bounty—Merry Rous **I. Parvizi**
89 **SWEET KISS (USA)**, gr f Yes It's True (USA)—Always Freezing (USA) **Gold Group International Ltd**
90 **SWIFT GIFT**, b c Cadeaux Genereux—Got To Go **Social & Affordable Racing Partnership**
91 **TEN HOUR LUNCH**, br g Averti (IRE)—Long Tall Sally (IRE) **The Strawberries To A Donkey Partnership**
92 **TOASTED SPECIAL**, ch f Johannesburg (USA)—Sajjaya (USA) **Iona Equine**
93 **WAVE HILL (IRE)**, b g Mujadil (USA)—Bryna (IRE) **Favourites Racing XIII**

TWO-YEAR-OLDS

94 B c 4/3 Lion Heart (USA)—Adored Slew (USA) (Seattle Slew (USA)) (58309) **I. Parvizi**
95 **ARABIAN MIRAGE**, b f 8/3 Oasis Dream—Bathilde (IRE) (Generous (IRE)) (210000) **Mr D. F. O'Rourke**
96 B c 26/4 Dr Fong (USA)—Band (USA) (Northern Dancer) (55000) **J. L. Allbritton**
97 B f 18/2 Sadler's Wells (USA)—Blanche Dubois (Nashwan (USA)) (75000) **Sangster Family & Partners**
98 B f 14/2 Daylami (IRE)—Blue Water (USA) (Bering) **Mrs R. Philipps**
99 Ch c 13/4 Peintre Celebre (USA)—Blushing Gleam (Caerleon (USA)) (30000) **I. Parvizi**
100 B f 22/2 Pivotal—Bolshaya (Cadeaux Genereux) (115000) **A. Rosen**
101 Ch f 8/4 Giant's Causeway (USA)—Chalamont (IRE) (Kris) (55000) **Sangster Family & Matthew Green**

MR B. J. MEEHAN—continued

102 CRAFT (FR), b c 19/3 Numerous (USA)—
Anyone For Tennis (IRE) (Night Shift (USA)) (16000) P. Abbott & A. Merritt
103 Gr f 21/2 King's Best (USA)—Crepe Ginger (IRE) (Sadler's Wells (USA)) T. W. Bloodstock Ltd
104 B c 23/3 Reset (AUS)—Crinkle (IRE) (Distant Relative) (24000) Mr N. Attenborough, Mrs L. Mann, Mrs L. Way
105 Ch c 21/3 Speightstown (USA)—Day Mate (USA) (Dayjur (USA)) (102040) Saleh Al Homaizi & Imad Al Sagar
106 B c 5/4 One Cool Cat (USA)—Dissidentia (IRE) (Dancing Dissident (USA)) (35000) M. C. Denmark
107 DREAM HUNTRESS, ch f 24/1 Dubai Destination (USA)—
Dream Lady (Benny The Dip (USA)) (40000) Wyck Hall Stud Ltd
108 B c 18/2 Bahri (USA)—Ecco Mi (IRE) (Priolo (USA)) (15000)
109 B f 14/2 Auction House (USA)—Ellway Queen (USA) (Bahri (USA)) (60000) The Comic Strip Heroes
110 EXCELSIOR ACADEMY, b c 6/3 Montjeu (IRE)—
Birthday Suit (IRE) (Daylami (IRE)) (260000) Lady M. C. Laidlaw
111 Ch c 28/1 Piccolo—Fiamma Royale (IRE) (Fumo di Londra (IRE)) (58000) Clipper Group Holdings Ltd
112 B f 24/4 Marju (IRE)—Flatter (IRE) (Barathea (IRE)) (47000) M. Green
113 FLY BUTTERFLY, ch f 23/3 Bahamian Bounty—Aconite (Primo Dominie) (37000) Mrs J. P. E. Cunningham
114 FROGNAL (IRE), b c 26/3 Kheleyf (USA)—Shannon Dore (Turtle Island (IRE)) (46000) R. C. Tooth
115 GEORGE REX (USA), b br c 25/4 Johannesburg (USA)—
Royal Linkage (USA) (Linkage (USA)) (45044) Tumbleweed Partnership
116 B f 4/4 Selkirk (USA)—Gold Bar (IRE) (Barathea (IRE)) Ballymacoll Stud
117 B c 23/2 Fasliyev (USA)—Graffiti Girl (IRE) (Sadler's Wells (USA)) (36000) Mrs S. Tucker
118 Ch c 2/2 Pivotal—Grandalea (Grand Lodge (USA)) (125000) The Comic Strip Heroes
119 GREENSWARD, b c 12/3 Green Desert (USA)—Frizzante (Efisio) Lady Rothschild
120 Gr c 4/2 Verglas (IRE)—Halicardia (Halling (USA)) (74001) The Comic Strip Heroes
121 Ch f 1/3 Birdstone (USA)—Heat Lightning (USA) (Summer Squall (USA)) Mr A. Rosen
122 B f 6/3 Halling (USA)—Hesperia (Slip Anchor) (50000) M. C. Denmark
123 HI FLING, b c 12/4 Oasis Dream—Crafty Buzz (USA) (Crafty Prospector) (220000) Lady M. C. Laidlaw
124 B f 3/4 Selkirk (USA)—Hiddendale (IRE) (Indian Ridge) Mrs S. Roy
125 HIGHLAND LASSIE (IRE), b f 17/3 Oasis Dream—
Arlesiana (USA) (Woodman (USA)) (160000) Lady M. C. Laidlaw
126 IN HER SHOES, ch f 1/2 Pivotal—Ebaraya (IRE) (Sadler's Wells (USA)) (165000) S. Dartnell
127 JEWELLED, b f 16/2 Fantastic Light (USA)—Danemere (IRE) (Danehill (USA)) Wyck Hall Stud Ltd
128 B c 28/1 Indian Haven—Kathy Desert (Green Desert (USA)) (38000)
129 KLYNCH, b c 28/3 Kyllachy—Inchcoonan (Emperor Jones (USA)) (32000) L P R Partnership
130 B c 6/3 Giant's Causeway (USA)—Lady Carla (Caerleon (USA)) (48000) E. H. Jones (Paints) Ltd.
131 B c 21/2 Royal Applause—Les Hurlants (IRE) (Barathea (IRE)) (50000) R. C. Tooth
132 Ch f 28/4 Rock of Gibraltar (IRE)—Lindesberg (Doyoun) (77220) Sangster Family & Matthew Green
133 MYSTIC PRINCE, b g 8/4 Dubai Destination (USA)—Hazy Heights (Shirley Heights) Wyck Hall Stud Ltd
134 B c 23/2 Fasliyev (USA)—Nawazi (USA) (Trempolino (USA)) (32174) Favourites Racing XV
135 PAGAN FLIGHT (IRE), b c 27/4 Hawk Wing (USA)—Regal Darcey (IRE) (Darshaan) (78000) GAP Partnership
136 B f 26/4 Refuse To Bend (IRE)—Park Charger (Tirol) (250000) F. C. T. Wilson
137 B f 22/3 Barathea (IRE)—Perils of Joy (IRE) (Rainbow Quest (USA)) (180000) F. C. T. Wilson
138 B c 26/2 Johannesburg (USA)—
Perovskia (USA) (Stravinsky (USA)) (102960) Sangster Family & Matthew Green
139 PISTE, b f 14/5 Falbrav (IRE)—Arctic Char (Polar Falcon (USA)) Miss G. J. Abbey
140 B c 24/3 Soviet Star (USA)—Putout (Dowsing (USA)) (61132)
141 B f 25/4 Oasis Dream—Rada's Daughter (Robellino (USA)) (65000) Highclere Thoroughbred Racing (St Simon)
142 ROCKABOUT (IRE), b f 26/2 Rock of Gibraltar (IRE)—
Capades Dancer (USA) (Gate Dancer (USA)) Lady Rothschild
143 Ch c 8/2 Bahamian Bounty—Roo (Rudimentary (USA)) (115000) Manton Thoroughbred Partnership
144 B c 2/3 Invincible Spirit (IRE)—Rouge Noir (USA) (Saint Ballado (CAN)) (95000) J. L. Allbritton
145 B f 27/4 Royal Applause—Sabina (Prince Sabo) (80000) I. Parvizi
146 B c 16/2 Hawk Wing (USA)—Savignano (Polish Precedent (USA)) (61132) Manton Thoroughbred Partnership
147 B f 19/5 Selkirk (USA)—Sciunfona (IRE) (Danehill (USA)) (15000)
148 Ch f 15/2 Compton Place—Shifting Mist (Night Shift (USA)) (80000) F. C. T. Wilson
149 SISTER ROSE (FR), b f 30/1 One Cool Cat (USA)—Lady of St Kilda (Mark of Esteem (IRE)) (48000) B. J. Meehan
150 B br f 9/4 Street Cry (IRE)—Something Mon (USA) (Maria's Mon (USA)) (167309) Mr A. Rosen
151 B f 16/5 Rock of Gibraltar (IRE)—Speak Softly To Me (USA) (Ogygian (USA)) (106177) Mr A. Rosen
152 B c 17/3 Invincible Spirit (IRE)—Special Park (USA) (Trempolino (USA)) (47000)
153 Ch c 13/3 Indian Ridge—Sun On The Sea (IRE) (Bering) Swordlestown Stud
154 SUPER SLEUTH (IRE), ch f 26/1 Selkirk (USA)—Enemy Action (USA) (Forty Niner (USA)) Mrs L. J. Freedman
155 B f 19/3 Yes It's True (USA)—Sweetheart (USA) (Mr Prospector (USA)) (230806) A. Rosen & R. Clay
156 Ch f 26/2 Noverre (USA)—Tiger Desert (GER) (Desert King (IRE)) (58000) Mrs S. M. Roy
157 B c 28/3 Kyllachy—Triple Sharp (Selkirk (USA)) (130000) Saleh Al Homaizi & Imad Al Sagar
158 B br f 15/4 Giant's Causeway (USA)—Vantive (USA) (Mr Prospector (USA)) (55000) Sangster Family & Partner
159 Ch f 18/2 Hawk Wing (USA)—Waratah (IRE) (Entrepreneur) (35392)
160 Ch c 22/3 Rainbow Quest (USA)—Wiener Wald (USA) (Woodman (USA)) (75000)

MR B. J. MEEHAN—continued

161 B br f 9/3 Giant's Causeway (USA)—Win's Fair Lady (USA) (Dehere (USA)) (583090) **Mr A. Rosen**
162 Ch f 19/2 Danehill Dancer (IRE)—
　　　　Wondrous Story (USA) (Royal Academy (USA)) (83654) **Sangster Family & Lady Bamford**

Other Owners: Mrs Ferdi Abbott, G. D. Anderson, Mr E. K. Baker, Mr A. Black, Mr John M. Carroll, Mrs J. Cash, Mrs Heather Spangler Clubb, T. S. M. Cunningham, W. A. L. Duff Gordon, Lady E. V. Duff Gordon, Mr J. R. Eburne, Miss Helen English, Miss Alice English, Family Amusements Ltd, Gold Group International Ltd, Mr Charles A. Green, Mrs B. D. Hall, Mr J. P. M. Main, Mrs Judy Maynard, Mr Harry McCalmont, Mr Ed McCormack, Ms Charlotte Musgrave, Ruairi O'Coileain, William O'Donnell, Denis O'Flynn, Miss P. M. O'Flynn, T. S. Palin, N. J. F. Robinson, Mr G. E. Sangster, Mr B. V. Sangster, Dr E. S. G. Semple, J. S. Threadwell, Mr Brian Wallace, Wood Hall Stud Limited.

Assistant Trainer: R. O'Dowd, P. McEwan

Apprentice: K. May.

---

395 MS M. A. MEEK, Eastbury
Postal: **Castle Piece Racing Stables, Grange Road, Eastbury, Hungerford, Berkshire, RG17 7JR**
Contacts: **PHONE** (01488) 670100 **FAX** (01488) 670100 **MOBILE** (07810) 866992
E-MAIL marymeek@btinternet.com

1 ADVERSANE, 4, ch g Alhaarth (IRE)—Cragreen **Ms M. A. Meek**
2 ANTY WREN, 6, gr g Tragic Role (USA)—Granny Nix **Ms M. A. Meek**
3 BARON BROOKDALE, 9, gr g Puissance—Baroness Blakeney **Miss L. Meek**
4 EDGE OF ITALY, 6, ch m Bold Edge—Brera (IRE) **Ms M. A. Meek**
5 ENLIST, 4, b g Beat Hollow—Dawna **Ms M. A. Meek**
6 IMAYDANCE, 4, ch f Dancing Spree (USA)—Inherit The Earth **Ms M. A. Meek**

---

396 MR A. MIDDLETON, Granborough
Postal: **Hogshaw Road Farm, Hogshaw Road, Granborough, Buckingham, Buckinghamshire, MK18 3NL**
Contacts: **PHONE** (01844) 292463 **FAX** (01844) 292463 **MOBILE** (07894) 909542
E-MAIL tony@granboroughracing.co.uk

1 MOSSMANN GORGE, 6, b g Lujain (USA)—North Pine **Mrs C. J. Middleton**
2 5, B g Sure Blade (USA)—Parsons Lass (IRE)
3 4, B c Emperor Fountain—Parsons Lass (IRE)
4 SMOOTH MOVER, 6, b g Mister Baileys—Dancing Heights (IRE) **Mrs C. J. Middleton**
5 TOOKA, 7, b g Sure Blade (USA)—Parsons Lass (IRE) **Mr A. Middleton**

Assistant Trainer: Mrs C. Middleton

Conditional: C. Poste, T. Molloy.

---

397 MR P. T. MIDGLEY, Westow
Postal: **Sandfield Farm, Westow, York**
Contacts: **PHONE** (01759) 373812 **FAX** (01759) 373812 **MOBILE** (07976) 965220

1 BOPPYS DANCER, 5, b g Clan of Roses—Dancing Mary **Mrs S. Bond**
2 BOPPYS DIAMOND, 4, b f Clan of Roses—Dancing Mary **Mrs S. Bond**
3 BOPPYS DREAM, 6, ch m Clan of Roses—Laurel Queen (IRE) **Mrs S. Bond**
4 COMPTON SPARK, 6, ch g Compton Place—Rhinefield Beauty (IRE)
5 DEADLINE (UAE), 4, ch c Machiavellian (USA)—Time Changes (USA) **W. B. Imison**
6 DRIZZI (IRE), 7, b g Night Shift (USA)—Woopi Gold (IRE) **Mr M. E. Elsworthy**
7 EXIT SMILING, 6, ch g Dr Fong (USA)—Away To Me **P. J. Mee**
8 HIGHLAND WARRIOR, 9, b g Makbul—Highland Rowena **Frank & Annette Brady**
9 JA MYFORD, 4, b g Auction House (USA)—Daleside Ladybird **A. D. Copley**
10 JUST OBSERVING, 5, ch g Observatory (USA)—Just Speculation (IRE) **O. R. Dukes**
11 MING VASE, 6, b g Vettori (IRE)—Minstrel's Dance (CAN) **M. Ng**
12 MISS TABOO (IRE), 4, b f Tobougg (IRE)—Miss Croisette **Mrs S. Bond**
13 MYFRENCHCONNECTION (IRE), 4, b g Tendulkar (USA)—Papinette (IRE) **J. F. Wright**
14 NOMOREBLONDES, 4, ch f Ishiguro (USA)—Statuette **A. D. Copley**
15 OUTLOOK, 5, ch g Observatory (USA)—Area Girl **M. E. Elsworthy**
16 PENEL (IRE), 7, b g Orpen (USA)—Jayess Elle **Mrs K. L. Midgley**

MR P. T. MIDGLEY—continued

17 **RANN NA CILLE (IRE)**, 4, br f Agnes World (USA)—Omanah (USA) **Enjoy A Day Out Partnership**
18 **SAPPHIRE STORM (IRE)**, 5, b m Elnadim (USA)—Blu Tu Miami (USA) **Mr J. F. Wright & Miss K. Watson**
19 **SEDGE (USA)**, 8, b g Lure (USA)—First Flyer (USA) **C. Alton**
20 **SHOPFITTER**, 5, b g Sugarfoot—Madam Wurlitzer **J. Watson**
21 **WILTSHIRE (IRE)**, 6, br g Spectrum (IRE)—Mary Magdalene **D. Mann**

THREE-YEAR-OLDS

22 **BELLAS CHICAS (IRE)**, ch f Captain Rio—Persian Light (IRE) **A. D. Copley**
23 **EVERYTHING**, bl f Namid—Flight Sequence **A. D. Copley**
24 **HANDSINTHEMIST (IRE)**, b f Lend A Hand—Hollow Haze (USA) **J. F. Wright**
25 **LOVELY LILLING**, ch f Presidium—Coney Hills **Mrs S. Johnson**
26 **PERSISTENT (IRE)**, b c Cape Cross (IRE)—Insistent (USA) **Mr Peter Mee & Mr Colin Alton**
27 **TENTH NIGHT (IRE)**, b c Mujadil (USA)—Starlight Venture (IRE) **D. Mann**
28 **WHISPERING DESERT**, b f Distant Music (USA)—Nullarbor **J. F. Wright**

TWO-YEAR-OLDS

29 B f 8/4 Xaar—Aidin And Abetting (IRE) (Entrepreneur) (1286)
30 B c 27/1 Millkom—Club Oasis (Forzando)
31 B f 23/4 Mujadil (USA)—Corynida (USA) (Alleged (USA)) (1029)
32 Ch f 26/2 Noverre (USA)—Deep Ravine (USA) (Gulch (USA)) (3800)
33 B f 20/1 Clodovil (IRE)—Eveam (IRE) (Mujadil (USA)) (2059)
34 B c 10/3 Pursuit of Love—Far Clan (Clantime) (500)
35 B f 8/4 Pyrus (USA)—Fizz Up (Alzao (USA)) (3860)
36 Ch c 17/4 Diesis—Garden Rose (IRE) (Caerleon (USA)) (12000)
37 **GEE GINA**, b f 21/5 Hunting Lion (IRE)—La Thuile (Statoblest) (6200)
38 B c 18/5 Raise A Grand (IRE)—Hever Rosina (Efisio) (1800)
39 B f 6/4 Mull of Kintyre—Jet Lock (Crafty Prospector (USA)) (1608)
40 B f 1/2 Mull of Kintyre—Jungle Story (IRE) (Alzao (USA)) (2000)
41 B f 20/3 Deportivo—Kingston Rose (GER) (Robellino (USA)) (1800)
42 B c 22/3 Lucky Owners (NZ)—Miles (Selkirk (USA)) (400)
43 B f 24/3 Spartacus (IRE)—Miri (IRE) (Sillery (USA))
44 B f 18/4 Catcher In The Rye (IRE)—Mrs Evans (IRE) (College Chapel) (6434)
45 B f 24/2 Tagula (IRE)—My Mimi (USA) (Diesis)
46 Ch f 9/5 Fath (USA)—Mystic Oak (IRE) (Waajib) (642)
47 B c 6/5 Best of The Bests (IRE)—Pain Perdu (IRE) (Waajib) (2500)
48 B c 10/4 Bertolini (USA)—Perfect Poppy (Shareef Dancer (USA)) (1000)
49 B f 8/4 Kheleyf (USA)—Professional Mom (USA) (Spinning World (USA)) (2059)
50 B f 13/1 Tobougg (IRE)—Skiddaw Bird (Bold Owl) (800)
51 Ch f 28/1 Bahamian Bounty—Spain (Polar Falcon (USA)) (1600)
52 B f 29/4 Captain Rio—Special One (Aragon) (3217)
53 Ch f 16/3 Reel Buddy (USA)—Waltzing Star (USA) (Danehill (USA)) (1500)

Other Owners: Mr Colin Alton, F. Brady, Mrs A. Brady, Mr P. T. Midgley, Mr Michael Ng, Mr E. I. Pruchniewicz, Miss K. Watson.

Jockey (flat): Mickey Fenton. **Amateur:** Mr S. Walker.

398

MISS M. K. MILLIGAN, Middleham

Postal: **Castle Stables, Middleham, Leyburn, North Yorkshire, DL8 4QQ**
Contacts: **OFFICE (01969) 623221 HOME (01969) 624105 FAX (01969) 623221**
MOBILE (07721) 529857
E-MAIL **kate@mkmracing.fsnet.co.uk**

1 **AMJAD**, 11, ch g Cadeaux Genereux—Babita **Miss M. K. Milligan**
2 **DARK BEN (FR)**, 8, b g Solar One (FR)—Reine d'auteuil (FR) **J. D. Gordon**
3 **HIGH BIRD HUMPHREY**, 9, ch g Nomadic Way (USA)—Miss Kewmill **P. G. Forster**
4 **MIDDLEWAY**, 12, b g Milieu—Galway Gal **Mrs J. M. L. Milligan**
5 **MINSTER LAKE**, 6, ch g Minster Son—Cullane Lake (IRE) **Mrs J. M. L. Milligan**
6 **OBARA D'AVRIL (FR)**, 6, gr m April Night (FR)—Baraka de Thaix II (FR) **J. D. Gordon**
7 **OF COURSE (FR)**, 6, ch g Adnaan (FR)—Intelectuelle (FR) **The Aunts & Mrs J M L Milligan**
8 **PENNEY LANE**, 7, ch m Minster Son—Cullane Lake (IRE) **Miss M. K. Milligan**
9 **SPIDERS STAR**, 5, br m Cayman Kai (IRE)—Kiss In The Dark **Miss M. K. Milligan**
10 **SPRINGAWAY**, 9, ch g Minster Son—Galway Gal **Mrs J. M. L. Milligan**

Other Owners: Mrs D. L. Barrett, Mrs Judith Robson.

Amateur: Miss T. Jackson.

399   MR B. R. MILLMAN, Cullompton

Postal: The Paddocks, Kentisbeare, Cullompton, Devon, EX15 2DX
Contacts: PHONE/FAX (01884) 266620 MOBILE (07885) 168447
E-MAIL rod.millman@ic24.net

1 **ADANTINO**, 9, b g Glory of Dancer—Sweet Whisper **Tarka Two Racing**
2 **CARLITOS SPIRIT (IRE)**, 4, ch g Redback—Negria (IRE) **Karmaa Racing Limited**
3 **CASTANO**, 4, br g Makbul—Royal Orchid (IRE) **H.G.Gooding & Mrs A.A.Gooding**
4 **CERIS STAR (IRE)**, 4, b g Cadeaux Genereux—Midsummernitedream (GER) **Mrs S. A. J. Kinsella-Hurley**
5 **DAVENPORT (IRE)**, 6, b g Bold Fact (USA)—Semence D'or (FR) **M. A. Swift & A. J. Chapman**
6 **DOWN THE BRICK (IRE)**, 4, b g Daggers Drawn (USA)—Damezao **Brick Racing**
7 **EL BOSQUE (IRE)**, 4, b g Elnadim (USA)—In The Woods **Wessex Racing**
8 **GOLDEN SPRITE**, 5, b m Bertolini (USA)—Shalad'or **G. J. & Mrs M. Palmer**
9 **HAWRIDGE MISS**, 4, b f Piccolo—In The Stocks **E. J. S. Gadsden**
10 **HAWRIDGE PRINCE**, 8, b g Polar Falcon (USA)—Zahwa **E. J. S. Gadsden**
11 **MAKABUL**, 5, b g Makbul—Victoria Sioux **M S T Partnership**
12 **MASAI MOON**, 4, b g Lujain (USA)—Easy To Imagine (USA) **Mr C. Roper**
13 **MONTZANDO**, 5, b g Forzando—Clashfern **The Links Partnership**
14 **MUSTAJED**, 7, b g Alharath (IRE)—Jasarah (IRE) **Mustajed Partnership**
15 **OCEAN BLAZE**, 4, b f Polar Prince (IRE)—La Belle Vie **Ocean View Properties International Ltd**
16 **OLIMPO (FR)**, 7, ch g Starborough—Emily Allan (IRE) **Pot Black Racing**
17 **PHANTOM WHISPER**, 9, b g Makbul—La Belle Vie **Mrs T. A. Dormer**
18 **PINAFORE**, 6, ch m Fleetwood (IRE)—Shi Shi **Mrs J. A. M. Willment**
19 **PRINCESS ZADA**, 4, ch f Best of The Bests (IRE)—Barnacla (IRE) **S. Laws**
20 **ROYAL STORM**, 9, b h Royal Applause—Wakayi **Mrs H. Brain**
21 **VOGARTH**, 4, ch g Arkadian Hero (USA)—Skara Brae **Mr P. Millman**
22 **WHITBARROW (IRE)**, 9, b g Royal Abjar (USA)—Danccini (IRE) **Mrs H. Brain**

THREE-YEAR-OLDS

23 **ALTO SINGER (IRE)**, b f Alhaarth (IRE)—Sonatina **The Beaker Racing Partnership**
24 B f Kyllachy—April Stock **E. J. S. Gadsden**
25 **BALATA**, b g Averti (IRE)—Manila Selection (USA) **The Links Partnership**
26 **BATHWICK MAN**, b g Mark of Esteem (IRE)—Local Abbey (IRE) **Mrs S. Clifford**
27 **BILBOA**, b g Averti (IRE)—Anita Marie (IRE) **P. Murphy**
28 **BOBSTER**, b f Best of The Bests (IRE)—Astelia **East Burrow Racing**
29 **BRAMAPUTRA (IRE)**, b f Choisir (AUS)—Bayalika (IRE) **Mrs M. Campbell-Andenaes**
30 **BRASSINI**, br gr g Bertolini (USA)—Silver Spell **The Links Partnership**
31 **FLYING SEASONS**, b g Elnadim (USA)—Silvereine (FR) **B. R. Millman**
32 **HIGHLAND HOMESTEAD**, b g Makbul—Highland Rossie **Mrs G. J. Rowe**
33 **KING BATHWICK (IRE)**, b g Golan (IRE)—Princess Sabaah (IRE) **H. M. W. Clifford**
34 **MILLDOWN BAY**, b f Bertolini (USA)—Barnacla (IRE) **Mrs J. E. Laws**
35 **MINERTON MOUNTAIN**, b g Carnival Dancer—Eau Rouge **Treatcourt Ltd**
36 **NEW MINERTON (IRE)**, b f Trans Island—Irish Lover (USA) **Treatcourt Ltd**
37 **OPERACHY**, b g Kyllachy—Sea Music **Wessex Racing**
38 **ORONSAY**, ch f Elmaamul (USA)—Glenfinlass **Mrs J. A. M. Willment**
39 **PIERIS**, b g Mujahid (USA)—Forest Fire (SWE) **Tarka Racing**
40 **STAGE ACCLAIM (IRE)**, b g Acclamation—Open Stage (IRE) **B. R. Millman**

TWO-YEAR-OLDS

41 B c 28/1 One Cool Cat (USA)—Angry Bark (USA) (Woodman (USA)) (32000)
42 B f 29/3 Monsieur Bond (IRE)—Anita Marie (IRE) (Anita's Prince) (10000) **P. Murphy**
43 **CAPTAIN PEACHY**, b c 27/1 Pursuit of Love—Dekelsmary (Komaite (USA)) **The Peachy Syndicate**
44 B f 22/4 Deportivo—Catriona (Bustino) (13000)
45 Ch f 12/3 Bahamian Bounty—Crofters Ceilidh (Scottish Reel) **P. Murphy**
46 B c 5/2 Xaar—Crozon (Peintre Celebre (USA)) (7000)
47 **HI SHINKO**, b c 14/3 Shinko Forest (IRE)—Up Front (IRE) (Up And At 'em) (10000) **Always Hopefull**
48 Ch c 2/4 Monsieur Bond (IRE)—Kastaway (Distant Relative) (9000) **J. J. Brummitt**
49 **MATTAMIA (IRE)**, b c 8/2 Makbul—Lady Dominatrix (IRE) (Danehill Dancer (IRE)) (32000) **Mr C. Roper**
50 B c 22/2 Lend A Hand—Miss Maisey (IRE) (Entrepreneur) (7600) **Clear Racing**
51 Ch c 7/2 Reset (AUS)—Naomi Wildman (USA) (Kingmambo (USA)) (5000) **The Mustajed Partnership**
52 Ch c 21/2 Kheleyf (USA)—Opalescent (IRE) (Polish Precedent (USA)) (30000) **The Links Partnership**
53 Br c 28/2 Makbul—Piccolo Cativo (Komaite (USA)) (11000)
54 **SOLDIER BAY**, ch c 8/3 Tobougg (IRE)—Little Tramp (Trempolino) (3500) **Mrs L. S. Millman**
55 Ch f 31/3 Observatory (USA)—St Edith (IRE) (Desert King (USA)) (10000) **Lucky Generals Racing**
56 **SWIFT CHAP**, b c 25/3 Diktat—Regent's Folly (IRE) (Touching Wood (USA)) (18000) **M. A. Swift**
57 B c 10/2 Forzando—Victoria Sioux (Ron's Victory (USA)) (13000) **D. J. Lowe**

MR B. R. MILLMAN—continued

58 B f 1/4 Kheleyf (USA)—Villafranca (IRE) (In The Wings) (7500) **Lucky Generals Racing**
59 B c 22/3 Royal Applause—Warning Belle (Warning) (20000)
60 Ch f 3/5 Systematic—Water Flower (Environment Friend) **Mr P. Allen**

Other Owners: Mr Ian Abercrombie, Mr M. Bevan, Mr J. P. Boulton, Mr A. J. Chapman, Mrs Jasmine B. Chesters, Mr A. J. Conway, Mr C. Dormer, Mr Pip Elson, Lady Margaret Fortescue, Mrs A. A. Gooding, Mr H. Gooding, Mr Hugh Griffith, C. E. Grover, Mr Dave Harris, J. W. Haydon, Mr N. W. Lake, Mr V. B. Lewer, Mr Colin Lewis, Mr D. A. Little, L. J. Loake, A. Loze, Mrs C. Loze, Mr B. R. Millman, Mr G. Palmer, Mrs M. Palmer, Mr S. M. Perry, Mr Tom Pridmore, Mr A. Richings, J. L. Rowsell, Mr M. J. Smith, Mr M. A. Swift, Mr C. Tayler, Mr E. M. Thornton, Mr G. M. Thornton, Mrs S. Thornton, Mr David Whitefield, J. L. Whitten, Mr D. R. Windebank, Mr Christopher Wood.

Assistant Trainer: Louise Millman

Jockey (flat): A Munro. **Apprentice:** James Millman. **Amateur:** Mr P. Millman.

---

400 MR T. G. MILLS, Epsom
Postal: **Loretta Lodge, Tilley Lane, Headley, Epsom, Surrey, KT18 6EP**
Contacts: **PHONE (01372) 377209 FAX (01372) 386578**
E-MAIL lorettalodge@aol.com

1 CHARLTON, 5, b g Inchinor—Sabina **T. G. Mills**
2 DIRICULOUS, 4, b g Diktat—Sheila's Secret (IRE) **Sherwoods Transport Ltd**
3 GOLDEN DESERT (IRE), 4, b g Desert Prince (IRE)—Jules (IRE) **Mr S. M. Parker**
4 MURRIN (IRE), 4, b br g Trans Island—Flimmering **Mr C. A. Faulkner**
5 NEW WORLD ORDER (IRE), 4, b c Night Shift (USA)—Kama Tashoof **Vetlab Supplies Ltd**
6 NORTON (IRE), 11, ch g Barathea (IRE)—Primrose Valley **T. G. Mills**
7 ORCHESTRATOR (IRE), 4, b g Docksider (USA)—Summerhill **Mrs L. M. Askew**
8 PETARA BAY (IRE), 4, b c Peintre Celebre (USA)—Magnificient Style (USA) **Mrs S. Ecclestone**
9 SAVIOURS SPIRIT, 7, ch g Komaite (USA)—Greenway Lady **J. E. Harley**
10 STRIKEEN (IRE), 4, ch g Intikhab (USA)—Sheen Falls (IRE) **Buxted Partnership**
11 WANDLE, 4, b c Galileo (IRE)—Artistic Blue (USA) **J. Daniels**

THREE-YEAR-OLDS

12 EVENTIDE, ch f Where Or When (IRE)—Evening Guest (FR) **Mrs A. R. Ruggles**
13 GREYLAMI (IRE), gr g Daylami (IRE)—Silent Crystal (USA) **J. Daniels**
14 HENNESSY ISLAND (USA), ch c Hennessy (USA)—Heavenly Dawn (USA) **J. Humphreys**
15 HI HOPES, ch g Where Or When (IRE)—Chelsea (USA) **Miss Jean Leighs**
16 PEGASUS AGAIN (USA), b c Fusaichi Pegasus (USA)—Chit Chatter (USA) **T. G. Mills**
17 SALT OF THE EARTH (IRE), b c Invincible Spirit (IRE)—Get The Accountant **Mrs Y. R. Russell**
18 SOOMAR, gr c Act One—Bint Shihama (USA) **Mr B. G. Chamley**
19 SUMMER WINDS, ch g Where Or When (IRE)—Jetbeeah (IRE) **J. Humphreys**
20 TYRRELLS WOOD (IRE), b g Sinndar (IRE)—Diner de Lune (IRE) **Mr P. C. Ryan**

TWO-YEAR-OLDS

21 Ch c 8/5 Fantastic Light (USA)—Artistic Blue (USA) (Diesis) (40000) **J. Daniels**
22 B c 18/2 Danehill Dancer (IRE)—Fragrant (Cadeaux Genereux) (30000) **Mrs L. M. Askew**
23 B br c 9/3 Fusaichi Pegasus (USA)—Louju (USA) (Silver Hawk (USA)) (100000) **J. Daniels**
24 B f 12/2 Cape Cross (IRE)—Royal Devotion (IRE) (Sadler's Wells (USA)) (141569) **Mrs Johnny Eddis**

Other Owners: Mrs L. M. Askew, Mr J. Daniels, Mrs B. Ecclestone, Mr R. Green, Mr Jim Hanifin, Mr John Humphreys, Mr T. Jacobs, Mr T. G. Mills, Mr Dennis Russell, Mrs J. Ruthven.

---

401 MR N. R. MITCHELL, Dorchester
Postal: **East Hill Stables, Piddletrenthide, Dorchester, Dorset, DT2 7QY**
Contacts: **PHONE/FAX (01300) 348739 MOBILE (07775) 843136**

1 APATURA DIK, 7, b g Deltic (USA)—Apatura Hati **Mrs R. O. Hutchings**
2 DELCOMBE, 7, b g Deltic (USA)—Nellie's Joy VII **Mrs R. O. Hutchings**
3 DIANA BISCOE, 5, b m Riverwise—Cut Above The Rest **Mrs P. M. Butler**
4 GRAND SEFTON, 5, br g Pivotal—Nahlin **J. R. Boughey**
5 GROUND PATROL, 7, b g Ashkalani (IRE)—Good Grounds (USA) **Mrs E. Mitchell**
6 KILTIMONEY (IRE), 8, gr g Kasmayo—Rosie's Midge **Dunplush**

MR N. R. MITCHELL—continued

7 MASSINI SUNSET (IRE), 8, b g Dr Massini (IRE)—Burgundy Sunset (IRE) **Mr & Mrs Andrew May**
8 PITTON PRINCE, 9, gr g Classic Cliche (IRE)—Curious Feeling **Martin Blandford**

Other Owners: Mr N. P. I. Harrison, Mr P. J. Hiscock, A. J. May, Mrs S. May.

Assistant Trainer: Mrs E. Mitchell

---

402 MR D. J. MOFFATT, Grange-Over-Sands
Postal: **Pit Farm Racing Stables, Cartmel, Grange-Over-Sands, Cumbria, LA11 6PJ**
Contacts: **PHONE (01539) 536689 FAX (01539) 536236 MOBILE (07767) 367282**
E-MAIL james@jamesmoffatt.co.uk WEBSITE www.jamesmoffatt.co.uk

1 AMBIT, 9, br g Krisfield—Minster Pecari **Alison Walker Sarah Cousins**
2 BALL GAMES, 10, b g Mind Games—Deb's Ball **Mrs J. A. Moffatt**
3 BORDER TALE, 8, b g Selkirk (USA)—Likely Story (IRE) **DJM - Arnold Headdock**
4 CABBYL DOO, 5, b h Killer Instinct—Chipewyas (FR) **Mrs A. Stamper**
5 CHAVEZ (IRE), 4, b c Desert Style (IRE)—Ballerina Gold (USA) **The Vyner-Brooks Family & D J M**
6 CHIEF DAN GEORGE (IRE), 8, b g Grand Americo—Colleen Donn **Maurice W. Chapman**
7 DEVILS DELIGHT (IRE), 6, b m Desert King—Devil's Crown (USA) **D. J. Moffatt**
8 ERGO (FR), 4, b c Grand Lodge (USA)—Erhawah **Mrs E. M. Milligan**
9 GREAT QUEST (IRE), 6, b m Montjeu (IRE)—Paparazzi (IRE) **Mr Arnold Headdock & Mrs Kath Headdock**
10 KINGS MAIDEN (IRE), 5, b m King's Theatre (IRE)—Maidenhair (IRE) **Mrs S. C. Huntley**
11 LETS GO GIRLS, 4, b f Sir Harry Lewis (USA)—Bee Pushi **Mr R. C. Helliwell**
12 MASTEROFCEREMONIES, 5, ch g Definite Article—Darakah **Mr C. Macleod**
13 MULLIGAN'S PRIDE (IRE), 7, b g Kahyasi—Babs Mulligan (IRE) **The Sheroot Partnership**
14 PIMBO LANE (IRE), 6, br m Bob's Return—Wire To Wire **Maurice W. Chapman**
15 RICH GIRL (IRE), 6, ch m Beneficial—Kitty Supreme (IRE) **Maurice W. Chapman**
16 ROBIN DE LA FOLIE (FR), 6, b g Robin des Pres (FR)—Cazeres (FR) **David & Nicky Robinson**
17 ROMAN ARMY (IRE), 6, b g Trans Island—Contravene (IRE) **The Vilprano Partnership**
18 SAMIZDAT (FR), 5, b g Soviet Star (USA)—Secret Account (USA) **Mrs F. C. Rayson**
19 SEA STORM (IRE), 10, b g Dolphin Street (FR)—Prime Interest (IRE) **Maurice W. Chapman**
20 SHARP DANIEL, 5, ch g Prince Daniel (USA)—Bromley Rose **A. Eubank**
21 THANKYOU MAAM, 6, b m Bahamian Bounty—Barefoot Landing (USA) **Alison Walker Sarah Cousins**
22 THUNDERWING (IRE), 6, b g Indian Danehill (IRE)—Scandisk (IRE) **David & Nicky Robinson**

Other Owners: Mr K. Bowron, Miss Sarah Cousins, Mr Arnold Headdock, Mrs Kath Headdock, Mr A. R. Mills, Mr D. J. Moffatt, Mr David Robinson (Little Langdale), Mr N. G. Robinson, Mr V. R. Vyner-Brooks, Mrs G. E. Vyner-Brooks, Mr C. S. Vyner-Brooks, Miss Alison Walker.

Assistant Trainer: Jennie Moffatt

Conditional: B. Hughes. **Amateur:** Mr M. Garnet.

---

403 MRS L. J. MONGAN, Epsom
Postal: **Condover Stables, Langley Vale Road, Epsom, Surrey, KT18 6AP**
Contacts: **PHONE (01372) 271494 FAX (01372) 271494 MOBILE (07788) 122942**
E-MAIL laura@lauramongan.co.uk WEBSITE www.lauramongan.co.uk

1 ALSADAA (USA), 5, b g Kingmambo (USA)—Aljawza (USA) **Mrs P. J. Sheen**
2 ALWAYSONTHEMOVE, 4, b g Mujahid (USA)—Royal Roulette **Mrs P. J. Sheen**
3 ARISTOXENE (FR), 8, b g Start Fast (FR)—Petite Folie **Mrs P. J. Sheen**
4 BALERNO, 9, b g Machiavellian (USA)—Balabina (USA) **K. M. Santana**
5 BEST SELECTION, 4, ch f Inchinor—Manila Selection **Mrs P. J. Sheen**
6 BRAVE QUEST (IRE), 4, b g Indian Danehill (IRE)—Mill Rainbow (FR) **The Most Welcome Partnership**
7 DARING RACER (GER), 5, ch g Big Shuffle—Daring Action **Condover Racing**
8 JEU D'ESPRIT (IRE), 5, b m Montjeu (IRE)—Cielo Vodkamartini (USA) **Mrs P. J. Sheen**
9 MASTER DARCY, 6, b g Cloudings—Swift Conveyance (IRE) **Mrs P. J. Sheen**
10 MISSIE BAILEYS, 6, ch m Mister Baileys—Jilly Woo **Mrs P. J. Sheen**
11 ORANGE STREET, 8, b g Primitive Rising (USA)—Arctic Oats **Mrs P. J. Sheen**
12 PEPITO COLLONGES (FR), 5, b g Brier Creek (USA)—Berceuse Collonges (FR) **Mrs P. J. Sheen**
13 PINK SALMON, 4, ch f Dr Fong (USA)—West Humble **Mrs P. J. Sheen**
14 PRINCESSE DE MEE (FR), 5, b m Ungaro (GER)—Une de Mee (FR) **Mrs P. J. Sheen**
15 REVOLVE, 8, b g Pivotal—Alpine Time (IRE) **Mrs P. J. Sheen**

MRS L. J. MONGAN—continued

16 **SARABA (FR)**, 7, gr m Soviet Star (USA)—Sarliya (IRE) **Mrs P. J. Sheen**
17 **TOP GEAR**, 6, b g Robellino (USA)—Bundle **Mrs P. J. Sheen**

THREE-YEAR-OLDS

18 **ON THE RED**, b g Bertolini (USA)—Royal Roulette **Mrs P. J. Sheen**

TWO-YEAR-OLDS

19 **MAYBE BLUE**, b f 23/1 Josr Algarhoud (IRE)—Rosina May (IRE) (Danehill Dancer (IRE)) **Mr M. Daly**

Other Owners: Mrs R. Buck, Ms P. J. Carter, Mr M. Daly, Mr David Harrison, Mrs L. J. Mongan, Mr K. Santana.

---

404 **MR W. P. MONTEITH, Rosewell**
Postal: **Whitebog Farm, Rosewell, Midlothian**
Contacts: **PHONE (0131) 4402309 FAX (0131) 4402226 MOBILE (07885) 060296**
E-MAIL pmonteith945@aol.com

1 **CANTGETON (IRE)**, 8, b g Germany (USA)—Lahana (IRE) **D. A. Johnson**
2 **CHARLIE GEORGE**, 7, ch g Idris (IRE)—Faithful Beauty (IRE) **Mrs M. Coppola**
3 **CLASSY CHAV (IRE)**, 6, b g Classic Cliche (IRE)—
Gavotte du Cochet (FR) **Mr & Mrs Raymond Anderson Green**
4 **FIELD ROLLER (IRE)**, 8, ch g High Roller (IRE)—Cathedral Road **D. A. Johnson**
5 **FIRST LOOK (FR)**, 8, b g Acatenango (GER)—First Class (GER) **D. A. Johnson**
6 **GETON (IRE)**, 8, b g Glacial Storm (USA)—Monavale **D. A. Johnson**
7 **HAWKIT (USA)**, 7, b g Silver Hawk (USA)—Hey Ghaz (USA) **A. McLuckie**
8 **JORDANS ELECT**, 8, ch g Fleetwood (IRE)—Cal Norma's Lady (IRE) **B. A. Jordan**
9 **KARABURAN (GER)**, 4, ch g Samum (GER)—Kimora **G. M. Cowan**
10 **KRISTIANSAND**, 8, b g Halling (USA)—Zonda **Mr D. J. Coppola**
11 **KWITARA (GER)**, 4, b f Acatenango (GER)—Kirona **B. A. Jordan**
12 **LOS NADIS (GER)**, 4, ch g Hernando (FR)—La Estrella (GER) **I. G. M. Dalgleish**
13 **LOUISA (GER)**, 4, b f Seattle Dancer (USA)—La Ola (GER) **G. M. Cowan**
14 **LUTEA (IRE)**, 8, ch g Beneficial—Francie's Treble **D. A. Johnson**
15 **MARCEL (FR)**, 8, b g Bateau Rouge—Une Risette (FR) **D. A. Johnson**
16 **MEDISON (FR)**, 8, br g Video Rock (FR)—Colombia III (FR) **D. A. Johnson**
17 **MILLIE THE FILLY**, 5, b m Erhaab (USA)—Life Is Life (FR) **Mr & Mrs Raymond Anderson Green**
18 **NELSON DU RONCERAY (FR)**, 7, b g Lute Antique (FR)—Trieste (FR) **D. A. Johnson**
19 **NERONE (GER)**, 7, gr g Sternkoenig (IRE)—Nordwahl (GER) **D. A. Johnson**
20 **NEWS OF THE DAY (IRE)**, 4, ch f Diesis—Etoile Ascendante (USA) **E. R. H. Nisbet**
21 **POLYPHON (FR)**, 10, b g Murmure (FR)—Petite Folie **Mr & Mrs Raymond Anderson Green**
22 **QUICUYO (GER)**, 5, ch g Acatenango (GER)—Quila (IRE) **Mr D. J. Coppola**
23 **RAYSROCK (IRE)**, 6, br g Anshan—Sovereign Leader (IRE) **A. Irvine**
24 **ROSSIN GOLD (IRE)**, 6, b g Rossini (USA)—Sacred Heart (IRE) **A. W. Melville**
25 **SHARES (IRE)**, 8, b g Turtle Island (IRE)—Glendora **The Dregs Of Humanity**
26 **SINATAS (GER)**, 5, b g Lomitas—Sylvette (USA) **I. W. Bell**
27 **STAND ON ME**, 9, ch g Bob's Return (IRE)—Weldcome **D. A. Johnson**
28 **STANDIN OBLIGATION (IRE)**, 9, ch g Pierre—Clonroche Floods **D. A. Johnson**
29 **TIGER KING (GER)**, 7, b g Tiger Hill (IRE)—Tennessee Girl (GER) **Mr & Mrs Raymond Anderson Green**
30 **TO MAKE TRACKS (FR)**, 6, b g Exit To Nowhere (USA)—Tokay **Mr & Mrs Raymond Anderson Green**
31 **TO TIGER (GER)**, 7, b g Tiger Hill (IRE)—The Mood (GER) **G. M. Cowan**
32 **TOSHI (USA)**, 6, b g Kingmambo (USA)—Majestic Role (FR) **E. Nisbet & Miss L. McFadzean**
33 **TWELVE PACES**, 7, b g Double Trigger (IRE)—Raise The Dawn **D. A. Johnson**
34 **UNCLE NEIL (IRE)**, 11, gr g Roselier (FR)—Bobs My Uncle **Major-Gen C. A. Ramsay**
35 **YOURMAN (IRE)**, 8, b g Shernazar—Lantern Lover **D. A. Johnson**

Other Owners: R. M. S. Allison, R. A. Green, Mrs A. Green, A. G. Guthrie, B. Jordan, Miss L. McFadzean, W. P. Monteith.

Assistant Trainer: Doreen Monteith

Jockey (flat): P. Fessey. **Jockey (NH):** W. Renwick, G. Lee. **Conditional:** Jenny Riding. **Amateur:** Mr D. Blacker, Mr S. Waley-Cohen, Mr J. Wallace.

405 MR A. L. MOORE, Naas

Postal: Dereens, Naas, Co. Kildare, Ireland
Contacts: PHONE (00353) 4587 6292 FAX (00353) 4589 9247 MOBILE (00353) 8725 52535
E-MAIL arthurlmoore@eircom.net

1 **BACK ON THE ROAD (IRE)**, 6, br g Broken Hearted—Special Trix (IRE) C. Jones
2 **BASIC PRINCIPLE**, 8, b g Rudimentary (USA)—Rhyming Moppet Mr D. Cox
3 **BEHIND THE SCENES (IRE)**, 6, br g Presenting—Run For Cover (IRE) Mr R. Croacke
4 **CAPTAIN LYFORD (IRE)**, 6, b g Kahyasi—Tinozakia (IRE) Sir A. J. O'Reilly
5 **CONSCRIPT (IRE)**, 6, b h Mujadil (USA)—Battle Queen F. Cruess Callaghan
6 **DARLING HARBOUR (IRE)**, 5, b g Cadoudal (FR)—Chattoga (FR) J. P. McManus
7 **FISTOULIG (FR)**, 4, ch g Urban Ocean (FR)—Milyseme (FR) Arr Dubs Racing Syndicate
8 **FRANCIS DU MESNIL (FR)**, 6, b g Saint Preuil (FR)—Franciscaine (FR) Kenneth T. Murphy
9 **FRAUDSTER (UAE)**, 5, b g Jade Robbery (USA)—Anaam Gigginstown House Stud
10 **GLORIEUX (IRE)**, 7, b h Perugino (USA)—Gloria (GER) Emerald Isle Syndicate
11 **GRAND LAHOU (FR)**, 5, ch g Cyborg (FR)—Yota (FR) T. Bailey
12 **GREEN BLACK (FR)**, 8, gr g Glaieul (USA)—Tipmosa (FR) Mr M. Beresford
13 **HAVAGOODSIP (IRE)**, 6, gr g Good Thyne (USA)—Lady Sipash C. Hanbury
14 **HIDDEN AGENT (IRE)**, 6, b g Pistolet Bleu (IRE)—Midnight Pond Mr C. Jones
15 **IMPERIAL STORM (IRE)**, 8, br g Glacial Storm (USA)—Call Girl (IRE) B. Kane
16 **IN TECHNICOLOR (IRE)**, 9, b g Germany (USA)—Light Argument (IRE) Dominic J. Jones
17 **JAFFONNIEN (FR)**, 5, b g Mansonnien (FR)—Ostenne (FR) Plantation Stud
18 **JAQUOUILLE (FR)**, 11, b g Agent Bleu (FR)—Topeka (FR) Mr F. Clarke
19 **JIMRAP (FR)**, 7, b g Jimble (FR)—La Rapaille (IRE) Hotsprey Syndicate
20 **JOHN DILLINGER (FR)**, 5, b br g Saddlers' Hall (FR)—Red Bush
21 **KING JOHNS CASTLE (IRE)**, 9, gr g Flemensfirth (USA)—Caislain Darai (IRE) J. P. McManus
22 **KRANJI (FR)**, 8, b g Take Risks (FR)—Vertevoie (FR) Sir A. J. O'Reilly
23 **LENREY (IRE)**, 8, b g Zaffaran (USA)—Sally Smith Mr T. Bailey
24 **LUERN QUERCUS (FR)**, 6, ch g Villez (USA)—Olle France (FR) Mr T. Bailey
25 **MAJOR SENSATION (FR)**, 6, b g Saddlers' Hall (FR)—Minorettes Girl J. P. McManus
26 **MANSONY (FR)**, 9, b g Mansonnien (FR)—Hairly (FR) Mr M. Mulholland
27 **MERITORIOUS (IRE)**, 5, b g Beat All (USA)—Little Serena J. P. McManus
28 **MON OISEAU (FR)**, 8, b g Port Lyautey (FR)—Amour d'oiseau (FR) Mrs A. Dunlop
29 **NATIVE CLAN (FR)**, 5, b g Dernier Empereur (USA)—Freccia (IRE) N. Langan
30 **NIT EN DO'S (FR)**, 7, b g Passing Sale (FR)—Ombrelle II (FR) Lyreen Syndicate
31 **NOTABLE D'ESTRUVAL (FR)**, 7, b g Nononito (FR)—Vocation (FR) Mr P. McCarthy
32 **O'GARA (IRE)**, 5, b g New Frontier (IRE)—Daring Hen (FR) Exors of the Late C. Ryan
33 **PANZER CHIEF (FR)**, 5, b g Assessor (IRE)—First Filly (FR) Gigginstown House Stud
34 **PIN D'ESTRUVAL (FR)**, 5, ch g Lute Antique (FR)—Haie d'estruval (FR) S. Haughey
35 **PLAISIR D'ESTRUVAL (FR)**, 5, ch g Fragrant Mix (USA)—Aluette (FR) P. Yale
36 **POMMIER D'ESTRUVAL (FR)**, 5, gr h Saint Preuil (FR)—Javelle d'estruval (FR) M. Beresford
37 **PORT LA CHAINE (FR)**, 5, b g Port Lyautey (FR)—Last Fury (FR) Wee Remy Syndicate
38 **QBUSTER (IRE)**, 7, b g Turtle Island (IRE)—Torbay (IRE) Mrs J. Magnier
39 **REGAL RUMPUS**, 6, br g Rakaposhi King—Avena Mrs A. L. T. Moore
40 **ROYALDOU (FR)**, 7, b g Cadoudal (FR)—Royale Sea (FR) J. P. McManus
41 **SEISMOLOGIE**, 5, ch g Zilzal (USA)—Miss Bussell L. Breslin
42 **SOLE BONNE FEMME (IRE)**, 6, b g Rudimentary (USA)—Ardnacrusha (IRE) Mr E. Fitzpatrick
43 **STEWARTS HOUSE (IRE)**, 5, b g Overbury (IRE)—Osocool C. Jones
44 **TAHITIEN FIX (FR)**, 6, bl g Mansonnien (FR)—Ifafy (FR) Mrs B. Mulryan
45 **TAKENDO**, 6, b h Acatenango (GER)—Tiyi (FR) F. Cruess Callaghan
46 **TAMAYO (IRE)**, 8, b br g In The Money (IRE)—Cassies Girl (IRE) R. A. Bartlett
47 **THE RAILWAY MAN (IRE)**, 9, b g Shernazar—Sparky Sue (IRE) Mr C. Ryan
48 **THEATRE FESTIVAL (IRE)**, 6, b g King's Theatre (IRE)—Karmisymixa (FR) Mrs N. McNamara
49 **TIGER CRY (IRE)**, 10, b g Germany (USA)—Dream Academy Mr C. Jones
50 **TRAIGA SUERTE (FR)**, 5, b g Adieu Au Roi (FR)—Nuovo Style (IRE) Mrs A. L. T. Moore
51 **UP THERE (IRE)**, 7, b g Supreme Leader—Avro Avian Mrs A. L. T. Moore
52 **VINTAGE CLASS (IRE)**, 5, b g Hernando (FR)—Native Bid (FR) Exors of the Late C. Ryan
53 **WELL TUTORED (IRE)**, 9, b g Master Willie—Knockaverry (IRE) Mr M. Bailey
54 **WELL YOUNG MAN (IRE)**, 7, b g Saddlers' Hall (IRE)—Iram Mr G. McManus

Assistant Trainer: Aurelion Micheau

Jockey (NH): D. J. Casey, D.N. Russell, P. A. Carberry. **Conditional:** S. G. Carey. **Amateur:** Mr N. Kelly, Mr M. O'Sullivan, Mr J. D. Moore.

406 MR G. L. MOORE, Brighton
Postal: **4 Downland Close, Woodingdean, Brighton, Sussex, BN2 6DN**
Contacts: HOME **(01273) 620106** YARD **(01273) 620405** MOBILE **(07753) 863123**

1 ADECCO (IRE), 9, b g Eagle Eyed (USA)—Kharaliya (FR) **The Ashden Partnership**
2 ADOPTED HERO (IRE), 8, b g Sadler's Wells (USA)—Lady Liberty (NZ) **N. J. Jones**
3 ALESSANO, 6, ch g Hernando (FR)—Alessandra **D. J. Deer**
4 ALMIZAN (IRE), 8, b g Darshaan—Bint Albaadiya (USA) **Heart Of The South Racing**
5 ALPES MARITIMES, 4, b g Danehill Dancer (USA)—Miss Riviera **R. Green**
6 ALRAFID (IRE), 9, ch g Halling (USA)—Ginger Tree **Gillespie Brothers**
7 ALTILHAR (USA), 5, b g Dynaformer (USA)—Al Desima **H. Hunt**
8 AMEEQ (USA), 6, b br g Silver Hawk (USA)—Haniya (USA) **C. E. Stedman**
9 AMICHI, 4, b f Averti (IRE)—Friend For Life **D. J. Deer**
10 AMNESTY, 9, ch g Salse (USA)—Amaranthus **Mr G.A.Jackman, Mr J.F.Jackman**
11 ANTICIPATING, 8, b g Polish Precedent (USA)—D'azy **D. R. Hunnisett**
12 APACHE DAWN, 4, ch g Pursuit of Love—Taza **R. Kiernan, Paul Chapman**
13 ARDMADDY (IRE), 4, b g Generous (IRE)—Yazmin (IRE) **Blue Crocodile**
14 ART MAN, 5, b g Dansili—Persuasion **M. R. Green**
15 ART MODERN (IRE), 6, ch g Giant's Causeway—Sinead (USA) **M. R. Green**
16 ARTREJU (GER), 5, ch g Perugino (USA)—Art of Easter (GER) **The Winning Hand**
17 BARRANCO (IRE), 7, b g Sadler's Wells (USA)—Belize Tropical (IRE) **Mr R. Henderson**
18 BLACKTHORN BOY (IRE), 6, b g Zaffaran (USA)—First And Foremost (IRE) **J. B. Hobbs**
19 BRIDGEWATER BOYS, 7, b g Atraf—Dunloe (IRE) **Matthew Green & Richard Green**
20 BRING IT ON HOME, 4, b g Beat Hollow—Dernier Cri **Mr C. E. Stedman & Mr A. R. Blaxland**
21 CAVALLIAN (USA), 6, b br g Bianconi (USA)—Taylor Park (USA) **D. J. Deer**
22 CAVALRY TWILL (IRE), 4, b g Alhaarth (IRE)—Blue Mantle (IRE) **The Winning Hand**
23 CELTIC SPIRIT (IRE), 5, ch g Pivotal—Cavernista **Miss S. K. Bowles**
24 COCKATOO (USA), 5, b g Dynaformer—Enticed (USA) **C. E. Stedman**
25 COEUR COURAGEUX (FR), 6, b g Xaar—Linoise (USA) **William Wallace Partnership**
26 COLD TURKEY, 8, b br g Polar Falcon (USA)—South Rock **A. P. Grinter**
27 DARK PARADE (ARG), 7, b g Parade Marshal (USA)—Charming Dart (ARG) **N. J. Jones**
28 DUNDRY, 7, b g Bin Ajwaad (IRE)—China's Pearl **D. J. Deer**
29 DUSKY WARBLER, 9, br g Ezzoud (IRE)—Bronzewing **Mike Charlton & Rodger Sargent**
30 EARL KRAUL (IRE), 5, b g Imperial Ballet (IRE)—Bu Hagab (IRE) **M. C. Killoran**
31 ENTHUSIUS, 5, b g Generous (IRE)—Edouna (FR) **Fontwell Park Partnership**
32 EQUILIBRIA (USA), 6, b g Gulch (USA)—Julie La Rousse (IRE) **Dr C. A. Barnett**
33 FIX THE RIB (IRE), 5, b g Dr Massini (USA)—Hot Curry (IRE) **Mr A. Wade**
34 FLAMING WEAPON, 6, b g Unfuwain (USA)—Flame Valley (USA) **B. T. M. Racing**
35 FLYING SPIRIT (IRE), 9, b g Flying Spur (AUS)—All Laughter **Richard Green (Fine Paintings)**
36 GABIER, 5, b g Galileo (IRE)—Contare **B. Siddle & B. D. Haynes**
37 GARRULOUS (UAE), 5, b g Lomitas—Friendly (USA) **Dr C. A. Barnett**
38 GRASP, 6, b g Kayf Tara—Circe **R. Green**
39 GUARDIAN OF TRUTH (IRE), 4, ch g Barathea (IRE)—Zarara (USA) **Bryan Fry & The Toerags**
40 GURU, 10, b g Slip Anchor—Ower (IRE) **W. Bennett**
41 HARRY TRICKER, 4, b g Hernando (FR)—Katy Nowaitee **Mr R. A. Green**
42 HAWK ARROW (IRE), 6, ch g In The Wings—Barbizou (FR) **The Horse Players Two**
43 HEATHCOTE, 6, b g Unfuwain (USA)—Chere Amie (USA) **B. Siddle & B. D. Haynes**
44 HERE WE GO (IRE), 9, b g Bob Back (USA)—Bold Lyndsey **D. N. Green**
45 HIGHEST ESTEEM, 4, b g Mark of Esteem (IRE)—For More (FR) **P. C. Green**
46 HONDURAS (SWI), 7, gr g Daylami (IRE)—High Mare (FR) **The Pink Punters**
47 HURRICANE THOMAS (IRE), 4, b g Celtic Swing—Viola Royale (IRE) **B. Siddle & B. D. Haynes**
48 I HAVE DREAMED (IRE), 6, b g Montjeu (IRE)—Diamond Field (USA) **D. R. Hunnisett**
49 IDRIS (GER), 7, ch g Generous (USA)—Idraak **RDM Racing**
50 IRISH TOAST (IRE), 6, b g Presenting—Brymar Lass (IRE) **Warm Bread**
51 JACK ROLFE, 6, b g Polish Precedent (USA)—Haboobti **Mrs Sarah Diamandis & Mrs Celia Woollett**
52 KARASAKAL (IRE), 5, b g Kahyasi—Karasta (IRE) **T. J. Painting**
53 KAVACHI (IRE), 5, b g Cadeaux Genereux—Answered Prayer **Mr Bryan Pennick & Mr Roy Martin**
54 KAVALOTI (IRE), 4, b c Kahyasi—Just As Good (FR) **Gillespie Brothers**
55 KERAYASI (FR), 6, b g Kahyasi—Good Blend (FR) **J. Brown, B. Spiby**
56 KING OF CHARM (IRE), 5, ch g King Charlemagne (USA)—Pumpona (USA) **Greystar Partnership**
57 KING'S HEAD (IRE), 5, b g King's Best—Ustka **The Gingerbread Men**
58 KRASIVI'S BOY (USA), 6, b br g Swain (USA)—Krasivi (USA) **Mrs E. A. Kiernan**
59 L'HOMME DE NUIT (GER), 4, b c Samum (GER)—La Bouche (GER) **David & Jane George**
60 LATALANTA (FR), 5, b g Lost World (IRE)—Belle De Saigon (FR)
61 LORD HECCLES (IRE), 9, b g Supreme Leader—Parsons Law **P. C. Collins**
62 LORD OF DREAMS (IRE), 6, ch g Barathea (IRE)—The Multiyorker (IRE) **N. J. Jones**
63 LORIKEET, 9, b g Rainbow Quest (USA)—Destiny Dance (USA) **The Tribesmen Syndicate**

MR G. L. MOORE—continued

64 **LUPANAR (IRE)**, 4, ch g Galileo (IRE)—Louve Sacree (USA)
65 **MACLEAN**, 7, b g Machiavellian (USA)—Celtic Cross **P. C. Collins**
66 **MADRIGALE**, 4, b f Averti (IRE)—Shy Minstrel (USA) **D. J. Deer**
67 **MARC OF BRILLIANCE (USA)**, 5, ch g Sunday Silence (USA)—Rahcak (IRE) **D. R. Hunnisett**
68 **MASTER T (USA)**, 9, b g Trempolino (USA)—Our Little C (USA) **G. L. Moore**
69 **MATARAZZO (IRE)**, 6, gr g Linamix (FR)—Altamira (FR) **Brighton Racecourse Partnership**
70 **MAXIMIX**, 5, gr g Linamix (FR)—Time Will Show (FR) **Mr W. G. Slee**
71 **MON MICHEL (IRE)**, 5, b g Montjeu (IRE)—Miniver (IRE) **The Gingerbread Men**
72 **MR BOO (IRE)**, 9, b g Needle Gun (IRE)—Dasi **The Hon Mrs C. Cameron**
73 **MR NAPOLEON (IRE)**, 6, gr g Daylami (IRE)—Dathuil (IRE) **Mr J. Gibbons**
74 **NATION STATE**, 7, b g Sadler's Wells (USA)—Native Justice (USA) **J. D. Brownrigg**
75 **NAWAMEES (IRE)**, 10, b g Darshaan—Truly Generous (IRE) **P. Stamp**
76 **NICE TO KNOW (FR)**, 4, ch f Machiavellian (USA)—Entice (USA) **Mr C. S. C. Hancock**
77 **NUMIDE (FR)**, 5, b h Highest Honor (FR)—Numidie (FR)
78 **OR JAUNE (FR)**, 6, ch g Grand Tresor (FR)—Vancia (FR) **Fontwell Park Partnership**
79 **OURAGAN LAGRANGE (FR)**, 6, b g Panoramic—
                        Fannie de Lagrange (FR) **The Betting Room Southsea Partnership**
80 **PACE SHOT (IRE)**, 6, b g Montjeu (IRE)—Pacific Grove **R. Green**
81 **PANJO BERE (FR)**, 5, b g Robin des Pres (FR)—Honeymoon Suite (FR) **Mr Paul Chapman Mr R. Kiernan**
82 **PEINTURE DE GUERRE (FR)**, 5, b g Loco (IRE)—Dani Kris (FR) **Mr A. J. Taylor**
83 **PREMIER DES MARAIS (FR)**, 5, b g Kalmoss (FR)—Imghard (FR) **Marais Racing**
84 **PRIME CONTENDER**, 6, b g Efisio—Gecko Rouge **Matthew Green & Richard Green**
85 **PRINCE VALENTINE**, 7, b g My Best Valentine—Affaire de Coeur **D. R. Hunnisett**
86 **RAHY'S CROWN (USA)**, 5, b g Rahy (USA)—Inca Princess (USA) **The Swag Partners**
87 **RANDWICK ROAR (IRE)**, 9, b g Lord Americo—Le Bavellen **D. R. Hunnisett**
88 **SAHF LONDON**, 5, b g Vettori (IRE)—Lumiere d'espoir (IRE) **Longshot Racing**
89 **SALUT SAINT CLOUD**, 7, b g Primo Dominie—Tiriana **A. P. Grinter**
90 **SAND CAT**, 5, b g Cadeaux Genereux—Desert Lynx (IRE) **EERC**
91 **SANDYMAC (IRE)**, 8, b m Oscar (IRE)—Molly Owen **P. C. Collins**
92 **SCARLET FLYER (USA)**, 5, b g Gilded Time (USA)—Tennis Partner (USA) **The Optima Partnership**
93 **SEBASTIANO (IRE)**, 5, ch g Ski Chief (USA)—Femme Rouge (IRE) **The Leap Of Faith Partnership**
94 **SHARDAKHAN (IRE)**, 6, b g Dr Devious (IRE)—Sharamana (IRE) **P. W. Middleton**
95 **SHE'S SO PRETTY (IRE)**, 4, ch f Grand Lodge (USA)—Plymsole (USA) **Miss S. Bowles**
96 **SOLE AGENT (IRE)**, 6, b g Trans Island—Seattle Siren (USA) **Mr B. & Mr J. Crainey**
97 **SPACE COWBOY (IRE)**, 8, b g Anabaa (USA)—Lady Moranbon (USA) **The Sanderson Partnership**
98 **STANCE**, 9, b g Salse (USA)—De Stael (USA) **S. Packham**
99 **STORMY SKYE (IRE)**, 12, b g Bluebird (USA)—Canna **Jayne Moore, T Pollock, J Driscoll**
100 **SUPER SENSATION (GER)**, 7, ch g Platini (GER)—Studford Girl **The Sanderson Partnership**
101 **TAVALU (USA)**, 6, b g Kingmambo (USA)—Larrocha (USA) **Mrs C. A. Painting**
102 **TIKRAM**, 11, ch g Lycius (USA)—Black Fighter (USA) **Mike Charlton & Rodger Sargent**
103 **TRIGGER GUARD**, 6, ch g Double Trigger (IRE)—Harlequin Walk (IRE) **The Harlequin Walk Partnership**
104 **TURNER'S TOUCH**, 6, ch g Compton Place—Chairmans Daughter **G. L. Moore**
105 **TWILL (IRE)**, 5, ch g Barathea (IRE)—Khafaya **T. J. Painting**
106 **VANADIUM**, 6, b g Dansili—Musianica **A V Racing**
107 **VERASI**, 7, b g Kahyasi—Fair Verona (USA) **F. Ledger J. Bateman**
108 **VINMIX DE BESSY (FR)**, 7, gr g River Bay (USA)—Hesse (FR) **P. W. Middleton**
109 **WAIT FOR THE WILL (USA)**, 12, ch g Seeking The Gold (USA)—You'd Be Surprised (USA) **RDM Racing**
110 **WAR PENNANT**, 6, b g Selkirk (USA)—Bunting **P.Collins J.Hinds J.Shea G.L.Moore**
111 **WATERSIDE (IRE)**, 9, ch g Lake Coniston (IRE)—Classic Ring (IRE) **N. R. Shields**
112 **WHISTLING**, 5, br m Piccolo—All The Time **Giles W. Pritchard-Gordon**
113 **WHITE ON BLACK (GER)**, 7, b g Lomitas—White On Red (GER) **B. V. Pennick**
114 **WIESENFURST (GER)**, 4, ch g Artan (IRE)—Wiesenblute (GER) **G. L. Moore**
115 **WINGMAN (IRE)**, 6, b g In The Wings—Precedence (IRE) **Gillespie Brothers**
116 **WITHYWOOD (USA)**, 4, b br f Woodman (USA)—Castellina (USA) **D. J. Deer**
117 **ZERO COOL (USA)**, 4, br c Forestry (USA)—Fabulous (USA) **Dedman Properties Limited**

THREE-YEAR-OLDS

118 **CAPRICCIOSO**, b f Cape Cross (IRE)—Heart of India (IRE) **G. C. Scudder**
119 **HITCHENS (IRE)**, b c Acclamation—Royal Fizz (IRE) **R. Green**
120 **LOVE AND GLORY (IRE)**, b c Intikhab (USA)—La Splendide (USA) **Mr P. Hancock**
121 **MAXWIL**, b c Storming Home—Lady Donatella **H. Hunt**
122 **MOUNTAINEER (FR)**, b g Saint des Saints (FR)—Mistica (FR) **C. E. Stedman**
123 **PAUL THE CARPET (UAE)**, ch c Halling (USA)—Favoured **A. P. Grinter**
124 **PINNACLE POINT**, ch g Best of The Bests (IRE)—Alessandra **D. J. Deer**
125 **PRINCESS LIVIUS (IRE)**, ch f Titus Livius (FR)—Last Shaambles (IRE) **Mr C. E. Stedman**

MR G. L. MOORE—continued

126 **ROYAL TARTAN (USA)**, b f Lemon Drop Kid (USA)—Castellina (USA) **D. J. Deer**
127 **SABRE LIGHT**, b g Fantastic Light (USA)—Good Grounds (USA) **D. J. Deer**
128 **SMOKEY RYE**, b f Bertolini (USA)—Another Secret **Darrell Hinds Susan Bell Pat Butcher**
129 **VINO GRIEGO (FR)**, b g Kahyasi—Vie de Reine (FR) **C. E. Stedman**

Other Owners: A. Amin, Mr M. C. Armstrong, Mrs E. Avery, Mr Wayne Barr, Mr J. Bateman, Mrs Susan Bell, Mr A. Black, Miss V. L. Blake, Mr A. R. Blaxland, J. T. Brown, Rev L. M. Brown, R. Brown, Mrs S. K. Bush, Mr J. M. Bush, Mrs P. M. Butcher, Mrs Rebecca Byrne, Mr Justin Byrne, A. Carr, Mr W. H. Carson, Mr Paul Chapman, Mr M. R. Charlton, Mr Dean Clark, Mrs Cynthia Connolly, Mr Brian Crainey, Mr Jackie Craney, Mrs Sarah J. Diamandis, Mr John Driscoll, Mr Bryan Fry, Mr S. W. Gandon, Mr D. W. George, Mrs J. George, Mr T. G. Gillespie, Mr G. S. Gillespie, Mr M. Goodrum, Mr A. Graham, Mr Paul Hancock, Mr W. D. Hawkes, Mr B. D. Haynes, T. D. Hide, Mr Peter Higgins, Mr Darrell Hinds, Mrs Jill Ho, Mr G. A. Jackman, Mr J. F. Jackman, P. J. Jacobs, Mr K. Jeffery, Mr Gordon Keith, Mr C. Lacy, Mrs F. Ledger, Mr Thomas Manley, Mr K. Marsden, R. N. Martin, M. C. Mason, Mr Frank McHugh, Mrs J. Moore, Mr Mike O'Brien, Mrs Christine Painting, Mr A. W. Payne, T. Penniket, M. T. Penniket, Mr John Penny, Mrs Caroline Penny, Mr T. Pollock, Mr John Ripley, H. J. Rix, Prof A. R. Sanderson, Ms Helen Sanderson, Mr Rodger Sargent, Mr J. Shea, Mr R. M. Siddle, W. P. Smith, B. Spiby, Mr Paul Stamp, Vogue Development Company (Kent) Ltd, Mr D. P. Walsh, Mr Tommy Ware, Mr D. A. Wilson, Mrs Celia Woollett.

Assistant Trainer: David Wilson

Jockey (flat): G. Baker, R. L. Moore, F. Sweeney. **Jockey (NH):** A. P. McCoy, P. Hide, J. E. Moore. **Conditional:** E. Dehdashti, D. Hutchinson. **Apprentice:** J. Marshall, R. Atkinson. **Amateur:** Miss Hayley Moore.

---

407 **MR G. M. MOORE, Middleham**
Postal: **Warwick Lodge Stables, Middleham, Leyburn, North Yorkshire, DL8 4PB**
Contacts: **PHONE (01969) 623823 FAX (01969) 623823 MOBILE (07711) 321117**
E-MAIL georgeandcarolmoore@hotmail.co.uk WEBSITE www.george-moore-racing.co.uk

1 **AD MURUM (IRE)**, 9, ch g Hubbly Bubbly (USA)—Cailin Cainnteach **W. J. Laws**
2 **ALL FOR THE CAUSE (IRE)**, 6, b g Gothland (FR)—Hurricane Hattie **D. Neale**
3 **APSARA**, 7, br m Groom Dancer (USA)—Ayodhya (IRE) **Mrs Mary & Miss Susan Hatfield**
4 **AVIATION**, 6, b g Averti (IRE)—Roufontaine **G. R. Orchard**
5 **BENTONS CHOICE**, 5, b g Sir Harry Lewis (USA)—Joley Blake **Bentons Racing**
6 **BIJOU DAN**, 7, ch g Bijou d'inde—Cal Norma's Lady (IRE)
7 **BOGSIDE THEATRE (IRE)**, 4, b f Fruits of Love (USA)—Royal Jubilee (IRE) **Brian Lappin**
8 **CHARITY LANE (IRE)**, 5, b g Indian Danehill (IRE)—In Behind (IRE) **M. R. Johnson**
9 **DOLANS BAY (IRE)**, 7, b g Old Vic—Kyle House VII **S. P. Graham**
10 **EASBY PARK**, 5, b g Tamure—Mossfield **G. R. Orchard**
11 **ELWICK PRINCESS**, 4, b f Averti (IRE)—Aldevonie **Geoff & Sandra Turnbull**
12 **FINLAY'S FOOTSTEPS**, 4, ch g Dr Fong (USA)—Bay Shade (USA) **D. Parker**
13 **FROGS' GIFT (IRE)**, 6, gr m Danehill Dancer (IRE)—Warthill Whispers **Mrs I. I. Plumb**
14 **GIBBOGHSTOWN (IRE)**, 5, b m Second Empire (IRE)—Take My Pledge (IRE) **Mrs A. M. O'Sullivan**
15 **GREENBELT**, 7, b g Desert Prince (IRE)—Emerald (USA) **Mrs A. Roddis**
16 **IN DREAM'S (IRE)**, 6, b g Dr Fong (USA)—No Sugar Baby (FR) **Castle Racing**
17 **INDIAN STORM (IRE)**, 6, b g Ridgewood Ben—Brushes Bride (IRE) **Mrs Mary & Miss Susan Hatfield**
18 **ISLAND KEY (IRE)**, 6, b g Insan (USA)—Kilkinamurry Home (IRE) **Mrs I. I. Plumb**
19 **JUNGLE JINKS (IRE)**, 13, b g Proud Panther (FR)—Three Ladies **Mrs Mary & Miss Susan Hatfield**
20 **KEENE SPIRIT**, 5, ch g Keen—High Penhowe **Ontario Flag Partnership**
21 **LIFES A MYSTERY (IRE)**, 5, b g Luso—Life of A Lady (IRE) **S. P. Graham**
22 **LUNAN BAY**, 5, b m Defacto (USA)—Tangalooma
23 **MACORVILLE (USA)**, 5, b g Diesis—Desert Jewel (USA) **Geoff & Sandra Turnbull**
24 **MUNDO'S MAGIC**, 4, b g Foxhound (USA)—Amber's Bluff **Fishing 4 Fun**
25 **NELSONS COLUMN (IRE)**, 5, b g Benny The Dip (USA)—Sahara Rose **Ribble Valley Racing**
26 **NUMERO DUE**, 6, b g Sinndar (IRE)—Kindle **J. W. Andrews**
27 **O'SOGOOD (IRE)**, 6, b g Oscar (IRE)—Bula Supreme (IRE) **J. B. Wallwin**
28 **PAGAN RIVER**, 7, b g River Falls—Pagan Star **Richard J. Phizacklea**
29 **PAGAN STARPRINCESS**, 4, b f Robertico—Pagan Star **Richard J. Phizacklea**
30 **PERLY SPENCER (IRE)**, 6, b g Bob's Return (IRE)—Never Dawned (IRE) **D. Neale**
31 **SAMRAANIAN DANCER**, 4, b g Samraan (USA)—Chipewyas (FR) **Mrs Mary & Miss Susan Hatfield**
32 **SHINKOSAN (IRE)**, 5, b g Shinko Forest (IRE)—Dashing Rocksville **B. P. Bradshaw**
33 **SPIRIT OF ECSTACY**, 4, b f Val Royal (FR)—Isla Negra (IRE) **A. M. Campion**
34 **SPRING GAMBLE (IRE)**, 9, b g Norwich—Aurora Run (IRE) **J. B. Wallwin**
35 **SPRINGVIC (IRE)**, 8, b g Old Vic—Spring Beauty (IRE) **Mrs J. M. Gray**
36 **THE KEALSHORE KID (IRE)**, 4, grg Saddlers' Hall (IRE)—Rongai (IRE) **J. Pickavance**
37 **THE LONGFELLA**, 7, b g Petong—Miss Tri Colour **Mrs S. M. Pearson**
38 **THE SHY MAN (IRE)**, 5, b g Grand Plaisir (IRE)—Black Betty **S. P. Graham**

MR G. M. MOORE—continued

39 **TOLDO (IRE)**, 6, gr g Tagula (IRE)—Mystic Belle (IRE) **J. Armstrong**
40 **YOUNG BOBBY**, 8, b g Gunner B—Trikkala Star **John J. Thompson & Cyril D. Butler**

THREE-YEAR-OLDS

41 **CALZA DI SETA**, b f Lujain (USA)—Isla Negra (IRE) **Mrs S. M. Pearson**
42 **HARRISON'S STAR**, gr g Erhaab (USA)—Gentle Gypsy **D. Parker**
43 **KEARA**, b f Kayf Tara—Lavender Lady (IRE)
44 **MILL ANNIE**, ch f Karinga Bay—Brookhill (GER) **M. T. Bloore**
45 **MILL BEATTIE**, b f Beat All (USA)—Step On Degas **M. T. Bloore**
46 **PRINCE'S DECREE**, br c Diktat—Rock Face **J. V. Lishman**
47 **REEL BUDDY STAR**, ch g Reel Buddy—So Discreet **J. W. Armstrong & M. J. Howarth**
48 **RUNSWICK BAY**, b c Intikhab (USA)—Upend **J. V. Lishman**
49 **VERONICAS WAY**, b f High Estate—Mimining **J. Stevenson**

TWO-YEAR-OLDS

50 B C 30/1 Mujahid (USA)—Janiceland (IRE) (Foxhound (USA)) (7500)
51 B f 30/3 Soviet Star (USA)—Aldevonie (Green Desert (USA))
52 Ch c 17/3 Traditionally (USA)—La Sylphide (Rudimentary (USA)) **Geoff & Sandra Turnbull**
53 Ch f 2/4 Bertolini (USA)—Mint Royale (Cadeaux Genereux)
54 **ORIENTAL ROSE**, b f 6/2 Dr Fong (USA)—Sahara Rose (Green Desert (USA))
55 **VERONICAS BOY**, br c 9/2 Diktat—Thamud (IRE) (Lahib (USA)) (2000) **J. Stevenson**

Other Owners: M. J. Bagshaw, Mr A. G. Benton, C. D. Butler, Mr S. R. Counsell, Mr H. T. Hair, Mrs Mary Hatfield, Mr M. J. Howarth, Mrs Susan Kramer, Mr A. K. Mitchell, Mr Steven Nightingale, Mr J. Reardon, Mr N. Ricioppo, C. G. Simpson, Mr Rodney Tennant, John J. Thompson, Mr W. A. Tunstall, Mr G. Turnbull, Mrs S. E. Turnbull, Mr J. R. Warne.

Assistant Trainer: Mrs Susan Moore

Jockey (NH): F. Keniry. **Conditional:** Matthew Dickinson.

---

408   MR J. S. MOORE, Upper Lambourn
Postal: Top Yard, Uplands, Upper Lambourn, Hungerford, Berkshire, RG17 8QJ
Contacts: PHONE (01488) 73353 FAX (01488) 73363 MOBILE (07860) 811127/(07900) 402856
E-MAIL jsmoore.racing@btopenworld.com WEBSITE uplandsracing.com

1 **AZAROLE (IRE)**, 7, b g Alzao (USA)—Cashew **Mrs F. H. Hay**
2 **DAYLAMI DREAMS**, 4, gr g Daylami (IRE)—Kite Mark **Mrs F. H. Hay**
3 **DUBAI BUILDER**, 4, b g Tobougg (IRE)—Roseum **Mrs F. H. Hay**
4 **EMMA JEAN LAD (IRE)**, 4, ch g Intikhab (USA)—Swing City (IRE) **Roger Ambrose William Reilly Stan Moore**
5 **FAIRY FESTIVAL (IRE)**, 4, b f Montjeu (IRE)—Escape To Victory **Coleman Bloodstock Limited**
6 **FINAL VERSE**, 5, b g Mark of Esteem (IRE)—Tamassos **Mrs F. H. Hay**
7 **IMPELLER (IRE)**, 9, ch g Polish Precedent (USA)—Almaaseh (IRE) **Mrs F. H. Hay**
8 **LARAD (IRE)**, 7, br g Desert Sun—Glenstal Priory **J. S. Moore**
9 **MACEDON**, 5, b g Dansili—Hypnotize **Mrs F. H. Hay**
10 **MONTALEMBERT (USA)**, 4, b br g Kalanisi (IRE)—Garendare **W. McKay**
11 **MR BILBO BAGGINS**, 5, ch g Magic Ring (IRE)—I'll Try **Mrs Derek Strauss**
12 **MULL OF DUBAI**, 5, b g Mull of Kintyre (USA)—Enlisted (IRE) **Mrs F. H. Hay**
13 **NEPOTISTA (BRZ)**, 6, b g Know Heights (IRE)—Wekilinda (BRZ) **Mrs F. H. Hay**
14 **POLISH POWER (GER)**, 8, br h Halling (USA)—Polish Queen **J. Wells**
15 **RYAN'S FUTURE (IRE)**, 8, b h Danetime (IRE)—Era **V. Khosla**
16 **SGT SCHULTZ (IRE)**, 5, b g In The Wings—Ann's Annie (IRE) **J. E. Barnes**
17 **SNOQUALMIE BOY (IRE)**, 5, b g Montjeu (IRE)—Seattle Ribbon (USA) **Mrs F. H. Hay**
18 **SOUTHANDWEST (IRE)**, 4, ch g Titus Livius (FR)—Cheviot Indian (IRE) **Mr B. McNicholas & Mr M. Feehan**
19 **TRAFFIC GUARD (USA)**, 4, b c More Than Ready (USA)—Street Scene (IRE) **Mrs F. H. Hay**
20 **YELLOWSTONE (IRE)**, 4, b c Rock of Gibraltar (IRE)—Love And Affection (USA) **Mrs F. H. Hay**

THREE-YEAR-OLDS

21 **BANJO BANDIT (IRE)**, b c Mujadil (USA)—Common Cause **Mr K. Bailey & Mr J. S. Moore**
22 **BLUE ZENITH (IRE)**, ch f Daggers Drawn (USA)—Secret Combe (IRE) **Miss K. Theobald & Mr J. S. Moore**
23 **COOL THE HEELS (IRE)**, b g Catcher In The Rye (IRE)—Alinea (USA) **Wall To Wall Partnership**
24 **DUBAI DYNAMO**, b c Kyllachy—Miss Mercy (IRE) **Mrs F. H. Hay**
25 **DUBAI PETAL (IRE)**, b f Dubai Destination (USA)—Out of Egypt (USA) **Mr S. A. Belton**
26 **GALVASHIELD**, b c Nayef (USA)—Star **Mrs F. H. Hay**

MR J. S. MOORE—continued

27 **HER NAME IS RIO (IRE)**, ch f Captain Rio—L'harmonie (USA) **Mr Tom Yates,Mrs Evelyn Yates,J.S.Moore**
28 **INFINITE PATIENCE**, b br f High Chaparral (IRE)—Idma **J. S. Moore**
29 **LIZARD ISLAND (USA)**, b c Danehill Dancer (IRE)—Add (USA) **Mrs F. H. Hay**
30 **PRECISION BREAK (USA)**, b c Silver Deputy (CAN)—Miss Kitty Cat (USA) **Uplands Acquisitions Limited**
31 **RANKAYO HITAM (USA)**, b c Yonaguska (USA)—Catala (USA) **Uplands Acquisitions Limited**
32 **SOLENT RIDGE (IRE)**, b c Namid—Carrozzina **Mrs L. Bloxsome, Mr T. Wilkinson & Mr J. S. Moore**
33 **SOUTHWEST STAR (IRE)**, b g No Excuse Needed—Christeningpresent (IRE) **Wall To Wall Partnership**

TWO-YEAR-OLDS

34 B c 12/1 Diktat—Ann's Annie (IRE) (Alzao (USA)) (26000)
35 **CRUIKADYKE**, b c 24/4 Kyllachy—Shoshone (Be My Chief (USA)) (77220) **Uplands Acquisitions Limited**
36 **FITRIANI**, ch f 21/2 Pivotal—Aunt Pearl (Seattle Slew (USA)) (100000) **Mrs F. H. Hay**
37 **FONG'S ALIBI**, b f 11/2 Dr Fong (USA)—
                  Alchemy (IRE) (Sadler's Wells (USA)) (4825) **Mr T. & Mrs J. Cunningham & Mr R. Frost**
38 Ch c 18/4 Captain Rio—Hilites (IRE) (Desert King (IRE)) (13000) **Mr & Mrs Yates**
39 **LAVA STEPS (USA)**, b c 17/4 Giant's Causeway (USA)—
                  Miznah (IRE) (Sadler's Wells (USA)) (115000) **Uplands Acquisitions Limited**
40 B c 5/4 One Cool Cat (USA)—Lillibits (USA) (Kingmambo (USA)) (21000)
41 **LOIS DARLIN (USA)**, ch f 15/3 Indian Haven—Miriana (IRE) (Bluebird (USA)) (4503) **Indian Haven Syndicate**
42 B br c 20/4 Officer (USA)—Luv to Stay n Chat (Candi's Gold (USA)) (17006)
43 B br c 7/2 Songandaprayer (USA)—Mama G (USA) (Prospector's Bid (USA)) (1523) **Mr J. Wells & Mr J. Wade**
44 Ch f 22/4 Indian Haven—Mystery Hill (USA) (Danehill (USA)) (12869)
45 B f 4/3 Chapel Royal (USA)—Oldupai (USA) (Gulch (USA)) (10689)
46 B c 23/3 Royal Applause—Roses of Spring (Shareef Dancer (USA)) (1238) **Bigwigs Bloodstock Ltd**
47 B f 12/2 Monsieur Bond (IRE)—Shirley Collins (Robellino (USA)) (3539) **P. Colley**
48 B c 17/3 Pyrus (USA)—Spot In Time (Mtoto) (17000)

Other Owners: Mr R. Ambrose, Mr K. B. Bailey, Mrs L. H. Bloxsome, Mr Gerry Connor, Mr Frank Connor, L. Conway, T. S. M. Cunningham, Mrs J. P. E. Cunningham, Mr P. G. Dalton, Mr K. Duncan, Mr M. Feehan, Mr R. E. Frost, P. J. Gleeson, Mr M. Khan, Mr Mustafa Khan, Mr B. McNicholas, Mr J. S. Moore, Mr A. E. Purser, Mr W. J. Reilly, Miss Karen Theobald, T. V. Wilkinson, Mr T. Yates, Mrs Evelyn Yates.

Assistant Trainer: Mrs S. Moore

Jockey (flat): John Egan, Liam Keniry. **Jockey (NH):** S. Durack. **Apprentice:** Tolley Dean. **Amateur:** Mrs S. Moore.

---

409 | **MR K. A. MORGAN, Ledbury**
Postal: **The Hop Kiln, Lilly Hall Farm, Little Marcle, Ledbury, Herefordshire, HR8 2LD**
Contacts: **PHONE (01531) 633122 MOBILE (07768) 996103**

1 **AJZAL (IRE)**, 4, b g Alhaarth (IRE)—Alkaffeyeh (IRE) **Mr P. J. Manser**
2 **CAMERA SHY (IRE)**, 4, ch c Pivotal—Shy Danceuse (FR) **Mr M. D. Ogburn**
3 **COLOPHONY (USA)**, 8, ch g Distant View (USA)—Private Line (USA) **Mr H.A.Blenkhorn & Miss C.J.Blenkhorn**
4 **CRY ALOT BOY**, 5, ch g Spinning World—Intellectuelle **D. S. Cooper**
5 **GROOMS AFFECTION**, 8, b g Groom Dancer (USA)—Love And Affection (USA) **P. Doughty**
6 **JEBAL SURAAJ (USA)**, 8, b g Gone West (USA)—Trishyde (USA) **D. S. Cooper**
7 **KINGKOHLER (IRE)**, 9, b g King's Theatre (IRE)—Legit **P. Doughty, J. Champion, E. Barlow, H. Morgan**
8 **LANNACOMBE CLOVER**, 5, b g Kayf Tara—Persian Clover **R. W. Mitchell**
9 **LOST SOLDIER FOUR**, 5, b g In The Wings—Donya **D. S. Cooper**
10 **MACREATER**, 10, b m Mazaad—Gold Caste **J. N. Stokes**
11 **MARKAB**, 5, b h Green Desert (USA)—Hawafiz **Tight Lines Partnership**
12 **MENELAUS**, 7, b g Machiavellian (USA)—Mezzogiorno **R. J. Norton**
13 **POSTAGE (USA)**, 5, b br g Chester House (USA)—Nimble Mind (USA) **P. Doughty**
14 **RAIDER OF THE EAST (IRE)**, 6, b g Darshaan—Convenience (IRE) **D. S. Cooper**
15 **SAHARA PRINCE (IRE)**, 8, b g Desert King (IRE)—Chehana **D. S. Cooper**
16 **SELKIRK GRACE**, 8, b g Selkirk (USA)—Polina **D. S. Cooper**
17 **SLOW TO PART (IRE)**, 11, gr g Roselier (FR)—Comeragh Queen **K. A. Morgan**
18 **TAKAAMUL**, 5, ch g Almutawakel—Mafaatin (IRE)

THREE-YEAR-OLDS

19 **ARCHILINI**, b c Bertolini (USA)—Dizzy Knight **S. R. Carter**
20 **FORCED OPINION (USA)**, gr c Distant View (USA)—Kinetic Force (USA) **K. A. Morgan**
21 **SAFASEEF (IRE)**, b f Cadeaux Genereux—Asaafeer (USA) **P. Doughty**

MR K. A. MORGAN—continued

Other Owners: Mr H. A. Blenkhorn, Miss C. J. Blenkhorn, Mrs Jo Champion, Mr E. B. De Giles, Mr T. Gould, Mr H. Morgan.

Assistant Trainer: Miss Laura Morgan

Jockey (flat): James Doyle. **Jockey (NH):** S. Durack, Josh Byrne, James Diment. **Amateur:** Miss Kelly Morgan.

---

410 MR C. P. H. MORLOCK, Wantage
Postal: **Raceyard Cottage Stables, Kingston Lisle, Wantage, Oxfordshire, OX12 9QH**
Contacts: **HOME/FAX** (01367) 820510 **MOBILE** (07768) 923444
E-MAIL charlie@charliemorlockracing.com **WEBSITE** www.charliemorlockracing.com

1 **AINTNONANCY,** 6, b m Rakaposhi King—Threads **Court House Racing**
2 **BEING THERE,** 5, b g Bien Bien (USA)—Segsbury Belle **R. A. Instone**
3 **BULL MARKET (IRE),** 5, b g Danehill (USA)—Paper Moon (IRE) **F. Jones**
4 **COSTA COURTA (FR),** 6, b g Marly River (FR)—Tosca de Bellouet (FR) **Pell-mell Partners**
5 **DEEP WOODS,** 5, b g Nashwan (USA)—Moss **Pell-mell Partners**
6 **DELIGHTFUL TOUCH (FR),** 7, gr g Villez—Fagaras (FR) **Baird,King,Philip & Rennie Partnership**
7 **EASEMENT,** 5, b g Kayf Tara—Raspberry Sauce **Miss Sarah E Williams**
8 5, B g Kahyasi—Fair Maid Marion (IRE)
9 **FLAMAND (FR),** 7, b g Double Bed (FR)—Rays Honor **S. R. C. Philip**
10 **GENARI,** 5, b g Generous (IRE)—Sari **R. A. Instone**
11 **GOOD EFFECT (USA),** 4, ch g Woodman (USA)—River Dreams (USA) **Newnham, Lewis, Patterson**
12 **KOUROSH (IRE),** 8, b g Anshan—Pit Runner **Mrs C. Kendrick**
13 **KRIKKET,** 4, ch f Sinndar (IRE)—Star of The Course (USA) **Miss Sarah E Williams**
14 **MAGIC MERLIN,** 7, b g Magic Ring (IRE)—St James's Antigua (IRE) **Mrs J. L. C. Philip**
15 **MISS JAFFA,** 6, gr m Bold Edge—Excelled (IRE) **Mrs J. W. Melbourne**
16 **NEW MISCHIEF (IRE),** 10, b g Accordion—Alone Party (IRE) **S. R. C. Philip**
17 **NICTOS DE BERSY (FR),** 7, b g Useful (FR)—Tropulka God (FR) **The Fortuna Five**
18 **PATRIXBOURNE,** 5, ch m Double Trigger (IRE)—Lady Buck **S. R. C. Philip**
19 5, B g Kayf Tara—Pollys Perk (IRE) **Mrs C. Kendrick**
20 7, B h Petoski—Red River (IRE) **Mrs J. W. Melbourne**
21 **SACRED BULL,** 6, b g Shambo—Strollaway (IRE) **S. R. C. Philip**
22 **THE BOFFINATOR,** 7, b g Terimon—Free Travel **Kendrick,Bromley,Wellington & Spooner**
23 **TWICE CHARMED,** 5, b m Lomitas—Native Charm (IRE) **Pell-mell Partners**
24 **WALKING IN MEMPHIS (IRE),** 4, b g Golan—Delta Blues (IRE) **S. R. Philip**
25 **WIDE RECEIVER (IRE),** 5, b g Taipan (IRE)—The Plud (IRE) **Girls Allowed**

Other Owners: Mr Michael Baird, Mr G. I. K. Bromley, Mrs Toby Bulgin, Mr J. Chromiak, Mr Richard Gilder, Mr D. P. King, The Hon Mrs Penelope Makins, Mr Michael McCarthy, Mr J. A. Osborne, Mr Simon Philip, Ms L. A. Rennie, Mr Howard Spooner, Mr D. W. Watts, Mr Nic Wellington.

Assistant Trainer: Miss C. Illingworth

Jockey (NH): J. A. McCarthy. **Amateur:** Mr M. Stanley, Mr Ed Cumberpatch.

---

411 MR M. MORRIS, Fethard
Postal: **Everardsgrange, Fethard, Co. Tipperary, Ireland**
Contacts: **PHONE** (00353) 523 1474 **FAX** (00353) 523 1654
E-MAIL mouse@eircom.net **WEBSITE** www.mousemorris.com

1 **ANCESTRAL GIFT (IRE),** 6, br g Presenting—Ancestral Voices (IRE) **Gigginstown Stud**
2 **BAILY BREEZE (IRE),** 9, b g Zaffaran (USA)—Mixed Blends **R. A. Scott**
3 **BAILY ROCK (IRE),** 5, b br g Supreme Leader—Knapping Princess (IRE) **R. A. Scott**
4 **BAILY STORM (IRE),** 6, br g Anshan—Euroblend (IRE) **R. A. Scott**
5 **BAILY VIEW (IRE),** 5, b g Flemensfirth (USA)—King's Linnet (IRE) **R. A. Scott**
6 **BOTTLEFORTHEBATTLE (IRE),** 5, b g Oscar—Divebomb **Horse Island Syndicate**
7 **BROWNS BAILY (IRE),** 6, b g Zaffaran (USA)—Frizzball (IRE) **R. A. Scott**
8 **CONTESSA MESSINA (IRE),** 8, b m Dr Massini—Reoss **M. Errange**
9 **DODGEY DREAM,** 6, ch g Zaffaran (USA)—Dinnys Dream (IRE) **Burnt Toast Ltd**
10 **DRAKERATH (IRE),** 6, br g Presenting—Sound Case (IRE) **T. Clinton**
11 **FANTASY BLUE (IRE),** 5, b m Darnay—Wild Fantasy (IRE) **L. Curtin, Dr. T. Dorman, & D. McEneff**
12 **FRIAR'S HALL (IRE),** 6, b g Saddlers' Hall (IRE)—Native Monk (IRE) **M. Morris**
13 **GOLDEN KILFEACLE (IRE),** 6, ch g Aboo Hom—Rosies Daughter (IRE)

MR M. MORRIS—continued

14 **GUNNER MASON (IRE)**, 6, b g Rudimentary (USA)—Villaexpress (IRE) **T. Kilduff**
15 **HAAKAISER (IRE)**, 7, ch g City Honours (USA)—Poor Times (IRE) **M. Maher**
16 **HEAR THE ECHO (IRE)**, 7, b g Luso—Echo Creek (IRE) **Gigginstown House Stud**
17 **IS HE SERIOUS (IRE)**, 6, b g Sea Raven (IRE)—Inamuddle (IRE) **M. O'Flynn**
18 **JOHNNIE DILLINGER (IRE)**, 8, b br g Supreme Leader—Kilbrien Star **Mrs J. Magnier**
19 **MICKATAINE (IRE)**, 7, b g Presenting—Inamuddle (IRE) **M. O'Flynn**
20 **POLAMALU (IRE)**, 5, b g Turtle Island (IRE)—Linda's Leader (IRE) **Sir. A. J. O'Reilly**
21 **ROCKFIELD (IRE)**, 5, b g Oscar (IRE)—Archdall Lady (IRE) **M. O'Flynn**
22 **RUSHANE LODGE (IRE)**, 6, b g Oscar (IRE)—Pafelto **Sir A. J. O'Reilly**
23 **RUSSET PRINCE (IRE)**, 7, b g Supreme Leader—Autumn Queen **J. P. McManus**
24 **SARALUSO (IRE)**, 5, b m Luso—An Imp For Sarah (IRE) **Fat Baldies Syndicate**
25 **SCAVENGER (IRE)**, 6, b g Presenting—Forest Pride (IRE) **Gigginstown Stud**
26 **SHANGHIDE**, 7, br h Supreme Leader—My Adventure (IRE) **J. Fitzgerald**
27 **SIR MALIK (IRE)**, 5, b g Oscar (IRE)—La Lucilla (IRE) **B. Maloney, M. O'Flynn**
28 **STEEL BAND**, 10, ch h Kris—Quaver (USA) **Irish World's Partners Syndicate**
29 **STEEL MAGNATE (IRE)**, 5, ch g Presenting—Black Gayle (IRE) **Gigginstown Stud**
30 **SYMPHONICA (IRE)**, 5, ch m Definite Article—Double Symphony (USA) **S. Vasicek**
31 **THE DEADLY (IRE)**, 8, b g Safety Catch (USA)—Seaside Lady (IRE) **WAB Syndicate**
32 **THE GLOVES ARE OFF (IRE)**, 5, b g Oscar (IRE)—Reapers Dream (IRE) **Gigginstown Stud**
33 **THE HURL (IRE)**, 5, b g Supreme Leader—No Dunce (IRE) **C. Ryan**
34 **THE PHANTOM PIPER (IRE)**, 5, b g Snurge—Pepsi Starlet (IRE) **We've Bought Tha Hats Syndicate**
35 **VENALMAR**, 6, b g Kayf Tara—Elaine Tully (IRE) **M. O' Flynn**
36 **WAR OF ATTRITION (IRE)**, 9, br g Presenting—Una Juna (IRE) **M. O'Leary**
37 **WAR OF THE WORLD (IRE)**, 6, b g Shernazar—Fairpark (IRE) **Gigginstown Stud**
38 **WAR OFFICER (IRE)**, 5, b g Luso—Art Lover (IRE) **Gigginstown Stud**

Jockey (NH): Paddy Flood.

412
MISS THERESA MORRIS, Droitwich
Postal: **The Treehouse, New Farm, Rushock, Droitwich, Worcestershire, WR9 0NR**
Contacts: **PHONE (01299) 851625 FAX (01299) 851581**
E-MAIL info@treehouseonline.co.uk WEBSITE www.treehouseonline.co.uk

1 **CARTHAGO (IRE)**, 11, b g Roselier (FR)—Hi Cousin **Mrs T. Morris**

413
MR H. MORRISON, East Ilsley
Postal: **Summerdown, East Ilsley, Newbury, Berkshire, RG20 7LB**
Contacts: **PHONE (01635) 281678 FAX (01635) 281746 MOBILE (07836) 687799**
E-MAIL hughie@hughiemorrison.co.uk

1 **AFRICAN PURSUITS (USA)**, 4, b g Johannesburg (USA)—Woodland Orchid (IRE) **The Pursuits Partnership**
2 **BLUE JAVA**, 7, ch g Bluegrass Prince (IRE)—Java Bay **Pangfield Partners**
3 **FLIRTATIOUS**, 5, b m Generous (IRE)—Mayfair Minx **Mrs M. D. W. Morrison**
4 **GLENCAL**, 4, ch f Compton Place—Raindrop **The Caledonian Racing Society**
5 **INTREPID JACK**, 6, b h Compton Place—Maria Theresa **Mr M. Lynch**
6 **KASUMI**, 5, ch m Inchinor—Raindrop **Viscountess Trenchard**
7 **KYLKENNY**, 13, b g Kylian (USA)—Fashion Flow **Mrs M. D. W. Morrison**
8 **MACADEMY ROYAL (USA)**, 5, b g Royal Academy (USA)—Garden Folly (USA) **H. Morrison**
9 **MOUNT HERMON (IRE)**, 4, b g Golan (IRE)—Machudi **Mr M. Lynch**
10 **NUR TAU (IRE)**, 4, b g Peintre Celebre (USA)—Litchfield Hills (USA) **Mrs R. C. A. Hammond**
11 **PALMETTO POINT**, 4, ch g Bahamian Bounty—Forum **M. T. Bevan**
12 **REALT NA MARA (IRE)**, 5, b br g Tagula (IRE)—Dwingeloo (IRE) **Mrs G. C. Maxwell & Mr J. D. N. Tillyard**
13 **SAKHEE'S SECRET**, 4, ch c Sakhee (USA)—Palace Street (USA) **Miss B. E. Swire**
14 **SALSA STEPS (USA)**, 4, ch f Giant's Causeway (USA)—Dance Design (IRE) **Ben & Sir Martyn Arbib**
15 **SCUBA**, 6, b g Indian Danehill (USA)—March Star (IRE) **Graham Doyle & Hazel Lawrence**
16 **SECRET PLOY**, 8, b g Deploy—By Line **A. M. Carding**
17 **SOHRAAB**, 4, b g Erhaab (USA)—Riverine **Pangfield Racing**
18 **STARZAAN (IRE)**, 9, b g Darshaan—Stellina (IRE) **Mr B. G. Arbib**
19 **STOCKMAN**, 4, b g Kylian (USA)—Fabriana **H. Morrison**
20 **SULARNO**, 4, ch g Medicean—Star Precision **Miss B. E. Swire**
21 **SUPASEUS**, 5, b g Spinning World (USA)—Supamova (USA) **Ben & Sir Martyn Arbib**
22 **YONDER**, 4, br f And Beyond (IRE)—Dominance **Mrs M. D. W. Morrison**
23 **YOUNG BERTIE**, 5, ch g Bertolini (USA)—Urania **Mr M. T. Bevan, Mr G. Swire & Mr M. Bryant**

MR H. MORRISON—continued

THREE-YEAR-OLDS

24 **BA DREAMFLIGHT**, b g Noverre (USA)—Aunt Tate **BA Racing**
25 **BRAZILIAN BRUSH (IRE)**, ch g Captain Rio—Ejder (IRE) **M. Kerr-Dineen**
26 **EMIR BAGATELLE**, gr g Dubai Destination (USA)—Giorgia Rae (IRE) **The End-R-Ways Partnership**
27 **EUROCELEB (IRE)**, ch f Peintre Celebre—Eurobird **Stonethorn Stud Farms Ltd**
28 **FERVENT PRINCE**, b g Averti (IRE)—Maria Theresa **Thurloe Finsbury II**
29 **GARTER STAR**, b f Mark of Esteem (IRE)—Palace Affair **Miss B. E. Swire**
30 **GOLDEN PENNY**, b g Xaar—Dog Rose (SAF) **Mrs B. Oppenheimer**
31 **ISLAND TREASURE**, b c Cadeaux Genereux—Gallivant **Mrs M. F. Meredith**
32 **KING OF PENTACLES**, b c King's Best (USA)—Maid To Perfection **N. G. Cooper**
33 **LAKE NAYASA**, b f Nayef (USA)—Lady of The Lake **Capt J. Macdonald-Buchanan**
34 **LOVESPELL (USA)**, ch f Diesis—Loose Arrow (USA) **De La Warr Racing**
35 **MANCHESTERMAVERICK (USA)**, ch g Van Nistelrooy (USA)—
                                              Lydia Louise (USA) **Mr D. P. Barrie & Mr M. J. Rees**
36 **MISS GLITTERS (IRE)**, b f Chevalier (IRE)—Geht Schnell **Mrs M. D. W. Morrison**
37 **MISS MOZART**, b f Bahamian Bounty—Papillon de Bronze (IRE) **Lord J. Blyth**
38 **MISTA ROSSA**, br g Red Ransom (USA)—Cloud Hill **Wood Street Syndicate IV**
39 **MOLUCCELLA**, b f Marju (IRE)—Pine Needle **Thurloe Thoroughbreds XXI**
40 **MOODY MARGARET**, b f Bahamian Bounty—Sound of Laughter (FR) **Exors of the Late A. J. Richards**
41 **MRS SUMMERSBY (IRE)**, ch f King's Best (USA)—Kournikova (SAF) **Mrs S. M. Rogers**
42 **PALACE MOON**, b c Fantastic Light (USA)—Palace Street (USA) **Miss B. E. Swire**
43 Gr f Environment Friend—Pang Valley Girl **Pangfield Partners**
44 B g Lando (GER)—Purple Haze (GER) **Thurloe Thoroughbreds XXII**
45 **RED TWIST**, b g Red Ransom (USA)—Spinning The Yarn **Castle Down Racing**
46 **ROCK PEAK (IRE)**, b c Dalakhani (IRE)—Convenience (USA) **Thurloe Finsbury II**
47 **ROCKJUMPER**, br c Cape Cross (IRE)—Bronzewing **Sir Thomas Pilkington**
48 **SELFISH OPTION (IRE)**, ch c Selkirk (USA)—Pride In Me **Ian Cameron**
49 **SIREN SOUND**, br f Singspiel (IRE)—Warning Belle **Helena Springfield Ltd**
50 **SLEEPY HOLLOW**, b g Beat Hollow—Crackling **Lady Blyth**
51 **SMETANA**, b g Kylian (USA)—Shimmer **Margadale, Tufnell, Wilson & Bryant**
52 **STIMULATION (IRE)**, b c Choisir (AUS)—Damiana (IRE) **M. Kerr-Dineen & Mr R. P. Tullett**
53 **STOW**, ch g Selkirk (USA)—Spry **Lady Howard De Walden**
54 **SUPAVERDI (USA)**, br f Green Desert (USA)—Supamova (USA) **Ben & Sir Martyn Arbib**
55 **TAIKOO**, b c Dr Fong (USA)—So True **Miss B. E. Swire**
56 **WELLINGTON SQUARE**, b g Millkom—Tempestosa **Mr Roger Barby & Sir T. Cassel**
57 **WING PLAY (IRE)**, b c Hawk Wing (USA)—Toy Show (IRE) **Watching Brief**

TWO-YEAR-OLDS

58 **ASK THE ORACLE**, ch c 10/3 Where Or When (IRE)—Delphic Way (Warning) **Miss B. E. Swire**
59 **ASSAIL**, b c 26/2 Bertolini (USA)—Roofer (IRE) (Barathea (IRE)) **Mike Watson**
60 **BENOZZO GOZZOLI**, ch c 5/2 Medicean—Star Precision (Shavian) **Miss B. E. Swire**
61 **BREADSTICK**, br f 21/1 Diktat—Poilane (USA)—Fethat **Mrs P. Bossom & Bloomsbury Stud**
62 B f 22/4 Piccolo—Cape Charlotte (Mon Tresor) (16000) **Mrs Anne Usher, Mrs Isabel Eavis & Partners**
63 B f 1/5 High Chaparral (IRE)—Damiana (IRE) (Thatching) (58000) **M. Kerr-Dineen & R. P. Tullett**
64 B f 10/3 Compton Place—Dancing Nelly (Shareef Dancer (USA)) (5000) **Lady Hardy**
65 B f 13/4 Dr Fong (USA)—Dead Certain (Absalom) **Crichel Racing**
66 B f 12/4 Milan—Emilia Romagna (GER) (Acatenango (GER)) **Mrs G. C. Maxwell & Mr J. D. N. Tillyard**
67 **ESCAPIST**, b c 16/2 Dubai Destination (USA)—Elude (Slip Anchor) **Lady Howard De Walden**
68 B f 21/3 Danehill Dancer (IRE)—Eurostorm (USA) (Storm Bird (CAN)) **Stonethorn Stud Farms Ltd**
69 B c 6/2 King's Best (USA)—
                          Footlight Fantasy (Nureyev (USA)) (20000) **Miss B. E. Swire &
                                              Mrs Annie Usher & Castle Down Racing**
70 B br c 29/1 Fusaichi Pegasus (USA)—Gracie Lady (IRE) (Generous (IRE)) (111758) **De La Warr Racing**
71 B c 19/3 Reset (AUS)—Great Verdict (AUS) (Christmas Tree (AUS)) **Mrs B. Oppenheimer**
72 B f 6/4 Fasliyev (USA)—Green Castle (IRE) (Indian Ridge) **Stonethorn Stud Farms Ltd**
73 B f 1/3 Rock of Gibraltar (IRE)—Gwen John (USA) (Peintre Celebre (USA)) (30000) **Usk Valley Stud**
74 B c 30/3 Hawk Wing (USA)—Kafayef (USA) (Secreto (USA)) (32174) **Mr R. C. Tooth**
75 **KING'S STARLET**, b f 13/3 King's Best (USA)—Brightest Star (Unfuwain (USA)) **Helena Springfield Ltd**
76 **LA POLKA**, ch f 6/5 Carnival Dancer—Indubitable (Sharpo) **Miss B. E. Swire**
77 **LADY PHILADELPHIA (IRE)**, b f 6/3 Night Shift (USA)—Miss Moore (IRE) (Tagula (IRE)) **Mr Robin Cutler**
78 Ch c 13/2 Sakhee (USA)—Marah (Machiavellian (USA)) (48000) **Thurloe Thoroughbreds**
79 Gr c 17/1 Compton Place—Molly Moon (IRE) (Primo Dominie) (75000) **Mr & Mrs H. Scott-Barrett & Partners**
80 B c 2/3 Bahamian Bounty—Monaiya (Shareef Dancer (USA)) (115000) **Mrs R. C. A. Hammond**

MR H. MORRISON—continued

81 **MOUNTAIN FOREST (GER)**, b c 12/4 Tiger Hill (IRE)—
Moricana (GER) (Konigsstuhl (GER)) (57915) **H. Y. Scott-Barrett**
82 **MY KINGDOM**, b c 23/3 King's Best (USA)—Nebraas (Green Desert (USA)) (45044) **Wood Street Syndicate**
83 Ch f 10/2 Peintre Celebre (USA)—Petite-D-Argent (Noalto) **D. A. Couper**
84 **PRESENT ALCHEMY**, ch c 27/3 Cadeaux Genereux—Desert Alchemy (Green Desert (USA)) **Normandie Stud**
85 Ch f 7/4 Compton Place—Raindrop (Primo Dominie) (5714) **Lord Margadale**
86 **SCRABBLE**, b f 3/2 Montjeu (IRE)—Spry (Suave Dancer (USA)) **Lady Howard De Walden**
87 **SOME SUNNY DAY**, ch f 29/3 Where Or When (IRE)—Palace Street (USA) (Secreto (USA)) **Miss B. E. Swire**
88 **SPRING GREEN**, b f 29/1 Bahamian Bounty—Star Tulip (Night Shift (USA)) **Nicholas Jones**
89 **SUAKIN DANCER (IRE)**, ch f 19/1 Danehill Dancer (IRE)—
Wedding Morn (IRE) (Sadler's Wells (USA)) (75000) **Dr Ornella Carlini Cozzi & J Bernstein**
90 Ch f 11/2 Peintre Celebre (USA)—Suntory (IRE) (Royal Applause) **Stonethorn Stud Farms Ltd**
91 **THERE AND THEN**, b c 22/5 Where Or When (IRE)—Cugina (Distant Relative) **Miss B. E. Swire**
92 **ULTIMATE**, b c 3/3 Anabaa (USA)—Nirvana (Marju (IRE)) **Lady Howard De Walden**

Other Owners: Mr Ben Arbib, Sir Martyn Arbib, Mr Jon Bailey, Mr Roger Barby, Mr D. P. Barrie, Mr J. Bernstein, Mr T. J. Billington, Mrs Gemma Billington, Mr Paul Blaydon, M. Bryant, Mrs Penny Burgess, John Byrne, Patsy Byrne, Mrs O. Carlini Cozzi, Sir Timothy Cassel, Mr Anthony E. Chapman, Major D. N. Chappell, Mr J. C. Condon, Lord De La Warr, Lady De La Warr, Mr Sam Dibb, Mrs Vicky Downie, Mr Graham Doyle, Mrs H. S. Ellingsen, Mrs J. Forbes, Miss C. A. Green, Andrew Holmes, Miss Hazel Lawrence, Lady Margadale, Mr Ricardo Marin, Nickola Markham, Mrs G. C. Maxwell, Michael McCalmont, Ms F. Melrose, Mrs Carole Middleton, Brendan Moran, Mr H. Morrison, Oscar O'Herlihy, Mrs Tsa Palmer, Mr B. G. W. Parker, Mr Oliver Pawle, Mr Keith Perrett, Mr James M. Polk, Mr K. B. Purcell, Mr M. J. Rees, Mr M. M. J. Rees, Mr J. P Repard, Mr Adrian Ryan, Mrs Catherine Seagrim, Mr J. A. B. Stafford, Mr M. R. Stokes, Jeremy Strutt, Mr G. D. W. Swire, Mr D. J. Taylor, Mr M. Taylor, Mr J. D. N. Tillyard, David Townsend, Mr R. P Tullett, Mr Edmund B. B. Vickers, Mr Malcolm Walker, Mr M. Weinfeld, Mr A. W. Wood.

Assistant Trainer: Hugo Palmer

Apprentice: Travis Block. **Amateur:** Miss Victoria Cartmel.

414
MR G. P. MOSS, Bay Horse
Postal: **Newland Hall, Bay Horse, Lancaster, Lancashire, LA2 9AA**
Contacts: **PHONE (01524) 791514 MOBILE (07962) 021526**

1 **FERN HOUSE (IRE)**, 6, b g Xaar—Certain Impression (USA) **J. W. Barrett**
2 **STANLEY WOLFE (IRE)**, 5, b g City On A Hill (USA)—Quatredil (IRE) **J. W. Barrett**

THREE-YEAR-OLDS

3 **BECKY QUICK (IRE)**, b f Fantastic Light (USA)—Private Bluff (USA) **J. W. Barrett**
4 **CARIBBEAN CRUISER**, b g Diktat—Caribbean Star **J. W. Barrett**
5 **DUBAI TO BARNSLEY**, b c Superior Premium—Oakwell Ace **J. A. Bower**
6 **RASCASSE**, b c Where Or When (IRE)—Sure Flyer (IRE) **J. W. Barrett**
7 **UGLY BETTY**, b f Where Or When (IRE)—Dancing Steps **J. W. Barrett**

Other Owners: Mr Zeph Wilkinson.

415
MISS D. MOUNTAIN, Newmarket
Postal: **Carriageway Stables, Hamilton Road, Newmarket, Suffolk, CB8 7JQ**
Contacts: **FAX (01638) 666665 MOBILE (07765) 964402 (07833) 510473**
E-MAIL debbie.mountain@hotmail.co.uk WEBSITE www.saharastables.co.uk

1 **BEHRUSI (IRE)**, 4, b br c Singspiel (IRE)—Behra (IRE) **D. P. Fremel**
2 **CHANCELLOR (USA)**, 4, b c Deputy Minister (CAN)—Cozzene's Angel (USA)
3 **DONT LOOK SIDEWAYS**, 4, br f Singspiel (IRE)—Live Your Dreams (USA)
4 **INCH LODGE**, 6, ch h Grand Lodge (USA)—Legaya **D. P. Fremel**
5 **ITALSTAR (IRE)**, 4, ch f Galileo (IRE)—Jorghinia (FR) **Mr I. Mian**
6 **PRIOR WARNING**, 4, ch c Barathea (IRE)—Well Warned
7 **RUSTY SLIPPER**, 8, b m Slip Anchor—Run For Russ (IRE)
8 **SCEILIN (IRE)**, 4, b f Lil's Boy (USA)—Sharifa (IRE) **Mr I. Mian**
9 **TRICKLE (USA)**, 4, ch f Rahy (USA)—Avitrix (USA) **D. P. Fremel**

THREE-YEAR-OLDS

10 **COLMAR MAGIC (IRE)**, b f Dixie Union (USA)—On View (USA) **Mr I. Mian**

MISS D. MOUNTAIN—continued

11 HULA HULA, ch f Cadeaux Genereux—Eurolink Sundance
12 TOON ARMY, gr f Tobougg (IRE)—Align **Mr A. Kobeissi**

TWO-YEAR-OLDS

13 B c 5/4 Catcher In The Rye (IRE)—Imposition (UAE) (Be My Guest (USA)) (5000) **Moubarak Racing Ltd.**
14 B c 29/3 Sky Mesa (USA)—Not a Solution (USA) (Grand Slam (USA)) (5000) **Moubarak Racing Ltd.**
15 Ch f 13/2 Nayef (USA)—Raydaniya (IRE) (In The Wings) (2000) **Moubarak Racing Ltd.**
16 Ch f 20/3 Auction House (USA)—Sweet Harriet (Hector Protector (USA)) (1200) **A. Kobeissi**
17 B f 29/3 Beat Hollow—Valagalore (Generous (IRE)) (10000) **Moubarak Racing Ltd.**
18 B c 23/4 Tobougg (IRE)—Wrong Bride (Reprimand) (21000) **Moubarak Racing Ltd.**

Other Owners: D. Fremel, A. Kobeissi, Mr I. Miah, Moubarak Racing Ltd.

Assistant Trainer: Ahmad Kobeissi

Jockey (flat): Paul Eddery.

---

416 MR WILLIAM R. MUIR, Lambourn
Postal: **Linkslade, Wantage Road, Lambourn, Hungerford, Berkshire, RG17 8UG**
Contacts: **OFFICE (01488) 73098 HOME (01488) 73748 FAX (01488) 73490**
MOBILE (07831) 457074
E-MAIL williamr.muir@virgin.net WEBSITE www.williammuir.com

1 AEGEAN PRINCE, 4, b g Dr Fong (USA)—Dizzydaisy **Theobalds Stud**
2 BIG ROBERT, 4, b c Medicean—Top Flight Queen **M. P. Graham**
3 BLUEBELLE DANCER (IRE), 4, b f Danehill Dancer (IRE)—Spring To Light (USA) **M. J. Caddy**
4 BUY ON THE RED, 7, b g Komaite (USA)—Red Rosein **R. Haim**
5 CARMENERO (GER), 5, b g Barathea (IRE)—Claire Fraser (USA) **Middleham Park Racing XXXVIII**
6 MISTER GENEPI, b g Mister Baileys—Ring Queen **M. J. Caddy**
7 PARK VALLEY PRINCE, 4, ch c Noverre (USA)—Santorini (USA) **Middleham Park Racing XXI**
8 ROCK 'N' ROLLER (FR), 4, b br g Sagacity (FR)—Diamond Dance (FR) **D. G. Clarke & C. L. A. Edginton**
9 TONY THE TAP, 7, b g Most Welcome—Laleston **Mr K. J. Mercer & Mrs S. Mercer**

THREE-YEAR-OLDS

10 ARTISTIC LIGHT, ch f Fantastic Light (USA)—Artisia (IRE) **Foursome Thoroughbreds**
11 ASK NICELY, b f Red Ransom (USA)—Oiselina (FR) **Foursome Thoroughbreds**
12 AWESOME LIGHT (IRE), b br c Catcher In The Rye (USA)—Stardance (USA) **David & Gwyn Joseph**
13 BERMACHA, ch f Bertolini (USA)—Machaera **Essex Racing Club**
14 BLUE JACK, b c Cadeaux Genereux—Fairy Flight (IRE) **M. P. Graham**
15 ENODOC, b g Efisio—Raindrop **Mrs D. L. Edginton**
16 ENROLLER (IRE), b c Marju (IRE)—Walk On Quest (FR) **D. G. Clarke & C. L. A. Edginton**
17 FABULEUX CHERIE, b f Noverre (USA)—Ashover Amber **David & Gwyn Joseph**
18 GOWER BELLE, b f Fantastic Light (USA)—Polish Belle **David & Gwyn Joseph**
19 HAWK FLIGHT (IRE), b c Hawk Wing (USA)—Rapid Action (USA) **David & Gwyn Joseph**
20 KAMAL, ch g Bahamian Bounty—Star Tulip **Mr. C. L. A. Edginton**
21 KING'S WONDER, ch c King's Best (USA)—Signs And Wonders **D. G. Clarke & C. L. A. Edginton**
22 MELODY FAIR (IRE), b f Montjeu (IRE)—Manchaca (FR) **The Ewe & Lamb Partnership**
23 MICK'S DANCER, b c Pivotal—La Piaf (FR) **Perspicacious Punters Racing Club**
24 MOON BOUND (IRE), b c Observatory (USA)—Inspiring (IRE) **A. J. De V. Patrick & M. J. Caddy**
25 NEMO SPIRIT (IRE), gr c Daylami (IRE)—La Bayadere **Mrs M. V. Bruce Copp**
26 OKAFRANCA (IRE), b g Okawango (USA)—Villafranca (IRE) **The Eastwood Partnership**
27 OUR ACQUAINTANCE, ch g Bahamian Bounty—Lady of Limerick (IRE) **Quaintance Partnership**
28 RESPLENDENT LIGHT, b c Fantastic Light (USA)—Bright Halo (USA) **Middleham Park Racing XLIX**
29 RUBYTWOSOX (IRE), b f Redback—Policy **Linkslade Optimists**
30 SAPHIRA'S FIRE (IRE), b f Cape Cross (IRE)—All Our Hope (USA) **M. J. Caddy**
31 SHESHA BEAR, b f Tobougg (IRE)—Sunny Davis (USA) **Joe Bear Racing**
32 SISTER MOONSHINE, b f Averti (IRE)—Cal Norma's Lady (IRE) **M. J. Caddy**
33 SOLAR EXPRESS, b g Fantastic Light (USA)—Jumairah Sun **M. J. Caddy**
34 SWEET LIGHTNING, b g Fantastic Light (USA)—Sweetness Herself **A. J. De V. Patrick & M. J. Caddy**
35 TANK COMMANDER, b c Polish Precedent (USA)—Herminoe **S. D. Jones, C. R. Lamplough & P. Kelly**
36 THIRTYFOURTHSTREET (IRE), gr f Beat Hollow—Peacock Alley (IRE) **Mr & Mrs G. Middlebrook**
37 WE HAVE A DREAM, b br c Oasis Dream—Final Shot **The Dreaming Squires**

MR WILLIAM R. MUIR—continued

TWO-YEAR-OLDS

38 B c 6/1 Mull of Kintyre (USA)—Birthday (IRE) (Singspiel (IRE)) (14500)
39 DEFECTOR (IRE), b c 9/4 Fasliyev (USA)—Rich Dancer (Halling (USA)) (21000) **Mr David Knox & Partners**
40 DIKTALINA, b f 18/2 Diktat—Oiselina (FR) (Linamix (FR)) (12000) **Foursome Thoroughbreds**
41 B c 15/3 Bahamian Bounty—Dress Design (IRE) (Brief Truce (USA)) (16000) **A. N. Brackley**
42 Ch f 21/2 Fath (USA)—Eimkar (Junius (USA)) (3539)
43 ENTRANCER (IRE), b c 19/2 Key of Luck (USA)—
                              Corn Futures (Nomination) (30000) **D. G. Clarke & C. L. A. Edginton**
44 B br c 28/2 Rock of Gibraltar (IRE)—For Criquette (IRE) (Barathea (IRE)) (10000) **Linkslade Partnership**
45 B c 15/3 Bachelor Duke (USA)—Gronchi Rosa (IRE) (Nashwan (USA)) (14000)
46 HALLING GAL, b f 2/5 Halling (USA)—Saik (USA) (Riverman (USA)) (25000) **David & Gwyn Joseph**
47 B c 1/2 Celtic Swing—Indian Myth (USA) (Lear Fan (USA)) (20000)
48 KING'S MASQUE, b c 31/3 Noverre (USA)—
                              Top Flight Queen (Mark of Esteem (IRE)) (14000) **A. Patrick, C. Edginton & M. Caddy**
49 B c 25/4 Kyllachy—La Piaf (FR) (Fabulous Dancer (USA)) (28000) **Perspicacious Punters Racing Club**
50 C b c 25/3 King's Best (USA)—Lightsabre (Polar Falcon (USA)) (21000) **Mr S. Jones**
51 ROSY MANTLE, b f 20/3 Daylami (IRE)—
                              Dominion Rose (USA) (Spinning World (USA)) (10000) **Foursome Thoroughbreds**
52 B f 13/4 Singspiel (IRE)—Seven of Nine (IRE) (Alzao (USA)) **M. J. Caddy**
53 SILVADOR, gr c 5/4 Selkirk (USA)—Dali's Grey (Linamix (FR)) (160000) **C. Edginton, K. Jeffery & P. Wheatley**
54 TRIP SWITCH, b c 12/3 Reset (AUS)—Caribbean Star (Soviet Star (USA)) (15000) **Andrew & Jo Patrick**
55 Ch c 16/3 Bachelor Duke (USA)—Truly Bewitched (USA) (Affirmed (USA)) (50000) **M. J. Caddy**

Other Owners: Mr. & Mrs. D. Quaintance, Mr. R. Antell, Mr. D. Boyd, Mr. & Mrs. A. Brackley, Mrs R. B. Brackley, Mrs. Monique Bruce-Copp, Mr. R. Burden, R. J. Burden, Mr. D. G. Clarke, D. G. Clarke, Mr. J. D. Clements, Mr. I. Collins, Mr I. E. Collins, Mr. P. Crawford, Mr. J. Davies, Dulverton Equine, C. L. A. Edginton, Mr John H. W. Finch, Mr Martin P. Graham, Mr. F. M. Green, Ms. J. Greenwell, Ms J. M. Greenwell, Mr R. Haim, Mr. S. Howard, S. J. Howard, Mr. K. Jeffery, K. Jeffery, Mr D. M. Joseph, Mr D. G. Joseph, Mr Paul Kelly, Mr I. G. Knightley, D. P. Knox, Mr R. C. Lamplough, Mr. R. Lardner, Mr R. A. Lardner, Mr. A. P. McCarthy, Mr A. P. McCarthy, Mr K. J. Mercer, Mrs S. Mercer, G. Middlebrook, Mrs L. A. Middlebrook, William R. Muir, Mr T. S. Palin, Mr. T. Palin, Mr J. Panos, G. K. Panos, K. Panos, Mr A. J. de V. Patrick, Mrs J. V. Patrick, Mrs. J. Patrick, Mr M. Prince, Mr. P. Quaintance, Mr P. D. Quaintance, Mr D. L. Quaintance, Mr Christopher Ransom, Mr S. M. Ransom, Mr. G. Roberts, R. B. Root, Mrs J. P. Root, Mr Mikir Shah, Mr Graham Stacey, Mr. M. Wass, Mr M. A. Wass, Mr. P. Wheatley, P. J. Wheatley, Mr. D. White, D. F. White, Mr. B. Whittal-Williams, Miss D. A. Williams, Mr. & Mrs. G. Wood, Mr G. E. Wood, Mrs G. E. G. Wood.

---

417 MR C. A. MULHALL, Scarcroft
Postal: **Scarcroft Hall Farm, Thorner Lane, Scarcroft, Leeds**
Contacts: **PHONE/FAX** (01132) 893095 **MOBILE** (07979) 527675
E-MAIL clive@scarcrofthallracing.co.uk **WEBSITE** www.clivemulhallracing.co.uk

1 ABZUSON, 11, b g Abzu—Mellouise **Abzuson Syndicate**
2 CLOISTERS HILL, 6, b g Minster Son—Hillmilly **W. R. Robinson**
3 CUMBERLAND ROAD, 5, ch g Efisio—Thatcher's Era (IRE)
4 DOESLESSTHANME (IRE), 4, ch g Definite Article—Damemill (IRE) **Mrs C. M. Mulhall**
5 FIT TO FLY (IRE), 7, b g Lahib—Maid of Mourne **Mrs C. M. Mulhall**
6 HABANERO, 7, b g Cadeaux Genereux—Queen of Dance (USA) **Mr K. Sivills**
7 INSTRUCTOR, 7, ch g Groom Dancer (USA)—Doctor's Glory (USA) **Mr K. Sivills**
8 MISS EMPEROR, 5, b m Emperor Fountain—Marquesa Juana **Mrs T. Corrigan-Clark**
9 MISTRAL DE LA COUR (FR), 8, bl g Panoramic—
                              Gracieuse Delacour (FR) **Mr K. Sivills, Ms D. Rafferty, Mrs M. Mulhall**
10 SIMHAL, 4, b g Minster Son—Busky Girl
11 SUPER BOSTON, 8, b g Saddlers' Hall (IRE)—Nasowas (IRE) **M. K. Oldham**

Other Owners: C. R. Green, Ms D. Rafferty, P. Scholefield.

Assistant Trainer: Mrs Martina Mulhall

Jockey (flat): P. Hanagan, P. Mulrennan. **Jockey (NH):** L. McGrath, P. Whelan. **Conditional:** Michael O'Connell. **Amateur:** Mr C. Mulhall.

418 MR M. MULLINEAUX, Tarporley

Postal: **Southley Farm, Alpraham, Tarporley, Cheshire, CW6 9JD**
Contacts: PHONE **(01829) 261440** FAX **(01829) 261622** MOBILE **(07753) 650263**
E-MAIL **southlearacing@btinternet.com** WEBSITE **www.cheshiretrainer.co.uk**

1 **ALWAYS OPTIMISTIC,** 5, b h Puissance—Glorious Aragon **The Hon Mrs Susan Pakenham**
2 **CARTOONIST (IRE),** 5, ch g Fruits of Love (USA)—Verusa (IRE)
3 **CARYS'S LAD,** 5, b g Exit To Nowhere (USA)—Dawn Spinner **The Bellflower Cary's Lad Partnership**
4 **CHARMING ROGUE,** 6, gr g Robellino (USA)—Silver Charm **Mr P. J. Lawton**
5 **CHICAMIA,** 4, b f Kyllachy—Inflation **Abbey Racing**
6 **DIAMOND JOSH,** 6, ch g Primo Dominie—Exit **G. Hankinson**
7 **DRIVING SEAT,** 4, b g Daylami (IRE)—Zorleni **The Bellflower Driving Seat Partnership**
8 **DRYUREYESMATE (IRE),** 6, br g Supreme Leader—Vidi Vici **Bellflower Dryureyesmate Partnership**
9 **DUSKY DANCER,** 4, b f Ziggy's Dancer (USA)—Hot Java (USA) **J. Connor**
10 **ELLAFINESSE,** 4, ch f Elmaamul (USA)—Dolfinesse (IRE) **M. Mullineaux**
11 **FAST FRED (IRE),** 6, b g Gothland (FR)—Tullibards Again (IRE) **Bellflower Racing Ltd**
12 **FOURPOINTONE,** 7, b g Overbury (IRE)—Praise The Lord **Bellflower Racing Ltd**
13 **HALLYS GOAL (IRE),** 6, b g Fourstars Allstar (USA)—Glenties **Bluestone Partnership**
14 **KIMOE WARRIOR,** 10, ch g Royal Abjar (USA)—Thewaari (USA) **D. Ashbrook & M. Mullineaux**
15 **KIRSTYS LAD,** 6, b g Lake Coniston (IRE)—Killick **S. A. Pritchard**
16 **LAKE WAKATIPU,** 6, b m Lake Coniston (IRE)—Lady Broker **Esprit De Corps Racing**
17 **LUCKY FIND (IRE),** 5, b m Key of Luck (USA)—Recherchee **Mr P. Danby**
18 **LYON'S HILL,** 4, ch g Generous (IRE)—New Abbey **The Bellflower Lyons Hill Partnership**
19 **METHAALY (IRE),** 5, b g Red Ransom (USA)—Santorini (USA) **The Bellflower Methaaly Partnership**
20 **MYSTIK MEGAN,** 7, gr m Wizard King—Sian's Girl **P. Currey**
21 **NEPAL (IRE),** 6, ch m Monashee Mountain (USA)—Zetonic **P. T. Hollins**
22 **NOSEY GUNNER,** 6, b m Gunner B—Out of Sorts **Mr Peter & Mrs Irene Danby**
23 **OVERSTAYED (IRE),** 5, ch g Titus Livius (FR)—Look Nonchalant (IRE) **R. Reid**
24 **PHOENIX EYE,** 7, b g Tragic Role (USA)—Eye Sight **J. R. Williamson**
25 **REVEUR,** 5, b m Rossini (USA)—Without Warning (USA) **A. Jones**
26 **RUDRY WORLD (IRE),** 5, ch g Spinning World (USA)—
                       Fancy Boots (IRE) **The Bellflower Rudry World Partnership**
27 **SAILOR A'HOY,** 12, b g Handsome Sailor—Eye Sight **J. R. Williamson**
28 **SPARTAN WARRIOR,** 6, b g Overbury (IRE)—La Coupee **Bellflower Racing Ltd**
29 **SUNNY PARKES,** 5, ch m Arkadian Hero (USA)—Janette Parkes **G. Hankinson**
30 **THE HISTORY MAN (IRE),** 5, b g Titus Livius (FR)—
                       Handsome Anna (IRE) **D. E. Simpson & R. Farrington-Kirkham**
31 **THE POSH NIPPER,** 9, b g Rakaposhi King—Jindabyne **Mrs R. Farrington-Kirkham**
32 **WEE ELLIE COBURN,** 4, ch f Bold Edge—Wathbat Mtoto **G. Coburn**
33 **WIZARD OF US,** 8, b g Wizard King—Sian's Girl **P. Currey**

THREE-YEAR-OLDS

34 **BRICK (IRE),** b f Averti (IRE)—Wicked **Mr P. J. Canton & Mr J. Donald**
35 **DANZIG FOX,** b c Foxhound (USA)—Via Dolorosa **Southley Racing Partnership**
36 Gr c Paris House—Diamond Rouge **M. Mullineaux**
37 **SCANNO (IRE),** b c Captain Rio—In Denial (IRE) **Mr A. Jones**

TWO-YEAR-OLDS

38 **BOXER SHORTS,** b c 19/3 Puissance—Lady Boxer (Komaite (USA)) **M. Mullineaux & Mr G. Coburn**
39 B f 14/2 Reel Buddy (USA)—Bullion (Sabrehill (USA)) **Bearstone Stud**
40 B f 29/3 Reel Buddy (USA)—Manderina (Mind Games) **Bearstone Stud**
41 Ch c 23/2 Fantastic Light (USA)—Maureena (IRE) (Grand Lodge (USA)) **Mr B. Buckley**

419 MR J. W. MULLINS, Amesbury

Postal: **Wilsford Stables, Wilsford-Cum-Lake, Amesbury, Salisbury, Wiltshire, SP4 7BL**
Contacts: PHONE/FAX **(01980) 626344** MOBILE **(07702) 559634**
E-MAIL **info@jwmullins.co.uk** WEBSITE **www.jwmullins.co.uk**

1 **A SEA COMMANDER (GER),** 6, b g Winged Love (IRE)—As Tu As (USA) **First Impressions Racing Group**
2 **APPACH (FR),** 9, gr g Riche Mare (FR)—Simply Red (FR) **A. M. Day**

MR J. W. MULLINS—continued

3 AVESOMEOFTHAT (IRE), 7, b g Lahib (USA)—Lacinia K. J. Pike
4 4, B g Quws—Coca's Well (IRE) Wilsford Racing Partnership
5 COLD MOUNTAIN (IRE), 6, b g Inchinor—Streak of Silver (USA) Woodford Valley Racing
6 DALAYLA (IRE), 4, gr f Midhish—Polocracy (IRE) Mr D. Anderson
7 DELANEYS TRIUMPH (IRE), 8, b br g Taipan (IRE)—Hoodsgrove Lady (IRE) B. R. Edgeley
8 FEMME D'AVRIL (FR), 6, b m Homme de Loi (IRE)—Free Demo (FR) Chris & Stella Watson, Seamus Mullins
9 FOREIGN KING (USA), 4, b g Kingmambo (USA)—Foreign Aid (USA) Mr J. Collins
10 FOREST SILVER, 6, gr g Silver Patriarch (IRE)—Miss Orphan (IRE) New Forest Racing Partnership
11 HENDRE HOTSHOT, 6, b m Exit To Nowhere (USA)—Mutual Decision (IRE) Hendre Racehorses
12 HEYNEWBOY, 8, ch g Keen—Clown Around K. J. Pike
13 HILL FORTS HENRY, 10, ch g Karinga Bay—Maggie Tee Mrs J. C. Scorgie
14 HILL FORTS TIMMY, 8, b g Thowra (FR)—Queen of The Suir (IRE) Mrs J. C. Scorgie
15 JOCKSER (IRE), 7, b g Desert Story (IRE)—Pupa Fiorini (ITY) The D. M. L. Partnership
16 JUST STANDEESE (IRE), 6, b g Shahrastani (USA)—Vaguely Deesse (USA) F. G. Matthews
17 KAWAGINO (IRE), 8, b g Perugino (USA)—Sharakawa (IRE) K. J. Pike
18 KENTFORD MIST, 5, gr m Silver Patriarch (IRE)—Kentford Duchess D. I. Bare
19 LE TOTO, 5, b g Mtoto—La Dolce Vita CPM Group Limited
20 LETS GET BUSY (IRE), 8, ch m Presenting—Mindyourown (IRE) Mrs M. M. Rayner
21 MALAGA BOY (IRE), 11, b g Nordic Brave—Ardglass Mist A. J. M. Trowbridge
22 MISS DOUBLET, 7, ch m Double Trigger (IRE)—Bournel N. R. Bowden
23 MISTIFIED (IRE), 7, b g Ali-Royal (IRE)—Lough N Uisce (IRE) Cum-Lake Racing
24 NOT FOR DIAMONDS (IRE), 8, b g Arctic Lord—Black-Crash M. J. & J. M. Scott
25 OR SING ABOUT (FR), 6, b g Le Balafre (FR)—Grande Folie A. M. Day
26 ORION STAR (IRE), 6, ch g Fourstars Allstar (USA)—Rosies Sister (USA) C. A. Green
27 PETITO (IRE), 5, b g Imperial Ballet (IRE)—Fallacy D. E. Hazzard
28 RADBROOK HALL, 9, b g Teenoso (USA)—Sarah's Venture Andrew Cocks & Tara Johnson
29 RAWCLIFFE BAY, 6, ch g Karinga Bay—Pedrosa (IRE) Mr B. R. Haigh
30 SANDY DENNY (IRE), 5, b m Desert Story (IRE)—Tatra J. W. Mullins
31 SEE YOU SOMETIME, 13, b g Sharp Deal—Shepani J. A. G. Meaden
32 SHORTGATE LANE (IRE), 7, b g Needle Gun (IRE)—Two-Penny Rice A. G. C. Russell
33 SILVER GORA, 5, gr m Silver Patriarch (IRE)—Just Steffi Mr R. Sivlal
34 SPECIAL CONQUEST, 10, b g El Conquistador—Kellys Special F. G. Matthews
35 SPOT THE LADY (IRE), 6, b m Gothland (FR)—Bayviewlady (IRE) Church Racing Partnership
36 STRAWBERRY (IRE), 7, b m Beneficial—Ravaleen (IRE) Dr R. Jowett
37 STUDENT LOAN, 4, b f Tamure (IRE)—Hops And Pops The Read Family & Mr B. Dennett
38 THE SPEAKER (FR), 7, b g Nikos—Ostenne (FR) F. W. K. Griffin
39 VALASSINI, 8, b m Dr Massini (IRE)—Running Valley Mrs K. Stone

THREE-YEAR-OLDS

40 THE NAME IS FRANK, b g Lujain (USA)—Zaragossa D. E. Hazzard

Other Owners: P. R. Attwater, J. E. Bone, Mr A. P. Cocks, Mr P. Collins, B. Dennett, P. Everard, R. Hatchard, Mrs T. P. James, Ms H. C. E. Jodrell, Miss T. Johnson, J. Kavanagh, Ms J. E. S. Llewellyn, Mr J. Moran, Mrs S. A. Mullins, Mrs C. A. E. Pearce, Mr J. Read, M. J. Scott, Mrs J. M. Scott, C. R. Watson, Mrs S. Watson, J. H. Young.

Jockey (NH): A. Thornton, R. Young. Conditional: W. P. Kavanagh.

MR WILLIAM P. MULLINS, Carlow
420

Postal: Closutton, Bagenalstown, Co. Carlow, Ireland
Contacts: PHONE (00353) 5997 21786 FAX (00353) 5997 21786 MOBILE (00353) 8725 64940
E-MAIL wpmullins@eircom.net WEBSITE www.wpmullins.com

1 A BIT PLEASED, 6, b m Alflora (IRE)—Lady High Sheriff (IRE) Teahon Consulting Ltd
2 A THOUSAND MEN (FR), 5, b g Kahyasi—Nouka (IRE) Douglas Taylor
3 ADAMANT APPROACH (IRE), 14, b g Mandalus—Crash Approach Greenstar Syndicate
4 ALEXANDER TAIPAN (IRE), 8, b br g Taipan (IRE)—Fayafi Mrs N. O'Callaghan
5 ALPHAZAR (IRE), 13, b g Alphabatim (USA)—Ravaleen (IRE) CCR Racing Syndicate
6 ARBOR SUPREME (IRE), 6, b g Supreme Leader—Peter's Well (IRE) John P. McManus
7 AVOCA MIST (IRE), 8, b br m Luso—Apicat T. Merrigan
8 BALLYGOE (IRE), 9, b g Flemensfirth (USA)—Handy Lady Mrs R. Boyd
9 BALLYTRIM (IRE), 8, b g Luso—Helynsar Mrs V. O'Leary
10 BLACK HARRY (IRE), 8, b br g Flemensfirth (USA)—Raise An Ace Sean O'Driscoll
11 BOTHAR NA (IRE), 9, ch g Mister Lord (USA)—Country Course (IRE) Mrs M. O'Dwyer
12 BOXER GEORG (IRE), 6, b g Taipan (IRE)—Country Course (IRE) William Murray

MR WILLIAM P. MULLINS—continued

13 **C'EST CA**, 4, b c Groom Dancer (USA)—Known Class (USA) **Mrs J. M. Mullins**
14 **CADSPEED (FR)**, 5, b g Vertical Speed (FR)—Cadmina (FR) **T. J. Heneghan**
15 **CANDY GIRL (IRE)**, 9, b m Un Desperado (FR)—Dynamic Venture (IRE) **T. Merrigan**
16 **CAPEL LAD (IRE)**, 5, b g Turtle Island (IRE)—Lady Perfect (IRE) **MCR Syndicate**
17 **CELTIC SUPREME (IRE)**, 7, b g Supreme Leader—Sorimak Gale (IRE) **John J. Fallon**
18 **CLEAR RIPOSTE (IRE)**, 6, b m King's Theatre (IRE)—Niamh Cinn Oir (IRE) **Heritage Syndicate**
19 **CLER (IRE)**, 5, b h Second Empire (IRE)—Spirit Of The Nile (FR) **P. Burke**
20 **COBHAM**, 8, ch g Rakaposhi King—Faint Praise **New Court Syndicate**
21 **COOLDINE (IRE)**, 6, b g Beneficial—Shean Alainn (IRE) **Mrs V. O'Leary**
22 **CRENAUN BRIDGE (IRE)**, 8, b g Dr Massini (IRE)—Persian Desert (IRE) **T. Gilligan**
23 **CRU (IRE)**, 4, b f Desert Style (IRE)—Crohal di San Jore **Magnum Cru Syndicate**
24 **CUCHULAINS SON (IRE)**, 6, b g Bob Back (USA)—Gallic Approach (IRE) **J. J. Brennan**
25 **CYRIL LORD (FR)**, 6, b g Cyborg (FR)—Allee Du Port (FR) **Axminster Syndicate**
26 **DANI CALIFORNIA**, 4, br f Beat All (USA)—Auntie Bob **W. K. McCarthy**
27 **DAVENPORT DEMOCRAT (IRE)**, 10, ch g Fourstars Allstar (USA)—Storm Court (IRE) **PM Racing Syndicate**
28 **DEFINITE EDGE (IRE)**, 6, ch g Definite Article—Itkan (IRE) **Friends In The North Syndicate**
29 **DERRYMORE DAWN (IRE)**, 4, b g Rossini (USA)—Ghayaat (USA) **B. Dobbin**
30 **DEUTSCHLAND (USA)**, 5, b g Red Ransom (USA)—Rhine Valley (USA) **A. McLuckie**
31 **DIEGO GARCIA (IRE)**, 8, b h Sri Pekan (USA)—Chapel Lawn **J. J. Brennan**
32 **DOONEYS GATE (IRE)**, 7, b g Oscar (IRE)—Park Breeze (IRE) **T. Gilligan**
33 **DRUMDERRY (IRE)**, 6, b m Shernazar—Karlybelle (FR) **Does Size Matter Syndicate**
34 **DUAL GALES (IRE)**, 7, b g Lord of Appeal—Freshfield Gale (IRE) **Killeedy Syndicate**
35 **EBAZIYAN (IRE)**, 7, gr g Daylami (IRE)—Ebadiyla (IRE) **Mr P. Garvey**
36 **EBONY SHADES (IRE)**, 7, br g Bob Back (USA)—Silks Princess **J. Ramsbottom**
37 **EQUUS MAXIMUS (IRE)**, 8, b g Flemensfirth (USA)—Sambara (IRE) **Greenstar Syndicate**
38 **EURO LEADER (IRE)**, 10, b g Supreme Leader—Noreaster (IRE) **J. Cox**
39 **FINAL ALERT (USA)**, 6, ch g Distant View (USA)—Flaming Torch **A. Fanning**
40 **FINANCIAL REWARD (IRE)**, 5, b h Fruits of Love (USA)—Lamp of Phoebus (USA) **Mrs M. Warde**
41 **FIRE OF KEN (FR)**, 7, b h Kendor (FR)—Terre de Feu (FR) **D. Flynn**
42 **FIVEFORTHREE (IRE)**, 6, gr g Arzanni—What A Queen **Olde Crowbars Syndicate**
43 **FRANKLINS TRAIL (IRE)**, 7, b h Imperial Ballet—Nettle **J. J. Brennan**
44 **FREDS BENEFIT (IRE)**, 7, ch g Beneficial—Welsh Ana (IRE) **D. Power**
45 **GILLIGANS HALL (IRE)**, 8, b g Saddlers' Hall (IRE)—Charming Mo (IRE) **T. Gilligan**
46 **GLANN BOY (IRE)**, 7, b g Darazari (IRE)—Osiery Girl (IRE) **Mrs M. Sarkar**
47 **GLENCOVE MARINA (IRE)**, 4, b g Spectrum (IRE)—Specifiedrisk (IRE) **J. J. Brennan**
48 **GOOD REPUTE**, 5, b h Benny The Dip (USA)—Reddening **Mrs M. Warde**
49 **HARD ACT (IRE)**, 5, b g Oscar (IRE)—Annaelaine (IRE) **T. J. Hemmings**
50 **HEDGEHUNTER (IRE)**, 12, b g Montelimar—Aberedw (IRE) **T. J. Hemmings**
51 **HOLLYWOOD LAW (IRE)**, 7, ch g Zaffaran (USA)—Whoareyoutoday (IRE) **D. Lawlor**
52 **HOMER WELLS (IRE)**, 10, b g Arctic Cider (USA)—Run And Shine **Mrs M. McMahon**
53 **HUCKLE BUCK SHOE (IRE)**, 5, b g King's Theatre (IRE)—Bold Nora (IRE) **M. J. Hanrahan**
54 **HURRICANE DEAN (IRE)**, 5, b g Flemensfirth (USA)—Ankor Belle (IRE) **Mrs B. Deane**
55 **IMPERIAL HILLS (IRE)**, 4, b g Imperial Ballet—Sixhills (IRE) **T. I. Naughton**
56 **IRISH INVADER (IRE)**, 7, b g Bob Back (USA)—Idealist **Sackcloth & Ashes Syndicate**
57 **JAYO (FR)**, 5, ch g Grape Tree Road—Joie de Nuit (USA) **P. Garvey**
58 **JOSEPHINE CULLEN (IRE)**, 6, ch m Daggers Drawn (USA)—Moycullen **Mrs J. M. Mullins**
59 **KNOCKNABOOLY (IRE)**, 9, ch g John French—Valiyist (IRE) **Margaret O'Rourke**
60 **LILYWHITEDANCER (IRE)**, 6, b br g King's Theatre (IRE)—Relief Map **Sarsfield Racing Syndicate**
61 **LITTLE PALM (IRE)**, 5, gr g Great Palm (USA)—Alzenia (IRE) **J. Kennefick**
62 **LIVINGSTONEBRAMBLE (IRE)**, 12, b g Supreme Leader—Killiney Side **Favorites Racing Syndicate**
63 **LOUGH HYNE HILL (IRE)**, 5, ch g Bob's Return (IRE)—El Zaana **Ilen Syndicate**
64 **MACS MANDALUS**, 8, b g Presenting—My Gonny (IRE) **Mrs Margaret McManus**
65 **MAGNUM FORCE (IRE)**, 4, b c Redback—Dalal **Magnum Cru Syndicate**
66 **MAN ON THE NILE (IRE)**, 8, b h Snurge—Spirit of The Nile (FR) **D. Flynn**
67 **MISTER HIGHT (FR)**, 6, b/ g Take Risks (FR)—Miss High (FR) **Mr P. Garvey**
68 **MR BRIGHTSIDE (IRE)**, 6, ch g Carroll House—Lissanuhig **David Flynn**
69 **MULLAGH NA SI**, 4, b c Poliglote—Fatale (IRE) **T. Gilligan**
70 **NANCY WAKE (IRE)**, 8, b m Mister Lord (USA)—Monadante (IRE) **Closutton Racing Club**
71 **NORWICH BOY (IRE)**, 6, b g Norwich—Saffron Spirit **Surr & Liffey Syndicate**
72 **O'HANA (FR)**, 6, b m Nononito (FR)—Isati's (FR) **Closutton Racing Club**
73 **ORGE D'ETE (FR)**, 6, gr g April Night (FR)—Fee Mousse (FR) **Two Tricia's Syndicate**
74 **OTAY KAWN (IRE)**, 5, b g Soviet Star (USA)—Fox Glen **Teahon Consulting**
75 **OUR BEN**, 9, ch g Presenting—Forest Pride (IRE) **T. J. Hemmings**
76 **OUR BOB (IRE)**, 6, gr g Bob Back (USA)—Mondeo Rose (IRE) **T. J. Hemmings**
77 **OUR MATTI**, 7, b g Supreme Leader—Haudello (FR) **T. J. Hemmings**
78 **PALACE MERANO (IRE)**, 5, b g Antarctique (IRE)—Domage II (FR) **T. J. Hanrahan**

MR WILLIAM P. MULLINS—continued

79 **POLAR CALL (IRE)**, 9, b g Shernazar—Acres Lady (IRE) **I. Farnan**
80 **POLAR SPEED (FR)**, 5, ch g Vertical Speed (FR)—Zvezda Danica (FR) **We Used To Be Friends Syndicate**
81 **PRESLEY (IRE)**, 7, b g Presenting—Charmere's Beauty (IRE) **Mrs J. K. Powell**
82 **QUATRE HEURES (FR)**, 6, b g Vertical Speed (FR)—Macyrienne (FR) **John Mc's Winchester Syndicate**
83 **RATHER DELIGHTED (IRE)**, 4, b g Indian Danehill (IRE)—Tiller Girl (IRE) **Mrs J. M. Mullins**
84 **ROSY CYBORG (FR)**, 5, b g Cyborg (FR)—Rosy Junior (FR) **T. Gilligan**
85 **ROYAL HERITAGE (IRE)**, 9, b h Carroll House—Call Me Anna **Heritage Syndicate**
86 **SADLERS WINGS (IRE)**, 10, b h In The Wings—Anna Comnena (IRE) **J. J. Brennan**
87 **SCAN THE MAN (IRE)**, 7, b g Shernazar—Eagles Joy (IRE) **D K D Syndicate**
88 **SCOTSIRISH (IRE)**, 7, b g Zaffaran (USA)—Serjitak **RR Stable LLP Syndicate**
89 **SESENTA (IRE)**, 4, b f King's Theatre (IRE)—Cincuenta (IRE) **Michael Carroll**
90 **SHADY WILLOW (IRE)**, 6, b g Unfuwain (USA)—Shady Leaf (IRE) **T. Gilligan**
91 **SHAKERVILZ (FR)**, 5, b g Villez (USA)—Zamsara (FR) **T. Gilligan**
92 **SHEDAN (IRE)**, 6, b m Perpendicular—Larry's Peach **Teahon Consulting Limited**
93 **SIMPLE APPROACH (IRE)**, 6, b g Simply Great (FR)—Musical Approach (IRE) **John J. Brennan**
94 **SNOWY MORNING (IRE)**, 8, b g Moscow Society (USA)—Miss Perky (IRE) **Quayside Syndicate**
95 **SOI (IRE)**, 6, b m Bob Back (USA)—Despute (IRE) **T. Conroy**
96 **SONNE CINQ (IRE)**, 9, b br m Old Vic—Ring Four (IRE) **Scones Syndicate**
97 **SONNIUM (IRE)**, 4, ch g Lomitas—Cutting Glance (USA) **Mrs J. M. Mullins**
98 **STARINTING (IRE)**, 7, b g Presenting—Star With A Glimer **Starry Things Syndicate**
99 **TAIPAN'S WAY (IRE)**, 6, b g Taipan (IRE)—Wayward Bride (IRE) **John O. Browne**
100 **TANGO FOXTROT (IRE)**, 6, b g Foxhound (USA)—Tango Two Thousand (IRE) **D. Kavanagh**
101 **TAX EXEMPTION (IRE)**, 7, b m Bob Back (USA)—Tourist Attraction (IRE) **NKR Syndicate**
102 **TEMLETT (IRE)**, 4, b g Desert Prince (IRE)—Bering Down (USA) **Double R Stables LLP Syndiacte**
103 **TEMPLERS HALL (IRE)**, 9, b g Majed (IRE)—Connaught Lace **K. O'Brien**
104 **THE BOXER COFFEY (IRE)**, 6, b h Spectrum (IRE)—Gipsy Anna (IRE) **J. O. Mahon**
105 **THE PATRIARCH GAME (IRE)**, 6, bl g Gothland (FR)—Glacial Lady (IRE) **Down The Hatch Syndicate**
106 **THEMOONANDSIXPENCE (IRE)**, 5, ch g Presenting—Elphis (IRE) **Mrs S. Ricci**
107 **UNCLE JUNIOR (IRE)**, 7, b g Saddlers' Hall (IRE)—Caslain Nua **Mrs M. McManus**
108 **VISO (FR)**, 5, gr g Take Risks (FR)—Vouivre (FR) **P. Burke**
109 **WARRENS CASTLE (IRE)**, 11, b g Fourstars Allstar (USA)—Jerusalem Cruiser (IRE) **J. J. Brennan**
110 **YOUNG MILLY (IRE)**, 5, ch m Accordion—Reign Onmee (IRE) **John Small**

THREE-YEAR-OLDS

111 **COFFEE TEA OR ME**, b c Vettori (IRE)—Cockatrice **Mrs S. Ricci**
112 **MIS FANCY THAT (IRE)**, b br f Trans Island—Mega Tassa (IRE) **Peter B. Kelly**

Jockey (NH): D. J. Condon, R. Walsh. **Apprentice:** Paul Townend. **Amateur:** Ms K. Walsh, Mr P. W. Mullins.

---

421 **MR F. MURPHY, West Witton**
Postal: Wynbury Stables, West Witton, Leyburn, North Yorkshire, DL8 4LR
Contacts: PHONE (01969) 622289 (01969) 624200 FAX (01969) 625278 MOBILE (07703) 444398
E-MAIL office@wynburystables.fsnet.co.uk WEBSITE www.ferdymurphyracing.co.uk

1 **ACES FOUR (IRE)**, 9, ch g Fourstars Allstar (USA)—Special Trix (IRE) **The DPRP Aces Partnership**
2 **AJAY (IRE)**, 7, ch g Posidonas—Gothic Shadow (IRE) **Mr I. A. Todd**
3 **ALDERBRIDGE (IRE)**, 5, b g Alderbrook—Gallic Honey (IRE) **T. J. Hemmings**
4 **AMBROSIA'S PROMISE (IRE)**, 5, ch m Minster Son—Snape (IRE) **Geoff Hubbard Racing**
5 **ANGLICAN (FR)**, 7, ch g Starborough—Anglaise (FR) **D. Parry**
6 **ANOTHER PROMISE (IRE)**, 9, ch g Presenting—Snape (IRE) **Geoff Hubbard Racing**
7 **APRIL SAN**, 5, b h Nashwan (USA)—April Lee (USA) **Whitechurch Stud**
8 **ASK THE CHIEF**, 7, b g Silver Patriarch (IRE)—Kev's Lass (IRE) **Geoff Hubbard Racing**
9 **AUBURN DRIVE (IRE)**, 7, b g Shernazar—Finnisk Dream (IRE) **Sean J. Murphy**
10 **BARTON SUN (IRE)**, 9, b g Indian Ridge—Sun Screen **One Day Soon Rodney Partnership**
11 **BEGGARS CAP (IRE)**, 6, ch g Lord of Appeal—Ann's Cap (IRE) **T. J. Hemmings**
12 **BEWERY MAN (IRE)**, 7, b g Heron Island (IRE)—Rumi **Mrs M. J. P. Kane**
13 **BIG BURROWS (IRE)**, 6, b g Supreme Leader—Bula Vogue **Mrs J. Morgan**
14 **BLACKPOOL BILLY (IRE)**, 6, br g Overbury (IRE)—Ina's Farewell **F. Murphy**
15 **BLASKNOCK (IRE)**, 6, br m Lord Americo—Vixen's Cry (IRE) **Mrs R. D. Cairns**
16 **BOBATIM (IRE)**, 7, gr m Alphabatim (USA)—Rose Wood **Mrs J. Knight**
17 **BONNETA (FR)**, 5, b m Bonnet Rouge (FR)—Incognito (FR) **RedHotGardogs**
18 **CAIPIROSKA**, 9, b g Petoski—Caipirinha (IRE) **T. J. Hemmings**
19 **CARDINAL SPIRIT**, 6, b g Selkirk (USA)—Answered Prayer **Betfair Club ROA**
20 **CARRICK STAR (IRE)**, 6, b g Supreme Leader—Chatty Di **Mr John Dollard & Miss Mollie Power**

MR F. MURPHY—continued

21 **CARRYDUFF**, 7, b g Deploy—Pink Brief (IRE) **Plantation Stud**
22 **CEILIDH LASS (FR)**, 4, gr f Saint Preuil (FR)—Cybertina (FR) **S & K Larson, C Whittaker & Mrs A Yeoman**
23 **CLEMAX (IRE)**, 7, gr g Linamix (FR)—Chauncy Lane (IRE) **The DPRP Clemax Partnership**
24 **CONISTON**, 5, b m Cotation—Laughing Pet **B. Leatherday**
25 **CYBORA (FR)**, 6, ch m Cyborg (FR)—Jolie Rapide (FR) **D. Clinton, S. Gale, M. Milns, F. Murphy**
26 **DANCER'S SERENADE (IRE)**, 6, b g Almutawakel—Dance Serenade (IRE) **Red Lion Racing Limited**
27 **DEJA VU (IRE)**, 9, b g Lord Americo—Khalkeys Shoon **The SGS Partnership**
28 **DELRAY BEACH (FR)**, 6, b m Saint Preuil—Icone (FR) **The DPRP Delray Partnership**
29 **DEVIL'S DISGUISE**, 6, b g Atraf—Dunloe (IRE) **S. L. Rodwell**
30 **EARVEE (IRE)**, 6, b g Raphane (USA)—Lady Redford **Sean J. Murphy**
31 **FAIR HILLS BABA (FR)**, 5, b g Milford Track (IRE)—Babacha (FR) **Hill, Trembath, Bryan & Outhart**
32 **FAITH AND FORTUNE**, 6, b m Mtoto—Snape (IRE) **Geoff Hubbard Racing**
33 **FOLK TUNE (IRE)**, 5, b h Danehill (USA)—Musk Lime (USA) **J. N. Blackburn**
34 **GALANT NUIT (FR)**, 4, b g Comte du Bourg (FR)—Little Blue (FR) **D. Parry**
35 **GENEROUS PARK**, 4, b g Generous (IRE)—Sadler's Park (USA) **S. L. Rodwell**
36 **GLACIAL DELIGHT (FR)**, 9, b g Glacial Storm (USA)—Annagh Delight **Mrs A. Sulin & Mrs J. Morgan**
37 **GREENOCK**, 7, b g Silver Patriarch (IRE)—Merilena (IRE) **J. & A. Millar**
38 **HELLO MY LOVELY**, 7, b m Presenting—Snape (IRE) **Geoff Hubbard Racing**
39 **HOT WELD**, 9, b g Weld—Deb's Ball **S. L. Rodwell**
40 **ITS A RINKY DINK (IRE)**, 8, b g Shardari—Choice Display **B.M.P.P. Partners**
41 **IVOIRE DE BEAULIEU (FR)**, 12, b g Port Etienne (FR)—Kashmonde (FR) **I Todd, F Murphy, C Leigh, S Holman**
42 **JOES EDGE (FR)**, 11, b br g Supreme Leader—Right Dark **Chemipetro Limited**
43 **KALAHARI KING (FR)**, 7, b br g Kahyasi—Queen of Warsaw (FR) **Mrs J. Morgan**
44 **KALMO BAY (FR)**, 5, b g Alamo Bay (USA)—Kermesse (USA) **The DPRP Kalmo Partnership**
45 **KING OF CONFUSION (IRE)**, 9, br g Topanoora—Rich Desire **Mr B. J. O'Rourke**
46 **KINGSBURY (FR)**, 9, b g Norwich—Glen Na Mban (IRE) **Reg Joseph & Miss J. V. Morgan**
47 **L'ANTARTIQUE (FR)**, 8, b g Cyborg (FR)—Moomaw **Mrs A. N. Durkan**
48 **LADY RHINESTONE (IRE)**, 4, b f Presenting—Rare Gesture (IRE) **S. L. Rodwell**
49 **LE ROI ROUGE (FR)**, 6, ch g Bateau Rouge—Reine de Lutece (FR) **G. T. W. Fenwicke-Clennell**
50 **LE VERT GALANT (FR)**, 5, b g Vertical Speed (FR)—
         Marie Prends Garde (FR) **C. McHugh, C. Eliades, W. O'Connor & F. Montanaro**
51 **LEADING MAN (IRE)**, 8, b g Old Vic—Cudder Or Shudder (IRE) **Mrs Catriona M. McKeane**
52 **LUCKY NELLERIE (FR)**, 9, ch g Grand Tresor (FR)—British Nellerie (FR) **The DPRP Nellerie Partnership**
53 5, B g Bob Back (USA)—Lucy Glitters **Mr John Dollard**
54 **LUZENIE (FR)**, 5, b m Cadoudal (FR)—Luzenia (FR) **The DPRP Luzenie Partnership**
55 **MACS ISLAND (IRE)**, 7, br g Heron Island (IRE)—Lady Clara (IRE) **B. McEntaggart**
56 **MAJORCA**, 7, b g Green Desert (USA)—Majmu (USA) **Chiltern**
57 **MANSION LEDA (IRE)**, 5, b m Mansonnien (FR)—Oleada (IRE) **Simon & Mark Hubbard Rodwell**
58 **MARSHALL HALL (IRE)**, 7, b g Saddlers' Hall (IRE)—Nocturnal Pleasure (IRE) **Plantation Stud**
59 **MASTER BUILDER (FR)**, 7, b g Lute Antique (FR)—Solaine (FR) **Mrs A. N. Durkan**
60 **MEDIA MAN (IRE)**, 8, br g Presenting—Derravarragh Lady (IRE) **J. B. Stead**
61 6, B br m Heron Island (IRE)—Miss Flic **F. Murphy**
62 **MONGORNO (FR)**, 5, b g Kizitca (FR)—Modiana (FR) **C. W. Cooper**
63 **MR FLOPPY (IRE)**, 7, b g Un Desperado (FR)—Bright Future (IRE) **W. J. Gott**
64 **MR JACK DANIELLS (IRE)**, 7, b g Mujadil (USA)—Neat Shilling (IRE) **Sean J. Murphy**
65 **NAIAD DU MISSELOT (FR)**, 7, b g Dom Alco (FR)—Une Nuit (FR) **Hill, Trembath, Bryan & Outhart**
66 **NEGUS DE BEAUMONT (FR)**, 7, b g Blushing Flame (USA)—Givry (FR) **Mr W. Roberts & Mr J. Tierney**
67 **NEW ALCO (FR)**, 7, b br g Dom Alco (FR)—Cabira des Saccart (FR) **Mr D. McGowan & Mr S. Murphy**
68 **NINE DE SIVOLA (FR)**, 7, b g Video Rock (FR)—Quine de Chalamont (FR) **The DPRP Sivola Partnership**
69 **NOIR ET VERT (FR)**, 7, b g Silver Rainbow—Danse Verte (FR) **Plantation Stud**
70 **NOT TALKING (IRE)**, 5, b g Supreme Leader—View of The Hills **J. N. Blackburn**
71 **OCKEY DE NEULLIAC (FR)**, 6, ch g Cyborg (FR)—Graine de Neulliac (FR) **F. Murphy**
72 **ORKI DES AIGLES (FR)**, 6, b g Le Balafre (FR)—Rose des Aigles (FR) **Mr W. H. Winlow & Mrs C. Seymour**
73 **PAKINEO DES PICTONS (FR)**, 5, b g Kadalko (FR)—Akinea (FR) **The DPRP Pictons Partnership**
74 **PALES (GER)**, 7, ch g Secret 'n Classy (CAN)—Parlez Moi D'amour (FR) **Geoff Hubbard Racing**
75 **PERCUTANT (FR)**, 5, b g April Night (FR)—Holliday's (FR) **W. J. Gott**
76 **PERSIAN TONIC (IRE)**, 4, b g Son of Sharp Shot—Arme Fatale (IRE) **Tony Pye & Masoud Khadem**
77 **PETERPAN DE SOLZEN (FR)**, 5, b g Passing Sale (FR)—Cymphonie (FR) **Mrs R. D. Cairns**
78 **PISTOL BASC (FR)**, 4, ch c Maille Pistol (FR)—Moldane (FR) **D. Parry**
79 **POKER DE SIVOLA (FR)**, 5, b g Discover d'auteuil (FR)—Legal Union **D. A. Johnson**
80 **POLYBE DES OBEAUX (FR)**, 5, b g Maresca Sorrento (FR)—Infinie II (FR) **Plantation Stud**
81 **PORT ERNE (IRE)**, 5, b g Stowaway—Little Nonnie (IRE) **Sean J. Murphy**
82 **PRE TOKEN**, 7, b g Presidium—Pro-Token **D. A. Johnson**
83 **PRINCIPAL LAD (IRE)**, 5, b g Supreme Leader—Marcontess (IRE) **T. J. Hemmings**
84 **QUALITY CONTROL (IRE)**, 7, b g Tiraaz (USA)—Booking Note (IRE) **Universal Recycling Company**
85 6, B br g Oscar (IRE)—Rich Desire

MR F. MURPHY—continued

86 **RICH LORD**, 4, b g Zamindar (USA)—Al Corniche (IRE) **The DPRP Lord Partnership**
87 **SEIZE**, 6, gr g Silver Patriarch (IRE)—Sleepline Princess **Mrs S. Mizel**
88 **SENORA SNOOPY (IRE)**, 7, b m Un Desperado (IRE)—Lovely Snoopy (IRE) **Racegoers Club Owners Group**
89 **SHARKEYS DREAM (FR)**, 7, gr g Dom Alco (FR)—Dame Au Diamant (FR) **Chemipetro Limited**
90 **SHOULDHAVEHADTHAT (IRE)**, 6, b g Definite Article—Keep The Pace (IRE) **Unchartered Waters**
91 **SILVER DESTINY**, 7, gr m Cloudings (IRE)—Tibbi Blues **Miss B. Spittal**
92 **SPEED UP (FR)**, 5, ch g Vertical Speed (FR)—Haiya (FR) **Mr D. McGowan & Mr S. Murphy**
93 **SPRING BREEZE**, 7, ch g Dr Fong (USA)—Trading Aces **J. N. Blackburn**
94 **START ROYAL (FR)**, 4, b g Starborough—Marie Des Epeires (FR) **Mr & Mrs J. D. Cotton**
95 **SUPREME BUILDER**, 7, b g Supreme Leader—Osocool **Mrs A. N. Durkan**
96 **SURRICATE (FR)**, 6, b m True Brave (USA)—Sweet Normania (FR) **Mr I. A. Todd**
97 **THE DUKE'S SPEECH (IRE)**, 7, b g Saddlers' Hall (IRE)—Dannkalia (IRE) **Mrs A. N. Durkan**
98 **THE HOLLINWELL**, 5, b g Classic Cliche (IRE)—Action de Balle (IRE) **Mr & Mrs Neil Iveson**
99 **THREE MIRRORS**, 8, b g Cloudings (IRE)—Aliuska (IRE) **Sean J. Murphy**
100 **TISSAIA (FR)**, 5, gr m Lute Antique (FR)—Miss Apple (FR) **F. Murphy**
101 **TOP CLOUD (IRE)**, 7, b g Cloudings (IRE)—Top Dresser (IRE) **T. J. Hemmings**
102 **TOPSHAM BELLE (IRE)**, 4, b f Presenting—Ara Blend (IRE) **S. L. Rodwell**
103 **TRISONS STAR (IRE)**, 10, b g Roselier (FR)—Delkusha **Taylor, Martin & White**
104 **UNDERWRITER (USA)**, 8, b br g With Approval (CAN)—Night Risk (USA) **Mrs D. K. O' Rourke**
105 **VICE VERSA (IRE)**, 6, b g Pistolet Bleu (IRE)—Suny Salome **Plantation Stud**
106 **WALLY WONDER (IRE)**, 10, ch g Magical Wonder (USA)—Sally Gap **A. Long**
107 **WATER TAXI**, 7, ch g Zafonic (USA)—Trellis Bay **G Wilson.R Wheeler.King.McHugh.Wade**
108 **WOODMASTER (IRE)**, 5, b g Oscar (IRE)—Allatrim (IRE) **T. J. Hemmings**
109 **YOU'RE SPECIAL (IRE)**, 11, b g Northern Flagship (USA)—Pillow Mint (USA) **Mrs D. K. O' Rourke**

THREE-YEAR-OLDS

110 **ERIN DANCER (IRE)**, b g Chevalier (IRE)—Negria (IRE) **J. & A. Millar**

Other Owners: Mr Tom Berrigan, Mr R. G. Capstick, Mr A. Coldron, Mr J. D. Cotton, Mrs B. Cotton, Mr John Dollard, Mr C. Eliades, Mr M. Hill (Taunton), Miss Sarah Holman, Mr D. N. Iveson, Mrs J. E. Iveson, Mr P. A. Jackson, Mr R. Joseph, Miss Mollie Power, Mr Masoud Khadem, Mrs S. Larson, Miss K. Larson, Lord Leigh, Mr R. Martin, Mr D. McGowan, Mr Chris McHugh, Mr A. Millar, Mrs J. Millar, Mr F. Montanaro, Miss J. V. Morgan, Mr Sean J. Murphy, Mr W. O'Connor, Mr D. F. O'Rourke, Mrs Perle O'Rourke, Mrs Rebecca Parry, Mr Tony Pye, Mr Brian Rafferty, Mrs J. Reader, Mr J. E. H. Reader, Mr Hugh T. Redhead, Mr Warren Roberts, Mrs Sandra Rodwell, Mr M. Hubbard Rodwell, Mr John Ryan, Mr K. Scoular, Mrs C. Seymour, Mr P. K. Starks, Mrs A. Sulin, Mr P. Sullivan, Mr J. Tierney, Mr Ian Allan Todd, Mr C. R. Trembath, Mr M. Waters, Mr R. Wheeler, Mr C. R. Whittaker, Mr J. Whittle, Mr G. V. Wilson, Mr W. H. Winlow, Mrs K. L. Yates, Mrs Angela Yeoman.

Assistant Trainer: Niall Hannity

Jockey (NH): G. Lee, K. Mercer. **Apprentice:** P. J. McDonald. **Conditional:** T. J. Dreaper, Mick O'Connell, Joe Palmowski, Ewan Whillans. **Amateur:** Mr N. Moscrop, Mr J. Winston.

---

422 **MR P. G. MURPHY, Hungerford**
Postal: Glebe House Stables, School Lane, East Garston, Nr Hungerford, Berkshire, RG17 7HR
Contacts: OFFICE (01488) 648473 FAX (01488) 649775 MOBILE (07831) 410409
E-MAIL pat@mabberleys.freeserve.co.uk

1 **BACK TO NORMAL (IRE)**, 5, ch m Muharib (USA)—Abi Normal (IRE) **Mrs D. E. Murphy**
2 **BALLYKILN (IRE)**, 7, br g Petoski—Hunt The Thimble (FR) **J. Cooper**
3 **BLUE PLANET (IRE)**, 10, b g Bluebird (USA)—Millie Musique **Miss J. Collison**
4 **GARSTON STAR**, 7, ch g Fleetwood (IRE)—Conquista **Mr P. G. Murphy**
5 **GREENWOOD**, 10, ch g Emarati (USA)—Charnwood Queen **P. G. Murphy**
6 **IMPROMPTU**, 4, b g Mujadil (USA)—Pie In The Sky **The Golden Anorak Partnership**
7 **LA CORTEZANA**, 4, ch f Piccolo—Blushing Belle **C. H. Shankland**
8 **MARIAVERDI**, 4, b f Diktat—Belinda **North Farm Stud**
9 **PEDLERS BRIDGE (IRE)**, 6, b g Moonax—Lochda **Arkley Racing**
10 **POWER SHARED (IRE)**, 4, gr g Kendor (FR)—Striking Pose (IRE) **The Golden Anorak Partnership**
11 **SALUTE (IRE)**, 9, b g Muhtarram (USA)—Alasib **The Golden Anorak Partnership**
12 **SCOBIE NAIL (IRE)**, 6, b g Presenting—Legendra **P. G. Murphy**
13 **SUN CATCHER (IRE)**, 5, b g Cape Cross (IRE)—Taalluf (USA) **Golden Anorak Partnership & Mike Conway**
14 **TARATEENO**, 5, b g Kayf Tara—Shalateeno **G. J. & Mrs M. Palmer**
15 **TREATY FLYER (IRE)**, 7, ch m Anshan—Highways Daughter (IRE) **Mrs D. E. Murphy**

MR P. G. MURPHY—continued

THREE-YEAR-OLDS

16 **BEN**, b c Bertolini (USA)—Bold Byzantium **K. W. Anidjah**
17 **MAYBE I WONT**, b c Kyllachy—Surprise Surprise **Ms P. M. Marks**
18 **OUR JANE**, b f Apprehension—Honey Mill **K. W. Anidjah**

TWO-YEAR-OLDS

19 **ALBERT HENRY (IRE)**, b c 21/4 Apprehension—Eastbury Rose (Beveled (USA)) (1904) **K. W. Anidjah**

Other Owners: Mr M. Conway, Mrs K. M. Graham, David J. Muir, Mrs A. Muir, G. J. Palmer, Mrs M. Palmer, A. D. Potts.

Assistant Trainer: Mrs Dianne Murphy

Jockey (flat): R. Havlin, S. Drowne. **Jockey (NH):** C. Bolger. **Amateur:** Mr Frank Fairchild.

---

423 MR P. T. J. MURPHY, Middleham
Postal: **Cappall Lodge, Coverham, Middleham, Leyburn, North Yorkshire, DL8 4TL**
Contacts: **MOBILE (07720) 404646**

1 **CALLINGWOOD (IRE)**, 8, ch g Pierre—Clonroche Artic **Mrs J. Morgan**
2 **CAPTAIN TIMELESS**, 5, b g Timeless Times (USA)—The Lady Captain **Patrick Cranney**
3 **CONTRABAND**, 10, b g Red Ransom (USA)—Shortfall **F. G. Wilson**
4 **ELZAHANN**, 6, b m Apprehension (IRE)—Serpentine Artiste **P. T. J. Murphy**
5 **FILM FESTIVAL (USA)**, 5, ch g Diesis—To Act (USA) **W. Durkan**
6 **GOODNIGHT DICK (IRE)**, 8, b br g Luso—Morning Susan **W. J. Foley**
7 **HAS SCORED (IRE)**, 10, b g Sadler's Wells (USA)—City Ex **The Extra Time Partnership**
8 **HIGH MOON (USA)**, 12, b g Alleged (USA)—Eclipse de Lune (USA) **F. G. Wilson**
9 **KAYAKA (FR)**, 4, b f Kahyasi—Falika (FR)
10 **LONGY THE LASH**, 5, b g Contract Law (USA)—Hello Hobson's (IRE) **A. Long**
11 **MARRIED (IRE)**, 10, ch g Pursuit of Love—Mistreat **F. G. Wilson**
12 **METEORIC RISE (IRE)**, 5, b m Heron Island (IRE)—Majestic Mind (IRE) **Mr O. Bonville**
13 **NOQUINA (FR)**, 7, ch g Epervier Bleu—Goquina (FR) **Mrs L. J. Hammond**
14 **PRYDERI DE KERION (FR)**, 5, b g Cadoubel (FR)—Alicia de Kerpaul (FR) **P. T. J. Murphy**
15 **ROSIE BEAR**, 5, b m Saddlers' Hall (IRE)—Minerstown (IRE) **S & S Hubbard Rodwell**
16 **SILVER FEATHER (IRE)**, 6, gr g Silver Patriarch (IRE)—Merilena (USA) **S & S Hubbard Rodwell**
17 **SYBELLIUS D'ARTAIX (FR)**, 8, b g Sassanian (USA)—Kadisha (FR) **F. G. Wilson**
18 4, B c Cloudings (IRE)—Tibbi Blues **Miss B. Spittall**
19 **WEE WALLIS**, 5, b m Windsor Castle—Cudder Or Shudder (IRE) **Mrs Catriona M. McKeane**

TWO-YEAR-OLDS

20 **ON THE FEATHER**, br f 18/4 Josr Algarhoud (IRE)—Fotheringhay (Loup Sauvage (USA)) **Mrs Jenny Willment**
21 **WOLFS BANE**, b f 5/3 Generous (IRE)—Loriner's Lady (Saddlers' Hall (IRE)) **Mrs Jenny Willment**

Other Owners: Dr Morgan Feely, Mrs Mary Feely, Mr S. Hubbard Rodwell, Mrs Sandra Rodwell.

---

424 MR D. J. G. MURRAY SMITH, Tarporley
Postal: **Rob Lloyd Racing Ltd, Haycroft Farm, Peckforton Hall Lane, Spurstow, Tarporley, Cheshire, CW6 9TF**
Contacts: **PHONE (01829) 261318 FAX (01829) 261331 MOBILE (07515) 483466**
E-MAIL info@roblloydracing.co.uk WEBSITE www.roblloydracing.co.uk

1 **CENTREBOARD (USA)**, 4, gr ro f Mizzen Mast (USA)—Corsini **Rob Lloyd Racing Limited**
2 **DREAM OF PARADISE (USA)**, 5, ch m Atticus (USA)—Scrumptious (USA) **Rob Lloyd Racing Limited**
3 **PIPER'S SONG (IRE)**, 5, gr g Distant Music (USA)—Dane's Lane (IRE) **Rob Lloyd Racing Limited**
4 **RUBENSTAR (IRE)**, 5, b g Soviet Star (USA)—Ansariya (USA) **Rob Lloyd Syndications**
5 **SANDY'S LEGEND**, 6, ch g Tale of The Cat (USA)—Avasand (USA) **Rob Lloyd Racing Limited**

THREE-YEAR-OLDS

6 **ANACOT STEEL (IRE)**, ch c Danehill Dancer (IRE)—Paper Moon (IRE) **Rob Lloyd Racing Limited**
7 **BROKEN APPLAUSE (IRE)**, br f Acclamation—Pink Cashmere (IRE) **Rob Lloyd Racing Limited**
8 **ELUSIVE DEAL (USA)**, ch f Elusive Quality (USA)—Peacefally (IRE) **Rob Lloyd Racing Limited**

MR D. J. G. MURRAY SMITH—continued

9 **OCEAN GLORY (IRE)**, b g Redback—Finty (IRE) **Lloyd Partnership**
10 **QUEST FOR SUCCESS (IRE)**, b c Noverre (USA)—Divine Pursuit **Rob Lloyd Racing Limited**

TWO-YEAR-OLDS

11 **AMERICAN CHAMP (IRE)**, b c 28/4 Pyrus (USA)—
Sandy Fitzgerald (IRE) (Last Tycoon) (22521) **Mr & Mrs Washer**
12 **ANFIELD STAR (IRE)**, b c 23/5 Celtic Swing—Shenkara (IRE) (Night Shift (USA)) (64349) **Mr Rob Lloyd**
13 **BEST BIDDER (USA)**, b br f 1/3 Mr Greeley (USA)—Party Stripes (USA) (Candy Stripes (USA)) (96524) **Rob Lloyd Racing Limited**
14 **DIAMOND JO (IRE)**, b f 1/2 Johannesburg (USA)—
Still As Sweet (IRE) (Fairy King (USA)) (32000) **Rob Lloyd Racing Limited**
15 **FIFER (IRE)**, b f 10/5 Soviet Star (USA)—Fife (IRE) (Lomond) (41183) **Rob Lloyd Racing Limited**
16 **GOLIATHS BOY (IRE)**, ch c 5/3 Medecis—Green Belt (FR) (Tirol) (44000) **Rob Lloyd Racing Limited**
17 **GOODISON GLORY (IRE)**, br c 26/4 Tout Seul (IRE)—Thorbella (Deploy) (25740) **Rob Lloyd Racing Limited**
18 **GRAYCLIFFE (IRE)**, gr c 14/2 Val Royal (FR)—
Popiplu (USA) (Cozzene) (25000) **Rob Lloyd Racing Limited**
19 **HIT THE SWITCH**, b c 3/3 Reset (AUS)—
Scenic Venture (IRE) (Desert King (IRE)) (51480) **Rob Lloyd Racing Limited**
20 **HONEY BERRY (IRE)**, ch f 22/2 Captain Rio—
Daggers At Dawn (IRE) (Daggers Drawn (USA)) (7500) **Rob Lloyd Racing Limited**
21 **ICE ATTACK (IRE)**, gr f 18/3 Verglas (IRE)—
Little Whisper (IRE) (Be My Guest (USA)) (96524) **Rob Lloyd Racing Limited**
22 **MAIGH EO (IRE)**, b c 16/4 Elusive City (USA)—
Princess Magdalena (Pennekamp (USA)) (32000) **Rob Lloyd Racing Limited**
23 **MARY WEST (IRE)**, b f 29/4 Pyrus (USA)—Pivot d'amour (Pivotal) (17000) **Rob Lloyd Racing Limited**
24 **MORE TEA VICAR (IRE)**, b f 11/2 Bahhare (USA)—
Grand Splendour (Shirley Heights) (20000) **Mrs & Mrs McLeod**
25 **OCEANIC DANCER (IRE)**, b f 5/4 Danetime (IRE)—Almasa (Faustus (USA)) (38609) **Rob Lloyd Racing Limited**
26 **PECKFORTON (GB)**, b f 2/2 Needwood Blade—Boavista (IRE) (Fayruz) (9000) **Rob Lloyd Racing Syndications**
27 **SILK STAR (IRE)**, b f 24/1 Pyrus (USA)—Silk Feather (USA) (Silver Hawk (USA)) (4000) **Mr & Mrs Mather**
28 **SIMPLY SENSATIONAL (IRE)**, ch c 19/4 Tendulkar (USA)—
Grange Clare (IRE) (Bijou d'inde) (3100) **Mr & Mrs Banner**
29 **TEDDY WEST (IRE)**, b c 14/3 Trans Island—Duckmore Bay (IRE) (Titus Livius (FR)) (4000) **Mrs P. P. McDonald**
30 **VIRGIN KING (IRE)**, b c 14/4 Century City (IRE)—
Jay's Renny (USA) (El Prado (IRE)) (70000) **Rob Lloyd Racing Limited**
31 **WATERSTOWN (IRE)**, ch c 20/4 Noverre (USA)—Twany Angel (Double Form) (11582) **Lloyd Partnership**

Assistant Trainer: Rob Lloyd

Jockey (flat): Pat Cosgrave, Dale Gibson. **Amateur:** Miss R. Bolton.

---

425 **MR F. MURTAGH**, Carlisle
Postal: Hurst Farm, Ivegill, Carlisle, Cumbria, CA4 0NL
Contacts: PHONE (01768) 484649 FAX (01768) 484744 MOBILE (07714) 026741
E-MAIL sue@suemurtagh.wanadoo.co.uk

1 **BULLIES ACRE (IRE)**, 8, b g Arctic Cider (USA)—Clonminch Lady **Mr J. M. Murtagh**
2 **CARRIETAU**, 5, b g Key of Luck (USA)—Carreamia **A. R. White**
3 **CORROBOREE (IRE)**, 11, b g Corrouge (USA)—Laura's Toi **Mrs G. C. Robinson**
4 **EMOTIVE**, 5, b g Pursuit of Love—Ruby Julie **Hurst Farm Racing**
5 **HIGH CLASS PET**, 8, b m Petong—What A Pet **R. Millican**
6 **HIGH COMMISSION**, 8, ch g Bob's Return (IRE)—Florencebray **J. R. Callow**
7 **HOLLOWS MILL**, 12, b g Rudimentary—Strawberry Song **The Great Expectations Sporting Club**
8 **HOLLOWS MIST**, 10, b g Missed Flight—Joyfulness (FR) **The Great Expectations Sporting Club 2**
9 **I'M A DARK HORSE**, 7, b g Alzao (USA)—Romoosh **R. Millican**
10 **IVEGILL**, 6, b m Overbury (IRE)—My Dawn **F. Murtagh**
11 **JUBILEE FLIGHT**, 6, b g Missed Flight—Hand On Heart (IRE) **Irving,Littleton,Blamire,Murtagh,Irving**
12 **LADY PICKPOCKET**, 4, b f Benny The Dip (USA)—Circe **J. R. Callow**
13 **LEGAL JOY**, 6, ch g Double Trigger (IRE)—Raglan Lady **Mr Don O'Connor & Mr Derek Wilson**
14 **MOSCOW MANDATE (IRE)**, 5, ch m Moscow Society (USA)—Madam Rocher **S. Agnew**
15 **PETE**, 5, b g Overbury (IRE)—Fen Terrier **Mrs S. Murtagh**
16 **PUGNACITY**, 4, b f Zilzal (USA)—Attention Seeker (USA) **Auldyn Stud Limited**
17 **SHE'S SO LUCKY (IRE)**, 6, b m Rudimentary (USA)—Laura's Pursuit (IRE) **The Most Wanted Partnership**
18 **SOLWAY GUNNER**, 7, ch g Gunner B—Lady Mag **David A. Harrison**

MR F. MURTAGH—continued

19 SUBSIDISE (IRE), 5, br g Key of Luck (USA)—Haysong (IRE) **D. O'Connor**
20 THE EVENT MASTER (IRE), 6, b g Darnay—Alvinru **Eventmasters Ltd**
21 TON-CHEE, 9, b g Vettori (IRE)—Najariya **A. R. White**

THREE-YEAR-OLDS

22 SONG OF SPRING, b f Myfontaine—Marycee (IRE) **D. O'Connor**

Other Owners: Mrs Stella Barclay, Mr I. Blamire, Mr Paul Clarkson, Mrs M. Irving, Mr W. A. Irving, Mr T. H. Littleton, Mr F. P. Murtagh, Mr D. O'Connor, Mr Clarence Smith, Mr T. D. Watson, Mr T. W. Wilson, Mr Derek Wilson.

Assistant Trainer: S. A. Murtagh.

426

MR W. J. MUSSON, Newmarket
Postal: **Saville House, St Mary's Square, Newmarket, Suffolk, CB8 0HZ**
Contacts: **PHONE (01638) 663371 FAX (01638) 667979**
E-MAIL williemusson@btconnect.com

1 AMICAL RISKS (FR), 4, bl g Take Risks (FR)—Miss High (FR) **The City Boys**
2 BEAR BOTTOM, 4, b g Imperial Ballet (IRE)—Pigeon Hole **W. J. Musson**
3 BOLD ADVENTURE, 4, ch g Arkadian Hero (USA)—Impatiente (USA) **Mustard Cord Cads**
4 BUSKER ROYAL, 5, ch g Shahrastani (USA)—Close Harmony **Mrs Rita Brown**
5 DARGHAN (IRE), 8, b g Air Express (IRE)—Darsannda (IRE) **S. Rudolf**
6 ESPEJO (IRE), 4, b g City On A Hill (USA)—Beechwood Quest (IRE) **W. J. Musson**
7 FOLIO (IRE), 8, b g Perugino (USA)—Bayleaf **Goodey & Broughton**
8 ITSY BITSY, 6, b m Danzig Connection (USA)—Cos I Do (IRE) **W. J. Musson**
9 KORTY, 4, b g Averti (IRE)—Promissory **Mrs Rita Brown Mrs Lorraine Irani**
10 MAGICALMYSTERYTOUR (IRE), 5, b g Sadler's Wells (USA)—Jude **Mr M. J. Dunne**
11 MANDALAY PRINCE, 4, b g Tobougg (IRE)—Autumn Affair **McGregor Bloodstock & Gillings**
12 MARAJAA (IRE), 6, b g Green Desert (USA)—Ghyraan (IRE) **J. D. Jacques**
13 MEDIEVAL MAIDEN, 5, gr m Zaha (CAN)—Brillante (FR) **K. L. West & J. Gunnell**
14 MOUNTAIN CAT (IRE), 4, b g Red Ransom (USA)—Timewee (USA) **S. Rudolf**
15 NIQAAB, 4, ch f Alhaarth (IRE)—Shanty **Broughton Thermal Insulations**
16 PIPER ROYAL, 4, b g Erhaab (USA)—Close Harmony **Mrs Rita Brown**
17 RUWAIN, 5, gr g Lujain (USA)—Ruwaya (USA) **I. K. Johnson**
18 SARWIN (USA), 5, gr g Holy Bull (USA)—Olive The Twist (USA) **S. Rudolf**
19 STREET LIFE (IRE), 10, ch g Dolphin Street (USA)—Wolf Cleugh (IRE) **W. J. Musson**
20 WILLIE EVER, 4, b g Agnes World (USA)—Miss Meltemi (IRE) **C. Bryce H. Scott N. Dower**

THREE-YEAR-OLDS

21 ARTS GUILD (USA), b c Theatrical—Gilded Edge **C. Bryce**
22 BETTYS TOUCH, b f Lujain (USA)—Fadaki Hawaki (USA) **T. S. Child**
23 BLACK COFFEE, b g Vettori (IRE)—In The Woods **H. Spooner & I. Weaver**
24 BROTHER BARRY (USA), b br g Forestry—Saratoga Sugar (USA) **S. Rudolf**
25 BROUGHTONS FLIGHT (IRE), ch f Hawk Wing (USA)—Aldburgh **Broughton Bloodstock**
26 CARLETON, b g Hunting Lion (IRE)—Canadian Capers **The Square Table**
27 COZY TIGER (USA), gr g Hold That Tiger (USA)—Cozelia (USA) **McHugh & Partners**
28 DUNEEN DREAM (USA), ch g Hennessy (USA)—T N T Red (USA) **EACH Partnership**
29 GANG SHOW (IRE), b g Desert Prince (USA)—Terry Jean (FR) **Mr Keith Brown & Mr Robin Heffer**
30 HEAVENLY STELLA (USA), b br f Wild Wonder (USA)—Nijivision (USA) **S. Rudolf**
31 MISTRESS COOPER, b br f Kyllachy—Litewska (IRE) **Mrs Rita Brown**
32 MOSS WAY, b g Zaha (CAN)—Ruwaya (USA) **R.U. Away Partnership**
33 POLICE OFFICER, b g Mark of Esteem (IRE)—No Rehearsal (FR) **H. Spooner & I. Weaver**
34 RAMBLIN BOB, b c Piccolo—Bijan (IRE) **The Roofer Guys**
35 B f Desert Style (IRE)—Serape
36 STILL SMALL VOICE, b f Polish Precedent (USA)—Mill Line **C. Bryce**
37 B f Kaldounevees (FR)—Welsh Motto (USA) **The City Boys**

TWO-YEAR-OLDS

38 B f 17/2 Royal Applause—Amankila (IRE) (Revoque (IRE)) (38000) **Broughton Thermal Insulations**
39 B f 24/2 Kyllachy—Broughton Bounty (Bahamian Bounty) (4000) **Broughton Thermal Insulations**
40 B c 21/3 Where Or When (IRE)—Keep Quiet (Reprimand) **Broughton Thermal Insulations**
41 B c 29/4 Statue of Liberty (USA)—My Enigma (Rainbow Quest) (USA) (32000) **B. N. Fulton**
42 Ch f 2/4 Alhaarth (IRE)—Noble Dane (IRE) (Danehill (USA)) (46000) **Mr H. Q. Spooner**

MR W. J. MUSSON—continued

43 B c 14/2 Dubai Destination (USA)—Red Rita (IRE) (Kefaah (USA)) (38000)
44 B c 28/4 Tobougg (IRE)—Robin Lane (Tenby) (17000)
45 **RYAN STYLE (IRE),** b c 5/4 Desert Style (IRE)—Westlife (IRE) (Mind Games) (57914) **Mr M. Dunne**
46 **SPARKAWAY,** ch c 7/2 Gold Away (IRE)—West River (USA) (Gone West (USA)) (22000) **KCS Partnership**
47 **STELLARINA (IRE),** b f 31/3 Night Shift (USA)—Accelerating (USA) (Lear Fan (USA)) (41826) **Mr S. Rudolf**
48 B c 16/2 Mark of Esteem (IRE)—Trefoil (FR) (Blakeney) (2500)

Other Owners: Miss Alice Abdullah, Mr M. E. Broughton, Mrs C. J. Broughton, Mr Keith Brown, Mr K. D. Clarke, Mr G. Clarke, Mr P. Cornwell, Mr Neil Dower, Mr Con Dower, Mr C. Eliades, Mr T. Evans, Mr A. Gillings, M. W. Goodey, Mr J. Gunnell, Mrs L. Hartman, Mr H. Robin Heffer, Mrs Lorraine Irani, Mr Jonny King, Mr David Lobban, Mr D. M. McCarthy, Mr Chris McHugh, Mr Ian Munday, Mr W. J. Musson, Mr R. D. Musson, Mr Paul Prince, Mr C. Savoury, Mr Howard Scott, Mr Bryan Taylor, Mr John Taylor, Mr I. L. Weaver, Mr K. L. West.

Jockey (flat): N. Pollard, T. Queally. **Apprentice:** Debra England.

---

427 MRS A. M. NAUGHTON, Richmond
Postal: **High Gingerfield, Hurgill Road, Richmond, North Yorkshire, DL10 4TD**
Contacts: **PHONE (01748) 822803 FAX (01748) 821816 MOBILE (07977) 576712**
E-MAIL murie1naughton@hotmail.co.uk

1 **LERIDA,** 6, ch g Groom Dancer (USA)—Catalonia (IRE) **Mrs A. M. Naughton**
2 **NEEDWOOD SPIRIT,** 13, b g Rolfe (USA)—Needwood Nymph **Famous Five Racing**
3 **SILLOTH SPIRIT,** 8, b g Atraf—Gaelic Air **Famous Five Racing**
4 **TRIUMPH OF LOVE (IRE),** 4, b f Indian Danehill (IRE)—Flower Child (IRE) **Mrs A. M. Naughton**

Other Owners: Mr R. Allen, Mr M. E. Ferguson, Mr A. J. Markley, Mr D. H. Montgomerie, Mr F. Previtali.

Assistant Trainer: Sarah Naughton

Jockey (NH): G. Supple. **Amateur:** Mr D. McCubbin.

---

428 DR J. R. J. NAYLOR, Shrewton
Postal: **The Cleeve, Elston Lane, Shrewton, Wiltshire, SP3 4HL**
Contacts: **PHONE (01980) 620804 FAX (01980) 621999 MOBILE (07771) 740126**
E-MAIL info@jeremynaylor.com WEBSITE www.jeremynaylor.com

1 **ACOSTA,** 4, b c Foxhound (USA)—Dancing Heights (IRE) **The Abchurch Partnership**
2 **BEN GOUGH,** 6, gr g Meadowbrook—Piecemeal **Mrs L. G. Stokes**
3 **GALANDORA,** 8, b m Bijou d'inde—Jelabna **The Kemp & Naylor Partnership**
4 4, B f Alflora (IRE)—Hays Lodge
5 **HEART SPRINGS,** 8, b m Parthian Springs—Metannee **Mrs T. M. Galton**
6 **INDIAN CHASE,** 11, b g Terimon—Icy Gunner **The Indian Chase Partnership**
7 **INDIAN DOCTOR,** 8, b g Dr Massini (IRE)—Icy Miss **The Abchurch Partnership**
8 **INDIAN GUNNER,** 15, b g Gunner B—Icy Miss **The Indian Gunner Partnership**
9 **JAMBLES,** 4, ch f Muhtarram (USA)—Jadidh **Mrs S. L. Brimble**
10 **JAU,** 5, b g Kayf Tara—Jadidh **Mrs S. L. Brimble**
11 **KATIE CONISTON,** 4, b f Lake Coniston (IRE)—Lycius Touch **Cleeve Stables Racing Partnership**
12 **LAGAN TURBO,** 4, b g Kayf Tara—Bichette **Mrs S. E. Clarke**
13 **PLAIN CHAMPAGNE (IRE),** 6, b m Victory Note (USA)—
                                       Paddys Cocktail (IRE) **Cleeve Stables Racing Partnership**
14 **QUEEN MUSA,** 6, b m Parthian Springs—Metannee **Queen Musa Partnership**
15 **SEE MORE JOCK,** 10, b g Seymour Hicks (FR)—Metafan **The See More Jock Partnership**
16 **SWEET REQUEST,** 4, ch f Best of The Bests (IRE)—Sweet Revival **Mrs S. P. Elphick**
17 **TRUE RUBY,** 5, b m Josr Algarhoud (IRE)—St James's Antigua (IRE) **Ascot Brew Racing**
18 **ZAMELIANA,** 4, ch f Zaha (CAN)—Amelia's Field **Mrs S. P. Elphick**

THREE-YEAR-OLDS

19 **LADY MAYA,** br f Prince Sabo—Monte Mayor Lady (IRE) **Free Spirit Racing Limited**
20 **POPPY GREGG,** b f Tamure (IRE)—Opalette **R. Biggs**
21 **RIVER N' BLUES (IRE),** ch f Touch of The Blues (FR)—Feather River (USA) **Free Spirit Racing Limited**

TWO-YEAR-OLDS

22 B c 29/3 Baryshnikov (AUS)—Daphne's Doll (IRE) (Polish Patriot (USA)) **Mrs. S. P. Elphick**

DR J. R. J. NAYLOR—continued

23 Gr c 26/2 Lend A Hand—Due To Me (Compton Place) **Mrs S. E. Clarke**
24 JAUBERTIE, b f 7/3 Bertolini (USA)—Jucinda (Midyan (USA)) (9000)

Other Owners: Mrs S. Z. Bates, Mrs D. Crow, Mr P. D. Dure, Mrs S. P. Elphick, Mr Toby Greenwood, Mr P. R. Kemp, Dr J. R. J. Naylor, Mrs S. Shepherd, Ms A. J. B. Smalldon, Mrs Lucinda Stokes.
Apprentice: M. Cosham.

---

429 MR J. L. NEEDHAM, Ludlow
Postal: **Gorsty Farm, Mary Knoll, Ludlow, Shropshire, SY8 2HD**
Contacts: **PHONE (01584) 872112/874826 FAX (01584) 873256 MOBILE (07811) 451137**

1 ANOTHER JOKER, 13, b g Commanche Run—Just For A Laugh **Miss J. C. L. Needham**
2 BELLASSINI, 8, b m Dr Massini (IRE)—Carlingford Belle **J. L. Needham**
3 BRINGEWOOD FOX, 6, gr g Cloudings (IRE)—Leinthall Fox **Miss J. C. L. Needham**
4 5, B m Kayt Tara—Carlingford Belle **J. L. Needham**
5 DEEPWOOD FOX, 7, b g Saddlers' Hall (IRE)—Leinthall Fox **Miss J. C. L. Needham**
6 FOUR BELLES, 9, ch m Fourstars Allstar (USA)—Carlingford Belle **J. L. Needham**
7 6, Gr g Cloudings (IRE)—Just For A Laugh **Miss J. C. L. Needham**
8 5, B h Kayt Tara—Leinthall Fox **Miss J. C. L. Needham**
9 MORTIMERS CROSS, 7, b g Cloudings (IRE)—Leinthall Doe **J. L. Needham**
10 ONE MORE NATIVE (IRE), 11, ch g Be My Native (USA)—Romany Fortune **Miss J. C. L. Needham**
11 TUDOR LACE (IRE), 6, ch m Fourstars Allstar (USA)—Elinor Glyn (IRE) **J. L. Needham**

Assistant Trainer: P. Hanly

Jockey (NH): J. Maguire, P. Moloney. **Conditional:** W. McCarthy. **Amateur:** Mr A. Hanly.

---

430 MR P. NEEDHAM, Barnard Castle
Postal: **Woolhouse Farm, Marwood, Barnard Castle, Co. Durham, DL12 8RG**
Contacts: **PHONE (01833) 690155**

1 CHEERY MARTYR, 10, b m Perpendicular—Kate O'kirkham **P. Needham**
2 PAINT THE LILY (IRE), 7, b m Barathea (IRE)—Chocolate Box **P. Needham**

Assistant Trainer: Sally Richardson

Jockey (NH): F. Keniry.

---

431 MRS H. R. J. NELMES, Dorchester
Postal: **Warmwell Stables, 2 Church Cottages, Warmwell, Dorchester, Dorset, DT2 8HQ**
Contacts: **PHONE/FAX (01305) 852254 MOBILE (07977) 510318**
WEBSITE www.warmwellracing.co.uk

1 DARING APPROACH (IRE), 7, b g Saddlers' Hall (IRE)—Nicks Approach (IRE) **Trickle Treat Partnership**
2 KOVA HALL (IRE), 6, ch g Halling (USA)—My Micheline **C. T. & A. Samways**
3 KRISTOFFERSEN, 8, ch g Kris—Towaahi (IRE) **J. P. Duffy**
4 ORVITA (FR), 6, b g Lute Antique (FR)—Ulvita (FR) **K. A. Nelmes**
5 OYEZ (IRE), 11, b g Jurado (USA)—Gleann Oisin (IRE) **C. T. & A. Samways**
6 SALYM (FR), 9, ch g Limnos (JPN)—Tina's Crest (FR) **K. A. Nelmes**
7 WILD POWER (GER), 10, b g Turtle Island (IRE)—White On Red (GER) **K. A. Nelmes**
8 WILDGOOSECHASE (IRE), 4, br f Marathon (USA)—Three-Mile-Limit (IRE) **T M W Partnership**

Other Owners: Mrs C. Knowles, Mrs J. M. Pengelly, Mr D. Price, C. T. Samways, Mrs A. Samways, Mrs J. Swaffield.
Jockey (NH): O. Nelmes.

---

432 MR C. NENADICH, Sutton
Postal: **Lakes Farm, Sutton, Herefordshire, HR1 3NS**
Contacts: **PHONE (01432) 880278 MOBILE (07860) 484400**

1 MUSIMARO (FR), 10, b g Solid Illusion (USA)—Musimara (FR) **C. Nenadich & N. Nenadich**
2 TAMREEN (IRE), 7, b g Bahhare (USA)—Na-Ayim (IRE) **C. Nenadich & N. Nenadich**
3 WEET WATCHERS, 8, b g Polar Prince (IRE)—Weet Ees Girl (IRE) **C. Nenadich**

MR C. NENADICH—continued

Other Owners: Mr Nick Nenadich.

Assistant Trainer: Marion Collins

---

433 **MR A. G. NEWCOMBE, Barnstaple**
Postal: Lower Delworthy, Yarnscombe, Barnstaple, Devon, EX31 3LT
Contacts: **PHONE/FAX (01271) 858554 MOBILE (07785) 297210**

1 BECHARM, 4, b f Singspiel (IRE)—Zuleika Dobson **DXB Bloodstock Ltd**
2 CABOZA, 4, ch g Zaha (CAN)—Cats Bottom **M. K. F. Seymour**
3 ELVINA, 7, b m Mark of Esteem (IRE)—Pharaoh's Joy **Capel, Eagle & Newcombe**
4 FUSTAAN (IRE), 4, b f Royal Applause—Alhufoof (USA) **M. K. F. Seymour**
5 GAELIC PRINCESS, 8, b m Cois Na Tine (IRE)—Berenice (ITY) **M. K. F. Seymour**
6 GRACIE'S GIFT (IRE), 6, b g Imperial Ballet (IRE)—Settle Petal **S. E. Hussey**
7 HISTORY PRIZE (IRE), 5, b g Celtic Swing—Menominee **S. F. Turton**
8 JOCHESKI (IRE), 4, b g Mull of Kintyre (USA)—Ludovica **The Grubbing Well Partnership**
9 KATEAL, 5, b m Supreme Leader—Quiet City **Yeo Racing Partnership**
10 KENTUCKY BULLET (USA), 12, b g Housebuster (USA)—Exactly So **Mrs E. M. Sherwin**
11 LESMOIR, 6, b g Wizard King—Paprika (IRE) **A. G. Newcombe**
12 MAJEHAR, 6, b g Marju (IRE)—Joonayh **J. R. Salter**
13 MIDDLETON GREY, 10, gr g Ashkalani (IRE)—Petula **A. G. Newcombe**
14 MISS SKIPPY, 9, b m Saddlers' Hall (IRE)—Katie Scarlett **Lymington Arms Racing Partnership**
15 MONTGOMERY, 7, b g In Command (IRE)—Lightening Reef **A. G. Newcombe**
16 NIMELLO (USA), 12, b g Kingmambo (USA)—Zakota (IRE) **Mrs J. Bramhill**
17 NOAH JAMEEL, 6, ch g Mark of Esteem (IRE)—Subtle One (IRE) **S. D. Langridge**
18 PEDLAR OF LUCK, 5, ch h Zaha (CAN)—Victoriet **A. G. Newcombe**
19 PRINCESS ZAHA, 6, b m Zaha (CAN)—Otaru (IRE) **A. G. Newcombe**
20 RESONATE (IRE), 10, b h Erins Isle—Petronelli (USA) **S. D. Langridge**
21 SHOOT THE GUEST, 6, b m Double Trigger (IRE)—Hosting **S. F. Turton**
22 SOVIETTA (IRE), 7, b m Soviet Star (USA)—La Riveraine (USA) **S. F. Turton**
23 TAXMAN (IRE), 6, ch g Singspiel (IRE)—Love of Silver (USA) **B. P. Ryan**
24 THE TEUCHTER, 9, b g First Trump—Barefoot Landing (USA) **The Devonian Partnership**
25 TWO ACRES (IRE), 5, b g Danetime (IRE)—Raise-A-Secret (IRE) **S. Jefford**
26 WIND CHIME (IRE), 11, ch h Arazi (USA)—Shamisen **M. K. F. Seymour**

THREE-YEAR-OLDS

27 BERRYNARBOR, b f Tobougg (IRE)—River Art (USA) **Mrs J. Bramhill**
28 HOLDEN EAGLE, b c Catcher In The Rye (IRE)—Bird of Prey (IRE) **DXB Bloodstock,Patel,Ryan & Newcombe**
29 LITTLE LOVELY (IRE), ch f Mizzen Mast (USA)—Copper Play (USA) **A. J. Sendell**

TWO-YEAR-OLDS

30 Ch c 22/1 Bertolini (USA)—Bird of Prey (IRE) (Last Tycoon) (6000) **I. Bloomfield**
31 Ch f 6/3 Best of The Bests (IRE)—Cyber Babe (IRE) (Persian Bold) **A. G. Newcombe**
32 B c 1/2 Best of The Bests (IRE)—Dune Safari (IRE) (Key of Luck (USA)) **A. G. Newcombe**
33 Gr f 20/4 Compton Place—How Do I Know (Petong) (12000) **D. Bramhill**
34 Gr f 2/2 King Charlemagne (USA)—Jugendliebe (IRE) (Persian Bold) (8000) **A. G. Newcombe**
35 B c 17/1 Groom Dancer (USA)—Owtaar (IRE) (Royal Applause) **M. K. F. Seymour**
36 Ch f 27/2 Reset (AUS)—Palace Green (IRE) (Rudimentary) **R. Eagle & M. Bevan**
37 B c 15/4 Lujain (USA)—Prickly Poppy (Lear Fan (USA)) **A. G. Newcombe**
38 B c 25/2 Bertolini (USA)—Quartermark (IRE) (General Monash (USA)) **A. G. Newcombe**
39 Ch c 22/3 Mark of Esteem (IRE)—Second Affair (IRE) (Pursuit of Love) (8000) **A. G. Newcombe**
40 Ch c 25/1 Best of The Bests (IRE)—Victoriet (Hamas (IRE)) **A. G. Newcombe**

Other Owners: Mr S. Baker, Mr M. Blagg, Mr C. C. Capel, DXB Bloodstock Ltd, Mr R. Eagle, Mr J. Heal, Mr Tristan Johnson, Mr Stephen Kemp, Mr A. G. Newcombe, Mr K. B. W. Parkhouse, Mr M. Patel, Mr C. S. Pike, Mr B. P. Ryan, Mr H. Wetter, Mrs K. D. Yeo.

Assistant Trainer: John Lovejoy

Jockey (flat): D. O'Neill, C. Catlin, L. Keniry. S. Whitworth. **Jockey (NH):** A. Thornton. **Amateur:** Miss C. Hannaford.

434 DR R. D. P. NEWLAND, Claines
Postal: Newland Associates Ltd, Linacres Farm, Egg Lane, Claines, Worcester, WR3 7SB
Contacts: PHONE (07956) 196535
E-MAIL richard.newland1@btopenworld.com

1 ALAM (USA), 9, b g Silver Hawk (USA)—Ghashtah (USA) **Dr R. D. P. Newland**
2 ARAFAN (IRE), 6, b g Barathea (IRE)—Asmara (USA) **CE Stedman,Dr RDP & Mrs LJ Newland**
3 BARTON LEGEND, 8, b g Midnight Legend—Home From The Hill (IRE) **The Five Nations Partnership**
4 BURNTOAKBOY, 10, b g Sir Harry Lewis (USA)—Sainte Martine **Dr R. D. P. & Mrs L. J. Newland**
5 COSMIC STRING (IRE), 6, ch g In The Wings—Continuous (IRE) **J. A. Provan**
6 DUNE RAIDER (USA), 7, b g Kingmambo—Glowing Honor (USA) **Prof D. E. Newland**
7 HEEZ A WONDER (IRE), 9, b g Naheez (USA)—Honey Wonder **R. Baylis & D. Ward**
8 HERNANDO ROYAL, 5, b g Hernando (FR)—Louis' Queen (IRE) **P. Murphy**
9 ODIHAM, 7, b g Deploy—Hug Me **C. E. Stedman**
10 OVERSTRAND (IRE), 9, b g In The Wings—Vaison La Romaine **Dr RDP & Mrs LJ Newland, CE Stedman**
11 XELLANCE (IRE), 11, b g Be My Guest—Excellent Alibi (USA) **Dr R. D. P. Newland**

Other Owners: Mr R. Baylis, Mrs L. J. Newland, S. R. Trow, Mr D. J. Ward.

Assistant Trainer: S. R. Trow.

Amateur: Mr T. Weston.

435 MISS A. M. NEWTON-SMITH, Polegate
Postal: Bull Pen Cottage, Jevington, Polegate, East Sussex, BN26 5QB
Contacts: PHONE (01323) 488354 FAX (01323) 488354 MOBILE (07970) 914124
E-MAIL anna@annanewton-smith.co.uk WEBSITE www.annanewton-smith.co.uk

1 COME BYE (IRE), 12, b g Star Quest—Boreen Dubh **PPS Racing**
2 ENGLISH JIM (IRE), 7, b g Saddlers' Hall (IRE)—Royal Folly (IRE) **P Hempenstall**
3 MISSUS JONES (IRE), 4, b f King's Theatre (IRE)—Seductive Dance **J. P. Smith**
4 MUNAAHEJ (IRE), 7, b g Soviet Star (USA)—Azyaa **Miss S. E. Harler**
5 MUSTAMAD, 5, b g Anabaa (USA)—Nasanice (IRE) **The MustBMad Partnership**
6 PETE THE FEAT (IRE), 4, b g King's Theatre (IRE)—Tourist Attraction (IRE) **Mr G. J. Larby & Mr P. J. Smith**
7 PORTRAIT ROYALE (IRE), 6, b m Portrait Gallery (IRE)—Crows Cross (IRE) **PPS Racing**
8 QUAYSTONE LADY (IRE), 5, b m Saddlers' Hall (IRE)—Royal Folly (IRE) **P Hempenstall**
9 4, B f Sonus (IRE)—Sight'n Sound **J. P. Smith**
10 THE HARDY BOY, 8, br g Overbury (IRE)—Miss Nero **Mrs S. B. S. Grist**

THREE-YEAR-OLDS

11 SEVEN ROYALS (IRE), b g Val Royal (FR)—Seven Notes **Miss S. E. Harler**

Other Owners: M. O. Coates, G. J. Larby, His Honour Judge A. Patience, J. R. Peppitt, P. J. Smith, Mrs P. A. Wilkins.

Jockey (flat): Hayley Turner. **Jockey (NH):** M. Batchelor, H. Oliver. **Conditional:** A. Martin, R. Lucey-Butler.

436 MR D. NICHOLLS, Thirsk
Postal: Tall Trees Racing Ltd, Tall Trees, Sessay, Thirsk, North Yorkshire, YO7 3ND
Contacts: PHONE (01845) 501470 FAX (01845) 501666 MOBILE (07971) 555105
E-MAIL david.nicholls@btconnect.com WEBSITE www.davidnichollsracing.com

1 BAHAMIAN PIRATE (USA), 13, ch g Housebuster (USA)—
    Shining Through (USA) **Lucayan Stud & G G N Bloodstock**
2 BIGALOS BANDIT, 6, ch g Compton Place—Move Darling **Bill Wallace / Gary Butters**
3 BLUE TOMATO, 7, b g Orpen (USA)—Ocean Grove (IRE) **Dab Hand Racing**
4 BUACHAILL DONA (IRE), 5, b g Namid—Serious Contender (IRE) **M. F. Browne**
5 CHICKEN GEORGE (IRE), 4, ch g Observatory (USA)—Missing **Roses Partnership**
6 CHOREOGRAPHY, 5, ch g Medicean—Stark Ballet (USA) **Bill Wallace / Gary Butters**
7 CIRCUIT DANCER (IRE), 8, b g Mujadil (USA)—Trysinger (IRE) **D. T. Fish**
8 CONTINENT, 11, ch g Lake Coniston (IRE)—Krisia **Lucayan Stud & G G N Bloodstock**
9 CROCODILE BAY (IRE), 5, b g Spectrum (IRE)—Shenkara (IRE) **Mr I. Bishop**
10 DREAM THEME, 5, b g Distant Music (USA)—Xaymara (USA) **Untouchable Partnership**
11 FIRE UP THE BAND, 9, b g Prince Sabo—Green Supreme **Mr A Barker Mr D Nicholls & Mr S A Short**
12 FREMEN (IRE), 8, ch g Rahy (USA)—Northern Trick (USA) **Miss C King Mrs A Seed Ms Finola Devaney**

MR D. NICHOLLS—continued

13 **FUNFAIR WANE**, 9, b g Unfuwain (USA)—Ivory Bride **The Wayward Lads**
14 **GARNICA (FR)**, 5, gr h Linamix (FR)—Gueridia (IRE) **Lady C. J. O'Reilly, Mr E. Maher**
15 **GIFT HORSE**, 8, ch g Cadeaux Genereux—Careful Dancer **Alfi & Partners**
16 **GUEST CONNECTIONS**, 5, b g Zafonic (USA)—Llyn Gwynant **Middleham Park Racing L**
17 **HAMAASY**, 7, b g Machiavellian (USA)—Sakha **J. P. Honeyman**
18 **HEYWOOD**, 4, b g Tobougg (IRE)—Owdbetts (IRE) **D. Nicholls**
19 **HYPNOTIC**, 6, ch g Lomitas—Hypnotize **Bill Wallace / Gary Butters**
20 **ICE PLANET**, 7, b g Polar Falcon (USA)—Preference **Middleham Park Racing**
21 **INDIAN TRAIL**, 8, ch g Indian Ridge—Take Heart **M. P. Love**
22 **JOSEPH HENRY**, 6, b g Mujadil (USA)—Iris May **Mr R. W. Hughes**
23 **KABIS AMIGOS**, 6, ch g Nashwan (USA)—River Saint (USA) **I. W. Glenton**
24 **KINGS POINT (IRE)**, 7, b h Fasliyev (USA)—Rahika Rose **Wetherby Racing Bureau**
25 **KUNTE KINTEH**, 4, b g Indian Lodge (IRE)—Summer Siren (FR) **Mr Ian Guise & Mr Warren Smith**
26 **LAGO D'ORTA (IRE)**, 8, ch g Bahhare (USA)—Maelalong (IRE) **Chalfont Foodhalls Ltd**
27 **LOST SOLDIER THREE (IRE)**, 7, b g Barathea (IRE)—Donya **Chalfont Foodhalls Ltd**
28 **LUCAYAN DANCER**, 8, b g Zieten (USA)—Tittle Tattle (IRE) **J. E. Greaves**
29 **MACHINIST (IRE)**, 8, br g Machiavellian (USA)—Athene (IRE) **Berry & Gould Partnership**
30 **MAIA**, 4, ch f Observatory (USA)—Preference
31 **MANDURAH (IRE)**, 4, b g Tagula (IRE)—Fearfully Grand **M. S. Hignett**
32 **MASTA PLASTA (IRE)**, 5, b g Mujadil (USA)—Silver Arrow **Lady C. J. O'Reilly**
33 **MINORITY REPORT**, 8, b g Rainbow Quest (USA)—Queen Sceptre (IRE) **S. C. B. Limited**
34 **MR ROONEY (IRE)**, 5, b g Mujadil (USA)—Desert Bride (USA) **T. G. Meynell**
35 **MR TOSHIWONKA**, 4, b g Compton Place—Victoria **I. Guise**
36 **NORTHERN DARE (IRE)**, 4, b g Fath (USA)—Farmers Swing (IRE) **J. H. Dale**
37 **NORTHERN FLING**, 4, b g Mujadil (USA)—Donna Anna **Mr Jim Dale / Mr Jason Berry**
38 **OBE GOLD**, 6, b g Namaqualand (USA)—Gagajulu
39 **PEACE OFFERING (IRE)**, 8, b g Victory Note (USA)—Amnesty Bay **Lady C. J. O'Reilly**
40 **PRINCE SAMOS (IRE)**, 6, b g Mujadil (USA)—Sabaniya (FR) **Mrs D. Plant**
41 **PURE IMAGINATION (IRE)**, 7, ch g Royal Academy (USA)—Ivory Bride **Dab Hand Racing**
42 **QUAI DU ROI (IRE)**, 6, ch g Desert King (IRE)—Emly Express (IRE) **D. Nicholls F. Devaney**
43 **RED LANCER**, 7, ch g Deploy—Miss Bussell **Gould & Rifat Partnership**
44 **REGAL PARADE**, 4, ch g Pivotal—Model Queen (USA) **Dab Hand Racing**
45 **ROYAL DIGNITARY (USA)**, 8, br g Saint Ballado (CAN)—Star Actress (USA) **Middleham Park Racing XXXVI**
46 **ROYAL POWER (IRE)**, 5, b h Xaar—Magic Touch **D. Nicholls**
47 **SHOT TO FAME (USA)**, 9, b g Quest For Fame—Exocet (USA) **Middleham Park Racing VII**
48 **SOMETHING (IRE)**, 6, b g Trans Island—Persian Polly **Middleham Park Racing**
49 **SPIRIT OF CONISTON**, 5, b g Lake Coniston (IRE)—Kigema (IRE) **Richardson Kelly O'Gara Partnership**
50 **STRIKE UP THE BAND**, 5, b g Cyrano de Bergerac—Green Supreme **Barker Moser Nicholls Power & Short**
51 **TAJNEED (IRE)**, 5, b g Alhaarth (USA)—Indian Express **Mrs A. A. Nicholls**
52 **TAX FREE (IRE)**, 6, b g Tagula (IRE)—Grandel **I. Hewitson**
53 **TENCENDUR (IRE)**, 4, ch g King Charlemagne (USA)—Jallaissine (IRE) **Mrs L. Scaife, Mrs S. Radford**
54 **TOURNEDOS (IRE)**, 6, b g Rossini (USA)—Don't Care (IRE) **M. F. Browne**
55 **TURNKEY**, 6, br g Pivotal—Persian Air **Middleham Park Racing XXIII**
56 **UMPA LOOMPA (IRE)**, 4, ch g Indian Lodge (IRE)—Bold Fashion (FR) **Chocolate Factory**
57 **VALDEMAR VICTORY**, 4, b g Inchinor—Park Crystal (IRE) **B S Racing Sarl**
58 **VALERY BORZOV (IRE)**, 4, b g Iron Mask (USA)—Fay's Song (IRE) **D Kilburn / I Hewitson / D Nicholls**
59 **VARADOURO (BRZ)**, 6, b g A Good Reason (BRZ)—Orquidea Vermelha (BRZ) **Clarke & Harlow Partnership**
60 **WHITE DEER (USA)**, 4, b g Stravinsky (USA)—Brookshield Baby (IRE) **Mr I. Bellamy**

THREE-YEAR-OLDS

61 **BINARIO UNO**, b g Bertolini (USA)—Madame Curie **DMQA Holdings & Mr Ian Blakey**
62 **BLASTIE**, b g Josr Algarhoud (IRE)—Passerella (FR) **David Faulkner**
63 **BOY BLUE**, b c Observatory (USA)—Rowan Flower (IRE) **Mr I. Bishop**
64 **CAPE VALE (IRE)**, b c Cape Cross (IRE)—Wolf Cleugh (IRE) **Lady C. J. O'Reilly**
65 **FOL HOLLOW (IRE)**, b g Monashee Mountain (USA)—Constance Do **Middleham Park Racing**
66 **HE'S A GEEZER**, br c Royal Applause—Golden Symbol **H. Redknapp**
67 **INXILE (IRE)**, b g Fayruz—Grandel **I. Hewitson**
68 **IVESTAR (IRE)**, b g Fraam—Hazardous **Middleham Park Racing XXII**
69 **MA NADRI**, b f Red Ransom (USA)—Frustration **I. W. Glenton**
70 **NORTHERN BOLT**, b c Cadeaux Genereux—Shafir (IRE) **Mr Jim Dale / Mr Jason Berry**
71 **OUR SUNNIE**, b g Averti (IRE)—Barawin (FR) **Mrs Jackie Love & Mr D. Nicholls**
72 **VAN BOSSED (CAN)**, ch c Van Nistelrooy (USA)—Embossed (CAN) **Mike & Maureen Browne**

TWO-YEAR-OLDS

73 Br c 19/2 Statue of Liberty (USA)—Athlacca Image (IRE) (Grand Lodge (USA)) (11000)

MR D. NICHOLLS—continued

74 **BOOTLEG,** b c 4/2 Bahamian Bounty—Asbo (Abou Zouz (USA)) (18000) **Untouchable Partnership**
75 **CAPO REGIME,** ch c 1/3 Captain Rio—Ashtree Belle (Up And At 'em) (26000) **Mr M Love**
76 B c 6/4 Makbul—Dee Dee Girl (IRE) (Primo Dominie) (6500)
77 **FOL LIAM,** b c 24/4 Observatory (USA)—Tide of Fortune (Soviet Star (USA)) (4000) **Middleham Park Racing**
78 Ch c 24/1 Night Shift (USA)—Just One Smile (IRE) (Desert Prince (IRE)) (19304) **Untouchable Partnership**
79 B c 26/3 Lucky Story (USA)—La Grace (Lahib (USA)) (6200) **Middleham Park Racing**
80 B f 9/1 Primo Valentino (IRE)—Mania (IRE) (Danehill (USA)) (13500)
81 **MURRAYS MAGIC (IRE),** b f 10/1 Bahri (USA)—Fiina (Most Welcome) (5000)
82 **NORTHERN ACRES,** b c 4/3 Mtoto—Bunting (Shaadi (USA)) (70000) **J. H. Dale**
83 **PARISIAN PYRAMID (IRE),** gr c 14/4 Verglas—Sharadja (IRE) (Doyoun) (9000) **D. Nicholls**
84 **PEACEFUL RULE (USA),** b c 12/2 Peace Rules (USA)—
                                      La Cat (USA) (Mr Greeley (USA)) (50000) **Chalfont Foodhalls**
85 **RED BARON DANCER,** ch c 23/4 Fraam—Reamzafonic (Grand Lodge (USA)) (6000) **Middleham Park Racing**
86 B f 22/2 Choisir (AUS)—Royal Mistress (Fasliyev (USA)) (54697) **Ms F. Devaney**
87 B c 10/2 Fasliyev (USA)—Sassari (IRE) (Darshaan) (28000) **Untouchable Partnership**
88 B c 12/4 Deportivo—Senobar (Mtoto) (1000) **Wetherby Racing Bureau**
89 B c 26/3 Mull of Kintyre (USA)—Serious Contender (IRE) (Tenby) (48000)
90 Ch c 15/2 Auction House (USA)—Thicket (Wolfhound (USA)) (6000) **Middleham Park Racing**
91 B c 21/4 Zaha (CAN)—Tinkerbird (Music Boy) (6200) **Middleham Park Racing**
92 **YORKSHIRE HUNTER,** ch c 29/3 Rambling Bear—Out of Hours (Lochnager) (3200)

Other Owners: Mr A. Barker, Mr Jason Berry, Mr Ian Blakey, Mr Mike Browne, Mrs Maureen Browne, Mr Gary Butters, Mr Ian Clarke, Mr Jim Dale, Mr D. Deadman, Ms Finola Devaney, G G N Bloodstock Ltd, Mr T. Gould, Mr Ian Guise, Mr L. Harlow, Mr Ian Hewitson, Mr D. Kilburn, Mr T. Letcher, Mrs Jackie Love, Lucayan Stud, Mr David Marshall, Miss Hayley Moser, Mr D. Nicholls, Mrs Alex Nicholls, Mr P. O'Gara, Mr T. S. Palin, Mr D. Pearson, Mr J. Peavoy, Mr Alan Pirie, Mr D. J. Power, Mr M. Prince, Mrs S. Radford, Mr J. Rifat, Mrs Angela C. Seed, Mr S. A. Short, Mr Warren Smith, Mr Martin Waite, Mr Bill Wallace.

Assistant Trainer: Ben Beasley, Ernie Greaves

Jockey (flat): Adrian Nicholls, Silvestre De Sousa.

---

437 **MR P. F. NICHOLLS, Shepton Mallet**
Postal: **Manor Farm Stables, Ditcheat, Shepton Mallet, Somerset, BA4 6RD**
Contacts: **PHONE** (01749) 860656 **FAX** (01749) 860523 **MOBILE** (07977) 270706
E-MAIL info@paulnichollsracing.com WEBSITE www.paulnichollsracing.com

1 **ALBUHERA (IRE),** 10, b g Desert Style (IRE)—Morning Welcome (IRE) **D. J. & F. A. Jackson**
2 **ANDREAS (FR),** 8, b g Marchand de Sable (USA)—Muscova Dancer (FR) **T. J. Hemmings**
3 **APOCAL (IRE),** 4, b g Anabaa Blue—Always Glitter (FR) **The Eight Amigos Racing Syndicate**
4 **ARMATURK (FR),** 11, ch g Baby Turk—Armalita (FR) **T. J. Hemmings**
5 **ARTADI (FR),** 5, b g Cadoudal (FR)—Vol Sauvage (FR) **Mrs M. Campbell-Andenaes**
6 **ARTURIO (FR),** 5, b g Astarabad (USA)—La Pitchoun (FR) **The Sparkes Family**
7 **BEAU MICHEL (FR),** 6, b g Saint Preuil (FR)—Rosacotte (FR) **C. G. Roach**
8 **BIG BUCK'S (FR),** 5, b br g Cadoudal (FR)—Buck's (FR) **The Stewart Family**
9 **BIG FELLA THANKS,** 6, b g Primitive Rising (USA)—Nunsdream **Mrs M. Findlay & P. K. Barber**
10 **BLU TEEN (FR),** 8, ch g Epervier Bleu—Teene Hawk (FR) **The Stewart Family**
11 **BLUSHING BULL,** 9, b g Makbul—Blush **Blushing Bull Partnership**
12 **BOBBY ON THE BEAT (IRE),** 4, b g Bob Back (USA)—Supreme Kellycarra (IRE) **The Stewart Family**
13 **BOLD FIRE,** 6, b m Bold Edge—Kirkby Belle **Mrs S. Craven**
14 **BOLD POLICY (IRE),** 5, b g Shernazar—Lady Vic (IRE) **Mrs S. Craven & Mrs E. Jackson**
15 **BOYASTARA (FR),** 5, b g Astarabad (USA)—Boya Girl (FR) **ROA Racing Partnership V**
16 **BREEDSBREEZE (IRE),** 6, b g Fresh Breeze (USA)—Godfreys Cross (IRE) **F. E. J. Lewis**
17 **BUMP IN THE NIGHT,** 5, b g Midnight Legend—Cornwood **R. A. Webb**
18 **CELESTIAL HALO (IRE),** 4, b g Galileo (IRE)—Pay The Bank **The Stewart Family**
19 **CERIUM (FR),** 7, b g Vaguely Pleasant (FR)—Tantatura (FR) **B Fulton, T Hayward, S Fisher, L Brady**
20 **CHAPOTURGEON (FR),** 4, gr g Turgeon (USA)—Chapohio (FR) **D. A. Johnson**
21 **COLORADO PEARL (IRE),** 7, br m Anshan—Flying Silver **Dr M. Nicholls**
22 **CORNISH SETT (IRE),** 9, b g Accordion—Hue 'n' Cry (IRE) **P. L. Hart**
23 **DANNY ZUKO (IRE),** 5, ch g Anshan—Lezies Last (IRE) **Mrs K. A. Stuart**
24 **DEAR VILLEZ (FR),** 6, b g Villez (USA)—Distant Meteor **Mr & Mrs J. D. Cotton**
25 **DEFINITE EDGE (IRE),** 6, ch g Definite Article—Itkan (IRE) **Mrs A. E. Fulton**
26 **DELENA,** 7, b m Classic Cliche (IRE)—Formal Affair **Mrs A. E. R. Goodwin**
27 **DENMAN (IRE),** 8, ch g Presenting—Polly Puttens **P. K. Barber & Mrs M. Findlay**
28 **DERRY CITY (IRE),** 5, b g Old Vic—Callmartel (IRE) **Mrs M. Findlay & P. K. Barber**
29 **DESERT QUEST (IRE),** 8, b g Rainbow Quest (USA)—Jumilla (USA) **Mrs M. Findlay**

MR P. F. NICHOLLS—continued

30 **DREAM LEADER (IRE)**, 6, gr m Supreme Leader—Run Away Dream (IRE) **R. P. Fry**
31 **EARTH DREAM (IRE)**, 5, b g Old Vic—Barbaras Mews (IRE) **Mrs C. E. Penny**
32 **EARTH MAN (IRE)**, 9, b g Hamas (IRE)—Rajaura (IRE) **R. M. Penny**
33 **EARTH PLANET (IRE)**, 6, b g Kayf Tara—Arctic Rose (IRE) **R. M. Penny**
34 **EIGHT PALMS (IRE)**, 4, b g Great Palm (IRE)—Nordic Union (IRE) **The Eight Amigos Racing Syndicate**
35 **ELUSIVE DREAM**, 7, b g Rainbow Quest (USA)—Dance A Dream **Mrs M. Findlay**
36 **FIVE DREAM (FR)**, 4, b g Take Risks (FR)—Jenny Pous (FR) **Scott-Macdonald, Kilduff, Donlon & Doyle**
37 **FLORADORADO**, 6, b m Afflora (IRE)—Cream By Post **J. M. Dare**
38 **FONT**, 5, b g Sadler's Wells (USA)—River Saint (USA) **Mr & Mrs P Mason & Mr & Mrs G Mason**
39 **FOREST GREEN**, 6, b g Green Tune (USA)—Farama (USA) **G. A. Mason**
40 **FOREST PENNANT (IRE)**, 6, b br g Accordion—Prudent View (IRE) **P. L. Hart**
41 **FROSTY SPRING**, 5, gr m Terimon—Springaleak **T. G. A. Chappell**
42 **GANSEY (IRE)**, 6, br g Anshan—Ebony Jane **T. J. Hemmings**
43 **GEEVEEM (IRE)**, 8, b g Supreme Leader—Glacial Field (IRE) **Mr M. Calvert & Mr Colin E. Lewis**
44 **GREAT MATES (IRE)**, 4, b g Bob's Return—All Set (IRE) **F. E. J. Lewis**
45 **GULLIBLE GORDON (IRE)**, 5, ch g Anshan—Cronohill (IRE) **Mrs M. Findlay & P. K. Barber**
46 **GUNGADU**, 8, ch g Beneficial—Tsarella **P. K. Barber & Mrs M. Findlay**
47 **GWANAKO (FR)**, 5, b br g Sin Kiang (FR)—Vaubecourt (FR) **The Stewart Family**
48 **HELL'S BAY (FR)**, 6, b g Supreme Leader—Queen's Flagship (IRE) **C. G. Roach**
49 **HERECOMESTHETRUTH (IRE)**, 6, ch g Presenting—Beagan Rose (IRE) **P. K. Barber & Mrs M. Findlay**
50 **HIVIKOS (FR)**, 5, ch g Nikos—Hijika (FR) **The Sparkes Family**
51 **HOO LA BALOO (FR)**, 7, b g Unfuwain (USA)—Via Saleria (USA) **The Stewart Family**
52 **I'MSINGINGTHEBLUES (IRE)**, 6, b g Pistolet Bleu (IRE)—Nova Rose **J. R. Hales**
53 **INDIAN BLOOD (IRE)**, 4, b g Indian Ridge—Miss Mistletoes (IRE) **D. A. Johnson**
54 **IROQUOIS WARRIOR (FR)**, 7, b g Lord Americo—Auntie Honnie (IRE) **M. J. P. Fordham**
55 **JUST AMAZING (IRE)**, 5, b g Presenting—Just Precious **Mr & Mrs J. D. Cotton**
56 **KALDOUAS (FR)**, 7, bl br g Kaldou Star—Popie D'ecorcei (FR) **Mrs A. Tincknell**
57 **KAUTO STAR (FR)**, 8, b g Village Star (FR)—Kauto Relka (FR) **C. D. Smith**
58 **KERRY'S GIRL (IRE)**, 5, b m Flemensfirth (USA)—Guess Twice **Mr J. Hewitt**
59 **KICKS FOR FREE (IRE)**, 7, b g Flemensfirth (USA)—Keep The Change (IRE) **T. J. Hemmings**
60 **KING CAINE (IRE)**, 6, b g King's Theatre (IRE)—Kadarassa (IRE) **J. R. Barber, A. J. Norman & A. G. Sim**
61 **KING FONTAINE (IRE)**, 5, b g King's Theatre (IRE)—Kerfontaine **T. J. Hemmings**
62 **L'AVENTURE (FR)**, 9, b m Cyborg (FR)—Amphitrite (FR) **C. J. Harriman**
63 **LAMANVER HOMERUN**, 6, b m Relief Pitcher—Bizimki **Dr D. Christensen**
64 **LE DUC (FR)**, 9, b g Villez (USA)—Beberova (FR) **The Stewart Family**
65 **LE PASSING (FR)**, 9, b g Passing Sale (FR)—Petite Serenade (FR) **The Hon Mrs C. A. Townshend**
66 **LE VOLFONI (FR)**, 7, b g Sicyos (USA)—Brume (FR) **Mr A. F. A. Banks**
67 **LEADING ATTRACTION (IRE)**, 7, b g Mister Mat (FR)—Cerise de Totes (FR) **Mrs J. Smith**
68 **LOU DU MOULIN MAS (FR)**, 9, b g Sassanian (USA)—Houf (FR) **The Hon Mrs C. A. Townshend**
69 **LOW DELTA**, 8, ch g Old Vic—La-Greine **Hector's Dream**
70 **MAHONIA (IRE)**, 5, b g Turtle Island (IRE)—Bell Walks Run (IRE) **MessrsLewis,Deal,Holder,Tincknell,Warner**
71 **MARODIMA (FR)**, 5, b g Robin des Pres (FR)—Balbeyssac (FR) **D. A. Johnson**
72 **MASSASOIT (IRE)**, 6, br g Supreme Leader—Lady Margaretta **The Stewart Family**
73 **MASTER MINDED (FR)**, 5, b g Nikos—Haute Tension (FR) **C. D. Smith**
74 **MICHAEL MUCK**, 6, b g Overbury (IRE)—Country Choice (IRE) **Mrs E. Banks**
75 **MICHEL LE BON (FR)**, 5, b g Villez (USA)—Rosacotte (FR) **C. G. Roach**
76 **MISTER KNIGHT (IRE)**, 9, ch g Mister Lord (USA)—Knights Bounty (IRE) **R. H. Dunn**
77 **MOBAASHER (USA)**, 9, b g Rahy (USA)—Balistroika (USA) **Seasons Holidays**
78 **MR POINTMENT (IRE)**, 9, b g Old Vic—Bettyhill **Stockton Heath Racing**
79 **NAKAI (FR)**, 7, b g Esprit du Nord (USA)—Hermes de Beaulieu (FR) **C. G. Roach**
80 **NANGA PARBAT (FR)**, 7, b g True Brave (USA)—Celeste (FR) **Mrs K. A. Stuart**
81 **NATAL (FR)**, 7, b g Funny Baby—Donitille (FR) **Mrs M. Hackett**
82 **NEPTUNE COLLONGES (FR)**, 7, gr g Dom Alco (FR)—Castille Collonges (FR) **J. R. Hales**
83 **NEVADA ROYALE (FR)**, 7, gr g Garde Royale—Ahhotep (FR) **P. K. Barber & Mrs M. Findlay**
84 **NEW LITTLE BRIC (FR)**, 7, ch g Bricassar (USA)—Doulina (FR) **Mrs K. A. Stuart**
85 **NIPPY DES MOTTES (FR)**, 7, b g Useful (FR)—Julie des Mottes (FR) **P. C. Green**
86 **NODFORMS PAULA (IRE)**, 5, b g Rashar (USA)—Monamandy (IRE) **J. R. Hales**
87 **NOLAND**, 7, b g Exit To Nowhere (USA)—Molakai (USA) **J. R. Hales**
88 **NYCTEOS (FR)**, 7, ch g Chamberlin (FR)—Cynthia (FR) **The Stewart Family**
89 **O'MALEY (FR)**, 6, b g Sleeping Car (FR)—Salse Pareille (FR) **Sir Robert Ogden C.B.E., LLD**
90 **OBERON MOON (FR)**, 7, gr g New Frontier (IRE)—Kemal's Princess **M. J. P. Fordham**
91 **OCEAN DU MOULIN (FR)**, 6, b g Robin des Champs (FR)—Hacienda du Moulin (FR) **Mrs J. Smith**
92 **OFAREL D'AIRY (FR)**, 6, b g Cadouhel (FR)—Farali d'airy (FR) **The Stewart Family**
93 **OFFICIER DE RESERVE (FR)**, 6, br g Sleeping Car (FR)—Royaute (FR) **Seasons Holidays**
94 **OPERA MUNDI (FR)**, 6, b g Discover d'auteuil—Gymnastique II (FR) **Sir Robert Ogden C.B.E., LLD**
95 **ORNAIS (FR)**, 6, b g Michel Georges—Imperia II (FR) **The Stewart Family**

MR P. F. NICHOLLS—continued

96 **OSCAR D'ANGRON (FR)**, 6, b g Robin des Pres (FR)—Quovaria d'angron (FR) **Million in Mind Partnership**
97 **OSLOT (FR)**, 6, b g Passing Sale (FR)—Une de Lann (FR) **The Stewart Family**
98 **OUMEYADE (FR)**, 6, b g Smadoun (FR)—Debandade (FR) **F. E. J. Lewis**
99 **PACHA D'OUDAIRIES (FR)**, 5, b g Ungaro (FR)—Forlane V (FR) **S. C. Botham**
100 **PASCO (SWI)**, 5, ro g Selkirk (USA)—Palena **J. T. Warner**
101 **PENNELLIS (FR)**, 4, b br g Alderbrook—Muchsorrylady (IRE) **R. M. Penny**
102 **PERTINENT (FR)**, 5, b g Sleeping Car (FR)—Jamais de La Vie (FR) **Mrs A. B. Yeoman & Mr C. R. Whittaker**
103 **PETIT LORD (FR)**, 6, ch g Lord of Men—Petite Majeste (FR) **Mr & Mrs J. D. Cotton**
104 **PHENIX JACK (FR)**, 5, b g Agent Bleu (FR)—Dzaoudzie (FR) **Mrs K. A. Stuart**
105 **PIERROT LUNAIRE (USA)**, 4, b g War Chant (USA)—Playact (IRE) **Mrs A. Tincknell**
106 **PISTE AUX ETOILES (FR)**, 4, gr g Ski Chief (USA)—Desert's Flower (FR) **Kingairloch Estate LLP**
107 **PLAY ON WORDS (FR)**, 5, b g Nikos—Snow Drop (FR) **T. J. Hemmings**
108 **POQUELIN (FR)**, 5, bl g Lahint (USA)—Babolna (FR) **The Stewart Family**
109 **PREDATEUR (FR)**, 5, b g Nikos—Fia Rosa (FR) **T Kilduff, C Donlon L Scott-Macdonald**
110 **PREDICTIVE (FR)**, 5, gr g Smadoun (FR)—Dacca de Thaix (FR) **Mrs K. A. Stuart**
111 **PRIDE OF DULCOTE (FR)**, 5, b g Kadalko (FR)—Quenice (FR) **Mrs A. B. Yeoman**
112 **QRACKERS (FR)**, 4, b g Lahint (USA)—Babolna (FR) **Seasons Holidays**
113 **QUIDEO DE TOUZAINE (FR)**, 4, b g Video Rock (FR)—Domitia (FR) **Mrs M. Hackett**
114 **RIPPLING RING (SAF)**, 5, b g Saumarez—Rippling Star (SAF) **The Stewart Family**
115 **ROBIN DE SHERWOOD (FR)**, 5, b g Robin des Champs (FR)—Hereke **Sir Robert Ogden C.B.E., LLD**
116 **ROBY DE CIMBRE (FR)**, 5, gr g Myrakalu (FR)—Belle de Liziere (FR) **J. T. Warner**
117 **ROYAL AUCLAIR (FR)**, 11, ch g Garde Royale—Carmonera (FR) **C. D. Smith**
118 **SAINTSAIRE (FR)**, 9, b g Apeldoorn (FR)—Pro Wonder (FR) **The Stewart Family**
119 **SENDANI (FR)**, 5, b g Grand Lodge (USA)—Sendana (FR) **Mr & Mrs R Nevinson & Mr & Mrs G Mason**
120 **SILVERBURN (IRE)**, 7, b g Presenting—Polly Puttens **P. C. Green**
121 **SIMONDIUN (FR)**, 5, b g Hernando (FR)—Jetbeeah (IRE) **K. A. Murphy**
122 **SMART CAVALIER (FR)**, 9, b g Terimon—Smart Topsy **J. M. Dare**
123 **SO NOW (IRE)**, 7, b g Heron Island (IRE)—Monty's Gayle (IRE) **Notalotterry**
124 **SPORAZENE (IRE)**, 9, gr g Cozzene (USA)—Sporades (USA) **G. A. Mason**
125 **STAR DE MOHAISON (FR)**, 7, b g Beyssac (FR)—Belle De Mohaison (FR) **Sir Robert Ogden C.B.E., LLD**
126 **SUPER FORMEN (FR)**, 4, b g Kizitca (FR)—Daly Turk (FR) **Mr Bill Bolsover & Mr Peter Hart**
127 **SUPREME HUNTRESS (IRE)**, 8, b g Supreme Leader—Luminous Girl (IRE) **The Stewart Family**
128 **TAKE ME THERE**, 5, b g Cape Cross (IRE)—Mill Path **Mr P. Devereaux**
129 **TAKE THE BREEZE (FR)**, 5, gr g Take Risks (FR)—Reine Breeze (FR) **G. Calder**
130 **TARALINA**, 6, b m Kayf Tara—La Princesse **The Oak Partnership**
131 **TATENEN (FR)**, 4, b g Lost World (FR)—Tamaziya (FR) **The Stewart Family**
132 **THE LUDER (IRE)**, 7, b g Naheez (USA)—Secret Sensation (IRE) **J. G. Hordle**
133 **THE NIGHTINGALE (FR)**, 5, b br g Cadoudal (FR)—Double Spring (FR) **C. G. Roach**
134 **THE TOTHER ONE (IRE)**, 7, b g Accordion—Baden (IRE) **C. G. Roach**
135 **THISTHATANDTOTHER (IRE)**, 12, b g Bob Back (USA)—Baden (IRE) **C. G. Roach**
136 **TRUST FUND (IRE)**, 10, ch g Rashar (USA)—Tuney Blade **T. R. Collins**
137 **TURKO (FR)**, 6, gr g Turgeon (USA)—Cambaria (FR) **The Stewart Family**
138 **TURTHEN (FR)**, 7, ch g Turgeon (USA)—Majathen (FR) **C. D. Smith**
139 **TWIST MAGIC (FR)**, 6, b g Winged Love (IRE)—
                                        Twist Scarlett (GER) **Barry Fulton Tony Hayward Michael Lynch**
140 **VITRAY (FR)**, 6, ch g Morespeed—Tarde (FR) **D. J. & F. A. Jackson**
141 **WHAT A FRIEND**, 5, b g Alflora (IRE)—Friendly Lady **Mr Ged Mason & Sir Alex Ferguson**
142 **WHITENZO (FR)**, 12, b g Lesotho (USA)—Whitengy (FR) **Exors of the Late Mr G. Z. Mizel**
143 **WOOLCOMBE FOLLY (IRE)**, 5, b br g Presenting—Strong Gara (IRE) **The Hon Mrs C. A. Townshend**

Other Owners: P.K. Barber, R. Barber, J. R. Barber, Mrs J. M. Blackshaw, J. P Blakeney, Mr G. W. Bolsover, Mr R. G. Botham, A. R. Bromley, M. Calvert, Mr J. L. Coombs, J. D. Cotton, Mr B. Cotton, Lord Daresbury, A. S. Davies, P.A. Deal, Mrs J. E. Derham, Mr C. A. Donlon, Mr A. Doyle, Mr K. B. Ellis, Sir A. C. Ferguson, Mr S. D. Fisher, Mr J. M. Fitzpatrick, B. N. Fulton, T. R. Gittins, G. F. Goode, Miss L. J. Hales, A. A. Hayward, D. C. Holder, Mr M. J. Holman, Mrs E W. Jackson, F. A. Jackson, D. J. Jackson, A. M. Johnson, R. A. Johnson, Mr C. N. Jones, J. A. Jones, Mr M. J. Jooste, T. Kilduff, Mr M. W. King, C. E. Lewis, Mr M. Lynch, Mr D. P Mcevoy, D. G. Millard, P. J. Mills, W. D. C. Minton, M. Morgan, Mrs C. Nevinson, Mrs D. C. Nicholson, A. J. Norman, T. H. Northwood, M. A. Osborne, Mr C. I. Poulter, Mr C. D. Preston, Mrs A. H. Robson, Mrs L. Scott-MacDonald, Prof D. B. A. Silk, A. G. Sim, Mr K. Sparkes, Mrs K. M. Sparkes, Mr A. Stewart, Mrs J. A. Stewart, W. C. Tincknell, C. R. Whittaker.

Assistant Trainer: Daniel Skelton, Richard Barber, Harry Fry

Jockey (NH): Sam Thomas, R. Walsh. **Conditional:** Harry Skelton, Liam Heard. **Amateur:** Mr N. Scholfield, Mr Ryan Mahon, Mr Robert Lee.

438 **MR P. D. NIVEN, Malton**
Postal: **Clovafield, Barton-Le-Street, Malton, North Yorkshire, YO17 6PN**
Contacts: PHONE **(01653) 628176** FAX **(01653) 627295** MOBILE **(07860) 260999**
E-MAIL pruniven@btinternet.com

1 AL FALCON, 6, ch g Alflora (IRE)—Northern Falcon **Gay & Peter Hartley**
2 ALIBA (IRE), 7, ch g Ali-Royal (IRE)—Kiba (IRE) **C. D. Carr**
3 APRIL LEADER (IRE), 6, b g Supreme Leader—April's Baby **Gay & Peter Hartley**
4 BALLYHALE (IRE), 10, br g Mister Lord (USA)—Deep Inagh **The Little Ice Club 2**
5 BATTIES DEN (IRE), 8, br g Corrouge (USA)—Miners Society **Aboukir Hotel Limited**
6 BEN TIRRAN, 5, b g Rock City—Clova **Mrs J. A. Niven**
7 COUNTRY SERVANT (USA), 5, b g Swain (IRE)—Night Drama (IRE) **The Cattlemen Syndicate**
8 DEPUTY MAYOR (IRE), 8, b g Saddlers' Hall (IRE)—Nora's Charm (IRE) **The Cattlemen Syndicate**
9 DICTATRIX, 5, gr m Diktat—Apennina (USA) **Crown Select**
10 FALCONS THEATRE (IRE), 5, b m King's Theatre (IRE)—Catch Those Kisses **Falcons Line Ltd**
11 FRANCESCAS BOY (IRE), 5, b g Titus Livius (FR)—Mica Male (ITY) **Mr M. J. Bennett**
12 MYSTIC GLEN, 9, b m Vettori (IRE)—Mystic Memory **Mrs J. A. Niven**
13 NABIR (FR), 8, gr g Linamix (FR)—Nabagha (FR) **Sandy Lodge Racing Club & Mr P.D.Niven**
14 NAPALM (IRE), 7, b g Warcraft (USA)—Cross My Palm (IRE) **Mrs J. A. C. Lundgren**
15 ROCKNEST ISLAND (IRE), 5, b m Bahhare (USA)—Margin Call (IRE) **Mrs K. J. Young**
16 SILENT LUCIDITY (IRE), 4, ch g Ashkalani (IRE)—Mimansa **Mrs J. A. Niven**
17 SIMPLY MYSTIC, 8, ch m Simply Great (FR)—Mystic Memory **A. Needham & Mrs J. A. Niven**
18 TALARIVE (USA), 12, ch g Riverman (USA)—Estala **I. G. M. Dalgleish**
19 THREE STRINGS (USA), 5, b g Stravinsky (USA)—Just Cause **The Wednesday Club**
20 THUNDERCLAP, 9, b br g Royal Applause—Gloriana **The Wednesday Club**
21 WEDNESDAYS BOY (IRE), 5, b g Alhaarth (IRE)—Sheen Falls (IRE) **The Wednesday Club**

Other Owners: Mr Stuart Barker, Mr C. Bracher, Mr M. Feneron, Miss V. C. Frith, Mrs P. A. H. Hartley, Mr P. A. H. Hartley, Mr D. Holgate, Mr Ken Little, Mr Andrew Needham, Mr P. D. Niven, Mr Michael Paley, Mr G. A. S. Reid, I. Simpson, Ms Joanne Thompson, Ms Lynn Tomkins, Mr J. S. Watson, Mrs Kate Young.

Amateur: Mr R. Tierney.

439 **MR G. R. S. NIXON, Selkirk**
Postal: **Oakwood Farm, Ettrickbridge, Selkirk, Selkirkshire, TD7 5HJ**
Contacts: PHONE **(01750) 52245** FAX **(01750) 52313**

1 HUSH TIGER, 7, br g Moshaajir (USA)—Just Hush **Rayson & Susan Nixon**
2 JUST POSH, 6, b m Moshaajir (USA)—Split The Wind **Rayson & Susan Nixon**
3 KEMPSKI, 8, b g Petoski—Little Katrina **Rayson & Susan Nixon**
4 NORMINSTER, 7, ch g Minster Son—Delightfool **Rayson & Susan Nixon**
5 POLITICAL ELEMENT, 6, b m Endoli—Political Mandate **Rayson & Susan Nixon**
6 POLITICAL PADDY, 6, b g Vitus—Political Mill **Rayson & Susan Nixon**
7 POLITICAL SOX, 14, br g Mirror Boy—Political Mill **Rayson & Susan Nixon**
8 SPIVITUS, 7, br g Vitus—Split The Wind **Rayson & Susan Nixon**
9 4, B f Supreme Sound—Split The Wind **Rayson & Susan Nixon**
10 TEMPO SOUND, 5, br m Supreme Sound—Split The Wind **Rayson & Susan Nixon**

Other Owners: G. R. S. Nixon, Mrs S. Nixon.

Assistant Trainer: Mrs S Nixon

Conditional: Gareth Thomas, Ryan Mania. **Amateur:** Mr Mark Ellwood.

440 **MRS S. NOCK, Stow-on-the-Wold**
Postal: **Smenham Farm, Icomb, Stow-on-the-Wold, Cheltenham, Gloucestershire, GL54 1JQ**
Contacts: PHONE **(01451) 831688** FAX **(01451) 831404**

1 DICTUM (GER), 10, ch g Secret 'n Classy (CAN)—Doretta (GER) **Camilla & Rosie Nock**
2 MISTRESS TO NO ONE, 5, b m Exit To Nowhere—Frosty Mistress **G. Nock**
3 MOLOSTIEP (FR), 8, b g Video Rock (FR)—Unetiepy (FR) **Camilla & Rosie Nock**
4 MYLORD COLLONGES (FR), 8, bl g Video Rock (FR)—Diane Collonges (FR) **G. Nock**
5 NABOUKO (FR), 7, br g Kadalko (FR)—Badrapette (FR) **G. Nock**
6 ROSS LEADER (IRE), 11, b g Supreme Leader—Emmagreen **G. Nock**
7 TOO MUCH TALK (IRE), 8, b br g Luso—Credora Bay **G. Nock**

Other Owners: Miss R. Nock, Miss C. D. Nock.

441 MR D. A. NOLAN, Wishaw
Postal: **Deer Park Farm, Mill Road, Morningside, Newmains, Wishaw, North Lanarkshire**
Contacts: **PHONE (01698) 383850 FAX (01698) 383850 MOBILE (07900) 918471**

1 ALFIE LEE (IRE), 11, ch g Case Law—Nordic Living (IRE) **Miss M. Mcfadyen-Murray**
2 ARDENT NUMBER, 8, b g Alderbrook—Pretty Average **Miss M. Mcfadyen-Murray**
3 COMPTON LAD, 5, b g Compton Place—Kintara **Miss M. Mcfadyen-Murray**
4 DEER PARK LORD, 4, b g Compton Admiral—Pretty Average **Miss M. Mcfadyen-Murray**
5 HOWARDS DREAM (IRE), 10, b g King's Theatre (IRE)—Keiko **Miss M. Mcfadyen-Murray**
6 HOWARDS PRINCE, 5, gr g Bertolini (USA)—Grey Princess (IRE) **Miss M. Mcfadyen-Murray**
7 MISTER MARMADUKE, 7, b g Marju (IRE)—Lalique (IRE) **Miss M. Mcfadyen-Murray**
8 MUTAYAM, 8, b g Compton Place—Final Shot **Miss M. Mcfadyen-Murray**
9 PAYS D'AMOUR (IRE), 11, b g Pursuit of Love—Lady of The Land **Miss M. Mcfadyen-Murray**
10 SENORA LENORAH, 4, ch f Tumbleweed Ridge—Blue Diamond **Hibernian Racing**
11 SOKOKE, 7, ch g Compton Place—Sally Green (IRE) **Miss M. Mcfadyen-Murray**
12 STRAVONIAN, 8, b g Luso—In The Evening (IRE) **Miss M. Mcfadyen-Murray**
13 TAILI, 7, b m Taipan (IRE)—Doubtfire **Mrs K. S. Dow**
14 THE PURPLEPUSSYCAT, 5, b m Captain Maverick (USA)—Valley of Time (FR) **Miss M. Mcfadyen-Murray**
15 VONDOVA, 6, b m Efisio—Well Proud (IRE) **Miss M. Mcfadyen-Murray**
16 WOLF PACK, 6, b g Green Desert (USA)—Warning Shadows (IRE) **Miss M. Mcfadyen-Murray**

THREE-YEAR-OLDS

17 JAZZ STICK (IRE), ch c Choisir (AUS)—Basin Street Blues (IRE) **Miss M. Mcfadyen-Murray**
18 LA GUANCHA, b f Timeless Times (USA)—Westcourt Ruby **W. G. Young**

Other Owners: Mr W. A. Boak, Mr Michael B. Gielty.

Assistant Trainer: Miss M McFadyen-Murray

Jockey (flat): P. Fessey, P. Mathers.

442 MRS L. B. NORMILE, Glenfarg
Postal: **Duncrievie, Glenfarg, Perthshire, PH2 9PD**
Contacts: **PHONE (01577) 830330 FAX (01577) 830658 MOBILE (07721) 454818/(07855) 755914**
E-MAIL lucy@normileracing.co.uk WEBSITE www.normileracing.co.uk

1 BOBBING COVE, 9, b g Bob's Return (IRE)—Candlebright **L. B. N. Racing Club**
2 5, B m Shambo—Carbery Spirit (IRE)
3 DO IT FOR DALKEY, 6, b g Silver Patriarch (IRE)—Dalkey Sound **G. S. Brown**
4 ENGLISH CITY (IRE), 5, ch h City On A Hill (USA)—Toledana (IRE) **Mr P. Carnaby**
5 FLAMING HECK, 11, b g Dancing High—Heckley Spark **D. A. Whitaker**
6 FRANCESCO (FR), 4, gr g Kaldounevees (FR)—Mount Gable
7 FRITH (IRE), 6, b g Benny The Dip (USA)—Melodist (USA) **Twentys Plenty**
8 5, B gr g Silver Patriarch (IRE)—Gale
9 4, B c Weldnaas (USA)—Good Job
10 HECKLEY FOXTROT, 7, ch g Dancing High—Heckley Charter **R. Green & A. J. Neill**
11 MIND YOUR MANNERS, 4, b g Courteous—Fond Farewell (IRE)
12 MISS CARRY ON, 6, gr m Wizard King—Carbery Spirit (IRE) **Carry On Racing**
13 MODARAB, 6, b g Barathea (IRE)—Jathaabeh **K. J. Fehilly**
14 6, B m Busy Flight—Pejawi
15 PENDRAGON (USA), 5, ch g Rahy (USA)—Turning Wheel (USA) **Mr J. Gallacher**
16 PRIMROSE TIME, 5, gr m Alflora (IRE)—The Whirlie Weevil **The Explorers**
17 ROYAL CITADEL (IRE), 5, b m City On A Hill (USA)—Royal Baldini (USA) **Mr S. W. Dick**
18 SILVER BY NATURE, 6, b g Silver Patriarch (IRE)—Gale **G. S. Brown**
19 STORMONT DAWN (IRE), 7, b m Glacial Storm (USA)—Andros Dawn (IRE) **A. J. Neill**
20 STROBE, 4, ch g Fantastic Light (USA)—Sadaka (USA) **Miss P. A. & Mr P. J. Carnaby**
21 THE AMPLE HAMPER, 10, gr g Alflora (IRE)—The Whirlie Weevil **The Explorers**
22 THE SALTIRE TIGER, 7, b g Busy Flight—Candlebright **Saltire Racing Club**
23 TURBULENT FLIGHT, 7, b m Busy Flight—Pejawi **Mrs J. C. Cross**
24 TYCHEROS, 6, b g Polar Falcon (USA)—Marie de Flandre (FR) **Twentys Plenty**
25 WISE CHOICE, 5, b g Green Desert (USA)—Ballykett Lady (USA) **Miss P. A. & Mr P. J. Carnaby**

THREE-YEAR-OLDS

26 ROLLER LAGRANGE (FR), gr c Persian Ruler—Fannie de Lagrange (FR)

MRS L. B. NORMILE—continued

Other Owners: Mr S. A. Brand, Miss P. A. Carnaby, Mr P. J. Carnaby, Mr K. J. Fehilly, Miss F. M. Fletcher, Mrs S. Gould, Mrs L. M. A. Johnston-Brand, Mrs S. D. B. Lyons, Mr B. F. Lyons, Mrs J. Nicol, Mrs L. Normile, Mr A. C. Rodger, Mr B. Thomson.

Assistant Trainer: Alan Normile

Jockey (NH): N. Mulholland, J. A. McCarthy. **Amateur:** Miss R Cowie.

443

MR J. R. NORTON, Barnsley
Postal: **Globe Farm, High Hoyland, Barnsley, South Yorkshire, S75 4BE**
Contacts: **PHONE/FAX (01226) 387633 MOBILE (07970) 212707**
E-MAIL johnrnorton@hotmail.com

1 FOXXY, 4, b f Foxhound (USA)—Fisher Island (IRE) **C. Holder**
2 INTO THE DAWN (IRE), 6, b m Insan (USA)—Cameo Dawn (IRE) **H. Kidd**
3 NALEDI, 4, b g Indian Ridge—Red Carnation (IRE) **Mrs J. Thompson**
4 QUAY MEADOW (IRE), 6, b br g Alderbrook—Harp Song **Jaffa Racing Syndicate**
5 RED RIVER REBEL, 10, b g Inchinor—Bidweaya (USA) **J. Slaney**
6 4, B g Classic Cliche (IRE)—Sahara Reem (IRE) **J. Norton**
7 SQUARE DEALER, 7, b g Vettori (IRE)—Pussy Foot **Jaffa Racing Syndicate**
8 TROMBONE TOM, 5, b g Superior Premium—Nine To Five **Mrs H. Tattersall**
9 WINTER LANE, 4, b g Hernando (FR)—Winding (USA) **Mrs H. Tattersall**

THREE-YEAR-OLDS

10 ALWAYS ENGAGED, b f Compton Place—Good Standing (USA) **J. R. Norton Ltd**
11 LIANI (IRE), b f Modigliani (USA)—Well Wisher (USA) **J. R. Norton Ltd**
12 B c Sir Harry Lewis (USA)—Sahara Reem (IRE) **Mr. Rhys Flint**
13 STRICTLY ELSIE (IRE), b f No Excuse Needed—Sophrana (IRE) **M. R. & T. Simcox**

TWO-YEAR-OLDS

14 B f 8/5 Almaty (IRE)—Captive Heart (Conquistador Cielo (USA)) (2000) **J. R. Norton Ltd**
15 Ch c 4/4 Where Or When (IRE)—Ela Aphrodite (Halling (USA)) (1000) **J. R. Norton Ltd**
16 B c 17/4 Josr Algarhoud (IRE)—Miss Koen (IRE) (Barathea (IRE)) (1500) **J. R. Norton Ltd**
17 B c 11/6 Sir Harry Lewis (USA)—Sahara Reem (IRE) (Don't Forget Me) **J. Norton**
18 B f 29/4 Almaty (IRE)—Undercover Girl (IRE) (Barathea (IRE)) (800) **J. Norton**

Other Owners: Mr R. M. Firth, Mr P. J. Marshall, Mr Tim Simcox.

Jockey (flat): P. Mulrennan. **Jockey (NH):** P. Aspell.

444

MR J. J. NOSEDA, Newmarket
Postal: **Shalfleet, 17 Bury Road, Newmarket, Suffolk, CB8 7BX**
Contacts: **PHONE (01638) 664010 FAX (01638) 664100 MOBILE (07710) 294093**
E-MAIL jeremy.noseda@virgin.net WEBSITE www.jeremynoseda.com

1 ARABIAN GLEAM, 4, b c Kyllachy—Gleam of Light (IRE)
2 EXPRESS WISH, 4, b c Danehill Dancer (IRE)—Waffle On
3 KAFUU (IRE), 4, b c Danehill Dancer (IRE)—Nausicaa (USA)
4 MILNE GRADEN (IRE), 4, b g Montjeu (IRE)—Glen Rosie (IRE)
5 SECRET WORLD (IRE), 5, ch g Spinning World (USA)—Classic Park
6 SIXTIES ICON, 5, b h Galileo (IRE)—Love Divine
7 SOLDIER'S TALE (USA), 7, ch h Stravinsky (USA)—Myrtle
8 VALRHONA (IRE), 4, b br f Spectrum (IRE)—Minerva (IRE)

THREE-YEAR-OLDS

9 ACCLAIMED (IRE), b c Hawk Wing (USA)—Park Charger
10 ACCUSED (IRE), b g Xaar—Danedrop (IRE)
11 ART EXHIBITION (IRE), ch c Captain Rio—Miss Dilletante
12 BLESSING (USA), b br f Pulpit (USA)—My Prayer (USA)
13 BLOW HOLE (USA), ch c Mr Greeley (USA)—Nevis (USA)
14 CAPTAIN BRILLIANCE (USA), ch c Officer (USA)—Bloomin Genius (USA)
15 CHARISMATIC (IRE), b f Galileo (IRE)—Darling

MR J. J. NOSEDA—continued

16 **CHECKLOW (USA)**, b c Street Cry (IRE)—Comstock Queen (USA)
17 **DAZZLING COLOURS**, b c Oasis Dream—Dazzle
18 **DEER LAKE (IRE)**, b c King's Best (USA)—Atlantic Desire (IRE)
19 **DUBROVNICK (IRE)**, b c Montjeu (IRE)—Aquila Oculus (IRE)
20 **ENDLESS LOVE (IRE)**, b f Dubai Destination (USA)—La Vita E Bella (IRE)
21 **FANJURA (IRE)**, b c Marju (IRE)—Accelerating (USA)
22 **FLEETING SPIRIT (IRE)**, b f Invincible Spirit (IRE)—Millennium Tale (FR)
23 **FLYING HAWK (IRE)**, ch c Hawk Wing (USA)—Two Clubs
24 **FORGOTTEN VOICE (IRE)**, b c Danehill Dancer (IRE)—Asnieres (USA)
25 **FRANCESCA D'GORGIO (USA)**, b f Proud Citizen (USA)—Betty's Solutions (USA)
26 **FULL MARKS**, b f Dansili—Flying Wanda
27 **GRANDE ANNEE (USA)**, b f Gone West (USA)—Bollinger (AUS)
28 **GULCH'S ROSE (USA)**, b f Gulch (USA)—England's Rose (USA)
29 **ICY COOL (IRE)**, b c Galileo (IRE)—Epping
30 **IMILOA (USA)**, b br f Kingmambo (USA)—Aldebaran Light (USA)
31 **IN CLOSE (USA)**, b c Empire Maker (USA)—Cozzy Corner (USA)
32 **ISABELLA GLYN (IRE)**, b f Sadler's Wells (USA)—Questina (FR)
33 **KAROUSH (USA)**, b br c Gone West (USA)—Victorica (USA)
34 **KING'S CHARM (FR)**, b c King's Best (USA)—On Fair Stage (IRE)
35 **KIRKUM (IRE)**, b c Selkirk (USA)—Jumilla (IRE)
36 **KNOWSALL**, ch g Kyllachy—Ecstatic
37 **LADDIES POKER TWO (IRE)**, gr f Choisir (AUS)—Break of Day (USA)
38 **LAST HERO (IRE)**, b c Danehill Dancer (IRE)—Sweet Retreat
39 **LEMON N SUGAR (USA)**, b f Lemon Drop Kid (USA)—Altos de Chavon (USA)
40 **LIBERATION SPIRIT (USA)**, b c Gone West (USA)—Katherine Seymour
41 **LIGHT HEARTED**, b f Green Desert (USA)—Gay Gallanta (USA)
42 **MASTER OF SPIES (GER)**, b c Red Ransom (USA)—Madame Cerito (USA)
43 **MESSIAS DA SILVA (USA)**, b br f Tale of The Cat (USA)—Indy Power (USA)
44 **MEYDAN PRINCESS (IRE)**, b f Choisir (AUS)—Miss Assertive
45 **MYANMAR (IRE)**, ch c Rock of Gibraltar (IRE)—Bold As Love
46 **NAYEF STAR**, b c Nayef (USA)—Satin Bell
47 **ONCE A GULCH (USA)**, b br c Gulch (USA)—Once Around (CAN)
48 **PRIDE OF INDIA (USA)**, b c Johannesburg (USA)—How Could You (USA)
49 **RESURGE (IRE)**, b c Danehill Dancer (IRE)—Resurgence
50 **ROYAL DESTINATION (IRE)**, b c Dubai Destination (USA)—Royale (IRE)
51 **SALEIMA (IRE)**, b f Rock of Gibraltar (USA)—Lumber Jill (USA)
52 **SEGAL (IRE)**, b c Cadeaux Genereux—Camcorder
53 **SILK STORM (IRE)**, b c Barathea (IRE)—Showering
54 **SIR BILLY NICK**, b c Bertolini (USA)—Follow Flanders
55 **SPICE TRADE**, ch c Medicean—Nutmeg (USA)
56 **STORM SIR (USA)**, ch c Johannesburg (USA)—Robust (USA)
57 **STRIKE THE DEAL (USA)**, ch c Van Nistelrooy (USA)—Countess Gold (USA)
58 **THE GALLOPING SHOE**, b g Observatory (USA)—My Way (IRE)
59 **THE WHICH DOCTOR**, b g Medicean—Oomph
60 **VISIONS OF JOHANNA (USA)**, b c Johannesburg (USA)—Belle Turquoise (FR)
61 **WANNABE FREE**, b f Red Ransom (USA)—Wannabe Grand (IRE)
62 **WITHOUT PREJUDICE (USA)**, ch c Johannesburg (USA)—Awesome Strike (USA)

TWO-YEAR-OLDS

63 **ADORN**, b f 22/4 Kyllachy—Red Tiara (USA) (Mr Prospector))
64 Gr c 6/2 Tobougg (IRE)—Anotheranniversary (Emarati (USA)) (65000)
65 **AUTHORITATIVE**, b f 2/2 Diktat—Australian Dreams (Magic Ring (IRE)) (65000)
66 Gr c 17/2 Verglas (IRE)—Badee'a (IRE) (Marju (IRE)) (95000)
67 B f 11/4 Danehill Dancer (IRE)—Bex (USA) (Explodent (USA)) (360000)
68 B c 1/2 Gone West (USA)—Bowl of Emeralds (USA) (A P Indy (USA)) (242954)
69 B c 24/1 Montjeu (IRE)—Bright Halo (IRE) (Bigstone (IRE)) (200000)
70 B c 8/2 Clodovil (IRE)—Cafe Creme (IRE) (Catrail (USA)) (135000)
71 B f 9/2 Indian Ridge—Damsel (Danzero (AUS)) (230000)
72 B f 23/4 Cape Cross (IRE)—Dinka Raja (USA) (Woodman (USA)) (140000)
73 B c 12/5 Elusive City (USA)—Diplomats Daughter (Unfuwain (USA)) (72000)
74 **ENTANGLE**, b f 26/4 Pivotal—Entwine (Primo Dominie)
75 **ERROL FLYNN (IRE)**, b br c 28/4 Danehill Dancer (IRE)—Warusha (GER) (Shareef Dancer (USA)) (180000)
76 B c 9/2 Oasis Dream—Esteemed Lady (IRE) (Mark of Esteem (IRE)) (40000)
77 B f 25/2 Oasis Dream—Habariya (IRE) (Perugino (USA)) (180180)
78 B c 9/2 Kyllachy—Haste (Halling (USA)) (120000)

MR J. J. NOSEDA—continued

79 **HIGHTIME HEROINE (IRE)**, b f 2/3 Danetime (IRE)—Esterlina (IRE) (Highest Honor (FR)) (135000)
80 B f 29/3 Galileo (IRE)—Hoh Dear (IRE) (Sri Pekan (USA)) (88000)
81 B c 22/2 Invincible Spirit (IRE)—Jupiter Inlet (IRE) (Jupiter Island) (100000)
82 B f 20/4 Cape Cross (IRE)—Kootenay (IRE) (Selkirk (USA))
83 B c 6/2 Danehill Dancer (IRE)—Lady Miletrian (IRE) (Barathea (IRE)) (210000)
84 B f 6/2 One Cool Cat (USA)—Latest Chapter (IRE) (Ahonoora) (148004)
85 B f 26/4 Danetime (IRE)—Lindfield Belle (IRE) (Fairy King (USA)) (260000)
86 Ch c 6/4 Galileo (IRE)—Llia (Shirley Heights) (450000)
87 **MEDLOCK**, b c 21/2 Johannesburg (USA)—Marcelia (Coronado's Quest (USA)) (102960)
88 B c 22/2 King's Best (USA)—Minerva (IRE) (Caerleon (USA))
89 B f 8/1 Danehill Dancer (IRE)—Moonavvara (IRE) (Sadler's Wells (USA))
90 B f 25/3 Stravinsky (USA)—Myrtle (Batshoof) (121477)
91 B f 5/4 Invincible Spirit (IRE)—Nassma (IRE) (Sadler's Wells (USA)) (193049)
92 Gr c 6/4 Johannesburg (USA)—Paiute Princess (FR) (Darshaan) (176961)
93 B c 26/4 Kris Kin (USA)—Pattimech (USA) (Nureyev (USA)) (67000)
94 **PEZULA BAY**, b c 20/1 Oasis Dream—Easy To Love (USA) (Diesis) (45000)
95 B c 6/3 Kyllachy—Polish Descent (IRE) (Danehill (USA))
96 B c 10/5 Galileo (IRE)—Poule de Luxe (IRE) (Cadeaux Genereux) (65000)
97 **QUEEN OF PENTACLES (IRE)**, b f 13/2 Selkirk (USA)—Maid To Perfection (Sadler's Wells (USA))
98 **REBECCA ROLFE**, b f 10/3 Pivotal—Matoaka (USA) (A P Indy (USA))
99 **ROCKY'S PRIDE (IRE)**, b c 28/3 Rock of Gibraltar (IRE)—L'animee (Green Tune (USA)) (135000)
100 Br f 26/1 One Cool Cat (USA)—Salagama (IRE) (Alzao (USA)) (40000)
101 B c 13/4 Kheleyf (USA)—Saphire (College Chapel) (115829)
102 B c 15/2 Where Or When (IRE)—Secret Flame (Machiavellian (USA)) (115000)
103 **SECRET WITNESS**, ch c 12/4 Pivotal—It's A Secret (Polish Precedent (USA))
104 B c 27/3 Green Desert (USA)—Silver Bracelet (Machiavellian (USA)) (65000)
105 B f 13/2 King's Best (USA)—Silver Rhapsody (USA) (Silver Hawk (USA))
106 B f 6/2 Acclamation—Snap Crackle Pop (IRE) (Statoblest) (350000)
107 B f 2/4 Danehill Dancer (IRE)—Sniffle (IRE) (Shernazar) (57914)
108 **THOUSAND KNIGHTS (USA)**, ch f 31/1 Grand Slam (USA)—
                                    Our Josephina (USA) (Tale of The Cat (USA)) (97181)
109 B c 15/2 Cape Cross (IRE)—Walkamia (FR) (Linamix (FR))
110 Ch f 7/4 Beat Hollow—Welsh Dawn (Zafonic (USA)) (42000)
111 B c 25/4 Dansili—Woodwin (IRE) (Woodman (USA)) (65000)
112 B c 6/4 Sadler's Wells (USA)—Zarawa (IRE) (Kahyasi) (170000)
113 B c 29/3 Fasliyev (USA)—Ziffany (Taufan (USA))

Owners: Malih L. Al Basti, I. J. Al-Sagar, Arashan Ali, Ballygallon Stud, Mr Syd Belzberg, Mr T. Benson, Mr A. Brazil, Mr P. Byrne, Budget Stable, Cheveley Park Stud, Mrs P. A. Cooke, Mr J. D. Cotton, Mrs B. Cotton, Mrs D. Curran, D. Curran, Sir Alex Ferguson, Mr C. Fox, Franconson Partners, Mr M. Green, Mr T. F. Harris, Mrs E. A. Harris, The Hon H. M. Herbert, Hesmonds Stud, Mrs Judy B. Hicks, Highclere Thoroughbred Racing Ltd, Saleh Al Homaizi, Mrs P. Jamison, Jayeff B Stables, Mr Edward J. Kelly JR, Mr Gregory S. Kelly, Mr Michael M. Kelly, Ms G. Khosla, Ladbrokes International Ltd, Mr G. Lansbury, Mr Robert Levitt, M. W. Lightbody, Mrs J. G. Lightbody, Mr R. M. Lightbody, Lordship Stud, Mr J. Lovat, Mr T. Ludt, Capt. J. Macdonald-Buchanan, Mrs J. Magnier, Mrs S. Magnier, Mr N. Mandell, Mr D. Margolis, Mr B. McAllister, Mr A. L. Michaels, Mr P. Mitchell, Mountgrange Stud, N17 Partnership, Netherfield House Stud, Ms Kathryn Nikkel, Normandie Stud, Sir Robert Ogden, C.B.E., LLD, Mr G. J. Prussin, Mr S. Robertson, Mr T. G. Roddick, Mr H. Rosenblatt, Duke of Roxburghe, Mrs S. Roy, Royal Ascot Racing Club, Exors of the late Cathal M. Ryan, Mr Richard Santulli, The Searchers, Mr Derrick Smith, Mr G. Stevens, Mr Andrew Stewart, Saeed Suhail, Mr M. Tabor, Lady Carolyn Warren, Wood Hall Stud, Mr J. Wright

Assistant Trainer: Dave Bradley

---

445 MR D. C. O'BRIEN, Tonbridge
Postal: **Knowles Bank, Capel, Tonbridge, Kent, TN11 0PU**
Contacts: **PHONE (01892) 824072**

1 **ACHIEVED**, 5, b g Lahib (USA)—Equity's Darling (IRE) **Mrs Valerie O'Brien**
2 **BELSHAZZAR (USA)**, 7, b g King of Kings (USA)—Bayou Blues (USA) **D. C. O'Brien**
3 **CONSTABLE BURTON**, 7, b g Foxhound (USA)—Actress **D. C. O'Brien**
4 **DOCTORED**, 7, ch g Dr Devious (IRE)—Polygueza (FR) **D. C. O'Brien**
5 **STRIDER**, 7, ch g Pivotal—Sahara Belle (USA) **Mrs Valerie O'Brien**
6 **SUZIEBLUE (IRE)**, 4, b f Redback—Blue Holly (IRE) **D. C. O'Brien**

Assistant Trainer: Christopher O'Bryan

Jockey (NH): M. Batchelor, W. Marston.

446 MR E. J. O'GRADY, Thurles

Postal: Killeens, Ballynonty, Thurles, Co. Tipperary, Ireland
Contacts: PHONE (00353) 525 6156 FAX (00353) 525 6466 MOBILE (00353) 086 2590764
E-MAIL edward@edwardogrady.com

1 ACAPULCO (IRE), 4, b c Galileo (IRE)—Harasava (FR) **Joe Higgins**
2 ADENAUER (IRE), 5, b g Presenting—Vul Gale **Go West Racing Syndicate**
3 AH COME ON TOM (IRE), 9, b g Distinctly North (USA)—Gooseneck **Mach One Syndicate**
4 ALLEZ LES BLEU (IRE), 6, b g Pistolet Bleu (IRE)—Miss Betsy (IRE) **J. P. McManus**
5 ALLGROWNUP (IRE), 6, gr m Sea Raven (IRE)—Penny Pincher (IRE) **The Star Syndicate**
6 ANYAAB (IRE), 5, ch g Halling (USA)—Femme Fatale **S. Davis**
7 ARMARAMAK (IRE), 4, b c Mark of Esteem (IRE)—Armarama **Cathedral Syndicate**
8 ASPOLAN (GER), 5, b g Spectrum (IRE)—Arkona (GER) **Dr Ingleborg Von Schubert**
9 BAD BOY BONNEY, 4, b g King's Theatre (IRE)—Wild Dream **Noel F. Murphy**
10 BE HUMBLE (IRE), 5, ch g Presenting—Easter Bee (IRE) **James Gleeson**
11 BERNABEU (USA), 6, ch h Kris S (USA)—Set In Motion (USA) **Mrs A. C. Ryan**
12 CALTRA PRINCESS (IRE), 4, gr f Traditionally (USA)—Supercal **Ballylinch Stud**
13 CATCH ME (GER), 6, b g Law Society (USA)—Calcida (GER) **Mr J. O'Shea**
14 CHAMPION CHARLIE (IRE), 7, b g Entrepreneur—Campestral (USA) **Robert Sinclair**
15 4, B f Definite Article—Clandestine **Glenview House Stud**
16 CLOPF (IRE), 7, b g Dr Massini (IRE)—Chroma **Mr B. Heffernan**
17 COCKLESHELL ROAD (IRE), 5, b g Sinndar (IRE)—Soeur Ti (FR) **Mr E. Duignan**
18 COOMNAHORNA (IRE), 4, b f Saddlers' Hall (IRE)—Santa Suzanna (IRE) **Lady Melissa Brooke**
19 DEAL OR NO DEAL (IRE), 7, br g Darazari (IRE)—Artistic Thyne (IRE) **Mr J. O'Grady**
20 DIOPHAS (GER), 5, b h Acatenango (GER)—Dadrala (IRE) **J. P. McManus**
21 DISCREET, 5, b m Kahyasi—Loving Around (IRE) **Bloomsbury Stud**
22 FEN GAME (IRE), 6, b g Montjeu (IRE)—Hatton Gardens **Easter Syndicate**
23 4, B g King's Theatre (IRE)—Gayephar **Mrs E. J. O'Grady**
24 GRAPEVINE SALLY (IRE), 7, b m Saddlers' Hall (IRE)—Mrs Battleaxe (IRE) **Mrs P. Wallace**
25 HAVING A CUT (IRE), 6, br g Supreme Leader—Top Her Up (IRE) **J. P. McManus**
26 HERKEL (IRE), 4, b c Hernando (FR)—Kelang **Merry Tatcher Syndicate**
27 IN THE FAMILY (IRE), 4, b g Dr Massini (IRE)—Rossa Lougha (IRE) **Family Estate Syndicate**
28 INDIAN SPRING (IRE), 4, br c Indian Danehill (USA)—Lille Hammer **Noel F. Murphy**
29 JACK FINCH, 6, b g Overbury (IRE)—Quick Profit **Mr P. Blee**
30 JUDGE ROY BEAN (IRE), 5, b g Sadler's Wells (USA)—Be My Hope (IRE) **Mrs J. Magnier**
31 KASIMALI (IRE), 5, b h Soviet Star (USA)—Kassiyda **P. Wilmott**
32 KNOCKNAGOW LEADER (IRE), 6, b g Supreme Leader—Knocknagow **J. P. McManus**
33 L'ACAJOU (IRE), 7, br g Supreme Leader—Kim's Choice **Mr B. Walsh**
34 LETTERMAN (IRE), 8, br g Presenting—Papoose (IRE) **Mr S. P. Tindall**
35 MAC'S MY MATE, 7, b g Overbury (IRE)—Ballon **Mr R. Macdonald**
36 MACKENZIE MILLER (IRE), 5, b g Dr Massini (IRE)—Brehon Law (IRE) **Mrs Paul Shanahan**
37 MARSEILLAISE (USA), 4, ch g Royal Anthem (USA)—It's a Gherkin (USA) **P. Sweeney**
38 MEDICINAL (IRE), 7, gr g Linamix (FR)—Pharmacist (IRE) **Mr S. Mulryan**
39 MISTER BUTTONS (IRE), 7, b g Mister Mat (FR)—Our Buttons (IRE) **Mr D. O'Connor**
40 MONEY BELT (IRE), 5, b g Presenting—Kitty Maher (IRE) **J. P. McManus**
41 MUTTIAH, 8, ch g Muhtarram (USA)—Loving Around (IRE) **S. P. Tindall**
42 NEGUS (GER), 4, ch c Samum—Noble House (GER) **K. T. Clancy**
43 4, Ch g Presenting—Nick's Jule (IRE) **Mrs C. McCabe**
44 O'HEOCHAGAIN (IRE), 5, b b g Accordion—Curraghmeela (IRE) **Mrs W. T. O'Grady**
45 O'MUIRCHEARTAIGH (IRE), 8, b g Accordion—Brian's Delight (IRE) **Mrs W. T. O'Grady**
46 ODARSHAAN (IRE), 7, b g Darshaan—Odalisque (IRE) **Mr G. Terrioni**
47 OOLA LAD (IRE), 7, ch g Definite Article—Algonquin Park **Mr L. Hooton**
48 PEPLUM (FR), 5, b g Subotica (FR)—Great Filly (FR) **Noel F. Murphy**
49 POSH PAULA (IRE), 5, b m Saddlers' Hall (IRE)—Santa Suzanna (IRE) **Peter Magnier**
50 QUERIDO (USA), 6, b h Spectrum (IRE)—Polent **M. A. L. M. Syndicate**
51 RARE COMMODITY (IRE), 4, b g Definite Article—Soul Mate (IRE) **Mrs P. Wallace**
52 ROCCO'S HALL (IRE), 6, b g Saddlers' Hall (IRE)—Miss San Siro (IRE) **Mr G. Terrioni**
53 ROCK STEADY (IRE), 5, b g Rudimentary (USA)—Stonehallqueen **Thomas Barr**
54 ROMEOS JULIET (IRE), 4, ch f Definite Article—Beyshira (IRE) **Glenview House Stud**
55 SALT LAKE (GER), 6, b h Monsun (GER)—Shine (GER) **The Pacmen Syndicate**
56 SESAME ROSE (IRE), 5, b m Saddlers' Hall (IRE)—Sesame Cracker **R. Jenks**
57 SHAZAND (FR), 5, b h Daylami (IRE)—Shawara (IRE) **Mr S. P. Tindall**
58 SILEX (GER), 5, b g Zilzal (USA)—Shine (GER) **Dr Ingelborg Von Schubert**
59 SIMONAY (IRE), 4, br g Bob Back (USA)—Silks Princess **Mr S. P. Tindall**
60 SKY'S THE LIMIT (FR), 7, gr h Medaaly—Highness Lady **Mr R. Rooney**
61 SOME LEGEND (IRE), 8, b g Flying Legend (USA)—Albeit **The Tir Conaill Syndicate**
62 THE BIG PICTURE (IRE), 5, b g Dushyantor (USA)—Wakt **Mrs T. Hyde**

MR E. J. O'GRADY—continued

63 **TRANQUIL SEA (IRE),** 6, b g Sea Raven (IRE)—Silver Valley (IRE) **Mr D. Cox**
64 **TURTLEANDESCARGOT (IRE),** 5, b g Turtle Island (IRE)—Miss San Siro (IRE) **A. G. Terrinoni**
65 **VALENTIA LADY (IRE),** 7, b m Tiraaz (USA)—Burnpark Lady **Blues Brothers Syndicate**
66 **WARNE (IRE),** 4, b g Bob Back (USA)—Dusky Diva (IRE) **Noel F. Murphy**
67 **WHATEVER YOU THINK (IRE),** 8, b g Luso—Hug In A Fog (IRE) **N. Hayes**
68 **WHIZBANG (USA),** 7, b g Gold Token (USA)—Perfect Patience (USA) **J. P. McManus**
69 **WOLF CREEK (IRE),** 8, b g Anshan—Sleeven Lady **Warren Syndicate**
70 **WRIGHT FLYER (IRE),** 6, ch g Accordion—Deep Estee (IRE) **Mrs M. Cotter**

Other Owners: Sir F. Brooke, Mrs E. Thompson.

447 MR J. O'KEEFFE, Leyburn
Postal: **Highbeck Lodge, Brecongill, Coverham, Leyburn, North Yorkshire, DL8 4TJ**
Contacts: **PHONE (01969) 640330 FAX (01969) 640397 MOBILE (07710) 476705**
E-MAIL jedd@jeddokeefferacing.co.uk WEBSITE www.jeddokeefferacing.co.uk

1 **BID FOR GOLD,** 4, b g Auction House (USA)—Gold And Blue (USA) **Paul Chapman & Ba'Tat Investments**
2 **CELTIC EMPIRE (IRE),** 5, b g Second Empire (IRE)—Celtic Guest (IRE) **WRB Racing 56 (wrbracing.com)**
3 **EMERALD DESTINY (IRE),** 6, b g Key of Luck (USA)—Green Belt (FR) **WRB Racing 53 (wrbracing.com)**
4 **FLOODLIGHT FANTASY,** 5, b g Fantastic Light (USA)—Glamadour (USA) **D. Gennard**
5 **HABITUAL DANCER,** 7, b g Groom Dancer (USA)—Pomorie (IRE) **The Country Stayers**
6 **KENTUCKY BOY (IRE),** 4, b g Distant Music (USA)—Delta Town (USA) **The Kentuckians**
7 **LUNA LANDING,** 5, ch g Allied Forces (USA)—Macca Luna (IRE) **WRB Racing 47 (wrbracing.com)**
8 **MOONWALKING,** 4, b g Danehill Dancer (IRE)—Macca Luna (IRE) **WRB Racing 38 (wrbracing.com)**
9 **PRINCE OF LOVE (IRE),** 5, b h Fruits of Love (USA)—Teodora (IRE) **Jedd O'Keeffe**
10 **SIR NIGHT (IRE),** 8, b g Night Shift (USA)—Highly Respected (IRE) **Highbeck Racing**
11 **SNOW BUNTING,** 10, ch g Polar Falcon (USA)—Marl **WRB Racing 49 (wrbracing.com)**

THREE-YEAR-OLDS

12 **AQUARIAN DANCER,** b f Mujahid (USA)—Admonish **The Fatalists**
13 **DON'T BE SO SAKHEE,** ch f Sakhee (USA)—Native Ring (FR) **Mrs J. Mear**
14 **FLASHY MAX,** b c Primo Valentino (IRE)—Be Practical **WRB Racing 50 (wrbracing.com)**
15 **HIGHLAND LOVE,** b g Fruits of Love (USA)—Diabaig **Ken & Delia Shaw-KGS Consultants Ltd**
16 **JONTOBEL,** b g Tobougg (IRE)—Belinda **D. Gennard**
17 **NORTHGATE MAISIE,** b f Sugarfoot—Chasetown Cailin **J. J. Scott**
18 **RAGNARR,** b g Bertolini (USA)—Desert Dawn **A. Walker**
19 **SOCIETY VENUE,** b g Where Or When (IRE)—Society Rose **Ken & Delia Shaw-KGS Consultants Ltd**

TWO-YEAR-OLDS

20 Br c 24/2 Fantastic Light (USA)—Bitwa (USA) (Conquistador Cielo (USA)) (8000) **A. Walker**
21 B f 24/2 Mull of Kintyre (USA)—Buddy And Soda (IRE) (Imperial Frontier (USA)) (4500) **Three Coins Racing**
22 **DARK ECHOES,** bl c 12/4 Diktat—Calamanco (Clantime) (28000) **Ken & Delia Shaw-KGS Consultants Ltd**
23 B c 20/3 Statue of Liberty (USA)—Go For Grace (Shalford (IRE)) (17000) **A. Walker**
24 B c 1/5 Generous (IRE)—Inya Lake (Whittingham (IRE)) (5000) **A. Walker**
25 **LUCKY BUDDHA,** gr c 20/2 Kyllachy—
　　　　Heaven-Liegh-Grey (Grey Desire) (6500) **Ken & Delia Shaw-KGS Consultants Ltd**
26 **SECRET VENUE,** ch c 1/2 Where Or When (IRE)—
　　　　Sheila's Secret (IRE) (Bluebird (USA)) (32000) **Ken & Delia Shaw-KGS Consultants Ltd**
27 B c 21/2 Daylami (IRE)—Shallat (IRE) (Pennekamp (USA)) (10000) **A. Walker**

Other Owners: Mr D. Altham, Mr Andrew Bates, Mr Richard Berry, Mr P. Blackburn, Mrs A. Bradley, Mr Michael Chapman, P. Chapman, Mr P. Chapman, Mr C. Ellwood, Mr H. English, Mr S. Fountain, Mrs E. Fountain, Mr A. Henderson, Mr B. Hickson, Mr & Mrs P. Hutchinson, E. R. D. Johnson, Mr E. R. D. Johnson, Mrs G. McKenna, Mr S. J. Mear, Colin & Melanie Moore, Mr J. Murphy, Mr Jedd O'Keeffe, Mr P. Ord, Mr E. Rider, Mr & Mrs H. M. Sadler, Mr J. Scott, Mrs D. M. Shaw, Mr & Mrs K. Shaw, Mr T. Shepherd, Mr S. C. C. Skey, Wetherby Racing Bureau Ltd.

Assistant Trainer: Andrea O'Keeffe.

Jockey (NH): B. Harding.

448 MR RONNIE O'LEARY, Co. Clare
Postal: **Willow Farm Stables, Carrowbaun, Ogonnelloe, Killaloe, Co. Clare**
Contacts: **PHONE (00353) 1376574 FAX (00353) 1376574 MOBILE (00353) 086 2640037**
E-MAIL ronandvicky@eircom.net

1 AURA OF CALM (IRE), 6, b g Grand Lodge (USA)—Perils of Joy (IRE) **Mrs M. M. Hanrahan**
2 FOLLOW THE SUN (IRE), 4, br g Tertullian (USA)—Sun Mate (IRE) **Vicky O' Leary**
3 LUNABARATO (FR), 4, b c Barathea (IRE)—Luna Mareza **Mr Gerry McManus**
4 SCHELM (GER), 6, b g Alwuhush (USA)—Shoba (GER) **Mr Paul Hillis**
5 SUNDECK (FR), 8, br h Dr Devious (IRE)—Mystery Tune (IRE) **Mr Gerry McManus**
6 VELOSO (FR), 6, gr g Kaldounevees (FR)—Miss Recif (IRE) **Mrs R. O'Leary**

Other Owners: MR. J. P. McManus.

449 MR J. G. O'NEILL, Bicester
Postal: **Hall Farm, Stratton Audley, Nr Bicester, Oxfordshire, OX27 9BT**
Contacts: **PHONE (01869) 277202 FAX (01869) 227096 MOBILE (07785) 394128**
E-MAIL jgoneill@lineone.net

1 IRISH GUARD, 7, b g Infantry—Sharp Practice **J. G. O'Neill**
2 THE STROKER, 5, b g Overbury (IRE)—Sharp Practice

450 MR J. J. O'NEILL, Cheltenham
Postal: **Jackdaws Castle, Temple Guiting, Cheltenham, Gloucestershire, GL54 5XU**
Contacts: **PHONE (01386) 584209 FAX (01386) 584219**
E-MAIL enquiries@jonjooneillracing.com WEBSITE www.jonjooneillracing.com

1 ALBERTAS RUN (IRE), 7, b g Accordion—Holly Grove Lass **T. J. Hemmings**
2 ALRIGHT NOW M'LAD (IRE), 8, b g Supreme Leader—Chattering **J. P. McManus**
3 ALTERNATOR (IRE), 6, ch g Pistolet Bleu (IRE)—Marello **C. D. Carr**
4 ANOTHER BROTHER (IRE), 6, b g Supreme Leader—Sister Rosza **T. J. Hemmings**
5 AYEMDEE (IRE), 5, b g Flemensfirth (USA)—Deep Coral (IRE)
6 BASIC FACT (IRE), 6, b g Rudimentary (USA)—Native Emma (IRE) **Mrs G. K. Smith**
7 BERINGS EXPRESS (FR), 5, b g Bering—Ess Express (FR) **Mrs G. K. Smith**
8 BLACK JACK KETCHUM (IRE), 9, b g Oscar (IRE)—Cailin Supreme (IRE) **Mrs G. K. Smith**
9 BOB HALL (IRE), 7, b g Sadler's Wells (USA)—Be My Hope (IRE) **J. P. McManus**
10 BUCKSHAW (IRE), 5, b g Supreme Leader—Bucktime (IRE) **T. J. Hemmings**
11 BUSY HENRY, 8, ch g Busy Flight—Haliguen Royal **J. P. McManus**
12 BUTLER'S CABIN (FR), 8, b g Poliglote—Strictly Cool (USA) **J. P. McManus**
13 CAN'T BUY TIME (IRE), 6, b g Supreme Leader—Sales Centre **J. P. McManus**
14 CAPTAIN CRACKERS (IRE), 4, b g King's Theatre (IRE)—Love The Lord (IRE)
15 CARNIVAL TOWN, 7, b g Classic Cliche (IRE)—One of Those Days **Mrs G. K. Smith**
16 CASTLECROSSINGS (IRE), 5, br m Broken Hearted—Peacefull River (IRE) **J. P. McManus**
17 CROCODILES ROCK (IRE), 6, b g Heron Island (IRE)—That's The Bonus (IRE) **J. P. McManus**
18 CROSS COMPLIANCE (IRE), 5, b g Turtle Island (IRE)—Pima (IRE) **Mrs S. Magnier**
19 CRUCHAIN (IRE), 5, ch g Shernazar—Mack Tack (IRE) **P. McCarthy**
20 DE SOTO, 7, b g Hernando (FR)—Vanessa Bell (IRE) **Mrs G. K. Smith**
21 DON'T PUSH IT (IRE), 8, b g Old Vic—She's No Laugh Ben (USA) **J. P. McManus**
22 DONALDSON (GER), 6, b g Lando (GER)—Daytona Beach (GER) **F. S. Williams**
23 DR MCFAB, 4, ch g Dr Fong (USA)—Barbera **Mr Chris Grant & Mr Michael H. Burke**
24 DRIVING MISS SUZIE, 4, br f Diktat—Santa Isobel **J C & S R Hitchins**
25 DYNAMIC LEAP, 5, b g Turtle Island (IRE)—Caramello **Mrs G. K. Smith**
26 EXOTIC DANCER (IRE), 8, b g Turgeon (USA)—Northine (FR) **Sir Robert Ogden C.B.E., LLD**
27 FIER NORMAND (FR), 9, b g Cyborg (FR)—Moomaw **J. P. McManus**
28 FIRTH OF FORTH (IRE), 8, b g Flemensfirth (USA)—Penny Star (IRE) **J. P. McManus**
29 FORTYSHADESOFGREEN (IRE), 5, b g Oscar (IRE)—Irian (IRE) **Mrs S. Magnier**
30 FRESH AIR AND FUN (IRE), 5, b br g Trans Island—Executive Ellie (IRE) **McGrath, Beighton, Griffin, Hancock**
31 GIVEUSACLUE (IRE), 7, b br g Presenting—Branscombe (IRE) **Mrs G. K. Smith**
32 GOLD BEACH (IRE), 8, b g Jurado (USA)—Grange Park (IRE) **Mrs C. S. Baylis**
33 GRANITE MAN (IRE), 8, b g Glacial Storm (USA)—Silkaway (IRE) **Mrs G. K. Smith**
34 GRECIAN GROOM (IRE), 6, b g Groom Dancer (USA)—Danse Grecque (FR) **Mrs G. K. Smith**
35 GUN SMITH, 6, b g Pistolet Bleu (IRE)—Bayariyka (IRE) **Mrs G. K. Smith**
36 HASTY PRINCE, 10, ch g Halling (USA)—Sister Sophie (USA) **J. P. McManus**
37 HOT ZONE (IRE), 6, b g Bob Back (USA)—Trixskin (IRE) **Mrs G. K. Smith**
38 I'M THE DECIDER (IRE), 6, b g Presenting—Donegal Thyne (IRE) **J. P. McManus**

MR J. J. O'NEILL—continued

39 ICE MELTED (IRE), 7, ch g Old Vic—Warren Thyne (IRE) **J. P. McManus**
40 IMMENSE (IRE), 4, b g Montjeu (IRE)—Admiring (USA) **Paul Downing & Tony Eaves**
41 INARO (IRE), 7, b g Bahhare (USA)—Doo Han (IRE) **J. P. McManus**
42 INTERSKY MUSIC (USA), 5, b g Victory Gallop (CAN)—Resounding Grace (USA) **Destiny Racing Club**
43 ISN'T THAT LUCKY, 5, b g Afflora (IRE)—Blast Freeze (IRE) **Mrs V. F. Burke**
44 JAM PACKED (IRE), 6, ch g Beneficial—Mad House **J. P. McManus**
45 KEEPATEM (IRE), 12, ch g Be My Native (USA)—Ariannrun **J. P. McManus**
46 KEEPITSECRET (IRE), 7, b g Topanoora—Try Your Case **Mrs G. K. Smith**
47 KIA KAHA, 6, b g Sir Harry Lewis (USA)—Not Enough **J. P. McManus**
48 LIKE A BEE (IRE), 10, b g Montelimar (USA)—Dasdilemma (IRE) **J. P. McManus**
49 MALAKIYA (IRE), 5, b g Sadler's Wells (USA)—State Crystal (IRE) **J. P. McManus**
50 MATCHO PIERJI (FR), 6, b g Cadoudal (FR)—La Brindille (FR) **J. P. McManus**
51 MCGARRY'S LANE (IRE), 5, b g Lahib (USA)—Braw Lass **Mrs N. Gillioz**
52 MINKOWSKI, 5, b g Galileo (IRE)—Abitara (IRE) **M. Tabor**
53 MOTOWN (IRE), 5, b g Luso—Meldrum Lass **T. J. Hemmings**
54 MOUNTAIN (IRE), 5, b g Montjeu (IRE)—Skidmore Girl (USA) **Mrs G. K. Smith**
55 MY OLD PIANO (IRE), 6, b g Dr Massini (IRE)—Tenbo (IRE) **Steven Ashley & Adrian Purvis**
56 NEWMAN DES PLAGES (FR), 7, b br g Passing Sale (FR)—
        Reine Des Plages (FR) **Sir Robert Ogden C.B.E., LLD**
57 OLAY OLAY (IRE), 8, b g Charnwood Forest (IRE)—Maria Renata **J. P. McManus**
58 OPTION MONEY (IRE), 6, b g Kotashaan (FR)—Be My Bargain (IRE) **Barry Connell**
59 PANTHERUS (IRE), 5, b g Montjeu (IRE)—Panthere (GER) **M & E Stobart**
60 PARKINSON (IRE), 7, br g Presenting—Be My Citizen (IRE) **T. J. Hemmings**
61 PASS IT ON (IRE), 9, br g Accordion—Windswept Lady (IRE) **J. P. McManus**
62 PEAU AIME (FR), 5, b g Passing Sale (FR)—Carvine d'or (FR) **Sir Robert Ogden C.B.E., LLD**
63 PHOUDAMOUR (FR), 5, b g Le Balafre (FR)—Grande Folie (FR) **J. P. McManus**
64 PIAMONTINI (IRE), 5, b g Alhaarth (IRE)—Actualite **Sir Robert Ogden C.B.E., LLD**
65 RAISE YOUR GAME (IRE), 7, b g Saddlers' Hall (IRE)—Roscrea Travel (IRE) **J. P. McManus**
66 RAPID INCREASE (IRE), 5, br g Sonus (IRE)—Lady Margaretta **Mrs G. K. Smith**
67 REFINEMENT (IRE), 9, b m Oscar (IRE)—Maneree **M. Tabor**
68 SASSO, 6, b g Efisio—Sioux **J. P. McManus**
69 SHE'S BEAUTIFUL (IRE), 5, b m Darnay—Anck Su Namun (IRE) **BMAP Partnership**
70 SPECTAIT, 6, b g Spectrum (IRE)—Shanghai Girl **J. P. McManus**
71 SUNNYHILLBOY (IRE), 5, b g Old Vic—Sizzle **J. P. McManus**
72 THE KING OF ANGELS (IRE), 6, b g Presenting—Vul Gale **J C & S R Hitchins**
73 THE VERY MAN (IRE), 6, b g Flemensfirth—Christian Lady (IRE) **J. P. McManus**
74 THEATRICAL MOMENT (USA), 5, b g Royal Anthem (USA)—Given Moment (USA) **Masterson Holdings Limited**
75 THUNDER ROCK (IRE), 6, b g King's Best—Park Express **Mrs G. K. Smith**
76 TOASTMASTER (IRE), 6, b g Oscar (IRE)—Melodic Tune (IRE) **Mrs G. K. Smith**
77 TRUCKERS DELIGHT (IRE), 7, b g Darazari (IRE)—Windmill Star (IRE) **Barry Connell**
78 VEDELLE (IRE), 9, b g Flemensfirth (USA)—Romitch **J. P. McManus**
79 WICHITA LINEMAN (IRE), 7, b g King's Theatre (IRE)—Monumental Gesture **J. P. McManus**
80 YOULL DO FOR ME (IRE), 6, b g Beneficial—Eurocurrency (IRE) **Mrs G. K. Smith**

Other Owners: Mr Brook Alder, Mr Phillip Ambler, Mr Steve Ashley, Mr P. Beighton, Mr Michael Burke, Mr P.A. Downing, A. C. Eaves, Mr C. I. Grant, R. F. Griffin, Mr J. D. Hancock, Mr J. C. Hitchins, Mr S. R. Hitchins, Mr C. Kelly, Mr Johnny McGrath, J. C. McGrath, Mrs Jonjo O'Neill, Mr A. Purvis, Mr E. Stobart.

---

451 MR J. G. M. O'SHEA, Westbury-on-Severn
Postal: Tudor Racing Stables, Elton, Westbury-on-Severn, Gloucestershire, GL14 1JN
Contacts: (01452) 760835 FAX (01452) 760972 MOBILE (07917) 124717
WEBSITE www.johnoshearacing.co.uk

1 ABSOLUTELYTHEBEST (IRE), 7, b g Anabaa (USA)—Recherchee **K. W. Bell**
2 BERRY HILL LASS (IRE), 4, b f Alhaarth (IRE)—Gold Mist **K. W. Bell**
3 BOTHAR BRUGHA (IRE), 4, b g Alexius (USA)—Denise's Stride (IRE) **Quality Street Racing Syndicate**
4 BRADS HOUSE (IRE), 6, b g Rossini (USA)—Gold Stamp **K. W. Bell & Son Ltd**
5 CHEVY TO THE LEVY (IRE), 6, b g Saddlers' Hall (USA)—Be The One (IRE) **K. W. Bell & Son Ltd**
6 COME ON NELLIE (IRE), 4, b f Diktat—Bauci (USA) **Preece Haden Partnership**
7 DR DREAM (IRE), 4, b g Dr Fong (USA)—Only In Dreams **GLK Partnership**
8 FOREST LASS (IRE), 5, b m Almutawakel—Gold Stamp **K. W. Bell & Son Ltd**
9 GO FREE, 7, gr g Easycall—Miss Traxdata **Pete Smith Car Sales**
10 HESTER BROOK (IRE), 4, b f Soviet Star (USA)—Keen To Please **Mr W. R. Baddiley**
11 HIGH REACH, 8, b g Royal Applause—Lady of Limerick (IRE) **Mr W. R. Baddiley**
12 KANPAI (IRE), 6, br g Trans Island—David's Star **Samurai Racing Syndicate**

MR J. G. M. O'SHEA—continued

13 **LOOKTHEOTHERWAY (IRE)**, 4, br f Val Royal (FR)—Gold Stamp **The Cross Racing Club**
14 **LORD OROKO**, 4, ch g Lord of Men—Wannaplantatree **A. G. Craddock**
15 **LULOAH**, 5, b m Mujahid (USA)—Bangles **Mr W. R. Baddiley**
16 **MEASURED RESPONSE**, 6, ch g Inchinor—Seal Indigo (IRE) **Pete Smith Car Sales**
17 **MICKEY PEARCE (IRE)**, 6, b g Rossini (USA)—Lucky Coin **The Lovely Jubbly's**
18 **PHARAON DE TOUZAINE (FR)**, 5, b g Subotica (FR)—Diana de Vonnas (FR) **K. W. Bell & Son Ltd**
19 **PRETTY POSEY**, 4, b f Dolpour—Aegean Glory **R. K. Mehta**
20 **RADMORES REVENGE**, 5, b g Overbury (IRE)—Harvey's Sister **J. R. Salter**
21 **STAFFORD WILL (IRE)**, 4, b g Rossini (USA)—Firstrusseofsummer (USA) **N. G. H. Ayliffe**
22 **SUMMEROFSIXTYNINE**, 5, b h Fruits of Love (USA)—Scurrilous **Quality Pipe Supports (Q.P.S.) Ltd**
23 **TERANDEIL**, 4, b f Auction House (USA)—Frisson **GLK Partnership**
24 **THE JAILER**, 5, b m Mujahid (USA)—Once Removed **N. M. Lowe**
25 **WALRAGNEK**, 4, gr g Mind Games—Eastern Lyric **Quality Pipe Supports (Q.P.S.) Ltd**

THREE-YEAR-OLDS

26 B br c Indian Danehill (IRE)—Gold Stamp **Mr K. W. Bell**
27 **MAGNOL**, gr f Tobougg (IRE)—Magnolia **Pete Smith Car Sales**
28 **MAMA LEO**, ch f Forzando—Milady Lillie (IRE) **Mr W. R. Baddiley**
29 **NEVER SOLD OUT (IRE)**, ch c Captain Rio—Vicious Rosie **Mr W. R. Baddiley**
30 **O'CASEY (IRE)**, b c Bold Fact (USA)—Miss Scott (IRE) **GLK Partnership**
31 **TEN ON LINE (IRE)**, ch c Rossini (USA)—Fastnet **J. R. Salter**
32 **XARAVELLA (IRE)**, b f Xaar—Walnut Lady **The Cross Racing Club**

TWO-YEAR-OLDS

33 B f 19/4 Hamas (IRE)—Ballerina Bay (Myjinski (USA) **Mrs P. Wallace**
34 **SHES BILLIE**, ch f 27/3 Auction House (USA)—Wintzig (Piccolo) (2666) **S. Martin**

Other Owners: Mr N. G. H. Ayliffe, Mr Patrick Brady, Mr F. J. Brady, Mr C. L. Dubois, Mr A. J. Haden, Mr L. Herbert, Mr Martyn James, Mr Brian Kermode, Mr J. P. O'Rourke, Mr J. S. Preece, Mr Gary Roberts, Mr Pete Smith, Mrs Sarah Smith, Mr Kenneth Stephens.

Assistant Trainer: Greg Richards

Jockey (flat): R. Havlin, D. Sweeney. **Jockey (NH):** David Crosse.

---

452 **MR J. A. B. OLD, Wroughton**
Postal: **Upper Herdswick Farm, Hackpen, Burderop, Wroughton, Swindon, Wiltshire, SN4 0QH**
Contacts: **CAR (07836) 721459 OFFICE (01793) 845200 FAX (01793) 845201**
E-MAIL racing@jimold.co.uk

1 **ATTORNEY GENERAL (IRE)**, 9, b g Sadler's Wells (USA)—Her Ladyship **W. E. Sturt**
2 **BACK AMONG FRIENDS**, 9, b g Bob Back (USA)—Betty's Girl **Mrs J. A. Fowler**
3 **BARRYS ARK (IRE)**, 10, b br g Commanche Run—Hand Me Down **M. E. Sturt**
4 5, Br g Hubbly Bubbly (USA)—Bold Shilling (IRE)
5 **BROUGHTON GREEN (IRE)**, 7, b g Shernazar—Lucy Walters (IRE) **W. E. Sturt**
6 **CAMINO REAL**, 5, ch m Benny The Dip (USA)—Kingdom Ruby (IRE) **W. E. Sturt**
7 **CAPTAIN AUBREY (IRE)**, 9, b g Supreme Leader—Hamers Girl (IRE) **W. E. Sturt**
8 **CNOC AOIBHINN (IRE)**, 7, b m Presenting—Inse Na Rince (IRE) **J. A. B. Old**
9 **COLLINE DE FLEURS**, 8, b m Alflora (IRE)—B Greenhill **The Wheels Have Come Off**
10 **COUNTING HOUSE (IRE)**, 5, ch g King's Best (USA)—Inforapenny **W. E. Sturt**
11 **DROPPY'S (IRE)**, 7, br g Houmayoun (FR)—Whizaway (IRE) **W. E. Sturt**
12 **DURANTE (IRE)**, 10, ch g Shernazar—Sweet Tune **W. E. Sturt**
13 **FREDDIES RETURN (IRE)**, 7, b g Flemensfirth (USA)—Rachael's Dawn **M. J. Lovatt**
14 **GALA EVENING**, 6, b g Daylami (IRE)—Balleta (USA) **W. E. Sturt**
15 **GUNNASAYSO**, 7, b m Gunner B—Sayshar **J. A. B. Old**
16 **HAVEYOURBEEN (IRE)**, 5, b m Accordion—Princess Tino (IRE) **W. E. Sturt**
17 **JERSEY COUNTESS (IRE)**, 5, br m Supreme Leader—Regents Prancer **W. E. Sturt**
18 **KELV**, 7, gr g Karinga Bay—Pendle Princess **P. D. Guntrip**
19 **KILDONNAN**, 9, b g Bob's Return (IRE)—Celtic Tore (IRE) **W. E. Sturt**
20 5, B m Moscow Society (USA)—Kim Mews (IRE)
21 **MONTEFORTE**, 10, b g Alflora (IRE)—Double Dutch **W. E. Sturt**
22 **MRS FAWLTY**, 5, b m Kayf Tara—Hannigan's Lodger (IRE) **W. E. Sturt**
23 **MY FRIEND SANDY**, 7, ch g Anshan—Gaye Fame **W. E. Sturt**
24 **OWLSLEY**, 6, b g Terimon—Black H'penny **A. J. Britten**

MR J. A. B. OLD—continued

25 **PATSY FINNEGAN**, 6, b g Sir Harry Lewis (USA)—Bampton Fair **Mr P. Finnegan**
26 5, B h Karinga Bay—Pendil's Niece
27 **PIP MOSS**, 13, ch g Le Moss—My Aisling **Mrs A. M. Old**
28 **RONAN THE WARRIOR (IRE)**, 8, b g Dr Massini (IRE)—Gracemarie Kate (IRE) **W. E. Sturt**
29 **ROUND THE HORN (IRE)**, 8, ch g Master Willie—Gaye Fame **W. E. Sturt**
30 **SHEILA RYAN**, 7, b m Bob's Return (IRE)—Bronze Sunset **Wise King Partnership**
31 **SHERNATRA (IRE)**, 9, b g Shernazar—Miss Nancy **W. E. Sturt**
32 **SIDNEY CHARLES (IRE)**, 6, br g Mister Baileys—Distant Music **P. D. Guntrip**
33 **SIZEABLE RETURN**, 7, b g Bob's Return (IRE)—Dutch Czarina **P. D. Guntrip**
34 **SMEATHE'S RIDGE**, 10, b g Rakaposhi King—Mrs Barty (IRE) **Smeathes Ridge Partnership**
35 **SNAKECHARM (IRE)**, 6, b g Taipan (IRE)—Sparkling Opera **W. E. Sturt**
36 **SUPER LADY (IRE)**, 7, br m Mister Lord (USA)—Daisy's Dream **W. E. Sturt**
37 **SUPER LORD (IRE)**, 10, br g Mister Lord (USA)—Daisy's Dream **W. E. Sturt**
38 **TEAM CHASER (IRE)**, 7, b g Dr Massini (IRE)—New Chello (IRE) **Mrs S. A. Smith**
39 **THE BOSS ROCK (IRE)**, 5, b g Shernazar—Lake Garden Park **Mrs A. M. Old**
40 **THE DUCKPOND (IRE)**, 11, ch g Bob's Return (IRE)—Miss Gosling **W. E. Sturt**
41 **THE HUDNALLS (IRE)**, 7, ch g Shernazar—Toposki (FR) **C. J. Jenkins**
42 **THEDREAMSTILLALIVE (IRE)**, 8, ch g Houmayoun (FR)—State of Dream (IRE) **W. E. Sturt**
43 **THENFORD SNIPE (IRE)**, 7, b g Clerkenwell (USA)—Peas (IRE) **W. E. Sturt**
44 **TOP RAM (IRE)**, 8, ch g Topanoora—Aries Girl **W. E. Sturt**
45 **TUESDAY CLUB (IRE)**, 9, ch g Old Vic—Asfreeasthewind (IRE) **Old Fools Partnership**
46 **WAIN MOUNTAIN**, 12, b g Unfuwain (USA)—Mountain Memory **Old Fools Partnership**
47 **WHITEWATER DASH**, 8, b g Bob Back (USA)—Skiddaw Samba **W. E. Sturt**
48 **WHOSETHATFOR (IRE)**, 8, b g Beneficial—Native Craft (IRE) **W. E. Sturt**
49 **YOUNG COLLIER**, 9, b g Vettori (IRE)—Cockatoo Island **W. E. Sturt**

Other Owners: S. M. Couling, Lt Cdr P. S. Emmet.

Assistant Trainer: Emma Grierson

Jockey (NH): J. Maguire, M. Bradburne.

---

453 MR G. R. OLDROYD, Malton
Postal: Flint Hall Farm, Moor Lane, Brawby, Malton, North Yorkshire, YO17 6PZ
Contacts: PHONE (01653) 668279

1 **BOND BECKS (IRE)**, 8, ch g Tagula (IRE)—At Amal (IRE) **R. C. Bond**
2 **BOND CASINO**, 4, b f Kyllachy—Songsheet **R. C. Bond**
3 **BOND CITY (IRE)**, 6, b g Trans Island—Where's Charlotte **R. C. Bond**
4 **BOND PLAYBOY**, 8, b g Piccolo—Highest Ever (FR) **R. C. Bond**
5 **JUST BOND (IRE)**, 6, b g Namid—Give Warning (IRE) **R. C. Bond**
6 **MISS SURE BOND (IRE)**, 5, ch m Danehill Dancer (IRE)—Desert Rose **R. C. Bond**
7 **SIR BOND (IRE)**, 7, ch g Desert Sun—In Tranquility (IRE) **R. C. Bond**
8 **THE DIAMOND BOND**, 4, bl g Josr Algarhoud (IRE)—Alsiba **R. C. Bond**
9 **TUMBLEWEED DI**, 4, ro f Tumbleweed Ridge—Peggotty **P. Drewery**

THREE-YEAR-OLDS

10 **ADMIRAL BOND (IRE)**, ch c Titus Livius (FR)—Where's Charlotte **R. C. Bond**
11 **BENITEZ BOND**, ch c Bahamian Bounty—Triple Tricks (IRE) **R. C. Bond**
12 **BOND SCISSORSISTER (IRE)**, b f Xaar—Musical Refrain (IRE) **R. C. Bond**
13 **CHOSEN FOREVER**, b g Choisir (AUS)—Forever Bond **R. C. Bond**
14 **FIRENZA BOND**, b g Captain Rio—Bond Stasia (IRE) **R. C. Bond**
15 **INFINITY BOND**, b c Forzando—Bond Girl **R. C. Bond**
16 **PEEDEE**, b f Elmaamul (USA)—Dispol Diamond **P. Drewery**

TWO-YEAR-OLDS

17 B f 11/3 Monsieur Bond (IRE)—Bond Girl (Magic Ring (IRE)) **R. C. Bond**
18 Ch f 18/4 Monsieur Bond (IRE)—Bond Royale (Piccolo) **Impossible Dreams Racing Limited**
19 Ch f 18/2 Monsieur Bond (IRE)—Bond Shakira (Daggers Drawn) **R. C. Bond**
20 B f 25/2 Monsieur Bond (IRE)—Chicago Bond (Real Quiet (USA)) **Impossible Dreams Racing Limited**
21 B f 14/2 Monsieur Bond (IRE)—Forever Bond (Danetime (IRE)) **R. C. Bond**
22 Ch f 28/1 Monsieur Bond (IRE)—Kanisfluh (Pivotal) **R. C. Bond**
23 B f 11/4 Auction House (USA)—Pawsible (IRE) (Mujadil (USA)) (500) **G. Sanderson**

MR G. R. OLDROYD—continued

Other Owners: Mr B. Abbott, Mr S. Ryan.

Assistant Trainer: Sarah Perry

Apprentice: Slade O'Hara.

---

454 **MR J. A. OSBORNE, Upper Lambourn**
Postal: Kingsdown, Upper Lambourn, Hungerford, Berkshire, RG17 8QX
Contacts: PHONE (01488) 73139 FAX (01488) 73084 MOBILE (07860) 533422
E-MAIL jamieosborne@dial.pipex.com WEBSITE www.jamieosborne.com

1 DOCOFTHEBAY (IRE), 4, ch c Docksider (USA)—Baize
2 ENJOY THE MOMENT, 5, b g Generous (IRE)—Denial
3 GEORDIELAND (FR), 7, gr h Johann Quatz (FR)—Aerdee (FR)
4 LASCELLES, 4, b c Halling (USA)—Poppy's Song
5 MORSE (IRE), 7, b g Shinko Forest (IRE)—Auriga
6 STICKY TAPE, 4, b f Royal Applause—Golden Symbol
7 TEARS OF A CLOWN (IRE), 5, b g Galileo (IRE)—Mood Swings (IRE)

THREE-YEAR-OLDS

8 BENEATH THE TREES (USA), b c Forestry (USA)—Arabis (USA)
9 BERTHA, b f Bertolini (USA)—Thea (USA)
10 BORROWDALE, b g Royal Applause—Night Mirage (USA)
11 BOY ON A SWING (USA), ch c Hold That Tiger (USA)—Balancoire (USA)
12 CEE BARGARA, b g Acclamation—Balsamita (FR)
13 CLUELESS COPSE (USA), b f Forest Camp (USA)—Miff Crypto (USA)
14 COUP DE TORCHON (FR), b f Namid—Tashtiyana (IRE)
15 DANDY ERIN (IRE), b c Danehill Dancer (IRE)—Sanctuary Line (IRE)
16 DAYS OF PLEASURE (IRE), b g Fraam—Altizaf
17 DRAWNFROMTHEPAST (IRE), ch c Tagula (IRE)—Ball Cat (FR)
18 DREAM IN BLUE, b c Oasis Dream—Blue Birds Fly
19 DUBAI PRINCESS (IRE), b f Dubai Destination (USA)—Blue Iris
20 GROUP THERAPY, ch c Choisir (AUS)—Licence To Thrill
21 HAWK EYED LADY (IRE), b f Hawk Wing (USA)—Danccini (IRE)
22 LITTLE WING (IRE), b c Hawk Wing (USA)—Hartstown House (IRE)
23 MEDIA STARS, gr c Green Desert (USA)—Starine (FR)
24 MISTERISLAND (IRE), b c Spectrum (IRE)—Carranita (IRE)
25 NAGS TO RICHES (IRE), b g Acclamation—Beauharnaise (FR)
26 PREMIER YANK (USA), br c Johannesburg (USA)—Sallybrooke (USA)
27 ROCKFIELD LODGE (IRE), b g Stravinsky (USA)—La Belle Simone (IRE)
28 ROCKFIELD ROSE, ch f Kyllachy—Owdbetts (IRE)
29 ROCKFIELD TIGER (IRE), b c Dubai Destination (USA)—Aljazeera (USA)
30 SNOW BOUNTY, b g Bahamian Bounty—Christmas Rose
31 TANTRIS (IRE), b g High Chaparral (IRE)—Emerald Cut
32 TEN DOWN, b g Royal Applause—Upstream
33 TENJACK KING, b c Kyllachy—Rash
34 TENSE (IRE), b f Invincible Spirit (IRE)—Roses From Ridey (IRE)
35 TENSION MOUNTS (IRE), b g Daggers Drawn (USA)—Dazzling Maid (IRE)
36 THANKUFORTHEMUSIC (IRE), b g Shinko Forest (IRE)—Auriga
37 THE RIDDLER (IRE), b c Daylami (IRE)—Wimple (USA)
38 TOLLISHILL (IRE), b c Sadler's Wells (USA)—Prospect Dalia (USA)

TWO-YEAR-OLDS

39 B c 23/3 Stroll (USA)—Afleet Summer (USA) (Afleet (CAN)) (57914)
40 Ch f 2/3 Redback—Ball Cat (FR) (Cricket Ball (USA)) (30000)
41 B f 26/4 Marju (IRE)—Bel Sole (ITY) (Spectrum (IRE)) (10617)
42 B f 29/3 Monsieur Bond (IRE)—Bond Stasia (IRE) (Mukaddamah (USA)) (10000)
43 CHEAP THRILLS, ch f 19/4 Bertolini (USA)—Licence To Thrill (Wolfhound (USA)) (150000)
44 B f 10/4 Danetime (IRE)—Clandolly (IRE) (Burslem) (23165)
45 B f 25/2 Royal Applause—Clincher Club (Polish Patriot (USA)) (90000)
46 B c 16/2 Mujadil (USA)—Danestar (Danehill (USA)) (27026)
47 Br c 12/2 Millkom—Discoed (Distinctly North (USA)) (28000)
48 B c 28/4 Key of Luck (USA)—Disregard That (IRE) (Don't Forget Me) (48261)

MR J. A. OSBORNE—continued

49 Ch c 16/3 Compton Place—Dunloe (IRE) (Shaadi (USA)) (32000)
50 B c 17/3 Desert Sun—Emma Peel (Emarati (USA))
51 B c 28/4 Tillerman—Fey Rouge (IRE) (Fayruz) (33461)
52 B f 17/3 Acclamation—Final Trick (Primo Dominie) (50000)
53 B f 28/3 Monsieur Bond—Fizzy Treat (Efisio) (14000)
54 B f 14/4 Royal Applause—Hiraeth (Petong) (23000)
55 B f 30/3 Royal Applause—Jezyah (USA) (Chief's Crown (USA)) (13513)
56 B c 14/4 Bahamian Bounty—Joonayh (Warning) (36000)
57 Ch f 17/1 Indian Ridge—Kathy College (IRE) (College Chapel) (40000)
58 B c 25/3 Elusive City (USA)—King of All (IRE) (King of Clubs) (26382)
59 Ch f 19/4 Kyllachy—La Caprice (USA) (Housebuster (USA)) (14000)
60 LIGHTENING LYNDA (USA), b f 13/2 Grand Slam (USA)—Easabeau Fille (USA) (Capote (USA)) (14577)
61 B f 19/1 Pivotal—Magic Cove (Kingmambo (USA)) (90000)
62 B c 6/2 Tagula—Marliana (IRE) (Mtoto) (27000)
63 Ch f 2/1 Captain Rio—Metisse (IRE) (Indian Ridge) (35392)
64 B c 6/4 Noverre (USA)—Monarchy (IRE) (Common Grounds) (52000)
65 B f 2/3 Monsieur Bond (IRE)—My Poppet (Midyan (USA)) (4000)
66 Br c 21/4 Lend A Hand—Peruvian Jade (Petong) (18000)
67 B f 8/3 Tagula (IRE)—Prima Marta (Primo Dominie)
68 B br c 2/4 Danetime (IRE)—Primo Supremo (IRE) (Primo Dominie) (18017)
69 B f 11/3 Redback—Respectful (IRE) (College Chapel) (15000)
70 B f 4/3 Johannesburg (USA)—Settling In (USA) (Green Desert (USA)) (30126)
71 B br c 14/2 More Than Ready (USA)—Short Shadow (USA) (Out of Place (USA)) (25000)
72 B c 5/3 Noverre (USA)—Stately Princess (Robellino) (27000)
73 B gr g 21/3 Kheleyf (USA)—Strelitzia (IRE) (Bluebird (USA)) (3217)
74 B f 2/2 Invincible Spirit (IRE)—Tarbela (IRE) (Grand Lodge (USA)) (68000)
75 B f 8/5 Elnadim (USA)—Vahine (USA) (Alysheba (USA)) (25740)
76 B f 19/2 Redback—Wee Merkin (IRE) (Thatching) (42000)

---

455 **MR JOHN M. OXX, Kildare**
Postal: **Creeve, Curragbeg, Kildare, Ireland.**
Contacts: **PHONE (00353) 4552 1310**

1 ALARAZI (IRE), 4, b c Spectrum (IRE)—Alaya (IRE) **D. Reddan**
2 ARCH SWING (USA), 4, b f Arch (USA)—Gold Pattern (USA) **P. Garvey**
3 DAWN VALENTINO (IRE), 4, b f Inchinor—Keepers Dawn (IRE) **P. McCarthy**
4 ELBASANA (IRE), 4, b f Indian Ridge—Ebaziya (IRE) **H. H. Aga Khan**
5 FLASH MCGAHON (IRE), 4, b g Namid—Astuti (IRE) **Dundalk Racing Club**
6 HASANKA (IRE), 4, b f Kalanisi (IRE)—Hasainiya (IRE) **H. H. Aga Khan**
7 JOSHUA'S PRINCESS, 4, b f Danehill (USA)—Josh's Pearl **Mrs A. Coughlan**
8 MOURILYAN (IRE), 4, b c Desert Prince (IRE)—Mouramara (IRE) **H. H. Aga Khan**

THREE-YEAR-OLDS

9 ADATARA (IRE), b f Celtic Swing—Adalya (IRE) **H. H. Aga Khan**
10 AGE OF CHIVALRY (IRE), b f Invincible Spirit (IRE)—Aravonian **Plantation Stud**
11 ALANDI (IRE), b c Galileo (IRE)—Aliya (IRE) **H. H. Aga Khan**
12 ALANIYA (IRE), b f Alhaarth (IRE)—Alaya (IRE) **H. H. Aga Khan**
13 ARIZONA JOHN (IRE), b c Rahy (USA)—Preseli (IRE) **N. Jones**
14 AT ALL, ch c Dalakhani (IRE)—Ballymore Celebre (IRE) **Mr H. Q. Spooner**
15 BAKULA (IRE), b f Fasliyev (USA)—Winona (IRE) **Lady Clague**
16 BE SMART (IRE), b f Statue of Liberty (USA)—Alaynia (IRE) **D. Reddan**
17 CARBONIA (IRE), ch f Alhaarth (IRE)—Piacenza (IRE) **G. A. Oldham**
18 DABASARI (IRE), b c Rainbow Quest (USA)—Dabousiya (IRE) **H. H. Aga Khan**
19 DABISTA (IRE), gr f Highest Honor (FR)—Dabaya (IRE) **H. H. Aga Khan**
20 DAHINDAR (IRE), b c Invincible Spirit (IRE)—Daftara (IRE) **H. H. Aga Khan**
21 DAWAL (IRE), ch c Polish Precedent (USA)—Dawana (IRE) **H. H. Aga Khan**
22 DUNVEGAN (IRE), ch c Galileo (IRE)—Blueberry (USA) **T. Barr**
23 EBADIYAN (IRE), gr ch c Daylami (IRE)—Ebatana (IRE) **H. H. Aga Khan**
24 EBALISTA (IRE), ch f Selkirk (USA)—Ebadiyla (IRE) **H. H. Aga Khan**
25 ELOUANA (IRE), b f Kalanisi (IRE)—Edabiya (IRE) **H. H. Aga Khan**
26 ERZEN (IRE), b c Daylami (IRE)—Ebaziya (IRE) **H. H. Aga Khan**
27 GALIYAN, b c Dalakhani (IRE)—Gold Field (IRE) **H. H. Aga Khan**
28 HADARAMA (IRE), ch f Sinndar (IRE)—Handaza (IRE) **H. H. Aga Khan**
29 HANOVERIAN BARON, b c Green Desert (USA)—Josh's Pearl (IRE) **Mrs A. M. Coughlan**

MR JOHN M. OXX—continued

30 **KALIDAHA (IRE)**, ch f Cadeaux Genereux—Kalimanta (IRE) **H. H. Aga Khan**
31 **KARGALI (IRE)**, gr c Invincible Spirit (IRE)—Karliyka (IRE) **H. H. Aga Khan**
32 **KATIYRA (IRE)**, b f Peintre Celebre (USA)—Katiykha (IRE) **H. H. Aga Khan**
33 **KERIYKA (IRE)**, b f Indian Ridge—Kermiyana (IRE) **H. H. Aga Khan**
34 **KHARSYA (IRE)**, b f Kahyasi—Kharsaka (IRE) **H. H. Aga Khan**
35 **KILSHANNIG (IRE)**, ch c Galileo (IRE)—Surf The Web (IRE) **P. Sugrue**
36 **LADY OF SUBSTANCE (IRE)**, b f Sadler's Wells (USA)—Hill of Snow **N. Jones**
37 **LIDANA (IRE)**, b f King's Best (USA)—Lidakiya (IRE) **H. H. Aga Khan**
38 **LISANI (IRE)**, ch c Dalakhani (IRE)—Littlefeather (IRE) **H. H. Aga Khan**
39 **MASIYMA (IRE)**, ch f Dalakhani (IRE)—Masilia (IRE) **H. H. Aga Khan**
40 **MONTELAGO (IRE)**, b c High Chaparral (IRE)—Miss a Note (USA) **P. Sugrue**
41 **ODIN'S RAVEN (IRE)**, ch c Dalakhani (IRE)—Oriane **Lady Clague**
42 **PAREESA (IRE)**, gr f Dalakhani (IRE)—Persian Lass (IRE) **H. H. Aga Khan**
43 **POINTED ARCH (IRE)**, ch f Rock of Gibraltar (IRE)—Gothic Dream (IRE) **Lady Clague**
44 **RAYDIYA (IRE)**, b f Marju (IRE)—Raydaniya (IRE) **H. H. Aga Khan**
45 **RAYINA (IRE)**, b f Sinndar (IRE)—Rayyana (IRE) **H. H. Aga Khan**
46 **RED EYE EXPRESS (IRE)**, b c Giant's Causeway (USA)—Snowfire **N. Jones**
47 **RIDAWANA (IRE)**, gr f Daylami (IRE)—Ridakiya (IRE) **H. H. Aga Khan**
48 **SEA'S LEGACY (IRE)**, b c Green Desert (USA)—Urban Sea (USA) **C. Tsui**
49 **SHAMIRAN (IRE)**, b c Polish Precedent (USA)—Sharemata (IRE) **H. H. Aga Khan**
50 **SHARLEEZ (IRE)**, b f Marju (IRE)—Sharesha (IRE) **H. H. Aga Khan**
51 **SHARP DROP (USA)**, b f Stormin Fever (USA)—Precipice (USA) **R. S. Evans**
52 **SHAUNA'S PRINCESS (IRE)**, b f Soviet Star (USA)—Azyaa **D. Gardiner**
53 **SIGNORA FRASI (IRE)**, b f Indian Ridge—Sheba (IRE) **E. Keena**
54 **SIMAWA (IRE)**, b f Anabaa (USA)—Sinntara (IRE) **H. H. Aga Khan**
55 **SOUL MURMUR (IRE)**, br c Indian Ridge—My Potters (USA) **Lady Clague**
56 **SYDNEY SLING (IRE)**, b c Xaar—Cherry Hills **C. Jones**
57 **TARALGA (IRE)**, b f Sinndar (IRE)—Tarabaya (IRE) **H. H. Aga Khan**
58 **TARKARI (IRE)**, ch g Fantastic Light (USA)—Taraza (IRE) **H. H. Aga Khan**
59 **TARVINI (IRE)**, b c Kalanisi (IRE)—Tarwila (IRE) **H. H. Aga Khan**
60 **THOROUGHLY RED (IRE)**, b c King's Best (USA)—Red Liason (IRE) **Lady Clague**
61 **TILABAY (IRE)**, b c Sadler's Wells (USA)—Tilimsana (IRE) **H. H. Aga Khan**
62 **TIMARI (IRE)**, gr c Dalakhani (IRE)—Timarida (IRE) **H. H. Aga Khan**
63 **ZAFAYRA (IRE)**, b f Nayef (USA)—Zafayana (IRE) **H. H. Aga Khan**
64 **ZAMIYLA (IRE)**, gr f Daylami (USA)—Zanara (IRE) **H. H. Aga Khan**
65 **ZARIZIYNA (IRE)**, b f Dalakhani (IRE)—Zarabaya (IRE) **H. H. Aga Khan**
66 **ZAZIYRA (IRE)**, gr f Dalakhani (IRE)—Zafzala (IRE) **H. H. Aga Khan**

TWO-YEAR-OLDS

67 **A GIRL (IRE)**, b f 28/4 Sadler's Wells (USA)—Preseli (IRE) (Caerleon (USA)) **N. Jones**
68 **ADAIYRA (IRE)**, b f 15/2 Sinndar (IRE)—Adirika (IRE) (Miswaki (USA)) **H. H. Aga Khan**
69 **ADJALIYA (IRE)**, b f 14/4 Sinndar (IRE)—Adalya (IRE) (Darshaan) **H. H. Aga Khan**
70 **ALAIYMA (IRE)**, b f 23/3 Refuse To Bend (IRE)—Alasana (IRE) (Darshaan) **H. H. Aga Khan**
71 B c 7/3 Alhaarth (IRE)—Alasha (IRE) (Barathea (IRE)) **H. H. Aga Khan**
72 B c 24/3 Kalanisi (IRE)—Alaya (IRE) (Ela-Mana-Mou) **H. H. Aga Khan**
73 **ALIYFA (IRE)**, b f 12/4 Spinning World (USA)—Aliya (IRE) (Darshaan) **H. H. Aga Khan**
74 B f 26/2 Theatrical—Amanda Louise (IRE) (Perugino (USA)) (32174) **H. O'Neill**
75 **ANAK (IRE)**, b c 30/3 Sinndar (IRE)—Akdara (IRE) (Sadler's Wells (USA)) **H. H. Aga Khan**
76 B c 29/1 Anabaa (USA)—Asmara (USA) (Lear Fan (USA)) **H. H. Aga Khan**
77 B f 22/1 Dalakhani (IRE)—Balanka (IRE) (Alzao (USA)) **H. H. Aga Khan**
78 B f 22/3 Sadler's Wells (USA)—Ball Chairman (USA) (Secretariat (USA)) **C. Fipke**
79 **BEAUTY O' GWAUN (IRE)**, b f 2/5 Rainbow Quest (USA)—
    Angel of The Gwaun (IRE) (Sadler's Wells (USA)) **N. Jones**
80 B c 10/2 Kalanisi (IRE)—Behra (IRE) (Grand Lodge (USA)) **H. H. Aga Khan**
81 **BIG GAME HUNTER (IRE)**, b c 24/4 Sadler's Wells (USA)—Hill of Snow (Reference Point) **Mr L. N. Jones**
82 B f 5/5 Oasis Dream—Catch The Blues (IRE) (Bluebird (USA)) **Mrs H. Keaveney**
83 B f 17/3 Daylami (USA)—Dabaya (IRE) (In The Wings) **H. H. Aga Khan**
84 Br gr f 10/2 Daylami (IRE)—Dabousiya (IRE) (Barathea (IRE)) **H. H. Aga Khan**
85 **DANCE OF THE MAMBO (USA)**, b f 2/2 Kingmambo (USA)—Ballerina (IRE) (Dancing Brave (USA)) **N. Jones**
86 B f 14/4 Selkirk (USA)—Dawnsio (IRE) (Tate Gallery (USA)) **Lady Clague**
87 B c 9/4 King's Best (USA)—Ebadiyla (IRE) (Sadler's Wells (USA)) **H. H. Aga Khan**
88 B f 4/2 Kalanisi (IRE)—Ebatana (IRE) (Rainbow Quest (USA)) **H. H. Aga Khan**
89 Ch f 19/4 Dubai Destination (USA)—Ebaziya (IRE) (Darshaan) **H. H. Aga Khan**
90 Ch c 13/5 Peintre Celebre (USA)—Edabiya (IRE) (Rainbow Quest (USA)) **H. H. Aga Khan**
91 **ERDIYNA (IRE)**, b f 27/2 Selkirk (USA)—Ebareva (IRE) (Machiavellian (USA)) **H. H. Aga Khan**

MR JOHN M. OXX—continued

92 B c 20/1 Sinndar (IRE)—Haratila (IRE) (Marju (IRE)) **H. H. Aga Khan**
93 B f 22/3 Sadler's Wells (USA)—Ibtikar (USA) (Private Account (USA)) (138483) **P. McCarthy**
94 B f 19/4 Montjeu (IRE)—Ingozi (Warning) (60000) **Mrs C. McStay**
95 B c 31/3 Dalakhani (IRE)—Josh's Pearl (IRE) (Sadler's Wells (USA)) **Mrs A. M. Coughlan**
96 B f 8/5 Selkirk (USA)—Kalamba (IRE) (Green Dancer (USA)) **H. H. Aga Khan**
97 B c 11/3 Traditionally (USA)—Karkiyla (IRE) (Darshaan) **H. H. Aga Khan**
98 **KASTALANA (IRE)**, b f 10/5 Key of Luck (USA)—Kassana (IRE) (Shernazar) **H. H. Aga Khan**
99 B c 3/3 Peintre Celebre (USA)—Key Change (IRE) (Darshaan) **Lady Clague**
100 **MARIYCA (IRE)**, gr f 2/2 Daylami (IRE)—Masakala (IRE) (Cadeaux Genereux) **H. H. Aga Khan**
101 B c 22/3 Alhaarth (IRE)—Mouramara (USA) (Kahyasi) **H. H. Aga Khan**
102 B f 19/3 Arch (USA)—Move (USA) (Forty Niner (USA)) **P. Garvey**
103 **QUIET LANE**, ch f 23/2 Cadeaux Genereux—Blue Sirocco (Bluebird (USA)) **H. Spooner**
104 Ch c 2/4 Indian Ridge—Rayyana (IRE) (Rainbow Quest (USA)) **H. H. Aga Khan**
105 B f 2/3 Danetime (IRE)—Rose Vibert (Caerleon (USA)) (31000) **Byerley Racing Limited**
106 **ROSES FOR THE LADY (IRE)**, br f 19/2 Sadler's Wells (USA)—
                   Head In The Clouds (IRE) (Rainbow Quest (USA)) **N. Jones**
107 B c 7/3 Hawk Wing (USA)—Roystonea (Polish Precedent (USA)) (19304) **D. Reddan**
108 Br c 22/5 Dansili—Sahara Slew (USA) (Seattle Slew (USA)) **Lady C. J. O'Reilly**
109 B f 23/2 Speightstown (USA)—Sapphire n' Silk (USA) (Pleasant Tap (USA)) (174927) **T. Jones**
110 **SEA THE STARS (IRE)**, b c 6/4 Cape Cross (IRE)—Urban Sea (USA) (Miswaki (USA)) **C. Tsui**
111 B c 23/2 Kahyasi—Sharesha (IRE) (Ashkalani (IRE)) **H. H. Aga Khan**
112 B f 1/4 Peintre Celebre (USA)—Sinnariya (IRE) (Persian Bold) **H. H. Aga Khan**
113 B c 17/3 Marju (IRE)—Takaliya (IRE) (Darshaan) **H. H. Aga Khan**
114 **TAKASIMA (IRE)**, b f 19/1 Daylami (IRE)—Takariya (IRE) (Arazi (USA)) **H. H. Aga Khan**
115 **TANOURA (IRE)**, b f 27/3 Dalakhani (IRE)—Takarouna (IRE) (Green Dancer (USA)) **H. H. Aga Khan**
116 C c 25/1 Selkirk (USA)—Tarakala (IRE) (Dr Fong (USA)) **H. H. Aga Khan**
117 B f 3/4 Red Ransom (USA)—Taraza (IRE) (Darshaan) **H. H. Aga Khan**
118 B f 2/4 Fantastic Light (USA)—Tillmsana (IRE) (Darshaan) **H. H. Aga Khan**
119 B gr f 1/5 Linamix (FR)—Timarida (IRE) (Kalaglow) **H. H. Aga Khan**
120 B f 3/4 Bachelor Duke (USA)—Truly Generous (IRE) (Generous (IRE)) (82000) **Byerley Racing**
121 **VITRUVIAN MAN**, b c 29/1 Montjeu (IRE)—Portrait of A Lady (IRE) (Peintre Celebre (USA)) **Plantation Stud**
122 B c 23/4 Pivotal—Zafaraniya (IRE) (Doyoun) **H. H. Aga Khan**
123 Ch f 16/2 Danehill Dancer (IRE)—Zarannda (IRE) (Last Tycoon) **H. H. Aga Khan**

Jockey (flat): M. J. Kinane, F. M. Berry. **Apprentice:** J. P. Fahy.

---

456 MR BRYN PALLING, Cowbridge
Postal: **Ty-Wyth-Newydd, Tredodridge, Cowbridge, South Glam**
Contacts: **PHONE (01446) 760122 FAX (01446) 760067 MOBILE (07831) 422492**

1 **ADDIENA**, 4, b f Golan (USA)—Nurse Goodbody (USA) **Mr Wayne Devine**
2 **ALWAYS SPARKLE (CAN)**, 4, ch c Grand Slam (USA)—Dancing All Night (USA) **Mrs A. J. Quinn**
3 **ARTHUR'S EDGE**, 4, b g Diktat—Bright Edge **Mrs A. L. Mason**
4 **AUCTION OASIS**, 4, b f Auction House (USA)—Shining Oasis (IRE) **Mr Bryn Palling**
5 **BIDABLE**, 4, b f Auction House (USA)—Dubitable **Flying Eight Partnership**
6 **CORRIB (IRE)**, 5, b m Lahib (USA)—Montana Miss (IRE) **Derek & Jean Clee**
7 **CYFRWYS (IRE)**, 7, b m Foxhound—Divine Elegance (IRE) **Mr Bryn Palling**
8 **DANIELLE'S LAD**, 12, b g Emarati (USA)—Cactus Road (FR) **Mr Bryn Palling**
9 **INDIAN EDGE**, 7, ch g Indian Rocket—Beveled Edge **Nigel Thomas & Christopher Mason**
10 **INKA DANCER (IRE)**, 6, ch m Intikhab—Grannys Reluctance (IRE) **Mrs A. J. Quinn**
11 **MIGHTY MOVER (IRE)**, 6, ch g Bahhare (USA)—Ericeira (IRE) **Bryn Palling**
12 **MY MICHELLE**, 7, b m Ali-Royal (IRE)—April Magic **Flying Eight Partnership**
13 **PELHAM CRESCENT (IRE)**, 5, ch g Giant's Causeway (USA)—Sweet Times **Flying Eight Partnership**
14 **SNAKE HIPS**, 4, b g Golden Snake (USA)—Royal Loft **Flying Eight Partnership**
15 **SOFIA ROYALE**, 4, b f Royal Applause—Once In My Life (IRE) **Mr W. M. Brackstone**
16 5, B g King Charlemagne—Tinsel **Mr D. H. Jones**

THREE-YEAR-OLDS

17 **BALAIS FOLLY (FR)**, ch g Act One—Bhima **Los Cabelleros**
18 **CASLA BEAG (IRE)**, b f Acclamation—Carna (IRE) **Mrs A. J. Quinn**
19 **EDGE OF GOLD**, ch f Choisir (AUS)—Beveled Edge **C. J. Mason**
20 **EDGE OF LIGHT**, b f Xaar—Bright Edge **Nigel Thomas & Christopher Mason**
21 **FOLLOW YOUR SPIRIT**, b g Compton Place—Ymlaen (IRE) **Derek & Jean Clee**
22 B f Lend A Hand—Mystic Oak (IRE) **Mr Bryn Palling**

MR BRYN PALLING—continued

TWO-YEAR-OLDS

23 B f 24/4 Auction House (USA)—Away Win (Common Grounds) **Mr Bryn Palling**
24 B f 17/5 Exceed And Excel (AUS)—Beveled Edge (Beveled (USA)) **Mr C. J. Mason**
25 B f 12/4 Spartacus (IRE)—Carna (IRE) (Anita's Prince) (6112) **Mr Bryn Palling**
26 Ch f 24/2 Auction House (USA)—Cashiki (IRE) (Case Law) **N. Thomas**
27 B f 8/4 Tillerman—Ervedya (IRE) (Doyoun) (3667) **Mr Bryn Palling**
28 Ch c 14/5 Hawk Wing (USA)—Grannys Reluctance (IRE) (Anita's Prince) (18017) **Mrs Anita Quinn**
29 Ch c 22/4 Rainbow Quest (USA)—Londonerdotcom (IRE) (Night Shift (USA)) (20000) **Derek & Jean Clee**
30 B c 24/3 Reset (AUS)—Miss Brooks (Bishop of Cashel) **Partnership**
31 B f 29/4 Tillerman—Phintia (IRE) (Tagula (IRE)) **Mr Bryn Palling**
32 B f 20/1 Desert Prince (IRE)—Royal Rival (IRE) (Marju (IRE)) **Partnership**
33 B f 14/3 Auction House (USA)—Sontime (Son Pardo) **Mr Bryn Palling**
34 B f 26/4 Daggers Drawn (USA)—Winged Victory (IRE) (Dancing Brave (USA)) (3539) **Mr W. M. Brackstone**
35 B f 4/2 One Cool Cat (USA)—Ymlaen (IRE) (Desert Prince (IRE)) (15000) **Derek & Jean Clee**

Other Owners: Mr D. Baker, Mr Wayne Brackstone, Mr Derek D. Clee, Mrs Jean P. Clee, Exors of the Late Mrs N. J. Funnell, Mr Martyn Lloyd, Mr Christopher J. Mason, Mr S. C. Moore, Mr Peter Morgan, Mrs Michelle Morgan, Mr K. A. Morris, Mr Larry Newton, Mr Bryn Palling, Mr B. Reynolds, Mr K. M. Rideout, Mr P. A. Rowley, Mr S. E. Salimeni, Mr Derek Thorne, Mr M. Unsworth, Mr Paul A. Young.

Assistant Trainer: Miss Jennifer Thomas

Amateur: Mrs Janet M. Berry.

---

457 MR J. F. PANVERT, Tiverton
Postal: **Steart Farm Racing Stables, Stoodleigh, Tiverton, Devon, EX16 9QA**
Contacts: **MOBILE (07764) 579175/(07732) 273837**
E-MAIL willowtreeracingstables@tesco.net

1 ACCORDING TO PLAN (IRE), 8, br g Accordion—Clonaheen Joy (IRE) **G. P. Brown**
2 ALEEMDAR (IRE), 11, b g Doyoun—Aleema (IRE) **G. P. Brown**
3 COMMANCHE GENERAL (IRE), 11, b g Commanche Run—Shannon Amber (IRE) **J. F. Panvert**
4 GALANT EYE (IRE), 9, ch g Eagle Eyed (USA)—Galandria **R. C. Palmer**
5 MIDNIGHT MARINE, 7, b g Midnight Legend—The Bizzo **J. F. Panvert**
6 NODDIES WAY, 5, b g Nomadic Way (USA)—Sharway Lady **W. Cox**
7 OLD TIME DANCING, 5, b m Danehill Dancer (IRE)—Rare Old Times (IRE) **G. P. Brown**
8 4, B f Nomadic Way (USA)—Sharway Lady **W. Cox**
9 WUN CHAI (IRE), 9, b g King's Theatre (IRE)—Flower From Heaven **G. P. Brown**

THREE-YEAR-OLDS

10 B f Exit To Nowhere (USA)—Sovereign **J. F. Panvert**

Assistant Trainer: Miss J Clark

Jockey (flat): J. Crowley. **Jockey (NH):** P. J. Brennan. **Conditional:** D. Jacob. **Apprentice:** L. Morris, L. Jones.

---

458 MR ANDREW PARKER, Lockerbie
Postal: **The Orchard, Ecclefechan, Lockerbie, Dumfriesshire, DG11 3JH**
Contacts: **PHONE (01576) 300238 FAX (01576) 300238 MOBILE (07968) 325650**
E-MAIL parker-racing@fsmail.net WEBSITE www.racingpeople.com

1 AIRFORCE, 6, b g Cloudings (IRE)—Preacher's Gem **D. Mossop**
2 CHERRY TOT, 7, ch g Karinga Bay—Cherry Lane **Distillery Racing Club**
3 DAUNTSEY BAY, 7, b g Primitive Rising (USA)—Penny Falls **M. C. MacKenzie**
4 EM'S ROYALTY, 11, b g Royal Fountain—Gaelic Empress **J. J. Paterson**
5 HARLOV (FR), 13, ch g Garde Royale—Paulownia (FR) **Mr & Mrs Raymond Anderson Green**
6 MARKSMORE, 5, b g Shahrastani (USA)—Admire-A-More
7 MERIGO (FR), 7, ch g Pistolet Bleu (IRE)—Muleta (FR) **Mr & Mrs Raymond Anderson Green**
8 NOMORE CLOUDYDAYS (IRE), 5, ch m Ridgewood Ben—Forever Silver (IRE) **Mrs W. Wright**
9 SILVER BREESE, 6, gr g Silver Patriarch (IRE)—Rymolbreese **Distillery Racing Club**
10 STING (GER), 6, b g Turtle Island (IRE)—Simply Red (GER) **Mr & Mrs Raymond Anderson Green**

MR ANDREW PARKER—continued

11 **THE LAST VIKING**, 8, b g Supreme Leader—Viking Rocket **Mr & Mrs Raymond Anderson Green**
12 **WINDYGATE (IRE)**, 8, b br g Supreme Leader—Moscow Maid (IRE) **A P & We Know It**

Other Owners: E. Graham, R. A. Green, Mrs A. Green, Mr L. McNulty, Mr M. J. McNulty, Andrew Parker, R. Robinson.

Assistant Trainer: Miss Gillian Kerr

---

459 **MR J. R. PAYNE, Dulverton**
Postal: **Lower Holworthy Farm, Brompton Regis, Dulverton, Somerset, TA22 9NY**
Contacts: **HOME/FAX (01398) 371244**
E-MAIL **holworthyfarm@aol.co.uk WEBSITE** www.holworthyfarm.com

1 **DOWN THE STRETCH**, 8, b g Rakaposhi King—Si-Gaoith **J. R. Payne**
2 **KNAPP BRIDGE BOY**, 8, b g Wimbleball—Toll Bridge **R. J. Payne**
3 **SKIPPERHAM WELL**, 6, b m Wimbleball—Spirit Level **R. J. Payne**

---

460 **MR P. S. PAYNE, Pyle**
Postal: **Oakfield House, Pen Y Bryn, Pyle, Mid-Glamorgan, CF33 6RA**
Contacts: **PHONE (01656) 740652 MOBILE (07775) 591094**

1 **ARIODANTE**, 6, b g Groom Dancer (USA)—Maestrale **D. A. Rosenbaum**
2 **OAKFIELD LEGEND**, 7, b g Midnight Legend—Kins Token **P. S. Payne**
3 **THE WHISPERING OAK (IRE)**, 6, gr m Silver Patriarch (IRE)—Celtic Remorse **Mrs P. Davies**

---

461 **MR R. E. PEACOCK, Tenbury Wells**
Postal: **Elliott House Farm, Vine Lane, Kyre, Tenbury Wells, Worcestershire, WR15 8RL**
Contacts: **PHONE (01885) 410772 MOBILE (07748) 565574/(07881) 440135**

1 **CANDY ANCHOR (FR)**, 9, b m Slip Anchor—Kandavu **R. E. Peacock**
2 **KOMREYEV STAR**, 6, b g Komaite (USA)—L'ancressaan **Mrs G. Whittaker**
3 **LITTLE GIRL**, 10, b m Homo Sapien—Dancing Returns **E. Turner**
4 **WHITE LEDGER (IRE)**, 9, ch g Ali-Royal (IRE)—Boranwood (IRE) **R. E. Peacock**

Assistant Trainer: Mrs C Peacock

Jockey (flat): S. Sanders. **Jockey (NH):** T. Siddall, Christian Williams. **Amateur:** Miss S. Peacock.

---

462 **MR J. PEARCE, Newmarket**
Postal: **Wroughton House, 37 Old Station Road, Newmarket, Suffolk, CB8 8DT**
Contacts: **PHONE (01638) 664669 FAX (01638) 669891 MOBILE (07876) 444456/(07787) 517876**

1 **AGILETE**, 6, b g Piccolo—Ingerence (FR) **Mr J. Pearce**
2 **BID FOR FAME (USA)**, 11, b br g Quest For Fame—Shroud (USA) **Mr J. Pearce**
3 **BORDER ARTIST**, 9, ch g Selkirk (USA)—Aunt Tate **B & G Racing & Friends**
4 **CHEVELEY FLYER**, 5, ch g Forzando—Cavern Breeze **The Cheveley Red Lion Partnership**
5 **CUMAE (USA)**, 4, b f King Cugat (USA)—Jubilee Walk **S. Birdseye**
6 **DAYIA (IRE)**, 4, br f Act One—Masharik (IRE) **Lady Green**
7 **EMILY'S PLACE (IRE)**, 5, b m Mujadil (USA)—Dulcinea **Macniler Racing Partnership**
8 **FANTASY RIDE**, 6, b g Bahhare (USA)—Grand Splendour **M. M. Foulger, A. Puddick, J. Pearce**
9 **FELIX REX (GER)**, 8, ch g Tempeltanz (GER)—Figlia D'oro (GER) **M. L. Wakefield**
10 **FORMIDABLE GUEST**, 4, b f Dilshaan—Fizzy Treat **Macniler Racing Partnership**
11 **GENEROUS STAR**, 5, ch g Generous (IRE)—Elegant Dance **Mrs E. C. Sheehan**
12 **GRANARY GIRL**, 6, b m Kingsinger (IRE)—Highland Blue **Mrs P. O'Shea, Mr N. Pally**
13 **HITS ONLY CASH**, 6, b g Inchinor—Persian Blue **Oceana Racing**
14 **KHANJAR (USA)**, 8, ch g Kris S (USA)—Alyssum (USA) **Mr P. J. Stephenson**
15 **MAGICAL MUSIC**, 5, b m Fraam—Magical Flute **Killarney Glen & Mrs E. M. Clarke**
16 **QUINCE (IRE)**, 5, b g Fruits of Love (USA)—Where's Charlotte **D. Leech**
17 **SOL ROJO**, 6, b g Efisio—Shining Cloud **Mrs J. R. Marsh**
18 **TEASING**, 4, b f Lujain (USA)—Movieland (USA) **D. Leech**
19 **TOP SPEC (IRE)**, 7, b g Spectrum (IRE)—Pearl Marine (IRE) **Mrs M. Renee**
20 **ZALKANI (IRE)**, 8, ch g Cadeaux Genereux—Zallaka (IRE) **Mrs J. R. Marsh, C. Whiting, J. Pearce**

MR J. PEARCE—continued

THREE-YEAR-OLDS

21 DAZZLING BEGUM, br f Okawango (USA)—Dream On Me **S. Birdseye**
22 HITS ONLY TIME, ch c Bertolini (USA)—South Wind **C. A. F. Whiting, M. L. Wakefield, R. Casey**
23 KLARITY, b f Acclamation—Clarice Orsini **Jay Three Racing**
24 LADY LONGCROFT, ch f Tobougg (IRE)—Top of The Morning **J. R. Furlong**
25 SPACE PIRATE, b c Bahamian Bounty—Science Fiction **Oceana Racing**
26 VISCONTE (GER), b c Law Society (USA)—Vicenca (USA) **J. R. Furlong**

TWO-YEAR-OLDS

27 B f 8/2 Green Tune (USA)—Follow The Girl (FR) (Saumarez) **J. R. Furlong**
28 Gr c 12/3 Bertolini (USA)—Incatinka (Inca Chief (USA)) (2500)
29 Ch c 23/4 Kris Kin (USA)—Lokapala (GER) (Alwuhush (USA))
30 B f 26/1 Ishiguru (USA)—Notable Lady (IRE) (Victory Note (USA)) (10000) **Killarney Glen & Mrs E. M. Clarke**
31 SIR CLAD, b c 7/3 Fantastic Light (USA)—Katina (USA) (Danzig (USA)) (33000) **Mrs M. Baxter & Mr H. Bunn**
32 B f 7/5 Desert Sun—Top of The Morning (Keen) **J. R. Furlong**

Other Owners: Mr Stuart Andrews, Mr Alexander Baker, Mr R. Casey, Mrs E. M. Clarke, Mr K. P. D. Cooper, Mr E. Dawson, T. E. Edge, Mr N. M. Hanger, Mr John Harrison, Mr M. A. Nayampally, Mrs Lydia Pearce, Mr Jeff Pearce, Mrs M. Rennie, Mr R. G. Thurston, Mr M. Wakefield, Mr A. Watford, Mr Clive Whiting, Mr S. D. York.

Assistant Trainer: Mrs Lydia Pearce

Jockey (flat): J. Quinn. Conditional: Matty Roe. Apprentice: Josephine Bruning. Amateur: Mr Simon Pearce

---

463 MR O. J. PEARS, Malton
Postal: **The Office, Old Farmhouse, Beverley Road, Norton, Malton, North Yorkshire, YO17 9PJ**
Contacts: **PHONE (01653) 696452 FAX (01653) 696452 MOBILE (07760) 197103**
E-MAIL olliepears@hotmail.co.uk

1 CALOW GREEN (IRE), 6, b br m Lord Americo—Wake Me Gently (IRE) **Miss S. L. Shaw**
2 ILVIZ (FR), 6, gr g Medaaly—Move The Mouse (IRE) **David Scott & Co (Pattern Makers) Ltd**
3 LOCAL POET, 7, b g Robellino (USA)—Laugharne **K. C. West**
4 NORTHAW LAD (IRE), 10, ch g Executive Perk—Black Tulip **Diamond Racing Ltd**
5 NOTA LIBERATA, 4, b g Spinning World (USA)—Kyda (USA) **O. J. Pears**
6 ONE MORE ROUND (USA), 10, b g Ghazi (USA)—Life of the Party (USA) **Diamond Racing Ltd**
7 ROWAN LODGE (IRE), 6, ch g Indian Lodge (IRE)—Tirol Hope (IRE) **F. K. Baxter**
8 SUALDA (IRE), 9, b g Idris (IRE)—Winning Heart **Diamond Racing Ltd**
9 SUPERJAIN, 4, b f Lujain (USA)—Plie **O. J. Pears**
10 THAT'S RACING, 8, ch g Classic Cliche (IRE)—All On **N. Hetherton**

THREE-YEAR-OLDS

11 COOL FASHION (IRE), b f Orpen (USA)—Fun Fashion (IRE) **21st Century Racing**
12 LU'S HILL, b g Lujain (USA)—Cinder Hills **O. J. Pears**
13 LUJANO, b g Lujain (USA)—Latch Key Lady (USA) **David Scott & Co (Pattern Makers) Ltd**

Other Owners: A. W. Catterall, Mrs B. Catterall.

Jockey (flat): Tom Eaves, Paul Mulrennan. Conditional: Brian Hughes. Amateur: Miss V. Coates.

---

464 MR D. PEARSON, High Peak
Postal: **Lower Fold Farm, Rowarth, High Peak, Derbyshire, SK22 1ED**
Contacts: **PHONE (01663) 741471 MOBILE (07775) 842009**

1 ANSHABIL (IRE), 9, br g Anshan—Billeragh Thyne (IRE) **D. Pearson**
2 DEAR OH DEAR, 7, ch g Alflora (IRE)—Flagg Flyer VII **D. Pearson**
3 HEVER ROAD (IRE), 9, ch g Anshan—The Little Bag **D. Pearson**
4 PER AMORE (IRE), 10, ch g General Monash (USA)—Danny's Miracle **D. Pearson**
5 THE CLIENT (IRE), 7, b g Rakaposhi King—Woodram Delight **D. Pearson**

Assistant Trainer: Eileen Pearson

465 MR M. A. PEILL, Liversedge
Postal: **Parkin Hall Stud, Hartshead Hall Lane, Hartshead, Liversedge, West Yorkshire, WF15 8AZ**
Contacts: **PHONE (01274) 850970 FAX (01274) 850970 MOBILE (07875) 669883**
E-MAIL peillmark@hotmail.com

1 BARNEY KNOWS (IRE), 13, b g In The Wings—Afeefa **C. N. Barnes**
2 BLACK FALCON (IRE), 8, ch g In The Wings—Muwasim (USA) **C. N. Barnes**
3 BREAKING SHADOW (IRE), 6, br g Danehill Dancer (IRE)—Crimbourne **G. Morrill**
4 CLASSY LASSIE (IRE), 8, ch m Goldmark (USA)—Okay Baby (USA) **A. R. Barnes**
5 DR LIGHT (IRE), 4, b g Medicean—Allumette **C. N. Barnes**
6 FIGURATIVE (IRE), 6, b g Machiavellian (USA)—Marble Maiden **A. R. Barnes**
7 KINGS PASS (FR), 4, b g Saint des Saints (FR)—Allee Sarthoise (FR) **Parkin Hall Stud Farm**
8 MILITAMAN (IRE), 6, gr g Rudimentary (USA)—Forest Lady (IRE)
9 MISS MOLLY BE RUDE (IRE), 6, b m Perugino (USA)—Ediyrna (IRE) **Be Rude Not To Syndicate**
10 5, B g Exit To Nowhere (USA)—Mrs Parker (IRE)
11 NOT WELL (IRE), 8, b g Germany (USA)—Bonnie Jean's Girl (USA) **Miss A. Bramall**
12 ORANA CONTI (FR), 6, b m Robin des Champs (FR)—Cadoudaline (FR) **Parkin Hall Stud Farm**
13 OXFORD DE LAGARDE (FR), 6, b g Sleeping Car (FR)—Gamine de Tanues (FR) **C. N. Barnes**
14 PADDY LIVE (FR), 5, b g Brier Creek (USA)—Iona Will (FR) **A. R. Barnes**
15 PALANCIA CONTI (FR), 5, ch m Bulington (FR)—Tatiana Lulu (FR) **Parkin Hall Stud Farm**
16 PALOS CONTI (FR), 5, ch g Robin des Champs (FR)—Dona Mirande (FR) **C. N. Barnes**
17 PAOLO CONTI (FR), 5, ch g Bulington (FR)—Crack'ela (FR) **Parkin Hall Stud Farm**
18 PATCHOULIE CONTI (FR), 5, b m Robin des Champs (FR)—
Lady In Love (FR) **Kathryn Richard M. Walker Carl N. Barnes**
19 QUICK LIVE (FR), 4, gr g Dom Alco (FR)—Iona Will (FR) **Parkin Hall Stud Farm**
20 QUOVER BAY (FR), 4, b f Ultimately Lucky (IRE)—Djeti (FR) **Mr K. J. Hickey**
21 ROBIN DES BANK (FR), 5, b g Robin des Champs (FR)—Millesimee (FR) **Parkin Hall Stud Farm**
22 SIR MARK (IRE), 4, ch g In The Wings—Web of Intrigue **Kathryn Richard M. Walker Carl N. Barnes**
23 THE FABRICATOR (FR), 5, b g Video Rock (FR)—Escopette (FR) **R. Barnes, A. Barnes, C. Barnes**
24 TRIPLE SHADOW, 4, ch g Compton Place—Arctic High **G. Morrill**

THREE-YEAR-OLDS

25 LIGHTING SHADOW, b g Captain Rio—Bonny Ruan **G. Morrill**
26 REEL CLASSY, ch f Reel Buddy (USA)—Classy Lassie (IRE) **A. R. Barnes**

Other Owners: Mr C. N. Barnes, Mr A. Barnes, Mr R. Barnes, Mr K. J. Hickey, Mr K. Tunney, Mr Richard M. Walker, Mrs Kathryn Walker.

466 MISS L. A. PERRATT, Carluke
Postal: **Belstane Racing Stables, Belstane Road, Carluke, Lanarkshire, ML8 5HN**
Contacts: **PHONE (01555) 773335 FAX (01555) 772243 MOBILE (07931) 306147**
E-MAIL linda.perratt@btconnect.com

1 ABBONDANZA (IRE), 5, b g Cape Cross (IRE)—Ninth Wonder (USA) **Joseph Leckie & Sons Ltd**
2 ACROPOLIS (IRE), 7, b g Sadler's Wells (USA)—Dedicated Lady (IRE) **Newkeylets**
3 ALIMACDEE, 4, ch f Compton Place—Howards Heroine (IRE) **G. McDowall**
4 ANCIENT PRIDE, 4, br g Inchinor—Carrie Pooter **Mrs K. Cullen**
5 APPALACHIAN TRAIL (IRE), 7, b g Indian Ridge—Karinski (USA) **G L S Partnership**
6 ART BANK, 5, b g Saddlers' Hall (IRE)—Langton Lass **The Racing Foursome**
7 BIG TIMER (USA), 4, b c Street Cry (IRE)—Moonflute (USA) **G. McDowall**
8 CITY MISS, 5, br m Rock City—Miss Pigalle **The Hon Miss H. Galbraith**
9 COOPERSTOWN, 5, ch g Dr Fong (USA)—Heckle **G. McDowall**
10 CURTAIL (IRE), 5, b g Namid—Nipitinthebud (USA) **G. McDowall**
11 DEFI (IRE), 6, b g Rainbow Quest (USA)—Danse Classique (IRE) **G. McDowall**
12 DISTANT SUN (IRE), 4, b g Distant View (USA)—The Great Flora (USA) **G. McDowall**
13 EASIBET DOT NET, 8, gr g Atraf—Silvery **Raeburn Brick Limited**
14 EMERALD BAY (IRE), 6, b g King's Best (USA)—Belle Etoile (IRE) **C. Boon**
15 FIRST ORDER, 7, b g Primo Dominie—Unconditional Love (IRE) **G. McDowall**
16 FORREST FLYER (IRE), 4, b c Daylami (IRE)—Gerante (USA) **Mrs V. C. Macdonald**
17 GREY OUTLOOK, 5, ch m Observatory (USA)—Grey Galava **J. K. McGarrity**
18 HOWARDS TIPPLE, 4, b g Diktat—Grey Princess (IRE) **G. McDowall**
19 JAMIESON GOLD (IRE), 5, b g Desert Style (IRE)—Princess of Zurich (IRE) **P. Tsim**
20 JEWELLED DAGGER (IRE), 4, b g Daggers Drawn (USA)—Cappadoce (IRE) **A. R. M. Galbraith**
21 KAMES PARK (IRE), 6, b g Desert Sun—Persian Sally (IRE) **Mrs J. Delaney**
22 MANDARIN ROCKET (IRE), 5, ch g Titus Livius (FR)—Two Thousand (IRE) **Mrs Francesca Mitchell**

MISS L. A. PERRATT—continued

23 **MARY FROM MARYHILL (IRE)**, 4, b f Fath (USA)—Kentucky Wildcat **Partick Thistle Racing Club**
24 **MAYADEEN (IRE)**, 6, b g King's Best (USA)—Inaaq **Cheesie & The Quiet Men**
25 **MINERAL RIGHTS (USA)**, 4, ch g Gulch (USA)—Long Vacation (IRE) **Belstane Park Racing**
26 **MYSTICAL AYR (IRE)**, 6, br m Namid—Scanno's Choice (IRE) **Ayrshire Racing**
27 **NEIL'S LEGACY (IRE)**, 6, br m Second Empire (IRE)—Eliade (IRE) **J. K. McGarrity**
28 **NELSON VETTORI**, 4, ch c Vettori (IRE)—Eskimo Nel (IRE) **First Chance Racing**
29 **NERO WEST (FR)**, 7, ch g Pelder (IRE)—West River (USA) **Mr & Mrs Charles Villiers**
30 **OBE BRAVE**, 5, b g Agnes World (USA)—Pass The Rose (IRE) **Mrs J. Penman**
31 **OEUF A LA NEIGE**, 8, b g Danehill (USA)—Reine de Neige **P. Tsim**
32 **OPAL NOIR**, 4, b g Lujain (USA)—Wrong Bride **R. C. Hyndman**
33 **OPTICAL ILLUSION (USA)**, 4, b g Theatrical—Paradise River (USA) **Mr J. Gaffney**
34 **PRIMO WAY**, 7, b g Primo Dominie—Waypoint **G. McDowall**
35 **ROYAL AMNESTY**, 5, br g Desert Prince (IRE)—Regal Peace **Mrs Francesca Mitchell**
36 **SARRAAF (IRE)**, 12, ch g Perugino (USA)—Blue Vista (IRE) **G. McDowall**
37 **SEAFIELD TOWERS**, 8, ch g Compton Place—Midnight Spell **Mr Ken McGarrity & Mr Tim Finch**
38 **SIMBA'S PRIDE**, 4, b g Dansili—Welcome Aboard **Mrs K. Cullen**
39 **SUNRISE SAFARI (IRE)**, 5, b g Mozart (IRE)—Lady Scarlett **Mrs J. Penman**
40 **THE SALWICK FLYER (IRE)**, 5, b g Tagula (IRE)—Shimla (IRE) **The Irish Mafia**
41 **TOMMY TOBOUGG**, 4, ch g Tobougg (IRE)—Celebrate (IRE) **Semple Racing**
42 **WRIT (IRE)**, 6, ch g Indian Lodge (IRE)—Carnelly (IRE) **C. Boon**
43 **ZEITGEIST (IRE)**, 7, b g Singspiel (IRE)—Diamond Quest **R. C. Hyndman**

THREE-YEAR-OLDS

44 **CIRCUS CLOWN (IRE)**, b c Vettori (IRE)—Comic (IRE) **D. L. McKenzie**
45 **DOON HAYMER (IRE)**, b c Barathea (IRE)—Mutige **G. McDowall**
46 **FORREST STAR**, ch f Fraam—Starfleet **Miss L. A. Perratt**
47 **HOWARDS HOPE**, ch g Kyllachy—Howards Heroine (IRE) **G. McDowall**
48 **HOWARDS WAY**, b g Bertolini (USA)—Love Quest **G. McDowall**
49 Ch c Fleetwood (IRE)—Kiveton Komet **T. P. Finch**
50 **MUFASA**, ch c Cayman Kai (USA)—Petticoat Rule **R. M. Mitchell**
51 **PARISIENNE GEM**, b f Kris (USA)—Miss Pigalle **The Hon Miss H. Galbraith**
52 **PRINCE RHYDDARCH**, b c Josr Algarhoud (IRE)—Nova Zembla **Mr & Mrs Charles Villiers**
53 **THUNDER BAY**, b g Hunting Lion (IRE)—Floral Spark **Mrs J. Penman**

TWO-YEAR-OLDS

54 Ch c 4/4 Bertolini (USA)—Rose of America (Brief Truce (USA)) (20000) **Miss L. A. Perratt**

Other Owners: Mr G. A. Bannerman, W. Brand, I. Burns, P.J. Burns, I. Crawford, J. G. H. Fenton, J. D. Groves, T. Hughes, Mr J. Jenkins, Mr J. King, Mr G. R. Leckie, D. McIntyre, Mr J. Nimmo, D. G. Savala, I. Semple, Mrs S. Sherriff, Mr D. T. Spratt, J. S. Sterry, C. Villiers, Mrs E. M. J. Villiers, Mr A. Wilson.

Assistant Trainer: Mr Ian Semple

Jockey (flat): R. Winston, Nicky Mackay, R. Ffrench, Phillip Makin, T. Eaves, M. J. Kinane. **Jockey (NH):** A. Dobbin, G. Lee.

---

467 **MRS A. J. PERRETT, Pulborough**
Postal: **Coombelands Racing Stables, Pulborough, West Sussex, RH20 1BP**
Contacts: **OFFICE** (01798) 873011 **HOME** (01798) 874894 **FAX** (01798) 875163
MOBILE (07803) 088713 **WEBSITE** www.amandaperrett.com

1 **ALFIE NOAKES**, 6, b g Groom Dancer (USA)—Crimson Rosella **G. C. Stevens**
2 **BANDAMA (IRE)**, 5, b h Green Desert (USA)—Orinoco (USA) **Mrs S. L. Whitehead**
3 **CAMPS BAY (USA)**, 4, b c Cozzene (USA)—Seewillo (USA) **Mr & Mrs R. Scott**
4 **CHOCOLATE CARAMEL**, 6, b g Storm Creek (USA)—Sandhill (BRZ) **Mrs P. S. Graham**
5 **JOHN TERRY**, 5, b g Grand Lodge (USA)—Kardashina (FR) **A. D. Spence**
6 **NIGHT CRESCENDO (USA)**, 5, b br g Diesis—Night Fax (USA) **J. P. Connolly**
7 **SUNBURN (IRE)**, 4, b g Mark of Esteem (IRE)—Sundrenched (IRE) **Fred & Sacha Cotton**
8 **TUNGSTEN STRIKE (USA)**, 7, ch g Smart Strike (CAN)—Bathilde (IRE) **J. P. Connolly**

THREE-YEAR-OLDS

9 **APPOINTMENT**, ch f Where Or When (IRE)—Shoshone **Highclere Thoroughbred Racing (Brunel)**
10 **BENEDETTO**, b c Fasliyev (USA)—Inchyre **Woodcote Stud Ltd**
11 **BLUE CITADEL (USA)**, ch c Dubai Destination (USA)—Cloud Castle **The Green Dot Partnership**

MRS A. J. PERRETT—continued

12 **CELTIC DRAGON,** b c Fantastic Light (USA)—Zanzibar (IRE) **Mr M. Dawson & Mr Kevin Mercer**
13 **COASTING,** b g Cape Cross (IRE)—Sweeping **Sir John Ritblat, Sir David & Lady Jennifer Sieff**
14 **COLOURWAYS (IRE),** b f Singspiel (IRE)—Chartres (IRE) **Lady Clague**
15 **DADDY'S BOY,** ch g Selkirk (USA)—Narva **Woodcote Stud Ltd**
16 **DANCING DIK,** b g Diktat—Maureena (IRE) **Sir John Ritblat, Sir David & Lady Jennifer Sieff**
17 **DRIVEN (IRE),** b c Domedriver (IRE)—Wonderful World (GER) **A. D. Spence**
18 **EVERY WHISPER (IRE),** b f High Chaparral (IRE)—Heavenly Whisper (IRE) **D. G. Hardisty Bloodstock**
19 **FLASH OF COLOUR,** b c Averti (IRE)—Big Pink (IRE) **S Barnett, J Deer, R Doel & T Wellard**
20 **FORESIGHT,** ch c Observatory (USA)—Avoidance (USA) **K. Abdulla**
21 **GAIA PRINCE (USA),** b br c Forestry (USA)—Castlebrook (USA) **J. P. Connolly**
22 **GREEK THEATRE (USA),** ch c Smoke Glacken (USA)—
Theatre Flight (USA) **Mr J E Bodie,Mr R Wells & Mr G Harwood**
23 **INQUEST,** b g Rainbow Quest (USA)—Katy Nowaitee **J. H. Richmond-Watson**
24 **LOBBY,** ch c Dr Fong (USA)—Real Trust (USA) **K. Abdulla**
25 **MIDSHIPS (USA),** gr c Mizzen Mast (USA)—Interim **K. Abdulla**
26 **MYSTERY SAIL (USA),** b f Mizzen Mast (USA)—Questonia **K. Abdulla**
27 **REGAL BEST (IRE),** b c King's Best (USA)—Carranza (USA) **A. D. Spence**
28 **RIVERSCAPE (IRE),** ch f Peintre Celebre (USA)—Orinoco (IRE) **Lady Clague**
29 **SILVER REGENT (USA),** b c Silver Deputy (USA)—Alexine (ARG) **P Graham, R D Hubbard & R Masterson**
30 **SPECTRANA,** b f Spectrum (IRE)—Anapola (GER) **D. M. James**
31 **TIVERS DIXIE (USA),** b br g Dixieland Band (USA)—
Gracious Living (USA) **Mrs Priscilla Graham & Mr G. Harwood**

TWO-YEAR-OLDS

32 **ADMIRAL SANDHOE (USA),** ch c 24/4 Diesis—Dancing Sea (USA) (Storm Cat (USA)) (31584) **D. M. Slade**
33 Br c 18/4 Key of Luck (USA)—Anne Boleyn (Rainbow Quest (USA)) (20000) **Coombelands Racing Syndicate**
34 **BLUE DYNASTY (USA),** b c 29/1 Dynaformer (USA)—
Saudia (USA) (Gone West (USA)) (82604) **The Green Dot Partnership**
35 **BLUE TANGO (IRE),** ch c 18/2 Noverre (USA)—
It Takes Two (IRE) (Alzao (USA)) (47000) **The Green Dot Partnership**
36 B c 25/1 Sakhee (USA)—Bourbonella (Rainbow Quest (USA)) (60000) **Mrs A. J. Perrett**
37 B c 20/3 El Prado (IRE)—
Cellars Shiraz (USA) (Kissin Kris (USA)) (170068) **R & P Scott A & J Powell Gallagher Stud**
38 **CHASCA (IRE),** b f 23/3 Namid—Daganya (IRE) (Danehill Dancer (USA)) **Lady Clague**
39 **CRY FOR THE MOON (USA),** b c 1/5 Street Cry (IRE)—
Kafaf (USA) (Zilzal (USA)) (92322) **Mr A Christodoulou Mr JH Richmond-Watson**
40 **DIMANDER (IRE),** b c 15/1 Namid—Red Liason (IRE) (Selkirk (USA)) **Lady Clague**
41 **DUBAI CREST,** b c 17/3 Dubai Destination (USA)—On The Brink (Mind Games) (120000) **A. D. Spence**
42 **GREEN ENDEAVOUR (CAN),** b c 27/2 Forestry (USA)—
Zuri Ridge (USA) (Cox's Ridge (USA)) (72886) **The Green Dot Partnership**
43 **HURAKAN (IRE),** b c 23/4 Daylami (IRE)—Gothic Dream (IRE) (Nashwan (USA)) **Lady Clague**
44 **JAZACOSTA (USA),** ch c 14/2 Dixieland Band (USA)—
Dance With Del (USA) (Sword Dance) (80174) **J. P. Connolly**
45 **KING'S LA MONT (IRE),** b c 6/4 King's Best (USA)—
La Leuze (IRE) (Caerleon (USA)) (21000) **Winterfields Farm Ltd, A.Brooke, A.Black**
46 Gr ro c 4/4 Mizzen Mast (USA)—Kithira (Danehill (USA)) **K. Abdulla**
47 **KYLLACHY KING,** b c 21/2 Kyllachy—
Baileys Dancer (Groom Dancer (USA)) (34000) **Cotton, James, Slade, Tracey**
48 B c 26/2 Captain Rio—Lady Nasrana (FR) (Al Nasr (FR)) (40000) **Mrs A. J. Perrett**
49 Ch c 23/3 Cadeaux Genereux—Living Daylights (IRE) (Night Shift (USA)) (30000) **Mrs A. J. Perrett**
50 B f 2/2 Dansili—Nashmeel (USA) (Blushing Groom (USA)) **K. Abdulla**
51 **PAGAN FORCE (IRE),** b c 21/3 Green Desert (USA)—
Brigitta (IRE) (Sadler's Wells (USA)) (68000) **The Gap Partnership**
52 **ROCOPPELIA (USA),** ch c 6/2 Hennessy (USA)—
Eternally (USA) (Timeless Moment (USA)) (72886) **J. P. Connolly**
53 **SABORIDO (USA),** gr c 2/5 Dixie Union (USA)—
Alexine (ARG) (Runaway Groom (CAN)) (60738) **Cotton, James, Slade, Tracey**
54 **SAINT CHAPELLE (IRE),** b f 13/1 Noverre (USA)—Chartres (IRE) (Danehill (USA)) **Lady Clague**
55 **SPANISH CYGNET (USA),** b f 11/3 El Corredor (USA)—
Dixie Dos (USA) (Dixieland Band (USA)) (48590) **Cotton, James, Slade, Tracey**
56 B c 13/4 Silver Deputy (CAN)—
Starry Farrari (USA) (Inherent Star (USA)) (63168) **Jason Hathorn & Tessona Racing Limited**
57 **SUPERNOVERRE (IRE),** b c 4/3 Noverre (USA)—
Caviare (Cadeaux Genereux) (50000) **Cotton, James, Slade, Tracey**

MRS A. J. PERRETT—continued

58 TOTTIE, b f 4/4 Fantastic Light (USA)—Katy Nowaitee (Komaite (USA)) **J. H. Richmond-Watson**
59 B f 2/5 Theatrical—Vinista (USA) (Jade Hunter (USA)) (145772) **Mr & Mrs R. Scott**

Other Owners: P. R. Anders, Mr S. W. Barnett, A. M. Black, J. E. Bodie, Mrs M. Brody, A. W. Brooke, A. Christodoulou, F. G. Cotton, Mrs S. H. Cotton, S. R. Counsell, M. V. Dawson, D. J. Deer, Mrs R. J. Doel, Mrs J. M. V. Freeman, D. G. Hardisty, Mrs E. Hardisty, Guy Harwood, J. J. Hathorn, The Hon H. M. Herbert, Highclere Thoroughbred Racing Ltd, Mr R. D. Hubbard, Mr R. E. Masterson, G. D. P. Materna, K. J. Mercer, Mr A. E. Powell, Mrs J. Powell, Sir J. H. Ritblat, R. Scott, Mrs P. M. Scott, Sir David Sieff, Lady J. R. Sieff, Mrs V. J. M. Slade, Tessona Racing Ltd, Mr M. Tracey, T. W. Wellard, J. R. L. Wells, Winterfields Farm Ltd.

Assistant Trainer: Mark Perrett

Amateur: Miss L. J. Crowley.

468
MR G. R. PEWTER, Halstead
Postal: **Great Lodge Farm, Castle Hedingham, Halstead, Essex, CO9 3AJ**
Contacts: PHONE **(01787) 460964** FAX **(01787) 462150** MOBILE **(07966) 489541**

1 DALLIGAN (IRE), 14, b g Executive Perk—Comeragh Queen **N. J. Pewter**
2 GENERAL HOPKINS (IRE), 13, b g Cataldi—Kewanee **N. J. Pewter**
3 HOMELEIGHWILDCHILD, 7, ro m Silver Patriarch (IRE)—Give It A Bash (IRE) **Mrs H. C. Edwards**
4 MR MIGHTY (IRE), 12, br g Montelimar (USA)—Laurie Belle **N. J. Pewter**
5 PACHA NOIR (IRE), 8, br g Lord Americo—Brennan For Audits (IRE) **N. J. Pewter**

Jockey (NH): Gerry Supple. **Amateur:** Mr Guy Pewter.

469
MR P. M. PHELAN, Epsom
Postal: **Ermyn Lodge, Shepherds Walk, Epsom, Surrey, KT18 6DF**
Contacts: PHONE **(01372) 229017** FAX **(01372) 229001** MOBILE **(07917) 762781**
E-MAIL pat.els@btconnect.com

1 EDE'S, 8, ch g Bijou d'inde—Ballagarrow Girl **Ede's (UK) Ltd**
2 EDE'S THE BEST, 4, b f Kayf Tara—Irish Impulse (USA) **Ede's (UK) Ltd**
3 THE BIG ORSE, 6, b g Benny The Dip (USA)—Polar Queen **Ermyn Lodge Stud Limited**

THREE-YEAR-OLDS

4 BUCK CANNON (IRE), b g High Chaparral (IRE)—Folgore (USA) **Ermyn Lodge Stud Limited**

Jockey (flat): Ian Mongan. **Jockey (NH):** Colin Bolger. **Apprentice:** Jack Mitchell. **Amateur:** Mr Sam Hanson.

470
MR R. T. PHILLIPS, Moreton-in-Marsh
Postal: **Adlestrop Stables, Adlestrop, Moreton-in-Marsh, Gloucestershire, GL56 0YN**
Contacts: PHONE **(01608) 658710** FAX **(01608) 658713** MOBILE **(07774) 832715**
E-MAIL info@richardphillipsracing.com WEBSITE www.richardphillipsracing.com

1 ALDERMAN ROSE, 8, b g Alderbrook—Rose Ravine **Mrs Nicholas Jones/Martin Broughton**
2 ANOTHER CHAT (IRE), 8, ch g Executive Perk—Lucky Fiver **A. Beard, B. Beard, J. Barnes, P. Doble**
3 ANOTHER LATE NIGHT (IRE), 7, b g Gothland (FR)—
　　　　　　　　　　　　　　　　　　Miss Executive (IRE) **Bellflower Anotherlatenight Partnership**
4 ASHWELL LAD (IRE), 6, gr g Sea Raven (IRE)—Irene's Call (IRE) **Mr P. Surtees & Mr G. Taylor**
5 ASSUMPTALINA, 8, b m Primitive Rising (USA)—New Broom (IRE) **M. R. Barnes**
6 BALLYKELLY (IRE), 7, b g Insan (USA)—Lady Oakwell (IRE) **Nut Club Partnership**
7 BARON ROMEO (IRE), 8, gr g Baron Blakeney—Langretta (IRE) **Mrs C. Skan**
8 BAUHAUS (IRE), 7, b g Second Empire (IRE)—Hi Bettina **The Hot Tub Club**
9 BOBBY DONALD (IRE), 6, b g Lord Americo—River Rescue **The Bellflower Bobby Donald Partnership**
10 CAPTAIN TIDDS (IRE), 7, b g Presenting—Kilmana (IRE) **C. Pocock**
11 CHANCERY LAD (IRE), 7, b g Leading Counsel (USA)—Carrigbuck (IRE) **Keweedee**
12 Ch g Fraam—Cheeky Monkey (USA) **R. T. Phillips**
13 CHOPNEYEV (FR), 10, b g Goldneyev—Pierre de Soleil (FR) **Mr F. J. Allen & Partners**
14 COLINETTE, 5, b m Groom Dancer (USA)—Collide **The Bellflower Colinette Partnership**
15 CORTESIA (IRE), 5, ch m Courteous—Cecina **Hintlesham Racing**
16 CROSSGUARD (USA), 5, b g Royal Anthem (USA)—Foible (USA) **Brigadier Racing 2006**

MR R. T. PHILLIPS—continued

17 **DELAYED APPROACH (IRE)**, 6, b m Bob's Return (IRE)—Becca's Approach (IRE) **The Ducksters Syndicate**
18 **DIAMOND CUTTER (NZ)**, 9, br g Strike Diamonds (NZ)—
Lough Allen (NZ) **Gryffindor II (www.racingtours.co.uk)**
19 **DRUMROE**, 6, b m Vettori (IRE)—Red Leggings **R. T. Phillips**
20 **EARLY WINGS (GER)**, 6, b g Winged Love (IRE)—Emy Coasting (USA) **Mr & Mrs R. Scott**
21 **EASTWELL SMILES**, 4, gr g Erhaab (USA)—Miss University (USA) **Eastwell Manor Racing Ltd**
22 **EVENING CLASS**, 5, br m Classic Cliche (IRE)—Evening Dusk (IRE) **Mr & Mrs F. C. Welch**
23 5, B g Pasternak—Flying Fur (IRE) **Mr F. Cooke & Mr R. Phillips**
24 **FOREST MILLER**, 9, b g Classic Cliche (IRE)—Its My Turn **The Old Foresters Partnership**
25 **GIOVANNA**, 7, b m Orpen (USA)—Red Leggings **Dozen Dreamers Partnership**
26 **GLAD BIG (GER)**, 6, b g Big Shuffle (USA)—Glady Sum (GER) **The Bellflower Glad Big Partnership**
27 **GO HARVEY GO (IRE)**, 9, b g Supreme Leader—Python Wolf (IRE) **Mrs S. J. Harvey**
28 **GRUMPY BEE (IRE)**, 6, br g Needle Gun (IRE)—Flapping Freda (IRE) **Mr S. J. Jenkins**
29 **HEEZAGREY (IRE)**, 5, gr g Naheez (USA)—Silver Belle (IRE) **Miss S. Troughton**
30 **HONEY MAKES MONEY**, 6, gr m Environment Friend—Silver Madam **P. G. Hepworth**
31 **JOKING ASIDE (IRE)**, 4, b br f Winged Love (IRE)—Listen Up **The Listeners**
32 **KAYF KEEL**, 5, gr m Kayf Tara—Royal Keel **Mrs Peter Matthey & John F. Horn**
33 **KHUMBU**, 6, b g Zaffaran (USA)—Kirov Royale **Garry & Catriona Braybrooke Jones**
34 6, B g Taipan (IRE)—Kilbally Quilty (IRE) **The Adlestrop Club**
35 **KING JACK**, 6, b g Classic Cliche (IRE)—Hack On **Gryffindor I (www.racingtours.co.uk)**
36 **LINDSAY (FR)**, 9, b g Chamberlin (FR)—Oliday (FR) **Mrs K. F. Lansbury**
37 **MARK OF LOVE (IRE)**, 4, ch g Mark of Esteem (IRE)—Dazilyn Lady (USA) **7 Day Catering Limited**
38 **MR AITCH (IRE)**, 6, b g Soviet Star (USA)—Welsh Mist **The Bellflower Mr Aitch Partnership**
39 **MR MERLOT**, 6, ch g Alflora (IRE)—Eloquent Lawyer **The Red Winers**
40 **NORMAN BECKETT**, 5, b g Beckett (IRE)—Classic Coral (USA) **The Bellflower Norman Beckett Partnership**
41 **ON Y VA (FR)**, 10, b g Goldneyev (USA)—Shakna (FR) **The Adlestrop Club**
42 **ON YER OWN**, 5, br m Terimon—Soloism **Mr & Mrs M. J. Hawley**
43 **PAK JACK (FR)**, 8, ch g Pitchounet (FR)—Miss Noir Et Or (FR) **The Bellflower Pak Jak Partnership**
44 **PELO DU BIEF (FR)**, 5, b g Useful (FR)—Hopeful of Silver (FR) **The After Eights**
45 **PETROUPETROV (FR)**, 5, br g Ungaro (GER)—Harlem (FR) **The Bellflower Petroupetrov Partnership**
46 **PHARDESSA**, 7, b m Pharly (FR)—Mardessa **Robert Brown & Partners**
47 **PIPER HAYES (IRE)**, 7, b g Tiraaz (USA)—Promised Path **Mr & Mrs R. Scott**
48 **ROARINGWATER (IRE)**, 9, b g Roselier (FR)—Supreme Cherry **The Adlestrop Club**
49 **SHARP JACK (IRE)**, 10, b g Be My Native (USA)—Polly Sharp **The Bellflower Sharp Jack Partnership**
50 **SHIELD OF ZEUS (IRE)**, 6, b g Sea Raven (IRE)—The Furnituremaker **Mr S. J. Jenkins**
51 **SMART TOM (IRE)**, 4, b g Un Desperado (FR)—Paper Merchant **The Bellflower Smart Tom Partnership**
52 **STOP THE SHOW (IRE)**, 7, b g King's Theatre (IRE)—Rathsallagh Tartan **D. M. Mason**
53 **SYCHO FRED (IRE)**, 7, b g Buster King—Rebecca Steel (IRE) **Glass Holdings Ltd**
54 **THOMPSON**, 4, br g Averti (IRE)—Sewards Folly **Mr & Mrs M. J. Hawley**
55 **TIGER MOSS**, 6, b m Classic Cliche (IRE)—Mighty Phantom (USA) **S. Smith**
56 6, B g Fourstars Allstar (USA)—Treble Base (USA) **R. T. Phillips**
57 **YANN'S (FR)**, 12, b g Hellios (USA)—Listen Gyp (USA) **The Bellflower Yann's Partnership**
58 **ZALZAAR (IRE)**, 6, b g Xaar—Zalamalec (USA) **The Adlestrop Club**

THREE-YEAR-OLDS

59 **BREATHE**, b f Dansili—Starfan (USA) **Mr S. L. Keswick**
60 **JUMPIN JOHNNIE**, ch g Compton Place—Trump Street **The Bellflower Jumpin Johnnie Partnership**

TWO-YEAR-OLDS

61 **BLUE CELESTE**, b f 14/3 Sakhee (USA)—Ellie Ardensky (Slip Anchor) (3000) **Mr R. Pennant Jones**

Other Owners: D. Allan, Mrs Y. Allan, F. J. Allen, J. E. Barnes, Alan Beard, B. M. Beard, S. Bell, Bellflower Racing Ltd, Mrs C. M. Braybrooke Jones, M. F. Broughton, S. W. Broughton, R. Brown, W. V. P. Bullingham, D. J. Bussell, C. W. Campbell, B. J. Cockerell, Mrs F. R. Colling, Mr F. G. Cooke, P. R. Doble, B. J. Duckett, D. G. Duggan, Mr D. E. Ford, Mr M. J. Hawley, Mrs A. J. Hawley, M. B. Hawtin, J. F. Horn, Mrs E. Jennings, G. P. Jones, Mrs N. Jones, Mrs M. J. Matthey, Mr A. N. Miller, T. H. Milson, C. F. Newman, C. J. Newport, Mrs H. M. Nixseaman, M. T. Phillips, R. Scott, Mrs P. M. Scott, C. B. Smith, P. J. Surtees, Mr G. R. Taylor, Mrs R. B. Weaver, Mrs S. C. Welch, F. C. Welch, T. C. Wilson.

Jockey (NH): R. Johnson, W. Marston. **Conditional:** S. Quinlan.

471 MR J. A. PICKERING, Hinckley
Postal: **Cottage Farm, Wigston Parva, Hinckley, Leicestershire, LE10 3AP**
Contacts: **PHONE (01455) 220535**

1 MUJART, 4, b f Mujahid (USA)—Artifact **J. A. Pickering**
2 TEMTATION (IRE), 4, b f Trans Island—Ish (IRE) **P. V. Charlesworth**

THREE-YEAR-OLDS

3 AVIAN FLEW, b f Averti (IRE)—Ice Bird **T.Pears,Mrs H.Morrish,G.Higginbotham**
4 JASTAANHI, b f Superior Premium—Cavern Breeze **Mrs H. A Morrish**
5 RAISA LILY, ch f Bold Edge—Raisa Point **J. A. Pickering**
6 SILVER DEAL, b f Lujain (USA)—Deal In Facts **S. Kitching**

Other Owners: Mr G. C. Higginbotham, J. E. Morgan, T. G. Pears.

472 MR STEWART PIKE, Sidmouth
Postal: **Synderborough Farm, Sidbury, Sidmouth, Devon, EX10 0QJ**
Contacts: **PHONE/FAX (01395) 597485 MOBILE (07836) 335293**
E-MAIL monique@pikes.eclipse.co.uk

1 BLUE MAGNUM (FR), 8, b g Pistolet Bleu (IRE)—Dalticia (FR) **S. L. Pike**
2 FRONT PAGE, 5, b m Alflora (IRE)—Front Cover **S. L. Pike**
3 GUN COVER, 7, ch m Gunner B—Front Cover **S. L. Pike**
4 KAY SERA (FR), 5, b m Kahyasi—Dalticia (FR) **S. L. Pike**
5 SOVIETICA (FR), 7, b m Subotica (FR)—Vieille Russie **S. L. Pike**
6 TOKAHY (FR), 5, b m Kahyasi—Vieille Russie **S. L. Pike**

Assistant Trainer: Mrs M P Pike

Jockey (NH): R. Thornton. Amateur: Miss Rachel Green, Mr. Nick Scholfield.

473 MR DAVID PINDER, Wantage
Postal: **Little Farm, Fawler Road, Kingston Lisle, Wantage, Oxfordshire, OX12 9QH**
Contacts: **PHONE (01367) 820280 FAX (01367) 821037 MOBILE (07711) 396191**
E-MAIL david@davidpinderracing.com WEBSITE www.davidpinderracing.com

1 ADAGE, 5, b m Vettori (FR)—Aymara **Ms L. Burns**
2 GAZBOOLOU, 4, b g Royal Applause—Warning Star **Mrs A. M. Pinder**
3 GOLDEN BROWN (IRE), 4, b g Kyllachy—Sand Grouse (USA) **Ms L. Burns**
4 LUNAR RIVER (FR), 5, b m Muhtathir—Moon Gorge **The Little Farm Partnership**
5 TIPSY PRINCE, 4, b g Tipsy Creek (USA)—Princess of Garda **Ambermarley Partnership**

THREE-YEAR-OLDS

6 APRIL'S QUEST (IRE), ch f Spectrum (IRE)—Coastal Jewel (IRE) **Mrs A. M. Pinder**
7 HOUSE OF TUDOR, b g Medicean—Wrong Bride **Miss N. M. Haine**

Other Owners: R. M. Pinder, Ms R. V. Richards.

474 MR D. E. PIPE, Wellington
Postal: **Pond House, Nicholashayne, Wellington, Somerset, TA21 9QY**
Contacts: **PHONE (01884) 840715 FAX (01884) 841343**
E-MAIL david@davidpipe.co.uk WEBSITE www.davidpipe.co.uk

1 ABRAGANTE (IRE), 7, b g Saddlers' Hall (IRE)—Joli's Girl **D. A. Johnson**
2 ACAMBO (GER), 7, gr g Acambaro (GER)—Artic Lady (FR) **D. A. Johnson**
3 ALAMINOS (FR), 4, b g Maille Pistol (FR)—Sandsea (IRE) **A. J. White & Mrs A. Underhill**
4 AMIR EL JABAL (FR), 5, b g Enrique—Premonitory Dream (FR) **Stefanos Stefanou**
5 AN ACCORDION (IRE), 7, b g Accordion—Jennie's First **B. A. Kilpatrick**
6 ARMENIAN BOY (FR), 5, b h Simon du Desert (FR)—Jade d'eau (IRE) **Mrs T. S. M. Cunningham**
7 ASHKAZAR (FR), 4, b g Sadler's Wells (USA)—Asharna (IRE) **D. A. Johnson**
8 AVANT GARDISTE (FR), 4, b g Victory Note (USA)—Lady For A Day (FR) **Twice Lucky**
9 BATHWICK BREEZE, 4, ch g Sugarfoot—She's A Breeze **H. M. W. Clifford**
10 BATHWICK SHANNON (IRE), 7, ch m Anshan—Glacier Lilly (IRE) **H. M. W. Clifford**

MR D. E. PIPE—continued

11 **BIG EARED FRAN (IRE)**, 5, gr g Danehill (USA)—Zarawa (IRE) **Mr Thomas Barr**
12 **BOULEVARDOFDREAMS (IRE)**, 7, b g Beau Sher—Cap The Waves (IRE) **D. A. Johnson**
13 **BRAVE BRONCHO (IRE)**, 6, b g Taipan (IRE)—Bro Ella (IRE) **D. A. Johnson**
14 **BROUSSE EN FEUX (FR)**, 5, ch m April Night (FR)—
Antoniola (FR) **Lord Donoughmore & Countess Donoughmore**
15 **BUENA VISTA (IRE)**, 7, b g In The Wings—Park Special **Matt Archer & The Late Miss Jean Broadhurst**
16 **CADOULITIQUE (FR)**, 5, b g Antarctique (FR)—Cadoulie Wood (FR) **Roger Stanley & Yvonne Reynolds III**
17 **CELESTIAL GOLD (IRE)**, 10, b g Persian Mews—What A Queen **D. A. Johnson**
18 **CELTIC SON (FR)**, 9, b g Celtic Arms (FR)—For Kicks (FR) **D. A. Johnson**
19 **CHOUMAKEUR (FR)**, 6, ch g Mansonnien (FR)—Feuille de Chou (FR) **P. A. D. Scouller**
20 **CHRISTDALO (IRE)**, 8, ch m Glacial Storm (USA)—Benbradagh Vard (IRE) **D. A. Johnson**
21 **COMMANDER VIC (IRE)**, 6, b g Old Vic—Miss Agarbie (IRE) **D. A. Johnson**
22 **COMPLY OR DIE (IRE)**, 9, b g Old Vic—Madam Madcap **D. A. Johnson**
23 **CONSIGLIERE (FR)**, 5, ch g Trempolino—Gianna Nannini (ITY) **P. A. D. Scouller**
24 **CRICKET BOY**, 4, b g Alflora (IRE)—Lady Cricket (FR) **D. A. Johnson**
25 **DADA CUP (FR)**, 5, b g Dadarissime (FR)—Colonial Cup (FR) **D. Harper & S. J. Crockett I**
26 **DIFFERENT LOT (IRE)**, 5, ch g Old Vic—Clonfert Sue (IRE) **A. J. White & Mrs A. Underhill**
27 **DOC ROW (IRE)**, 8, b g Dr Massini (IRE)—Roberto Moss **D. A. Johnson**
28 **DOM D'ORGEVAL (FR)**, 8, b g Belmez (USA)—Marie D'orgeval (FR) **A. J. White & Mrs A. Underhill**
29 **EL BANDINOS (IRE)**, 7, b g Darazari (IRE)—Supreme Weasel (IRE) **D. A. Johnson**
30 **ESTATE**, 6, b g Montjeu (IRE)—Fig Tree Drive (USA) **Mr R. S. Brookhouse**
31 **FIGARO DU ROCHER (FR)**, 8, ch g Beyssac (FR)—Fabinou (FR) **Pipe Monkees**
32 **FLASH CUMMINS (FR)**, 8, b br g Corrouge (USA)—Corshanna River (IRE) **D. A. Johnson**
33 **FOURTY ACERS (IRE)**, 8, ch g Bob Back (USA)—Guest Cailin (IRE) **David Manning Associates**
34 **FUL OF GRACE (IRE)**, 4, b f Marju (IRE)—Mitawa (IRE) **Mr D. Harper**
35 **GASPARA (FR)**, 5, b m Astarabad (USA)—Gaspaisie (FR) **P. McMahon**
36 **GIBRALTAR STAR (IRE)**, 4, b g Bering—Ciudadella (USA) **James & Antoinette Kennedy I**
37 **GUERABAD (FR)**, 6, b g Astarabad (USA)—Guerville (FR) **M. C. Pipe**
38 **HELEN WOOD**, 5, b m Lahib (USA)—Last Ambition (IRE) **Mrs E. King**
39 **HITAAF (IRE)**, 6, b g Montjeu (IRE)—Heaven Only Knows **Teddington Racing Club II**
40 **I'M SO LUCKY**, 6, b g Zilzal (USA)—City of Angels **Mrs S. J. Brookhouse**
41 **IDIAN MIX (FR)**, 7, b g Indian River (FR)—Nashamix (FR) **Idian Partnership**
42 **ITSMYBOY (IRE)**, 8, br g Frimaire—Hawkfield Lass (IRE) **D. A. Johnson**
43 **JOAACI (IRE)**, 8, b g Presenting—Miss Sarajevo (IRE) **D. A. Johnson**
44 **JUST CLASSIC**, 8, gr g Classic Cliche (IRE)—Misty View **D. A. Johnson**
45 **KAVATCHA (FR)**, 5, gr g Nikos—Kaleigh's Jovite (USA) **Mr Chris Grant & Mr Michael H. Burke**
46 **KILTY STORM (IRE)**, 9, b g Glacial Storm (USA)—Hogan's Cherry **S. Lucey**
47 **LAUSTRA BAD (FR)**, 5, b g Astarabad (USA)—Love Crazy (FR) **Mrs S. J. Ling**
48 **LE BEAU BAI (FR)**, 5, b g Cadoudal (FR)—Dame Blonde (FR) **The Arthur White Partnership**
49 **LEARNING THE BLUES (FR)**, 5, ch g Trempolino (USA)—Cure The Blues (IRE) **Lady H. J. Clarke**
50 **LEO'S LUCKY STAR (USA)**, 6, b g Forestry (USA)—Leo's Lucky Lady (USA) **Mrs S. J. Brookhouse**
51 **LOOM (GER)**, 6, b g Tiger Hill (IRE)—La Curamalal (IRE) **Mr D. C. Manasseh**
52 **LOUGH DERG (FR)**, 8, b g Apple Tree (FR)—Asturias (FR) **W. F. Frewen**
53 **LUCIFER BLEU (FR)**, 9, b g Kadalko (FR)—Figa Dancer (FR) **A. J. White**
54 **LUSAKA DE PEMBO (FR)**, 9, b g Funny Baby (FR)—Crackeline (FR) **Swanvista Limited**
55 **MADISON DU BERLAIS (FR)**, 7, b g Indian River (FR)—
Anais du Berlais (FR) **Roger Stanley & Yvonne Reynolds II**
56 **MAMLOOK (IRE)**, 4, br g Key of Luck (USA)—Cradle Brief (IRE) **P. A. Deal & G. Lowe**
57 **MANX ROYAL (FR)**, 9, b g Cyborg (FR)—Badj II (FR) **James & Antoinette Kennedy**
58 **MARIDAY**, 7, br g Trifolio—Classic Hand **M. C. Pipe**
59 **MASTER OVERSEER (IRE)**, 5, b g Old Vic—Crogeen Lass **T. Barr**
60 **MILAN DEUX MILLE (FR)**, 6, b g Double Bed—Uberaba (FR) **F. G. & J. E. Wilson**
61 **MILORD LESCRIBAA (FR)**, 8, b g Cadoudal (FR)—Mona Lisaa (FR) **M. C. Pipe**
62 **MONSIEUR VILLEZ (FR)**, 6, b g Villez (USA)—Dame De Trefles (FR) **The Liskey Partnership**
63 **MUTUAL FRIEND (USA)**, 4, gr g Aljabr (USA)—Dubai Visit (USA) **Pond House Racing**
64 **MY IMMORTAL**, 6, b g Monsun (GER)—Dame Kiri (FR) **Major P. Arkwright & Mrs I. C. Sellars**
65 **NACADOUR (FR)**, 7, b g Port Lyautey (FR)—Digit II (FR) **The West Coast Syndicate**
66 **NANARD (FR)**, 7, br g Double Bed (FR)—Isabellita (FR) **James & Antoinette Kennedy I**
67 **NIKE WALKER (FR)**, 5, b g Bering—Albiatra (USA) **Pipe Monkees**
68 **NOBLE SHAM**, 7, b g Shambo—Shamana **D. A. Johnson**
69 **NOBODY TELLS ME (FR)**, 7, b br g Lute Antique (FR)—Becebege (FR) **B. A. Kilpatrick**
70 **NOT LEFT YET (IRE)**, 7, b br g Old Vic—Dalus Dawn **D. A. Johnson**
71 **OCEAN PRIDE (IRE)**, 5, b g Lend A Hand—Irish Understudy (ITY) **Churston & Partners**
72 **OSANA (FR)**, 6, b g Video Rock (FR)—Voilette (FR) **T. Barr**
73 **OUR VIC (IRE)**, 10, b g Old Vic—Shabra Princess **D. A. Johnson**
74 **OVER THE CREEK (FR)**, 9, br g Over The River (FR)—Solo Girl (IRE) **D. A. Johnson**

MR D. E. PIPE—continued

75 **PABLO DU CHARMIL (FR)**, 7, ch g Lyphard's Wish (FR)—Pacifie du Charmil (FR) **J. Moran**
76 **PARADI (FR)**, 5, b br g Video Rock (FR)—Gintonique (FR) **D. A. Johnson**
77 **PAUILLAC (FR)**, 5, b g Useful (FR)—Jolie Mome (FR) **D. A. Johnson**
78 **PENNY PICTURES (IRE)**, 9, b g Theatrical—Copper Creek **T. Neill**
79 **PEUT ETRE SIVOLA (FR)**, 5, b g Robin des Champs (FR)—Largentiere (FR) **Third Time Lucky**
80 **PITFUL TERCAH (FR)**, 5, b g Useful (FR)—Perle des Mers (FR) **S. E. Munir**
81 **POLINAMIX (FR)**, 5, b g Loup Solitaire (USA)—Polynamia (FR) **Lord Donoughmore&Countess Donoughmore I**
82 **PRINCE ARY**, 5, b g Desert Prince (IRE)—Aryaf (CAN) **A. W. Black**
83 **PRINCE BERE (FR)**, 5, b g Epistolaire (FR)—Known Alibi (USA) **J. T. Ennis**
84 **PRINCE DE BERSY (FR)**, 5, b g Useful (FR)—Tropulka God (FR) **Mr Chris Grant & Mr Carl Turpin**
85 **PUNTAL (FR)**, 12, b g Bering—Saveur **T. Neill**
86 **PURE GENIUS (IRE)**, 5, gr m Exit To Nowhere (USA)—Lady of Gortmerron (IRE) **Cloud Nine**
87 **QUADDICK LAKE (IRE)**, 5, br g Blueprint (IRE)—Wondermac (IRE) **D. A. Johnson**
88 **QUILLYGHAM (FR)**, 4, b g Vertical Speed (FR)—Baikal Bunch (FR) **Mrs J. E. Wilson**
89 **QUINTE DU CHÂTELET (FR)**, 4, b g Lavirco (GER)—Grandeur Royale (FR) **Brocade Racing**
90 **RASLAN**, 5, b g Lomitas—Rosia (IRE) **D. J. Reid**
91 **RED ECHO (FR)**, 7, b g Subotica (FR)—Volniste (FR) **T. Neill**
92 **RED RIBAND**, 5, b m Bandmaster (USA)—Miss Match **Mrs S. J. Faulks**
93 **REIDWIL (FR)**, 5, b g Bonnet Rouge (FR)—Reine Du Mont (FR) **Betfair Club ROA**
94 **RONALD JACK (FR)**, 6, b g Villez (USA)—Gatine de Bissy (FR) **S. M. Mercer**
95 **ROYAL RATIONALE (IRE)**, 4, b g Desert Prince (IRE)—Logic **Pond House Racing**
96 **RURAL REBEL (IRE)**, 6, br g New Frontier (IRE)—Patsy Donnellan (IRE) **D. A. Johnson**
97 **SABRE HONGROIS (FR)**, 5, b g Ungaro (GER)—L'arme Au Poing (FR) **T. S. M. Cunningham**
98 **SAINTE KADETTE (FR)**, 4, b f Kadalko (FR)—Sainte Albane (FR) **S. M. Mercer**
99 **SARATOGANE (FR)**, 6, b m Saratoga Springs (CAN)—Asturias (FR) **Pipe Monkees**
100 **SCOTLAND YARD (UAE)**, 5, b g Jade Robbery (USA)—Aqraba **J. M. Brown & M. J. Blackburn**
101 **SEVEN IS LUCKY (IRE)**, 6, b g Old Vic—Green Legend (IRE) **D. A. Johnson**
102 **SEVEN IS MY NUMBER (IRE)**, 6, b g Pistolet Bleu (IRE)—Waterloo Ball (IRE) **D. A. Johnson**
103 **SHALI SAN (FR)**, 4, b f Saint des Saints (FR)—Shillagh (FR) **A. J. White & Mrs A. Underhill**
104 **SIXO (IRE)**, 11, gr g Roselier (FR)—Miss Mangaroo **Mr Matt Archer & The Late Jean Broadhurst**
105 **SOLIYA (FR)**, 4, b f Vaguely Pleasant (FR)—Solimade (FR) **Eminence Grise Partnership**
106 **TAMARINBLEU (FR)**, 8, b g Epervier Bleu—Tamainia (FR) **The Arthur White Partnership**
107 **TANGO ROYAL (FR)**, 12, gr g Royal Charter (FR)—Nazia (FR) **B. A. Kilpatrick**
108 **TARAN TREGARTH**, 4, b f Tobougg (IRE)—Little Change **Mr Stephen Jones**
109 **THE PACKAGE**, 5, br g Kayf Tara—Ardent Bride **D. A. Johnson**
110 **THIRTYTHREEBLACK (IRE)**, 5, b g Oscar (IRE)—Chance My Native (IRE) **D. A. Johnson**
111 **TIME BANDIT (IRE)**, 8, b g Luso—Over The Green (IRE) **D. A. Johnson**
112 **TINO TINO (FR)**, 4, ch g Epaphos (GER)—Tinozakia (FR) **D. A. Johnson**
113 **TOM KNOWS (IRE)**, 5, b g Old Vic—Bk Lass (IRE) **D. A. Johnson**
114 **TRAVELLING LIGHT (IRE)**, 6, b g Old Vic—Donaghmore Lady (IRE) **D. A. Johnson**
115 **TROIALINI**, 4, b g Bertolini (USA)—Troia (IRE) **Chris Grant & Martin Jones**
116 **VERY COOL**, 6, b g Sir Harry Lewis (USA)—Laurel Diver **N. G. Mills**
117 **VIVID IMAGINATION (IRE)**, 9, b g Moonax (IRE)—Sezu (IRE) **M. C. Pipe**
118 **VODKA BLEU (FR)**, 9, b g Pistolet Bleu (IRE)—Viva Vodka (FR) **D. A. Johnson**
119 **WEE DINNS (IRE)**, 7, b m Marju (IRE)—Tir-An-Oir (IRE) **Lord Donoughmore&Countess Donoughmore I**
120 **WELL CHIEF (GER)**, 9, ch g Night Shift (USA)—Wellesiena (GER) **D. A. Johnson**
121 **WHISPERED PROMISES (USA)**, 7, b g Real Quiet (USA)—Anna's Honor (USA) **Mrs S. J. Brookhouse**
122 **WHISPERED SECRET (GER)**, 9, b g Selkirk (USA)—Wells Whisper (FR) **Mr D. C. Manasseh**
123 **WISE OWL**, 6, b g Danehill (USA)—Mistle Thrush (USA) **The Wise Partners**
124 **WOLF WARNING**, 6, b g Loup Sauvage (USA)—Light Ship **Burnt Toast Ltd**
125 **ZORRO DE LA VEGA (FR)**, 5, b g Marathon (USA)—Shinobie (FR) **Fergus, Judith & Tanya Wilson**

Other Owners: M. Archer, Mr Matt Archer, Mr Philip Arkwright, Mr T. Barr, Mr C. M. Batterham, Mrs R. F. Batterham, Mr B. J. Batterham, Mr T. Bedford, Mr Michael Blackburn, Exors of the Late Miss E. V. Broadhurst, R. S. Brookhouse, Mrs J. Brookhouse, Mr G. R. Broom, Mr G. Broom, Mrs A. Broom, Mrs A. E. M. Broom, Mr J. M. Brown, Mr Michael Burke, Burnt Toast Limited, Mr D. G. Churston, Mr W. Clifford, Mr S. J. Crockett, Mr T. S. M. Cunningham, Mr P.A. Deal, Lord Donoughmore, Countess of Donoughmore, Mr W. Frewen, Mr Tom Gittins, Mr C. I. Grant, Mr Robert B. Gray, Mr R. E. Greatorex, Mr Darren Harper, Mr T. M. Hely-Hutchinson, Mr K. W. R. Hodge, Ms Emma Hughes, Mr Malcolm B. Jones, Mr Martin L. Jones, Mr Stephen Jones, Mr J. P. Kennedy, Mrs Antoinette Kennedy, Mr R. Lambert, Mr James Langridge, Mrs Sarah Ling, Mr A. J. Lomas, Mr D. J. Long, Mr E. Long, Mr G. Lowe, Mr Sean Lucey, Mr Peter R. Masters, Mrs Kim E. Masters, Mr Stuart M. Mercer, Mr Ron Middleton, Mr Stuart J. Middleton, Mr Terry Neill, Mr C. G. Paletta, Mr G. L. Phippen, Mr M. C. Pipe, Mrs Y. J. Reynolds, Mr David G. Robinson, Mrs Sadie Ryan, Mrs Ian Sellars, Mr Michael Shufflebotham, Mr R. Stanley, Mr David Stones, The Late Jean Broadhurst, Mr Carl Turpin, Mrs A. Underhill, Mr B. E. Westcott, Mrs G. W. I. Westcott, Mr Bob Whitby, Mr A. J. White, Mr F. G. Wilson, Miss T. Wilson, Mrs J. E. Wilson.

MR D. E. PIPE—continued

Assistant Trainer: Mr M. C. Pipe C.B.E.

Jockey (NH): Tom Scudamore, Timmy Murphy, Gerry Supple. **Conditional:** Johnny Farrelly, Tom Malone. **Amateur:** Mr Charlie Wallis, Mr Danny Cook, Mr Daniel Pick, Mr John Monk.

---

475 **MR T. J. PITT, Malton**
Postal: **The Bottom Yard, Norton Grange, Norton, Malton, North Yorkshire, YO17 9EA**
Contacts: **PHONE (01653) 696159 FAX (01653) 696159 MOBILE (07917) 541341**
E-MAIL timjoelpitt@aol.com WEBSITE www.timpittracing.com

1 **BAAHER (USA),** 4, b c War Chant (USA)—Raajiya (USA) **Mr Alf Chadwick**
2 **BASALT (IRE),** 4, b g Rock of Gibraltar (IRE)—Sniffle (IRE) **Mr Tim Kelly**
3 **CADWELL,** 4, b g Pivotal—Sur Les Pointes (IRE) **The Rycroft Racers**
4 **CANTLEY SPIRIT,** 5, b m Compton Admiral—Foxy Alpha (IRE) **John Collier & Tim Pitt**
5 **KING'S MAJESTY (IRE),** 6, b g King's Best (USA)—Tiavanita (USA) **Ferrybank Properties Limited**
6 **MARIST MADAME,** 4, ch f Tomba—Linda's Schoolgirl (IRE) **T. G. N. Burrage**
7 **YOUNG ALF,** 5, b g Balnibarbi—Sciacca (IRE) **Mrs L. Dyer**

THREE-YEAR-OLDS

8 **CAPAL DUBH ALAINN (IRE),** b br g Kalanisi (IRE)—Tarifana (IRE) **Burke, Daly, Boyle, Prosser, McConnon**
9 **FOCAIL EILE,** b g Noverre (USA)—Glittering Image (IRE) **Mr C. Fegan**
10 **GURTAVALLIG,** ch f Starborough—Alcadia (IRE) **The Wedge 'n' Wad Partnership**

TWO-YEAR-OLDS

11 B f 14/5 Fusaichi Pegasus (USA)—Chateau Beach (IRE) (Danehill (USA)) (18000)
12 **IRISH SAINT (IRE),** ch c 28/4 Kheleyf (USA)—Tarifana (IRE) (Dr Devious (IRE)) **Saintly Racing**
13 B c 20/4 Fath (USA)—John's Ballad (IRE) (Ballad Rock) (10000) **Bigwigs Bloodstock**
14 **KANNIE ANNIE,** ch f 1/4 Cayman Kai (IRE)—Minskip Miss (Lucky Wednesday) **The Minskip Merlin Partnership**
15 B f 30/4 Red Ransom (USA)—Tessara (GER) (Big Shuffle (USA)) (11000) **Mr Sean Burke**

Other Owners: Mr P. Bhardwaj, Mr Matty Boyle, Mr Joseph Burke, Mr Sean Daly, Mr P. Evans, Mr Brian McConnon, Mr T. J. Pitt, Mr M. J. Pitt, Mr B. J. Pitt, Mr Ed Prosser, Mr D. Waddicor.

Jockey (flat): Francis Norton, Robert Havlin, Greg Fairley, Neil Callan.

---

476 **MR C. T. POGSON, Newark**
Postal: **Allamoor Farm, Mansfield Road, Farnsfield, Nottinghamshire, NG22 8HZ**
Contacts: **PHONE (01623) 882275 MOBILE (07977) 016155**

1 **BRONSON F'SURE,** 9, b g Overbury (IRE)—T'be Sure (IRE) **C. T. Pogson**
2 **EMMASFLORA,** 10, b m Alflora (IRE)—Charlotte's Emma **C. T. Pogson**
3 **KINGSCOURT LAD (IRE),** 10, b g Norwich—Mrs Minella **C. T. Pogson**
4 **LORD BASKERVILLE,** 7, b g Wolfhound (USA)—My Dear Watson **C. T. Pogson**
5 **MAJOR CATCH (IRE),** 9, b g Safety Catch (USA)—Inch Tape **C. T. Pogson**
6 **OSCARDEAL (IRE),** 9, b g Oscar (IRE)—Sleepy Bye Byes (IRE) **C. T. Pogson**
7 **RAVENSCAR,** 10, b g Thethingaboutitis (USA)—Outcrop **C. T. Pogson**
8 **REEL MISSILE,** 9, b g Weld—Landsker Missile **C. T. Pogson**
9 **SEYMOUR WELD,** 8, ch g Weld—Seymour News **C. T. Pogson**
10 **THIMBLESFIRTH (IRE),** 7, b m Flemensfirth (USA)—Miss Thimble (IRE) **C. T. Pogson**

Assistant Trainer: Adam Pogson

Conditional: A. Pogson.

---

477 **MR B. N. POLLOCK, Market Harborough**
Postal: **Station House, Medbourne, Market Harborough, Leicestershire, LE16 8ED**
Contacts: **PHONE (01858) 565225 MOBILE (07968) 032774**
E-MAIL ben@nbpracing.com WEBSITE www.bnpracing.com

1 **A GLASS IN THYNE (IRE),** 10, br g Glacial Storm (USA)—River Thyne (IRE) **Mrs J. R. Dale**
2 **ARCHENEMEE (IRE),** 6, b g Perpendicular—Community Service (IRE) **D. Mee**

MR B. N. POLLOCK—continued

3 BALLYNONTY (IRE), 7, b g Carroll House—Carrigkem (IRE) **Mrs E J Merriam & Mrs H Robson**
4 BEAU TORERO (IRE), 10, gr g True Brave (USA)—Brave Lola (FR) **Mrs K Lloyd Mrs L Pollock Mr L Stilwell**
5 CELTIC SOCIETY (IRE), 7, ch g Moscow Society (USA)—Final Peace (IRE) **R. G. Catton**
6 ENGLISH BAY, 5, b g Commanche Run—Strong Attraction **R. J. W. Hall**
7 FURZE HILL (IRE), 7, b g Topanoora—Zigina (IRE) **Medbourne Racing Club**
8 4, Ch g Sir Harry Lewis (USA)—Jowoody **A. W. K. Merriam**
9 LAUNDE (IRE), 9, b g Norwich—Carbia's Last **D. Mee**
10 LITTLE SHILLING (IRE), 6, ch g Bob's Return—Minouette (IRE) **Mrs L. M. Pestell**
11 NO TELLING (IRE), 6, b g Supreme Leader—Kissantell (IRE) **Mrs J. R. Dale**
12 QUICK JUDGEMENT (IRE), 6, b g Norwich—Bit of A Diva (IRE) **Mrs Z. Pruhs**
13 REBEL RAIDER (IRE), 9, b g Mujadil (USA)—Emily's Pride **Mrs Z. Pruhs**
14 SAFE INVESTMENT (USA), 4, b g Gone West (USA)—Fully Invested (USA) **R. G. Catton**
15 SAMIKIN (IRE), 10, b br g Topanoora—Samika (IRE) **Mrs N. Pollock**
16 SHAMPERS, 6, b g Shambo—Sparkling Spirit **Mrs K Lloyd Mrs L Pollock Mr L Stilwell**
17 SMART ALEX (IRE), 6, b g Topanoora—Berkim (IRE) **R Triple H**
18 TOBOUGG WELCOME (IRE), 4, ch g Tobougg (IRE)—Three White Sox **A. W. K. Merriam**
19 TYSSAC (FR), 7, ch g Beyssac (FR)—Aktia (FR) **Mrs S. E. M. Platt**

Other Owners: T. M. Hailstone, J. R. Holmes, Mrs K. M. Lloyd, Mrs E. J. Merriam, Mrs L. G. Pollock, Mrs A. H. Robson, Mr I. T. Stevens, L. F. Stilwell, K. Thompson, Mrs E. Townsend.
Jockey (flat): Vince Slattery. **Jockey (NH):** A. Thornton. **Conditional:** T. Messenger. **Amateur:** Mr Alex Merriam.

---

478 MR N. J. POMFRET, Tilton-on-the-Hill
Postal: **Red Lodge Farm, Marefield Lane, Tilton-on-the-Hill**, Leicester
Contacts: **PHONE (01162) 597537**

1 BITESIZE, 4, b f Commanche Run—Intrepid Gal **N. J. Pomfret**
2 REDD RAGUSA, 6, b m Busy Flight—Riva La Belle **Mr F. Hutchinson**

THREE-YEAR-OLDS

3 KIS KING, ch g Karinga Bay—Keep Ikis **J. N. Cheatle**

---

479 MRS N. N. M. POOK, Marlborough
Postal: **Team Pook Racing, Temple Farm, Rockley, Nr Marlborough**, Wiltshire, SN8 1RU
Contacts: **MOBILE (07861) 385260**
E-MAIL teampookracing@hotmail.co.uk **WEBSITE** www.teampookracing.co.uk

1 ALLONBY BAY, 5, ch g Karinga Bay—Castle Country **Dr John Wilson & Mrs Norma Pook**
2 ASHPATRICK, 4, b g Beat All (USA)—Emma-Lyne **Dr John Wilson & Mr Ray Blackman**
3 BAKER'S GIRL (IRE), 5, gr m Silver Patriarch (IRE)—Bewitch
4 CHICO TIME (IRE), 7, b m Presenting—Hilldalus (IRE) **The Chico Clique**
5 DARAMOON (IRE), 7, b m Darazari (IRE)—Yellow Moon (IRE) **Mrs L. J. Robins**
6 DARAZ ROSE (IRE), 7, br m Darazari (IRE)—Miss Rose (IRE) **Mrs L. J. Robins**
7 KARINGA MAGIC, 5, b g Karinga Bay—Foxgrove **R Stuart A Taylor P Bates N Pook**
8 MAGIC RUSH, 6, b g Almaty (IRE)—Magic Legs **Kine, Antell, Donovan, Barry's Bar, Pook**
9 MIDSUMMER LEGEND, 4, ch f Midnight Legend—Sabeel
10 4, B f Alflora (IRE)—Miss Orchestra (IRE) **Mr Paul Bates**
11 4, B c Kahtan—Missy Gee (IRE) **Mr R. Nutland & P. Bates**
12 MOONCOIN MAN (IRE), 8, br g Needle Gun (IRE)—Mooncoin Magic (IRE) **Mrs L. Kine**
13 SHROPSHIRELASS, 5, b m Beat All (USA)—Emma-Lyne **Mrs C. M. Ball**
14 TALKIN ROXY, 5, b m Flemensfirth (USA)—Queen of All Gales (USA) **Bates & Sian**

Other Owners: Mr Ray Antell, Mr Paul Bates, G. F. Bear, Mr R. C. Blackman, Mrs Norma Pook, Mrs Liz Sian, Mr Ronald. A. Stuart, A. J. Taylor, Dr John Wilson (Beaconsfield).

---

480 MR C. L. POPHAM, Taunton
Postal: **Bashford Racing Stables, West Bagborough, Taunton, Somerset, TA4 3EF**
Contacts: **PHONE (01823) 432769 MOBILE (07967) 506430**
E-MAIL bashfordstables@hotmail.com

1 ABOVE GROUND (IRE), 6, b g Presenting—What A Topper (IRE) **Mrs S. J. Popham**

MR C. L. POPHAM—continued

2 KALANTERA (IRE), 5, b g Kalanisi (IRE)—Tintera (IRE) **Friends Of Eddy Hall**
3 THUNDER CHILD, 8, gr g Cloudings (IRE)—Double Dutch **The Four Bucks**
4 TRUE DOVE, 6, b m Kayf Tara—Pasja (IRE) **Mr C & Mrs G Scott & Mr P & Mrs G Turner**

THREE-YEAR-OLDS

5 EPHESIAN (IRE), b f Efisio—Maddie G (USA) **Miss H. Wynne**

Other Owners: Mr Tim Harris, Mr L. A. Heard, Mr P. Littlejohns, Mrs Mandy Rossiter, Mrs Gill Scott, Mr C. Scott, Mr A. S. Skidmore, Mrs G. S. Turner, Mr P. R. Turner, Mr Richard Weeks.

---

481 MR J. G. B. PORTMAN, Compton
Postal: **Hamilton Stables, Hockham Road, Compton, Newbury, Berkshire, RG20 6QJ**
Contacts: **OFFICE** (01635) 578031 **FAX** (01635) 579323 **MOBILE** (07798) 824513
E-MAIL portman.hamiltonstables@virgin.net

1 AMAZING PROPOSAL (IRE), 8, b g Oscar (IRE)—Parsonage **Valiyar Racing**
2 BOB'S YOUR UNCLE, 5, br g Zilzal (USA)—Bob's Princess **A. S. B. Portman**
3 DESERT SECRETS (IRE), 6, b m Almutawakel—Shaping Up (USA) **M. J. Vandenberghe**
4 FINMERE (IRE), 5, b g Glacial Storm (USA)—Water Stratford (IRE) **Five Counties Partnership**
5 L'OISEAU (FR), 9, br g Video Rock (FR)—Roseraie (FR) **Milady Partnership**
6 LIVE THE LIFE (IRE), 6, ch m Good Thyne—Living A Dream (IRE) **A. R. Boswood**
7 MEASURELESS, 13, ch g Lion Cavern (USA)—Magnetic Point (USA) **J. G. B. Portman**
8 MIKADO MELODY (IRE), 9, b g Supreme Leader—Double Symphony (IRE) **Valiyar Racing**
9 NECKAR VALLEY (IRE), 9, b g Desert King (IRE)—Solar Attraction (IRE) **Mr P. E. Walters**
10 NED LUDD (IRE), 5, b g Montjeu (IRE)—Zanella (IRE) **M. J. Vandenberghe**
11 ROCKMOOR POND (IRE), 6, br m Fraam—Native Novel (IRE) **T. M. Curtis**

THREE-YEAR-OLDS

12 COCABANA, b f Captain Rio—Hiraeth **Hockham Racing**
13 FEASIBLE, ch g Efisio—Zoena **Berkeley Racing**
14 FIELDER (IRE), b g Catcher In The Rye (IRE)—Miss Garuda **S. J. Skinner**
15 GOLDDIGGING (IRE), b f Acclamation—On The Make (IRE) **Out To Grass Partnership**
16 ILLUSIONARY, b c Observatory—Tease (IRE) **Mrs D. O. Joly**
17 JANSHE GOLD, ch f Bertolini (USA)—Rekindled Flame (IRE) **Good Connections II**
18 LOOPING THE LOOP (USA), gr ro c Alphabet Soup (USA)—Citidance Missy (USA) **A. S. B. Portman**
19 Ch f Traditionally (USA)—Machikane Akaiito (IRE) **J. G. B. Portman**
20 MERIDIAN LINE (IRE), b f Trans Island—Meranie Girl (IRE) **Berkeley Racing**
21 POPPY DEAN (IRE), ch f Night Shift (USA)—Miss Devious (IRE) **Prof C. D. Green**
22 SPANISH BOUNTY, b g Bahamian Bounty—Spanish Gold **The Farleigh Court Racing Partnership**
23 TEADANCER (IRE), b f Traditionally (USA)—Dance Up A Storm (USA) **The Traditionalists**
24 TRUMPET LILY, b f Acclamation—Periwinkle (FR) **Mrs J. N. Edwards-Heathcote**
25 ZEN FACTOR, b g Josr Algarhoud (IRE)—Zabelina (USA) **Mr J. T. Habershon-Butcher**

TWO-YEAR-OLDS

26 Gr f 24/4 Verglas (IRE)—Abbey Park (USA) (Known Fact (USA)) (40000) **T. J. Parrott**
27 ACCEDE, b f 10/3 Acclamation—Here To Me (Muhtarram (USA)) (24000) **Mrs D. O. Joly**
28 B f 13/4 Captain Rio—Anneliina (Cadeaux Genereux) (10295) **A. S. B. Portman**
29 BAYCAT (IRE), b c 3/3 One Cool Cat (USA)—
                                   Greta d'argent (IRE) (Great Commotion (USA)) (21000) **A. S. B. Portman**
30 Ch f 29/4 Halling (USA)—Covet (Polish Precedent) (11000) **Prof C. D. Green**
31 B c 5/3 Mind Games—Exotic Forest (Dominion) (22000) **J. G. B. Portman**
32 HEARTSEASE, b f 31/3 Pursuit of Love—Balsamita (FR) (Midyan (USA)) **The Hon Mrs R. Pease**
33 Ch f 16/2 Redback—Miss Caoimhe (IRE) (Barathea (IRE)) (16000) **Prof C. D. Green**
34 Ch c 3/5 Captain Rio—Miss Garuda (Persian Bold) (12869) **J. G. B. Portman**
35 Ch f 22/3 Captain Rio—Presently (Cadeaux Genereux) (15000) **Hockham Racing**
36 RUSSIAN RAVE, ch f 16/2 Danehill Dancer (IRE)—Russian Ruby (FR) (Vettori (IRE)) (45000) **The Traditionalists**
37 SAPPHIRE ROSE, b f 5/3 Tobougg (IRE)—Pearly River (Elegant Air) **M. P. Redditt**
38 B f 20/2 Bahamian Bounty—Sharena (IRE) (Kahyasi) (2500) **J. G. B. Portman**
39 Br f 24/3 Where Or When (IRE)—Tancholo (So Factual (USA)) (6000) **Hockham Racing**

MR J. G. B. PORTMAN—continued

Other Owners: Mr H. J. Anson, Mr Jeremy Brownlee, G. F. Clark, Mr. G. Clark, Mr. W. Clifford, Mr. J. Cook, Mr L. Cox, Mr Charles Curtis, Mr. S. Davies, Mr S. E. Dawes, Mr. P. Deal, Mr. R. Dollar, Mr. K. Dougall, Mr. R. Eaple, Mr. T. Edwards, Mrs. J. Garvin, Mrs T. Haiton, Mr. G. Harris, Mr. J. Hawkings-Byars, Mr J. A. Hawkings-Byass, Mrs. N. Haywood Cole, J. S. Hobhouse, Mr. J. Hobhouse, Mr N. C. Hussey, Miss. J. Kempsey, Mrs S. Matthews, Mrs H. Parrott, Mr. J. Pearson, The Hon Mrs R. Pease, Mr. P. Pett, Miss J. Philip-Jones, Mrs S. J. Portman, Mr. D. Powell, Lt Cdr N. S. Seddon-Brown, Mr. N. Seddon-Brown, Mr. C. Shankland, Mr. R Trotter, Mr. C. Vites.

Assistant Trainer: Sophie Portman

---

482 **MR B. G. POWELL, Upper Lambourn**
Postal: Newlands Stables, Upper Lambourn, Hungerford, Berkshire, RG17 8QX
Contacts: **PHONE** (01488) 73650 **HOME** (01962) 717705 **FAX** (01488) 73650
MOBILE (07785) 390737
E-MAIL brendan.powell@aol.com **WEBSITE** www.brendanpowellracing.com

1 **ACES OR BETTER (IRE)**, 7, b g Saddlers' Hall (IRE)—Aon Dochas (IRE) **R. A. H. Evans**
2 **ALLFORTARA (IRE)**, 4, b f Saddlers' Hall (IRE)—Nethertara **M C C Partnership**
3 **AMERICAN WORLD (FR)**, 4, b br g Lost World (IRE)—Rose Laura (FR) **B. G. Powell**
4 **ARISEA (IRE)**, 5, b m Cape Cross (IRE)—Castelfranca (IRE) **J. Studd**
5 **ATACAMA STAR**, 6, ch g Desert King (IRE)—Aunty (FR) **R. H. Gunn**
6 **AWARD WINNER**, 5, b g Alflora (IRE)—Blackwater Bay (IRE) **Mrs C. Argeband**
7 **BATHWICK QUEST (IRE)**, 4, b f Barathea (IRE)—Ninth Quest (USA) **H. M. W. Clifford**
8 **BAY HAWK**, 6, b g Alhaarth (IRE)—Fleeting Vision (IRE) **Miss K. E. Anderson**
9 **BIG ROB (IRE)**, 9, b g Bob Back (USA)—Native Shore (IRE) **P. H. Betts**
10 **BILLYBOB BATHWICK (IRE)**, 6, b g Fourstars Allstar (USA)—One Eyed Lucy (IRE) **H. M. W. Clifford**
11 **BLUEBERRY ICE (IRE)**, 10, b m Glacial Storm (USA)—Call Me Honey **Mrs B. A. M. Studd**
12 **BOSHAM MILL**, 10, ch g Nashwan (USA)—Mill On The Floss **M. D. Gichero**
13 **BRAVE KATIE (IRE)**, 6, b m Pasternak—The Marching Lass (IRE) **Mr & Mrs D. A. Gamble**
14 **BUBBLE BOY (IRE)**, 9, ch g Hubbly Bubbly (USA)—Cool Charm **Exors of the Late J. G. Plackett**
15 **CALUSA SPIRIT**, 5, ch g Rakaposhi King—Gentle Echo **Peter Luff**
16 **CARETTA CARETTA**, 6, b m Mtoto—Salty Girl (IRE) **Miss J. E. Reed**
17 **CHANCES GO**, 5, b g Fraam—Schizo-Phonic **Munster Syndicate**
18 **CLASSIC DREAM (GER)**, 5, b g Grape Tree Road—Classic Queen (GER) **D. A. Johnson**
19 **CONTRA MUNDUM (USA)**, 5, ch g Giant's Causeway (USA)—Speak Softly To Me (USA) **D. J. Coles**
20 **DEFINITELY IT**, 4, b f Definite Article—Bin It (IRE) **The G. V. Syndicate**
21 **DONT EVEN ASK**, 4, ch g Elmaamul (USA)—Gold Halo (IRE) **Mrs M. Devine**
22 **DR HART (IRE)**, 8, b g Dr Massini (IRE)—Christy's Heart (IRE) **Geoff & The Jem Racing Team**
23 **FILM QUEEN (IRE)**, 4, b br f Desert Style (IRE)—Filmgame (IRE) **A. Head**
24 **FONDNESS**, 5, ch m Dr Fong (USA)—Island Story **S. Mannion**
25 **GAELIC GIFT (IRE)**, 6, b m Presenting—Gaelic Leader (IRE) **Leith Hill Chasers**
26 **GELSMOOR LADY**, 6, b m Presenting—Murchan Tyne (IRE) **C. F. Harrington**
27 **HECTOR BARBOSSA**, 5, ch g Fleetwood (IRE)—Salty Girl (IRE) **Mrs P. Smith & Miss Juliet Reed**
28 **ICE AND SODA (IRE)**, 8, b g Arctic Lord—Another Vodka (IRE) **Mrs A. Ellis**
29 **INCHLOCH**, 6, ch g Inchinor—Lake Pleasant (IRE) **Jubert Family & Miss J. Semple**
30 **INDIANA FOX**, 5, b m Foxhound (USA)—Ridgewood Ruby (IRE) **Woodhaven Racing Syndicate**
31 **JOB ONE (FR)**, 5, gr g Kahyasi—Corrossol (FR) **Pertemps Ltd**
32 **JUST PADDY**, 7, b g Supreme Leader—Zaffaran Run (IRE) **Mrs M. Devine**
33 **KERRIEMUIR LASS (IRE)**, 5, b m Celtic Swing—Shabby Chic (USA) **J. P. McManus**
34 **KNIGHTSWOOD (IRE)**, 7, b g Simply Great (FR)—Brymar Lass (IRE) **Mr & Mrs D. A. Gamble**
35 **LAY THE CASH (USA)**, 4, ch g Include (USA)—Shanade (USA) **Peter Webb & Peter Lay**
36 **LISATHEDADDY**, 6, br m Darnay—Erith's Chill Wind **Mrs P. S. Wilson**
37 **LORD NELLERIE (FR)**, 9, b g Panoramic—Epsom Nellerie (FR) **The Opperman Racing Partnership**
38 4, B f Saddlers' Hall (IRE)—Loshian (IRE) **Mr & Mrs W. J. Williams**
39 **LOWLANDER**, 9, b g Fuji Kiseki (JPN)—Lake Valley (USA) **The Opperman Racing Partnership**
40 **LUPITA (IRE)**, 4, ch f Intikhab (USA)—Sarah (IRE) **Mr K. R. E. Rhatigan**
41 **MANDINGO CHIEF (IRE)**, 9, b g Flying Spur (AUS)—Elizabethan Air **Mrs A. Ellis**
42 **MANYOSHU (IRE)**, 4, b g Shinko Forest (IRE)—Poetry (IRE) **Mr J. P. R. Hannon**
43 **MEN OF DESTINY (IRE)**, 7, b g Sadler's Wells (USA)—Caladira (IRE) **L. Gilbert**
44 **METHODICAL**, 6, b m Lujain (USA)—Simple Logic **Woodhaven Racing Syndicate**
45 **MONEY ORDER (IRE)**, 6, b g Supreme Leader—Dipper's Gift (IRE) **J. P. McManus**
46 **MOSHAHED**, 5, ch g Nashwan (USA)—Nafhaat (USA) **Fontwell Park Partnership**
47 **MR NICK (IRE)**, 8, b g Naheez (USA)—Brave Express **Felix Rosenstiel's Widow & Son Ltd**
48 **MYSTIC STORM**, 5, b g Medicean—Mrs Nash **B. G. Powell**
49 **NOBLE BEN (IRE)**, 6, ch g Beneficial—I'm Happy Now (IRE) **D. A. Johnson**

MR B. G. POWELL—continued

50 **OKOUM (FR)**, 6, gr g Dadarissime (FR)—Belle Brune (FR) **Mrs K. Stone**
51 **OPTIMISTIC ALFIE**, 8, b g Afzal—Threads **The Optimists**
52 **PARK LODGE**, 5, b g Clerkenwell (USA)—Gilsan Grey **Mrs A. Ellis**
53 **PRINCESS FLAME (GER)**, 6, br m Tannenkonig (IRE)—Pacora (GER) **Mr & Mrs D. A. Gamble**
54 **PSYCHOMODO**, 6, b g Mark of Esteem (IRE)—En Vacances (IRE) **The Arkle Bar Partnership**
55 **SADLER'S STAR (GER)**, 5, b g Alwuhush (USA)—Sadlerella (IRE) **P. C. Green**
56 **SERGHEYEV**, 5, b g King's Best—Schezerade (USA) **D. A. Johnson**
57 **SIR BATHWICK (IRE)**, 9, b g Oscar (IRE)—Karenda **Mrs S. Clifford**
58 **SITTING DUCK**, 9, b g Sir Harry Lewis (USA)—Fit For Firing (FR) **Mr M. D. Powers**
59 **SONOMA (IRE)**, 8, ch m Dr Devious (IRE)—Mazarine Blue (USA) **D. J. Coles**
60 **STANDING ORDER**, 5, ch g Arkadian Hero (USA)—Simple Logic **Miss J. E. Reed**
61 **STRATN JACK**, 4, b g Rambling Bear—Strat's Quest **P. Banfield**
62 **SWEET ROBINIA (IRE)**, 5, b m Bob Back (USA)—Native Shore (IRE) **P. H. Betts**
63 **TAKE A MILE (IRE)**, 6, ch g Inchinor—Bu Hagab (IRE) **R. E. Williams**
64 **TENDER THE GREAT (IRE)**, 5, br m Indian Lodge (IRE)—Tender Guest (IRE) **Miss K. A. Yip**
65 **THE SILENT KING (IRE)**, 6, b g Muroto—Phar From Men (IRE) **M. D. Gichero**
66 **THESE ARE THE DAYS**, 5, b m Sir Harry Lewis (USA)—Threads **B. P. McNamee**
67 **TORA BORA (GER)**, 6, b br g Winged Love (IRE)—Tower Bridge (GER) **D. A. Johnson**
68 **WARNE'S WAY (IRE)**, 5, ch g Spinning World (USA)—Kafayef (USA) **N. J. Stafford**
69 **WEST RIDGE**, 7, ch g Ridgewood Ben—Western Ploy **C. F. Harrington**
70 **WHICH POCKET (IRE)**, 10, br g Norwich—Toran Pocket **A. D. Peachey**
71 **WHO'S WINNING (IRE)**, 7, ch g Docksider (USA)—Quintellina **Tony Head & Caroline Andrus**
72 **WILD GROUND (IRE)**, 7, ch m Simply Great (FR)—Rapid Ground **L. Gilbert**
73 5, B m Golden Snake (USA)—Zaffaran Run (IRE) **Mrs M. Devine**

THREE-YEAR-OLDS

74 **CAFFE CORETTO**, b f Mark of Esteem (IRE)—Sempre Sorriso **P. J. & Mrs J. P. Haycock**
75 **COOLE DODGER (IRE)**, ch c Where Or When (IRE)—Shining High **Kempton Park Racecourse Ltd**
76 **MORESTEAD (IRE)**, ch g Traditionally—Itsy Bitsy Betsy (USA) **L. Gilbert & R. Gunn**
77 **PICCOLO PRIDE**, ch g Piccolo—Jaycat (USA) **D. J. Coles**

TWO-YEAR-OLDS

78 B c 5/3 Indian Danehill (IRE)—San Jovita (CAN) (St Jovite (USA)) (20000)

Other Owners: Miss C. J. Andrus, A. Cowing, A. S. W. Cutler, Mr B. Downes, G. M. Flood, Mrs A. Gamble, D. A. Gamble, P. J. Haycock, Mrs J. P. Haycock, Mr M. Johnstone, Mrs P. D. Jubert, Exors of the Late P. R. Jubert, Paul Jubert, Mr P. J. Lay, C. A. Leafe, D. Leon, Mr N. F. Maltby, Mrs J. Maltby, Mrs A. May, Mr L. P. McNamee, C. R. Millington, Mr D. O'Flaherty, J. M. Opperman, Mr G. T. Opperman, J. R. Penny, Mrs C. Penny, Miss J. Semple, J. D. V. Seth-Smith, Mrs P. A. Smith, G. D. Thompson, P. R. Webb, W. J. Williams, Mrs M. Williams.

Jockey (flat): G. Baker, M. Hills, T. Quinn. **Jockey (NH):** M. A. Fitzgerald. **Conditional:** C. Studd, S. P. Jones, C. Davies. **Apprentice:** Kylie Manser. **Amateur:** Mr Brian Toomey, Miss C. L. Wills.

483
MR G. J. POWELL, Abbeydore
Postal: Tan House, Abbeydore, Hereford, HR2 6AA
Contacts: **PHONE (01981) 240204**
E-MAIL jppowell@ereal.net

1 **GOODNIGHT TOM**, 9, b g Midnight Legend—Rosealeena **G. J. Powell**
2 **MR POSTMAN**, 7, ch g Private Despatch (USA)—Palm Lady **G. J. Powell**

Assistant Trainer: Katherine Powell

Jockey (NH): R. Johnson, R. Thornton. **Amateur:** Mr J. Mahot.

484
MR K. M. PRENDERGAST, Ross-On-Wye
Postal: Groom Cottage, Caradoc Estate, Sellack, Ross-On-Wye, Herefordshire, HR9 6LS
Contacts: **PHONE (01989) 730314 MOBILE (07795) 363992**
E-MAIL kevin@prendergastracing.com **WEBSITE** www.prendergastracing.com

1 **ALIBY (IRE)**, 8, ch g Ali-Royal (IRE)—Byliny (IRE) **Stanleys Horse & Golf Society**
2 **AWE**, 4, b g Muhtarram (USA)—Fleet of Light **M. J. Langdell**
3 **MUNCHING MIKE (IRE)**, 5, br g Orpen (USA)—Stargard **Wye Diamonds**

MR K. M. PRENDERGAST—continued

4 OUH JAY, 10, ch m Karinga Bay—Creeping Jane **K. M. Prendergast**
5 RED WHARF BAY, 6, b g Ashkalani (IRE)—Forest Heights **K. M. Prendergast**
6 ROUSSEA (IRE), 10, ch g Boyne Valley—River Regent **Mr W. C. Watkins**
7 THE CAYTERERS, 6, b g Cayman Kai (IRE)—Silky Smooth (IRE) **Mr R. D. Willis & Mr M. C. Watts**
8 WATT A WILL, 5, ch m Karinga Bay—Wilming **Mr T. S. Watts**
9 ZANTERO, 6, b g Danzero (AUS)—Cruinn A Bhord **K. M. Prendergast**

Other Owners: Mr Ted Bennett, Mr Paul Stobbart, Mr Dave Thompson, Mr M. C. Watts, Mr T. D. J. Williams, Mr R. D. Willis.

Assistant Trainer: M. G. Prendergast

Jockey (NH): Lee Stephens.

---

485   MR P. J. PRENDERGAST, Co. Kildare
Postal: **Melitta Lodge Stables, Kildare, Co. Kildare, Irish Republic.**
Contacts: **PHONE (00353) 5521401 FAX (00353) 521875 MOBILE (086) 2550079**
E-MAIL prendergastpj@gmail.com/prendergastpj@eircom.net

1 GLASHEEN (USA), 4, b br f Take Me Out (USA)—Just Cuz (USA) **Mrs Catherine O'Flynn**
2 GRAND ARTICLE (IRE), 4, ch g Definite Article—Grand Morning (IRE) **High Hopes Syndicate**
3 TIS MIGHTY (IRE), 5, b br m Fruits of Love (USA)—Floating Agenda (USA) **Joseph P. Daly**

THREE-YEAR-OLDS

4 ANN KASTAN, b f Red Ransom (USA)—Marguerite de Vine **Mrs Mary Murphy**
5 CUMBERLAND FALLS (IRE), b g Tagula (IRE)—Lunar Rainbow (IRE) **Anthony Rogers**
6 WILLOUGHBY BAY (IRE), b c Invincible Spirit (IRE)—Grand Morning (IRE) **Mrs Patrick Prendergast**

TWO-YEAR-OLDS

7 B f 17/3 Invincible Spirit (IRE)—Askmoll (IRE) (Peintre Celebre (USA)) **Baron Peter Von Kap-herr**
8 B f 29/3 Chevalier (IRE)—Beverley Macca (Piccolo) (9973) **Mr Anthony O'Callaghan, Mr John O'Meara**
9 B c 5/4 Atraf—Common Bond (IRE) (Common Grounds) (11582) **Niamh Gannon**
10 INDIAN JEWEL (IRE), b f 27/4 Indian Haven (IRE)—Fag End (IRE) (Treasure Kay) (25000) **Mrs B. Miley**
11 Gr f 14/4 Verglas (IRE)—Lanasara (Generous (IRE)) (20591) **Mr William Durkan**
12 B c 10/5 Viking Ruler (AUS)—Shydico (Nordico (USA)) **Mr J. P. Kenny**

Apprentice: Conor O'Farrell.

---

486   SIR MARK PRESCOTT BT, Newmarket
Postal: **Heath House, Newmarket, Suffolk, CB8 8DU**
Contacts: **PHONE (01638) 662117 FAX (01638) 666572**

1 ALGARADE, 4, b f Green Desert (USA)—Alexandrine (IRE) **Miss K. Rausing**
2 ALLEVIATE, 4, br f Indian Ridge—Alleluia **Mrs S. M. Rogers**
3 ALMA MATER, 5, b m Sadler's Wells (USA)—Alouette **Miss K. Rausing**
4 CARAVEL (IRE), 4, ch g Medicean—Caraiyma (IRE) **Neil Greig - Osborne House**
5 COME APRIL, 4, b f Singspiel (IRE)—So Admirable **Faisal Salman**
6 MY MENTOR (IRE), 4, b g Golan—Vanille **Mr & Mrs Arthur Finn**
7 SOFT MORNING, 4, b f Pivotal—Summer Night **Miss K. Rausing**
8 SPANISH CONQUEST, 4, b g Hernando (FR)—Sirena (GER) **Neil Greig - Osborne House II**
9 TILAPIA (IRE), 4, ch g Daggers Drawn (USA)—Mrs Fisher (IRE) **G. D. Waters**
10 WICKED DAZE (IRE), 5, ch g Generous (IRE)—Thrilling Day **R. T. Ferris**

THREE-YEAR-OLDS

11 ALEATRICIS, br gr g Kingmambo (USA)—Alba Stella **The Green Door Partnership**
12 ALIZADORA, b f Zilzal (USA)—Ballymac Girl **Miss K. Rausing**
13 ALMAMIA, b f Hernando (FR)—Alborada **Miss K. Rausing**
14 ALTITUDE, gr f Green Desert (USA)—Alouette **Miss K. Rausing**
15 ASTRODOME, b g Domedriver (IRE)—Alexandrine (IRE) **W. E. Sturt - Osborne House II**
16 BE FREE, b f Selkirk (USA)—Showdown **Faisal Salman**
17 BUDDHIST MONK, b g Dr Fong (USA)—Circle of Light **Lord Derby**
18 CASUAL GARCIA, gr g Hernando (FR)—Frosty Welcome (USA) **Ne'er Do Wells II**
19 CELESTE, b f Green Desert (USA)—Heavenly Ray (USA) **Cheveley Park Stud Limited**

SIR MARK PRESCOTT BT—continued

20 **CHINA PINK**, b f Oasis Dream—Red Bouquet **Faisal Salman**
21 **CHORAL SINGER**, gr f Daylami (IRE)—Choirgirl **Cheveley Park Stud Limited**
22 **FANDANGERINA**, b f Hernando (FR)—Fantastic Belle (IRE) **Miss K. Rausing**
23 **GENERAL TING (IRE)**, b c Daylami (IRE)—Luana **Lady K. M. Watts**
24 **GOLDEN BUTTON (IRE)**, ch f Trans Island—Velvet Appeal (IRE) **William Charnley & Tweenhills Racing**
25 **IRON CROSS (IRE)**, b g Cape Cross (IRE)—Alithini (IRE) **L. A. Larratt - Osborne House**
26 **LADY CALIDO (USA)**, b br f El Prado (IRE)—Hydro Calido (USA) **Lordship Stud**
27 **LIMELIGHT (USA)**, gr f Dalakhani (IRE)—Last Second (IRE) **Faisal Salman**
28 **MASTER OF ARTS (USA)**, b br g Swain (IRE)—Grazia **Eclipse Thoroughbreds-Osborne House III**
29 **POINTS OF VIEW**, b g Galileo (IRE)—On Point **G. Moore - Osborne House**
30 **PRESCRIPTION**, ch gr f Pivotal—Doctor's Glory (USA) **Cheveley Park Stud Limited**
31 **RECLAMATION (IRE)**, b f Red Ransom (USA)—Overruled (IRE) **Sir E. J. Loder**
32 **ROUGH SKETCH (USA)**, b g Peintre Celebre (USA)—Drama Club (USA) **Mr E. S. A. Belcher**
33 **STARLIT SANDS**, b f Oasis Dream—Shimmering Sea **Miss K. Rausing**
34 **SUITE FRANCAISE**, gr f Hernando (FR)—Entente Cordiale (USA) **Miss K. Rausing**
35 **TORCH OF FREEDOM (IRE)**, b g Statue of Liberty (USA)—Danse Royale (IRE) **J. Fishpool - Osborne House**
36 **ULTIMATE QUEST (IRE)**, ch c Rainbow Quest (USA)—Crepe Ginger (IRE) **Syndicate 2006**

TWO-YEAR-OLDS

37 **AESTIVAL**, b c 29/4 Falbrav (IRE)—Summer Night (Nashwan (USA)) (100000) **Lady K. M. Watts**
38 **AIR MAZE**, b f 16/1 Dansili—Begueule (FR) (Bering) (386100) **Plantation Stud**
39 **ALICANTE**, gr f 17/4 Pivotal—Alba Stella (Nashwan (USA)) **Miss K. Rausing**
40 **ARTY CRAFTY (USA)**, b f 25/2 Arch (USA)—Princess Kris (Kris) **Mrs S. M. Rogers**
41 **ASCENDANT**, ch c 23/4 Medicean—Ascendancy (Sadler's Wells (USA)) **Cheveley Park Stud Limited**
42 **BRAVEHEART MOVE (IRE)**, b c 24/4 Cape Cross (IRE)—
                          Token Gesture (IRE) (Alzao (USA)) (102960) **Moyglare Stud Farms Ltd**
43 **BRETT VALE (IRE)**, br g 13/4 Sinndar (IRE)—Pinta (IRE) (Ahonoora) (35392) **G. D. Waters**
44 **BY REQUEST**, b f 16/2 Giant's Causeway (USA)—Approach (Darshaan) **Faisal Salman**
45 **CASTLE HEIGHTS**, b c 22/4 Selkirk (USA)—Cheviot Hills (Gulch (USA)) **Cheveley Park Stud Limited**
46 **CHORAL FESTIVAL**, b f 31/1 Pivotal—Choirgirl (Unfuwain (USA)) **Cheveley Park Stud Limited**
47 **CROSSFIRE (IRE)**, b c 19/3 Cape Cross (IRE)—
                          Cinnamon Rose (USA) (Trempolino (USA)) (120000) **Charles C. Walker - Osborne House**
48 **DULCE DOMUM**, b f 21/3 Dansili—Enclave (USA) (Woodman (USA)) **N. M. H. Jones**
49 **ELOISE**, ch f 10/2 Hernando (FR)—Eternelle (Green Desert (USA)) **Miss K. Rausing**
50 **FLORENTIA**, ch f 8/4 Medicean—Area Girl (Jareer (USA)) (45000) **W. N. Greig**
51 **FORTUNI (IRE)**, b c 13/4 Montjeu (IRE)—
                          Desert Ease (IRE) (Green Desert (USA)) (193049) **Pacific International Management**
52 **GLIMMER**, b f 17/3 Royal Applause—Mythic (Zafonic (USA)) **Dr C. M. H. Wills**
53 **GOOD HUMOURED**, b c 4/5 Rock of Gibraltar (IRE)—
                          Humouresque (Pivotal) (62000) **Charles C. Walker - Osborne House II**
54 **HAVEN'T A CLUE**, b f 9/4 Red Ransom (USA)—Cool Question (Polar Falcon (USA)) **Lady Fairhaven**
55 **INFLAMMABLE**, b f 5/5 Montjeu (IRE)—Flame Valley (USA) (Gulch (USA)) **Cheveley Park Stud Limited**
56 **INGENUE**, b f 15/3 Hernando (FR)—I Do (Selkirk (USA)) **Miss K. Rausing**
57 **KIND HEART**, b f 6/3 Red Ransom (USA)—Portorosa (Irish River (FR)) **B. Haggas**
58 **NIGHT OF FORTUNE**, b c 16/4 Key of Luck (USA)—
                          La Nuit Rose (FR) (Rainbow Quest (USA)) (35392) **P. J. McSwiney-Osborne House**
59 **OASIS QUEEN**, b f 22/2 Oasis Dream—Odette (Pursuit of Love) **C. G. Rowles Nicholson**
60 **OUR LAST CALL (IRE)**, gr f 7/5 Hernando (FR)—On Call (Alleged (USA)) **Lady C. J. O'Reilly**
61 **PAMPERED KING (USA)**, b c 21/3 Kingmambo (USA)—
                          Last Second (IRE) (Alzao (USA)) (157920) **Faisal Salman**
62 **PASSKEY**, b f 15/3 Medicean—Revival (Sadler's Wells (USA)) **Cheveley Park Stud Limited**
63 **PATRONNE**, b f 7/5 Domedriver (IRE)—Pat Or Else (Alzao (USA)) **Miss K. Rausing**
64 **POINT OF LIGHT**, b c 3/3 Pivotal—Lighthouse (Warning) (90000) **Syndicate 2007**
65 **PREDICT**, b f 31/1 Oasis Dream—Procession (Zafonic (USA)) **Faisal Salman**
66 **RAPID RELEASE (CAN)**, ch c 7/3 Action This Day (USA)—
                          Bail Money (USA) (St Jovite (USA)) (48261) **W. E. Sturt - Osborne House III**
67 **ROCK RELIEF (IRE)**, gr c 17/2 Daylami (IRE)—Sheer Bliss (IRE) (Sadler's Wells (USA)) (128700) **S. E. Munir**
68 **ROYAL DIAMOND (IRE)**, b c 9/2 King's Best (USA)—
                          Irresistible Jewel (USA) (Danehill (USA)) (45044) **E. B. Rimmer-Osborne House**
69 **SPECIAL CUVEE**, b c 23/2 Diktat—Iris May (Brief Truce (USA)) **John Brown & Megan Dennis**
70 **SPEED DATING**, ch c 23/5 Pivotal—Courting (Pursuit of Love) **Cheveley Park Stud Limited**
71 **STARRY SKY**, b f 10/4 Oasis Dream—Succinct (Hector Protector (USA)) **Dr C. M. H. Wills**
72 **ULZANA (IRE)**, b c 18/4 High Chaparral (IRE)—Maritsa (IRE) (Danehill (USA)) (66500) **Rectory Racing**
73 **UNCLE BRIT**, b c 29/5 Efisio—Tarneem (USA) (Zilzal (USA)) (60000) **P. J. D. Pottinger**
74 **VALID POINT (IRE)**, b c 25/2 Val Royal (FR)—Ricadonna (Kris) (68000) **W. E. Sturt - Osborne House**

SIR MARK PRESCOTT BT—continued

75 **VEILED**, b f 17/5 Sadler's Wells (USA)—Evasive Quality (FR) (Highest Honor (FR)) **Cheveley Park Stud Limited**
76 **WATERGATE (IRE)**, gr c 26/4 Verglas (IRE)—
Moy Water (IRE) (Tirol) (38609) **Charles C. Walker-Osborne House III**

Other Owners: Mr Robert Aird, Mr Timothy Bunting, Mr B. D. Burnet, Mr Thomas J. Carroll, Mr Yagnish Chotai, Mr Nigel Cobby, Mrs Megan Dennis, Mr Fred Done, Mr J. Donnelly, Mr Frank Dunne, Mr J. J. Durkin, Mr P Fewell, Mrs S. A. Finn, The Hon Mrs G. Greenwood, Mrs Caroline Gregson, Mr David Harding, Mr Trevor Harris, Mr Chris Jenkins, Mrs Jennifer Lambert, The Hon Pearl Lawson Johnston, Mr David Lowrey, Mr Donald Mackenzie, Mrs Mackenzie, Mr David Redvers, Mrs Jane Rimmer, Skymarc Farm Inc., Mr Ian Spearing, Mr Barry Taylor, Tessona Racing Ltd, The Hon Lady Troubridge, Mrs S. L. Warman, Mr William West, Mr Kevin Wilde, Mr E. J. Williams, Mr David Williams.

Assistant Trainer: William Butler, Pupil Assistant: Robert Stephens
Jockey (flat): S. Sanders. **Apprentice:** R. Jessop.

---

487 MRS A. PRICE, Presteigne
Postal: **The Meeting House, Norton, Presteigne, Powys, LD8 2HA**
Contacts: PHONE **(01544) 267221** FAX **(01544) 267221**

1 **HOH NELSON**, 7, b g Halling (USA)—Birsay **Mrs A. Price**
2 **LET'S ROCK**, 10, b g Rock City—Sizzling Sista **Mrs A. Price**
3 **LOOK THE PART (IRE)**, 8, br g Presenting—Friary Hill **Mrs A. Price**
4 **MARKET BOB (IRE)**, 6, br g Bob Back (USA)—Market Lass (IRE) **Mrs A. Price**
5 **TUFF JOINT (IRE)**, 10, b br g Good Thyne (USA)—The Furnituremaker **Mrs A. Price**
6 **TYUP POMPEY (IRE)**, 7, ch g Docksider (USA)—Cindy's Baby **Mrs A. Price**

Jockey (NH): Lee Stephens. **Amateur:** Mr R. Hodges.

---

488 MR A. E. PRICE, Leominster
Postal: **Eaton Hall Farm, Leominster, Herefordshire, HR6 0NA**
Contacts: PHONE **(01568) 611137** FAX **(01568) 611137** MOBILE **(07729) 838660**
E-MAIL **helen@aepriceracing.plus.com**

1 **CASTLE FROME (IRE)**, 9, b g Spectrum (IRE)—Vendimia **M. G. Racing**
2 4, B c Fraam—Flakey Dove **Mrs M. Price**
3 **FLAMESTONE**, 4, b g Piccolo—Renee **Mrs H. L. Price**
4 **HEARTY DOVE**, 6, b m Overbury (IRE)—Coney Dove **Mrs G. M. Price**
5 **JAUNTY DOVE**, 6, b m Atraf—Flossy Dove **Mrs G. M. Price**
6 **JUST SMUDGE**, 6, b g Fraam—Flakey Dove **Sastastic Partnership**
7 **KNEAD THE DOUGH**, 7, b g Wolfhound (USA)—Ridgewood Ruby (IRE) **Mr N. Field**
8 **MIDNIGHT GUNNER**, 14, b g Gunner B—Light Tonight **M. G. Racing**
9 **PRINCE ROSSI (IRE)**, 4, b g Royal Applause—Miss Rossi **Business Development Consultants Ltd**
10 **SISTEMA**, 7, b g Danzero (AUS)—Shahdiza (USA) **Sastastic Partnership**

THREE-YEAR-OLDS

11 **PRETTY BONNIE**, b f Kyllachy—Joonayh **Mr N. Field**

TWO-YEAR-OLDS

12 B f 9/3 Fraam—Castanet (Pennekamp (USA)) **Mrs C. Davis**

Other Owners: Miss S. Bather, Mr A. G. Bathurst, Mr E. J. Bywater, Mrs Carol Davis, Mr B. S. Jones, Mrs E. R. Kitt, Mr J. C. Penfold, Mr A. E. Price, Mr R. E. Smith.
Assistant Trainer: Mrs H L Price

---

489 MR J. K. PRICE, Ebbw Vale
Postal: **41 Beaufort Terrace, Ebbw Vale, Gwent, NP23 5NW**
Contacts: PHONE **(01495) 306113** MOBILE **(07870) 475156**

1 **MELVINO**, 6, b g Josr Algarhoud (IRE)—Safe Secret **J. K. Price**
2 **PENRIC**, 8, b g Marju (IRE)—Nafhaat (USA) **J. K. Price**

Assistant Trainer: A J Price

490 MR RICHARD J. PRICE, Hereford
Postal: **Criftage Farm, Ullingswick, Hereford, Herefordshire, HR1 3JG**
Contacts: PHONE **(01432) 820263** FAX **(01432) 820785** MOBILE **(07929) 200598**

1 ALASIL (USA), 8, b br g Swain (IRE)—Asl (USA) **Miss V. J. Price**
2 BILLESEY (IRE), 10, b g King's Ride—Rose Runner (IRE) **W. T. Gavan**
3 BOULEVIN (IRE), 8, b br g Perugino (USA)—Samika (IRE) **E. J. Whilding**
4 BUSINESS TRAVELLER (IRE), 8, ch g Titus Livius (FR)—Dancing Venus **Karl & Patricia Reece**
5 CANTIQUE (IRE), 4, b f Danetime (IRE)—Bethania **Tom Thornton, Tony Reynolds, Helen R. Davies**
6 DESERT LOVER (IRE), 6, b g Desert Prince (IRE)—Crystal Flute **Multi Lines Partnership**
7 HARARE, 7, b g Bahhare (USA)—Springs Eternal **Mrs P. A. Wallis**
8 MAPLEDURHAM (IRE), 6, ch g Grand Lodge (USA)—Gold Mist **K. Reece**
9 MONMOUTHSHIRE, 5, b g Singspiel (IRE)—Croeso Cariad **Dick's Neighbours**
10 SON OF SAMSON (IRE), 7, ch g Diesis—Delilah **M. H. Ings**
11 SUPSONIC, 5, br h Marju (IRE)—Nicely (IRE) **W. T. Gavan**
12 WILD KNIGHT (IRE), 11, b g Jurado (USA)—Knight's Maid **Richard J. Price**

THREE-YEAR-OLDS
13 MISTER BEANO (IRE), b c Mull of Kintyre (USA)—Subtle Move (USA) **Mrs K. E. Oseman**
14 PRINCESS ZHUKOVA (IRE), b f Terroir (USA)—Miss Bussell **Fox & Cub Partnership**

Other Owners: Mrs N. J. V. Barrett, A. G. Chapman, S. S. Hill, B. S. Hill, Mr L. J. Macey, Mr J. Macey, Mr N. J. Panniers, Mrs P. Reece, Mr A. N. Reynolds, Ms H. V. Rowley Davies, Mr T. Thornton.

Assistant Trainer: Jane Price

Amateur: Mr M Price, Miss V. Price.

491 MISS J. PRIEST, Kidderminster
Postal: **Parlour Stables, Bank Lane, Abberley, Worcestershire, WR6 6BQ**
Contacts: PHONE **(01299) 896559** FAX **(01299) 896559** MOBILE **(07885) 349266**

1 HEAVY WEATHER (IRE), 10, ch g Glacial Storm (USA)—Tinkers Lady **Miss J. Priest**
2 HISTORY MASTER (IRE), 6, b g Dr Massini (IRE)—Native Emigrant (IRE) **A. G. Goodwin**
3 KARINGA LANE, 11, b g Karinga Bay—Handy Lane **Miss J. Priest**
4 ROGER'S ACCORDION (IRE), 6, b g Accordion—Molly Blaney **The Leppington Partnership**
5 SOMEWIN, 8, b m Goldmark (USA)—Janet Oliphant **Three Men & A Lady**
6 THE POWER OF PHIL, 4, b g Komaite (USA)—Starboard Tack (FR) **A. D. Solomon**

Other Owners: Mrs C. A. Leppington, J. A. C. Leppington, W. D. Leppington, M. A. Lloyd, Mr D. J. Weaver.

Jockey (NH): Jason Maguire. **Conditional:** Liam Treadwell. **Amateur:** Mr R. Burton.

492 DR P. L. J. PRITCHARD, Purton
Postal: **Timber Pond House, Purton, Berkeley, Gloucestershire, GL13 9HY**
Contacts: PHONE **(01453) 811989** FAX **(01453) 521557** MOBILE **(07709) 701531**
E-MAIL **jockeysdoc@msn.com**

1 ADMIRAL PEARY (IRE), 12, b br g Lord Americo—Arctic Brief **Lady Maria Coventry**
2 ANNO JUBILO (GER), 11, b g Lando (GER)—Anna Maria (GER) **Lady Maria Coventry**
3 ARGENTO, 11, b g Weldnaas (USA)—Four M's **Mr I. M. Whistondale**
4 ASHGAN (IRE), 15, br g Yashgan—Nicky's Dilemma **Timber Pond Racing Club**
5 HAPPY HUSSAR (IRE), 15, b g Balinger—Merry Mirth **Mrs T. A. C. Pritchard**
6 HI TECH, 9, b g Polar Falcon (USA)—Just Speculation (IRE) **Timber Pond Racing Club**
7 IDEALKO (FR), 12, b g Kadalko (FR)—Belfaster (FR) **Mr I. Whistondale**
8 JALOUX D'ESTRUVAL (FR), 11, b g Kadalko (FR)—Pommette III (FR) **Lady Maria Coventry**
9 KNOCKRIGG (IRE), 14, ch g Commanche Run—Gaiety Lass **Timber Pond Racing Club**
10 PREDICAMENT, 9, b g Machiavellian (USA)—Quandary (USA) **P. Nurcombe**
11 SUNDAY HABITS (IRE), 14, ch g Montelimar (USA)—Robertina (USA) **The It's My Job Partnership**

Other Owners: Mr C. D. Hazelwood, Mrs T. Pritchard, Dr P. Pritchard, Miss C. J. Shearer.
Assistant Trainer: Mrs T. Pritchard
Jockey (NH): R. Greene, J. Mogford. **Conditional:** Oliver Dayman.

493 MR G. PRODROMOU, East Harling
Postal: Georges Farm, Bryants Bridge, East Harling, Norfolk, NR16 2JR
Contacts: OFFICE (01953) 717224 FAX (01953) 717317 MOBILE (07899) 071001

1 AL RAYANAH, 5, b m Almushtarak (IRE)—Desert Bloom (FR) F. Al-Nassar
2 KING OF KNIGHT (IRE), 7, gr g Orpen (USA)—Peace Melody (IRE) M. M. Foulger
3 LUCY BABE, 5, ch m Groom Dancer (USA)—La Puce Volante M. M. Foulger
4 MEANTIME (USA), 5, b g Point Given (USA)—Interim M. M. Foulger
5 NASSAR (IRE), 5, b h Danehill (USA)—Regent Gold (USA) F. Al-Nassar
6 PHARAOH PRINCE, 7, b g Desert Prince (IRE)—Kinlochewe What R U Like Partnership
7 SHAIKA, 5, b m Almushtarak (IRE)—Subtle Girl F. Al-Nassar
8 SIR MIKEALE, 5, b h Easycall—Sleep Standing (IRE) M. M. Foulger
9 TIA JADE, 4, gr f Imperial Ballet (IRE)—Sunningdale (IRE) Mr I. Mann
10 WAHHAJ, 4, b c Muhtarram (USA)—Scottish Royal (USA) F. Al-Nassar
11 WATTYS THE CRAIC, 4, ch c Erhaab (USA)—La Puce Volante Chris Watkins & David N. Reynolds

Other Owners: Mrs A. Butler, Mr F. Butler, Mr D. N. Reynolds, Mr C. D. Watkins.

Assistant Trainer: Anna Savage

Jockey (flat): O. Urbina. Jockey (NH): R. Thornton. Conditional: M. Roe. Apprentice: Kirsty Milczarek. Amateur: Mr Mathew Smith.

494 MR P. D. PURDY, Bridgwater
Postal: Fyne Court Farm, Broomfield, Bridgwater, Somerset, TA5 2EQ
Contacts: PHONE/FAX (01823) 451632 MOBILE (07860) 392786

1 COURT EMPRESS, 11, ch m Emperor Fountain—Tudor Sunset P. D. Purdy
2 COURT FINALE, 7, ch g One Voice (USA)—Tudor Sunset P. D. Purdy
3 COURT HUMOUR, 5, b g Joligeneration—Tudor Sunset P. D. Purdy
4 COURT NANNY, 14, ch m Nicholas Bill—Tudor Sunset P. D. Purdy
5 COURT OLIVER, 10, ch g One Voice (USA)—Tudor Sunset P. D. Purdy
6 COURT SENOR, 12, gr g Gran Alba (USA)—Tudor Sunset P. D. Purdy
7 SUNRISE COURT, 9, ch g One Voice (USA)—Tudor Sunset P. D. Purdy

THREE-YEAR-OLDS

8 JOLI'S DAUGHTER, b f Joligeneration—Tudor Sunset P. D. Purdy
9 THE BLONDE EMPEROR, ch g Emperor Fountain—Tudor Blonde P. D. Purdy

Assistant Trainer: Alison J Purdy

Amateur: Miss A. Purdy.

495 MR M. QUINLAN, Newmarket
Postal: 93 St Johns Avenue, Newmarket, Suffolk, CB8 8DE
Contacts: OFFICE (01638) 603530 FAX (01638) 603488 MOBILE (07815) 072946

1 DEV (IRE), 8, b g Anshan—Local Dream L. Mulryan
2 DREAM OF FORTUNE (IRE), 4, b g Danehill Dancer (IRE)—Tootling (IRE) N. J. Jones
3 ENCORES, 4, b g Tobougg (IRE)—Western Applause Mr J. H. Moore
4 FINAL BID (IRE), 5, b g Mujadil (USA)—Dusky Virgin L. Mulryan
5 FLASH HARRY, 4, ch g Fantastic Light (USA)—Woodyousmileforme (USA) Mrs J. Johnson
6 FLIGHT DREAM (FR), 5, gr h Highest Honor (FR)—Flight Night Mr P. Moran
7 FRANK SONATA, 7, b h Opening Verse (USA)—Megdale (IRE) W. P. Flynn
8 MARSAM (IRE), 5, gr g Daylami (IRE)—Dancing Prize (IRE) L. Mulryan & M. C. Fahy
9 MOLLY HUSSEY (IRE), 5, b m Flemensfirth (USA)—Tree Oaks (IRE) Mr P. T. Quinlan
10 NO SUPPER (IRE), 4, ch c Inchinor—Be Thankfull (IRE) L. Mulryan
11 PRETTY DEMANDING (IRE), 4, b f Night Shift (USA)—Absolute Glee (USA) L. Mulryan & M. C. Fahy
12 5, Ch g Presenting—Rahan Bridge (IRE) L. Mulryan
13 4, B c Oscar (IRE)—Robo's Sister (IRE) L. Mulryan
14 STEAM CUISINE, 4, ch f Mark of Esteem (IRE)—Sauce Tartar Burns Farm Racing

MR M. QUINLAN—continued

THREE-YEAR-OLDS

15 **CALTIRE (GER)**, b g Pentire—Caluna (SWI) **N. J. Jones**
16 **CHERISHED SONG**, b f Mark of Esteem (IRE)—Waseyla (IRE) **Mrs J. M. Quinlan**
17 **CHINESE TEMPLE (IRE)**, b c Choisir (AUS)—Savage (IRE) **L. Mulryan**
18 **DIDANA (IRE)**, br f Diktat—Daanat Nawal **The Spurs**
19 **LONGORIA (IRE)**, b br f Fasliyev (USA)—Shangri La (IRE) **John Hanly**
20 B f Acclamation—Mind Song **L. Mulryan**
21 **NOWZDETIME (IRE)**, b c Statue of Liberty (USA)—Sensitive (IRE) **N. J. Jones**
22 **REDARSENE**, ch c Sakhee (USA)—Triple Zee (USA) **N. J. Jones**
23 **SILK AFFAIR (IRE)**, b f Barathea (IRE)—Uncertain Affair (IRE) **L. Mulryan & M. C. Fahy**

TWO-YEAR-OLDS

24 B f 8/5 Diktat—Dignify (IRE) (Rainbow Quest (USA)) (26000) **T. Cummins**
25 B f 6/3 Piccolo—Easy Beat (IRE) (Orpen (USA)) **Peter Quinlan**
26 B f 16/5 Clodovil (IRE)—El Corazon (IRE) (Mujadil (USA)) (7000)
27 B f 21/3 One Cool Cat (USA)—Exultate Jubilate (USA) (With Approval (CAN)) (24000) **Mr R. J. Turner**
28 B f 1/3 Needwood Blade—Fauna (IRE) (Taufan (USA))
29 Ch f 15/1 Barathea (IRE)—Grecian Grail (IRE) (Rainbow Quest (USA)) **L. Mulryan**
30 B c 13/3 Polish Precedent (USA)—Herminoe (Rainbow Quest (USA)) (16000) **Dr A. Macchi**
31 B f 10/3 Namid—Inspiring (IRE) (Anabaa (USA)) (32000) **Burns Farm Racing**
32 Ch f 2/5 Bachelor Duke (USA)—Isadora Duncan (IRE) (Sadler's Wells) (4181) **Mrs N. J. McGreavy**
33 B c 4/4 High Chaparral (IRE)—Jumbo Delight (IRE) (Don't Forget Me) (12869) **M. Lowrey TD**
34 B c 25/3 Falbrav (IRE)—Kanzina (Machiavellian (USA)) (6000) **Dr A. Macchi**
35 B c 24/3 Lahib (USA)—La Fija (USA) (Dixieland Band (USA)) (10000) **Mrs N. J. McGreavy**
36 B f 6/4 Zamindar (USA)—Least Said (USA) (Trempolino (USA)) (2000) **Dr A. Macchi**
37 B f 6/4 Bahamian Bounty—Lets Be Fair (Efisio) (4500) **Burns Farm Racing**
38 Ch c 4/4 Storm Day (USA)—Miss N Texas (USA) (Dehere (USA)) (9652) **O'Connor Racing**
39 Gr f 26/1 Act One—Night Over Day (Most Welcome) **D. Jackson**
40 B f 30/3 Namid—Pearl Bright (FR) (Kaldoun (FR)) (28000) **W. P. Flynn**
41 Ch c 7/4 Where Or When (IRE)—Persian Blue (Persian Bold) (8000) **N. J. Jones**
42 B f 14/3 Millkom—Plum (Pivotal) (8000) **Mrs N. J. McGreavy**
43 B c 20/1 Barathea (IRE)—Rebel Clan (IRE) (Tagula (IRE)) **L. Cashman**
44 B f 15/3 Trans Island—Second Omen (Rainbow Quest (USA)) (15500) **L. Mulryan**
45 Ch c 31/3 Namid—She Legged It (IRE) (Cape Cross (IRE))
46 B c 7/5 Lemon Drop Kid (USA)—Tolltally Light (USA) (Majestic Light (USA)) (29000) **P. C. Ashmore**
47 B f 5/4 Acclamation—Waseyla (IRE) (Sri Pekan (USA)) (17000) **Reg Simpson**
48 B f 19/5 Titus Livius (FR)—Zurarah (Siberian Express (USA)) (6200) **A. Pettinari**

Other Owners: Mr Wayne Asquith, Mr P. Asquith, Mr J. P. Constable, Miss T. Coulson, Mr M. C. Fahy, Mrs S. Magnier, Mr M. T. Neville, Mr John O'Connor, Mrs H. V. Palmer, D. Smith, M. Tabor.

Assistant Trainer: N Quinlan

Jockey (flat): T. P. Queally, J. Quinn, R. L. Moore. **Jockey (NH):** Jamie Moore. **Apprentice:** Jerry O'Dwyer, Jamie Jones.

---

496 MR J. J. QUINN, Malton
Postal: **Bellwood Cottage Stables, Settrington, Malton, North Yorkshire, YO17 8NR**
Contacts: **PHONE** (01944) 768370 **FAX** (01944) 768261 **MOBILE** (07899) 873304
E-MAIL johnquinnracing@btconnect.com

1 **AHMEDY (IRE)**, 5, b g Polish Precedent (USA)—Nawaji (USA) **Lady Anne Bentinck**
2 **ALERON (IRE)**, 10, b g Sadler's Wells (USA)—High Hawk **G. Liles**
3 **AMBER WARRIOR (IRE)**, 8, b br g College Chapel—Book Choice **Lady Anne Bentinck**
4 **ARMAND**, 5, b g Observatory (USA)—Guillem (USA) **Lady Anne Bentinck**
5 **AUNTIE KATHLEEN**, 8, gr m Terimon—Lady High Sheriff (IRE) **S. C. B. Limited**
6 **BASINET**, 10, b g Alzao (USA)—Valiancy **Tara Leisure**
7 **BELLANEY JEWEL (IRE)**, 8, gr m Roselier (FR)—Sister of Gold **J. W. Rosbotham**
8 **BLYTHE KNIGHT (IRE)**, 8, ch g Selkirk (USA)—Blushing Barada (USA) **Maxilead Limited**
9 **BOY DANCER (IRE)**, 5, ch g Danehill Dancer (IRE)—Mary Gabry (FR) **Mr A. Turton & Mr S. Brown**
10 **BROOK NO ARGUMENT**, 6, ch m Alderbrook—Gloriana **Lady Legard**
11 **CARAMAN (IRE)**, 10, ch g Grand Lodge (USA)—Caraiyma (IRE) **A. Mann**
12 **CARIBBEAN CORAL**, 9, ch g Brief Truce (USA)—Caribbean Star **Mr J. Quinn & Mr R. Dawson**
13 **CHARACTER BUILDING (IRE)**, 8, ch gr g Accordion—Mrs Jones (IRE) **Mrs E. Wright**

MR J. J. QUINN—continued

14 CROW WOOD, 9, b g Halling (USA)—Play With Me (IRE) **Mrs M. Taylor**
15 DAY TO REMEMBER, 7, gr g Daylami (IRE)—Miss Universe (IRE) **Lady Anne Bentinck**
16 DIG DEEP (IRE), 6, b g Entrepreneur—Diamond Quest **Roberts Green Whittall-Williams Savidge**
17 DOUBLE DEPUTY (IRE), 7, b g Sadler's Wells (USA)—Janaat **Stone Taylor Withey Woods**
18 EDAS, 6, b h Celtic Swing—Eden (IRE) **SCB Ltd**
19 EL CHICO, 4, b c Bollin William—Bred For Pleasure **Ticketee Racing Syndicate**
20 FANTASY BELIEVER, 10, b g Sure Blade (USA)—Delicious **Fantasy Fellowship B**
21 FANTASY EXPLORER, 5, b g Compton Place—Zinzi **Fantasy Fellowship E**
22 FOCUS GROUP (USA), 7, b g Kris S (USA)—Interim **Mr R. Harmon**
23 FORSTERS PLANTIN, 4, ch f Muhtarram (USA)—Ischia **Robert Miller-Bakewell & Mrs A. C. Robson**
24 FUEL CELL (IRE), 7, b g Desert Style (IRE)—Tappen Zee **Mr J. Morris**
25 GAELIC PRINCE (IRE), 5, b g Imperial Ballet (IRE)—Zapata (IRE) **Dawson & Quinn**
26 GLOUCESTER, 5, b g Montjeu (IRE)—Birdlip (USA) **Mr R. Harmon**
27 GOLD HEART (FR), 6, gr g Turgeon (USA)—Shannondore (FR) **Mr & Mrs J. D. Cotton**
28 GRAZEON GOLD BLEND, 5, ch g Paris House—Thalya **Mr J. Rowbottom**
29 HALL OF FLAME (IRE), 8, b g Saddlers' Hall (IRE)—Fleming Run **J. Henderson**
30 HIGH COTTON (IRE), 13, gr g Ala Hounak—Planalife **R. Burridge, H. Burridge, J. H. W. Lloyd**
31 HOLIDAY COCKTAIL, 6, b g Mister Baileys—Bermuda Lily **Estio Racing**
32 KINGS QUAY, 6, b h Montjeu (IRE)—Glen Rosie (IRE) **Mrs M. Taylor**
33 LESLINGTAYLOR (IRE), 6, b g Orpen (USA)—Rite of Spring **Mrs M. Taylor**
34 MASTER NIMBUS, 8, b g Cloudings (IRE)—Miss Charlie **Mr J. Hewitt**
35 MASTERSHIP (IRE), 4, ch g Best of The Bests (IRE)—Shady Point (IRE) **Dark Horse Racing**
36 MAZZAREME (IRE), 10, b g Supreme Leader—Mazza **P. A. H. Hartley**
37 OR D'OUDAIRIES (FR), 6, b g April Night (FR)—Belle Truval (FR) **Gay & Peter Hartley**
38 PACIFIC PRIDE, 5, b g Compton Place—Only Yours **Maxilead Ltd**
39 PEVENSEY (IRE), 6, b g Danehill (USA)—Champaka (IRE) **Dum Spiro Spero**
40 RIODAN (IRE), 6, ch m Desert King (IRE)—Spirit of The Nile (FR) **Mr Lawrence Mullaney & Mr John Marson**
41 ROBEMA, 5, b m Cadeaux Genereux—Germane **Mrs J. O'Connor**
42 SOLENT (IRE), 6, b g Montjeu (IRE)—Stylish **Mrs M. Taylor**
43 TICKET TO FREEDOM (NZ), 6, bl g Cape Cross (IRE)—Macrowave (NZ) **Lady Anne Bentinck**
44 VEILED APPLAUSE, 5, b g Royal Applause—Scarlet Veil **Far 2 Many Sues**
45 VIOLENT VELOCITY (IRE), 5, b g Namid—Lear's Crown (USA) **Mrs S. Quinn**
46 WINTHORPE (IRE), 8, b g Tagula—Zazu **Green Roberts Savage Whittall Williams**
47 ZOMERLUST, 6, b g Josr Algarhoud (IRE)—Passiflora **Dawson & Quinn**

THREE-YEAR-OLDS

48 B br f Marju (IRE)—Anna Kareena (IRE) **Mr Colm McEvoy**
49 BEST SUITED, b f Averti (IRE)—Scarlett Holly **Hutchinson & Waltham**
50 FANTASY FIGHTER (IRE), b g Danetime (IRE)—Lady Montekin **The Fantasy Fellowship F**
51 GRAZE ON AND ON, ch f Elmaamul (USA)—Laena **J. R. Rowbottom**
52 HAWK MOUNTAIN (UAE), b g Halling (USA)—Friendly (USA) **P. Morrison & N. Luck**
53 HIPPOLYTUS, ch g Observatory (USA)—Pasithea (IRE) **Lady Legard**
54 ISLAND MUSIC (IRE), b f Mujahid (USA)—Ischia **Robert Miller-Bakewell & Mrs A.C. Robson**
55 KING FINGAL (IRE), b g King's Best (USA)—Llia **G. N. van Cutsem**
56 KNOW NO FEAR, b g Primo Valentino (IRE)—Alustar **F D C Racing Club**
57 RIVINGTON PIKE (IRE), b g Catcher In The Rye (USA)—Bean Island (USA) **Maxilead Limited**
58 SELECT COMMITTEE, b g Fayruz—Demolition Jo **Which Bits Mine Syndicate**
59 SERENA'S STORM (IRE), gr f Statue of Liberty (USA)—Princess Serena (USA) **R. A. Donworth**
60 TARA'S FORCE (IRE), b f Acclamation—Tara's Girl (IRE) **Tara Leisure**
61 THANXFORTHAT (USA), gr g Alphabet Soup (USA)—Paper Princess (USA) **Mrs E. Wright**
62 UNCLE HARRY, b g Mind Games—Lapadar (IRE) **Mr N. S. Cooper**

TWO-YEAR-OLDS

63 Ch f 5/4 Halling (USA)—Cairns (UAE) (Cadeaux Genereux) (57914) **Mr James McEvoy**
64 DALMUNZIE (IRE), ch f 1/2 Choisir (AUS)—Berenice (ITY) (Marouble) (42000) **G. N. van Cutsem**
65 SOLIS, b c 2/3 Josr Algarhoud (IRE)—Passiflora (Night Shift (USA)) (44000) **Mr R. Harmon**
66 WOTEVA, b f 28/2 Kyllachy—Happy Omen (Warning) (13500) **Mr M. Laverack**

Other Owners: Mr P. Allen, B. Bargh, A. M. Blewitt, Mr S. W. Brown, R. T. H. Burridge, Lady H. L. N. Burridge, P. Coll, Mr J. D. Cotton, Mrs B. Cotton, Mr J. B. Dobson, M. A. Enright, Mr Martin Green, Mr F. M. Green, Mrs P. A. H. Hartley, Mr P. A. H. Hartley, Mr G. P. Henderson, Mr Les Lawson, Mr J. H. W. Lloyd, N. E. F. Luck, Mr D. C. Macdonald, Mr J. Marson, Mr D. P. McEvoy, Mr Robert Miller-Bakewell, P. R. C. Morrison, Mr L. A. Mullaney, Mr G. J. Paver, Mr P. Rainton, Mr A. P. Reed, Mr G. A. Roberts, Mrs A. C. Robson, Mr M. G. Savidge, Mrs Vanessa J. Stone, Mr Robert Turner, Mr Andrew Turton, Mr E. B. Whittall-Williams, Mrs Sue Withey, Mr T. G. S. Wood, Mr E. J. Worrell.

MR J. J. QUINN—continued

Assistant Trainer: Mark Walford

Jockey (flat): Graham Gibbons. **Jockey (NH):** Douglas Costello. **Apprentice:** Keith McDonnell. **Amateur:** Mr Mark Walford.

---

497 MR M. QUINN, Newmarket
Postal: **Trillium Place Stables, Birdcage Walk, Newmarket, Suffolk, CB8 ONE**
Contacts: PHONE **(01638) 660017** FAX **(01638) 660017** MOBILE **(07973) 260054**
E-MAIL **mick@quinn2562.fsnet.co.uk**

1 ANGUS NEWZ, 5, ch m Compton Place—Hickleton Lady (IRE) **Mr M. J. Quinn, Mr J. Dooley, Flanagans**
2 BLACKMALKIN (USA), 4, b f Forest Wildcat (USA)—Farrlesheena (USA) **B. Walsh**
3 BOLD MINSTREL (IRE), 6, br g Bold Fact (USA)—Ponda Rosa (IRE) **The Boys from the Shed Partnership**
4 DRAGON FLAME (IRE), 5, b g Tagula (IRE)—Noble Rocket **Mr A. Newby**
5 FOLEY MILLENNIUM (IRE), 10, ch g Tagula (IRE)—Inshirah (USA) **M. Quinn**
6 MANGO MUSIC, 5, ch m Distant Music (USA)—Eurolink Sundance **Mr B. Morton**
7 RAIN STOPS PLAY (IRE), 6, b g Desert Prince (IRE)—Pinta (IRE) **P. Montgomery**
8 SWAYZE, 5, b g Marju (IRE)—Dance of Love (IRE) **The Pathway Partnership**

THREE-YEAR-OLDS

9 BOOKIEBASHER BABE (IRE), b f Orpen (USA)—Jay Gee (IRE) **Mr J. Henry & Mr J. Blake**
10 HARDCASE, b c Hunting Lion (IRE)—Nordesta (IRE) **M. Quinn**
11 JALONS BRIDEWELL, b c Compton Place—Inflation **Mr J. Dooley**
12 MINWIR (IRE), b g Green Desert (USA)—Elshamms **S. Astaire**
13 REDSENSOR, b c Redback—Xtrasensory **B. Morton**
14 THE DRAGON (IRE), b f Statue of Liberty (USA)—Noble Rocket **Mr A. Newby & Mr J. Dooley**
15 WATERLOO DOCK, b c Hunting Lion (IRE)—Scenic Air **Mr M. J. Quinn**

TWO-YEAR-OLDS

16 ELSIE JAY, br f 7/3 Fraam—Lara Falana (Tagula (IRE)) (3500)
17 MAJ WILLIAM MARTIN, ch c 4/4 Ishiguru (USA)—Hagley Park (Petong) **Mr S. Astaire**
18 B f 28/2 Fayruz—Truly Grand (Grand Lodge (USA)) (3000)

Other Owners: Mr J. Blake, Mr I. Crompton, Mr B. Dunn, Mr J. G. Henry, Mr G. Norris, Mr R. Prime.

Assistant Trainer: Miss Karen Davies

Jockey (flat): F. Norton.

---

498 MR W. J. H. RATCLIFFE, Leyburn
Postal: **Bolton Hall Racing Stables, Wensley, Leyburn, North Yorkshire, DL8 4UF**
Contacts: PHONE **(01969) 624444** FAX **(01969) 624444** MOBILE **(07767) 745471**
E-MAIL **enquiries@billratcliffracing.co.uk** WEBSITE **www.billratcliffracing.co.uk**

1 BEL CANTOR, 5, b h Largesse—Palmstead Belle **W. J. H. Ratcliffe**
2 BINGO ONE (IRE), 5, b m Mujahid (USA)—Barque Bleue (USA) **Bill Ratcliffe Racing**
3 DARK CHAPEL, 5, b g College Chapel—Possibility **Bill Ratcliffe Racing**
4 GUTO, 5, b g Foxhound (USA)—Mujadilly **Bill Ratcliffe Racing**
5 JIMINOR MACK, 5, b m Little Jim—Copper Trader **Bill Ratcliffe Racing**
6 MISSYCOMELIGHTLY, 5, bl m Killer Instinct—Clean Singer **Mr J. N. Sheard**
7 SHARP INDIAN, 4, ch f Gorse—Indian Wardance (ITY) **Camela Racing Limited**

THREE-YEAR-OLDS

8 COSMETIC, ch f Where Or When (IRE)—Cosmology (USA) **J. Hamilton**
9 ETON FABLE (IRE), b c Val Royal (FR)—Lina Story **The Gathering**
10 MY KAISER CHIEF, b c Paris House—So Tempted **Camela Racing Limited**
11 Br g Compton Admiral—Patrician Fox (IRE) **Mr R. W. North**
12 PRIMER LUGAR, b f Primo Valentino (IRE)—Up Front (IRE) **Ms L. Grasby**
13 STYLE AWARD, b f Acclamation—Elegant (IRE) **Bolton Hall Partnership 1**
14 B f Royal Applause—World's End (USA) **Bill Ratcliffe Racing**

MR W. J. H. RATCLIFFE—continued

TWO-YEAR-OLDS

15 B f 13/3 Primo Valentino (IRE)—Bombay Sapphire (Be My Chief (USA)) (3200) **Bill Ratcliffe Racing**
16 B c 1/1 Shinko Forest (IRE)—Patrician Fox (IRE) (Nicolotte) **Mr R. W. North**
17 Ch f 21/4 Needwood Blade—Trilby (In The Wings) (1100) **W. J. S. Ratcliffe**

Other Owners: Mr Louis Bebb, Mr A. Longbottom, Mr B. Pratt, Mr B. Turner.

Assistant Trainer: Elena Ratcliffe

Apprentice: Andrew Mullen.

MR W. J. REED, Umberleigh
Postal: **Stowford Farm, East Stowford, Chittlehampton, Umberleigh, Devon, EX37 9RU**
Contacts: **PHONE (01769) 540292 MOBILE (07967) 130991**

1 ALMOST HERE (IRE), 5, b g Lear Spear (USA)—Second Violin (IRE) **W. J. Reed**
2 QARAARAT (IRE), 5, ch g In The Wings—Filfilah **W. J. Reed**
3 SUNSET KING (USA), 8, b g King of Kings—Sunset River (USA) **W. J. Reed**
4 WADHAM HILL, 6, b m Bandmaster (USA)—Sport of Fools (IRE) **W. J. Reed**

---

500   MR D. REES, Haverfordwest
Postal: **The Grove Yard, Clarbeston Road, Haverfordwest, Pembrokeshire, SA63 4SP**
Contacts: **PHONE (01437) 731308 FAX (01437) 731551 MOBILE (07831) 800172/(07775) 662463**
E-MAIL davidreesfencing@lineone.net

1 AHEADOFHISTIME (IRE), 9, b g Supreme Leader—Timely Run (IRE) **Bar Five Racing**
2 ASBURY PARK, 5, b g Primo Valentino (IRE)—Ocean Grove (IRE) **Mr D.A.Rees, Mr J.McAndrew, Mr R.T.Voyle**
3 GUNSMOKE BLUE (IRE), 8, b g Luso—Linda's Course (IRE) **Dai & Mac**
4 KISHA KING (IRE), 7, b g Dr Massini (IRE)—Lady Elise (IRE) **D. Rees**
5 MISAMON (FR), 5, b g Simon du Desert (FR)—Misaline (FR) **The Supreme Racing Club**
6 RED BUTTONS, 8, b g Parthian Springs—Lady Pokey **D. Rees**
7 REVALLEY, 4, ch c Dreams End—Steppintyme **Mrs J. Hill**
8 RUNNING LORD (IRE), 10, b g Mister Lord (USA)—Craic Go Leor **D. Rees**

Other Owners: Mr N. Adams, Mr K. Bowen, Mr M. Connellan, Mr J. C. McAndrew, Mr D. Rees, Mr R. T. Voyle.

Assistant Trainer: Mr Marc Barber

Amateur: Mr Marc Barber, Mr Lee Inston-Evans.

---

501   MRS G. S. REES, Preston
Postal: **Moor Farm, Sollom, Preston, Lancashire, PR4 6HR**
Contacts: **PHONE (01772) 812780 MOBILE (07789) 436991**

1 BRYNRIS, 4, gr g Perryston View—Isle of Mull **B. R. Podmore**
2 FINAL DYNASTY, 4, b f Komaite (USA)—Malcesine (IRE) **TBN Racing**
3 PITBULL, 5, b g Makbul—Piccolo Cativo **Mrs G. Rees**
4 SWEET SEVILLE (FR), 4, b f Agnes World (USA)—Hispalis (IRE) **P. Bamford**
5 TOPFLIGHTCOOLRACER, 4, b f Lujain (USA)—Jamarj **P. Bamford**

THREE-YEAR-OLDS

6 BRASINGAMAN HIFIVE, b f High Estate—Our Miss Florence **Mr R. J. Morgan**
7 FITOLINI, ch f Bertolini (USA)—Miss Fit (IRE) **The Top Banana Partnership**
8 GULNAZ, b f Tobougg (IRE)—Hymn Book (IRE)
9 KOOL KATIE, b f Millkom—Katie Komaite **Mrs G. Rees**
10 PRINCESS RHIANNA (IRE), ch f Fath (USA)—Persian Sally (IRE) **Aricabeau Racing Limited**
11 TOPFLIGHTREBELLION, b f Mark of Esteem (IRE)—Jamarj **P. Bamford**

TWO-YEAR-OLDS

12 B f 19/4 Fath (USA)—Crimada (IRE) (Mukaddamah (USA)) (24000) **Aricabeau Racing Limited**
13 KATIE GIRL, b f 23/3 Makbul—Katie Komaite (Komaite (USA)) (5000) **Mrs G. Rees**

MRS G. S. REES—continued

14 B f 1/3 Bertolini (USA)—Making Waves (IRE) (Danehill (USA)) **P. Bamford**
15 MINIBUZZ, b g 10/4 Superior Premium—Amy Leigh (IRE) (Imperial Frontier (USA)) (6000) **Mrs G. Rees**
16 SHANAVAZ, gr f 8/3 Golden Snake (USA)—Safinaz (Environment Friend)
17 SUSURRAYSHAAN, b g 26/2 Dilshaan—Magic Mistral (Thowra (FR)) (9000) **Maggie & Eric Hemming**

Other Owners: E. R. Hemming, Mrs M. E. Hemming.

Assistant Trainer: Capt J H Wilson

Apprentice: Ian Craven.

---

502 MRS H. E. REES, Dorchester
Postal: **Distant Hills, Chalmington, Dorchester, Dorset, DT2 0HB**
Contacts: **PHONE (01300) 320683 MOBILE (07715) 558289**
E-MAIL **helen.rees@hotmail.co.uk**

1 GROUVILLE, 7, b g Groom Dancer (USA)—Dance Land (IRE) **Mrs H. E. Rees**
2 HUMID CLIMATE, 8, ch g Desert King (IRE)—Pontoon **Mrs H. E. Rees**

Assistant Trainer: Mr Rupert Rees

---

503 MR A. S. REID, Mill Hill, London
Postal: **Highwood Lodge, Highwood Hill, Mill Hill, London, NW7 4HB**
Contacts: **PHONE (02089) 061255 FAX (02089) 061255 MOBILE (07747) 751603**

1 BARTON SANDS (IRE), 11, b g Tenby—Hetty Green **A. S. Reid**
2 OBSTRUCTIVE, 4, ch g Zilzal (USA)—Emily-Mou (IRE) **A. S. Reid**

THREE-YEAR-OLDS

3 HIGHLAND PATRIOT, b g Pursuit of Love—Gentle Irony **Ms C. F. Bithell**
4 LITTLE KNICKERS, b f Prince Sabo—Pants **A. S. Reid**
5 MR PLOD, ch g Silver Patriarch (IRE)—Emily-Mou (IRE) **A. S. Reid**
6 TESSIE BEAR, b f Red Ransom (USA)—Macaerleon (IRE) **A. S. Reid**
7 TOPHORSNOPEDIGREE, b g Teofilio (IRE)—Happy And Blessed (IRE) **A. S. Reid**

TWO-YEAR-OLDS

8 BAGGY BLOOMERS, b f 31/3 Pursuit of Love—Pants (Pivotal) (13333) **A. S. Reid**
9 EFFECTIVE, b g 21/2 Teofilio (IRE)—Kirriemuir (Lochnager) (6190) **A. S. Reid**

Other Owners: Dr D. S. Myers.

Assistant Trainer: Steve Peirson

Jockey (flat): J. Crowley.

---

504 MR K. G. REVELEY, Saltburn
Postal: **Groundhill Farm, Lingdale, Saltburn-by-the-Sea, Cleveland, TS12 3HD**
Contacts: **OFFICE (01287) 650456 FAX (01287) 653095 MOBILE (07971) 784539**

1 ACCORDELLO (IRE), 7, b m Accordion—Marello **Mr & Mrs W. J. Williams**
2 ALONG THE NILE, 6, b g Desert Prince (IRE)—Golden Fortune **W. J. Hoey**
3 ANTONIUS CAESAR (FR), 5, b g Mansonnien (FR)—Kandania (FR) **Sir Robert Ogden C.B.E., LLD**
4 BARDOLET (IRE), 5, b g Snurge—Bonne Atthenagh **Mrs S. A. Smith**
5 BOLD RANSOM (IRE), 6, b g Lord of Appeal—Bodalmore Rose (IRE) **Mrs G. P. Furness**
6 BRACKENMOSS (IRE), 5, b m Supreme Leader—
Shean Bracken (IRE) **Home & Away Partnership & Reveley Farms**
7 BRAVE REBELLION, 9, b g Primitive Rising (USA)—Grand Queen **Cristiana's Crew**
8 CATEGORICAL, 5, b g Diktat—Zibet **Rug, Grub & Pub Partnership**
9 CEBONNE (FR), 7, b g Pistolet Bleu (IRE)—Northine (FR) **Sir Robert Ogden C.B.E., LLD**
10 CELTIC CARISMA, 6, b m Celtic Swing—Kathryn's Pet **H. G. W. Brown**
11 COLOURFUL LIFE (IRE), 12, ch g Rainbows For Life (CAN)—Rasmara **Merchant Rentals Plc**
12 CRIPSEY BROOK, 10, ch g Lycius (USA)—Duwon (IRE) **The Mary Reveley Racing Club**

MR K. G. REVELEY—continued

13 **DARAZARI BAY (IRE)**, 7, b g Darazari (IRE)—Conna Dodger (IRE) **The Eleven O'Clock Club**
14 **DON'T TELL LOUIE**, 5, gr m Terimon—Wellwotdouthink **A. Flannigan**
15 **FLORAROSSA**, 4, b f Alflora (IRE)—Bayrouge (IRE) **Mrs A. Fulton**
16 **FRIEND TO ALL**, 6, gr m Environment Friend—Noreasonatall **J. M. & Mrs M. R. Edwardson**
17 **HAPENEY (IRE)**, 5, b m Saddlers' Hall (IRE)—Pennys Pride (IRE) **J. J. G. Good**
18 **HEATHCLIFF (IRE)**, 6, b g Glacial Storm (USA)—Gaye Le Moss **Sir Robert Ogden C.B.E., LLD**
19 **HEAVENLY CHORUS**, 6, b m Key of Luck (USA)—Celestial Choir **The Mary Reveley Racing Club**
20 **HERNANDO'S BOY**, 7, b g Hernando (FR)—Leave At Dawn **Crack of Dawn Partnership**
21 **HIDDEN BOUNTY (IRE)**, 12, b g Generous (IRE)—Sought Out (IRE) **M. E. Foxton**
22 **ITS TEESCOMPONENTS (IRE)**, 6, b m Saddlers' Hall (IRE)—Windswept Lady (IRE) **Tees Components Ltd**
23 **JASS**, 6, b g Robellino (USA)—Iota **The Scarth Racing Partnership**
24 **LA RESERVE (FR)**, 7, b br g Cadoudal (FR)—La Domengere (FR) **Sir Robert Ogden C.B.E., LLD**
25 **LE ROYAL (FR)**, 9, b g Garde Royale—Caucasie (FR) **Jemm Partnership Limited**
26 **LEOS QUEST**, 4, b g Robertico—La Femme En Rouge **Mr & Mrs M. Hutton, Mrs Mary Laing**
27 **LET IT BE**, 7, ch m Entrepreneur—Noble Dane (IRE) **A. Frame**
28 **MALECH (IRE)**, 5, b g Bahhare—Choral Sundown **Reveley Farms**
29 5, Br m Turtle Island (IRE)—Marello **Mr & Mrs W. J. Williams**
30 4, Ch f Bach (IRE)—Marello **Mr & Mrs W. J. Williams**
31 **OUTDOOR SALLY (IRE)**, 7, ch m Accordion—Outdoor Holly (IRE) **Mr Godfrey Deacon**
32 4, B f Alflora (IRE)—Pennys Pride (IRE) **J. G. Good, C. Anderson, Reveley Farms**
33 **PERFECT PUNCH**, 9, b g Reprimand—Aliuska (IRE) **Reveley Farms**
34 **PRESQUE PERDRE**, 4, ch g Desert Prince (IRE)—Kindle **J. W. Andrews**
35 **RAMBLING MINSTER**, 10, b g Minster Son—Howcleuch **The Lingdale Optimists**
36 **ROBBIE**, 4, b g Robellino (USA)—Corn Lily **Mrs S. McDonald, Reveley Farms**
37 **SHEKAN STAR**, 6, b m Sri Pekan (USA)—Celestial Welcome **D. Young**
38 **SILVER SYD**, 4, gr f Silver Patriarch—Celtic Sky **The Thoughtful Partnership**
39 **SMART STREET**, 6, b g Silver Patriarch—Smart Spirit **Mrs S. A. Smith**
40 **SOLID SILVER**, 7, gr g Pharly (FR)—Shadows of Silver **Mr & Mrs Paul Mayall**
41 **STAR BEAT**, 5, b g Beat All (USA)—Autumn Leaf **Blyth, Buttery, Tanfield & Wilson**
42 **STARBOUGG**, 4, b f Tobougg (IRE)—Celestial Welcome **Star Alliance (II) & Reveley Farms**
43 **SUN KING**, 11, ch g Zilzal (USA)—Opus One **G. Renton**
44 **SUPREME'S LEGACY (IRE)**, 9, b g Supreme Leader—Lucylet **The Supreme Alliance**
45 **TAZBAR (IRE)**, 9, b g Tiraaz (USA)—Candy Bar (IRE) **The Supreme Partnership**
46 **THE RING (IRE)**, 8, b g Definite Article—Renata's Ring **P. D. Savill**
47 **TIME MARCHES ON**, 10, b g Timeless Times (USA)—Tees Gazette Girl **Mrs M. B. Thwaites**
48 **TIME TO ACT**, 6, b m Rakaposhi King—Bayrouge (IRE) **J. M. & Mrs M. R. Edwardson**
49 **TOSS THE CABER (IRE)**, 6, ch g Dr Devious (IRE)—Celtic Fling **A. Flannigan**
50 **TOTALLY SCOTTISH**, 12, b g Mtoto—Glenfinlass **The Phoenix Racing C.O.**
51 **TRUCKERS LADY (IRE)**, 9, b m Presenting—Classie Claire (IRE) **Mrs C. Reed**
52 **UNGARO (FR)**, 9, b g Epervier Bleu—Harpyes (FR) **Sir Robert Ogden C.B.E., LLD**
53 **VALENTINES LADY (IRE)**, 7, b m Zaffaran (USA)—Jessica One (IRE) **I. Valentine**

THREE-YEAR-OLDS

54 **CASHMERE JACK**, b g Daylami (IRE)—Cashmere **The J. P. B. & D. A. G. Partnership**
55 **SAMBELUCKY (IRE)**, b g Barathea (IRE)—Kalimar (IRE) **The J. P. B. & D. A. G. Partnership**
56 **STAR NATIVE**, ch g Alflora (IRE)—Northern Native (IRE) **Mrs S. Smith**

TWO-YEAR-OLDS

57 **HARVEY'S HOPE**, b c 15/5 Sinndar (IRE)—
           Ancara (Dancing Brave (USA)) (38000) **The J. P. B. & D. A. G. Partnership**
58 **HYDROGEN HIGHWAY**, ch g 31/3 Karinga Bay—Northern Native (IRE) (Be My Native (USA)) **Mrs S. Smith**
59 B c 22/5 Sulamani (IRE)—Pennys Pride (IRE) (Pips Pride) **J. G. Good, C. Anderson, Reveley Farms**
60 **THURNHAM**, b g 3/3 Tobougg (IRE)—Nobratinetta (FR) (Celtic Swing) **J. M. & Mrs M. R. Edwardson**

Other Owners: Mr. R. J. Ainscough, Mr C. Anderson, Mrs J. Bailey, Bard Entertainments Limited, Mrs Marilyn Bauckham, Mr Douglas Bauckham, Mr D. E. Baxter, Mrs Christine Baxter, Mr Neil Bendelow, Mr R. A. Black, Mr J. P. Bladen, Mr John Bladen, Mr D. Blyth, Mr M. Bradley, Mr A. E. Brown, M. J. Burns, Mr Mervyn Burns, Mrs Angela Chatterton, Mr Hugh Chatterton, Mrs Joane Clanson, Mrs M. Clark-Wright, Ms J. Clarson, Mr Dave Clewes, Mr J. W. Coates, Mr E. Coll, Mr A. E. Corbett, Mr J. Crow, Mr Paul Dean, Mr Eric Dean, Mr N. Derbyshire, Mr Bernard Drinkall, Mrs Pamela Drinkall, Mr Michael Dunbar, Mr. J. M. Edwardson, Mrs M. R. Edwardson, Mr J. A. Evans, Mrs H. J. Fish, Mr Michael Flynn, Mr David A. Green, Mrs D. Greenhalgh, Mr R. M. Halliday, Mr Roger Hart, Mrs A. S. Heley, Mr C. Iredale, Mrs V. Iredale, Mr Ernest Johnson, Mr S. F. Lincoln, Mr P. Longstaff, Mr Ron MacDonald, Mr A. Macdonald, Mrs M. S. Mayall, Mr T. M. McKain, Mr Paul Monks, Mr Ian Nicol, Mrs D. A. Oliver, R. R. Parker, Mr Robert Parker, Mr Alexander J. Paterson, Mrs D. L. Pink, Mr Tony Poolay, Mr Clive Purdy, Mr Douglas Renton, Mr John Renton, Mr Graeme Renton, Reveley Farms, Mr M. G. Roberts, Mr Denis Robinson, Mr Jim Rogers, Mr Craig Sanders, Mr J. Scarth, Mr Dave Scott, Mrs Carol Anne Sewell, Mr D. J. Shelley, Exors of the Late Miss E.

MR K. G. REVELEY—continued

Shepherd, Mr Philip Shepherd, Mrs M. Sherwood, Mr Gerry Slater, Mr R. V. Smith, Mr Richard V. Smith, Mrs Ann Starkie, Mr Richard Stephens, Mrs E. Steven, Mr V. P Stevens, Mr S. G. Storr, Mr James Struth, Mr Peter Tabbinor, Mrs Pru Turpin, Mr Michael Walsh, Mr Ron Whitehead, Mr David Wild, Mrs M. Williams, Mr W. J. Williams, Mr John Wilson, Mr Owen Watson Wilson, M. Wood, Mr Malcolm Wood, Mrs C. M. Yates, Lord Zetland.

Assistant Trainer: Fiona Reveley

Jockey (NH): R. McGrath. **Conditional:** Philip Kinsella, James Reveley.

505	**MRS LYDIA RICHARDS, Chichester**
	Postal: **Lynch Farm, Hares Lane, Funtington, Chichester, West Sussex, PO18 9LW**
	Contacts: **YARD (01243) 574379 HOME (01243) 574882 MOBILE (07803) 199061**
	E-MAIL lydiarichards.racing@zoom.co.uk

1 **ACOMB**, 8, b g Shaamit (IRE)—Aurora Bay (IRE) **Mrs E. F. J. Seal**
2 **ATLANTIC CITY**, 7, ch g First Trump—Pleasuring **The Atlantic City Partnership**
3 **DOUBLE M**, 11, ch g First Trump—Girton Degree **Mrs Lydia Richards**
4 **HENRY HOLMES**, 5, b g Josr Algarhoud (IRE)—Henrietta Holmes (IRE) **Mrs E. F. J. Seal**
5 **KAPPELHOFF (IRE)**, 11, b g Mukaddamah (USA)—Miss Penguin **Mrs Lydia Richards**
6 **KING ALFRED (IRE)**, 8, b g Doubletour (USA)—Society Girl **L. Howard**
7 **WORCESTER LODGE**, 7, ch g Grand Lodge (USA)—Borgia **B. M. Mathieson**
8 **YOUNG ERIC**, 6, ch g Midnight Legend—Slippery Fin **The Young Eric Partnership**

Other Owners: Mr A. J. Mills, Mrs Lydia Richards, Mrs Judy Seal.

506	**MR N. G. RICHARDS, Greystoke**
	Postal: **The Old Rectory, Greystoke, Penrith, Cumbria, CA11 0UJ**
	Contacts: **OFFICE (01768) 483392 HOME (01768) 483160 FAX (01768) 483933**
	MOBILE (07771) 906609 E-MAIL n.g.richards@virgin.net

1 **A BIT CHANCY**, 5, b m Hi Nod—Jungle Jeopardy **Mrs J. MacInnes & Partners**
2 **ACCORDING TO JOHN (IRE)**, 8, br g Accordion—Cabin Glory **Sir Robert Ogden C.B.E., LLD**
3 **ALAN'S LEGACY (IRE)**, 5, b g Presenting—Dedham Gale (IRE) **C. Bennett**
4 **ALL FOR LUCK (IRE)**, 7, b g Heron Island (IRE)—Castle Graigue (IRE) **Mr & Mrs Duncan Davidson**
5 **ANDYTOWN (IRE)**, 5, ch g Old Vic—Pitfire (IRE) **R. G. Kelvin-Hughes**
6 **AUTUMN HARVEST**, 4, b g Beat Hollow—Welsh Autumn **C. H. McGhie**
7 **BALLYVOGE (IRE)**, 7, b g Presenting—Ardnurcher (IRE) **C. Bennett**
8   4, ch g Beneficial—Bavards Girl (IRE) **The Market Grafters Syndicate**
9 **BEDLAM BOY (IRE)**, 7, br g Broken Hearted—Evening Fashion (IRE) **Mr A. S. Ambler**
10 **BEN BRITTEN**, 9, ch g Sabrehill (USA)—Golden Panda **J. R. Callow**
11 **BENMADIGAN (IRE)**, 6, ch g Presenting—Dont Tell Nell (IRE) **J. R. Hales**
12 **BENNO'S BOY (IRE)**, 5, b g Accordion—Arctic Tartan **C. Bennett**
13 **BOHEMIAN SPIRIT (IRE)**, 10, b g Eagle Eyed (USA)—Tuesday Morning **Mr & Mrs Duncan Davidson**
14 **BOX WALLAH (IRE)**, 5, b g Accordion—Jacks Girl (IRE) **A. D. Stewart & M. H. Matheson**
15 **BRETTON WOODS (IRE)**, 6, b g Supreme Leader—Bella Velutina **J. D. Flood**
16 **BROADWAY STAR (FR)**, 5, b g Broadway Flyer (USA)—Starry Dust (FR) **Mr & Mrs Duncan Davidson**
17 **CASH BONANZA (IRE)**, 8, ch g Beneficial—Vulcash (IRE) **R. H. T. Barber**
18 **CASHBACK ROSE (IRE)**, 7, b br m Aflora (IRE)—Grayrose Fleur **Niel Manning & Mary Lewis**
19 **CASTLE CRAIGS (IRE)**, 6, b g Bob's Return (IRE)—Graigue Glen **Ashleybank Investments Limited**
20 **CHAPEL FLOWERS (IRE)**, 6, b g Pistolet Bleu (IRE)—Stormweather Girl (IRE) **D. Wesley-Yates**
21 **CLUELESS**, 6, b g Royal Applause—Pure **C. H. McGhie**
22 **COLOUR CLASH**, 5, b g Rainbow Quest (USA)—Ancara **Mr & Mrs Duncan Davidson**
23 **COMMONBURN (IRE)**, 5, ch g Flemensfirth (USA)—Two Choices (IRE) **Mr & Mrs Duncan Davidson**
24 **COOLERBIE HILL**, 7, b g Tragic Role (USA)—Coole Pilate **Miss R. Jeffreys**
25 **CORNERBACK (IRE)**, 6, b m Bob Back (USA)—
                                Dinny Kenn (IRE) **Mrs DMcGawn JDudgeon DKempton PLaverty**
26 **DOCKBRIDGE (IRE)**, 6, br g Presenting—Rahan Bridge (IRE) **T. J. Hemmings**
27 **DOUBLE DEFAULT (IRE)**, 7, ch g Beneficial—Over The Risc (IRE) **Sir Robert Ogden C.B.E., LLD**
28 **DOWD'S DESTINY (IRE)**, 5, b g Flemensfirth (USA)—Windy Run **C. Bennett**
29 **ECHO POINT (IRE)**, 8, b g Luso—Lady Desart (IRE) **The Border Reivers**
30 **ETCHED IN STONE (IRE)**, 9, gr g Roselier (FR)—Wilton Castle (IRE) **Mr & Mrs Duncan Davidson**
31 **EVER PRESENT (IRE)**, 10, ch g Presenting—My Grand Rose (IRE) **R. D. Brown**
32 **FAASEL (IRE)**, 7, b g Unfuwain (USA)—Waqood (USA) **J. T. Ennis**

MR N. G. RICHARDS—continued

33 **FLEMMINGSBOND (IRE)**, 4, ch g Flemensfirth (USA)—Got To Fly (IRE) **R. G. Kelvin-Hughes**
34 **FLYING DOCTOR**, 5, b g Mark of Esteem (IRE)—Vice Vixen (CAN) **Mr T. McNicholas**
35 **FORMBY (IRE)**, 5, b br g Presenting—Northern Elation (IRE) **T. J. Hemmings**
36 **GLEN ROUGE (IRE)**, 7, ch g Fourstars Allstar (USA)—Charcol **David & Nicky Robinson**
37 **GLINGERBANK (IRE)**, 8, b g Supreme Leader—Mauradante (IRE) **James Westoll**
38 **GRAND THEATRE (IRE)**, 6, b g King's Theatre (IRE)—La Grande Dame **Mrs E. E. R. Sloan**
39 **GRANGECLARE FLIGHT (IRE)**, 6, b m Old Vic—Grangeclare Rose (IRE) **Mr & Mrs Duncan Davidson**
40 **GREAT APPROACH (IRE)**, 7, b g Simply Great (FR)—Gayles Approach **Sir Robert Ogden C.B.E., LLD**
41 **GUNADOIR (IRE)**, 6, b m Needle Gun (IRE)—Rent Day **J. R. Callow**
42 **GUNNER JACK**, 7, b g Gunner B—Wayuphill **T. J. Hemmings**
43 **GUNS AND BUTTER (IRE)**, 6, b g Definite Article—Clairification (IRE) **Mr & Mrs Duncan Davidson**
44 **HARMONY BRIG (IRE)**, 9, ch g Accordion—Bridges Daughter (IRE) **It's a Bargain Syndicate**
45 **HAWKWELL (IRE)**, 7, b g Topanoora—Royal Daisy **It's a Bargain Syndicate**
46 **HEY CHARLIE (IRE)**, 6, b g Mister Mat (FR)—Reynards Run **Hey Charlie Partnership**
47 **I'M DELILAH**, 6, b m Overbury (IRE)—Gallants Delight **Mr C. S. Johnston**
48 **JAZZ D'ESTRUVAL (FR)**, 11, gr g Bayolidaan (FR)—Caro d'estruval (FR) **Ashleybank Investments Limited**
49 **JORVEYBROOK (IRE)**, 6, b g Alderbrook—Webb Find (IRE) **C. Bennett**
50 **KING PENDA (IRE)**, 5, br g Presenting—Peacock Feather **R. G. Kelvin-Hughes**
51 **KYALAMI (FR)**, 10, gr g Royal Charter (FR)—Reine Margot III (FR) **R. G. Kelvin-Hughes**
52 **LAHIB THE FIFTH (IRE)**, 8, br g Lahib (USA)—Bob's Girl (IRE) **J. T. Ennis**
53 **LINDA'S THEATRE**, 8, b g King's Theatre (IRE)—Sorara **J. R. Wills**
54 **LORD RAGNAR (IRE)**, 5, b g King's Theatre (IRE)—Shaiymara (IRE) **R. G. Kelvin-Hughes**
55 **MEERTRIX (IRE)**, 7, gr g Lord Americo—Deer Trix **Ashleybank Investments Limited**
56 **MERRYDOWN (IRE)**, 5, b g Oscar (IRE)—Euro Coin Lady (IRE) **Mrs E. E. R. Sloan**
57 **MIDAS (FR)**, 5, b g Grand Tresor (FR)—Mifiguemiraisin (FR) **Mr & Mrs Duncan Davidson**
58 **MIDDLETON DENE (IRE)**, 6, b g Oscar (IRE)—Sharonamar (IRE) **Mr & Mrs Duncan Davidson**
59 **MODICUM (USA)**, 6, b g Chester House (USA)—Wandesta **Mr & Mrs Duncan Davidson**
60 **MONET'S GARDEN (IRE)**, 10, gr g Roselier (FR)—Royal Remainder (IRE) **D. Wesley-Yates**
61 **MONEY TRIX (IRE)**, 8, gr g Old Vic—Deer Trix **C. Bennett**
62 **MR BARNACLE (IRE)**, 7, br g Zaffaran (USA)—Going Native (IRE) **R. H. T. Barber**
63 **NATIVE CORAL (IRE)**, 10, ch g Be My Native (USA)—Deep Coral (IRE) **City Rovers Partnership**
64 **NEW LODGE**, 5, b g Grand Lodge (USA)—New Abbey **Mr & Mrs Duncan Davidson**
65 **NOBLE ALAN (GER)**, 5, b g King's Theatre (IRE)—Nirvavita (FR) **C. Bennett**
66 **NORTHERN LAD (IRE)**, 6, ch g Lord of Appeal—Deep Green **Dark Horse Racing Partnership One**
67 **OFF DUTY**, 4, ch g Beat Hollow—Petralona (USA) **Mr & Mrs Duncan Davidson**
68 **OH YAH DANCER (IRE)**, 6, ch g Portrait Gallery (IRE)—Croi Na Greine (IRE) **Kingdom Taverns Ltd**
69 **ONCE BEFORE (IRE)**, 6, b g Windsor Castle—Poll's Fontaine (IRE) **R. G. Kelvin-Hughes**
70 **ONE SNIFF (IRE)**, 9, b g Mister Lord (USA)—Deep Fern **J. R. Hales**
71 **OSRIC (IRE)**, 5, b g Mister Mat (FR)—Miss Ondee (FR) **R. G. Kelvin-Hughes**
72 **PALOMAR (USA)**, 6, b br g Chester House (USA)—Ball Gown (USA) **Sir Robert Ogden C.B.E., LLD**
73 **PERAMBULATION**, 4, ch g Selkirk (USA)—Rive (USA) **Mr & Mrs Duncan Davidson**
74 **POSSEXTOWN (IRE)**, 10, b g Lord Americo—Tasse du The **J Dudgeon S Leece P Montgomery D Neale**
75 **PREMIER DANE (IRE)**, 6, b g Indian Danehill (USA)—Crystal Blue (IRE) **Jim Ennis Construction Ltd**
76 **PREMIER SAGAS (FR)**, 4, b g Sagacity (FR)—Estampe (FR) **D. Wesley-Yates & Partners**
77 **PRINCE AMONG MEN**, 11, b g Robellino (USA)—Forelino (USA) **Greystoke Stables Ltd**
78 **QUICK MAN (FR)**, 4, ch g Agent Bleu (FR)—Honfleur (FR) **David & Nicky Robinson**
79 **RANDOM NATIVE (IRE)**, 10, br g Be My Native (USA)—Random Wind **J. T. Ennis**
80 **RAYSHAN (IRE)**, 8, b g Darshaan—Rayseka (IRE) **Mr & Mrs Duncan Davidson**
81 **ROLE ON (IRE)**, 6, gr g Bob's Return (IRE)—Banderole (IRE) **Mr & Mrs Duncan Davidson**
82 **RUN TO SPACE**, 7, b g Zahran (IRE)—Need Some Space **It's a Bargain Syndicate**
83 **RUSHWEE (IRE)**, 5, b g Oscar (IRE)—My Baloo **Mr & Mrs J. Timmons**
84 **RYDALE LAD (IRE)**, 6, b g Presenting—Shuil Na Mhuire (IRE) **T. J. Hemmings**
85 **SAIF SAREEA**, 8, b g Atraf—Slipperose **Mr & Mrs Duncan Davidson**
86 **SALSERO (IRE)**, 5, gr g Turgeon (USA)—Mankirella (FR) **Mr & Mrs J. Timmons**
87 **SCARVAGH DIAMOND (IRE)**, 7, b m Zaffaran (USA)—Bucks Slave **M S Borders Racing Club**
88 **SILVER SNITCH (IRE)**, 8, gr g Supreme Leader—Banderole (IRE) **Mrs L. M. Lamyman**
89 **SILVER STEEL (IRE)**, 5, b g Robin des Pres (FR)—Oliver's Queen (FR) **T. J. Hemmings**
90 **STEADY TIGER (IRE)**, 6, b g Presenting—Mindyourown (IRE) **Kingdom Taverns Ltd**
91 **STORMY WATERS (IRE)**, 5, br m Karinga Bay—Chinook's Daughter (IRE) **Lord Cavendish & Partners**
92 **TAMIMI'S HISTORY**, 4, b g Kalanisi (IRE)—Polish Pink (IRE) **J. T. Ennis**
93 **THAT'LL DO NICELY (IRE)**, 5, b g Bahhare (USA)—Return Again (IRE) **J. D. Flood**
94 **THE WHISPERER (IRE)**, 7, b g Supreme Leader—Ring Mam (IRE) **Mr & Mrs Duncan Davidson**
95 **TOPAZ LADY (IRE)**, 7, ch m Zaffaran (USA)—Miss Top (IRE) **Lowthian, Blakeney & Porter**
96 **TRITON**, 5, ch g Observatory (USA)—Questionable **Mr & Mrs Duncan Davidson**
97 **TURPIN GREEN (IRE)**, 9, b g Presenting—Coolshamrock (IRE) **T. J. Hemmings**
98 **TYRRHENIAN**, 5, gr g Blueprint (IRE)—Calabria **Mr & Mrs Duncan Davidson**

MR N. G. RICHARDS—continued

99 **VIKING REBEL (IRE)**, 6, b g Taipan (IRE)—Clodagh's Dream **R. G. Kelvin-Hughes**
100 **WATCH MY BACK**, 7, b g Bob Back (USA)—Gallants Delight **Mr A. S. Ambler**
101 **WEATHER FRONT**, 4, b g Sakhee (USA)—Bright And Clear **Mr & Mrs Duncan Davidson**
102 **WESTGROVE BERRY (IRE)**, 8, br m Presenting—Mulberry (IRE) **West Coast Fiddlers**
103 **YOUNG ALBERT (IRE)**, 7, br g Taipan (IRE)—Smooth Leader (IRE) **T. J. Hemmings**

Other Owners: Mr A. Armstrong, Mr E. Briggs, Mrs J. M. Dodd, Mr Raymond Donn, Mr G. Dowd, Mr G. Dowling, Mr John J. Elliot, Mrs R. L. Elliot, Mr Keith Elliott, Mrs G. B. Fairbairn, Mr G. B. Fairbairn, Mr Mike Futter, Mr G. Grithin, Miss L. Hales, Mr Andrew Hamilton, Mr Marten Julian, Mr D. L. Kempton, Mr S. Keogh, Mr P. J. Laverty, Mr Stephen Lowthian, Col R. J. Martin, Mr R. Paisley, Lord Reay, Miss Joey Richards, Mrs T. R. Riley.

Assistant Trainer: Miss Joey Richards

Jockey (NH): A. Dobbin, B. Harding. **Conditional:** F. Davis, J. Reveley. **Amateur:** Miss R. Davidson, Mr H. Haynes, Mr C. J. Callow, Miss J. R. Richards.

---

507 **MRS P. A. RIGBY, Llangollen**
Postal: **Tower Cottage, Garth, Trevor, Llangollen**
Contacts: **PHONE (01978) 822198 MOBILE (07926) 961504**

1 **FENELLA MERE**, 5, b m Sir Harry Lewis (USA)—Sharp Pet **Mrs P. A. Rigby**
2 **ROCKMAN**, 7, b g Daywelpacificgold (NZ)—Broken Paws **Mrs P. A. Rigby**
3 **SAWYER'S GOLD**, 6, b g Daywelpacificgold (NZ)—Broken Paws **Mrs J. E. Webster**

Assistant Trainer: Keith Rigby

Jockey (NH): Tom Messenger.

---

508 **MR M. G. RIMELL, Witney**
Postal: **Fairspear Racing Stables, Fairspear Road, Leafield, Witney, Oxfordshire, OX29 9NT**
Contacts: **PHONE (01993) 878551 FAX (01993) 878823 MOBILE (07778) 648303/(07973) 627054**
E-MAIL rimell@rimellracing.com **WEBSITE** www.rimellracing.com

1 6, B m Lugana Beach—American Pie **The Beachcombers**
2 4, Ch g Karinga Bay—Azulada (FR) **W. E. Dudley**
3 **COVE MOUNTAIN (IRE)**, 6, br m Indian Danehill (IRE)—Nordic Pride **J & L Wetherald - M & M Glover**
4 **CROSSBOW CREEK**, 10, b g Lugana Beach—Roxy River **M. G. Rimell**
5 **FLIRTY BABE**, 5, ch m Killer Instinct—Flirty Lady **Mrs J. Harmsworth**
6 **HAVE YOU SEEN ME?**, 5, b g Beneficial—Silent Supreme (IRE) **M. G. Rimell**
7 **JUST PLAYFULL**, 6, b g Sure Blade (USA)—Miss Millie **W. W. Stroud**
8 **JUST UNIQUE**, 4, ch g Sure Blade (USA)—Miss Millie **W. W. Stroud**
9 5, Ch m Karinga Bay—Ming Blue
10 **NESNAAS (USA)**, 7, ch g Gulch (USA)—Sedrah (USA) **M. G. Rimell**
11 **ONEWAY (IRE)**, 11, b g Bob's Return (IRE)—Rendezvous **M. G. Rimell**
12 **PERKIN WARBECK**, 6, ch g Karinga Bay—Supreme Lady (IRE)
13 5, Ch m Exit To Nowhere (USA)—Roxy River **M. G. Rimell**
14 4, B g Loup Sauvage (USA)—Sherwani (IRE) **M. G. Rimell**
15 **SOUTHERN EXIT**, 5, b m Poliglote—Southern Sky **L. J. Strangman**
16 **TAKE TIME**, 9, b g Teenoso—Fernessa **Mrs S. J. Cole**
17 **THE MAIN MAN**, 7, b g Double Trigger (IRE)—Papirusa (IRE) **J & L Wetherald - M & M Glover**
18 **THYNE SUPREME (IRE)**, 9, b g Good Thyne (USA)—Lisfuncheon Adage **Mrs S. E. Lindley**
19 **TRUMPED UP CHARGE**, 7, b br g First Trump—Bright-One **Over The Sticks**

Other Owners: Lady Blyth, Mr R. J. Davis, Lady Davis, Mr M. J. Duffin, Mr M. Glover, Ms M. Glover, R. Kidnel, C. Oram, Mr D. J. Pratt, Mrs M. R. T. Rimell, The Postie Partnership, Mr Jim Wetherald, Mrs Lilian Wetherald.

Assistant Trainer: Anne Rimell

Jockey (flat): J. Crowley, L. Morris. **Jockey (NH):** J. Moore, R. Johnson, G. Lee. **Amateur:** Mr M. G. Rimell.

509 MRS P. ROBESON, Newport Pagnell
Postal: Fences Farm, Tyringham, Newport Pagnell, Buckinghamshire, MK16 9EN
Contacts: PHONE/FAX (01908) 611255 MOBILE (07831) 579898
E-MAIL robesons@attglobal.net

1 **BOBBY GEE**, 7, ch g Bob's Return (IRE)—Country Orchid **Nick Brown Racing**
2 **CETTI'S WARBLER**, 10, gr m Sir Harry Lewis (USA)—Sedge Warbler **Mrs P. Robeson**
3 **COLLEGE ACE (IRE)**, 7, b g Taipan (IRE)—Frantesa **Mrs E. A. Prowting**
4 **CYD CHARISSE**, 6, b m Kayf Tara—Silk Stockings (FR) **Dale Hing & Nicole Langstaff**
5 **DAREYNA**, 5, gr m Dansili—Tereyna **Mrs P. Robeson**
6 **DUSKY LORY**, 5, ch m Shahrastani (USA)—Mountain Lory **Mrs P. Robeson**
7 5, B g Selkirk (USA)—Fantastic Belle (IRE)
8 **HEEBIE JEEBIE**, 6, b m Overbury (IRE)—Avec Le Vent (IRE) **Mrs E. A. Prowting**
9 **IMPORTANT BUSINESS (IRE)**, 5, ch g Mutamam—Opus One **The Tyringham Partnership**
10 **MATTAKING (IRE)**, 5, b g Mister Mat (FR)—Kings Comfort (IRE) **The Ravenstone Partnership**
11 **OGEE**, 5, ch g Generous (IRE)—Aethra (USA) **Sir Evelyn de Rothschild**
12 **PALILA**, 6, b m Petoski—Mountain Lory **Mrs P. Robeson**
13 **PLEASURABLE**, 4, ch f Polish Precedent (USA)—Les Hurlants (IRE) **Mrs P. Robeson**
14 **ROCK WREN**, 5, ch g Shahrastani (USA)—Wren Warbler **Mrs P. Robeson**
15 **TISH TOO**, 4, ch f Sir Harry Lewis (USA)—Sister-In-Law

Other Owners: Mr N. J. Brown, D. J. Hing, Miss N. J. Langstaff, D. Yates.

510 MISS P. ROBSON, Capheaton
Postal: Kidlaw Farm, Capheaton, Newcastle Upon Tyne, NE19 2AW
Contacts: PHONE (01830) 530241 MOBILE (07721) 887489
E-MAIL pauline.robson@virgin.net

1 **BENBEOCH**, 9, ch g Hatim (USA)—Phantom Singer **Mrs E. J. Deans**
2 **OVERSERVED**, 9, b b g Supreme Leader—Divine Comedy (IRE) **Mr & Mrs Raymond Anderson Green**
3 **SAFARI RUN (IRE)**, 7, b m Supreme Leader—Fraulein Koln (IRE) **Mr & Mrs Duncan Davidson**

Other Owners: Mr D. Davidson, Mrs D. Davidson, Mr Raymond Anderson Green, Mrs Anita Green.

Assistant Trainer: David Parker

Jockey (NH): R. McGrath, D. Costello. **Amateur:** Mr Luke Morgan, Miss P. Robson.

511 MR P. R. RODFORD, Martock
Postal: Lavenoak Racing Stables, Ash, Martock, Somerset, TA12 6NZ
Contacts: PHONE (01935) 823459 MOBILE (07909) 547249
E-MAIL judith.holton@btconnect.com

1 **GOTONTHELUCKYONE (IRE)**, 8, b g Eagle Eyed (USA)—Notluckytochange (IRE) **P. R. Rodford**
2 **KIRBYS GLEN (IRE)**, 6, b g Charente River (IRE)—Silence To Silence (IRE) **B. A. Derrick**
3 **LAVENOAK LAD**, 8, b g Cloudings (IRE)—Halona **Mrs E. A. Heal**
4 **OUTSIDE INVESTOR (IRE)**, 8, b br g Cadeaux Genereux—Desert Ease (IRE) **E. T. Wey**
5 **SHAZOOM**, 7, b g Regal Embers (IRE)—Dusky Nancy **P. R. Rodford**
6 **TREASULIER (IRE)**, 11, gr g Roselier (FR)—Flashy Treasure **Mrs E. A. Heal**

Other Owners: Mr P. R. Rodford.

Conditional: Kieran Burke.

512 MR W. M. ROPER, Curragh
Postal: French Furze, Maddenstown, The Curragh, Co. Kildare, Ireland
Contacts: PHONE (00353) 4544 1821 FAX (00353) 4544 1821 MOBILE (00353) 8682 34279

1 **BELLEVUE HERO (NZ)**, 11, b g Heroicity (AUS)—Rummage (NZ) **Bellevue Ltd**
2 5, B m Beckett (IRE)—Bianca Cappello (IRE) **Mr M. J. Keogh**
3 **BILLY BRAY**, 8, b g Alflora (IRE)—Chacewater **J. P. Williams**
4 **EDIRNELI (IRE)**, 11, b g Ela-Mana-Mou—Eviyrna (USA)
5 **KINGSDALE PACIFIC (IRE)**, 4, b c Charente River (IRE)—Madmosel John (IRE) **Mrs J. Devey**
6 **M'BOYO**, 6, gr g M'bebe—Parodia **The Cilwych Partnership**

MR W. M. ROPER—continued

7 4, B f Galileo (IRE)—Miss Plum **Mrs J. Devey**
8 **MRS HARDY (IRE)**, 7, b m Flemensfirth (USA)—Laurenca's Girl (IRE)
9 **NELL PETERS (IRE)**, 5, b m Singspiel (IRE)—Hejraan (USA)
10 **PARQUETRY (IRE)**, 7, br m Idris (IRE)—Marquetterie (USA) **Mr M. J. Keogh**
11 **RAILSIDE LADY (IRE)**, 6, b m Nazar (IRE)—Gravina **Mr M. Doyle**
12 **TOGHERSTOWN HOUSE (IRE)**, 9, b h Flying Legend (USA)—Exclusive Edition (IRE)

THREE-YEAR-OLDS

13 **KINGSDALEMILLENIUM**, b f Hawk Wing (USA)—Jinsiyah (USA) **Mrs J. Devey**
14 **LADY NOVA (IRE)**, b f Noverre (USA)—The Woodstock Lady **Michael H. Keogh**
15 **MRS LAUREL**, ch f Atraf—Simply Beautiful (IRE) **Mr W. M. Roper**
16 **TYPICAL JIG**, br c Atraf—Achates (IRE) **Mr W. M. Roper**

TWO-YEAR-OLDS

17 Br g 15/4 Morozov (USA)—Achates (IRE) (Charnwood Forest (IRE))
18 Ch f 30/3 Frenchmans Bay (FR)—Surabaya (FR) (Galetto (FR)) (6112)
19 Ch c 19/1 Indian Ridge—Tout A Coup (Ela-Mana-Mou) (28313)

Other Owners: Mrs V. Cresswell, Miss L. V. Cresswell.

---

513 **MR J-C ROUGET, Pau**
Postal: **Chemin de la Foret Bastard, Domaine de l'Aragnon, 64000 Pau, France**
Contacts: **PHONE (0033) 5593 32790 FAX (0033) 5593 32930 MOBILE (0033) 6102 70335**

1 **ALWAYS KING (FR)**, 7, b h Desert King (IRE)—Always On Time **Mr J.F. Gribomont**
2 **BANDIAMIR (FR)**, 6, b g Keos (USA)—Suadif (FR) **Jean-Claude Weill**
3 **BORN FOR GLORY (IRE)**, 5, b g Sadler's Wells (USA)—Elegant As Always (USA) **Rouget**
4 **CASTELLINA**, 4, ch f Medicean—Protectorate **Mr Le Comte L. De Quintanilla**
5 **CHILL (FR)**, 4, b f Verglas (IRE)—Calithea (IRE) **Mr R. Bousquet**
6 **CICEROLE (FR)**, 4, ch f Baratchea (IRE)—Uryale **Baron G. de Rothschild**
7 **CRISTOBAL (USA)**, 4, b c Aptitude (USA)—Balenciaga (USA) **Mme P. Shanahan**
8 **DARALARA (FR)**, 4, b f Baratchea (USA)—Darakiyla (IRE) **H.H. Aga Khan**
9 **GRANDRETOUR**, 4, br c Grand Lodge (USA)—Entail (USA) **Mr C. Gour**
10 **ILBARITZ (FR)**, 4, ch c Zilzal (USA)—Radiant **Mr A. Lapoterie**
11 **MADANI (FR)**, 7, b g Royal Applause—First Served (FR) **Mr A. Caro**
12 **MEZZO FORTE (USA)**, 4, ch c Stravinsky (USA)—Calming (USA) **Ecurie Brindor**
13 **MISK (FR)**, 4, gr f Linamix (FR)—Gontcharova (IRE) **Prince F. Salman**
14 **MISTER CHARM (FR)**, 8, gr h Linamix (FR)—Miss Sacha (IRE) **Mr J. Ng**
15 **POLY DANCE (FR)**, 7, br h Le Triton (USA)—Dancing Machine (FR) **Mme L. Rabineau**
16 **QUESTION DAY (FR)**, 4, gr c Charge d'affaires—Kings Widow **Mr P. Beziat**
17 **SARUHAN (IRE)**, 4, b br c Danehill Dancer (USA)—Safe And Sound **Mr E. Puerari**
18 **TANDORI (FR)**, 6, b h Loup Solitaire (USA)—Tamaziya (IRE) **Mr A. Caro**
19 **VIVARTIC (FR)**, 5, gr m Verglas (IRE)—Artic Bride (USA) **Mr J.F. Gribomont**
20 **YORKTOWN BATTLE (IRE)**, 4, ch c Pivotal—Moonbaby (FR) **Edmund Gann**

THREE-YEAR-OLDS

21 **ALASKAN WAY (USA)**, b f Giant's Causeway (USA)—Alaskan Idol (USA) **Mr J.P. Dubois**
22 **ALL IN ORDER (USA)**, b f Kingmambo (USA)—Rose Gypsy **Mr Fares**
23 **ANACARDE (FR)**, b c Anabaa Blue—Genuine (USA) **Mr A. Caro**
24 **ARTIKING (FR)**, b c Kingsalsa (USA)—Artic Bride (USA) **Mr Gribomont**
25 **AVANT PREMIERE (USA)**, b f Vindication (USA)—Committed Actress (USA) **Mr J.L. Tepper**
26 **BAHIA NOOR (USA)**, b f Johannesburg (USA)—Bahia Gold (USA) **I. M. Fares**
27 B f Rock of Gibraltar (IRE)—Bells Are Ringing (USA) **I. M. Fares**
28 **BLIND SHAFT (FR)**, gr c Linamix (FR)—Mysterious Guest (FR)
29 **BLOODY WINTER (FR)**, gr c Verglas (IRE)—Embattle (FR)
30 **BLUE EXIT (USA)**, b c Pulpit (USA)—Black Speck (USA) **Mr J. Allen**
31 **BLUE EXPECTATION (FR)**, b f Anabaa Blue—Shining Molly (FR) **Mr A. Caro**
32 **BOCASTAR (FR)**, b f Kaldounevees (FR)—Bocanegra (FR) **Baron G. de Rothschild**
33 **CAIPIRINO (FR)**, gr c Linamix (FR)—Zabumba (BRZ) **Mme L. Rabineau**
34 **CARLIOR (FR)**, b c Orpen (USA)—Carlitta (USA) **H.H. Aga Khan**
35 **CHANGE THE WORLD (IRE)**, b c Sakhee (USA)—Mrs Seek **Lydia Rabineau**
36 **CIGARRAL (FR)**, b c Poliglote—Parallel Universe **Mr A. Caro**
37 **CIRCUS KEY (IRE)**, b f Key of Luck (USA)—Circassienne (USA) **Baron E. de Rothschild**

MR J-C ROUGET—continued

38 **CORONEL MOLDES (USA)**, b c Repent (USA)—Dead Ender (USA) **Anthony Holmes**
39 **CORPS DE GARDE (FR)**, b c Kingsalsa (USA)—Jazzie (FR) **Mr D. Treves**
40 **DESERT NIGHTS (IRE)**, b f Desert Style (IRE)—Midnight Partner (IRE) **Marc de Chambure**
41 **DIXIE GIRL (FR)**, gr f Green Desert (USA)—Diasilixa (FR) **H.H. Aga Khan**
42 B f Thunder Gulch (USA)—Drina (USA) **Ecurie des Monceaux**
43 **ENFANT MODELE**, gr f Peintre Celebre (USA)—Sage Et Jolie **H.H. Aga Khan**
44 **ENTRE NOUS (IRE)**, b f Sadler's Wells (USA)—Dayanata **Micheal Tabor**
45 **FAIR WEST (USA)**, b f Gone West (USA)—Fair Kris (USA) **Mr S. Boucheron**
46 **FALSEN (USA)**, b f Fasliyev (USA)—Ellen (IRE) **Mr Geffroy**
47 **FEVER FEVER (USA)**, b f Elusive Quality (USA)—Valley Fever (USA) **I. M. Fares**
48 **FORGE (USA)**, b c Tale of The Cat (USA)—My Annette (USA) **Mr J. Allen**
49 **GASCOGNE (CAN)**, b f Empire Maker (USA)—Gandria (CAN) **Ecurie des Monceaux**
50 **GATEAU RUSSE (FR)**, b c Fasliyev (USA)—Saralea (FR) **Team Valor**
51 **GENEROZ (FR)**, b c Cadeaux Genereux—Eoz (IRE) **Mr S. Boucheron**
52 **GIPSON DESSERT (USA)**, b br f Orientate (USA)—Gypsy Hollow (USA) **Mr Fares**
53 **GOLDEN SWING (FR)**, b c Miesque's Son (USA)—Belle d'arbois (FR) **Mme L. Rabineau**
54 **GOLDEN THAI**, b f Red Ransom (USA)—Mouriyana (IRE) **Mme la Marquise De Moratalla**
55 **GRADIVA (USA)**, b f Grand Slam (USA)—Ascension (IRE) **Noel Forgeard**
56 **GRANDE APHRODITE (USA)**, b f Grand Slam (USA)—Sweet November (USA) **I. M. Fares**
57 **GRENADIA (USA)**, b f Thunder Gulch (USA)—Great Lady Slew (USA) **Nelson Radwan**
58 **GRIS TENDRE (FR)**, gr c Slickly (FR)—Tendre Pensee (FR) **Baron G. de Rothschild**
59 **GROIX (IRE)**, b c Hawk Wing (USA)—Miss Asia Quest **Mr R. Bousquet**
60 **HAMIDA (USA)**, b br f Johannesburg (USA)—Pertuisane **Robert Bousquet**
61 **HELTER HELTER (USA)**, b f Seeking The Gold (USA)—Moon Queen (IRE) **Mr J. Allen**
62 **HIGH ROCK (IRE)**, ch c Rock of Gibraltar (IRE)—Hint of Silver (USA) **Robert Bousquet**
63 **HIMARIYA (IRE)**, b f Marju (IRE)—Hariya (IRE) **Betty Hermelin**
64 B c Stravinsky (USA)—Histoire Sainte (FR) **Daniel Treves**
65 **HOPES AND FEARS (IRE)**, b c Captain Rio—Saibhreas (IRE) **Mme B. Hermelin**
66 **ILLIZMIT (FR)**, b c Miesque's Son (USA)—Izmit (FR)
67 **INDIAN DAFFODIL (IRE)**, b c Hernando (FR)—Danseuse Indienne (IRE) **Baron E. de Rothschild**
68 B f Poliglote—Irish Arms (FR) **Haras d'Etreham**
69 **KALAN (FR)**, b c Sinndar (IRE)—Kalana (FR) **H.H. Aga Khan**
70 **KING GREELEY (USA)**, b c Mr Greeley (USA)—Royal Terminal (USA) **Mr Puerari**
71 **KITAJ**, br c Sakhee (USA)—Jumairah Sunset **Daniel Treves**
72 **KOMFORT (IRE)**, b c Montjeu (IRE)—Kabuki (GER) **Mme B. Hermelin**
73 **L'AMANDIER (FR)**, gr c Poliglote—L'authie (FR) **Mr Seche**
74 **LAST CAST (FR)**, b f Marju (IRE)—Femme de Fer (FR) **Mr Soriano**
75 **LEONALDO (USA)**, b c Silver Deputy (CAN)—Electric Talent (USA) **Mr Geffroy**
76 **LOBAU (USA)**, b c Fasliyev (USA)—Calico Moon (USA) **Mr D. Treves**
77 **MAGIC BRENT (FR)**, b c Singspiel (IRE)—Silver Singing (USA) **Mme Rabineau**
78 **MAREE BASSE (IRE)**, b f Royal Applause—Mabalane (IRE) **Baron E. de Rothschild**
79 B f Vindication (USA)—Marie J (USA) **I. M. Fares**
80 **MARQUIS YI (USA)**, ch c Hennessy—Belle du Bois (USA) **Mr J.L. Tepper**
81 **MAYWEATHER**, ch c Nayef (USA)—Misplace (IRE) **Mr R. Bousquet**
82 **MEGA BACK**, br c Zamindar (USA)—Gitane (FR) **Jean-Claude Gour**
83 **MESS AROUND (FR)**, b c Sagacity (FR)—Bubba Gump (IRE) **Mme L. Rabineau**
84 **MISS MAYBE (IRE)**, b f Hawk Wing (USA)—Pintada de Fresco (FR) **Andrew James Smith**
85 **MOUSSE AU CHOCOLAT (USA)**, b f Hennessy—Muskoka Dawn (USA) **Mr Fares**
86 **MR DOB (USA)**, b c Dynaformer (USA)—Dorcinea (USA) **Mr J.L. Tepper**
87 **NANCY SPAIN (IRE)**, b f Sadler's Wells (USA)—Alleged Devotion (USA) **Susan Magnier**
88 **NARALINA (FR)**, gr f Linamix (FR)—Narasimha (USA) **H.H. Aga Khan**
89 **NEVER ON SUNDAY (FR)**, gr c Sunday Break (JPN)—Hexane (FR) **Mr D. Treves**
90 **NOOR FOREVER (FR)**, gr f Highest Honor (FR)—Lovely Noor (USA) **Mr Fares**
91 **OSSUN (FR)**, b br f Anabaa (USA)—Lamballe (USA) **Mr J.P. Dubois**
92 **PARFUM DES DIEUX**, b c Cape Cross (IRE)—Moonbaby (FR) **Mme B. Hermelin**
93 **PASBA (USA)**, b f Danehill Dancer (USA)—Peach Out of Reach (IRE) **Mr Radwan**
94 **PEACHMELBA (USA)**, b f Theatrical—Peachtree City (USA) **Mr Fares**
95 **PERROTIN (IRE)**, b c King's Best (USA)—Street Opera **Mr J.L. Tepper**
96 **PERRUCHE GRISE (FR)**, gr f Mark of Esteem (IRE)—Tadorne (FR) **Baron G. de Rothschild**
97 **QUARAYED (USA)**, b f Dynaformer (USA)—Golden Aster (USA) **Mr Keller**
98 **QUEPHAETON (FR)**, b f Trempolino (USA)—Lyphard's Dream (IRE) **Mr Gribomont**
99 **RAUH (USA)**, b c Vindication (USA)—English Lady (USA) **Mr D. Treves**
100 **RECIT BIBLIQUE (FR)**, gr c Kendor (FR)—Biblique (FR) **Mr Seche**
101 **RIPPLE (FR)**, b c Rock of Gibraltar (IRE)—Slipstream Queen (USA) **H.H. Aga Khan**
102 **SABBATH (USA)**, b f Pulpit (USA)—Cuando Puede (USA) **Stuart Janney**
103 **SAN SICHARIA (IRE)**, ch f Daggers Drawn (USA)—Spinamix **Marc de Chambure**

MR J-C ROUGET—continued

104 **SATAN'S CIRCUS (USA)**, b f Gone West (USA)—Delmonico Cat (USA) **Edmund Gann**
105 **SHAKILA**, b f Cadeaux Genereux—Alliata (USA) **Mr Bousquet**
106 **SHEPTON MALLET (FR)**, ch f Ocean of Wisdom (USA)—Ivory Coast (FR) **Edmund Gann**
107 **SHORT STACK (IRE)**, br c Hawk Wing (USA)—Street Maya (FR) **Daniel Treves**
108 **SNOWY DAY IN LA (IRE)**, gr f Sadler's Wells (USA)—Mabrova **David Nagle**
109 B f Kingmambo (USA)—Sophisticat (USA) **Mr Radwan**
110 **SOVIET SUPREME (FR)**, b c Soviet Star (USA)—Praline Rouge (USA) **Mr D. Treves**
111 **STAR ROSE (FR)**, ch c Starborough—Valleyrose (IRE) **Antonio Caro**
112 **STEP SOFTLY**, b f Golan (IRE)—Step Aloft **Joseph Allen**
113 **STOA (IRE)**, b f Peintre Celebre (USA)—Mer Noire (IRE) **Mr R. Bousquet**
114 **TALL PERFECTION (USA)**, b f Distorted Humor (USA)—Above Perfection (USA) **I. M. Fares**
115 **TICOZ (USA)**, b c Cozzene (USA)—Transition Time (USA) **Robert Bousquet**
116 **TRIP TO GLORY (FR)**, gr f Where Or When (IRE)—Trip To Fame (FR) **Baron G. de Rothschild**
117 **TWOMBLY (USA)**, ch c Diesis—Thunder Maid (USA) **Daniel Treves**
118 **WAR OFFICER (USA)**, b br c Grand Slam (USA)—Wonder Woman (USA) **Mr J. Allen**
119 **WEDGE (USA)**, ch f Storm Cat (USA)—Kentucky Rose (FR) **I. M. Fares**
120 B f Langfuhr (CAN)—Western Girl (USA) **Patrick Bellaiche**
121 **WHISPEROR (IRE)**, b gr c Linamix (FR)—Quiet Splendor (USA) **H.H. Aga Khan**
122 **YORKTOWN (FR)**, b c Red Ransom (USA)—Wedding Night (FR) **Mr Mack**
123 **ZALAMA (FR)**, b f Red Ransom (USA)—Zalaiyka (FR) **H.H. Aga Khan**
124 **ZALIYM (FR)**, ch c Cadeaux Genereux—Zalafira (FR) **H.H. Aga Khan**
125 **ZAMORANO (FR)**, b c Zamindar (USA)—Macotte (FR) **Mr A. Caro**
126 Gr c Zamindar (USA)—Zankara (FR) **H.H. Aga Khan**
127 **ZANORA (FR)**, b f Kalanisi (IRE)—Zanadiyka (FR) **H.H. Aga Khan**
128 B c Mujahid (USA)—Zarkana (IRE) **H.H. Aga Khan**

TWO-YEAR-OLDS

129 Ch f 29/3 Distant View (USA)—Affirm Miss (USA) (Sky Classic (CAN))
130 B c 12/2 Hawk Wing (USA)—Always On Time (Lead On Time (USA)) (19305)
131 **ARMY STRONG (USA)**, gr ro c 27/3 Unbridled's Song (USA)—Wonder Woman (USA) (Storm Cat (USA))
132 Ch f 10/2 Johannesburg (USA)—Ascension (IRE) (Night Shift (USA))
133 Ch c 5/2 Giant's Causeway (USA)—Bahia Gold (USA) (Woodman (USA)) (92322)
134 **BAINORAMA (FR)**, b f 12/4 Anabaa (USA)—Lake Baino (Highest Honor (FR))
135 B c 30/1 Langfuhr (CAN)—Baldellia (FR) (Grape Tree Road) (57915)
136 **BELLE CHASSE**, b f 9/3 Kyllachy—Cosmology (Distant View (USA)) (28957)
137 B f 5/4 Tale of The Cat (USA)—Belle Turquoise (FR) (Tel Quel (USA)) (60738)
138 Ch f 2/3 Aldebaran (USA)—Berine (IRE) (Bering)
139 B f 5/3 Fusaichi Pegasus (USA)—Big Hurry (FR) (Red Ransom (USA)) (70456)
140 **BOCAMIX (FR)**, gr c 16/4 Linamix (FR)—Bocanegra (FR) (Night Shift (USA))
141 B f 16/4 Mr Greeley (USA)—Boubskaia (Niniski (USA)) (360360)
142 **CANDIDATA (FR)**, ch f 25/2 Kendor (FR)—La Cibeles (FR) (Cardoun (FR)) (141570)
143 **CARVALLO (FR)**, gr c 23/3 American Post—Starvalla (FR) (With Approval (CAN)) (32175)
144 B c 15/4 Fasliyev (USA)—Catalane (USA) (Septieme Ciel (USA)) (46332)
145 B f 23/3 Elusive Quality (USA)—Charming Lauren (USA) (Meadowlake (USA)) (121477)
146 B f 12/4 Street Cry (IRE)—Chelsey Dancer (USA) (Affirmed (USA)) (97181)
147 **CHERUBINO (FR)**, b c 21/4 Loup Solitaire (USA)—Bubba Gump (IRE) (Charnwood Forest (IRE)) (19305)
148 B br f 17/2 Theatrical—Crafty Atlantic (USA) (Crafty Prospector (USA)) (29154)
149 Ch f 1/4 Choisir (AUS)—Crepusculaire (FR) (Hernando (FR)) (15000)
150 B c 1/1 Dubai Destination (USA)—Darakiyla (IRE) (Last Tycoon)
151 Gr c 27/1 Numerous (USA)—Dibenoise (FR) (Kendor (FR)) (128700)
152 B f 8/4 Gone West (USA)—Dixie Holiday (USA) (Dixieland Band) (102040)
153 **DREAMETTE (USA)**, b br f 26/4 Fusaichi Pegasus (USA)—Volga (USA) (Caerleon (USA))
154 **DUC D'ALENCON (IRE)**, b c 4/3 Nayef (USA)—Ma Paloma (FR) (Highest Honor (FR)) (48262)
155 **ENDLESS TRIUMPH (IRE)**, b f 23/2 Gone West (USA)—Bush Triumph (USA) (Trempolino (USA))
156 B c 3/2 Grand Slam (USA)—Extra Fancy (USA) (Danzig (USA)) (64350)
157 **FAISEUR DE ROI (FR)**, gr c 13/3 Nombre Premier—Seal of Cause (IRE) (Royal Academy (USA))
158 B c 4/3 Sakhee (USA)—Fascinating Hill (FR) (Danehill (USA)) (64350)
159 **FULL SNOW MOON (USA)**, b f 27/1 Vindication (USA)—Netherland (ARG) (Roy (USA)) (48590)
160 **GAELIC SILVER (FR)**, b c 14/4 Lando (GER)—Galatza (FR) (Johann Quatz (FR)) (32175)
161 **GALUPIN (FR)**, b c 13/2 Loup Solitaire (FR)—Magic Kaldoun (FR) (Kaldoun (FR)) (10296)
162 B c 21/4 Giant's Causeway (USA)—Graceful Manor (FR) (Cure The Blues (USA)) (77745)
163 **GRANITIK**, b c 29/1 Intikhab (USA)—Grosgrain (USA) (Diesis) (74002)
164 B c 4/4 Lando (GER)—Green Way (FR) (Green Tune (USA)) (19305)
165 **GREYLADY (FR)**, gr f 3/3 Poliglote—Lady Stella (FR) (Shining Steel)
166 Gr ro f 25/1 Pleasantly Perfect (USA)—Grisonnante (FR) (Kaldoun (FR)) (90090)

MR J-C ROUGET—continued

167 **HIGH PERFECTION (IRE)**, b f 31/1 High Chaparral (IRE)—Pedicure (Atticus (USA)) (57915)
168 **HISTORY BOY (USA)**, b c 21/4 Grand Slam (USA)—Rare Blend (USA) (Bates Motel (USA))
169 **HOMEBOUND (USA)**, b br f 12/5 Dixie Union (USA)—Black Speck (USA) (Arch (USA))
170 Ch f 4/3 Seeking The Gold (USA)—Hopes and Fears (USA) (Mt Livermore (USA)) (97181)
171 **INTERIOR (USA)**, b f 22/2 Fusaichi Pegasus (USA)—Binya (GER) (Royal Solo (IRE))
172 B c 26/2 Giant's Causeway (USA)—Kristi (USA) (St Jovite (USA)) (58309)
173 Gr f 21/4 Linamix (FR)—Labour of Love (USA) (Silver Deputy (CAN)) (61132)
174 **LAGO DI GARDA**, gr c 9/4 Linamix (FR)—Narasimha (USA) (Nureyev (USA)) (48262)
175 **LANGRUNE (IRE)**, b f 14/1 Fasliyev (USA)—Habilea (FR) (Grand Lodge (USA)) (64350)
176 **LE HAVRE (IRE)**, b c 4/2 Noverre (USA)—Marie Rheinberg (GER) (Surako (GER)) (64350)
177 B f 4/2 Grand Slam (USA)—Lemon Lady (USA) (Lemon Drop Kid (USA)) (72886)
178 B f 2/2 Dixie Union (USA)—Libertaire (USA) (Highest Honor (FR)) (63168)
179 B c 25/4 Grand Slam (USA)—Light Show (USA) (Pleasant Colony (USA)) (68027)
180 **LITTLE GAME**, b c 25/3 Kendor (FR)—Isalou (FR) (Unfuwain (USA))
181 **LONIA BLUE (FR)**, b f 11/4 Anabaa Blue—Lonia (GER) (Royal Academy (USA)) (18661)
182 **LOS GIGANTES (FR)**, b c 1/2 Kendor (FR)—Suerte (Halling (USA)) (51480)
183 B f 18/1 Zamindar (USA)—Louve de Saron (FR) (Loup Solitaire (USA)) (135135)
184 Gr c 14/3 Slickly (FR)—Luna Hill (FR) (Danehill (USA)) (48262)
185 **LUNA JOLIE (FR)**, b f 18/2 Septieme Ciel (USA)—Lignite (FR) (Priolo (USA)) (4504)
186 B c 19/3 Fusaichi Pegasus (USA)—Luna Wells (IRE) (Sadler's Wells (USA)) (131195)
187 B f 4/3 Diktat—Lunaba (FR) (Anabaa (USA)) (54697)
188 B f 1/1 Fasliyev (USA)—Lunatoria (IRE) (Vettori (IRE))
189 B f 12/5 A P Indy (USA)—Macoumba (USA) (Mr Prospector (USA))
190 **MAD MASTER (IRE)**, ch f 30/3 Tale of The Cat (USA)—Madam Minister (CAN) (Deputy Minister (CAN))
191 **MAGANY (FR)**, b c 11/3 American Post—Miryea (FR) (Shining Steel) (20592)
192 B c 1/1 Rainbow Quest (USA)—Massatixa (FR) (Linamix (FR))
193 **MONEY HUMOR (IRE)**, ch f 7/5 Distorted Humor (USA)—Paulette (USA) (Deputy Minister (CAN))
194 Br c 11/4 Diktat—Mouriyana (IRE) (Akarad (FR)) (26000)
195 **NAVAL OFFICER (USA)**, b c 22/4 Tale of The Cat (USA)—Wandering Star (USA) (Red Ransom (USA))
196 B c 31/3 Orpen (USA)—Nefouda (FR) (Neverneyev (USA)) (16087)
197 B f 18/2 Anabaa (USA)—Night Tune (FR) (Night Shift (USA)) (51480)
198 **NIZAMABAD (FR)**, ch c 25/1 Gold Away (IRE)—Nasriyda (FR) (Darshaan)
199 B c 2/2 Arch (USA)—Nobilissime (Halling (USA)) (54697)
200 **NOORISSUN (IRE)**, b f 20/3 Chapel Royal (USA)—Sunburst (Gone West (USA))
201 Gr c 13/5 Linamix (FR)—Peace Talk (FR) (Sadler's Wells (USA)) (77220)
202 B f 25/1 Grand Slam (USA)—Perilous Night (USA) (Coronado's Quest (USA)) (97181)
203 B c 16/3 Linamix (FR)—Pink And Red (USA) (Red Ransom (USA))
204 **POLITEO (FR)**, ch c 13/3 Lando (GER)—Italienne (USA) (Distant View (USA)) (35392)
205 **PULPIT POINT (USA)**, b c 1/2 Pulpit (USA)—Point Gained (USA) (Hennessy (USA)) (22837)
206 B f 31/3 Gone West (USA)—Que Belle (CAN) (Seattle Dancer (USA)) (218658)
207 Gr f 1/1 Clodovil (IRE)—Quiet Splendor (USA) (Unbridled (USA))
208 B f 27/3 Red Ransom (USA)—Raisonnable (Common Grounds) (70785)
209 **RASHDINGUE (FR)**, gr c 27/1 Rashbag—Flutixoa (FR) (Linamix (FR)) (11583)
210 Gr c 9/3 Linamix (FR)—Rashiqa (USA) (Diesis)
211 **REGISTERED NURSE (USA)**, gr ro f 28/4 Unbridled's Song (USA)—Moon Queen (IRE) (Sadler's Wells (USA))
212 **REX REGINA (IRE)**, b f 23/3 King's Best (USA)—Mrs Ting (USA) (Lyphard (USA)) (80437)
213 Ch f 31/3 Pleasantly Perfect (USA)—Ring of Fire (USA) (Nureyev (USA)) (28957)
214 B c 27/1 Johannesburg (USA)—Rose Bourbon (USA) (Woodman (USA)) (48590)
215 **RYMAN (USA)**, b c 30/4 Elusive Quality (USA)—Letgomyecho (USA) (Menifee (USA)) (48590)
216 B f 5/2 Stravinsky (USA)—Sachet (USA) (Royal Academy (USA))
217 B c 1/1 Cape Cross (IRE)—Saga d'ouilly (FR) (Linamix (FR))
218 **SAINTE ADRESSE**, b f 25/1 Elusive City (USA)—Queseraisjesanstoi (FR) (Rainbow Quest (USA)) (48262)
219 **SANTA BIATRA (FR)**, b f 25/5 Highest Honor (FR)—Albiatra (USA) (Dixieland Band (USA))
220 B c 1/1 Red Ransom (USA)—Santiago Blue (USA) (Relaunch (USA))
221 Gr c 10/4 Linamix (FR)—Sarkala (IRE) (Caerleon (USA))
222 B c 9/4 The Cliff's Edge (USA)—Satin Breeze (USA) (Fly So Free (USA)) (5830)
223 B f 4/4 Malibu Moon (USA)—Scalene (USA) (Dehere (USA)) (19436)
224 B f 19/3 Highest Honour (FR)—Shawara (IRE) (Barathea (IRE))
225 B c 14/1 Smarty Jones (USA)—Shemita (IRE) (Sadler's Wells (USA)) (72886)
226 B f 3/4 Grand Slam (USA)—Sigatoka (USA) (Storm Cat (USA)) (82604)
227 B c 21/2 Giant's Causeway (USA)—Starry Dreamer (USA) (Rubiano (USA))
228 Gr f 7/4 Linamix (FR)—Stellar Waltz (FR) (Starborough) (51480)
229 B c 12/4 Night Shift (USA)—Street Maya (FR) (Mtoto) (16731)
230 Gr c 1/1 Linamix (FR)—Super View (USA) (Distant View (USA))
231 B c 11/5 Okawango (USA)—Super Vite (USA) (Septieme Ciel (USA)) (33462)
232 **SYMBA'S DREAM (USA)**, gr ro f 30/1 Vindication (USA)—Lyphard Gal (USA) (Lyphard (USA))

MR J-C ROUGET—continued

233 B f 5/5 Giant's Causeway (USA)—Takesmybreathaway (USA) (Gone West (USA)) (279397)
234 B c 10/3 Linamix (FR)—Valses Pour Moi (USA) (Gate Dancer (USA)) (22522)
235 B br f 30/3 Red Ransom (USA)—Vayeva (IRE) (Kahyasi)
236 B f 6/4 Hawk Wing (USA)—Viva Maria (FR) (Kendor (FR)) (51480)
237 **VOLVER (IRE)**, ch f 30/1 Danehill Dancer (IRE)—Chanteleau (USA) (A P Indy (USA)) (48262)
238 B f 20/4 Galileo (IRE)—Wait For Spring (USA) (Seeking The Gold (USA)) (89893)
239 Gr ro f 11/4 El Prado (USA)—Walker's Gal (USA) (Woodman (USA)) (155490)
240 **WANGOKAYE (FR)**, b c 3/2 Okawango (USA)—River Ballade (USA) (Irish River (FR)) (27027)
241 **WAR POWER (USA)**, b br c 5/2 Pulpit—Tempo West (USA) (Rahy (USA))
242 B c 30/3 Grand Slam (USA)—Wilderness Area (USA) (Deputy Minister (CAN)) (46161)

---

514 **MR R. ROWE, Pulborough**
Postal: Ashleigh House Stables, Sullington Lane, Storrington, Pulborough, West Sussex, RH20 4AE
Contacts: PHONE (01903) 742871 FAX (01903) 740110 MOBILE (07831) 345636
E-MAIL r.rowe.racing@virgin.net WEBSITE www.richardrowe-racing.co.uk

1 **ACERTACK (IRE)**, 11, b g Supreme Leader—Ask The Madam **K. Hunter**
2 **ALPHA GAMBLE (IRE)**, 8, ch g Alphabatim (USA)—Caher Cross (IRE) **Capt A. Pratt**
3 **BROADCASTING (IRE)**, 5, b br g Presenting—Supreme Parsonetta (IRE) **Mr R. N. Alwen**
4 **BURREN LEGEND (IRE)**, 7, b g Flying Legend (USA)—Burren View (IRE) **T. Thompson**
5 **CHARLESTON**, 7, ch g Pursuit of Love—Discomatic (USA) **R. Rowe**
6 **ELLIOTT**, 6, b g I'm Supposin—Kiloran Bay **Mrs L. I. Scott**
7 **FRENCH DIRECTION (IRE)**, 9, ch g John French—Shelikesitstraight (IRE) **Mrs P. E. Proctor**
8 **FUNNY FELLOW**, 6, b g Defacto (USA)—Royal Comedian **T. L. Clowes**
9 **HALF COCKED**, 6, b g Double Trigger (IRE)—Half Asleep **Richard Rowe Racing Partnership**
10 **HEY PRESTO**, 8, b g Piccolo—Upping The Tempo **R. Rowe**
11 **ISLAND STREAM (IRE)**, 9, b g Turtle Island (IRE)—Tilbrook (IRE) **M. J. Deasley**
12 **KING COAL (IRE)**, 9, b br g Anshan—Lucky Trout **Richard Rowe Racing Partnership**
13 **KING LOUIS (FR)**, 7, b g Nikos—Rotina (FR) **Capt A. Pratt**
14 **LORD 'N' MASTER (IRE)**, 12, b g Lord Americo—Miss Good Night **Exors of the Late Dr W. B. Alexander**
15 **LORD APPELLARE (IRE)**, 7, ch g Lord of Appeal—Rainbow Alliance (IRE) **The Reality Partnership**
16 **MANELE BAY**, 5, ch m Karinga Bay—Lacounsel (FR) **Capt Adrian Pratt & Friends**
17 **MISTER PINK**, 8, gr g Accordion—Place Stephanie **H. P. J. Lowe**
18 **MOUNT OSCAR (IRE)**, 9, b g Oscar (IRE)—Sweet Mount (IRE) **Mrs J. R. Bishop**
19 **MUTTLEY MAGUIRE (IRE)**, 9, b g Zaffaran (USA)—Alavie (FR) **Mrs J. R. Bishop**
20 **POCKET ACES (IRE)**, 6, b g Dr Massini (IRE)—Mrs Mustard (IRE) **The Encore Partnership III**
21 **RYDERS STORM (USA)**, 9, b br g Dynaformer (USA)—Justicara **Ms E. J. Southall**
22 **SATIN STARLIGHT**, 7, b m I'm Supposin (IRE)—Taciturn (USA) **Winterfields Farm Ltd**
23 **SUNNY AFTERNOON**, 8, ch m Atraf—Pinup **R. Rowe**
24 **SUPPOSE I'M STUPID**, 6, b m I'm Supposin (IRE)—Stupid Cupid **Winterfields Farm Ltd**
25 **UNCLE ELI (IRE)**, 6, b g Raintrap—Yosna (FR) **Mrs J. R. Bishop**

Other Owners: A. Blades, Mr D. M. Bradshaw, Mrs H. C. G. Butcher, Mrs J. Case, Mr S. Davies, Mrs J. E. Debenham, K. E. Gregory, Ms C. M. A. Kirby, N. J. Mckibbin, Mrs S. M. Murdoch, P. A. Naret-Barnes, Lady B. M. P. Neville, C. W. D. Poore, C. G. Turner, T. W. Wellard, Mr P. R. Wilby.

Assistant Trainer: Mr Paul Hacking

Jockey (NH): B. Fenton. **Apprentice:** Richard Rowe. **Amateur:** Miss Anna Wallace.

---

515 **MISS M. E. ROWLAND, Lower Blidworth**
Postal: Kirkfields, Calverton Road, Lower Blidworth, Nottingham, Nottinghamshire, NG21 0NW
Contacts: PHONE (01623) 794831 MOBILE (07768) 224666

1 **BESSEMER (JPN)**, 7, b g Carnegie (IRE)—Chalna (IRE) **Hall Farm Racing**
2 **DOUBLE MONEY**, 6, ch m Double Trigger (IRE)—We're In The Money **A Chinn P Foster S Deeman M Rowland**
3 **FINAL TUNE (IRE)**, 5, ch g Grand Lodge (USA)—Jackie's Opera (FR) **M. E. Rowland Hall Farm M. Shirley**
4 **GIOVANNI D'ORO (IRE)**, 4, b g Johannesburg (USA)—Maddie G (USA) **racingowners.co.uk**
5 **HI SPEC (IRE)**, 5, b m Spectrum (IRE)—Queen of Fibres (IRE) **Miss M. E. Rowland**

MISS M. E. ROWLAND—continued

6 **HOLLYWOOD GEORGE**, 4, b c Royal Applause—Aunt Tate **M. Shirley M. E. Rowland**
7 **INTEGRATION**, 8, b g Piccolo—Discrimination **Miss M. E. Rowland**
8 **MR CHOCOLATE DROP (IRE)**, 4, b g Danetime (IRE)—Forest Blade (IRE) **Mr D. R. Mitchell**
9 **SAVING OLIVER**, 4, ch g Courteous—We're In The Money **Double Ten Racing**

THREE-YEAR-OLDS

10 **EMMA'S SECRETS**, b br f Fraam—Hopping Higgins (IRE) **M. Shirley M. E. Rowland**
11 **LITTLE FIRECRACKER**, b f Cadeaux Genereux—El Hakma **Hall Farm Racing**
12 **ONLY A GAME (IRE)**, b c Foxhound (USA)—Compendium **Hall Farm Racing**

Other Owners: Mrs A. J. Chinn, S. M. Deeman, P. W. Foster, S. P. Giles, Mrs M. E. Giles, Mr D. J. Haddrell, Mr C. S. Mellor, M. C. Shirley.

Jockey (flat): A. Culhane. Jockey (NH): J. Mogford. Conditional: A. Pogson. Amateur: Mrs K. Darmody.

---

516 MRS L. V. RUSSELL, Kinross
Postal: **Arlary House Stables, Milnathort, Kinross, Tayside, KY13 9SJ**
Contacts: PHONE (01577) 862482 YARD (01577) 865512 OFFICE (01577) 865512
FAX (01577) 861171 MOBILE (07970) 645261
E-MAIL lucinda@arlary.fsnet.co.uk WEBSITE www.lucindarussellracing.com

1 **ALAGON (IRE)**, 8, b g Alzao (USA)—Forest Lair **P. J. S. Russell**
2 **ARIGNA (IRE)**, 9, b g Sri Pekan (USA)—Shanntabariya (IRE) **D. G. Pryde**
3 **ARRAN LAW (IRE)**, 4, ch g Flemensfirth (USA)—Windy Run **Mr I. D. Miller**
4 **ASRAR (IRE)**, 6, b m King's Theatre (IRE)—Zandaka (IRE) **Bissett Racing**
5 **AUGUST ROSE (IRE)**, 8, b br m Accordion—Lockerslebay (IRE) **Mr S. A. Rose**
6 **AUGUSTINE**, 7, b br g Machiavellian (USA)—Crown of Light **Dunalastair Estates Ltd**
7 **BALLYNURE (IRE)**, 10, b br g Roselier (FR)—Fresh Partner (IRE) **Mrs J. M. Fraser**
8 **BARRA LAD (IRE)**, 5, b g Quws—Love For Lydia (IRE) **Mr I. D. Miller**
9 **BRACKEN LAD (IRE)**, 5, b g Presenting—Up The Mountain (IRE) **Mr I. D. Miller**
10 **BREAKWATER HOUSE (IRE)**, 6, b g Supreme Leader—Millicent Bridge (IRE) **Dunalastair Estates Ltd**
11 5, B m Kornado—Bukowina (GER) **Mr S. A. Rose**
12 **CATCH THE PERK**, 11, b g Executive Perk—Kilbally Quilty (IRE) **A. A. Bissett**
13 **COPPER'S GOLD (IRE)**, 4, b g Presenting—West Hill Rose (IRE) **John R. Adam**
14 **CRACKERJACK LAD (IRE)**, 5, br g Exit To Nowhere (USA)—Crowther Homes **Mr I. D. Miller**
15 **CULCABOCK (IRE)**, 8, b g Unfuwain (USA)—Evidently (IRE) **Mrs E. B. Ferguson**
16 **DUKE OF MALFI (IRE)**, 5, b g Alflora (IRE)—Princess Maxine (IRE) **Miss G. Joughin**
17 **DUKE ORSINO (IRE)**, 8, b g Old Vic—Deselby's Choice **P. K. Dale**
18 **ETHAN'S STAR (IRE)**, 5, b g Taipan (IRE)—Ethans Rose (IRE) **Mrs Sandra Giles & Mr Chris Giles**
19 **ETXALAR (FR)**, 5, b g Kingsalsa (USA)—Tender To Love **Mrs E. B. Ferguson**
20 **EVER SPECIAL (IRE)**, 5, b g Fruits of Love (USA)—El Corazon (IRE) **Suzanne & Nigel Williams**
21 **GRAFTON TRUCE (IRE)**, 11, gr g Brief Truce (USA)—Grafton Street (GER) **Bissett Racing**
22 **GRAY MOUNTAIN (USA)**, 5, gr ro g Lasting Approval—Cuando Quiere (USA) **Miss J. A. Buchanan**
23 **INCAS (FR)**, 12, br g Video Rock (FR)—Amarante II (FR) **D. G. Pryde**
24 **INNOMINATE (IRE)**, 6, b g Saddlers' Hall (USA)—Tip Marie (IRE) **Mr & Mrs T. P. Winnell**
25 **INSIDE JOB (IRE)**, 4, b g Jade Robbery (USA)—Ines Bloom (IRE) **Mr J. A. Morrow**
26 **ISLA PEARL FISHER (IRE)**, 5, b g Supreme Sound—Salem Beach **Mrs P. M. Gammell**
27 **JEFERTITI (FR)**, 11, ch g Le Nain Jaune (FR)—Nefertiti (FR) **W. Powrie**
28 **KERRY LADS (IRE)**, 13, ch g Mister Lord—Minstrel Top **Mrs A. M. Greig**
29 **KILBRICKEN ROSE (IRE)**, 6, b m Presenting—Lockerslebay (IRE) **Mr S. A. Rose**
30 **LAUDERDALE**, 12, b g Sula Bula—Miss Tullulah **P. J. S. Russell**
31 **LORD GILBERT (FR)**, 4, b g Lord of Men—Parla (FR) **J. Petterson**
32 **LOW REACTOR (IRE)**, 7, b g Taipan (IRE)—Strong Opinion **Suzanne & Nigel Williams**
33 **MAJESTIC CHIEF**, 4, b g Xaar—Grand Splendour **Mr & Mrs T. P. Winnell**
34 **MANADAM (FR)**, 5, b g Mansonnien (FR)—Cadoudame (FR) **Mr & Mrs Duncan Davidson**
35 **MASTER SEBASTIAN**, 9, ch g Kasakov—Anchor Inn **Mrs J. M. Grimston**
36 **MIRAGE DORE (FR)**, 5, b g Muhtathir—Rose Venitien (FR) **Mr & Mrs Duncan Davidson**
37 **MOSCOW MISCHIEF**, 4, ch f Moscow Society (USA)—Desperate Measures **A. D. Stewart**
38 **MR PREACHER MAN**, 6, b g Sir Harry Lewis (USA)—Praise The Lord **Mr & Mrs A. D. Stewart**
39 **NAMED AT DINNER**, 7, ch g Halling (USA)—Salanka (IRE) **Dig In Racing**
40 **NICKY TAM (IRE)**, 6, b br g Presenting—Wigmore (IRE) **Mrs Sandra Giles & Mr Chris Giles**
41 **OLIVERJOHN (IRE)**, 11, ch g Denel (FR)—Graeme's Gem **Dig In Racing**
42 **ORMELLO (IRE)**, 6, b g Cyborg (FR)—Galante V (FR) **Dunalastair Estates Ltd**
43 **PRINCE TAM (IRE)**, 4, bl g Terimon—Princess Maxine (IRE) **Miss G. Joughin**

MRS L. V. RUSSELL—continued

44 PROSECCO (IRE), 6, b g Perpendicular—Bay Gale (IRE) **Miss J. A. Buchanan**
45 QUIVER HILL (IRE), 5, b g Dr Massini (IRE)—Alana (IRE) **Suzanne & Nigel Williams**
46 QUWS LAW (IRE), 6, b g Quws—Love For Lydia (IRE) **Mr I. D. Miller**
47 RECKLESS VENTURE (IRE), 7, ch g Carroll House—Satin Talker **Mrs A. M. Greig**
48 ROOM AT THE TOP (IRE), 5, b g Singspiel (IRE)—Questina (FR) **Mrs E. B. Ferguson**
49 ROSCHAL (IRE), 10, gr g Roselier (FR)—Sunday World (USA) **John R. Adam**
50 4, B g Dancing High—Sandholes (IRE) **Mrs E. S. Russell**
51 SCRAPPIE (IRE), 8, b g Fourstars Allstar (USA)—Clonyn **John R. Adam & Sons Ltd**
52 SEE YOU THERE (IRE), 9, br g Religiously (USA)—Bye For Now **John R. Adam**
53 SEEKING STRAIGHT (IRE), 5, b g Rainbow Quest (USA)—Alignment (IRE) **J. Petterson**
54 SEEYAAJ, 8, b g Darshaan—Subya **Brahms & Liszt**
55 SILVERDALES, 6, b g Silver Patriarch (IRE)—Swallowfield **Peter K. Dale Ltd**
56 SPIRIT CALLING (IRE), 7, br g Lord Americo—Satco Street (IRE) **John R. Adam & Sons Ltd**
57 SPORTS EXPRESS, 10, ch m Then Again—Lady St Lawrence (USA) **Bissett Racing**
58 STORM PROSPECT, 5, b g Mujahid (USA)—Bajan Blue **Mutual Friends**
59 STRONG COMMAND (IRE), 7, b g Norwich—Farmerette **Kelso Members Lowflyers Club**
60 STRONG RESOLVE (IRE), 12, gr g Roselier (FR)—Farmerette **Jim Beaumont, Maguire, Pryde, Buchanan**
61 SUMMER SOUL (IRE), 6, b g Danehill (USA)—Blend of Pace (IRE) **Tay Valley Chasers Racing Club**
62 TINTO VERANO (IRE), 6, b br m Good Thyne (USA)—Sweet Roselier (IRE) **G. Houldsworth**
63 TOP MARK, 6, b g Mark of Esteem (IRE)—Red White And Blue **Don't Tell A Soul**

THREE-YEAR-OLDS

64 LIVVY INN (USA), ch g Woodman (USA)—London Be Good (USA) **Mrs E. B. Ferguson**

Other Owners: Mr Jim Beaumont, Mr A. A. Bissett, Mrs J. Bissett, Mrs Nicky Buchanan, Mr D. Davidson, Mrs D. Davidson, Mrs Sandra Giles, Mr C. M. Giles, Ms Brenda J. Johnston, Mrs L. R. Joughin, Mr Michael F. Maguire, Mr A. Miller, Mrs Suzanne Ramsay, Mrs Margaret Rees, Miss Lucinda V. Russell, Mrs V. M. Stewart, Mr N. Williams, Mr T. P. Winnell, Mrs M. Winnell.

Assistant Trainer: Jaimie Duff

Jockey (NH): P. Buchanan. **Conditional:** C. I. Gillies.

---

517 **MR B. J. M. RYALL, Yeovil**
Postal: **Higher Farm, Rimpton, Yeovil, Somerset, BA22 8AD**
Contacts: **PHONE/FAX (01935) 850222 MOBILE (07970) 876248**
E-MAIL johnryall@rimpton.freeserve.co.uk

1 ALCATRAS (IRE), 11, b br g Corrouge (USA)—Kisco (IRE) **Mr I. & Mrs K. G. Fawcett**
2 CHIPLESS (IRE), 5, b g Tel Quel (FR)—Emerald Forest **Mr I. & Mrs K. G. Fawcett**
3 CYPRESS GROVE (IRE), 5, b g Windsor Castle—Grecian Queen **Mr P. J. O'Donovan**
4 FAIR COPPELIA, 5, b m Saddlers' Hall (IRE)—Formal Affair **Mrs G. C. Pritchard**
5 GREY TOPPER, 6, gr g Wizard King—Parlez Moi d'amour (IRE) **Mrs R. E. Parker**
6 HOT CHOC (IRE), 6, br g Darnay—Vulcan Belle **The Chocoholics**
7 MICHIGAN D'ISOP (FR), 8, b g Cadoudal (FR)—Julie Du Berlais (FR) **B. J. M. Ryall**
8 NICHOLAS THE SPARK (IRE), 6, b g Saddlers' Hall (IRE)—Merapi **R. J. Hart**
9 SKY BY NIGHT, 7, b m Riverwise (USA)—Purbeck Polly **Mrs A. E. M. Davis**
10 THE GRIFTER, 6, b g Thowra (FR)—Spring Grass **B. J. M. Ryall**
11 THIS WAY (IRE), 6, b g Exit To Nowhere (USA)—Hawthorn's Way (IRE) **J. F. Tucker**
12 TIN SYMPHONY, 10, ch m Opera Ghost—Bronze Age **The Wessex Cornflower Partnership**

Other Owners: I. Fawcett, Mrs K. G. Fawcett, Miss G. N. Pope, Mrs M. Reeve, Mrs R. C. Ryall.

Assistant Trainer: Mrs R C Ryall

---

518 **MR J. B. RYAN, Newmarket**
Postal: **John Ryan Racing, Cadland House Stables, Old Station Road, Newmarket, Suffolk, CB8 8DT**
Contacts: **PHONE (01638) 664172 MOBILE (07739) 801235**
E-MAIL john.ryan@jryanracing.com WEBSITE www.jryanracing.com

1 AIR GUITAR (IRE), 8, b g Blues Traveller (IRE)—Money Talks (IRE) **Miss C. R. Mooney**
2 ASK NO MORE, 5, b g Pyramus (USA)—Nordesta (IRE) **Mr H. J. Bell**
3 AUNTIE CRAIK, 4, b f Cotation—Mrs Poppyford **Dr L. G. Parry**

MR J. B. RYAN—continued

4 **BEST WARNING**, 4, br f Best of The Bests (IRE)—Just Warning **Back 4 More Partnership**
5 **DREAM MASTER (IRE)**, 5, b g Priolo (USA)—Pip's Dream **M. Byron & M. Wray**
6 **IRON PEARL**, 4, b f Iron Mask (USA)—Fast Tempo (IRE) **Mr J. B. Ryan**
7 **LINDBERGH**, 6, b g Bold Edge—Halland Park Girl (IRE) **John Ryan Racing Partnership**
8 **NODDLEDODDLE (IRE)**, 4, b f Daggers Drawn—En Retard (IRE) **John Ryan Racing Partnership**
9 **ROCKATORRI**, 5, b m Vettori (IRE)—Lady Rockstar **John Ryan Racing Partnership**
10 **ROYAL SAILOR (IRE)**, 6, b g Bahhare (USA)—Old Tradition (IRE) **Mr J. McMinn**
11 **SIRAJ**, 9, b g Piccolo—Masuri Kabisa (USA) **T. C. Gilligan**
12 **STOLEN SONG**, 8, b g Sheikh Albadou—Sparky's Song **John Ryan Racing Partnership**
13 **WAVERTREE ONE OFF**, 6, b g Diktat—Miss Clarinet **Wavertree Racing Partnership C**

THREE-YEAR-OLDS

14 **L'ORAGE**, b f Storming Home—Rosa Canina **T. C. Gilligan**
15 **LADY BOWER**, b f Bertolini (USA)—Noble Water (FR) **Mr M. Kirby**
16 **LORD OF ESTEEM**, ch c Mark of Esteem (IRE)—Lady Rockstar **Masters Stud**
17 **NANCYMAY**, b f Millkom—Just Eliza **B. J. Liversage**
18 **PATSYMARTIN**, ch g Bertolini (USA)—Souadah (USA) **T. C. Gilligan**
19 **UNA AURORABOREALIS**, br f Fantastic Light (USA)—Aly McBe (USA) **B. J. Liversage**

TWO-YEAR-OLDS

20 B f 22/2 Deportivo—Eurolink Artemis (Common Grounds) (5000) **B. J. Liversage**
21 B c 23/3 Tobougg (IRE)—La Suquet (Puissance) (4000) **B. J. Liversage**
22 Ch g 12/5 Zaha (CAN)—Lady At Leisure (IRE) (Dolphin Street (FR)) (9047) **John Ryan Racing Partnership**
23 B f 14/3 Forzando—Polar Peak (Polar Falcon (USA)) (2200) **John Ryan Racing Partnership**

Other Owners: Mr M. Byron, Miss L. M. Collins, Ms Anne Dixon, D. Donaldson, D. G. Kennedy, K. Pattinson, Mr M. T. Stokes, Mr M. Wray.

Amateur: Mr David McMinn.

519
MR K. A. RYAN, Hambleton
Postal: Hambleton Lodge, Hambleton, Thirsk, North Yorkshire, YO7 2HA
Contacts: **PHONE** Office (01845) 597010/(01845)597622 **FAX** (01845) 597622
MOBILE (07768) 016930 **E-MAIL** kevin.hambleton@virgin.net

1 **ADVANCED**, 5, b h Night Shift (USA)—Wonderful World (GER) **T. Doherty & McHeen**
2 **ALEXANDER HURICANE (IRE)**, 4, b c Danetime (IRE)—Alpine Lady (IRE) **Mr N. O'Callaghan**
3 **CAPTAIN JACKSPARRA (IRE)**, 4, b c Danehill (USA)—
Push A Venture **J.Duddy,B.McDonald,A.Heeney,M.McMenamin**
4 **CHA CHA CHA**, 4, b f Efisio—Shall We Dance **Guy Reed**
5 **COLEORTON DANCER**, 6, ch g Danehill Dancer (IRE)—Tayovullin (IRE) **Coleorton Moor Racing**
6 **DANETIME LORD (IRE)**, 5, b g Danetime (IRE)—Seven Sisters (USA) **Bull & Bell Partnership**
7 **DECIBEL**, 4, ch g Zamindar (USA)—Xaymara (USA) **J. Duddy**
8 **DESERT LORD**, 8, b g Green Desert (USA)—Red Carnival (USA) **Bull & Bell Partnership**
9 **DISTINCTLY GAME**, 6, b g Mind Games—Distinctly Blu (IRE) **Mr & Mrs Julian & Rosie Richer**
10 **EVENS AND ODDS (IRE)**, 4, ch c Johannesburg (USA)—Coeur de La Mer (IRE) **Mrs C. O'Flynn**
11 **EVERYMANFORHIMSELF (IRE)**, 4, b c Fasliyev (USA)—Luisa Demon (IRE) **J Duddy B Mcdonald & A Heeney**
12 **GODFREY STREET**, 5, ch g Compton Place—Tahara (IRE) **Club ISM**
13 **GOLDEN DAGGER (IRE)**, 4, ch f Daggers Drawn—Santarene (USA) **Mr & Mrs K. Hughes & Dr J. Gozzard**
14 **GREEN MANALISHI**, 7, b g Green Desert (USA)—Silca-Cisa **T.Fawcett,S.McCarthy,J.Brennan&J.Smith**
15 **GRIMES FAITH**, 5, b g Woodborough (USA)—Emma Grimes (IRE) **Mrs A. Bailey**
16 **HARRY UP**, 7, ch g Piccolo—Faraway Lass **The Fishermen**
17 **HE'S A HUMBUG (IRE)**, 4, b g Tagula (IRE)—Acidanthera **David Fravigar, Kathy Dixon**
18 **HEAVEN'S GATES**, 4, ch g Most Welcome—Arcady **J. H. Henderson**
19 **HIGH CURRAGH**, 5, b g Pursuit of Love—Pretty Poppy **Mrs J Nattrass Mrs D Davenport & R Fawcett**
20 **KAMANDA LAUGH**, 7, ch g Most Welcome—Kamada (USA) **Jamie Newell Racing Ltd**
21 **KING ORCHISIOS (IRE)**, 5, ch g Tagula (IRE)—Wildflower **Mr & Mrs Julian & Rosie Richer**
22 **MAKSHOOF (IRE)**, 4, b g Kyllachy—Tres Sage **F. Gillespie**
23 **MELALCHRIST**, 6, b g Almaty (IRE)—Lawless Bridget **Mr T. G. S. Wood**
24 **MY PARIS**, 7, b g Paris House—My Desire **J. D. & M. A. Spensley**
25 **NEW DANCER**, 6, b g Zafonic (USA)—Paradise Soul **Mrs R. G. Hillen**
26 **NORTHERN EMPIRE (IRE)**, 5, ch g Namid—Bumble **R. Peel**

MR K. A. RYAN—continued

27 **PEGASUS DANCER (FR)**, 4, b g Danehill Dancer (IRE)—Maruru (IRE) **Rievaulx Racing Syndicate**
28 **PHILANTHROPY**, 4, ch g Generous (IRE)—Clerio **Mr N. Cable & Mr M. Smith**
29 **RASAMAN (IRE)**, 4, b g Namid—Rasana **Mrs J. H. Ryan**
30 **RIVER THAMES**, 5, b g Efisio—Dashing Water **Whitestonecliffe Racing Partnership**
31 **SOVIET PALACE (IRE)**, 4, b g Jade Robbery (USA)—Daisy Hill **D. P. Reilly**
32 **TAMAGIN (USA)**, 5, b h Stravinsky (USA)—Luia (USA) **Mr T. Al Nisf**
33 **TRIMLESTOWN (IRE)**, 5, b g Orpen (USA)—Courtier **Mrs J. H. Ryan**
34 **WESTPORT**, 5, b g Xaar—Connemara (IRE) **The C H F Partnership**
35 **WI DUD**, 4, b c Elnadim (USA)—Hopesay **J. Duddy, L.Duddy, P. McBride, E. Duffy**
36 **WIGWAM WILLIE (IRE)**, 6, b g Indian Rocket—Sweet Nature (IRE) **Neil & Anne Dawson Partnership**
37 **YES ONE (IRE)**, 4, ch c Peintre Celebre (USA)—Copious (IRE) **J. Duddy, L. Duddy, P. McBride & E. Duffy**

THREE-YEAR-OLDS

38 **ALEXANDER CASTLE (USA)**, b c Lemon Drop Kid (USA)—Palapa (USA) **Mr N. O'Callaghan**
39 B c Tomba—Amamus **Mrs P. Good**
40 **ANOSTI**, b f Act One—Apennina (USA) **Theobalds Stud**
41 **ARCETRI (IRE)**, b f Galileo (IRE)—Shewillifshewants (IRE) **J. Browne T. Doherty D. Reilly C. Reilly**
42 **ARGANIL (USA)**, ch c Langfuhr (CAN)—Sherona (USA) **The Big Moment**
43 **COACHHOUSE LADY (USA)**, b f Rahy (USA)—Secret Advice (USA) **Iona Equine**
44 **COBO BAY**, b c Primo Valentino (IRE)—Fisher Island (IRE) **The C H F Partnership**
45 **EASTERN ROMANCE**, b f Oasis Dream—Ocean Grove (IRE) **Mr T. G. & Mrs M. E. Holdcroft**
46 **ERRIGAL LAD**, ch c Bertolini (USA)—La Belle Vie **Errigal Racing**
47 **FAST FEET**, b g Statue of Liberty (USA)—Landowska (USA) **J.Duddy,B.McDonald,A.Heeney,M.McMenamin**
48 **GLENVEAGH (IRE)**, b c Catcher In The Rye (IRE)—Limone (IRE) **J. Duddy, L.Duddy, P. McBride, E. Duffy**
49 **HAMMADI (IRE)**, b c Red Ransom (USA)—Ruby Affair (IRE) **Malih L. Al Basti**
50 **HASTY LADY**, b f Dubai Destination (USA)—Hasten (USA) **G. B. Frankland**
51 **HELLFIRE BAY**, b c Diktat—Composition **Chris & Antonia Deuters**
52 **HOLLY GOLIGHTLEY**, b f Choisir (AUS)—Breakfast Bay (IRE) **Mr J. E. Nattrass**
53 **HORATIO CARTER**, b c Bahamian Bounty—Jitterbug (IRE) **T. Alderson**
54 **IMPERIAL MINT (IRE)**, ch c Tagula (IRE)—Escudo (IRE) **David Fravigar, Kathy Dixon**
55 **JAZENIO**, b f Auenadler (GER)—Jade Chequer **Zen Racing**
56 **KINOUT (IRE)**, b g Invincible Spirit (IRE)—Kinn (FR) **B. T. McDonald**
57 B f Apprehension—Knayton Lass **Naughty Diesel Ltd**
58 **LA FORTALESA (IRE)**, b c Rock of Gibraltar (IRE)—
Another Legend (USA) **Joseph Ogden, J. Hanson, John Ogden**
59 **LE TOREADOR**, ch c Piccolo—Peggy Spencer **Guy Reed**
60 **LOVE CAT (USA)**, b br c Stormin Fever (USA)—Remuda (USA) **Mr J. E. Nattrass**
61 **MINUS FIFTEEN (IRE)**, ch c Trans Island—Bumble **Clipper Group Holdings Ltd**
62 **MONTIBOLI (IRE)**, ch f Bahamian Bounty—Aunt Sadie **Dales Homes Ltd**
63 **MOON SPRAY (USA)**, ch g Malibu Moon (USA)—Sun Spray (USA) **J. Reilly,D.Reilly & M.Reilly**
64 **MRS BUN**, b f Efisio—Card Games **Guy Reed**
65 **ORPEN ELLA**, b f Orpen (USA)—M N L Lady **Hambleton Racing Ltd IV**
66 **PETER'S STORM**, ch c Van Nistelrooy (USA)—
Fairy Land Flyer (USA) **Peter & Richard Foden Racing Partnership**
67 **RED APHRODITE**, b f Oasis Dream—Peony **Malih L. Al Basti**
68 **ROMANTIC DESTINY**, b f Dubai Destination (USA)—My First Romance **Mr T. G. & Mrs M. E. Holdcroft**
69 B f Val Royal (FR)—Roos Rose (IRE) **Naughty Diesel Ltd**
70 **ROYAL APPLROD**, b c Royal Applause—Known Class **Bull & Bell Partnership**
71 **SHADY GLOOM (IRE)**, b c Traditionally (USA)—Last Drama (IRE) **B. P. Hayes**
72 **SMILEFORAWHILE (IRE)**, b g Green Desert (USA)—Woodyousmileforme (USA) **Mrs G. O'Driscoll**
73 **SPLASH THE CASH**, b g Lomitas—Bandit Queen **The Armchair Jockeys**
74 **SWEET HOPE (USA)**, b br f Lemon Drop Kid (USA)—High Heeled Hope (USA) **Highbank Syndicate**
75 **THE LADY GRANUAILE (USA)**, b f More Than Ready (USA)—
Marlene (USA) **Mr Henry Bourke & Mr Colm Gavin**
76 **THUNDERSTRUCK**, b g Bertolini (USA)—Trustthunder **P. J. Dixon**
77 **TIGER DREAM**, b c Oasis Dream—Grey Way (USA) **J Duddy A Bailey T Marnane B McDonald**
78 **TOBAR SUIL LADY (IRE)**, b f Statue of Liberty (USA)—Stellarette (IRE) **Eye Opener Syndicate**
79 **TUGALU (IRE)**, b c Tagula (IRE)—Merci (IRE) **Hambleton Racing Ltd III**
80 **WILLKANDOO (USA)**, b br c Unbridled's Song (USA)—
Shannkara (IRE) **M. Forsyth,J.Turner & M.F.Logistics Ltd**
81 **WISEMAN'S DIAMOND (USA)**, b f Wiseman's Ferry (USA)—Aswhatilldois (IRE) **Wright, Hillen & Hatta**
82 **WOTASHIRTFULL (IRE)**, ch g Namid—Madrina **Sporting Gunners Syndicate Two**

MR K. A. RYAN—continued

TWO-YEAR-OLDS

83 B c 4/3 Compton Place—Adhaaba (USA) (Dayjur (USA)) (32000)
84 B c 24/3 Reset (AUS)—Aegean Blue (Warning) (10000)
85 B f 22/1 Montjeu (IRE)—Almond Mousse (FR) (Exit To Nowhere (USA)) (70784)
86 B f 5/1 Choisir (AUS)—Ardent Lady (Alhaarth (IRE)) (16000) **J. K. Shannon**
87 B c 12/3 Johannesburg (USA)—Bello Cielo (USA) (Conquistador Cielo (USA)) (199222)
88 Br c 24/3 Statue of Liberty (USA)—Brave Truth (IRE) (Brief Truce (USA)) (10000)
89 CARNABY HAGGERSTON (IRE), gr c 6/2 Invincible Spirit (IRE)—
　　　　Romanylei (IRE) (Blues Traveller (IRE)) **Mr & Mrs Duncan Davidson**
90 CHARCOAL, br f 3/5 Primo Valentino (IRE)—Waterfowl Creek (IRE) (Be My Guest (USA)) (4000)
91 Ch c 9/5 Giant's Causeway (USA)—Christmas In Aiken (USA) (Affirmed (USA)) (68027) **Errigal Racing**
92 COLEORTON CHOICE, ch c 8/3 Choisir (AUS)—
　　　　Tayovullin (IRE) (Shalford (IRE)) (19000) **Coleorton Moor Racing**
93 COUNT ALMAVIVA (USA), ch c 27/2 Rossini (USA)—Mimi Kat (USA) (Storm Cat (USA)) **Mr Catesby W. Clay**
94 COUNTRYWIDE SPIRIT (IRE), b c 18/3 Colossus (IRE)—Lovere (St Jovite (USA)) (7500) **Countrywide Racing**
95 B c 7/5 Rock of Gibraltar (IRE)—Daftiyna (IRE) (Darshaan) (45044)
96 DARK OASIS, b c 9/1 Dubai Destination (USA)—
　　　　Silent Waters (Polish Precedent (USA)) (22000) **Mr G. C. Woodall**
97 DISTINCTIVE SPIRIT (IRE), b c 20/3 Elusive City (USA)—Prince's Passion (Brief Truce (USA)) (20000) **Mr I. Hill**
98 DRACHENFELS, b c 13/4 Mind Games—Its Another Gift (Primo Dominie) (52000) **J. Erhardt**
99 DUKE OF URBINO, ch c 22/4 Medicean—Nefeli (First Trump) (70000) **Mr & Mrs Duncan Davidson**
100 ED'S PRIDE, b c 9/4 Catcher In The Rye (IRE)—Queenliness (Exit To Nowhere (USA)) (16000)
101 ESPRIT DE MIDAS, b c 9/2 Namid—
　　　　Spritzeria (Bigstone (IRE)) (100000) **Joseph Ogden, J. Hanson, John Ogden**
102 B c 11/5 Reel Buddy (USA)—Fisher Island (IRE) (Sri Pekan (USA)) (8000)
103 FOLLOWING WIND, ch f 23/4 Reel Buddy (USA)—
　　　　Cyclone Flyer (College Chapel) (20000) **Mr T. G. & Mrs M. E. Holdcroft**
104 B f 9/4 Red Ransom (USA)—Give Warning (IRE) (Warning) (19947)
105 B c 23/3 Night Shift (USA)—Gold Bust (Nashwan (USA)) (26000) **Hambleton Racing Ltd VI**
106 B f 8/2 Fasliyev (USA)—Happy Memories (IRE) (Thatching) (13513) **Wooster Partnership**
107 B f 7/5 Dixie Union (USA)—Hazino (USA) (Hazaam (USA))
108 Ch c 14/4 Deportivo—Hidden Meaning (Cadeaux Genereux) (20000) **Mrs M. Forsyth**
109 Ch f 26/1 Spinning World (USA)—High Spot (Shirley Heights) (57914) **Highbank Syndicate**
110 ISABELLA GREY, gr f 12/4 Choisir (AUS)—Karsiyaka (IRE) (Kahyasi) (14000) **Mr T. G. & Mrs M. E. Holdcroft**
111 B c 30/1 Invincible Spirit (IRE)—March Star (IRE) (Mac's Imp (USA)) (16730)
112 B c 11/5 Fraam—Medina de Rioseco (Puissance) (25000) **J. K. Shannon**
113 B c 19/3 Kyllachy—Mi Amor (IRE) (Alzao (USA)) (21000) **Hambleton Racing Ltd VII**
114 MONTMARTRE (USA), b c 30/3 Awesome Again (CAN)—
　　　　Sacre Coeur (USA) (Saint Ballado (CAN)) **Mr Catesby W. Clay**
115 B c 28/2 Diktat—Omission (Green Desert (USA)) (36000) **R. Peel**
116 Ch f 16/2 Spartacus (IRE)—Party Bag (Cadeaux Genereux) (47000)
117 Ch c 11/5 Tomba—Princess Sadie (Shavian) **Mrs P. Good**
118 B f 4/2 Johannesburg (USA)—Rababah (USA) (Woodman (USA)) (52000)
119 B c 25/1 Lemon Drop Kid (USA)—Radu Cool (USA) (Carnivalay (USA)) (38872) **K. Lee & L. M. Rutherford**
120 B c 12/2 Tagula (IRE)—Red Letter (Sri Pekan (USA)) (3217)
121 B c 25/2 Spartacus (IRE)—Reddish Creek (USA) (Mt Livermore (USA)) (24000) **S. J. Carr**
122 Br f 13/3 Hawk Wing (USA)—Ruby Affair (IRE) (Night Shift (USA)) (55000) **Malih L. Al Basti**
123 B c 25/4 Johannesburg (USA)—Rumored (USA) (Royal Academy (USA)) (53449) **Hambleton Racing Ltd V**
124 B c 27/1 Danetime (IRE)—Scarlet Empress (Second Empire (IRE)) (32174)
125 Ch f 31/1 Monsieur Bond (IRE)—Secret Circle (Magic King (IRE)) (18000) **M. G. White**
126 Ch c 10/3 Indian Ridge—Seraphina (IRE) (Pips Pride) (90090) **Mr A. Heeney**
127 SWEET SMILE (IRE), b c 9/3 Catcher In The Rye (IRE)—Quivala (USA) (Thunder Gulch (USA))
128 B f 19/3 Red Ransom (USA)—Triomphale (USA) (Nureyev (USA)) (77000) **Highbank Syndicate**
129 B c 16/1 Gone West (USA)—Weekend in London (USA) (Belong To Me (USA))
130 YSING YI, b c 11/3 Singspiel (USA)—Hsi Wang Mu (IRE) (Dr Fong (USA)) **Mr Catesby W. Clay**

Other Owners: Mr Mark Allen, Mrs Angie Bailey, Mr J. M. Birkett, Mr H. Bourke, Mr J. J. Brennan, Mr John Browne, Mr N. Cable, Mr S. Carter, Mr Simon Cordingley, Mr Michael Cunningham, Mrs J. M. Davenport, D. H. Davidson, Mrs S. K. Davidson, Mrs A. Dawson, Mr R. N. Dawson, A. Day, Mr Chris Deuters, Mrs Chris Deuters, Mr T. C. Dewhirst, Miss Kathy Dixon, Mr Thomas Doherty, Mr Neale Dougan, Mr L. Duddy, Mr John Duddy, Mr E. Duffy, P. J. Dunkley, Mr C. J. Edwards, Mr Rob Fawcett, A. R. Fawcett, Mr S. L. Feast, Mr K. H. Fischer, Mr C. H. Fischer, Mr E. P. Foden, Mr R. P. Foden, J. A. Forsyth, Mr D. Fower, Mr David Fravigar, Mr C. Gavin, Mr Julian Gouder, Dr J. Gozzard, Mr O. Greene, Hambleton Racing Ltd, Mr J. P. Hames, Mr P. Hampshire, Mr J. Hanson, Hatta Bloodstock Int'l Ltd, Mr A. C. Henson, Mr M. P. Higson, Mrs R. G. Hillen, Mrs Alison Hole, Mr A. Holmes, Mr J. H. A. Hopkinson, Mr K. Hughes, Mrs Debbie Hughes, Mr Brian Hutchinson, Mr Jimmy Kelly, M. K. Lee, M F Logistics (UK) Ltd, Mrs T. Marnane, D. McAllister, Mr P. McBride, Mrs Sandra McCarthy, Mr B. T. McDonald,

MR K. A. RYAN—continued

Exors of the late Mr Colin McRae, Mr D. Minton, Mr Francis Moll, Mr J. Nattrass, Mr N. J. O'Brien, Mr Denis O'Flynn, Miss P. M. O'Flynn, Mr Joseph Ogden, Mr John Ogden, Mr K. Panos, Mr G. K. Panos, R. Parlour, I. J. Poulter, R J H Limited, Mr Arthur Reeves, Mr David Reilly, Mrs Candice Reilly, Mrs Rosie Richer, Mr J. Richer, Mr P Ringer, L. M. Rutherford, Mr R. A. Sankey, Mr M. Smith (Lancashire), J. D. T. Smith, Mr Matthew Taylor, Mr N. J. Titterton, Mr S. R. H. Turner, Mrs J. K. Turner, Mrs I. M. Wainwright, Mr M. Wainwright, Mr B. Walsh, Mr Lee Westwood, Mr Simon Wildsmith, Mr A. Williams, Dr D. H. Wood, Mrs C. M. Wood, Mr C. G. Wright.

Jockey (flat): N. Callan, D. O'Donohoe. **Amateur:** Miss Amy Ryan.

---

520 MR A. M. SADIK, Kidderminster
Postal: **Wolverley Court Coach House, Wolverley, Kidderminster, Worcestershire, DY10 3RP**
Contacts: **PHONE (01562) 852362 MOBILE (07803) 040344**

1 CENGIZ (IRE), 6, b g Taipan (IRE)—Gypsy Kelly (IRE) **A. M. Sadik**
2 GOOD MAN AGAIN (IRE), 10, b g Arctic Lord—Amari Queen **A. M. Sadik**

---

521 MRS K. M. SANDERSON, Tiverton
Postal: **New Cottage, Rackenford Road, Calverleigh, Tiverton, Devon, EX16 8BE**
Contacts: **PHONE (01884) 254217 (01884) 258930**

1 HOLLANDIA (IRE), 7, gr g Needle Gun (IRE)—Steel Mariner **Mrs K. M. Sanderson**
2 OPERA SINGER, 7, b g Ali-Royal (IRE)—Wheeler's Wonder (IRE) **Mrs K. M. Sanderson**

Jockey (NH): T. J. O'Brien. **Amateur:** Mr W. Biddick.

---

522 MR M. S. SAUNDERS, Wells
Postal: **Blue Mountain Farm, Wells Hill Bottom, Haydon, Wells, Somerset, BA5 3EZ**
Contacts: **OFFICE/FAX (01749) 841011 MOBILE (07771) 601035**
E-MAIL malcolm@malcolmsaunders.co.uk WEBSITE www.malcolmsaunders.co.uk

1 CRIMSON FERN (IRE), 4, ch f Titus Livius (FR)—Crimada (IRE) **M. S. Saunders**
2 FAIRFIELD PRINCESS, 4, b f Inchinor—Cool Question **Lockstone Business Services Ltd**
3 MATTEROFACT (IRE), 5, b m Bold Fact (USA)—Willow Dale (IRE) **Prempro Racing**
4 SWEET AFTON (IRE), 5, b m Mujadil (USA)—Victory Peak **Lockstone Business Services Ltd**
5 THREE HALF CROWNS (IRE), 4, b c Barathea (IRE)—My-Lorraine (IRE) **L. Sheridan**
6 THREE THIEVES (UAE), 5, ch g Jade Robbery (USA)—Melisendra (FR) **Prempro Racing**
7 VALEESHA, 4, b f Erhaab (USA)—Miss Laetitia (IRE) **T. H. Chadney**

THREE-YEAR-OLDS

8 DANCING RHYTHM, b g Piccolo—Will You Dance **B. C. Scott**
9 DIDNTCOMEBACK, b g Oasis Dream—Latin Beauty (IRE) **M. S. Saunders**
10 PENNYSPIDER (IRE), b f Redback—Malacca (USA) **B. C. Scott**
11 POLAR ANNIE, b f Fraam—Willisa **Lockstone Business Services Ltd**

TWO-YEAR-OLDS

12 B c 31/1 Masterful (USA)—Be Magic (Persian Bold) (25740) **M. S. Saunders**
13 B c 26/2 Fraam—Brigadiers Bird (IRE) (Mujadil (USA)) (10000) **M. S. Saunders**
14 INTO MY ARMS, gr f 3/4 Kyllachy—True Love (Robellino (USA)) (30000) **P. P. Thorman**
15 Ch c 19/3 Needwood Blade—Willisa (Polar Falcon (USA)) (12000) **Lockstone Business Services Ltd**

Other Owners: D. Adcock, D. J. Collier, D. R. Febry, Mr P. S. G. Nicholas, Mr S. R. Williams.

Amateur: Miss K Jones.

---

523 MR J. SAVILLE, Gisburn
Postal: **The Stables Cottage, Gisburn Park, Gisburn, Lancashire, BB7 4HU**
Contacts: **PHONE (01200) 445687 FAX (08716) 661323**
E-MAIL joss@josssavilleracing.co.uk WEBSITE www.josssavilleracing.co.uk

1 ANGLERZAR (IRE), 8, ch m Shernazar—Anglers Girl (IRE) **Mrs S. Saville**
2 APADI (USA), 12, ch g Diesis—Ixtapa (USA) **Mrs A. Kenny**

MR J. SAVILLE—continued

3 **BALLYBOE BOY (IRE)**, 9, b g Flying Spur (AUS)—Born To Fly (IRE) **Mrs A. Kenny**
4 **BALLYS JOY (IRE)**, 7, b m Executive Perk—Moonshee (IRE) **Formulated Polymer Products Ltd**
5 **COLLEGE CITY (IRE)**, 9, b g College Chapel—Polish Crack (IRE) **Mrs A. Kenny**
6 **COVERDALE LADY**, 6, b m Prince Daniel (USA)—Lisband Lady (IRE) **Three J's Racing**
7 6, b m Beneficial—Deep Serve **Mrs S. Saville**
8 5, B m Norwich—Executive Dream (IRE) **E. Astal & J. Saville**
10 **FARINGTON LODGE (IRE)**, 10, b g Simply Great (FR)—Lodge Party (IRE) **Ownaracehorse Ltd**
10 **FLASHING FLOOZIE**, 5, ch m Muhtarram (USA)—High Habit **Mrs A. Kenny**
11 **FREEDOM FLYING**, 5, b m Kalanisi (IRE)—Free Spirit (IRE) **Mrs A. Kenny**
12 **GOLDEN SNOOPY (IRE)**, 11, ch g Insan (USA)—Lovely Snoopy (IRE) **Alpha Gold Partnership**
13 **IT'S MY PARTY**, 7, b g Danzero (AUS)—Addicted To Love **Ley Inn Racing Academy & Joss Saville**
14 **MINSTER LANE**, 8, ch g Minster Son—Coverdale Lane **Three J's Racing**
15 **MUNNINGS TOUCH (IRE)**, 7, b g Bob Back (USA)—Castle Mews (IRE) **J. Saville**
16 **ON THE MAP**, 4, b f Agnes World (USA)—Noor El Houdah (IRE) **Ownaracehorse.co.uk (Panama)**
17 **PANAMA AT ONCE**, 8, ch g Commanche Run—Cherry Sip **Ownaracehorse.co.uk (Panama)**
18 **PANAMA THREE KNOTS**, 8, b m Primitive Rising (USA)—Emu (IRE) **Gisburn Racing**
19 **PLATINUM KING (IRE)**, 6, gr g Beauchamp King—Carmenoura (IRE) **Joss Saville & Harry Eckersall**
20 **RED DAWN (IRE)**, 9, ch g Presenting—West Tour **Gisburn Racing**
21 **SPRINGFIELD SNIPER**, 6, ch g Gunner B—Springfield Rhyme **S & J Whitaker**
22 **STAR OF RAVEN**, 11, b m Sea Raven (IRE)—Lucy At The Minute **J. Saville**
23 **TARA FOR NOW**, 5, b g Kayf Tara—Swallow Breeze **ownaracehorse.co.uk (Gisburn)**
24 7, B m Luso—Wingfield Lady (IRE) **J. Saville**
25 **WORLD SIXTEEN (IRE)**, 7, b m Naheez (USA)—Karawill (IRE) **Gisburn Racing**
26 **YOULUCKYMAN (IRE)**, 7, b g Zaffaran (USA)—Laffan's Bridge (IRE) **Four Blokes & A Bird**

THREE-YEAR-OLDS

27 **LEKIN SEDONA (IRE)**, ch g Namid—Abrahamsdotter (IRE) **Formulated Polymer Products Ltd**
28 **SWEET VERA**, ch f Double Trigger (IRE)—Inesse **J. Saville**

Other Owners: Mr M. R. Cope, Mr J. H. Eckersall, Mr S. W. Ford, Mr K. B. Hanover, Mr P. G. Haworth, Mr D. Jones, Dr R. M. F. Klein, Mrs S. Klein, Mr J. O'Brien, Ownaracehorse Ltd (ownaracehorse.co.uk), Mr Jim Pilkington, Miss C. D. Richardson, Mr Joss Saville, Mr I. N. Walsh, Mr S Whitaker, Mr J. S. Whitaker, Mrs C. M. Wibberley.

Conditional: Tom Messenger, David Cullinane, Bernie Wharfe.

524 MRS H. D. SAYER, Penrith
Postal: **Town End Farm, Hackthorpe, Penrith, Cumbria, CA10 2HX**
Contacts: PHONE (01931) 712245 MOBILE (07980) 295316

1 **DARK GENTLEMAN**, 5, bl g Rock City—Panic Button (IRE) **Mr A. Slack & Mr R. Lyle**
2 **FRONT RANK (IRE)**, 8, b g Sadler's Wells (USA)—Alignment (IRE) **J. A. Sayer**
3 **GETINBYBUTONLYJUST**, 9, b g King's Ride—Madame President (IRE) **J. A. Sayer**
4 **TROODOS JET**, 7, b g Atraf—Costa Verde **A. R. White**

Other Owners: Mr Michael Burley, Mr R. Lyle, Mr A. Slack.

Assistant Trainer: Mr Andrew Sayer

Amateur: Miss Joanna Sayer, Miss Natalie Sayer.

525 DR J. D. SCARGILL, Newmarket
Postal: **Red House Stables, Hamilton Road, Newmarket, Suffolk, CB8 0TE**
Contacts: PHONE (01638) 663254 MOBILE (07785) 350705
E-MAIL scargill@redhousestables.freeserve.co.uk WEBSITE www.drjonscargill.co.uk

1 **BIG NOISE**, 4, b c Lake Coniston (IRE)—Mitsubishi Video (IRE) **Theme Tune Partnership**
2 **BOBBY CHARLES**, 7, ch g Polish Precedent (USA)—Dina Line (USA) **Silent Partners**
3 **DEFECTIVEDETECTIVE**, 4, b g Terimon—Afterthought **Basil White**
4 **GENERATOR**, 6, ch g Cadeaux Genereux—Billie Blue **R. A. Dalton**
5 **PAINTED SMILE (IRE)**, 4, b f Iron Mask (USA)—Hope And Glory (USA) **J P T Partnership**
6 **SILENT APPLAUSE**, 5, b g Royal Applause—Billie Blue **J P T Partnership**
7 **TORVER**, 4, br f Lake Coniston (IRE)—Billie Blue **R. A. Dalton & Silent Partners**

DR J. D. SCARGILL—continued

THREE-YEAR-OLDS

 8 **DEADLY SILENCE (USA)**, b c Diesis—Mill Guineas (USA) **Silent Partners**
 9 **FLIGHT OF FASHION (IRE)**, ch f Hawk Wing (USA)—Fashion **Silent Partners**
10 **LATIMER HOUSE (IRE)**, ch f Observatory (USA)—Tramonto **D. W. Johnson OBE**

TWO-YEAR-OLDS

11 Ch f 10/1 Compton Place—Billie Blue (Ballad Rock) **R. A. Dalton**
12 B f 22/2 Bahamian Bounty—Emerald Fire (Pivotal) (24000) **Strawberry Fields Stud**
13 Gr f 15/2 Noverre (USA)—Esperada (ARG) (Equalize (USA)) (26000) **Strawberry Fields Stud**
14 **LADY ANGELICA**, ch f 26/2 Piccolo—
                              Fine Frenzy (IRE) (Great Commotion (USA)) (2500) **Ms Angelica Fernandez Flores**
15 B f 16/2 Johannesburg (USA)—
                              School of Deelites (USA) (Afternoon Deelites (USA)) (22000) **Strawberry Fields Stud**

Other Owners: Mr G. Brigford, Mrs C. Cobb, Mrs M. Coppitters, Mr J. Dutton, Mr A. Holness, Mr D. Meilton, Mr Andrew Millar, Mr G. F. L. Robinson, Mrs Andrea Rose, Mr G. Rose, Mr K. Ruttle, Mrs N. Ruttle, Mr P. J. Scargill, Mrs Susan Scargill, Mr P. Stanton, Mrs M. Stanton, Mr I. Wagstaffe, Mr B. Watson, Mrs R. Watson, Mr Basil White.

---

526 **MR D. D. SCOTT, Minehead**
Postal: **East Lynch, Minehead, Somerset, TA24 8SS**
Contacts: **PHONE (01643) 702430 FAX (01643) 702430**

1 **IMPORTANT BOY (ARG)**, 11, ch g Equalize (USA)—Important Girl (ARG) **Mrs D. D. Scott**
2 **MASTER RAT**, 7, b g Thowra (FR)—Race Against Time **Mrs D. D. Scott**

---

527 **MR J. SCOTT, Dulverton**
Postal: **Higher Holworthy Farm, Brompton Regis, Dulverton, Somerset, TA22 9NY**
Contacts: PHONE **(01398) 371414 MOBILE (07709) 279483**
E-MAIL holworthyfarm@yahoo.com

1 **DOVEDALE**, 8, b m Groom Dancer (USA)—Peetsie (IRE) **S. G. Searle**
2 5, B g Baryshnikov (AUS)—Fairy Ballerina
3 **GONE TO LUNCH (IRE)**, 8, ch g Mohaajir (USA)—Jayells Dream **G. T. Lever**
4 **KUZNETSKY MOST (IRE)**, 5, ch g Moscow Society (USA)—Calm Waters (IRE) **G. T. Lever**
5 **LYRICAL CHANT (IRE)**, 4, ch f Deploy—Vic Melody (FR) **Mrs N. A. Ward & Mrs N. Welby**
6 **PURPLE PATCH**, 10, b m Afzal—My Purple Prose **Mrs C. C. Scott**
7 **SHEIKH MCMURRAY**, 6, b g Supreme Leader—Shannon Native (IRE) **I. R. Murray**

Other Owners: Mrs C. W. Ward, Mrs N. J. Welby.

---

528 **MRS J. SCRASE, Pulborough**
Postal: **Lee Place Farm, Scrase Farms, Pulborough, West Sussex, RH20 1DF**
Contacts: **PHONE (01403) 700525 FAX (01403) 701119 MOBILE (07789) 888013**

1 **NELTINA**, 12, gr m Neltino—Mimizan (IRE) **Mrs J. E. Scrase**

---

529 **MR B. SCRIVEN, Taunton**
Postal: **Cogload Farm, Durston, Taunton, Somerset, TA3 5AW**
Contacts: **PHONE (01823) 490208**

1 **DUNBELL BOY (IRE)**, 10, b br g Over The River (FR)—Whipper Snapper **B. Scriven**

Assistant Trainer: Miss Kay Scriven

530 MR M. J. SCUDAMORE, Bromsash
Postal: **Eccleswall Court, Bromsash, Ross-On-Wye, Herefordshire, HR9 7PP**
Contacts: **PHONE** (01989) 750844 **FAX** (01989) 750281
E-MAIL peter.scu@ic24.net

1 **A PERFECT GENT (IRE)**, 5, b g Exit To Nowhere (USA)—First And Foremost (IRE) **The Tainton Partnership**
2 **ADRENALINE ALLEY (IRE)**, 6, ch g Clerkenwell (USA)—Pepper Star (IRE) **Burnt Toast Ltd**
3 **ALBARINO (IRE)**, 9, ch g Royal Abjar (USA)—Miss Lee Ann **Mr M. R. Blandford**
4 **ARUMUN (IRE)**, 7, b g Posidonas—Adwoa (IRE) **Mr M. R. Blandford**
5 **AZULEJO (FR)**, 10, b g Pistolet Bleu (FR)—Junta (FR) **J. E. Wilson & T. J. Wilson**
6 **BOBBY BULLOCK (IRE)**, 6, b g Old Vic—Miss Chickabee (IRE) **The Yes No Wait Sorries**
7 **COMMAND MARSHAL (FR)**, 5, b g Commands (AUS)—Marsakara (IRE) **S. W. Molloy**
8 **COUNTESS TRIFALDI (IRE)**, 8, b m Flemensfirth (USA)—Course Royal **Woolf & Wilkinson**
9 **DARK ENERGY**, 4, br g Observatory (USA)—Waterfowl Creek (IRE) **The Yes No Wait Sorries**
10 **DIRECTA'S DIGGER (IRE)**, 4, b c Daggers Drawn (USA)—Chita Rivera **Mr I. J. Anderson**
11 **FINZI (IRE)**, 10, b g Zaffaran (USA)—Sporting Talent (IRE) **E. W. Moss**
12 **FLOW GENTLY ALONG (IRE)**, 5, b m Norwich—Over The Pond (IRE) **The Honfleur Syndicate**
13 **GRAHAM'S GIRL**, 5, b m Alflora (IRE)—Pendil's Delight **A. P. Barwell**
14 **GUNNER ROSE**, 5, ch g Gunner B—Fortria Rosie Dawn **M. J. & W. J. Fenn**
15 **HEMINGTON**, 5, gr g Shahrastani (USA)—Race To The Rhythm **Horse Passport Agency Ltd**
16 **JACKSONS PIER (IRE)**, 8, b g Accordion—Uhuru (IRE) **A. P. Barwell**
17 **KEMPLEY GREEN (IRE)**, 5, b g Revoque (IRE)—Alaroos (IRE) **F. K. Jennings**
18 **MONTY'S PANESAR (IRE)**, 6, b m Zaffaran (USA)—Union Day (IRE) **The Yes No Wait Sorries**
19 **MYSTIC KING**, 5, b g Rakaposhi King—Just Lynn **E. W. Moss**
20 **NORSEMAN CATELINE (FR)**, 7, b g Poplar Bluff—Dame Jaune (FR) **The Yes No Wait Sorries**
21 **NOTANOTHERDONKEY (IRE)**, 8, b g Zaffaran (USA)—Sporting Talent (IRE) **A. Brush**
22 **OAKS BAY**, 5, b m Gildoran—Bonnet **Bernard S. Hicks**
23 **PENFULL (FR)**, 5, b g Useful (FR)—Donebola (USA) **The Yes No Wait Sorries**
24 **PREMIERSHIP (IRE)**, 12, b br g Zinaad—Fadaki Hawaki (USA) **J. E. Wilson & T. J. Wilson**
25 **PRINCESSE D'AGNOUN (FR)**, 4, ch f Grand Seigneur (FR)—Sweet Julie (FR) **M. J. Scudamore**
26 **RAKI ROSE**, 6, b g Rakaposhi King—Fortria Rosie Dawn **M. J. & W. J. Fenn**
27 **ROSEVINA (IRE)**, 8, b m Saint Preuil (FR)—Galvina (FR) **Miss H. Smith**
28 **SAIL AND RETURN**, 4, b g Kayf Tara—Maidwell **Horse Passport Agency Ltd**
29 **SILLY WUPPLE**, 6, b g Syrtos—Lily The Lark **Mr S. M. Smith & Keith Hunter**
30 **THE NIMBLE TIMPLE (IRE)**, 8, b g Accordion—Gale Belle **Mrs N. M. Barcoe**
31 **WILL EXELL (IRE)**, 5, b m Exit To Nowhere (USA)—Woodhouse Bay (IRE) **Tim Exell & Will Unwin**

Other Owners: S. A. Baker, C. S. J. Coley, T. J. F. Exell, M. J. Fenn, W. J. Fenn, K. Hunter, D. M. Hussey, Mrs M. E. Pritchard, Dr S. M. Readings, S. Smith, Mr J. Tainton, Mr W. R. J. Unwin, Mr C. A. Wilkinson, Mrs J. E. Wilson, Miss T. E. Wilson, Mr J. M. Woolf.

Assistant Trainer: Peter Scudamore & Michael Scudamore (Jnr)

Jockey (NH): T. Scudamore. **Conditional:** John Kington.

531 MR D. SHAW, Newark
Postal: **Stubby Nook Lodge, Danethorpe Hill, Danethorpe, Newark, Nottinghamshire, NG24 2PD**
Contacts: **PHONE** (01636) 605683 **MOBILE** (07721) 039645
E-MAIL mail@derekshawracing.com **WEBSITE** www.derekshawracing.com

1 **ALTOS REALES**, 4, b f Mark of Esteem (IRE)—Karsiyaka (IRE) **Danethorpe Racing Partnership**
2 **ALUCICA**, 5, b m Celtic Swing—Acicula (IRE) **Mr. Joe Tucker**
3 **BABY STRANGE**, 4, gr c Superior Premium—The Manx Touch (IRE) **Market Avenue Racing Club Ltd**
4 **BENTLEY**, 4, b g Piccolo—April Lee **Danethorpe Racing Partnership**
5 **BILLY ONE PUNCH**, 6, b g Mark of Esteem (IRE)—Polytess (IRE) **Norcroft Park Stud**
6 **COME WHAT JULY (IRE)**, 7, b g Indian Rocket—Persian Sally (IRE) **R. Milward**
7 **COOL SANDS (IRE)**, 6, b g Trans Island—Shalerina (USA) **P. Swann**
8 **DANCING DUO**, 4, b f Groom Dancer—Affaire Royale (IRE) **Ownaracehorse.co.uk (Danethorpe)**
9 **DESERT LIGHT (IRE)**, 7, b g Desert Sun—Nacote (IRE) **Ownaracehorse.co.uk (Shaw)**
10 **EBRAAM (USA)**, 5, b g Red Ransom (USA)—Futuh (USA) **The Circle Bloodstock I Limited**
11 **ELUSIVE DREAMS (USA)**, 4, ch g Elusive Quality (USA)—Bally Five (USA) **The Circle Bloodstock I Limited**
12 **EPIDAURIAN KING (IRE)**, 5, b g King's Best (USA)—Thurayya **Mr D. Shaw**
13 **GALLANTRY**, 6, b g Green Desert (USA)—Gay Gallanta (USA) **The Circle Bloodstock I Limited**
14 **GRAND PALACE (IRE)**, 5, b g Grand Lodge (USA)—Pocket Book (IRE) **Ownaracehorse.co.uk (Shakespeare)**
15 4, B g Namid—It's So Easy **Danethorpe Racing Partnership**
16 **JETE (IRE)**, 4, b g Imperial Ballet (IRE)—Jet Lock (USA) **Danethorpe Racing Partnership**

MR D. SHAW—continued

17 **JULIAN JOACHIM (USA)**, 4, b g Officer (USA)—Seeking the Jewel (USA) **G. Houghton**
18 **LORD OF THE REINS (IRE)**, 4, b g Imperial Ballet (IRE)—Waroonga (IRE) **Danethorpe Racing Partnership**
19 **LUCIUS VERRUS (USA)**, 8, b g Danzig (USA)—Magic of Life (USA) **Danethorpe Racing Partnership**
20 **MIND ALERT**, 7, b g Mind Games—Bombay Sapphire **Mr R. G. Botham**
21 **MONTE MAJOR (IRE)**, 7, b g Docksider (USA)—Danalia (IRE) **The Circle Bloodstock I Limited**
22 **MUKTASB (USA)**, 7, b g Bahri (USA)—Maghaarb **Miss Claire Comery**
23 **NAMIR (IRE)**, 6, b g Namid—Danalia (IRE) **Ownaracehorse.co.uk (Shakespeare)**
24 **PARKVIEW LOVE (USA)**, 7, b br g Mister Baileys—Jerre Jo Glanville (USA) **Danethorpe Racing Partnership**
25 **PRINCE TUM TUM (USA)**, 8, b g Capote (USA)—La Grande Epoque (USA) **The Circle Bloodstock I Limited**
26 **RABBIT FIGHTER (IRE)**, 4, ch c Observatory (USA)—Furnish **Market Avenue Racing Club Ltd**
27 **RAIHANAH**, 4, b f Dr Fong (USA)—Al Shadeedah (USA) **Ownaracehorse.co.uk (Danethorpe)**
28 **ROYAL EMBRACE**, 5, b g Bertolini (USA)—Tight Spin **Mrs B. E. Wilkinson**
29 **ROYAL ENVOY (IRE)**, 5, b g Royal Applause—Seven Notes **The Circle Bloodstock I Limited**
30 **SANDS CROONER (IRE)**, 5, b h Imperial Ballet (IRE)—Kurfuffle **Danethorpe Racing Partnership**
31 **SPARKWELL**, 6, b g Dansili—West Devon (USA) **The Circle Bloodstock I Limited**
32 **STAND GUARD**, 4, b g Danehill (USA)—Protectress **The Circle Bloodstock I Limited**
33 **TARTARTUFATA**, 6, b m Tagula (IRE)—It's So Easy **Danethorpe Racing Partnership**
34 **THEFLYINGSCOTTIE**, 6, gr g Paris House—Miss Flossa (FR) **R. Milward**

THREE-YEAR-OLDS

35 **ALABAMA SPIRIT (USA)**, b br f Dixie Union (USA)—Appealing Spirit (USA) **The Circle Bloodstock I Limited**
36 **CAPTAIN CROONER (IRE)**, ch g Captain Rio—Kurfuffle **Danethorpe Racing Partnership**
37 Br g Celtic Swing—Deerskin (USA) **Mrs A.J. Cornwell**
38 **JAZZ ROMANCE (IRE)**, ch f Choisir (AUS)—Music In My Life (IRE) **Danethorpe Racing Partnership**
39 **PLANET PARADISE (IRE)**, b f Spinning World (USA)—Just Heavens Gate **D. R. Tucker**
40 **SILVER SPRITE**, gr g Best of The Bests (IRE)—Nightingale **Danethorpe Racing Partnership**
41 B g Dixie Union (USA)—Starboard Stinger (USA) **Mrs B. E. Wilkinson**
42 B g High Chaparral (IRE)—Stop Press (USA) **Danethorpe Racing Partnership**
43 **STOREY HILL (USA)**, b br g Richter Scale (USA)—Crafty Nan (USA) **D. J. Goose**
44 **TOBOUGGORNOTOBOUGG**, ch g Tobougg (IRE)—Douce Maison (IRE) **Danethorpe Racing Partnership**
45 **VIOLA ROSA (IRE)**, b f Fraam—Bleu Cerise **Danethorpe Racing Partnership**

TWO-YEAR-OLDS

46 B f 27/3 Smart Strike (CAN)—Cataballerina (USA) (Tabasco Cat (USA)) (19436) **Mrs B. E. Wilkinson**
47 Ch f 18/3 Ecton Park (USA)—Dear Abigail (USA) (Dehere (USA)) **D. Shaw**
48 **EXPRESSO STEPS**, b br f 5/5 Medaglia d'oro (USA)—
                                Walk On Gold (Seeking The Gold (USA)) (17006) **The Circle Bloodstock I Limited**
49 Br f 4/3 Piccolo—Kitty Kitty Cancan (Warrshan (USA)) **Mr D. Shaw**
50 B f 30/3 Lujain (USA)—Polytess (IRE) (Polish Patriot (USA)) **Norcroft Park Stud**

Other Owners: Mr M. Kevin Delaney, Mr A. J. Hollis, Mr M. D. Hollis, Mr Tim Lively, Ownaracehorse Ltd
(ownaracehorse.co.uk), Mr Peter Swann, Mr P. A. Whiteman, Mr S. A. Whiteman.

Jockey (flat): D. McKeown. **Apprentice:** T. Dean, L. Topliss. **Amateur:** Mrs M. Morris.

---

532 MR M. I. SHEPPARD, Ledbury
Postal: **Home Farm Cottage, Eastnor, Ledbury, Herefordshire, HR8 1RD**
Contacts: **FAX** (01531) 634846 **MOBILE** (07770) 625061
E-MAIL matthew.sheppard@cmail.co.uk **WEBSITE** mattsheppardracing.co.uk

1 **BEESNEEZ (IRE)**, 8, b g Naheez (USA)—Kings Run (IRE) **Miss S. Troughton**
2 **BOOT 'N TOOT**, 7, b m Mtoto—Raspberry Sauce **The Aftertimers**
3 **BRAVE VILLA (FR)**, 9, b g Villez (USA)—Brave Lola (FR) **S. L. K. Racing**
4 **CRICKIE PITCH**, 4, b g Chaddleworth (IRE)—Dane Rose **Mrs N. Sheppard**
5 **FAIR SHAKE (IRE)**, 8, b g Sheikh Albadou—Shamrock Fair (IRE) **Lost In The Summer Wine**
6 **MADAM BLAZE**, 8, gr m Overbury (IRE)—Roslin **R. Allsop**
7 **PARADISE EXPECTED**, 5, ch m North Briton—Phenomenon **M. E. & A. D. I. Harris**
8 **SARAHS GIFT (IRE)**, 5, ch g Spectrum (IRE)—Trigger Happy (IRE) **Mr A. J. Scrivin**
9 **SUPER JUDGE (IRE)**, 7, b g Saddlers' Hall (IRE)—Supreme Control (IRE) **S. J. D. Gegg**
10 **SYROCO (FR)**, 9, b g Homme de Loi (IRE)—La Pommeraie (FR) **The Blues Partnership**
11 **WENGER (FR)**, 8, b g Unfuwain (USA)—Molly Dance (FR) **Worcester Racing Club**
12 **YOUNG YOZZA**, 6, b g Kayf Tara—Swift Messenger **Mr D. & Mrs L. Yearsley**

MR M. I. SHEPPARD—continued

Other Owners: Mr J. M. Basquill, M. R. Bown, Mr P. Brook, Mrs K. P. Brown, Mr M. E. Harris, A. D. I. Harris, M. P. Hill, Mrs L. J. Johnson, R. A. Kujawa, Mr R. Nicholls, Mr P. R. W. Smith, Mrs S. A. Ward, D. K. Yearsley, Mrs L. I. Yearsley.

Amateur: Mr L. Payter.

---

533 **MR O. M. C. SHERWOOD, Upper Lambourn**
Postal: Rhonehurst House, Upper Lambourn, Hungerford, Berkshire, RG17 8RG
Contacts: **PHONE (01488) 71411 FAX (01488) 72786 MOBILE (07979) 591867**
E-MAIL oliver.sherwood@virgin.net WEBSITE www.oliversherwood.com

1 ARGENTO LUNA, 5, gr m Mtoto—Dissolve **P. K. Gardner**
2 ARRAYOU (FR), 7, b g Valanjou (FR)—Cavatine (FR) **J. P. Ledwidge**
3 BALLYGALLEY BOB (IRE), 7, br g Bob Back (USA)—Follow The Guide (IRE) **A. L. Cohen**
4 BELLEDESARO (IRE), 8, br m Un Desperado (FR)—Cedarbelle (IRE) **Mrs S. Griffiths**
5 BLACK VEN (IRE), 7, b g Presenting—Mini Minor (IRE) **The Chamberlain Addiscott Partnership**
6 BRUMOUS (IRE), 8, b g Glacial Storm (USA)—Ath Leathan **J. M. Dougall**
7 CARIBOU (FR), 6, b g Epervier Bleu—Cardoudalle (FR) **It Wasn't Us**
8 CELEBRITY CALL (IRE), 7, ch g Fourstars Allstar (USA)—Callerbann **The Celebrity Call Partnership**
9 CIRCUS OF DREAMS, 5, b g Kayf Tara—Foehn Gale (IRE) **D. B. Knox**
10 CNOC MOY (IRE), 4, b g Mull of Kintyre (USA)—Ewar Sunrise **Mrs C. M. Hardman**
11 ELLWAY PROSPECT, 8, ch m Pivotal—Littlemisstrouble (USA) **Mrs M. L. Luck**
12 ERIC'S CHARM (FR), 10, b g Nikos—Ladoun (FR) **M. St Quinton & P. Deal**
13 FASSAROE, 6, b g Kayf Tara—Kosheen (IRE) **M. G. St Quinton**
14 FINNEY, 6, b g Supreme Leader—Haudello (FR) **T. J. Hemmings**
15 GLOBAL STRATEGY, 5, b g Rainbow Quest (USA)—Pleasuring **E. P. Duggan**
16 GRANDAGE, 5, b g Courteous—Casting Vote (USA) **D. Allan**
17 INGHWUNG, 6, b m Kayf Tara—Mossy Fern **G. R. Waters**
18 IRON MAID, 7, b m Shambo—Brass Castle (IRE) **The Cottage Coterie**
19 IT'S A PLEASURE (IRE), 8, b g Lord Americo—Kiria Mou (USA) **Mrs S. Griffiths**
20 JAUNTY FLIGHT, 6, b m Busy Flight—Jaunty June **P. A. Deal**
21 LITTLE AL, 5, b g Alflora (IRE)—Mossy Fern **G. R. Waters**
22 LUNAR ROCK (IRE), 6, b g Rock Hopper—Firey Comet (IRE) **Mrs S. Griffiths**
23 LYES GREEN, 7, gr g Bien Bien (USA)—Dissolve **P. K. Gardner**
24 MAJOR FAUX PAS (IRE), 6, b g Barathea (IRE)—Edwina (IRE) **The St Joseph Partnership**
25 MANDALAY LADY, 6, gr m Environment Friend—Pretty Scarce **C. I. C. Munro**
26 MANORSON (IRE), 9, ch g Desert King (IRE)—Familiar (USA) **Byrne Bros (Formwork) Limited**
27 MINSTER ABBI, 8, b m Minster Son—Elitist **R. C. Tooth**
28 MOUNT SANDEL (IRE), 7, b g Supreme Leader—Droichidin **T. J. Hemmings**
29 PACCO (FR), 5, b g Assessor (IRE)—Uguette IV (FR) **Ray & Marian Elbro**
30 PUERTO AZUL (IRE), 4, ch g Beneficial—Droichidin **B. T. Stewart-Brown & J. Palmer-Brown**
31 ROSCREA (IRE), 6, b g Oscar (IRE)—Village Bridge (IRE) **E. P. Duggan**
32 SILVER BAY, 7, b g Silver Patriarch (IRE)—Sheriff **G. R. Waters**
33 SIX DAY WAR (IRE), 6, b g Barathea (IRE)—Risarshana (FR) **Martyn & Elaine Booth & Andrew L Cohen**
34 SOURICEAU (FR), 4, b g Maille Pistol (FR)—Saural (FR) **Million in Mind Partnership**
35 SPROSSER (IRE), 8, b g Alflora (IRE)—Dark Nightingale **W. S. Watt**
36 STRONG COFFEE, 6, b g Classic Cliche—Foehn Gale (IRE) **David Knox & John Rathbone**
37 SUPERROLLERCOASTER, 8, b g Classic Cliche (IRE)—Foehn Gale (IRE) **R. J. Bassett**
38 TYTHEKNOT, 7, b g Pursuit of Love—Bundled Up (USA) **B. R. Marsden**
39 WIDELY ACCEPTED (IRE), 6, b g Mujadil (USA)—Costume Drama (USA) **Mrs S. Griffiths**
40 WILKINSON, 5, br g Anshan—Brown Gillette **T. J. Hemmings**

Other Owners: Mrs D. L. Addiscott, G. Addiscott, J. W. M. Barlow, Mr A. M. K. Barlow, M. Booth, Mrs E. Booth, W. J. B. Bridge, A. R. Bromley, Mrs P. C. Chamberlain, N. J. Chamberlain, S. M. Chapman, Lord Daresbury, Mr A. Douglas, Mrs M. Elbro, Mr R. J. Elbro, Mrs M. F. Feilden, G. F. Goode, W. D. C. Minton, Mrs D. C. Nicholson, J. A. Osborne, J. S. Palfreyman, J. Palmer-Brown, H. M. J. Pope, Mrs M. E. Powney-Jones, Mr J. C. D. Rathbone, O. M. C. Sherwood, B. T. Stewart-Brown Esq, V. J. Walsh, D. P. Walsh.

Assistant Trainer: Warren Greatrex

Jockey (NH): D. Elsworth, P. C. O'Neill. **Amateur:** Mr J. Quintin.

534 MR S. E. H. SHERWOOD, Bromyard
Postal: **The Day House, Bredenbury, Bromyard, Herefordshire, HR7 4TL**
Contacts: **OFFICE (01885) 488567 FAX (01885) 488677 MOBILE (07836) 215639**
E-MAIL **seh.sherwood@virgin.net**

1 LAURIER D'ESTRUVAL (FR), 9, ch g Ragmar (FR)—Grive d'estruval (FR) **T. N. Siviter**
2 MILLITANT MAN, 6, b g Kayf Tara—Ruby Laser **Lady Thompson**
3 5, B g Kayf Tara—Ruby Laser **Lady Thompson**
4 SERENGETI SUNSET (IRE), 7, b m Luso—Crotty's Bridge (IRE) **G. C. Vos**
5 SUB ARTIC (IRE), 10, b g Arctic Lord—Suba (GER) **H. A. Murphy**

Jockey (NH): J. Tizzard.

535 MR R. SHIELS, Jedburgh
Postal: **Thickside Farm, Jedburgh, Roxburghshire, TD8 6QY**
Contacts: **PHONE (01835) 864060 MOBILE (07790) 295645**

1 HURRICANE BASIL (IRE), 6, gr g Good Thyne (USA)—Toureen Gale (IRE) **R. Shiels**
2 JUST JED, 9, b g Presidium—Carrapateira **R. Shiels**
3 KING RASCAL, 5, b g Rakaposhi King—Royal Blaze **R. Shiels**
4 LIVELY DESSERT (IRE), 15, b g Be My Native (USA)—Liffey Travel **R. Shiels**
5 LOCKSTOCKANDBARREL (IRE), 9, b g Needle Gun (IRE)—Quill Project (IRE) **R. Shiels**

536 MR S. H. SHIRLEY-BEAVAN, Hawick
Postal: **Gatehousecote, Bonchester Bridge, Hawick, Roxburghshire, TD9 8JD**
Contacts: **PHONE (01450) 860210**

1 CUIGNY (FR), 5, b g Freedom Cry—Kaolombe (FR) **Mrs P. M. Shirley-Beavan**
2 PLAISIR DE MONTÔT (FR), 5, ch g Video Rock (FR)—Idylle de Montot (FR) **Mrs P. M. Shirley-Beavan**
3 QUOQUILLE DES SACART (FR), 4, b f Ragmar (FR)—Entiqua des Sacart (FR) **S. H. Shirley-Beavan**

Amateur: Miss Kelly Bryson.

537 MISS L. C. SIDDALL, Tadcaster
Postal: **Stonebridge Farm, Colton, Tadcaster, North Yorkshire, LS24 8EP**
Contacts: **PHONE (01904) 744291 FAX (01904) 744291 MOBILE (07778) 216692/4**

1 DAY DU ROY (FR), 10, b g Ajdayt (USA)—Rose Pomme (FR) **G. Kennington**
2 EXPLODE, 11, b g Zafonic (USA)—Didicoy (USA) **Lynn Siddall Racing II**
3 FRILL A MINUTE, 4, b f Lake Coniston (IRE)—Superfrills **Podso Racing**
4 GAGARIN (FR), 8, b g Quest For Fame—Good To Dance (IRE) **Stonebridge Racing**
5 HENBECK LADY (IRE), 6, b m Chickawicka (IRE)—Landsbury Lass (IRE) **Miss L. C. Siddall**
6 LAZY LENA (IRE), 9, b m Oscar (IRE)—Magnum Gale (IRE) **Miss L. C. Siddall**
7 LEAHSTAR, 9, ch m In The Wings—Moondance **Mrs D. J. Morris**
8 ONE ACCORD, 7, b g Accordion—Not So Prim **Mrs D. Ibbotson**
9 WESTWIRE TOBY, 6, ch g Anshan—Ware It Well (IRE) **Stonebridge Racing II**
10 WINDFOLA, 9, b m Sovereign Water (FR)—Sainte Martine **Miss J. M. Slater**

Other Owners: Mrs P. J. Clark, Mrs E. W. Cooper, Mr B. Donkin, Mr I. Grice, Mrs P. M. Hornby, Mr T. Humphrey, Mrs K. M. Kennington, Miss S. Lythe, Mr. D. McGhee, Miss Sue Vinden.

Assistant Trainer: Stephen Hackney

Jockey (NH): Tom Siddall.

538 MR D. M. I. SIMCOCK, Newmarket

Postal: The Office, Trillium Place, Birdcage Walk, Newmarket, Suffolk, CB8 ONE
Contacts: PHONE/FAX (01638) 662968 MOBILE (07808) 954109
E-MAIL davidsimcock@ukonline.co.uk or david@davidsimcock.co.uk
WEBSITE www.davidsimcock.co.uk

1 BUSHMAN, 4, gr g Maria's Mon (USA)—Housa Dancer (FR)
2 CLASSIC ENCOUNTER (IRE), 5, b g Lujain (USA)—Licence To Thrill
3 CONTENTIOUS (IRE), 4, b f Danetime (IRE)—Serious Contender (IRE)
4 GOLDEN WAVE (IRE), 4, b f Green Desert (USA)—Gold Bust
5 HAZZARD COUNTY (USA), 4, ch c Grand Slam (USA)—Sweet Lexy May (USA)
6 METROPOLITAN MAN, 5, ch h Dr Fong (USA)—Preceder
7 MINAASH (USA), 4, b c Dixie Union (USA)—Metanoia (USA)
8 PADLOCKED (IRE), 4, b c Key of Luck (USA)—Accelerating (USA)
9 RUSSKI (IRE), 4, b c Fasliyev (USA)—Rose of Mooncoin (IRE)
10 VAINGLORY (USA), 4, ch c Swain (IRE)—Infinite Spirit (USA)

THREE-YEAR-OLDS

11 AINIA, b f Alhaarth (IRE)—Vayavaig
12 ANY GIVEN DAY (IRE), gr g Clodovil (IRE)—Five of Wands
13 DANCE THE STAR (USA), b br c Dynaformer (USA)—Dance The Slew (USA)
14 FLEURS DE CENSIER, b f Vettori (IRE)—April Lee (USA)
15 GONE FAST (USA), ch f Gone West (USA)—Abita (USA)
16 LADY ZABEEN (IRE), b f Singspiel (IRE)—Britannia House (USA)
17 NOBLE CITIZEN (USA), b c Proud Citizen (USA)—Serene Nobility (USA)
18 QUICK RELEASE (IRE), b c Red Ransom (USA)—Set The Mood (USA)
19 SAPPHIRE QUEEN, ch f Sakhee (USA)—Celtic Sapphire (FR)
20 SEEKING THE STAR (CAN), b g Seeking The Gold (USA)—Water Music (CAN)
21 TIMBALIER (USA), ch c Dixieland Band (USA)—Gabacha (USA)
22 TOP TICKET (IRE), ch c Alhaarth (IRE)—Tathkara (USA)
23 WABBRAAN (USA), b g Aldebaran (USA)—Madame Modjeska (USA)
24 ZAARMIT (IRE), b c Xaar—Tender Is Thenight (IRE)

TWO-YEAR-OLDS

25 B f 8/2 Barathea (IRE)—Anthyllis (IRE) (Night Shift (USA)) (27000)
26 B br f 18/2 Gone West (USA)—Blue Moon (FR) (Lomitas) (85034)
27 DOWNSTREAM, b f 21/1 Marju (IRE)—Sister Moonshine (FR) (Piccolo)
28 DUBAI LEGEND, ch f 2/5 Cadeaux Genereux—Royal Future (IRE) (Royal Academy (USA)) (34000)
29 B c 27/2 Oasis Dream—Egoli (USA) (Seeking The Gold (USA)) (35000)
30 B br f 22/3 Harlan's Holiday (USA)—Henderson Band (USA) (Chimes Band (USA)) (58309)
31 Br f 1/5 Dubai Destination (USA)—In Full Cry (USA) (Seattle Slew (USA)) (55000)
32 B f 20/2 Cape Cross (IRE)—Joharra (USA) (Kris S (USA)) (30000)
33 B c 6/3 Dubai Destination (USA)—Lady Bankes (IRE) (Alzao (USA)) (52000)
34 B c 21/4 Auction House (USA)—Lady Ploy (Deploy) (8000)
35 Ch c 29/3 Singspiel (IRE)—Lady Zonda (Lion Cavern (USA)) (70000)
36 B f 15/2 King's Best (USA)—Loire Valley (IRE) (Sadler's Wells (USA)) (30000)
37 B br f 7/3 Gone West (USA)—Magicalmysterycat (USA) (Storm Cat (USA)) (68027)
38 Gr c 23/2 Orpen (USA)—Man Eater (Mark of Esteem (IRE)) (10000)
39 Ch c 2/5 King's Best (USA)—Needles And Pins (IRE) (Fasliyev (USA)) (37000)
40 Ch f 14/1 Refuse to Bend (IRE)—Oulianovsk (IRE) (Peintre Celebre (USA)) (45000)
41 B f 1/3 Dubai Destination (USA)—Paper Chase (FR) (Machiavellian (USA)) (32000)
42 B c 7/4 Kheleyf (USA)—Premier Amour (Salmon Leap (USA)) (18000)
43 B f 6/4 Oasis Dream—Royal Alchemist (USA) (Royal Academy (USA)) (60000)
44 B c 13/4 Tiger Hill (IRE)—Sagamartha (Rainbow Quest (USA)) (90089)
45 B br f 30/1 Singspiel (IRE)—Shepherd's Moon (USA) (Silver Hawk (USA)) (41302)
46 SPIRIT OF DUBAI (IRE), b f 5/4 Cape Cross (IRE)—Questina (FR) (Rainbow Quest (USA)) (85000)
47 B c 15/4 King's Best (USA)—Tegwen (USA) (Nijinsky (CAN)) (90000)
48 B f 4/5 Diktat—Zibet (Kris) (10000)

Owners: Saif Ali, Sultan Ali, S. H. Altayer, Mrs J. Annable, A. S. Belhab, Mr Malcolm Caine, DXB Bloodstock Ltd, K. A. Dasmal, Mr Carl Davis, D. J. Erwin, Mrs T. A. Foreman, S. R. Hope, S. Misfer, S. Misleh, Miss S. J. Moses, M. A. Nabouda, Dr A. Ridha, A. A. Shaikh, Shamsudeen, Mr Graham Tysom.

Jockey (flat): Richard Mullen. **Apprentice:** Chris Hough.

539 **MR RODNEY SIMPSON, Lambourn**
Postal: **Upshire Racing, Greenways, Lambourn, Hungerford, Berkshire, RG17 7LE**
Contacts: **PHONE (01488) 73333 FAX (01488) 73333 MOBILE (07852) 312319**
E-MAIL rod@carnivalquest.com WEBSITE www.carnivalquest.com

1 COOL EBONY, 5, br g Erhaab (USA)—Monawara (IRE) **Liza Judd/Wedgewood Estates**
2 EVEN BOLDER, 5, ch g Bold Edge—Level Pegging (IRE) **Carnival Quest**
3 MULTEEN GUNNER, 11, b g Homo Sapien—Sister Delaney **Miss J. H. Jenner**
4 ORANGE ZEUS, 4, ch g Most Welcome—Linea-G **Mr Paul Harvey Mr Phil Shepley**
5 RAY'S DREAM, 4, b g Sure Blade (USA)—Polar Queen **Miss V. C. Dunn**
6 SIMPLY THE QUEST, 4, br f Mtoto—Wydah **Carnival Quest**
7 UNLIMITED, 6, b g Bold Edge—Cabcharge Blue **Carnival Quest**

THREE-YEAR-OLDS

8 ANGELS QUEST, b f Piccolo—Tamara **Carnival Quest**
9 CHRISTOPHERS QUEST, b c Forzando—Kaprisky (IRE) **Carnival Quest**
10 ELIZABETH'S QUEST, b f Piccolo—Reina **Carnival Quest**
11 MONASHEE ROCK (IRE), b f Monashee Mountain (USA)—Polar Rock **Mr Lewin & Mr Grieve**

TWO-YEAR-OLDS

12 SAHARAN ROYAL, b f 13/3 Val Royal (FR)—Saharan Song (IRE) (Singspiel (IRE)) **Mr Lewin Mr Grieve**
13 B c 3/5 Golan (IRE)—Women In Love (IRE) (Danehill (USA)) **Mr H. Davies, Mrs V. Dunn**

Other Owners: D. E. Grieve, Mr Paul Harvey, M. J. Lewin, Mr P. Shepley, Mr Rod Simpson, Mrs A. Wise.

Assistant Trainer: Ann Marie Wise

Apprentice: Ryan Clark. Amateur: Miss Jackie Jenner.

540 **MRS D. E. SLACK, Appleby**
Postal: **Stoneriggs, Hilton, Appleby, Cumbria, CA16 6LS**
Contacts: **PHONE (01768) 351354 MOBILE (07936) 372529**

1 BARNEY (IRE), 7, b g Basanta (IRE)—Double Or Nothing (IRE) **A. Slack**
2 CASH MAN (IRE), 7, b g Flemensfirth (USA)—Bollero (IRE) **A. Slack**
3 KING DANIEL, 7, br g Prince Daniel (USA)—Panic Button (USA) **A. Slack**
4 MIGHTY FELLA, 6, gr g Cloudings (IRE)—Zany Lady **Mrs D. E. Slack**
5 SMART MAN, 6, gr g Silver Patriarch (IRE)—Run Tiger **A. Slack**
6 STONERIGGS MERC (IRE), 7, gr g Alderbrook—Betseale (IRE) **Mrs D. E. Slack**
7 STONERIGGS SILVER, 7, gr g Silver Patriarch (IRE)—Carole's Crusader **A. Slack**
8 WHATCANYASAY, 7, gr g Prince Daniel (USA)—Snowys Pet **A. Slack**

Amateur: Miss Natalie Sayer.

541 **MRS P. M. SLY, Peterborough**
Postal: **Singlecote, Thorney, Peterborough, Cambridgeshire, PE6 0PB**
Contacts: **PHONE (01733) 270212 FAX (01733) 270212 MOBILE (07850) 511267**

1 BEDIZEN, 5, b g Fantastic Light (USA)—Barboukh **D. Bayliss, T. Davies, G. Libson & P. M. Sly**
2 CAPISTRANO, 5, b g Efisio—Washita **C. B. Goodyear**
3 CAYMAN CALYPSO (IRE), 7, ro g Danehill Dancer (IRE)—Warthill Whispers **T. R. Pryke**
4 CIRCUS ROSE, 6, ch m Most Welcome—Rosie Cone **Mrs P. M. Sly**
5 CORKAGE (IRE), 5, b g Second Empire (IRE)—Maslam (IRE) **Mrs P. M. Sly**
6 DELIGHTFUL CLICHE, 7, b g Classic Cliche (IRE)—Ima Delight **Mrs V. M. Edmonson**
7 DHEHDAAH, 7, b g Alhaarth (IRE)—Carina Clare **D. Bayliss, T. Davies, G. Libson & P .Sly**
8 FULLARDS, 10, b g Alderbrook—Milly Kelly **Mrs P. M. Sly**
9 GLINTON, 6, ch g Most Welcome—Chichell's Hurst **G. A. Libson, D. L. Bayliss, G. Taylor, P. M. Sly**
10 HARLEY, 10, ch g Alderbrook—Chichell's Hurst **Thorney Racing Club**
11 HELPSTON, 4, b g Sir Harry Lewis—Chichell's Hurst **Mrs P. M. Sly**
12 NOBLE RAIDER (IRE), 6, gr g Deploy—Smooth Princess (IRE) **E. M. Kirtland**
13 PHEIDIAS (IRE), 4, ch g Spectrum (IRE)—Danse Grecque (IRE) **Mrs P. M. Sly**
14 PIKASSO (FR), 5, b br g Sleeping Car (FR)—Roseraie (FR) **M. H. S. Sly**
15 SAMARINDA (USA), 5, ch g Rahy (USA)—Munnaya (USA) **D. Bayliss, T. Davies, G. Libson & P. M. Sly**
16 SAN ANTONIO, 8, b g Efisio—Winnebago **S. W. R. Brazier**

MRS P. M. SLY—continued

17 UPRIGHT IMA, 9, b m Perpendicular—Ima Delight **Mrs P. M. Sly**
18 VIABLE, 6, b g Vettori (IRE)—Danseuse Davis (FR) **Thorney Racing Club**
19 WISTOW, 4, b f Sir Harry Lewis (USA)—River Bay (IRE) **Mrs P. M. Sly**

THREE-YEAR-OLDS

20 MISS SERENA, gr f Singspiel (IRE)—Valnerina (IRE) **Mr E. Amlie**
21 MWINDAJI, b g Hunting Lion (IRE)—Gayane **Mrs R. J. Kettle**
22 OVTHENIGHT (IRE), b c Noverre (USA)—Night Beauty **D. Bayliss, T. Davies, G. Libson & P. M. Sly**

TWO-YEAR-OLDS

23 Ch f 10/2 Golden Missile (USA)—Gal of Mine (USA) (Mining (USA)) (17978)
24 B br f 10/5 More Than Ready (USA)—
　　　　　Woodman's Dancer (USA) (Woodman (USA)) (36443) **M. H. Sly, Dr T. Davies & Mrs P. M. Sly**

Other Owners: Mr David L. Bayliss, Dr T. J. W. Davies, Mrs S. E. Godfrey, Mr G. A. Libson, Mr Derek Sly, Mr G. Taylor.

Jockey (flat): M. Fenton, A. Culhane. **Jockey (NH):** W. Marston. **Amateur:** Miss Louise Allan.

542　MR D. SMAGA, Lamorlaye
Postal: **17 Voie de la Grange des Pres, 60260 Lamorlaye, France**
Contacts: **PHONE (0033) 3442 15005 FAX (0033) 3442 15356**

1 ALEXANDRIA BLUE (IRE), 4, ch f Anabaa Blue—Sudden Storm Bird (USA) **Mme Dominique Smaga**
2 BEAU VENGEROV (IRE), 4, b c Danehill (USA)—Arpege (IRE) **Mr M. Parrish**
3 BOOKEND, 4, b g Dansili—Roupala (USA) **Prince Khalid Abdullah**
4 DREAM'S DUNE, 4, b f Anabaa Blue—Finir En Beaute (FR) **Haras De Bernesq**
5 HIDDEN RAINBOW (IRE), 5, ch g Spectrum (IRE)—Grecian Urn **Mme Dominique Smaga**
6 IRISH WAY (FR), 6, ch h Giant's Causeway (USA)—Irish Arms (FR) **Mme R. Ades**
7 KABOURA (FR), 5, b m Kabool—Colour Scheme (FR) **Baron T. Van Zuylen**
8 KASLIK (FR), 7, b g Desert Prince (USA)—Mrs Ting (USA) **Mme Dominique Smaga**
9 SARGASSO SEA (FR), 4, bl c Ocean of Wisdom (USA)—Sangrilla (FR) **Baron T. Van Zuylen**
10 SKAGERRAK (USA), 4, gr ro c Dynaformer (USA)—Si Je N'avais Plus (IRE) **Mr Maurice Lagasse**
11 VICTORIA COLLEGE (FR), 4, b f Rock of Gibraltar (IRE)—Uruk **Mr O. El Sharif**

THREE-YEAR-OLDS

12 A LA PLAGE, b f Galileo (IRE)—Ocean Reef **Mr S. Chiboub**
13 ANDRE MON AMI (USA), ch c Peintre Celebre (USA)—Steno **Mr Frank Pagano**
14 AORNOS (FR), b c Dashing Blade—Semenova (FR) **Ecurie Chalhoub**
15 ATHINEOS (IRE), b c Anabaa (USA)—Greek Air (IRE) **Mme Dominique Smaga**
16 AZTEC GOLD (IRE), b c Oasis Dream—China Moon (USA) **Prince Khalid Abdullah**
17 B c Diesis—Baldellia (FR) **Mr Maurice Lagasse**
18 BIZERTE (IRE), ch c King's Best (USA)—Verzasca (IRE) **Mr Slim Chiboub**
19 BOISLEDUC (IRE), b c Numerous (USA)—Dame Edith (FR) **Baron T. Van Zuylen**
20 BUNSEN BURNER, b c Langfuhr (CAN)—Navarene (USA) **Prince Khalid Abdullah**
21 B f Enrique—Capework (USA) **Woodside Farms**
22 CLECAME, b gr f Slickly (FR)—Amazing Story (FR) **Mr Malcolm Parrish**
23 DANCE DANCE (IRE), ch c Daylami (IRE)—Latifolia **Mr Slim Chiboub**
24 GREY STYLE (FR), gr c Daylami (IRE)—Style For Life (IRE) **Mr Slim Chiboub**
25 HANNOUMA, b c Anabaa (USA)—Red Blossom (USA) **Mr M. Parrish**
26 HEAD OF DEFENCE (USA), b c Cozzene (USA)—Tsar's Pride **Prince Khalid Abdullah**
27 HORSEGUARD, b c Beat Hollow—Londonnet (IRE) **Prince Khalid Abdullah**
28 HURRICAN GIRL, gr f Slickly (FR)—Hold The Gold (GER) **Mr S. Chiboub**
29 LEADING ARTIST, ch f Peintre Celebre (USA)—I Will Lead (USA) **Prince Khalid Abdullah**
30 MODERN LOOK, b f Zamindar (USA)—Prophecy (IRE) **Prince Khalid Abdullah**
31 REALLY BEST (FR), b f King's Best (USA)—Scripture (IRE) **Mr Slim Chiboub**
32 RETIENS LA NUIT, ch f Grand Slam (USA)—Rodericka (USA) **Mr M. Lagasse**
33 SEAL BAY (IRE), ch c Hernando (FR)—Torrealta **Mr A. Morice**
34 SECOND ACT, b f Sadler's Wells (USA)—Tuning **Prince Khalid Abdullah**
35 SHARGA (IRE), b c Highest Honor (FR)—Glebe Place (FR) **Mr O. El Sharif**
36 SUBLISSIME (IRE), b f Rock of Gibraltar (IRE)—Reem Albaraari **Mr Malcolm Parrish**
37 TRULLY BELLE, b f Bahri (USA)—Truly A Gift (IRE) **Mr A. Chiboub**
38 VASCO MARENGO, ch c Hernando (FR)—Moon Is Up (USA) **M. E. Parrish**

MR D. SMAGA—continued

TWO-YEAR-OLDS

39 Ch f 31/3 Johannesburg (USA)—Ardere (USA) (El Prado (IRE)) **Mr Wafic Said**
40 B f 16/5 Orpen (USA)—Dame Edith (FR) (Top Ville) (22522) **Baron T. Van Zuylen**
41 **DESERT RALLY (IRE),** b c 11/3 Green Desert (USA)—
          Blanche (FR) (Loup Solitaire (USA)) (57915) **Mr Slim Chiboub**
42 **DON JO,** b c 1/3 Johannesburg (USA)—Zinziberine (USA) (Zieten (USA)) (83655) **Mr Slim Chiboub**
43 **EQUERRIA (FR),** b f 28/1 Equerry (USA)—Phaleria (USA) (Lyphard (USA)) **Mme Dominique Smaga**
44 **FRENCH GARDEN (FR),** b c 1/1 Kendor (FR)—Girl of France (Legend of France (USA)) **Baron T. Van Zuylen**
45 B c 1/1 Kalanisi (IRE)—Glebe Place (FR) (Akarad (FR)) **Baron T. Van Zuylen**
46 **HANDSOME MAESTRO (IRE),** b c 12/3 Dansili—Graceful Bering (USA) (Bering) (115830) **Mr Slim Chiboub**
47 Ch f 10/3 Choisir (AUS)—Haskilclara (FR) (Green Tune (USA)) (57915) **Mr Jean-Michel Hegesippe**
48 **KOROMANDEL (FR),** b f 8/1 Numerous (USA)—Thank Heavens (FR) (Octagonal (NZ)) **Baron T. Van Zuylen**
49 B f 1/1 Daylami (IRE)—Lady Time (FR) (Orpen (USA)) **Baron T. Van Zuylen**
50 Ch c 4/4 Bering—Loretta Gianni (FR) (Classic Account (USA)) **Mr Philippe Druon**
51 **POMME D'AMOUR (IRE),** b f 11/2 Dansili—Seditieuse (IRE) (Night Shift (USA)) (28957) **Mr Robert Bellaiche**
52 B c 10/3 Elusive City (USA)—Queen of Fairies (IRE) (Fairy King (USA)) **Mr Maurice Lagasse**
53 **SUDDEN SURPRISE (FR),** b f 1/1 Bahri (USA)—Sudden Storm Bird (USA) (Storm Bird (CAN)) **Mr Slim Chiboub**
54 **TU T'LAISSES ALLER,** b f 4/2 Hernando (FR)—Tashkiyla (FR) (Alzao (USA)) (25740) **Mr Maurice Lagasse**

Jockey (flat): D. Boeuf. **Apprentice:** Mr Frankie Leroy.

---

543 **MR B. SMART, Thirsk**
Postal: **Hambleton House, Sutton Bank, Thirsk, North Yorkshire, YO7 2HA**
Contacts: **PHONE (01845) 597481 FAX (01845) 597480 MOBILE (07748) 634797**
E-MAIL office@bryansmart.plus.com WEBSITE www.bryansmart-racing.com

1 **AEGEAN DANCER,** 6, b g Piccolo—Aegean Flame **Pinnacle Piccolo Partnership**
2 **ANGARIC (IRE),** 5, ch g Pivotal—Grannys Reluctance (USA) **A. D. Gee**
3 **ANSELLS PRIDE (IRE),** 5, b g King Charlemagne (USA)—Accounting **Ansells Of Watford**
4 **AVERTUOSO,** 4, b g Averti (IRE)—First Musical **Pinnacle Averti Partnership**
5 **BOLD NEVISON (IRE),** 4, b g Danehill Dancer (IRE)—La Pieta (IRE) **Ceffyl Racing**
6 **CASSIE'S CHOICE (IRE),** 4, b f Fath—Esteraad (IRE) **EKOS Pinnacle Partnership**
7 **FATHOM FIVE (IRE),** 4, b g Fath (USA)—Ambria (ITY) **Hintlesham Racing**
8 **IL CASTAGNO (IRE),** 5, ch g Night Shift—Cartesian **Pinnacle Night Shift Partnership**
9 **JACK RACKHAM,** 4, ch g Kyllachy—Hill Welcome **Mrs F. Denniff**
10 **JEMBER RED,** 5, b m Polish Precedent (USA)—Arabellajill **R. J. Mullan**
11 **MISS DOUBLE DAISY,** 5, ch m Compton Place—Stealthy **J. R. Wills**
12 **SADEEK,** 4, ch c Kyllachy—Miss Mercy (IRE) **Mrs P. M. Brown**
13 **SIR XAAR (IRE),** 5, b br g Xaar—Cradle Brief **Pinnacle Smart Partnership**
14 **UNTIL WHEN (USA),** 4, b g Grand Slam (USA)—Chez Cherie **B. Smart**

THREE-YEAR-OLDS

15 B f Cape Cross (IRE)—Advancing (IRE) **S. J. Macdonald**
16 **AMBER ISIS,** ch f Captain Rio—Mammas F-C (IRE) **Pinnacle Captain Rio Partnership**
17 **BERTIE BOO,** b g Where Or When (IRE)—Lucy Boo **Ron & Vera Hopkins**
18 **C'MON YOU IRONS (IRE),** b c Orpen (USA)—Laissez Faire (IRE) **Hintlesham Racing**
19 **CAPTAIN GERRARD (IRE),** b c Oasis Dream—Delphinus **R. C. Bond**
20 **CAPTAIN MACARRY (IRE),** ch c Captain Rio—Grannys Reluctance (USA) **A. D. Gee**
21 **CHIVOLA (IRE),** b c Invincible Spirit (IRE)—Boudica (IRE) **Prime Equestrian**
22 **CHOISETTE,** b f Choisir (AUS)—Final Pursuit **Pinnacle Choisir Partnership**
23 **CHOSEN ONE (IRE),** ch c Choisir (AUS)—Copious (IRE) **Ceffyl Racing**
24 **DORIC DREAM,** ch f Ishiguru (USA)—Generous Share **Doric Dream Partnership**
25 **EASY TARGET (FR),** ch c Danehill Dancer (IRE)—Aiming **Prime Equestrian**
26 **FIREWALKER,** b f Bertolini (USA)—Crystal Canyon **L. Shillito & Julie Martin & David R Martin**
27 **GREAT DESTINATION,** b g Dubai Destination (USA)—Bella Chica (IRE) **Pinnacle Dubai Destination Partnership**
28 **IRISH BROOKE (IRE),** ch f Night Shift (USA)—Away With The Wind **EERC**
29 **KYLLIS,** b f Kyllachy—Princess Latifa **Darling Girls**
30 **MAID IN BLOOM,** b f Averti (IRE)—Fille de Fleurie **Miss N. A. Jefford**
31 **MANGHAM (IRE),** b c Montjeu (IRE)—Lovisa (USA) **Mr R. Hull**
32 **MAZE (IRE),** ch c Dr Fong (USA)—Aryadne **Pinnacle Dr Fong Partnership**
33 **MILL CREEK,** ch f Ishiguru (USA)—Hollia **Destiny Racing Club**
34 **NICKEL SILVER,** ro c Choisir (AUS)—Negligee **M. Barber**
35 **NIZHONI (USA),** ch f Mineshaft (USA)—Carinae (USA) **Crossfields Racing**

MR B. SMART—continued

36 **NORTUNE (USA)**, b c Street Cry (IRE)—Gilded Leaf (USA) **Prime Equestrian**
37 **ON INSTINCT (IRE)**, b f Clodovil (IRE)—Julius (IRE) **S. J. Macdonald**
38 **PEGGYS POINT (IRE)**, b f Fantastic Light (USA)—Just Call Me (NZ) **H.E. Sheikh R. Al Maktoum**
39 **PRIME PERFORMER (IRE)**, b f Acclamation—Storming Kate (IRE) **Prime Equestrian**
40 **PRINCE HAMLET (IRE)**, b c Fantastic Light (USA)—Hamsaat Hi Haat (USA) **H.E. Sheikh R. Al Maktoum**
41 **RED TARN**, gr g Fraam—Cumbrian Melody **Pinnacle Fraam Partnership**
42 **ROGER'S REVENGE**, ch g City On A Hill (USA)—Resemblance **B. Smart**
43 **SOOPACAL (IRE)**, b c Captain Rio—Fiddes (IRE) **Brian Grieve & Jeff Evans**
44 **STRAWBERRY MOON (IRE)**, b f Alhaarth (IRE)—Dancing Drop **Mrs J. M. T. Martin**
45 **SWEET DESTINY**, b f Namid—Cinnamon Lady **Destiny Racing Club**
46 **TANGERINE TREES**, b g Mind Games—Easy To Imagine (USA) **Tangerine Trees Partnership**
47 **TRANSMISSION (IRE)**, b g Galileo (IRE)—Individual (USA) **M. Barber**
48 **UNILATERAL (IRE)**, ch f Rock of Gibraltar (IRE)—Mira Adonde (USA) **Prime Equestrian**
49 **VIRTUALITY (USA)**, b br f Elusive Quality (USA)—Hold To Ransom (USA) **Crossfields Racing**
50 **WELLS LYRICAL (IRE)**, b c Sadler's Wells (USA)—Lyrical **M. Barber**
51 **WING DIVA (IRE)**, b f Hawk Wing (USA)—Sasimoto (USA) **M. Barber**

TWO-YEAR-OLDS

52 B c 30/3 Dr Fong (USA)—All Glory (Alzao (USA)) (34000) **A. M. A. Al Shorafa**
53 B c 27/1 Haafhd—Annapurna (IRE) (Brief Truce (USA)) (100000) **H.E. Sheikh R. Al Maktoum**
54 Ch c 12/2 Monsieur Bond (IRE)—Annie Harvey (Fleetwood (IRE)) (16000) **Mrs V. Smart**
55 B f 29/1 Refuse To Bend (IRE)—Atnab (USA) (Riverman (USA)) (128700) **H.E. Sheikh R. Al Maktoum**
56 B br c 6/4 Royal Applause—Avila (Ajdal (USA)) (88000) **H.E. Sheikh R. Al Maktoum**
57 Ch f 24/4 Choisir (AUS)—Beausite (Grand Lodge (USA)) (3200) **P. A. Darling**
58 Ch c 18/3 Refuse To Bend (IRE)—Bella Bella (IRE) (Sri Pekan (USA)) (148004) **H.E. Sheikh R. Al Maktoum**
59 B c 27/2 Invincible Spirit (IRE)—Bella Michela (IRE) (Superpower) (122264) **H.E. Sheikh R. Al Maktoum**
60 B c 11/2 Falbrav (IRE)—Bunty Boo (Noalto) (34000) **Pinnacle Falbrav Partnership**
61 B c 30/3 Refuse To Bend (IRE)—Bush Cat (Kingmambo (USA)) (50000) **EKOS Pinnacle Partnership**
62 Ch c 15/2 Montbrook (USA)—Catalina Cat (Tabasco Cat (USA)) (16000) **A. M. A. Al Shorafa**
63 B f 16/2 Exceed And Excel (AUS)—Cefira (Distant View (USA)) (50000) **M. Barber**
64 Ch f 22/4 Reel Buddy (USA)—Compact Disc (IRE) (Royal Academy (USA)) (2000) **Mr T. G. & Mrs M. E. Holdcroft**
65 Ch f 20/2 Exceed And Excel (AUS)—
    Coolrain Lady (IRE) (Common Grounds) (120000) **H.E. Sheikh R. Al Maktoum**
66 B c 5/3 Bahamian Bounty—Dark Eyed Lady (IRE) (Exhibitioner) (32174) **Prime Equestrian**
67 B c 11/3 Elusive City (USA)—Foresta Verde (USA) (Green Forest (USA)) (10000) **Mr R. Hull**
68 B c 25/2 Kyllachy—Go Between (Daggers Drawn (USA)) (64000) **H.E. Sheikh R. Al Maktoum**
69 Ch c 25/4 Bahamian Bounty—Goodwood Blizzard (Inchinor) (8000) **Pinnacle Bahamian Bounty Partnership**
70 B c 22/3 Dubai Destination (USA)—Hill Welcome (Most Welcome) (95000) **H.E. Sheikh R. Al Maktoum**
71 Ch f 19/2 Exceed And Excel (AUS)—Ikan (IRE) (Sri Pekan (USA)) (110000) **H.E. Sheikh R. Al Maktoum**
72 B c 11/2 Royal Applause—Incise (Dr Fong (USA)) (42000) **H.E. Sheikh R. Al Maktoum**
73 B f 6/4 Hawk Wing (USA)—Innocence (Unfuwain (USA)) (28957) **Prime Equestrian**
74 B c 6/3 Exceed And Excel (AUS)—Jakarta (IRE) (Machiavellian) (88000) **H.E. Sheikh R. Al Maktoum**
75 B c 14/2 Bertolini (USA)—Latour (Sri Pekan (USA)) (36000) **B. Smart**
76 **LAZYBLUES (USA)**, ch c 7/1 Dixieland Band (USA)—
    Society Column (USA) (Seeking The Gold (USA)) (15000) **Crossfields Racing**
77 B c 11/2 War Chant (USA)—Leopard Hunt (USA) (Diesis) (19000) **Pinnacle War Chant Partnership**
78 Ch c 11/3 Van Nistelrooy (USA)—Longing To Dance (USA) (Nureyev (USA)) (7288) **Prime Equestrian**
79 B c 10/1 Elusive Quality (USA)—Lucky (IRE) (Sadler's Wells (USA)) (300000) **H.E. Sheikh R. Al Maktoum**
80 B c 28/4 Exceed And Excel (AUS)—Magic Lady (Bigstone (IRE)) (14000) **Destiny Racing Club**
81 B c 23/3 Dr Fong (USA)—Mail The Desert (IRE) (Desert Prince (IRE)) (200000) **H.E. Sheikh R. Al Maktoum**
82 Ch f 18/4 Monsieur Bond (IRE)—Mammas F-C (IRE) (Case Law) **Mr Phil Williams**
83 B c 16/2 Include (USA)—Many Thanks (USA) (Mi Cielo (USA)) (20000) **A. M. A. Al Shorafa**
84 B f 22/2 Johannesburg (USA)—Margay (IRE) (Marju (IRE)) (54697) **S. J. Macdonald**
85 B c 5/3 Nayef (USA)—Mauri Moon (Green Desert (USA)) (175000) **H.E. Sheikh R. Al Maktoum**
86 Ch f 15/2 Rahy (USA)—Meiosis (Danzig (USA)) **H.E. Sheikh R. Al Maktoum**
87 B f 18/1 Elusive Quality (USA)—Mistle Song (Nashwan (USA)) (86872) **H.E. Sheikh R. Al Maktoum**
88 **MYTHICISM**, b f 23/3 Oasis Dream—Romantic Myth (Mind Games) (40000) **Crossfields Racing**
89 Ch c 18/2 Refuse To Bend (IRE)—Nesaah's Princess (Sinndar (IRE)) (62000) **H.E. Sheikh R. Al Maktoum**
90 **NET VALUE (USA)**, b c 13/3 Van Nistelrooy (USA)—Gritsie Girl (USA) (Boone's Mill (USA)) **Prime Equestrian**
91 B c 11/3 Oasis Dream—Ocean View (USA) (Gone West (USA)) (95000) **H.E. Sheikh R. Al Maktoum**
92 B br f 9/4 Tale of The Cat (USA)—Out of Sync (USA) (Out of Place (USA)) (67566) **Prime Equestrian**
93 B c 6/3 Bertolini (USA)—Pewter Lass (Dowsing (USA)) (32000) **A. Turton & S. Brown**
94 Ch f 7/3 Monsieur Bond (IRE)—Pretty Pollyanna (General Assembly (USA)) (5000) **Mrs F. Denniff & Mr B. Smart**
95 B f 31/3 Monsieur Bond (IRE)—Princess Latifa (Wolfhound (USA)) (3000) **P. A. Darling**
96 Ch f 5/4 Exceed And Excel (AUS)—Princess Nutley (IRE) (Mujtahid (USA)) (32174) **Prime Equestrian**

MR B. SMART—continued

97 QUATERMAIN, ch c 8/3 Peintre Celebre (USA)—Fancy Lady (Cadeaux Genereux) (64349) **Prime Equestrian**
98 Ch f 29/3 Exceed And Excel (AUS)—Quiz Show (Primo Dominie) (96000) **H.E. Sheikh R. Al Maktoum**
99 B c 1/5 Rock of Gibraltar (IRE)—Rills (USA) (Clever Trick (USA)) (38609) **Prime Equestrian**
100 B c 3/2 Monsieur Bond (IRE)—Silca Boo (Efisio) (28000) **R. C. Bond**
101 B f 11/4 Kheleyf (USA)—Silver Arrow (USA) (Shadeed (USA)) (148004) **H.E. Sheikh R. Al Maktoum**
102 B c 5/3 Exceed And Excel (AUS)—Spinamix (Spinning World) (USA) (84000) **H.E. Sheikh R. Al Maktoum**
103 B c 25/3 Nayef (USA)—St Radegund (Green Desert (USA)) (85000) **H.E. Sheikh R. Al Maktoum**
104 B f 20/3 Red Ransom (USA)—String Quartet (IRE) (Sadler's Wells (USA)) (110000) **H.E. Sheikh R. Al Maktoum**
105 B c 1/4 Refuse To Bend (IRE)—Style of Life (USA) (The Minstrel (CAN)) (200000) **H.E. Sheikh R. Al Maktoum**
106 Gr f 21/2 Pivotal—Tamarillo (Daylami (IRE)) **H.E. Sheikh R. Al Maktoum**
107 B c 2/3 Acclamation—Teodora (IRE) (Fairy King (USA)) (65000) **H.E. Sheikh R. Al Maktoum**
108 Ch c 27/3 Choisir (AUS)—There With Me (USA) (Distant View (USA)) (74001) **Prime Equestrian**
109 B c 13/3 Dr Fong (USA)—Trick (IRE) (Shirley Heights) (70000) **H.E. Sheikh R. Al Maktoum**
110 Ch c 19/4 Monsieur Bond (IRE)—Triple Tricks (IRE) (Royal Academy (USA)) (50000) **R. C. Bond**
111 B c 28/1 Invincible Spirit (IRE)—Turtulla (IRE) (Night Shift (USA)) (74001) **Prime Equestrian**
112 Ch f 1/3 Noverre (USA)—Twiggy's Sister (IRE) (Flying Spur (AUS)) (30243) **Prime Equestrian**
113 B f 6/2 Elusive Quality (USA)—Via Borghese (USA) (Seattle Dancer (USA)) (51480) **Prime Equestrian**
114 B c 27/4 Royal Applause—Wildwood Flower (Distant Relative) (58000) **H.E. Sheikh R. Al Maktoum**
115 B br c 16/2 Cape Cross (IRE)—Wimple (USA) (Kingmambo (USA)) (300000) **H.E. Sheikh R. Al Maktoum**
116 Ch c 19/3 Dr Fong (USA)—Wondrous Maid (GER) (Mondrian (GER)) (10000) **Mrs J. M. T. Martin**

Other Owners: Mr David Allan, Mrs Yoshiko Allan, Mr Phillip Ambler, Mr B. C. Ansell, Mrs B. C. Ansell, Mr R. L. Ansell, Mrs Patricia Barrell, Mr Andrew Bird, Mr M. G. Bullock, Mrs Tina Bullock, Mrs Rebecca Byrne, Mr Justin Byrne, Mrs Ann Darling, Mr Dave Elders, Mr Jeff Evans, Mr M. Ford, Mr Bill Fraser, Mr Brian Grieve, Miss J. A. Helliwell, R. Hopkins, Mrs V. Hopkins, Mrs A. C. Hudson, Mr S. Iyyappan, Mr David R. Martin, Mrs B. A. Matthews, Mr Richard Page, Miss Lesley Shillito, Miss Emma Smith, Mr N. H. Tritton.

Assistant Trainer: Mrs V. R. Smart, Mr K. Edmunds

Jockey (flat): Tom Eaves. **Jockey (NH):** Graham Lee. **Apprentice:** Mark Lawson.

---

544 MR G. J. SMITH, Melton Mowbray
Postal: **Fox Covert Farm, Narrow Lane, Wymeswold, Loughborough, Leicestershire, LE12 6SD**
Contacts: **PHONE** (01509) 881250 **Assistant** (07967) 720758 **FAX** (01509) 881250
MOBILE (07831) 531765

1 BRAVE HIAWATHA (FR), 6, b g Dansili—Alexandrie (USA) **The Wishful Partnership**
2 DESPERATE DEX (IRE), 8, b g Un Desperado (FR)—Too Sharp **Crossed Fingers Partnership**
3 FISHERMAN JACK, 13, b g Carlingford Castle—Troublewithjack **The Wishful Partnership**
4 GROUND BREAKER, 8, b g Emperor Jones (USA)—Startino **Slow Donkey Partnership**
5 IRISH SECRET (CZE), 4, ch g Secret 'n Classy (CAN)—Irska Sipka (IRE) **G. J. Smith**
6 MR TIM (IRE), 10, br g Naheez (USA)—Ari's Fashion **The Mr Tim Partnership**
7 WYSALL WIZARD, 4, b g Wizard King—Rose Alto **Mrs J. Osbaldeston**

THREE-YEAR-OLDS

8 NOVESTAR (IRE), ch c Noverre (USA)—Star of Cayman (IRE) **G. J. Smith**

Other Owners: Mr D. A. Atherton, Mr J. M. Fawbert, Mrs D. Key, Mrs H. Renshaw, Mr N. Williamson, Mrs A. L. Wilson, Mr D. A. Yates.

Assistant Trainer: Mrs Debbie Topping

---

545 MR JULIAN SIMON SMITH, Tirley
Postal: **Tirley Court, Tirley, Gloucester**
Contacts: **PHONE** (01452) 780461 **FAX** (01452) 780461 **MOBILE** (07880) 732337
E-MAIL tcracing@tirleycourt.orangehome.co.uk

1 FINE BY ME (IRE), 9, b g Accordion—Girseach **Mrs J. A. Benson**
2 FRANCINES-BOY (IRE), 12, b g Namaqualand (USA)—Nancy Drew **D. E. S. Smith**
3 GLEN WARRIOR, 12, b g Michelozzo (USA)—Mascara VII **D. E. S. Smith**
4 GREAT CHARACTER (IRE), 9, b g Shernazar—Ask Breda **R. P. Taylor**
5 MIDNIGHT OCEAN, 7, br m Sovereign Water (FR)—Mascara VII **R. P. Taylor**
6 RETURN HOME, 9, b g Bob's Return (IRE)—Welgenco **D. E. S. Smith**

MR JULIAN SIMON SMITH—continued

- 7 **SAILOR'S SOVEREIGN**, 7, b g Sovereign Water (FR)—Tirley Pop Eye **D. E. S. Smith**
- 8 **SEA ROBBER (IRE)**, 5, b g Shernazar—Bright Future (IRE) **Mrs J. A. Benson**
- 9 5, B br h Overbury (IRE)—Selective Rose **Mr D. Smith**
- 10 6, Br m Nomadic Way (USA)—Sense of Value **Mr D. Smith**
- 11 5, Br m Overbury (IRE)—Sense of Value **Mr D. Smith**
- 12 **VALLEY WARRIOR**, 11, b g Michelozzo (USA)—Mascara VII **Mrs J. A. Benson**

Other Owners: Miss S. N. Benson, Mr Donald Smith.

Assistant Trainer: Mrs Nicky Smith

Jockey (NH): T. J. Murphy, P. Malonoy, W. Marston. **Conditional:** Gerald Tumelty.

---

546 MR M. SMITH, Kirkheaton
Postal: **The Tofts, Kirkheaton, Newcastle-upon-Tyne, Tyne and Wear, NE19 2DH**
Contacts: **PHONE (01830) 530044 MOBILE (07976) 903233**

- 1 **FORTUNATE DAVE (USA)**, 9, b g Lear Fan (USA)—Lady Ameriflora (USA) **Mrs S. Smith**
- 2 4, Br g Anshan—Mrs Byrne (IRE) **Mrs S. Smith**
- 3 **SPECIAL FLIGHT (IRE)**, 7, b g Topanoora—Swinging Sari (IRE) **Mrs S. Smith**

---

547 MRS NADINE SMITH, Pulborough
Postal: **Hillside Cottage Stables, Hillside Fruit Farm, Bury, Pulborough, West Sussex, RH20 1NR**
Contacts: **PHONE (01798) 831206 MOBILE (07761) 044890**

- 1 **ALTENBURG (FR)**, 6, b g Sadler's Wells—Anna of Saxony **C.Dower B.Fulton T.Hayward K.A.Little**
- 2 **FOREST DANE**, 8, b g Danetime (IRE)—Forest Maid **The Ember Partnership**
- 3 **IRISH CAPE**, 5, br m Cape Cross (IRE)—Praglia (IRE) **J. J. Whelan**
- 4 **PAPEETE (GER)**, 7, b m Alzao (USA)—Prairie Vela **Mrs Judith Laycock & Eddie Gleeson**
- 5 **RUNNING SUPREME (GB)**, 4, b f Josr Algarhoud (IRE)—Running Glimpse (IRE) **The Team Supreme**
- 6 **SPEAR THISTLE**, 6, ch g Selkirk (USA)—Ardisia (USA) **Tony Hayward & Sue Head**
- 7 **TIGER TRAIL (GER)**, 4, b g Tagula (IRE)—Tweed Mill **Mrs H. Remmington**
- 8 **WHIST DRIVE**, 8, ch g First Trump—Fine Quill **Tony Hayward & Barry Fulton**

TWO-YEAR-OLDS

- 9 **SUPREME GLIMPSE**, b f 22/3 Piccolo—Running Glimpse (IRE) (Runnett) **The Team Supreme**

Other Owners: Mr Con Dower, Mr B. N. Fulton, Mr Eddie Gleeson, Mr Tony Hayward, Mrs Sue Head, Mr A. P. King, Mr M. A. King, Mrs J. M. Laycock, Mr K. A. Little, J. R. O'Leary, Mrs S. F. O'Leary.

Assistant Trainer: A. M. Smith

---

548 MISS S. SMITH, Lewes
Postal: **County Stables, The Old Racecourse, Lewes, East Sussex, BN7 1UR**
Contacts: **PHONE (01273) 477173 FAX (01273) 477173 MOBILE (07970) 550828**
E-MAIL countystables@hotmail.co.uk WEBSITE www.suzysmithracing.co.uk

- 1 **AIMIGAYLE**, 5, b m Midnight Legend—Cherrygayle (IRE) **P. J. Mercer**
- 2 **BOARDROOM DANCER (IRE)**, 11, b g Executive Perk—Dancing Course (IRE) **Dr DJ Meecham Jones & Mr TA Fowler**
- 3 4, B br g Heron Island (IRE)—Brennan For Audits (IRE)
- 4 **CRAFTY LADY (IRE)**, 9, b br m Warcraft (USA)—Kilmana (IRE) **Miss S. Smith**
- 5 **DADS LAD (IRE)**, 14, b g Supreme Leader—Furryvale **Miss S. Smith**
- 6 **GOLDEN CREW**, 8, b h Busy Flight—Goldenswift (IRE) **Sue Addington-Smith & David Tribe**
- 7 **JORDAN**, 5, b m Golden Snake (USA)—Formula One Affair
- 8 **JUST SILVER**, 7, gr g Silver Patriarch (IRE)—Silver Mood Saloop
- 9 **LE MILLENAIRE (FR)**, 9, b br g Ragmar (FR)—Ezaia (FR) **Dr DJ Meecham Jones & Mr TA Fowler**
- 10 **MAGNIFICENT SEVEN (FR)**, 9, ch g Un Desperado (FR)—Seven Hills (FR) **G. E. Tobitt**
- 11 **MATERIAL WORLD**, 10, b m Karinga Bay—Material Girl **Southern Bloodstock**
- 12 **MIDLETON MADNESS (IRE)**, 6, b g Alphabatim (USA)—Craic Go Leor **The Cat Weazle Wizards**
- 13 **MISSOULA (IRE)**, 5, b m Kalanisi (IRE)—Medway (IRE) **Mr M J Weaver & Pollards Bloodstock**
- 14 **PEARLSFORTHEGIRLS**, 8, gr m Cloudings (IRE)—Rim of Pearl **The Pearls Of Wisdom**

MISS S. SMITH—continued

15 **PRINCE OF ARAGON**, 12, b g Aragon—Queens Welcome **Miss S. Smith**
16 **RUAIRI (IRE)**, 7, b g Mister Mat (FR)—By Golly (IRE) **C. J. Bennett**
17 **SILVER SERG**, 7, b g Silver Patriarch (IRE)—Ranyah (USA) **Saloop**
18 **SON OF KARINGA**, 4, ch g Karinga Bay—Sister Dee **Mr S. J. Antram**
19 **STARTENGO (IRE)**, 5, ch g Nashwan (USA)—Virgin Hawk (USA) **Ten Green Bottles Racing**
20 **THE BIG FELLA (IRE)**, 6, ch g Shernazar—Gemmodee (IRE) **Miss S. Smith**

Other Owners: Mr J. Adams, Mrs S. A. Addington-Smith, Mrs D. J. Arstall, Mr L. Arstall, Mr J. L. Barrott, Mrs C. S. Braga, Mr M. D. Elliott, T. A. Fowler, Mrs A. A. Hawkins, J. A. A. S. Logan, Dr D. J. Meecham Jones, R. A. Muddle, R. F. Smith, Mr D. R. Tribe, M. J. Weaver.

Assistant Trainer: Mr S E Gordon-Watson

Conditional: C. Bolger.

---

549 **MRS S. J. SMITH, Bingley**
Postal: Craiglands Farm, High Eldwick, Bingley, West Yorkshire, BD16 3BE
Contacts: PHONE (01274) 564930 FAX (01274) 560626
E-MAIL craiglandsracing@yahoo.co.uk

1 **ACCEPTING**, 11, b g Mtoto—D'azy **Mr M. T. Bloore & Mrs J. E. Lockwood**
2 **ALFABET SOUK**, 7, b g Alflora (IRE)—Levantine Rose **Sultans Of Swing**
3 **ALLISTATHEBARRISTA (IRE)**, 9, b g Leading Counsel (USA)—Rechime **M. B. Scholey & R. H. Scholey**
4 **AURORAS ENCORE (IRE)**, 6, b g Second Empire (IRE)—Sama Veda (IRE) **Mrs Alicia Skene & W. S. Skene**
5 **AUTOGRAPH**, 7, b m Polar Prince—Seraphim (FR) **Mrs B. Ramsden**
6 **BAMBY (IRE)**, 8, b m Glacial Storm (USA)—Ardfallon (IRE) **Mrs S. Granger**
7 **BELMORE BARON**, 6, ch g Double Trigger (IRE)—Belmore Cloud **Mrs S. J. Smith**
8 **BOBDAMAN (IRE)**, 8, b br g Supreme Leader—Mary Kate Finn **Mrs S. J. Smith**
9 **BUSHIDO (IRE)**, 9, br g Brief Truce (USA)—Pheopotstown **Mrs B. Ramsden**
10 **CLEAR THE WAY (IRE)**, 8, b br g Simply Great (FR)—Casheral **Mrs S. J. Smith**
11 **CLOUDY TIMES (IRE)**, 5, gr g Cloudings (IRE)—Khalsheva **T. J. Hemmings**
12 **COE (IRE)**, 6, br g Presenting—Dante's Skip (IRE) **J. T. Hemmings**
13 **DALDINI**, 6, b g Josr Algarhoud (IRE)—Arianna Aldini **P. J. Dixon**
14 **DARINA'S BOY**, 12, b g Sula Bula—Glebelands Girl **Mrs C. Steel**
15 **ELA RE**, 9, ch g Sabrehill (USA)—Lucia Tarditi (IRE) **K. Nicholson**
16 **FLAKE**, 8, ch g Zilzal (USA)—Impatiente (USA) **K. Nicholson**
17 **GEE DEE (IRE)**, 7, gr g Arzanni—Silver Haired (IRE) **Mrs S. J. Smith**
18 **GERSHWINNER (IRE)**, 5, b g Classic Cliche (IRE)—Dalton Lady **The Red Oak Partnership**
19 **GINO**, 6, gr g Cloudings (IRE)—Old Betsy **Mrs S. J. Smith**
20 **GNILLISH**, 8, b g Bob's Return (IRE)—Spring Flyer (IRE) **Mrs S. J. Smith**
21 **GOLDEN RUN**, 5, b m Commanche Run—Goldengirlmichelle (IRE) **The Cartmel Syndicate**
22 **GOT THE GIFT (IRE)**, 7, b g Norwich—Kylemore Rose (IRE) **Mrs S. J. Smith**
23 **GREY EAGLE**, 9, gr g White Sorrel—Mam'zelle Angot **Mrs S. J. Smith**
24 **HIMALAYAN TRAIL**, 9, b g Nomadic Way (USA)—Hindu Lady **K. Nicholson**
25 **HOLD THE BID (IRE)**, 8, b br g Luso—Killesk Castle (IRE) **Formulated Polymer Products Ltd**
26 **IMTIHAN (IRE)**, 9, ch g Unfuwain (USA)—Azyaa **K. Nicholson**
27 **IZZYKEEN**, 9, b g Keen—Washita **A. A. Thomason**
28 **JEMEZ (IRE)**, 7, b g Supreme Leader—Our Sioux (IRE) **T. J. Hemmings**
29 **LEAC AN SCAIL (IRE)**, 7, b g Lord Americo—Swings'n'things (USA) **Mrs S. J. Smith**
30 **LEWIS'S WORLD**, 5, br gr g Overbury (IRE)—Brenig **The Broken Knights**
31 **MILL SIDE**, 8, b g Milieu—Little Greyside **The TWT Group**
32 **MISTER MCGOLDRICK**, 11, b g Sabrehill (USA)—Anchor Inn **R. J. Longley**
33 **MR STRACHAN (IRE)**, 7, b g Zaffaran (USA)—Call Girl **Mrs S. Granger**
34 **MURPHYS BEAU (IRE)**, 6, b br g Beau Sher—Royal Broderick (IRE) **Mrs S. J. Smith**
35 **NIRVANA SWING (FR)**, 7, b g Chamberlin (FR)—Ukrainia II (FR) **Mrs S. J. Smith**
36 **OSO MAGIC**, 10, b g Teenoso (USA)—Scottish Clover **Michael Thompson**
37 **OUR SPRING**, 7, b g Parthian Springs—Little Sail **Mrs S. J. Smith**
38 **PARTLY CLOUDY**, 7, b g Cloudings (IRE)—Old Betsy **T. J. Hemmings**
39 **PASS THE CLASS (IRE)**, 8, b g Classic Cliche (IRE)—Passchendaele (IRE) **K. Nicholson**
40 **PIPPISTREL**, 6, b m Alflora (IRE)—Colmarann (IRE) **Mrs S. J. Smith**
41 **PRAIRIE LORD (IRE)**, 8, b g Lord of Appeal—Johara (USA) **Mrs S. J. Smith**
42 **PRESENTING ALF (IRE)**, 8, b g Presenting—Hilary's Penny **K. Nicholson**
43 **PRESUMPTUOUS**, 8, ch g Double Trigger (IRE)—
T O O Mamma's (IRE) **Mr & Mrs C. Bradford-Nutter, Mr & Mrs Jack Berry**

MRS S. J. SMITH—continued

44 RAGADOR, 7, b g El Conquistador—Ragsi **Widdop Wanderers**
45 RARE SOCIETY (IRE), 10, b g Deep Society—Rare Glen **Mrs J. McCullough**
46 REBEL RHYTHM, 9, b g Robellino (USA)—Celt Song (IRE) **The Fees R Us Syndicate**
47 ROSS COMM, 12, gr g Minster Son—Yemaail (IRE) **K. G. Treanor**
48 ROYAL EMPEROR (IRE), 12, gr g Roselier (FR)—Boreen Bro **Widdop Wanderers**
49 SCOTT'S MILL, 6, ch g Unfuwain (USA)—Mill On The Floss **K. Nicholson**
50 SHARP BELLINE (IRE), 11, b g Robellino (USA)—Moon Watch **Townville C. C. Racing Club**
51 SOMETHING GOLD (FR), 8, gr g Baby Turk—Exiled (USA) **Mrs S. J. Smith**
52 SPARE DAYS, 4, b g Cloudings (IRE)—Spare Set (IRE) **T. J. Hemmings**
53 SPARE ME, 5, b g Cloudings (IRE)—Spare Set (IRE) **T. J. Hemmings**
54 SPARKLING TAFF, 9, b g Alderbrook—Sparkling Time (USA) **Mrs S. J. Smith**
55 ST MATTHEW (USA), 10, b g Lear Fan (USA)—Social Crown (USA) **K. Nicholson**
56 STAGECOACH AMBER (USA), 6, b g Bright Launch (USA)—Clan Lake (USA) **Mrs J. Conroy**
57 STAGECOACH DIAMOND, 9, b g Classic Cliche (IRE)—Lyra **Mrs J. Conroy**
58 STAGECOACH OPAL, 7, b g Komaite (USA)—Rag Time Belle **John Conroy Jaqueline Conroy**
59 SUPER ROAD TRAIN, 9, b g Petoski—Foehn Gale (IRE) **Worcester Racing Club**
60 TEENANDO (IRE), 8, b g Teenoso (USA)—Ananda **Mrs S. J. Smith**
61 THE MASTERS LESSON, 5, ch g Minster Son—Japedone **M. F. Spence**
62 THE QUIET KING, 8, b g Commanche Run—Kings Athlete (USA) **Mrs S. J. Smith**
63 TIMETWOGO, 6, b g Double Trigger (IRE)—Golden Mile (IRE) **The Red Oak Partnership**
64 TOMENOSO, 10, b gr g Teenoso (USA)—Guarded Expression **K. Nicholson**
65 TOUS CHEZ (IRE), 9, b g Carroll House—Sixfoursix **K. Nicholson**
66 UNDENIABLE, 10, b g Unfuwain (USA)—Shefoog **K. Nicholson**
67 UNION DEUX (FR), 9, ch g Nikos—Sanhia (USA) **M. B. Scholey & R. H. Scholey**
68 WHATDOIDOWITHTHAT, 5, ch g Minster Son—Wynyard Lady **M. F. Spence**
69 WILLIE THE FISH (IRE), 11, b g King's Ride—Bricon Lady **Mrs S. J. Smith**
70 WILLIES WAY, 8, ch g Nomadic Way (USA)—Willies Witch **K. Nicholson**
71 WORK BOY, 7, b g Nomadic Way (USA)—Swift Reward **Mrs S. J. Smith**
72 YOUNG SMOKEY (IRE), 7, gr g Cloudings (IRE)—Miss Aylesbury **T. J. Hemmings**

Other Owners: J. Berry, Mrs J. M. Berry, M. T. Bloore, C. Bradford-Nutter, Mrs J. M. Bradford-Nutter, J. Conroy, Mr P. E. Cranston, M. P Hill, A. D. Hollinrake, Mrs J. E. L. Lockwood, C. C. S. MacMillan, B. McLean, D. Musgrave, Mr R. Nicholls, C. P. Norbury, Mr D. Oakley, Mrs J. B. Pye, Mr A. Redmond, Mr R. A. Robson, Mrs M. B. Scholey, R. H. Scholey, Mrs J. C. Short, W. S. Skene, Mrs A. Skene, Mr J. S. Whittaker.

Jockey (NH): S. Durack, D Elsworth.

---

550   ## MRS S. J. SMITH, Gentleshaw
Postal: Coldwell Cottage, Gentleshaw, Rugeley, Staffordshire, WS15 4NJ
Contacts: PHONE (01543) 686587 MOBILE (07791) 347860

1 CELTIC ROMANCE, 9, b m Celtic Swing—Southern Sky **Mrs S. J. Smith**
2 FOUR KISSES (IRE), 8, b m Supreme Leader—Danjo's Lady (IRE) **J. P. Smith**
3 WEET A HEAD (IRE), 7, b g Foxhound (USA)—Morale **Mrs S. J. Smith**

---

551   ## MR V. SMITH, Newmarket
Postal: Exeter Stables, Church Street, Exning, Newmarket, Suffolk, CB8 7EH
Contacts: PHONE/FAX (01638) 608542 MOBILE (07780) 853232
E-MAIL vincesmith2@hotmail.com

1 CAPITALISE (IRE), 5, b g City On A Hill (USA)—Prime Interest (IRE) **Tilen Electrics Ltd**
2 FASCINATIN RHYTHM, 4, br f Fantastic Light (USA)—Marguerite de Vine **W. A. Harrison-Allan**
3 IMPERIAL HARRY, 5, b g Alhaarth (IRE)—Serpentara **CGA Racing Partnership**
4 JOUSTING, 4, b g Josr Algarhoud (IRE)—Sweet Wilhelmina **D. E. Jenkins**
5 JUST INTERSKY (USA), 5, gr g Distant View—Hexane (FR) **Tapas Partnership & Mr J. Pepper**
6 MAJESTICAL (IRE), 6, b g Fayruz—Haraabah (USA) **V. Smith**
7 NOTHINGTODECLAIRE, 4, b c Tobougg (IRE)—Double Fault (IRE) **Mr D. Hanafin**
8 SONNY PARKIN, 6, b g Spinning World (USA)—No Miss Kris (USA) **F. O'Brien**

THREE-YEAR-OLDS

9 DALKEY GIRL (IRE), ch f Raise A Grand (IRE)—Tosca **A. Pettinari**
10 DIADEMAS (USA), b br c Grand Slam (USA)—Kona Kat (USA) **V. Smith**
11 DIAMOND SEEKER, ch f Erhaab (USA)—Slavonic Dance **Mr J. W. J. McCullough**

MR V. SMITH—continued

12 DOVETAIL (IRE), b f Acclamation—Daniella Drive (USA) **R. C. Tooth**
13 MISS TILEN, ch f Tipsy Creek (USA)—Ashleen **Tilen Electrics Ltd**
14 TAPAS LAD (IRE), b c Modigliani (USA)—Missish **F. O'Brien**
15 WOULDN'TITBENICE, ch f Dr Fong (USA)—Krista **M. Caine**

TWO-YEAR-OLDS

16 B c 3/2 Reset (AUS)—Ewenny (Warrshan (USA)) (20000) **V. Smith**
17 Ch c 1/4 Beat Hollow—Judiam (Primo Dominie) **R. J. H. West**
18 B c 16/3 Lear Spear (USA)—Lola Lola (IRE) (Piccolo) (1904) **R. C. Tooth**
19 Ch f 5/4 Distant Music (USA)—Tosca (Be My Guest (USA)) (1619) **Mr G. Gaffney**

Other Owners: Exors of the Late A. C. D. Ingleby-Mackenzie, Mr A. T. Murphy, J. Pepper, A. Walmsley.

Jockey (flat): N. Callan, D. Holland, J. Quinn, M. A. Tebbutt. Jockey (NH): P. Hide.

---

552 ### MISS J. A. SOUTHCOMBE, Chard
Postal: Holemoor Farm Bungalow, Combe St Nicholas, Chard, Somerset, TA20 3AE
Contacts: PHONE (01460) 68865 MOBILE (07968) 178121
E-MAIL jane@janesouthcomberacing.co.uk WEBSITE www.janesouthcomberacing.co.uk

1 BENJAMIN (IRE), 10, b g Night Shift (USA)—Best Academy (USA) **M. Savill**
2 DORIES DREAM, 4, b f Foxhound (USA)—Milliscent **Mr K. A. Parr**
3 GALANTOS (GER), 7, b g Winged Love (IRE)—Grey Metal (GER) **The Top Tottys Racing Partnership**
4 RED PERFECTION, 5, b m Lahib (USA)—Perfect Poppy **Picture Perfect Partnership**
5 ROGUE, 6, b m Royal Applause—Mystique **M. Savill**

Other Owners: Miss K. V. Fuller, Miss V. Vivian.

---

553 ### MR M. E. SOWERSBY, York
Postal: Southwold Farm, Goodmanham Wold, Market Weighton, York, East Yorkshire, YO43 3NA
Contacts: PHONE (01430) 810534 MOBILE (07855) 551056

1 CHATEAU (IRE), 6, ch g Grand Lodge (USA)—Miniver (IRE) **C. N. Richardson**
2 HARDYBUCK (IRE), 7, b g Saddlers' Hall (IRE)—Miss Beaufleur (IRE) **A. H. Milner**
3 KARATHAENA (IRE), 8, b m Barathea (IRE)—Dabtara (IRE) **The Southwold Set**
4 MAMORE GAP (IRE), 10, b g General Monash (USA)—Ravensdale Rose **The Southwold Set**
5 MOON MELODY (GER), 5, b g Montjeu (IRE)—Midnight Fever (IRE) **Mrs J. H. Cooper**
6 NAMARIAN (IRE), 4, b f Namid—Zalamera **The Southwold Set**
7 NUMERICAL (IRE), 4, ch g Numerous (USA)—Conspiracy **The Southwold Set**
8 RUDAKI, 6, ch g Opening Verse (USA)—Persian Fountain (IRE) **Keith Brown Properties (Hull) Ltd**

THREE-YEAR-OLDS

9 ARABIAN FERN, b f Tobougg (IRE)—Cryptogam **R. D. Seldon**
10 DAWN WHISPER, ch f Rock City—Doodle Wood **Mrs D. Wood**
11 HANDSOME CHAP, b c Tumbleweed Ridge—Dolphin Beech (IRE) **Keith Brown Properties (Hull) Ltd**
12 PENNY ARCADE, ch f Arkadian Hero (USA)—Concentration (IRE) **Mrs J. Robinson**

TWO-YEAR-OLDS

13 B c 28/2 Lujain (USA)—Cryptogam (Zamindar (USA)) (800) **R. D. Seldon**

Other Owners: Mr Paul Clifton, Mr P. Laverack, Mr J. Payne, Jean W. Robinson, Mr R. Robinson, Mr M. E. Sowersby, Mr R. Waite.

Assistant Trainer: Mary Sowersby

Jockey (flat): Tom Eaves, Greg Fairley, R. Ffrench. Jockey (NH): K. Mercer. Conditional: Fearghal Davis, Phil Kinsella.
Amateur: Miss K. Searby, Mr G. Brewer.

---

554 ### MR J. L. SPEARING, Kinnersley
Postal: John Spearing Racing Ltd, Kinnersley Racing Stables, Kinnersley, Severn Stoke, Worcestershire, WR8 9JR
Contacts: PHONE (01905) 371054 FAX (01905) 371054 MOBILE (07801) 552922
E-MAIL jlspearing@aol.com

1 ABIT IRISH (NZ), 7, ch g Oregon (USA)—Irish Talk (NZ) **T. N. Siviter**
2 AMBROSINNI, 6, b g Dr Massini (IRE)—Macfarly (IRE) **R. Doody**

MR J. L. SPEARING—continued

3 BLUE SOVEREIGN, 8, gr g Sovereign Water (FR)—Slack Alice **T. N. Siviter**
4 BLUE SPEEDWELL, 6, gr m Sovereign Water (FR)—Slack Alice **Mr D. C. Spearing**
5 BOLD SHUFFLE (IRE), 4, b g Revoque (IRE)—Alaroos (IRE) **Kinnersley Partnership**
6 CROESO BACH, 4, b f Bertolini (USA)—Croeso-I-Cymru **Mrs S. A. Evans**
7 6, B m Cloudings (IRE)—Dara's Course (IRE) **D. A. Hunt**
8 EQUULEUS PICTOR, 4, br g Piccolo—Vax Rapide **Masonaires**
9 FILLY SO FICKLE, 6, b m Kayf Tara—Mavourneen (IRE) **James Thorburn-Muirhead&John Kevin Lomax**
10 HAKIM (NZ), 14, ch g Half Iced (USA)—Topitup (NZ) **T. N. Siviter**
11 HIGH STANDARD (NZ), 7, b g Cicerao (IRE)—For Today (NZ) **Bache Silk**
12 IGUACU, 4, b g Desert Prince (IRE)—Gay Gallanta (USA) **Derek & Cheryl Holder**
13 ISOBEL ROSE (IRE), 4, b f Royal Applause—Total Love **Mrs R. F. Knipe**
14 JUCEBABE, 5, b m Zilzal (USA)—Jucea **G. M. Eales**
15 KAYF ARAMIS, 6, b g Kayf Tara—Ara **Mrs Isobel Phipps Coltman**
16 LOCH VIC (IRE), 7, br g Old Vic—Miss Chickabee (IRE) **J. H. Bebbington**
17 MCGRUDERS CROSS (IRE), 10, b g Toulon—Kayanna **L. Kinsella**
18 MISTER ELEGANT, 6, b h Fraam—Risky Valentine **M. Lawrence & W. Cooper**
19 MOCHO (IRE), 7, b g Accordion—Supreme Kellycarra (IRE) **Mr T. J. & Mrs H. Parrott**
20 NO WORRIES YET (IRE), 4, b f Orpen (USA)—Charming Victoria (IRE) **J. L. Spearing**
21 NOBILISSIMA (IRE), 4, b f Orpen (USA)—Shadow Smile (IRE) **Nine Traders Syndicate**
22 NORTHSTAR EXPRESS (IRE), 5, b m Tagula (IRE)—Ramich John **East Coast Coolers Syndicate**
23 QUILLAN HILL, 8, ch g Environment Friend—Bowland Girl (IRE) **L. Kinsella**
24 RAJEH (IRE), 5, b g Key of Luck (USA)—Saramacca (IRE) **Miss C. J. Ive**
25 RISING FORCE (IRE), 5, b g Selkirk (USA)—Singing Diva (IRE) **Masonaires**
26 SASHENKA, 6, b m Silver Patriarch (IRE)—Annie Kelly **Major H. R. M. Porter**
27 SAWPIT SUNSET, 7, br m Classic Cliche (IRE)—Moonlight Air **D. A. Hunt**
28 SIMON, 9, b g Overbury (IRE)—Gaye Memory **Mrs Mercy Rimell**
29 SOULARD (USA), 5, b g Arch (USA)—Bourbon Blues (USA) **Mrs H. M. Haddock**
30 TRUE TARA, 5, b m Kayf Tara—True Ring **Mr & Mrs R.M.Phillips & Mr J.Spearing**
31 WATERSPRAY (AUS), 10, ch g Lake Coniston (IRE)—Forain (NZ) **Bache Silk**
32 WILD JACK (IRE), 5, b g Sunshine Street (USA)—Mullard View (IRE) **L. Kinsella**

THREE-YEAR-OLDS

33 Ch c Kyllachy—Arkadia Park (IRE) **R. Heathcote**
34 CROESO CUSAN, b f Diktat—Croeso Croeso **Mrs S. A. Evans**
35 ROSSINI BYLINE (IRE), b f Rossini (USA)—Byliny (IRE) **Seaview Partnership**
36 SAWPIT SOLITAIRE, ro f Daylami (IRE)—Balleta (USA) **D. A. Hunt**
37 SAWPIT SUNSHINE (IRE), b f Mujadil (USA)—Curie Express (IRE) **D. A. Hunt**
38 WHITEOAK LADY (IRE), ch f Medecis—French Toast (IRE) **L. Kinsella**
39 ZEFFIRELLI, ch g Tomba—Risky Valentine **Miss C. J. Ive**

TWO-YEAR-OLDS

40 Ch f 30/3 Namid—Corryvreckan (IRE) (Night Shift (USA)) (15443)
41 B f 3/5 Key of Luck (USA)—Crystal Blue (IRE) (Bluebird (USA)) (16730) **D. A. Hunt**
42 B f 15/3 City On A Hill (USA)—Fraamtastic (Fraam) (6434)
43 Ch f 26/4 Captain Rio—Khawafi (Kris) (6434)
44 B f 17/3 Orpen (USA)—Lucayan Star (IRE) (First Trump) (3860) **D. A. Hunt**
45 NATIVITY, ch f 22/2 Kyllachy—Mistral's Dancer (Shareef Dancer (USA)) (20000) **R. Heathcote**
46 B f 23/3 Pyrus (USA)—Peking Dancer (USA) (King of Kings (IRE)) (5469)
47 Ch f 14/5 Bertolini (USA)—Risky Valentine (Risk Me (FR))
48 B g 20/3 Trans Island—Tread Softly (IRE) (Roi Danzig (USA)) (5791) **A. A. Campbell**

Other Owners: Mr Peter Bache, R. M. Bluck, H. Calvey, Mr W. H. Cooper, Mr S. J. Court, J. Folan, Mr W. J. Goddard, Mr Joseph Heavey, Mr Derek C. Holder, Mrs Cheryl Holder, Mr P. L. Jackson, Mr M. T. Lawrance, Mr Kevin Lomax, Mr Paul Madden, Mr Martin Molloy, Mr T. J. Parrott, Mrs H. Parrott, Mr R. M. Phillips, Mrs M. J. Phillips, Mr G. Hampson Silk, Mr J. Spearing, Mr James Thorburn-Muirhead, Mr Thomas Whearty, Mr Barry Whearty.

Assistant Trainer: Miss C Ive

Jockey (flat): S. Drowne. **Jockey (NH):** A. Evans, A. P. McCoy, H. Oliver, R. Thornton.

555 MISS T. S. SPEARING, Kinnersley
Postal: 2nd Yard, Kinnersley Racing Stables, 14-16 Kinnersley, Severn Stoke, Worcester, Worcestershire, WR8 9JR
Contacts: PHONE (01905) 371304 FAX (01905) 371054 MOBILE (07970) 939506

1 FOURTH DIMENSION (IRE), 9, b g Entrepreneur—Isle of Spice (USA) **Advantage Chemicals Holdings Ltd**
2 STORM PRINCE (IRE), 11, ch g Prince of Birds (USA)—Petersford Girl (IRE) **D. J. Oseman**
3 VALENTINO SWING (IRE), 5, ch g Titus Livius (FR)—Farmers Swing (IRE) **D. J. Oseman**
4 YANKEY, 6, b g Amfortas (IRE)—Key **J. T. Jones**

556 MR T. STACK, Golden
Postal: Thomastown Castle, Golden, Co. Tipperary, Ireland
Contacts: PHONE (00353) 625 4129 FAX (00353) 625 4399
E-MAIL tommystack@eircom.net

1 COCHLEAR (IRE), 4, b g Danetime (IRE)—Rahwah
2 DANTE HALL (IRE), 7, b h Saddlers' Hall (IRE)—Bettys The Boss (IRE)
3 G'DAY TO YOU (IRE), 6, b g Entrepreneur—Zing Ping (IRE)
4 PERCE ROCK, 6, b h Dansili—Twilight Secret
5 WANANGO (GER), 7, ch g Acatenango (GER)—Wanateluthspilgrim (USA)

THREE-YEAR-OLDS

6 AINE, ch f Danehill Dancer (IRE)—Antinnaz (IRE)
7 ARIES BALLERINA, b f Peintre Celebre (USA)—March Hare
8 BALLYGOLOGUE, b f Montjeu (IRE)—Admiring (USA)
9 B c Danehill Dancer (IRE)—Breyani
10 CASSIQUE LADY, b f Langfuhr (CAN)—Palacoona (FR)
11 ERIN'S GIFT, b f Danetime (IRE)—Tawala (IRE)
12 GOLDEN TOKYO (IRE), b c Danetime (IRE)—Oraplata (USA)
13 LIBERTY BRIDGE (USA), gr c Mr Greeley (USA)—Gray Cashmere (USA)
14 LOCO GRANDE (IRE), ch c Raise A Grand (IRE)—Locorotondo (IRE)
15 MAGEN'S STAR (IRE), b f Galileo (IRE)—Bluffing (IRE)
16 MYBOYCHARLIE, b c Danetime (IRE)—Dulceata (IRE)
17 ORPEN WINGER, b c Orpen (USA)—Tahdid
18 PAVANNE, ch c Hawk Wing (USA)—Pillars of Society (IRE)
19 B br f Stravinsky (USA)—Sadler's Profile (USA)
20 SECRET MEMOIRS, b f Marju (IRE)—Flower Child (IRE)
21 SHIVERING, b f Royal Applause—Snowing
22 SINNJICA (IRE), b c Sinndar (IRE)—Fiaba (USA)
23 SUPERIUS, b c High Chaparral (IRE)—Zing Ping (IRE)
24 THE LOAN EXPRESS, b f Choisir (AUS)—Mamma's Too
25 TRISKEL, b f Hawk Wing (USA)—Pat Or Else
26 UNSUNG HEROINE (IRE), b f High Chaparral (IRE)—Thermopylae
27 B f Catcher In The Rye (IRE)—Vespers (IRE)
28 WARDY'S WONDER, ch f Choisir (AUS)—Beucaire (IRE)

TWO-YEAR-OLDS

29 B f 24/4 Choisir (AUS)—Alexander Express (IRE) (Sri Pekan (USA)) (7000)
30 B f 27/3 Danehill Dancer (IRE)—An Mosey (USA) (Royal Academy (USA)) (70784)
31 B c 8/3 Exceed And Excel (AUS)—Angel Alydar (USA) (Alysheba (USA)) (46000)
32 Ch f 10/2 Danehill Dancer (IRE)—Bluebell Wood (IRE) (Bluebird (USA)) (50000)
33 Ch c 7/5 Danehill Dancer (IRE)—Castilian Queen (USA) (Diesis (USA)) (51480)
34 B f 21/3 Fasliyev (USA)—College of Arms (Lujain (USA)) (20000)
35 B c 1/4 Danetime (IRE)—Defined Feature (IRE) (Nabeel Dancer (USA)) (34000)
36 Ch c 6/4 Rock of Gibraltar (IRE)—Delilah (IRE) (Bluebird (USA))
37 B f 10/3 Smarty Jones (USA)—Djebel Amour (Mt Livermore (USA)) (165208)
38 B f 23/4 Imperial Ballet (IRE)—Dulceata (IRE) (Rousillon (USA)) (38000)
39 Ch c 14/4 Spartacus (IRE)—Eastern Ruby (Be My Chief (USA)) (12000)
40 B f 20/4 Danehill Dancer (IRE)—Feather Bride (IRE) (Groom Dancer (USA)) (125481)
41 B c 9/4 Dansili—Heckle (In The Wings) (54697)
42 Ch c 28/3 Medicean—In Luck (In The Wings) (34000)
43 B f 1/3 Royal Applause—Leukippids (IRE) (Sadler's Wells (USA)) (119047)
44 B f 21/2 High Chaparral (IRE)—Lucky Achievement (USA) (St Jovite (USA)) (50000)
45 B c 25/4 Danetime (IRE)—Mauradell (IRE) (Mujadil (USA)) (42000)
46 B c 24/2 Exceed And Excel (AUS)—Mikara (FR) (Midyan (USA)) (41826)

MR T. STACK—continued

47 B c 27/2 Exceed And Excel (AUS)—Miss Tardy (JPN) (Lammtarra (USA)) (20591)
48 B f 7/4 Royal Applause—Mohican Princess (Shirley Heights) (83654)
49 Ch f 6/2 Choisir (AUS)—No Reservations (IRE) (Commanche Run) (25740)
50 B c 5/2 Catcher In The Rye (IRE)—No Way (IRE) (Rainbows For Life (CAN)) (41000)
51 B f 24/2 Mull of Kintyre (USA)—Otherwise (IRE) (Dr Devious (IRE)) (9008)
52 B f 9/4 Galileo (IRE)—Pillars of Society (IRE) (Caerleon (USA)) (150000)
53 **RUTLAND WATER (IRE)**, b f 27/3 Hawk Wing (USA)—Rutledge (IRE) (Entrepreneur) (32174)
54 B f 7/3 Danetime (IRE)—Sarah Stokes (IRE) (Brief Truce (USA)) (50192)
55 **SUGAR FREE (IRE)**, b f 20/2 Oasis Dream—Much Faster (IRE) (Fasliyev (USA))
56 B f 5/5 Fasliyev (USA)—Tamise (USA) (Time For A Change (USA)) (77220)
57 B f 28/4 Sadler's Wells (USA)—Tarascon (IRE) (Tirol) (193049)
58 **THALA TLASS (IRE)**, gr f 20/4 Diktat—Acciacatura (USA) (Stravinsky (USA))
59 B f 9/4 Danetime (IRE)—Unfortunate (Komaite (USA)) (37322)
60 B f 13/3 Danetime (IRE)—Villa Nova (IRE) (Petardia) (160000)
61 B c 3/3 Exceed And Excel (AUS)—Vinicky (IRE) (Kingmambo (USA)) (19304)
62 B f 26/4 Danehill Dancer (IRE)—Wannabe (Shirley Heights) (240000)

Owners: Mr Rick Barnes, Mr M. A. Begley, Mr A. Boyle, Mr P. A. Byrne, CO2 Financial Partnership, Mr T. Corden, Mrs Ann Gaffney, Giggonstown Stud, Hammersboy Syndicate, W. M. Hickey, John Hughes, IRS Syndicate, Killiney Golf Club Syndicate, Miss C. Lynch, Mrs John Magnier, Mr T. V. Magnier, Mr John P. McManus, Mrs Diane Nagle, Newtownanner Stud, N. O'Callaghan, Roger O'Callaghan, Michael O'Flynn, Mrs Wendy O'Leary, Lady O'Reilly, Mr Liam O'Toole, Mrs W. L. O'Toole, Mr Peter Piller, Pollard Stables, Mrs Jane Rowlinson, Mrs P. Shanahan, Trevor Stewart, The 05 Syndicate, The Boston Syndicate, Ms K. Vaughan.

Jockey (flat): W. J. Lee, W. M. Lordan. **Apprentice:** C. D. Allen.

---

557 MR D. O. STEPHENS, Newport
Postal: **The Knoll, St Brides Netherwent, Caldicott, Newport, Gwent, NP26 3AT**
Contacts: **PHONE (01633) 400909 FAX (01633) 400203 MOBILE (07771) 878652**
E-MAIL James@stephens.orangehome.co.uk

1 EDEN ROSE, 7, b m Gildoran—Belhelvie **O. J. Stephens**
2 SAXON LEADER (IRE), 6, b g Supreme Leader—Bronica (IRE) **Castle Farm Racing**
3 TRECELYN, 7, b m Sooty Tern—Trevella **O. J. Stephens**

Other Owners: D. O. Stephens, Mrs J. L. Williams.

---

558 MR J. T. STIMPSON, Newcastle-under-Lyme
Postal: **Park House, Park Road, Butterton, Newcastle-under-Lyme, Staffordshire, ST5 4DZ**
Contacts: **PHONE (01782) 636020 FAX (01782) 633533 MOBILE (07768) 213531**
E-MAIL info@jtsintltd.co.uk

1 ARTE ET MARTE (IRE), 9, b br g Accordion—Glen's Gale (IRE) **E. Ashford**
2 BOLCKOW, 5, b g Marju (IRE)—Stamatina **J. T. Stimpson**
3 CARNT SPELL, 7, b g Wizard King—Forever Shineing **J. T. Stimpson & B. W. Trubshaw**
4 DANDYGREY RUSSETT (IRE), 7, gr m Singspiel (IRE)—
 Christian Church (IRE) **Bevan Holmes Underwood & Partners**
5 DON PASQUALE, 6, br g Zafonic (USA)—Bedazzling (IRE) **J. T. Stimpson**
6 ELAALA (USA), 6, ch m Aljabr (USA)—Nufuth (USA) **Moorland Racing**
7 HILL FARM SHANTY, 6, b g Slip Anchor—Hill Farm Blues **D. Newton**
8 ICE AND FIRE, 9, b g Cadeaux Genereux—Tanz (IRE) **J. T. Stimpson & B. W. Trubshaw**
9 KIRKHAMMERTON (IRE), 6, ch g Grand Lodge (USA)—Nawara **B. D. Leavy**
10 LLIZAAM, 4, b f Foxhound (USA)—Mazilla **M. Rhodes**
11 MCQUEEN (IRE), 8, ch g Barathea (IRE)—Bibliotheque (USA) **Moorland Racing**
12 MEGA SHOCKER, 4, b g Fasliyev (USA)—Girlie Set (IRE) **J. T. S. (International) Ltd**
13 MR JAWBREAKER (IRE), 9, b g Sadler's Wells (USA)—Abury (IRE) **J. T. S. (International) Ltd**
14 OCEAN VALENTINE, 5, gr g King Charlemagne (USA)—Dolly Bevan **Ocean View Properties International Ltd**
15 OPTIMUM (IRE), 6, br g King's Best (USA)—Colour Dance **J. T. Stimpson**
16 PICTURE FRAME, 4, ch g Fraam—Floral Spark **J. T. Stimpson**
17 PINKERTON MILL, 8, b m Rudimentary—Real Silver **Mrs Maria Del Rosario Stimpson**
18 ROYAL MASTER, 6, b g Royal Applause—High Sevens **J. T. Stimpson**
19 SHADOW JUMPER (IRE), 7, b g Dayjur—Specifically (USA) **J. T. Stimpson**
20 SONIC ANTHEM (USA), 6, b g Royal Anthem (USA)—Whisperifyoudare (USA) **Shearstud Ltd**
21 STAR TENOR (IRE), 6, b g Fourstars Allstar (USA)—Coco Opera (IRE) **S. H. Riley**

MR J. T. STIMPSON—continued

22 **WONDERWINDER (IRE)**, 6, b g Kayf Tara—Girlie Set (IRE) **J. T. S. (International) Ltd**
23 **ZED CANDY (FR)**, 5, b g Medicean—Intrum Morshaan (IRE) **J. T. S. (International) Ltd**

THREE-YEAR-OLDS

24 **EMERALD TOFFEE (IRE)**, ch c Tagula (IRE)—Spirit of Hope (IRE) **J. T. S. (International) Ltd**
25 **SIR JOEY**, ch g Forzando—Estabella (IRE) **S. H. Riley**

Other Owners: Mrs P. J. Bevan, Mr S. A. Mace, Mr A. P. Simmill, Mr J. T. Stimpson, Mr B. W. Trubshaw, Mrs Margaret Underwood.

Assistant Trainer: Barry Leavy (07710) 374989

---

559 **MRS M. K. STIRK, Ripon**
Postal: **Buck House Farm, Kirkby Moor Road, Kirkby Malzeard, Ripon, North Yorkshire, HG4 3QW**
Contacts: **PHONE (01765) 658202 MOBILE (07759) 295989**
E-MAIL maxinestirk@talktalk.net WEBSITE www.chaserstore.co.uk

1 **ELIZA DOALOTT (IRE)**, 6, b m Oscar (IRE)—Alottalady (IRE) **Mrs M. K. Stirk**
2 **SEEK THE TRUTH (IRE)**, 5, b g Witness Box (USA)—Country Project (IRE) **Mrs M. K. Stirk**

Assistant Trainer: A J Stirk

Jockey (NH): B. Harding. **Amateur:** Mr G. Brewer, Mr M. Walford.

---

560 **MISS ANN STOKELL, Richmond**
Postal: **Castle Stables, Gatherley Road, Brompton on Swale, Richmond, North Yorkshire, DL10 7JN**
Contacts: **MOBILE (07814) 579982**

1 **BLACK SABBETH**, 7, br g Desert Story (IRE)—Black Orchid (IRE) **Ms C. Stokell**
2 **GIFTED FLAME**, 9, b g Revoque (IRE)—Little Lady Leah (USA) **Ms C. Stokell**
3 **JUNIPER BANKS**, 7, ch g Night Shift (USA)—Beryl **Ms C. Stokell**
4 **LEGAL SET (IRE)**, 12, ch g Second Set (IRE)—Tiffany's Case (IRE) **Ms C. Stokell**
5 **PAWAN (IRE)**, 8, ch g Cadeaux Genereux—Born To Glamour **Ms C. Stokell**
6 **PERCY DOUGLAS**, 8, b g Elmaamul (USA)—Qualitair Dream **Ms C. Stokell**
7 **SAFRANINE (IRE)**, 11, b m Dolphin Street (FR)—Webbiana **Ms C. Stokell**
8 **TARAS KNIGHT (IRE)**, 6, b g Indian Danehill (IRE)—Queen of Art (IRE) **Ms C. Stokell**
9 **UNDERSCORE (USA)**, 6, ch g Spinning World (USA)—Speed Dialer (USA) **Ms C. Stokell**

TWO-YEAR-OLDS

10 B f 17/4 Rambling Bear—Animal Cracker (Primo Dominie) (1200) **John Medley**

Assistant Trainer: Caron Stokell

---

561 **MR W. B. STONE, Horseheath**
Postal: **The Meadow, Streetly End, West Wickham, Cambridge, Cambridgeshire, CB21 4RP**
Contacts: **PHONE (01223) 894617 MOBILE (07788) 971094**

1 **CARRIAGE RIDE (IRE)**, 10, b g Tidaro (USA)—Casakurali **Miss C. M. Scott**
2 **DARKSHAPE**, 8, b g Zamindar (USA)—Shapely (USA) **Miss C. M. Scott**
3 **DELORAIN (IRE)**, 5, b g Kalanisi (IRE)—Lady Nasrana (FR) **Miss C. M. Scott**
4 **HOOFBEATS TOUR**, 6, b g Vettori (IRE)—Sprite **Mrs M. Stone**
5 **LACONICOS (IRE)**, 6, ch g Foxhound (USA)—Thermopylae **Miss C. M. Scott**
6 **RIVER TIGRIS (IRE)**, 6, b m Dr Devious (IRE)—La Riveraine (USA) **Miss C. M. Scott**

562 MR B. STOREY, Kirklinton

Postal: **Low Dubwath, Kirklinton, Carlisle, Cumbria, CA6 6EF**
Contacts: PHONE **(01228) 675376** FAX **(01228) 675977** MOBILE **(07912) 898740**
E-MAIL bstoreyracing@aol.com

1 BRONZE DANCER (IRE), 6, b g Entrepreneur—Scrimshaw **Miss J. Hutchinson**
2 CARNDALE (IRE), 11, b g Black Monday—Inamuddle (IRE) **J. R. Callow**
3 COASTLEY (IRE), 6, b g Lord Americo—Cosima (IRE) **D. Carr**
4 DANEHILL SILVER, 4, b g Silver Patriarch (IRE)—
  Danehill Princess (IRE) **Miss J. Hutchinson, Mr I. A. Gibson, Mr Colin Scott**
5 DO L'ENFANT D'EAU (FR), 9, ch g Minds Music (USA)—L'eau Sauvage **Mr W J E Scott & Mrs M A Scott**
6 DOTTY'S DAUGHTER, 4, ch f Forzando—Colonel's Daughter **Miss J. Hutchinson**
7 EXIT TO SAUMUR (FR), 7, b g Exit To Nowhere (USA)—Mercalle (FR) **Mr & Mrs Raymond Anderson Green**
8 FAIRFIELD, 7, b m Afflora (IRE)—April City **Mr & Mrs T. I. Gourley**
9 5, ch g Windsor Castle—Final Touch (IRE) **Mr & Mrs Raymond Anderson Green**
10 GALAHAD (FR), 7, b g Apple Tree (FR)—Reine Elodie (FR) **Mr & Mrs Raymond Anderson Green**
11 GRAPHEX, 6, b br g Inchinor—Allegra **Mr & Mrs T. I. Gourley**
12 HAROUM (USA), 5, ch g Diesis—Up Her Sleeve (USA) **The Border Raiders**
13 HUMOUROUS (IRE), 6, b g Darshaan—Amusing Time (IRE) **Graham & Storey**
14 5, B g Weldnaas (USA)—Joyful Imp **Mr & Mrs J. E. Dixon**
15 ONE ROSE, 5, b m Roi de Rome (USA)—Solo Rose **Phil & Jane Coward**
16 SCARECROW (IRE), 7, b g Presenting—Rossacrowe Gale (IRE) **Larry Parker & Drummond Wilson**
17 SECRET TALK, 5, b m Classic Cliche (IRE)—Strumpet **Miss J. Hutchinson**
18 SILK AND ROSES, 5, gr m Roi de Rome (USA)—Joetta (IRE) **Miss J. Hutchinson**
19 VERSUS (GER), 8, gr g Highest Honor (FR)—Very Mighty (FR) **Mr & Mrs W. J. E. Scott**
20 WORLD VISION (IRE), 11, ch g Denel (FR)—Dusty Lane (IRE) **B. Storey**
21 WYN DIXIE (IRE), 9, b g Great Commotion (USA)—Duchess Affair (IRE) **Miss J. Hutchinson**

Other Owners: Mrs Jane Coward, Mr Philip Coward, Mr I. A. Gibson, Mr T. I. Gourley, Mrs M. Gourley, Mr W. Graham, Mr Raymond Anderson Green, Mrs Anita Green, Mr M. G. Hall, Mr E. W. Mallinson, Mr Larry Parker, Mr W. J. E. Scott, Mrs M. A. Scott, Mr Colin Scott, Mr B. Storey, Mr F. S. Storey, Mr Drummond Wilson.

Assistant Trainer: Miss Jackie Hutchinson

Jockey (NH): B. Harding, R. McGrath. **Apprentice:** P. J. McDonald. **Amateur:** Miss A. L. Hutchinson, Mr M. Walford.

563 MR W. STOREY, Consett

Postal: **Grange Farm & Stud, Muggleswick, Consett, Co. Durham, DH8 9DW**
Contacts: PHONE **(01207) 255259** FAX **(01207) 255259** MOBILE **(07860) 510441**
E-MAIL wlstorey@metronet.co.uk WEBSITE www.wilfstorey.com

1 BAZIL POINT, 6, b g Environment Friend—On The Bay **M. D. Townson**
2 FLY KICKER, 11, ch g High Kicker (USA)—Double Birthday **M. D. Townson**
3 INTO ACTION, 4, b c Sendawar (IRE)—Syrian Dancer (IRE) **P. Singh**
4 JERSEY MARY, 5, ch m River Falls—Sylvan Maid **P. Bailey**
5 MADGE, 6, br m Marju (IRE)—Aymara **Regent Decorators Ltd**
6 MISTER PETE (IRE), 5, b g Piccolo—Whistfilly **W. Storey**
7 OVER THE ODDS, 6, b m Overbury (IRE)—Ashniader (IRE) **J. Herring**
8 PEREZ (IRE), 6, b g Mujadil (USA)—Kahla **H. S. Hutchinson**
9 RAINBOW ZEST, 5, b h Rainbow Quest (USA)—Original **R. C. Tooth**
10 ROCA REDONDA (IRE), 4, b f Fasliyev (USA)—Devil's Crown (USA) **W. Storey**
11 VIE A DEUX (FR), 5, b m Jeune Homme (USA)—Callithea **Mr D. Tindale**

THREE-YEAR-OLDS

12 MCHEPPLE, b f Fleetwood (IRE)—Roleover Mania **A. McCormick**
13 PAINT STRIPPER, b g Prince Sabo—Passing Fancy **Gremlin Racing**
14 B c Rock City—Princess Diva **W. Storey**
15 SPOOKY, br g Vettori (IRE)—Aneen Alkamanja **H. S. Hutchinson**

Other Owners: Mr D. D. Gillies, Mr A. Henderson, Mr W. Moore.

Assistant Trainer: Miss S Storey

564 MRS S. P. STRETTON, Sherborne
Postal: **Beech Farm, Sigwells, Charlton Horethorne, Sherborne, Dorset, DT9 4LN**
Contacts: **PHONE (01963) 220524 FAX (01963) 220524 MOBILE (07816) 173657**
E-MAIL stretton@beechfarmsigwells.freeserve.co.uk

1 5, B m Emperor Fountain—Cinnamon Cruise **Mrs S. P. Stretton**
2 **CORTON COPSE**, 6, b g Sylvan Express—Corton Hill **Mrs S. P. Stretton**
3 **HONEYCOMBE**, 7, b m Relief Pitcher—Hanglands **Mrs S. P. Stretton**
4 5, B h Commanche Run—Patrita Park **Mrs S. P. Stretton**
5 4, B f Courteous—Sea Pearl **Mrs S. P. Stretton**

Other Owners: Mr J. K. Stretton.

Assistant Trainer: Claire Stretton

Jockey (NH): Claire Stretton.

565 MR R. M. STRONGE, Newbury
Postal: **Woods Folly, Beedon Common, Newbury, Berkshire, RG20 8TT**
Contacts: **PHONE/FAX (01635) 248710 MOBILE (07887) 521333**
E-MAIL robert@strong4380.freeserve.co.uk

1 **BENELLINO**, 5, b g Robellino (USA)—Benjarong **TestValleyPartnership & Bernice Stronge**
2 **COURT SPEEDING (IRE)**, 6, b g Courtship—Dalana's Pet VII **Mrs Bernice Stronge**
3 **LETHAM ISLAND (IRE)**, 4, b f Trans Island—Common Cause **Mr T. J. Whiting**
4 **MIX N MATCH**, 4, b c Royal Applause—South Wind **Mr T. J. Whiting**
5 **MOST DEFINITELY (IRE)**, 8, b g Definite Article—Unbidden Melody (USA) **Mr T. J. Whiting**
6 **RED**, 4, ch f Fraam—Great Tern **Mr J & Mrs P Cantrill**
7 **WATER KING (USA)**, 9, b g Irish River (FR)—Brookshield Baby (IRE) **Mrs Bernice Stronge**

Other Owners: Mr D. J. Baker, J. S. Cantrill, Mrs P. J. Cantrill, Mr A. C. Phillips.

Assistant Trainer: Bernice Stronge

Jockey (NH): B. Fenton. **Conditional:** S. Walsh.

566 MRS L. STUBBS, Malton
Postal: **Beverley House Stables, Beverley Road, Malton, North Yorkshire, YO17 9PJ**
Contacts: **PHONE (01653) 698731 FAX (01653) 698724 MOBILE (07747) 613962/(07801) 167707**
E-MAIL l.stubbs@btconnect.com

1 **SFORZANDO**, 7, b m Robellino (USA)—Mory Kante (USA) **Mrs L. Stubbs**
2 **STRADOCASTER**, 4, ch f Rock City—Hill Farm Blues **Miss Carol A. Jewell**
3 **TOBAGO REEF**, 4, b g Tobougg (IRE)—Silly Mid-On **V. Lee**

THREE-YEAR-OLDS

4 **MENSADIL**, b g Mind Games—Jezadil (IRE) **O. J. Williams**
5 **TERRY'S TIP (IRE)**, b g Namid—Kadarassa (IRE) **D. M. Thurlby**

TWO-YEAR-OLDS

6 B g 12/3 Reset (AUS)—Bint Makbul (Makbul) (2500) **Mr D. Arundale**
7 **CALLEY HO**, b g 30/4 Kyllachy—Lucayan Belle (Cadeaux Genereux) (9000) **D. M. Thurlby**
8 **HUXAAR**, b g 28/4 Xaar—Green Song (FR) (Green Tune) (USA)) (10500) **Tyme Partnership**
9 **JATMAN**, b g 8/5 Choisir (AUS)—Partenza (USA) (Red Ransom (USA)) (10000) **D. M. Thurlby**
10 **JUST BUZZIN**, b g 10/3 Kyllachy—Smoke Signal (IRE) (College Chapel) (12500) **Cos We Can Partnership**
11 **RUSSET REWARD**, b g 24/3 Bahamian Bounty—Appleacre (Polar Falcon (USA)) (10000) **P. G. Shorrock**

Other Owners: Mr D. Arundale, M. S. Martin, T. T. G. Osborne, Mrs Valerie Pittman, Mr I. Roche, Mrs L. Stubbs, Mr A. J. Wittering.

Jockey (flat): T. Eaves. **Apprentice:** Kristin Stubbs.

567 MISS TOR STURGIS, Lambourn

Postal: **Delamere Cottage Stables, Folly Road, Lambourn, Hungerford, Berkshire, RG17 8QG**
Contacts: **PHONE (07909) 977722 FAX (01488) 73703**
E-MAIL info@torsturgisracing.co.uk WEBSITE www.torsturgisracing.co.uk

1 BE TELLING (IRE), 9, b g Oscar (IRE)—Manhattan King (IRE) **The Windrush Mob**
2 CHAMPAGNE SHADOW (IRE), 7, b g Kahyasi—Moet (IRE) **Mr J. Roberts**
3 CHUNKY'S CHOICE (IRE), 4, b g Key of Luck (USA)—Indian Imp **Roger Davis & Ann Sturgis**
4 DABARATSA (FR), 5, b m Astarabad (USA)—Miss Reddy (FR) **Fightheban Racing Partnership**
5 GENERAL FLUMPA, 7, b g Vettori (IRE)—Macca Luna (IRE) **S. Astaire**
6 IMMOLA (FR), 12, b br g Quart de Vin (FR)—Jessica (FR) **Mrs S. V. M. Stevens**
7 MIKA'S FABLE (FR), 5, ch m Muhtathir—Baie des Anges **Ladyswood Stud Ltd**
8 OCEAN WAVES (IRE), 5, ch m Barathea (IRE)—We've Just Begun (USA) **H. M. Stanley**
9 PARK DRIVE (IRE), 7, b h Daggers Drawn (USA)—Flying Clouds **Miss V. C. Sturgis**
10 PATSY BEE (IRE), 7, b g Saddlers' Hall (IRE)—Strong Profit (IRE) **Roger Davis & David Thomas**
11 SALOON (USA), 4, b c Sadler's Wells (USA)—Fire The Groom (USA)
12 WATCHMAKER, 5, b g Bering—Watchkeeper (IRE) **Miss A. Sturgis**
13 WELSH MAIN, 11, b g Zafonic (USA)—Welsh Daylight **Miss V. C. Sturgis**
14 WOTARIDE (IRE), 6, b g Clerkenwell (USA)—Yokki Moppie (USA) **The Wotaride Partnership**

THREE-YEAR-OLDS

15 WHISKEY CREEK, ch g Tipsy Creek (USA)—Judiam **Mrs L. L. Wheeler**

Other Owners: Ms Joan Bell, Mr Roger Davis, Mr P. J. Foley, Mr Tom Gittins, Mrs Jacky Hopkins, Mr P. B. Mitford-Slade, Mr D. Redvers, Miss Ann Sturgis, Mr D. M. Thomas.

568 MR B. R. SUMMERS, Solihull

Postal: **Hill Farm, Pigtrot Lane, Tanworth-In-Arden, Solihull, West Midlands, B94 5BJ**
Contacts: **PHONE (01564) 742667 MOBILE (07775) 898327**

1 ARCTIC ECHO, 9, b g Alderbrook—Arctic Oats **R. P. D. T. Dineen**
2 BOOMERANG BUD, 5, b g Kayf Tara—Blossoming **Mr T. E. Bucknall**
3 NELSON (FR), 7, ch g Blushing Flame (USA)—Fleur des Marais II (FR) **O. P. J. Meli**
4 OCEAN FOU (FR), 6, b g Lute Antique (FR)—Vieille Folle (FR) **O. P. J. Meli**
5 PHOTOGENIQUE (FR), 5, b m Cyborg (FR)—Colombia (FR) **Mrs G. M. Summers**
6 ROMEO (FR), 10, ch g Mansonnien (FR)—Dona Rahotep (FR) **Mr B. P. Breheny**
7 SAINT ESPIEGLE (FR), 4, b g Saint Preuil (FR)—Pointe Espiegle (FR) **O. P. J. Meli**
8 SURAGOT (FR), 6, ch g Dyhim Diamond (IRE)—Miss Bugey (FR) **Mr M. Mccormick**

Assistant Trainer: Mrs G. M. Summers

569 MR CHARLIE SWAN, Cloughjordan

Postal: **Modreeny, Cloughjordan, Co. Tipperary, Ireland**
Contacts: **PHONE (00353) 5054 2128 FAX (00353) 2054 2128 MOBILE (00353) 8625 73194**
E-MAIL cswan@iol.ie

1 ADAJAL (IRE), 5, b g Zilzal (USA)—Adalya (IRE) **J. P. McManus**
2 BACK TO SQUARE ONE (IRE), 6, b g Bob Back (USA)—Fortune And Favour (IRE) **J. P. McManus**
3 BAT OUT OF HELL (IRE), 5, b g Anshan—Be My Citizen (IRE) **Gigginstown House Stud**
4 BERKELEY HOUSE (IRE), 8, b m Beneficial—Danny's Charm (IRE) **Berkeley Racing Club**
5 BET OUT OF IT (IRE), 6, ch g Pistolet Bleu (IRE)—Autumn Sky (IRE) **Walk Of Shame Syndicate**
6 BONIFACIO (IRE), 4, b c Sadler's Wells (USA)—Anaza **Mr P. Moore**
7 BOULAVOGUE (IRE), 5, b g Turtle Island (IRE)—Nilousha **Mr Noel O'Flaherty**
8 CHECKPOINTCHARLIE (IRE), 5, b g Supreme Leader—Ramble Bramble **Orpendale Racing**
9 CLOONE RIVER (IRE), 12, b br g Un Desperado (FR)—Grangemills **Mrs K. Gillane**
10 CLOONE ROCKET (IRE), 6, b g Pistolet Bleu (IRE)—Site-Leader (IRE) **Mrs K. Gillane**
11 COME TO THE PARTY (IRE), 5, b g Taipan (IRE)—Iron Mariner (IRE) **Mrs C. Swan**
12 CROOKED THROW (IRE), 9, br g Anshan—Mary's View (IRE) **Hogan, Woods, Whelan Syndicate**
13 DAB HAND (IRE), 5, b g Alzao (USA)—Deft Touch **Derek Williams**
14 DALUCCI (IRE), 5, gr g Daylami (IRE)—Coigach **Mr J. McCarthy**
15 DRIVE ON JIM (IRE), 5, b g Alderbrook—Garryduff Princess (IRE) **Mr N. O'Flaherty**
16 DRUNKEN DISORDERLY (IRE), 8, b g Luso—Slave Hero (IRE) **Gigginstown House Stud**
17 EMMPAT (IRE), 10, b g Bigstone (IRE)—Nordic Abu (IRE) **Mr M. D. Mee**
18 EX EX AL (NZ), 7, ch g Sandtrap—Just Sayonara (NZ) **Mr D. Taylor**

MR CHARLIE SWAN—continued

19 **FOREMAN (GER)**, 10, ch g Monsun (GER)—Fleurie (GER) **J. P. McManus**
20 **FORTY FOOT (IRE)**, 5, b g King's Theatre (IRE)—Ride The Tide (IRE) **Barry Connell**
21 **GALLEY LIGHT (IRE)**, 5, b g Turtle Island (IRE)—Coola Cross (IRE) **Mr N. O'Flaherty**
22 **GARRYOWEN STAR (IRE)**, 6, br g Supreme Leader—Swing Into Action (IRE) **Frank Hogan Motors**
23 **GLAMIS CASTLE (USA)**, 5, b g Selkirk (USA)—Fairy Godmother **Mrs A. F. Lee**
24 **GO SILVER BULLET (FR)**, 7, gr g Simon du Desert (FR)—
Bouge De La (USA) **D. Brennan Accountants Syndicate**
25 **GRIGG OAK (IRE)**, 5, b g Rashar (USA)—Head of The Gang **Ms T. Foreman**
26 **GRIPIT N TIPIT (IRE)**, 7, b g Saddlers' Hall (IRE)—Savanagh (IRE) **The Doonbeg Golf Syndicate**
27 **HAPPY REUNION (IRE)**, 5, br m Fantastic Light (USA)—Queen Sceptre (IRE) **Mr J. Sullivan**
28 **HOTTERTHANJULY (IRE)**, 6, b g Oscar (IRE)—Sunsets Girl (IRE) **Mr B. Connell**
29 **HOUSE OF BOURBON (IRE)**, 5, ch g Rainbow Quest (USA)—Her Ladyship **Arabian Ranches Syndicate**
30 **ICKLINGHAM (IRE)**, 8, b g Sadler's Wells (USA)—Braiswick **Mr Dennis J. Reddaw**
31 **JALMIRA (IRE)**, 7, b m Danehill Dancer (IRE)—Jaldini (IRE) **Green Dragon Syndicate**
32 **JET PROPELLED (IRE)**, 7, b g Oscar (IRE)—Fahy Quay **J. P. McManus**
33 **KICKING BULL (IRE)**, 6, b g Supreme Leader—Loch Mor (IRE) **Mrs M. A. Healy**
34 **KING OF THE CHASE (IRE)**, 7, b g Accordion—Beglawella **Mr T. Keane**
35 **KIRKSTALL**, 6, b g Selkirk (USA)—Stilleta **Mr D. Taylor**
36 **LADY HILLINGDON**, 5, b m Overbury (IRE)—Ecologically Kind **Mrs C. Swan**
37 **LAST DRAW (IRE)**, 5, ch g Accordion—Marble Miller (IRE) **Trotters Ind. Trading Syndicate**
38 **LAUREDEAN BELLE (IRE)**, 7, b m Supreme Leader—Calora (USA) **D. Brennan Accountants Syndicate**
39 **LET'S TALK (IRE)**, 5, b g Saddlers' Hall (IRE)—Savanagh (IRE) **J. P. McManus**
40 **MINNIESCOTTAGE (IRE)**, 6, ch m Moscow Society (USA)—Tanyas Cottage (IRE) **Mr E. Crawford**
41 **MISTER MONTH (IRE)**, 11, ch g Roselier (FR)—Croghan Heather **Mr Noel O'Flaherty**
42 **NEXTHINGWAS (IRE)**, 6, ch g Presenting—Jessica One (IRE) **Gigginstown House Stud**
43 **NINE INCH NAIL (IRE)**, 6, ch g Weld—Still Hoping **Gigginstown House Stud**
44 **OFFSHORE ACCOUNT (IRE)**, 8, b g Oscar (IRE)—Park Breeze (IRE) **Mr B. Polly**
45 **ONE COOL COOKIE (IRE)**, 7, ch g Old Vic—Lady Bellingham (IRE) **Gigginstown House Stud**
46 **ONE MORE MINUTE (IRE)**, 8, ch g Zaffaran (USA)—Wollongong (IRE) **Mr Robert Butler Racing Ltd**
47 **OODACHEE**, 9, b g Marju (IRE)—Lady Marguerrite **Modreeny Syndicate**
48 **OZARA (IRE)**, 6, b m Oscar (IRE)—Conzara (IRE) **Moore Syndicate**
49 **PAMPER MEE (IRE)**, 4, b f King Charlemagne (USA)—Courtier **Durkan Bloodstock Ltd**
50 **PORTICCIO (IRE)**, 5, ch h Lomitas—Rekindled Affair (IRE) **J. P. McManus**
51 **ROCK BELTER (IRE)**, 5, b g Norwich—Kilmington Breeze (IRE) **Santas Little Helper Syndicate**
52 **RORY'S PLEASURE (IRE)**, 7, b g Tiraaz (USA)—Great Pleasure (IRE) **Mr E. Kavanagh**
53 **RORY'S SISTER (IRE)**, 7, b m Little Bighorn—Dunany Star (IRE) **Mr E. Kavanagh**
54 **ROYAL MAN (FR)**, 7, ch g Garde Royale—Fayolia (FR) **Gigginstown House Stud**
55 **SAALBACK (USA)**, 6, ch m King of Kings (IRE)—Parker's Cove (USA) **The Wrong Ones Syndicate**
56 **SAINTLY RACHEL (IRE)**, 10, b m Religiously (USA)—Ursha (IRE) **The Whitethorn Syndicate**
57 **SECURITY TIGER (IRE)**, 4, b f Desert Prince (IRE)—Nuit Chaud (USA) **Mrs C. Swann**
58 **SILVER PORTRAIT (IRE)**, 7, gr g Portrait Gallery (IRE)—Mary Oliver (IRE) **Mr Edward Nugent**
59 **SIR EJAY (IRE)**, 5, b br g Saddlers' Hall (IRE)—Coumeenoole Lady **Mr E. Crawford**
60 **SLASH AND BURN (IRE)**, 6, b g Presenting—Force Seven **Gigginstown House Stud**
61 **SOFT SPOKEN (IRE)**, 5, b g Turgeon (USA)—Miss Planette (FR) **Brian Polly**
62 **SORRY AL (IRE)**, 8, ch g Anshan—Just A Second **Mr Donal Carey**
63 **SUTHERLAND BELLE (IRE)**, 7, b m Bob Back (USA)—First Strike (IRE) **Mr P. McNelney**
64 **TEEMING RAIN (IRE)**, 9, b g Supreme Leader—Lady Graduate (IRE) **J. P. McManus**
65 **THAT'S AN IDEA (IRE)**, 10, b g Arctic Lord—Annsgrove Polly (IRE) **J. P. McManus**
66 **THE NEXT KING (IRE)**, 6, ch g Oscar Schindler (IRE)—Little Nikita **The Diggers Syndicate**
67 **THE OLD BUCCANEER (IRE)**, 5, b g Turtle Island (IRE)—Claycastle (IRE) **Mr P. Byrne**
68 **THE WARRIOR KANE (IRE)**, 7, b g Bob Back (USA)—Tynaghs Thyne (IRE) **Mr P. McCormack**
69 **VALAIN (IRE)**, 5, b br g Grand Lodge (USA)—Literary **J. P. McManus**
70 **VICTOR GRUMPS (IRE)**, 5, b g Old Vic—Nil Faic (IRE) **Mrs C. Swan**
71 **WINTERWOOD (IRE)**, 5, b g Definite Article—Miss Dolly (IRE) **Mr Robert Butler Racing Ltd**
72 **YELENA'S GOLD (IRE)**, 6, b m High Roller—Lady Moskva (IRE) **Mrs M. Cashman**
73 **YOUCANOTBESERIOUS (IRE)**, 5, b m Sonus (IRE)—Womans Heart (IRE) **Mrs M. Byrne**
74 **ZARALABAD (IRE)**, 4, b c Fantastic Light (USA)—Zarannda (IRE) **Mr N. O'Flaherty**

THREE-YEAR-OLDS

75 **YOUR NIGHT OUT (FR)**, b f Dubai Destination (USA)—Happy Hour (GER) **Durkan Bloodstock Ltd**

Other Owners: R. G. W. Brown, The Hon R. T. A. Goff.

Jockey (NH): D. J. Casey. **Conditional:** D. G. Hogan. **Amateur:** Miss A. K. Grace, Mr W. Hayes, Mr L. Flynn, Miss Louisa Williams.

570 MR M. S. SWEETLAND, Honiton
Postal: **Abbeywood Farm, Dunkeswell, Honiton, Devon, EX14 4RW**
Contacts: **PHONE (01823) 680287 FAX (01823) 680287**

1 ABBEY SHADOW, 9, gr g Lir—Silver Zip **M. S. Sweetland**
2 BASILIR, 9, b g Lir—Zara Express **M. S. Sweetland**
3 FENNY LILY, 10, br m Lir—Zara Express **M. S. Sweetland**
4 FIESTY MADAM, 7, ch m Bien Bien (USA)—Riverine **M. S. Sweetland**
5 MISS PATCHWORK, 6, b m El Conquistador—Moorland Mews **M. S. Sweetland**

Amateur: Mr Martin Sweetland.

571 MR G. A. SWINBANK, Richmond
Postal: **Thorndale Farm, Melsonby, Richmond, North Yorkshire, DL10 5NJ**
Contacts: **PHONE (01325) 377318 FAX (01325) 377796 MOBILE (07860) 368365/(07711) 488341**
E-MAIL info@alanswinbank.com WEBSITE www.alanswinbank.com

1 ALFIE FLITS, 6, b g Machiavellian (USA)—Elhilmeya (IRE) **Dom Flit**
2 ALTO STRATUS, 7, gr m Cloudings (IRE)—Legata (IRE) **Tracey Gaunt & David Gibbons**
3 BIVOUAC (UAE), 4, b g Jade Robbery (USA)—Tentpole (USA) **P. J. Hughes Developments Ltd**
4 CAREFREE, 4, b f Medicean—Hertha **Geraldine Degville & Lawrence Degville**
5 COLLIER RIDGE, 4, b g Tobougg (IRE)—Amal **R. H. Hall**
6 CONTEMPLATION, 5, b g Sunday Silence (USA)—Wood Vine (USA) **R. L. Crowe**
7 COOL MISSION (IRE), 4, ch g Definite Article—Mettlesome **Richard Haggas**
8 COTTON EYED JOE (IRE), 7, b g Indian Rocket—Cwm Deri (IRE) **Mrs S. L. Sanbrook**
9 DESERTED DANE (USA), 4, b c Elusive Quality (USA)—Desertion (IRE) **Mr A. Flower & Mr R. H. Hall**
10 DORIS'S GIFT, 7, gr g Environment Friend—Saxon Gift **Elliott Brothers**
11 ELLA, 4, b f Pivotal—Flossy **Guy Reed**
12 EVELITH REGENT (IRE), 5, b g Imperial Ballet (IRE)—No Avail (IRE) **A. Stennett**
13 EZDYAAD (USA), 4, b g Lemon Drop Kid (USA)—August Storm (USA) **Elsa Crankshaw & G. Allan**
14 FERRANDO, 6, b g Hernando (FR)—Oh So Misty **S P Racing Investments & Matthew Green**
15 FIRST BUDDY, 4, ch g Rock of Gibraltar (IRE)—Dance Treat (USA) **W. J. Gredley**
16 FLAGSTONE (USA), 4, ch g Distant Vine (USA)—Navarene (USA) **S. L. Gray**
17 FLYING VALENTINO, 4, b f Primo Valentino (IRE)—Flying Romance (IRE) **A. Butler**
18 GIVE HER A WHIRL, 4, b f Pursuit of Love—Peggy Spencer **Guy Reed**
19 GYRATION (IRE), 4, ch g Spinning World (USA)—Tomori (USA) **D J Fish, David Gibbons & Tracey Gaunt**
20 HARTSHEAD, 9, b g Machiavellian (USA)—Zalitzine (USA) **B. Valentine**
21 HILL BILLY ROCK (IRE), 5, b g Halling (USA)—Polska (USA) **Mr W. Powrie & Mrs S. Sandbrook**
22 IGNOTUS, 6, b g Vitus—Linns Heir **M. R. Green**
23 ISIDORE BONHEUR (IRE), 7, b g Mtoto—Way O'gold (USA) **Mr J. McAleese**
24 KARLANI (IRE), 5, b br g Fantastic Light (USA)—Karliyka (IRE) **Elliott Brothers**
25 KATAPULT (GER), 5, b g Dashing Blade—Katharina (GER) **Mrs B Watson & Copskam Partnership**
26 KEY DECISION (IRE), 4, br g Key of Luck (USA)—Adalya (IRE) **A. Butler**
27 KINGSBEN, 5, b g King's Best (USA)—Bluebelle **Mr A. Butler & Mr J. David Abell**
28 KIRKBY'S TREASURE, 10, gr g Mind Games—Gem of Gold **Kirkby Lonsdale Racing**
29 LITTLE LU (IRE), 6, b m Danehill Dancer (IRE)—Tales of Wisdom **Dom Flit**
30 MAGIC MEL, 5, br m Overbury (IRE)—Gospel Echo **Mr M. Miller,Mrs C. Miller,Mrs J Penney**
31 MASRA, 5, b g Silver Patriarch (IRE)—Go Sally Go (IRE) **C P M Racing**
32 MISS KECK, 4, b f Inchinor—En Vacances (IRE) **Mr A. Wright**
33 NORTHERN BLAZE, 6, ch g North Col—Blazer's Baby **The Four Tops**
34 PACKERS HILL (IRE), 4, b g Mull of Kintyre (USA)—Head For The Stars (IRE) **B. Valentine**
35 PERSIAN PERIL, 4, br g Erhaab (USA)—Brush Away **Mrs J. Porter**
36 PETERS PRIDE, 6, b g Silver Patriarch (IRE)—Manzanilla **Miss L Davis & The Peaks Partnership**
37 PRESENT GESTURE (IRE), 5, b m Presenting—Rare Gesture (IRE) **Mr J. M. Hussey**
38 PRINCE EVELITH (GER), 5, b g Dashing Blade—Peace Time (GER) **A. Stennett**
39 PROGRAMME GIRL (IRE), 6, ch m Definite Article—Targhyb (IRE) **G Houghton & David C Young**
40 PUY D'ARNAC (FR), 5, b g Acteur Francais—Chaumeil (FR) **Barrow Brook Racing**
41 REASONTOBECHEERFUL, 5, b m Parthian Springs—Lisband Lady (IRE) **Foxwood Hillhouse Stables**
42 SAM'S SECRET, 6, b m Josr Algarhoud (IRE)—Twilight Time **Copskam Partnership**
43 SCALE BANK (IRE), 5, b g Indian Danehill (USA)—Cory Everson (IRE) **Mr R. H. Hall & Mr J. A. Kavanagh**
44 SELLJ, 4, b g Sakhee (USA)—Taqreem (IRE) **Elsa Crankshaw & G. Allan II**
45 SHIWAWA, 4, b g Halling (USA)—I Will Lead (USA) **Mr G. Holmes**
46 SILVER GOAL (GER), 4, b c Tiger Hill (IRE)—Salka (GER) **J. Watson**
47 SIR BOREAS HAWK, 6, b g Overbury (IRE)—Fringe Benefit **W. Powrie**
48 SIR MULBERRY HAWK, 4, b g Overbury (IRE)—Fringe Benefit (IRE) **Powrie, Valentine & McManus Br 2**
49 SIR TANTALLUS HAWK, 4, b g Overbury (IRE)—Mobile Miss (IRE) **Highland Racing 4 & Mrs E. Melrose**

MR G. A. SWINBANK—continued

50 **SISELLA (IRE)**, 5, gr m Bob Back (USA)—Slavica **P. E. Atkinson**
51 **SOCCERJACKPOT (USA)**, 4, b g Mizzen Mast (USA)—Rahbaby (USA) **Sporta Racing & George Houghton**
52 **SOUTHERN WATERS (FR)**, 4, br g Sinndar (IRE)—Due South **D. C. Mitchell**
53 **SPRINGFIELD DANTE**, 7, b g Pharly (FR)—Mythical Storm **Mrs M. A. Pinney**
54 **STARTING POINT**, 6, br g Monashee Mountain (USA)—Louise Moillon **Lothian Recycling Limited**
55 **STEVIE GEE (IRE)**, 4, b g Invincible Spirit (IRE)—Margaree Mary (CAN) **S. L. Gray**
56 **TANNENBERG (IRE)**, 7, b g Polish Precedent (USA)—Upper Strata **N. Shutts**
57 **TOUCH OF IRISH**, 6, b g Kayf Tara—Portland Row (IRE) **W. A. Walker**
58 **TURBO LINN**, 5, b m Turbo Speed—Linns Heir **J. Nelson**
59 **TWENTYNINEBLACK (FR)**, 4, b br g Valanour (IRE)—Grange Cunault (FR) **D. Gibbons & T. Gaunt**
60 **VIVONA HILL**, 4, b g Overbury (IRE)—Lets Go Dutch **Mrs V. Birnie & Mrs F. Crone**
61 **WIND STAR**, 5, ch g Piccolo—Starfleet **Mr D. G. Williams & Mr R. H. Hall**

THREE-YEAR-OLDS

62 **APPLAUDE**, b c Royal Applause—Flossy **Guy Reed**
63 **BAR BLU (IRE)**, b f Mull of Kintyre (USA)—Ruwy **Mr B. Harker & Mrs V. McGee**
64 **BORN TO PERFORM**, br g Theatrical—My Hansel (USA) **Mr J. N. Swinbank**
65 **CAERLAVEROCK (IRE)**, b g Statue of Liberty (USA)—Daziyra (IRE) **Mr & Mrs Duncan Davidson**
66 **CARR ON FIRE (USA)**, b br g Hook and Ladder (USA)—Escarrgot (USA) **Dusktilldawn Racing II**
67 **CASTLEBURY (IRE)**, b g Spartacus (IRE)—La Vie En Rouge (IRE) **A. Butler**
68 **CHATANOOGACHOOCHOO**, ch f Piccolo—Taza **Guy Reed**
69 **CHICKINI (IRE)**, b f Rossini (USA)—Fast Chick **J. V. Layton**
70 **CULLYBACKEY (IRE)**, ch f Golan (IRE)—Leitrim Lodge (IRE) **Mr H. Brown Kerr**
71 **DAREIOS (GER)**, ch g Numerous (USA)—Desert Chiara (USA) **Mr A. W. Bult**
72 **DESERT LARK**, b c Sakhee (USA)—Oyster Catcher (IRE) **David Gibbons & Tracey Gaunt**
73 **DEVINIUS (IRE)**, ch f Choisir (AUS)—Vampress (IRE) **The Jags Syndicate**
74 **FULL SPEED (GER)**, b g Sholokhov (IRE)—Flagny (FR) **P. J. Carr**
75 **IF YOU KNEW SUZY**, b f Efisio—Sioux **Guy Reed**
76 **KALHAN SANDS (IRE)**, b g Okawango (USA)—Night Spirit (IRE) **Elsa Crankshaw & Gordon Allan**
77 **KAMA NIGHT (IRE)**, b g Night Shift (USA)—Kamalame (USA) **B. Valentine**
78 **KASHIMIN (IRE)**, b c Kyllachy—Oh So Misty **Mrs A. M. Noble**
79 **LOUIS SEFFENS (USA)**, b c Elusive Quality (USA)—Miss Seffens (USA) **R. L. Crowe**
80 **MERCHANT OF DUBAI (IRE)**, b c Dubai Destination (USA)—Chameleon **Highland Racing 2**
81 **MR LU**, b g Lujain (USA)—Libretta **The Greens Committee**
82 **NEXT OF KIN (IRE)**, b g Kris Kin (USA)—Lady of Shalott **Mrs K. S. Pratt**
83 **NOBLE SCHOLAR (IRE)**, b c Anabaa (USA)—Lisieux Rose (IRE) **John Watson**
84 **PAR AVION**, b f Efisio—Blow Me A Kiss **Guy Reed**
85 **PRINCE KALAMOUN (IRE)**, ch g Desert Prince (IRE)—Grenouillere (USA) **Mr J. P. F. Dixon**
86 **RED ROUGE**, b f Celtic Swing—Red To Violet **P. A. Jarvis**
87 **RIO SABOTINI (IRE)**, ch c Captain Rio—Sabotini **The Rio Sabotini Partnership**
88 **SALINGERS STAR (IRE)**, b f Catcher In The Rye (USA)—Head For The Stars (IRE) **Hokey Cokey Partnership**
89 **SCOTTY THE SAMURAI (IRE)**, b g Oguri Cap (JPN)—Waka Shirayuki (JPN) **S. C. Bellwood**
90 **SHAKEDOWN**, b c Domedriver (IRE)—Stormy Weather **Mrs L. M. Lamyman**
91 **SIR ROYAL (USA)**, b c Diesis—Only Royale (IRE) **Mr L. Ferdinand**
92 **SOLAR SPIRIT (IRE)**, b c Invincible Spirit (IRE)—Misaayef (USA) **Mr C. J. Allan**
93 **STEVIE THUNDER**, ch g Storming Home—Social Storm **S. L. Gray**
94 Ch g Spartacus (IRE)—Susan (IRE) **Elsa Crankshaw**
95 **TAKE IT EASEE (IRE)**, b f Noverre (USA)—Fairy Lore (IRE) **Mr D. M. FitzGerald**
96 **TALON (IRE)**, ch g Indian Ridge—Brief Lullaby (IRE) **Mr S. S. Anderson**
97 **TARKHEENA PRINCE (USA)**, b g Aldebaran (USA)—Tarkheena (USA) **Mr G. H. Bell**
98 **WHIRLIJIG (IRE)**, ch f Spinning World (USA)—Dariyba (IRE) **Mrs T. Blackett**

TWO-YEAR-OLDS

99 **ACCLABEN (IRE)**, b c 29/4 Acclamation—Jour de Grace (SWE) (Steve's Friend (USA)) (25740) **Mr A. Butler**
100 B br c 17/4 One Cool Cat (USA)—Amizette (USA) (Forty Niner (USA)) (27026) **Mrs J. Porter**
101 Gr c 21/3 Val Royal (FR)—Aneydia (IRE) (Kenmare (FR)) (12869) **Miss S. Haynes**
102 B c 10/2 Marju (IRE)—Anniversary (Salse (USA)) (32000) **The County Set**
103 B c 7/5 Danehill Dancer (IRE)—Band of Angels (IRE) (Alzao (USA)) (23809) **Mrs J. Peat**
104 B c 4/4 Val Royal (FR)—Boley Lass (IRE) (Archway (IRE)) (23165) **Mr R. Haggas**
105 B c 18/4 Hawk Wing (USA)—Danccini (IRE) (Dancing Dissident (USA)) (24000) **W. Powrie**
106 **FREYA'S FLIGHT (IRE)**, ch f 14/3 Viking Ruler (AUS)—
Polish Saga (Polish Patriot (USA)) (1930) **Mrs T. Gaunt & Mr D. Gibbons**
107 **GEORGE ADAMSON (IRE)**, b g 10/3 Where Or When (IRE)—
Tactile (Groom Dancer (USA)) (5000) **Mrs S. Sandbrook**
108 B c 7/5 Pyrus (USA)—Ghayaat (USA) (Lyphard (USA)) (9330) **Mrs S. Sandbrook**

MR G. A. SWINBANK—continued

109 Br c 29/3 Tillerman—Grey Pursuit (IRE) (Pursuit of Love) (10939) **Mrs J. Porter**
110 **ISLAND FELLOW,** b c 16/5 Turbo Speed—Island Path (IRE) (Jupiter Island) **Mr J. Nelson**
111 **IVOR NOVELLO (IRE),** b c 14/4 Noverre (USA)—Pearly Brooks (Efisio) (43000) **Duncan Davidson**
112 Ch c 5/5 Bertolini (USA)—Jodeeka (Fraam) (15000) **Mr J. Nelson**
113 B c 4/4 Bernstein (USA)—Lady Carson (USA) (Carson City) (12147) **Mr R. H. Hall**
114 **LADY COUNSELLOR,** b f 7/6 Turbo Speed—Linns Heir (Leading Counsel (USA)) **Mr S. C. Bellwood**
115 B c 4/4 Statue of Liberty (USA)—Lady Justice (Compton Place) (9652) **Brian Harker**
116 B f 3/5 Invincible Spirit (IRE)—Misaayef (USA) (Swain (IRE)) (19304) **Mr W. Moloney**
117 **NORTHSIDE PRINCE (IRE),** b g 19/2 Desert Prince (IRE)—
                              Spartan Girl (IRE) (Ela-Mana-Mou) (12869) **Mrs S. Anderson**
118 B f 18/2 Elusive City (USA)—Pantera Piceno (IRE) (College Chapel) (8364) **Mr G. Stephenson**
119 Ch c 7/3 Kheleyf (USA)—Rising Spirits (Cure The Blues (USA)) (18000) **Mr D. Bamlett**
120 B c 12/3 Fantastic Light (USA)—Russian Snows (IRE) (Sadler's Wells) (7721) **Mr A. Butler**
121 B c 29/1 Rock of Gibraltar (IRE)—Sakkara (IRE) (Sadler's Wells) (16086) **Mr G. Allan & Elsa Crankshaw**
122 B c 8/2 Mull of Kintyre (USA)—Soden (IRE) (Mujadil (USA)) (10295) **Brian Valentine**
123 B c 1/4 High Chaparral (IRE)—Southey (USA) (Broad Brush (USA)) (20000) **W. J. Gredley**
124 B f 1/4 Fasliyev (USA)—Sugar (Hernando (FR)) (5469) **Mrs J. Porter**
125 **TALE OF SILVER (IRE),** b g 11/2 Pyrus (USA)—Bajan Belle (IRE) (Efisio) (14156) **Mrs I. Gibson**
126 **TILERIUM'S DREAM (IRE),** b g 15/4 Tillerman—
                              Thai Princess (IRE) (Hamas) (14156) **Mr D. Gibbons & Mrs T. Gaunt**
127 B c 29/5 Fath (USA)—Tropical Zone (Machiavellian (USA)) (13500) **Mr P. Clark**
128 Ch c 20/4 Danehill Dancer (IRE)—Uriah (GER) (Acatenango (GER)) (28957) **Mrs T. Blackett**
129 Gr c 1/5 Needwood Blade—Wandering Stranger (Petong) (7078) **Mr D. G. Williams**
130 B c 22/2 Najran (USA)—What's Up Kittycat (USA) (Tabasco Cat (USA)) (20591) **Mr G. Allan & Elsa Crankshaw**
131 B c 23/4 Halling (USA)—Woven Silk (USA) (Danzig (USA)) (10295) **Mr B. Valentine**

Other Owners: Mr J. David Abell, G. Allan, R. D. Anderson, Mr J. Babb, Mr D. Bamlett, Mr E. N. Barber, I. M. Bennett, I. M. Buchan, A Cadger, Mr P. Copson, Miss E. Crankshaw, Lord Daresbury, D. H. Davidson, Mrs S. K. Davidson, Miss L. I. Davis, Mrs G. J. Degville, Mr L. W. Degville, Mr Andrew Dick, Mr Brian Dunn, Mr J. A. Elliott, Mr John Elliott, Mr Colin Elliott, Dr C. I. Emmerson, Mr D. J. Fish, Mr Gary Flitcroft, S. A. Flower, Mrs Tracey Gaunt, B. Gaunt, Mr D. M. Gibbons, Mrs I. Gibson, G. Godsman, Mr R. H. Hall, Mr Brian Harker, Mr B. Harker, Miss Sally R. Haynes, Mr F. Hendry, G. Houghton, Mrs A. Iles, N. E. M. Jones, Mr J. A. Kavanagh, Mr S. E. Kennedy, Mr P. J. Kenny, R. Lee, Mrs M. Lee, Mr T. Mallen, A. Mallen, P. H. Marron, Mr G. Marshall, Mr D. Matteo, Mrs V. McGee, Mrs V. McGee, Mr A. McManus, Mrs Eleanor Melrose, Mr Melvyn Miller, Mrs C. Miller, T. Minnis, Mr J. M. Murphy, P. R. Nodder, Mr D. Nuttall, Mr S. P O'Connor, Mrs K. E. Parkinson, Mrs J. M. Penney, Mr William A. Powrie, SP Racing Investments S.A., Mrs E. L. Sampson, A. W. Sinclair, Mr N. D. Skinner, P Swift, Miss M. Swinbank, G. A. Swinbank, G. R. Taylor, Mr Peter Thompson, Mr P. Thompson, Miss K. T. Thompson, Mrs C. A. Todd, Mr J. Townson, Mrs B. Watson, Mr D. G. Williams, D. C. Young.

Assistant Trainer: Mr W.W. Haigh & Mr R. Lappin

Jockey (flat): N. Callan, Dean McKeown. **Jockey (NH):** A. Dobbin. **Conditional:** Brian Hughes, D. C. Costello. **Apprentice:** P. J. McDonald.

---

572 MR W. R. J. SWINBURN, Berkhamsted
Postal: **Church Farm, Station Road, Aldbury, Tring, Hertfordshire, HP23 5RS**
Contacts: PHONE **(01442) 851134 (01442) 851328 FAX (01442) 851063**
WEBSITE www.walterswinburnracing.co.uk

1 **ADENIUM (IRE),** 4, b g Desert Style (IRE)—Kelsey Rose
2 **BEE STING,** 4, b g Selkirk (USA)—Desert Lynx (IRE)
3 **CAPE DIAMOND (IRE),** 5, b g Cape Cross (IRE)—Jemalina (USA)
4 **CONFUCHIAS (IRE),** 4, b c Cape Cross (IRE)—Schust Madame (IRE)
5 **CONSTANT CHEERS (IRE),** 5, b g Royal Applause—Juno Marlowe (IRE)
6 **EASTERN EMPEROR,** 4, ch g Halling (USA)—B Beautiful (IRE)
7 **ETAIN (IRE),** 4, b f Alhaarth (IRE)—Brogan's Well (IRE)
8 **GRAND SHOW,** 6, b g Efisio—Christine Daae
9 **HAARTH SOVEREIGN (IRE),** 4, b g Alhaarth (IRE)—Summer Queen
10 **IDESIA (IRE),** 4, b f Green Desert (USA)—Inabda (IRE)
11 **JUZILLA (IRE),** 4, b f Marju (IRE)—Mizillablack (IRE)
12 **OVERTURN (IRE),** 4, b g Barathea (IRE)—Kristal Bridge
13 **PENDULUM STAR,** 4, gr f Observatory (USA)—Pendulum
14 **PINPOINT (IRE),** 6, b g Pivotal—Alessia (GER)
15 **POLISH PRIZE,** 4, b g Polish Precedent (USA)—Forest Prize
16 **REZZAGO (USA),** 8, b g Night Shift (USA)—Western Friend (USA)
17 **SERRE CHEVALIER (IRE),** 7, b g Marju (IRE)—Ski Lodge (IRE)

MR W. R. J. SWINBURN—continued

18 **STOTSFOLD**, 5, b g Barathea (IRE)—Eliza Acton
19 **THE ALDBURY FLYER**, 5, b g Royal Applause—Fantasy Ridge
20 **VALLEY OBSERVER (FR)**, 4, ch g Observatory (USA)—Valleyrose (IRE)
21 **VELMA KELLY**, 4, b f Vettori (IRE)—Possessive Artiste
22 **VIKING SPIRIT**, 6, b g Mind Games—Dane Dancing (IRE)
23 **WHO'S THIS (IRE)**, 4, b g Xaar—Tarafiya (USA)
24 **WILLOW DANCER (IRE)**, 4, ch g Danehill Dancer (IRE)—Willowbridge (IRE)

THREE-YEAR-OLDS

25 **AMIR PASHA (UAE)**, br c Halling (USA)—Clarinda (IRE)
26 B f Cape Cross (IRE)—Annette Vallon (IRE)
27 **APOTHEOSIS**, ch c Dr Fong (USA)—Carradale
28 B c King's Best (USA)—Belle Allemande (CAN)
29 **BET NOIR (IRE)**, b f King's Best (USA)—Ivowen (USA)
30 B g Marju (IRE)—Blue Mantle (IRE)
31 **CANDY ROCK (IRE)**, b f Rock of Gibraltar (IRE)—Paquita (IRE)
32 **CARNIOLAN**, b g Royal Applause—Dancing Feather
33 B c More Than Ready (USA)—Celestic (USA)
34 **CHARMEL'S LAD**, ch g Compton Place—Fittonia (FR)
35 **CRACKING NICK (IRE)**, b g Cape Cross (IRE)—Enrich (USA)
36 **CRYPTONITE DIAMOND (USA)**, ch f Hennessy (USA)—Cryptotoo (USA)
37 **DESERT KISS**, b f Cape Cross (IRE)—Kiss And Don'tell (USA)
38 **DISTANT DIAMOND (IRE)**, b c Distant Music (USA)—La Belle Katherine (USA)
39 **ERLYDORS (IRE)**, b f Captain Rio—Moonlight Path (IRE)
40 B g Fasliyev (USA)—Fairy Contessa (IRE)
41 **FIYERO (USA)**, b g Theatrical—Wassifa
42 **FLEUR DE MONTJEU (IRE)**, b f Montjeu (IRE)—Dancing Sensation (USA)
43 **FURZEWOOD (IRE)**, b f Montjeu (IRE)—Lila
44 **GOLD AGAIN (USA)**, b f Touch Gold (USA)—Miss Insync (USA)
45 **GREYSTOKE PRINCE**, gr g Diktat—Grey Princess (IRE)
46 **HENDERSYDE (USA)**, ch c Giant's Causeway (USA)—Cimmaron Lady (USA)
47 **HEVELIUS**, b c Polish Precedent (USA)—Sharp Terms
48 **HLA TUN (USA)**, b g Johannesburg (USA)—Sophie (USA)
49 Ch f Spinning World (USA)—Kristal Bridge
50 **LA ROSA NOSTRA**, ch f Dr Fong (USA)—Rose Quantas (IRE)
51 **LA TAMBORA (USA)**, b br f Golden Missile (USA)—Nortena (USA)
52 **LEKITA**, b f Kyllachy—Tender Moment (IRE)
53 **LINDORO**, b g Marju (IRE)—Floppie (FR)
54 **LYTTON**, b c Royal Applause—Dora Carrington (IRE)
55 **MARCIA DAY**, b f Marju (IRE)—Camerlata
56 **MOONLIGHT ANGEL**, b f Kyllachy—Far Post (USA)
57 B br c Street Cry (IRE)—Object of Virtue (USA)
58 Gr ro f Act One—Oops Pettie
59 **OUTSIDE EDGE (IRE)**, b g Danetime (IRE)—Naraina (IRE)
60 **PEGASUS GOLD (USA)**, ch g Fusaichi Pegasus (USA)—Little Treasure (FR)
61 **REHABILITATION**, ch c Dr Fong (USA)—Lamees (USA)
62 **SAINTLY GAZE**, ch g Observatory (USA)—St Edith (IRE)
63 B f Street Cry (IRE)—Saintly Speaking (USA)
64 **SAM'S CROSS (IRE)**, b c Cape Cross (IRE)—Fancy Lady
65 **SHIFTING STAR (IRE)**, ch g Night Shift (USA)—Ahshado
66 **SOFT SHOE SHUFFLE (IRE)**, ch f Danehill Dancer (IRE)—Why So Silent
67 **STAYING ON (IRE)**, b c Invincible Spirit (IRE)—Lakatoi
68 **TWO LEFT FEET**, b g Groom Dancer (USA)—Sardegna
69 **VALLANI (IRE)**, ch f Vettori (IRE)—Hecuba
70 **WINTERCAST**, ch c Spinning World (USA)—Bright Hope (IRE)

TWO-YEAR-OLDS

71 B c 27/2 Fasliyev (USA)—Albavilla (Spectrum (IRE))
72 **ALECTRONA (FR)**, b f 26/3 Invincible Spirit (IRE)—Dom Pennion (Dominion) (125481)
73 B c 27/1 Royal Applause—Anna Frid (GER) (Big Shuffle (USA)) (67566)
74 Ch c 10/5 Zilzal (USA)—Annette Vallon (IRE) (Efisio)
75 B c 5/5 Bahamian Bounty—April Lee (Superpower) (27000)

MR W. R. J. SWINBURN—continued

76 B br f 4/4 Grand Slam (USA)—Baltic Sea (CAN) (Danzig (USA)) (77745)
77 B br f 13/2 Pulpit (USA)—Banksia (Marju (IRE)) (70456)
78 B c 2/5 Bahamian Bounty—
        Bombalarina (IRE) (Barathea (IRE)) (45044)   **79** Br f 1/3 Diktat—Bright Hope (IRE) (Danehill (USA))
80 B c 7/4 Polish Precedent (USA)—Camerlata (Common Grounds)
81 Ch c 9/2 Tagula (IRE)—Carpet Lady (IRE) (Night Shift (USA)) (50000)
82 **CHAMPAGNE FUTURE,** b f 27/3 Compton Place—Jade Pet (Petong) (30000)
83 Br c 5/3 Primo Valentino (IRE)—Christina's Dream (Spectrum (IRE))
84 B c 24/3 Royal Applause—Copy-Cat (Lion Cavern (USA)) (55000)
85 B f 3/3 Successful Appeal (USA)—Cup Match (Kingmambo (USA)) (24295)
86 B c 3/2 Royal Applause—Dorothea Brooke (IRE) (Dancing Brave (USA))
87 B f 19/3 Dansili—Eliza Acton (Shirley Heights)
88 B f 23/4 Danehill Dancer (IRE)—Healing Music (FR) (Bering) (37322)
89 Ch c 3/5 Danehill Dancer (IRE)—Karla June (Unfuwain (USA)) (20000)
90 Ch f 17/4 Night Shift (USA)—Koukla Mou (Keen) (18000)
91 B br f 13/1 Forestry (USA)—Lakefront (USA) (Deputy Minister (CAN)) (77745)
92 B c 14/3 Hawk Wing (USA)—Lifting (IRE) (Nordance (USA)) (40000)
93 B c 25/2 Royal Applause—Lochmaddy (Selkirk (USA)) (50000)
94 Ch c 20/3 Smart Strike (CAN)—Luminance (USA) (Deputy Minister (CAN)) (65597)
95 B c 6/4 Danehill Dancer (IRE)—Lydia Maria (Dancing Brave (USA))
96 Gr c 15/1 Dalakhani (IRE)—Majoune (FR) (Take Risks (FR)) (90000)
97 B c 19/3 Bertolini (USA)—Markova's Dance (Mark of Esteem (IRE)) (30000)
98 B c 28/3 Key of Luck (USA)—Meadow Pipit (CAN) (Meadowlake (USA)) (20591)
99 Ch c 10/4 Proud Citizen (USA)—Near Mint (Dehere (USA)) (77745)
100 B c 5/3 Green Desert (USA)—Pericardia (Petong) (68000)
101 B f 5/3 Diktat—Persian Lass (IRE) (Grand Lodge (USA))
102 B f 1/3 Noverre (USA)—Pink Sovietstaia (FR) (Soviet Star (USA)) (42000)
103 B f 5/2 Mind Games—Poppy Carew (IRE) (Danehill (USA))
104 Ch c 16/3 Mr Greeley (USA)—Really Quick (USA) (In Reality) (41302)
105 **RED HOT DESERT,** b c 9/4 Green Desert (USA)—Red Carnation (IRE) (Polar Falcon (USA)) (70000)
106 **RINKY DINK LADY (IRE),** b f 1/5 Tiger Hill (IRE)—Glady Starlet (GER) (Big Shuffle (USA)) (8364)
107 B c 25/3 Green Desert (USA)—Rise (Polar Falcon (USA)) (40000)
108 Gr ro c 13/4 Maria's Mon (USA)—Shutterbug (USA) (Deputy Minister (CAN)) (68027)
109 Ch c 24/3 Nayef (USA)—Sokoa (USA) (Peintre Celebre (USA)) (35000)
110 B c 12/4 Where Or When (IRE)—Tender Moment (IRE) (Caerleon (USA))
111 B c 19/3 King's Best (USA)—Triple Try (IRE) (Sadler's Wells (USA)) (25740)
112 B f 2/3 Polish Precedent (USA)—Triplemoon (USA) (Trempolino (USA))
113 Ch f 1/3 Sakhee (USA)—Tuppenny (Salse (USA)) (36000)
114 B c 26/1 Kyllachy—Two Step (Mujtahid (USA)) (75000)
115 B f 11/5 Cape Cross (IRE)—Why So Silent (Mill Reef (USA))

Jockey (flat): Adam Kirby. **Apprentice:** Benario De Paiva.

---

573 **MR T. J. TAAFFE, Co. Kildare**
Postal: **Portree Stables, Boston, Strappan, Co. Kildare, Irish Republic**
Contacts: **PHONE (00353) 1627 3604 FAX (00353) 1627 4231**
E-MAIL portreestables@eircom.net

1 **AN CLASACH (IRE),** 5, b g Luso—Galvina (FR)
2 **BAKER'S BRIDGE (IRE),** 7, b g King's Theatre (IRE)—Back To The Nest (IRE)
3 **BEAUTIFUL VISION (IRE),** 8, ch g Moscow Society (USA)—Rumi
4 **BORN SUPREME (IRE),** 6, b g Supreme Leader—Stormy Miss (IRE)
5 **BRAVE MO CHROI (IRE),** 6, b g Brave Act—Portree
6 **BREAKING SILENCE (IRE),** 7, b g Simply Great (IRE)—Lady of Tara
7 **CANE BRAKE (IRE),** 9, b g Sadler's Wells (USA)—Be My Hope (IRE)
8 **CHARMING GAEL (IRE),** 7, b g Charmer—Carney Native (IRE)
9 **CLOSESTHINGTOCRAZY,** 4, b c King's Theatre (IRE)—Cheyenne Squaw (IRE)
10 **DEAD SOUND (IRE),** 8, ch g Bob Back (USA)—Tonto's Girl
11 **DUNEGAN CASTLE (IRE),** 4, b g Luso—Benrue Adventure (IRE)
12 **EMOTIONAL ARTICLE (IRE),** 8, ch g Definite Article—Cairo Lady (IRE)
13 **EMOTIONAL MELODY (IRE),** 6, b m Saddlers' Hall (IRE)—Rosceen Bui (IRE)
14 **EMOTIONAL MOMENT (IRE),** 11, b g Religiously (USA)—Rosceen Bui (IRE)

MR T. J. TAAFFE—continued

15 FINGER ONTHE PULSE (IRE), 7, b g Accordion—Quinnsboro Ice (IRE)
16 FOLLOW UR INSTINCT (IRE), 4, b g Luso—Dejani (IRE)
17 GLENFIDDICK (IRE), 7, br g Scribano—Edermine Sunset (IRE)
18 GLENFINN CAPTAIN (IRE), 9, br g Alderbrook—Glenfinn Princess
19 GOGO GIZMO (IRE), 6, ch g Accordion—Saphfanna (IRE)
20 GOOD THING (IRE), 6, b g Good Thyne (USA)—Bridgequarter Lady (IRE)
21 HAPPINESS IS FREE (IRE), 5, br g Bob Back (USA)—Ennel Lady (IRE)
22 HONOURABLE RETREAT (IRE), 6, b g Luso—No Blues (IRE)
23 ICE WARRIOR (IRE), 6, b g New Frontier (USA)—Quinnsboro Ice (IRE)
24 IN THE HIGH GRASS (IRE), 7, b g In The Wings—Gale Warning (IRE)
25 INTHE NAME OF LOVE (IRE), 6, b br g Presenting—Mr K's Winterblues (IRE)
26 KESKESAY (FR), 4, b g Key of Luck (USA)—Karolo (IRE)
27 KICKING KING (IRE), 10, b g Old Vic—Fairy Blaze (IRE)
28 KING'S FAVOUR (IRE), 6, b g Luso—Strong Grove (IRE)
29 KNOCKLAYDE EURO (IRE), 4, b g Beneficial—Eurolink Sea Baby
30 KNOCKLAYDE VIC (IRE), 4, ch g Old Vic—Laughing Lesa (IRE)
31 MANHATTAN BABE (IRE), 4, b f Definite Article—Rosceen Bui (IRE)
32 MERDEKA (IRE), 8, b g Luso—Gentle Reef (IRE)
33 NINETIETH MINUTE (IRE), 5, b g Old Vic—Myown (IRE)
34 PERSIAN HUNTER (IRE), 5, b g Luso—Persian Honey (IRE)
35 ROS CLIATH (IRE), 5, b g Exit To Nowhere (USA)—Wealthy And Wise (IRE)
36 SCHINDLER'S DAME (IRE), 5, b m Oscar Schindler (IRE)—Saraemma
37 SCHINDLER'S GOLD (IRE), 6, ch g Oscar Schindler (IRE)—Saraemma
38 SHINDIG, 6, b g Classic Cliche (IRE)—Cloud Cuckoo
39 SHOULDERTOSHOULDER (IRE), 5, b g Luso—Whipa-D-Bu
40 SKETCH ON THE PAGE (IRE), 7, b g Scribano—Cool Aga (IRE)
41 SLIM PICKINGS (IRE), 9, b g Scribano—Adapan
42 SMOKING ACES (IRE), 4, b g Old Vic—Callmartel (IRE)
43 STREETSHAVENONAME (IRE), 7, b g Old Vic—Glore River (IRE)
44 SUPREME RULER (IRE), 5, b g Supreme Leader—Twin Gale (IRE)
45 TABLE TALK (IRE), 5, b g Old Vic—Fairy Blaze (IRE)
46 TEARS TO CHEERS (IRE), 4, b g Oscar (IRE)—Lantern Lark (IRE)
47 THE TALL TEXAN (IRE), 5, b g Oscar (IRE)—Smokey River
48 THURSDAY'S KNIGHT (IRE), 5, b g Oscar (IRE)—Chaparral Reef (IRE)
49 TREACLE (IRE), 7, ch g Zaffaran (USA)—Current Liability
50 TUMBLING DICE (IRE), 9, b g King's Theatre (IRE)—Eva Fay (IRE)
51 WALLS OF JERICHO (IRE), 5, b g Oscar (IRE)—Tim The Lord (IRE)
52 WATERLOO CHATEAU (IRE), 5, br g Presenting—Be My Flower (IRE)
53 WINDOW OF HOPE (IRE), 6, ch g Accordion—By All Means
54 ZAMINDAR QUEEN (IRE), 4, b f Zamindar (USA)—Fineline

---

574 **MR T. P. TATE, Tadcaster**
Postal: **Castle Farm, Hazelwood, Tadcaster, North Yorkshire, LS24 9NJ**
Contacts: PHONE (01937) 836036 FAX (01937) 530011 MOBILE (07970) 122818
E-MAIL tomtate@castlefarmstables.fsnet.co.uk WEBSITE www.tomtate.co.uk

1 CELTIC SULTAN (IRE), 4, b c Celtic Swing—Farjah (IRE) **Mrs Sylvia Clegg and Louise Worthington**
2 CHARLIE CRAB, 5, b g Tamure (IRE)—Minigale **The Ivy Syndicate**
3 CRYSTAL PRINCE, 4, b g Marju (IRE)—Crystal Ring (IRE) **D. A. Halsall**
4 DR SHARP (IRE), 8, ch g Dr Devious (IRE)—Stoned Imaculate (IRE) **The Ivy Syndicate**
5 EXCITING CAR (FR), 4, b g Sleeping Car (FR)—Union Sacree (FR) **A. R. Trotter**
6 FINAL VETO, 5, ch g Vettori (IRE)—Robin Lane **Phil Martin & Richard Longley**
7 GREEK ENVOY, 4, br g Diktat—South Shore **T. P. Tate**
8 HONEST JOHN, 4, b g Alzao (USA)—Tintera (IRE) **T. P. Tate**
9 RAUCOUS (GER), 5, b g Zinaad—Roseola (GER) **The Ivy Syndicate**
10 RUMPUS (GER), 4, ch g Medaaly—Roseola (GER) **T. P. Tate**
11 SUITS ME, 5, ch g Bertolini (USA)—Fancier Bit **D. E. Cook**
12 WALAMO (GER), 4, b g Mujahid (USA)—Walkona (IRE) **P. J. Martin**
13 WELSH EMPEROR (IRE), 9, b g Emperor Jones (USA)—Simply Times (USA) **Mrs S. Clegg**

MR T. P. TATE—continued

THREE-YEAR-OLDS

14 ADMIRALCOLLINGWOOD, b g Reel Buddy (USA)—Chocolate (IRE) **Havelock Racing 2**
15 CELTIC STRAND (IRE), b g Celtic Swing—Mur Taasha (USA) **Mrs S. L. Worthington**
16 ELK TRAIL (IRE), ch g Captain Rio—Panpipes (USA) **Mrs S. L. Worthington**
17 INSPECTOR CLOUSEAU (IRE), gr g Daylami (IRE)—Claustra (FR) **T. P. Tate**
18 LATERLY (IRE), b g Tiger Hill—La Candela (GER) **S. M. Racing**
19 PICCOLO PETE, b c Piccolo—Goes A Treat (IRE) **Havelock Racing**
20 REEL BUDDY BLAZE, ch g Reel Buddy (USA)—Hope Chest **T. P. Tate**
21 SHANAFARAHAN (IRE), b g Marju (IRE)—Sedna (FR) **The Ivy Syndicate**
22 TOTO SKYLLACHY, b c Kyllachy—Little Tramp **Phil Martin & Richard Longley**
23 WEST WITH THE WIND, b c Fasliyev (USA)—Midnight Angel (GER) **The Ivy Syndicate**

TWO-YEAR-OLDS

24 B c 20/1 Royal Applause—A Ma Guise (USA) (Silver Hawk (USA)) (31000)
25 B c 26/2 Royal Applause—Alignment (IRE) (Alzao (USA)) (27670)
26 B c 9/3 Kyllachy—All Business (Entrepreneur) (17000) **Phil Martin & Richard Longley**
27 B c 26/3 Falbrav (IRE)—Amathia (IRE) (Darshaan) (48261)
28 Ch c 18/4 Dr Fong (USA)—Arabis (Arazi (USA)) (19304)
29 DROP THE HAMMER, b f 12/4 Lucky Story (USA)—Paperweight (In The Wings) (1500) **A. Crowther**
30 FASTNET STORM (IRE), br c 23/2 Rock of Gibraltar (IRE)—
Dreams (Rainbow Quest (USA)) (22000) **The Kittywake Partnership**
31 B c 10/4 Captain Rio—Imperialist (IRE) (Imperial Frontier (USA)) (13000)
32 B c 1/4 Captain Rio—In Denial (IRE) (Maelstrom Lake) (12500)
33 KNOW BY NOW, b c 14/2 Piccolo—
Addicted To Love (Touching Wood (USA)) (52000) **Mrs Sylvia Clegg and Louise Worthington**
34 Ch c 12/3 Sendawar (IRE)—Mannsara (IRE) (Royal Academy) (13000)
35 Ch c 18/1 Compton Place—Marie La Rose (FR) (Night Shift (USA)) (26000)
36 Gr c 22/3 Graphite (IRE)—Nirvavita (FR) (Highest Honor (FR)) (14000)
37 STACEYS GIRL, b f 2/5 Timeless Times (USA)—Lavernock Lady (Don't Forget Me) (1200) **A. Crowther**
38 Br c 14/2 Diktat—Timewee (USA) (Romanov (IRE)) (12869)
39 B g 25/1 King's Best (USA)—White Rose (GER) (Platini (GER)) (28000)

Other Owners: A. Clark, Mr D. M. W. Hodgkiss, Mrs S. Hodgkiss, Mr G. R. Hunnam, Mr Richard Longley, Mr P. J. Martin.

Assistant Trainer: Hazel Tate

Jockey (flat): Micky Fenton. **Jockey (NH):** Jason Maguire.

575	**MR COLIN TEAGUE, Wingate** Postal: **Bridgefield Farm, Trimdon Lane, Station Town, Wingate, Co. Durham, TS28 5NE** Contacts: **PHONE** (01429) 837087 **MOBILE** (07967) 330929 **E-MAIL** colin.teague@btopenworld.com

1 ABBEYJADE (IRE), 4, b g Redback—In The Papers
2 ANGELOFTHENORTH, 6, b m Tomba—Dark Kristal (IRE) **Collins Chauffeur Driven Executive Cars**
3 BETTERLATETHANEVER (IRE), 4, ch g Titus Livius (FR)—First Nadia **Thomas Downey**
4 DIKTALEX (IRE), 5, b m Diktat—Kingdom Royale (IRE) **Collins Chauffeur Driven Executive Cars**
5 DUCAL REGANCY DUKE, 4, gr g Bertolini (USA)—Fun Run (USA) **Regancy Bloodstock**
6 DUCAL REGANCY LAD, 5, gr g Silver Patriarch (IRE)—Grafter (IRE) **Regancy Bloodstock**
7 DUCAL REGANCY RED, 4, ch f Bertolini (USA)—One For Jeannie **Regancy Bloodstock**
8 FORREST GUMP, 8, ch g Zilzal (USA)—Mish Mish **Collins Chauffeur Driven Executive Cars**
9 HAMBURG SPRINGER (IRE), 6, b g Charnwood Forest (IRE)—Kyra Crown (IRE) **Bosco Racing**
10 MONTE PATTINO (USA), 4, ch c Rahy (USA)—Jood (USA) **Richardson Kelly O'Gara**
11 PRINCESS CHARLMANE (IRE), 5, b m King Charlemagne (USA)—Bint Alreeys **M. N. Emmerson**
12 RONNIES GIRL, 4, b f Tobougg (IRE)—Tryptonic (FR) **Mr J. R. Bowman**
13 SPARKY VIXEN, 4, b f Mujahid (USA)—Lucy Glitters (USA) **Carlton Leisure**
14 TOMBALINA, 5, ch m Tomba—Ashkernazy (IRE) **Collins Chauffeur Driven Executive Cars**
15 VIBRATO, 6, b g Stravinsky (USA)—She's Fine (USA) **Reg Richardson & Noel Kelly**
16 VILLAGE STORM (IRE), 5, b g Mujadil (USA)—First Nadia **Thomas Downey**
17 WINGATE WARRIOR, 5, ch h Tipsy Creek (USA)—Jeethgaya (USA) **Collins Chauffeur Driven Executive Cars**

MR COLIN TEAGUE—continued

THREE-YEAR-OLDS

18 B c Cois Na Tine (IRE)—Always Daring
19 B c Forzando—Fun Run (USA)
20 B c Tomba—Trinity Hall

TWO-YEAR-OLDS

21 B c 29/3 Hunting Lion (IRE)—Always Daring (Atraf)
22 Gr f 3/1 Pursuit of Love—Fun Run (USA) (Skip Away (USA))
23 B c 19/4 Rambling Bear—Transylvania (Wolfhound (USA))

Other Owners: T. Burton, Mr W. M. Cadman, Mr S. R. James, Mr Terry Johnson, Mr T. N. Kelly, Mr P. O'Gara, Mr G. Pritchard, Mr Reg Richardson.

Amateur: Mr L. Bates.

---

576 **MR R. A. TEAL, Epsom**
Postal: **Thirty Acre Barn Stables, Shepherds Walk, Epsom, Surrey, KT18 6BX**
Contacts: **PHONE (01372) 279535 FAX (01372) 279535 MOBILE (07710) 325521**
E-MAIL rteal@thirtyacre.co.uk

1 **ALPH**, 11, b g Alflora (IRE)—Royal Birthday **Andy Chard Boris Thompson Alan Jackson**
2 **AND AGAIN (USA)**, 5, b m In The Wings—Garah **A. J. Morton**
3 **BURGUNDY**, 11, b g Lycius (USA)—Decant **Mrs S. Sheldon**
4 **ESTEEM MACHINE (USA)**, 4, b c Mark of Esteem (IRE)—Theme (IRE) **Mr M. Vickers**
5 **NORTH SOUTH DIVIDE (IRE)**, 4, b g Namid—Bush Rose **Wonforthefrog Partnership**
6 **PRINCE OF CHARM (USA)**, 4, ch g Mizzen Mast (USA)—Pretty Clear (USA) **J. R. Stephens**
7 **PURUS (IRE)**, 6, b g Night Shift (USA)—Pariana (USA) **A. J. Morton**
8 **SIMPSONS GAMBLE (IRE)**, 5, b g Tagula (IRE)—Kiva **A. C. Simpson**
9 **SIR LIAM (USA)**, 4, b c Monarchos (USA)—Tears (USA)
10 **TWILIGHT STAR (IRE)**, 4, b c Green Desert (USA)—Heavenly Whisper (IRE) **Mr G. Harris**

THREE-YEAR-OLDS

11 **HIGHLY REGAL (IRE)**, b c High Chaparral (IRE)—Regal Portrait (IRE) **A. J. Morton**
12 **PETIT PARC**, b f Bahamian Bounty—Alkarida (FR) **Mr M. Vickers**
13 **SPIRITOFTHESTORM (USA)**, b f Mizzen Mast (USA)—Southern Issue (USA) **A. J. Morton**
14 **SPIRITOFTHETIGER (USA)**, ch f Hold That Tiger (USA)—Royal Malt (IRE) **A. J. Morton**
15 **STEELE TANGO (USA)**, ch c Okawango (USA)—Waltzing Around (IRE) **The Thirty Acre Racing Partnership**

TWO-YEAR-OLDS

16 B f 20/4 Mujadil (USA)—Changari (USA) (Gulch (USA)) (30000) **A. J. Morton**
17 Ch f 24/3 Compton Place—Sophielu (Rudimentary (USA)) (2000) **A. J. Morton**

Other Owners: Mr Andy Chard, Mr A. A. W. Jackson, Mr B. Reilly, Mrs Toni Steele, Mr B. P. Thompson, Mr Darren Waterer.

---

577 **MRS D. THOMAS, Bridgend**
Postal: **Pen-Y-Lan Farm, Aberkenfig, Bridgend, Mid Glam**
Contacts: **PHONE (01656) 720254 FAX (01656) 720254 MOBILE (07989) 462130**
E-MAIL philjones1226@aol.com

1 **FINISHED ARTICLE (IRE)**, 11, b g Indian Ridge—Summer Fashion **Mrs D. Thomas**
2 **ICE CRYSTAL**, 11, b g Slip Anchor—Crystal Fountain **Mrs D. Thomas**
3 **JAZZ CITY**, 8, br g Rock City—Hullo Mary Doll **Mrs D. Thomas**
4 **VANISHING DANCER (SWI)**, 11, ch g Llandaff (USA)—Vanishing Prairie (USA) **Mrs D. Thomas**

Assistant Trainer: Miss D C Thomas

Conditional: Shane Walsh. **Amateur:** Mr Ryan Cummings.

578 MR KEITH S. THOMAS, Carlisle
Postal: **Murray Holme, Roadhead, Bewcastle, Carlisle, CA6 6PJ**
Contacts: **PHONE (01697) 748157 FAX (01697) 748159 MOBILE (07770) 462839**
E-MAIL keiththomas@equilaw.co.uk WEBSITE www.equilaw.co.uk

1 DOUBLE RUNNER, 6, b m Doubletour (USA)—Running Frau **Keith S. Thomas**
2 RUCOLINO (IRE), 8, ch g Rock Hopper—Tasmania Star **Keith S. Thomas**
3 THE FLIGHTY FRAU, 5, ch m Missed Flight—Running Frau **Ann Holt**

THREE-YEAR-OLDS

4 Ch c Roi de Rome (USA)—Running Frau **Keith S. Thomas & Ann Holt**

Assistant Trainer: Ann Holt

Jockey (NH): Gareth Thomas.

579 MR D. W. THOMPSON, Darlington
Postal: **South View Racing, Ashley Cottage, South View, Bolam, Darlington, Co. Durham, DL2 2UP**
Contacts: **PHONE (01388) 835806 (01388) 832658 FAX (01325) 835806 MOBILE (07795) 161657**
E-MAIL svr@dwthompson.co.uk WEBSITE www.dwthompson.co.uk

1 ALLORO, 4, ch g Auction House (USA)—Minette **Hiflyer Partnership**
2 4, Ch c Supreme Sound—Barn Stripper **Mr A. Graham**
3 4, Ch c Supreme Sound—Camorra **Mr A. Graham**
4 CHEERS THANK YOU (IRE), 8, b g Humbel (USA)—Turbo Run **J. A. Moore**
5 DARK PLANET, 5, ch g Singspiel (IRE)—Warning Shadows (IRE) **Mr A. Duffeild**
6 DAVIDIA (IRE), 5, b g Barathea (IRE)—Green Life **Mr A. Davis**
7 DEE JAY WELLS, 4, b g Ishiguru (USA)—Stravaig (IRE) **K. Middleton**
8 4, Ch f Minster Son—Dom One **Mr J. Greenbank**
9 FLUOREE (FR), 4, b br f Xaar—Floridene (FR) **P. J. Harle**
10 KILMORE BAY (IRE), 7, b g Karinga Bay—Becca's Rose (IRE) **The Ramp Organisation**
11 KYATHOS (GER), 7, br g Dashing Blade—Kajaana **Mr A. Duffeild**
12 LANE MARSHAL, 6, ch g Danzig Connection (USA)—Evening Falls **Mrs A. Davis**
13 PIQUE DU JOUR (FR), 5, b m Turgeon (USA)—Wackie (USA) **Mr A. Duffeild**
14 SAAMEQ (IRE), 7, b g Bahhare (USA)—Tajawuz **Mrs L. Irving**
15 SOVEREIGN STATE (IRE), 11, b g Soviet Lad (USA)—Portree **Mr D. W. Thompson**

THREE-YEAR-OLDS

16 CAUGHT IN PARADISE (IRE), b c Catcher In The Rye (IRE)—Paradis **Mr D. Morland**

TWO-YEAR-OLDS

17 B c 22/3 Tobougg (IRE)—Heavens Above (FR) (Pistolet Bleu (IRE)) (10500) **Mrs A. Suddes**

Other Owners: Mr M. A. Bissett, Mr B. Bradbury, Mrs A. Davis, Mr A. Duffield, Mr A. Graham, Mr J. Greenbank, Mr L. Irving, Mr K. Middleton, Mr J. A. Moore, Mr D. Morland, Mr P. H. Muirhead, Mr D. Patterson, Mr David W. Thompson.

Assistant Trainer: J. A. Moore

Jockey (flat): T. Hamilton. **Apprentice:** A. Elliott. **Amateur:** Mr Richard Smith.

580 MR C. W. THORNTON, Leyburn
Postal: **Dale House, Rectory Farm, Wensley, Leyburn, North Yorkshire, DL8 4HS**
Contacts: **YARD (01969) 625446 HOME (01969) 623350 FAX (01969) 623629**
MOBILE (07976) 648965
E-MAIL christopher.thornton@talk21.com WEBSITE www.chris-thornton.com & www.luxury-villa-disney.com

1 DANCE SAUVAGE, 5, ch g Groom Dancer (USA)—Peace Dance **Guy Reed**
2 DANZATRICE, 6, b m Tamure (IRE)—Miss Petronella **980 Racing**
3 FLORAL MAGIC, 5, b m Alflora (IRE)—Auntie Alice **Mr K. H. Rainbow**
4 FLORENTINO, 4, b f Efisio—Sirene Bleu Marine (USA) **Guy Reed**
5 FLYING SPRAY, 4, b br g Emperor Fountain—April Rain **Mr C. W. Thornton**
6 FRESCHEZZA, 6, b m Tamure (IRE)—Minigale **D. B. Dennison**

MR C. W. THORNTON—continued

7 **JAYNE DEAN,** 4, b f Rock City—Otterington Girl **Mrs D. S. Wilkinson**
8 **LETS ROLL,** 7, b g Tamure (IRE)—Miss Petronella **A. Crute & Partners**
9 **RODEO,** 5, ch g Pivotal—Flossy **Guy Reed**
10 **ROLL EM OVER,** 5, b m Tamure (IRE)—Miss Petronella **Mrs D. S. Wilkinson**
11 **ROLL OF DRUMS,** 6, b m Tamure (IRE)—Mossfield **Mrs D. S. Wilkinson**
12 **SEA VENTURE (IRE),** 6, b g Sea Raven (IRE)—Good Highlights (IRE) **Mr P. I. Herman & Mr C. N. Herman**
13 **SMARTIES PARTY,** 5, b m Tamure (IRE)—Maries Party **Team 30**
14 **SPRINKLER,** 5, b m Emperor Fountain—Ryewater Dream **Mrs F. R. Wilson**
15 **TAMMY,** 5, b m Tamure (IRE)—Heather Honey **The Rollettes**
16 **TIMARA QUEEN,** 4, b f Tamure (IRE)—Mossfield **Mr C. W. Thornton**
17 **VESUVIO,** 4, br g Efisio—Polo **Guy Reed**

THREE-YEAR-OLDS

18 **BRAVE OPTIMIST (IRE),** b f Diktat—Maine Lobster (USA) **Mr J. H. Davey**
19 **ETERNAL OPTIMIST (IRE),** b f Bahri (USA)—Shore Lark (USA) **Mr J. H. Davey**
20 **MATHOOL (IRE),** b f Alhaarth (IRE)—Mathaayl (USA) **D. B. Dennison**

TWO-YEAR-OLDS

21 **PETELLA,** b f 31/3 Tamure (IRE)—Miss Petronella (Petoski) **A. Crute & Susan Davies**
22 **SPRUZZO,** b g 28/5 Emperor Fountain—Ryewater Dream (Touching Wood (USA)) (7800) **Racing 980**

Other Owners: Mr. J. Attridge, Mr. G. Bloom, Mr. O. Burrows, Mr A. Crute, Mr. A. Davies, MR. M. Denbow, Mr. G. Fowler, Mr. T. Garry, Mr. E. Gray, Mrs V. Gregson, Mrs. K. Hardie, Mr P.I. Herman, Mr C. N. Herman, Mr. A. Lacey, Mr Gavin Renton, Mr. M. Ross, Mr. J. Russell, Mr. S. Sands, Mr. H. Sheldon, Mr C. W. Thornton, Mr. J. Tomlinson, Mr J. M. Tozer, Mr M. D. Tozer, Mr. T. Wooldridge, Mr Karl Zanft.

Jockey (flat): T. Eaves, Dean McKeown. **Jockey (NH):** R. McGrath, F. Keniry. **Conditional:** G. Berridge.

---

581 **MRS A. M. THORPE, Carmarthen**
Postal: Felinfach, Bronwydd, Carmarthen, Carmarthenshire, SA33 6BE
Contacts: PHONE (01267) 253595 or (01267) 253783 MOBILE (07795) 832004 or (07901) 528500
E-MAIL amthorpe@racingstables.freeserve.co.uk

1 **BAYBERRY KING (USA),** 5, b g Lear Fan (USA)—Myrtle **D. Jenkins**
2 **CLEYMOR HOUSE (IRE),** 10, ch g Duky—Deise Lady **Mrs A. M. Thorpe**
3 **CUSP,** 8, b m Pivotal—Bambolona **West Wales Racing Club**
4 **DILMOUN (IRE),** 6, b g Darshaan—Mannakea (USA) **Lindie Donaldson & Regan King**
5 **DISHDASHA (IRE),** 6, b g Desert Prince (IRE)—Counterplot (IRE) **Tristar**
6 **DOONIGAN (IRE),** 4, b g Val Royal (FR)—Music In My Life (IRE) **Mrs A. M. Thorpe**
7 **DOUBLE BRANDY,** 4, gr f Alflora (IRE)—Cheeky Mare **P. J. Hughes Developments Ltd**
8 **FULL OF ZEST,** 6, ch m Pivotal—Tangerine **Clear Racing**
9 **GEM MILL (IRE),** 6, b g Exit To Nowhere—Cara Gail (IRE) **Mrs J. Fleetham**
10 **GOLD GUN (USA),** 6, b g Seeking The Gold (USA)—Possessive Dancer **Tristar**
11 **HENRY'S PRIDE (IRE),** 8, ch g Old Vic—Hightown Girl (IRE) **P. J. Hughes Developments Ltd**
12 **IL PENSEROSO (IRE),** 10, br g Norwich—Railstown Phairy (IRE) **Tristar**
13 **INMATE (IRE),** 7, b g Needle Gun—Highland Spirit **J. Rogers**
14 **INSIGNIA (IRE),** 6, b g Royal Applause—Amathea (FR) **Clear Racing**
15 **JIM BOBS GIRL (IRE),** 7, b m Flemensfirth—Sinfonietta **Mrs A. M.Thorpe**
16 **JOROBADEN (FR),** 8, gr g Poliglote—Mercalle (FR) **P. J. Hughes Developments Ltd**
17 **LIBERIA (FR),** 9, b g Kadalko (FR)—Unica Iv (FR) **Mrs T. J. Stone-Brown**
18 **LIMESTONE BOY (IRE),** 6, b br g Beneficial—Limestone Lady (IRE) **P. J. Hughes Developments Ltd**
19 **LIT UP (IRE),** 5, ch g Fantastic Light (USA)—High Spirited **Mrs J. Fleetham**
20 **MAXIMINUS,** 8, b g The West (USA)—Candarela **Three A's Caravans**
21 **ME AND PAT (IRE),** 7, b g Supreme Leader—Martins Times (IRE) **Tristar**
22 **MODEL SON (IRE),** 10, b g Leading Counsel (USA)—Miss Mutley **P. J. Hughes Developments Ltd**
23 **OVERCLEAR,** 6, b g Overbury (IRE)—Callope (USA) **Exe Valley Racing**
24 **PRINCE VECTOR,** 6, b g Vettori—The In-Laws (IRE) **Whistlejacket Partnership**
25 **PUBLIC ESTEEM (IRE),** 7, b br g Carroll House—Spindle Tree **P. J. Hughes Developments Ltd**
26 **RIO (IRE),** 6, ch g Namid—Renashaan (FR) **Mrs A. M. Thorpe**
27 **ROCKYS GIRL,** 6, b m Piccolo—Lady Rockstar **Formula One Racing**
28 **SCARLET MIX (FR),** 7, gr g Linamix (FR)—Scarlet Raider (USA) **D. Jenkins**
29 **SCHINDLERS SON (IRE),** 7, ch g Oscar Schindler—Belle Perk (IRE) **Mrs A. M. Thorpe**
30 **SHALATI PRINCESS,** 7, b m Bluegrass Prince (IRE)—Shalati (FR) **T. Reffell**
31 **SONAR SOUND (GER),** 4, b g Slickly (FR)—Samothrace (IRE) **Lindie Donaldson & Regan King**

MRS A. M. THORPE—continued

32 TALKINGSTICK (IRE), 6, br m Bob Back (USA)—Shaunies Lady (IRE) A. T. Bailey
33 TAMPA BOY (IRE), 8, b h Montjeu (IRE)—Tirolean Dance (IRE) Mrs A. M. Thorpe
34 TUTOR (IRE), 4, ch g Dr Fong (USA)—Glandore (IRE) Mrs A. M. Thorpe
35 VALIANT SHADOW (GER), 6, b g Winged Love (IRE)—Vangelis Tristar
36 WOLFMAN, 6, ch g Wolfhound (USA)—Madam Millie Mrs A. M. Thorpe

Other Owners: Miss L. M. Donaldson, Mr L. H. Evans, Mrs T. Evans, Mr B. Greening, Mr W. Jenks, Mr H. Jones, Mr Regan King, Ms M. M. Richardson, Mr Mike Rowe, Mrs Joyce Taylor, Mr J. Thorpe, Mr Gwyn Williams, Mrs June Williams, Dr D. Woodhouse, Mr J. Woodhouse, Mr A. Yorke.

Conditional: P. J. Tolman. **Amateur:** Miss Jodie Hughes.

---

582 MR C. L. TIZZARD, Sherborne
Postal: **Venn Farm, Milborne Port, Sherborne, Dorset, DT9 5RA**
Contacts: **PHONE (01963) 250598 FAX (01963) 250598 MOBILE (07976) 778656**

1 AMBLE FORGE (IRE), 6, b g Needle Gun (IRE)—La Mode Lady Robert and Sarah Tizzard
2 ARE YOU THERE, 7, br m Presidium—Scoffera C. Tizzard
3 AVEC MOI CE SOIR (IRE), 5, b g Marignan (USA)—Claregary (IRE) Singing & Dancing Racing
4 BLAKENEY COAST (IRE), 11, b g Satco (FR)—Up To More Trix (IRE) The Jam Boys
5 BOB BOB BOBBIN, 9, gr g Bob Back (USA)—Absalom's Lady Mrs S. L. Tizzard
6 BRING ME SUNSHINE (IRE), 7, ch g Alderbrook—Hilarys Pet Robert and Sarah Tizzard
7 CAPTAIN MARLON (IRE), 7, b g Supreme Leader—Marlonette (IRE) Grass Roots Racing
8 CHILLA CILLA, 5, ch m Glacial Storm (USA)—Priscilla H. T. Cole
9 CLASSIC CLOVER, 8, ch g Classic Cliche (IRE)—National Clover John & Heather Snook
10 CLIFDEN BOY (IRE), 6, br g Anshan—Pharandom (IRE) The Jam Boys
11 DO THE LOCOMOTION (IRE), 6, b g Presenting—Torekulu Brocade Racing
12 ENROBLIM TROP (IRE), 6, b g Supreme Leader—Crafty Women (IRE) The Con Club
13 FLASHY CONQUEST, 6, b g El Conquistador—Craberi Flash Foot D. V. Stevens
14 FLIGHT LEADER (IRE), 8, b g Supreme Leader—Stormy Petrel (IRE) John & Heather Snook
15 GO JOHNNY GO (IRE), 6, b g Moonax (IRE)—The Helmet (IRE) Singing & Dancing Racing
16 HEY BIG SPENDER (IRE), 5, b g Rudimentary (USA)—Jims Monkey Brocade Racing
17 HYDROMATIC (IRE), 8, b g Sovereign Water (FR)—Missile Lady Miss J. Tizzard
18 IRONSIDE (IRE), 9, b g Mister Lord (USA)—The Helmet (IRE) D. J. Hinks
19 JOE LIVELY (IRE), 9, b g Flemensfirth (USA)—Forest Gale R. E. Dimond
20 JUSTABOUT, 5, br g Classic Cliche (IRE)—Dubacilla Brocade Racing
21 LEADING AUTHORITY (IRE), 7, br g Supreme Leader—Bonnie Thynes (IRE) Robert and Sarah Tizzard
22 LORD KILLESHANRA (IRE), 9, br g Mister Lord (USA)—Killeshandra Lass (IRE) G. F. Gingell
23 LORD WEST, 7, ch g The West (USA)—Flair Lady A. P. Hedditch
24 MISS PENFOLD, 6, b m Emperor Fountain—Speckyfoureyes A. J. M. Trowbridge
25 MISTER QUASIMODO, 8, b g Busy Flight—Dubacilla J. M. Dare, T. Hamlin, J. W. Snook
26 NESOTHO (FR), 7, b g Lesotho (USA)—Epopee II (FR) A. G. Fear
27 NOUGAT DE L'ISLE (FR), 7, b g Kadalko (FR)—Ceres de L'isle (FR) K S B Bloodstock
28 PASS ME A DIME, 9, b g Past Glories—Hand Out Cherry Bolberry Partnership
29 RUDIVALE (IRE), 6, ch g Rudimentary (USA)—Conjure Up (IRE) Blackmore Vale Syndicate
30 SERGEANT HARPER (IRE), 5, br g Insan (USA)—Quelle Femme (IRE) K S B Bloodstock
31 SONG SUNG BLUE (IRE), 5, b g Supreme Leader—Greenflag Princess (IRE) Singing & Dancing Racing
32 SOU'WESTER, 8, b g Fleetwood (IRE)—Mayfair Robert and Sarah Tizzard
33 THE JAZZ MUSICIAN (IRE), 6, b g Tiraaz (USA)—Royal Well The Jazz Club
34 TRIGGERNOMETRY, 7, b g Double Trigger (IRE)—Dubacilla The Butterwick Syndicate
35 WISE MEN SAY (IRE), 6, br g Grand Plaisir (IRE)—Queen Alda Singing & Dancing Racing
36 WOTASHAMBLES (IRE), 7, b g Shambo—Rent Day Mrs K Harvey & Mr S J Kail

Other Owners: Mrs S. J. Biggins, Mr K. W. Biggins, W. J. Brockway, Mr G. R. Broom, Mrs A. E. M. Broom, Mr A. J. Callow, J. M. Dare, R. Dibble, T. Hamlin, Mrs K. Harvey, Mr M. G. Hatcher, Mr E. J. Highnam, Mrs C. M. Hinks, Mr S. J. Kail, Mrs P. O. Perry, C. Raymond, J. W. Snook, Mrs H. A. Snook, R. G. Tizzard, Mrs P. T. Tizzard, Mr E. R. Vickery.

Assistant Trainer: Mrs K. Gingell

Jockey (NH): J. Tizzard.

583 MR D. M. TODHUNTER, Penrith

Postal: The Park, Orton, Penrith, Cumbria, CA10 3SD
Contacts: PHONE (01539) 624314 FAX (01539) 624811 MOBILE (07976) 440082
WEBSITE www.martintodhunter.co.uk

1 BAAWRAH, 7, ch g Cadeaux Genereux—Kronengold (USA) **J. D. Gordon**
2 BEN NELLY (IRE), 7, b g Taipan (IRE)—Cothu Na Slaine (IRE) **B. Dunn**
3 BENNY THE BUS, 6, b g Komaite (USA)—Amy Leigh (IRE) **P. G. Airey**
4 BOG OAK (IRE), 8, b g Accordion—Miss Amy (IRE) **The Cartmel Race Club**
5 CALCULAITE, 7, b g Komaite (USA)—Miss Calculate **Highbank Syndicate**
6 COZWECAN (IRE), 5, br m Blueprint (IRE)—Gale Spring (IRE) **The Coz Syndicate**
7 CRATHORNE (IRE), 8, b g Alzao (USA)—Shirley Blue (IRE) **The Centaur Group Partnership IX**
8 DIAMOND MICK, 8, ch g Pivotal—Miss Poll Flinders **M. S. Borders Racing Club 2**
9 EXIT FORTY FOUR (IRE), 6, br g Exit To Nowhere (USA)—De Derri (IRE) **K. Fitzsimons**
10 GRAND UNION (IRE), 4, b g Bob Back (USA)—Queens Mark (IRE) **Sir Robert Ogden C.B.E., LLD**
11 JUST FOR MEN (IRE), 8, gr g Glacial Storm (USA)—Regents Ballerina (IRE) **Sir Robert Ogden C.B.E., LLD**
12 JUST IN DEBT (IRE), 12, b br g Montelimar (USA)—No Debt **Gill & Bill Hazeldean**
13 KILMACKILLOGE, 9, b g Lancastrian—Garjun (IRE) **S. Currie**
14 KIT CARSON (IRE), 8, b g Dr Massini (IRE)—Roses Niece (IRE) **B. Dunn**
15 LE ROUGE FATAL (FR), 6, ch g Bateau Rouge—Fatal Attraction (IRE) **J. R. Callow**
16 LONGDALE, 10, b g Primitive Rising (USA)—Gunnerdale **David Curr, Donald Ponsonby, Dr Will Ponsonby**
17 MONTCHARA (IRE), 5, b g Montjeu (IRE)—Mochara **Gill & Bill Hazeldean**
18 MY ARCH, 6, b g Silver Patriarch (IRE)—My Desire **Mr J. D. Spensley & Mrs M. A. Spensley**
19 NEVSKY BRIDGE, 6, b m Soviet Star (USA)—Pontressina (USA) **The Carlisle Cavaliers**
20 ROYAL GAME, 6, b g Vettori (IRE)—Ground Game **The Hexham Handicappers**
21 RUSSIAN FLAG (FR), 5, b g Kingsalsa (USA)—Nousa Nousa (FR) **Sir Robert Ogden C.B.E., LLD**
22 SADDLERS' SUPREME (IRE), 6, b m Saddlers' Hall (IRE)—
Festival Leader (IRE) **The Northern Echo Partnership**
23 SILVER JACK (IRE), 10, gr g Roselier (FR)—Consharon (IRE) **Mrs J. Batey**
24 STYLISH SHOT (IRE), 4, b g Desert Style (IRE)—Lady Sharp Shot (IRE) **The Surf & Turf Partnership**
25 TELL HENRY (IRE), 8, ch g Broken Hearted—Valleymay (IRE) **Don't Tell Henry**
26 TEN CARAT, 8, ch g Grand Lodge (USA)—Emerald (IRE) **Ian Hall Racing**
27 TEVIOT BRIG, 7, b g Weldnaas (USA)—Here Comes Tibby **Mrs S. J. Matthews**
28 THAT'S RHYTHM (FR), 8, b g Pistolet Bleu (IRE)—Madame Jean (FR) **Sir Robert Ogden C.B.E., LLD**
29 WALDO WINCHESTER (IRE), 5, b g Second Empire (IRE)—Zeddaana (FR) **Dig Deep Racing**

Other Owners: Mrs S. E. Barclay, Mr C. Bewick, P.M. Clarkson, Mr A. J. Cork, Mr M. Croan, David Curr, Mrs R. L. Elliot, J. W. Hazeldean, Ms G. Hazeldean, Mr S. G. Joicey, H. R. Kerslake, Dr W. J. C. Ponsonby, Mr P. W. D. Ponsonby, K Sobey, Mrs M. A. Spensley, Mr J. D. Spensley, S. T. Uprichard, Mrs I. M. Wainwright, Mr M. A. Wainwright.

Jockey (NH): B. Harding, G. Lee.

---

584 MR J. A. R. TOLLER, Newmarket

Postal: Eve Lodge Stables, Hamilton Road, Newmarket, Suffolk, CB8 0NY
Contacts: PHONE (01638) 668918 FAX (01638) 669384 MOBILE (07887) 942234
E-MAIL james.toller@btconnect.com

1 AFFRETTANDO (IRE), 4, b g Danetime (IRE)—Trading Aces **Lady Sophia Topley**
2 BASSINET (USA), 4, b f Stravinsky—Berceau (USA) **J. R. Drew**
3 PAGAN BELIEF, 4, b g Fraam—Au Contraire **The Gap Partnership**
4 PARADISE DANCER (IRE), 4, b f Danehill Dancer (IRE)—Pintada de Fresco (FR) **Dr B. Drew & J. Drew**
5 PERFECT TREASURE (IRE), 5, ch m Night Shift (USA)—Pitrizza (IRE) **J. R. Drew**
6 SECRET NIGHT, 5, gr m Dansili—Night Haven **Hants & Herts**
7 WOODNOOK, 5, b m Cadeaux Genereux—Corndavon (USA) **Mrs J. M. M. Scott**

THREE-YEAR-OLDS

8 BAHAMIAN BLISS, b f Bahamian Bounty—Fragrance **Ms F. R. E. Dakers**
9 BURNBRAKE, b c Mujahid (USA)—Duena **Michael E. Wates**
10 CRABAPPLE, b f Alhaarth (IRE)—Crodelle (IRE)
11 DANCING BELLE, b f Fasliyev (USA)—May Ball **Goldrock Partnership**
12 DANISH ART (IRE), b c Danehill Dancer (IRE)—Lady Ounavarra (IRE) **M. R. Green**
13 DORIC LADY, b f Kyllachy—Tanasie **Buckingham Thoroughbreds I**
14 GLOBAL GLORY (IRE), ch c Spinning World (USA)—Crimson Glory **P. C. J. Dalby & R. Schuster**
15 KENTON STREET, ch c Compton Place—Western Applause **Byculla Thoroughbreds**
16 PERSONDY (IRE), b f Desert Style (IRE)—Sharadja (IRE) **J. White**

MR J. A. R. TOLLER—continued

17 B br f Tiznow (USA)—Quelle Affaire (USA) **G. B. Partnership**
18 RIVER NAIAD, ch f Nayef (USA)—Waqood (USA) **G. B. Partnership**
19 SHINDY (FR), b f Intikhab (USA)—Sheriya (USA) **P. C. J. Dalby & R. Schuster**

TWO-YEAR-OLDS

20 Ch c 17/4 Lucky Story (USA)—Au Contraire (Groom Dancer (USA)) (17000) **M. A. Whelton**
21 CAKE STAND, b c 10/5 Haafhd—Galette (Caerleon (USA)) (20000) **P. C. J. Dalby & R. Schuster**
22 Br c 17/4 Bachelor Duke (USA)—Complication (Compton Place) **Julia Staughton**
23 B c 19/3 Bachelor Duke (USA)—Creme Caramel (USA) (Septieme Ciel (USA)) (20000) **M. R. Green**
24 B c 7/4 Orpen (USA)—Pagan Princess (Mujtahid (USA)) **G. Materna**
25 PEACE IN PARADISE (IRE), b f 27/1 Dubai Destination (USA)—
Paola Maria (Daylami (IRE)) (9000) **Michael E. Wates**

Other Owners: Mr P. R. Anders, Miss Catherine Bates, Mr R. G. W. Brown, Mr N. J. Charrington, Mr James Corden, Mr P. C. J. Dalby, Dr Bridget Drew, Ms Pippa Drew, Mr N. R. R. Drew, Mrs Sue Glasgow, Mr Tom Goff, Mrs A. M. Goor, Mr J. A. Grabham, Mr M. G. H. Heald, Mrs J. E. Lee-Smith, Mr G. D. P Materna, Mr D. A. Poole, Mr Richard Schuster, Mrs David Staughton, Mr L. Straszewski, Mr E. B. C. Van Cutsem, Mr Davies Webb, Mrs Jacqueline Williams.

Jockey (flat): A. Munro, E. Ahern, R. Havlin.

585 MR M. H. TOMPKINS, Newmarket
Postal: **Flint Cottage Stables, Rayes Lane, Newmarket, Suffolk, CB8 7AB**
Contacts: **PHONE (01638) 661434 FAX (01638) 668107 MOBILE (07799) 663339**
E-MAIL mht@marktompkins.co.uk WEBSITE www.marktompkins.co.uk

1 ASTROANGEL, 4, b f Groom Dancer (USA)—Nutmeg (IRE) **Mystic Meg Limited**
2 ASTROLIBRA, 4, b f Sakhee (USA)—Optimistic **Mystic Meg Limited**
3 BABODANA, 8, ch h Bahamian Bounty—Daanat Nawal **M. P. Bowring**
4 DON'TCALLMEGINGER (IRE), 5, ch g Fruits of Love (USA)—Scotia Rose **Trott Knight Jenkins**
5 FORCE GROUP (IRE), 4, b g Invincible Spirit (IRE)—Spicebird (IRE) **The Force Group Of Companies Ltd**
6 FOUR MIRACLES, 4, b f Vettori (IRE)—North Kildare (USA) **Pat Swayne & Partners**
7 GEE DEE NEN, 5, b g Mister Baileys—Special Beat **Mr D. P. Noblett**
8 GEORGE HENSON (IRE), 4, b br g Desert Style (USA)—Alexandria (IRE) **D. G. Tompkins**
9 INCHPAST, 7, ch g Inchinor—Victor Ludorum **Marcoe Racing Welwyn**
10 KINSYA, 5, ch g Mister Baileys—Kimono (IRE) **Roalco Ltd**
11 MARVO, 4, b c Bahamian Bounty—Mega (IRE) **The Marvo Partnership**
12 MIKAO (IRE), 7, b g Tagula (IRE)—Oumaladia (IRE) **Mr Ben & Mrs Carole Allen**
13 RAJAYOGA, 7, ch g Kris—Optimistic **Mystic Meg Limited**
14 RIVER DEUCE, 4, b g Zaha (CAN)—Light Hand **R. M. Levitt**
15 SMOKEY OAKEY (IRE), 4, b c Tendulkar (USA)—Veronica **Judi Dench & Mr Bryan Agar**
16 SPELL CASTING (USA), 5, b g Kingmambo (USA)—Copper Play (USA) **Mrs A. M. Tompkins**
17 STEENBERG (IRE), 9, ch g Flying Spur (AUS)—Kip's Sister **Miss C. L. Hollest**
18 TOP TIGER, 4, b c Mtoto—Topatori (USA) **C. Tremewan**
19 TOPARUDI, 7, b g Rudimentary (USA)—Topatori (IRE) **M. P. Bowring**
20 TREW STYLE, 6, ch g Desert King (IRE)—Southern Psychic (USA) **Russell Trew Ltd**
21 WHITE MOSS (IRE), 4, b f Peintre Celebre (USA)—Saint Ann (USA) **Mr & Mrs G. Middlebrook**
22 YOSSI (IRE), 4, b g Montjeu (IRE)—Raindancing (IRE) **R. D. Trew**

THREE-YEAR-OLDS

23 ALAN DEVONSHIRE, br c Mtoto—Missed Again **Russell Trew Ltd**
24 ASTRODONNA, ch f Carnival Dancer—Mega (IRE) **Mystic Meg Limited**
25 AZURE MIST, ch f Bahamian Bounty—Inquirendo (USA) **Mr D. P. Noblett**
26 BELLA MEDICI, ch f Medicean—Missouri **Carole & Ben Allen**
27 BENEDICT SPIRIT (IRE), b c Invincible Spirit (IRE)—Kathy Caerleon (IRE) **Miss F. L. Corrigan**
28 BLIMEY O'RILEY (IRE), b c Kalanisi (IRE)—Kafayef (USA) **Mr T. J. Benton**
29 BLUE ADMIRAL, ch g Fleetwood (IRE)—Poly Blue (IRE) **Roalco Ltd**
30 BOWDER STONE (IRE), b c Rock of Gibraltar (IRE)—Ghita (IRE) **Mr & Mrs G. Middlebrook**
31 CREATIVE (IRE), b g Acclamation—Pride of Pendle **Newmarket All Stars**
32 FORCE TRADITION (IRE), ch g Traditionally (USA)—Kind of Loving **The Force Group Of Companies Ltd**
33 FORTUNES MAID (IRE), b f Raise A Grand (IRE)—Where's The Money **Maggie Gallop & Partners**
34 HERE AND HOW, b f Where Or When (IRE)—Qilin (IRE) **I. C. Lochhead**
35 INDIAN SKIPPER (IRE), b c Indian Danehill (USA)—Rosy Lydgate **Roalco Ltd**
36 KURIYAMA (IRE), ch c Raise A Grand (IRE)—Gobolino **Carole & Ben Allen**
37 LOCUM, ch g Dr Fong (USA)—Exhibitor (USA) **Ray Smith & Partners**

MR M. H. TOMPKINS—continued

38 **LOUGH DIVER (IRE)**, b g Act One—Spicebird (IRE) **Sir Thomas Pilkington**
39 **MYSTERY STAR (IRE)**, ch c Kris Kin (USA)—Mystery Hill (USA) **J. Brenchley**
40 **NO RULES**, b c Fraam—Golden Daring (IRE) **Raceworld Thoroughbreds**
41 **PEGGLE**, b f Tobougg (IRE)—Grove Dancer **David Morgan & Partners**
42 **SERGEANT SHARPE**, ch g Cadeaux Genereux—Halcyon Daze **Miss C. L. Hollest**
43 **SLEEPING**, b f Mujahid (USA)—Tenpence **Dullingham Park Stud**
44 **SOGGY DOLLAR**, ch g Bahamian Bounty—Ninia (USA) **Lordship Stud 2**
45 **SONNY SAM (IRE)**, b g Black Sam Bellamy (IRE)—Purple Risks (FR) **M. F. Browne**
46 **TEVEZ**, b c Sakhee (USA)—Sosumi **Sakal Family**
47 **THE GATEKEEPER**, b c Mujahid (USA)—Tiempo **Mrs S. Ashby**
48 **TORTOLA (IRE)**, ch c Cadeaux Genereux—Slipper **Lordship Stud 2**
49 **TRAWLERMAN (IRE)**, b c High Chaparral (IRE)—Forest Lair **J. Brenchley**

TWO-YEAR-OLDS

50 B c 23/2 Hawkeye (IRE)—Alycus (USA) (Atticus (USA)) (11000)
51 **ASTROBRAVA**, ch f 28/2 Falbrav (IRE)—Nutmeg (IRE) (Lake Coniston (IRE)) **Mystic Meg Limited**
52 **ASTROLEO**, ch c 1/3 Groom Dancer (USA)—Astrolove (IRE) (Bigstone (IRE)) (9000) **Mystic Meg Limited**
53 B f 30/1 Where Or When (IRE)—Astromancer (USA) (Silver Hawk (USA)) (3500)
54 **BERTIE SMALLS**, b c 29/1 Xaar—Largo (IRE) (Selkirk (USA)) (12000) **The Grass Partnership**
55 **BRUSHING**, ch f 9/3 Medicean—Seasonal Blossom (IRE) (Fairy King (USA)) (10000) **Dullingham Park Stud**
56 **CALL IT ON**, ch c 11/4 Raise A Grand (IRE)—
                                     Birthday Present (Cadeaux Genereux) (23165) **GPD Investments (Uk) Ltd**
57 **DAREDEVIL DAN**, b c 21/3 Golden Snake (USA)—Tiempo (King of Spain) **Dullingham Park Stud**
58 **DAZINSKI**, ch c 13/2 Sulamani (IRE)—Shuheb (Nashwan (USA)) (20000) **Mrs B. M. Lockey**
59 **DERRINGBAY (IRE)**, b c 16/4 Mull of Kintyre (USA)—
                                     Rustle In The Wind (Barathea (IRE)) (7721) **Mrs B. M. Lockey**
60 **DRUM DRAGON**, b f 28/5 Beat Hollow—Qilin (IRE) (Second Set (IRE)) **I. C. Lochhead**
61 B f 2/3 Hernando (FR)—Dulcinea (Selkirk (USA)) **Dullingham Park Stud**
62 **FINGER SPIN**, b f 17/3 Vettori (IRE)—Light Hand (Star Appeal) **R. M. Levitt**
63 B c 11/4 Alhaarth (IRE)—High Barn (Shirley Heights)
64 **INTIKAMA (IRE)**, ch f 2/3 Intikhab (USA)—
                                     Really Gifted (IRE) (Cadeaux Genereux) (11904) **Vallance, John & Kelly**
65 **JACOBITE PRINCE (IRE)**, b c 28/3 Chevalier (IRE)—Kind Gesture (IRE) (Alzao (USA))
66 **KHAYAR (IRE)**, b c 11/4 Refuse To Bend (IRE)—Khatela (IRE) (Shernazar) (26000) **Mrs Sallie Lloyd**
67 Ch f 22/2 Traditionally (USA)—Kind of Loving (Diesis) (2573)
68 B f 3/5 Kheleyf (USA)—Kiva (Indian Ridge) (9330) **M. A. W. Winter**
69 Br c 14/3 Indian Haven—Lady Cinders (IRE) (Dance of Life (USA)) (34748) **M. H. Tompkins**
70 Ch f 29/3 Spartacus (IRE)—Lauretta Blue (IRE) (Bluebird (USA)) (6112) **M. H. Tompkins**
71 **MOON LIGHTNING (IRE)**, b c 18/3 Desert Prince (IRE)—
                                     Moon Tango (IRE) (Last Tycoon) (12869) **Mr D. P. Noblett**
72 **MT KINTYRE (IRE)**, b c 16/3 Mull of Kintyre (USA)—
                                     Nihonpillow Mirai (IRE) (Zamindar (USA)) (45044) **Mrs G. A. E. Smith**
73 **MY GIRL JODE**, ch f 27/3 Haafhd—Brush Strokes (Cadeaux Genereux) **Mrs G. A. E. Smith**
74 Ch f 31/3 Tagula (IRE)—Nicea (IRE) (Dominion) (10939)
75 **OLAUDAH EQUIANO**, ch c 6/5 Dubai Destination (USA)—
                                     Magongo (Be My Chief (USA)) (22000) **The Countess of Halifax**
76 **ORTHOLOGY (IRE)**, b c 5/4 Kalanisi (IRE)—Al Shakoor (Barathea (IRE)) (13000)
77 **PREMIER SUPERSTAR**, ch f 18/1 Bertolini (USA)—Absolve (USA) (Diesis) (9008) **Mr R. M. Jones**
78 **ROYAL ACCLAIM**, b f 28/1 Royal Applause—Movie Queen (Danehill (USA)) **J. H. Ellis**
79 Gr c 26/2 Indian Haven—Sensuality (IRE) (Idris (IRE))
80 **SNOOZING**, b f 9/3 Where Or When (IRE)—Tenpence (Bob Back (USA)) **Dullingham Park Stud**
81 Ch f 17/1 Medicean—Sosumi (Be My Chief (USA)) **Sakal Family**
82 **TOP TINKER**, b c 29/4 Vettori (IRE)—Topatori (IRE) (Topanoora) **M. P. Bowring**

Other Owners: Miss Christina Blockley, Mr N. Davey, Mr M. V. Deegan, Mr Tony Fitzpatrick, Mr P. S. Green, Mr Kevin Hodges, Mr W. J. Jones, Mr C. Lockey, Mrs P. M. Rickett, Mrs Sonia Rogers, Mr P. Spencer, Mr R. J. Thornalley.

Assistant Trainer: Steven Avery

Apprentice: Nicol Polli, Ashley Morgan.

586 MISS J. R. TOOTH, Upper Lambourn
Postal: **Saxon Gate, Upper Lambourn, Hungerford, Berkshire, RG17 8QH**
Contacts: PHONE **(01488) 72712** FAX **(01488) 72716** MOBILE **(07767) 641263**
E-MAIL **j.tooth@btconnect.com**

1 **FIZZLEPHUT (IRE)**, 6, b g Indian Rocket—Cladantom (IRE) **Warwick Racing Partnership**
2 **FOXY DIPLOMAT**, 4, b g Foxhound (USA)—Diplomatist **R. C. Tooth**
3 **GULF (IRE)**, 9, ch g Persian Bold—Broken Romance (IRE) **R. C. Tooth**
4 **PSYCHIATRIST**, 7, ch g Dr Devious (IRE)—Zahwa **Miss J. R. Tooth**
5 **PULSE**, 10, b g Salse (USA)—French Gift **R. C. Tooth**
6 **TRISKAIDEKAPHOBIA**, 5, b g Bertolini—Seren Teg **Mr Raymond Tooth & Mr Steve Gilbey**
7 **TRIUMPHUS**, 4, b g Lear Spear (USA)—Sarcita **R. C. Tooth**
8 **WHISTLER**, 11, ch g Selkirk (USA)—French Gift **Warwick Racing Partnership**

THREE-YEAR-OLDS

9 **BOOT STRAP BILL**, ch g Timeless Times (USA)—Nuthatch (IRE) **Miss J. R. Tooth**
10 **LAWTON**, b c Lear Spear (USA)—First Veil **R. C. Tooth**
11 B g Lear Spear (USA)—Milladella (FR) **R. C. Tooth**
12 **POPPY RED**, ch f Lear Spear (USA)—Pooka's Daughter (IRE) **Miss J. R. Tooth**
13 B f Daggers Drawn (USA)—Sarooh's Love (USA) **R. C. Tooth**

TWO-YEAR-OLDS

14 B c 9/4 Bertolini (USA)—Pooka's Daughter (IRE) (Eagle Eyed (USA))
15 B c 15/3 Lear Spear (USA)—Sarcita (Primo Dominie) (14285)

Other Owners: Mr Steve Gilbey, Mr Conal Kelly, Miss J. R. Tooth.

Jockey (flat): P. Fitzsimons. **Jockey (NH):** J. E. Moore.

---

587 MR K. TORK, Leigh
Postal: **Westcoats Farm, Clayhill Road, Leigh, Reigate, Surrey, RH2 8PB**
Contacts: PHONE **(01306) 611616** MOBILE **(07988) 206544**

1 **BEAREEN LAD (IRE)**, 6, b g Close Conflict (USA)—Baby Brown (IRE) **K. Tork**
2 **GRAND SILENCE (IRE)**, 5, ch g Grand Lodge (USA)—Why So Silent **Miss D. Tork**
3 **MYSAYNOWAY**, 6, br m Overbury (IRE)—Chinook's Daughter (IRE) **K. Tork**
4 **PODIUM PETE (IRE)**, 4, ch g Barathea (IRE)—Annemasse (FR) **K. Tork**

THREE-YEAR-OLDS

5 **L'AUBERE (USA)**, gr ro g Aljabr (USA)—Ishtak **K. Tork**

Amateur: Mr G. Gallagher.

---

588 MRS P. TOWNSLEY, Godalming
Postal: **Mendips, The Common, Dunsfold, Godalming, Surrey, GU8 4LA**
Contacts: PHONE **(01483) 200849** FAX **(01483) 200555** MOBILE **(07887) 726363**
E-MAIL **pruetownsley@classicsecurity.co.uk**

1 **ARDGLASS (IRE)**, 6, b g Danehill Dancer (IRE)—Leggagh Lady (IRE) **Pink Fizz**
2 **CUDOWNA (POL)**, 4, ch f Two-Twenty-Two (IRE)—Czerwona Roza (POL) **The Pole to Pole Partnership**
3 **DAUPHIN DES CARRES (FR)**, 10, ch g Dauphin du Bourg (FR)—Hypne (FR) **The Pole to Pole Partnership**
4 **ESCOBAR (POL)**, 7, b g Royal Court (IRE)—Escola (POL) **The Pole to Pole Partnership**
5 **GRAFT**, 9, b g Entrepreneur—Mariakova (USA) **Classic Security UK Ltd**
6 **MISTER ROBIN**, 4, ch g Tumbleweed Ridge—Ell Gee
7 **NARLEN (CZE)**, 6, ch g Rainbows For Life (CAN)—Neris (POL) **The Pole to Pole Partnership**
8 **NONONONOYES**, 4, ch g My Best Valentine—Kinkajoo **Classic Security UK Ltd**

TWO-YEAR-OLDS

9 **RENTAL ROY**, ch c 23/3 Mark of Esteem (IRE)—Kinkajoo (Precocious) **P. Townsley**

Other Owners: J. P. Butler, Mr S. F. Johnstone, Mrs C. A. Thompson.

Assistant Trainer: C Thompson

Jockey (flat): A. Culhane. **Jockey (NH):** M. Batchelor. **Conditional:** A. Martin. **Amateur:** Mrs C Thompson.

589 MR M. P. TREGONING, Lambourn

Postal: **Kingwood House Stables, Lambourn, Berkshire, RG17 7RS**
Contacts: **PHONE (01488) 73300 FAX (01488) 71728 MOBILE (07767) 888100**
E-MAIL enquiries@kingwood-stables.co.uk WEBSITE www.kingwood-stables.co.uk

1 **AJHAR (USA)**, 4, b g Diesis—Min Alhawa (USA) **Hamdan Al Maktoum**
2 **AQALEEM**, 4, b c Sinndar (IRE)—Dalayil (IRE) **Hamdan Al Maktoum**
3 **AUDLEY'S BREAK**, 4, ch f Midnight Break **Major & Mrs R. Kennard & Partner**
4 **BRONTE'S HOPE**, 4, ch f Gorse—General Jane **The Cheamsters**
5 **ENFORCE (USA)**, 5, b br m Kalanisi (IRE)—Kinetic Force (USA) **Mr & Mrs A. Pakenham**
6 **EZDIYAAD (IRE)**, 4, b c Galileo (IRE)—Wijdan (USA) **Hamdan Al Maktoum**
7 **FORMAX (FR)**, 6, gr g Marathon (USA)—Fortuna (FR) **Mr and Mrs A. E. Pakenham**
8 **MULTAKKA (IRE)**, 5, b g Alhaarth (IRE)—Elfaslah (IRE) **Hamdan Al Maktoum**
9 **RAYHANI (USA)**, 5, b g Theatrical—Bahr Alsalaam (USA) **Sheikh Ahmed Al Maktoum**
10 **SHAHIN (USA)**, 5, b h Kingmambo (USA)—String Quartet (IRE) **Hamdan Al Maktoum**
11 **YAB ADEE**, 4, b g Mark of Esteem (IRE)—Kotdiji **Kingwood House Stables**

THREE-YEAR-OLDS

12 **AJRA (IRE)**, b f Sakhee (USA)—Taqreem (IRE) **Hamdan Al Maktoum**
13 **AMHOOJ**, br f Green Desert (USA)—Harayir (USA) **Hamdan Al Maktoum**
14 **ANFAASS (USA)**, b f Belong To Me (USA)—Awtaan (USA) **Hamdan Al Maktoum**
15 **ASFURAH'S DREAM (IRE)**, b f Nayef (USA)—Asfurah (USA) **Hadi Al-Tajir**
16 **ASKAR TAU (FR)**, b c Montjeu (IRE)—Autriche (IRE) **N. Bizakov**
17 **BALIGHA**, ch f Alhaarth (IRE)—Najmat Jumairah (USA) **Sheikh Ahmed Al Maktoum**
18 **BLESSINGS ABOUND (IRE)**, b f Nayef (USA)—Nanda **Mr J. McCann & Mr R. Cutler**
19 **CANDY ROSE**, b f Tobougg (IRE)—Cottage Maid **Exors of the Late S. J. Sharp**
20 **CINERAMA (IRE)**, b f Machiavellian (USA)—Disco Volante **Mrs A. E. Morris**
21 **GHAIYATH**, gr c Dalakhani (IRE)—Sundus (USA) **Hamdan Al Maktoum**
22 **HADA MEN (USA)**, b g Dynaformer (USA)—Catchy (USA) **Sheikh Ahmed Al Maktoum**
23 **HADAF (IRE)**, b c Fasliyev (USA)—Elhida (IRE) **Hamdan Al Maktoum**
24 **HALL HEE (IRE)**, br f Invincible Spirit (IRE)—Lionne **Sheikh Ahmed Al Maktoum**
25 **HAMMER**, b g Beat Hollow—Tranquil Moon **Mrs H. T. Jones**
26 **HARTING HILL**, b g Mujahid (USA)—Mossy Rose **Exors of the Late S. J. Sharp**
27 **IL WARRD (IRE)**, b c Pivotal—Demure **Sheikh Ahmed Al Maktoum**
28 **JASOORA**, b f Mark of Esteem (IRE)—Kotdiji **Sheikh Ahmed Al Maktoum**
29 **KARA TAU**, b g Efisio—Donna Anna **N. Bizakov**
30 **KING'S ICON (IRE)**, b g King's Best—Pink Sovietstaia (FR) **Lady Tennant**
31 **LADY MARGUERITE**, b f Dubai Destination (USA)—Shimaal **Mr and Mrs A. E. Pakenham**
32 **LIKE A TIGRESS (USA)**, ch f Hold That Tiger (USA)—Rima (USA) **Mr and Mrs A. E. Pakenham**
33 **LILLE IDA**, br f Hawk Wing (USA)—Fur Will Fly **Mrs M. Campbell-Andenaes**
34 **MARRAASI (USA)**, ch f Rahy (USA)—Bashayer (USA) **Hamdan Al Maktoum**
35 **MASAALEK (USA)**, b c Green Desert (USA)—Hammiya (USA) **Hamdan Al Maktoum**
36 **MAWATHEEQ (USA)**, b c Danzig (USA)—Sarayir (USA) **Hamdan Al Maktoum**
37 **MIN SHAAN SHOO LA**, b br f Storming Home—Bilad (USA) **A. Merza**
38 **MISS CARLOTTA**, b f Helissio (FR)—Ninfa of Cisterna **N.A.Penston,R.J.Penston & A.R.O'Donnell**
39 **MOWOUDD (USA)**, b c Elusive Quality (USA)—United Kingdom (USA) **Sheikh Ahmed Al Maktoum**
40 **NASAQ (USA)**, b c Gulch (USA)—Irtahal (USA) **Hamdan Al Maktoum**
41 **PROPHET'S STAR**, b g Daylami (IRE)—Profit Alert (IRE) **Mr. I. Popham**
42 **QUAIL LANDING**, b f Mark of Esteem (IRE)—Tarneem (USA) **Mrs H. B. Raw**
43 **REALLY SO SHARP (USA)**, b f Lear Fan (USA)—Devil's Needle (USA) **Exors of the late S. J. Sharp**
44 **ROWAAD**, ch c Compton Place—Level Pegging (IRE) **Hamdan Al Maktoum**
45 **RUTBA**, b f Act One—Elhilmeya (IRE) **Hamdan Al Maktoum**
46 **SHABIBA (USA)**, b f Seeking the Gold (USA)—Misterah **Hamdan Al Maktoum**
47 **SHADAYID KHANUM (IRE)**, b f Mujahid (USA)—Ashjaan (USA) **John McCann & Robin Cutler**
48 **SHUBAAN (USA)**, b br c Kingmambo (USA)—Sayedah (IRE) **Hamdan Al Maktoum**
49 **SINAAF**, b f Nayef (USA)—Elutrah **Hamdan Al Maktoum**
50 **SLIP**, b c Fraam—Niggle **Mrs H. T. Jones**
51 **ST MICHAEL'S MOUNT**, b g Mark of Esteem (IRE)—Marithea (IRE) **The Arber Bottriell Partnership**
52 **STAR OF THE WEST**, b f Galileo (IRE)—Apache Star **A. E. Oppenheimer**
53 **TALAYEB**, b br g Nayef (USA)—Paper Chase (FR) **Hamdan Al Maktoum**
54 **TAYARAT (IRE)**, b g Noverre (USA)—Sincere (IRE) **Hamdan Al Maktoum**
55 **TODBER**, b f Cape Cross (IRE)—Dominica **Major & Mrs R. B. Kennard & Partner**
56 **UROOBAH (USA)**, b f Dynaformer (USA)—Manwah (USA) **Hamdan Al Maktoum**
57 **WALHALLA (IRE)**, b c Sinndar (IRE)—Imitation **Mr J. A. Tabet**
58 **WIKAALA (USA)**, ch g Diesis—Roseate Tern **Hamdan Al Maktoum**
59 **WORLD VIEW (IRE)**, br f Golan (IRE)—Athene (IRE) **Ballymacoll Stud Farm Ltd**

MR M. P. TREGONING—continued

TWO-YEAR-OLDS

60 **ALKHARSAA (IRE)**, b f 4/5 Sakhee (USA)—Raghba (USA) (Gulch (USA)) **Hamdan Al Maktoum**
61 **ALMUTAWAAZIN**, b c 20/4 Nayef (USA)—
        Crown Water (USA) (Chief's Crown (USA)) (120000) **Hamdan Al Maktoum**
62 **ALSAHIL (USA)**, ch c 30/1 Diesis—Tayibah (IRE) (Sadler's Wells (USA)) **Hamdan Al Maktoum**
63 **ARWAAH (IRE)**, b f 18/2 Dalakhani (IRE)—Sahool (Unfuwain (USA)) **Hamdan Al Maktoum**
64 **BEDAYAAT**, ch f 16/5 Alhaarth (IRE)—Elhida (Mujtahid (USA)) **Hamdan Al Maktoum**
65 **BOWSERS BOY (IRE)**, b c 31/1 Daylami (IRE)—Surval (IRE) (Sadler's Wells (USA)) (50000)
66 **COLORADO DAWN**, ch f 15/4 Fantastic Light (USA)—Colorspin (FR) (High Top) **Meon Valley Stud**
67 **DIAMOND HEIST**, ch c 2/1 Domedriver (IRE)—Carenage (IRE) (Alzao (USA)) (11000)
68 B c 15/2 Desert Style (IRE)—Double Edge (IRE) (Common Grounds) (52000) **Hamdan Al Maktoum**
69 **DREAM CITY (IRE)**, b f 20/3 Elusive City (USA)—On View (IRE) (Distant View (USA)) (13513)
70 **FARNCOMBE (IRE)**, ch f 10/3 Where Or When (IRE)—Promenade (Primo Dominie) (20000)
71 **FINJAAN**, b c 12/3 Royal Applause—Alhufoof (USA) (Dayjur (USA)) **Hamdan Al Maktoum**
72 **HASEILA (USA)**, b f 21/4 Forestry (USA)—Unify (USA) (Farma Way (USA)) (242954) **Hamdan Al Maktoum**
73 B f 30/3 Medicean—Invincible (Slip Anchor)
74 **ISTISHARRY**, b f 28/1 Haafhd—Eshaadeh (USA) (Storm Cat (USA)) **Hamdan Al Maktoum**
75 **JANADIL**, b c 2/5 Green Desert (USA)—Amenixa (FR) (Linamix (FR)) (78000) **Hamdan Al Maktoum**
76 **KHAN TENGRI (IRE)**, gr c 1/5 Sadler's Wells (USA)—Ela Athena (Ezzoud (USA)) (190000) **N. Bizakov**
77 **MAKAAM (USA)**, ch c 28/4 Giant's Causeway (USA)—Elaflaak (USA) (Gulch (USA)) **Hamdan Al Maktoum**
78 **MARSOOL**, br c 9/2 Key of Luck (USA)—Chatifa (IRE) (Titus Livius (FR)) **Hamdan Al Maktoum**
79 **MAWAASEEM (IRE)**, b c 5/4 Elusive City (USA)—
        Justine Au Jardin (USA) (Black Tie Affair) (44000) **Hamdan Al Maktoum**
80 **MOBAGHIT (USA)**, ch c 26/4 Dixieland Band (USA)—Hazimah (USA) (Gone West (USA)) **Hamdan Al Maktoum**
81 **MUBTADA**, br c 18/2 Sakhee (USA)—Shawahid (USA) (A P Indy (USA)) **Hamdan Al Maktoum**
82 **MUTARAAMI**, b c 6/3 Cape Cross (IRE)—Esloob (USA) (Diesis) **Hamdan Al Maktoum**
83 **OASIS KNIGHT (IRE)**, b c 21/2 Oasis Dream—Generous Lady (Generous (IRE)) (100000) **Lady Tennant**
84 **OKBA (USA)**, b f 9/4 Diesis—Awtaan (USA) (Arazi (USA)) **Hamdan Al Maktoum**
85 B c 25/3 Royal Applause—Princess Miletrian (IRE) (Danehill (USA)) (80000) **Sheikh Ahmed Al Maktoum**
86 **QELAAN**, b f 14/2 Dynaformer (USA)—Irtahal (IRE) (Swain (USA)) **Hamdan Al Maktoum**
87 B c 24/2 Exceed And Excel (AUS)—Reunion (IRE) (Be My Guest (USA)) (14156)
88 **SAHAAL (USA)**, b c 18/2 Rahy (USA)—Thaminah (USA) (Danzig (USA)) **Hamdan Al Maktoum**
89 B f 28/4 Oasis Dream—Shadow Dancing (Unfuwain (USA)) **Minster Stud & Mrs Hugh Dalgety**
90 **STERLING SOUND (USA)**, b f 24/4 Street Cry (IRE)—Lady In Silver (USA) (Silver Hawk (USA)) (58309)
91 **SUMBE (USA)**, b br c 16/4 Giant's Causeway (USA)—Sumoto (Mtoto) (290000) **N. Bizakov**
92 **TA ALEEM (USA)**, b c 22/4 Galileo (IRE)—Tadris (USA) (Red Ransom (USA)) **Hamdan Al Maktoum**
93 **TAAMEER**, b c 10/3 Beat Hollow—Vayavaig (Damister (USA)) (150000) **Hamdan Al Maktoum**
94 **TAFAOOL (IRE)**, b f 2/5 Green Desert (USA)—Sundus (USA) (Sadler's Wells (USA)) **Hamdan Al Maktoum**
95 **TAHKEEM**, b f 2/3 Green Desert (USA)—Katayeb (IRE) (Machiavellian (USA)) **Hamdan Al Maktoum**
96 **TANFIDH**, b f 6/3 Marju (IRE)—Wijdan (USA) (Mr Prospector (USA)) **Hamdan Al Maktoum**
97 **UNA SANCTA (GER)**, br f 10/3 Lando (GER)—
        Urena (GER) (Dschingis Khan) (15444) **Mrs Mette Campbell-Andenaes**
98 **UNCLE KEEF (IRE)**, b c 20/4 Sadler's Wells (USA)—Love For Ever (IRE) (Darshaan) (100000)
99 Ch c 5/3 Nayef (USA)—Valthea (FR) (Antheus (USA)) (220000) **Hamdan Al Maktoum**
100 B f 20/2 Kheleyf (USA)—Victoria Regia (IRE) (Lomond (USA)) (180000) **Sheikh Ahmed Al Maktoum**
101 **WOODLARK ISLAND (IRE)**, b c 27/2 Tagula (IRE)—Be My Lover (Pursuit of Love) (50000) **Lady Tennant**

Other Owners: Mr Hadi Al-Tajir, Mrs S. Aldridge, Mrs Romilla Arber, Mrs W. Biggs, Mr N. Bizakov, Mr W. Bottriell, Mrs Mette Campbell-Andenaes, Mr R. S. Cutler, Mrs Hugh Dalgety, Mrs Sarah J. Diamandis, Mr R. A. H. Evans, Mr R. F. U. Gaskell, Mr & Mrs Geoffry Hobby, Mr M. Horne, Major R. B. Kennard, Mrs R. B. Kennard, Mr John McCann, Mr Aziz Merza, Mrs Hugo Morris, Mr A. R. O'Donnell, Mr A. R. O'Donnell, Mr A. Oppenheimer, Mr A. E. Pakenham, Mrs Victoria Pakenham, O. J. W. Pawle, Mr N. A. Penston, Mr R. J. Penston, Mr K. B. S. Purcell, Mrs S. J. Sharp, Mr J. A. Tabet, Mrs H. Thomson-Jones, Mr M. P. N. Tregoning, Mrs Celia Woollett, Mr N. H. T. Wrigley.

Jockey (flat): P. Dobbs, M. Dwyer, R. Hills. **Apprentice:** Katia Scallan, Talib Hussain.

---

590 MR E. TUER, Northallerton
Postal: Home Farm, Great Smeaton, Northallerton, North Yorkshire, DL6 2EP
Contacts: **PHONE** (01609) 881214 **FAX** (01609) 881214 **MOBILE** (07808) 330306

1 **BAMBINO ROSSI**, 7, ch m Classic Cliche (IRE)—Leading Note (USA) **E. Tuer**
2 **COMPTON COMMANDER**, 10, ch g Barathea (IRE)—Triode (USA) **E. Tuer**
3 **DOUBLE DEPUTY (IRE)**, 7, b g Sadler's Wells (USA)—Janaat **Miss L. V. Horner**
4 **DYNAMIC RHYTHM (USA)**, 5, b g Kingmambo (USA)—Palme d'or (IRE) **Miss L. V. Horner**

MR E. TUER—continued

5 **EURO AMERICAN (GER)**, 8, br g Snurge—Egyptale **Shore Property Developments**
6 **KAFAMBER**, 4, b f Kayf Tara—Leading Note **E. Tuer**
7 **MANEKI NEKO (IRE)**, 6, b g Rudimentary (USA)—Ardbess **Mr & Mrs C. Tompkins & Mr E. Tuer**
8 **MRDEEGEETHEGEEGEE (IRE)**, 6, b g Sadler's Wells (USA)—Department (USA) **Shore Property Developments**
9 **MT DESERT**, 6, b g Rainbow Quest (USA)—Chief Bee **Far Distant Partnership**
10 **PARADISE WALK**, 4, b f Sakhee (USA)—Enclave **E. Tuer**
11 **PATAVIUM (IRE)**, 5, b g Titus Livius (FR)—Arcevia (IRE) **Mr J. A. Nixon**
12 **PICCOLOMINI**, 6, b g Diktat—La Dama Bonita (USA) **E. Tuer**
13 **RAIN AND SHADE**, 4, ch g Rainbow Quest (USA)—Coretta (IRE) **E. Tuer**
14 **RUBY SUNDAY**, 5, b g Kayf Tara—Leading Note (USA) **E. Tuer**
15 **SPHINX (FR)**, 10, b g Snurge—Egyptale **E. Tuer**
16 **TOP ROCKER**, 4, b g Rock City—Top Hand **E. Tuer**

THREE-YEAR-OLDS

17 **BULAS BOY**, ch g Exit To Nowhere (USA)—Bula Rose (IRE) **E. Tuer**

Other Owners: E. Carr, M. J. Molloy, A. C. Tompkins, Mrs A. R. Tompkins.

591
MR G. F. TUER, Northallerton
Postal: **Granary Barn, Wiske House Farm, Birkby, Northallerton, North Yorkshire, DL7 0EF**
Contacts: PHONE **(01609) 881094** FAX **(01609) 881094** MOBILE **(07879) 698869**
E-MAIL **granttuer@btinternet.com**

1 **ANNIBALE CARO**, 6, b g Mtoto—Isabella Gonzaga **G. F. Tuer**
2 **BARNEY'S DREAM (IRE)**, 5, b g Orpen (USA)—Guama Lass (IRE) **G. F. Tuer**
3 **FUNKY TOWN (IRE)**, 6, b g Anshan—Dance Rhythm (IRE) **G. F. Tuer**
4 **NINETYNINETREBLE (IRE)**, 5, b g Grand Lodge (USA)—Licorne **Nice to See You Euro-Racing**
5 **PRESENTABLE (IRE)**, 7, ch g Presenting—Crashrun **G. F. Tuer**
6 **SHANAPOVA (IRE)**, 8, br m Anshan—Native Gale (IRE) **G. F. Tuer**
7 **SNOWY DAY (FR)**, 5, b g Pennekamp (USA)—Snow White **G. F. Tuer**
8 **THROUGH THE RYE**, 12, ch g Sabrehill (USA)—Baharlilys **Nice to See You Euro-Racing**

Other Owners: Mr T. Bosomworth, I. C. Forsyth.

Jockey (NH): Paddy Aspell.

592
MRS A. F. TULLIE, Whitemire
Postal: **Whitemire Stud, Whitemire, Duns, Berwickshire, TD11 3PY**
Contacts: PHONE **(01890) 818743 (01890) 818255** FAX **(01890) 818791** MOBILE **(07714) 022903**
E-MAIL **a.tullie@btconnect.com**

1 **ASHTONMORE**, 5, b g Classic Cliche (IRE)—Sillymore **Mrs A. F. Tullie**
2 **MITEY PERK (IRE)**, 9, b g Executive Perk—More Dash (IRE) **Mrs A. F. Tullie**
3 **MORE EQUITY**, 6, b m Classic Cliche (IRE)—Sillymore **Mrs A. F. Tullie**
4 **MORE LIKELY**, 7, b m Shambo—Admire-A-More **Mrs A. F. Tullie**
5 **TRY CATCH PADDY (IRE)**, 10, ch g Safety Catch (USA)—Blackwater Rose VII **Mrs A. F. Tullie**

593
MR ANDREW TURNELL, Swindon
Postal: **Elm Cross House, Broad Hinton, Swindon, Wiltshire, SN4 9PF**
Contacts: PHONE **(01793) 731481** FAX **(01793) 739001** MOBILE **(07973) 933450**
E-MAIL **a.turnell@virgin.net** WEBSITE **andyturnellracing.com**

1 **BAWN BOY (NZ)**, 9, gr g Haayil (AUS)—Lissom (NZ) **Marlborough Racing Partnership**
2 **BIBLE LORD (IRE)**, 7, ch g Mister Lord (USA)—Pharisee (IRE) **Mr M. J. Tedham**
3 **BLUE BAJAN (IRE)**, 6, b g Montjeu (IRE)—Gentle Thoughts **Dr J. Hollowood**
4 **CAPTAIN AMERICO (IRE)**, 6, b g Lord Americo—Excitable Lady **Mr M. J. Tedham**
5 **CELTIC GOLD (USA)**, 4, b g Elusive Quality (USA)—Fortune (IRE) **L. G. Kimber**
6 **CHEATING CHANCE (IRE)**, 7, b g Oscar (IRE)—Clochban Clonroche (IRE) **Mr M. J. Tedham**
7 **DOUBLE THE TROUBLE**, 7, ch g Double Trigger (IRE)—Upton Lass **Mrs M. R. Taylor**
8 **FINNISH MELODY**, 4, ch f Karinga Bay—Myrtilla **Mrs A. J. Long**
9 **HAAR**, 4, ch g Selkirk (USA)—Chilly Start (IRE) **Mrs R. M. Hill**
10 **HIGH CAROL (IRE)**, 6, ch g Presenting—Madam Chloe **Mr M. J. Tedham**

MR ANDREW TURNELL—continued

11 HIGH JACK (IRE), 6, b g Supreme Leader—Pharisee (IRE) **Mr M. J. Tedham**
12 INTERACTIVE (IRE), 5, b g King's Best (USA)—Forentia **Griffiths Gifts Limited**
13 JIGSAW DANCER (IRE), 6, ch g Old Vic—Moonshee (IRE) **Robinson Webster (Holdings) Ltd**
14 KEW JUMPER (IRE), 9, b g Mister Lord (USA)—Pharisee (IRE) **Robinson Webster (Holdings) Ltd**
15 KING GABRIEL (IRE), 6, b g Desert King (IRE)—Broken Spirit (IRE) **Miss Alison Jones**
16 LADY LORINS, 4, ch f Tomba—Charleigh Keary **Mrs M. R. Taylor**
17 LORDSBRIDGE (USA), 6, b g Lord Avie (USA)—Victorian Style **Griffiths Gifts Limited**
18 MOVES GOODENOUGH, 5, ch g Woodborough (USA)—
                                                                      Rekindled Flame (IRE) **D. Goodenough Removals & Transport**
19 MY MATILDA, 5, gr m Silver Patriarch (IRE)—Upton Lass (IRE) **L. G. Kimber**
20 NAUGHTY THOUGHTS (IRE), 4, b f Grand Lodge (USA)—Gentle Thoughts **Mrs C. Hollowood**
21 OUTLANDISH, 5, b g Dr Fong (USA)—Velvet Lady **L. G. Kimber**
22 PINE CONQUEST, 7, b m El Conquistador—Rakaposhi Queen **Mrs D. J. Hues**
23 READY TO CROWN (USA), 4, b f More Than Ready (USA)—Dili (USA) **S. Kimber**
24 SEEFIN MOUNTAIN (IRE), 4, gr g Linamix (FR)—Paldouna (IRE) **Marlborough Racing Partnership**
25 SHANNON SPRINGS (IRE), 6, b g Darshaan—Our Queen of Kings **Mr M. J. Tedham**
26 SO BRASH (IRE), 8, ch g Rashar (USA)—Oak Tavern Lady **Miss S. Douglas-Pennant**
27 SPANISH CRUISE (IRE), 4, gr g Daylami (IRE)—Baldemara (FR) **Griffiths Gifts Limited**
28 SQUIRES LANE (IRE), 9, b g Mister Lord (USA)—Perks Glory (IRE) **Mr M. J. Tedham**
29 TOOLENTIDHAAR (USA), 4, b f Swain (IRE)—Rababah **Griffiths Gifts Limited**
30 TRADINGUP (IRE), 9, b g Arctic Lord—Autumn Queen **Miss S. Douglas-Pennant**

THREE-YEAR-OLDS

31 CONNOR'S CHOICE, b g Bertolini (USA)—Susan's Dowry **Dr J. Hollowood**
32 HIGH COINCIDENCE, b br g Diktat—Our Pleasure (IRE) **Mr M. J. Tedham**

Other Owners: M. P. Hill.

Conditional: Jason Favell.

---

594   MR D. C. TURNER, Plymouth
Postal: **Higher Collard Farm, Wotter, Plymouth, Devon, PL7 5HU**
Contacts: **PHONE (01752) 839231**

1 DUKE'S VIEW (IRE), 7, b g Sadler's Wells (USA)—Igreja (ARG) **Mrs M. E. Turner**
2 GLOBAL PARTY (IRE), 6, b g Portrait Gallery (IRE)—Fionas Party (IRE) **Mrs M. E. Turner**

Assistant Trainer: Sally Palmer

Jockey (NH): R. Greene.

---

595   MR J. R. TURNER, Helperby
Postal: **Mayfield Farm, Norton-le-Clay, Helperby, York**
Contacts: **PHONE (01423) 322239 FAX (01423) 322239**

1 BLUEBELL FLYER (IRE), 6, gr m Pistolet Bleu (IRE)—Hurst Flyer **A. J. & Mrs J. Ward**
2 FILEY FLYER, 8, ch m Weldnaas (USA)—Chasers' Bar
3 HEIDI HI, 4, b f High Estate—Alwal **J. R. Turner**
4 LUKEY LUKE, 5, b g Kayf Tara—Skiddaw Samba **G. Towersey**
5 MARLBOROUGH SOUND, 9, b g Overbury (IRE)—Dark City **J. R. Turner**

Other Owners: Mr G. Towersey, Mr A. J. Ward, Mrs Janet Ward.

Assistant Trainer: Oliver J Turner

Jockey (NH): G. Lee, A. Dobbin, P. Aspell. **Amateur:** Mr R. Wakeham.

---

596   MR W. G. M. TURNER, Sherborne
Postal: **Sigwells Farm, Sigwells, Corton Denham, Sherborne, Dorset, DT9 4LN**
Contacts: **PHONE (01963) 220523 FAX (01963) 220046 MOBILE (07932) 100173**

1 A DOUBLE EWE BEE, 7, b m Kingsinger (IRE)—Some Dream **R. A. Bracken**
2 DADDY COOL, 4, b g Kyllachy—Addicted To Love **Mascalls Stud**

MR W. G. M. TURNER—continued

3 **DUSTY DANE (IRE),** 6, b g Indian Danehill (IRE)—Teer On Eer (IRE) **Trowbridge Office Cleaning Services Ltd**
4 **EDE'IFF,** 11, b m Tragic Role (USA)—Flying Amy **Hawks & Doves Racing Syndicate**
5 **ELLE ROSE,** 5, b m Emperor Fountain—Elle Flavador **Mr E. R. Vickery**
6 **HALFWAYTOPARADISE,** 5, b m Observatory (USA)—Always On My Mind **Mascalls Stud**
7 **LOOKS THE BUSINESS (IRE),** 7, b g Marju (IRE)—Business Centre (IRE) **M J B Racing**
8 **MERCHANT BANKES,** 5, b h Observatory (USA)—Lady Bankes (IRE) **Mrs J. S. Lightbowne**
9 **MISS HOOLIE,** 4, b f Danehill Dancer (IRE)—Silky Dawn (IRE) **J. M. Troy**
10 **MOLLYANKO,** 4, gr f Komaite (USA)—Molly Malone **G. S. Tuck**
11 **PERFECT STORM,** 9, b g Vettori (IRE)—Gorgeous Dancer (IRE) **P. P. Thorman**
12 **SAD TIMES (IRE),** 4, b f Tendulkar (USA)—Mrs Kanning **Nutty Partners**
13 **STARGAZY,** 4, b g Observatory (USA)—Romantic Myth **Kachina Racing**
14 **TANG,** 4, ch f Bahamian Bounty—Hymne (FR) **Mr A. W. F. White**
15 **WESTERN PRIDE,** 5, b m Classic Cliche (IRE)—Llanfihangel Lass **Pride of the West Racing Club**

THREE-YEAR-OLDS

16 **AGGLESTONE ROCK,** b g Josr Algarhoud (IRE)—Royalty (IRE) **T. Lightbowne**
17 **JUST MOSSIE,** ch g Ishiguru (USA)—Marinsky (USA) **M. O'Connell**
18 **JUST PUDDIE,** b f Piccolo—Miss Laetitia (IRE) **T. H. Chadney**
19 **LORD DEEVERT,** br g Averti (IRE)—Dee-Lady **Mrs M. S. Teversham**
20 **MY SHEILAS DREAM (IRE),** b f Acclamation—Triphibious **J. McGrath**
21 **SYLROY,** b f Silver Patriarch (IRE)—Celtic Island **Mr H. G. W. Brown**

TWO-YEAR-OLDS

22 **BLAKENEYS PET (IRE),** b f 27/2 Celtic Swing—Kathryn's Pet (Blakeney) **Mr H. G. W. Brown**
23 **DANCING WAVE,** b f 26/3 Baryshnikov (AUS)—Wavet (Pursuit of Love) **Mr B. J. Goldsmith**
24 **DAZZLING DUST (IRE),** b c 17/4 Tagula (IRE)—Dusty Dazzler (IRE) (Titus Livius (FR)) **T.O.C.S Ltd**
25 Ch gr f 26/3 Baryshnikov (AUS)—Dusty Bankes (Greensmith) **T.O.C.S Ltd & W. G. M. Turner**
26 **GRAYSLAND,** bl f 5/4 Silver Patriarch (IRE)—Celtic Island (Celtic Swing) **Mr H. G. W. Brown**
27 **JOLI HAVEN (IRE),** ch f 17/3 Indian Haven—
Game Leader (IRE) (Mukaddamah (USA)) (1672) **The Game Leader Partnership**
28 Ch g 6/5 Karinga Bay—Magical Day (Halling (USA)) **M J B Racing**
29 **MAKALUNA,** b g 26/4 Makbul—Easter Moon (FR) (Easter Sun) (5000) **Coombes Burwell Eddowes**
30 B c 10/5 Mull of Kintyre (USA)—Princesse Sonia (FR) (Ashkalani (IRE)) (8800) **Hong Kong Breeders Club**
31 B f 11/4 Makbul—Sheik'n Swing (Celtic Swing) **W. G. M. Turner**

Other Owners: Mr G. E. Amey, Mr C. S. J. Beek, Mrs S. Burwell, D. Coombes, G. Cosburn, Mrs S. J. Drewett, Mr A. G. Drewett, Mr E. G. Eddowes, Mr R. A. Grant, Mrs Margaret Ann Grant, Mrs Susan Hearn, Mr Barry Hearn, Mr John McGrath, Mr P. Packman, G. G. Payne, Mr J. P. Rawlins, Mr John Sunnucks, Trading Research, Mr Peter Yip.

Jockey (NH): Tom O'Connor, **Conditional:** Robert Lucey-Butler. **Apprentice:** Jack Dean. **Amateur:** Mr G. Loader.

---

597 **MRS K. J. TUTTY, Northallerton**
Postal: Trenholme House Farm, Osmotherley, Northallerton, North Yorkshire, DL6 3QA
Contacts: PHONE (01609) 883624 FAX (01609) 883624 MOBILE (07967) 837406
E-MAIL karentutty@btinternet.com

1 **CEDAR POINT,** 5, ch g Keen—Jay-Dee-Jay **N. D. Tutty**
2 **DARK THUNDER (IRE),** 11, br g Religiously (USA)—Culkeern **N. D. Tutty**
3 **IRON WARRIOR (IRE),** 8, b g Lear Fan (USA)—Robalana (USA) **N. D. Tutty**
4 **JEY JEY KEEN,** 9, ch g Keen—Jay-Dee-Jay **N. D. Tutty**
5 **MANDALAY BAY (IRE),** 8, b g Humbel (USA)—Molly Bigley (IRE) **N. D. Tutty**
6 **REFLEX BLUE,** 11, b g Ezzoud (IRE)—Briggsmaid **N. D. Tutty**

TWO-YEAR-OLDS

7 **NIGELLA EXPRESS,** b f 1/1 Keen—Crimson Brocade **N. D. Tutty**

Amateur: Miss P. Tutty.

598 MR N. A. TWISTON-DAVIES, Cheltenham

Postal: T/a Grange Hill Farm Limited, Grange Hill Farm, Naunton, Cheltenham, Gloucestershire, GL54 3AY
Contacts: PHONE (01451) 850278 FAX (01451) 850101 MOBILE (07836) 664440
E-MAIL nigel@nigeltwistondavies.co.uk WEBSITE www.nigeltwistondavies.co.uk

1 AMBER BROOK (IRE), 7, ch m Alderbrook—Me Grannys Endoors (IRE) **The Yes No Wait Sorries**
2 ANDREW NICK (IRE), 6, b g Riberetto—Legal Tour (IRE) **N. A. Twiston-Davies**
3 APOLLO CREED (IRE), 6, b g Rudimentary (USA)—Persian Argument (IRE) **Mr C. Cornes**
4 ARDAGHEY (IRE), 9, b br g Lord Americo—Mrs Pepper **D. J. & S. A. Goodman**
5 BALLYFITZ, 8, b g Overbury (IRE)—Running For Gold **Mr F. J. Mills & Mr W. Mills**
6 BALLYSHAN (IRE), 10, b g Synefos (USA)—Bramble Leader (IRE) **Jump For Fun Racing**
7 BANTRY BERE (IRE), 4, b g Distant Music (USA)—Tirana (USA) **The Yes No Wait Sorries**
8 BARON WINDRUSH, 10, b g Alderbrook—Dame Scarlet **The Double Octagon Partnership**
9 BATTLECRY, 7, b br g Accordion—Miss Orchestra (IRE) **Hamsard 2363 Limited**
10 BEAT THE BOYS (IRE), 7, gr g Portrait Gallery (IRE)—Portia's Delight (IRE) **New Club Ladies**
11 BERMUDA POINTE (IRE), 6, ch g Lahib (USA)—Milain (IRE) **D. J. & S. A. Goodman**
12 BILLYANDI (IRE), 8, ch g Zaffaran (USA)—Top Dart **Hamsard 2363 Limited**
13 BUCK THE LEGEND (IRE), 6, b br g Anshan—Patience of Angels (IRE) **Alan Parker, C. Fell & A. Harris**
14 CALL ME EDWARD (IRE), 7, b g Safety Catch (USA)—Smith's Cross (IRE) **Mrs Sally & Miss Isobel Noott**
15 CHAMPAGNE HARRY, 10, b g Sir Harry Lewis (USA)—Sparkling Cinders **G. Nock**
16 CHAN BAHLUM (IRE), 5, ch g Accordion—Bar Flute (IRE) **Mrs V. Scott**
17 CLISHMACLAIVER (IRE), 5, b g Classic Cliche (IRE)—Kingussie Flower **Mrs V. J. R. Ramm**
18 COMMEMORATION DAY (IRE), 7, b g Daylami (USA)—Bequeath (USA) **C. A. Bosley**
19 CRESCENT ISLAND (IRE), 5, b g Presenting—Island Crest **Sarah Bays Jill Scott Sarah MacEchern**
20 DARK CORNER, 8, b g Supreme Leader—Made For A King **H. R. Mould**
21 DISTILLER (IRE), 4, b g Invincible Spirit (IRE)—Bobbydazzle **H. R. Mould**
22 EASY PEASY, 7, gr m Cloudings (IRE)—Easy Horse **C. W. Jenkins**
23 EILA, 5, b m Turtle Island (IRE)—Brambly Hedge **Mrs Orton & Exors of the Late P. Orton**
24 ELEGANT CLUTTER (IRE), 10, b g Petorius—Mountain Hop (IRE) **J. K. Emmerson-Briggs**
25 FIRST DE LA BRUNIE (FR), 7, ch g Mansonnien (FR)—Samisti (BEL) **Mrs C. E. M. R. Mackness**
26 FLEMISH INVADER (IRE), 5, b g Flemensfirth (USA)—Lite 'n Easy (IRE) **A. M. Armitage**
27 FLORIDA DREAM (IRE), 9, b g Florida Son—Ice Pearl **D. J. & S. A. Goodman**
28 FREDDIE ED, 7, b g Makbul—Miss Mirror **The Elegant Eds**
29 FREDDIE THE THIRD (IRE), 6, b g Good Thyne (USA)—Actress Mandy (IRE) **S D Samuels Ltd**
30 FUNDAMENTALIST (IRE), 10, b g Supreme Leader—Run For Shelter **Mr C. Cornes**
31 GOSPEL BAY, 4, b g Karinga Bay—Gospel Echo **Mrs L. M. Berryman**
32 GRENFELL (IRE), 9, br m Presenting—Arumah **Mrs J. K. Powell**
33 HUNTERS PLOY (IRE), 6, ch g Deploy—Hunt The Thimble (FR) **Mr C. Cornes**
34 IMPERIAL COMMANDER (IRE), 7, b g Flemensfirth (USA)—Ballinlovane **Our Friends in the North**
35 IRISH RAPTOR (IRE), 9, b br g Zaffaran (USA)—Brownskin **Mrs C. S. C. Beresford-Wylie**
36 ITS CRUCIAL (IRE), 8, b g Beneficial—Balda Girl **Mrs C. S. C. Beresford-Wylie**
37 JACKIE BOY (IRE), 9, b g Lord Americo—Riverpauper (IRE) **J. F. Bance**
38 KNOWHERE (IRE), 10, b g Lord Americo—Andarta **H. R. Mould**
39 LEAMINGTON LAD (IRE), 5, gr g Beckett (IRE)—Nicea (IRE) **Three Off The Tee Partnership**
40 LORD BROCK, 9, b g Alderbrook—Mariner's Air **Graham & Alison Jelley**
41 MAHOGANY BLAZE (FR), 6, b g Kahyasi—Mahogany River **Mrs L. M. Berryman**
42 MAJOR MALARKEY (IRE), 5, b g Supreme Leader—Valley (IRE) **Baker Dodd & Cooke**
43 MISS SHAKIRA (IRE), 10, b m Executive Perk—River Water **Mr F. J. Mills & Mr W. Mills**
44 MORGAN THE MIGHTY (IRE), 6, b br g Presenting—Another Grouse **N. A. Twiston-Davies**
45 MOULIN DE LA CROIX, 4, b f Muhtarram (USA)—Brambly Hedge **N. A. Twiston-Davies**
46 MR IRONMAN, 7, b g Jendali (USA)—Carly-J **J. White**
47 NAUNTON BROOK, 9, b g Alderbrook—Give Me An Answer **D. J. Langdon**
48 NIKOLA (FR), 7, b g Roi de Rome (USA)—Envie de Chalamont (FR) **Graham & Alison Jelley**
49 NUDGE AND NURDLE (IRE), 7, b g Shernazar—Firey Comet (IRE) **The Yes No Wait Sorries**
50 OLLIE MAGERN, 10, b g Alderbrook—Outfield **R. Nicholls**
51 OURAGAN DE PRAIRIE (FR), 6, ch g Brier Creek (USA)—Airelle de Prairie (FR) **Graham & Alison Jelley**
52 PATMAN DU CHARMIL (FR), 6, b g Robin des Pres (FR)—Pacifie du Charmil (FR) **H. R. Mould**
53 PEACOCK (FR), 5, ch g Bulington (FR)—Algue Rouge (FR) **H. R. Mould**
54 PEN GWEN (FR), 5, b r Le Balafre (FR)—Dans Dro (FR) **Million in Mind Partnership**
55 PETITE MARGOT, 9, b m Alderbrook—Outfield **R. Nicholls**
56 PETTIFOUR (IRE), 6, b g Supreme Leader—Queen of Natives (IRE) **Pettifer Group Limited**
57 PIGEON ISLAND, 5, gr g Daylami (IRE)—Morina (IRE) **H. R. Mould**
58 PLATIN GROUNDS (GER), 6, ch g Waky Nao—Platin Queen (IRE) **D. J. & S. A. Goodman**
59 RANDOLPH O'BRIEN (IRE), 8, b g Zaffaran (USA)—Gala's Pride **Geoffrey & Donna Keeys**
60 RAZOR ROYALE (IRE), 6, b g Oscar (IRE)—Maypole Gayle **Mr C. Cornes**
61 REDEMPTION, 13, b g Sanglamore (USA)—Ypha (USA) **N. A. Twiston-Davies**

MR N. A. TWISTON-DAVIES—continued

62 **RIMSKY (IRE)**, 7, gr g Silver Patriarch (IRE)—Mistinguett (IRE) **D. J. & S. A. Goodman**
63 **ROWDY YEATS (IRE)**, 7, ch g Un Desperado (IRE)—Summerhill Express (IRE) **Hamsard 2363 Limited**
64 **SCRIBANO EILE (IRE)**, 7, b g Scribano—Ean Eile (IRE) **H. R. Mould**
65 **SPARKLING BROOK (IRE)**, 5, b m Alderbrook—
Auntie Prickle Pin (IRE) **Jilly Scott, Sarah MacEchern, Scilla Phillips**
66 **THE GANGERMAN (IRE)**, 8, ch g Anshan—Ivy Lane (IRE) **Agetur (UK) Ltd**
67 **THE GREAT ALFIE**, 5, b g Alflora (IRE)—Like Manner **D. J. & S. A. Goodman**
68 **TRAMANTANO**, 9, b g Muhtarram (USA)—Hatta Breeze **H. R. Mould**
69 **VICTORBANO (IRE)**, 5, b g Scribano—Augusta Victoria **Mr C. Cornes**

Other Owners: Mr J. B. Baker, C. J. Barker, Mrs E. M. Bathurst, Mrs S. Bays, R. N. Bevis, A. R. Bromley, C. S. J. Coley, Mr P. G. Cooke, W. Craig, J. Craig, Mr G. T. G. Dodd, Mr J. Fell, G. F. Goode, D. J. Goodman, Mrs S. A. Goodman, Mrs F. V. C. Gregory, Mr A. R. Harris, D. M. Hussey, G. S. Jelley, Mrs A. D. Jelley, G. F. Keeys, Mrs C. M. Keeys, Mrs S. A. MacEchern, Mrs P. Mason, F. J. Mills, W. R. Mills, W. D. C. Minton, Mrs D. C. Nicholson, Mrs S. A. Noott, P. R. Noott, Mrs S. V. Orton, Exors of the Late P.C. Orton, A. G. Parker, Mrs P. M. Phillips, T. J. Pope, G. M. Powell, I. Robinson, Mrs G. C. Robinson, G. W. Sanders, Mrs J. Scott, R. I. Sims, Mrs M. Whitfield, E. E. Williams.

Jockey (NH): P. Brennan. **Conditional:** D. England, R. Killoran.

599 | **MR J. R. UPSON, Towcester**
Postal: **Glebe Stables, Blakesley Heath, Maidford, Towcester, Northamptonshire, NN12 8HN**
Contacts: **PHONE (01327) 860043 FAX (01327) 860238**

1 **ALBERT PARK (IRE)**, 7, ch g Presenting—Victoria Belle (IRE) **Middleham Park Racing XXXV**
2 **BACKSCRATCHER**, 14, b g Backchat (USA)—Tiernee Quintana **Mrs D. Upson**
3 **BAYLOCK BOY (IRE)**, 7, b br g Accordion—She Insists (IRE) **Mrs A. F. Key**
4 **BLUNHAM HILL (IRE)**, 10, ch g Over The River (FR)—Bronach **The Reserved Judgment Partnership**
5 **CELTIC TREASURE (IRE)**, 6, b g Second Empire (IRE)—Future Treasure **Middleham Park Racing XXXV**
6 **GRITTI PALACE (IRE)**, 8, b g Duky—Glittering Grit (IRE) **Sir Nicholas Wilson**
7 **HE'S A ROCKET (IRE)**, 7, b g Indian Rocket—Dellua (IRE) **Belinda Clarke & James D. Smith**
8 **LAKE BARRINE**, 5, b g Bahhare (USA)—North Kildare (USA) **Middleham Park Racing XXXV**
9 **MAJOR BELLE (FR)**, 9, ch m Cyborg (FR)—Mistine Major (FR) **Bar Snacks Partnership**
10 **MAJOR UPSET (IRE)**, 5, b g Oscar (IRE)—Ikdam Valley (IRE) **Bar Snacks Partnership**
11 **MENKAURA**, 5, b g Pivotal—Nekhbet **The Peter Partnership**
12 **REGAL RIVER**, 11, b g Over The River (FR)—My Friend Fashion **Middleham Park Racing XXXV**
13 **SILVER TERRA**, 6, gr g Environment Friend—Highly Sociable **The Nap Hand Partnership**
14 **STROLLING VAGABOND (IRE)**, 9, ch g Glacial Storm (IRE)—Found Again (IRE) **J. F. Bath**

Other Owners: Mr M. H. Beesley, Exors of the Late Mr P. Bromfield, Ms F. H. Brunton, Mrs Belinda Clarke, Mr D. Deveney, Mr James Knight, Mr Graeme P. McPherson, Mrs S. M. McPherson, Mr T. S. Palin, Mr M. Prince, Mr James D. Smith, Mr Mick White, Mr P. F. Williams.

600 | **MR M. D. I. USHER, Lambourn**
Postal: **Saxon House Stables, Upper Lambourn, Hungerford, Berkshire, RG17 8QH**
Contacts: **PHONE (01488) 72598 FAX (01488) 73630 MOBILE (07831) 873531**
E-MAIL markusherracing@btconnect.com WEBSITE www.markusherracing.co.uk

1 **AUBURN GREY**, 6, gr g Environment Friend—Odyn Dancer **G. A. Summers**
2 **CALCULATING (IRE)**, 4, b g Machiavellian (USA)—Zaheemah (USA) **Mr B. C. Rogan**
3 **COUNT CEPRANO (IRE)**, 4, b g Desert Prince (IRE)—Camerlata **Mr I. Sheward**
4 **DIMINUTO**, 4, b f Iron Mask (USA)—Thicket **R. H. Brookes**
5 **GOLDEN ALCHEMIST**, 5, ch g Woodborough (USA)—Pure Gold **Midweek Racing**
6 **KELAMON**, 4, b g Keltos (FR)—Faraway Moon **Mr & Mrs Richard Hames & Friends**
7 **LADY DUXYANA**, 5, b m Most Welcome—Duxyana (IRE) **Bryan Fry & The Toerags**
8 **PAJADA**, 4, b f Bertolini (USA)—Last Ambition (IRE) **Ron Goddard & Partners**
9 **PIANO KEY**, 4, ch f Distant Music (USA)—Ivorine (USA) **Donaghey Usher**
10 **RULING REEF**, 6, b m Diktat—Horseshoe Reef **Midweek Racing**
11 **SCOTTISH RIVER (USA)**, 9, b g Thunder Gulch (USA)—Overbrook **M. D. I. Usher**
12 **SOUTH GEORGIA**, 4, b f First Trump—East Rose **J. A. Stansfield**

THREE-YEAR-OLDS

13 **ADMIRAL TROY**, b c Umistim—Troia (IRE) **Mark Usher & Partners**
14 **BAHIA PALACE**, b f Zamindar (USA)—Inya Lake **The Goodracing Partnership**

MR M. D. I. USHER—continued

15 **KING'S ALCHEMIST**, b c Slickly (FR)—Pure Gold **The Ridgeway Partnership**
16 **LADY JINKS**, ch f Kirkwall—Art Deco Lady **The High Jinks Partnership**
17 **OUR KALLY**, b br f Kyllachy—Rendition **Ron Goddard & Partners**
18 **RIDGEWAY JAZZ**, b f Kalanisi (IRE)—Billie Holiday **The Ridgeway Bloodstock Company Ltd**
19 **SAXON BLUE**, b g Josr Algarhoud (IRE)—Highland Blue **M. D. I. Usher**
20 **SEDUCTIVE WITCH**, ch f Zamindar (USA)—Thicket **Bryan Fry & The Toerags**
21 **TALLULAH SUNRISE**, b f Auction House (USA)—Tallulah Belle **Ron Goddard & Partners**

TWO-YEAR-OLDS

22 B c 17/2 Minardi (USA)—Allegedly (IRE) (Alhaarth (IRE)) (5500) **The Paymasters**
23 Ch f 10/5 Generous (IRE)—Art Deco Lady (Master Willie) **M. D. I. Usher**
24 Ch f 10/4 Bold Edge—Bowden Rose (Dashing Blade) (3500) **M. D. I. Usher**
25 B c 13/3 Lucky Story (USA)—Eleonora d'arborea (Prince Sabo) (6500) **Ushers Court**
26 B f 28/2 Compton Place—Faraway Moon (Distant Relative) (8500) **Mr & Mrs Richard Hames & Friends**
27 **INDIAN BLADE (IRE)**, ch c 16/3 Daggers Drawn (USA)—Belle Bijou (Midyan (USA)) (4825) **Midweek Racing**
28 **RIDGEWAY SILVER**, b f 29/1 Lujain (USA)—
　　　　　　　　　　Barefooted Flyer (USA) (Fly So Free (USA)) **The Ridgeway Bloodstock Company Ltd**

Other Owners: Mr J. Donaghey, Mr Bryan Fry, Mr R. A. Goddard, Mr M. Goodrum, Mrs Richard Hames, Mr Richard Hames, Mrs A. C. Hill, Miss D. G. Kerr, Mr Barry Minty, Mr Carl West-Meads.

Jockey (flat): Hayley Turner, Richard Smith. **Jockey (NH):** Dave Crosse. **Amateur:** Mr L. Newnes.

---

601 **MR E. F. VAUGHAN, Newmarket**
Postal: **Grange House Stables, Hamilton Road, Newmarket, Suffolk, CB8 0TE**
Contacts: **PHONE (01638) 667411 FAX (01638) 667452 MOBILE (07799) 144901**
E-MAIL ed@efvaughan.com WEBSITE www.efvaughan.com

1 **BARON'S PIT**, 8, b g Night Shift (USA)—Incendio **A. M. Pickering**
2 **CONVIVIAL SPIRIT**, 4, b g Lake Coniston (IRE)—Ruby Princess (IRE) **A. M. Pickering**
3 **COSMIC DESTINY (IRE)**, 6, b m Soviet Star (USA)—Cruelle (USA) **A. M. Pickering**
4 **COYOTE CREEK**, 4, b g Zilzal (USA)—High Barn Gibson, Goddard, Hamer & Hawkes
5 **MEDICEA SIDERA**, 4, br f Medicean—Broughtons Motto **M. A. Whelton**
6 **MINNIS BAY (CAN)**, 4, b g Royal Academy (USA)—Aly's Daylite (USA) **John Ferguson Spares Ltd**
7 **PELICAN WATERS (IRE)**, 4, b f Key of Luck (USA)—Orlena (USA) **M. Sammon**
8 **SHADOW THE WIND (IRE)**, 4, b g Val Royal (FR)—Kesh Kumay (USA) **M. J. C. Hawkes & E. J. C. Hawkes**
9 **VEENWOUDEN**, 4, b f Desert Prince (IRE)—Delauncy **Wood Hall Stud Limited**

THREE-YEAR-OLDS

10 **BEGGARS END (USA)**, gr ro g Mizzen Mast (USA)—Hasardeuse (USA) **E. F. Vaughan**
11 **BOBAL GIRL**, ch f Tobougg (IRE)—Al Guswa **Sir Robert Stewart & A M Pickering**
12 **KOTSI (IRE)**, b f Nayef (USA)—Ingozi **A. E. Oppenheimer**
13 **SENORITA PARKES**, ch f Medicean—Lucky Parkes **J. Heler**

TWO-YEAR-OLDS

14 Gr c 17/3 Dubai Destination (USA)—Amellnaa (IRE) (Sadler's Wells (USA)) **Mr M. Rashid**
15 **AWANI**, b f 1/4 Sakhee (USA)—Hatton Gardens (Auction Ring (USA)) (100000) **Mrs E. Kennedy**
16 **BICKSTA**, b f 27/1 Haafhd—Premiere Dance (IRE) (Loup Solitaire (USA)) (35000) **M. J. C. Hawkes**
17 B c 19/4 Royal Applause—Caldy Dancer (IRE) (Soviet Star (USA)) **Mr M. Rashid**
18 B c 19/4 Falbrav (IRE)—Countess Sybil (IRE) (Dr Devious (IRE)) **Lady Cobham**
19 **CRYSTAL FEATHER**, ch f 21/3 Monsieur Bond (IRE)—
　　　　　　　　　　Prince's Feather (IRE) (Cadeaux Genereux) (17000) **Featherbed Ladies**
20 **DOCTOR PARKES**, b c 21/2 Diktat—Lucky Parkes (Full Extent (USA)) **J. Heler**
21 **GREY GHOST**, gr c 22/2 Linamix (FR)—Isla Azul (IRE) (Machiavellian (USA)) **A. E. Oppenheimer**
22 **KONKA (USA)**, ch c 25/3 Johannesburg (USA)—
　　　　　　　　　　Defining Style (USA) (Out of Place (USA)) (58309) **M. J. C. Hawkes**
23 B c 30/3 Choisir (AUS)—Lady Ounavarra (IRE) (Simply Great (FR)) (38000) **The Comic Strip Heroes**
24 B c 23/3 Law Society (USA)—Lilac Dance (Fabulous Dancer (USA)) (20000) **E. F. Vaughan**
25 B f 26/2 Barathea (IRE)—Ludynosa (USA) (Cadeaux Genereux) (62000) **Saif Ali & Saeed H. Altayer**
26 B c 11/2 Diktat—Noble Desert (FR) (Green Desert (USA)) (10000) **C. J. Murfitt**
27 **OCEANS EDGE**, br c 22/3 Needwood Blade—Lady Roxanne (Cyrano de Bergerac) (46000) **Sir J. W. Robb**
28 **PACHAKUTEK (USA)**, ch c 14/4 Giant's Causeway (USA)—Charlotte Corday (Kris) (90000) **El Catorce**
29 **PRINCESS REBECCA**, ch f 21/3 Compton Place—Sunley Stars (Sallust) (14000) **P. Webb**

MR E. F. VAUGHAN—continued

30 Ch c 5/3 Galileo (IRE)—Sena Desert (Green Desert (USA)) **Mr M. Obaida**
31 SINCHIROKA (FR), b c 10/3 Della Francesca (USA)—Great Care (USA) (El Gran Senor (USA)) (30000) **El Catorce**
32 STARLIGHT WISH, ch c 9/2 Fantastic Light (USA)—
　　　　　　　　　　　　　　Aliena (IRE) (Grand Lodge (USA)) (10000) **Four Winds Racing**

Other Owners: S. Ali, S. H. Altayer, A. W. Black, Mr A. Black, Mr A. Cohen, Mrs Joanna Dolan, Mr John Ferguson, Mr B. Gibson, Mr Arthur Goddard, Mr C. M. Hamer, Mrs Stella Harvey, Mr E. J. C. Hawkes, Mrs Toby Hunter, Mr Toby Hunter, Mr O. H. Kingsley, S. J. Mear, Mr S. J. Mear, Mr A. V. Nicoll, Mrs Rosalynd Norman, Mr C. Pizarro, Mrs Karla Pizarro, Mr S. C. C. Skey, Mr S. C. C. Skey, Sir Robert Stewart, J. P. Wray, Mr J. Wray.

---

602 MR N. J. VAUGHAN, Malpas
Postal: **Manor House Stables, Hampton, Malpas, Cheshire, SY14 8AB**
Contacts: **PHONE (01948) 820485 FAX (01948) 820495 MOBILE (07771) 700183**
E-MAIL nicky@manorhousestables.com WEBSITE manorhousestables.com

1 DERRICKS DOTTY, 4, br g Beat All (USA)—Pass The Rose (IRE) **Derricks Dotty Syndicate**
2 DON JOSE (USA), 5, b br g Dynaformer (USA)—Panthera (USA) **Mike & Maureen Browne**
3 FOUR TEL, 4, gr g Vettori (IRE)—Etienne Lady (IRE) **Owen Promotions Limited**
4 LILAC MOON (GER), 4, b f Dr Fong (USA)—Luna de Miel **A. W. Black**
5 MONDOVI, 4, b f Kyllachy—Branston Fizz **Mr K Dyer & Mr C Bellamy**
6 PRAIRIE TIGER (GER), 4, b c Tiger Hill (IRE)—Prairie Lilli (GER) **Owen Promotions Limited**
7 PRIVATE SOLDIER, 5, gr g Dansili—Etienne Lady (IRE) **Owen Promotions Limited**
8 SKY CHART (IRE), 4, ch g Fantastic Light (USA)—Marion Haste (IRE) **Manor House Stables LLP**
9 STILL CALM, 4, b g Zamindar (USA)—Shining Water **Mr D. J. Simpson**
10 SUPERCAST (IRE), 5, b g Alhaarth (USA)—Al Euro (FR) **S. Walker**

THREE-YEAR-OLDS

11 DASHING DANIEL, gr c Zamindar (USA)—Etienne Lady (IRE) **Owen Promotions Limited**
12 EMERALD ROCK (CAN), b c Johannesburg (USA)—Classic Jones (CAN) **The Whack Pack**
13 GINGER MINX (IRE), ch f Raise A Grand (IRE)—Glenmalure (USA) **Manor House Stables LLP**
14 GO GLOW, b c Lomitas—Glossary **Mike & Maureen Browne**
15 HOLOKO HEIGHTS, br g Pivotal—Treble Heights (IRE) **Owen Promotions Limited**
16 JUST KENKO, ch c Primo Valentino (IRE)—Coffee To Go **Betfair Club ROA**
17 LADY SOUGHTON (IRE), b gr f Daylami (IRE)—Indaba (IRE) **Owen Promotions Limited**
18 LISBON LION (IRE), br gr c Mull of Kintyre (USA)—Ludovica
19 LUCKY CHARACTER, b c Key of Luck (USA)—Gay Heroine **Aykroyd & Sons Limited**
20 MARYOLINI, b f Bertolini (USA)—Mary Jane **A. Charlton, P. Jones, I. Smith, K. Warth**
21 MOSCOW OZNICK, b br c Auction House (USA)—Cozette (IRE) **MO, SP, NB, CM**
22 MR MACATTACK, b c Machiavellian (USA)—Aunty Rose (IRE) **Manor House Stables LLP**
23 B c Namid—Mrs Cee (IRE) **Manor House Stables LLP**
24 PEARL DEALER (IRE), b c Marju (IRE)—Anyaas (IRE) **Manor House Stables LLP**
25 RIO L'OREN (IRE), ch f Captain Rio—Princess Sofie **Super Saturday Syndicate**
26 ROYAL MANOR, b f King's Best (USA)—She's Classy (USA) **Manor House Stables LLP**
27 SHEPHERDS WARNING (IRE), ch f Vettori (IRE)—Sky Red **A. W. Black**
28 THE STAFFY (IRE), b g Redback—Lady Charlotte **MO, SP, NB, CM**
29 UNCLE BERTIE, b c Bertolini (USA)—Resourceful (IRE) **Manor House Stables LLP**

TWO-YEAR-OLDS

30 B f 21/3 Shinko Forest (IRE)—Abbaleva (Shaddad (USA)) (22000) **K. Gannon**
31 Br c 20/3 Golan (IRE)—Danish Gem (Danehill (USA)) (21000)
32 JONNY MUDBALL, b c 20/4 Oasis Dream—Waypoint (Cadeaux Genereux) (50000) **Woodgate Family**
33 B c 18/2 Domedriver (IRE)—Lavinia's Grace (USA) (Green Desert (USA)) (40000)
34 B c 19/3 Mtoto—Morgannwg (IRE) (Simply Great (FR)) (30000) **Manor House Stables LLP**
35 B c 10/3 Iron Mask (USA)—Starisa (IRE) (College Chapel) (8000)
36 B c 9/3 Pivotal—Treble Heights (IRE) (Unfuwain (USA)) **Owen Promotions Limited**

Other Owners: Mr C. Bellamy, Mr Mike Browne, Mrs Maureen Browne, Mr Nicky Butt, Mr S. J. Carr, Mr Andrew Charlton, Mr D. Duff, Mr K. Dyer, Mr Tom Gittins, Mr S. Given, Mr J. R. Healey, Mr Peter Jones (Flintshire), Mr Craig Moore, Mr Michael Owen, Mrs L. Owen, Mr L. T. Owen, Mr S. Parker, Mrs Sadie Ryan, Mr Ian Smith (Staffs), Mr Keith Warth, Mr J. Woodgate, Mr A. W. Woodgate.

603 **MR T. E. VAUGHAN, Bridgend**
Postal: **Mount Pleasant, Rhiwceiliog, Pencoed, Mid-Glamorgan, CF35 6NE**
Contacts: **PHONE** (01656) 862012 **FAX** (01656) 862012 **MOBILE** (07841) 800081
E-MAIL tim@timvaughanracing.com **WEBSITE** www.timvaughanracing.com

1 BRINKMANSHIP (USA), 6, b g Red Ransom—Whist **Mrs G. M. Owens**
2 CITY AFFAIR, 7, b g Inchinor—Aldevonie **optimumracing.co.uk**
3 KINGS EURO (IRE), 8, b g Eurobus—Jewell For A King (IRE) **N. B. Jones**
4 MAD PROFESSOR (IRE), 5, b g Mull of Kintyre (USA)—Fancy Theory (USA) **M. Glastonbury**
5 MOORLANDS TERI, 5, b m Terimon—Sandford Springs (USA) **Mrs L. M. Williams**
6 PRESIDENT PARK (FR), 6, b g Northern Park (USA)—Miss Alida (FR) **optimumracing.co.uk**
7 SUNGATES (IRE), 12, ch g Glacial Storm (USA)—Live It Up **D. J. Wallis**
8 WYCHWOODS LEGEND, 5, b m Midnight Legend—Miss Millbrook **K. J. Glastonbury**

Other Owners: Mr Andrew Lowrie, Mrs J. Lowrie.

Assistant Trainer: Mrs Abbi Vaughan.

604 **MR CHRISTIAN VON DER RECKE, Weilerswist**
Postal: **Rennstall Recke, Hovener Hof, D-53919, Weilerswist, Germany**
Contacts: **(0049)** 2254 845314 **FAX** (0049) 2254 845315 **MOBILE** (0049) 171 5425050
E-MAIL recke@t-online.de **WEBSITE** www.rennstall-recke.de

1 A CE SOIR (GER), 7, b m Laroche (GER)—Acatonia (GER) **Th. Volz**
2 AL BALDID (GER), 5, b h Auenadler (GER)—Al Coq (GER) **Stall Roggen**
3 ALRESCHA (GER), 4, b c Dictator's Song (USA)—Alpenkonigin (GER) **U. Schwirz**
4 ANSWERING (IRE), 9, b g King's Theatre (IRE)—Ansariya (USA) **A. Putsch**
5 ASKANT (GER), 11, b g Goofalik (USA)—Askura (GER) **U. Potofski u.a.**
6 ASKURANT (GER), 4, b g Goofalik (USA)—Askura (GER) **Stall Stromberg**
7 AUENWIESE (GER), 4, b f Lando (GER)—Anatina (GER) **Stall Jenny**
8 BAYSIDE, 7, ch g Docksider (USA)—Sister Sophie (USA) **Stall Karlshorst**
9 BEAGLE (IRE), 4, b g Xaar—Bella Michela (GER) **Stall Burg Muggenhausen**
10 BOSS MAK (IRE), 5, ch g Shinko Forest (IRE)—Lucky Achievement (USA) **Stall Mohlenberg**
11 BRITANNIC, 5, ch g Rainbow Quest (USA)—Anka Britannia (USA) **Mr F. T. M. Meyer**
12 CAVAN GAEL (FR), 6, b g Dansili—Time Will Show (FR) **Frau P. u. G. v. Schmidt-Pauli**
13 CELTIC SNAKE, 4, b g Golden Snake (USA)—Thamud (IRE) **Stall Aron**
14 COLD MOUNTAIN (GER), 4, b g Samum (GER)—Charismatique (GER) **Stall Blankenese**
15 CONGRIO DORADO (USA), 6, b g Real Quiet (USA)—Cox Girl (USA) **Stall Chevalex**
16 COSEADROM (IRE), 6, b g Almutawakel—Madam Lightfoot (USA) **F. T. M. Meyer**
17 CROSS MY SHADOW (IRE), 6, b g Cape Cross (IRE)—Shadowglow **Stall Karlshorst**
18 DAILY NATION (GER), 6, b m Winged Love (IRE)—Daily Mail (GER) **M. Wittmann**
19 DANCERA (GER), 4, b f Johan Cruyff—Dancin' Doll **Gestut Erlenhof**
20 DANILO (IRE), 4, ch c Dr Fong (USA)—Dunnella (IRE) **F. W. Holtkotter**
21 DARDANTOS (GER), 6, b g Dashing Blade—Dark Lady (GER) **D. Rosport**
22 DASHING PRINCESS, 4, b f Dashing Blade—L'aspect (IRE) **Stall Wendelstein**
23 DESAFINADO (GER), 4, b c Lecroix (GER)—Dream of You (GER) **Stall Mimmi & Friends**
24 DO IT (GER), 6, b gr h Twen (GER)—Duas (GER) **Frau M. Wittman**
25 EARLSALSA (GER), 4, b g Kingsalsa (GER)—Earthly Paradise (GER) **Stall Blankenese**
26 EASYTANGO (GER), 4, ch g Acatenango (GER)—Estelle **Stall Mimmi & Friends**
27 FAIRY FOREST (IRE), 4, ch f Fath (USA)—Forest Treasure (USA) **Frau R. U. A. Hacker**
28 FESTERO (GER), 5, b g Silvano (GER)—Freni (GER) **Stall Blau-Weiss**
29 FIEPES SHUFFLE (GER), 8, b g Big Shuffle (USA)—Fiepe (EG) **Stall Jenny**
30 FURSTENBERG (IRE), 6, b g Monashee Mountain (USA)—Flagny (FR) **Stall Blau-Weiss**
31 GIANT GINO (GER), 5, b h Perugino (USA)—Glen Royal (GER) **Stall Weisser Stein**
32 GOLDEN MILLENIUM (GER), 7, b g Monsun (GER)—Gluckskind (GER) **BMK Racing**
33 HELMAC (GER), 7, br g Macanal (USA)—Helsinki (GER) **B. Raber**
34 HOME CALL (USA), 6, b g Chester House (USA)—Call Account (USA) **BMK Racing**
35 IBRIS (GER), 4, b c Big Shuffle (USA)—Innella (GER)
36 KATHEDRALE (GER), 4, b f Samum (GER)—Kampada (FR) **Stall K B S**
37 KRONOS (GER), 5, ch g Spectrum (IRE)—Kapitol (GER) **Stall Weissenhof**
38 LATINI (GER), 4, b c Desert Prince (IRE)—La Felicita **Stall Helena**
39 LE PAPILLON (GER), 4, b c Devil River Peek (USA)—La Filolie (FR) **Stall Blue Sky**
40 LINDSTROEM (GER), 6, b br g Kendor (FR)—Lindenblute **Stall Terry**
41 MAJOR KEY (FR), 5, ch g Majorien—Chanteuse de Jazz **Stall Aron**
42 MAKNOON, 5, ch g Muhtarram (USA)—Suhaad **A. Peitsch**
43 MALAFEMINA, 4, gr f Montjeu (IRE)—Lady Of The Turf (NZ) **H. Kagel**

MR CHRISTIAN VON DER RECKE—continued

44 **NAURETOS (GER)**, 4, b g Surako (GER)—Nicole (GER) **Gestut Schattauer Hof-Granum Zuc**
45 **ORFISIO (GER)**, 9, b g Efisio—Thelma **Stall Schmeer**
46 **ORGIE (GER)**, 4, gr f Samum (GER)—Otero (GER) **Dr R. Zurmaar**
47 **OSTER KONIG (GER)**, 5, b g Tannenkonig (IRE)—Oster Lady (GER) **Stall Much**
48 **OUR FIRST CHESNUT (GER)**, 6, ch g Java Gold (USA)—Orient Way (IRE) **B. Raber**
49 **OVER BROWN (GER)**, 4, b g Aeskulap (GER)—Odile (GER) **Frau D. Rickoll**
50 **PARADISE SEARCH (IRE)**, 4, b f Rainbow Quest (USA)—Moonlight Paradise (USA) **Schwindibode AG**
51 **PEREDUR (GER)**, 4, b c Protektor (GER)—Prairie Queen (GER) **Stall Aron**
52 **PERSONAL POWER (GER)**, 5, br g Dashing Blade—Personal Hope (GER) **Frau U. U. H. Alck**
53 **PRESS EXPRESS (IRE)**, 6, ch g Entrepreneur—Nawaji (USA) **H. Kronseder**
54 **PRIMUS (GER)**, 4, b g Goofalik (USA)—Palais (GER) **Stall Grimminger**
55 **PRINCESS ILEANA (IRE)**, 4, b f Danetime (IRE)—Uhud (IRE) **Stall Karlshorst**
56 **QUIRINO (GER)**, 7, b g Lagunas—Queen's Diamond (GER) **Stall Burg Muggenhausen**
57 **REDCLIFF (GER)**, 4, ch g Lomitas—Rhode Island (GER) **Gestut Am Schlossgarten**
58 **RIGHT TO PLAY (USA)**, 5, b br h Kingmambo (USA)—Possibly Perfect (USA) **BMK Racing**
59 **ROB ROY (GER)**, 5, b h Bluebird (USA)—Roxania **Stall Stromberg**
60 **ROSENBRIEF (GER)**, 9, ch g Brief Truce (USA)—Roseraie (GER) **Stall Grimminger**
61 **SCHOOLBOY (GER)**, 4, bl c Acatenango (GER)—Sylvette (USA) **J. M. B. O'Connor**
62 **SKY CRUSADER (GER)**, 6, b g Mujahid (USA)—Red Cloud (IRE) **Stall Saarbrucken**
63 **SONG OF PRIDE (GER)**, 4, ch c Platini (GER)—Song of Peace (GER) **Quadriga GmbH**
64 **SPECIAL EDITION (GER)**, 6, br g Big Shuffle (USA)—Safrane (GER) **Stall Tommy**
65 **SWEET DEVIL (GER)**, 4, gr g Goofalik (USA)—Safrane (GER) **Stall Tommy**
66 **SWORDSMAN (GER)**, 6, b h Acatenango (GER)—Saiga **Mr J. M. B. O'Connor**
67 **VEGANO (FR)**, 7, br g Waky Nao—Vega Sicilia **B. Raber**
68 **WILDBACH (IRE)**, 6, b g Law Society (USA)—Wurfspiel (GER) **J. Spence**
69 **WOODLAND TRAVELLER (USA)**, 4, b g Gone West (USA)—Iftiraas **Stall Aron**
70 **ZOOM (GER)**, 5, ch m Lomitas—Zizi Top **Stall Hanse**

THREE-YEAR-OLDS

71 **ARROW FLIGHT (IRE)**, b c Nayef (USA)—Lust **Miss A. Shaykhutdinova**
72 **CASPARI (GER)**, b c Chato (USA)—Cordona (GER) **G. Schmitz**
73 **CLASSICAL SONG (HOL)**, b c Volfonic (IRE)—Classic Royal (GER) **Biesdeel Stud**
74 **EASTERN EAGLE (GER)**, b g Auenadler (GER)—Egyptale **H. Kagel**
75 **ELBA (GER)**, b f Hawk Wing (USA)—Elisha (GER) **Stall Helena**
76 **GENETHNI**, b f Primo Valentino (IRE)—Mujadilly **F. T. M. Meyer**
77 **HILDAGO (IRE)**, b c Tagula (IRE)—Darling Smile (IRE) **Gestut Am Schlossgarten**
78 **IDELA (GER)**, b f Seattle Dancer (USA)—Ibelia (GER) **Quadriga GmbH**
79 Ch c Second Set (IRE)—Kayama (GER) **Stall Burg Munggenhausen**
80 **KING'S WISH**, b c King's Best (USA)—Secret Wish (IRE) **Miss A. Shaykhutdinova**
81 **MARALDO (GER)**, b c Bering—Marquesa Island (GER) **H. Kronseder**
82 **MISTER MINISTER (GER)**, ch c Artan (GER)—Misniniski **Stall Blau-Weiss**
83 **MONTIANO (IRE)**, b g Kris Kin (USA)—Ruby Setting **Gestut Am Schlossgarten**
84 **NUJOMA (GER)**, ch f Samum (GER)—New Berlin (IRE) **Gestut Am Schlossgarten**
85 **PEARL MINING (IRE)**, ch g Monashee Mountain (USA)—Palace Blue (IRE) **Quadriga GmbH**
86 **PIRQUINA (GER)**, b f Kahyasi—Pampa Mia **Stall Chevalex**
87 **SACO (GER)**, b g Pentire—Sang Sun (GER) **Stall Gelb-Blau**
88 **SPITZBUBE (GER)**, b c Dashing Blade—She's His Guest (IRE) **W. Frouhlich**
89 B br f Spectrum (USA)—Stefania (IRE) **Gestut Romerhof**
90 **TAPISSERIE (GER)**, b f Second Set (IRE)—Trance Dancer **M. E. Veek**
91 **THE LEMONPIE (GER)**, b c Next Desert (IRE)—Terra Novalis (GER) **R. Reutershan**

TWO-YEAR-OLDS

92 B c 25/4 Tiger Hill (IRE)—Aughamore Beauty (IRE) (Dara Monarch) **Gestut Romerhof**
93 **BLAUER KÖNIG**, ch c 25/2 Big Shuffle (USA)—Bubulina (GER) (Konigsstuhl) (6435) **Stall Blau-Weiss**
94 B f 23/3 Monsun (GER)—Classic Light (IRE) (Classic Secret (USA)) **Biesdeel Stud**
95 **DAINAH (GER)**, ch f 10/3 Dashing Blade—Dream of You (GER) (Music Boy) (8365) **Stall Aron**
96 B f 6/2 One Cool Cat (USA)—Eternal Beauty (USA) (Zafonic (USA)) (40000) **R. Shaykhutdinov**
97 **FINCA (IRE)**, b f 25/4 Pentire—Flagny (FR) (Kaldoun (FR)) **Frau R. U. A. Hacker**
98 Gr c 10/5 Eden Rock (GER)—Francisca (GER) (Lagunas) **Martin Schu**
99 **INDRAVADEN (GER)**, b c 1/1 Dashing Blade—Ibidem (GER) (Local Suitor (USA)) **Frau R. U. A. Hacker**
100 **ISHAN (GER)**, b c 1/1 Sholokhov (IRE)—Ishika (GER) (Lagunas) **Frau R. U. A. Hacker**
101 **ISI GOING (IRE)**, b f 5/4 King Charlemagne (USA)—Indian Goddess (IRE) (Indian Ridge) (7722) **P. Vogt**
102 **LADY ALIDA**, b f 12/4 Tobougg (IRE)—Lady Annina (FR) (Dashing Blade) (19305) **F. W. Holtkotter**
103 B c 28/2 Orpen (USA)—Mamma's Too (Skyliner) **Gestut Romerhof**
104 **PINTOR (GER)**, b c 1/1 Ransom O'war (USA)—Pampa Mia (Unblest) **Stall Chevalex**

MR CHRISTIAN VON DER RECKE—continued

105 **RIBELLO (GER)**, ch c 3/5 Sharp Prod (USA)—Roseola (GER) (Acatenango (GER)) (3217) **Quadriga GmbH**
106 **SABANTUY**, b c 6/3 Mujahid (USA)—Sabanila (GER) (In The Wings) (48262) **R. Shaykhutdinov**
107 **SPIRIT OF DUKE**, ch c 29/4 Bachelor Duke (USA)—See Me Well (IRE) (Common Grounds) (21879) **Stall Aron**
108 **VEGACINO (FR)**, b c 1/1 Septieme Ciel (USA)—Vega Sicilia (Environment Friend) **H. Kagel**
109 **ZIPPO (GER)**, ch c 17/4 Mondrian (GER)—Zizi Top (Robellino (USA)) (18018) **Stall P & P Bremen**

Other Owners: C. Bryce, Mrs E. M. Burke, A. J. Cousins, J. Dwight, V. Giesgen, Mrs J. Gleason, M. Himmelsbach, Ingrid Horlemann, R. T. Horrell, P Krug Handels GmbH, G. H. Leatham, Mr D. McCarthy, P. Murphy, Stall Four Friends, Stall Magarethe, Stall Mydlinghoven, Stall Valentina, R. E. Williams.

Assistant Trainer: Mrs Stephanie Nigge, Head Lad Mr Michael Berger

Jockey (flat): Rene Piechulek, Alex Pietch. **Jockey (NH):** Jan Korpas, A. P. McCoy. **Conditional:** A. K. Bromann. **Apprentice:** Angela Zander, Caroline Fuchs. **Amateur:** Mr O. Sauer, Mrs K. Schmitt.

---

605 MR J. WADE, Sedgefield
Postal: **Howe Hills, Mordon, Sedgefield, Cleveland, TS21 2HG**
Contacts: **PHONE (01740) 630310 FAX (01740) 630310 MOBILE (07831) 686968**

1 **ALWAYS RIGHT (IRE)**, 6, ch g Right Win (IRE)—Kemal Brave (IRE) **J. Wade**
2 **ATTICUS BOY (IRE)**, 7, ch g Atticus (USA)—Ring Beaune (USA) **Mr I. Herity**
3 **BLACK TOM TYRANT (IRE)**, 6, b g Synefos (USA)—Mis Fortune (IRE) **J. Wade**
4 **CASSIUS DIO (IRE)**, 6, ch g Anshan—Roisin Beag (IRE) **J. Wade**
5 **COUNT THE COST (IRE)**, 9, ch g Old Vic—Roseaustin (IRE) **J. Wade**
6 **DEUTERONOMY (IRE)**, 7, b g Beneficial—Good Heavens (IRE) **J. Wade**
7 **DEVIL'S RUN (IRE)**, 12, b g Commanche Run—She Devil **J. Wade**
8 **DOMINO DANCER (IRE)**, 4, b g Tagula (IRE)—Hazarama (IRE) **J. Wade**
9 **EYRE SQUARE (IRE)**, 5, b g Publisher (USA)—Eyre Eile (IRE) **Mr I. Herity**
10 **GENERAL HARDI**, 7, b g In Command (IRE)—Hardiprincess **J. Wade**
11 **GO FIGURE (IRE)**, 5, ch g Desert Prince (IRE)—Interpose **J. Wade**
12 **HARBOUR BUOY**, 7, ch g Bal Harbour—Elissa **J. Wade**
13 **IMPACT CRUSHER (IRE)**, 8, b g Sri Pekan (USA)—Costume Drama (USA) **J. Wade**
14 **JACK TAR (IRE)**, 6, b g Jolly Jake (NZ)—Pretty Furry **J. Wade**
15 **JERINGA**, 9, b g Karinga Bay—Jervandha **J. Wade**
16 **KING OF THE ARCTIC (IRE)**, 10, b g Arctic Lord—Ye Little Daisy **J. Wade**
17 **LE PLATINO (GER)**, 6, ch g Platini (GER)—La Paz (GER) **J. Wade**
18 **LOVE THAT BENNY (USA)**, 8, ch g Benny The Dip (USA)—Marie Loves Emma (USA) **J. Wade**
19 **LUCIUS RUFO (IRE)**, 6, b h Luso—Filli Rufo (IRE) **J. Wade**
20 **MARINERS WAY**, 5, b g Bal Harbour—Petaz **J. Wade**
21 **MUSICAL GIANT (USA)**, 5, ch g Giant's Causeway (USA)—Music House (USA) **J. Wade**
22 **PENZO (IRE)**, 5, gr g Shinko Forest (IRE)—Thatchabella (IRE) **J. Wade**
23 **PERSIAN PRINCE (IRE)**, 8, br g Anshan—Real Decent (IRE) **J. Wade**
24 **PERTINAX (IRE)**, 6, ch g Synefos (USA)—Echoes of Erin (IRE) **J. Wade**
25 **POLAR GALE (IRE)**, 8, ch g Anshan—Ali-Kin **J. Wade**
26 **POSEIDON (GER)**, 6, b g Tannenkonig (GER)—Pentagon Affairs **J. Wade**
27 **RECENT EDITION (IRE)**, 10, b g Roselier (FR)—Hi Millie **J. Wade**
28 **RED CEDAR (USA)**, 8, ch g Woodman (USA)—Jewell Ridge (USA) **J. Wade**
29 **ROLLING RIVER (IRE)**, 11, b g Over The River (FR)—Paddy's Dancer **J. Wade**
30 **RYMINSTER**, 9, ch g Minster Son—Shultan (IRE) **J. Wade**
31 **SHADY BARON (IRE)**, 9, b g Lord Americo—Glint of Baron **J. Wade**
32 **SHULMIN**, 8, ch m Minster Son—Shultan (IRE) **J. Wade**
33 **SILENT BAY**, 9, b g Karinga Bay—Lady Rosanna **J. Wade**
34 **STORMY LORD (IRE)**, 12, br g Lord Americo—Decent Shower **J. Wade**
35 **TRADING TROUBLE**, 11, b g Petoski—Marielou (FR) **J. Wade**
36 **WILFUL LORD (IRE)**, 11, b g Lord Americo—Dotties Girl (IRE) **J. Wade**
37 **ZAFFRAN GAIL (IRE)**, 7, ch g Zaffaran (USA)—Cara Gail (IRE) **J. Wade**

Assistant Trainer: Miss Maria Myco (07798) 775932

Jockey (NH): Paddy Aspell. **Amateur:** Mr Christopher Dawson.

606 MRS L. A. M. WADHAM, Newmarket
Postal: **The Trainer's House, Moulton Paddocks, Newmarket, Suffolk, CB8 7PJ**
Contacts: **PHONE (01638) 662411 FAX (01638) 668821 MOBILE (07980) 545776**

1 APPROVED FORCE (USA), 4, gr g With Approval (CAN)—Kinetic Force (USA) **Mr T. R. Wood**
2 BACKBORD (GER), 6, b g Platini (GER)—Bukowina (GER) **Mr & Mrs J. Timmons**
3 BOSS IMPERIAL (FR), 5, b g Raintrap—L'imperialis (FR) **Mr R. Davies**
4 CHAIM (IRE), 6, b br g Lord Americo—Furry Gran **Old Pals Partnership**
5 CORNELIA, 5, gr m Silver Patriarch (IRE)—Ludoviciana **Mrs G.Leigh & Mr G. W. Paul**
6 CRYSTAL DANCE (FR), 8, gr g Loup Solitaire (USA)—Somptueuse (FR) **Mr T. R. Wood**
7 DESERT INFERNO (FR), 6, b g Simon du Desert (FR)—Dora Dante (IRE) **Sir Peter & Lady Gibbings**
8 DIARIUS (GER), 5, b g Ungaro (GER)—Diavolessa (GER) **A. P. Racing**
9 DIVINE WISDOM, 7, ch m Silver Patriarch (IRE)—Ardent Bride **Mrs S. N. J. Embiricos**
10 DUSTY SPRINGHEELED (IRE), 5, br m Tragic Role—Majestic Di (IRE) **Ms K. J. Austin**
11 EMPEROR CONCERTO, 5, ch g Emperor Fountain—Busy Mittens **Waterhall Racing**
12 FENIX (GER), 9, b br g Lavirco (GER)—Frille (FR) **P. Philipps, T. Redman & J. Redman**
13 FORT SEVERN (IRE), 4, gr g Saddlers' Hall (IRE)—La Cabrilla **P. H. Betts**
14 HEIR TO BE, 9, b g Elmaamul (USA)—Princess Genista **R. B. Holt**
15 LADY ROISIN (IRE), 6, b m Luso—Curracloe Rose (IRE) **The Not Over Big Partnership**
16 LIGHT YIELD (USA), 4, ch g High Yield (USA)—Lisheba (USA) **Thurloe 50**
17 PERSONAL FLAIR, 5, ch m Alflora (IRE)—Lara's Princess
18 PUNJABI ARMY, 5, ch g Allied Forces—Punjabi Rose **Mrs J. May**
19 QUEEN POLINE (FR), 4, b f Trempolino (USA)—Queen Running (FR) **Mr R. Davies**
20 ROSENINDERIN (IRE), 4, b f Indian Danehill (IRE)—Roseraie (GER) **P. Philipps, T. Redman & J. Redman**
21 RUBY HARE, 7, ch g Classic Cliche (IRE)—Five And Four (IRE) **Campbell Gray Partnership**
22 SI GRAND (FR), 5, b g Solon (GER)—Secret Gold (GER) **Mr R. Davies**
23 SPECIAL DAY (FR), 4, gr c Daylami (IRE)—Plissetskaia (FR)
24 SURE FLAME (IRE), 6, b g Needle Gun (IRE)—Gallic Flame **The Hopkins Trower Partnership**
25 THE BLACK BARON (IRE), 6, br g Lord Americo—Royal Nora (IRE) **Mr and Mrs A. E. Pakenham**
26 THE DARK LORD (IRE), 11, b g Lord Americo—Khalkeys Shoon **Mr and Mrs A. E. Pakenham**
27 TOPFLIGHT WILDBIRD, 5, br m Diktat—Jamarj **P. Bamford**
28 UNITED (GER), 7, b m Desert King (IRE)—Una Kasala (GER) **R. B. Holt**
29 VICTORIAS GROOM (GER), 6, b br g Lavirco (GER)—Valda (RUS) **P. H. Betts (Holdings) Ltd**

Other Owners: Mr D. Allatt, Mrs C. P. Campbell, Mr Colin Campbell, Mr S. N. J. Embiricos, Sir Peter Gibbings, Lady Gibbings, Mr S. B. Glazer, Mr R. M. Harris, Mr James Hopkins, Mr James Hopkins, Mr Paul G. Jacobs, Mrs G. Leigh, Mr Peter O'Neill, Mr A. E. Pakenham, Mrs Victoria Pakenham, Mr G. W. Paul, Mr Oliver Pawle, Mr P. A. Philipps, Mr T. S. Redman, Mr J. S. Redman, Mr P. J. H. Rowe, Mr Andrew Thompson, Mr John Timmons, Mrs Marie Timmons, Mr William Trower, Mr Richard Venn, Mr J. J. W. Wadham.

Jockey (NH): D. Elsworth. **Conditional:** M. Roe.

607 MR N. WAGGOTT, Spennymoor
Postal: **Ingledene, Vyners Close, Merrington Lane, Spennymoor, Co. Durham, DL16 7HB**
Contacts: **PHONE (01388) 819012**

1 AAHJIMLAD (IRE), 7, b g Aahsaylad—Aunty Catherine (IRE) **Mrs J. Waggott**
2 ARCANGELA, 5, b m Galileo (IRE)—Crafty Buzz (USA) **Mrs J. Waggott**
3 BAILEYS SURPRISE (IRE), 6, ch g Mister Baileys—Sight'n Sound **N. Waggott**
4 DANEHILL WARRIOR (IRE), 4, b g Indian Danehill (IRE)—Karatisa (IRE) **Mrs J. Waggott**
5 FUTOO (IRE), 7, b g Foxhound—Nicola Wynn **Mrs J. Waggott**

Amateur: Mr J. J. Waggott.

608 MISS T. WAGGOTT, Spennymoor
Postal: **Awaitening Stables, Merrington Lane, Spennymoor, Co. Durham, DL16 7HB**
Contacts: **MOBILE (07979) 434498**

1 AWAKEN, 7, b m Zafonic (USA)—Dawna **Miss T. Waggott**
2 DENISON DANCER, 5, b g Paris House—Let's Hang On (IRE) **Mr R. R. Irvine**
3 GOOD INVESTMENT, 6, b g Silver Patriarch (IRE)—Bundled Up (USA) **H. Conlon**
4 KALIBS DREAM, 6, b g Minster Son—Primitive Countess **H. Conlon**
5 NUFOUDH (IRE), 4, b g Key of Luck (USA)—Limpopo **H. Conlon**
6 ROMAN HISTORY (IRE), 5, b g Titus Livius (FR)—Tetradonna (IRE) **B. Douglas**

MISS T. WAGGOTT—continued

7 **SEYAADI**, 6, b g Intikhab (USA)—Sioux Chef **H. Conlon**
8 **THE BRAT**, 4, b f Perryston View—Kalarram **H. Conlon**
9 **WINGSINMOTION (IRE)**, 4, b f Indian Lodge (IRE)—Coulisse (IRE) **Mr R. Orton**

Jockey (flat): M. Tebbutt. **Amateur:** Mr J. J. Waggott.

---

609 MR J. S. WAINWRIGHT, Malton

Postal: **Hanging Hill Farm, Kennythorpe, Malton, North Yorkshire, YO17 9LA**
Contacts: **PHONE (01653) 658537 FAX (01653) 658658 MOBILE (07798) 778070**

1 **BOBANSHEIL (IRE)**, 4, b f Dushyantor (USA)—Bobanlyn (IRE) **Mrs S. M. Walker**
2 **CAPE DANCER (IRE)**, 4, b f Cape Cross (IRE)—Yankee Dancer **C. V. Wentworth**
3 **GUNFIGHTER (IRE)**, 5, ch h Machiavellian (USA)—Reunion (IRE) **M. Sawers**
4 **LINDSEYFIELD LODGE (IRE)**, 7, br g Presenting—Missusan (IRE) **M. Sawers**
5 **LITTLE TASK**, 10, b g Environment Friend—Lucky Thing **K. Jackson**
6 **MISTER FIZZBOMB (IRE)**, 5, b g Lend A Hand—Crocus (IRE) **S. Enwright**
7 **MORRISTOWN MUSIC (IRE)**, 4, b f Distant Music (USA)—Tongabezi (IRE) **Hurn Racing**
8 **NESSEN DORMA (IRE)**, 7, b g Entrepreneur—Goldilocks (IRE) **Ms J. A. French**
9 **ONIZ TIPTOES (IRE)**, 7, ch g Russian Revival (USA)—Edionda (IRE) **drawn2win.co.uk Partnership**
10 **POLISH STAR**, 4, b g Polish Precedent (USA)—Apennina (USA) **M. Sawers**
11 **RED LETTER GIRL (IRE)**, 7, b m Bob Back (USA)—Letterlore **Mr J. M. Liggett**
12 **REFLECTIVE GLORY (IRE)**, 4, ch f City On A Hill (USA)—Sheznice (IRE) **A. Longbottom**
13 **SANDWITH**, 5, ch g Perryston View—Bodfari Times **M. Sawers**
14 **SLIVOVIC (IRE)**, 4, b f Fruits of Love (USA)—Ned's Contessa (IRE) **C. V. Wentworth**
15 **SOLDIER FIELD**, 4, b g Fantastic Light (USA)—Khambani (IRE) **J. S. Wainwright**

THREE-YEAR-OLDS

16 **BERTOLINI SPICE**, b f Bertolini (USA)—Scottish Spice
17 **BOURSE (IRE)**, b g Dubai Destination (USA)—Quarter Note (USA) **M. Sawers**
18 **CALL OF KTULU (IRE)**, b g Noverre (USA)—Yankee Dancer **C. V. Wentworth**
19 **FYODOROVICH (USA)**, b c Stravinsky (USA)—Omnia (USA) **C. V. Wentworth**
20 **LOCH JIPP (USA)**, b f Belong To Me (USA)—Miss Keyonna (USA) **Mr I Barran & Mr P Rhodes**

TWO-YEAR-OLDS

21 Gr ro c 5/4 Cozzene (USA)—Amber Token (USA) (Hennessy (USA)) (13119) **D. R. Brown**
22 B f 20/3 Traditionally (USA)—Catherinofaragon (USA) (Chief's Crown (USA)) (7721)
23 B c 15/2 Arch (USA)—Golden Show (Theatrical) **C. V. Wentworth**
24 B f 7/3 Prince Sabo—Landofheartsdesire (Up And At 'em)
25 B f 3/4 Kyllachy—Silver Blessings (Statoblest) (7000) **C. A. Maxted**

Other Owners: I. J. Barran, D. R. Brown, Mrs E. E. Brown, P. W. Cooper, Mr D. R. Jennings, J. G. Mitchell, Mr A. D. Renham, P. Rhodes, Miss Fiona Rodmell, Mr P. R. Walker.

Assistant Trainer: Miss Fiona Rodmell

Jockey (flat): R Winston, T. Eaves, T. Hamilton. **Jockey (NH):** P. Aspell. **Conditional:** Richard Tierney. **Amateur:** Mr M. D. Hill, Miss F. Rodmell.

---

610 MRS K. WALDRON, Tenbury Wells

Postal: **Woodstock Bower Farm, Stoke Bliss, Tenbury Wells, Worcestershire, WR15 8QN**
Contacts: **STABLES (01885) 410317 HOME (01885) 410309 FAX (01885) 410317 MOBILE (07779) 504580**

1 **AYURVEDA**, 7, b g Classic Cliche (IRE)—Herballistic **N. Shutts**
2 **COOLAVANNY LAD (IRE)**, 7, b g Needle Gun (IRE)—Thistletopper **N. Shutts**
3 **CORUM (IRE)**, 5, b g Galileo (IRE)—Vallee des Reves (USA) **N. Shutts**
4 **EXIT ROUTE**, 5, b g Exit To Nowhere (USA)—Nutcase **N. Shutts**
5 **FOLY PLEASANT (FR)**, 14, ch g Vaguely Pleasant (FR)—Jeffologie (FR) **N. Shutts**
6 **L'OISEAU DE FEU (USA)**, 4, b g Stravinsky (USA)—Off You Go (USA) **N. Shutts**
7 **LIVERPOOL ECHO (FR)**, 8, b g Poliglote—Miss Echo **N. Shutts**
8 **MAGNIFICO (FR)**, 7, b g Solid Illusion (USA)—Born For Run (FR) **N. Shutts**
9 **MERRY STORM (IRE)**, 9, b g Glacial Storm (USA)—Cap Reform (IRE) **N. Shutts**
10 **MILTON DES BIEFFES (FR)**, 8, gr g Princeton (FR)—Rose Fuschia (FR) **N. Shutts**

MRS K. WALDRON—continued

11 **RASH MOMENT (FR)**, 9, b g Rudimentary (USA)—Ashura (FR) **N. Shutts**
12 **SUMTOTOTAL**, 6, b g Mtoto—Garota De Ipanema (FR) **N. Shutts**
13 **TEWKESBURY (IRE)**, 4, b g King's Best—Zeferina (IRE) **N. Shutts**
14 **THE GENERAL LEE (IRE)**, 6, b br g Accordion—Catrionas Castle (IRE) **N. Shutts**
15 **YOUNG LORCAN**, 12, ch g Bay Tern (USA)—Naughty Nessie **N. Shutts**

Conditional: R. Spate.

MR R. B. WALEY-COHEN, Banbury
Postal: **Upton Viva, Banbury, Oxfordshire, OX15 6HT**
Contacts: **PHONE (02072) 446022 MOBILE (07831) 888778**
E-MAIL rwc@alliance.co.uk

1 **ANY THE WISER**, 4, br g Kahyasi—Best of The Best (FR) **R. B. Waley-Cohen**
2 **IRILUT (FR)**, 12, br g Lute Antique (FR)—Patchourie (FR) **R. B. Waley-Cohen**
3 **KATARINO (FR)**, 13, b g Pistolet Bleu (IRE)—Katevana (FR) **R. B. Waley-Cohen**
4 **MEL IN BLUE (FR)**, 10, b g Pistolet Bleu (IRE)—Calligraphie (FR) **R. B. Waley-Cohen**
5 **ORGANIZ (FR)**, 6, b br g Mansonnien (FR)—Madame Illusion (FR) **R. B. Waley-Cohen**
6 **PRELUDE D'ESTRUVAL (FR)**, 5, gr g Sheyrann—Kali d'estruval (FR) **R. B. Waley-Cohen**
7 **SOMETHING SMALL**, 8, br g Supreme Leader—Rachel C (IRE) **R. B. Waley-Cohen**

Assistant Trainer: Kate Mawle

Amateur: Mr S. Waley-Cohen.

612

MR T. D. WALFORD, Sheriff Hutton
Postal: **Cornborough Manor, Sheriff Hutton, York**
Contacts: **PHONE (01347) 878382 FAX (01347) 878547 MOBILE (07904) 237676**
E-MAIL g_walford@hotmail.com WEBSITE www.timwalford.co.uk

1 **BLAST THE PAST**, 6, b m Past Glories—Yours Or Mine (IRE) **Energytek (Yorkshire) Ltd**
2 **CALM SEAS (IRE)**, 4, b g Posidonas—Sunalina **Mrs R. Conway**
3 **GYPSY GEORGE**, 7, b br g Sovereign Water (FR)—Query Line **Mr M. C. Thuey**
4 **INDONESIA**, 6, ch g Lomitas—Idraak **G. E. Dempsey**
5 **ITS MOON (IRE)**, 4, b f Tobougg (IRE)—Shallat (IRE) **Jaass One Racing**
6 **MICKY MAC (IRE)**, 4, b g Lend A Hand—Gazette It Tonight **A. M. McArdle**
7 **MISS PROSS**, 8, br m Bob's Return (IRE)—Lucy Manette **D. Coates**
8 **NASEBY COVERT**, 6, br g Moscow Society (USA)—Buckby Folly **Mrs S. A. York**
9 **ROSA FINA**, 6, b m Luso—Baroness Rose **Mrs H. P. Spath**
10 **SHERIFF HUTTON (IRE)**, 5, b g Rudimentary (USA)—Will She What (IRE) **R. J. Adcock**

THREE-YEAR-OLDS

11 B g First Trump—Elle Reef

TWO-YEAR-OLDS

12 B g 14/4 First Trump—Faithful Beauty (IRE) (Last Tycoon) (14000)
13 B f 2/4 Bahri (USA)—Northern Goddess (Night Shift (USA)) (9000) **Mrs W. A. D. Craven**

Other Owners: D. F. L. Bishop, J. R. Burns, E. R. Clark, D. J. Dickson, C. J. Grindal, Mr N. J. Maher, Mr C. Moss, I. C. Phillips, N. Skinner, Mrs G. B. Walford, J. P. Wilcox.

Assistant Trainer: Mrs G B Walford

Jockey (NH): R. Walford. Amateur: Mr M. Walford.

613

MR C. F. WALL, Newmarket
Postal: **Induna Stables, Fordham Road, Newmarket, Suffolk, CB8 7AQ**
Contacts: **OFFICE (01638) 661999 HOME (01638) 668896 FAX (01638) 667279**
MOBILE (07764) 940255
E-MAIL christianwall@btconnect.com WEBSITE www.chriswallracing.co.uk

1 **ACE OF HEARTS**, 9, b g Magic Ring (IRE)—Lonely Heart **Archangels 1**
2 **CURZON PRINCE (IRE)**, 4, b c Mujadil (USA)—Smooth Spirit (USA) **Mr H. Alsabah**

MR C. F. WALL—continued

3 **DALMATIAN**, 4, b g Mtoto—Patria (USA) **Alan & Jill Smith**
4 **EMULATE**, 4, b f Alhaarth (IRE)—Aquarelle
5 **ESPOIR DE LUMIERE**, 4, b f Mark of Esteem (IRE)—Lumiere d'espoir (FR) **Aldis, Caunce & Sigsworth**
6 **FOLLOW THE FLAG (IRE)**, 4, ch g Traditionally (USA)—Iktidar **Follow The Flag Partnership**
7 **GRAND VIZIER (IRE)**, 4, b g Desert Style (IRE)—Distant Decree (USA) **Hintlesham SP Partners**
8 **HABSHAN (USA)**, 8, ch g Swain (IRE)—Cambara **Alan & Jill Smith**
9 **KEIDAS (FR)**, 4, b f Lomitas—Kahina (GER) **M. Tilbrook**
10 **MASTER PEGASUS**, 5, b g Lujain (USA)—Seeking Utopia **Mrs S. P. Roberts**
11 **NAVENE (IRE)**, 4, b f Desert Style (IRE)—Majudel (IRE) **Dr P. J. Brown**
12 **OH SO SAUCY**, 4, b f Imperial Ballet (IRE)—Almasi (IRE) **The Eight of Diamonds**
13 **PREMIO LOCO (USA)**, 4, ch g Prized (USA)—Crazee Mental **B. R. Westley**
14 **ROYAL ROCK**, 4, b g Sakhee (USA)—Vanishing Point (USA) **S. Fustok**
15 **SUNDAE**, 4, b g Bahamian Bounty—Merry Rous **P. A. Gregory**
16 **ZOWINGTON**, 6, gr g Zafonic (USA)—Carmela Owen **O. Pointing**

THREE-YEAR-OLDS

17 **ADDWAITYA**, br c Xaar—Three White Sox **L. McLaughlin**
18 **ANTILLIA**, b f Red Ransom (USA)—Milly of The Vally **A. Saeed**
19 **BEAU FIGHTER**, b g Tobougg (IRE)—Belle de Jour **P. G. Kingston & P. T. Kingston**
20 **CARMELA MARIA**, b f Medicean—Carmela Owen **O. Pointing**
21 **CHARLEVOIX (IRE)**, b f King Charlemagne (USA)—Cayman Sound **M. Sinclair**
22 **DALLA FINESTRA**, ch f Bahamian Bounty—Spinning Mouse **Doreen M Swinburn & Lady Juliet Tadgell**
23 **GIADINIERA**, b f Bahri (USA)—Rose des Andes (IRE) **Lady Juliet Tadgell**
24 **LADY CAROLLINA**, b f Bertolini (USA)—Carollan (IRE) **Moss & Vaessen**
25 **LUMINOUS GOLD**, b f Fantastic Light (USA)—Nasaieb (IRE) **Dr P. J. Brown**
26 **MANGO LADY**, gr f Dalakhani (IRE)—Generous Lady **S. Fustok**
27 **MINISTEROFINTERIOR**, b g Nayef (USA)—Maureen's Hope (USA) **S. Fustok**
28 **MORNING DELIGHT**, b f Daylami (USA)—All Glory **P. R. Pritchard**
29 **PLAISTERER**, b f Best of The Bests (IRE)—Lumiere d'espoir (FR) **David Andrews Plastering**
30 **SO GLAMOROUS**, b f Diktat—Gena Ivor (USA) **M. L. Ayers**
31 **SPATE RIVER**, b g Zaha (CAN)—Rion River (IRE) **Firman Webster Racing**
32 **STAR GRAZER**, ch f Observatory (USA)—Oatey **Racingeight Partners**
33 **THE HONORABLE (IRE)**, b c Sadler's Wells (USA)—Bonita Francita (CAN) **E. I. Mack**
34 **TOMATINA**, ch f Kyllachy—Sunningdale (IRE) **Hintlesham JMS Partners**
35 **VALATRIX (IRE)**, b f Acclamation—Dramatic Entry (IRE) **Mrs V. A. Gordon**
36 **VIVE LES ROUGES**, b f Acclamation—Bible Box (IRE) **J. E. Sims**
37 **XANDRA (IRE)**, b f Xaar—Talah **Mrs P Neave,Batting & Tweenhills Racing**

TWO-YEAR-OLDS

38 **BEAU MILITAIRE**, b c 2/5 Tobougg (IRE)—Belle de Jour (Exit To Nowhere (USA)) **P. G. Kingston & P. T. Kingston**
39 **BOUNTY BOX**, b f 17/2 Bahamian Bounty—Bible Box (Bin Ajwaad (IRE)) **J. E. Sims**
40 **DUBAI DIVA**, b f 27/1 Dubai Destination (USA)—Marine City (JPN) (Carnegie (IRE)) (62000) **P. J. W. Botham**
41 **FORTEZZA**, b f 3/4 Efisio—Donna Anna (Be My Chief (USA)) **Lady Juliet Tadgell**
42 **GALIOTTO (IRE)**, b c 18/4 Galileo (IRE)—Welsh Motto (Mtoto) (45000) **Archangels 2**
43 B c 23/4 Sakhee (USA)—Gena Ivor (USA) (Sir Ivor (USA)) (4000) **Mr M. Ayers**
44 **MERRY DIVA**, b f 29/4 Bahamian Bounty—Merry Rous (Rousillon (USA)) **Mrs. P. Green**
45 **MOON BOY**, b c 17/2 Medicean—Summer Daze (Swain (USA)) (30000) **S. Fustok**
46 **PRECIOUS SECRET (IRE)**, b f 15/3 Fusaichi Pegasus (USA)—
Gharam (USA) (Green Dancer (USA)) **Stourbank Racing**
47 **PYRRHA**, b f 19/1 Pyrus (USA)—Demeter (USA) (Diesis) (7000) **Lady Juliet Tadgell**
48 **RAFIQA (IRE)**, b f 8/3 Mujahid (USA)—Shamara (USA) (Spectrum (USA)) (20000) **The Equema Partnership**
49 **RIPTIDE**, b c 28/1 Val Royal (FR)—
Glittering Image (IRE) (Sadler's Wells (USA)) (60000) **Gone To The Bar Racing**
50 **SHARAXIA**, b f 23/3 Xaar—Shioda (USA) (Bahri (USA)) (40000) **Induna Racing Partners (Two)**
51 **STANLEY RIGBY**, b c 25/3 Dr Fong (USA)—
Crystal (IRE) (Danehill (USA)) (45000) **Dean Hardman & Stella Kelsall**
52 B f 12/2 Cadeaux Genereux—Star Profile (Sadler's Wells (USA)) (40000) **Mr. P. Botham & Partners**
53 **SUNSPEAR (IRE)**, b f 18/2 Montjeu (IRE)—Out West (USA) (Gone West (USA)) **S. Fustok**
54 B f 28/2 Red Ransom (USA)—Surprise Visitor (IRE) (Be My Guest (USA)) (40000) **The Leap Year Partnership**
55 **WAKE UP CALL**, b f 28/3 Noverre (USA)—Up And About (Barathea (IRE)) (30000) **The Hon John Lambton**
56 **WINTERFELL**, b f 16/1 Haafhd—It Girl (Robellino (USA)) **S. Fustok**

MR C. F. WALL—continued

Other Owners: D. Ablitt, Mrs A. Aldis, D. Allan, Mr S. Atkin, Mr T. Bater, Mrs J. M. T. Batting, Mr. N. Belcher, Mr Giles Bovill, Mr Hugo Bovill, Mr W. J. Bridge, P. W. Brown, Mr P Brown, Mrs Billy Carbutt, Mrs J. Carlisle, S. A. Caunce, Mr John F. Chapman, MR D. Cherry, Mrs J. M. Clement, Mrs Rex Cooper, Mrs S E. Cunningham, Mr. P. Cunningham Snr., Mrs J. E. Dobie, MR M. Donnellan, Mr J. Firman, Mr R. Fraiser, Mr J. N. Gosling, Mr. R. Haim, Mr D. Hanafin, Mr Dean Hardman, Mr. C. Harker, Mr. S. Harrar, The Hon Mrs J. Haslam, Mr. D. Hilton, Miss M. C. Jackman, Ms Stella Kelsall, Mrs Jill Kerr-Smiley, Mr. M. Key, Mrs P. G. Kingston, Mr P. T. Kingston, Mr. R. Mone, Mr Alwyn Moss, Mr Roger Nash, Mrs R. M. S. Neave, Mr. J. Norden, Mrs Charles Park, Mr D. Popely, Mr R. A. Popely, Mr. I. Radford, Mr D. Redvers, Mr Ray Rice, Mr. D. Rice, Mr J. Roberts, Prudence Lady Salt, Mrs R. Skeels, Mr R. A. Smith, Mr. S. Smith, Mrs Jill Smith, Lady Stuttaford, Mrs Doreen M. Swinburn, A. Taylor, MR. A. A. Thomas, Mr. P. Tuckwell, Mr L. J. Vaessen, P. H. Veenbaas, Mrs P. I. Veenbaas, Vogue Development Company (Kent) Ltd, Mrs C. J. Walker, Mr J. Wall, D. P. Walsh, Mr. M. Wayman, Mr. R. Wayman, Mr S. L. Webster, Mrs P. H. Williams.

Assistant Trainer: Kerry Cournane

Apprentice: Jack Mitchell.

---

614 **MRS S. WALL, Dallington**
Postal: **Little Pines, Bakers Lane, Dallington, Nr. Heathfield, East Sussex, TN21 9JS**
Contacts: **PHONE/FAX (01435) 831048**
E-MAIL sarah55french@btinternet.com

1 **CONNA COURT (IRE)**, 5, b g Witness Box (USA)—My Mavourneen **Mrs S. Wall**
2 **SHANLYRE QUEST (IRE)**, 8, b g Eurobulo—Manta Vision (IRE) **Mrs S. Wall**
3 **SHIKOKU LASS (IRE)**, 8, br m Muroto—Miss Josephine (IRE) **J. P. C. Wall**
4 **TALLOW BAY (IRE)**, 13, b g Glacial Storm (USA)—Minimum Choice (IRE) **Mrs S. Wall**

Assistant Trainer: Jeremy Wall

Amateur: Mr S. P. Hanson.

---

615 **MR T. R. WALL, Church Stretton**
Postal: **Harton Manor, Harton, Church Stretton, Shropshire, SY6 7DL**
Contacts: **PHONE (01694) 724144 FAX (01694) 724144**

1 **ALWAYS BAILEYS (IRE)**, 5, ch g Mister Baileys—Dubiously (USA) **Mr Derek & Mrs Marie Dean**
2 **ARCHIMBOLDO (USA)**, 5, ch g Woodman (USA)—Awesome Strike (USA) **The Wenlock Edge Optimists**
3 **ARDFRY (IRE)**, 9, b g Courtship—Chestnut Park (IRE) **Over the Edge**
4 **CAT SIX (USA)**, 4, b f Tale of The Cat (USA)—Hurricane Warning (USA) **Mr Derek & Mrs Marie Dean**
5 **ELLIES HORSE (IRE)**, 6, gr g Saddlers' Hall (IRE)—Place Stephanie (IRE) **C. G. Johnson**
6 **GLENEAGLES (IRE)**, 4, ch g Pivotal—Embassy **Mr Derek & Mrs Marie Dean**
7 **LITTLE VILLAIN (IRE)**, 10, b g Old Vic—Party Woman (IRE) **T. R. Wall**
8 **LYON**, 8, ch g Pivotal—French Gift **Mr & Mrs J D Lomas & Mrs S Orme**
9 **MIND THAT FOX**, 6, b g Mind Games—Foxie Lady **T. R. Wall**
10 8, Ch h El Conquistador—Sanber **Mrs M. Lomas**
11 **SHADY OLIVE**, 4, gr f Terimon—Shady Emma **D. Pugh**
12 **SPY GUN (USA)**, 8, ch g Mt Livermore (USA)—Takeover Target (USA) **Mr Derek & Mrs Marie Dean**
13 **STAR BERRY**, 5, b m Mtoto—Star Entry **Mr Derek & Mrs Marie Dean**

THREE-YEAR-OLDS

14 **MARINO PRINCE (FR)**, b c Dr Fong (USA)—Hula Queen (USA) **Mr Derek & Mrs Marie Dean**

TWO-YEAR-OLDS

15 Ch c 3/5 Central Park (IRE)—E Minor (IRE) (Blushing Flame (USA)) (2500) **Mr Derek & Mrs Marie Dean**

Other Owners: Mr A. H. Bennett, Mr Derek Dean, Mrs Marie Dean, Mr D. Evans, Mr J. D. Lomas, Mrs M. Lomas, Mr R. Mapp, Mrs S. Orme, Mr E. P. Parkes, Mr S. Pickering, Mr C. Sharratt, Mr T. Wall.

Assistant Trainer: Mrs J. A. Wall

Conditional: L. P. Edwards. **Apprentice:** Josh Wall. **Amateur:** Mr A. W. Edwards, Mr L. Johnson.

616 MRS K. WALTON, Middleham
Postal: Sharp Hill Farm, Middleham, Leyburn, North Yorkshire, DL8 4QY
Contacts: PHONE (01969) 622250 MOBILE (07718) 909356
E-MAIL Katewaltonracing@hotmail.com WEBSITE www.katewaltonracing.co.uk

1 CROP WALKER (IRE), 6, b br g Kotashaan (FR)—Miss Mutley I. M. Lynch
2 HUKA LODGE (IRE), 11, gr g Roselier (FR)—Derrella Mrs J. M. Jones
3 JIMMY BOND, 9, b g Primitive Rising (USA)—Miss Moneypenny Mr & Mrs P. Chapman
4 KISSINTHEPEACH (IRE), 7, b m Witness Box (USA)—Balinloop (IRE) S. Birchall
5 MASTERJOE, 6, b g Shambo—Littledrunkgirl Mrs P. M. Wilson
6 NEVERTIKA (FR), 7, b g Subotica (FR)—Griotte de Coddes (FR) Mrs J. M. Jones
7 OUR JOYCEY, 7, b m Shernazar—Charisse Dancer Stan Clough & Brian Ross
8 PHENIX MAG (FR), 5, b g Subotica (FR)—Feat (FR) Mrs C. E. Holroyd
9 ROMAN BURY, 5, b m Overbury (IRE)—Roman Uproar Keep The Faith Partnership
10 ROYAL FLYNN, 6, b g Royal Applause—Shamriyna (IRE) Mr & Mrs P. Chapman
11 SIR ORPEN (IRE), 5, gr g Orpen (USA)—Yalciyna J. P. Allen
12 SKIPPER'S LAD (IRE), 6, br g Flemensfirth (USA)—Spin N'win Mr & Mrs P. Chapman
13 STAR OF THE DESERT (IRE), 5, b br g Desert Story (IRE)—Cindy's Star (IRE) The Suffolk Punch Syndicate
14 TOP OFFICIAL (IRE), 6, ch g Beneficial—Lobby Nes (IRE) R. Manners

THREE-YEAR-OLDS

15 Br f Dr Fong (USA)—Inimitable J. P. Allen

Other Owners: J. Baker, Mr P. W. Chapman, Mrs J. Chapman, S. Clough, Mr J. Edwards, Mr D. Edwards, Mr M. Kane, Mr G. Pearson, Mr B. Ross, Mr B. R. Smith, Mr G. M. Spall, J. M. Swinglehurst, Mrs K. Walton.

Jockey (NH): R. McGrath. Conditional: R. Utley.

617 MRS BARBARA WARING, Ettington
Postal: Stone Cottage, Thornton Chase, Ettington, Stratford upon Avon
Contacts: MOBILE (07787) 516723

1 MALDOUN (IRE), 9, b g Kaldoun (FR)—Marzipan (IRE) Hodgkinson Shimmans Lister Wood Nicholls
2 MURAQEB, 8, ch g Grand Lodge (USA)—Oh So Well (IRE) Hughes Shimmans Roche
3 PRINCESS ARWEN, 6, b m Magic Ring (IRE)—Absolutelystunning Mrs Barbara Waring
4 SMILING APPLAUSE, 9, b g Royal Applause—Smilingatstrangers Eddys A Team
5 STUNNING MAGIC, 8, b g Magic Ring (IRE)—Absolutelystunning Bowler Shapter Macrae Wiggam Mundy
6 TAKEACHANCEONHIM, 10, b g Dilum (USA)—Smilingatstrangers Zebby & Friends

Other Owners: Mr John K. Barlow, Mr J. R. Barr, Mr P. O. Bowler, Ms Anna Brewer, Mr G. Coan, Mr B. Conneely, Mr V. R. Cooke, Mr Joe Cottington, Mr D. M. Finnigan, Mr A. Flint, Mr M. J. Flint, Mr R. E. Foulkes, Mr A. G. Gibbs, Mrs David Hodgkinson, Miss K. Hughes, Mr B. P. Jessup, Mr D. E. Jones, Mr Graham Lister, Mr J. Macrae, Mr M. Mitchell, Mr J. T. Morris, Mr C. Mundy, Mrs E. Nicholls, Mr Richard Parker, Mr S. Roche, Mr Kieran P. Ryan, Mr Hugh J. Shapter, Mr G. Shimmans, Mr P. Tinkler, Mr J. W. Waggott, Mrs Barbara Waring, Mr D. Waterman, Mr J. Wiggam, Mr Duncan Wood.

Assistant Trainer: H Chisman

Jockey (NH): M. Foley, J. Mogford, M. A. Fitzgerald. Conditional: J. Pritchard. Amateur: Mr M. Wall.

618 MR F. WATSON, Sedgefield
Postal: Beacon Hill, Sedgefield, Stockton-On-Tees, Cleveland, TS21 3HN
Contacts: PHONE (01740) 620582 MOBILE (07773) 321472

1 ATTILA THE HUN, 9, b g Piccolo—Katya (IRE) Mr K. Watt
2 BEACON RAMBLER, 6, ch g Cayman Kai (IRE)—Bunty's Friend F. Watson
3 BOTTOMLESS WALLET, 7, ch m Titus Livius (FR)—Furry Dance (USA) Mr K. Watt
4 CRUSHEA (IRE), 8, b g Shahanndeh—Cooleen Alainn F. Watson
5 DISTINCTLYTHEBEST, 8, b g Distinctly North (USA)—Euphyllia F. Watson
6 FLAMING CAT (IRE), 5, b br g Orpen (USA)—Brave Cat (IRE) J. D. Blythe
7 KAYRATI, 5, b m Cayman Kai (IRE)—Emmajoun F. Watson

MR F. WATSON—continued

THREE-YEAR-OLDS

8 **KAIOPPER**, b f Cayman Kai (IRE)—Great Hopper **F. Watson**

TWO-YEAR-OLDS

9 B c 17/2 Diktat—Birjand (Green Desert (USA)) (1200)
10 B c 5/5 Hunting Lion (IRE)—Deekazz (IRE) (Definite Article)
11 Ch f 18/2 Vettori (IRE)—Swallow Breeze (Salse (USA)) (800)

Amateur: Miss Victoria Casey.

---

619 **LADY S. WATSON, Bossall**
Postal: **Bossall Hall, Bossall, York, North Yorkshire, YO60 7NT**
Contacts: **PHONE (01904) 468315 MOBILE (07836) 578122**

1 4, Ch f Zaha (CAN)—Isabeau **Lady S. Watson**
2 **KISMET**, 10, b m Tirol—Belamcanda **Lady S. Watson**
3 **TO THE WIND**, 5, gr g Silver Patriarch (IRE)—Caution **Lady S. Watson**
4 **TURFTANZER (GER)**, 9, b g Lomitas—Tower Bridge (GER) **Lady S. Watson**

---

620 **MRS S. A. WATT, Richmond**
Postal: **Rosey Hill Farm, Scorton Road, Brompton on Swale, Richmond, North Yorkshire, DL10 7EQ**
Contacts: **PHONE (01748) 812064 FAX (01748) 812064 MOBILE (07970) 826046**
E-MAIL wattfences@aol.com

1 **BEAMISH PRINCE**, 9, ch g Bijou d'inde—Unconditional Love (IRE) **Forster Watt Boast**
2 **CASH FLOW**, 5, b m Mtoto—Little Change **Mrs J. E. M. Trotter**
3 **FEANOR**, 10, b m Presidium—Nouvelle Cuisine **Mrs S. A. Watt**
4 **LOOKING FORWARD**, 12, br g Primitive Rising (USA)—Gilzie Bank **Mrs N. M. Handley**
5 **OSCAR TRIAL (IRE)**, 6, b g Oscar (IRE)—The Polecat (IRE) **Major E. J. Watt**
6 **PRESSMAN**, 5, b g Alflora (IRE)—Scoop (IRE) **Mrs S. A. Watt**
7 **YOUNG BLADE**, 7, b g Cloudings (IRE)—Lady Shoco **C. Tremewan**

Other Owners: Mr L. Boast, Mrs Wendy Forster, Major E. J. Watt.

Assistant Trainer: S. Hole

Jockey (NH): K. Mercer. **Amateur:** Mr S. Byrne.

---

621 **MR R. I. WEBB-BOWEN, Wincanton**
Postal: **Sycamore Farm, Stoke Trister, Wincanton, Somerset, BA9 9PE**
Contacts: **PHONE (01963) 31647 (01722) 433402 FAX (01963) 31647 MOBILE (07919) 884895**
E-MAIL robert@webb-bowen.co.uk WEBSITE www.camrosestud.org.uk

1 **DEEP KING (IRE)**, 13, b br g King's Ride—Splendid Run **Mrs D. J. Webb-Bowen**
2 **HIGH BRAY (GER)**, 7, b g Zieten (USA)—Homing Instinct **Mrs D. J. Webb-Bowen**

Assistant Trainer: Mrs Dinah Webb-Bowen

---

622 **MR P. R. WEBBER, Banbury**
Postal: **Cropredy Lawn, Mollington, Banbury, Oxfordshire, OX17 1DR**
Contacts: **PHONE (01295) 750226 FAX (01295) 758482 MOBILE (07836) 232465**
E-MAIL paul@paulwebberracing.com WEBSITE www.paulwebberracing.com

1 **AISATSU (IRE)**, 4, ch f Courteous—Casting Vote (USA) **Fawley House Stud**
2 **APPLEADAY (IRE)**, 7, gr g Beneficial—Hello Aris (IRE) **D. C. R. Allen**
3 **ASTRAL BOY (IRE)**, 4, b br g Lahib (USA)—Astral Cake (CAN) **Mr S. Liebermann**
4 **AUSSIE BAY (IRE)**, 5, b g Clerkenwell (USA)—Bondi Bay (IRE) **Simon & Liz Packer**
5 **AUSTRALIA DAY (IRE)**, 5, gr g Key of Luck (USA)—Atalina (FR) **Samantha & Emma McQuiston Partnership**
6 **AUTUMN RED (IRE)**, 8, ch g Zaffaran (USA)—Ballygullen River (IRE) **Dodson & Partners**
7 **BEGUILING (IRE)**, 7, b m Dr Massini (IRE)—Belle Dame (IRE) **Mrs C. A. Waters**

MR P. R. WEBBER—continued

8 4, Ch g Flemensfirth (USA)—Bell Walks Run (IRE) **Sarah & Toby Drysdale**
9 **CAPTAIN'S LEGACY,** 7, b g Bob's Return (IRE)—Tuppence In Clover **Chartwell Racing**
10 **DON CASTILLE (USA),** 6, ch g Royal Anthem (USA)—Suzie Sparkle (USA) **Mr D. P. Barrie & Mr M. J. Rees**
11 **DREAM FOREST (IRE),** 5, b g Raise A Grand (IRE)—Theresa Green (IRE) **T. R. Pearson**
12 **EDGBRIAR (FR),** 6, br g Brier Creek (USA)—Harmonie de Valtat (FR) **D. C. R. Allen**
13 **EDGEBURY,** 5, br g Overbury (IRE)—Dusky Dante (IRE) **D. C. R. Allen**
14 **EDGEOVER,** 6, br g Overbury (IRE)—Dusky Dante (IRE) **D. C. R. Allen**
15 **EDGEVINE,** 4, b f Grape Tree Road—Vieille Russie **D. C. R. Allen**
16 **ERDELI (IRE),** 4, b g Desert Prince (IRE)—Edabiya (IRE) **P. A. Deal**
17 **FERMAT (FR),** 6, gr g Great Palm (USA)—Five Rivers (FR) **Mr M. J. Dowd**
18 **FIRST BLUE (IRE),** 5, b g Supreme Leader—Bilberry **R. M. Kirkland**
19 **FULL HOUSE (IRE),** 9, br g King's Theatre (IRE)—Nirvavita (FR) **The Chamberlain Addiscott Partnership**
20 4, B br g Tamayaz (CAN)—Gaye Gordon **David Carrington**
21 4, B g Beneficial—Good Times Ahead (IRE) **David Carrington**
22 **HALF HIB (IRE),** 5, br g Lahib (USA)—Half Irish **Burnt Toast Ltd**
23 **HERE'S THE KEY (IRE),** 4, b f Dark Moondancer—Hereke **D. C. R. Allen**
24 **IDIOME (FR),** 12, b g Djarvis (FR)—Asterie L'ermitage (FR) **Mrs L. C. Taylor & Miss M. Talbot BT**
25 **INWAAN (IRE),** 5, b g King's Best (USA)—Balaabel (USA) **The Eleventh Hour Racing Partnership**
26 **JAOKA DU GORD (FR),** 11, b g Concorde Jr (USA)—Theorie du Cochet (FR) **R. W. Barnett**
27 **JULY JOHNSON (IRE),** 6, b g Saddlers' Hall (IRE)—
          Miss Cripps (IRE) **Sir Martyn Arbib, Paul Dixon, John Harvey, Martin Myers**
28 **KANGRINA,** 6, b m Acatenango (GER)—Kirona **Patrick Burling Developments Ltd**
29 **KATE'S GIFT,** 7, b g Supreme Leader—Ardentinny **Mr & Mrs M. J. Dowd**
30 **KENTMERE (IRE),** 7, b g Efisio—Addaya (IRE) **D. C. R. Allen**
31 **KEY CUTTER (FR),** 4, b g Alderbrook—Two Roads **Mrs A. W. Timpson**
32 **KING OF CASTILE,** 4, ch g Hernando (FR)—Pato **Mr D. P. Barrie & Mr M. J. Rees**
33 **LADY BERNIE (IRE),** 7, b m Supreme Leader—Noon Hunting **The Large G & T Partnership**
34 **LAISH YA HAJAR (IRE),** 4, ch g Grand Lodge (USA)—Ya Hajar **The Auctionair Racing Partnership**
35 **LASKARI (FR),** 9, b g Great Palm (USA)—Hatzarie (FR) **Mrs W. Morrell & Mrs L. C. Taylor**
36 **LETS CAST AGAIN,** 6, ch g Mark of Esteem (IRE)—Alcalali (USA) **Mr D. P. Barrie & Mr M. J. Rees**
37 **LUXURIX (FR),** 7, gr g Linamix (FR)—Luxurious (USA) **P. C. Green**
38 **MAGIC CLOVER (ARG),** 7, ch h Candy Stripes (USA)—Magnanimity (ARG) **B. V. R. Racing**
39 **MAKHZOON (USA),** 4, b br g Dynaformer—Boubskaia **T. R. Pearson**
40 **MERCHANT RED (USA),** 5, b br g Red Ransom (USA)—Great Lady Slew (USA) **John Nicholls Ltd/David Kilburn**
41 **MISTER PAN (IRE),** 6, b g Taipan (IRE)—Forest Mist **Happy Days Racing**
42 **MORE TROUBLE (IRE),** 7, b g Zaffaran (USA)—Athas Liath (IRE) **Economic Security**
43 **NEFERTARI,** 6, b m Sir Harry Lewis (USA)—Kota Tinggi **Mrs C. A. Inglesant**
44 **OFF SPIN,** 8, b g Petoski—Re-Spin **M. C. Stoddart**
45 **ON SPEC,** 4, b g Spectrum (IRE)—Ann Veronica (IRE) **W. H. F. Carson**
46 **ONE GULP,** 5, b m Hernando (FR)—Elaine Tully (IRE) **R. J. McAlpine**
47 **ONE OF THE BOYS (IRE),** 7, ch g Shernazar—Easter Morning (FR) **D. E. Czarnetzki**
48 **ONE SCOOP,** 4, ch g Hernando (FR)—Bodfari Quarry **R. J. McAlpine**
49 **OPTIC,** 6, b m Kayf Tara—Mid Day Chaser (IRE) **J. A. Jenkins**
50 **PATRICKSNINETEENTH (IRE),** 11, b g Mister Lord (USA)—Many Miracles **The Large G & T Partnership**
51 **PIA JANE (IRE),** 8, b m Beneficial—Modile (IRE) **The Auctionair Racing Partnership**
52 **PRESSGANG,** 6, b g Unfuwain (USA)—Petralona (USA) **Mrs S. H. West**
53 **RADAR LOVE,** 6, ch m Classic Cliche (IRE)—Goldenswift (USA) **The Dream On Partnership**
54 **RED BIRR (IRE),** 7, b g Bahhare (USA)—Cappella (IRE) **John Nicholls (Trading) Ltd**
55 **RETURN OF THE KING,** 6, b g Nashwan (USA)—Someone Special **S. C. B. Ltd, G. Shiel & R. Stevenson**
56 **ROBERT THE BRAVE,** 4, b g Primo Valentino (IRE)—Sandicliffe (USA) **T. R. Pearson**
57 **RUBY ISABEL (IRE),** 4, gr f Great Palm (USA)—Royal Lucy (IRE) **R. A. Green, D. Taglight**
58 **SENIOR WHIM,** 6, b g Lahib (USA)—Euphorie (GER) **D. I. Bare**
59 **SLEEP TALK (USA),** 5, br g Theatrical—Sleep Easy (USA) **Bell Equino Partnership**
60 **SPACE MISSION (IRE),** 6, b g Kayf Tara—Jupiter's Message **Saif Ali**
61 **SPACE STAR,** 8, b g Cosmonaut—Sophiesue **P. R. Webber**
62 **SPINAROUND,** 10, gr g Terimon—Re-Spin **D. R. Stoddart**
63 **STAR SHOT (IRE),** 7, b g Cloudings (IRE)—B Final **R. M. Kirkland**
64 **STRONG SURVIVOR (USA),** 5, b g Kingmambo (USA)—Summer Solstice (IRE) **Mr D. P. Barrie & Mr M. J. Rees**
65 **SWAYTHE (USA),** 7, b m Swain (IRE)—Caithness (USA) **The Syndicators**
66 **TRIBE,** 6, b g Danehill (USA)—Leo Girl (USA) **Mr I. R. Watters**
67 **VIVARINI,** 4, b g Hernando (FR)—Venetian Red (USA) **R. C. Moody**
68 **WINCHESTER RED,** 6, ch g Gunner B—M I Babe **Jeremy Dougall, William Watt**

MR P. R. WEBBER—continued

THREE-YEAR-OLDS

69 **HARD TO RESIST (IRE)**, b c Statue of Liberty (USA)—Kelpie (IRE) **Mrs C. A. Waters & Mr E. Jordan**
70 **STAR ALLIANCE (IRE)**, b c Sadler's Wells (USA)—Angelica Tree (CAN) **M. H. Watt**

Other Owners: Mrs D. L. Addiscott, D. P. Barrie, Mr John T. Behrendt, Mr Michael Coghlan, Mrs A. L. Davies, Mr M. J. Dowd, Mrs H. J. Dowd, Mr R. J. Dyer, Mr Raymond Anderson Green, Mr D. W. Higgins, Mr D. R. D. M. Hilleary, John Nicholls (Trading) Ltd, Mr Joseph Kerrigan, Mr D. Kilburn, Mr S. M. Lloyd, Sir I. Magee, Mrs S. D. McGrath, Mr R. H. Mcgrath, Professor David Metcalf, Mr Simon Packer, Mrs Liz Packer, Mr Martin Pepper, Miss Julia Pike, Mr M. J. Rees, Mr Philip Rocher, Mr Tony Stephens, Mr Charles Street, Miss M. Talbot, Mrs L. C. Taylor, Mrs A. Timpson, Mr Geoffrey Vos, Mr R. L. Ward, Mr Graham Wilson.

Assistant Trainer: Caroline Fryer

Jockey (flat): J. Fortune. **Jockey (NH):** Dominic Elsworth, W. T. Kennedy, A. Tinkler, J. Davies, A. Thornton.

---

623 **MISS D. E. WEEDEN, Newmarket**
Postal: **Fieldview, 5 Little Ditton, Woodditton, Newmarket, Suffolk, CB8 9SA**
Contacts: **PHONE (01638) 730587 (01638) 730546 FAX (01638) 730546 MOBILE (07919) 975893**
E-MAIL dianaweedenracing@btinternet.com

1 **BROUHAHA**, 4, b g Bahhare (USA)—Top of The Morning **G. D. Newton**
2 **CANARY GIRL**, 5, br m Primo Valentino (IRE)—Cumbrian Concerto
3 **INTIMATE FRIEND (USA)**, 7, b m Expelled (USA)—Intimate (USA) **Miss D. E. Weeden**
4 **ONLY HOPE**, 4, b f Marju (IRE)—Sellette (IRE) **The Italian Job**

THREE-YEAR-OLDS

5 **CULZEAN BAY**, b f Mind Games—Florie Nightingale **G. D. Newton**
6 B c Mtoto—Star Princess **Young Roman Racing**

Other Owners: Miss Carmelina Favarulo, Mr Mark Fryers, Mrs Vivien Hamilton-Carroll, Miss Diana Weeden.

Assistant Trainer: Mr Cliff Lines

Jockey (flat): P. Eddery.

---

624 **MR P. WEGMANN, Gloucester**
Postal: **Maisemore Park, Maisemore, Gloucester, GL2 8HX**
Contacts: **PHONE (01452) 301332 FAX (01452) 505002 MOBILE (07785) 242857**
E-MAIL peter.wegmann@virgin.net

1 **ALLEGIANCE**, 13, b g Rock Hopper—So Precise (FR) **P. Wegmann**
2 **LOMAGUNDI ROAD (IRE)**, 8, b g Lycius (USA)—Olivana (GER) **P. Wegmann**
3 **SPRINGWELL BEAU**, 6, ch g Then Again—Logani **P. Wegmann**

Assistant Trainer: Miss V Williams

---

625 **MR D. K. WELD M.V.B. M.R.C.V.S., The Curragh**
Postal: **Rosewell House, The Curragh, Co. Kildare, Irish Republic.**
Contacts: **PHONE (00353) 4544 1273/441 476 FAX (00353) 4544 1119**
E-MAIL dkweld@eircom.net

1 **ANSAR (IRE)**, 12, b g Kahyasi—Anaza **Mrs K. Devlin**
2 **BOBS PRIDE (IRE)**, 6, b h Marju (IRE)—Vyatka **R. Blacoe**
3 **EXPLANATION**, 4, b c Peintre Celebre (USA)—Never Explain (IRE) **Dr M.W.J. Smurfit**
4 **GENTLEMAN JEFF (USA)**, 4, ch c Mr Greeley (USA)—Wooing (USA) **Dr Ronan Lambe**
5 **MAJESTIC CONCORDE (IRE)**, 5, b g Definite Article—Talina's Law (IRE) **Dr Ronan Lambe**
6 **PRINCE ERIK**, 4, gr c Indian Ridge—Miracle **Dr Ronan Lambe**
7 **PRINCELY HERO (IRE)**, 4, b g Royal Applause—Dalu (IRE) **Dr Ronan Lambe**
8 **PROFOUND BEAUTY (IRE)**, 4, b f Danehill (USA)—Diamond Trim (IRE) **Moyglare Stud Farm**
9 **TRULY MINE (IRE)**, 4, ch f Rock of Gibraltar (IRE)—Truly Yours (IRE) **Mrs C. L. Weld**

MR D. K. WELD M.V.B. M.R.C.V.S.—continued

THREE-YEAR-OLDS

10 **ALANEED**, b c Key of Luck (USA)—Banaadir (USA) **Hamdan Al Maktoum**
11 **ALMOLAHEK (IRE)**, b c Red Ransom (USA)—Daqtora **Hamdan Al Maktoum**
12 **ANAAWEEN (USA)**, b f Diesis—Vencera (FR) **Hamdan Al Maktoum**
13 **ANGEL DREAMER (USA)**, b f Street Cry (IRE)—L'extra Honor (USA) **Dr Ronan Lambe**
14 **ARTIC CRY (USA)**, b c Rahy (USA)—Sailing Minstrel (USA) **Mr Sean Mulryan**
15 **AWARD CEREMONY (IRE)**, b c Green Desert (USA)—Ripple of Pride (IRE) **Moyglare Stud Farm**
16 **BRAVELY FOUGHT (IRE)**, b c Indian Ridge—Amazing Tale **Moyglare Stud Farm**
17 **CAMPFIRE GLOW (IRE)**, b f Invincible Spirit (IRE)—Ski Lodge (IRE) **Dr Ronan Lambe**
18 **CARRIBEAN SUNSET (IRE)**, b f Danehill Dancer (IRE)—Bonheur (IRE) **Dr Ronan Lambe**
19 **CASUAL CONQUEST (IRE)**, b c Hernando (FR)—Lady Luck (IRE) **Moyglare Stud Farm**
20 **CENTRAL STATION (IRE)**, ch c Indian Ridge—Token Gesture (IRE) **Moyglare Stud Farm**
21 **CHINESE WHITE (IRE)**, gr f Dalakhani (IRE)—Chiang Mai (IRE) **Lady O'Reilly**
22 **CUSTOMARY CHORUS (IRE)**, br gr f Linamix (FR)—Magical Cliche (USA) **Moyglare Stud Farm**
23 **DAASIJ (IRE)**, b c Dalakhani (IRE)—Alyakkh (IRE) **Hamdan Al Maktoum**
24 **DAR ARAB (USA)**, b f Dynaformer (USA)—Grand Deed (USA) **Hamdan Al Maktoum**
25 **DAWRAAT (IRE)**, b f Dubai Destination (USA)—Hadeb **Hamdan Al Maktoum**
26 **DIAMOND STAR (IRE)**, b f Daylami (IRE)—Style of Life (USA) **Mrs C. L. Weld**
27 **DOMESTIC FUND (IRE)**, b c Sadler's Wells (USA)—Market Slide (USA) **Moyglare Stud Farm**
28 **FAMOUS NAME**, b c Dansili—Fame At Last (USA) **Mr K. Abdulla**
29 **GHIMAAR**, b c Dubai Destination (USA)—Charlecote (USA) **Hamdan Al Maktoum**
30 **GOING PUBLIC (IRE)**, b c Night Shift (USA)—Gifts Galore (IRE) **Moyglare Stud Farm**
31 **GRACEFUL STAR (IRE)**, b f Soviet Star (USA)—Amandian (IRE) **Mr Sean Mulryan**
32 **GRATIFIED (IRE)**, b c Sadler's Wells (USA)—Be Glad **Mr K. Abdulla**
33 **KI MANIERE (IRE)**, b f Sadler's Wells (USA)—Dress To Thrill (IRE) **Moyglare Stud Farm**
34 **KNOWING WINK (IRE)**, b f Big Shuffle (USA)—Sudden Stir (USA) **Moyglare Stud Farm**
35 **LABAQA (USA)**, b f Rahy (USA)—Rumansy (USA) **Hamdan Al Maktoum**
36 **LADY ALICIA (IRE)**, b f Hawk Wing (USA)—Dame Alicia (IRE) **Dr Ronan Lambe**
37 **LEO'S PRIDE (IRE)**, ch c Medicean—Alpine Park (IRE) **Mr Donald Keough**
38 **LUXIE (IRE)**, b f Acclamation—Cover Girl (IRE) **Mrs C. L. Weld**
39 **MAD ABOUT YOU (IRE)**, b f Indian Ridge—Irresistible Jewel (IRE) **Moyglare Stud Farm**
40 **MARYELLEN'S SPIRIT (IRE)**, b f Invincible Spirit (IRE)—Habariya (IRE) **N. Newtown Anner Stud Farm Ltd**
41 **MATTERS AT HAND (IRE)**, b c Red Ransom (USA)—Hint of Humour (USA) **Moyglare Stud Farm**
42 **PORTOFINO BAY (IRE)**, b f Montjeu (IRE)—Sallanches (USA) **Dr Ronan Lambe**
43 **PROVINCIAL (IRE)**, b c Aldebaran (USA)—Rustic (IRE) **Mr K. Abdulla**
44 **ROCK CRITIC (IRE)**, b c Pivotal—Diamond Trim (IRE) **Moyglare Stud Farm**
45 **SCARLET O' HARA (IRE)**, b f Sadler's Wells (USA)—Agnetha (GER) **Mrs C.L. Weld & Mrs J. Magnier**
46 **SECOND GLANCE (IRE)**, b f Lemon Drop Kid (USA)—Easy Sunshine (IRE) **Moyglare Stud Farm**
47 **SHINING ARMOUR (IRE)**, b c Green Desert (USA)—Perfect Touch (USA) **Dr Ronan Lambe & Mrs C.L. Weld**
48 **SOARING EMOTIONS (USA)**, b f Kingmambo (USA)—Luminous Beauty (USA) **Moyglare Stud Farm**
49 **SONG OF FREEDOM (IRE)**, b c Montjeu (IRE)—Hoity Toity **Dr Ronan Lambe**
50 **SPANISH CROSS (IRE)**, gr f Cape Cross (IRE)—Espana **Lady O'Reilly**
51 **STREET STYLE (IRE)**, b f Rock of Gibraltar (IRE)—Streetcar (IRE) **Lady O'Reilly**
52 **SUAILCE (IRE)**, gr f Singspiel (IRE)—Katch Me Katie **H. E. President Of Ireland**
53 **SURFER GIRL (IRE)**, b f Red Ransom (USA)—Imelda (USA) **Mr Paul Gould**
54 **TABAAHI (IRE)**, ch c Alhaarth (IRE)—Lovelyst (USA) **Hamdan Al Maktoum**
55 **UNWRITTEN RULE (IRE)**, gr c Dalakhani (IRE)—Triple Try (IRE) **Moyglare Stud Farm**
56 **WELANGA**, b f Dansili—Well Beyond (FR) **Mr K. Abdulla**
57 **WOODLAND BEAUTY (IRE)**, gr f Highest Honor (FR)—Algaira (USA) **Lady B. Oppenheimer**

TWO-YEAR-OLDS

58 **AADAAT (USA)**, b f 1/1 Dixie Union (USA)—Aljawza (USA) (Riverman (USA)) **Hamdan Al Maktoum**
59 **ALMEDAWAR (IRE)**, b c 24/1 Elusive Quality (USA)—
                          Lucky Rainbow (Rainbow Quest (USA)) (199484) **Hamdan Al Maktoum**
60 **ALTURISTIC (IRE)**, b c 13/8 Sadler's Wells (USA)—Market Slide (USA) (Gulch (USA)) **Moyglare Stud Farm**
61 B f 12/2 Refuse To Bend (IRE)—Angelic Sounds (IRE) (The Noble Player (USA)) (150000) **Lady C. J. O'Reilly**
62 **ANYWAYSMILE (IRE)**, ch f 25/2 Indian Ridge—
                          Genuine Charm (IRE) (Sadler's Wells (USA)) **Moyglare Stud Farm**
63 **APRIL (IRE)**, ch f 29/4 Rock of Gibraltar (IRE)—Agnetha (GER) (Big Shuffle (USA)) **Mrs C. L. Weld**
64 B c 7/5 Oasis Dream—Avoidance (USA) (Cryptoclearance (USA)) **Mr K. Abdulla**
65 B f 22/2 Galileo (IRE)—Beautiful Note (USA) (Red Ransom (USA)) (83654) **Mr Robert Blacoe**
66 **BLACKANGELHEART (IRE)**, b f 26/4 Danehill Dancer (IRE)—
                          Magical Cliche (USA) (Affirmed (USA)) **Moyglare Stud Farm**
67 **BLOND BEAUTY (USA)**, ch f 24/3 Theatrical—Luminous Beauty (USA) (A P Indy (USA)) **Moyglare Stud Farm**

MR D. K. WELD M.V.B. M.R.C.V.S.—continued

 68 **CAREFREE SMILE (IRE)**, b f 1/3 Invincible Spirit (IRE)—
Frippet (Ela-Mana-Mou) (128700) **Dr Ronan Lambe**
 69 Ch c 16/5 Rock of Gibraltar (IRE)—Claxton's Slew (USA) (Seattle Slew (USA)) (164092) **Newtown Anner Stud**
 70 Ch f 14/2 Medicean—Cochin (USA) (Swain (IRE)) **Mr K. Abdulla**
 71 B f 11/5 Elusive Quality (USA)—Committed Actress (USA) (Theatrical) (72886) **Mrs C. L. Weld**
 72 B f 9/2 Nayef (USA)—Costa Rica (IRE) (Sadler's Wells (USA)) **Mr K. Abdulla**
 73 **DANCE PASS (IRE)**, b f 3/2 Sadler's Wells (USA)—Super Gift (IRE) (Darshaan) **Moyglare Stud Farm**
 74 **DISCREET AFFAIR (IRE)**, b f 15/3 Invincible Spirit (IRE)—
Lady Elysees (USA) (Royal Academy (USA)) (173744) **Dr Ronan Lambe**
 75 **EASY MATE (IRE)**, ch f 18/4 Monsun (GER)—All To Easy (Alzao (USA)) **Moyglare Stud Farm**
 76 **ENCHANTED EVENING (IRE)**, b f 24/2 High Chaparral (IRE)—Glen Kate (Glenstal (USA)) **Mr D. K. Weld**
 77 **FIERY RED (IRE)**, ch f 6/2 Pivotal—Step With Style (USA) (Gulch (USA)) **Moyglare Stud Farm**
 78 **GHANAATI (USA)**, b f 27/3 Seeking The Gold (USA)—Nafisah (Lahib (USA)) **Hamdan Al Maktoum**
 79 **HASEILA**, b f 8/2 Oasis Dream—Miss Anabaa (Anabaa (USA)) **Hamdan Al Maktoum**
 80 **HIDDEN UNIVERSE (IRE)**, gr c 9/5 Linamix (FR)—
Hint of Humour (USA) (Woodman (USA)) (96524) **Dr Ronan Lambe**
 81 B c 16/5 Bahri (USA)—Idilic Calm (IRE) (Indian Ridge) (70000) **Newtown Anner Stud**
 82 B f 10/4 Cape Cross (IRE)—Indaba (IRE) (Indian Ridge) (74001) **Mr Hassen Adams**
 83 **INTIMATE SECRET (IRE)**, b f 8/4 Invincible Spirit (IRE)—Habaza (IRE) (Shernazar) (100000) **Dr Ronan Lambe**
 84 B c 19/2 Danehill Dancer (IRE)—Labrusca (Grand Lodge (USA)) (154440) **Newtown Anner Stud**
 85 **LEGEND OF GREECE (IRE)**, b c 17/4 Danetime (IRE)—Lodema (IRE) (Lycius (USA)) (51480) **Dr Ronan Lambe**
 86 B c 13/2 Bachelor Duke—Lidanna (Nicholas (USA)) (100000) **Mr Donald Keough**
 87 **LIEBERMANN (GER)**, b c 7/2 Big Shuffle (USA)—La Ola (GER) (Dashing Blade) (27670) **Lisselan Farms**
 88 B f 4/4 Dynaformer (USA)—Light Jig (Danehill (USA)) **Mr K. Abdulla**
 89 B f 21/3 Refuse To Bend (IRE)—Lionne (Darshaan) (140000) **Mrs C. L. Weld**
 90 **LUMINIOUS EYES (IRE)**, ch f 9/4 Bachelor Duke (USA)—
Mood Indigo (IRE) (Indian Ridge) (102960) **Dr Ronan Lambe**
 91 **MA ANI (USA)**, gr ro f 24/2 El Prado (IRE)—Hasheema (IRE) (Darshaan) **Hamdan Al Maktoum**
 92 B c 8/5 Sadler's Wells (USA)—Mabrova (Prince Mab (FR)) (200000) **Mr Donald Keough**
 93 B c 16/4 Celtic Swing—Magical Peace (IRE) (Magical Wonder (USA)) (140000) **Sir M. W. J. Smurfit**
 94 **MAJESTIC SILVER (IRE)**, br f 21/4 Linamix (FR)—
Diamond Trim (IRE) (Highest Honor (FR)) **Moyglare Stud Farm**
 95 **MAQSOOD (USA)**, ch c 14/3 Forestry (USA)—La Riviera (USA) (Affirmed (USA)) (165208) **Hamdan Al Maktoum**
 96 B f 10/4 Rock of Gibraltar (IRE)—March Hare (Groom Dancer (USA)) (80437) **Mr Ananda Krishnan**
 97 Gr f 23/2 Dalakhani (IRE)—Massarra (Danehill (USA)) (150000) **Lady C. J. O'Reilly**
 98 **MAZIONA**, b f 18/1 Dansili—Polygueza (FR) (Be My Guest (USA)) (250000)
 99 **MEDICIO (FR)**, b c 18/4 Medicean—Cospicua (IRE) (High Estate) (128700) **Hamdan Al Maktoum**
100 **MOVING HEART (IRE)**, b f 1/5 Anabaa (USA)—Lady Luck (IRE) (Kris) **Moyglare Stud Farm**
101 Ch f 3/2 Pivotal—My Giddy Aunt (IRE) (Danehill) (USA)) **Newtown Anner Stud**
102 **NAIAZEK**, ch c 2/5 Refuse To Bend (IRE)—Elshamms (Zafonic (USA)) **Hamdan Al Maktoum**
103 **NAVAJO PRINCESS (IRE)**, ch f 13/3 Indian Ridge—Perfect Touch (USA) (Miswaki (USA)) **Mrs C. L. Weld**
104 **NETHAAM (IRE)**, ro c 15/4 Dalakhani (IRE)—Balaabel (USA) (Sadler's Wells (USA)) **Hamdan Al Maktoum**
105 B c 16/5 Danetime (IRE)—Optional (Prince Sabo) (154440) **Dr Ronan Lambe**
106 B f 21/1 Exceed And Excel (AUS)—Pacific Grove (Persian Bold) (99741) **Mr Hassen Adams**
107 B f 7/3 Orpen (USA)—Peratus (IRE) (Mujadil (USA)) **Mr Bert Firestone**
108 **PERFECTLY CHILLED (IRE)**, gr f 15/2 Dalakhani (IRE)—
Ripple of Pride (IRE) (Sadler's Wells (USA)) **Moyglare Stud Farm**
109 B f 10/3 Empire Maker (USA)—Phantom Wind (USA) (Storm Cat (USA)) **Mr K. Abdulla**
110 **PIECES OF DREAM**, br c 17/4 Dalakhani (IRE)—Bedside Story (Mtoto) (128700) **Dr Ronan Lambe**
111 **PINNACLE WHISPER (IRE)**, ch f 24/2 Giant's Causeway (USA)—
Suitably Discreet (Mr Prospector (USA)) **Moyglare Stud Farm**
112 **POWERFUL PRESENCE (IRE)**, ch c 24/3 Refuse To Bend (IRE)—
Miss a Note (USA) (Miswaki (USA)) (109394) **Dr Ronan Lambe**
113 **PRECIOUS GEM (IRE)**, b f 3/4 Sadler's Wells (USA)—Ruby (IRE) (Danehill (USA)) (148004) **Mrs C. L. Weld**
114 **QASSAAR**, b c 15/4 Cape Cross (IRE)—Taqreem (IRE) (Nashwan (USA)) **Hamdan Al Maktoum**
115 B f 26/2 Oasis Dream—Rapid Ransom (USA) (Red Ransom (USA)) **Lady O'Reilly**
116 Ch c 6/2 Falbrav (IRE)—Revealing (Halling (USA)) **Mr K. Abdulla**
117 **SALAABA (IRE)**, b f 15/2 Nayef (USA)—Khulasah (IRE) (Darshaan) **Hamdan Al Maktoum**
118 B c 19/3 Fasliyev (USA)—Savieres (IRE) (Sadler's Wells (USA)) (50000) **M. R. Green**
119 B c 18/4 Galileo (IRE)—Sevi's Choice (USA) (Sir Ivor (USA)) (155000) **Sir M. W. J. Smurfit**
120 **SILVER FOR YOU (IRE)**, gr c 27/4 Verglas (IRE)—Sun Seasons (IRE) (Salse (USA)) **Moyglare Stud Farm**
121 **SILVER SHOON (IRE)**, gr f 18/3 Fasliyev (USA)—Limpopo (Green Desert (USA)) (165000) **Mrs C. L. Weld**
122 B c 5/2 Dalakhani (IRE)—Snug Dinner (IRE) (Jareer (USA)) (141570) **Mr Donald Keough**
123 B c 14/2 Rock of Gibraltar (IRE)—Soviet Moon (IRE) (Sadler's Wells (USA)) **Mr K. Abdulla**
124 **SPORTING ICON (IRE)**, b c 18/1 Sadler's Wells (USA)—
Dress To Thrill (IRE) (Danehill (USA)) **Moyglare Stud Farm**

MR D. K. WELD M.V.B. M.R.C.V.S.—continued

125 **SUBLIME TALENT (IRE)**, b c 13/2 Sadler's Wells (USA)—
Summer Trysting (USA) (Alleged (USA)) (90089) **Dr Ronan Lambe**
126 B c 31/3 Harlan's Holiday (USA)—Tee For Three (USA) (Lil E Tee (USA)) (145772) **Sir M. W. J. Smurfit**
127 **TELESCOPIC VISION (IRE)**, b c 6/2 Galileo (IRE)—
Silly Game (IRE) (Bigstone (IRE)) (122264) **Dr Ronan Lambe**
128 Gr ro c 13/3 Mizzen Mast (USA)—Tsar's Pride (Sadler's Wells (USA)) **Mr K. Abdulla**
129 Ch c 24/1 Indian Ridge—Upperville (IRE) (Selkirk (USA)) (141569) **Mr B. R. Firestone**
130 B f 7/3 Invincible Spirit (IRE)—Watch The Clock (Mtoto) (283140) **Newtown Anner Stud**
131 B c 24/2 Rainbow Quest (USA)—West Dakota (USA) (Gone West (USA)) **Mr K. Abdulla**
132 B f 10/2 Oasis Dream—Zathonia (Zafonic (USA)) **Mr K. Abdulla**

Jockey (flat): P. Shanahan, P. J. Smullen. **Apprentice:** S. M. Gorey.

---

626 **MR MARK WELLINGS, Bridgnorth**
Postal: Broad Acre Stables, Broadlanes, Quatt, Bridgnorth, Shropshire, WV15 6EG
Contacts: PHONE (01746) 781019 MOBILE (07973) 763469
E-MAIL mark@broadacre.fsnet.co.uk

1 **DIAMOND HURRICANE (IRE)**, 4, b g Mujadil (USA)—Christoph's Girl **Mark Wellings Racing**
2 **KING OF CONNACHT**, 5, b h Polish Precedent (USA)—Lady Melbourne (IRE) **Mr A. M. Gilbert**
3 **LITTLE RICHARD (IRE)**, 9, b g Alhaarth (IRE)—Intricacy **Mark Wellings Racing**
4 **YURCHENKO**, 4, b f Mamalik (USA)—Rajmata (IRE) **Lord Mutton Racing Partnership**

THREE-YEAR-OLDS

5 **BAGENALSTOWN (IRE)**, b c Fath (USA)—Rhapsani (IRE) **Mr P. F. Goulding**
6 **JIMMY DEAN**, b c Ishiguru (USA)—Sister Sal **Mark Wellings Racing**

Other Owners: Mr C. Fiford, Miss A. Poplar, A. Tranter, Mark Wellings.

Assistant Trainer: Mrs L A Wellings

---

627 **MR L. WELLS, Billingshurst**
Postal: Pallingham Manor Farm, Wisborough Green, Billingshurst, West Sussex, RH14 0EZ
Contacts: OFFICE (01403) 700119 HOME (01403) 700911 FAX (01403) 700899
MOBILE (07977) 144949 E-MAIL pmf@btinternet.com WEBSITE www.lawrencewells.co.uk

1 **CLASSIC ROLE**, 9, b g Tragic Role (USA)—Clare Island **L. Wells**
2 **DIVA OF NORWICH (IRE)**, 6, b b m Norwich—Sue's A Lady **P. Zetter**
3 **LEASE BACK (FR)**, 9, b g Sleeping Car (FR)—Salse Pareille (FR) **D. W. Cox**
4 **LORD LEONARDO (IRE)**, 8, b g Norwich—Sue's A Lady **Mrs C. J. Zetter-Wells**
5 **LORD NORMAN (IRE)**, 7, b g Norwich—Sue's A Lady **Mrs C. J. Zetter-Wells**
6 **NOVI SAD (IRE)**, 10, b g Norwich—Shuil Na Gale **Mrs C. J. Zetter-Wells**
7 **PRESENTING DIVA (IRE)**, 5, b m Presenting—Sue's A Lady **Mrs C. J. Zetter-Wells**
8 **THE STAFFORD (IRE)**, 7, b g Selkirk (USA)—Bint Zamayem (IRE) **P. Zetter**
9 **TIMON'S PRESENT**, gr f Presenting—Princess Timon **P. Zetter**
10 **ULLALUJAH**, 6, b m Josr Algarhoud (IRE)—Ulla Laing **P. Zetter**
11 **VICTREE (IRE)**, 9, b g Old Vic—Boro Glen **D. W. Cox**

Assistant Trainer: Mrs C J Zetter-Wells

---

628 **MISS S. WEST, Lewes**
Postal: 5 Balmer Farm Cottages, Brighton Road, Lewes, East Sussex, BN7 3JN
Contacts: PHONE (01273) 621303 FAX (01273) 622189 MOBILE (07748) 181804
E-MAIL sheenawest11@aol.com WEBSITE www.sheenawest.com

1 **CAMBO (FR)**, 7, b br g Mansonnien (FR)—Royal Lie (FR) **G. L. Flight**
2 **CLARA BUCK**, 6, b m Kayf Tara—Buck Comtess (USA) **G. West**
3 **DIZZY RASCAL**, 4, br f Bob Back (USA)—City Times (IRE) **Bellhouse Racing Limited**
4 **DOCTOR NED**, 4, b g Bahamian Bounty—Sangra (USA) **M. Moriarty**
5 **DUBAI ACE (USA)**, 7, b g Lear Fan (USA)—Arsaan (USA) **Mucky Duck II Partnership**
6 **FLAMEHAIRTEMPTRESS**, 5, ch m Dancing Spree (USA)—
It's Been Jilted (IRE) **The Stewkley Shindiggers Partnership**

MISS S. WEST—continued

7 HANSOMELLE (IRE), 6, b m Titus Livius (FR)—Handsome Anna (IRE) **M. Moriarty**
8 4, B c Dancing Spree (USA)—It's Been Jilted (IRE) **G. West**
9 ITSAWINDUP, 4, b g Elnadim (USA)—Topwinder (USA) **Wrb Racing 58 (wrbracing.Com)**
10 LADINO (FR), 8, b g Acatenango (GER)—Lauderdale (GER) **M. Moriarty**
11 MY MONNA, 4, b f Josr Algarhoud (IRE)—Albarsha **J. Baden White**
12 QUALIFY, 5, b g Mark of Esteem (IRE)—Raneen Alwatar **WRB Racing 58 (wrbracing.com)**
13 RUBILINI, 4, ch f Bertolini (USA)—Aunt Ruby (USA) **Heart Of The South Racing**
14 RUBYS BAY, 4, b f Docksider (USA)—Female Lead **Mucky Duck III Partnership**
15 SEA MAP, 6, ch g Fraam—Shchana (USA) **G. West**
16 SILBER MOND, 6, gr g Monsun (GER)—Salinova (FR) **M. K. George**
17 SMOKEY THE BEAR, 6, ch g Fumo di Londra (IRE)—Noble Soul **G. L. Flight**

THREE-YEAR-OLDS

18 B g Kayrawan (USA)—Hey Winnie (USA) **M. Moriarty**
19 TOBAGO BAY, b c Tobougg (IRE)—Perfect Dream **Heart Of The South Racing**

Other Owners: Mr Andrew Bates, Mr C. Cory, Mr M. W. Gregory, Mr J. E. Hall, Mr M. Kell, Mr John Penny, Mrs Caroline Penny, Miss Sheena West, Mr Gerald West, Wetherby Racing Bureau Ltd.

Assistant Trainer: Jamie Goldstein

Jockey (NH): J. Goldstein. **Conditional:** M. Goldstein.

---

629 **MR J. R. WEYMES, Middleham**
Postal: Ashgill, Coverham, Leyburn, North Yorkshire, DL8 4TJ
Contacts: **PHONE** (01969) 640420 **FAX** (01969) 640505 **MOBILE** (07753) 792515
E-MAIL johnweymes@aol.com **WEBSITE** www.johnweymes.co.uk

1 ALMATY EXPRESS, 6, b g Almaty (IRE)—Express Girl **Sporting Occasions Racing No 5**
2 ANOTHER RUM (IRE), 10, b g Zaffaran (USA)—Sharp Fashion VII **Mr A. J. R. Lilley**
3 ATTACCA, 7, b g Piccolo—Jubilee Place (IRE) **High Moor Racing 2**
4 CHRIS CORSA, 5, b g Mark of Esteem (IRE)—Risque Lady **G. Houghton**
5 CROSBY JEMMA, 4, ch f Lomitas—Gino's Spirits **Exors of the Late Don Raper**
6 FRANCESCO, 4, ch g Vettori (IRE)—Violet (IRE) **G. Houghton**
7 GRAND VIEW, 12, ch g Grand Lodge (USA)—Hemline **Sporting Occasions**
8 LADY SAMBURY, 6, b m Overbury (IRE)—Skiddaw Samba **High Moor Racing 4**
9 LINDEN'S LADY, 8, b m Compton Place—Jubilee Place (IRE) **Mr E. P. Kingsley**
10 MISS HAVISHAM (IRE), 4, b f Josr Algarhoud (IRE)—Agony Aunt **High Moor Racing 1**
11 ONYERGO (IRE), 6, b g Polish Precedent (USA)—Trick (IRE) **Exors of the Late Hon Mrs N. Napier**
12 RUE SOLEIL, 4, ch f Zaha (CAN)—Maria Cappuccini **Mr R. Burton**
13 SIMPLY ST LUCIA, 6, b m Charnwood Forest (IRE)—Mubadara (IRE) **J. R. Weymes**
14 THE RIMORIK, 7, ch g Cayman Kai (IRE)—Brook House **Mrs D. A. Bousfield**
15 TUXSUMDOIN, 4, ch f Zaha (CAN)—Roisin Clover **Mr R. Burton**
16 WELCOME APPROACH, 5, b g Most Welcome—Lucky Thing **T. A. Scothern**

THREE-YEAR-OLDS

17 B f Midnight Legend—Books Whirl
18 CASINO NIGHT, ch f Night Shift (USA)—Come Fly With Me **Mr T. B. Robson**
19 DUCAL DAMSEL, b f Best of The Bests (IRE)—Lucky Thing **T. A. Scothern**
20 ELUSIVE LADY (IRE), b f Clodovil (IRE)—Bella Vie (IRE) **T. A. Scothern**
21 JIM MARTIN, b g Auction House (USA)—Folly Finnesse **Mrs J. Morley**
22 MISS UNDERSTANDING, b f Dansili—Crossed Wire **C. E. Giblett**
23 PADDY JACK, ch g Rambling Bear—Bayrami **Mr T. W. Batchelor**
24 SOCIAL SPIRIT (IRE), br f Auction House (USA)—Sibilant **Mrs A. Birkett**

TWO-YEAR-OLDS

25 B c 11/4 Daggers Drawn (USA)—Aimee's Delight (Robellino (USA)) (20000) **Mrs J. Morley**
26 CAPTAIN CROMBY (IRE), ch c 2/3 Captain Rio—Ladycromby (IRE) (Lycius (USA)) (2500) **Mr E. P. Kingsley**
27 DIKTARAM, b c 19/2 Diktat—Aries (GER) (Big Shuffle (USA)) (4500) **High Moor Racing 5**
28 FIZZY FRIEND, ch f 7/4 Reel Buddy (USA)—Champenoise (Forzando)
29 B c 23/4 Kyllachy—Indian Gift (Cadeaux Genereux) (18000) **Mrs J. Morley**
30 B f 22/1 Primo Valentino (IRE)—Lapadar (IRE) (Woodborough (USA)) (10000)

MR J. R. WEYMES—continued

31 B f 6/2 Forzando—Lucky Thing (Green Desert (USA)) (800)
32 B f 22/4 Alderbrook—Miss Pout (Kris)
33 B f 9/3 Iron Mask (USA)—Mitchella (IRE) (Persian Bold) (2251)
34 Ch c 23/3 City On A Hill (USA)—Newtown Breeze (IRE) (Forest Wind (USA)) (2800)
35 Ch f 31/5 Kheleyf (USA)—Quick Flight (Polar Falcon (USA))
36 B br f 28/2 Pyrus (USA)—Ruby Julie (Clantime) (1930) **Mr J. Wilde**
37 B f 21/2 Xaar—Samsung Spirit (Statoblest)
38 **TRANSFORMATION (IRE),** b f 21/2 Trans Island—Gleam (Green Desert (USA)) (4200) **Mrs R. L. Heaton**
39 Ch f 31/1 Orientate (USA)—Vanessa's Gem (CAN) (Jade Hunter (USA)) (19304) **T. A. Scothern**
40 B f 28/4 Statue of Liberty (USA)—Whistfilly (First Trump) (4181)

Other Owners: Mr P. D. Bickley, Miss K. A. Buckle, Mr Mel Catlow, Mrs D. Catlow, Mr D. Dunford, Mr I. A. Gregg, Mr Neil Palamountain.

Assistant Trainer: Kirsty Buckle, kirsty@johnweymes.co.uk

Jockey (flat): D. Holland, P. Makin. **Jockey (NH):** K. Mercer, D. Costello. **Amateur:** Mr B. Stomie.

---

630 MR E. A. WHEELER, Pangbourne
Postal: Coombe Park Stables, Whitchurch on Thames, Pangbourne, Oxfordshire, RG8 7QT
Contacts: **PHONE** (07795) 844185 **FAX** (01189) 841924 **MOBILE** (07795) 844185

1 **BATCHWORTH BLAISE,** 5, b g Little Jim—Batchworth Dancer **Astrod Limited TA Austin Stroud & Co**
2 **DANCING MYSTERY,** 14, b g Beveled (USA)—Batchworth Dancer **Astrod Limited TA Austin Stroud & Co**
3 **FIREWORK,** 10, b g Primo Dominie—Prancing **Mrs P. Simmonds**
4 **MASTER MCGHEE,** ch g Beveled (USA)—Sandra Dee (IRE) **E. A. Wheeler**

THREE-YEAR-OLDS

5 B f High Estate—A Little Hot **Mr G. W. Witheford**
6 Ch f Bertolini (USA)—Fragrant Cloud **Mr Tony Arnold & Mr Nick Hill**
7 **YOUNG OLLIE,** ch f Piccolo—Miss Michelle **Mr E. A. Wheeler**

TWO-YEAR-OLDS

8 Ch f 7/4 Reel Buddy (USA)—Batchworth Breeze (Beveled (USA)) **Mr G. Witheford**

Assistant Trainer: Mr C. Witheford

Jockey (flat): S. Carson. **Amateur:** Miss C. Nosworthy.

---

631 MR D. W. WHILLANS, Hawick
Postal: Dodlands Steading, Hawick, Roxburghshire, TD9 8LG
Contacts: **BUSINESS** (01450) 373128 **HOME** (01450) 379810 **FAX** (01450) 376082
MOBILE (07771) 550556

1 **ALLEGEDLY SO (IRE),** 7, b g Flemensfirth (USA)—Celtic Lace
2 **BABY SISTER,** 9, ch m King Among Kings—Market Blues **C. N. Whillans**
3 **BEAU LARGESSE,** 6, b g Largesse—Just Visiting **Milsey Bay Racing**
4 **BEAU PEAK,** 9, ch m Meadowbrook—Peak A Boo **Mrs H. M. Whillans**
5 **BOLLIN FIONA,** 4, ch f Silver Patriarch (IRE)—Bollin Nellie **C. N. Whillans**
6 **BOLLIN RUTH,** 6, gr m Silver Patriarch (IRE)—Bollin Roberta **C. N. Whillans**
7 **GALE DANCER,** 6, b m Saddlers' Hall (IRE)—Barton Gale (IRE) **Mrs A. W. Whillans**
8 4, Ch f Alflora (IRE)—Gentle Approach
9 **HARRY FLASHMAN,** 7, ch g Minster Son—Youandi **A. Gilchrist M. Kent P. Wylie**
10 **LEITH WALK (IRE),** 5, ch m Posidonas—Gothic Shadow (IRE) **D. McComb**
11 **MEDA'S SONG,** 9, ch m Master Willie—Cala Conta **D. W. Whillans**
12 **MR MIDAZ,** 9, ch g Danzig Connection (USA)—Marmy **Chas N. Whillans, Dr Doreen M. Steele**
13 **POLLY WHITEFOOT,** 9, b m Perpendicular—Cream O The Border **Mrs J. Cowan**
14 **ROBBIE DYE,** 6, b m Minster Son—Youandi **Allan Gilchrist & Peter Wylie**
15 5, Ch g Sugarfoot—Stoproveritate **D. W. Whillans**
16 **THE MAYSTONE (IRE),** 8, b br g Thowra (FR)—Peg O The Wood (IRE) **Stoneage Paving**
17 **WELL DISGUISED (IRE),** 6, b m Beneficial—Executive Move (USA) **Alistair Duncan & David Leslie**
18 5, Ch g Weldnaas (USA)—Youandi **A. Gilchrist**

MR D. W. WHILLANS—continued

Other Owners: Mr J. Anderson, Mr A. J. M. Duncan, Mr G. Fairgrieve, M. Kent, D. R. Leslie, Dr D. Steele, P. A. Wylie.

Conditional: Garry Whillans. **Amateur:** Mr Callum Whillans.

632 MR R. M. WHITAKER, Scarcroft
Postal: **Hellwood Racing Stables, Hellwood Lane, Scarcroft, Leeds, West Yorkshire, LS14 3BP**
Contacts: **PHONE (01132) 892265 FAX (01132) 893680 MOBILE (07831) 870454**
E-MAIL liz.whitaker1@btconnect.com WEBSITE www.richardwhitaker.org

1 **AIREDALE LAD (IRE),** 7, b g Charnwood Forest (IRE)—Tamarsiya (USA) **R. M. Whitaker**
2 **AUSSIE BLUE (IRE),** 4, b g Bahamian Bounty—Luanshya **T. L. Adams**
3 **BLUE JET (USA),** 4, b g Black Minnaloushe (USA)—Clickety Click (USA) **Country Lane Partnership**
4 **BOLD DIKTATOR,** 6, b g Diktat—Madam Bold **R. M. Whitaker**
5 **DAMIKA (IRE),** 5, ch g Namid—Emly Express (IRE) **G. B. Bedford**
6 **INTERSKY CHARM (USA),** 4, ch c Lure (USA)—Catala (USA) **Intersky Bloodstock**
7 **JUST WAZ (USA),** 6, ch g Woodman (USA)—Just Tops (USA) **Waz Developments Ltd**
8 **MISTER JINGLES,** 5, ch g Desert Story—Fairy Free **Mr James Marshall & Mrs Susan Marshall**
9 **MOONSTREAKER,** 5, b g Foxhound (USA)—Ling Lane **I. B. Ender**
10 **MY LADY,** 4, b f Tobougg (IRE)—Be My Wish **R. M. Whitaker**
11 **NEON BLUE,** 7, b br g Atraf—Desert Lynx (IRE) **Country Lane Partnership**
12 **NEVADA DESERT (IRE),** 8, b g Desert King (IRE)—Kayanga **J. B. Pemberton**
13 **STEEL BLUE,** 8, b g Atraf—Something Blue **Country Lane Partnership**
14 **TABARET,** 5, ch h Bertolini (USA)—Luanshya **T. L. Adams**
15 **VICIOUS WARRIOR,** 9, b g Elmaamul (USA)—Ling Lane **Mr James Marshall & Mrs Susan Marshall**

THREE-YEAR-OLDS

16 **CURIO,** b f Captain Rio—Luanshya **G. F. Pemberton**
17 **IBROX (IRE),** b g Mujahid (USA)—Ling Lane **sportaracing.com**
18 **INTERSKY MELODY (USA),** b g Sky Mesa (USA)—Mayan Maiden (USA) **Intersky Bloodstock I**
19 **JAFRA (IRE),** ch g Choisir (AUS)—Polish Saga (IRE) **G. B. Bedford**
20 **JOINEDUPWRITING,** b g Desert Style (IRE)—Ink Pot (USA) **R. C. Dollar**
21 **MEY BLOSSOM,** ch f Captain Rio—Petra Nova **Waz Developments Ltd**
22 **PONDAPIE (IRE),** b g Highest Honor (FR)—Fruhling Feuer (FR) **Clipper Group Holdings Ltd**
23 **RIO SANDS,** b g Captain Rio—Sally Traffic **Barry & The Barflys**
24 **SHALOO DIAMOND,** b g Captain Rio—Alacrity **G. B. Bedford**
25 **STONES OF VENICE (IRE),** b f Barathea (IRE)—Midnight Fever (IRE) **Clipper Logistics**
26 B c Mull of Kintyre (USA)—Sylviani

TWO-YEAR-OLDS

27 B c 10/2 Bertolini (USA)—Compton Girl (Compton Place) (24000)
28 **DESERT FALLS,** b c 25/3 Pyrus (USA)—Sally Traffic (River Falls) (12000)
29 **HONESTY BLUE,** ch f 4/2 Compton Place—Just Deserts (Alhijaz) (2500) **Country Lane Partnership**
30 **QUANAH PARKER (IRE),** b c 26/3 Namid—Uncertain Affair (IRE) (Darshaan) **Robert Macgregor**
31 B c 3/3 Captain Rio—Scooby Dooby Do (Atraf)
32 **WOTATOMBOY,** ch f 15/5 Captain Rio—Keen Melody (USA) (Sharpen Up) (23000) **Giro Partnership**

Other Owners: A. Bell, Mr A. S. Crossan, J. R. Marshall, Mrs S. Marshall, S. R. McKeown, Terry Mcdermott, Mrs C. Mckeown, Mr M. P. R. Mclaren, W. Murphy, Miss G. P. Platt, Mrs R. M. Whitaker, Mrs J. M. Willows.

Assistant Trainer: Simon R Whitaker

Jockey (flat): V. Halliday, Dean McKeown. **Apprentice:** M. Stainton.

633 MR A. J. WHITEHEAD, Craven Arms
Postal: **Lawn Farm, Beambridge, Aston on Clun, Craven Arms, Shropshire, SY7 0HA**
Contacts: PHONE (01588) 660424

1 **ARCTIC CHERRY (IRE),** 10, b g Arctic Lord—Cherry Avenue **A. J. Whitehead**
2 **JEANRY (FR),** 5, b g Marathon (USA)—Envergure **A. J. Whitehead**
3 **LONESOME BOATMAN (IRE),** 8, b g Old Vic—Midnight Miss (NZ) **A. J. Whitehead**
4 **LUCKY SHAME (FR),** 6, ch g Lesotho (USA)—Shame (IRE) **A. J. Whitehead**

Conditional: Lee Edwards.

634 MR M. WIGHAM, Newmarket
Postal: Hamilton Stables, Hamilton Road, Newmarket, Suffolk, CB8 7JQ
Contacts: PHONE (01638) 668806 FAX (01638) 668806 MOBILE (07831) 456426

1 AVOCA DANCER (IRE), 5, ch m Compton Place—Kashra (IRE) **Have A Go Syndicate & Michael Wigham**
2 BENLLECH, 4, b g Lujain (USA)—Four Legs Good (IRE) **R. J. Lorenz**
3 BETHANYS BOY (IRE), 7, ch g Docksider (USA)—Daymoon (USA) **M. Wigham**
4 CLASSIC PORT (FR), 4, gr c Slickly (FR)—Portella (GER) **Ashards Partnership**
5 CONFIDENTIALITY (IRE), 4, b f Desert Style (IRE)—Confidential **J. Cullinan**
6 GRANAKEY (IRE), 5, b m Key of Luck (USA)—Grand Morning (IRE) **The Colourful Bunch**
7 KATIE KINGFISHER, 4, b f Fraam—Sonic Sapphire **J. Pearce**
8 LITTLEDODAYNO (IRE), 5, b m Mujadil (USA)—Perfect Welcome **Mr W L Bamforth & John Williams P'ship**
9 MOVERRA (IRE), 4, ch f Noverre (USA)—Muneera (USA)
10 MULTAHAB, 9, b br g Zafonic (USA)—Alumisiyah (USA) **Mr P J Burke & Dave Anderson**
11 PURR, 7, b g Pursuit of Love—Catawba **S. P. Rees**
12 SILVER HOTSPUR, 4, b g Royal Applause—Noble View (USA) **D. Hassan**
13 STRABINIOS KING, 4, b g King's Best (USA)—Strawberry Morn (CAN) **V. Kelly**
14 STRAIGHT FACE (IRE), 4, b g Princely Heir (IRE)—Dakota Sioux (IRE) **M. Wigham**
15 THOUGHTSOFSTARDOM, 5, b g Mind Games—Alustar **Eventmaker Racehorses**
16 TIME SHARE (IRE), 4, b f Danetime (IRE)—Clochette (IRE) **Eventmaker Racehorses**
17 TREES OF GREEN (USA), 4, b br c Elusive Quality (USA)—Grazia **A. W. Darke**

THREE-YEAR-OLDS

18 BAYTOWN BLAZE, ch f Zaha (CAN)—Lightning Blaze **Eventmaker Racehorses**
19 RUBY ROCKS, ch f Zaha (CAN)—Natural Grace **R. J. Gough**

Other Owners: D. J. Anderson, W. L. Bamforth, P. J. Burke, Mr P. E. Coggins, Mr K. J. Harvey, Mr M. A. Humphris, T. D. Johnson, M. Kelly, Mr G. O'Shea, Ms L. J. Roussel, Mr J. B. Williams.

Assistant Trainer: Mr Nick Hyde

Jockey (flat): Nicky Mackay, Jamie Mackay. **Apprentice:** Michael Murphy. **Amateur:** Mr Josh Pearce.

635 MR M. S. WILESMITH, Dymock
Postal: Bellamys Farm, Dymock, Gloucestershire, GL18 2DX
Contacts: PHONE (01531) 890410 FAX (01684) 893428 MOBILE (07970) 411638
E-MAIL martin@mswilesmith.co.uk

1 COTTON ON, 11, b g Henbit (USA)—Linen Leaf **M. S. Wilesmith**
2 LORD BELLAMY (IRE), 6, b g Lord Americo—Paean Express (IRE) **M. S. Wilesmith**
3 MOUNTAIN SINGER (IRE), 9, b g Carroll House—Mountain Grove **M. S. Wilesmith**
4 MRS WHITE (IRE), 8, b m Alflora (IRE)—Annicombe Run **M. S. Wilesmith**
5 THE HUMBEL BUTLER (IRE), 7, b g Humbel (USA)—Butler's Lady **M. S. Wilesmith**
6 THIS ONE IS A BOY (IRE), 12, b g Executive Perk—Belinda Vard **M. S. Wilesmith**

Assistant Trainer: Miss E C Wilesmith

Amateur: Mr M. C. Wilesmith.

636 MR I. P. WILLIAMS, Alvechurch
Postal: Dominion Racing Stables, Seafield Lane, Alvechurch, Birmingham, B48 7HL
Contacts: PHONE (01564) 822392 FAX (01564) 829475 MOBILE (07976) 645384
E-MAIL info@ianwilliamsracing.com WEBSITE ianwilliamsracing.com

1 ACT GOLD (GER), 6, b g Slip Anchor—Alisa (GER) **Macable Partnership**
2 ANGLICISME (FR), 6, b g Kahyasi—Anglaise (IRE) **J. T. Warner**
3 BAMBI DE L'ORME (FR), 9, gr g True Brave (USA)—Princesse Ira (FR) **Mr & Mrs John Poynton**
4 BRIGADORE (USA), 5, gr ro g Sandpit (BRZ)—Mersey **Mr & Mrs G.Middlebrook/Mr & Mrs P.Brain**
5 BULWARK (IRE), 6, b h Montjeu (IRE)—Bulaxie **Dr M. B. Q. S. Koukash**
6 CALLISTO MOON, 4, b g Mujahid (USA)—Nursling (IRE) **B. W. Bedford**
7 CLASSIC BLUE (IRE), 4, b f Tagula (IRE)—Palace Blue (IRE) **Boston R. S. Ian Bennett**
8 CRUISE DIRECTOR, 8, b g Zilzal (USA)—Briggsmaid **Mrs M. A. Bull**
9 DEVIL'S CREEK (IRE), 8, b g Shernazar—Auburn Park **B & S Vaughan**
10 EARNEST (IRE), 8, b g Oscar (IRE)—Unassisted (IRE) **Elliott Thomas Limited**

MR I. P. WILLIAMS—continued

11 **EURO IMPORT**, 10, ch g Imp Society (USA)—Upper Club (IRE) **I. P. Williams**
12 **HI FI**, 10, b g Homo Sapien—Baroness Orkzy **Mrs R. W. Paterson**
13 **HILL OF LUJAIN**, 4, b g Lujain (USA)—Cinder Hills **Pertemps Ltd**
14 **JIMMYTHEBLACKSMITH (IRE)**, 6, bl g Presenting—Wonder Woman (GER) **P. Kelly**
15 **KEENAN'S FUTURE (IRE)**, 7, ch g Safety Catch (USA)—The Singer (IRE) **P. Kelly**
16 **KICKAHEAD (USA)**, 6, b g Danzig (USA)—Krissante (USA) **Churchill Office Solutions Limited**
17 **LADY ASPEN (IRE)**, 5, b m Elnadim (USA)—Misty Peak (IRE) **Will Tyrrell Richard Tyrrell Andrew Dick**
18 **LAMY JACK (FR)**, 6, b g Villez (USA)—Line Lawyer (FR) **Willsford Racing Ltd**
19 **LIVINGONAKNIFEDGE (IRE)**, 9, b br g Classic Memory—Duhallow Fiveo **Concertina Racing**
20 **LUNAR PROMISE (IRE)**, 6, b g Mujadil (USA)—Lunadine (FR) **A. L. R. Morton**
21 **MISTER APPLE'S (FR)**, 8, ch g Video Rock (FR)—Doryane (FR) **P. J. Vogt**
22 **MITH HILL**, 7, b g Daylami (IRE)—Delirious Moment (IRE) **P. J. Vogt**
23 **MONTANEL (FR)**, 8, br g Assessor (IRE)—Ocre Elegance (FR) **Scott Rutherford & David Hughes**
24 **NEWBY ABBEY (IRE)**, 7, b g Lord of Appeal—Turramurra Girl (IRE) **Mr H. D. Ellis**
25 **NIMBY RUN (IRE)**, 10, ch g Commanche Run—Nimble Wind **Mr P. Tarrant**
26 **NO GREATER LOVE (FR)**, 6, b g Take Risks (FR)—Desperate Virgin (BEL) **The Ferandlin Peaches**
27 **NORWEGIAN**, 7, b g Halling (USA)—Chicarica (USA) **Mr R. Bee**
28 **OEIL D'ESTRUVAL (FR)**, 6, b g Sheyrann—Image d'estruval (FR) **The Last Resort Partnership**
29 **PHAREIGHT DEI (IRE)**, 10, b g Leading Counsel (USA)—Mullaghroe **Mr P. Tarrant**
30 **PRINCE EMMANUEL (FR)**, 5, gr g Take Risks (FR)—Princesse Mimi (FR) **P. Kelly**
31 **RATHCOR**, 6, b g Overbury (IRE)—Brenig **Cockbury Court Partnership**
32 **SILVERGINO (IRE)**, 8, b g Perugino (USA)—Silvretta (IRE) **Notalotterry**
33 **SPECTROMETER**, 11, ch g Rainbow Quest (USA)—Selection Board **Will Tyrrell Richard Tyrrell Andrew Dick**
34 **TAGULA BLUE (IRE)**, 8, b g Tagula (IRE)—Palace Blue (IRE) **Boston R. S. Ian Bennett**
35 **TERMINATE (GER)**, 6, ch g Acatenango (GER)—Taghareed (USA) **Dr M. B. Q. S. Koukash**
36 **THE GRANDCHILD (IRE)**, 6, b g Moscow Society (USA)—Just Placed (IRE) **P. Kelly**
37 **THE MICK WESTON**, 9, b g North Col—Zalina **M. Weston**
38 **TOP SEED (IRE)**, 7, b g Cadeaux Genereux—Midnight Heights **J. Tredwell**
39 **TUFTON**, 5, b g King's Best (USA)—Mythical Magic **Dr M. B. Q. S. Koukash**
40 **VANQUISHER (IRE)**, 8, b g Xaar—Naziriya (FR) **Dr M. B. Q. S. Koukash**
41 **WILLANDRICH (IRE)**, 6, b g Insan (USA)—Cool Mary **Will Tyrrell Richard Tyrrell Andrew Dick**
42 **WINTER CRUISE (IRE)**, 4, b g Lil's Boy—Arundhati (IRE) **P. Kelly**

Other Owners: Mr Richard Allen, Mrs Margaretha Allen, Mr Ian Bennett, Mr P. J. Brain, Mrs Yuriko Brain, Mr Anthony Callaghan, Mr M. N. Dennis, Mr A. Dick, Mr J. B. Duffy, Mr P.V. Harris, Ms R. J. Harris, Mr David M. Hughes, Mr Tim Kelly, Mr S. Mackintosh, Mr Paul Manning, Mr G. Middlebrook, Mrs L. Middlebrook, Mr M. Morgan, Mr P. R. Nodder, Mr T. H. Northwood, Mr John Poynton, Mrs Anne Poynton, Mr Scott J. Rutherford, Mr D. M. Stuart, Mr R. J. Tyrrell, Mr J. Tyrrell, Mrs S. A. Vaughan, Mr B. D. Vaughan.

Jockey (NH): D R Dennis. **Conditional:** M. Murphy. **Amateur:** Mr James Ravenall.

---

637 **MR N. S. L. WILLIAMS, South Molton**
Postal: Culverhill Farm, George Nympton, South Molton, Devon, EX36 4JE
Contacts: HOME (01769) 574174 FAX (01769) 573661 MOBILE (07855) 450379

1 **BESHABAR (IRE)**, 6, ch g Flemensfirth (USA)—In Our Intrest (IRE) **Mr A. H. H. Mole**
2 **BLANDINGS CASTLE**, 7, ro g Cloudings (IRE)—Country House **Mrs J. R. Williams**
3 **BOYTJIE (IRE)**, 8, b g Un Desperado (FR)—Miss Cali **Mrs J. R. Williams**
4 **CORNAS (NZ)**, 6, br g Prized (USA)—Duvessa (NZ) **Gascoigne Brookes Partnership**
5 **DIAMOND HARRY**, 5, b g Sir Harry Lewis (USA)—Swift Conveyance (IRE) **Paul Duffy Diamond Partnership**
6 **HE'S THE BIZ (FR)**, 9, b g Nikos—Irun (FR) **Mrs J. R. Williams**
7 **KALAMAZOO (IRE)**, 7, b g Flemensfirth (USA)—Cheryls Pet (IRE) **Mrs J. R. Williams**
8 **KINGS BROOK**, 8, br g Alderbrook—Kins Token **Mr A. P. Gale**
9 **LOS SUENOS (IRE)**, 7, br g Supreme Leader—Stormy Miss **Mrs J. R. Williams**
10 **MALJIMAR (IRE)**, 8, b g Un Desperado (FR)—Marble Miller (IRE) **Mrs J. R. Williams**
11 **MEET THE LEGEND (IRE)**, 7, b g Norwich—Rose Ana (IRE) **Gale Force Six**
12 **MIGHTY MOOSE (IRE)**, 8, b g Mister Lord (USA)—Brief Pace (IRE) **Gale Force Four**
13 **PHILSON RUN (IRE)**, 12, b g Un Desperado (FR)—Isis **Gale Force One**
14 **QUASAR D'OUDAIRIES (FR)**, 4, b g Epistolaire (IRE)—Hanebane (FR) **Paul Duffy Diamond Partnership**
15 **QUICK DRAW MCGRAW**, 5, ch g Double Trigger (IRE)—Cadal Queen (FR) **Mrs J. R. Williams**
16 **SANGFROID**, 4, gr g With Approval (CAN)—Affaire d'amour
17 **THE REAL DEAL (IRE)**, 7, b g Taipan (IRE)—Forest Mist **Mrs J. R. Williams**
18 **THE RISKY VIKING (IRE)**, 9, b g Supreme Leader—Queen's Flagship (IRE) **Gale Force Two**
19 **THEOCRITUS (GER)**, 7, b g Trempolino (USA)—Thyatira (FR) **Gale Force Three**

MR N. S. L. WILLIAMS—continued

THREE-YEAR-OLDS

20 **REVE DE SIVOLA (FR)**, b g Assessor (IRE)—Eva de Chalamont (FR) **Paul Duffy Diamond Partnership**

Other Owners: Mr Paul Duffy, Mr Tony Gale, Mr J. G. Storey.

Assistant Trainer: Mrs Jane Williams

---

638 **MR R. E. R. WILLIAMS, Llancarfan**
Postal: **Aberogwrn Farm, Llancarfan, Nr Barry, Vale of Glamorgan**
Contacts: PHONE **(01446) 754069** MOBILE **(07950) 381227**
E-MAIL **caroledavid@ewracing.com**

1 **ADEUS AYRTON (IRE)**, 4, b g Definite Article—Flawless Finish (IRE) **Mrs M. Findlay**
2 **ALEXANDER EXCHANGE (IRE)**, 7, ch g Alderbrook—Had Enough **The Hanningfield Syndicate**
3 **ARISTI (IRE)**, 7, b m Dr Fong (USA)—Edessa (IRE) **R. E. R. Williams**
4 **AXINIT (GER)**, 8, gr g Linamix (FR)—Assia (IRE) **R. E. R. Williams**
5 **BACK IN BUSINESS (IRE)**, 8, b g Bob Back (USA)—Rose of Burnett (IRE) **W. R. Thomas**
6 **BACKSTAGE (FR)**, 6, b g Passing Sale (FR)—Madame Nathalie (FR) **Sir Robert Ogden C.B.E., LLD**
7 **BLIND FAITH (IRE)**, 4, b g Beneficial—Drinadaly (IRE) **Mrs C. A. Waters & Phil Cunningham**
8 **BRENIN CWMTUDU**, 5, b g Saddlers' Hall (IRE)—Keel Row **T. H. Jones**
9 4, B f Kayf Tara—Cabriole Legs **G. Houghton**
10 **CAISLEAN NA DEIRGE (IRE)**, 10, b g Boyne Valley—Bramble Lane **Mr M. J. Harper**
11 **CAMDEN FOUR (IRE)**, 5, b g Fourstars Allstar (USA)—Camden Three (IRE) **Camden Four Partnership**
12 **CHRYSANDER**, 6, b g Cadeaux Genereux—Jumairah Sun (IRE) **Only Fools N Horses**
13 5, B m Saddler's Hall (IRE)—Clowns Glory **Keith & Sue Lowry**
14 **COOL CLICHE (IRE)**, 6, b g Classic Cliche (IRE)—Ardent Love (IRE) **I. C. Brice**
15 **CORRAN ARD (IRE)**, 7, b g Imperial Ballet (IRE)—Beeper The Great (USA) **Camden Four Partnership 2**
16 **COUNCILLOR JACK (IRE)**, 7, b g Oscar (IRE)—Kaysel (IRE) **R. E. R. Williams**
17 4, B f Classic Cliche (IRE)—Countessmarkievicz (IRE) **K. E. Stait**
18 **COUNTRYCOUSIN (IRE)**, 8, b g Oscar (IRE)—Garryduff Supreme (IRE) **R. E. R. Williams**
19 **COURT ALLIANCE**, 9, ch g Alhijaz—Fairfields Cone **Derek & Cheryl Holder**
20 **COURT PRINCESS**, 5, b m Mtoto—Fairfields Cone **Derek & Cheryl Holder**
21 **COURT RULER**, 6, b g Kayf Tara—Fairfields Cone **Derek & Cheryl Holder**
22 **DEARSON (IRE)**, 7, b g Definite Article—Petite Maxine **VJ, MJ, KJ & LJ**
23 **DEEP PURPLE**, 7, b g Halling (USA)—Seal Indigo (IRE) **P. C. Green**
24 **DEMI BEAU**, 10, b g Dr Devious (IRE)—Charming Life (NZ) **Cunningham Racing**
25 **DESERT TOMMY**, 7, b g Desert King (IRE)—Flambera (FR) **All Adda Winna Racing Club**
26 **ENLIGHTENMENT (IRE)**, 8, b g Presenting—Shaiybaniyda **T. H. Jones**
27 **FABULOUS JET (FR)**, 8, ch g Starborough—Jetty (FR) **M. Edwards**
28 **FLYING ENTERPRISE (IRE)**, 8, b g Darshaan—Flying Kiss (IRE) **M. Edwards**
29 **GAN EAGLA (IRE)**, 9, b g Paris House—Mafiosa **T. H. Jones**
30 **GHIZAO (GER)**, 4, b g Tiger Hill (IRE)—Glorosia (FR)
31 **GRANPA'S GONE GREY (IRE)**, 6, gr g Sea Raven (IRE)—Grandpa's River **R. E. R. Williams**
32 **HARRY POTTER (GER)**, 9, b g Platini (GER)—Heavenly Storm (USA) **Billy Evans & Gareth Morse**
33 **HENRY BEAUCLERC**, 5, b g Hernando—Cullen Bay (IRE) **Mr & Mrs William Rucker**
34 **HEROES**, 4, b g Diktat—Wars (IRE) **Six Star Racing**
35 **HESIVORTHEDRIVER (GER)**, 4, b c King's Best—Homing Instinct **M. V. Dawson**
36 **HIGH CHIMES (IRE)**, 9, b g Naheez (USA)—Forward Gal **Mr & Mrs William Rucker**
37 **HIGHGLEN (IRE)**, 9, b g Old Vic—Nil Faic (IRE) **G. A. Moore**
38 **HIGHLAND GAMES (IRE)**, 8, b g Singspiel (IRE)—Highland Gift (IRE) **M. J. Haines**
39 **HORSHAM LAD (IRE)**, 4, b g Muroto—Comeragh Queen **Mr & Mrs William Rucker**
40 **HYPNOTIC VIBES (IRE)**, 4, b g Daylami (IRE)—Literary Lover (IRE) **I. Struel**
41 **IF ONLY I KNEW (IRE)**, 8, b br g Accordion—Girseach **M. J. Haines**
42 **IM SPARTACUS**, 6, b g Namaqualand (USA)—Captivating (IRE) **The Regulate Partnership**
43 **KNIGHT OF LIGHT (IRE)**, 5, b g Scribano—Quarry Lass (IRE) **R. E. R. Williams**
44 **KYLES PRINCE (IRE)**, 6, b g In The Wings—Comprehension (USA) **Get To The Bar Racing**
45 **LEADING ARTICLE (IRE)**, 6, ch g Definite Article—Jameela (IRE) **R. E. R. Williams**
46 **LIMIT (GER)**, 4, gr g Paris House—Lerida (GER) **R. E. R. Williams**
47 **LORD JAY JAY (IRE)**, 8, b g Lord of Appeal—Mesena **Mrs J. M. Johnson**
48 **MAC HALEN (IRE)**, 5, b g Lord Americo—Colleen Donn **Keith & Sue Lowry**
49 **MALETTON (FR)**, 5, b g Bering (FR)—Reine Dougla (FR) **M. Edwards**
50 **MAN OVERBOARD**, 6, b g Overbury (IRE)—Dublin Ferry **Mr & Mrs William Rucker**
51 **MCEVOY (IRE)**, 8, ch g Accordion—Molly Blaney **P. M. Cunningham**
52 **MICKMACMAGOOLE (IRE)**, 6, b g Sadler's Wells (USA)—Musk Lime (USA) **Mad Mick Partnership**

MR R. E. R. WILLIAMS—continued

53 **MR WISEGUY**, 5, b g Groom Dancer (USA)—Tassagh Bridge (IRE) **Mr I. Staples**
54 **MY FRIEND JOHNNIE (IRE)**, 8, ch g Broken Hearted—Pharaway Stream (IRE) **R. E. R. Williams**
55 **NICK JUNIOR (IRE)**, 9, b g Norwich—Paico Ana **I. C. Brice**
56 **NOADIBOU (FR)**, 10, b g Cadoudal (FR)—Bahia De Chalamont (FR) **R. E. R. Williams**
57 **NORDWIND (IRE)**, 7, b g Acatenango (GER)—Narola (GER) **R. E. R. Williams**
58 **NOUN DE LA THINTE (FR)**, 7, b m Oblat (FR)—Belis de La Thinte (FR) **M. Edwards**
59 **OLD SCHOOL (IRE)**, 8, b g Shernazar—Winterland Gale (IRE) **T. H. Jones**
60 **OVERLUT (FR)**, 6, bl g Discover d'auteuil (FR)—Lutsine (FR) **P. C. Green**
61 **PEBROCK (FR)**, 5, b g Video Rock (FR)—Envie de Chalamont (FR) **Mrs M. Findlay**
62 **PHILANTHROPIST**, 5, b g Fantastic Light (USA)—Someone Special **Cunningham Racing**
63 **PIRAN (IRE)**, 6, b g Orpen (USA)—Dancing At Lunasa (IRE) **The Welsh Valleys Syndicate**
64 **POLE STAR**, 10, b br g Polar Falcon (USA)—Ellie Ardensky **P. C. Green**
65 **ROCKVIEW LAD (IRE)**, 7, ch g Beneficial—Fourtowns (IRE) **P. M. De Wilde**
66 **ROYAL ARMS**, 6, b g Desert King—Opus One **Sir Robert Ogden C.B.E., LLD**
67 **ROYAL KATIDOKI (FR)**, 8, b g Rochesson (FR)—Miss Coco (FR) **R. E. R. Williams**
68 **SANTINHO (IRE)**, 5, b g Double Eclipse (IRE)—Gina's Love **Mr K. W. Peach**
69 **SCRAPE THE PAINT**, 5, b g Alflora (IRE)—Corn Lily **R. E. R. Williams**
70 **SEATTLE ROBBER**, 6, b g Robellino (USA)—Seattle Ribbon (USA) **R. E. R. Williams**
71 **SKY WARRIOR (FR)**, 10, b g Warrshan (USA)—Sky Bibi (FR) **R. E. R. Williams**
72 **SPRING LOVER (FR)**, 9, b g Fijar Tango (FR)—Kailasa (FR) **M. Edwards**
73 **STATE OF PLAY**, 8, b g Hernando (FR)—Kaprice (GER) **Mr & Mrs William Rucker**
74 **STUBBLE FORTROUBLE (IRE)**, 9, ch g Flemensfirth (USA)—Safe Hands **R. E. R. Williams**
75 **SUCH A MAN (IRE)**, 7, b g Saddlers' Hall (IRE)—You're So Fine (IRE) **Mr J. Grace**
76 **TEMPTING PARADISE (IRE)**, 5, ch g Grand Lodge (USA)—Summer Trysting (USA) **Norwester Racing Club**
77 **THE ACCORDION MAN (IRE)**, 7, b g Accordion—Gale Griffin (IRE) **Mr & Mrs William Rucker**
78 **THE HAIRY MART (IRE)**, 6, b g Presenting—Crash Approach **Philip & Charles Racing**
79 **THE LAST CAST**, 9, ch g Prince of Birds (USA)—Atan's Gem (USA) **R. E. R. Williams**
80 **TURKISH SULTAN (IRE)**, 5, b g Anabaa (USA)—Odalisque (IRE) **The Lovely Jubbly's**
81 **VIBE**, 7, gr g Danzero (AUS)—Courting **R. E. R. Williams**
82 **VICTORY PARADE (IRE)**, 5, ch g Old Vic—Charlotte's Moss **Mr & Mrs William Rucker**
83 **WALSINGHAM (IRE)**, 10, b g Presenting—Let's Compromise **Keith & Sue Lowry**
84 **WARPATH (IRE)**, 7, b g Alderbrook—Blake's Fable (IRE) **Mr R. J. Gambarini**
85 **WARRIOR DRIVE (IRE)**, 7, b g Beneficial—Deep Satisfaction **Mr R. J. Gambarini**
86 **WILDHUTER (GER)**, 4, b g Sendawar (IRE)—Wurfspiel (GER) **R. E. R. Williams**
87 **WITH SPEED (GER)**, 5, br g Spectrum (IRE)—Well Known (GER) **R. E. R. Williams**
88 **WOOLLY BULLY**, 5, b g Robellino (USA)—Belle Ile (USA) **Six Star Racing**

Other Owners: Mr D. S. Bryant, P. Cunningham, A. D. Dale, Mr A. M. Dale, Mr C. Davies, Mr W. J. Eaton, W. J. Evans, P. M. Evans, Mr D. Hanafin, D. C. Holder, Mrs C. R. Holder, M. P. James, V. H. Johnson, Mr M. Johnson, Mr P. M. Langford, Mrs N. P. Lloyd, D. G. Long, Mrs S. B. Lowry, K. R. Lowry, Mr P. Maloney, Charles J. McCarthy, Mr R. Mone, S. T. Morris, W. J. G. Morse, R. J. Pritchard, Mr P. Pyatt, W. J. Rucker, Mrs A. Rucker, P. J. Smith, P. Smith, Mr A. Turton, Mrs C. A. Waters.

Assistant Trainer: Mrs C. Williams, Mr James Tudor & Mr Nick Williams

Jockey (NH): C. Williams, P. Moloney. **Conditional:** J. Flavin. **Amateur:** Mr N. Williams, Mr J. Tudor, Mr R. Hughes.

---

639 **MR S. C. WILLIAMS, Newmarket**
Postal: Diomed Stables, Hamilton Road, Newmarket, Suffolk, CB8 0PD
Contacts: STABLES/OFFICE (01638) 663984 HOME (01638) 560143 FAX (01638) 560143
MOBILE (07730) 314102
E-MAIL stuart@stuartwilliamsracing.co.uk WEBSITE www.stuartwilliamsracing.co.uk

1 **APHRODISIA**, 4, b f Sakhee (USA)—Aegean Dream (IRE) **Bell House Racing Limited**
2 **BLACKTOFT (USA)**, 5, b br g Theatrical—Black Truffle (USA) **Chris Watkins & David N. Reynolds**
3 **CORNERSTONE**, 4, ch g Pivotal—Splice **J. W. Lovitt & Partners**
4 **DANIEL O'DONNELL**, 6, b h Komaite (USA)—Light Slippers (IRE) **L. McGarrigle**
5 **HOGMANEIGH (IRE)**, 5, b g Namid—Magical Peace **Mrs L. B. K. Bone**
6 **LITTLE CARMELA**, 4, gr f Beat Hollow—Carmela Owen **O. Pointing**
7 **MAMBAZO**, 6, b g Dansili—Kalindi **D. G. Burge**
8 **MARAAGEL (USA)**, 5, b h Danzig (USA)—Hasnaael Reef (USA) **J. W. Lovitt**
9 **MINNOW**, 4, b f Averti (IRE)—Tharwa (IRE) **M. A. Hammond**
10 **NOBLE MINSTREL**, 5, ch g Fantastic Light (USA)—Sweetness Herself **Alasdair Simpson**
11 **RATIONALE**, 5, b g Singspiel (IRE)—Logic **Alasdair Simpson**
12 **THE CITY KID (IRE)**, 5, b m Danetime (IRE)—Unfortunate **L. McGarrigle**
13 **VOLIERE**, 5, b m Zafonic (USA)—Warbler **J. W. Parry**

MR S. C. WILLIAMS—continued

THREE-YEAR-OLDS

14 BILLBERRY, gr c Diktat—Elderberry **Pascoe, Enticknap & Sullivan**
15 EARLSMEDIC, ch c Dr Fong (USA)—Area Girl **Mad Man Plus One**
16 FELICIA, b f Diktat—Gracia **D. A. Shekells**
17 HAPI, b c Groom Dancer (USA)—Nekhbet **Mr M. Bush**
18 LA ZARZA, b f Domedriver (IRE)—La Fazenda **Alasdair Simpson**
19 LUNATICO (GER), b g Bertolini (USA)—La Playa **Mr K. A. Boothby**
20 MAD MAN WILL (IRE), b g Namid—Native Queen (FR) **Mad Man Partnership**
21 REGAL VEIL, b f Royal Applause—Shararah **J. W. Parry**
22 SCOTS W'HAE, b c Piccolo—Ionian Secret **Gordon Coburn & Robert Reid Partnership**
23 SOUTH WALES, b c Sakhee (USA)—Santorini (USA) **K. J. Mercer**
24 VANN HELSING, gr c Sakhee (USA)—Eurolis (USA) **J. A. Peters**

TWO-YEAR-OLDS

25 B c 24/3 Gilded Time (USA)—Beyond The Fence (USA) (Grand Slam (USA)) (70000) **J. W. Parry**
26 Ch c 27/2 Auction House (USA)—Buddug (Formidable (USA)) **Lloyd Brothers**
27 CAPTAIN FLASHEART (IRE), ch c 21/4 Captain Rio—Catfoot Lane (Batshoof) (22000) **P. W. Stevens**
28 B f 22/3 Mujahid (USA)—Carrie Kool (Prince Sabo) (9000)
29 B f 15/4 Oasis Dream—Degree (Warning) **D. A. Shekells**
30 B c 2/3 Rossini (USA)—Grazia (Sharpo) (3000) **Mr J. Parry**
31 B f 19/4 Reset (AUS)—In Love Again (IRE) (Prince Rupert (FR)) (5200)
32 Ch f 30/4 Dr Fong (USA)—Jamrat Jumairah (IRE) (Polar Falcon (USA)) (7500) **Redmyre Bloodstock**
33 B c 17/5 Singspiel (IRE)—Massomah (USA) (Seeking The Gold (USA)) (18000) **Mr J. Parry**
34 B f 17/4 Acclamation—Maugwenna (Danehill (USA)) (25000) **Bruce McAllister**
35 B gr f 28/3 Falbrav (IRE)—Miss University (USA) (Beau Genius (CAN)) **D. A. Shekells**
36 B c 26/2 Fasliyev (USA)—Rose of Mooncoin (IRE) (Brief Truce (USA)) (29000) **C. D. Watkins & D. Reynolds**
37 Ch f 8/3 Fantastic Light (USA)—Sadaka (USA) (Kingmambo (USA)) (9000) **D. A. Shekells**
38 Br f 9/3 Diktat—Shararah (Machiavellian (USA)) (6000) **S. C. Williams**
39 SIRCOZY (IRE), b c 21/4 Celtic Swing—Furnish (Green Desert (USA)) (6435)
40 B c 15/3 Ishiguru (USA)—Sumitra (Tragic Role (USA)) (3000)
41 B f 17/2 Storming Home—Sweet Cando (IRE) (Royal Applause) (5000) **Mrs Lucille Bone**

Other Owners: Mr J. J. Brummitt, Mr M. Bush, Mr G. Coburn, Mr A. Demetri, Mr W. E. Enticknap, Mr John W. Lovitt, Mr B. McGarrigle, Mrs S. Mercer, Mr Ross Pascoe, Mr A. Pointing, Mr Robert Reid, Mr D. N. Reynolds, Mr D. A. Shekells, Mr L. Stewart, Mr A. J. Sullivan, Mr G. Thompson.

Assistant Trainer: Michael Hammond

Apprentice: William Carson.

---

640 MISS V. M. WILLIAMS, Hereford
Postal: **Aramstone, Kings Caple, Hereford, Herefordshire, HR1 4TU**
Contacts: PHONE **(01432) 840646** FAX **(01432) 840830** MOBILE **(07770) 627108**

1 ABERDEEN PARK, 6, gr m Environment Friend—Michelee **Chemipetro Limited**
2 ABSTRACT ART (USA), 5, ch g Distorted Humor (USA)—Code From Heaven (USA) **Hills of Ledbury Ltd**
3 ALDERLEY ROVER (IRE), 4, gr g Beneficial—St Anne's Lady (IRE) **Alec Craig & Andrew Dick**
4 4, B g Accordion—American Chick (IRE) **M. L. Shone**
5 ANCHOR BRIDGE (IRE), 7, b g King's Theatre (IRE)—Retinue (IRE) **Cotton, Clarke, Lanigan-O'Keeffe**
6 ART PROFESSOR (IRE), 4, b g In The Wings—Itab (USA) **M. R. Green**
7 ASHGREEN, 11, b g Afzal—Space Kate **C. J. Green**
8 ATOUCHBETWEENACARA (IRE), 7, b br g Lord Americo—Rosie Lil (IRE) **P. W. Beck**
9 BACK ON LINE (IRE), 8, br m Bob Back (USA)—Ballyvooney **ROA Arkle Partnership**
10 BERGERAC (NZ), 10, b g Just A Dancer (NZ)—Guiding Star (NZ) **P. W. Beck**
11 BLENCATHRA BAY (IRE), 6, b g Saddlers' Hall (IRE)—Back To School (IRE) **You Can Be Sure**
12 BLEU SUPERBE (FR), 13, b g Epervier Bleu—Brett's Dream (FR) **P.A. Deal, A. Hirschfeld & J. Tyndall**
13 CASH FOR HONOURS, 5, b g City Honours (USA)—Copper Breeze (IRE) **A. D. Dick & A. J. Duckworth**
14 CASH KING (IRE), 8, b g Beneficial—On The Bridle (IRE) **A. D. Dick & A. J. Duckworth**
15 CHERY D'OR (FR), 7, b g Kizitca (FR)—Robe De Gala **T & Z Racing Club**
16 CHIEF YEOMAN, 8, b g Machiavellian (USA)—Step Aloft **B. Moore & E. C. Stephens**
17 CHIVALRY, 9, b g Mark of Esteem (IRE)—Gai Bulga **P. W. Beck**
18 CLIMATE CHANGE (USA), 6, ch g Langfuhr (CAN)—Summer Mist (USA) **The Weather Girls**
19 COACH LANE, 7, b g Barathea (IRE)—Emplane (USA) **B. Moore & E. C. Stephens**

MISS V. M. WILLIAMS—continued

20 **CRACKING CLICHE**, 6, ch m Classic Cliche (IRE)—Calametta **Mrs R. F. Knipe**
21 **CROFTERS LAD (IRE)**, 6, gr g Almutawakel—Hariyana (IRE) **B. C. Dice**
22 **DANSIMAR**, 4, gr f Daylami (IRE)—Hylandra (USA) **Let's Live Racing**
23 **DE BLANC (IRE)**, 8, b m Revoque (IRE)—Queen's Share **J. P. Hancock**
24 **ELSIE'S PRIDE (IRE)**, 6, gr g Turgeon (USA)—Magnissima (FR) **R. J. Cadoret**
25 **EMILE ZOLA**, 6, b g Singspiel (IRE)—Ellie Ardensky **Colin Brown, Ian Ganney & Peter Shawyer**
26 4, b g Flemensfirth (USA)—Estacado (IRE) **A. D. Dick & A. J. Duckworth**
27 **EVER SO SLIGHTLY (IRE)**, 7, b g Good Thyne (USA)—Loch Lomond (IRE) **A. D. Dick & A. J. Duckworth**
28 **FAIR QUESTION (IRE)**, 10, b g Rainbow Quest (USA)—Fair of The Furze **The Merseyclyde Partnership**
29 **FLANAGAN (IRE)**, 4, b g Old Vic—Fosterandallen (IRE) **M. L. Shone**
30 **FLEUR DE VASSY**, 4, ch f Alflora—Royale De Vassy **Len Jakeman Jeanette Davies Roger Downes**
31 **FLINTOFF (USA)**, 7, ch g Diesis—Sahibah (USA) **Andrew Flintoff & Paul Beck**
32 **FLYING FALCON**, 9, b g Polar Falcon (USA)—Lemon Balm **Burnt Toast Ltd**
33 **FRETWORK**, 4, b f Galileo (IRE)—Celtic Cross **The Old Dutches**
34 **GODS TOKEN**, 10, gr g Gods Solution—Pro-Token **The Silver Cod Partnership**
35 **GREEN BELT ELITE (FR)**, 4, b g Astarabad (USA)—Vallee Bleue (FR) **Green Belt Foresters**
36 **GREEN BELT FLYER (IRE)**, 10, b g Leading Counsel (USA)—Current Liability **Green Belt Foresters**
37 **GREYT BIG STUFF (USA)**, 4, gr g Aljabr (USA)—Dixie Eyes Blazing (USA) **T & Z Racing Club**
38 **GUSTAVO**, 7, b g Efisio—Washita **Gay & Peter Hartley**
39 **HAMMER TIME**, 5, b g Rudimentary (USA)—Miss Franco (IRE) **The Whatevers**
40 **HERALD ANGEL (FR)**, 5, b g Priolo (USA)—Heavenly Music (USA) **Countrywide Steel & Tubes Ltd**
41 **HINTON THUNDERBOLT**, 6, b g Primitive Rising (USA)—Hinton Grace **Mrs N. L. M. Moores**
42 **HOLY JOE (FR)**, 11, b g Pharly (USA)—Niffy Nora **Mrs J. Scarisbrick**
43 **JEEPSTAR**, 8, b g Muhtarram (USA)—Jungle Rose **Mr I. R. P. Josephs**
44 **JERICHO III (FR)**, 11, b g Lute Antique (FR)—La Salamandre (FR) **P. W. Beck**
45 **JIMMY TENNIS (FR)**, 11, b br g Video Rock (FR)—Via Tennise (FR) **Derek & Jean Clee**
46 **JOE'S A BOY (IRE)**, 6, ch g Beneficial—Replica (IRE) **Mr A. Dick**
47 **JUST JAFFA (IRE)**, 9, ch g Zaffaran (USA)—East Link (IRE) **John Nicholls (Trading) Ltd**
48 4, B g Witness Box (USA)—Kinsellas Rose (IRE) **Mrs P. Brown, Mrs O. P. Dakin**
49 **KOCK DE LA VESVRE (FR)**, 10, b g Sassanian (USA)—Csardas (FR) **O. P. Dakin**
50 **KRAKOW BABA (FR)**, 8, b g Sleeping Car (FR)—Babacha (FR) **Flintham, King, Jakeman & Roberts**
51 **LATANIER (FR)**, 5, b g Cadoudal (FR)—Lattaquie (FR) **F. M. P. Mahon**
52 **LIGHTNING STRIKE (GER)**, 5, ch g Danehill Dancer (IRE)—La Capilla **John Nicholls (Trading) Ltd**
53 **LORD TOMNODDY**, 6, b g Tragic Role (USA)—Rosemoss **M. D. C. Jenks**
54 **MA YAHAB**, 7, ch g Dr Fong (USA)—Bay Shade (USA) **M. J. Pilkington**
55 **MAKE HASTE (IRE)**, 4, b g Sadler's Wells—Mosaique Bleue **T. J. Hemmings**
56 **MAMBO DES MOTTES (FR)**, 8, b g Useful (FR)—
Julie des Mottes (FR) **John Nicholls, Roy Robbins, David Nash**
57 **MARAAFEQ (USA)**, 4, b br g Bahri (USA)—Tabrir (IRE) **Taylor, Burrows, Johnstone, Brooks**
58 **MARS ROCK (FR)**, 8, b g Video Rock (FR)—Venus de Mirande (FR) **John Nicholls (Trading) Ltd**
59 **MENDOSINO (GER)**, 9, b g Acatenango (GER)—Maji **D & J Racing Ltd**
60 **MISTY DANCER**, 9, gr g Vettori (IRE)—Light Fantastic **Pinks Gym & Leisure Wear Ltd**
61 **MON MOME (FR)**, 8, b g Passing Sale (FR)—Etoile du Lion (FR) **Mrs V. A. Bingham**
62 **NAXOX (FR)**, 7, ch g Cupidon (FR)—Frou Frou Lou (FR) **P. W. Beck & Andrew Flintoff**
63 **NECROMANCER (IRE)**, 5, b g Broken Hearted—Black Trix **M. L. Shone**
64 **NEVER SO BLUE (FR)**, 7, gr g April Night (FR)—Etiane Bleue (FR) **The Moody Blues**
65 **NICE TRY (IRE)**, 9, b g Lord Americo—Lyntim **The Juggins Partnership**
66 **NIRVANA DU BOURG (FR)**, 7, b br g Cadoudal (FR)—Gnosca (FR) **T. J. Hemmings**
67 **NO MORE TOM (IRE)**, 6, b g Clerkenwell (USA)—Miss Caitlin (IRE) **Six Blokes & A Scouser**
68 **NOBLE FUTURE**, 6, b g Averti (IRE)—Gold Luck (USA) **ROA Arkle Partnership**
69 **OMME ANTIQUE (FR)**, 6, b g Lute Antique (FR)—Saturbaine (FR) **W. E. Prichard**
70 **OUTAOUAIS (FR)**, 6, b g Sleeping Car (FR)—Hatilade (FR) **P. W. Beck**
71 **PASS ME BY**, 9, b g Balnibarbi—Errol Emerald **P. W. Beck**
72 **PING PONG SIVOLA (FR)**, 5, ch m Blushing Flame (USA)—Clio de Chalamont (FR) **Mrs J. Yeomans**
73 **PLEIN POUVOIR (FR)**, 5, b g Maresca Sorrento (FR)—Dellerie (FR) **Dr M. A. Hamlin**
74 **PTERODACTYL (IRE)**, 6, b g Montjeu (IRE)—Blue Kestrel (IRE) **Mrs A. Burrows Mr B. C. Dice**
75 **QUICKBEAM (IRE)**, 6, b g Lord Americo—Your Life **Miss M. Coughlan**
76 **ROBIN DE VASSY (FR)**, 5, b g Robin des Champs (FR)—
Provenchere (FR) **Downes Ferrand Flintham Jakeman King**
77 **ROYAL HERON (IRE)**, 5, b g Exit To Nowhere (USA)—Royal Shares (IRE) **Mrs V. A. Bingham**
78 **SAMURAI WAY**, 6, b g Darshaan—Truly Special **M. L. Shone**
79 **SARIN**, 10, b g Deploy—Secretilla (USA) **R. J. Stevenson**
80 **SHARP DRESSER (USA)**, 4, ch f Diesis—A La Mode (USA) **GSM Properties Ltd**
81 **SIMPLE GIFTS**, 5, ch m Double Trigger (IRE)—Chanson d'amour (IRE) **R. Stewart**
82 **SOMETHING WELLS (FR)**, 7, b g Dolpour—Linsky Ball (FR) **Favourites Racing XVIII**
83 **SPARTACUS BAY (IRE)**, 7, b g Simply Great (FR)—Decent Slave **You Can Be Sure**

MISS V. M. WILLIAMS—continued

84 **SPIT (IRE)**, 5, b g Flemensfirth (USA)—Red Supporter **M. P. Graham**
85 **STAN (NZ)**, 9, b g Super Imposing (NZ)—Take Care (NZ) **P. W. Beck**
86 **SUPREME LEADER (IRE)**, 7, b g Supreme Leader—Nic An Ree (IRE) **T. J. Hemmings**
87 **THE OUTLIER (IRE)**, 10, gr g Roselier (FR)—Shuil A Cuig **Mr P. J. Murphy**
88 **THEATRE DIVA (IRE)**, 7, b m King's Theatre (IRE)—Rigobertha (IRE) **Let's Live Racing**
89 **TIGHTEN YOUR BELT (IRE)**, 11, b g Phardante (FR)—Hi' Upham **The MerseyClyde Partnership**
90 **TRUMP CALL (IRE)**, 4, b g Mull of Kintyre (USA)—Trumped (IRE) **Mr G. G. Mezzone**
91 **TUSKAR ROCK (FR)**, 5, br g Turgeon (USA)—Shannondore (FR) **Anthony Pye-Jeary & Mel Smith**
92 **VENICE ROAD (IRE)**, 7, ch g Halling (USA)—Croeso Cynnes **Razzle Racing Partnership**
93 **VILCABAMBA**, 6, b g Hernando (FR)—Makounji (FR) **Lady H. J. Clarke**
94 **WALK TALL (IRE)**, 5, b g Blueprint (IRE)—Dikler Gale (IRE) **T. J. Hemmings**
95 **WEIRD AL (IRE)**, 5, b g Accordion—Bucks Gift (IRE) **Brannon Dennis Dick Holden**
96 **ZACHAROVA (IRE)**, 5, b g Lil's Boy (USA)—Voronova (IRE) **The Leadenhall Partnership**

THREE-YEAR-OLDS

97 **MISTER ROSS**, b g Medicean—Aqualina (IRE) **Mrs P. Pink**

Other Owners: Dr Martin Booth, Mr A. Brooks, Mr J. S. Broomfield, Mr Andrew Brown, Mr Colin B. Brown, Mr T. W. Burrows, Mr David Cliff, Mrs Philippa Clunes, Dr Chris Cowell, Mr David Currie, Mr J. S. Dale, Lord Daresbury, Mr P.A. Deal, Mrs P.A. Deal, Mr M. N. Dennis, Mr J. R. Eburne, Mr Melvyn Edwards, Mrs Douglas Graham, Mrs F. M. Hallett, Mr Simon Hill, Mr Tony Hirschfield, Mrs J. Holleran, Mr D. Jinks, Mr J. W. Johnstone, Mr J. D. King, Mr Geoffrey Martin, Mr C. D. Massey, Mr C. R. Nugent, Mr John O'Reilly, Mr D. Redvers, Mr T. D. Rose, Mr P. Ryan, Mr Maurice Ryan, Mr K. Shaw, Mr D. M. Stuart, Mr S. Stuart, Mr Julian Taylor, Mr A. Taylor, Mr John Tyndall, Mr Terrence White.

Jockey (NH): L. Stephens, A. O'Keeffe, P. C. O'Neill, S. Thomas. **Conditional:** L. Treadwell, C. Thompson, A. Coleman. **Amateur:** Mr W. Biddick.

---

641 MRS L. V. WILLIAMSON, Chester
Postal: **Saighton Hall, Saighton, Chester, Cheshire, CH3 6EE**
Contacts: **PHONE** (01244) 314254 **MOBILE** (07970) 437679
E-MAIL info@lisawilliamson.co.uk **WEBSITE** www.lisawilliamson.co.uk

1 **BLYTHE SPIRIT**, 9, b g Bahamian Bounty—Lithe Spirit (IRE) **Bithell/Garner Partnership**
2 **COLLIERS COURT**, 11, b g Puget (USA)—Rag Time Belle **The Castle Bend Syndicate**
3 **CORNISH REBEL (IRE)**, 11, br g Un Desperado (FR)—Katday (FR) **Halewood International Ltd**
4 **FLEMEN LOON (IRE)**, 9, b g Flemensfirth (USA)—Dancing Course (IRE) **Mr F. Keegan**
5 **FLY TIME**, 4, b f Fraam—Kissing Time **Bithell, Garner Partnership**
6 **GLENISLAND**, 4, br f Diktat—Glider (IRE) **Mr C. T. O'Donnell**
7 **INCORPORATION**, 9, b g In The Wings—Danishkada **Ms R. J. Haydn-Lloyd**
8 **LAMBRINI BIANCO (IRE)**, 10, br g Roselier (FR)—Darjoy **Halewood International Ltd**
9 **LAMBRINI CLASSIC**, 5, gr g Classic Cliche (IRE)—Lizzy Lamb **Halewood International Ltd**
10 **LAMBRINI MIST**, 10, gr g Terimon—Miss Fern **Halewood International Ltd**
11 **LOST IN NORMANDY (IRE)**, 11, b g Treasure Hunter—Auntie Honnie (IRE) **Please Hold UK**
12 **MIDNIGHT DIAMOND (IRE)**, 5, b h Alzao (USA)—Derena (FR) **The Jet Set Syndicate**
13 **REASONABLY SURE (IRE)**, 8, b g Presenting—No Reason **D & D Coatings Ltd**
14 **REBOND (FR)**, 6, ch g Trempolino (USA)—Lattaquie (FR) **Halewood International Ltd**
15 5, B g Accordion—Rosearro (IRE) **Halewood International Ltd**
16 **SKIDDAW FOX**, 4, ch c Foxhound (USA)—Stealthy Times **Mr G. Kendrick**
17 **SMART PICK**, 5, ch m Piccolo—Nevita **D & D Coatings Ltd**

THREE-YEAR-OLDS

18 **LAMBRINI LACE (IRE)**, b f Namid—Feather 'n Lace (IRE) **Mrs J. M. Halewood**
19 B g Beat All (USA)—Miss Lambrini **Halewood International Ltd**

TWO-YEAR-OLDS

20 B f 21/2 Reel Buddy (USA)—Anita In Wales (IRE) (Anita's Prince) (3800) **Mr G. Kendrick**
21 B c 17/2 Night Shift (USA)—Carrie Pooter (Tragic Role (USA)) (24000) **Mr T. Conway**
22 **DR JAMESON (IRE)**, b c 25/2 Orpen (USA)—Touraneena (Robellino (USA)) (18000) **Black Velvet Racing**
23 B c 24/4 Mind Games—Makeover (Priolo (USA)) (2200) **Mr G. Kendrick**
24 B f 17/4 Fair Mix (IRE)—Miss Lambrini (Henbit (USA)) **Halewood International Ltd**
25 B f 27/4 Captain Rio—Mysterious Plans (IRE) (Last Tycoon) (7000) **Mr T. Conway**

MRS L. V. WILLIAMSON—continued

Other Owners: Mr Anthony Bithell, Mr J. Clarke, Mr P. Cummins, Mrs Judy Halewood, Mr J. B. Hughes, Ms S. Lee, Mr John Wills.

Assistant Trainer: Mark Williamson

Jockey (flat): T. Eaves. **Jockey (NH):** D. Crosse. **Conditional:** D. Laverty.

---

642 MR A. C. WILSON, Penrith
Postal: **Silver Howe, Orton, Penrith, Cumbria, CA10 3RQ**
Contacts: PHONE **(01539) 624071** MOBILE **(07813) 846768**

1 **MISS CHAMPAGNE (IRE)**, 5, b m Tagula (IRE)—Champagne Lady (IRE) **Mrs H. J. Wilson**
2 **REXMEHEAD (IRE)**, 7, b g Fort Morgan (USA)—Moon Rose (IRE) **Mrs H. J. Wilson**

---

643 MR A. J. WILSON, Cheltenham
Postal: **Glenfall Stables, Ham, Charlton Kings, Cheltenham, Gloucestershire, GL52 6NH**
Contacts: PHONE **(01242) 244713** FAX **(01242) 226319** MOBILE **(07932) 157243**
E-MAIL ajwglenfall@aol.com

1 **BITTA DASH**, 8, ch g Bandmaster (USA)—Letitica **Mrs M. J. Wilson**
2 **BOB'S TEMPTATION**, 9, br g Bob's Return (IRE)—Temptation (IRE) **The Cotswold Partnership**
3 **MAKELLY**, 5, b g Makbul—Electric Avenue (IRE) **E. T. D. Leadbeater**
4 **NISHNASH**, 5, b g Commanche Run—Rosehall **Mrs T. D. Pilkington**
5 **RUBY VALENTINE (FR)**, 5, b m Kayf Tara—A Ma Valentine (FR) **The Wimbledon Partnership**
6 **TICKET TO RIDE (FR)**, 10, ch g Pistolet Bleu (IRE)—Have A Drink (FR) **E. T. D. Leadbeater**

Other Owners: Mr R. S. Alexander, I. R. Anderson, J. W. Griffin, B. J. Hughes, D. B. O'Beirne.

---

644 MR C. R. WILSON, Darlington
Postal: **Manor Farm, Manfield, Darlington, Co. Durham, DL2 2RW**
Contacts: PHONE **(01325) 374595** FAX **(01325) 374595** MOBILE **(07815) 952306/(07721) 379277**
E-MAIL wilsonracing@aol.com

1 **CELTIC FLOW**, 10, b m Primitive Rising (USA)—Celtic Lane **Mrs J. Wilson**
2 4, B g Compton Admiral—Celtic Lane **Mrs J. Wilson**
3 4, Br f Hunting Lion (IRE)—Dragons Daughter **Mrs J. Wilson**
4 **ORMUS**, 5, b g Rambling Bear—Adar Jane **D. A. J. Bartlett**
5 **PENNYBID (IRE)**, 6, b g Benny The Dip (USA)—Stamatina **W. Martin**
6 **ZEYDNAA (IRE)**, 8, b g Bahhare (USA)—Hadawah (USA) **Mrs J. Wilson**

THREE-YEAR-OLDS

7 **URSUS**, ch g Rambling Bear—Adar Jane **D. A. J. Bartlett**

TWO-YEAR-OLDS

8 B g 6/5 Lear Spear (USA)—Hana's Pride (IRE) (Pips Pride) **Bill Martin**

Other Owners: S. R. Bainbridge.

Assistant Trainer: Julie Wilson

Jockey (flat): T. Hamilton. **Jockey (NH):** B. Harding, P. Aspell, K. Mercer.

---

645 MR N. WILSON, York
Postal: **Woodcroft, Flaxton, York, North Yorkshire, YO60 7QZ**
Contacts: PHONE **(01904) 468151** WORK **(01904) 468035** FAX **(01904) 468035**
MOBILE **(07808) 162631**
E-MAIL noelwilson@racing845.orangehome.co.uk WEBSITE www.noelwilsonracing.com

1 **ARCTIC GHOST**, 8, gr g Environment Friend—Saxon Gift **Paul & Linda Dixon**
2 **BEAUCHAMP TURBO**, 6, ch g Pharly (FR)—Compton Astoria (USA) **B Plows PM Watson J Owen**

MR N. WILSON—continued

3 **DEMOLITION**, 4, ch g Starborough—Movie Star (IRE) **Mrs N. C. Wilson**
4 **DODAA (USA)**, 5, b g Dayjur (USA)—Ra'a (USA) **Paul & Linda Dixon**
5 **HAATMEY**, 6, b g Josr Algarhoud (IRE)—Raneen Alwatar **Naughty Diesel Ltd**
6 **HUNTERS BELT (IRE)**, 4, b g Intikhab (USA)—Three Stars **Nigel Sennett & Nicola Wilson**
7 **MAFTEN (IRE)**, 5, b g City Honours (USA)—Mafiosa **Mrs H. Scotto**
8 **MAYOR OF SEAHAM (IRE)**, 5, ch g Titus Livius (FR)—Torrmana (IRE) **Mayor Of Seaham Partnership**
9 **MICHAELS DREAM (IRE)**, 9, b g Spectrum (IRE)—Stormswept (USA) **Mrs C. K. Paver**
10 **NANTON (USA)**, 6, gr ro g Spinning World (USA)—Grab The Green (USA) **Themackemracers**
11 **PRIMUS INTER PARES (IRE)**, 7, b g Sadler's Wells (USA)—Life At The Top **The Pip Partnership**
12 **RED ROMEO**, 7, ch g Case Law—Enchanting Eve **Six Pound Note Club**
13 **RIGHTFUL RULER**, 6, b g Montjoy (USA)—Lady of the Realm **The Centaur Group Partnership II**
14 **RUN FREE**, 4, b g Agnes World (USA)—Ellie Ardensky **The Run Free Partnership**
15 **STOLT (IRE)**, 4, b g Tagula (IRE)—Cabcharge Princess (IRE) **Dixon, McIntyre, Tobin**
16 **TIROL LIVIT (IRE)**, 5, ch g Titus Livius (FR)—Orange Royale (IRE) **Mrs N. C. Wilson**
17 **TURN OF PHRASE (IRE)**, 9, b g Cadeaux Genereux—Token Gesture (IRE) **Naughty Diesel Ltd**
18 **UNITED NATIONS**, 7, ch g Halling (USA)—Congress (IRE) **Beverley Embassy Syndicate**

THREE-YEAR-OLDS

19 **LIGHTING SHADOW**, b g Captain Rio—Bonny Ruan **G. Morrill**
20 **RED SKIPPER (IRE)**, ch g Captain Rio—Speed To Lead (IRE) **Six Pound Note Club**
21 **RIDLEY DIDLEY (IRE)**, b g Tagula (IRE)—Dioscorea (IRE) **D. McIntyre**

Other Owners: T. Alderson, E. Bell, C. E. Bell, Mr D. Branchflower, Mr A. J. Cork, P. Dixon, Mrs L. J. Dixon, Mr S. M. Goodwin, Mr M. B. Goodwin, G. Hamilton, J. L. Holdroyd, D. Kilburn, T. P. Maguire, Mr B. Midgley, Mr M. N. Oughtred, J. R. Owen, D. B. Plows, N. P. Sennett, K Sobey, F. P. Tobin, P. M. Watson, J. Yates.

Assistant Trainer: Mrs N. C. Wilson

Jockey (flat): Jimmy Quinn, D. Tudhope. **Jockey (NH):** K. Renwick. **Apprentice:** Samuel Drury.

---

646   MR K. G. WINGROVE, Bridgnorth

Postal: **6 Netherton Farm Barns, Netherton Lane, Highley, Bridgnorth, Shropshire, WV16 6NJ**
Contacts: **HOME (01746) 861534 MOBILE (07974) 411267**

1 **MAGICAL MIMI**, 7, b m Magic Ring (IRE)—Naval Dispatch **M. M. Foulger**
2 **MILLERS TOPAZ**, 4, ch f Sly—Old Castle Liziann **L. T. Woodhouse**
3 4, ch g Gorse—Naval Dispatch **M. M. Foulger**
4 **SOMEWHERE MY LOVE**, 7, br m Pursuit of Love—Grand Coronet **L. T. Woodhouse**

THREE-YEAR-OLDS

5 **MILLERS SAPHIRE**, b f Sly—So Welcome **L. T. Woodhouse**

Assistant Trainer: Isobel Willer

---

647   MR P. L. WINKWORTH, Chiddingfold

Postal: **Robins Farm Racing Stables, Fisher Lane, Chiddingfold, Surrey, GU8 4TB**
Contacts: **PHONE (01428) 685025 FAX (01483) 200878 MOBILE (07968) 799950**
E-MAIL peter.winkworth@cbgplc.com

1 **ALE HOUSE (IRE)**, 6, b g Taipan (IRE)—Vultang Lady **Mrs Olivia Donovan, Mrs Gina Barrett**
2 **DESERT SPRINGS**, 5, b m Parthian Springs—Desert Project (IRE) **Mrs V. Palmer**
3 **DUNSFOLD DUKE**, 8, b g Cloudings (IRE)—Rositary (FR) **P. L. Winkworth**
4 **FRUITY O'ROONEY**, 5, b g Kahyasi—Recipe **Mrs T. A. Winkworth**
5 **HIGH CLASS PROBLEM (IRE)**, 5, b g Mozart (IRE)—Sarah-Clare **Ashplace Stud & Joshua Russell**
6 **OSBOURNE**, 9, ch g Blushing Flame (USA)—Glenlinass **Mrs Jenny Willment**
7 **PRAGMATIST**, 4, b f Piccolo—Shi Shi **Mrs Jenny Willment**
8 **ROZNIC (FR)**, 10, b g Nikos—Rozamie (FR) **Etoile Racing**
9 **SAFARI ADVENTURES (IRE)**, 6, b g King's Theatre (IRE)—Persian Walk (FR) **Mrs T. A. Winkworth**
10 **SAFARI MISCHIEF**, 5, b g Primo Valentino (IRE)—Night Gypsy **Foxtrot Racing Partnership**
11 **SAFARI SUNDOWNER (IRE)**, 4, b g Daggers Drawn (USA)—Acadelli (IRE) **P. L. Winkworth**
12 **SAFARI SUNSET (IRE)**, 6, b g Fayruz—Umlani (IRE) **P. L. Winkworth**
13 **SHERIFF ROSCOE**, 8, b g Roscoe Blake—Silva Linda **The Ten Gallon Partnership**
14 **SIGNATURE TUNE (IRE)**, 9, b g Gothland (FR)—Divine Affair (IRE) **S. N. Martyn**

MR P. L. WINKWORTH—continued

15 **THE WICKED WITCH**, 5, gr m Terimon—Welgenco **Mrs L. J. Munnis**
16 **UP IN ARMS (IRE)**, 4, b g Daggers Drawn (USA)—Queenliness **Robins Farm Racing 1**

THREE-YEAR-OLDS

17 **AMIE MAGNIFICENT (IRE)**, b f Mujahid (USA)—Darbela (IRE) **Mr D. C. Holden**
18 **COLOUR TROOPER (IRE)**, ch c Traditionally (USA)—Viola Royale (IRE) **Kennet Valley Thoroughbreds I**
19 **DEAL FLIPPER**, b f Xaar—Zibet **Badger's Set**
20 **MISTRESS EVA**, br f Diktat—Foreign Mistress **Mrs F. A. Veasey**
21 **PRINCESS INDIA (IRE)**, ch f Hawk Wing (USA)—Litchfield Hills (USA) **The Hon Mrs C. Cameron**
22 **SAFARI SUNUP (IRE)**, b c Catcher In The Rye (IRE)—Nuit des Temps **P. L. Winkworth**
23 **SAFARI TIME (IRE)**, b f Danetime (IRE)—Laurel Delight **P. L. Winkworth**
24 **SHY**, ch f Erhaab (USA)—Shi Shi **Mrs Jenny Willment**
25 **SOFIA'S STAR**, b br c Lend A Hand—Charolles **Mr D. C. Holden**
26 **SPARKLER**, b f Best of The Bests (IRE)—Gem **N H Bloodstock Ltd**
27 **STARLIGHT SAFARI (IRE)**, b f Hawk Wing (USA)—Don't Care (IRE) **Tweenhills Racing**
28 **THE WILLOWY WIGEON**, b f Josr Algarhoud (IRE)—The Dark Eider **Mrs F. A. Veasey**

TWO-YEAR-OLDS

29 B c 8/2 Xaar—Antigone (IRE) (Cape Cross (IRE)) (20000) **Mrs Jessica Muddle**
30 B g 13/4 Baryshnikov (USA)—Aunt Hilda (Distant Relative) (2095) **Badger's Second Set**
31 **CATENACCIO (IRE)**, b c 18/4 Spartacus (IRE)—Montessori (Akarad (FR)) (10000) **The Defence Rests**
32 Ch f 3/4 Alhaarth (IRE)—Far Reaching (USA) (Distant View (USA)) (4000) **Ash Place Stud**
33 **FOXTROT ALPHA (IRE)**, b f 27/4 Desert Prince (IRE)—
Imelda (USA) (Manila (USA)) (23809) **Foxtrot Racing Partnership**
34 **FOXTROT BRAVO (IRE)**, b c 6/3 Noverre (USA)—
Standcorrected (Shareef Dancer (USA)) (23000) **Foxtrot Racing Partnership**
35 **FOXTROT CHARLIE**, b c 4/5 Lucky Story (USA)—Holy Smoke (Statoblest) (9500) **Foxtrot Racing Partnership**
36 **GO COMMANDO**, b c 19/3 Fraam—Magic Moment (Magic Ring (IRE)) (6000) **The Landing Strip Partnership**
37 **HATCHET MAN**, ch c 22/2 Needwood Blade—
Mayfair (Green Desert (USA)) (32000) **Kennet Valley Thoroughbreds VII**
38 **HEY HO**, b f 4/2 Primo Valentino (IRE)—Beauty (IRE) (Alzao (USA)) (2200) **C. V. Cruden**
39 Gr f 28/1 Verglas (IRE)—Ladylishandra (IRE) (Mujadil (USA)) (27026) **Team Safari**
40 **LAVENDER GIRL**, b f 9/3 Lucky Owners (NZ)—Lavender Dancer (Tragic Role (USA)) (571) **Mrs Judy Munnis**
41 **MONEY MONEY MONEY**, b f 25/1 Generous (IRE)—Shi Shi (Alnasr Alwasheek) (USA) **Mrs Jenny Willment**
42 **NOW**, b f 11/4 Where Or When (IRE)—Tup Tim (Emperor Jones (USA)) (10000) **Mrs Jenny Willment**
43 **ON THE FEATHER**, br f 18/4 Josr Algarhoud (IRE)—Fotheringhay (Loup Sauvage (USA)) **Mrs Jenny Willment**
44 B c 13/5 Piccolo—Oriel Girl (Beveled (USA)) (1047) **Mrs F. A. Veasey & Partners**
45 **PENTON HOOK**, gr g 12/3 Lucky Owners (NZ)—
Cosmic Star (Siberian Express (USA)) (3238) **Mrs T. A. Winkworth**
46 **PORTUGESE CADDY (IRE)**, b g 2/3 Great Palm (USA)—
Paintbrush (IRE) (Groom Dancer (USA)) (2095) **Mrs T. A. Winkworth**
47 B f 21/4 Reset (AUS)—Princess of Garda (Komaite (USA)) (15000) **Badger's Second Set**
48 **REEL ALE**, ch c 3/2 Reel Buddy (USA)—Betty Stogs (IRE) (Perugino (USA)) (4000) **The Cricketers At Duncton**
49 **SAFARI SUNSHINE (IRE)**, b f 5/3 Marju (IRE)—
Alexandra S (IRE) (Sadler's Wells (USA)) (25096) **P. L. Winkworth**
50 **SENORITA PAPAGENA**, b f 12/5 Piccolo—Foreign Mistress (Darshaan) (10476) **Mrs F. A. Veasey**
51 **SONHADOR**, b c 12/3 Compton Place—Fayre Holly (IRE) (Fayruz) (26000) **Mr D. C. Holden**
52 **THE SAUCY SNIPE**, b f 18/2 Josr Algarhoud (IRE)—The Dark Eider (Superlative) (1047) **Mrs F. A. Veasey**
53 **WOLFS BANE**, b f 5/3 Generous (IRE)—Loriner's Lady (Saddlers' Hall (UK)) **Mrs Jenny Willment**

Other Owners: G. D. Anderson, Mrs G. E. Barrett, Mr Andy Billett, Mr Rob Brook, Mr Nick Bryant, Mr Alan Burnett, Mrs Cax du Pon, Mr Greg Chamberlain, Mr S. Champ, Mr Greg Clerkson, Mr Guy Convert, Mr Mike Davies, Mr Angus Donaldson, Mrs O. Donovan, Mr Michael Eaton, Mr Keith Ellis, Mr Rupert Fleming, T. R. Gittins, Mr Jason Golder, Mr Andy Goodsir, Mrs Rosemary Gourlay, Mr Martin Green, P. W. Haddock, Mr P. G. C. Hall, Dr Carolyn Heeps, Mr David Holden, Mr Ed Horner, Mr Scott Hunt, Mr Nicho Jenkins, Mr Chris Lewis, Mr Tom Little, Mr David Lock, Mr James Lock, Mr A. Lowrie, Mrs Victoria Lowrie, Mr Tom Marshall, Mr James Matthews, Mr David McFadzean, Mr Mark Miles, Mr P.Molony, Mr Carl Morris, Mr Jamie Moyes, Mr Jim Nolan, S. T. Norton, Mrs Angela Norton, Mr A. N. Palmer, Mr Alex Phillipson, Mr D. Redvers, Mr N. J. F. Robinson, Mrs A. Russell, Mr J. N. T. Russell, Mr Giles Salmon, Mr Dan Scott, Mr C. C. Shand Kydd, Mr Phil Spencer, Mr Tom Spencer, Mr John Steward, Mr Paul Tabor, Mr Rod Tayler, Mr Ross Tayler, Mr R. B. Taylor, Mr Alex Thistlewayte, Mrs Y. C. Timberlake, Mr John Tyndall, Mr A. J. Viall, Mr Angus Wink, Mr Ed Worsley, Mr James Young.

Assistant Trainer: Anton Pearson

Jockey (flat): J. Crowley, S. Carson. **Jockey (NH):** B. Fenton, P. Hide.

648 MR D. J. WINTLE, Cheltenham

Postal: **Lavender Hill Stud, Naunton, Cheltenham, Gloucestershire, GL54 3AZ**
Contacts: PHONE **(01451) 850182/850893** FAX **(01451) 850187** MOBILE **(07798) 822477**
E-MAIL info@lavenderhillstud.co.uk WEBSITE www.lavenderhillstud.co.uk

1 BARON BLITZKRIEG, 10, b g Sir Harry Lewis (USA)—Steel Typhoon **Bish Mezzogori-Curran, Holmes, Keast**
2 CEOPERK (IRE), 9, ch m Executive Perk—Golden Mela **Willjoman Partnership**
3 CHICAGO ALLEY, 7, br m Bob Back (USA)—Winnetka Gal (USA) **L & P Partnership**
4 FLYING SQUAD (UAE), 4, b g Jade Robbery (USA)—Sandova **M. D. Coulson**
5 GO FOR ONE (IRE), 9, b g Muroto—Barntown **Mrs B. B. Grainger**
6 HAOYUNMA (IRE), 6, ch m Old Vic—A Bit of Luck (IRE) **J. W. Egan**
7 HELLO BUD (IRE), 10, b g Jurado (USA)—Orchestral Sport (IRE) **Mr Seamus Murphy**
8 ILLOGICAL HOPE (IRE), 6, b br g Fourstars Allstar (USA)—Queen Street (IRE) **The League Of Gentlemen**
9 KEY PHIL (FR), 10, ch g Beyssac (FR)—Rivolie (FR) **The Key Partnership**
10 KRAKATAU (FR), 4, b g Noverre (USA)—Tomanivi **Ocean Trailers Ltd**
11 LES BAUX BELLE (IRE), 8, b m Supreme Leader—
                Sister Stephanie (IRE) **Mr Chris White & Mrs Margaret Turner**
12 LIZARAZU (GER), 9, b g Second Set (IRE)—Lilly (GER) **J. W. Egan**
13 NARVAL D'AVELOT (FR), 7, b g Video Rock (FR)—Reine Des Planches (FR) **D. A. Thorpe**
14 OUTCLASS (FR), 6, b m Classic Cliche (IRE)—Winnetka Gal (USA) **Lavender Hill Stud L.L.C.**
15 PHAMTOM DU LAC (FR), 5, b g Phantom Breeze—Oochigeas (FR) **Ocean Trailers Ltd**
16 PIVOLANT (FR), 5, br g Nononito (FR)—Rivolie (FR) **The Key Partnership**
17 SEVENEIGHTSIX, 8, ch m Old Vic—Necochea **D. J. Wintle**
18 TIARA BOOM DE AY (IRE), 4, b f Fasliyev (USA)—Fez **Tiara Syndicate**
19 YAKIMOV (USA), 9, ch g Affirmed (USA)—Ballet Troupe (USA) **B. E. T. Partnership**

Other Owners: Mrs J. M. Banks, R. J. Beggan, Mrs A. Bish, T. G. Bish, D. Bishop, Mr C. Bowkley, Mrs S. A. Thorpe, M. Tuerks, Mrs M. K. B. Turner, J. T. Warner, C. J. White.

Assistant Trainer: Mr Graham McCourt

Jockey (flat): V. Slattery. **Jockey (NH):** W. Marston.

649 MR I. A. WOOD, Upper Lambourn

Postal: **Neardown Stables, Upper Lambourn, Hungerford, Berkshire, RG17 8QP**
Contacts: PHONE **(01488) 72324** FAX **(01488) 72877** MOBILE **(07775) 508111**
E-MAIL ianwood@chase3c.com WEBSITE neardownracing.com

1 ALFRESCO, 4, b g Mtoto—Maureena (IRE) **Mrs A. M. Riney**
2 ANTHILL, 4, b f Slickly (FR)—Baddi Heights (FR) **C. S. Tateson**
3 BEE STINGER, 6, b g Almaty (IRE)—Nest Egg **Sporting Occasions No. 11**
4 BOWL OF CHERRIES, 5, b g Vettori (IRE)—Desert Nomad **G. Bradbury**
5 DETONATE, 6, b g Mind Games—Bron Hilda (IRE) **J. Purcell**
6 FATEFUL ATTRACTION, 5, b m Mujahid (USA)—Heavens Above (FR) **M. I. Forbes**
7 GAME LADY, 4, b f Mind Games—Highland Gait **C. S. Tateson**
8 GOLAN WAY, 4, b g Golan—Silk Daisy **Lewis Caterers**
9 HOLYFIELD WARRIOR (IRE), 4, b g Princely Heir (IRE)—Perugino Lady (IRE) **Neardown Stables**
10 MA'AM (USA), 6, ch m Royal Anthem (USA)—Hide the Bride (USA) **Neardown Stables**
11 MEDITATION, 6, ch m Inchinnor—Trojan Desert **P. E. Barrett**
12 SLAVONIC LAKE, 4, b g Lake Coniston (IRE)—Slavonic Dance **Sporting Occasions No. 14**
13 THAAYER, 13, b g Wolfhound (USA)—Hamaya (USA) **Mrs Joyce Wood**
14 WADNAGIN (IRE), 4, b f Princely Heir (IRE)—Band of Colour (IRE) **J. Browne**
15 WILLIAM'S WAY, 6, b g Fraam—Silk Daisy **Lewis Caterers**

THREE-YEAR-OLDS

16 BLACK OR RED (IRE), b c Cape Cross (IRE)—Gentle Thoughts **Cherries Racing**
17 CHERRIES ON TOP (IRE), ch c Elnadim (USA)—Easy Going **Cherries Racing**
18 EASY WONDER (GER), b f Royal Dragon (USA)—Emy Coasting (USA) **P. E. Barrett**
19 IT'S JOSR, b g Josr Algarhoud (IRE)—It's So Easy **Graham Jones & Joyce Wood**
20 KING HAFHAFAH, ch c King Charlemagne (USA)—Hafhafah **Neardown Stables**
21 RANDAMA BAY (IRE), b br c Frenchmans Bay (FR)—Randama **Neardown Stables**
22 SECONDITIS, b c Spinning World (USA)—Hairy Night (IRE) **Lewis Caterers**
23 TOWY BOY (IRE), b c King Charlemagne (USA)—Solar Flare (IRE) **Lewis Caterers**
24 WHENINEEDYOU, ch f Best of The Bests (IRE)—Party Turn **Neardown Stables**
25 WOGAN'S SISTER, b f Lahib (USA)—Dublivia **Neardown Stables**

MR I. A. WOOD—continued
TWO-YEAR-OLDS

26 Ch f 23/2 Kris Kin (USA)—Band of Colour (IRE) (Spectrum (IRE)) (11582) **Kilna Moragh Stud**
27 B f 7/3 Reset (AUS)—Be My Tinker (Be My Chief (USA)) **Mr C. Tateson**
28 Ch f 9/3 Zaha (CAN)—Chevin (Danzig Connection (USA)) (800) **A Partnership**
29 B f 21/4 Fraam—Desert Nomad (Green Desert (USA)) (300) **Writtle College**
30 Ch c 2/4 Lucky Story—Dijital Power (Pivotal) **A Partnership**
31 **DOTCO,** br f 13/4 Reel Buddy (USA)—Josifina (Master Willie) **A Partnership**
32 B f 15/4 Princely Heir (IRE)—Dublivia (Midyan (USA)) (6112) **Kilna Moragh Stud**
33 Ch c 20/3 Generous (IRE)—Dusty Shoes (Shareef Dancer (USA)) **Miss Stephanie Robinson**
34 C c 2/4 Needwood Blade—Generous Share (Cadeaux Genereux) (23000) **W. H. R. John & Partners**
35 B f 23/3 Josr Algarhoud (IRE)—Huwaidah (Shareef Dancer (USA)) (800) **Mr Andy Middleton**
36 B c 30/1 Mujahid (USA)—Janiceland (IRE) (Foxhound (USA)) (7500) **Mrs K. Kettlewell**
37 B f 18/2 Royal Applause—Liberty Bound (Primo Dominie) (22000) **A Partnership**
38 Gr c 5/2 First Trump—Mrs Dawson (Sharrood (USA)) **Mr Michael Young**
39 Ch g 19/4 Needwood Blade—My Bonus (Cyrano de Bergerac) (12000) **W. H. R. John & Partners**
40 B f 4/3 Olden Times—Pink Supreme (Night Shift (USA)) (857) **C. S. Tateson**
41 B f 14/3 Forzando—Polar Peak (Polar Falcon (USA)) (2200) **Mr Michael Young**
42 Ch c 24/2 Needwood Blade—Polish Girl (Polish Precedent (USA)) **Helshaw Grange Stud**
43 Ch f 11/2 Bold Edge—Princess Carranita (IRE) (Desert Sun) **A Partnership**
44 B gr c 6/3 Piccolo—Princess Maud (Irish River (FR)) (10000) **Summertree Stud**
45 B c 16/3 Needwood Blade—Princess Oberon (IRE) (Fairy King (USA)) **Mrs D. Smith-Hooper**
46 Ch c 30/4 Congaree (USA)—Queens Wild (USA) (Spectacular Bid (USA)) (16000)
47 **RABBIT WELL,** ch c 25/3 Dream Well (FR)—Celinda (FR) (Bering) **Mr Andy Middleton**
48 Ch c 1/4 Ishiguru (USA)—Red Head And Dotty (Risk Me (FR)) **Writtle College**
49 Ch f 6/5 Frenchmans Bay (FR)—Second Dream (Second Set (IRE)) (1930) **Kilna Moragh Stud**
50 B f 11/5 Imperial Dancer—Shalad'or (Golden Heights) **Summertree Stud**
51 B c 10/3 Josr Algarhoud (IRE)—Special Gesture (Brief Truce (USA)) (8000) **Mrs Clair Murphy**
52 B c 10/4 Catcher In The Rye (IRE)—Straight And True (Lake Coniston (IRE)) **Maesgwyn Farm**
53 B c 21/4 Zaha (CAN)—Tinkerbird (Music Boy) (6200) **Mr J. Cleeve**
54 B c 8/5 Statue of Liberty (USA)—Tragic Point (Tragic Role (USA))
55 B c 17/5 Cape Town (IRE)—Trinity Hall (Hallgate) **A Partnership**
56 **WHERE'S CHARLIE,** br c 16/3 Where Or When (IRE)—Kennedys Prima (Primo Dominie) **Middleton Stud**
57 B c 2/4 Auction House (USA)—Yo-Cando (IRE) (Cyrano de Bergerac) (10000) **A Partnership**

Other Owners: Mr Graham Bradbury, Mr Mel Catlow, Mrs D. Catlow, Mr G. R. Jones, Mrs Joyce Wood, Mr I. A. Wood.

Jockey (flat): James Doyle. **Amateur:** Mr C. Martin.

---

650 **MR R. D. E. WOODHOUSE, Thirsk**
Postal: **Breckenbrough Racing Stables, Breckenbrough, Thirsk, North Yorkshire, YO7 4EL**
Contacts: **PHONE (01845) 587872 FAX (01845) 587872 MOBILE (07885) 651348**
E-MAIL woodhouseracing@btconnect.com

1 4, Ch g Alflora (IRE)—Alphacall **J. W. Nellis**
2 **ELLIE BEE,** 9, b m Primitive Rising (USA)—Hutcel Loch **R. D. E. Woodhouse**
3 **FLAYGRAY,** 4, gr g Terimon—I'll Skin Them (IRE)
4 4, B g Terimon—Hutcel Loch **R. D. E. Woodhouse**
5 **LOCH OSCAIG,** 8, b g Sir Harry Lewis (USA)—Paddys Cherub **W. D. S. Murdoch**
6 **LUCE BAY,** 5, b g Picea—Mary Macblain **R. D. E. Woodhouse**
7 **MR BOND (IRE),** 5, ch g Moscow Society (USA)—Wise Wish **C. F. Colquhoun**
8 **ON AND UP,** 4, bl f Terimon—Bobupandown **Shade Oak Stud**
9 **OVERTHROW,** 5, b m Overbury (IRE)—My Adventure (IRE) **Mr & Mrs A. C. Wakeham**
10 **SALVEO (IRE),** 6, b g Saddlers' Hall (IRE)—Devil Worship **R. D. E. Woodhouse**
11 **THE ONLY WAY,** 5, b m Yaheeb (USA)—Way Home **Team Bonnie**
12 **TICKATEAL,** 8, ch g Emperor Fountain—Mary Hand (IRE) **R. D. E. Woodhouse**

THREE-YEAR-OLDS

13 B g Alflora (IRE)—Hutcel Loch **R. D. E. Woodhouse**
14 B g Picea—Morticia **R. D. E. Woodhouse**

TWO-YEAR-OLDS

15 **UPTON OLA,** b f 26/3 Josr Algarhoud (IRE)—Hispaniola (IRE) (Barathea (IRE)) **R. D. E. Woodhouse**
16 **UPTON SEAS,** b f 24/3 Josr Algarhoud (IRE)—Crystal Seas (Zamindar (USA)) **R. D. E. Woodhouse**

MR R. D. E. WOODHOUSE—continued

Other Owners: Dr C. A. Browning, Mr Antony Wakeham, Mrs A. C. Wakeham.

Assistant Trainer: Ben R. Woodhouse

Amateur: Mr B. R. Woodhouse.

---

651 **MR S. WOODMAN, Chichester**
Postal: **Parkers Barn Stables, 8 Pook Lane, East Lavant, Chichester, West Sussex, PO18 0AU**
Contacts: **OFFICE (01243) 527136 FAX (01243) 527136 MOBILE (07889) 188519**
E-MAIL stevewoodman83@msn.com

1 GOOD WEE GIRL (IRE), 6, b m Tagula (IRE)—Auriga **Mrs S. B. Woodman**
2 IVORY LACE, 7, b m Atraf—Miriam **Sally Woodman J Lenaghan D Mortimer**
3 TINTAWN GOLD (IRE), 8, b m Rudimentary (USA)—Clear Ahead **Mrs S. B. Woodman**

THREE-YEAR-OLDS

4 B g Josr Algarhoud (IRE)—Its Your Bid

Other Owners: Mrs J. Lenaghan, Mr D. Mortimer.

---

652 **MRS A. M. WOODROW, High Wycombe**
Postal: **Crookswood Stud Farm, Wycombe Road, Studley Green, High Wycombe, Buckinghamshire, HP14 3XB**
Contacts: **PHONE (01494) 482557 MOBILE (07901) 858874**
E-MAIL john@woodrow.com

1 LESCER'S LAD, 11, b g Perpendicular—Grange Gracie **Mrs A. M. Woodrow & Mr J. G. Woodrow**
2 SIR PELINORE, 13, b g Caerleon (USA)—Soemba **Mrs A. M. Woodrow & Mr J. G. Woodrow**

Other Owners: Mr J. G. Woodrow.

Assistant Trainer: John Woodrow

Jockey (NH): S. Durack, J. A. McCarthy. **Conditional:** Felix De Giles, Ryan Cummings. **Amateur:** Mr A. G. L. Merriam.

---

653 **MR G. WOODWARD, Tickhill**
Postal: **21 Camden Grove, Maltby, Rotherham, South Yorkshire, S66 8GE**
Contacts: **HOME (01709) 813431 WORK (07739) 382052**
E-MAIL gwoodwardracing@aol.com WEBSITE www.garrywoodward.co.uk

1 ALI D, 10, b g Alhijaz—Doppio **G. Woodward**
2 DOUBLE CARPET (IRE), 5, b g Lahib (USA)—Cupid Miss **R. W. Empson**
3 HAUGHTON HOPE, 5, b g Daawe (USA)—Kandymal (IRE) **Hammered On Friday Racing Partnership**

Other Owners: Mr J. N. Bloom, Mr G. W. B. Noble.

Jockey (flat): T.G. McLaughlin.

---

654 **MR GEOFFREY WRAGG, Newmarket**
Postal: **Abington Place, Bury Road, Newmarket, Suffolk, CB8 7BT**
Contacts: **OFFICE (01638) 662328 FAX (01638) 663576**
E-MAIL gwragg@btclick.com

1 APPLE BLOSSOM (IRE), 4, b f Danehill Dancer (IRE)—Silk (IRE) **Dr A. J. F. Gillespie**
2 CONVALLARIA (FR), 5, b m Cape Cross (IRE)—Scarlet Davis (FR) **Mrs C. Lilley**
3 DRAGON DANCER, 5, b h Sadler's Wells (USA)—Alakananda **J. L. C. Pearce**
4 FOLLY LODGE, 4, ch f Grand Lodge (USA)—Marika **Mr O F Waller & Mr T D Rootes**
5 GRAND PASSION (IRE), 8, b g Grand Lodge (USA)—Lovers' Parlour **H. H. & Mrs H. H. Morriss**
6 HERON BAY, 4, b c Hernando (FR)—Wiener Wald (USA) **Mollers Racing**
7 HOTEL DU CAP, 5, br h Grand Lodge (USA)—Miss Riviera Golf **J. L. C. Pearce**
8 IVY CREEK (USA), 5, b h Gulch (USA)—Ivy Leaf (IRE) **Mollers Racing**

MR GEOFFREY WRAGG—continued

9 **JACK OF TRUMPS (IRE)**, 8, b g King's Theatre (IRE)—Queen Caroline (USA) **Mollers Racing**
10 **PRINCESS LAVINIA**, 5, ch m Fraam—Affaire de Coeur **D. R. Hunnisett**
11 **SELL OUT**, 4, gr f Act One—Nordica **T. D. Rootes**
12 **THE CARLTON CANNES**, 4, b c Grand Lodge (USA)—Miss Riviera Golf **J. L. C. Pearce**
13 **THE WILY WOODCOCK**, 4, b g Mark of Esteem (IRE)—Lonely Shore **Mrs E. Y. Hunnisett & Mrs F. A. Veasey**

THREE-YEAR-OLDS

14 **ANDAMAN SUNSET**, b c Red Ransom (USA)—Miss Amanpuri **J. L. C. Pearce**
15 **ARTHUR'S GIRL**, b f Hernando (FR)—Maid of Camelot **A. E. Oppenheimer**
16 **HARRY GEE**, b g Averti (IRE)—Mentro (IRE) **Mollers Racing**
17 **HAWK ISLAND (IRE)**, b c Hawk Wing (USA)—Crimphill (IRE) **Mollers Racing**
18 **MISS RIVIERA CHIC**, b f Cadeaux Genereux—Miss Riviera **J. L. C. Pearce**
19 **MISS ST TROPEZ**, b f Danehill Dancer (IRE)—Miss Riviera Golf **J. L. C. Pearce**
20 **MONTERRICO**, b c Dubai Destination (USA)—Mezzogiorno **Mrs R. Philipps**
21 **MOYENNE CORNICHE**, ch c Selkirk (USA)—Miss Corniche **J. L. C. Pearce**
22 **PORT QUIN**, ch c Dr Fong (USA)—Saphila (IRE) **Mollers Racing**
23 **ST JEAN CAP FERRAT**, b br c Domedriver (IRE)—Miss Cap Ferrat (IRE) **J. L. C. Pearce**
24 **THE LADY LAPWING**, b f Mark of Esteem (IRE)—Lonely Shore **Mrs F. A. Veasey**

TWO-YEAR-OLDS

25 **FLECHE D'OR**, b f 21/5 Dubai Destination (USA)—Nuryana (Nureyev (USA)) **Mr A. E. Oppenheimer**
26 **GASSIN**, b c 18/2 Selkirk (USA)—Miss Riviera Golf (Hernando (FR)) **J. L. C. Pearce**
27 **LOMBOK**, b c 20/2 Hernando (FR)—Miss Rinjani (Shirley Heights) **J. L. C. Pearce**
28 **MISS EZE**, b f 23/2 Danehill Dancer (IRE)—Miss Corniche (Hernando (FR)) **J. L. C. Pearce**
29 **ROYAL RIVIERA**, b c 23/2 Nayef (USA)—Miss Cap Ferrat (Darshaan) **J. L. C. Pearce**

---

655 MR G. H. YARDLEY, Malvern
Postal: **Upper Woodsfield Farm, Newland, Malvern, Worcestershire, WR13 5BE**
Contacts: **PHONE (01905) 830245**

1 5, B g Classic Cliche (IRE)—Burnt Honey (IRE)
2 **COMANCHE KRIEK**, 5, ch g Commanche Run—Cherry Sip **P. J. Jones**
3 **EASTERN PRINCESS**, 4, b f Almutawakel—Silvereine (FR) **Battlefield Brook Racing**
4 **GATECRASHER**, 5, gr g Silver Patriarch (IRE)—Girl At The Gate **Battlefield Brook Racing**
5 **NATIVE CHERRY**, 7, b m Commanche Run—Cherry Sip **P. J. Jones**
6 **STREET WARRIOR (IRE)**, 5, b g Royal Applause—Anne Bonny **Battlefield Brook Racing**
7 **TUXEDO BAY**, 4, b g Muhtarram (USA)—Shoof (USA) **C. J. Shelton**

Other Owners: Mrs Jan Kerr, Mr Paul Morrison.

Assistant Trainer: Alison Yardley

Jockey (NH): V. Slattery.

---

656 MR R. H. YORK, Cobham
Postal: **Newmarsh Farm, Horsley Road, Cobham, Surrey, KT11 3JX**
Contacts: **PHONE (01932) 863594 FAX (01932) 860703 MOBILE (07808) 344131**
E-MAIL ray.york@virgin.net

1 **APPLECROSS BAY**, 5, b m Mohaajir (USA)—Glenda Ross **S. Cargill**
2 **AYA**, 6, b m Double Trigger (IRE)—Upper Mount Street (IRE) **R. H. York**
3 **DESERT SOUL**, 4, b g Fantastic Light (USA)—Jalousie (IRE) **F. D. Camis**
4 5, Br m Darnay—Dunbrody Duchess (IRE) **R. H. York**
5 **MEREWORTH MONARCH**, 5, ch g Double Trigger (IRE)—Royal Credit **Miss D. T. Hamblin**
6 **NAMIBIAN PINK (IRE)**, 4, b f Cape Cross (IRE)—Sky Pink
7 **ROSIE'S MATE (IRE)**, 5, b m Needle Gun (IRE)—Empress Nicki **Mrs H. E. Moore**
8 **SHAMMY BUSKINS**, 6, b g Shambo—Quistaquay **P. J. Morgan**
9 **SOVIET THREAT (IRE)**, 7, ch g Soviet Star (USA)—Veiled Threat (IRE) **R. H. York**
10 **STAR GLOW**, 14, b g Dunbeath (USA)—Betrothed **R. H. York**

Amateur: Mr N. Kinnon, Mr P. York.

657 MR W. G. YOUNG, Carluke

Postal: Overton Farm, Crossford, Carluke, Lanarkshire, ML8 5QF
Contacts: PHONE (01555) 860226 FAX (01555) 860137 MOBILE (07900) 408210
E-MAIL peppersyoung@aol.com

1 **ELLANDSHE (IRE)**, 8, b br g Topanoora—Fox Glen **W. G. Young**
2 **GALA QUEEN**, 8, gr m Accondy (IRE)—Miss Jedd **W. G. Young**
3 **HANDEL WITH CARE (IRE)**, 6, b g King of Kings (IRE)—La Pepite (USA) **W. G. Young**
4 **HATTINGTON**, 10, b g Polish Precedent (USA)—Ruffle (FR) **W. G. Young**
5 **KAIKOVRA (IRE)**, 12, ch g Toulon—Drefflane Supreme **W. G. Young**
6 **KALATIME (IRE)**, 5, b br m Kalanisi (IRE)—Dream Time **W. G. Young**
7 **LEPRECHAUN'S MAITE**, 6, b g Komaite (USA)—Leprechaun Lady **W. G. Young**
8 **NOSHINANNIKIN**, 14, ch g Anshan—Preziosa **W. G. Young**
9 **ROADWORTHY (IRE)**, 11, b m Lord Americo—Henry Woman (IRE) **W. G. Young**
10 **ROSEBANK (IRE)**, 6, b m Heron Island (IRE)—Molls Rose (IRE) **W. G. Young**

Assistant Trainer: W. G. Young Jnr.

INDEX TO HORSES

The Figure before the name of the horse refers to the number of the team in which it appears and **The Figure after** the horse supplies a ready reference to each animal. Horses are indexed strictly alphabeticaly, e.g. THE CARROT MAN appears in the T's, MR BUSBY in the MR's, ST MELLION WAY in the ST's etc.

538 **AINIA** (GB) 11
410 **AINTNONANCY** (GB) 1
166 **AIR CHIEF** (GB) 6
375 **AIR FORCE ONE** (GER) 1
518 **AIR GUITAR** (GB) 1
124 **AIR LION** (USA) 17
486 **AIR MAZE** (GB) 38
632 **AIREDALE LAD** (IRE) 1
203 **AIRES ROCK** (IRE) 1
458 **AIRFORCE** (GB) 1
33 **AIRMAN** (IRE) 2
622 **AISATSU** (GB) 1
283 **AITCH DOUBLEYOU** (IRE) 1
377 **AITCHJAYEM** (GB) 1
99 **AJAAN** (GB) 1
421 **AJAY** (IRE) 2
167 **AJEEL** (IRE) 1
589 **AJHAR** (GB) 1
589 **AJRA** (IRE) 12
409 **AJZAL** (GB) 1
115 **AKA LADY** (FR) C 77
36 **AKABAR** (GB) 45
83 **AKAREM** (GB) 2
311 **AKILAK** (IRE) 5
167 **AKMAL** (GB) 69
165 **AKUNA BAY** (USA) F 65
237 **AL AQABAH** (IRE) 3
167 **AL AZY** (IRE) 17
604 **AL BALDID** (GER) 2
105 **AL BARIZ** (GB) 7
302 **AL COBRA** (IRE) 17
438 **AL FALCON** (GB) 1
56 **AL GILLANI** (IRE) 26
165 **AL KHALEEJ** (IRE) 1
200 **AL MOULATHAM** (GB) 2
67 **AL MUHEER** (IRE) 14
105 **AL QASI** (IRE) 1
493 **AL RAYANAH** (GB) 1
364 **AL RECIBIR** (FR) 1
167 **AL TAMOOH** (IRE) 70
332 **AL TAYYARA** (GB) 2
302 **AL THERAAB** (USA) C 82
531 **ALABAMA SPIRIT** (USA) 35
305 **ALABJAR** (GB) 32
87 **ALACITY** (IRE) 19
302 **ALAFOOR** (FR) 83
343 **ALAGHIRAAR** (IRE) 1
516 **ALAGON** (IRE) 1
302 **ALAINMAAR** (FR) 84
455 **ALAIYMA** (IRE) 70
434 **ALAM** (USA) 1
474 **ALAMINOS** (FR) 3
209 **ALAMKHAN** (IRE) 1
585 **ALAN DEVONSHIRE** (GB) 23
506 **ALAN'S LEGACY** (IRE) 3
455 **ALANDI** (IRE) 11
625 **ALANEED** (GB) 10
455 **ALANIYA** (IRE) 11
169 **ALANNAH** (IRE) 11
215 **ALAPOUR** (IRE) 10
455 **ALARAZI** (IRE) 1
30 **ALARMED** (GB) 11
50 **ALAS** (FR) 23
455 **ALASHA** (IRE) C 71
490 **ALASIL** (USA) 1
513 **ALASKAN WAY** (USA) 21
107 **ALASPIEL** (IRE) 10
455 **ALAYA** (IRE) C 72
302 **ALAZEYAB** (USA) 85
67 **ALBABILIA** (IRE) 15
340 **ALBACORA** (IRE) C 84
67 **ALBADI** (GB) 1
167 **ALBAHER** (GB) 1
165 **ALBAIYDA** (IRE) C 66
257 **ALBANOV** (IRE) 2

311 **ALBANY** (IRE) 6
530 **ALBARINO** (IRE) 3
302 **ALBAROUCHE** (GB) 18
572 **ALBAVILLA** (GB) 71
348 **ALBERT HALL** (USA) 10
422 **ALBERT HENRY** (IRE) 19
599 **ALBERT PARK** (IRE) 1
450 **ALBERTAS RUN** (IRE) 1
20 **ALBINUS** (GB) 1
115 **ALBISOLA** (IRE) 44
282 **ALBRIGHTON** (GB) 1
437 **ALBUHERA** (IRE) 1
517 **ALCATRAS** (IRE) 1
105 **ALCIMEDES** (GB) 8
421 **ALDERBRIDGE** (IRE) 3
135 **ALDERBROOK GIRL** (IRE) 1
141 **ALDERBURN** (GB) 1
640 **ALDERLEY ROVER** (IRE) 3
216 **ALDERLUCK** (IRE) 1
470 **ALDERMAN ROSE** (GB) 1
407 **ALDEVONIE** (GB) F 51
95 **ALDIRUOS** (IRE) 1
114 **ALDIZA** (USA) C 53
647 **ALE HOUSE** (IRE) 1
486 **ALEATRICIS** (GB) 11
20 **ALECIA** (IRE) 2
572 **ALECTRONA** (IRE) 72
457 **ALEEMDAR** (IRE) 2
181 **ALEGRIA** (GB) C 17
496 **ALERON** (IRE) 1
406 **ALESSANO** (IRE) 1
211 **ALEXANDER BALLET** (GB) C 35
519 **ALEXANDER CASTLE** (USA) 38
638 **ALEXANDER EXCHANGE** (IRE) 2
556 **ALEXANDER EXPRESS** (IRE) F 29
48 **ALEXANDER GURU** (IRE) 1
519 **ALEXANDER HURICANE** (IRE) 2
222 **ALEXANDER OATS** (GB) 1
420 **ALEXANDER TAIPAN** (IRE) 4
542 **ALEXANDRIA BLUE** (IRE) 1
225 **ALEXIA REVEUSE** (IRE) C 89
549 **ALFABET SOUK** (GB) 2
259 **ALFADORA** (GB) 1
332 **ALFASONIC** (GB) 3
239 **ALFATHAA** (GB) 16
320 **ALFATRIX** (IRE) 1
571 **ALFIE FLITS** (GB) 1
441 **ALFIE LEE** (IRE) 1
467 **ALFIE NOAKES** (GB) 1
56 **ALFIE TUPPER** (IRE) 1
320 **ALFRED'S TOWER** (GB) 2
649 **ALFRESCO** (GB) 1
276 **ALGAAWIA** (USA) 82
39 **ALGAIRA** (USA) F 23
486 **ALGARADE** (GB) 1
340 **ALHAURIN** (USA) 12
167 **ALHUDHUD** (IRE) 72
653 **ALI D** (GB) 1
39 **ALI FORTUNA** (IRE) F 24
257 **ALI'S DIPPER** (IRE) F 3
438 **ALIBA** (IRE) 2
484 **ALIBY** (IRE) 1
486 **ALICANTE** (GB) 39
174 **ALICE BLACKTHORN** (GB) C 22
173 **ALICE SMITH** F 1
229 **ALICE STRAND** (IRE) 1
193 **ALICEDALE** (USA) C 14
364 **ALIFIERI** (GER) 2
574 **ALIGNMENT** (IRE) C 25
102 **ALIKA'S DANCE** (USA) F 34
188 **ALIKHLAS** (GB) F 28
466 **ALIMACDEE** (GB) 3
59 **ALINGHI** (GER) 1
128 **ALISAR** (IRE) 1
50 **ALIX ROAD** (FR) 1

455 **ALIYFA** (IRE) 73
486 **ALIZADORA** (GB) 12
390 **ALIZAR** (IRE) F 15
165 **ALKHAFIF** (GB) 67
589 **ALKHARSAA** (IRE) 60
340 **ALKIVIA** (FR) 13
18 **ALL ABOUT TRIGGER** (FR) 1
107 **ALL ABOUT YOU** (IRE) 61
574 **ALL BUSINESS** (GB) C 26
133 **ALL DIAMONDS** (IRE) 1
506 **ALL FOR LUCK** (IRE) 4
407 **ALL FOR THE CAUSE** (IRE) 2
543 **ALL GLORY** (GB) C 52
302 **ALL GUNS FIRING** (IRE) 86
513 **ALL IN ORDER** (USA) 22
320 **ALL IN THE STARS** (IRE) 3
292 **ALL IS FAIR** (GB) C 102
332 **ALL LIT UP** (GB) 178
360 **ALL OUT FOR SEVEN** (IRE) 1
328 **ALL SONSILVER** (FR) 1
58 **ALL SQUARE** (FR) C 53
269 **ALL STAR** (GER) 5
302 **ALL THE ACES** (IRE) 19
285 **ALL YOU NEED** (IRE) 1
600 **ALLEGEDLY** (IRE) C 22
631 **ALLEGEDLY SO** (IRE) 1
624 **ALLEGIANCE** (GB) 1
486 **ALLEVIATE** (IRE) 2
56 **ALLEXES** (IRE) 46
9 **ALLEY KITTEN** (IRE) C 39
249 **ALLEZ LES BLEU** (IRE) 4
482 **ALLEZ MELINA** (IRE) 2
446 **ALLFORTARA** (IRE) 1
446 **ALLGROWNUP** (IRE) 5
37 **ALLIED POWERS** (IRE) 18
131 **ALLIGRAM** (USA) C 64
549 **ALLISTATHEBARRISTA** (IRE) 3
276 **ALLIUM** (IRE) 10
115 **ALLODIAL LAND** (USA) 1
479 **ALLONBY BAY** (GB) 1
579 **ALLORO** (GB) 1
311 **ALLOVERAGAIN** (IRE) 7
320 **ALLUMEE** (GB) 4
363 **ALLURING PARK** (IRE) C 37
340 **ALLYBAR** (IRE) 85
486 **ALMA MATER** (IRE) 1
101 **ALMAHABA** (IRE) 1
486 **ALMAMIA** (GB) 13
225 **ALMANSA** (IRE) C 90
282 **ALMANSHOOD** (USA) 2
629 **ALMATY EXPRESS** (IRE) 1
346 **ALMAYDAN** (GB) 1
167 **ALMAZAR** (GB) 73
625 **ALMEDAWAR** (IRE) 59
289 **ALMIER** (IRE) 3
302 **ALMIQDAAD** (GB) 87
57 **ALMIRE DU LIA** (FR) 1
406 **ALMIZAN** (IRE) 4
625 **ALMOLAHEK** (IRE) 11
519 **ALMOND MOUSSE** (FR) F 85
66 **ALMORA GURU** (GB) 3
499 **ALMOST HERE** (IRE) 1
221 **ALMOST MARRIED** (IRE) 1
276 **ALMOUTAZ** (USA) 11
302 **ALMOUTEZAH** (USA) 20
302 **ALMUSHKHAS** (USA) 1
589 **ALMUTAWAAZIN** (GB) 61
132 **ALNWICK** (GB) 1
163 **ALOMA'S REALITY** (USA) F 53
263 **ALONE HE STANDS** (IRE) 1
504 **ALONG THE NILE** (GB) 2
56 **ALONSO DE GUZMAN** (IRE) 2
172 **ALPENGLOW** (GB) F 83
406 **ALPES MARITIMES** (GB) 5
576 **ALPH** (GB) 1

530 **AZULEJO** (FR) 5
585 **AZURE MIST** (GB) 25
165 **AZWA** (GB) 71
1 **AZYGOUS** (GB) 1
126 **B BEAUTIFUL** (IRE) F 40
107 **B BEAUTIFUL** (IRE) F 62
413 **BA DREAMFLIGHT** (GB) 24
475 **BAAHER** (USA) 1
67 **BAALBEK** (GB) F 74
105 **BAARIQ** (GB) 50
191 **BAARRIJ** (GB) 1
583 **BAAWRAH** (GB) 1
1 **BABA GHANOUSH** (GB) 3
64 **BABE HEFFRON** (IRE) 1
29 **BABICA** (USA) 2
220 **BABILU** (GB) 22
585 **BABODANA** (GB) 3
115 **BABOUCHE** (FR) 3
44 **BABY FANE** (IRE) G 2
225 **BABY HOUSEMAN** (GB) 15
265 **BABY LOVES** (GB) F 45
277 **BABY PRINCESS** (BRZ) 2
631 **BABY SISTER** (GB) 2
531 **BABY STRANGE** (GB) 3
452 **BACHELOR DAYS** (IRE) 41
452 **BACK AMONG FRIENDS** (GB) 2
638 **BACK IN BUSINESS** (IRE) 5
292 **BACK IS BACK** (IRE) 4
640 **BACK ON LINE** (IRE) 9
405 **BACK ON THE ROAD** (IRE) 1
422 **BACK TO NORMAL** (IRE) 1
569 **BACK TO SQUARE ONE** (IRE) 2
269 **BACK TO THE WIND** (IRE) 8
311 **BACKBEAT** (IRE) 14
606 **BACKBORD** (GER) 2
95 **BACKLASH** (GB) 5
599 **BACKSCRATCHER** (GB) 2
638 **BACKSTAGE** (FR) 6
310 **BAD BARON** (IRE) 21
446 **BAD BOY BONNEY** (GB) 9
257 **BAD DAY BAD DAY** (GB) 7
1 **BAD MOON RISING** (GB) 24
37 **BADALONA** (GB) 22
444 **BADEE'A** (IRE) C 66
107 **BADGE** (GB) 63
170 **BADGER BAY** (IRE) F 5
257 **BADGERLAW** (IRE) 8
324 **BADLY BRUISED** (IRE) 1
167 **BADWEIA** (USA) 20
311 **BAFANA BOY** (GB) 15
375 **BAGAN** (FR) 4
166 **BAGBER** (GB) 26
626 **BAGENALSTOWN** (IRE) 5
503 **BAGGY BLOOMERS** (GB) 8
115 **BAHALI** (FR) 79
260 **BAHAMARAMA** (IRE) 24
37 **BAHAMIAN BABE** (GB) 69
43 **BAHAMIAN BALLAD** (GB) 16
68 **BAHAMIAN BAY** (GB) 2
584 **BAHAMIAN BLISS** (GB) 8
166 **BAHAMIAN BLUE** (GB) 7
83 **BAHAMIAN DUKE** (GB) 6
68 **BAHAMIAN GIFT** (GB) 16
285 **BAHAMIAN KID** (GB) 32
285 **BAHAMIAN LAD** (GB) 33
436 **BAHAMIAN PIRATE** (USA) 1
285 **BAHAMIAN PRINCESS** (GB) 34
67 **BAHAR SHUMAAL** (IRE) 2
325 **BAHHMIRAGE** (IRE) 1
269 **BAHIA BLANCA** (FR) 9
238 **BAHIA BREEZE** (GB) 2
513 **BAHIA GOLD** (USA) C 133
513 **BAHIA NOOR** (USA) 26
600 **BAHIA PALACE** (GB) 14
67 **BAHIANO** (IRE) 3

172 **BAHIRAH** (GB) F 86
254 **BAIE DES FLAMANDS** (USA) 4
30 **BAILA MORENA** (FR) 60
394 **BAILEY** (IRE) 20
336 **BAILEYS APPLAUSE** (GB) F 27
220 **BAILEYS BENCHMARK** (GB) 3
253 **BAILEYS CREAM** (GB) F 91
220 **BAILEYS OUTSHINE** (GB) 1
607 **BAILEYS SURPRISE** (IRE) 3
411 **BAILY BREEZE** (IRE) 2
411 **BAILY ROCK** (IRE) 3
411 **BAILY STORM** (IRE) 4
411 **BAILY VIEW** (IRE) 5
335 **BAINISTEOIR** (GB) 8
513 **BAINORAMA** (FR) 134
115 **BAKARAT DU BERLAIS** (FR) 4
332 **BAKBENSCHER** (GB) 8
573 **BAKER'S BRIDGE** (IRE) 2
479 **BAKER'S GIRL** (IRE) 3
358 **BAKERS BOY** (GB) 1
455 **BAKULA** (IRE) 15
172 **BAL BIRNIE** (GB) 5
456 **BALAIS FOLLY** (IRE) 17
156 **BALAKIREF** (GB) 2
254 **BALAMORY DAN** (IRE) 5
455 **BALANKA** (IRE) F 77
399 **BALATA** (GB) 25
513 **BALDELLIA** (IRE) C 135
542 **BALDELLIA** (FR) C 17
83 **BALDEMAR** (GB) 34
340 **BALDORIA** (IRE) 2
403 **BALERNO** (GB) 4
305 **BALI BELONY** (GB) 4
589 **BALIGHA** (GB) 17
340 **BALIUS** (IRE) 3
178 **BALKAN KNIGHT** (GB) 2
454 **BALL CAT** (FR) F 40
455 **BALL CHAIRMAN** (USA) F 78
402 **BALL GAMES** (GB) 2
68 **BALL GOWN** (GB) F 48
111 **BALLA D'AIRE** (IRE) 1
383 **BALLABRIGGS** (IRE) 1
383 **BALLABROOK** (IRE) 2
295 **BALLAD MAKER** (IRE) 1
332 **BALLAMUSIC** (IRE) 9
37 **BALLANTRAE** (IRE) 70
6 **BALLARINA** (GB) 11
451 **BALLERINA BAY** (GB) F 33
326 **BALLINTENI** (GB) 2
105 **BALLISODARE** (GB) 15
276 **BALLOCHROY** (GB) 14
304 **BALLURE BAY** (IRE) 5
337 **BALLY CONN** (IRE) 4
253 **BALLYALLA** (GB) 92
523 **BALLYBOE BOY** (IRE) 3
333 **BALLYBOLEY** (IRE) 1
275 **BALLYBOUGH JACK** (IRE) 1
355 **BALLYBUNION** (IRE) 1
53 **BALLYCASSIDY** (IRE) 3
16 **BALLYCROY BOY** (IRE) 10
279 **BALLYDUB** (IRE) 2
212 **BALLYFIN** (IRE) 4
292 **BALLYFINNEY** (IRE) 5
598 **BALLYFITZ** (GB) 1
213 **BALLYFOY** (IRE) 1
533 **BALLYGALLEY BOB** (IRE) 3
420 **BALLYGOE** (IRE) 8
556 **BALLYGOLOGUE** 8
148 **BALLYGOREY** (IRE) 2
438 **BALLYHALE** (IRE) 4
298 **BALLYHEALY LADY** (GB) 19
470 **BALLYKELLY** (IRE) 6
422 **BALLYKILN** (IRE) 2
70 **BALLYLIFFEN BOY** (IRE) 2
212 **BALLYMAN** (IRE) 5

383 **BALLYNALTY EXPRESS** (IRE) 3
477 **BALLYNONTY** (IRE) 1
516 **BALLYNURE** (IRE) 7
308 **BALLYRAINEY** (IRE) 1
242 **BALLYROBERT** (IRE) 2
523 **BALLYS JOY** (IRE) 4
598 **BALLYSHAN** (IRE) 6
199 **BALLYSHANNON LADY** (IRE) 3
420 **BALLYTRIM** (IRE) 9
322 **BALLYVADEN** (IRE) 7
506 **BALLYVOGE** (IRE) 7
49 **BALMORAL STAR** (GB) 2
167 **BALNAGORE** (GB) 2
131 **BALTHAZAAR'S GIFT** (IRE) 2
231 **BALTIC BEACH** (IRE) F 54
572 **BALTIC SEA** (CAN) F 76
172 **BALTIMORE JACK** (IRE) 6
311 **BALYAN** (IRE) 16
115 **BAMAROK** (FR) 3
636 **BAMBI DE L'ORME** (FR) 3
590 **BAMBINO ROSSI** (GB) 1
549 **BAMBY** (GB) 6
109 **BANAKILL** (FR) F 51
391 **BANANA GROVE** (IRE) 3
109 **BANANA TROPIC** (GB) 14
172 **BANCHORY TWO** (IRE) 7
342 **BANCO SOLO** (GB) C 3
394 **BAND** (USA) C 96
571 **BAND OF ANGELS** (IRE) C 103
649 **BAND OF COLOUR** (IRE) F 26
371 **BANDA SEA** (IRE) 30
467 **BANDAMA** (IRE) 2
302 **BANDERAZ** (GB) 25
513 **BANDIAMIR** (FR) 2
165 **BANDIT QUEEN** (GB) F 72
369 **BANDITS PISTOL** (NZ) 1
286 **BANDORAN** (GB) 15
408 **BANJO BANDIT** (IRE) 21
321 **BANJO PATTERSON** (GB) 3
131 **BANKABLE** (IRE) 3
20 **BANKNOTE** (GB) 3
572 **BANKSIA** (GB) F 77
383 **BANNISTER LANE** (GB) 4
360 **BANOGE** (IRE) 4
9 **BANOO** (IRE) 2
598 **BANTRY BERE** (IRE) 7
279 **BAODAI** (FR) 3
571 **BAR BLU** (GB) 63
167 **BARAARI** (USA) 1
285 **BARACHOIS PRINCESS** (USA) C 44
92 **BARAFUNDLE** 1
36 **BARAKAT** (GB) F 50
311 **BARASHI** (GB) 143
31 **BARATARIA** (GB) 1
258 **BARATI** (IRE) 2
83 **BARAWIN** (GB) 35
37 **BARBARY BOY** (FR) 23
269 **BARBERS SHOP** (GB) 10
66 **BARBIROLLI** (GB) 4
165 **BARBIZOU** (FR) F 73
382 **BARBOSSA** (GB) 25
66 **BARDEN LADY** (GB) F 48
504 **BARDOLET** (IRE) 4
30 **BARILOCH** (FR) 15
177 **BARKASS** (UAE) 2
321 **BARLEY MOON** (GB) 4
112 **BARLIFFEY** (GB) 9
579 **BARN STRIPPER** (GB) C 2
138 **BARNBROOK EMPIRE** (IRE) 1
540 **BARNEY** (IRE) 1
465 **BARNEY KNOWS** (IRE) 1
156 **BARNEY MCGREW** (IRE) 3
591 **BARNEY'S DREAM** (GB) 2
91 **BARNEYS LYRIC** (GB) 1

306 **BELVILLEZ** (GB) 1
422 **BEN** (GB) 16
214 **BEN AMI** (GB) 1
273 **BEN BACCHUS** (IRE) 3
40 **BEN BHRAGGIE** (IRE) 2
506 **BEN BRITTEN** (GB) 10
342 **BEN CHORLEY** (GB) 1
428 **BEN GOUGH** (GB) 2
292 **BEN MORE ASSYNT** (IRE) 6
583 **BEN NELLY** (IRE) 2
438 **BEN TIRRAN** (GB) 6
364 **BEN VETO** (FR) 4
292 **BEN VRACKIE** (IRE) 7
186 **BENANDONNER** (USA) 3
355 **BENAYOUN** (GB) 2
510 **BENBEOCH** (GB) 1
107 **BENCOOLEN** (GB) 15
93 **BENDED KNEE** (GB) 35
221 **BENE LAD** (IRE) 2
454 **BENEATH THE TREES** (USA) 8
467 **BENEDETTO** (GB) 10
212 **BENEDICT BAY** (GB) 6
585 **BENEDICT SPIRIT** (IRE) 27
391 **BENEFICIAL GUEST** (IRE) 2
80 **BENEKING** (GB) 2
565 **BENELLINO** (GB) 1
142 **BENETWOOD** (IRE) 2
151 **BENGO** (IRE) 1
157 **BENGUERRA** (FR) 76
167 **BENHAVIS** (GB) 22
453 **BENITEZ BOND** (GB) 11
552 **BENJAMIN** (IRE) 1
634 **BENLLECH** (GB) 2
506 **BENMADIGAN** (IRE) 11
302 **BENMALK** (IRE) 89
337 **BENMORE BOY** (IRE) 5
103 **BENNETT** (IRE) 2
506 **BENNO'S BOY** (IRE) 12
583 **BENNY THE BUS** (GB) 3
34 **BENNYNTHEJETS** (IRE) 2
115 **BENODET** (IRE) 7
413 **BENOZZO GOZZOLI** (GB) 60
298 **BENS GEORGIE** (IRE) 1
531 **BENTLEY** (GB) 4
114 **BENTONG** (IRE) 2
407 **BENTONS CHOICE** (GB) 5
363 **BENWILT BREEZE** (IRE) 3
302 **BERAIMI** (IRE) 90
302 **BERAYSIM** (GB) F 91
253 **BERBICE** (IRE) 22
184 **BERE DAVIS** (FR) 28
84 **BERENGARIO** (IRE) 1
184 **BERENICA** (GB) G 40
50 **BERENICE PANCRISIA** (FR) 2
640 **BERGERAC** (NZ) 10
211 **BERGO** (GER) 1
311 **BERGONZI** (IRE) 19
513 **BERINE** (FR) F 138
450 **BERINGS EXPRESS** (FR) 7
569 **BERKELEY HOUSE** (IRE) 4
416 **BERMACHA** (GB) 13
598 **BERMUDA POINTE** (IRE) 3
134 **BERNABEU** (IRE) 2
446 **BERNABEU** (USA) 11
30 **BERNANDO** (FR) 1
45 **BERNARD** (GB) 3
451 **BERRY HILL LASS** (IRE) 2
172 **BERRYMEAD** (GB) 69
433 **BERRYNARBOR** (GB) 27
52 **BERTBRAND** (GB) 16
454 **BERTHA** (GB) 9
543 **BERTIE BOO** (GB) 17
45 **BERTIE MAY** (GB) 4
585 **BERTIE SMALLS** 54
42 **BERTIE SOUTHSTREET** (GB) 1

208 **BERTIE SWIFT** (GB) 1
64 **BERTIES BROTHER** (GB) 2
609 **BERTOLINI SPICE** (GB) 16
298 **BERTOLIVER** (GB) 1
360 **BERWICK LAW** (IRE) 6
637 **BESHARAH** (GB) 2
261 **BESPOKE BOY** (GB) 23
515 **BESSEMER** (JPN) 1
209 **BESSIE SMITH** (IRE) 2
311 **BEST ACCOLADE** (GB) 20
356 **BEST ACTOR** (IRE) 6
424 **BEST BIDDER** (USA) 13
378 **BEST DANCER** (GB) 11
98 **BEST DEAL** (GB) 8
353 **BEST OF THE WEST** (GB) 15
279 **BEST OF THREE** (IRE) 5
67 **BEST ONE** (GB) 4
282 **BEST PLEASED** 48
156 **BEST PROSPECT** (IRE) 4
403 **BEST SELECTION** (GB) 5
496 **BEST SUITED** (GB) 49
518 **BEST WARNING** (GB) 4
311 **BESTOFTHEBROWNIES** (IRE) 21
225 **BESTOWED** (GB) 18
572 **BET NOIR** (IRE) 29
364 **BET ON ME** (GER) 5
569 **BET OUT OF IT** (IRE) 5
279 **BETAVIX** (GB) 6
634 **BETHANYS BOY** (IRE) 3
340 **BETILLA** (IRE) 18
331 **BETOULA** (GB) 15
229 **BETT'S SPIRIT** (IRE) 24
166 **BETTER IN HEAVEN** (GB) 8
77 **BETTER MOMENT** (IRE) 1
216 **BETTER TOGETHER** (GB) 5
575 **BETTERLATETHANEVER** (IRE) 3
304 **BETTERTHANLIKELY** (GB) 49
343 **BETTYS TOUCH** (GB) 22
16 **BETWS Y COED** (IRE) 16
456 **BEVELED EDGE** (FR) 24
485 **BEVERLEY MACCA** (GB) F 8
332 **BEVERLY HILL BILLY** (GB) 10
212 **BEWARE CHALK PIT** (IRE) 7
184 **BEWDLEY** (GB) 29
421 **BEWERY MAN** (IRE) 12
311 **BEWLEYS BERRY** (IRE) 22
444 **BEX** (USA) F 67
207 **BEYOND MOONBEAMS** (GB) 1
639 **BEYOND THE FENCE** (USA) C 25
188 **BIANCA CAPELLO** (GB) 31
512 **BIANCA CAPPELLO** (IRE) F 2
131 **BIANCA NERA** (GB) F 67
593 **BIBLE LORD** (IRE) 2
601 **BICKSTA** (GB) 16
20 **BID ART** (IRE) 38
462 **BID FOR FAME** (USA) 2
116 **BID FOR GLORY** (GB) 1
447 **BID FOR GOLD** (GB) 1
116 **BID TO THE BEAT** (GB) 14
456 **BIDABLE** (GB) 5
229 **BIDALIA** (IRE) 3
326 **BIENHEUREUX** (GB) 3
250 **BIG BERTHA** (GB) 3
437 **BIG BUCK'S** (FR) 8
421 **BIG BURROWS** (IRE) 13
340 **BIG DAY TODAY** (FR) 19
474 **BIG EARED FRAN** (FR) 11
437 **BIG FELLA THANKS** (GB) 1
455 **BIG GAME HUNTER** (IRE) 81
67 **BIG HUG** (GB) 19
513 **BIG HURRY** (USA) F 139
363 **BIG JOE** (ITY) 38
525 **BIG NOISE** (GB) 1

216 **BIG PADDY** (IRE) 6
277 **BIG PINK** (IRE) F 44
298 **BIG RALPH** (GB) 3
482 **BIG ROB** (IRE) 9
416 **BIG ROBERT** (IRE) 1
68 **BIG SLICK** (IRE) 17
466 **BIG TIMER** (USA) 7
436 **BIGALOS BANDIT** (GB) 2
83 **BIGFANOFTHAT** (IRE) 36
305 **BIJAN** (IRE) C 41
407 **BIJOU DAN** (GB) 6
333 **BIJOU LOVE** (IRE) 2
93 **BIKINI** (GB) 14
399 **BILBOA** (GB) 27
172 **BILL ON THE HILL** (GB) 88
639 **BILLBERRY** (GB) 14
490 **BILLESEY** (IRE) 2
525 **BILLIE BLUE** F 11
89 **BILLION DOLLAR KID** (GB) 9
241 **BILLSGREY** (IRE) 1
241 **BILLSLEGACY** (IRE) 2
512 **BILLY BRAY** (GB) 1
186 **BILLY DANE** (IRE) 4
36 **BILLY HOT ROCKS** (IRE) 8
125 **BILLY MURPHY** (IRE) 1
531 **BILLY ONE PUNCH** (GB) 5
305 **BILLY RED** (GB) 5
66 **BILLY THE SHIFTER** (GB) 6
598 **BILLYANDI** (IRE) 2
482 **BILLYBOB BATHWICK** (IRE) 10
141 **BILLYVODDAN** (IRE) 3
220 **BIMBOLA** (FR) C 45
37 **BIN END** (GB) 71
102 **BINANITI** (GB) 2
436 **BINARIO UNO** (GB) 61
301 **BINGO MEETING** (USA) F 27
498 **BINGO ONE** (IRE) 2
124 **BINIOU** (GB) 2
63 **BINNION BAY** (IRE) 1
269 **BINOCULAR** (FR) 11
566 **BINT MAKBUL** (GB) G 6
433 **BIRD OF PREY** (GB) C 30
277 **BIRETTA** (USA) C 45
618 **BIRJAND** (GB) C 9
96 **BIRKSIDE** (GB) 3
158 **BIRKSPIEL** (GER) 1
416 **BIRTHDAY** (IRE) C 38
389 **BIRTHDAY BELLE** (GB) F 25
319 **BIRTHDAY STAR** (IRE) 1
314 **BISCAR TWO** (IRE) 1
225 **BISHAARA** (IRE) 92
343 **BISHOP'S BRIDGE** (IRE) 5
185 **BISHOPS HEIR** (GB) 12
106 **BISHOPS PLOY** (IRE) 5
292 **BISHOPSTOWN BOY** (IRE) 8
228 **BIT OF A MONKEY** (GB) 1
146 **BITE UN FIGHT** (GB) 1
478 **BITESIZE** (GB) 1
215 **BITHIA** (GB) 12
643 **BITTA DASH** (GB) 1
447 **BITWA** (USA) C 20
571 **BIVOUAC** (UAE) 3
542 **BIZERTE** (IRE) 18
199 **BIZET** (IRE) 6
292 **BLACK APALACHI** (IRE) 9
179 **BLACK CLOUD** (GB) 2
426 **BLACK COFFEE** (GB) 23
382 **BLACK DAHLIA** (GB) 26
5 **BLACK DE BESSY** (FR) 4
28 **BLACK EYED PEA** (GB) 3
465 **BLACK FALCON** (IRE) 10
420 **BLACK HARRY** (IRE) 10
52 **BLACK HEART** (GB) 11
212 **BLACK HILLS** (GB) 8
332 **BLACK JACARI** (IRE) 179

554 **BOLD SHUFFLE** (IRE) 5
183 **BOLD TRUMP** (GB) 4
571 **BOLEY LASS** (IRE) C 104
166 **BOLIVIA** (USA) F 28
97 **BOLLICINA** (USA) G 2
345 **BOLLIN FERGUS** (GB) 1
631 **BOLLIN FIONA** (GB) 5
358 **BOLLIN FRANNY** (GB) 1
357 **BOLLIN FREDDIE** (GB) 1
631 **BOLLIN RUTH** (GB) 6
126 **BOLLIN VICTORIA** (GB) F 41
63 **BOLLYWOOD** (IRE) 2
42 **BOLLYWOOD STYLE** (GB) 26
186 **BOLODENKA** (IRE) 6
394 **BOLSHAYA** (GB) F 100
186 **BOLTON HALL** (IRE) 6
336 **BOLUISCE** (IRE) 2
572 **BOMBALARINA** (IRE) C 78
310 **BOMBARDIER WELLS** (GB) 14
498 **BOMBAY SAPPHIRE** (GB) F 15
277 **BOMBER COMMAND** (USA) 3
105 **BOMBINA** (GB) 52
301 **BON MARCHE** (GB) F 29
253 **BON TON ROULET** (GB) 25
279 **BON VIVEUR** (IRE) 9
382 **BONA FIDELIS** (IRE) 27
269 **BONCHESTER BRIDGE** (GB) 13
453 **BOND BECKS** (IRE) 1
453 **BOND CASINO** (GB) 2
453 **BOND CITY** (IRE) 3
453 **BOND GIRL** (GB) F 17
453 **BOND PLAYBOY** (GB) 4
453 **BOND ROYALE** (GB) 5
453 **BOND SCISSORSISTER** (IRE) 12
453 **BOND SHAKIRA** (GB) F 19
93 **BOND SOLITAIRE** (GB) F 37
454 **BOND STASIA** (IRE) F 42
212 **BONE OF CONTENTION** (IRE) G 9
569 **BONIFACIO** (IRE) 6
269 **BONIKOS** (IRE) 14
132 **BONITA BEE** (GB) F 10
163 **BONJOUR ALLURE** (IRE) 17
115 **BONJOUR L'AFRICAN** (FR) 81
83 **BONKERS** (GB) F 78
37 **BONNE** (GB) 24
56 **BONNE D'ARGENT** (IRE) 4
365 **BONNET O'BONNIE** (GB) 2
421 **BONNETA** (FR) 17
276 **BONNIE PRINCE BLUE** (GB) 1
106 **BONNIE ROCK** (IRE) 2
291 **BONZO** (GB) 16
290 **BOOGIE DANCER** (GB) 7
98 **BOJUM** (GB) F 25
244 **BOOK OF FACTS** (FR) 1
542 **BOOKEND** (GB) 3
497 **BOOKIEBASHER BABE** (IRE) 9
305 **BOOKIESINDEX BOY** (GB) 6
629 **BOOKS WHIRL** (GB) F 17
141 **BOOMERANG** (IRE) 4
568 **BOOMERANG BUD** (GB) 2
269 **BOOMSHAKALAKA** (IRE) 15
219 **BOOSTER DIVIN** (FR) 2
532 **BOOT 'N TOOT** (GB) 2
363 **BOOT BOY** (IRE) 19
586 **BOOT STRAP BILL** (GB) 9
436 **BOOTLEG** (GB) 7
257 **BOOTSANDSLIPPERS** (IRE) 11
397 **BOPPYS DANCER** (GB) 1
397 **BOPPYS DIAMOND** (GB) 2
397 **BOPPYS DREAM** (GB) 3
186 **BOPPYS PRIDE** (GB) 8
29 **BORASCO** (USA) 27
462 **BORDER ARTIST** (GB) 3
265 **BORDER CASTLE** (GB) 3
49 **BORDER DEFENCE** (IRE) 21

63 **BORDER EDGE** (GB) 3
360 **BORDER FOX** (GB) 7
7 **BORDER MIST** (IRE) 3
20 **BORDER MUSIC** (GB) 4
253 **BORDER OWL** (IRE) 26
107 **BORDER PATROL** (GB) 67
241 **BORDER SOVEREIGN** (GB) 3
402 **BORDER TALE** (GB) 3
31 **BORDERLESCOTT** (GB) 2
20 **BORDERS LANE** (GB) 40
142 **BOREHILL JOKER** (GB) 3
375 **BORERO** (FR) 7
332 **BORMO** (FR) 14
513 **BORN FOR GLORY** (IRE) 3
289 **BORN HIGH** (IRE) 7
332 **BORN LEADER** (IRE) 15
166 **BORN ROMANTIC** (GB) 29
573 **BORN SUPREME** (FR) 4
571 **BORN TO PERFORM** (GB) 5
99 **BORN TOBOUGGIE** (GER) 17
28 **BORODINSKY** (GB) 4
346 **BORORA** (GB) 3
454 **BORROWDALE** (GB) 10
257 **BORYENKA** (GB) 12
265 **BOSAMCLIFF** (IRE) 29
219 **BOSCALL HILL** (IRE) 3
482 **BOSHAM MILL** (GB) 12
606 **BOSS IMPERIAL** (FR) 3
604 **BOSS MAK** (IRE) 10
26 **BOSTON MONDAIN** (FR) 1
137 **BOSUN BREESE** (GB) 8
451 **BOTHAR BRUGHA** (IRE) 7
420 **BOTHAR NA** (IRE) 11
36 **BOTHY** (GB) 54
411 **BOTTLEFORTHEBATTLE** (IRE) 6
618 **BOTTOMLESS WALLET** (GB) 3
513 **BOUBSKAIA** F 141
257 **BOUCHARD** (GB) 13
126 **BOUGGIE DAIZE** (GB) 42
90 **BOUGGLER** (GB) 13
105 **BOUGUEREAU** (GB) 16
569 **BOULAVOGUE** (IRE) 7
172 **BOULEVARD ROUGE** (USA) C 89
474 **BOULEVARDOFDREAMS** (IRE) 12
490 **BOULEVIN** (IRE) 3
3 **BOUNCING BOB** (GB) 1
383 **BOUNCING KING** (GB) 9
83 **BOUNDLESS BEAUTY** (GB) F 79
326 **BOUNDLESS PROSPECT** (USA) 2
394 **BOUNTIFUL BAY** (GB) 22
613 **BOUNTY BOX** (GB) 39
163 **BOURBON BALISTIC** (GB) 18
261 **BOURBON HIGHBALL** (IRE) 24
467 **BOURBONELLA** (GB) C 36
131 **BOURNE** (GB) 68
609 **BOURSE** (IRE) 17
364 **BOUVINE** (FR) 124
39 **BOVERED** (IRE) 1
172 **BOW PEEP** (IRE) C 90
600 **BOWDEN ROSE** (GB) F 24
585 **BOWDER STONE** (IRE) 30
258 **BOWDLANE BARB** (GB) 4
241 **BOWERHOPE** (GB) 4
649 **BOWL OF CHERRIES** (GB) 4
444 **BOWL OF EMERALDS** (USA) C 68
5 **BOWLEAZE** (IRE) 5
589 **BOWSERS BOY** (IRE) 65
506 **BOX WALLAH** (IRE) 14
420 **BOXER GEORG** (IRE) 12
418 **BOXER SHORTS** (GB) 38
436 **BOY BLUE** (GB) 63
496 **BOY DANCER** (IRE) 9
454 **BOY ON A SWING** (USA) 11
216 **BOY'S HURRAH** (IRE) 7
437 **BOYASTARA** (FR) 15

279 **BOYCHUK** (IRE) 10
637 **BOYTJIE** (IRE) 3
131 **BOZ** (GB) 5
114 **BOZEMAN TRAIL** (GB) 20
516 **BRACKEN LAD** (IRE) 9
504 **BRACKENMOSS** (IRE) 6
343 **BRACKENRIDGE** (GB) 8
204 **BRACKNEY HALL** (IRE) 2
35 **BRADDOCK ISLAND** (GB) 2
451 **BRADS HOUSE** (IRE) 4
107 **BRAEMAR GAMES** (GB) 16
394 **BRAKEY HILL** (USA) 23
136 **BRAMANTINO** (IRE) 1
399 **BRAMAPUTRA** (IRE) 29
292 **BRAMDEAN** G 10
163 **BRANDANE** (IRE) 19
20 **BRANDON PRINCESS** (GB) G 79
20 **BRANDY BUTTER** (GB) 80
360 **BRANDY WINE** (GB) 8
193 **BRANDYWELL BOY** (IRE) 4
336 **BRANSTON LUCY** (GB) F 28
180 **BRASILIA PRINCE** (GB) 1
501 **BRASINGAMAN HIFIVE** (GB) 6
399 **BRASSINI** (GB) 30
285 **BRASTAR JELOIS** (FR) 3
166 **BRAVE BEAT** (GB) 30
166 **BRAVE BOOGIE** (GB) 9
474 **BRAVE BRONCHO** (IRE) 13
8 **BRAVE BUGSY** (IRE) 3
265 **BRAVE FACE** (GB) 4
302 **BRAVE HAWK** (GB) 28
544 **BRAVE HIAWATHA** (FR) 1
262 **BRAVE JO** (FR) 1
482 **BRAVE KATIE** (GB) 13
151 **BRAVE KNAVE** (GB) 21
303 **BRAVE MAVE** (GB) 16
573 **BRAVE MO CHROI** (IRE) 5
580 **BRAVE OPTIMIST** (IRE) 18
403 **BRAVE QUEST** (IRE) 6
504 **BRAVE REBELLION** (GB) 7
519 **BRAVE TRUTH** (IRE) C 88
174 **BRAVE VILLA** (FR) 3
486 **BRAVEHEART MOVE** (IRE) 42
625 **BRAVELY FOUGHT** (IRE) 16
18 **BRAYBROOKE LADY** (IRE) 4
142 **BRAYFORD LAD** (IRE) 4
413 **BRAZILIAN BRUSH** (IRE) 25
413 **BREADSTICK** (GB) 61
58 **BREAK OUT** (GB) 3
138 **BREAK THE ICE** (GB) 3
465 **BREAKING SHADOW** (IRE) 3
573 **BREAKING SILENCE** (IRE) 6
516 **BREAKWATER HOUSE** (IRE) 10
470 **BREATHE** (GB) 59
304 **BRECKS LANE** (GB) 6
437 **BREEDSBREEZE** (IRE) 16
212 **BREEZER** (GB) 10
139 **BREIZ DREAM'S** (FR) 4
279 **BREMEN** (GB) 11
41 **BRENDAR** (IRE) 1
638 **BRENIN CWMTUDU** (GB) 8
548 **BRENNAN FOR AUDITS** (IRE) G 3
68 **BRENTSVILLE** (USA) C 49
33 **BRET MAVERICK** (IRE) 6
486 **BRETT VALE** (IRE) 43
506 **BRETTON WOODS** (IRE) 15
126 **BREXCA** (IRE) 19
556 **BREYANI** C 9
360 **BRIAN'S JOURNEY** (GB) 9
358 **BRIANNSTA** (IRE) 3
20 **BRIAREUS** (GB) 5
360 **BRIARHILL BOY** (IRE) 10
360 **BRIARHILL LAD** (IRE) 11
99 **BRIBERY** (IRE) 62
418 **BRICK** (IRE) 34

484 RACEFORM

52 **CALISTOS QUEST** (GB) 19	
268 **CALL ACCOUNT** (USA) C 49	

52 **CALISTOS QUEST** (GB) 19
268 **CALL ACCOUNT** (USA) C 49
585 **CALL IT ON** 56
332 **CALL ME A LEGEND** (GB) 18
265 **CALL ME COURAGEOUS** (IRE) 49
148 **CALL ME DAVE** (GB) 3
598 **CALL ME EDWARD** (IRE) 14
265 **CALL ME MYRTLE** (GB) 5
220 **CALL ME ROSY** (IRE) 3
210 **CALL ME SIR** (IRE) 1
609 **CALL OF KTULU** (IRE) 18
9 **CALL OSCAR** (IRE) 5
566 **CALLEY HO** (GB) 7
52 **CALLING VICTORY** (FR) 43
423 **CALLINGWOOD** (IRE) 1
636 **CALLISTO MOON** (GB) 6
82 **CALLITWHATYALIKE** (GB) 3
352 **CALLOFF THE SEARCH** (GB) 1
612 **CALM SEAS** (IRE) 2
83 **CALMDOWNMATE** (IRE) 39
463 **CALMING WATERS** (GB) 6
463 **CALOW GREEN** (IRE) 1
495 **CALTIRE** (GER) 15
446 **CALTRA PRINCESS** (GB) 12
279 **CALUSA CRYSTAL** (FR) 14
482 **CALUSA SPIRIT** (GB) 15
37 **CALYPSO CHARMS** (GB) 25
302 **CALYPSO GRANT** (IRE) F 92
231 **CALYPSO KING** (GB) 4
407 **CALZA DI SETA** (IRE) 41
83 **CALZAGHE** (IRE) 10
257 **CAMAN SWINGER** (GB) 15
628 **CAMBO** (IRE) 1
638 **CAMDEN FOUR** (IRE) 11
365 **CAME BACK** (IRE) 3
383 **CAMELIA WALK** (GB) 11
163 **CAMELOT COMMUNION** (IRE) 39
66 **CAMEO ROLE** (GER) G 63
409 **CAMERA SHY** (IRE) 2
572 **CAMERLATA** (GB) C 80
452 **CAMINO REAL** (GB) 6
298 **CAMISSA** (GB) 5
579 **CAMORRA** C 3
18 **CAMPAIGN CHARLIE** (GB) 6
269 **CAMPANNELLO** (GB) 18
197 **CAMPASPE** (GB) G 1
197 **CAMPASPE** G 16
78 **CAMPDEN ANNIE** (IRE) 5
625 **CAMPFIRE GLOW** (IRE) 17
250 **CAMPLI** (IRE) 5
39 **CAMPO BUENO** (FR) 2
467 **CAMPS BAY** (USA) 3
220 **CAN CAN DANCER** (GB) 25
356 **CAN'T BUY A THRILL** (IRE) 9
450 **CAN'T BUY TIME** (IRE) 13
311 **CANADA STREET** (IRE) 27
124 **CANADIAN DANEHILL** (IRE) 2
176 **CANALTURN** (FR) 2
623 **CANARY GIRL** (GB) 2
165 **CANARY ISLANDS** (GB) 15
239 **CANDELA BAY** (IRE) 21
36 **CANDIDA'S BEAU** (GB) 10
513 **CANDIDATA** (FR) 142
239 **CANDIDATO ROY** (ARG) 2
93 **CANDLE** (IRE) 1
461 **CANDY ANCHOR** (IRE) 1
420 **CANDY GIRL** (IRE) 15
165 **CANDY RIDE** (IRE) 75
572 **CANDY ROCK** (IRE) 31
589 **CANDY ROSE** (GB) 19
383 **CANDY'S ROOM** (IRE) 12
573 **CANE BRAKE** (IRE) 7
232 **CANINA** (GB) 2
85 **CANNI THINKAAR** (IRE) 1
231 **CANNIKIN** (IRE) C 55

90 **CANNY BAY** (GB) 3
215 **CANONGATE** (GB) 2
280 **CANTABILY** (IRE) 3
363 **CANTERLOUPE** (IRE) C 40
404 **CANTGETON** (IRE) 1
490 **CANTIQUE** (IRE) 5
475 **CANTLEY SPIRIT** (GB) 4
279 **CAOBA** (GB) 15
88 **CAP IT IF YOU CAN** (IRE) G 2
88 **CAP IT IF YOU CAN** (IRE) C 8
285 **CAP ST JEAN** (IRE) 4
475 **CAPAL DUBH ALAINN** (GB) 8
184 **CAPANIA** (IRE) 3
257 **CAPE ALLSTAR** (IRE) 16
105 **CAPE AMBER** (IRE) 17
413 **CAPE CHARLOTTE** (GB) F 62
225 **CAPE COBRA** (GB) 2
174 **CAPE COD** (IRE) C 23
253 **CAPE COLONY** (GB) 28
609 **CAPE DANCER** (IRE) 2
572 **CAPE DIAMOND** (IRE) 3
302 **CAPE EXPRESS** (IRE) 29
105 **CAPE FLATTERY** (GB) C 55
253 **CAPE HAWK** (IRE) 2
74 **CAPE OF STORMS** (IRE) 3
288 **CAPE ROCK** (GB) 11
58 **CAPE ROYAL** (GB) 5
394 **CAPE SIREN** (GB) C 26
217 **CAPE THEA** (GB) 1
304 **CAPE TRIBULATION** (GB) 10
89 **CAPE TYCOON** (IRE) 10
436 **CAPE VALE** (IRE) 64
277 **CAPE VELVET** (IRE) 4
114 **CAPEFLY** (GB) 21
420 **CAPEL LAD** (IRE) 15
176 **CAPETONIAN** (FR) 3
39 **CAPETOWN GIRL** (GB) C 26
542 **CAPEWORK** (USA) F 21
541 **CAPISTRANO** (GB) 2
382 **CAPITAL LASS** (GB) 3
551 **CAPITALISE** (GB) 1
269 **CAPITANA** (GER) 19
253 **CAPITELLI** (IRE) 96
257 **CAPO DI CAPI** (IRE) 17
436 **CAPO REGIME** (GB) 75
292 **CAPPACURRY DAWN** (IRE) 11
156 **CAPPUCCINO** (GB) G 44
89 **CAPPUCHINO** (IRE) C 25
406 **CAPRICCIOSO** (GB) 118
1 **CAPRICHO** (IRE) 6
382 **CAPRICORN RUN** (USA) 4
68 **CAPRIMA** (IRE) 18
107 **CAPRIO** (IRE) 17
131 **CAPSTAN** (GB) 32
168 **CAPSTICK** (JPN) F 22
593 **CAPTAIN AMERICO** (IRE) 3
452 **CAPTAIN AUBREY** (IRE) 7
207 **CAPTAIN BECKET** (GB) 2
444 **CAPTAIN BRILLIANCE** (USA) 14
361 **CAPTAIN CAN CAN** (IRE) 1
105 **CAPTAIN CHURCHILL** (IRE) 56
279 **CAPTAIN CORELLI** (GB) 16
450 **CAPTAIN CRACKERS** (IRE) 14
629 **CAPTAIN CROMBY** (IRE) 26
531 **CAPTAIN CROONER** (GB) 36
276 **CAPTAIN DANCER** (IRE) 88
639 **CAPTAIN FLASHEART** (IRE) 27
543 **CAPTAIN GERRARD** (IRE) 19
519 **CAPTAIN JACKSPARRA** (IRE) 3
151 **CAPTAIN KIR** (IRE) 22
197 **CAPTAIN LING** (GB) 2
405 **CAPTAIN LYFORD** (FR) 4
543 **CAPTAIN MACARRY** (IRE) 20
353 **CAPTAIN MAINWARING** (GB) 16
582 **CAPTAIN MARLON** (IRE) 7

1 **CAPTAIN MARRYAT** (GB) 7
276 **CAPTAIN MARVELOUS** (IRE) 2
399 **CAPTAIN PEACHY** (GB) 43
191 **CAPTAIN SMOOTHY** (GB) 3
470 **CAPTAIN TIDDS** (IRE) 10
423 **CAPTAIN TIMELESS** (IRE) 7
25 **CAPTAIN TURBOT** (IRE) 19
308 **CAPTAIN WILLOUGHBY** (IRE) 2
622 **CAPTAIN'S LEGACY** (GB) 9
157 **CAPTAINE COURAGE** (IRE) 47
308 **CAPTIVATE** (GB) 2
443 **CAPTIVE HEART** F 14
225 **CAPUCCI** (GB) 7
269 **CARACCIOLA** (GER) 20
263 **CARAIYMA** (IRE) F 6
496 **CARAMAN** (IRE) 11
225 **CARAMBOLA** (IRE) C 93
178 **CARAMEL CRÈME** (GB) 26
322 **CARAPAX** (IRE) 4
285 **CARATI** (GB) F 45
486 **CARAVEL** (IRE) 4
442 **CARBERY SPIRIT** (IRE) F 2
371 **CARBON HOOFPRINT** (GB) 31
107 **CARBON PRINT** (USA) 18
455 **CARBONIA** (IRE) 17
184 **CARCINETTO** (IRE) 4
157 **CARD IN HAND** (FR) 77
212 **CARDENAS** (GER) 11
421 **CARDINAL** (GB) 19
421 **CARDINAL SPIRIT** (GB) 19
571 **CAREFREE** (GB) 4
625 **CAREFREE SMILE** (IRE) 68
394 **CARELESS FREEDOM** (GB) 27
253 **CARESSING** (GB) 97
482 **CARETTA CARETTA** (GB) 16
87 **CARHUE PRINCESS** (IRE) 21
302 **CARIBANA** (GB) 30
496 **CARIBBEAN CORAL** (GB) 12
414 **CARIBBEAN CRUISER** (GB) 4
68 **CARIBBEAN ESCAPE** (GB) F 50
533 **CARIBOU** (FR) 9
115 **CARLA SONG** (FR) 9
426 **CARLETON** (GB) 26
429 **CARLINGFORD BELLE** F 4
513 **CARLIOR** (FR) 34
399 **CARLITOS SPIRIT** (IRE) 2
87 **CARLTON MAC** (IRE) 16
180 **CARLY BAY** (GB) 2
364 **CARLYSSAR** (FR) 7
613 **CARMELA MARIA** (GB) 20
416 **CARMENERO** (GER) 5
285 **CARMINE ROCK** (GB) 35
456 **CARNA** (IRE) F 25
519 **CARNABY HAGGERSTON** (IRE) 89
562 **CARNDALE** (IRE) 2
215 **CARNET DES NUITS** (FR) 14
572 **CARNIOLAN** (GB) 32
260 **CARNIVAL DREAM** (GB) 25
450 **CARNIVAL TOWN** (GB) 15
29 **CARNIVORE** (GB) 4
558 **CARNT SPELL** (GB) 3
107 **CARO GEORGE** (USA) 20
244 **CAROLE OS** (IRE) 4
269 **CAROLE'S LEGACY** (GB) 21
30 **CAROLINA SHOOT** (GB) 65
282 **CAROLINES DREAM** (IRE) 8
239 **CARPE DIEM** (GB) 7
257 **CARPENTER** (IRE) 18
572 **CARPET LADY** (IRE) C 81
340 **CARPO** (FR) 21
345 **CARR HALL** (IRE) 2
571 **CARR ON FIRE** (USA) 66
43 **CARR SHAKER** (USA) C 27
163 **CARRADALE** (GB) F 40
340 **CARRATRACA** (GB) 22

83 **CHANGE OF HEART** (IRE) F 80
513 **CHANGE THE WORLD** (IRE) 35
394 **CHANGING SKIES** (IRE) 30
212 **CHANGIZ** (GB) 12
259 **CHANINBAR** (FR) 3
269 **CHANTACO** (IRE) 22
364 **CHANTEGRIL** (FR) 9
220 **CHANTERELLE** (IRE) C 46
124 **CHANTILLY JEWEL** (USA) 12
165 **CHANTILLY TIFFANY** (GB) 3
506 **CHAPEL FLOWERS** (IRE) 20
311 **CHAPEL HOUSE** (GB) 31
257 **CHAPMANS PEAK** (IRE) 20
437 **CHAPOTURGEON** (FR) 20
331 **CHAPTER** (IRE) 2
276 **CHAPTER AND VERSE** (IRE) 89
496 **CHARACTER BUILDING** (IRE) 13
223 **CHARANGO STAR** (GB) 1
519 **CHARCOAL** (GB) 90
105 **CHARGER** (GB) 57
141 **CHARINGWORTH** (GB) 6
51 **CHARIOT** (IRE) 3
444 **CHARISMATIC** (IRE) 15
137 **CHARISMATIC CHARLI** (IRE) 13
407 **CHARITY LANE** (IRE) 8
301 **CHARLENE LACY** (GB) F 30
48 **CHARLES DARWIN** (IRE) 2
156 **CHARLES PARNELL** (IRE) 7
227 **CHARLES STREET** (GB) 1
514 **CHARLESTON** (GB) 5
613 **CHARLEVOIX** (IRE) 21
83 **CHARLIE ALLNUT** (GB) 41
169 **CHARLIE BE** (IRE) 12
148 **CHARLIE BEAR** (GB) 5
94 **CHARLIE CHAN** (GB) 3
574 **CHARLIE CRAB** (GB) 2
58 **CHARLIE DELTA** (GB) 7
394 **CHARLIE FARNSBARNS** (IRE) 2
404 **CHARLIE GEORGE** (GB) 2
220 **CHARLIE GIRL** (GB) F 47
232 **CHARLIE GREEN** (GB) 8
320 **CHARLIE POOLE** (GB) 8
201 **CHARLIE TANGO** (IRE) 3
186 **CHARLIE TOKYO** (IRE) 9
42 **CHARLIES DOUBLE** (GB) 2
5 **CHARLIES FUTURE** (GB) 4
285 **CHARLIETOO** (GB) 46
277 **CHARLOCK** (IRE) C 49
250 **CHARLOTTE VALE** (GB) 6
337 **CHARLOTTES WEBB** (IRE) 12
297 **CHARLOTTEVALENTINA** (IRE) C 17
400 **CHARLTON** (GB) 1
280 **CHARLTON KINGS** (IRE) 4
225 **CHARM SCHOOL** (GB) 23
332 **CHARMAINE WOOD** (GB) 20
572 **CHARMEL'S LAD** (GB) 34
49 **CHARMING FELLOW** (IRE) 4
573 **CHARMING GAEL** (IRE) 3
513 **CHARMING LAUREN** (USA) F 145
78 **CHARMING OSCAR** (IRE) 2
418 **CHARMING ROGUE** (GB) 4
394 **CHARMING TALE** (USA) 31
253 **CHARTIST** (GB) 29
467 **CHASCA** (IRE) 38
375 **CHASE THE DAWN** (GB) 9
60 **CHASE THE FOX** (GB) 3
257 **CHASING CARS** (IRE) 21
363 **CHASING CLOUDS** (IRE) 20
223 **CHASING MEMORIES** (GB) 7
215 **CHASING MOONBEAMS** (IRE) 17
268 **CHASING STARS** (IRE) 3
157 **CHASSE CROISE** (FR) 78
571 **CHATANOOGACHOOCHOO** (GB) 68
553 **CHATEAU** (IRE) 1
475 **CHATEAU BEACH** (IRE) F 11

250 **CHATEAU ROUGE** (IRE) 7
95 **CHATSHOW** (USA) 8
161 **CHATTER'S PRINCESS** (GB) F 2
92 **CHAUSSENEIGE** (FR) F 20
402 **CHAVEZ** (IRE) 5
96 **CHE GAMBE** (USA) F 4
454 **CHEAP THRILLS** (GB) 43
593 **CHEATING CHANCE** (IRE) 6
311 **CHECKERBOARD** (IRE) 32
444 **CHECKLOW** (USA) 16
569 **CHECKPOINTCHARLIE** (IRE) 8
39 **CHEEKY CRUMPET** (GB) 27
165 **CHEEKY DOWNLOAD** (IRE) 5
470 **CHEEKY MONKEY** (USA) G 12
172 **CHEER US ON** (GB) 13
579 **CHEERS THANK YOU** (IRE) 4
25 **CHEERY CAT** (USA) 4
430 **CHEERY MARTYR** (GB) 1
360 **CHEF DE COUR** (FR) 13
301 **CHELSEA** (USA) C 31
126 **CHELSEA GIRL** (GB) 21
513 **CHELSEY DANCER** (USA) F 146
280 **CHEMISE** (IRE) 30
211 **CHEONMADO** (USA) 2
364 **CHERCHEUR D'OR** (FR) 10
276 **CHERISH THE MOMENT** (IRE) 90
242 **CHERISHED NUMBER** (GB) 6
495 **CHERISHED SONG** (GB) 16
250 **CHERNIK** (IRE) 8
34 **CHEROKEE STAR** (GB) 25
96 **CHERRI FOSFATE** (GB) 3
649 **CHERRIES ON TOP** (IRE) 17
287 **CHERRY FLORA** (GB) 2
20 **CHERRY PLUM** (GB) 83
458 **CHERRY TOT** (GB) 2
83 **CHERRYTREE ELLA** (IRE) 42
513 **CHERUBINO** (IRE) 147
640 **CHERRY D'OR** (IRE) 15
66 **CHESHIRE PRINCE** (GB) 10
29 **CHESHIRE ROSE** (GB) 29
120 **CHESIL BEACH BOY** (GB) 1
289 **CHEVAUX LOCO** (IRE) 8
462 **CHEVELEY FLYER** (GB) 4
282 **CHEVI** 51
649 **CHEVIN** (GB) F 28
394 **CHEVIOT RED** (GB) 32
451 **CHEVY TO THE LEVY** (IRE) 5
30 **CHEYENNE DREAM** (GB) F 66
157 **CHI WARA SHEBA** (FR) 48
264 **CHIA** (IRE) 1
229 **CHIA LAGUNA** (IRE) C 50
279 **CHIARO** (FR) 18
1 **CHIASSO** (USA) F 29
648 **CHICAGO ALLEY** (GB) 3
160 **CHICAGO BOND** (USA) F 20
418 **CHICAMIA** (GB) 5
383 **CHICKAPEAKRAY** (GB) 14
436 **CHICKEN GEORGE** (IRE) 5
571 **CHICKINI** (GB) 69
479 **CHICO TIME** (IRE) 4
402 **CHIEF DAN GEORGE** (IRE) 6
98 **CHIEF ERIC** (GB) 3
211 **CHIEF EXEC** (GB) 3
57 **CHIEF SCOUT** (GB) 2
640 **CHIEF YEOMAN** (GB) 16
254 **CHIGORIN** (GB) 7
364 **CHIHUAHUA** (IRE) 125
45 **CHILBURY HILL** (IRE) 5
513 **CHILI** (FR) 5
582 **CHILLA CILLA** (GB) 8
242 **CHILLY MILLY** (GB) 7
59 **CHIMICHURRI** (FR) 3
221 **CHIN WAG** (IRE) 4
37 **CHINA** (GB) F 76
158 **CHINA CHERUB** (GB) 2

486 **CHINA PINK** (GB) 20
201 **CHINCHON** (IRE) 23
98 **CHINE** (GB) F 26
60 **CHINESE PROFIT** (GB) 22
495 **CHINESE TEMPLE** (IRE) 5
625 **CHINESE WHITE** (IRE) 21
109 **CHINOISERIE** (GB) 16
112 **CHINON** (FR) F 14
167 **CHIOROSCURO** (GB) 24
517 **CHIPLESS** (IRE) 2
99 **CHIQUINKIRA** (IRE) 20
7 **CHIRAPATRE** (GB) 4
364 **CHITA MAGNETIC** (IRE) 126
279 **CHITA'S FLIGHT** (GB) 19
640 **CHIVALRY** (GB) 17
543 **CHIVOLA** (IRE) 21
30 **CHOBE** (GB) 18
115 **CHOCK A BLOCK** (IRE) 83
467 **CHOCOLATE CARAMEL** (USA) 4
174 **CHOISEAU** (IRE) 3
543 **CHOISETTE** (GB) 22
269 **CHOMBA WOMBA** (GB) 23
261 **CHOOSE YOUR MOMENT** (GB) 25
470 **CHOPNEYEV** (FR) 13
486 **CHORAL FESTIVAL** (GB) 46
239 **CHORAL SERVICE** (GB) 63
486 **CHORAL SINGER** (GB) 18
131 **CHORAL SUNDOWN** C 71
107 **CHORAL SYMPHONY** (GB) 21
383 **CHORD** (GB) 15
436 **CHOREOGRAPHY** (GB) 6
41 **CHOREOGRAPHY** (IRE) 2
453 **CHOSEN FOREVER** (GB) 13
543 **CHOSEN ONE** (GB) 23
474 **CHOUMAKEUR** (FR) 19
59 **CHOUROMANESCO** (FR) 4
269 **CHOUXDAMOUR** (FR) 24
629 **CHRIS CORSA** (GB) 4
205 **CHRISTALINI** (GB) 3
474 **CHRISTDALO** (FR) 20
291 **CHRISTIAN BENDIX** (GB) 4
572 **CHRISTINA'S DREAM** (GB) C 83
519 **CHRISTMAS IN AIKEN** (USA) C 91
278 **CHRISTMAS TRUCE** (IRE) 2
539 **CHRISTOPHERS QUEST** (GB) 9
638 **CHRYSANDER** (GB) 12
382 **CHRYSTAL VENTURE** (IRE) 28
567 **CHUNKY'S CHOICE** (IRE) 3
343 **CHUQUICAMATA** (GB) 9
289 **CHURCH ISLAND** (IRE) 8
340 **CHURRIANA** (IRE) 24
513 **CICEROLE** (GB) 1
276 **CIGALAS** (GB) 18
513 **CIGARRAL** (FR) 36
332 **CILLA BLACK** (GB) 21
196 **CINAMAN** (IRE) 2
56 **CINEMATIC** (GB) 6
589 **CINERAMA** (IRE) 20
564 **CINNAMON CRUISE** (GB) F 1
310 **CINNAMON HILL** (GB) 2
394 **CINQUANTE CINQ** (IRE) 3
311 **CIRCASSIAN** (IRE) 33
436 **CIRCUIT DANCER** (IRE) 7
466 **CIRCUS CLOWN** (GB) 44
513 **CIRCUS KEY** (GB) 37
533 **CIRCUS OF DREAMS** (GB) 9
66 **CIRCUS POLKA** (USA) 11
541 **CIRCUS ROSE** (GB) 4
165 **CITRINE SPIRIT** (IRE) F 79
225 **CITRON PRESSE** (USA) 24
603 **CITY AFFAIR** (GB) 2
225 **CITY BONUS** (IRE) 25
258 **CITY FOR CONQUEST** (IRE) 5
394 **CITY LEADER** (GB) 33
157 **CITY LOOK** (GB) 49

637 **DIAMOND HARRY** (GB) 5
589 **DIAMOND HEIST** 67
626 **DIAMOND HURRICANE** (IRE) 1
424 **DIAMOND JO** (IRE) 14
418 **DIAMOND JOSH** (GB) 6
186 **DIAMOND LASS** (IRE) 76
583 **DIAMOND MICK** (GB) 2
418 **DIAMOND ROUGE** (GB) C 36
165 **DIAMOND ROYAL** (IRE) 22
551 **DIAMOND SEEKER** (GB) 11
115 **DIAMOND SQUARE** (GB) 12
625 **DIAMOND STAR** (IRE) 26
42 **DIAMOND TWISTER** (USA) 45
394 **DIAMOND TYCOON** (GB) 5
288 **DIAMOND WORLD** (GB) 3
99 **DIAMOND YAS** (IRE) 23
401 **DIANA BISCOE** (GB) 3
50 **DIANE DE POITIERS** (IRE) 32
1 **DIANE'S CHOICE** (GB) 9
143 **DIAPASON** (IRE) 17
606 **DIARIUS** (GB) 8
172 **DIAVOLERIA** (GB) 15
340 **DIAVOLIKOS** (GB) 28
513 **DIBENOISE** (FR) C 151
131 **DICE** (IRE) 76
292 **DICERA** (IRE) 23
302 **DICHOH** (GB) 4
58 **DICKIE DEANO** (GB) 13
83 **DICKIE LE DAVOIR** (GB) 12
383 **DICKIE LEWIS** (GB) 25
51 **DICKIE VALENTINE** (GB) 11
438 **DICTATRIX** (GB) 9
440 **DICTUM** (GER) 1
382 **DIDACTIC** (GB) 8
495 **DIDANA** (IRE) 18
239 **DIDDUMS** (GB) 72
522 **DIDNTCOMEBACK** (GB) 9
345 **DIDOE** (GB) 4
420 **DIEGO GARCIA** (IRE) 31
474 **DIFFERENT LOT** (IRE) 26
277 **DIFFERENT STORY** (USA) F 51
496 **DIG DEEP** (IRE) 16
216 **DIGGER GETS LUCKY** (IRE) 14
311 **DIGITAL MEDIA** (IRE) 44
495 **DIGNIFY** (IRE) F 24
649 **DIJITAL POWER** (GB) C 30
207 **DIK DIK** (GB) 6
132 **DIKIKA** (GB) 12
575 **DIKTALEX** (IRE) 4
416 **DIKTALINA** (GB) 40
629 **DIKTARAM** (GB) 27
238 **DIKTAT QUEEN** 24
115 **DIKTATING** (GB) 86
82 **DIKTATIT** (GB) 5
311 **DIKTATORIAL** (GB) 45
92 **DIKTATORSHIP** (IRE) 6
213 **DILLAY BROOK** (IRE) 5
581 **DILMOON** (IRE) 4
467 **DIMANDER** (IRE) 40
600 **DIMINUTO** (GB) 4
82 **DINARIUS** (GB) 31
20 **DINGAAN** (IRE) 10
257 **DINGLE BELLE** (IRE) 28
444 **DINKA RAJA** (USA) F 72
321 **DINNER DATE** (GB) 8
340 **DIODOROS** (FR) 94
446 **DIOPHAS** (GER) 20
230 **DIOTIMA** (GB) C 95
142 **DIP ANCHOR** (GB) 11
6 **DIPLOMATIC DAN** (IRE) 1
444 **DIPLOMATS DAUGHTER** (GB) C 73
286 **DIRECT ACCESS** (IRE) 2
37 **DIRECT DEBIT** (GB) 1
257 **DIRECT EXIT** (IRE) 29
530 **DIRECTA'S DIGGER** (IRE) 10

191 **DIRECTOR'S CHAIR** (GB) 13
400 **DIRICULOUS** (GB) 2
245 **DIRTY' ARRY** (GB) 2
269 **DISALLOWED** (IRE) G 34
454 **DISCOED** (GB) C 47
111 **DISCOMANIA** (GB) 2
446 **DISCREET** (GB) 21
625 **DISCREET AFFAIR** (IRE) 74
99 **DISCREET BRIEF** (IRE) F 71
581 **DISHDASHA** (IRE) 5
303 **DISPATCH BOX** (GB) 1
29 **DISPOL ISLE** (IRE) 5
312 **DISPOL PETO** (GB) 3
454 **DISREGARD THAT** (IRE) C 48
394 **DISSIDENTIA** (GB) C 106
157 **DISTALINO** (FR) 5
572 **DISTANT DIAMOND** (IRE) 38
378 **DISTANT DIVA** (GB) C 13
378 **DISTANT DIVA** (GB) F 21
157 **DISTANT HORIZON** (USA) C 81
109 **DISTANT LOVER** (GB) F 54
74 **DISTANT NOBLE** (GB) 10
156 **DISTANT PLEASURE** (GB) 5
68 **DISTANT RAINBOW** (IRE) 20
229 **DISTANT ROCK** (GB) 29
466 **DISTANT SUN** (USA) 12
598 **DISTILLER** (IRE) 21
225 **DISTINCTIVE IMAGE** (USA) 30
519 **DISTINCTIVE SPIRIT** (IRE) 97
519 **DISTINCTLY GAME** (GB) 5
618 **DISTINCTLYTHEBEST** (GB) 5
342 **DITTO DITTO** (GB) 7
13 **DITZY DIVA** (GB) 22
87 **DIUM MAC** (GB) 4
627 **DIVA OF NORWICH** (IRE) 2
332 **DIVALI PRINCESS** (GB) 31
359 **DIVERS** (FR) 3
250 **DIVEX** (IRE) 12
264 **DIVINATORE** (GB) 15
103 **DIVINE GIFT** (GB) 6
36 **DIVINE POWER** (GB) 12
156 **DIVINE SPIRIT** (GB) 9
53 **DIVINE WHITE** (GB) 10
606 **DIVINE WISDOM** (GB) 9
229 **DIVINITUS** (GB) 30
35 **DIVVYS DREAM** (GB) 6
302 **DIXEY** (GB) 33
90 **DIXIE FAVOR** (USA) F 24
513 **DIXIE GIRL** (IRE) 41
513 **DIXIE HOLIDAY** (USA) F 152
628 **DIZZY RASCAL** (GB) 3
257 **DJANGO** (IRE) 30
556 **DJEBEL AMOUR** (USA) F 37
604 **DO IT** (GER) 24
442 **DO IT FOR DALKEY** (GB) 3
562 **DO L'ENFANT D'EAU** (FR) 5
371 **DO THE HUSTLE** (USA) G 17
582 **DO THE LOCOMOTION** (IRE) 11
289 **DOC REASON** (IRE) 16
474 **DOC ROW** (GB) 27
225 **DOCK LEAF** (USA) F 95
199 **DOCK STREET** (IRE) 13
506 **DOCKBRIDGE** (IRE) 26
454 **DOCOFTHEBAY** (IRE) 1
359 **DOCTOR COLLINS** (GB) 4
17 **DOCTOR DAVID** (GB) 3
215 **DOCTOR DINO** (FR) 3
34 **DOCTOR KILBRIDE** (IRE) 4
628 **DOCTOR NED** (GB) 4
601 **DOCTOR PARKES** (GB) 20
143 **DOCTOR ROBERT** (GB) 5
445 **DOCTORED** (GB) 4
645 **DODAA** (USA) 4
6 **DODGER MCCARTNEY** (GB) 6
411 **DODGEY DREAM** (GB) 9

417 **DOESLESSTHANME** (IRE) 4
363 **DOHASA** (IRE) 21
407 **DOLANS BAY** (IRE) 9
188 **DOLCETTO** (IRE) 37
25 **DOLLY NO HAIR** (GB) 20
474 **DOM D'ORGEVAL** (FR) 28
579 **DOM ONE** (GB) F 8
338 **DOME ROCKET** (GB) 25
305 **DOMENICO** (IRE) 10
247 **DOMESTIC FLIGHT** (IRE) 1
625 **DOMESTIC FUND** (IRE) 7
9 **DOMINICAN MONK** (IRE) 10
605 **DOMINO DANCER** (IRE) 8
622 **DON CASTILLE** (GB) 10
384 **DON FREDERIKO** (FR) 1
542 **DON JO** 42
602 **DON JOSE** (USA) 2
558 **DON PASQUALE** (GB) 5
49 **DON PICOLO** (GB) 23
340 **DON RAMIRO** (FR) 29
447 **DON'T BE SO SAKHEE** (GB) 13
126 **DON'T FORGET FAITH** (USA) 23
450 **DON'T PUSH IT** (IRE) 1
277 **DON'T STOP ME NOW** (IRE) 21
504 **DON'T TELL LOUIE** (GB) 14
9 **DON'T TELL SUE** (GB) 11
13 **DON'T TELL TRIGGER** (IRE) F 23
585 **DON'TCALLMEGINGER** (IRE) 4
167 **DONA ALBA** (IRE) 27
17 **DONALD WILL DO** (IRE) 4
450 **DONALDSON** (GER) 22
139 **DONASTRELA** (IRE) 8
375 **DONATESSA** (GER) 11
20 **DONEGAL** (USA) 41
388 **DONNA'S DOUBLE** (GB) 2
34 **DONT BE CROSS** (IRE) 5
4 **DONT CALL ME DEREK** (GB) 1
482 **DONT EVEN ASK** (GB) 21
415 **DONT LOOK SIDEWAYS** (GB) 3
333 **DONT TELL JILL** (IRE) 6
289 **DOODLE EILE** (IRE) 17
311 **DOODLEBOP** (IRE) 46
115 **DOOKUS** (IRE) 48
466 **DOOM HAYMER** (IRE) 45
420 **DOONEYS GATE** (IRE) 32
581 **DOONIGAN** (IRE) 6
311 **DORAFLORA** (GB) 47
290 **DORIAN** (GB) G 12
543 **DORIC DREAM** (GB) 24
584 **DORIC LADY** (GB) 13
552 **DORIES DREAM** (GB) 3
571 **DORIS'S GIFT** (GB) 10
25 **DORN DANCER** (IRE) 7
572 **DOROTHEA BROOKE** (IRE) C 86
168 **DORSO ROSSO** (IRE) 12
292 **DOSCO** (IRE) 24
41 **DOT'S DELIGHT** (GB) 4
649 **DOTCO** (GB) 31
337 **DOTTIE** (GB) 16
163 **DOTTY'S BROTHER** 48
562 **DOTTY'S DAUGHTER** (GB) 6
167 **DOUBLE BANDED** (IRE) 4
114 **DOUBLE BILL** (USA) 4
581 **DOUBLE BRANDY** (GB) 7
653 **DOUBLE CARPET** (IRE) 2
171 **DOUBLE CHIMES** (GB) C 1
188 **DOUBLE DAD** (IRE) 79
506 **DOUBLE DEFAULT** (IRE) 27
496 **DOUBLE DEPUTY** (IRE) 3
590 **DOUBLE DEPUTY** (IRE) 3
78 **DOUBLE DIZZY** (GB) 6
394 **DOUBLE DUTY** (IRE) 38
257 **DOUBLE EAGLE** (FR) 31
383 **DOUBLE EAGLE** (GB) 26
589 **DOUBLE EIGHT** (IRE) C 68

25 **EASTER BUNNY** (GB) 29
282 **EASTER FOLLY** (IRE) 11
343 **EASTER LEGEND** (GB) 14
337 **EASTER PRESENT** (IRE) 17
222 **EASTER VIC** (GB) 3
257 **EASTERN CANAL** (IRE) 33
147 **EASTERN DAGGER** (GB) 5
604 **EASTERN EAGLE** (GER) 74
253 **EASTERN EMBER** C 106
572 **EASTERN EMPEROR** (GB) 6
253 **EASTERN GIFT** (GB) 36
49 **EASTERN PRIDE** (GB) 24
655 **EASTERN PRINCESS** (GB) 3
519 **EASTERN ROMANCE** (GB) 45
556 **EASTERN RUBY** (GB) C 39
55 **EASTFIELDS LAD** (GB) 2
470 **EASTWELL SMILES** (GB) 21
495 **EASY BEAT** (IRE) F 25
625 **EASY MATE** (IRE) 75
598 **EASY PEASY** (GB) 22
126 **EASY STREET** (GB) 25
543 **EASY TARGET** (FR) 25
649 **EASY WONDER** (GER) 18
289 **EASYFIX** (IRE) 18
604 **EASYTANGO** (GB) 26
104 **EAU GOOD** (GB) 4
1 **EAU SAUVAGE** (GB) 11
455 **EBADIYAN** (IRE) 23
455 **EBADIYLA** (GB) C 87
455 **EBALISTA** (IRE) 24
455 **EBATANA** (IRE) F 88
455 **EBAZIYA** (IRE) F 89
420 **EBAZIYAN** (IRE) 35
302 **EBIAYN** (FR) 98
302 **EBN MALK** (IRE) 34
420 **EBONY SHADES** (IRE) 36
531 **EBRAAM** (USA) 10
394 **ECCO MI** (IRE) C 108
89 **ECHO DANCER** (GB) 27
374 **ECHO FALLS** (IRE) 4
506 **ECHO POINT** (IRE) 29
115 **ECLAIR FILANTE** (GB) 13
115 **ECLAIR MAGIQUE** (IRE) 49
36 **ECSTASY** (GB) F 58
90 **ECSTATIC** (GB) F 25
519 **ED'S PRIDE** 100
455 **EDABIYA** (IRE) C 90
496 **EDAS** (GB) 18
37 **EDDIE BOY** (GB) 78
308 **EDDYSTONE** (IRE) 6
596 **EDE'IFF** (GB) 4
469 **EDE'S** (GB) 1
469 **EDE'S THE BEST** (GB) 2
156 **EDEN PARK** (GB) 48
174 **EDEN ROCK** (IRE) 4
557 **EDEN ROSE** (GB) 1
622 **EDGBRIAR** (FR) 12
253 **EDGE CLOSER** (GB) 5
189 **EDGE END** (GB) 3
456 **EDGE OF GOLD** (GB) 19
395 **EDGE OF ITALY** (GB) 4
456 **EDGE OF LIGHT** (GB) 20
622 **EDGEBURY** (GB) 13
98 **EDGEFOUR** (GB) 4
622 **EDGEOVER** (GB) 14
622 **EDGEVINE** (GB) 15
370 **EDIE SUPERSTAR** (USA) 5
99 **EDINBOROUGH** (GB) 24
512 **EDIRNELI** (IRE) 4
282 **EDUCATED THIEF** (IRE) 12
369 **EDWARD** (IRE) 4
503 **EFFECTIVE** (GB) 9
93 **EFFIGY** (GB) 3
276 **EFFINGHAM** (IRE) 26
276 **EFFORTLESS** (GB) 27

87 **EFIDIUM** (GB) 5
358 **EFISIO PRINCESS** (GB) 7
291 **EGLANTINE** (GB) C 25
167 **EGLEVSKI** (IRE) 5
538 **EGOLI** (USA) C 29
231 **EGYPTIAN LORD** (GB) 5
289 **EIGHT FIFTY SIX** (IRE) 19
437 **EIGHT PALMS** (IRE) 34
67 **EIGHTEEN THOUSAND** (IRE) 27
172 **EIGHTY TWENTY** (IRE) 71
254 **EIJAAZ** (IRE) 12
598 **EILA** (GB) 23
416 **EIMKAR** F 42
109 **EIRE** (GB) 3
114 **EISTEDDFOD** (GB) 5
60 **EJAY** (GB) C 33
225 **EJEED** (USA) 32
165 **EKTIMAAL** (GB) 6
347 **EL ALAMEIN** (IRE) 4
474 **EL BANDINDOS** (IRE) 29
134 **EL BATAL** (IRE) 5
399 **EL BOSQUE** (IRE) 7
496 **EL CHICO** (GB) 19
495 **EL CORAZON** (IRE) F 26
286 **EL COTO** (GB) 3
211 **EL DIEGO** (IRE) 5
303 **EL DUENDE** (USA) 19
340 **EL FONTAN** (IRE) 32
371 **EL FUSER** (GB) 18
233 **EL HOMBRE DEL RIO** (IRE) 1
289 **EL JO** (IRE) 20
286 **EL POTRO** (GB) 4
30 **EL ROSA** (FR) 21
82 **EL SUENO** (IRE) 6
311 **EL VAQUERO** (IRE) 49
333 **EL ZORRO** (GB) 7
66 **ELA ALETHIA** (GB) G 64
443 **ELA APHRODITE** (GB) C 15
549 **ELA RE** (GB) 15
558 **ELAALA** (USA) 6
604 **ELBA** (GER) 75
455 **ELBASANA** (IRE) 4
159 **ELBDOUBLEU** (GB) 9
31 **ELBOW LANE** (IRE) 1
24 **ELBRUS** (USA) 22
211 **ELEANOR ELOISE** (GB) 6
194 **ELECTRIC BALOO** (GB) 1
83 **ELECTRIC WARRIOR** (IRE) 13
126 **ELECTROLYSER** (IRE) 26
598 **ELEGANT CLUTTER** (IRE) 24
109 **ELEGANT DANCER** (FR) 22
239 **ELEONORA** (FR) 24
600 **ELEONORA D'ARBOREA** (GB) C 25
251 **ELGAR** (GB) 2
335 **ELHAMRI** (GB) 3
29 **ELIJAH PEPPER** (USA) 31
56 **ELISIANO** (IRE) 31
87 **ELITE LAND** (GB) 1
115 **ELIXIR DU BERLAIS** (FR) 14
572 **ELIZA ACTON** (GB) F 87
559 **ELIZA DOALOTT** (IRE) 1
188 **ELIZA DOOLITTLE** (GB) 80
219 **ELIZABETH GARRETT** (GB) F 83
389 **ELIZABETH SPIRIT** (IRE) 2
253 **ELIZABETH SWANN** (GB) 37
382 **ELIZABETH'S QUEST** (GB) 10
411 **ELJARHA** (GB) F 35
574 **ELK TRAIL** (IRE) 16
90 **ELKHORN** (GB) 4
571 **ELLA** (GB) 11
83 **ELLA FALLS** (IRE) C 81
6 **ELLA WOODCOCK** (IRE) 2
184 **ELLA Y ROSSA** (GB) 8
418 **ELLAFINESSE** (GB) 10
657 **ELLANDSHE** (IRE) 1

612 **ELLE REEF** (GB) G 11
596 **ELLE ROSE** (GB) 5
298 **ELLEMUJIE** (GB) 20
332 **ELLEN TILLEY** (GB) 33
61 **ELLERSLIE ALI** (IRE) 2
311 **ELLERSLIE GEORGE** (IRE) 50
61 **ELLERSLIE LISA** (GB) 3
53 **ELLERSLIE TOM** (GB) 12
363 **ELLETELLE** (IRE) 22
650 **ELLIE BEE** (GB) 2
106 **ELLIE LOU** (GB) 3
87 **ELLIES FAITH** (GB) 7
615 **ELLIES HORSE** (IRE) 5
514 **ELLIOTT** (GB) 6
83 **ELLISTOWN LADY** (IRE) F 82
198 **ELLOPASSOFF** (GB) F 8
220 **ELLOVAMUL** (GB) C 49
533 **ELLWAY PROSPECT** (GB) 11
394 **ELLWAY QUEEN** F (GB) 109
167 **ELMALEEHA** (GB) 31
63 **ELMASONG** (GB) 4
291 **ELMS SCHOOLBOY** (GB) 5
394 **ELNA BRIGHT** (GB) 40
253 **ELNAWIN** (GB) 107
486 **ELOISE** (GB) 49
163 **ELOQUENT ISLE** (IRE) 20
163 **ELOQUENT ROSE** (IRE) 2
455 **ELOUANA** (IRE) 25
215 **ELOUGES** (IRE) 18
165 **ELSAFEER** (IRE) 24
497 **ELSIE JAY** (GB) 16
640 **ELSIE'S PRIDE** (IRE) 24
391 **ELSIES NOOK** (GB) 4
279 **ELTON** (GB) 36
424 **ELUSIVE DEAL** (USA) 8
437 **ELUSIVE DREAM** (GB) 35
531 **ELUSIVE DREAMS** (USA) 11
629 **ELUSIVE LADY** (IRE) 20
89 **ELUSIVE RONNIE** (IRE) 28
186 **ELUSIVE WARRIOR** (USA) 15
84 **ELUVAPARTY** (GB) 3
433 **ELVINA** (GB) 3
304 **ELVIS RETURNS** (GB) 15
407 **ELWICK PRINCESS** (GB) 11
302 **ELYSEE PALACE** (IRE) 35
423 **ELZAHANN** 4
165 **ELZEEZA** (USA) 25
458 **EM'S ROYALTY** (GB) 5
67 **EMAIL** (GB) 28
378 **EMAURA** (GB) F 22
466 **EMERALD BAY** (IRE) 14
394 **EMERALD CRYSTAL** (IRE) 41
447 **EMERALD DESTINY** (IRE) 3
227 **EMERALD DESTINY** (IRE) 4
525 **EMERALD FIRE** (GB) F 12
372 **EMERALD GREEN** (GER) 1
602 **EMERALD ROCK** (CAN) 12
558 **EMERALD TOFFEE** (IRE) 24
332 **EMERALD WILDERNESS** (IRE) 34
143 **EMERGENCY EXIT** (FR) C 18
158 **EMERGING LIGHT** (GB) 3
640 **EMILE ZOLA** (GB) 25
413 **EMILIA ROMAGNA** (GER) F 66
263 **EMILY BLAKE** (GB) 3
35 **EMILY'S FLORA** (GB) 1
462 **EMILY'S PLACE** (IRE) 7
413 **EMIR BAGATELLE** (GB) 26
172 **EMMA AMOUR** (GB) F 92
408 **EMMA JEAN LAD** (IRE) 4
454 **EMMA PEEL** (GB) C 50
515 **EMMA'S SECRETS** (GB) 10
476 **EMMASFLORA** (GB) 2
311 **EMMENSO** (IRE) 51
569 **EMMPAT** (IRE) 17
573 **EMOTIONAL ARTICLE** (IRE) 12

649 **GENEROUS SHARE** (GB) C 34
462 **GENEROUS STAR** (GB) 11
291 **GENEROUS THOUGHT** (GB) 19
513 **GENEROZ** (FR) 51
604 **GENETHNI** (GB) 76
269 **GENEVA BAY** (GB) 43
181 **GENEVRA** (IRE) C 21
356 **GENIES LAMP** (IRE) 18
107 **GENKI** (FR) 5
363 **GENNY LIM** (IRE) C 45
188 **GENOA** (GB) C 84
191 **GENTEEL** (IRE) C 14
631 **GENTLE APPROACH** (GB) F 8
216 **GENTLE CARIBOU** (IRE) 17
279 **GENTLE JOHN** (FR) 46
625 **GENTLEMAN JEFF** (USA) 4
332 **GENTLEMAN JIMMY** (IRE) 40
172 **GENTLEMAN'S DEAL** (IRE) 22
85 **GEOGRAPHY** (IRE) 2
221 **GEOJIMALI** (GB) 12
39 **GEORDIE DANCER** (IRE) 3
454 **GEORDIELAND** (FR) 3
571 **GEORGE ADAMSON** (IRE) 107
585 **GEORGE HENSON** (GB) 8
394 **GEORGE REX** (USA) 115
250 **GEORGE THE BEST** (IRE) 15
186 **GEORGE'S FLYER** (IRE) 23
316 **GEORGES BOY** (IRE) 2
332 **GEORGIAN KING** (GB) 41
96 **GEORGIE BEE** (GB) 49
91 **GEORGINA MACRAE** 91
363 **GEROBIES GIRL** (USA) F 46
22 **GERRARD** (GB) 2
279 **GERSHWIN** (IRE) 47
549 **GERSHWINNER** (IRE) 18
128 **GERTIE** (IRE) 5
524 **GETINBYBUTONLYJUST** (GB) 3
404 **GETON** (IRE) 6
292 **GETTING BACK** (IRE) 34
177 **GHAFEER** (USA) 8
302 **GHAIDAA** (IRE) 39
85 **GHAILL FORCE** (GB) 1
589 **GHAIYATH** (GB) 21
279 **GHALLAB** (GB) 48
625 **GHANAATI** (USA) 78
571 **GHAYAAT** (USA) C 108
625 **GHIMAAR** (GB) 29
638 **GHIZAO** (GB) 30
131 **GHOST DANCER** (GB) 7
613 **GIADINIERA** (GB) 23
102 **GIANT ACT** (GB) 22
604 **GIANT GINO** (GER) 31
221 **GIANT STAR** (USA) 13
100 **GIANT'S ROCK** (IRE) 1
105 **GIBB RIVER** (IRE) 61
407 **GIBBOGHSTOWN** (IRE) 14
474 **GIBRALTAR STAR** (FR) 36
365 **GIDAM** (IRE) 9
285 **GIDDYWELL** (GB) 10
300 **GIFFOINE** (GB) F 11
436 **GIFT HORSE** (GB) 15
338 **GIFT OF TIME** (GB) 27
560 **GIFTED FLAME** (GB) 2
231 **GIFTED GAMBLE** (GB) 8
16 **GIFTED HEIR** (IRE) 4
21 **GIFTED LASS** (GB) 3
174 **GIFTED LEADER** (USA) 15
157 **GIGANA** (FR) 50
276 **GIGANTICUS** (USA) 4
54 **GIGGLES O'SHEA** (IRE) 1
36 **GILBERTIAN** (GB) 59
285 **GILDED COVE** (GB) 11
93 **GILDED YOUTH** (GB) 4
82 **GILES** (GB) 10
58 **GILLANS INN** (GB) 47

420 **GILLIGANS HALL** (IRE) 45
383 **GILSLAND** (IRE) 29
126 **GILT EDGE GIRL** (GB) 16
9 **GIMME SOME LOVIN** (IRE) 13
30 **GIMPSIL** (GB) 25
602 **GINGER MINX** (IRE) 13
378 **GINGER POP** (GB) 3
146 **GINGER ROGERS** (GB) F 17
172 **GINGER'S LAD** (GB) 2
131 **GINGHAM** (GB) 39
549 **GINO** (GB) 19
52 **GINO'S SPIRITS** (GB) C 46
52 **GINOS DESTINATION** (GB) 26
25 **GIOACCHINO** (IRE) 21
199 **GIOLLA DE** (IRE) 17
470 **GIOVANNA** (GB) 25
515 **GIOVANNI D'ORO** (IRE) 4
168 **GIRL NEXT DOOR** (GB) C 23
165 **GIRL OF PANGAEA** (GER) 29
363 **GIVE A WHISTLE** (IRE) F 47
571 **GIVE HER A WHIRL** (GB) 18
257 **GIVE IT TIME** (GB) 49
216 **GIVE ME A DIME** (IRE) 18
319 **GIVE ME LOVE** (FR) 2
519 **GIVE WARNING** (IRE) F 104
220 **GIVEN A CHOICE** (IRE) 7
450 **GIVEUSACLUE** (IRE) 31
215 **GIVRE** (FR) 21
421 **GLACIAL DELIGHT** (IRE) 36
9 **GLACIAL SUNSET** (IRE) 14
470 **GLAD BIG** (GER) 26
20 **GLAM ROCK** (GB) C 92
569 **GLAMIS CASTLE** (USA) 23
164 **GLAMOROUS GIRL** (IRE) C 10
216 **GLANDORE MOON** (GB) 19
420 **GLANN BOY** (IRE) 46
485 **GLASHEEN** (USA) 1
337 **GLASKER MILL** (GB) 22
156 **GLASSHOUGHTON** (GB) 12
292 **GLAVEY** (IRE) 35
301 **GLEAMING SPIRIT** (IRE) 5
542 **GLEBE PLACE** (FR) C 45
107 **GLEEFUL** (GB) 34
276 **GLEN MOLLY** (IRE) 101
92 **GLEN OMEN** (IRE) 8
506 **GLEN ROUGE** (IRE) 36
391 **GLEN TANAR** (IRE) 8
17 **GLEN THYNE** (IRE) 7
545 **GLEN WARRIOR** (GB) 3
141 **GLENARY** (IRE) 11
292 **GLENBARROW** (IRE) 36
413 **GLENCAL** (GB) 4
1 **GLENCALVIE** (IRE) 12
420 **GLENCOVE MARINA** (IRE) 47
356 **GLENDA HODDLE** (GB) 19
298 **GLENDALE** (GB) 7
615 **GLENEAGLES** (IRE) 6
573 **GLENFIDICK** (IRE) 17
573 **GLENFINN CAPTAIN** (IRE) 18
311 **GLENGAP** (IRE) 58
209 **GLENGARRA** (IRE) 6
641 **GLENISLAND** (GB) 3
299 **GLENKILL** (IRE) 2
221 **GLENLIJJI** (GB) 36
220 **GLENRIDDING** (GB) 8
257 **GLENROCK LEADER** (IRE) 50
102 **GLENSARA** (GB) C 23
139 **GLENTANNA GIRL** (GB) G 11
519 **GLENVEAGH** (IRE) 48
383 **GLENWOOD KNIGHT** (IRE) 30
224 **GLIDE** (GB) 5
486 **GLIMMER** (GB) 52
73 **GLIMMER OF LIGHT** (IRE) 5
506 **GLINGERBANK** (IRE) 37

541 **GLINTON** (GB) 9
208 **GLISTENING SILVER** (GB) C 17
37 **GLITZ** (FR) 29
219 **GLOBAL ACHIEVER** (GB) 11
584 **GLOBAL GLORY** (IRE) 14
348 **GLOBAL HERO** (GER) 1
594 **GLOBAL PARTY** (IRE) 2
533 **GLOBAL STRATEGY** (GB) 15
184 **GLOBAL TRAFFIC** (GB) 8
30 **GLORIA DE CAMPEAO** (BRZ) 3
405 **GLORIEUX** (IRE) 10
378 **GLORIOUS ARAGON** (GB) F 24
205 **GLORIOUS CASTLEBAR** (GB) 6
105 **GLORIOUS GIFT** (IRE) 24
496 **GLOUCESTER** (GB) 26
146 **GLOWING DAWN** (IRE) 4
549 **GNILLISH** (GB) 20
305 **GO AMWELL** (GB) 12
543 **GO BETWEEN** (GB) C 68
166 **GO BUT GO** (GB) 1
647 **GO COMMANDO** (GB) 36
605 **GO FIGURE** (IRE) 11
447 **GO FOR GRACE** (FR) C 23
648 **GO FOR ONE** (FR) 5
451 **GO FREE** (GB) 9
602 **GO GLOW** (GB) 14
3 **GO GUNNER** (IRE) 4
470 **GO HARVEY GO** (IRE) 27
44 **GO HUNTING** (GB) G 4
582 **GO JOHNNY GO** (IRE) 15
124 **GO MO** (IRE) 5
120 **GO ON AHEAD** (IRE) 3
349 **GO ON GEORGE** (IRE) 6
195 **GO ON JACK** (GB) 1
569 **GO SILVER BULLET** (FR) 24
163 **GO SUNSHINE** (IRE) 51
139 **GO WEST** (IRE) 12
98 **GOBEJOLLY** (GB) 12
519 **GODFREY STREET** (GB) 12
640 **GODS TOKEN** (GB) 34
216 **GOFLO** (GB) 20
346 **GOFORTHEGAP** (IRE) 8
573 **GOGO GIZMO** (IRE) 19
107 **GOING FOR GOLD** (GB) 76
625 **GOING PUBLIC** (IRE) 30
649 **GOLAN WAY** (GB) 8
240 **GOLCONDA** (IRE) F 13
142 **GOLD AGAIN** (IRE) 16
572 **GOLD AGAIN** (USA) 44
269 **GOLD AWARD** (GB) 44
394 **GOLD BAR** (IRE) F 116
450 **GOLD BEACH** (IRE) 32
253 **GOLD BLENDED** (GB) C 116
519 **GOLD BUST** (GB) C 105
157 **GOLD EXCHANGE** (FR) 84
178 **GOLD FLAIR** F 59
581 **GOLD GUN** (USA) 10
496 **GOLD HEART** (FR) 27
279 **GOLD MEDALLIST** (GB) 49
37 **GOLD PROSPECT** (GB) 5
332 **GOLD REEF** (GB) 42
212 **GOLD RING** (GB) 22
451 **GOLD STAMP** (GB) C 26
311 **GOLD THREAD** (IRE) 59
96 **GOLDAN JESS** (IRE) 9
481 **GOLDDIGGING** (IRE) 15
600 **GOLDEN ALCHEMIST** (GB) 5
37 **GOLDEN BISHOP** (GB) 30
473 **GOLDEN BROWN** (IRE) 3
486 **GOLDEN BUTTON** (IRE) 24
548 **GOLDEN CREW** (GB) 6
519 **GOLDEN DAGGER** (IRE) 13
215 **GOLDEN DESERT** (FR) 22
400 **GOLDEN DESERT** (GB) 3
364 **GOLDEN FLIGHT** (FR) 15

422 **GREENWOOD** (GB) 5
332 **GREMLIN** (GB) 44
513 **GRENADIA** (USA) 57
184 **GRENANE** (IRE) 11
598 **GRENFELL** (IRE) 32
229 **GRENOUILLERE** (USA) F 54
39 **GRETHEL** (IRE) 4
253 **GREY AGAIN** (GB) C 118
159 **GREY BROTHER** (GB) 13
387 **GREY CAVALIER** (GB) 11
68 **GREY COMMAND** (USA) 26
95 **GREY DASLER** (IRE) 20
549 **GREY EAGLE** (GB) 23
601 **GREY GHOST** (GB) 21
177 **GREY GURKHA** (GB) 10
387 **GREY GURKHA** (GB) 12
360 **GREY LIGHT** (IRE) 24
466 **GREY OUTLOOK** (GB) 17
571 **GREY PURSUIT** (IRE) C 109
387 **GREY SAMURAI** (GB) 13
80 **GREY SHARK** (IRE) 6
542 **GREY STYLE** (IRE) 24
30 **GREY SWAN** (IRE) 26
517 **GREY TOPPER** (GB) 5
142 **GREYBROOK LASS** (IRE) F 17
124 **GREYCIOUSNESS** (USA) F 19
162 **GREYFIN** (GB) 1
513 **GREYLADY** (GB) 165
400 **GREYLAMI** (IRE) 13
572 **GREYSTOKE PRINCE** (GB) 45
640 **GREYT BIG STUFF** (USA) 37
569 **GRIGG OAK** (IRE) 25
519 **GRIMES FAITH** (GB) 15
311 **GRINGO** (GB) 63
569 **GRIPIT N TIPIT** (IRE) 26
513 **GRIS TENDRE** (FR) 18
513 **GRISONNANTE** (FR) F 166
599 **GRISSOM** (IRE) 32
599 **GRITTI PALACE** (IRE) 6
196 **GRIZEBECK** (IRE) 3
1 **GRIZEDALE** (IRE) 13
513 **GROIX** (IRE) 59
416 **GRONCHI ROSA** (IRE) C 45
409 **GROOMS AFFECTION** (GB) 5
143 **GROSS PROPHET** (GB) 7
544 **GROUND BREAKER** (GB) 4
401 **GROUND PATROL** (GB) 5
332 **GROUP CAPTAIN** (GB) 45
454 **GROUP THERAPY** (GB) 20
502 **GROUVILLE** (GB) 7
363 **GROVE VIEW STAR** (GB) 26
25 **GRUDGE** (GB) 22
470 **GRUMPY BEE** (IRE) 28
165 **GTAAB** (GB) 86
68 **GUADALOUP** (GB) 6
358 **GUAPISIMA** (GB) 11
336 **GUARDED EXPRESSION** (GB) F 20
406 **GUARDIAN OF TRUTH** (IRE) 39
474 **GUERABAD** (FR) 37
115 **GUERIDIA** (IRE) C 88
436 **GUEST CONNECTIONS** (GB) 16
176 **GUEST OF ANCHOR** (GB) C 34
336 **GUILDED WARRIOR** (GB) 7
291 **GUILDENSTERN** (IRE) 7
82 **GUILT** (GB) 11
257 **GUITAR RORY** (IRE) 53
444 **GULCH'S ROSE** (USA) 28
586 **GULF** (IRE) 3
276 **GULF STREAM LADY** (IRE) 31
37 **GULL WING** (IRE) 6
437 **GULLIBLE GORDON** (IRE) 45
501 **GULNAZ** (GB) 8
45 **GUMLEY GALE** (GB) 7
472 **GUN COVER** (GB) 3
450 **GUN SMITH** (GB) 35

506 **GUNADOIR** (IRE) 41
609 **GUNFIGHTER** (IRE) 3
437 **GUNGADU** (GB) 46
37 **GUNNADOIT** (USA) 32
452 **GUNNASAYSO** (GB) 15
186 **GUNNER FLY** (IRE) 82
506 **GUNNER JACK** (GB) 42
411 **GUNNER MASON** (IRE) 14
530 **GUNNER ROSE** (GB) 14
311 **GUNNER ROYAL** (GB) 64
179 **GUNNER'S VIEW** (GB) 5
82 **GUNPOINT** (IRE) 12
506 **GUNS AND BUTTER** (GB) 43
153 **GUNS OF LOVE** (IRE) 4
72 **GUNSHIP** (IRE) 2
500 **GUNSMOKE BLUE** (IRE) 3
7 **GUNSON HIGHT** (GB) 8
311 **GUPPY** (GB) 65
475 **GURTAVALLIG** 10
406 **GURU** (GB) 40
34 **GUS** (GB) 8
640 **GUSTAVO** (GB) 38
498 **GUTO** (GB) 4
289 **GUTS FOR GARTERS** (IRE) 26
279 **GUYMUR** (IRE) 50
437 **GWANAKO** (FR) 47
413 **GWEN JOHN** (USA) F 73
340 **GWENSEB** (FR) 5
264 **GWILYM** (GER) 3
19 **GWYNIE** (GB) 19
139 **GYPSY BOB** (IRE) 13
29 **GYPSY FAIR** (GB) F 55
612 **GYPSY GEORGE** (IRE) 3
167 **GYR** (IRE) 86
571 **GYRATION** (IRE) 19
387 **H HARRISON** (IRE) 14
143 **HAAFHD TIME** (IRE) 20
66 **HAAFHDS DELIGHT** (IRE) 68
411 **HAAKAISER** (IRE) 15
593 **HAAR** (GB) 8
572 **HAARTH SOVEREIGN** (IRE) 9
305 **HAASEM** (USA) 13
645 **HAATMEY** (GB) 5
102 **HAATMEY** (GB) 5
417 **HABANERO** (GB) 6
145 **HABANUS LIVIUS** (IRE) 1
444 **HABARIYA** (IRE) F 77
31 **HABBIE HEIGHTS** (GB) 17
447 **HABITUAL DANCER** (GB) 5
613 **HABSHAN** (USA) 8
589 **HADA MEN** (USA) 22
589 **HADAF** (IRE) 23
455 **HADARAMA** (IRE) 28
365 **HADITOVSKI** (GB) 10
253 **HADRON COLLIDER** (FR) 43
375 **HAGGLE TWINS** (IRE) 2
97 **HAIL THE KING** (USA) 1
7 **HAIR OF THE DOG** (GB) 9
554 **HAKIM** (NZ) 10
332 **HALCON GENELARDAIS** (FR) 46
277 **HALCYON DAZE** (GB) C 53
332 **HALDIBARI** (IRE) 47
25 **HALF A CROWN** (GB) 23
217 **HALF A TSAR** (IRE) 4
514 **HALF COCKED** (GB) 9
99 **HALF GLANCE** (GB) F 74
622 **HALF HIB** (IRE) 22
242 **HALFWAY CUT** (GB) 14
596 **HALFWAYTOPARADISE** (GB) 6
394 **HALICARDIA** (GB) C 120
589 **HALL HEE** (IRE) 24
496 **HALL OF FLAME** (IRE) 29
186 **HALLA SAN** (GB) 5
105 **HALLAND PARK LASS** (IRE) F 63
416 **HALLING GAL** (GB) 46

288 **HALLINGS OVERTURE** (USA) 5
225 **HALLIWELL HOUSE** (GB) 103
418 **HALLYS GOAL** (IRE) 13
109 **HALONG BAY** (FR) 24
42 **HALSION CHALLENGE** (GB) 28
42 **HALSION CHANCER** (GB) 7
436 **HAMAASY** (GB) 17
276 **HAMALKA** (IRE) 32
575 **HAMBURG SPRINGER** (IRE) 9
513 **HAMIDA** (USA) 60
519 **HAMMADI** (IRE) 49
589 **HAMMER** (GB) 25
60 **HAMMER OF THE GODS** (IRE) 8
640 **HAMMER TIME** (IRE) 39
68 **HAMMIYA** (IRE) C 56
105 **HAMPTON LUCY** (GB) F 64
220 **HAMSAH** (IRE) F 51
225 **HAMSAT ELQAMAR** (GB) 37
644 **HANA'S PRIDE** (IRE) G 8
153 **HANBRIN BHOY** (IRE) 5
335 **HANDBAGS AT DAWN** (IRE) 18
657 **HANDEL WITH CARE** (IRE) 3
397 **HANDSINTHEMIST** (IRE) 24
553 **HANDSOME CHAP** (GB) 11
186 **HANDSOME FALCON** (GB) 27
542 **HANDSOME MAESTRO** (IRE) 46
275 **HANDY CROSS** (GB) 2
105 **HANDY STATION** (IRE) C 65
68 **HANIYA** (IRE) F 57
366 **HANNAH PARK** (IRE) G 17
302 **HANNICEAN** (GB) 6
542 **HANNOUMA** 25
455 **HANOVERIAN BARON** (GB) 29
98 **HANS CRESCENT** (IRE) 21
98 **HANSINGER** (IRE) 22
628 **HANSOMELLE** (IRE) 7
366 **HANSOMIS** (IRE) 9
211 **HANTA YO** (IRE) 38
648 **HAOYUNMA** (IRE) 6
504 **HAPENEY** (IRE) 17
639 **HAPI** (GB) 17
573 **HAPPINESS IS FREE** (IRE) 21
27 **HAPPY BOY** (IRE) 5
492 **HAPPY HUSSAR** (IRE) 5
519 **HAPPY MEMORIES** (IRE) F 106
569 **HAPPY REUNION** (IRE) 27
240 **HAPPY STORY** (IRE) F 14
56 **HAPPY TALK** (IRE) F 51
307 **HAPTHOR** (GB) 3
188 **HARALD BLUETOOTH** (IRE) 44
172 **HARAMBEE** (IRE) F 97
490 **HARARE** (GB) 7
455 **HARATILA** (IRE) C 92
95 **HARBOUR BLUES** (GB) 54
92 **HARBOUR BREEZE** (IRE) 9
605 **HARBOUR BUOY** (GB) 12
171 **HARBOURS ROSE** (IRE) 3
369 **HARCOURT** (USA) 5
420 **HARD ACT** (IRE) 49
311 **HARD ACT TO FOLLOW** (IRE) 66
229 **HARD ROCK CITY** (USA) 8
622 **HARD TO RESIST** (GB) 69
276 **HARDA ARDA** (USA) F 104
197 **HARDANGER** (IRE) 17
497 **HARDCASE** (GB) 10
289 **HARDTOTAKE** (GB) 27
292 **HARDY EUSTACE** (IRE) 41
553 **HARDYBUCK** (IRE) 2
324 **HAREEM** (IRE) 2
34 **HARLAXTON** (GB) 9
114 **HARLECH CASTLE** (GB) 27
200 **HARLEQUIN HUGO** (GB) 13
167 **HARLESTONE GOLD** (GB) 38
167 **HARLESTONE SNAKE** (GB) 87
541 **HARLEY** (GB) 10

HERNANDO CORTES (GB) 37
HERNANDO ROYAL (GB) 8
HERNANDO'S BOY (GB) 20
HEROES (GB) 34
HEROIC LAD (GB) 33
HEROINE (FR) C 72
HEROLDS BAY (GB) 73
HERON (IRE) 18
HERON BAY (GB) 6
HERRBEE (IRE) 15
HESIVORTHEDRIVER (GER) 35
HESPERIA (GB) F 122
HESTER BROOK (IRE) 10
HEUREUX (USA) 69
HEVELIUS (GB) 47
HEVER ROAD (IRE) 3
HEVER ROSINA (GB) C 38
HEX (FR) 24
HEY BIG SPENDER (IRE) 16
HEY CHARLIE (IRE) 46
HEY HO (GB) 38
HEY PRESTO (GB) 10
HEY WINNIE (USA) G 18
HEYNEWBOY (GB) 12
HEYWOOD (GB) 18
HI CLOY (IRE) 28
HI DANCER (GB) 11
HI FI (GB) 12
HI FLING (GB) 123
HI HOPES (GB) 15
HI SHINKO 47
HI SPEC (IRE) 5
HI TECH (GB) 6
HI-TEC CLASSIC 52
HIAWATHA (IRE) 16
HIBIKI (IRE) 7
HIBOU DE NUIT (IRE) 33
HICCUPS (GB) 13
HIDDEN AGENT (IRE) 14
HIDDEN BOUNTY (IRE) 21
HIDDEN DOOR (IRE) 21
HIDDEN MEANING (GB) C 108
HIDDEN RAINBOW (IRE) 5
HIDDEN TALENTS (IRE) 6
HIDDEN UNIVERSE (IRE) 80
HIDDEN WEAPON (GB) 8
HIDDENDALE (IRE) F 124
HIDDENSEE (USA) 2
HIERARCHY (GB) F 15
HIGH 'N DRY (IRE) 2
HIGH ARCTIC (GB) 5
HIGH BARN (GB) C 63
HIGH BIRD HUMPHREY (GB) 3
HIGH BRAY (GER) 2
HIGH CAROL (IRE) 10
HIGH CHIMES (IRE) 36
HIGH CLASS PET (GB) 5
HIGH CLASS PROBLEM (IRE) 5
HIGH COINCIDENCE (GB) 32
HIGH COMMAND (IRE) 20
HIGH COMMISSION (GB) 6
HIGH COTTON (IRE) 30
HIGH COUNTRY (IRE) 17
HIGH CURRAGH (IRE) 19
HIGH EXPECTATIONS (IRE) 6
HIGH FIVE SOCIETY (GB) 4
HIGH FUN (IRE) 39
HIGH JACK (IRE) 11
HIGH LADY (GB) 24
HIGH LIFE (GB) 49
HIGH MOON (USA) 8
HIGH PERFECTION (IRE) 167
HIGH PETERGATE (IRE) C 98
HIGH PLAINS (FR) 44
HIGH POINT (IRE) 5

HIGH PRAISE (USA) C 76
HIGH REACH (GB) 11
HIGH RIDGE (GB) 20
HIGH ROCK (IRE) 62
HIGH SEASONS (GB) 10
HIGH SPOT (GB) F 109
HIGH STAND LAD (GB) 9
HIGH STANDARD (NZ) 11
HIGH STANDING (USA) 15
HIGH STEPPING (IRE) G 6
HIGH STEPPING (USA) 31
HIGH SUMMER (USA) F 52
HIGH TECH MADE (FR) 6
HIGH TWELVE (USA) 107
HIGH VOLTAGE (GB) 7
HIGH WINDOW (IRE) 1
HIGHAM (GB) 8
HIGHEST ESTEEM (GB) 45
HIGHGLEN (GB) 37
HIGHLAND CHIEF (GB) 50
HIGHLAND DAUGHTER (IRE) 28
HIGHLAND FLASH (GB) 35
HIGHLAND GAIT (GB) F 57
HIGHLAND GAMES (GB) 38
HIGHLAND HARVEST (IRE) 34
HIGHLAND HOMESTEAD (GB) 32
HIGHLAND LADDIE (GB) 25
HIGHLAND LASSIE (IRE) 125
HIGHLAND LEGACY (GB) 7
HIGHLAND LOVE (GB) 15
HIGHLAND PATRIOT (GB) 3
HIGHLAND SONG (IRE) 4
HIGHLAND STORM (GB) 52
HIGHLAND VENTURE (IRE) 34
HIGHLAND WARRIOR (IRE) 8
HIGHLY ACCLAIMED (GB) 54
HIGHLY REGAL (IRE) 11
HIGHMIX (GB) 97
HIGHTIME HEROINE (IRE) 79
HIGHWAY MAGIC (IRE) 35
HILAL (GB) 7
HILBRE COURT (USA) 48
HILDAGO (IRE) 77
HILITES (IRE) C 38
HILL BILLY ROCK (IRE) 21
HILL CLOUD (GB) 21
HILL FARM DANCER (GB) C 22
HILL FARM SHANTY (GB) 7
HILL FORTS HENRY (GB) 13
HILL FORTS TIMMY (GB) 14
HILL OF LUJAIN (GB) 13
HILL SUPREME (IRE) G 5
HILL WELCOME (GB) C 70
HILLRIDGE (GB) 6
HILLS OF ARAN (GB) 5
HILLS OF HOME (IRE) 51
HIMALAYAN TRAIL (GB) 24
HIMARIYA (IRE) 63
HIMBA (GB) 21
HINT OF SILVER (USA) F 73
HINTON THUNDERBOLT (GB) 41
HIP (GB) 32
HIPPOLYTUS (GB) 53
HIRAETH (GB) F 54
HIS TWEEDS (FR) 87
HISARONU (IRE) 77
HISHMAH (GB) 21
HISS AND BOO (GB) 20
HISTOIRE SAINTE (FR) C 64
HISTORIC PLACE (USA) 23
HISTORY BOY (USA) 168
HISTORY MASTER (IRE) 2
HISTORY PRIZE (IRE) 7
HIT THE ROOF (GB) 45
HIT THE SWITCH (GB) 19

HITAAF (IRE) 39
HITCHENS (IRE) 119
HITS ONLY CASH (GB) 13
HITS ONLY TIME (GB) 22
HITS ONLY VIC (USA) 10
HLA TUN (USA) 48
HO PANG YAU (GB) 16
HOBBS CHOICE (GB) G 2
HOBBS HILL (GB) 8
HOBBY (GB) 15
HOBOOB (USA) 88
HOBSON (GB) 16
HOCKENHEIM (FR) 70
HOGAN KNOWS BEST (IRE) 29
HOGMANEIGH (IRE) 5
HOH DEAR (IRE) F 80
HOH MIKE (IRE) 8
HOH NELSON (GB) 1
HOH VISS (GB) 22
HOH WOTANITE (GB) 14
HOHLETHELONELY (IRE) 4
HOLAMO (IRE) 47
HOLBECK GHYLL (IRE) 14
HOLD EM (IRE) 6
HOLD FIRE (GB) 21
HOLD THAT CALL (USA) 46
HOLD THE BID (IRE) 25
HOLD'S NIK (FR) 9
HOLDEN CAULFIELD (IRE) 10
HOLDEN EAGLE (GB) 28
HOLDING (GB) 74
HOLGERA (GER) F 87
HOLIDAY COCKTAIL (GB) 31
HOLIDAY ROCK (GB) 10
HOLLANDER (IRE) 10
HOLLANDIA (IRE) 1
HOLLINS (GB) 18
HOLLOW DREAM (IRE) 26
HOLLOW JO (GB) 14
HOLLOWS MILL (GB) 7
HOLLOWS MIST (GB) 8
HOLLY CLEUGH (GB) 46
HOLLY GOLIGHTLEY (GB) 52
HOLLYWOOD (GB) 1
HOLLYWOOD GEORGE (GB) 6
HOLLYWOOD LAW (IRE) 51
HOLOCENE (USA) 4
HOLOKO HEIGHTS (GB) 15
HOLY JOE (FR) 42
HOLY STORM (IRE) 17
HOLYFIELD WARRIOR (IRE) 9
HOME (GB) 34
HOME CALL (USA) 34
HOME COMING (IRE) 2
HOME FROM THE HILL (IRE) G 11
HOME FROM THE HILL (IRE) F 3
HOMEBOUND (USA) 169
HOMEBREW (IRE) 28
HOMECROFT BOY (GB) 12
HOMELEIGHWILDCHILD (GB) 3
HOMER WELLS (IRE) 52
HOMESPUN MAGIC (GB) 6
HOMETOWN (GB) 105
HONDALIA (IRE) 24
HONDURAS (SWI) 46
HONEST JOHN (GB) 8
HONEST LADY (USA) F 78
HONEST VALUE (IRE) 27
HONEST YANKEE (GB) 28
HONESTY BLUE (GB) 29
HONESTY PAYS (GB) 48
HONEY BERRY (IRE) 20
HONEY GEM (FR) 33
HONEY MAKES MONEY (GB) 30

131 **MAGALING** (IRE) 95
513 **MAGANY** (IRE) 191
238 **MAGDALENE** (GB) 8
141 **MAGE D'ESTRUVAL** (FR) 19
556 **MAGEN'S STAR** (IRE) 15
139 **MAGGIE BOON** (GB) 19
297 **MAGGIE KATE** (GB) 16
305 **MAGIC AMIGO** (GB) 16
334 **MAGIC BENGIE** (GB) 2
513 **MAGIC BRENT** (GB) 77
83 **MAGIC CAT** (GB) 92
262 **MAGIC CLICHE** (GB) 10
622 **MAGIC CLOVER** (ARG) 38
454 **MAGIC COVE** (USA) F 61
156 **MAGIC ECHO** (GB) 17
231 **MAGIC GLADE** (GB) 15
243 **MAGIC HAZE** (GB) 8
543 **MAGIC LADY** (IRE) C 80
571 **MAGIC MEL** (GB) 30
410 **MAGIC MERLIN** (GB) 14
34 **MAGIC OF THE ISLES** (GB) 27
479 **MAGIC RUSH** (GB) 3
115 **MAGIC SARAH** (IRE) 22
259 **MAGIC SKY** (FR) 14
205 **MAGIC WARRIOR** (GB) 11
596 **MAGICAL DAY** (GB) 28
121 **MAGICAL LEGEND** (GB) 8
646 **MAGICAL MIMI** (GB) 1
462 **MAGICAL MUSIC** (GB) 15
625 **MAGICAL PEACE** (IRE) C 93
49 **MAGICAL SONG** (GB) 28
378 **MAGICAL SPEEDFIT** (IRE) 16
121 **MAGICAL TREASURE** (GB) 9
121 **MAGICAL WONDERLAND** (GB) 10
538 **MAGICALMYSTERYCAT** (USA) F 37
426 **MAGICALMYSTERYTOUR** (GB) 10
302 **MAGISTRATE** (IRE) 10
257 **MAGNESIUM** (USA) 68
548 **MAGNIFICENT SEVEN** (IRE) 10
99 **MAGNIFICENT STAR** (USA) C 34
610 **MAGNIFICO** (GB) 28
239 **MAGNITUDE** (GB) 30
451 **MAGNOL** (GB) 27
420 **MAGNUM FORCE** (IRE) 65
99 **MAGNUSHOMESTWO** (IRE) 19
5 **MAGOT DE GRUGY** (FR) 21
2 **MAGPIE** (IRE) 55
280 **MAGROOM** (GB) 16
67 **MAHADEE** (IRE) 42
269 **MAHARBAL** (FR) 61
598 **MAHOGANY BLAZE** (FR) 41
437 **MAHONIA** (GB) 70
436 **MAIA** (GB) 30
109 **MAID FOR WINNING** (USA) 29
543 **MAID IN BLOOM** (GB) 30
239 **MAID OF AILSA** (USA) 31
99 **MAID OF CAMELOT** (GB) F 86
215 **MAID OF DAWKINS** (GB) F 44
212 **MAID OF MISCHIEF** (GB) C 57
167 **MAID TO BELIEVE** (GB) 8
211 **MAIDANNI** (USA) 13
352 **MAIDEN INVESTOR** (GB) 6
424 **MAIGH EO** (IRE) 22
543 **MAIL THE DESERT** (IRE) C 81
239 **MAIMOONA** (IRE) 32
181 **MAINE LOBSTER** (USA) C 24
115 **MAINMISE** (USA) F 92
85 **MAIREAD'S BOY** (IRE) 11
6 **MAISON DIEU** (GB) 5
277 **MAISONETTE** (GB) F 58
497 **MAJ WILLIAM MARTIN** (GB) 17
213 **MAJAALES** (USA) 18
239 **MAJEEN** (GB) 33
433 **MAJEHAR** (GB) 12

272 **MAJESTIC** (IRE) 11
516 **MAJESTIC CHIEF** (GB) 33
625 **MAJESTIC CONCORDE** (IRE) 5
156 **MAJESTIC ISSUE** (IRE) 18
163 **MAJESTIC MOVER** (IRE) 27
625 **MAJESTIC SILVER** (IRE) 94
551 **MAJESTICAL** (IRE) 6
364 **MAJESTIE WING** (IRE) 135
240 **MAJESTY'S DANCER** (IRE) C 17
172 **MAJIGAL** (GB) 77
157 **MAJIMOURIEN** (IRE) 19
599 **MAJOR BELLE** (FR) 9
253 **MAJOR CADEAUX** (GB) 10
476 **MAJOR CATCH** (IRE) 5
394 **MAJOR EAZY** (GB) 64
218 **MAJOR EURO** (IRE) 2
533 **MAJOR FAUX PAS** (IRE) 24
604 **MAJOR KEY** (GB) 41
156 **MAJOR MAGPIE** (IRE) 19
598 **MAJOR MALARKEY** (IRE) 42
269 **MAJOR MILLER** (GB) 62
332 **MAJOR RUMBLE** (GB) 77
405 **MAJOR SENSATION** (IRE) 5
141 **MAJOR SUSPECT** (GB) 20
599 **MAJOR UPSET** (IRE) 10
215 **MAJOR WING** (IRE) 25
421 **MAJORCA** (GB) 56
572 **MAJOUNE** (FR) C 96
172 **MAJURO** (IRE) 38
306 **MAJY D'AUTEUIL** (FR) 4
589 **MAKAAM** (USA) 77
276 **MAKAAMEN** (GB) 117
302 **MAKAASEB** (USA) 51
399 **MAKABUL** (GB) 11
278 **MAKAI** (GB) 5
596 **MAKALUNA** (GB) 29
7 **MAKE A MARK** (IRE) 11
640 **MAKE HASTE** (IRE) 55
284 **MAKE IT PLAIN** (GB) 8
208 **MAKE MY DREAM** (GB) 5
643 **MAKELLY** (GB) 3
641 **MAKEOVER** (GB) C 23
285 **MAKFLY** (GB) 18
276 **MAKHAALEB** (IRE) 118
622 **MAKHZOON** (USA) 39
236 **MAKING OVERTURES** (GB) 3
501 **MAKING WAVES** (IRE) F 14
604 **MAKNOON** (GB) 42
268 **MAKOKO** (IRE) 28
519 **MAKSHOOF** (IRE) 22
74 **MAKTAVISH** (GB) 5
268 **MALABA** (FR) 4
181 **MALABARISTA** (FR) 25
604 **MALAFEMINA** (GB) 43
419 **MALAGA BOY** (IRE) 21
450 **MALAKIYA** (IRE) 49
617 **MALDOUN** (IRE) 1
504 **MALECH** (IRE) 28
638 **MALETTON** (FR) 49
202 **MALGURU** (GB) 5
165 **MALIBU GIRL** (USA) 36
268 **MALIENNE** (FR) 5
282 **MALIN MIST** (USA) 24
177 **MALINSA BLUE** (IRE) 16
637 **MALJIMAR** (IRE) 10
359 **MALKO DE BEAUMONT** (FR) 11
156 **MALL QUEEN** (USA) G 52
139 **MALMO BOY** (GB) 20
360 **MALT DE VERGY** (FR) 29
164 **MALT EMPRESS** (IRE) 12
253 **MALT OR MASH** (USA) 11
225 **MALTA** (USA) 48
114 **MALTESE FALCON** (GB) 6
408 **MAMA G** (USA) C 43
451 **MAMA LEO** (GB) 28

360 **MAMBA** (GER) 30
639 **MAMBAZO** (GB) 7
640 **MAMBO DES MOTTES** (FR) 56
220 **MAMBO SPIRIT** (IRE) 13
474 **MAMLOOK** (GB) 56
604 **MAMMA'S TOO** (GB) C 103
543 **MAMMAS F-C** (IRE) F 82
553 **MAMORE GAP** (IRE) 4
394 **MAN APPEAL** (GB) 65
538 **MAN EATER** (GB) C 38
377 **MAN FROM HIGHWORTH** (GB) 7
184 **MAN OF GWENT** (UAE) 16
372 **MAN OF KENT** (GB) 2
169 **MAN OF LEISURE** (GB) 5
274 **MAN OF LETTERS** (UAE) 6
420 **MAN ON THE NILE** (IRE) 66
638 **MAN OVERBOARD** (GB) 50
143 **MANA POOLS** (IRE) F 24
516 **MANADAM** (FR) 34
394 **MANASSAS** (IRE) 66
314 **MANATHON** (FR) 4
250 **MANBOW** (IRE) 25
135 **MANCEBO** (GB) 9
413 **MANCHESTERMAVERICK** (USA) 35
597 **MANDALAY BAY** (GB) 5
533 **MANDALAY LADY** (GB) 25
426 **MANDALAY PRINCE** (GB) 11
466 **MANDARIN ROCKET** (IRE) 22
239 **MANDELIEU** (IRE) 34
418 **MANDERINA** (GB) F 40
225 **MANDHOOMA** (GB) 115
482 **MANDINGO CHIEF** (IRE) 41
378 **MANDRAGORE** (USA) C 27
436 **MANDURAH** (IRE) 31
142 **MANDYS GALE** (IRE) G 23
590 **MANEKI NEKO** (IRE) 7
514 **MANELE BAY** (GB) 16
167 **MANERE BAY** (GB) 47
95 **MANFORALLSEASONS** (GB) 30
39 **MANGANO** (GB) 6
82 **MANGE TOUT** (GB) 15
543 **MANGHAM** (FR) 31
613 **MANGO LADY** (GB) 26
198 **MANGO MASHER** (IRE) 3
497 **MANGO MUSIC** (GB) 6
573 **MANHATTAN BABE** (IRE) 31
279 **MANHATTAN BOY** (GER) 72
276 **MANHATTAN DREAM** (USA) 47
340 **MANHATTAN SUNSET** (GB) C 100
436 **MANIA** (IRE) F 80
349 **MANJAM** (IRE) 10
377 **MANNERS** (IRE) 8
574 **MANNSARA** (IRE) C 34
257 **MANOR PARK** (IRE) 114
533 **MANORSON** (IRE) 26
67 **MANSII** (GB) 43
421 **MANSONN LEDA** (FR) 57
405 **MANSONY** (FR) 26
311 **MANUKA BEE** (IRE) 147
371 **MANUKA TOO** (IRE) C 25
363 **MANUSCRIPT** (GB) F 55
474 **MANX ROYAL** (FR) 57
543 **MANY THANKS** (USA) C 83
99 **MANY VOLUMES** (USA) 2
482 **MANYOSHU** (IRE) 42
332 **MANYRIVERSTOCROSS** (IRE) 186
320 **MAORI LEGEND** (GB) 15
490 **MAPLEDURHAM** (IRE) 8
625 **MAQSOOD** (USA) 95
20 **MARA RIVER** (GB) F 102
640 **MARAAFEQ** (USA) 57
639 **MARAAGEL** (USA) 8
242 **MARAAKEZ** (GB) 23
302 **MARAASED** (GB) 52
413 **MARAH** (GB) C 78

MUJAADEL (USA) 43
MUJADA (GB) 28
MUJAHAZ (IRE) 31
MUJAHOPE (GB) 30
MUJAMEAD (GB) 35
MUJART (GB) 1
MUJOBLIGED (IRE) 17
MUJOOD (GB) 6
MUKHBER (GB) 55
MUKTASB (USA) 22
MULAAZEM (GB) 16
MULBERRY LAD (IRE) 10
MULL OF DUBAI (GB) 12
MULLACH NA SI (GB) 69
MULLEIN (GB) 26
MULLIGAN'S PRIDE (IRE) 13
MULTAHAB (GB) 10
MULTAKKA (IRE) 8
MULTEEN GUNNER (GB) 3
MULTICOLOUR WAVE (IRE) F 140
MULTIDIMENSIONAL (IRE) 3
MUMAATHEL (IRE) 3
MUMBLESWERVE (IRE) 1
MUMS CHATTERBOX (IRE) 5
MUMTAZ BEGUM (GB) 14
MUNAASHAH (IRE) 4
MUNAKASHAH (IRE) G 9
MUNCASTER CASTLE (IRE) 7
MUNCHING MIKE (IRE) 3
MUNDO'S MAGIC (GB) 24
MUNDYBASH (GB) 35
MUNJUM (GB) 99
MUNLOCHY BAY (GB) 13
MUNNINGS TOUCH (IRE) 15
MUNRO (IRE) 4
MUNSEF (GB) 9
MUNTAMI (IRE) 13
MURACO (GB) 8
MURAQEB (GB) 2
MURAWEG (IRE) 119
MURDOCH (GB) 4
MUREEFA (USA) F 48
MURFREESBORO (GB) 16
MURPHY (IRE) 36
MURPHY'S MATE (GB) 21
MURPHYS BEAU (IRE) 34
MURRAYS MAGIC (IRE) 81
MURRIN (IRE) 4
MUSAALEM (USA) 11
MUSANGO (GB) 9
MUSHARAHB (GB) 11
MUSHTAAQ (USA) 57
MUSIC CELEBRE (IRE) 11
MUSIC IN EXILE (USA) 53
MUSIC NOTE (GB) 10
MUSICAL AFFAIR (GB) 13
MUSICAL BAR (GB) 54
MUSICAL BEAT (GB) 2
MUSICAL CHAIRS (IRE) 35
MUSICAL DAY (GB) C 56
MUSICAL GIANT (USA) 21
MUSICAL GIFT (GB) 8
MUSICAL KEY (GB) F 26
MUSICAL LOCKET (IRE) 12
MUSICAL MAZE (USA) 74
MUSICAL SCRIPT (USA) 6
MUSIMARO (FR) 1
MUSTAJED (GB) 14
MUSTAMAD (GB) 5
MUSTAQER (IRE) 127
MUT'AB (USA) 49
MUTAJARRED (GB) 12
MUTAMAASEK (USA) 11
MUTAMAASHI (GB) 83
MUTARAAMI (GB) 82

MUTARED (IRE) 7
MUTAWAFFER (GB) 37
MUTAWARATH (IRE) 84
MUTAYAM (GB) 8
MUTHABARA (IRE) 51
MUTINEER (IRE) 60
MUTTIAH (GB) 46
MUTTLEY MAGUIRE (IRE) 19
MUTTON MANIAC (USA) F 72
MUTUAL FRIEND (USA) 63
MUTUAL RESPECT (IRE) 17
MWINDAJI (GB) 21
MY ABANNA G 61
MY ARCH (GB) 18
MY AUNT FANNY (GB) 56
MY BEAUTAFUL (GB) 8
MY BEAUTIFUL LOSER (IRE) 17
MY BOBBY (GB) 25
MY BONUS (GB) G 47
MY BONUS (GB) G 39
MY CONDOR (GB) 57
MY DANCER (GB) C 141
MY DEVON GIRL (GB) 16
MY DIXIE DARLING (USA) 142
MY ENIGMA (GB) C 41
MY FINAL BID (IRE) 1
MY FIRST PAIGE (GB) C 36
MY FLAME (GB) 28
MY FRIEND JOHNNIE (IRE) 54
MY FRIEND PAUL (GB) 8
MY FRIEND SANDY (GB) 23
MY FUNNY VALENTINE (IRE) C 128
MY GACHO (IRE) 16
MY GIDDY AUNT (IRE) F 101
MY GIRL JODE (GB) 73
MY IMMORTAL (GB) 64
MY JEANIE (GB) 13
MY KAISER CHIEF (GB) 10
MY KINGDOM 82
MY LADY (GB) 10
MY LEARNED FRIEND (IRE) 21
MY MATE MAX (GB) 39
MY MATE PETE (IRE) 27
MY MATILDA (GB) 19
MY MENTOR (IRE) 6
MY MICHELLE (GB) 12
MY MIMI (USA) F 45
MY MOMENT (IRE) 23
MY MONNA (GB) 11
MY OBSESSION (IRE) 7
MY OLD PIANO (IRE) 55
MY PARIS (GB) 24
MY PETRA (GB) 70
MY POPPET (GB) F 65
MY RETREAT (USA) 5
MY SARA (GB) 38
MY SHADOW (GB) 18
MY SHEILAS DREAM (IRE) 20
MY SKIPPER (GB) 36
MY SPRING ROSE (GB) 22
MY TURN KISSIN (USA) C 62
MY TURN NOW (IRE) 32
MY WAY DE SOLZEN (FR) 87
MYANMAR (IRE) 45
MYBOYCHARLIE 16
MYFRENCHCONNECTION (IRE) 13
MYLANIA (GB) C 86
MYLIE (FR) 2
MYLORD COLLONGES (FR) 4
MYMUMSAYSIMTHEBEST (GB) 60
MYRTLE (GB) F 90
MYSAYNOWAY (GB) 3
MYSHERAMOUR (IRE) 23
MYSHKIN (GB) 113

MYSTERIOUS PLANS (IRE) F 25
MYSTERIOUS WORLD (IRE) 7
MYSTERY HILL (USA) F 44
MYSTERY PLAY (IRE) C 26
MYSTERY SAIL (USA) 26
MYSTERY STAR (GB) 39
MYSTIC ART (IRE) 26
MYSTIC GLEN (GB) 12
MYSTIC KING (GB) 19
MYSTIC OAK (IRE) F 46
MYSTIC OAK (USA) F 22
MYSTIC PRINCE 133
MYSTIC SPIN (IRE) 17
MYSTIC STORM (GB) 48
MYSTIC TEMPO (USA) C 120
MYSTICAL AYR (IRE) 26
MYSTICAL BREEZE (IRE) 42
MYSTICAL STAR (FR) 3
MYSTIFIED (IRE) 8
MYSTIFY (GB) F 143
MYSTIK MEGAN (GB) 20
MYTHICAL CHARM (GB) 11
MYTHICAL GIRL (USA) C 55
MYTHICISM (GB) 88
MYTTONS MAID (GB) 22
NAAZEQ (GB) F 60
NABEEH (IRE) 38
NABIR (FR) 13
NABOUKO (FR) 5
NABRA (GB) 9
NACADOUR (FR) 65
NACARAT (FR) 23
NACHO LIBRE (GB) 55
NADOVER (FR) 33
NAGAM (FR) 7
NAGANO (FR) 32
NAGS TO RICHES (IRE) 25
NAIAD DU MISSELOT (FR) 65
NAIAZEK (GB) 102
NAIRANA (GB) 56
NAIZAK (GB) 101
NAJAABA (USA) F 25
NAJCA DE THAIX (FR) 29
NAKAI (FR) 79
NAKOMA (IRE) 24
NALEDI (GB) 3
NAMARIAN (IRE) 6
NAMED AT DINNER (GB) 39
NAMESAKE (GB) F 75
NAMIBIAN PINK (IRE) 6
NAMID REPROBATE (IRE) 7
NAMING PROBLEMS (GB) 32
NAMIR (GB) 23
NAMROUD (USA) 19
NAN JAN (GB) 7
NANARD (FR) 66
NANAVITS (IRE) G 26
NANCY SPAIN (IRE) 87
NANCY WAKE (FR) 70
NANCYMAY (GB) 17
NANGA PARBAT (FR) 80
NANNYS GIFT (IRE) 9
NANOSECOND (USA) 6
NANTON (GB) 10
NAOMI WILDMAN (USA) C 51
NAPALM (IRE) 14
NAPOLETANO (GER) 6
NAPOLI (FR) F 82
NAPOLITO (FR) 9
NARAINA (FR) F 36
NARALINA (FR) 88
NARLEN (CZE) 7
NARVAL D'AVELOT (FR) 13
NASAIEB (USA) F 89
NASAQ (USA) 40

340 **POMPEYANO** (IRE) 63
632 **PONDAPIE** (IRE) 22
184 **PONDICHERRY** (USA) F 49
242 **PONGO'S NEPHEW** (GB) 26
56 **PONTE VECCHIO** (IRE) 15
586 **POOKA'S DAUGHTER** (IRE) C 14
141 **POP** (FR) 34
191 **POP MUSIC** (IRE) 7
159 **POPCORN ROSIE** (GB) 20
265 **POPPET'S LOVEIN** (GB) 58
265 **POPPETS SWEETLOVE** (GB) 20
572 **POPPY CAREW** (IRE) F 103
481 **POPPY DEAN** (IRE) 21
428 **POPPY GREGG** (GB) 20
320 **POPPY MAROON** (GB) 20
586 **POPPY RED** (GB) 12
173 **POPPY SMITH** (GB) 4
387 **POPPY'S ROSE** (GB) 22
115 **POPULONIA** (FR) 28
437 **POQUELIN** (FR) 108
364 **PORDIOSERO** (FR) 141
268 **PORGY** (GB) 34
421 **PORT ERNE** (IRE) 81
364 **PORT GAUGAIN** (GB) 66
405 **PORT LA CHAINE** (FR) 37
115 **PORT MANECH** (IRE) 96
73 **PORT OF MOGAN** (IRE) 9
107 **PORT PROVIDENCE** (GB) 45
654 **PORT QUIN** (GB) 22
374 **PORTACARRON BAY** (IRE) 9
304 **PORTAVADIE** (GB) 33
107 **PORTELET** (GB) C 90
332 **PORTERS WAR** (IRE) 112
276 **PORTHOLE** (USA) 57
569 **PORTICCIO** (IRE) 50
82 **PORTLAND** (GB) 19
5 **PORTLAND BILL** (IRE) 38
99 **PORTODORA** (USA) 39
625 **PORTOFINO BAY** (IRE) 42
435 **PORTRAIT ROYALE** (IRE) 7
96 **PORTRUSH STORM** (GB) 36
647 **PORTUGESE CADDY** (IRE) 46
605 **POSEIDON** (GB) 26
141 **POSH DUDE** (GB) 35
280 **POSH EMILY** (GB) 22
446 **POSH PAULA** (IRE) 49
159 **POSH PENNY** (GB) 21
277 **POSSESSIVE ARTISTE** (GB) C 63
506 **POSSEXTOWN** (IRE) 74
409 **POSTAGE** (GB) 13
131 **POSTER** (IRE) 102
268 **POSTERITAS** (USA) F 58
297 **POSTMASTER** (GB) 8
332 **POTEMKIN** (USA) 187
277 **POTENTIALE** (IRE) 13
383 **POTTER'S GALE** (IRE) C 70
346 **POTTS OF MAGIC** (GB) 18
37 **POULAINE BLEUE** (GB) 45
444 **POULE DE LUXE** (IRE) C 96
157 **POUR CHANGER** (FR) 59
332 **POUVOIR** (FR) 113
348 **POUVOIR ABSOLU** (IRE) 19
102 **POWER AGAIN** (GB) 13
338 **POWER BALLAD** (GB) 6
349 **POWER KING** (GB) 13
208 **POWER OF SPEECH** (GB) 12
112 **POWER PLAYER** (GB) 3
422 **POWER SHARED** (GB) 10
117 **POWER STRIKE** (USA) 6
157 **POWERFUL** (IRE) 29
625 **POWERFUL PRESENCE** (IRE) 112
36 **POYLE DEE DEE** (GB) 28
36 **POYLE MEG** (GB) 71
647 **PRAGMATIST** (GB) 7
364 **PRAHDA** (FR) 67

549 **PRAIRIE LORD** (IRE) 41
20 **PRAIRIE STORM** (GB) 59
602 **PRAIRIE TIGER** (GER) 6
364 **PRALIN DE L'ISLE** (FR) 68
298 **PRANCING** (GB) C 33
114 **PRAVDA STREET** (GB) 39
340 **PRAXITHEA** (GB) F 64
300 **PRE EMINANCE** (IRE) 6
421 **PRE TOKEN** (GB) 82
280 **PREACHER BOY** (GB) 23
58 **PRECEDER** (GB) F 61
625 **PRECIOUS GEM** (IRE) 113
613 **PRECIOUS SECRET** (IRE) 46
96 **PRECIPICE** (GB) 37
408 **PRECISION BREAK** (USA) 30
83 **PRECOCIOUS STAR** (IRE) 21
112 **PRECURSOR** (IRE) 12
437 **PREDATEUR** (FR) 109
18 **PREDESTINE** (FR) 23
492 **PREDICAMENT** (GB) 10
486 **PREDICT** (GB) 65
172 **PREDICTABLE** (IRE) 79
437 **PREDICTIVE** (FR) 110
66 **PRELUDE** (GB) 30
611 **PRELUDE D'ESTRUVAL** (FR) 6
538 **PREMIER AMOUR** C 42
506 **PREMIER DANE** (IRE) 75
406 **PREMIER DES MARAIS** (FR) 83
343 **PREMIER HOPE** (IRE) 35
178 **PREMIER PRIZE** (GB) F 68
506 **PREMIER SAGAS** (IRE) 76
585 **PREMIER SUPERSTAR** (GB) 77
454 **PREMIER YANK** (USA) 26
268 **PREMIERE PARTIE** (FR) 35
530 **PREMIERSHIP** (IRE) 24
613 **PREMIO LOCO** (USA) 13
167 **PRESBYTERIAN NUN** (IRE) 56
486 **PRESCRIPTION** (GB) 30
343 **PRESENCE OF MIND** (IRE) 36
219 **PRESENT** (GB) 16
413 **PRESENT ALCHEMY** (GB) 84
571 **PRESENT GESTURE** (IRE) 37
9 **PRESENT GLORY** (GB) 21
5 **PRESENT M'LORD** (IRE) 39
104 **PRESENT ORIENTED** (USA) 14
591 **PRESENTABLE** (IRE) 5
549 **PRESENTING ALF** (IRE) 42
279 **PRESENTING COPPER** (IRE) 103
627 **PRESENTING DIVA** (IRE) 7
343 **PRESENTING EXPRESS** (IRE) 37
481 **PRESENTLY** (GB) F 35
29 **PRESIDENT ELECT** (IRE) 43
571 **PRESIDENT HILL** (IRE) 7
603 **PRESIDENT PARK** (FR) 6
420 **PRESIDENT ROYAL** (GB) 104
115 **PRESIDENTIABLE** (FR) 60
420 **PRESLEY** (IRE) 81
504 **PRESQUE PERDRE** (GB) 34
604 **PRESS EXPRESS** (IRE) 53
56 **PRESS THE BUTTON** (GER) 16
622 **PRESSGANG** (GB) 52
302 **PRESSING** (IRE) 10
6 **PRESSMAN** (GB) 6
215 **PRESTANCE** (IRE) 28
105 **PRESTIGIOUS BABY** (IRE) 73
67 **PRESTO VENTO** (GB) F 91
107 **PRESUMPTIVE** (FR) 7
549 **PRESUMPTUOUS** (GB) 43
131 **PRESVIS** (GB) 7
184 **PRET A PORTER** (UAE) 20
236 **PRET A THOU** (FR) 4
95 **PRETIOSA** (IRE) F 27
95 **PRETTILINI** (GB) 39
488 **PRETTY BONNIE** (GB) 11
364 **PRETTY BRUERE** (FR) 69

495 **PRETTY DEMANDING** (IRE) 11
93 **PRETTY MISS** (GB) 8
238 **PRETTY OFFICER** (USA) 16
543 **PRETTY POLLYANNA** F 94
451 **PRETTY POSEY** (GB) 19
211 **PRETTY SHARP** (GB) F 42
332 **PRETTY STAR** (GB) 114
188 **PREVAILING WIND** (GB) 61
433 **PRICKLY POPPY** (GB) C 37
437 **PRIDE OF DULCOTE** (GB) 111
444 **PRIDE OF INDIA** (USA) 48
124 **PRIDE OF MINE** (GB) 8
277 **PRIDE OF NATION** (GB) 14
332 **PRIDEUS** (GB) 115
454 **PRIMA MARTA** (GB) F 67
188 **PRIMAEVAL** (GB) 91
406 **PRIME CONTENDER** (GB) 84
276 **PRIME DEFENDER** (GB) 5
107 **PRIME EXHIBIT** (GB) 46
276 **PRIME FACTOR** (GB) 58
1 **PRIME NUMBER** (GB) 16
543 **PRIME PERFORMER** (GB) 39
192 **PRIME RECREATION** (GB) 3
498 **PRIMER LUGAR** (GB) 12
198 **PRIMESHADE PROMISE** (GB) 4
286 **PRIMITIVE ACADEMY** (GB) 77
338 **PRIMO DILETTANTE** (GB) 32
221 **PRIMO HEIGHTS** (GB) 40
454 **PRIMO SUPREMO** (GB) C 68
466 **PRIMO WAY** (GB) 34
45 **PRIMROSE PARK** (GB) 13
442 **PRIMROSE TIME** (GB) 16
604 **PRIMUS** (GER) 54
645 **PRIMUS INTER PARES** (IRE) 11
201 **PRINCE ADJAL** (IRE) 7
36 **PRINCE AFRAM** (GB) 29
506 **PRINCE AMONG MEN** (GB) 77
474 **PRINCE ARY** (GB) 82
474 **PRINCE BERE** (FR) 83
332 **PRINCE BROC** (FR) 116
332 **PRINCE BUSTER** (FR) 117
311 **PRINCE CAR** (FR) 106
83 **PRINCE CHARLEMAGNE** (IRE) 22
474 **PRINCE DE BERSY** (FR) 84
278 **PRINCE DES NEIGES** (FR) 7
143 **PRINCE DESIRE** (FR) 12
269 **PRINCE DU BEURY** (FR) 82
332 **PRINCE DU SEUIL** (FR) 118
324 **PRINCE DUNDEE** (FR) 8
156 **PRINCE EGOR** (IRE) 23
636 **PRINCE EMMANUEL** (FR) 30
625 **PRINCE ERIK** (GB) 6
571 **PRINCE EVELITH** (GER) 38
302 **PRINCE FOREVER** (IRE) 11
543 **PRINCE HAMLET** (GB) 40
571 **PRINCE KALAMOUN** (GER) 85
199 **PRINCE MASSINI** (IRE) 27
163 **PRINCE NAMID** (GB) 10
548 **PRINCE OF ARAGON** (GB) 15
576 **PRINCE OF CHARM** (USA) 6
36 **PRINCE OF DELPHI** (GB) 9
294 **PRINCE OF GOLD** (GB) 2
447 **PRINCE OF LOVE** (IRE) 9
42 **PRINCE OF MEDINA** (GB) 20
364 **PRINCE OF SURINAM** (FR) 70
1 **PRINCE OF THEBES** (IRE) 17
466 **PRINCE RHYDDARCH** (GB) 52
488 **PRINCE ROSSI** (GB) 9
253 **PRINCE SABAAH** (IRE) 16
436 **PRINCE SAMOS** (IRE) 40
20 **PRINCE SIEGFRIED** 112
279 **PRINCE TAIME** (FR) 105
516 **PRINCE TAM** (GB) 43
356 **PRINCE TOM** (GB) 39
531 **PRINCE TUM TUM** (USA) 25

311 **ROYAL ROSA** (FR) 110
518 **ROYAL SAILOR** (IRE) 10
288 **ROYAL SENGA** (GB) 10
311 **ROYAL SOVEREIGN** (IRE) 157
399 **ROYAL STORM** (IRE) 20
20 **ROYAL STRAIGHT** (GB) 65
36 **ROYAL SUPERLATIVE** (GB) 75
406 **ROYAL TARTAN** (USA) 126
338 **ROYAL TOERAG** (GB) 34
220 **ROYAL TROOPER** (IRE) 63
216 **ROYAL WEDDING** (IRE) 32
303 **ROYAL WILLY** (IRE) 49
405 **ROYALDOU** (FR) 40
109 **ROYALE DANEHILL** (IRE) 10
268 **ROYALE LIFE** (FR) 39
364 **ROYALE MAJESTY** (IRE) 146
183 **ROYALE RAG** (FR) 10
269 **ROYALEETY** (FR) 91
268 **ROYALEMIXA** (FR) 40
302 **ROYALIST** (GB) 66
269 **ROYALS DARLING** (GER) 92
4 **ROYALTIES** (GB) 7
8 **ROYMAR** (GB) 5
455 **ROYSTONEA** (GB) C 107
647 **ROZNIC** (FR) 8
67 **RSMIYA** (GB) 58
548 **RUAIRI** (IRE) 16
49 **RUB OF THE RELIC** (IRE) 32
167 **RUBAA** (IRE) 108
424 **RUBENSTAR** (IRE) 4
628 **RUBILINI** (GB) 13
304 **RUBIPRESENT** (IRE) 36
156 **RUBIROSA** (FR) 39
519 **RUBY AFFAIR** (IRE) F 122
116 **RUBY BLADE** (GB) 9
18 **RUBY CROWN** (GB) 27
132 **RUBY DELTA** (GB) 9
606 **RUBY HARE** (GB) 21
622 **RUBY ISABEL** (IRE) 57
629 **RUBY JULIE** (GB) F 36
534 **RUBY LASER** (GB) G 3
108 **RUBY MAY** (GB) 3
254 **RUBY QUEEN** (IRE) 24
634 **RUBY ROCKS** (GB) 19
60 **RUBY ROCKS** (GB) 29
590 **RUBY SUNDAY** (GB) 14
643 **RUBY VALENTINE** (FR) 5
21 **RUBY'S RAINBOW** (IRE) 11
58 **RUBY'S SONG** (IRE) 62
628 **RUBYS BAY** (GB) 14
416 **RUBYWOSOX** (IRE) 29
578 **RUCOLINO** (IRE) 2
553 **RUDAKI** (GB) 8
139 **RUDINERO** (IRE) 31
582 **RUDIVALE** (GB) 29
418 **RUDRY WORLD** (IRE) 26
115 **RUE PIGALLE** (IRE) C 99
115 **RUE ROYALE** (IRE) 66
629 **RUE SOLEIL** (GB) 12
42 **RUFF DIAMOND** (USA) 42
191 **RUFFIE** (GB) 9
387 **RULE FOR EVER** (GB) 25
276 **RULER OF ALL** (USA) 138
46 **RULES APPLY** (IRE) 4
600 **RULING REEF** (GB) 10
93 **RUM JUNGLE** (GB) 9
9 **RUMBLE OF THUNDER** (IRE) 45
212 **RUMBLED** (GB) 47
157 **RUMINA** (FR) 94
519 **RUMORED** (USA) C 123
574 **RUMPUS** (GB) 17
269 **RUN FOR MOOR** (IRE) 93
225 **RUN FOR THE HILLS** (GB) 127
388 **RUN FOREST RUN** (GB) 9
645 **RUN FREE** (GB) 14

40 **RUN FROM NUN** (GB) 14
64 **RUN ON** (GB) 14
326 **RUN TO ME** (GB) 13
506 **RUN TO SPACE** (GB) 82
204 **RUN TO THE SEA** (IRE) 15
16 **RUNNING BUCK** (USA) 13
578 **RUNNING FRAU** C 4
262 **RUNNING HOT** (GB) 20
500 **RUNNING LORD** (IRE) 8
547 **RUNNING SUPREME** (GB) 5
377 **RUNNING TIMES** (USA) 10
64 **RUNSHAN** (IRE) 15
407 **RUNSWICK BAY** (GB) 48
266 **RUPERT'S PRINCESS** (IRE) F 8
266 **RUPERT'S PRINCESS** (IRE) F 11
227 **RURAL PRIDE** (IRE) 15
474 **RURAL REBEL** (IRE) 96
335 **RUSH HOUR** (GB) C 55
411 **RUSHANE LODGE** (IRE) 22
506 **RUSHWEE** (GB) 83
199 **RUSSELLSTOWN BOY** (IRE) 30
411 **RUSSET PRINCE** (IRE) 23
566 **RUSSET REWARD** (GB) 11
13 **RUSSIAN ANGEL** (GB) 17
216 **RUSSIAN AROUND** (IRE) 33
258 **RUSSIAN CONSORT** (IRE) 16
302 **RUSSIAN EPIC** (GB) 21
583 **RUSSIAN FLAG** (FR) 21
332 **RUSSIAN INVADER** (IRE) 130
302 **RUSSIAN JAR** (IRE) 116
363 **RUSSIAN MUSE** (FR) F 60
107 **RUSSIAN MUSIC** (USA) 47
481 **RUSSIAN RAVE** (GB) 36
168 **RUSSIAN ROCKET** (IRE) 10
226 **RUSSIAN SKY** (GB) 11
571 **RUSSIAN SNOWS** (IRE) C 120
176 **RUSSIAN SYMPHONY** (USA) 14
142 **RUSSIAN TRIGGER** (GB) 30
538 **RUSSKI** (IRE) 9
332 **RUSTARIX** (FR) 131
377 **RUSTIC JOHN** (GB) 11
269 **RUSTLER** (GB) 94
415 **RUSTY SLIPPER** (GB) 7
589 **RUTBA** (GB) 45
556 **RUTLAND WATER** (IRE) 53
426 **RUWAIN** (GB) 17
426 **RYAN STYLE** (IRE) 45
408 **RYAN'S FUTURE** (IRE) 15
130 **RYDAL** (USA) 5
336 **RYDAL MOUNT** (IRE) 15
506 **RYDALE LAD** (IRE) 84
514 **RYDERS STORM** (USA) 21
83 **RYE ROCKET** (GB) 67
274 **RYEDALE OVATION** (IRE) 9
513 **RYMAN** (USA) 215
364 **RYME BERE** (FR) 147
605 **RYMISTER** (GB) 30
321 **SA NAU** (GB) 12
68 **SAADA ONE** (IRE) F 69
394 **SAAFEND GEEZER** (GB) 81
569 **SAALBACK** (USA) 55
579 **SAAMEQ** (IRE) 14
68 **SABAAH ELFULL** (GB) F 70
239 **SABANCAYA** (GB) 44
604 **SABANTUY** (GB) 106
513 **SABBATH** (USA) 102
213 **SABEEL** (GB) G 30
213 **SABEEL** (GB) G 31
225 **SABI STAR** (GB) 128
394 **SABINA** (GB) F 145
372 **SABO PRINCE** (GB) 4
467 **SABORIDO** (USA) 53
474 **SABRATA** (IRE) C 71
474 **SABRE HONGROIS** (FR) 97
406 **SABRE LIGHT** (GB) 127

245 **SABRE'S EDGE** (IRE) 11
356 **SABREFLIGHT** (GB) 47
37 **SABREON** (GB) F 92
121 **SABY** (FR) 17
513 **SACHET** (USA) F 216
604 **SACO** (GER) 87
410 **SACRED BULL** (GB) 21
394 **SACRED FLAME** (GB) 82
178 **SACRILEGE** (GB) 43
596 **SAD TIMES** (IRE) 12
639 **SADAKA** (USA) F 37
78 **SADDLER GEORGE** (IRE) 22
235 **SADDLERS MOT** (GB) 8
27 **SADDLERS SINGER** (IRE) 14
200 **SADDLERS' GAIT** (IRE) 25
583 **SADDLERS' SUPRÊME** (IRE) 22
543 **SADEEK** (GB) 12
98 **SADIKA** (IRE) C 28
67 **SADINGA** (FR) F 92
385 **SADLER'S HILL** (IRE) 3
186 **SADLER'S KINGDOM** (IRE) 48
556 **SADLER'S PROFILE** (USA) F 19
482 **SADLER'S STAR** (GER) 55
420 **SADLERS WINGS** (IRE) 86
647 **SAFARI ADVENTURES** (IRE) 9
510 **SAFARI RUN** (IRE) 3
647 **SAFARI SUNDOWNER** (IRE) 11
647 **SAFARI SUNSET** (IRE) 12
647 **SAFARI SUNSHINE** (IRE) 49
647 **SAFARI SUNUP** (IRE) 22
647 **SAFARI TIME** (IRE) 23
409 **SAFASEEF** (IRE) 21
477 **SAFE INVESTMENT** (USA) 14
318 **SAFIN** (GER) 14
560 **SAFRANINE** (IRE) 7
513 **SAGA D'OUILLY** (FR) C 217
240 **SAGAING** (GB) F 18
538 **SAGAMARTHA** (GB) C 44
150 **SAGASSA** (GB) 3
134 **SAGUNT** (GB) 17
253 **SAHAADI** (GB) 76
589 **SAHAAL** (USA) 88
409 **SAHARA PRINCE** (IRE) 15
443 **SAHARA REEM** (GB) G 6
443 **SAHARA REEM** (IRE) C 17
443 **SAHARA REEM** (IRE) C 12
455 **SAHARA SLEW** (USA) C 108
539 **SAHARAN ROYAL** (GB) 12
67 **SAHARIRI** (IRE) 59
406 **SAHF LONDON** (GB) 88
67 **SAHRATI** (GB) 12
261 **SAIBHREAS** (IRE) F 54
506 **SAIF SAREEA** (GB) 85
302 **SAIFAAN** (GB) 117
50 **SAIGA** (FR) F 35
530 **SAIL AND RETURN** (GB) 28
418 **SAILOR A'HOY** (GB) 27
298 **SAILOR KING** (IRE) 5
545 **SAILOR'S SOVEREIGN** (GB) 7
93 **SAINGLEND** (GB) 30
467 **SAINT CHAPELLE** (IRE) 54
103 **SAINT ERIC** (FR) 33
568 **SAINT ESPIEGLE** (FR) 7
364 **SAINT FONTENAILLES** (FR) 95
259 **SAINT GODEGRAND** (FR) 20
231 **SAINT REMUS** (IRE) 22
513 **SAINTE ADRESSE** (GB) 218
3 **SAINTE ETOILE** (GB) G 8
474 **SAINTE KADETTE** (FR) 98
364 **SAINTE NONO** (FR) 96
157 **SAINTE RUSSY** (FR) 70
364 **SAINTE SCOLASSE** (FR) 97
364 **SAINTENITOUCHE** (FR) 98
364 **SAINTETE** (FR) 99

169 **SHYBUTWILLING** (IRE) 15
485 **SHYDICO** (IRE) C 12
238 **SI BELLE** (IRE) 18
185 **SI BIEN** (FR) 14
606 **SI GRAND** (FR) 22
373 **SIAKIRA** (GB) 12
268 **SICILE** (FR) 42
167 **SICILIAN PINK** (GB) 112
37 **SICILIANDO** (GB) 95
238 **SICILY** (USA) F 31
165 **SIDDARTHA** (GB) 53
452 **SIDNEY CHARLES** (IRE) 32
292 **SIEGEMASTER** (GB) 83
83 **SIEM REAP** (USA) F 99
168 **SIENA** (GB) 7
352 **SIENA STAR** (IRE) 8
513 **SIGATOKA** (USA) F 226
435 **SIGHT'N SOUND** (GB) F 9
188 **SIGN OF THE CROSS** (GB) 22
647 **SIGNATURE TUNE** (IRE) 14
93 **SIGNOR PELTRO** (GB) 11
39 **SIGNOR WHIPPEE** (GB) 12
455 **SIGNORA FRASI** (IRE) 5
103 **SIGNS OF LOVE** (FR) 34
165 **SILAAH** (GB) 10
628 **SILBER MOND** (GB) 16
209 **SILBERHORN EXPRESS** (GB) 17
543 **SILCA BOO** (GB) C 100
332 **SILENCIO** (IRE) 142
190 **SILENT ANGEL** (GB) C 13
525 **SILENT APPLAUSE** (GB) 6
605 **SILENT DAY** (GB) 33
207 **SILENT CITY** (GB) 18
211 **SILENT DREAM** (GB) 28
438 **SILENT LUCIDITY** (IRE) 16
124 **SILENT MIRACLE** (IRE) C 29
161 **SILENT SCREAM** (IRE) F 5
60 **SILENT SCREAM** (IRE) C 31
260 **SILENT STAR** (IRE) C 35
231 **SILENT STORM** (IRE) 23
67 **SILENT TRIBUTE** (IRE) F 94
204 **SILENT WHISPER** (IRE) 19
446 **SILEX** (GER) 58
308 **SILISTRA** (GB) 19
346 **SILIVRI** (GB) 21
495 **SILK AFFAIR** (IRE) 23
562 **SILK AND ROSES** (GB) 18
165 **SILK COTTON** (USA) 109
311 **SILK DRUM** (GB) 158
37 **SILK GALLERY** (USA) 55
9 **SILK HALL** (UAE) 36
424 **SILK STAR** (IRE) 27
68 **SILK STOCKINGS** (FR) G 13
444 **SILK STORM** (IRE) 53
20 **SILKEN DALLIANCE** (GB) C 116
126 **SILKEN SANDS** (IRE) 58
163 **SILKEN SPELL** (GB) 33
142 **SILKWOOD TOP** (IRE) 32
371 **SILKY STEPS** (IRE) 28
427 **SILLOTH SPIRIT** (GB) 3
28 **SILLY GILLY** (IRE) 16
530 **SILLY WUPPLE** (GB) 29
347 **SILMI** (GB) 7
264 **SILVABELLA** (IRE) 9
416 **SILVADOR** (GB) 53
239 **SILVANUS** (IRE) 46
27 **SILVER ALIDANTE** (GB) 16
543 **SILVER ARROW** (USA) F 101
337 **SILVER BALLERINA** (GB) 46
533 **SILVER BAY** (GB) 32
609 **SILVER BLESSINGS** (GB) F 25
304 **SILVER BOW** (GB) 39
444 **SILVER BRACELET** (GB) C 104
458 **SILVER BREESE** (GB) 9
442 **SILVER BY NATURE** (GB) 18

290 **SILVER CHARMER** (GB) 9
267 **SILVER DAGGER** (GB) 3
471 **SILVER DEAL** (GB) 6
421 **SILVER DESTINY** (GB) 91
303 **SILVER DIAMOND** (GB) 33
290 **SILVER DREAMER** (IRE) 10
423 **SILVER FEATHER** (IRE) 16
625 **SILVER FOR YOU** (IRE) 120
571 **SILVER GOAL** (GER) 46
419 **SILVER GORA** (GB) 33
130 **SILVER HARRIET** (GB) 9
634 **SILVER HOTSPUR** (GB) 12
164 **SILVER HUT** (USA) C 18
5 **SILVER INNGOT** (IRE) 41
45 **SILVER ISLAND** (GB) 15
583 **SILVER JACK** (IRE) 23
282 **SILVER JARO** (FR) 38
18 **SILVER MISSILE** (GB) 29
52 **SILVER MITZVA** (IRE) 17
55 **SILVER MONT** (IRE) 11
340 **SILVER POINT** (IRE) 5
569 **SILVER PORTRAIT** (IRE) 58
298 **SILVER PRELUDE** (GB) 13
51 **SILVER PROPHET** (IRE) 10
467 **SILVER REGENT** (USA) 29
444 **SILVER RHAPSODY** (USA) F 105
253 **SILVER RIME** (FR) 79
219 **SILVER RING** (GB) 18
247 **SILVER SEDGE** (IRE) 6
548 **SILVER SERG** (GB) 17
625 **SILVER SHOON** (IRE) 121
207 **SILVER SISTER** (GB) 19
506 **SILVER SNITCH** (IRE) 88
332 **SILVER SPINNER** (GB) 143
389 **SILVER SPRUCE** (GB) 39
276 **SILVER STAR** (GB) F 145
506 **SILVER STEEL** (FR) 89
178 **SILVER SUITOR** (IRE) 17
504 **SILVER SYD** (GB) 38
599 **SILVER TERRA** (GB) 13
229 **SILVER TIDE** (USA) 18
178 **SILVER WATERS** (GB) 46
386 **SILVER WEDDING** (GB) F 13
437 **SILVERBURN** (IRE) 120
516 **SILVERDALES** (GB) 55
636 **SILVERGINO** (IRE) 32
121 **SILVERHAY** (GB) 18
29 **SILVERHAY GIRL** (GB) 69
36 **SILVERTONE** (FR) C 77
268 **SILVERY BAY** (GB) 10
259 **SILVO** (NZ) 22
455 **SIMAWA** (IRE) 54
332 **SIMBA SUN** (IRE) 144
466 **SIMBA'S PRIDE** (GB) 38
30 **SIMBAD** (FR) 8
417 **SIMHAL** (GB) 10
269 **SIMILAR FASHION** (GB) 99
554 **SIMON** (GB) 28
446 **SIMONAY** (IRE) 59
437 **SIMONDIUM** (GB) 121
107 **SIMONE MARTINI** (IRE) 53
56 **SIMONIDA** (IRE) G 56
177 **SIMONSIDE** (GB) 21
30 **SIMPLE ACT** (USA) 50
420 **SIMPLE APPROACH** (GB) 93
640 **SIMPLE GIFTS** (GB) 81
153 **SIMPLE GLORY** (IRE) 25
104 **SIMPLIFIED** (GB) 15
84 **SIMPLY BLUE** (GB) 5
438 **SIMPLY MYSTIC** (GB) 17
424 **SIMPLY SENSATIONAL** (IRE) 28
9 **SIMPLY SOOTY** (GB) C 46
629 **SIMPLY ST LUCIA** (GB) 13
539 **SIMPLY THE QUEST** (GB) 6

576 **SIMPSONS GAMBLE** (IRE) 8
186 **SIN CITY** (GB) 51
589 **SINAAF** (GB) 49
404 **SINATAS** (GER) 26
277 **SINBAD THE SAILOR** (GB) 35
601 **SINCHIROKA** (FR) 31
332 **SINDANNA** (GB) 145
263 **SINE QUA NON** (GB) 5
231 **SINEAD OF AGLISH** (IRE) 41
115 **SINGAPORE NICK** (FR) 69
115 **SINGAPORE PINK** (FR) 101
115 **SINGAPORE SPEED** (FR) 70
115 **SINGAPORE TRAMP** (FR) 71
115 **SINGAPORE TROY** (FR) 102
239 **SINGE** (GB) 47
99 **SINGED** (GB) C 100
106 **SINGHALONGTASVEER** (GB) 22
103 **SINGLE PLAYER** (IRE) 35
99 **SINGLE VOTE** (GB) 45
29 **SINGLEB** (IRE) 20
268 **SINGLETON** (GB) F 59
455 **SINNARIYA** (FR) F 112
556 **SINNJICA** (IRE) 22
258 **SION HILL** (IRE) 18
177 **SIR ARTHUR** (IRE) 22
482 **SIR BATHWICK** (IRE) 57
342 **SIR BERE** (FR) 21
444 **SIR BILLY NICK** (GB) 54
453 **SIR BOND** (IRE) 7
571 **SIR BOREAS HAWK** (GB) 47
462 **SIR CLAD** (GB) 31
364 **SIR DAL** (FR) 148
389 **SIR DON** (IRE) 8
260 **SIR DOUGLAS** (GB) 18
137 **SIR DUKE** (IRE) 3
569 **SIR EJAY** (FR) 59
271 **SIR FREDDIE** (GB) 19
382 **SIR GEOFFREY** 40
188 **SIR GERRY** (USA) 66
224 **SIR HARRY COOL** (GB) 14
332 **SIR HARRY ORMESHER** (GB) 146
159 **SIR HARRY ORMESHER** (GB) 25
305 **SIR HAYDN** (GB) 25
359 **SIR IAN** (IRE) 20
336 **SIR IKE** (IRE) 24
239 **SIR ISAAC** (GB) 95
269 **SIR JIMMY SHAND** (GB) 100
558 **SIR JOEY** (GB) 3
212 **SIR KYFFIN'S FOLLY** (GB) 60
343 **SIR LAUGHALOT** (GB) 45
305 **SIR LEONARD** (IRE) 26
576 **SIR LIAM** (USA) 9
81 **SIR LOIN** (GB) 3
411 **SIR MALIK** (IRE) 27
465 **SIR MARK** (IRE) 22
493 **SIR MIKEALE** (GB) 8
53 **SIR MONTY** (USA) 40
571 **SIR MULBERRY HAWK** (GB) 48
447 **SIR NIGHT** (IRE) 10
90 **SIR NOD** (GB) 12
616 **SIR ORPEN** (IRE) 11
355 **SIR PANDY** (IRE) 13
652 **SIR PELINORE** (GB) 2
141 **SIR PETER** (IRE) 43
142 **SIR REMBRANDT** (IRE) 33
279 **SIR RIQUE** (FR) 115
571 **SIR ROYAL** (USA) 91
66 **SIR SANDICLIFFE** (IRE) 37
571 **SIR TANTALLUS HAWK** (GB) 49
142 **SIR WINSTON** (IRE) 34
543 **SIR XAAR** (IRE) 13
518 **SIRAJ** (GB) 11
639 **SIRCOZY** (IRE) 39
364 **SIRE DES IFS** (FR) 102
131 **SIREN PARTY** (GB) 56

109 **VERTUEUX** (FR) 49	496 **VIOLENT VELOCITY** (IRE) 45	589 **WALHALLA** (IRE) 57
474 **VERY COOL** (GB) 116	114 **VIOLET SPRING** (IRE) C 84	640 **WALK TALL** (IRE) 94
331 **VERY GREEN** (FR) 12	285 **VIPER** (GB) 31	444 **WALKAMIA** (FR) C 109
273 **VERY WELL RED** (GB) 17	424 **VIRGIN KING** (IRE) 30	513 **WALKER'S GAL** (USA) F 239
239 **VERY WISE** (GB) 15	143 **VIRGIN STANZA** (USA) F 35	292 **WALKIN AISY** (GB) 95
556 **VESPERS** (IRE) F 27	364 **VIRGINIA DESIR** (FR) 115	410 **WALKING IN MEMPHIS** (IRE) 24
147 **VESTA FLAME** (GB) 5	225 **VIRTUAL** (GB) 86	99 **WALKING TALKING** (GB) 9
229 **VESTAVIA** (IRE) 45	543 **VIRTUALITY** (USA) 49	364 **WALKYRIE** (IRE) 153
580 **VESUVIO** (GB) 17	261 **VIRTUE** (GB) 22	345 **WALL STREET RUNNER** (GB) 12
52 **VETTORENJOY** (GB) 41	163 **VISCAYA** (IRE) 36	573 **WALLS OF JERICHO** (IRE) 51
205 **VEVERKA** (GB) 17	462 **VISCONTE** (GER) 26	421 **WALLY WONDER** (IRE) 106
184 **VHUJON** (IRE) 38	95 **VISCOUNT ROSSINI** (GB) 51	451 **WALRAGNEK** (GB) 25
543 **VIA BORGHESE** (USA) F 113	30 **VISIONS OF CLARITY** (IRE) F 102	638 **WALSINGHAM** (IRE) 83
322 **VIA DEL QUATRO** (IRE) F 13	444 **VISIONS OF JOHANNA** (USA) 60	20 **WALTON HOUSE** (USA) 73
541 **VIABLE** (GB) 18	420 **VISO** (IT) 108	273 **WALTON WAY** (GB) 18
59 **VIAL DE KERDEC** (FR) 16	239 **VITAL LINK** (IRE) 54	397 **WALTZING STAR** (IRE) F 53
638 **VIBE** (GB) 81	178 **VITAL STATISTICS** (GB) 22	556 **WANANGO** (GER) 5
575 **VIBRATO** (USA) 15	365 **VITELLI** (GB) 23	43 **WANDER LUST** (GB) 24
383 **VICARIO** (GB) 92	437 **VITRAY** (FR) 140	166 **WANDERING MINSTRAL** (GB) 5
172 **VICE ADMIRAL** (GB) 67	455 **VITRUVIAN MAN** (GB) 121	571 **WANDERING STRANGER** (GB) C 129
421 **VICE VERSA** (GB) 105	225 **VITUISA** (GB) F 142	400 **WANDLE** (GB) 11
197 **VICENTIO** (GB) 15	253 **VITZNAU** (IRE) 20	513 **WANGOKAYE** (IRE) 240
348 **VICHY** (IRE) 21	513 **VIVA MARIA** (FR) F 236	556 **WANNABE** (GB) F 62
129 **VICIOUS PRINCE** (IRE) 14	178 **VIVA VETTORI** (GB) 23	444 **WANNABE FREE** (GB) 61
632 **VICIOUS WARRIOR** (GB) 7	622 **VIVARINI** (GB) 67	342 **WANNABE GRAND** (IRE) C 25
126 **VICTOIRE FINALE** (GB) F 62	37 **VIVARTIC** (FR) 19	165 **WANNAROCK** (IRE) 62
139 **VICTOR DALY** (IRE) 38	613 **VIVE LES ROUGES** (GB) 36	269 **WANTAGE ROAD** (IRE) 121
569 **VICTOR GRUMPS** (IRE) 70	474 **VIVID IMAGINATION** (IRE) 117	271 **WAQAARR** (GB) 13
41 **VICTOR TRUMPER** (GB) 26	571 **VIVONA HILL** (GB) 60	176 **WAR ANTHEM** (GB) 20
157 **VICTOR VICTORIA** (GB) 74	225 **VIZ** (USA) F 143	181 **WAR ARTIST** (AUS) 5
598 **VICTORBANO** (GB) 69	58 **VLASTA WEINER** (GB) 45	337 **WAR FOOTING** (GB) 55
542 **VICTORIA COLLEGE** (FR) 11	474 **VODKA BLEU** (GB) 118	411 **WAR OF ATTRITION** (IRE) 36
20 **VICTORIA MONTOYA** (GB) 72	5 **VODKA BROOK** (IRE) 45	74 **WAR OF THE ROSES** (IRE) 8
253 **VICTORIA REEL** (GB) 84	37 **VODKA SHOT** (USA) 104	411 **WAR OF THE WORLD** (IRE) 37
589 **VICTORIA REGIA** (IRE) F 100	399 **VOGARTH** (GB) 21	411 **WAR OFFICER** (IRE) 38
399 **VICTORIA SIOUX** (GB) C 57	356 **VOICE OF REASON** (IRE) 62	513 **WAR OFFICER** (USA) 118
174 **VICTORIA'S SECRET** (IRE) C 33	169 **VOIR DIRE** (GB) 10	406 **WAR PENNANT** (GB) 110
352 **VICTORIAN BOUNTY** (GB) 13	302 **VOLE VOLE MONAMOUR** (USA) C 122	257 **WAR PILOT** 107
606 **VICTORIAS GROOM** (GER) 29	639 **VOLIERE** (GB) 13	513 **WAR POWER** (USA) 241
433 **VICTORIET** (GB) C 40	513 **VOLVER** (IRE) 237	394 **WARATAH** (IRE) F 159
259 **VICTORY MILE** (USA) 28	261 **VOLVORETAS RAINBOW** (GB) 37	302 **WARDATI** (GB) 123
638 **VICTORY PARADE** (IRE) 32	269 **VON GALEN** (IRE) 120	178 **WARDEN FIZZ** (GB) 52
341 **VICTORY QUEST** (IRE) 9	441 **VONDOVA** (GB) 15	556 **WARDY'S WONDER** (GB) 28
42 **VICTORY SHOUT** (USA) 43	112 **VOORTREKKER** (GB) 18	67 **WARMING UP** (IRE) 67
627 **VICTREE** (GB) 11	326 **VORTEX** (GB) 16	446 **WARNE** (GB) 66
563 **VIE A DEUX** (FR) 11	332 **VOY POR USTEDES** (IRE) 171	482 **WARNE'S WAY** (IRE) 68
292 **VIEL GLUCK** (IRE) 94	340 **VRAIMENT ROUGE** (FR) 79	31 **WARNERS BAY** (IRE) 7
188 **VIENNA AFFAIR** (GB) 72	340 **VRILISSOS** (FR) 111	399 **WARNING BELLE** (GB) C 59
111 **VIENNCHEE RUN** (GB) 6	311 **VULCAN PILOT** (GB) 135	271 **WARNINGCAMP** (GB) 14
79 **VIEWFORTH** (GB) 4	37 **WAAEDAH** (USA) F 105	340 **WAROLINO** (FR) 112
335 **VIGANO** (IRE) 31	167 **WAAHEJ** (GB) 116	220 **WAROONGA** (FR) C 71
349 **VIKING DREAM** (IRE) G 20	239 **WAARID** (GB) 55	638 **WARPATH** (IRE) 84
506 **VIKING REBEL** (IRE) 99	538 **WABBRAAN** (USA) 23	20 **WARRANTS ATTENTION** (IRE) 120
572 **VIKING SPIRIT** (GB) 22	499 **WADHAM HILL** (GB) 4	246 **WARREN BANK** (GB) 6
640 **VILCABAMBA** (GB) 93	67 **WADLIA** (GB) 66	420 **WARRENS CASTLE** (IRE) 109
556 **VILLA NOVA** (IRE) F 60	649 **WADNAGIN** (IRE) 14	288 **WARRIOR CONQUEST** (GB) 12
399 **VILLAFRANCA** (IRE) F 58	167 **WAHEEBA** (GB) 117	638 **WARRIOR DRIVE** (IRE) 85
575 **VILLAGE STORM** (IRE) 16	493 **WAHHAJ** (GB) 10	200 **WARRIOR KING** (GB) 35
364 **VILLENTIN** (FR) 114	25 **WAHOO SAM** (GB) 13	279 **WARSAW PACT** (IRE) 133
360 **VILLON** (IRE) 43	146 **WAIFER'S LAD** (IRE) 15	220 **WARSAW WALTZ** (GB) 43
89 **VILNA** (USA) 23	452 **WAIN MOUNTAIN** (GB) 46	25 **WASALAT** (USA) 14
176 **VINANDO** (GB) 18	115 **WAIT AND SEE** (FR) 76	165 **WASAN** (GB) 63
176 **VINCENZIO** (IRE) 19	257 **WAIT FOR GREEN** (IRE) 106	495 **WASEYLA** (IRE) F 47
363 **VINCENZIO GALILEI** (USA) 13	513 **WAIT FOR SPRING** (USA) F 238	362 **WASHANGO** (GB) 13
239 **VINEYARD** (GB) 53	347 **WAIT FOR THE LIGHT** (GB) 8	159 **WASTE NOT WANT NOT** (GB) 31
238 **VINGT ET UNE** (FR) F 34	406 **WAIT FOR THE WILL** (USA) 109	371 **WATAMU** (IRE) 15
340 **VINICIO** (FR) 78	109 **WAITING FOR JOHN** (IRE) 13	506 **WATCH MY BACK** (GB) 100
556 **VINICKY** (USA) C 61	225 **WAJAHA** (IRE) 144	245 **WATCH OUT** (GB) 15
467 **VINISTA** (GB) F 59	613 **WAKE UP CALL** (GB) 55	625 **WATCH THE CLOCK** (GB) F 130
406 **VINMIX DE BESSY** (FR) 108	279 **WAKEFUL** (GB) 132	98 **WATCH THE MASTER** (GB) 30
406 **VINO GRIEGO** (FR) 129	574 **WALAMO** (GER) 12	83 **WATCH THIS PLACE** (GB) 74
405 **VINTAGE CLASS** (IRE) 52	356 **WALDENSTROEM** (GER) 63	131 **WATCHFUL** (IRE) 25
262 **VINTAGE FABRIC** (USA) 26	109 **WALDMARK** (FR) F 71	567 **WATCHMAKER** (GB) 12
131 **VIOLA DA BRACCIO** (IRE) C 118	121 **WALDO PEPPER** (IRE) 21	399 **WATER FLOWER** (GB) F 60
531 **VIOLA ROSA** (IRE) 45	583 **WALDO WINCHESTER** (IRE) 29	107 **WATER HEN** (IRE) 101

LATE ENTRIES

MR S. A. EARLE, Warminster
Postal: The Beeches, Deverill Road, Sutton Veny, Warminster, Wiltshire, BA12 7BY
Contacts: PHONE (01985) 841166 FAX (01985) 840474 MOBILE (07850) 350116
E-MAIL simon@simonearleracing.com WEBSITE www.simonearleracing.com

1 ETENDARD INDIEN (FR), 7, b g Selkirk (USA)—Danseuse Indienne (IRE) R. L. Dacombe
2 HEAVENLY PLEASURE (IRE), 9, b m Presenting—Galynn (IRE) P. W. Urquhart
3 KAVI (IRE), 8, ch g Perugino (USA)—Premier Leap (IRE) R. L. Dacombe
4 MISS WIZADORA, 13, ch m Gildoran—Lizzie The Twig
5 SNARK (IRE), 5, b g Cape Cross (IRE)—Agoer Mrs P. L. Bridel
6 ZAIF (IRE), 5, b g Almutawakel—Colourful (FR) Miss R. Wakeford

ADDITIONAL TRAINERS

The following lists have not been supplied from the respective trainers. The lists are as accurate as possible at the time of going to press, and have been arrived at by using information in the public domain.

MR M. S. JOHNSTON, Middleham
Postal: Kingsley House Racing Stables, Middleham, Leyburn, North Yorkshire, DL8 4PH

1 BAAN (USA), 5, ch g Diesis—Madaen (USA)
2 CELTIC STEP, 4, br g Selkirk (USA)—Inchiri
3 CHAMPERY (USA), 4, b g Bahri (USA)—Ice Ballet (IRE)
4 COLORADO RAPID (IRE), 4, b c Barathea (IRE)—Rafting (IRE)
5 DENBERA DANCER (USA), 4, b c Danehill (USA)—Monevassia (USA)
6 DOLLAR CHICK (IRE), 4, b f Dansili—Dollar Bird (IRE)
7 DUBAI'S TOUCH, 4, b c Dr Fong (USA)—Noble Peregrine
8 ERADICATE (IRE), 4, b g Montjeu (IRE)—Coyote
9 GOLDEN QUEST, 7, ch g Rainbow Quest (USA)—Souk (IRE)
10 GREYFRIARS ABBEY, 4, b g Fasliyev (USA)—Mysistra (FR)
11 HEARTHSTEAD MAISON (IRE), 4, b c Peintre Celebre (USA)—Pieds de Plume (FR)
12 LAA RAYB (USA), 4, b c Storm Cat (USA)—Society Lady (USA)
13 LINAS SELECTION, 5, ch h Selkirk (USA)—Lines of Beauty (USA)
14 LOVELACE, 4, b c Royal Applause—Loveleaves
15 LUBERON, 5, b g Fantastic Light (USA)—Luxurious (USA)
16 MIZZLE (USA), 4, ch f Rahy (USA)—Loving Claim (USA)
17 NATCO, 4, b f Cois Na Tine (IRE)—Young Sue
18 PEPPERTREE LANE (IRE), 5, ch h Peintre Celebre (USA)—Salonrolle (IRE)
19 PETROSIAN, 4, b g Sakhee (USA)—Arabis
20 PLANE PAINTER (IRE), 4, b g Orpen (USA)—Flight Sequence
21 PLAYERS PLEASE (USA), 4, ch g Theatrical—Miss Tobacco (USA)
22 PRINCE OF LIGHT, 5, ch g Fantastic Light (USA)—Miss Queen (USA)
23 RECORD BREAKER (IRE), 4, b g In The Wings—Overruled (IRE)
24 ROAD TO LOVE (IRE), 5, ch g Fruits of Love (USA)—Alpine Flair (IRE)
25 SOAPY DANGER, 5, b br h Danzig (USA)—On A Soapbox (USA)
26 SWISS ACT, 4, ch g Act One—Dancing Mirage (IRE)
27 TARTAN TIE, 4, b c Grand Lodge (USA)—Trois Graces (USA)
28 VOODOO MOON, 4, b f Efisio—Lunasa (IRE)
29 WINGED FLIGHT (USA), 4, b g Fusaichi Pegasus (USA)—Tobaranama (IRE)
30 ZAHAM (USA), 4, ch g Silver Hawk (USA)—Guerre Et Paix (USA)

THREE-YEAR-OLDS

31 ACE OF SPIES (IRE), b c Machiavellian (USA)—Nadia
32 AL SAMHA (USA), b c Elusive Quality (USA)—Dubian
33 ALWAYS ATTRACTIVE (IRE), ch f King's Best (USA)—Fife (IRE)
34 ALWAYS BRAVE, ch g Danehill Dancer (IRE)—Digge Park (USA)

MR M. S. JOHNSTON—continued

35 **ALWAYS CERTAIN (USA)**, ch c Giant's Causeway (USA)—Mining Missharriet (USA)
36 **ARCTIC CAPE**, b c Cape Cross (IRE)—Arctic Air
37 **ATABAAS PRIDE**, b c Pivotal—Atabaa (FR)
38 **BAHAMA BAILEYS**, ch g Bahamian Bounty—Baileys Silver (USA)
39 **BARON'S COURT**, ch c Pivotal—Grafin (USA)
40 **BEAUJEU (IRE)**, ch c Singspiel (IRE)—Baya (USA)
41 **BONNY ROSE**, ch f Zaha (CAN)—Marina Park
42 **BOOKISH**, b f Dubai Destination (USA)—Daybook (IRE)
43 **BOOMTOWN**, b c Fantastic Light (USA)—Ville d'amore (USA)
44 **CALL OF DUTY (IRE)**, br c Storming Home—Blushing Barada (USA)
45 **CAMPANOLOGIST (USA)**, b c Kingmambo (USA)—Ring of Music
46 **CAPTAIN WEBB**, br c Storming Home—Criquette
47 **CHAENOMELES (USA)**, b br f Fusaichi Pegasus (USA)—Eliza (USA)
48 **CHANTEUSE DE RUE (IRE)**, b f Street Cry (IRE)—Mt Morna (USA)
49 **CLOVIS**, b c Kingmambo (USA)—Darling Flame (USA)
50 **DEBONNAIRE**, b f Anabaa (USA)—Ultra Finesse (USA)
51 **DETONATOR (IRE)**, b g Fantastic Light (USA)—Narwala
52 **DOUBLE ATTACK (FR)**, b f Peintre Celebre (USA)—Salome's Attack
53 **DRILL SERGEANT**, br c Rock of Gibraltar (IRE)—Dolydille (USA)
54 **EDGBASTON (IRE)**, ch c Pivotal—Pure Spin (USA)
55 **ELLIWAN**, b c Nayef (USA)—Ashbilya (USA)
56 **ENDLESS LUCK (USA)**, b br c Giant's Causeway (USA)—Endless Parade (USA)
57 **ESPECIALLY (IRE)**, b f Fantastic Light (USA)—Esperada (ARG)
58 **FITZROY CROSSING (USA)**, gr c Cozzene (USA)—Jaded Lady (USA)
59 **FLIGHT TO QUALITY**, ch c Where Or When (IRE)—Southern Psychic (USA)
60 **FLY WITH THE STARS (USA)**, ch g Fusaichi Pegasus (USA)—Forest Key (USA)
61 **FORSYTE SAGA**, br f Machiavellian (USA)—First of Many
62 **FUNSEEKER (UAE)**, b br f Halling (USA)—Silversword (FR)
63 **GIANT LOVE (USA)**, ch c Giant's Causeway (USA)—Morning Devotion (USA)
64 **GLITTERING PRIZE (UAE)**, b br f Cadeaux Genereux—Tanami
65 **GRAND FLEET**, b c Green Desert (USA)—Janaat
66 **GRAPES OF WRATH (UAE)**, ch f Halling (USA)—Muscadel
67 **GREEN DIAMOND**, b c Green Desert (USA)—Balisada
68 **HALLINGDAL (UAE)**, b f Halling (USA)—Saik (USA)
69 **HAMPTON COURT**, ch c King's Best (USA)—Rafting (IRE)
70 **HARLEM SHUFFLE (UAE)**, br f Halling (USA)—Badraan (USA)
71 **HAWAASS (USA)**, b c Seeking The Gold (USA)—Sheroog (USA)
72 **HIEROGLYPH**, b f Green Desert (USA)—Mighty Isis (USA)
73 **HOLLOW POINT (IRE)**, b c Cherokee Run (USA)—Squeak
74 **JAADULL**, b c Dubai Destination (USA)—Saafeya (IRE)
75 **JERRY HAMILTON (USA)**, b br c Cherokee Run (USA)—Helsinki
76 **JIM'S BOY (USA)**, ch g Street Cry (IRE)—Ella Eria (FR)
77 **KEENES DAY (FR)**, gr g Daylami (IRE)—Key Academy
78 **LEAMINGTON (USA)**, b f Pleasant Tap (USA)—Muneefa (USA)
79 **LOVE EMPIRE (USA)**, b c Empire Maker (USA)—Gioconda (USA)
80 **LOVE GALORE (IRE)**, b c Galileo (IRE)—Lobmille
81 **LOVE VALENTINE (IRE)**, b f Fruits of Love (USA)—Ridotto
82 **MAFIOSO**, b c Red Ransom (USA)—Lamarque (IRE)
83 **MAZAAYA (USA)**, b f Cozzene (USA)—Mariamme (USA)
84 **MIESKO (USA)**, b c Quiet American (USA)—Polish Style (USA)
85 **MISSIONER (USA)**, b c Rahy (USA)—Magic Mission
86 **MOOTHIR (USA)**, gr c Elusive Quality (USA)—Alattrah (USA)
87 **MUZMIN (USA)**, b br c Seeking The Gold (USA)—In On The Secret (CAN)
88 **NAOMH GEILEIS (USA)**, ch f Grand Slam (USA)—St Aye (USA)
89 **NAWAKHIDA (USA)**, ch c Mr Greeley (USA)—Silvester Lady
90 **NEYRAAN**, b f Lujain (USA)—Zaynaat
91 **OBERLIN (USA)**, ch c Gone West (USA)—Balanchine (USA)
92 **PARK ROYAL (UAE)**, b br f Cape Cross (IRE)—Shbakni (USA)
93 **PEARL TRADER (IRE)**, ch f Dubai Destination (USA)—Vintage Tipple (IRE)
94 **PENTATHLON (IRE)**, b g Storming Home—Nawaiet (USA)
95 **PIERMARINI**, b c Singspiel (IRE)—Allespagne (USA)
96 **PLANETARIUM**, gr c Fantastic Light (USA)—Karsiyaka (IRE)
97 **PRAGMATISM**, b c Kingmambo (USA)—Sheer Reason (USA)
98 **PREMIER DANSEUR (IRE)**, b c Noverre (USA)—Destiny Dance (USA)
99 **RAMATNI**, b f Green Desert (USA)—Wardat Allayl (USA)
100 **RED AND WHITE (IRE)**, b f Red Ransom (USA)—Candice (IRE)

MR M. S. JOHNSTON—continued

101 **ROBBY BOBBY,** ch c Selkirk (USA)—Dancing Mirage (IRE)
102 **SCREEN STAR (IRE),** gr f Tobougg (IRE)—Actoris (USA)
103 **SHAFTESBURY (IRE),** b g Lomitas—Vivid Concert (IRE)
104 **SIGNORA (IRE),** ch f Indian Ridge—Lady Catherine
105 **SILENT MASTER (USA),** b c Cherokee Run (USA)—Polent
106 **SIR JOHN LILLEY (USA),** ch c Gulch—Brackish (USA)
107 **SMOOTH SOVEREIGN (IRE),** ch c King's Best (USA)—Mellow Park (IRE)
108 **SOMERSET FALLS (UAE),** b f Red Ransom (USA)—Dunnes River (IRE)
109 **SOVIET (IRE),** b c Danehill Dancer (IRE)—Miss Sacha (IRE)
110 **SOXY DOXY (IRE),** ch f Hawk Wing (USA)—Feather Bride (IRE)
111 **STAGECOACH TOPAZ (USA),** b g Stravinsky (USA)—Indian Fashion (USA)
112 **SUZI SPENDS (IRE),** b f Royal Applause—Clever Clogs
113 **TAJWEED (IRE),** ch c Pivotal—Mannakea (USA)
114 **TAWZEEA (IRE),** ch c Cadeaux Genereux—Kismah
115 **TERRACOS DO PINHAL,** b c Selkirk (USA)—Sister Bluebird
116 **TOUCHDOWN,** b c Singspiel (IRE)—Salim Toto
117 **TOURISM (IRE),** b c Dubai Destination (USA)—Ribot's Guest (IRE)
118 **TRAITOR'S GATE,** b g Machiavellian (USA)—Wilayif (USA)
119 **UPPER CLASS (IRE),** b c Fantastic Light (USA)—Her Ladyship
120 **VICE CONSUL,** b c In The Wings—Wajina
121 **VISCOUNTESS (IRE),** b f Green Desert (USA)—Maria Isabella (USA)
122 **YES MR PRESIDENT (IRE),** b c Montjeu (IRE)—Royals Special (IRE)
123 **ZAKHAAREF,** gr c Daylami (IRE)—Shahaamah (IRE)

TWO-YEAR-OLDS

124 **AKBABEND,** b c 30/3 Refuse To Bend (IRE)—Akdariya (IRE) (Shirley Heights) (13000)
125 Ch c 24/4 Trans Island—Alpine Flair (IRE) (Tirol) (32174)
126 **ATEEB,** b c 8/2 Red Ransom (USA)—Design Perfection (USA) (Diesis) (180000)
127 B c 28/4 Anabaa (USA)—Capistrano Day (USA) (Diesis) (62000)
128 Gr ro c 19/2 Giant's Causeway (USA)—Fountain Lake (USA) (Vigors (USA)) (63168)
129 **GREEN DYNASTY (IRE),** ch c 10/2 Giant's Causeway (USA)—Rose Gypsy (Green Desert (USA)) (70785)
130 **LOVE PEGASUS,** b br c 27/1 Fusaichi Pegasus (USA)—Take Charge Lady (USA) (Dehere (USA)) (41302)
131 **MAKHAALEB (USA),** ch c 2/3 Mr Greeley (USA)—Guerre Et Paix (USA) (Soviet Star (USA)) (218658)
132 **MANNLICHEN,** ch c 3/2 Selkirk (USA)—Robe Chinoise (Robellino (USA)) (65000)
133 **PRIDE OF KINGS,** b c 31/3 King's Best (USA)—Aunty Mary (Common Grounds) (16000)
134 **TARZAN (IRE),** ch c 16/3 Spinning World (USA)—Run To Jane (IRE) (Doyoun) (135000)

MR A. P. O'BRIEN, Cashel
Postal: **Ballydoyle Stables, Cashel, Co. Tipperary, Ireland**

1 **ABRAHAM LINCOLN (IRE),** 4, b c Danehill (USA)—Moon Drop
2 **ASTRONOMER ROYAL (USA),** 4, b c Danehill (USA)—Sheepscot (USA)
3 **DUKE OF MARMALADE (IRE),** 4, b c Danehill (USA)—Love Me True (USA)
4 **HONOLULU (IRE),** 4, b c Montjeu (IRE)—Cerulean Sky (IRE)
5 **HONOURED GUEST (IRE),** 4, b c Danehill (USA)—Wind Silence (USA)
6 **MACARTHUR,** 4, b c Montjeu (IRE)—Out West (USA)
7 **MAHLER,** 4, b c Galileo (IRE)—Rainbow Goddess
8 **MOUNT NELSON (IRE),** 4, b c Rock of Gibraltar (IRE)—Independence
9 **PEEPING FAWN (USA),** 4, b f Danehill (USA)—Maryinsky (IRE)
10 **PORT OF SPAIN (USA),** 4, b c Danehill (USA)—Dietrich (USA)
11 **RED ROCK CANYON (IRE),** 4, b c Rock of Gibraltar (IRE)—Imagine (IRE)
12 **SEPTIMUS (IRE),** 5, b h Sadler's Wells (USA)—Caladira (IRE)
13 **SOLDIER OF FORTUNE (IRE),** 4, b c Galileo (USA)—Affianced (IRE)
14 **US RANGER (USA),** 4, B C Danzig (USA)—My Annette (USA)
15 **YEATS (IRE),** 7, b h Sadler's Wells (USA)—Lyndonville (USA)

THREE-YEAR-OLDS

16 **ACHILL ISLAND (IRE),** b br c Sadler's Wells (USA)—Prawn Cocktail (USA)
17 **ALESSANDRO VOLTA,** b c Montjeu (IRE)—Ventura Highway (USA)
18 **BASHKIROV,** ch c Galileo (IRE)—Tina Heights
19 **CALABASH (IRE),** b c Sadler's Wells (USA)—Multimara (USA)
20 **COACH AND FOUR (USA),** b c Storm Cat (USA)—Tacha (USA)
21 **DECREE (IRE),** b c Pivotal—Truly A Dream (IRE)
22 **EGYPTIAN HERO (USA),** b c Danzig (USA)—Al Theraab (USA)

MR A. P. O'BRIEN—continued

23 **FROZEN FIRE (GER)**, b c Montjeu (IRE)—Flamingo Sea (USA)
24 **GENTLE ON MY MIND (IRE)**, b f Sadler's Wells (USA)—Ezilla (IRE)
25 **GEORGEBERNARDSHAW (IRE)**, b c Danehill Dancer (IRE)—Khamseh
26 **GIANT AMONG MEN (USA)**, ch c Giant's Causeway (USA)—Dissemble
27 **GREAT BARRIER REEF (USA)**, ch c Mr Greeley (USA)—Song to Remember (USA)
28 **GREAT RUMPUSCAT (USA)**, b c Storm Cat (USA)—Monevassia (USA)
29 **GREATWALLOFCHINA (USA)**, b br c Kingmambo (USA)—Dietrich (USA)
30 **GREEK MYTHOLOGY (USA)**, b c Mr Greeley (USA)—Tell Me Now (USA)
31 **HALFWAY TO HEAVEN (IRE)**, gr f Pivotal—Cassandra Go (IRE)
32 **HENRYTHENAVIGATOR (USA)**, b br c Kingmambo (USA)—Sequoyah (IRE)
33 **HINDU KUSH (IRE)**, b c Sadler's Wells (USA)—Tambora
34 **HOLD ME LOVE ME (IRE)**, b f Sadler's Wells (USA)—Jude
35 **HONORIA (IRE)**, b f Sadler's Wells (USA)—Tedarshana
36 **ICE QUEEN (IRE)**, b f Danehill Dancer (IRE)—Wadud
37 **JANE AUSTEN (IRE)**, b br f Galileo (IRE)—Harasava (FR)
38 **JUPITER PLUVIUS (USA)**, b c Johannesburg (USA)—Saratoga Honey (USA)
39 **KING OF ROME (IRE)**, b c Montjeu (IRE)—Amizette (USA)
40 **KING OF THE NILE**, b c Oasis Dream—Grail (IRE)
41 **KING OF WESTPHALIA (USA)**, b c Kingmambo (USA)—Quarter Moon (IRE)
42 **KINGDOM OF NAPLES (USA)**, b c Sadler's Wells (USA)—Inkling (IRE)
43 **KITTY MATCHAM (IRE)**, b f Rock of Gibraltar (IRE)—Imagine (IRE)
44 **LISTEN (IRE)**, b f Sadler's Wells (USA)—Brigid (USA)
45 **LOVE TO DANCE (IRE)**, b f Sadler's Wells (USA)—Lagrion (USA)
46 **LUCIFER SAM (USA)**, b c Storm Cat (USA)—Rafina (USA)
47 **MIKHAIL FOKINE (IRE)**, b c Sadler's Wells (USA)—Rain Flower (IRE)
48 **MINNEAPOLIS (IRE)**, b c Sadler's Wells (USA)—Teggiano (IRE)
49 **MOONSTONE**, b f Dalakhani (IRE)—Solo de Lune (IRE)
50 **MY DARK ROSALEEN**, b f Sadler's Wells (USA)—Danilova (USA)
51 **NATIONAL HERITAGE**, b c High Chaparral (USA)—French Quartet (IRE)
52 **NEW ZEALAND (IRE)**, ch c Galileo (IRE)—Worlds Apart
53 **OBSERVATION POST (USA)**, b c Johannesburg (USA)—Bullville Belle (USA)
54 **ONE GREAT CAT (USA)**, br c Storm Cat (USA)—Blissful (USA)
55 **OPTIMO MAXIMO (USA)**, b c Kingmambo (USA)—Legend Maker (IRE)
56 **PLAN (USA)**, ch c Storm Cat (USA)—Spain (USA)
57 **POET**, b c Pivotal—Hyabella
58 **PSALM (IRE)**, b f Sadler's Wells (USA)—Litani River (USA)
59 **QUEEN OF THE NIGHT**, b f Sadler's Wells (USA)—Gift of The Night (USA)
60 **SAIL (IRE)**, b f Sadler's Wells (USA)—Pieds de Plume (FR)
61 **SAVETHISDANCEFORME (IRE)**, b f Danehill Dancer (IRE)—Bex (USA)
62 **SHOWCALL (USA)**, b f Kingmambo (USA)—Butterfly Cove (USA)
63 **SLIGO**, b c Sadler's Wells (USA)—Arabesque
64 **SOINLOVEWITHYOU (USA)**, b f Sadler's Wells (USA)—Love Me True (USA)
65 **SWEET SIXTEEN (IRE)**, b f Sadler's Wells (USA)—User Friendly
66 **TALE OF TWO CITIES (IRE)**, b c Sadler's Wells (USA)—Kasora (IRE)
67 **THE BOGBERRY (USA)**, ch c Hawk Wing (USA)—Lahinch (IRE)
68 **TROJAN WARRIOR (USA)**, b c Giant's Causeway (USA)—Hold to Fashion (USA)
69 **VIVALDI (IRE)**, b c Montjeu (IRE)—Parvenue (FR)
70 **WASHINGTON IRVING (IRE)**, b c Montjeu (IRE)—Shouk
71 **WASSILY KANDINSKY**, b c Montjeu (IRE)—Lady Storm (IRE)
72 **WILLIAM HOGARTH**, b c High Chaparral (USA)—Mountain Holly
73 **WINDSOR PALACE (IRE)**, b c Danehill Dancer (IRE)—Simaat (USA)
74 **YOU'RESOTHRILLING (USA)**, br f Storm Cat (USA)—Mariah's Storm (USA)
75 **ZULU CHIEF (USA)**, b c Fusaichi Pegasus (USA)—La Lorgnette (CAN)

TWO-YEAR-OLDS

76 84 Ch c 4/4 Danehill Dancer (IRE)—Ahdaab (USA) (Rahy (USA))
77 **AIGLEMONT**, ch c 8/3 Dansili—Abbatiale (FR) (Kaldoun (FR)) (611325)
78 B c 26/4 Montjeu (IRE)—Al Saqiya (USA) (Woodman (USA))
79 Gr c 17/3 Montjeu (IRE)—Alabastrine (Green Desert (USA))
80 B c 28/3 Galileo (IRE)—Amory (GER) (Goofalik (USA))
81 B c 11/4 Hawk Wing (USA)—Announcing Peace (Danehill (USA)) (225224)
82 Gr c 4/2 Dalakhani (IRE)—Bella Lambada (Lammtarra (USA)) (1000000)
83 B c 6/4 Galileo (IRE)—Belle Allemande (CAN) (Royal Academy (USA)) (310000)
84 Ch c 6/3 Giant's Causeway (USA)—Better Than Honour (USA) (Deputy Minister (CAN))
85 B c 5/5 Sadler's Wells (USA)—Caladira (IRE) (Darshaan) (140000)

MR A. P. O'BRIEN—continued

 86 B c 11/4 Montjeu (IRE)—Check Bid (USA) (Grey Dawn II) (96524)
 87 B c 13/4 Galileo (IRE)—Clara Bow (FR) (Top Ville) (900900)
 88 Ch c 4/3 Galileo (IRE)—Corrine (IRE) (Spectrum (IRE)) (353924)
 89 B c 11/5 Montjeu (IRE)—Crafty Example (USA) (Crafty Prospector (USA)) (289575)
 90 B c 28/3 Montjeu (IRE)—Dance Desire (IRE) (Caerleon (USA)) (238095)
 91 B c 28/3 Montjeu (IRE)—Dixielake (IRE) (Lake Coniston (IRE))
 92 B c 31/3 Kingmambo (USA)—Elegant As Always (USA) (Nashwan (USA))
 93 Ch c 22/1 Danehill Dancer (IRE)—Elite Guest (IRE) (Be My Guest (USA))
 94 B c 5/3 El Prado (IRE)—Favorite Funtime (USA) (Seeking The Gold (USA)) (364431)
 95 Ch c 14/2 Galileo (IRE)—Four Green (FR) (Green Tune (USA))
 96 B c 29/1 Montjeu (IRE)—Funsie (FR) (Saumarez)
 97 B c 10/2 Sadler's Wells (USA)—Grecian Bride (IRE) (Groom Dancer (USA)) (380000)
 98 B c 10/2 Galileo (IRE)—Green Rosy (USA) (Green Dancer (USA)) (375000)
 99 Ch c 22/4 Danehill Dancer (IRE)—Greenvera (USA) (Riverman (USA))
100 B c 20/3 Montjeu (IRE)—Gryada (Shirley Heights)
101 Ch c 13/5 Galileo (IRE)—Hishi Lover (USA) (Pleasant Colony (USA)) (170068)
102 B c 27/3 Sadler's Wells (USA)—I'll Get Along (USA) (Smile (USA))
103 B br c 3/2 Kingmambo (USA)—Imperial Beauty (USA) (Imperial Ballet (IRE))
104 B c 9/3 Sadler's Wells (USA)—Kasora (IRE) (Darshaan)
105 B c 24/4 Sadler's Wells (USA)—Katiyfa (Auction Ring (USA)) (270269)
106 B c 19/5 Fusaichi Pegasus (USA)—La Lorgnette (CAN) (Val de L'orne (FR))
107 Ch c 26/4 Giant's Causeway (USA)—Legend Maker (IRE) (Sadler's Wells (USA))
108 B c 4/5 Montjeu (IRE)—Litani River (USA) (Irish River (FR))
109 B c 5/5 Sadler's Wells (USA)—Lyrical (Shirley Heights)
110 B c 5/4 Montjeu (IRE)—Maskaya (IRE) (Machiavellian (USA)) (418275)
111 Ch f 14/4 Hawk Wing (USA)—Medicosma (USA) (The Minstrel (CAN)) (9008)
112 B c 19/2 Montjeu (IRE)—Miletrian (IRE) (Marju (IRE)) (128700)
113 B c 4/2 Montjeu (IRE)—Millennium Dash (Nashwan (USA)) (500000)
114 B c 6/4 Sadler's Wells (USA)—Miss Satamixa (FR) (Linamix (FR)) (160000)
115 B c 21/2 Danehill Dancer (IRE)—Mood Swings (IRE) (Shirley Heights) (340000)
116 B c 18/2 Sadler's Wells (USA)—Multimara (USA) (Arctic Tern (USA))
117 B br c 18/4 Giant's Causeway (USA)—Myth (USA) (Ogygian (USA))
118 Ch c 30/4 Storm Cat (USA)—Mythomania (USA) (Nureyev (USA)) (826044)
119 B c 16/2 Galileo (IRE)—Onereuse (Sanglamore (USA)) (418275)
120 B c 12/4 Montjeu (IRE)—Park Crystal (IRE) (Danehill (USA)) (370012)
121 B c 10/3 Galileo (IRE)—Patacake Patacake (USA) (Bahri (USA))
122 B c 4/5 Sadler's Wells (USA)—Peony (Lion Cavern (USA)) (380000)
123 B c 16/3 Montjeu (IRE)—Pescia (IRE) (Darshaan)
124 B c 25/3 Danehill Dancer (IRE)—Pharapache (USA) (Lyphard (USA))
125 B c 19/2 Storm Cat (USA)—Quarter Moon (IRE) (Sadler's Wells (USA))
126 B c 26/3 Dansili—Royal Flame (IRE) (Royal Academy (USA)) (140000)
127 B c 8/4 Sadler's Wells (USA)—Sabria (USA) (Miswaki (USA))
128 B c 30/1 Sadler's Wells (USA)—Shouk (Shirley Heights)
129 B c 13/2 Galileo (IRE)—Silver Colours (USA) (Silver Hawk (USA)) (750000)
130 B c 26/4 High Chaparral (IRE)—Sitara (Salse (USA))
131 Br c 23/2 Statue of Liberty (USA)—Skidmore Girl (USA) (Vaguely Noble) (27026)
132 B c 4/3 Sadler's Wells (USA)—Solo de Lune (IRE) (Law Society (USA))
133 B c 3/4 Montjeu (IRE)—Someone Special (Habitat) (200000)
134 B c 15/5 Rock of Gibraltar (IRE)—Sudden Hope (FR) (Darshaan) (7721)
135 B c 16/5 Sadler's Wells (USA)—Sweet Gypsy Rose (IRE) (Darshaan)
136 B c 16/5 Danehill Dancer (IRE)—Teslemi (USA) (Ogygian (USA))
137 B c 25/5 Sadler's Wells (USA)—Welsh Love (Ela-Mana-Mou) (244529)
138 B c 8/2 Montjeu (IRE)—Zivania (IRE) (Shernazar) (600000)

SIR M. STOUTE, Newmarket
Postal: **Freemason Lodge, Bury Road, Newmarket, Suffolk, CB8 7BY**

 1 **ALLEGRETTO (IRE)**, 5, ch m Galileo (IRE)—Alleluia
 2 **ARABIAN GULF**, 4, b c Sadler's Wells (USA)—Wince
 3 **ASK**, 5, b h Sadler's Wells (USA)—Request
 4 **AUDIT (IRE)**, 4, b g Fusaichi Pegasus (USA)—Amethyst (IRE)
 5 **CABINET (IRE)**, 4, b c Grand Lodge (USA)—Passe Passe (USA)
 6 **DANCE OF LIGHT (USA)**, 4, b f Sadler's Wells (USA)—Flamelight (IRE)
 7 **DISTINCTION (IRE)**, 9, b g Danehill (USA)—Ivy Leaf (IRE)
 8 **GALACTIC STAR**, 5, ch h Galileo (IRE)—Balisada

SIR M. STOUTE—continued

9 **GREAT HAWK (USA)**, 5, b h El Prado (IRE)—Laser Hawk (USA)
10 **GULF EXPRESS (USA)**, 4, b c Langfuhr (CAN)—Wassifa
11 **HEAVEN SENT**, 5, ch m Pivotal—Heavenly Ray (USA)
12 **HI CALYPSO (IRE)**, 4, b f In The Wings—Threefold (USA)
13 **KING'S EVENT (USA)**, 4, b c Dynaformer (USA)—Magic of Love
14 **LANG SHINING (IRE)**, 4, ch c Dr Fong (USA)—Dragnet (IRE)
15 **MARAAHEL (IRE)**, 7, b h Alzao (USA)—Nasanice (IRE)
16 **MOUNTAIN HIGH (IRE)**, 6, b h Danehill (USA)—Hellenic
17 **PAPAL BULL**, 5, b h Montjeu (IRE)—Mialuna
18 **PRAXITELES (IRE)**, 4, b c Sadler's Wells (USA)—Hellenic
19 **PROMISING LEAD**, 4, b f Danehill (USA)—Arrive
20 **QUEEN'S BEST**, 5, b m King's Best (USA)—Cloud Castle
21 **RED GALA**, 5, b h Sinndar (IRE)—Red Camellia
22 **SPANISH MOON (USA)**, 4, b c El Prado (IRE)—Shining Bright
23 **WINTER SUNRISE**, 4, b f Pivotal—Winter Solstice

THREE-YEAR-OLDS

24 **ADVERSITY**, b c Oasis Dream—Tuxford Hideaway
25 **ALBARAARI**, b f Green Desert (USA)—Brigitta (IRE)
26 **ALMAJD (IRE)**, b c Marju (IRE)—Irish Valley (USA)
27 **ALMONAFIS (IRE)**, gr c Sadler's Wells (USA)—Sulaalah (IRE)
28 **ALSERAAJ (USA)**, ch f El Prado (IRE)—Barzah (IRE)
29 **ASCOT LIME**, ch c Pivotal—Hector's Girl
30 **AUTOCUE**, b c Dansili—Sing For Fame (USA)
31 **BUGAKU**, b c Montjeu (IRE)—Bryony Brind (IRE)
32 **CERTAIN PROMISE (USA)**, b f El Prado (IRE)—Shining Bright
33 **CITY STABLE (IRE)**, b c Machiavellian (USA)—Rainbow City (IRE)
34 **COLONY (IRE)**, b c Statue of Liberty (USA)—Funoon (IRE)
35 **CONDUIT (IRE)**, ch c Dalakhani (IRE)—Well Head (IRE)
36 **CONFIDENCE TRICK (USA)**, ch c Rahy (USA)—Hiaam (USA)
37 **CONFRONT**, b c Nayef (USA)—Contiguous (USA)
38 **CRITERION**, b g Dr Fong (USA)—Film Script
39 **CRYSTAL CAPELLA**, b f Cape Cross (IRE)—Crystal Star
40 **DIAMOND IN DEMAND (IRE)**, ch c Danehill Dancer (IRE)—Sought Out (IRE)
41 **DOCTOR FREMANTLE**, b c Sadler's Wells (USA)—Summer Breeze
42 **DR FAUSTUS (IRE)**, gr c Sadler's Wells (USA)—Requesting
43 **DRUM MAJOR (IRE)**, b c Sadler's Wells (USA)—Phantom Gold
44 **E MAJOR**, ch c Singspiel (IRE)—Crystal Cavern (USA)
45 **EPHORUS (IRE)**, b c Galileo (IRE)—No Frills (IRE)
46 **FILIGREE LACE (USA)**, ch f Seeking The Gold (USA)—Yafill (USA)
47 **FLAWED GENIUS**, b c Fasliyev (USA)—Talented
48 **FRENCH RIVIERA**, b c Montjeu (IRE)—Arietta's Way (IRE)
49 **HERITAGE COAST (USA)**, b f Dynaformer (USA)—Bristol Channel
50 **HOUGHTON (IRE)**, b c Sadler's Wells (USA)—Love And Affection (USA)
51 **INSTITUTE**, ch c Pivotal—Constitute (USA)
52 **KENSINGTON OVAL**, b c Sadler's Wells (USA)—Request
53 **KINGDOM OF FIFE**, b c Kingmambo (USA)—Fairy Godmother
54 **LAMBDA (USA)**, b f Empire Maker (USA)—South of Saturn (USA)
55 **LAUGHTER (IRE)**, b f Sadler's Wells (USA)—Smashing Review (USA)
56 **LINDELAAN (USA)**, ch f Rahy (USA)—Crystal Symphony (USA)
57 **MAIN AIM**, b c Oasis Dream—Orford Ness
58 **MARAMBA (USA)**, ch f Hussonet (USA)—Coco (USA)
59 **MARCO POLO (USA)**, b c Kingmambo (USA)—Guiza (USA)
60 **MEETHAAQ (USA)**, b c Kingmambo (USA)—New Harmony (USA)
61 **MISTRESS GREELEY (USA)**, ch f Mr Greeley (USA)—My Reem (USA)
62 **NAVAL REVIEW (USA)**, b br c Storm Cat (USA)—Arutua (USA)
63 **PATKAI (IRE)**, ch c Indian Ridge—Olympienne (IRE)
64 **PERFECT STRIDE**, b c Oasis Dream—First
65 **QUOTATION**, b f Medicean—Eloquent
66 **SEASIDER**, b c Zamindar (USA)—Esplanade
67 **SELSEY**, b f Selkirk (USA)—Louella (USA)
68 **SNOWY INDIAN**, b f Indian Ridge—Snow Princess (IRE)
69 **SOVEREIGN'S HONOUR (USA)**, ch f Kingmambo (USA)—Chiming (IRE)
70 **STRIVING (IRE)**, b br f Danehill Dancer (IRE)—Wannabe
71 **TAJAAWEED (USA)**, br c Dynaformer (USA)—Uforia (USA)

SIR M. STOUTE—continued

72 **TANWEER (USA)**, ch c Seeking The Gold (USA)—Fitted Crown (USA)
73 **TARTAN BEARER (IRE)**, ch c Spectrum (IRE)—Highland Gift (IRE)
74 **TOMORROW'S WORLD (IRE)**, b f Machiavellian (USA)—Follow That Dream
75 **UCETEK (IRE)**, b f Kalanisi (IRE)—Dragnet (IRE)
76 **VISIT**, b f Oasis Dream—Arrive
77 **VOICE COACH (IRE)**, ch c Alhaarth (IRE)—Drama Class (IRE)
78 **WARRINGAH**, ch c Galileo (IRE)—Threefold (USA)
79 **WINNERS CHANT (IRE)**, b f Dalakhani (IRE)—Delilah (IRE)

TWO-YEAR-OLDS

80 **ALBAASHA (IRE)**, ch c 27/1 Lemon Drop Kid (USA)—Cozy Maria (Cozzene (USA)) (220000)
81 **CUSTODY (IRE)**, b c 21/1 Fusaichi Pegasus (USA)—Shahtoush (IRE) (Alzao (USA)) (65000)
82 **DANCOURT (IRE)**, b c 5/4 Cadeaux Genereux—Stage Struck (IRE) (Sadler's Wells (USA))
83 **DANIEL DEFOE (USA)**, ch c 21/2 Smart Strike (CAN)—Dear Daughter (Polish Precedent (USA))
84 B c 22/3 Montjeu (IRE)—Grain of Gold (Mr Prospector (USA)) (220000)
85 **HARBINGER**, b c 12/3 Dansili—Penang Pearl (FR) (Bering) (180000)
86 **HARVEST SONG (IRE)**, b c 5/4 Sadler's Wells (USA)—La Mouline (IRE) (Nashwan (USA)) (290000)
87 B c 6/2 Montjeu (IRE)—Hector's Girl (Hector Protector (USA))
88 **HIGHLAND GLEN**, b c 25/1 Montjeu (IRE)—Daring Aim (Daylami (IRE))
89 **ITHINKBEST**, b c 15/2 King's Best (USA)—Monturani (IRE) (Indian Ridge) (200000)
90 **JEDI**, ch c 9/2 Pivotal—Threefold (USA) (Gulch (USA))
91 **KING'S SONG (IRE)**, ch c 30/3 Indian Ridge—Alleluia (Caerleon (USA)) (386100)
92 **METRAASH**, ch c 2/2 Dubai Destination (USA)—Ballymore Celebre (IRE) (Peintre Celebre (USA)) (185000)
93 **MOHALHAL (IRE)**, b c 5/3 Cape Cross (IRE)—Madame Dubois (Legend of France (USA)) (210000)
94 **NAMIBIAN ORATOR (IRE)**, br c 31/3 Cape Cross (IRE)—Drama Class (IRE) (Caerleon (USA))
95 B c 21/2 Danehill Dancer (IRE)—On Fair Stage (IRE) (Sadler's Wells (USA)) (170000)
96 **PIED PIPER**, b c 2/3 Pivotal—Flight of Fancy (Sadler's Wells (USA))
97 **RAWAAJ**, gr c 13/3 Linamix (FR)—Inaaq (Lammtarra (USA))
98 B c 20/2 Pivotal—Red Tulle (USA) (A P Indy (USA)) (165000)
99 **SAPTAPADI (IRE)**, ch c 18/3 Indian Ridge—Olympienne (Sadler's Wells (USA))
100 Ch c 18/2 Kris Kin (USA)—Shell Garland (USA) (Sadler's Wells (USA))
101 B br c 19/3 Dynaformer (USA)—Surf N Sand (USA) (Boston Harbor (USA)) (218658)
102 **TEMPLAR KNIGHT**, b c 16/1 Montjeu (IRE)—Vas Y Carla (USA) (Gone West (USA))
103 **THESPIS OF ICARIA (IRE)**, b c 28/3 Sadler's Wells (USA)—Hellenic (Darshaan)

MR SAEED BIN SUROOR, Newmarket
Postal: **Godolphin Office, Snailwell Road, Newmarket, Suffolk, CB8 7YE**

1 **AFRASHAD (USA)**, 6, ch h Smoke Glacken (USA)—Flo White (USA)
2 **AL SHEMALI**, 4, ch c Medicean—Bathilde (IRE)
3 **AMARNA (USA)**, 4, b c Danzig (USA)—Mysterial (USA)
4 **ARMY OF ANGELS (IRE)**, 6, ch g King's Best (USA)—Angelic Sounds (IRE)
5 **BEST ALIBI (IRE)**, 5, b h King's Best (USA)—Chauncy Lane (USA)
6 **BEST NAME**, 5, b h King's Best (USA)—Flawly
7 **BLACKAT BLACKITTEN (IRE)**, 4, CH C Inchinor—Tara's Girl (IRE)
8 **BLUE KSAR (FR)**, 5, b h Anabaa (USA)—Delicieuse Lady
9 **BOOK OF MUSIC (IRE)**, 5, b h Sadler's Wells (USA)—Novelette
10 **BOSCOBEL**, 4, ch c Halling (USA)—Dunnes River (USA)
11 **BYGONE DAYS**, 7, ch g Desert King (USA)—May Light
12 **CALABASH COVE (USA)**, 4, ch c Rahy (USA)—I Need A Holiday (USA)
13 **CHERRY MIX (FR)**, 7, gr h Linamix (FR)—Cherry Moon (USA)
14 **COCOA BEACH (CHI)**, 4, b br f Doneraile Court (USA)—Visionera (CHI)
15 **COLORADO RAPID (IRE)**, 4, b c Barathea (USA)—Rafting (USA)
16 **COUNTERPUNCH**, 5, ch g Halling (USA)—Evil Empire (GER)
17 **CREACHADOIR (IRE)**, 4, b c King's Best (USA)—Sadima (IRE)
18 **CRIME SCENE (IRE)**, 5, b g Royal Applause—Crime (USA)
19 **DIJEERR (USA)**, 4, b c Danzig (USA)—Sharp Minister (CAN)
20 **EA (USA)**, 4, br c Dynaformer (USA)—Enthused (USA)
21 **EASTERN ANTHEM (IRE)**, 4, b c Singspiel (IRE)—Kazzia (GER)
22 **EMIRATES SKYLINE (USA)**, 5, b h Sunday Silence (USA)—The Caretaker
23 **EMIRATES TO DUBAI (USA)**, 5, ch h Storm Cat (USA)—Morn of Song (USA)
24 **EMPIRE DAY (UAE)**, 4, ch c Lomitas—Evil Empire (GER)
25 **ENVISAGE (IRE)**, 4, b g Singspiel (IRE)—Truly A Dream (IRE)
26 **EXTREME MEASURES**, 5, b h Montjeu (IRE)—Fade

MR SAEED BIN SUROOR—continued

27 **FAIRMILE**, 6, b g Spectrum (IRE)—Juno Marlowe (IRE)
28 **FAMILIAR TERRITORY**, 5, br h Cape Cross (IRE)—Forever Fine (USA)
29 **FIESTA LADY (ARG)**, 4, b f Southern Halo (USA)—Fiereze (ARG)
30 **FOLK OPERA (IRE)**, 4, ch f Singspiel (IRE)—Skiphall
31 **FORMAL DECREE (GER)**, 5, b br g Diktat—Formida (FR)
32 **GLEN NEVIS (USA)**, 4, b br c Gulch (USA)—Beating The Buzz (IRE)
33 **GOLD SOVEREIGN (IRE)**, 4, b c King's Best (USA)—Sassenach (IRE)
34 **GONGIDAS**, 4, b c Big Shuffle (USA)—Gonfalon
35 **GRAVITAS**, 5, ch h Mark of Esteem (IRE)—Bombazine (IRE)
36 **GREEK RENAISSANCE (IRE)**, 5, b h Machiavellian (USA)—Athene (IRE)
37 **IMPERIAL STAR (IRE)**, 5, br h Fantastic Light (USA)—Out West (USA)
38 **IMPERIALISTA (BRZ)**, 5, b h Voando Baixo (BRZ)—Zarumba Bis (BRZ)
39 **JALIL (USA)**, 4, br c Storm Cat (USA)—Tranquility Lake (USA)
40 **KIRKLEES (IRE)**, 4, b c Jade Robbery (USA)—Moyesii (USA)
41 **LAVEROCK (IRE)**, 6, b h Octagonal (NZ)—Sky Song (IRE)
42 **LITERATO (FR)**, 4, ch c Kendor (FR)—La Cibeles (FR)
43 **LOVE DANCING (ARG)**, 4, b f Salt Lake (USA)—Le Midi (ARG)
44 **MANY COLOURS**, 4, b f Green Desert (USA)—First of Many
45 **MINEFIELD (USA)**, 4, b c Silver Deputy (CAN)—Copperfield (CAN)
46 **MOFARIJ**, 4, ch c Bering—Pastorale
47 **MOON QUEST (IRE)**, 4, ch g Rainbow Quest (USA)—Midnight Line (USA)
48 **MY INDY (ARG)**, 4, br c Indygo Shiner (USA)—My Light (ARG)
49 **MYTHICAL KID (USA)**, 4, b br c Lemon Drop Kid (USA)—Myth To Reality (FR)
50 **NAIPE MARCADO (URU)**, 5, ch h Timber 'o (URU)—Nadinka Foss (URU)
51 **NEW GUINEA**, 5, b g Fantastic Light (USA)—Isle of Spice (USA)
52 **OLYMPIAN ODYSSEY**, 5, b h Sadler's Wells (USA)—Field of Hope (IRE)
53 **PALACE EPISODE (USA)**, 5, b br h Machiavellian (USA)—Palace Weekend (USA)
54 **POET LAUREATE**, 4, gr c Highest Honor (FR)—Desired
55 **PURPLE EMPEROR (USA)**, 4, b c Red Ransom (USA)—Checkerspot (USA)
56 **RALLYING CRY (USA)**, 4, b br c War Chant (USA)—Turning Wheel (USA)
57 **RAMONTI (FR)**, 6, b h Martino Alonso (IRE)—Falfast (ITY)
58 **REGAL FLUSH**, 4, b c Sakhee (USA)—Ruthless Rose (USA)
59 **RONDO (USA)**, 5, b h Grand Slam (USA)—Dama (USA)
60 **SAGARA (USA)**, 4, B C Sadler's Wells (USA)—Rangoon Ruby (USA)
61 **SCHIAPARELLI (GER)**, 5, ch h Monsun (GER)—Sacarina
62 **SHADOWY FIGURE**, 4, b c Machiavellian (USA)—Renashaan (FR)
63 **SPRING CITY (GER)**, 4, ch c Monsun (GER)—Spirit of Eagles (USA)
64 **STAGE GIFT (IRE)**, 5, ch g Cadeaux Genereux—Stage Struck (IRE)
65 **STROBILUS**, 4, b c Mark of Esteem (IRE)—Mount Elbrus
66 **TAM LIN**, 5, b h Selkirk (USA)—La Nuit Rose (FR)
67 **TESLIN (IRE)**, 4, b g In The Wings—Yukon Hope (USA)
68 **THE ILLIES (IRE)**, 4, b c Fasliyev (USA)—Velvet Appeal (IRE)
69 **THIRD SET (IRE)**, 5, b g Royal Applause—Khamseh
70 **TRUE CAUSE (USA)**, 5, ch h Storm Cat (USA)—Dearly
71 **TRULY ROYAL**, 4, b c Noverre (USA)—Her Ladyship
72 **WITH INTEREST**, 5, b h Selkirk (USA)—With Fascination (USA)

THREE-YEAR-OLDS

73 **CALMING INFLUENCE (IRE)**, b c King's Best (USA)—Idilic Calm (IRE)
74 **CLASSIC TALE**, ch c Dubai Destination (USA)—Persian Secret (FR)
75 **CRAIGSTOWN**, b c Cape Cross (IRE)—Craigmill
76 **DESERT CHILL (USA)**, b f Red Ransom (USA)—Storm Song (USA)
77 **DOVE (IRE)**, b f Sadler's Wells (USA)—Golden Digger (USA)
78 **EMMROOZ**, b c Red Ransom (USA)—Nasmatt
79 **ETCHED (USA)**, ch c Forestry (USA)—Unbridled Elaine (USA)
80 **ETOSHA (IRE)**, b c Cape Cross (IRE)—Zibilene
81 **ETRUSCAN (IRE)**, b c Selkirk (USA)—Maddelina (IRE)
82 **FAST COMPANY (IRE)**, b c Danehill Dancer (IRE)—Sheezalady
83 **FATEH FIELD (USA)**, b c Distorted Humor (USA)—Too Cool To Fool (USA)
84 **GLADIATORUS (USA)**, b c Silic (FR)—Gmaasha (IRE)
85 **GOTHENBURG (UAE)**, b c Halling (USA)—Poised (USA)
86 **HATTA FORT**, B C Cape Cross (IRE)—Oshiponga
87 **IBIS (USA)**, b br f Empire Maker (USA)—Sunlit Silence (USA)
88 **IBN KHALDUN (USA)**, ch c Dubai Destination (USA)—Gossamer
89 **IGUAZU FALLS (USA)**, ch c Pivotal—Anna Palariva (IRE)

MR SAEED BIN SUROOR—continued

90 IVONA, b f Indian Ridge—Mot Juste
91 LAURELDEAN GALE (USA), b br f Grand Slam (USA)—Ravnina (USA)
92 MCCARTNEY (GER), b br c In The Wings—Messina (GER)
93 OMNICAT (USA), br c Storm Cat (USA)—Onaga (USA)
94 PINK IVORY, ch f Sakhee (USA)—Anna of Saxony
95 PLAVIUS (USA), br c Danzig (USA)—Sharp Minister (CAN)
96 PONT DES SOUPIRS (USA), b c Harlan's Holiday (USA)—Flirted (USA)
97 QANAWAAT, b br c Almutawakel—Mouwadh (USA)
98 RIO DE LA PLATA (USA), ch c Rahy (USA)—Express Way (ARG)
99 SIYABONA (USA), b f Kingmambo (USA)—Relish (IRE)
100 SIYASA (USA), ch f Rahy (USA)—Jood (USA)
101 SKYCRUISER (IRE), ch c Dubai Destination (USA)—Maskunah (IRE)
102 STORM FORCE (IRE), b c Cape Cross (IRE)—Aguinaga (IRE)
103 WHISPERED DREAMS (GER), ch f Platini (GER)—Waconda (GER)
104 WINGBEAT (USA), b c Elusive Quality (USA)—Infinite Spirit (USA)
105 WOLGAN VALLEY (USA), ch c Mr Greeley (USA)—Dancing Naturally (USA)
106 WORLD OF CHOICE (USA), b c Distorted Humor (USA)—Palace Weekend (USA)

TWO-YEAR-OLDS

107 Ch c 22/2 Distorted Humor (USA)—Alchemist (USA) (A P Indy (USA)) (485908)
108 ANMAR (USA), ch c 28/2 Rahy (USA)—Ranin (Unfuwain (USA))
109 B c 30/4 Cape Cross (IRE)—Diminuendo (USA) (Diesis)
110 EMERGING ARTIST (FR), b c 4/4 Dubai Destination (USA)—Picture Princess (Sadler's Wells (USA))
111 B c 18/4 Seeking The Gold (USA)—Encandiladora (ARG) (Equalize (USA))
112 B c 5/5 Exceed And Excel (AUS)—Enrich (USA) (Dynaformer (USA))
113 B c 29/3 Cape Cross (IRE)—Evil Empire (GER) (Acatenango (GER))
114 Ch c 10/5 Pivotal—Fairy Contessa (IRE) (Fairy King (USA)) (230000)
115 B c 19/2 E Dubai (USA)—Fortune (IRE) (Night Shift (USA))
116 Ch c 24/3 Rahy (USA)—Forty Marinesca (ARG) (Roar (USA)) (170068)
117 Ch c 23/1 Rahy (USA)—Helwa (USA) (Silver Hawk (USA)) (175000)
118 B c 2/4 Cape Cross (IRE)—Humilis (IRE) (Sadler's Wells (USA)) (290000)
119 B c 7/3 Haathd—Janaat (Kris)
120 Ch c 6/2 Distorted Humor (USA)—Just A Bird (USA) (Storm Bird (CAN)) (388726)
121 Gr ro c 26/4 Rahy (USA)—Laiyl (IRE) (Nureyev (USA))
122 MATHAAQ, b c 19/2 Nayef (USA)—Mouwadh (Nureyev (USA))
123 MAWAZIN, br c 18/2 Red Ransom (USA)—Injaad (Machiavellian (USA))
124 Ch c 21/1 Pivotal—Moonshell (IRE) (Sadler's Wells (USA))
125 B c 12/2 Dansili—Morning Queen (GER) (Konigsstuhl (GER))
126 B c 22/2 Elusive Quality (USA)—Mysterial (USA) (Alleged (USA))
127 B c 30/3 Gone West (USA)—Myth To Reality (FR) (Sadler's Wells (USA)) (1000000)
128 B c 23/3 Halling (USA)—Poised (USA) (Rahy (USA))
129 B c 15/3 Halling (USA)—Polska (USA) (Danzig (USA))
130 B br c 17/5 Dynaformer (USA)—Preach (USA) (Mr Prospector (USA)) (1409135)
131 B c 21/2 Cape Cross (IRE)—Shimna (Mr Prospector (USA)) (200000)
132 Ch c 25/1 Distorted Humor (USA)—Stormy Bear (USA) (Storm Cat (USA)) (923226)
133 Ch c 8/4 Refuse To Bend (IRE)—Tanzania (USA) (Darshaan)
134 B c 23/3 Pivotal—Teggiano (IRE) (Mujtahid (USA)) (160000)
135 B c 28/1 Dalakhani (IRE)—Time Honoured (Sadler's Wells (USA)) (480000)
136 B c 27/3 King's Best (USA)—Time Saved (Green Desert (USA)) (150000)
137 B c 7/2 Singspiel (IRE)—Whisper To Dream (USA) (Gone West (USA))
138 B br c 12/5 Elusive Quality (USA)—Windsharp (USA) (Lear Fan (USA))

LOCATION OF TRAINING QUARTERS

References show squares as on map

IN SEVERAL CASES THE NEAREST MAIN CENTRE IS SHOWN TO LOCATE SITUATION OF STABLES

AKEHURST, JONATHAN, Epsom G5
ALEXANDER, N. W., Leslie A4
ALLEN, J. S., Alcester E4
ALLEN, M. A., Worthing G5
ALNER, R. H. & MRS S., Blandford G3
ALSTON, E. J., Preston D3
AMOS, W., Hawick B3
APPLEBY, M., Compton Verney E4
ARBUTHNOT, D. W. P., Compton F4
ARMSON, R. J., Melbourne E4
ATKINSON, P. G., Northallerton C5
ATTWATER, M. J., Epsom F5
AUVRAY, JEAN-RENE, Upper Lambourn F4
AYLIFFE, N. G., Minehead F2
AYNSLEY, J. W. F., Morpeth C5

BAILEY, A., Newmarket F6
BAILEY, MRS C., Northampton E5
BAILEY, K. C., Cheltenham F4
BAKER, MRS L. P., Maidstone F6
BALDING, A. M., Kingsclere F4
BALDING, J., Doncaster D5
BARCLAY, MRS A., Moreton-In-Marsh F4
BARCLAY, J., Kinnesswood A4
BARFOOT-SAUNT, MRS T. M., Wotton-under-Edge F3
BARKER, D. W., Richmond C5
BARLOW, SIR J., Nantwich F4
BARNES, M. A., Brampton C4
BARR, R. E., Middlesbrough C5
BARRON, T. D., Thirsk D5
BASTIMAN, R., Wetherby D5
BATEMAN, A. J., Minehead F2
BAUGH, B. P. J., Stoke-on-Trent E4
BEALBY, C. C., Grantham E5
BEAUMONT, P, Brandsby D5
BECKETT, R. M., Whitsbury G4
BELL, M. L. W., Newmarket F6
BENNETT, J. A., Wantage F4
BERRY, A., Cockerham D4
BERRY, J. C. DE P, Newmarket F6
BEST, J., Lewes G5
BEST, J. R., Maidstone F6
BETHELL, J. D., Middleham C5
BEWLEY, J. R., Jedburgh B4
BISHOP, K., Bridgwater F3
BLACKFORD, MISS L. A., Tiverton F2
BLACKMORE, A. G., Hertford F6
BLANSHARD, M. T. W., Upper Lambourn F4
BLOCKLEY, P. A., Lambourn F4
BOSLEY, M. R., Marlborough F4
BOTTI, M., Newmarket F6
BOWEN, P., Haverfordwest E1
BOWLBY, MRS A. J., Wantage F4
BOWRING, S. R., Edwinstowe D5
BOYLE, J, R., Epsom F5
BRADBURNE, MRS S. C., Cupar A4
BRADLEY, J. M., Chepstow F3
BRADSTOCK, M. F., Wantage F4
BRAVERY, G. C., Newmarket F6
BRENNAN, OWEN, Worksop D5
BREWIS, MISS RHONA, Belford B5
BRIDGER, J. J., Liphook G5

BRIDGWATER, D. G., Stow-on-the-Wold F4
BRIDGWATER, G. F., Shrewley F4
BRISBOURNE, W. M., Nesscliffe E3
BRITTAIN, C. E., Newmarket F6
BRITTAIN, M. A., Warthill D5
BROCKBANK, J. E., Carlisle C4
BROOKE, LADY S., Powys E2
BROOKHOUSE, R. S., Alcester F3
BROOKS, MRS A E., Towcester F5
BROOKSHAW, S. A., Alcester F3
BROTHERTON, R., Pershore F4
BROWN, I. A., Salton D5
BROYD, MISS A. E., Crickhowell F3
BRYANT, MISS M. P., Lewes G5
BUCKLER, R. H., Bridport G3
BUCKLEY, M. A., Stamford E5
BURCHELL, W. D., Ebbw Vale F3
BURGOYNE, P. V. J., Wincanton F3
BURKE, K. J., Northleach F4
BURKE, K. R., Leyburn C5
BURROUGH, S., Chard G3
BUTLER, P., Lewes G5
BUTT, T., Jedburgh B4
BYCROFT, N., Malton D6
CALDWELL, T. H., Warrington D3
CALLAGHAN, S. A., Newmarket F6
CAMACHO, MISS J. A., Malton D6
CAMPION, A. M., Malton D6
CANDLISH, MS J., Leek E4
CANDY, HENRY D. N. B., Wantage F4
CARR, MRS RUTH, York D5
CARROLL, A. W., Cropthorne F3
CARROLL, D., Warthill D5
CARSON, R. M., Lambourn F4
CASE, B. I., Banbury F4
CECIL, H. R. A., Newmarket F6
CHADWICK, S, G., Hayton C3
CHAMBERLAIN, A, J., Swindon F4
CHAMINGS, P. R., Basingstoke F4
CHANCE, N. T., Upper Lambourn F4
CHAPMAN, M. C., Market Rasen D5
CHAPPLE-HYAM, P. W., Newmarket F6
CHARLTON, G. A. G., Stocksfield C5
CHARLTON, ROGER J., Beckhampton F4
CLARK, R. M., West Lothian B4
CLINTON, P. L., Doveridge E4
CLUTTERBUCK, K. F., Newmarket F6
COAKLEY, D. J., West Ilsley F4
COBB, MRS H. J., Pulborough G5
COLE, P. F. I., Whatcombe F4
COLLINGRIDGE, H. J., Newmarket F6
COLTHERD, W. S., Selkirk B3
CONNELL, LADY, Brackley F5
COOGAN, A. B., Ely F6
COOMBE, M. J., Weymouth G3
CORCORAN, L, A., Kingsbridge G2
CORNWALL, J. R., Melton Mowbray E5
COUPLAND, J. F., Grimsby D6
COWELL, R. M. H., Newmarket F6
COWLEY, P. E., Banbury F4
COX, C. G., Lambourn F4
CRAGGS, R., Sedgefield C5

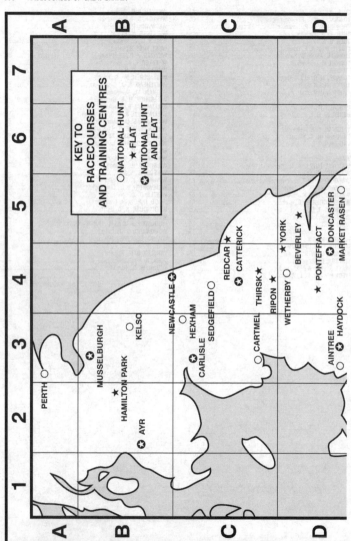

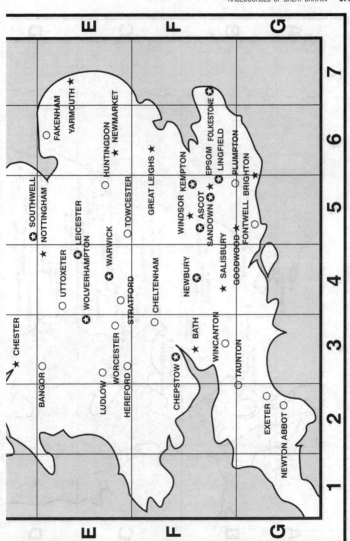

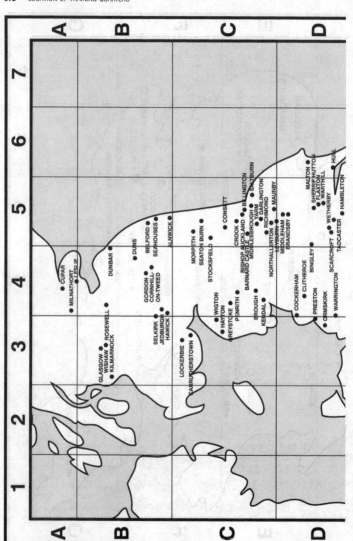

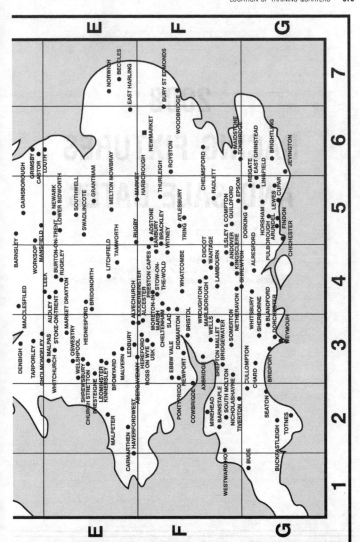

2008
RACING FIXTURES
AND SALE DATES

(SUBJECT TO ALTERATION)

Flat fixtures are in **Black Type**; Jump in Light Type; Irish in *Italic*;
asterisk (☆) indicates an evening meeting;
† *indicates an All Weather meeting. Sale dates are at foot of fixtures*

MARCH

Sun	Mon	Tues	Wed	Thur	Fri	Sat
30	**31**					**1**
Curragh *Downpatrick* Kempton Park Wincanton	**Lingfield Park**† **Southwell**† Wincanton					Doncaster Kelso Kempton Park *Navan* Newbury **Wolverhampton**†☆
2	**3**	**4**	**5**	**6**	**7**	**8**
Bangor-on-Dee *Clonmel* Huntingdon *Leopardstown*	**Lingfield Park**† Stratford-on-Avon **Wolverhampton**†	Exeter Newcastle **Southwell**†	Catterick Bridge Fontwell Park **Lingfield Park**† **Wolverhampton**†☆	Carlisle Lingfield Park *Thurles* Wincanton **Wolverhampton**†☆	Ayr *Dundalk*†☆ Leicester Sandown Park **Wolverhampton**†☆	Ayr Chepstow *Gowran Park* Sandown Park **Wolverhampton**†
		Fasig-Tipton Sale			*Goffs Sale*	
9	**10**	**11**	**12**	**13**	**14**	**15**
Market Rasen *Naas* Warwick	Plumpton Stratford-on-Avon Taunton	Cheltenham Sedgefield **Southwell**†	Cheltenham Huntingdon **Southwell**† **Wolverhampton**†☆	Cheltenham Hexham **Southwell**† **Wolverhampton**†☆	Cheltenham *Dundalk*†☆ Fakenham **Kempton Park**†☆ **Lingfield Park**†	**Kempton Park**†☆ *Limerick* **Lingfield Park**† Newcastle Uttoxeter Wetherby
16	**17**	**18**	**19**	**20**	**21**	**22**
Carlisle Fontwell Park *Limerick* *Navan*	*Down Royal* Lingfield Park Taunton *Wexford* **Wolverhampton**†	Exeter **Great Leighs**† Warwick	Chepstow *Dundalk*†☆ **Kempton Park**†☆ **Lingfield Park**† Market Rasen	*Clonmel* **Great Leighs**†☆ Ludlow **Southwell**† Wincanton		Carlisle *Cork* **Doncaster** *Fairyhouse* Haydock Park **Kempton Park**† Newton Abbot **Wolverhampton**†☆
23	**24**	**25**	**26**	**27**	**28**	**29**
Cork *Fairyhouse* **Musselburgh** Plumpton Towcester	Chepstow *Cork* *Fairyhouse* Fakenham Huntingdon Plumpton **Redcar** **Warwick** **Yarmouth**	*Fairyhouse* Fontwell Park **Pontefract** Sedgefield	**Great Leighs**† Kempton Park Newcastle **Wolverhampton**†☆	Ayr Exeter **Great Leighs**†☆ **Lingfield Park**† *Thurles*	*Dundalk*†☆ **Kempton Park**†☆ **Lingfield Park**† Newbury **Wolverhampton**†	*Bangor-on-Dee* **Doncaster** **Kempton Park**† *Navan* Newbury Stratford-on-Avon **Wolverhampton**†☆
			Doncaster Sale	*Doncaster Sale*	*Doncaster Sale*	

APRIL

Sun	Mon	Tues	Wed	Thur	Fri	Sat
		1 Folkestone **Great Leighs†** Wetherby	**2** Catterick Bridge *Gowran Park☆* **Kempton Park†☆** Lingfield Park† Nottingham	**3** Aintree **Great Leighs†☆** Leicester Taunton	**4** Aintree *Dundalk†☆* **Great Leighs†** Southwell *Wolverhampton†☆*	**5** Aintree Chepstow **Kempton Park†☆** *Limerick* **Lingfield Park†** Newcastle
						Fasig-Tipton Sale
6 Hexham *Leopardstown* *Limerick* Market Rasen Worcester	**7** Kelso **Kempton Park†** Plumpton	**8** **Lingfield Park†** Sedgefield **Southwell†**	**9** Bath **Kempton Park†☆** Ludlow Towcester	**10** Carlisle **Folkestone** Fontwell Park **Great Leighs†☆** *Tipperary☆* Towcester	**11** Ascot **Doncaster** *Dundalk†☆* Musselburgh **Wolverhampton†☆**	**12** Doncaster *Fairyhouse* **Great Leighs☆** **Kempton Park†** Newbury Uttoxeter
		Keeneland Sale	*Keeneland Sale*			
13 *Curragh* **Great Leighs†** Kelso Newton Abbot *Tramore*	**14** Newcastle *Tramore☆* **Windsor** **Wolverhampton†**	**15** Exeter Nottingham Warwick	**16** **Beverley** Cheltenham Newmarket **Wolverhampton†☆**	**17** Cheltenham *Dundalk†☆* **Great Leighs†☆** Newmarket Ripon *Tipperary☆*	**18** Ayr Cheltenham *Dundalk†☆* **Great Leighs†☆** Newbury Taunton☆ **Thirsk**	**19** Ayr Bangor-on-Dee *Naas* Newbury **Nottingham☆** **Thirsk** **Wolverhampton†☆**
		Tattersalls Sale	*Ascot Sale* *Tattersalls Sale*	*Tattersalls Sale*	*Arqana Sale*	*Arqana Sale*
20 *Cork* **Great Leighs†** *Leopardstown* Stratford-on-Avon Wincanton	**21** Hexham Plumpton **Pontefract** Sedgefield☆ **Windsor☆**	**22** **Bath☆** **Folkestone** **Kempton Park†** *Punchestown* **Southwell** Towcester☆	**23** Catterick Bridge **Kempton Park†☆** Nottingham Perth *Punchestown* Worcester☆	**24** **Beverley** Fontwell Park **Great Leighs†☆** Perth *Punchestown* **Southwell†☆**	**25** Bangor-on-Dee☆ Chepstow☆ Newton Abbot☆ Perth *Punchestown* Sandown (mixed) **Wolverhampton†**	**26** **Haydock Park☆** Leicester Market Rasen *Punchestown* **Ripon** Sandown (mixed) **Wolverhampton†☆**
	Ascot Sale					
27 Brighton *Gowran Park* Ludlow *Navan* Wetherby	**28** **Lingfield Park†** **Southwell†☆** Towcester **Windsor☆** Yarmouth	**29** Bath Sedgefield☆ **Southwell†** Wincanton **Wolverhampton†☆**	**30** Ascot *Ballinrobe☆* **Great Leighs†☆** Kelso☆ Pontefract Worcester			

MAY

Sun	Mon	Tues	Wed	Thur	Fri	Sat
				1 Folkestone *Great Leighs☆* Hereford Huntingdon☆ **Redcar** *Tipperary☆* Tattersalls Sale	**2** *Bangor-on-Dee☆* *Cork☆* *Dundalk†☆* *Fontwell Park☆* **Lingfield Park†** **Musselburgh** **Southwell** Tattersalls Sale	**3** *Doncaster☆* **Goodwood** *Hexham☆* *Kilbeggan☆* **Newmarket** **Thirsk** Uttoxeter
4 *Gowran Park* **Hamilton Park** **Newmarket** **Salisbury** *Sligo*	**5** *Curragh* *Down Royal* **Kempton Park†** *Limerick* **Newcastle** **Warwick** **Windsor**	**6** *Catterick Bridge☆* **Chepstow** *Exeter☆* **Kelso** **Southwell†**	**7** **Beverley** *Cheltenham☆* **Chester** **Fakenham** Huntingdon☆ *Punchestown☆* Goffs Sale	**8** *Chester☆* *Clonmel☆* **Goodwood** **Great Leighs†☆** Newton Abbot *Wetherby☆* *Wincanton☆*	**9** *Aintree☆* **Chester** *Downpatrick☆* **Hamilton Park☆** **Lingfield Park** **Nottingham** *Ripon☆* *Wexford☆*	**10** **Ascot** *Downpatrick* **Haydock (Mixed)** Hexham **Lingfield Park** **Nottingham** *Thirsk☆* *Warwick☆*
11 *Killarney* *Leopardstown* Plumpton Uttoxeter Worcester	**12** *Killarney☆* **Redcar** *Towcester☆* **Windsor☆** **Wolverhampton†** **Yarmouth**	**13** **Brighton** **Great Leighs†☆** *Killarney☆* Newton Abbot☆ **Southwell†** **Yarmouth**	**14** *Bath☆* Exeter Fontwell Park *Naas☆* *Perth☆* **York**	**15** *Folkestone☆* *Limerick☆* *Ludlow☆* **Newmarket†** Perth **Salisbury** **York**	**16** *Aintree☆* *Cork☆* *Dundalk†☆* **Hamilton Park☆** **Newbury** **Newcastle☆** **Newmarket** **York**	**17** *Bangor-on-Dee* *Doncaster☆* *Kilbeggan☆* **Newbury** **Newmarket** **Thirsk** *Uttoxeter☆*
18 Fakenham *Gowran Park* Market Rasen *Navan* **Ripon**	**19** **Bath** **Musselburgh** Newton Abbot *Roscommon☆* **Windsor☆** **Wolverhampton†☆** Doncaster Sale Fasig-Tipton Sale	**20** **Beverley** **Leicester☆** **Musselburgh** **Southwell†** Towcester☆ Doncaster Sale Fasig-Tipton Sale	**21** **Ayr** **Goodwood** Kelso *Leopardstown☆* **Sandown Park☆** Sedgefield☆ *Sligo☆* Doncaster Sale	**22** *Clonmel☆* **Goodwood** **Haydock Park** **Salisbury☆** Wetherby Worcester☆ Doncaster Sale	**23** **Brighton** **Haydock Park☆** **Newcastle** **Newmarket** Pontefract☆ Stratford-on-Avon☆ *Tipperary☆* *Wexford☆* Doncaster Sale	**24** **Beverley** *Cartmel☆* **Catterick Bridge** *Curragh* **Haydock Park** **Newmarket** Stratford-on-Avon *Tralee*
25 *Curragh* Fontwell Park **Newmarket** *Tralee* Uttoxeter	**26** *Ballinrobe☆* **Carlisle** Cartmel **Chepstow** **Leicester** **Redcar**	**27** *Ballinrobe☆* **Chepstow** Hexham☆ Huntingdon☆ **Leicester** **Redcar**	**28** **Beverley☆** Cartmel **Great Leighs†** *Leopardstown☆* *Punchestown☆* Southwell☆ **Yarmouth**	**29** **Ayr** **Great Leighs†** **Newcastle☆** **Sandown Park☆** *Wetherby☆* **Yarmouth**	**30** **Brighton** *Down Royal☆* **Goodwood** **Haydock Park☆** **Musselburgh☆** Towcester☆ *Tramore☆* **York**	**31** **Doncaster** **Goodwood** **Haydock Park** *Lingfield Park☆* **Newbury☆** *Tramore* **York**

JUNE

Sun	Mon	Tues	Wed	Thur	Fri	Sat
1	**2**	**3**	**4**	**5**	**6**	**7**
Bath	**Carlisle**	**Folkestone**☆	Fontwell Park	**Hamilton Park**	**Bath**☆	Curragh☆
Kilbeggan	**Leicester**	**Ripon**	Kempton Park☆	Lingfield Park†	**Catterick Bridge**	**Doncaster**
Listowel	Listowel	Sedgefield☆	Leopardstown☆	Newton Abbot	**Doncaster**☆	**Epsom Downs**
Perth	Naas	**Southwell**†	**Lingfield Park**	**Sandown Park**☆	**Epsom Downs**	Hexham
Stratford-on-Avon	Thirsk☆		**Nottingham**	Tipperary☆	**Goodwood**☆	**Lingfield Park**☆
	Windsor☆		**Ripon**☆	Uttoxeter☆	Navan☆	**Musselburgh**
				Wetherby☆	Wexford☆	**Newcastle**
					Wolverhampton†	Worcester
		Ascot Sale	*Ascot Sale*			
8	**9**	**10**	**11**	**12**	**13**	**14**
Brighton	**Folkestone**	**Chester**☆	**Beverley**	Fontwell Park☆	Aintree☆	**Bath**
Cork	Newton Abbot	**Redcar**	**Brighton**	**Haydock Park**	**Chepstow**☆	Hexham
Roscommon	**Pontefract**☆	**Salisbury**	Hamilton Park☆	**Newbury**	Clonmel☆	**Leicester**☆
Southwell†	Roscommon☆	Southwell☆	Kempton Park☆	Uttoxeter☆	**Goodwood**☆	Limerick☆
Worcester	**Windsor**☆		Leopardstown☆	**Yarmouth**	Market Rasen	**Lingfield Park**☆
			Nottingham		Navan☆	**Sandown Park**
					Sandown Park	**York**
					York	
	Goffs Sale	*Goffs Sale*	*Goffs Sale*	*Goffs Sale*	*Goffs Sale*	
15	**16**	**17**	**18**	**19**	**20**	**21**
Cork	Ballinrobe☆	**Ascot**	**Ascot**	**Ascot**	**Ascot**	**Ascot**
Doncaster	**Carlisle**	Newton Abbot☆	**Hamilton Park**	Fairyhouse☆	**Ayr**☆	Ayr
Salisbury	Sedgefield	**Thirsk**	Kempton Park☆	**Great Leighs**☆	Down Royal☆	Down Royal
Stratford-on-Avon	**Warwick**☆	**Yarmouth**☆	Leopardstown☆	**Leicester**☆	**Goodwood**☆	**Haydock Park**☆
	Windsor☆		**Ripon**☆	**Ripon**	Limerick☆	**Lingfield Park**☆
			Worcester	Tipperary☆	**Musselburgh**	**Newmarket**
				Towcester☆	**Newmarket**☆	**Redcar**
				Warwick	**Redcar**	
22	**23**	**24**	**25**	**26**	**27**	**28**
Down Royal	**Chepstow**☆	**Beverley**	**Bath**☆	Fairyhouse	**Chester**☆	**Chester**
Gowran Park	Kilbeggan☆	**Brighton**	**Carlisle**	**Great Leighs**†	Curragh☆	Curragh
Hereford	**Lingfield Park**†	**Newbury**☆	Kempton Park☆	Hamilton Park☆	**Doncaster**	**Doncaster**☆
Hexham	**Windsor**☆	Newton Abbot☆	Naas☆	**Leicester**☆	**Folkestone**	**Lingfield Park**☆
Pontefract	**Wolverhampton**†	Sligo☆	**Salisbury**	**Newcastle**	Market Rasen	**Newcastle**
			Worcester	**Warwick**	**Newcastle**☆	**Newmarket**
					Newmarket☆	**Windsor**
			Tattersalls (IRE) Sale	*Tattersalls (IRE) Sale*	*Tattersalls (IRE) Sale*	
29	**30**					
Curragh	**Musselburgh**☆					
Salisbury	**Pontefract**					
Uttoxeter	**Windsor**☆					
Windsor	**Wolverhampton**†					

JULY

Sun	Mon	Tues	Wed	Thur	Fri	Sat
		1	**2**	**3**	**4**	**5**
		Brighton Hamilton Park Lingfield Park†☆ Thirsk☆	Catterick Bridge Chepstow☆ Kempton Park☆ *Leopardstown*☆ *Perth* Worcester	*Bellewstown*☆ Haydock Park Newbury☆ *Perth* **Redcar**☆ Warwick☆ Yarmouth	*Bellewstown*☆ Beverley☆ Haydock Park☆ Salisbury☆ Sandown Park☆ Southwell† Warwick *Wexford*☆	*Bellewstown*☆ Beverley Carlisle☆ Haydock Park Leicester Nottingham☆ Sandown Park
			Arqana Sale	*Arqana Sale*		
6	**7**	**8**	**9**	**10**	**11**	**12**
Ayr Brighton *Gowran Park* *Limerick* Market Rasen	Brighton Musselburgh Ripon☆ *Roscommon*☆ **Windsor**☆	Pontefract *Roscommon*☆ **Southwell**†☆ Uttoxeter☆ Wolverhampton†	Catterick Bridge Kempton Park☆ Lingfield Park *Naas*☆ Newmarket Worcester☆	Doncaster☆ *Fairyhouse*☆ Folkestone Newmarket Nottingham☆ Warwick	Ascot Chepstow☆ Chester☆ *Cork*☆ Newbury☆ Newmarket York	Ascot Chester *Curragh* *Dundalk*† Hamilton Park☆ Nottingham Salisbury☆ York
Tattersalls Sale	*Tattersalls Sale*	*Tattersalls Sale*	*Tattersalls Sale*	*Tattersalls Sale*	*Tattersalls Sale*	
13	**14**	**15**	**16**	**17**	**18**	**19**
Curragh **Haydock Park** *Perth* *Sligo* Stratford-on-Avon	Ayr *Downpatrick* *Killarney*☆ Newton Abbot **Windsor**☆ Wolverhampton†☆	Beverley Brighton **Great Leighs**†☆ *Killarney*☆ Yarmouth☆	Catterick Bridge Kempton Park☆ *Killarney*☆ *Leopardstown*☆ Lingfield Park Uttoxeter Worcester☆	Bath☆ Cartmel Doncaster☆ *Fairyhouse*☆ Hamilton Park *Killarney* Leicester Sandown Park☆	Hamilton Park☆ *Kilbeggan*☆ Newbury☆ Newmarket Nottingham Pontefract☆ Southwell	Haydock Park☆ Lingfield Park☆ Market Rasen Newbury Newmarket Ripon *Tipperary*☆
	Fasig-Tipton Sale	*Ascot Sale* *Fasig-Tipton Sale*				
20	**21**	**22**	**23**	**24**	**25**	**26**
Fairyhouse Newton Abbot **Redcar** Stratford-on-Avon *Tipperary*	Ayr *Ballinrobe*☆ Beverley☆ **Windsor**☆ Yarmouth	*Ballinrobe*☆ Bangor-on-Dee☆ **Great Leighs**†☆ Salisbury Yarmouth	Catterick Bridge Leicester☆ Lingfield Park *Naas*☆ Sandown Park☆ Worcester	Bath Doncaster☆ Folkestone☆ Kempton Park☆ *Leopardstown*☆ *Limerick*☆ Sandown Park Uttoxeter	Ascot Chepstow☆ Newmarket☆ Thirsk☆ *Wexford*☆ Wolverhampton† York☆	Ascot Lingfield Park☆ Newcastle Newmarket Salisbury☆ York
27	**28**	**29**	**30**	**31**		
Ascot Carlisle *Curragh* Pontefract	*Galway* **Southwell**† Uttoxeter☆ **Windsor**☆ Yarmouth	Beverley *Galway*☆ **Goodwood** *Perth*☆ Worcester☆	*Galway* **Goodwood** Kempton Park☆ Leicester☆ *Perth* **Redcar**	*Galway* **Goodwood** Musselburgh☆ Nottingham Sandown Park☆ Stratford-on-Avon		

AUGUST

Sun	Mon	Tues	Wed	Thur	Fri	Sat
31					**1**	**2**
Curragh **Folkestone** *Killarney* **Musselburgh** Newton Abbot					Bangor-on-Dee **Bath**☆ *Galway*☆ **Goodwood** **Haydock Park**☆ **Newmarket**☆ **Thirsk**	**Doncaster** *Galway* **Goodwood** **Hamilton Park**☆ **Lingfield Park**☆ **Newmarket** **Thirsk**
3	**4**	**5**	**6**	**7**	**8**	**9**
Chester *Cork* *Galway* Market Rasen **Newbury**	**Carlisle**☆ *Cork* *Naas* Newton Abbot **Ripon** **Windsor**☆	**Catterick Bridge** **Chepstow** *Roscommon*☆	**Brighton** *Gowran Park*☆ **Kempton Park**† **Newcastle** **Pontefract** *Sligo*☆ **Yarmouth**☆	**Bath**☆ **Brighton** **Folkestone** **Haydock Park** **Sandown Park**☆ *Sligo*☆ *Tipperary*☆ **Yarmouth**	**Brighton** **Haydock Park** **Lingfield Park** **Newmarket**☆ *Wexford*☆ **Worcester**	**Ascot** *Ayr*☆ **Haydock Park** *Kilbeggan*☆ **Lingfield Park**☆ **Newmarket** **Redcar**
		Doncaster Sale *Fasig-Tipton Sale*	*Doncaster Sale*	*Doncaster Sale*		*Fasig-Tipton Sale*
Fasig-Tipton Sale						
10	**11**	**12**	**13**	**14**	**15**	**16**
Curragh *Downpatrick* **Leicester** **Redcar** **Windsor**	*Ballinrobe*☆ Southwell **Thirsk**☆ **Windsor**☆ **Wolverhampton**†	**Lingfield Park**† **Musselburgh**☆ Newton Abbot **Nottingham**☆	**Beverley** *Gowran Park*☆ **Hamilton Park**☆ **Salisbury** **Sandown Park**☆ **Yarmouth**	**Beverley** **Chepstow**☆ **Great Leighs**†☆ **Salisbury** **Sandown Park**☆ Stratford-on-Avon *Tramore*☆	**Catterick Bridge**☆ *Dundalk*† **Kempton Park**☆ **Newbury** **Newcastle** **Newmarket**☆ **Nottingham** *Tramore*☆	Bangor-on-Dee **Lingfield Park**☆ Market Rasen☆ **Newbury** **Newmarket** **Ripon** *Tramore*☆
Fasig-Tipton Sale		*Fasig-Tipton Sale* *Tattersalls (IRE) Sale*	*Tattersalls (IRE) Sale*	*Tattersalls (IRE) Sale*	*Arqana Sale* *Tattersalls (IRE) Sale*	*Arqana Sale*
17	**18**	**19**	**20**	**21**	**22**	**23**
Bath *Leopardstown* **Pontefract** Southwell *Tramore*	**Lingfield Park**† *Roscommon*☆ **Windsor**☆ **Wolverhampton**† **Yarmouth**☆	**Brighton** Newton Abbot☆ *Tralee* *Worcester*☆ **York**	**Carlisle** **Folkestone**☆ **Hamilton Park** Newton Abbot☆ *Tralee* **York**	**Chester**☆ *Fontwell Park*☆ **Great Leighs**† Stratford-on-Avon *Tralee* **York**	**Bath**☆ **Hamilton Park**☆ *Kilbeggan*☆ **Newbury** **Newcastle**☆ **Newmarket** *Tralee* **York**	**Beverley** *Cartmel* *Curragh* **Goodwood** **Newmarket** **Redcar**☆ *Tralee* **Windsor**☆
Arqana Sale	*Arqana Sale*					
24	**25**	**26**	**27**	**28**	**29**	**30**
Ballinrobe **Beverley** *Cork* **Goodwood** **Yarmouth**	*Cartmel* **Chepstow** *Downpatrick* Huntingdon **Kempton Park**† **Newcastle** **Ripon** **Warwick**	**Great Leighs**† **Ripon** *Sligo*☆	**Ayr** *Bellewstown*☆ **Catterick Bridge** **Great Leighs**†	**Ayr** *Bellewstown*☆ **Great Leighs**† **Lingfield Park** *Tipperary*☆	**Chester** *Down Royal*☆ **Hamilton Park**☆ **Salisbury**☆ **Sandown Park** *Wexford*☆ **Wolverhampton**†☆	**Bath**☆ **Chester** *Killarney* Market Rasen☆ Newton Abbot **Ripon** **Sandown Park**
	Fasig-Tipton Sale	*Ascot Sale* *Doncaster Sale* *Fasig-Tipton Sale*	*Doncaster Sale*	*Doncaster Sale*		

SEPTEMBER

Sun	Mon	Tues	Wed	Thur	Fri	Sat
	1	**2**	**3**	**4**	**5**	**6**
	Hamilton Park	Goodwood	Brighton	*Clonmel*☆	Catterick Bridge	Haydock Park
	Kempton Park†	Sedgefield	*Down Royal*☆	Great Leighs†☆	Chepstow	Kempton Park†
	Lingfield Park†	Southwell†	Hereford	Redcar	Kempton Park†☆	*Leopardstown*
	Roscommon☆		Kempton Park†☆	Salisbury	*Kilbeggan*☆	Stratford-on-Avon
			Lingfield Park	Warwick	Lingfield Park†	Thirsk
						Wolverhampton†
				Arqana Sale		
		Tattersalls (IRE) Sale	Tattersalls (IRE) Sale	Tattersalls (IRE) Sale		
7	**8**	**9**	**10**	**11**	**12**	**13**
Dundalk†	Bath	Beverley	Doncaster	Chepstow	Bangor-on-Dee	Chester
Fontwell Park	Folkestone	*Galway*☆	Doncaster	Doncaster	*Curragh*	*Curragh*
Thirsk	*Galway*☆	Leicester	Kempton Park†☆	Great Leighs†☆	Doncaster	Doncaster
Worcester	Newcastle	Lingfield Park	Uttoxeter	*Laytown*	Sandown Park	Goodwood
			Warwick	Sandown Park	Wolverhampton†☆	Great Leighs†
				Tipperary☆		Kempton Park†☆
			Doncaster Sale	Doncaster Sale		
	Keeneland Sale	Keeneland Sale	Keeneland Sale	Keeneland Sale	Keeneland Sale	Keeneland Sale
14	**15**	**16**	**17**	**18**	**19**	**20**
Curragh	Leicester	Haydock Park	Beverley	Ayr	Ayr	Ayr
Goodwood	*Listowel*	Lingfield Park†	Kempton Park†☆	Great Leighs†☆	*Listowel*	Catterick Bridge
Great Leighs☆	Musselburgh	*Listowel*	*Listowel*	*Listowel*	Newbury	*Listowel*
Listowel	Redcar	Yarmouth	Sandown Park	Pontefract	Newmarket	Newbury
Stratford-on-Avon			Yarmouth	Yarmouth	Wolverhampton†☆	Newmarket
						Wolverhampton†
Keeneland Sale	Keeneland Sale	Keeneland Sale	Keeneland Sale	Keeneland Sale	Keeneland Sale	Keeneland Sale
21	**22**	**23**	**24**	**25**	**26**	**27**
Hamilton Park	*Ballinrobe*	Beverley	*Downpatrick*	Fontwell Park	Ascot	Ascot
Plumpton	Hamilton Park	Folkestone	Goodwood	Great Leighs†☆	*Dundalk*†☆	Chester
Uttoxeter	Kempton Park†	Sedgefield	Kempton Park†☆	Perth	Haydock Park	*Gowran Park*
	Leicester		Perth	Pontefract	Wolverhampton†☆	Great Leighs†☆
			Redcar		Worcester	Haydock Park
						Market Rasen
						Navan
Keeneland Sale						
28	**29**	**30**				
Ascot	Bath	Sedgefield				
Clonmel	Brighton	Southwell†				
Market Rasen	*Roscommon*☆	Warwick				
Musselburgh	Windsor					
Naas						
	Fasig-Tipton Sale	Fasig-Tipton Sale				
	Goffs Sale	Goffs Sale				

OCTOBER

Sun	Mon	Tues	Wed	Thur	Fri	Sat
			1	**2**	**3**	**4**
			Kempton Park†☆ Newcastle Nottingham Salisbury *Sligo*	*Ayr* Goodwood Great Leighs†☆ Newmarket	*Dundalk†☆* *Gowran Park* Hexham Lingfield Park† Newmarket Wolverhampton†☆	Fontwell Park *Gowran Park* Kempton Park† Newmarket Redcar Wolverhampton†☆
			Fasig-Tipton Sale Goffs Sale	Goffs Sale	Goffs Sale	Arqana Sale
5	**6**	**7**	**8**	**9**	**10**	**11**
Dundalk† Huntingdon Kelso *Tipperary* Uttoxeter	Pontefract Warwick Windsor	Catterick Bridge Folkestone Leicester	Exeter Kempton Park†☆ *Navan* Nottingham Towcester	Great Leighs†☆ Newbury *Tramore* Wincanton Worcester	Ayr Carlisle *Dundalk†☆* Lingfield Park† Wolverhampton†☆	Ascot Bangor-on-Dee Chepstow *Fairyhouse* Hexham Musselburgh Wolverhampton†☆
		Tattersalls Sale	Tattersalls Sale	Tattersalls Sale	Tattersalls Sale	
12	**13**	**14**	**15**	**16**	**17**	**18**
Bath Goodwood Great Leighs† *Limerick* *Naas*	Kempton Park† Windsor Wolverhampton†☆	Huntingdon Leicester Newcastle	Kempton Park†☆ Lingfield Park† *Punchestown* Uttoxeter Wetherby	Brighton Great Leighs†☆ Ludlow Nottingham *Punchestown*	Cheltenham *Dundalk†☆* Kempton Park†☆ Newmarket Redcar	Catterick Bridge Cheltenham *Cork* Kelso Newmarket Wolverhampton†☆
		Ascot Sale Tattersalls Sale	Tattersalls Sale	Tattersalls Sale	Tattersalls Sale	Tattersalls Sale
19	**20**	**21**	**22**	**23**	**24**	**25**
Cork *Fairyhouse* Fontwell Park Kempton Park Southwell†	Plumpton Pontefract Windsor	Exeter Lingfield Park† Yarmouth	Bath Great Leighs† Kempton Park†☆ *Navan* Worcester	Brighton Carlisle Great Leighs†☆ Ludlow *Thurles*	Ayr Doncaster *Dundalk†☆* Fakenham Wolverhampton†☆	Aintree Chepstow Doncaster *Naas* Newbury Stratford-on-Avon *Wexford* Wolverhampton†☆
	Arqana Sale Doncaster Sale Fasig-Tipton Sale	Arqana Sale Doncaster Sale Fasig-Tipton Sale	Arqana Sale Doncaster Sale Fasig-Tipton Sale	Doncaster Sale	Doncaster Sale	
26	**27**	**28**	**29**	**30**	**31**	
Aintree *Galway* Towcester *Wexford* Wincanton	*Galway* Kempton Park† Leicester *Leopardstown* Lingfield Park†	Catterick Bridge Southwell† Yarmouth	Great Leighs† Huntingdon Kempton Park†☆ Nottingham *Punchestown*	*Clonmel* Great Leighs†☆ Lingfield Park† Newcastle Stratford-on-Avon	*Down Royal* Newmarket Uttoxeter Wetherby Wolverhampton†☆	
	Tattersalls Sale	Tattersalls Sale	Tattersalls Sale	Tattersalls Sale	Goffs Sale Tattersalls Sale	

NOVEMBER

Sun	Mon	Tues	Wed	Thur	Fri	Sat
30						**1**
Carlisle *Fairyhouse* **Kempton Park†** Leicester						Ascot **Ayr** *Down Royal* **Great Leighs†** **Newmarket** Wetherby
						Tattersalls Sale
2	**3**	**4**	**5**	**6**	**7**	**8**
Carlisle *Cork* Huntingdon *Leopardstown* **Southwell†**	Plumpton Warwick **Wolverhampton†**	**Catterick Bridge** Exeter **Southwell†**	Chepstow *Downpatrick* Huntingdon **Kempton Park†☆** **Nottingham**	**Great Leighs†☆** Haydock Park **Lingfield Park†** *Thurles* Towcester	*Dundalk†☆* Fontwell Park Hexham **Musselburgh** **Wolverhampton†☆**	**Doncaster** Kelso *Naas* Sandown Park Wincanton **Wolverhampton†**
Fasig-Tipton Sale Keeneland Sale	Keeneland Sale Tattersalls (IRE) Sale	Ascot Sale Keeneland Sale Tattersalls (IRE) Sale	Keeneland Sale Tattersalls (IRE) Sale	Fasig-Tipton Sale Keeneland Sale Tattersalls (IRE) Sale	Keeneland Sale Tattersalls (IRE) Sale	Keeneland Sale Tattersalls (IRE) Sale
9	**10**	**11**	**12**	**13**	**14**	**15**
Hereford **Kempton Park†** *Limerick* Market Rasen *Navan*	Carlisle *Limerick* **Southwell†** **Wolverhampton†**	Exeter Lingfield Park Sedgefield	Bangor-on-Dee Kempton Park **Southwell†** **Wolverhampton†☆**	*Clonmel* **Lingfield Park†** Ludlow Taunton	Cheltenham *Dundalk†☆* **Kempton Park†☆** Newcastle **Southwell†**	Cheltenham **Great Leighs†** *Punchestown* Uttoxeter Wetherby **Wolverhampton†**
Keeneland Sale Tattersalls (IRE) Sale	Keeneland Sale Tattersalls (IRE) Sale	Keeneland Sale Tattersalls (IRE) Sale	Keeneland Sale Tattersalls (IRE) Sale	Keeneland Sale Tattersalls (IRE) Sale	Keeneland Sale Tattersalls (IRE) Sale	Keeneland Sale Tattersalls (IRE) Sale
16	**17**	**18**	**19**	**20**	**21**	**22**
Cheltenham *Cork* Fontwell Park *Punchestown* Stratford-on-Avon	**Kempton Park†** Leicester **Wolverhampton†**	Fakenham Folkestone **Southwell†**	Hexham **Kempton Park†☆** **Lingfield Park†** Warwick	**Great Leighs†☆** Hereford Market Rasen *Thurles* Wincanton	Ascot *Dundalk†☆* Exeter Kelso **Wolverhampton†☆**	Ascot *Gowran Park* Haydock Park Huntingdon **Lingfield Park†** **Wolverhampton†**
Goffs Sale Tattersalls (IRE) Sale	Arqana Sale Goffs Sale	Arqana Sale Goffs Sale	Goffs Sale	Goffs Sale	Goffs Sale	Goffs Sale
23	**24**	**25**	**26**	**27**	**28**	**29**
Aintree *Navan* Plumpton Towcester	Ayr **Lingfield Park†** Ludlow	Lingfield Park Sedgefield **Southwell†**	Chepstow Kempton Park Wetherby **Wolverhampton†☆**	**Great Leighs†☆** Newbury Taunton *Thurles* Uttoxeter	*Dundalk†☆* *Fairyhouse* **Kempton Park†☆** **Lingfield Park†** Musselburgh Newbury	*Fairyhouse* **Kempton Park†** Newbury Newcastle Towcester *Wexford* **Wolverhampton†☆**
Goffs Sale	Tattersalls Sale	Tattersalls Sale	Tattersalls Sale	Tattersalls Sale	Tattersalls Sale	Tattersalls Sale

DECEMBER

Sun	Mon	Tues	Wed	Thur	Fri	Sat
	1	**2**	**3**	**4**	**5**	**6**
	Fakenham	Hereford	Ayr	*Great Leighs*†☆	*Dundalk*†☆	Chepstow
	Folkestone	**Lingfield Park**†	Catterick Bridge	Leicester	Exeter	**Great Leighs**†
	Wolverhampton†	**Southwell**†	**Kempton Park**†☆	Market Rasen	**Lingfield Park**†	*Navan*
			Plumpton	Wincanton	Sandown Park	Sandown Park
					Wolverhampton†☆	Wetherby
						Wolverhampton†☆
					Doncaster Sale	
	Tattersalls Sale	Tattersalls Sale	Tattersalls Sale	Tattersalls Sale	Tattersalls Sale	Arqana Sale
7	**8**	**9**	**10**	**11**	**12**	**13**
Clonmel	**Lingfield Park**†	Fontwell Park	Hexham	*Great Leighs*†☆	Cheltenham	Cheltenham
Kelso	Musselburgh	Sedgefield	**Kempton Park**†☆	Huntingdon	Doncaster	Doncaster
Lingfield Park†	**Wolverhampton**†	**Southwell**†	Leicester	Ludlow	*Gowran Park*	*Fairyhouse*
Punchestown			**Southwell**†	Taunton	**Southwell**†	Lingfield Park
Warwick					**Wolverhampton**†☆	**Southwell**†
						Wolverhampton†☆
	Arqana Sale					
Arqana Sale	Fasig-Tipton Sale	Arqana Sale	Arqana Sale			
Fasig-Tipton Sale	Goffs Sale	Goffs Sale	Goffs Sale	Goffs Sale	Doncaster Sale	Goffs Sale
14	**15**	**16**	**17**	**18**	**19**	**20**
Cork	Ayr	Catterick Bridge	Bangor-on-Dee	Exeter	Ascot	Ascot
Lingfield Park†	Plumpton	Folkestone	**Kempton Park**†	*Great Leighs*†☆	*Downpatrick*	Haydock Park
Musselburgh	**Wolverhampton**†	**Southwell**†	**Lingfield Park**†	Ludlow	**Southwell**†	**Lingfield Park**†
Navan			Newbury	**Southwell**†	Uttoxeter	*Navan*
					Wolverhampton†☆	Newcastle
						Wolverhampton†☆
Fasig-Tipton Sale	Tattersalls (IRE) Sale	Tattersalls (IRE) Sale	Tattersalls (IRE) Sale	Tattersalls (IRE) Sale		
21	**22**	**23**	**24**	**25**	**26**	**27**
Carlisle	Hereford	Fontwell Park			*Down Royal*	Chepstow
Great Leighs†	**Kempton Park**†	**Southwell**†			Huntingdon	**Great Leighs**†☆
Thurles	**Lingfield Park**†				Kempton Park	Kempton Park
					Leopardstown	*Leopardstown*
					Limerick	*Limerick*
					Market Rasen	**Southwell**†
					Sedgefield	Wetherby
					Towcester	
					Wetherby	
					Wincanton	
					Wolverhampton†	
	Ascot Sale					
28	**29**	**30**	**31**			
Catterick Bridge	**Great Leighs**†	Haydock Park	**Lingfield Park**†			
Leicester	*Leopardstown*	**Lingfield Park**†	*Punchestown*			
Leopardstown	*Limerick*	Taunton	*Tramore*			
Limerick	Musselburgh	**Wolverhampton**†☆	Uttoxeter			
Lingfield Park†	Newbury		Warwick			

DATES OF PRINCIPAL RACES

(SUBJECT TO ALTERATION)

JANUARY

Aquanti Group 'Dipper' Novices' Chase (Cheltenham)	1st
EBF High Sheriff Of Gloucestershire's Millennium Event "Junior" Standard Open Bumper (Cheltenham)	1st
Unicoin Homes Handicap Chase (Cheltenham)	1st
Phil Sweeney Chase (Thurles)	3rd
Anglo Irish Bank Tolworth Novices' Hurdle (Sandown Park)	5th
partybets.com Anne Boleyn Mares' Only Hurdle (Sandown Park)	5th
Slaney Novices' Hurdle (Naas)	6th
Intercasino.co.uk Lanzarote Handicap Hurdle (Kempton Park)	12th
Ballymore Properties Leamington Novices' Hurdle (Warwick)	12th
totesport.com Classic Handicap Chase (Warwick)	12th
totesport 0800 221 221 Standard Open Bumper (Warwick)	12th
Juvenile Hurdle (Punchestown)	12th
Fitzpatrick Novices' Chase (Leopardstown)	13th
Pierse Chase (Leopardstown)	13th
Pierse Handicap Hurdle (Leopardstown)	13th
Kinloch Brae Chase (Thurles)	17th
Coolmore EBF Mares Novices' Chase (Thurles)	17th
Victor Chandler Chase (Ascot)	19th
Montpelier Group Lightning Novices' Chase (Ascot)	19th
Betty Chandler Memorial Holloway's Hurdle (Limited Handicap) (Ascot)	19th
Oilexo Mares' Only Hurdle (Ascot)	19th
bonussprint.com Altcar Novices' Chase (Haydock Park)	19th
bonussprint.com Champion Hurdle Trial (Haydock Park)	19th
Anglo Irish Bank Novices' Hurdle (Haydock Park)	19th
Peter Marsh Chase (Limited Handicap) (Haydock Park)	19th
Woodlands Novices' Chase (Naas)	19th
Normans Grove Chase (Fairyhouse)	20th
Thyestes Handicap Chase (Gowran Park)	24th
Galmoy Hurdle (Gowran Park)	24th
Byrne Bros Cleeve Hurdle (Cheltenham)	26th
Letheby & Christopher Chase (Cheltenham)	26th
Ballymore Properties Novices' Hurdle (Cheltenham)	26th
Wragge & Co Juvenile Novices' Hurdle (Cheltenham)	26th
Ladbrokes Trophy Handicap Chase (Cheltenham)	26th
JCT600 Mercedes-Benz Doncaster Mares' Only Hurdle (Doncaster)	26th
Sky Bet Handicap Chase (Doncaster)	26th
Golden Cygnet Novices' Hurdle (Leopardstown)	27th
Clarkson Handicap Chase (Leopardstown)	27th
AIG Champion Hurdle (Leopardstown)	27th
Arkle Novices' Chase (Leopardstown)	27th

FEBRUARY

totesport.com Scilly Isles Novices' Chase (Sandown Park)	2nd
totescoop6 Sandown Handicap Hurdle (Sandown Park)	2nd
Agfa UK Hurdle (Sandown Park)	2nd
Agfa Diamond Handicap Chase (Sandown Park)	2nd
Brit Insurance Novices' Hurdle (Wetherby)	2nd
totepool Towton Novices' Chase (Wetherby)	2nd
digibet.com Ladybird Stakes (Kempton Park)	3rd
Hurdle Series Final (Punchestown)	3rd
Tied Cottage Chase (Punchestown)	3rd
Grand National Trial Chase (Punchestown)	3rd
Aon Chase (Newbury)	9th
totepool Game Spirit Chase (Newbury)	9th
tote Text Betting 60021 Standard Open Bumper (Newbury)	9th
totesport Trophy Handicap Hurdle (Newbury)	9th
totesport.com Kingmaker Novices' Chase (Warwick)	9th
totesport.com Novices' Hurdle (Exeter)	9th
Deloitte Novices' Hurdle (Leopardstown)	10th
Spring 4yo Hurdle (Leopardstown)	10th
Dr P J Moriarty Novices' Chase (Leopardstown)	10th
Hennessy Gold Cup (Leopardstown)	10th
Commercial First Ascot Chase (Ascot)	16th
John Smith's Reynoldstown Novices' Chase (Ascot)	16th
Brit Insurance Prestige Novices' Hurdle (Haydock Park)	16th

Casino 36 Stockport Rendlesham Hurdle (Haydock Park) 16th
Red Square Vodka Gold Cup (Handicap Chase) (Haydock Park) 16th
totesport.com Lord Gyllene Handicap Chase (Uttoxeter) 16th
Bathwick Tyres Kingwell Hurdle (Wincanton) 16th
Country Gentlemen's Association Chase (Limited Handicap) (Wincanton) 16th
Red Mills Trial Hurdle (Gowran Park) 16th
Red Mills Chase (Gowran Park) 16th
Ten Up Chase (Navan) 17th
Boyne Hurdle (Navan) 17th
Flyingbolt Novices' Chase (Navan) 17th
Anglo Irish Bank Novices' Hurdle (Kempton Park) 23rd
racingpost.co.uk Pendil Novices' Chase (Kempton Park) 23rd
Racing Post Adonis Juvenile Novices' Hurdle (Kempton Park) 23rd
Racing Post Handicap Chase (Kempton Park) 23rd
Go Pontin's Winter Derby Trial (Lingfield Park) 23rd
pontins.com Cleves Stakes (Lingfield Park) 23rd
totesport.com Eider Handicap Chase (Newcastle) 23rd
Winning Fair Juvenile Hurdle (Fairyhouse) 23rd
Bobbyjo Chase (Fairyhouse) 23rd
INHSO Series Final (Novices' Handicap Hurdle) (Fairyhouse) 23rd
totesport.com National Spirit Hurdle (Fontwell Park) 24th
Newlands Chase (Naas) 24th
Johnstown Novices' Hurdle (Naas) 24th
Nas Na Riogh Novices' Chase (Naas) 24th

MARCH

totepool Premier Kelso Novices' Hurdle (Kelso) 1st
Ashleybank Investments Scottish Borders National (Handicap Chase) (Kelso) 1st
VC Casino.com Gold Cup (Handicap Chase) (Newbury) 1st
Mick Holly Handicap Chase (Leopardstown) 2nd
Michael Purcell Memorial Novices' Hurdle (Thurles) 6th
EBF Sunderlands 'NH' Novices' Hurdle Final (Handicap) (Sandown Park) 8th
Sunderlands Imperial Cup (Handicap Hurdle) (Sandown Park) 8th
EBF/Doncaster Bloodstock Sales Mares' Only Standard Open Bumper Final (Sandown Park) 8th
williamhill.co.uk Lady Wulfruna Stakes (Wolverhampton) 8th
William Hill Lincoln Trial (Heritage Handicap) (Wolverhampton) 8th
Garryrichard Stud Handicap Chase (Gowran Park) 8th
Irish Independent Arkle Challenge Trophy (Novices' Chase) (Cheltenham) 11th
Anglo Irish Bank Supreme Novices' Hurdle (Cheltenham) 11th
Smurfit Kappa Champion Hurdle Challenge Trophy (Cheltenham) 11th
William Hill Trophy (Handicap Chase) (Cheltenham) 11th
Fred Winter Juvenile Novices' Handicap Hurdle (Cheltenham) 11th
Sporting Index Cross Country Handicap Chase (Cheltenham) 11th
Seasons Holidays Queen Mother Champion Chase (Cheltenham) 12th
Royal & SunAlliance Novices' Chase (Cheltenham) 12th
Ballymore Properties Novices' Hurdle (Cheltenham) 12th
Weatherbys Champion Bumper (Cheltenham) 12th
Coral Cup (Handicap Hurdle) (Cheltenham) 12th
Fulke Walwyn Kim Muir Challenge Cup (Handicap Chase) (Cheltenham) 12th
Ladbrokes World Hurdle (Cheltenham) 13th
Ryanair Chase (Cheltenham) 13th
Racing Post Plate (Handicap Chase) (Cheltenham) 13th
Jewson Novices' Handicap Chase (Cheltenham) 13th
Pertemps Final (Handicap Hurdle) (Cheltenham) 13th
NH Challenge Cup (Amateur Riders Novices' Chase) (Cheltenham) 13th
JCB Triumph Novices' Hurdle (Cheltenham) 14th
totesport Cheltenham Gold Cup Chase (Cheltenham) 14th
Brit Insurance Novices' Hurdle (Cheltenham) 14th
David Nicholson Mares' Only Hurdle (Cheltenham) 14th
Johnny Henderson Grand Annual Challenge Cup (Handicap Chase) (Cheltenham) 14th
Vincent O'Brien County Handicap Hurdle (Cheltenham) 14th
Christie's Foxhunter Challenge Cup Chase (Cheltenham) 14th
Bet Direct Winter Derby (Lingfield Park) 15th
betdirectuk.com Spring Cup (Lingfield Park) 15th
32Red.com Hever Sprint Stakes (Lingfield Park) 15th
John Smith's Midlands Grand National (Handicap Chase) (Uttoxeter) 15th
Dawn Run Mares Novices' Chase (Limerick) 16th
EBF Handicap Chase Final (Navan) 16th
Doncaster Mile (Doncaster) 22nd
intercasino.co.uk Magnolia Stakes (Kempton Park) 22nd
intercasino.co.uk Stakes (fillies) (Kempton Park) 22nd
intercasino.co.uk Rosebery Stakes (Heritage Handicap) (Kempton Park) 22nd
Murphys Handicap Hurdle (Cork) 23rd

Festival Novices' Hurdle (Fairyhouse)..23rd
EBF Mares Hurdle Final (Fairyhouse)..23rd
Powers Gold Cup Novices' Chase (Fairyhouse)...23rd
Irish Grand National (Handicap Chase) (Fairyhouse)...24th
Avon Ri Novices' Chase (Fairyhouse)..24th
Sherry Fitzgerald Hurdle (Fairyhouse)..24th
Menolly Homes Handicap Hurdle (Fairyhouse)..25th
Weatherbys Hurdle (Fairyhouse)...25th
Moore Memorial Handicap Chase (Fairyhouse)...25th
Dunboyne Castle Novices' Hurdle (Fairyhouse)...25th
DBS Spring Sales Standard Open Bumper (Newbury)..28th
williamhill.co.uk Cammidge Trophy (Doncaster)..29th
William Hill Spring Mile (Handicap) (Doncaster)..29th
William Hill Lincoln (Heritage Handicap) (Doncaster)...29th
intercasino.co.uk Dragonfly Stakes (Kempton Park)...29th
EBF/TBA Mares' Novices' Final (Handicap Chase) (Newbury)...29th
EBF Mares Only 'NH' Novices' Hurdle Final (Limited Handicap) (Newbury).......................................29th
An Uaimh Chase (Navan)...29th
Park Express Stakes (Curragh)...30th

APRIL

Weatherbys Bank 'Further Flight' Stakes (Nottingham)...2nd
John Smith's Anniversary 4yo Novices' Hurdle (Aintree)...3rd
Betfair Bowl Chase (Aintree)...3rd
John Smith's Liverpool Hurdle (Aintree)...3rd
Citroen C4 Picasso Mersey Novices' Hurdle (Aintree)..3rd
John Smith's Red Rum Handicap Chase (Aintree)...3rd
John Smith's Handicap Hurdle (Aintree)...3rd
John Smith's Fox Hunters' Chase (Aintree)...3rd
John Smith's Melling Chase (Aintree)...4th
Citroen C6 Sefton Novices' Hurdle (Aintree)..4th
John Smith's Mildmay Novices' Chase (Aintree)...4th
John Smith's Imagine Appeal Top Novices' Hurdle (Aintree)...4th
John Smith's Mares' Only Standard Open Bumper (Aintree)..4th
John Smith's Topham Handicap Chase (Aintree)...4th
John Smith's Maghull Novices' Chase (Aintree)..5th
Baltika Beer Aintree Hurdle (Aintree)...5th
John Smith's Champion Standard Open Bumper (Aintree)...5th
John Smith's Grand National (Handicap Chase) (Aintree)..5th
John Smith's Extra Cold Handicap Hurdle (Aintree)..5th
John Smith's Extra Smooth Handicap Hurdle (Aintree)..5th
betdirect.com International Trial Stakes (Lingfield Park)..5th
1000 Guineas Trial (Leopardstown)..6th
2000 Guineas Trial (Leopardstown)..6th
Hugh McMahon Memorial Novices' Chase (Limerick)...6th
intercasino.co.uk Easter Stakes (colts & geldings) (Kempton Park)...12th
intercasino.co.uk Masaka Stakes (fillies) (Kempton Park)...12th
Gladness Stakes (Curragh)..13th
Faucets for Mira Showers Silver Trophy (Limited Handicap Chase) (Cheltenham).............................16th
Leslie Harrison Memorial Nell Gwyn Stakes (fillies) (Newmarket)...16th
European Free Handicap Stakes (Newmarket)..16th
Connaught Access Flooring Feilden Stakes (Newmarket)..16th
Yorkshire Bank Mares' Only Handicap Hurdle (Cheltenham)..17th
banshahousestables.com Craven Stakes (Newmarket)..17th
Weatherbys Earl of Sefton Stakes (Newmarket)...17th
Abernant Stakes (Newmarket)...17th
Silver Bowl Stakes (Ripon)..17th
Ashleybank Investments Future Champion Novices' Chase (Ayr)...19th
Samsung Electronics Scottish Champion Hurdle (Limited Handicap) (Ayr)...19th
Coral Scottish Grand National (Handicap Chase) (Ayr)...19th
Dubai Duty Free Stakes (fillies) (Newbury)..19th
Dubai Tennis Championships Stakes (Newbury)...19th
Lane's End Greenham Stakes (colts & geldings) (Newbury)..19th
Ballysax Stakes (Leopardstown)...20th
VC Bet Novices' Hurdle (Punchestown)..22nd
Ellier Novices' Chase (Punchestown)...22nd
Evening Herald Handicap Hurdle (Punchestown)..22nd
Kerrygold Champion Chase (Punchestown)..22nd
S M Morris Handicap Chase (Punchestown)..23rd
Punchestown Gold Cup (Punchestown)..23rd
Bewleys Mares Hurdle (Punchestown)...23rd
Champion Bumper (Punchestown)...23rd
Champion 4yo Hurdle (Punchestown)..24th

Tipperkevin Hurdle (Punchestown) ... 24th
Swordlestown Novices' Chase (Punchestown) ... 24th
Pat Taaffe Handicap Chase (Punchestown) ... 24th
Gordon Richards Stakes (Sandown Park) ... 25th
Tickell Novices' Hurdle (Punchestown) ... 25th
Betfair Novices' Handicap Chase (Punchestown) ... 25th
Punchestown Champion Hurdle (Punchestown) ... 25th
totesport.com Leicestershire Stakes (Leicester) ... 26th
Celebration Chase (Sandown Park) ... 26th
Concept Hurdle (Sandown Park) ... 26th
Sandown Mile (Sandown Park) ... 26th
Classic Trial (Sandown Park) ... 26th
Sandown Park Gold Cup (Handicap Chase) (Sandown Park) ... 26th
Osberstown Development Handicap Hurdle (Punchestown) ... 27th
Prix Ganay (Longchamp) ... 29th
EBF Lansdown Stakes (fillies) (Bath) ... 30th
Woodcote Stud Sagaro Stakes (Ascot) ... 30th
Britain's Got Talent Paradise Stakes (Ascot) ... 30th
waterhomes.com Pavilion Stakes (Ascot) ... 30th

MAY

EBF Begbies-Traynor Conqueror Stakes (fillies) (Goodwood) ... 3rd
Stan James 2000 Guineas Stakes (colts & fillies) (Newmarket) ... 3rd
Stan James Dahlia Stakes (fillies) (Newmarket) ... 3rd
Stan James Newmarket Stakes (colts) (Newmarket) ... 3rd
Stan James Stakes (Heritage Handicap) (Newmarket) ... 3rd
Stan James 1000 Guineas Stakes (fillies) (Newmarket) ... 4th
Stan James Jockey Club Stakes (Newmarket) ... 4th
Stan James Palace House Stakes (Newmarket) ... 4th
Stan James Pretty Polly Stakes (fillies) (Newmarket) ... 4th
digibet Sports Betting Jubilee Handicap Stakes (Kempton Park) ... 5th
Athasi Stakes (Curragh) ... 5th
Mooresbridge Stakes (Curragh) ... 5th
Tetrarch Stakes (Curragh) ... 5th
Weatherbys Bank Cheshire Oaks (fillies) (Chester) ... 7th
totesport Chester Cup (Heritage Handicap) (Chester) ... 7th
Akkroball Huxley Stakes (Chester) ... 8th
MBNA Chester Vase (colts & geldings) (Chester) ... 8th
TurfTV Aubigny Stakes (Goodwood) ... 8th
Blue Square Ormonde Stakes (Chester) ... 9th
Aktiv Kapital UK Ltd Dee Stakes (colts & geldings) (Chester) ... 9th
Bovis Homes Buckhounds Stakes (Ascot) ... 10th
totesport.com Victoria Cup (Heritage Handicap) (Ascot) ... 10th
Betfred Swinton Handicap Hurdle (Haydock Park) ... 10th
Betfredpoker Spring Trophy (Haydock Park) ... 10th
totesport Derby Trial (colts & geldings) (Lingfield Park) ... 10th
totepool Chartwell Stakes (fillies) (Lingfield Park) ... 10th
totesport.com Oaks Trial (fillies) (Lingfield Park) ... 10th
totesportcasino.com Kilvington Fillies' Stakes (Nottingham) ... 10th
Amethyst Stakes (Leopardstown) ... 11th
Derrinstown 1000 Guineas Trial (Leopardstown) ... 11th
Derrinstown Derby Trial (Leopardstown) ... 11th
Murphys Handicap Hurdle (Killarney) ... 11th
Poule d'Essai des Poulains (Longchamp) ... 11th
Poule d'Essai des Pouliches (Longchamp) ... 11th
VC Casino.com Stakes (colts & geldings) (Windsor) ... 12th
Duke of York Hearthstead Homes Stakes (York) ... 14th
Tattersalls Musidora Stakes (fillies) (York) ... 15th
totesport.com Dante Stakes (York) ... 15th
totepool Middleton Stakes (fillies) (York) ... 15th
Bank of Scotland Corporate Hambleton Stakes (Handicap) (York) ... 15th
Montjeu Coolmore Prix Saint-Alary (Longchamp) ... 16th
Glasgow Stakes (Hamilton Park) ... 15th
McGrattan Piling Braveheart Stakes (Handicap) (Hamilton Park) ... 16th
Ultimate Travel Stakes (Newbury) ... 16th
Swettenham Stud Fillies' Trial Stakes (Newbury) ... 16th
Emirates Airline Yorkshire Cup (York) ... 16th
Langleys Solicitors EBF Marygate Stakes (fillies) (York) ... 16th
Michael Seely Memorial Stakes (fillies) (York) ... 16th
Mount Ruby Handicap Chase (Cork) ... 16th
Juddmonte Lockinge Stakes (Newbury) ... 17th
paddypower.com Stakes (Newbury) ... 17th
Prix d'Ispahan (Longchamp) ... 18th

Letheby & Christopher Festival Stakes (Goodwood) 21st
Peters Opal Stakes (colts & geldings) (Goodwood) 22nd
Raymarine Stakes (fillies) (Goodwood) 22nd
Betfair Temple Stakes (Haydock Park) 24th
EBF Joan Westbrook Pinnacle Stakes (fillies) (Haydock Park) 24th
Watts/McCrohan 50th Tribute Sandy Lane Stakes (Haydock Park) 24th
totesport.com Silver Bowl (Heritage Handicap) (Haydock Park) 24th
Darian Homes King Charles II Stakes (Newmarket) 24th
onerailway.com Fairway Stakes (Newmarket) 24th
Coral Sprint (Heritage Handicap) (Newmarket) 24th
Pertemps Cup Champion Hunters Chase (Stratford-on-Avon) 24th
Ridgewood Pearl Stakes (Curragh) 24th
Greenlands Stakes (Curragh) 24th
Irish 2000 Guineas Stakes (Curragh) 24th
Tattersalls Gold Cup (Curragh) 25th
Gallinule Stakes (Curragh) 25th
Irish 1000 Guineas Stakes (Curragh) 25th
totesport.com Zetland Gold Cup (Heritage Handicap) (Redcar) 26th
Hilary Needler Trophy (fillies) (Beverley) 28th
Betfair Henry II Stakes (Sandown Park) 29th
Betfair Heron Stakes (Sandown Park) 29th
Betfair Brigadier Gerard Stakes (Sandown Park) 29th
Betfair Mobile National Stakes (Sandown Park) 29th
Empire Property Group On The House Stakes (Goodwood) 31st
Timeform Silver Salver Stakes (fillies) (Haydock Park) 31st
Bentley Grand Cup (York) 31st
Coral Sprint Trophy (Handicap) (York) 31st

JUNE

Langvale Homes Charleston Grange Perth Gold Cup (Handicap Chase) (Perth) 1st
Prix du Jockey Club (Chantilly) 1st
SEI Investments Stakes (Windsor) 2nd
Swordlestown Stakes (Naas) 2nd
digibet Achilles Stakes (Kempton Park) 4th
Ballyogan Stakes (Leopardstown) 4th
Coronation Cup (Epsom Downs) 6th
Oaks (fillies) (Epsom Downs) 6th
Princess Elizabeth Stakes (fillies) (Epsom Downs) 6th
Surrey Stakes (Epsom Downs) 6th
Hildon Stakes (Goodwood) 6th
Derby (colts & fillies) (Epsom Downs) 7th
Diomed Stakes (Epsom Downs) 7th
Woodcote Stakes (Epsom Downs) 7th
The 'Dash' (Heritage Handicap) (Epsom Downs) 7th
Prix de Diane (Chantilly) 8th
Weatherbys Bank Pipalong Stakes (fillies) (Pontefract) 9th
Ballycorus Stakes (Leopardstown) 11th
Bank of Scotland Corporate Stakes (Haydock Park) 12th
Lord Weinstock Memorial Stakes (fillies) (Newbury) 12th
cherriesracing.com Scurry Stakes (Sandown Park) 14th
William Hill Trophy (Heritage Handicap) (York) 14th
Axminster Carpets Cathedral Stakes (Salisbury) 15th
Noblesse Stakes (Cork) 15th
Tweenhills Farm and Stud Warwickshire Oaks (fillies) (Warwick) 16th
Queen Anne Stakes (Royal Ascot) 17th
St James's Palace Stakes (colts) (Royal Ascot) 17th
Coventry Stakes (Royal Ascot) 17th
King's Stand Stakes (Royal Ascot) 17th
Windsor Castle Stakes (Royal Ascot) 17th
Ascot Stakes (Handicap) (Royal Ascot) 17th
Prince of Wales's Stakes (Royal Ascot) 18th
Queen Mary Stakes (fillies) (Royal Ascot) 18th
Windsor Forest Stakes (fillies & mares) (Royal Ascot) 18th
Jersey Stakes (Royal Ascot) 18th
Sandringham Handicap Stakes (fillies) (Royal Ascot) 18th
Royal Hunt Cup (Heritage Handicap) (Royal Ascot) 18th
Gold Cup (Royal Ascot) 19th
Ribblesdale Stakes (fillies) (Royal Ascot) 19th
Norfolk Stakes (Royal Ascot) 19th
Hampton Court Stakes (Royal Ascot) 19th
Britannia Stakes (Heritage Handicap) (colts & geldings) (Royal Ascot) 19th
King George V Stakes (Heritage Handicap) (Royal Ascot) 19th
Coronation Stakes (fillies) (Royal Ascot) 20th

King Edward VII Stakes (colts & geldings) (Royal Ascot) 20th
Albany Stakes (fillies) (Royal Ascot) 20th
Queen's Vase Stakes (Royal Ascot) 20th
Wolferton Handicap Stakes (Royal Ascot) 20th
Buckingham Palace Stakes (Heritage Handicap) (Royal Ascot) 20th
Golden Jubilee Stakes (Royal Ascot) 21st
Hardwicke Stakes (Royal Ascot) 21st
Chesham Stakes (Royal Ascot) 21st
Duke of Edinburgh Stakes (Heritage Handicap) (Royal Ascot) 21st
Queen Alexandra Stakes (Royal Ascot) 21st
Wokingham Stakes (Heritage Handicap) (Royal Ascot) 21st
totesport Pontefract Castle Stakes (Pontefract) 22nd
Carling Carlisle Bell Handicap Stakes (Carlisle) 25th
Grolsch Cumberland Plate (Handicap Stakes) (Carlisle) 25th
EBF/GNER Go Racing Hoppings Stakes (Newcastle) 26th
totesport.com Eternal Stakes (fillies) (Warwick) 26th
Newcastle Brown Ale 80th Birthday Chipchase Stakes (Newcastle) 28th
John Smith's Northumberland Plate (Heritage Handicap) (Newcastle) 28th
Criterion Stakes (Newmarket) 28th
Fred Archer Stakes (Newmarket) 28th
Empress Stakes (fillies) (Newmarket) 28th
totepool Midsummer Stakes (Windsor) 28th
Curragh Cup Stakes (Curragh) 28th
Pretty Polly Stakes (Curragh) 28th
Britannia Building Society English Summer National (Handicap Chase) (Uttoxeter) 29th
Irish Derby (Curragh) 29th
Railway Stakes (Curragh) 29th
Grand Prix de Saint-Cloud (Saint-Cloud) 29th

JULY

Brownstown Stakes (Leopardstown) 2nd
William Ewart Properties Gala Stakes (Sandown Park) 4th
Aim Dragon Stakes (Sandown Park) 4th
bet365 Lancashire Oaks (fillies) (Haydock Park) 5th
H20 Trophy Handicap Stakes (Haydock Park) 5th
bet365 Old Newton Cup (Heritage Handicap) (Haydock Park) 5th
Coral-Eclipse Stakes (Sandown Park) 5th
Laurent-Perrier Champagne Sprint Stakes (Sandown Park) 5th
Weatherbys VAT Services Stakes (Sandown Park) 5th
Addleshaw Goddard Stakes (fillies) (Sandown Park) 5th
totescoop6 Stakes (Heritage Handicap) (Sandown Park) 5th
EBF Land O'Burns Stakes (fillies) (Ayr) 6th
UAE Hydra Properties Falmouth Stakes (fillies) (Newmarket) 9th
Irish Thoroughbred Marketing Cherry Hinton Stakes (fillies) (Newmarket) 9th
Princess of Wales's wbx.com Stakes (Newmarket) 10th
TNT July Stakes (colts & geldings) (Newmarket) 10th
Bahrain Trophy (Newmarket) 10th
Darley July Cup (Newmarket) 11th
Weatherbys Superlative Stakes (Newmarket) 11th
Ladbrokes Bunbury Cup (Heritage Handicap) (Newmarket) 11th
Cuisine de France Summer Stakes (fillies) (York) 11th
Sony Summer Mile (Ascot) 12th
totesport.com City Wall Stakes (Chester) 12th
John Smith's Extra Smooth Silver Cup (Handicap) (York) 12th
John Smith's Cup (Heritage Handicap) (York) 12th
International Stakes (Curragh) 12th
Minstrel Stakes (Curragh) 13th
Irish Oaks (Curragh) 13th
Anglesey Stakes (Curragh) 13th
Prix Jean Prat (Chantilly) 13th
Giles Insurance 40th Anniversary Heritage Handicap (Ayr) 14th
Juddmonte Grand Prix de Paris (Longchamp) 14th
EBF Virginia Stakes (fillies) (Yarmouth) 15th
totesport.com Summer Plate Handicap Chase (Market Rasen) 19th
totescoop6 Summer Handicap Hurdle (Market Rasen) 19th
Uplands Racing Hackwood Stakes (Newbury) 19th
EBF Rose Bowl Stakes (Newbury) 19th
David Wilson Homes Steventon Stakes (Newbury) 19th
Weatherbys Super Sprint (Newbury) 19th
Plantation Stud Stakes (fillies) (Newmarket) 19th
Grimes Hurdle (Tipperary) 20th
Meld Stakes (Leopardstown) 20th
Beat Charity Star Stakes (fillies) (Sandown Park) 24th

Tyros Stakes (Leopardstown) 24th
EBF Valiant Stakes (fillies) (Ascot) 25th
King George VI and Queen Elizabeth Stakes (Ascot) 26th
Kleenex Winkfield Stakes (Ascot) 26th
totesport.com International Stakes (Heritage Handicap) (Ascot) 26th
Skybet York Stakes (York) 26th
Princess Margaret Stakes (fillies) (Ascot) 27th
Hong Kong Jockey Club Sprint (Heritage Handicap) (Ascot) 27th
Pomfret Stakes (Pontefract) 27th
Phoenix Stakes (Curragh) 27th
Betfair Cup (Goodwood) 29th
Gordon Stakes (Goodwood) 29th
Betfair Molecomb Stakes (Goodwood) 29th
BGC Sussex Stakes (Goodwood) 29th
Veuve Cliquot Vintage Stakes (Goodwood) 30th
Galway Plate (Handicap Chase) (Galway) 30th
ABN AMRO Goodwood Cup (Goodwood) 30th
Audi Stakes (Goodwood) 31st
Lillie Langtry Stakes (fillies & mares) (Goodwood) 31st
Galway Hurdle (Handicap) (Galway) 31st

AUGUST

Richmond Stakes (colts & geldings) (Goodwood) 1st
Oak Tree Stakes (fillies) (Goodwood) 1st
Coutts Glorious Stakes (Goodwood) 1st
totesport Mile (Heritage Handicap) (Goodwood) 1st
Turf Club Stewards' Sprint (Handicap Stakes) (Goodwood) 1st
Blue Square Nassau Stakes (fillies) (Goodwood) 2nd
Bluesquarepoker.com Thoroughbred Stakes (Goodwood) 2nd
bluesquare.com Stewards' Cup (Heritage Handicap) (Goodwood) 2nd
Prix Rothschild (Deauville) 2nd
M&S Money Queensferry Stakes (Chester) 3rd
EBF Chalice Stakes (fillies) (Newbury) 3rd
Give Thanks Stakes (Cork) 4th
Blue Square Shergar Cup Day (Ascot) 9th
totepool Rose of Lancaster Stakes (Haydock Park) 9th
skybet.com Sweet Solera Stakes (fillies) (Newmarket) 9th
Debutante Stakes (Curragh) 10th
Phoenix Sprint (Curragh) 10th
Royal Whip Stakes (Curragh) 10th
Prix Maurice de Gheest (Deauville) 10th
EBF Upavon Stakes (fillies) (Salisbury) 13th
totesport.com Sovereign Stakes (colts & geldings) (Salisbury) 14th
Newbury St Hugh's Stakes (fillies) (Newbury) 15th
Hungerford Stakes (Newbury) 16th
Geoffrey Freer Stakes (Newbury) 16th
Usk Valley Stud Stakes (Newbury) 16th
William Hill Great St Wilfrid Stakes (Heritage Handicap) (Ripon) 16th
EBF Dick Hern Stakes (fillies) (Bath) 17th
EBF Slatch Farm Stud Flying Fillies' Stakes (Pontefract) 17th
Ballyroan Stakes (Leopardstown) 17th
Desmond Stakes (Leopardstown) 17th
Prix du Haras de Fresnay-Le-Buffard Jacques le Marois (Deauville) 17th
Juddmonte International Stakes (York) 19th
Ladbrokes Great Voltigeur Stakes (colts & geldings) (York) 19th
Weatherbys Insurance Lonsdale Cup (York) 19th
Brandon Handicap Hurdle (Tralee) 19th
Ireland Gimcrack Stakes (colts & geldings) (York) 20th
Julian Graves Roses Stakes (York) 20th
totesport Ebor (Heritage Handicap) (York) 20th
Darley Yorkshire Oaks (fillies) (York) 21st
Jaguar Cars Lowther Stakes (fillies) (York) 21st
Grahame Stowe Bateson Family Law Unit Strensall Stakes (York) 21st
EBF Galtres Stakes (fillies) (York) 21st
Coolmore Nunthorpe Stakes (York) 22nd
Acomb Stakes (York) 22nd
SKF City of York Stakes (York) 22nd
totepool Beverley Bullet Sprint (Beverley) 23rd
totesport Celebration Mile (Goodwood) 23rd
Prestige Stakes (fillies) (Goodwood) 23rd
Windflower March Stakes (Goodwood) 23rd
Countrywide Steel and Tubes Hopeful Stakes (Newmarket) 23rd
totesport.com Winter Hill Stakes (Windsor) 23rd

totepool August Stakes (Windsor) 23rd
Futurity Stakes (Curragh) 23rd
Denny Handicap Chase (Tralee) 23rd
EBF Alice Keppel Handicap Stakes (fillies) (Goodwood) 24th
Darley Prix Morny (Deauville) 24th
Ripon Champion Two Yrs Old Trophy (Ripon) 25th
Weatherbys Bank Stonehenge Stakes (Salisbury) 29th
betterbetcorbett Chester Handicap Stakes (Chester) 30th
Iveco Daily Solario Stakes (Sandown Park) 30th
bluesquare.com Atalanta Stakes (fillies) (Sandown Park) 30th
Moyglare Stud Stakes (Curragh) 31st
Round Tower Stakes (Curragh) 31st
Flying Five Stakes (Curragh) 31st

SEPTEMBER

Charles Jones Homes Supreme Stakes (Goodwood) 2nd
EBF Dick Poole Stakes (fillies) (Salisbury) 4th
Betfred Sprint Cup (Haydock Park) 6th
Betfred "Treble Odds On All Luckys" Superior Mile (Haydock Park) 6th
betfredpoker.com Old Borough Cup (Heritage Handicap) (Haydock Park) 6th
totepool Sirenia Stakes (Kempton Park) 6th
totesport.com September Stakes (Kempton Park) 6th
Kilternan Stakes (Leopardstown) 6th
Matron Stakes (Leopardstown) 6th
Irish Champion Stakes (Leopardstown) 6th
Prix du Moulin de Longchamp (Longchamp) 7th
Scarbrough Stakes (Doncaster) 10th
£300,000 St Leger 2-y-o Stakes (Doncaster) 10th
Smirnoff Handicap Chase (Galway) 10th
Park Hill Stakes (fillies) (Doncaster) 11th
May Hill Stakes (fillies) (Doncaster) 11th
Weatherbys Bank Sceptre Stakes (fillies) (Doncaster) 11th
Fortune Stakes (Sandown Park) 11th
GNER Doncaster Cup (Doncaster) 12th
Flying Childers Stakes (Doncaster) 12th
Blandford Stakes (Curragh) 12th
Carlsberg Stand Cup (Chester) 13th
Betdaq the betting exchange Henry Gee Stakes (fillies & mares) (Chester) 13th
Ladbrokes St Leger (colts & fillies) (Doncaster) 13th
Park Stakes (Doncaster) 13th
Champagne Stakes (colts & geldings) (Doncaster) 13th
Ladbrokes Portland Stakes (Heritage Handicap) (Doncaster) 13th
Stardom Stakes (Goodwood) 13th
Starlit Stakes (Goodwood) 13th
Irish St Leger (Curragh) 13th
Renaissance Stakes (Curragh) 13th
National Stakes (Curragh) 14th
Select Racing UK on Sky 432 Stakes (Goodwood) 14th
Qatar Prix Vermeille (Longchamp) 14th
Solonoway Stakes (Curragh) 14th
Lartigue Handicap Hurdle (Listowel) 16th
EBF At The Races John Musker Stakes (fillies) (Yarmouth) 17th
Kerry National (Handicap Chase) (Listowel) 17th
Guinness Handicap Hurdle (Listowel) 18th
James Barr Chartered Surveyors Harry Rosebery Stakes (Ayr) 19th
Dubai Duty Free Arc Trial (Newbury) 19th
Dubai Duty Free Cup (Newbury) 19th
Laundry Cottage Stud Firth of Clyde Stakes (fillies) (Ayr) 20th
Doonside Cup (Ayr) 20th
totesport.com Ayr Gold Cup (Heritage Handicap) (Ayr) 20th
Dubai Duty Free Mill Reef Stakes (Newbury) 20th
Dubai International Airport World Trophy (Newbury) 20th
EBF Flower of Scotland Stakes (fillies) (Hamilton Park) 21st
Charles James Homes Foundation Stakes (Goodwood) 24th
PriceWaterhouseCoopers Princess Royal EBF Stakes (fillies) (Ascot) 26th
Watership Down Stud Sales Stakes (fillies) (Ascot) 26th
Meon Valley Stud Fillies' Mile (Ascot) 27th
Queen Elizabeth II Stakes (Ascot) 27th
Juddmonte Royal Lodge Stakes (colts & geldings) (Ascot) 27th
Space Group Rosemary Handicap (fillies) (Ascot) 27th
Miles & Morrison October Stakes (fillies) (Ascot) 27th
Cordell Lavarack Stakes (Gowran Park) 27th
John Guest Diadem Stakes (Ascot) 28th
Grosvenor Casinos Cumberland Lodge Stakes (Ascot) 28th
SIS Fenwolf Stakes (Ascot) 28th

Beresford Stakes (Naas) 28th
Park Stakes (Naas) 28th
Kilbegnet Novices' Chase (Roscommon) 29th

OCTOBER

Rous Stakes (Newmarket) 2nd
Noel Murless Stakes (Newmarket) 2nd
Somerville Tattersall Stakes (colts & geldings) (Newmarket) 2nd
£250,000 Tattersalls October Auction Stakes (Newmarket) 2nd
Cheveley Park Stakes (fillies) (Newmarket) 3rd
Shadwell Middle Park Stakes (colts) (Newmarket) 3rd
Shadwell Godolphin Stakes (Newmarket) 3rd
Shadwell Joel Stakes (Newmarket) 3rd
Shadwell Oh So Sharp Stakes (fillies) (Newmarket) 3rd
Kingdom of Bahrain Sun Chariot Stakes (fillies) (Newmarket) 4th
totesport.com Cambridgeshire (Heritage Handicap) (Newmarket) 4th
Tattersalls Timeform Million (Newmarket) 4th
Tattersalls Timeform Fillies' 800 (Newmarket) 4th
totepool Two-Year-Old Trophy (Redcar) 4th
Guisborough Stakes (Redcar) 4th
Langtons Handicap Hurdle (Gowran Park) 4th
National Lottery Chase (Gowran Park) 4th
Qatar Prix de la Foret (Longchamp) 4th
Qater Prix du Cadran (Longchamp) 4th
Concorde Stakes (Tipperary) 5th
Like A Butterfly Novices' Chase (Tipperary) 5th
Tipperary Hurdle (Tipperary) 5th
Joe Mac Novices' Hurdle (Tipperary) 5th
Qatar Prix de l'Arc de Triomphe (Longchamp) 5th
Qatar Prix Jean Luc Lagardere (Longchamp) 5th
Qatar Prix Marcel Boussac Criterium des Pouliches (Longchamp) 5th
Qatar Prix de l'Opera (Longchamp) 5th
Qatar Prix de l'Abbaye de Longchamp (Longchamp) 5th
Willmott Dixon Bengough Stakes (Ascot) 11th
Deloitte Autumn Stakes (Ascot) 11th
Willmott Dixon Cornwallis Stakes (Ascot) 11th
Grahame Stowe Bateson Family Law Unit Rockingham Stakes (to be confirmed) (Ascot) 11th
Sherry Fitzgerald Chase (Limerick) 12th
Munster National (Handicap Chase) (Limerick) 12th
Buck House Novices' Chase (Punchestown) 15th
Carvills Hill Chase (Punchestown) 16th
Georgia House Stud Darley Stakes (Newmarket) 17th
EBF Boadicea Stakes (fillies) (Newmarket) 17th
Lanwades Stud Severals Stakes (fillies) (Newmarket) 17th
Darley Dewhurst Stakes (colts & fillies) (Newmarket) 18th
Emirates Airline Champion Stakes (Newmarket) 18th
Rockfel Stakes (fillies) (Newmarket) 18th
VC Bet Challenge Stakes (Newmarket) 18th
Pride Stakes (Fillies) Newmarket 18th
Jockey Club Cup (Newmarket) 18th
totesport Cesarewitch (Heritage Handicap) (Newmarket) 18th
wbx.com Novices' Hurdle (Kempton Park) 19th
wbx.com Handicap Chase (Kempton Park) 19th
Dairygold Handicap Chase (Cork) 19th
totesport.com Silver Tankard Stakes (Pontefract) 20th
intercasino.co.uk Molyneux Novices' Chase (Aintree) 25th
Ballymore Ontario Tower Novices' Hurdle (Chepstow) 25th
Intercasino Silver Trophy (Handicap Hurdle) (Chepstow) 25th
Racing Post Trophy (colts & fillies) (Doncaster) 25th
Doncaster Stakes (Doncaster) 25th
Mountgrange Stud Stakes (colts & geldings) (Newbury) 25th
St Simon Stakes (Newbury) 25th
Heatherwold Stud Stakes (fillies) (Newbury) 25th
Brown Lad Handicap Hurdle (Naas) 25th
Poplar Square Chase (Naas) 25th
Bonusprint.com Old Roan Steeple Chase (Limited Handicap) (Aintree) 26th
Ballybrit Novices' Chase (Galway) 26th
Prix Royal-Oak (Longchamp) 26th
Killavullan Stakes (Leopardstown) 27th
Floodlit Stakes (Kempton Park) 29th
EBF River Eden Stakes (fillies & mares) (Lingfield Park) 30th
EBF Fleur de Lys Stakes (fillies) (Lingfield Park) 30th
EBF Bosra Sham Stakes (fillies) (Newmarket) 31st

Constant Security Wensleydale Juvenile Novices' Hurdle (Wetherby)..31st
bet365.com Handicap Chase (Wetherby)..31st
Anglo Irish Bank Hurdle (Down Royal)..31st
Scarvagh House Mares Novices' Hurdle (Down Royal)..31st

NOVEMBER

Byrne Group Handicap Chase (Ascot)..1st
bet365 James Seymour Stakes (Newmarket)..1st
bet365 Ben Marshall Stakes (Newmarket)..1st
EBF bet365.com EBF Montrose Stakes (fillies) (Newmarket)..1st
bet365 Charlie Hall Chase (Wetherby)..1st
John Smith's Hurdle (Wetherby)..1st
Daniel Gath Homes Mares' Only Hurdle (Wetherby)..1st
James Nicholson Chase (Down Royal)..1st
Killultagh Properties Chase (Down Royal)..1st
Cork Grand National (Handicap Chase) (Cork)..2nd
Criterium International (Saint-Cloud)..2nd
William Hill Gold Cup (Limited Handicap Chase) (Exeter)..4th
EBF Gillies Stakes (fillies) (Doncaster)..8th
totescoop6 Wentworth Stakes (Doncaster)..8th
totesport.com November Heritage Handicap (Doncaster)..8th
totepool Rising Stars Novices' Chase (Wincanton)..8th
£1 Million totetentofollow Elite Hurdle (Limited Handicap) (Wincanton)..8th
Badger Ales Trophy (Handicap Chase) (Wincanton)..8th
Fortria Chase (Navan)..9th
Lismullen Hurdle (Navan)..9th
For Auction Novices' Hurdle (Navan)..9th
Criterium de Saint-Cloud (Saint-Cloud)..12th
Clonmel Oil Chase (Clonmel)..13th
Anglo Irish Bank Private Banking Novices' Hurdle (Cheltenham)..14th
Ryman The Stationer Juvenile Novices' Hurdle (Cheltenham)..15th
Paddy Power Gold Cup (Handicap Chase) (Cheltenham)..15th
Servo Computer Services Trophy (Handicap Chase) (Cheltenham)..15th
Lombard Properties Handicap Hurdle (Cheltenham)..15th
Irish Field Novices' Chase (Punchestown)..15th
Independent Newspaper Novices' Chase (Cheltenham)..16th
Greatwood Handicap Hurdle (Cheltenham)..16th
Open Bumper (Cheltenham)..16th
Blackwater Handicap Hurdle (Cork)..16th
Craddockstown Novices' Chase (Punchestown)..16th
Morgiana Hurdle (Punchestown)..16th
Coral Ascot Hurdle (Ascot)..22nd
Amlin 1965 Limited Intermediate Handicap Chase (Ascot)..22nd
Betfair Chase (Haydock Park)..22nd
Newton Novices' Hurdle (Haydock Park)..22nd
totesport.com Peterborough Chase (Huntingdon)..22nd
Churchill Stakes (Lingfield Park)..22nd
Eastbourne Stakes (Lingfield Park)..23rd
totesport.com Becher Handicap Chase (Aintree)..23rd
Monksfield Novices' Hurdle (Navan)..23rd
Troytown Handicap Chase (Navan)..23rd
Friends of Nigel Clark Mares' Only Hurdle (Kempton Park)..26th
Marshall's Peugeot 308 Novices' Chase (Newbury)..27th
AIS Fire Tech Novices' Chase (Newbury)..28th
Hyde Stakes (Kempton Park)..29th
White Rose Stakes (Kempton Park)..29th
VC Casino.com Long Distance Hurdle (Newbury)..29th
Hennessy Cognac Gold Cup (Handicap Chase) (Newbury)..29th
Sodexho Prestige Intermediate Hurdle Race (Limited Handicap) (Newbury)..29th
wbx.com 'Fighting Fifth' Hurdle (Newcastle)..29th
Rehearsal Handicap Chase (Newcastle)..29th
Porterstown Handicap Chase (Fairyhouse)..29th
New Stand Handicap Hurdle (Fairyhouse)..29th
Juvenile Hurdle (Fairyhouse)..29th
Royal Bond Novices' Hurdle (Fairyhouse)..30th
Drinmore Novices' Chase (Fairyhouse)..30th
Hattons Grace Hurdle (Fairyhouse)..30th

DECEMBER

Ballymore Properties Novices' Hurdle (Sandown Park)..5th
Tingle Creek Chase (Sandown Park)..6th

The information contained within the Principal Races section is supplied by the BHA and is provisional. In all cases the dates and names of sponsors are correct at the time of going to press but subject to possible alteration.

RACECOURSES OF GREAT BRITAIN

AINTREE (L.H)
Grand National Course: Triangular, 2m 2f (16) 494y run-in with elbow. Perfectly flat. A severe test for both horse and rider, putting a premium on jumping ability, fitness and courage, although some of the fences were recently modified.
Mildmay Course: Rectangular, 1m 4f (8) 260y run-in. A very fast course with sharp bends.
Address: Aintree Racecourse, Ormskirk Road, Aintree, Liverpool, L9 5AS Tel: (0151) 523 2600
Fax: (0151) 522 2920 E-mail: aintree@rht.net www.aintree.co.uk
Clerk of the Course: Andrew Tulloch
Managing Director: Julian Thick
Going Reports: (0151) 523 2600.
Stabling: 176 boxes allocated in strict rotation. Facilities are available on the course for up to 100 stable staff. (0151) 523 2600.
By Road: North of the City, near the junction of the M57 and M58 with the A59 (Preston).
By Rail: Aintree Station is adjacent to the Stands, from Liverpool Central.
By Air: Liverpool (Speke) Airport is 10 miles. Helicopter landing facility by prior arrangement.

ASCOT (R.H)
Flat: Right-handed triangular track just under 1m 6f in length. The Round course descends from the 1m 4f start into Swinley Bottom, the lowest part of the track. It then turns right-handed and joins the Old Mile Course, which starts on a separate chute. The course then rises to the right-handed home turn over a new underpass to join the straight mile course. The run-in is about 3f, rising slightly to the winning post. The whole course is of a galloping nature with easy turns.
N.H. Triangular, 1m 6f (10) 240y mostly uphill. A galloping course with an uphill finish, Ascot provides a real test of stamina. The fences are stiff and sound jumping is essential, especially for novices.
Address: Ascot Racecourse, Ascot, Berkshire SL5 7JX Tel: (08707) 271 234 Fax: (08704) 601 238
www.ascot.co.uk
Clerk of the Course: Chris Stickels (07970) 621440
Chief Executive: TBA.
Going Reports: Day: (01344) 874567
Stabling: Free, with shavings, straw or paper provided. Tel: (01344) 625630 Fax: (01344) 873751
By Road: West of the town on the A329. Easy access from the M3 (Junction 3) and the M4 (Junction 6). Car parking adjoining the course and Ascot Heath.
By Rail: Regular service from Waterloo to Ascot (500y from the racecourse).
By Air: Helicopter landing facility at the course. London (Heathrow) Airport 15 miles, White Waltham Airfield 12 miles.

AYR (L.H)
Flat: A left-handed, galloping, flat oval track of 1m 4f with a 4f run-in. The straight 6f is essentially flat.
N.H. Oval, 1m 4f (9) 210y run-in. Relatively flat and one of the fastest tracks in Great Britain. It is a well-drained course and the ground rarely becomes testing. Suits the long-striding galloper.
Address: Ayr Racecourse, Whitletts Road, Ayr KA8 0JE Tel: (0870) 850 5666 Fax: (0870) 850 5667
Website: www.ayr-racecourse.co.uk
Clerk of the Course: Katherine Self
General Manager: William Gorol
Managing Director: Richard Johnstone
Going Reports: Contact Clerk of the Course as above.
Stabling: Free stabling and accommodation for lads and lasses. Tel: (01292) 264179.
By Road: East of the town on the A758. Free parking for buses and cars.
By Rail: Ayr Station (trains on the half hour from Glasgow Central). Journey time 55 minutes. Buses and taxis also to the course.
By Air: Prestwick International Airport (10 minutes), Glasgow Airport (1 hour).

BANGOR-ON-DEE (L.H)

N.H. Circular, 1m 4f (9) 325y run-in. Apart from some 'ridge and furrow', this is a flat course notable for three sharp bends, especially the paddock turn. Suits handy, speedy sorts and is ideal for front-runners.
Address: Bangor-On-Dee Racecourse, Overton Road, Bangor-On-Dee, Wrexham. LL13 0DA
Tel: (01978) 782081, Fax: (01978) 780985 Website: www.bangorondeeraces.co.uk
Clerk of the Course: Ed Gretton Tel: (01978) 780323 or Mobile (07855) 807718. Fax: (01978) 780985.
Chief Executive: Richard Thomas
General Manager: Jeannie Chantler
Going Reports: Contact Clerk of the Course as above.
Stabling: 84 stables, allotted on arrival. Shavings (straw on request). Applications to the Manager.
Tel: (01978) 780323.
By Road: 5 miles South-East of Wrexham, off the B5069.
By Rail: Wrexham Station (bus or taxi to the course).
By Air: Helicopters may land by prior arrangement with Clerk of the Course at entirely their own risk.

BATH (L.H)

Flat: Galloping, left-handed, level oval of 1m 4f 25y, with long, stiff run-in of about 4f which bends to the left. An extended chute provides for races over 5f 11y and 5f 161y.
Address: The Racecourse, Lansdown, Bath BA1 9BU. (01225) 424609 Fax: (01225) 444415.
Website: www.bath-racecouse.co.uk
Clerk of the Course: Tim Long Tel: (01255) 424609 (Office), (07966) 893531 (Mobile).
General Manager: Jon Williams
Going Reports: Contact Clerk of the Course as above.
Stabling: Free stabling and accommodation for lads and lasses. Tel: (01225) 444274
By Road: 2 miles North-West of the City (M4 Junction 18) at Lansdown. Unlimited free car and coach parking space immediately behind the stands. Special bus services operate from Bath to the racecourse.
By Rail: Bath Station (from Paddington), regular bus service from Bath to the course (3 miles).
By Air: Bristol or Colerne Airports. Helicopter landing facilities available by prior arrangement.

BEVERLEY (R.H)

Flat: A right-handed oval of 1m 3f, generally galloping, with an uphill run-in of two and a half furlongs. The 5f course is very stiff.
Address: Beverley Race Co. Ltd., York Road, Beverley, Yorkshire HU17 9QZ Tel: (01482) 867488/882645.
Clerk of the Course: James Hutchinson. Tel: (01765) 602156. Mobile (07860) 679904.
Racecourse Manager: Sally Iggulden (07850) 458605
Going Reports: Tel: (01482) 867488/882645 or Head Groundsman (Mr. S Jessop) mobile 07885 678186
Stabling: Free stabling. Accommodation available for lads and lasses Tel: (01482) 867488/882645.
By Road: 7 miles from the M62 (Junction 38) off the A1035. Free car parking opposite the course. Owners and Trainers use a separate enclosure.
By Rail: Beverley Station (Hull-Scarborough line). Occasional bus service to the course (1 mile).
By Air: Helicopter landings by prior arrangement. Light aircraft landing facilities at Linley Hill, Leven airport.

BRIGHTON (L.H)

Flat: Left-handed, 1m 4f horseshoe with easy turns and a run-in of three and a half furlongs. Undulating and sharp, the track suits handy types.
Address: Brighton Racecourse, Brighton, East Sussex BN2 2XZ Tel: (01273) 603580 Fax: (01273) 673267.
Clerk of the Course: Richard Aldous
General Manager: Matt Hudson
Going Reports: Available on brighton-racecourse.co.uk or contact main office/Clerk Of Course as above
Stabling: Stabling & accommodation: Tel: (01273) 603580, available on request.
By Road: East of the city on the A27 (Lewes Road). There is a car park adjoining the course.
By Rail: Brighton Station (from Victoria on the hour, London Bridge or Portsmouth). Special bus service to the course from the station (approx 2 miles).
By Air: Helicopters may land by prior arrangement.

CARLISLE (R.H)

Flat: Right-handed, 1m 4f pear-shaped track. Galloping and undulating with easy turns and a stiff uphill run-in of three and a half furlongs. 6f course begins on an extended chute.

N.H. Pear-shaped, 1m 5f (9) 300y run-in uphill. Undulating and a stiff test of stamina, ideally suited to the long-striding thorough stayer. Three mile chases start on a chute, and the first fence is only jumped once. Ground tends to be either very fast or very soft.
Address: Carlisle Racecourse, Durdar Road, Carlisle CA2 4TS Tel: (01228) 554700
Office: (01228) 554747 www.carlisle-races.co.uk
Clerk of the Course: Jonny Fenwicke-Clennell. Tel: Office (01228) 554700. Home (016974) 76589.
Mobile: (07860) 737729.
Managing Director: John Baker
Going Reports: (01228) 554700 (recorded) or contact Clerk of the Course above
Stabling: Stabling and accommodation available on request. Please phone Head Groundsman on (01228) 546188, or Stable Office on (01228) 549489 from 3pm day before racing.
By Road: 2 miles south of the city (Durdar Road). Easy access from the M6 (Junction 42). The car park is free (adjacent to the course). Trackside car parking £10.
By Rail: Carlisle Station (2 miles from the course).
By Air: Helicopter landing facility by prior arrangement.

CARTMEL (L.H)

N.H.: Oval, 1m 1f (6) 800y run-in. Almost perfectly flat but very sharp, with the longest run-in in the country, approximately half a mile. The fences are stiff but fair.
Address: Cartmel Racecourse, Cartmel, nr Grange-Over-Sands, Cumbria LA11 6QF Tel: (015395) 36340.
Out of season (015395) 33335 Fax: (01539) 536004
Clerk of the Course: Andrew Tulloch Tel: (0151) 523 2600 Fax: (0151) 522 2920 Car: (0411) 880123
Racedays: (01539) 536340.
Racecourse Manager: Sean Hodgson (07779) 315104
Club Secretary: Mrs Bray (015395) 33434
Going Reports: (015395) 36340 or contact Clerk Of Course as above.
Stabling: Boxes and accommodation for lads and lasses is limited. Prior booking is advisable.
By Road: 1 mile West of the town, 2 miles off the B5277 (Grange-Haverthwaite road). M6 (Junction 36).
By Rail: Cark and Cartmel Station (2½ miles) (Carnforth-Barrow line).
By Air: Light aircraft facilities available at Cark Airport (4 miles from the course). Helicopter landing facility at the course, by prior arrangement only.

CATTERICK (L.H)

Flat: A sharp, left-handed, undulating oval of 1m 180y with a downhill run-in of 3f.
N.H. Oval, 1m 1f (9) 240y run-in. Undulating, sharp track that favours the handy, front-running sort, rather than the long-striding galloper.
Address: The Racecourse, Catterick Bridge, Richmond, North Yorkshire DL10 7PE Tel: (01748) 811478
Fax: (01748) 811082 Website: www.catterickbridge.co.uk
Clerk of the Course: James Sanderson
Going Reports: Contact Clerk Of Course as above
Stabling: Boxes are allotted on arrival.
By Road: The course is adjacent to the A1, 1 mile North-West of the town on the A6136. There is a free car park.
By Rail: Darlington Station (special buses to course - 14 mile journey).
By Air: Helicopters can land by prior arrangement. Fixed wing planes contact RAF Leeming
Tel: 01677 423041

CHELTENHAM (L.H)

Old Course: Oval, 1m 4f (9) 350y run-in. A testing, undulating track with stiff fences. The ability to stay is essential.
New Course: Oval, 1m 5f (10) 220y run-in. Undulating, stiff fences, testing course, uphill for the final half-mile.
Address: Cheltenham Racecourse, Prestbury Park, Cheltenham, Gloucestershire GL50 4SH
Tel (01242) 513014 Fax: (01242) 224227 Website: www.cheltenham.co.uk
Managing Director: Edward Gillespie
Director of Racing & Clerk of the Course: Simon Claisse
Going Reports: Available from 6 days before racing (01242) 517900
Stabling: Ample stabling and accommodation for lads. Apply to the Stable Manager (01242) 513014
or 521950.
By Road: 1.5 miles North of the town on the A435. M5 (Junction 10 or 11).
By Rail: Cheltenham (Lansdowne) Station. Buses and taxis to course.
By Air: Helicopter landing site to the North-East of the stands.

CHEPSTOW (L.H)

Flat: A left-handed, undulating oval of about 2m, with easy turns, and a straight run-in of 5f. There is a straight track of 1m 14y.

N.H. Oval, 2m (11) 240y run-in. Many changing gradients, five fences in the home straight. Favours the long-striding front-runner, but stamina is important.

Address: Chepstow Racecourse, Chepstow, Monmouthshire NP16 6BE Tel: (01291) 622260
Fax: (01291) 627061 Website: www.chepstow-racecourse.co.uk

Clerk of the Course: Tim Long Tel: (01283) 711233 (Office), (07966) 893531 (Mobile).

Executive Director: Simon Lee

Going Reports: Contact Clerk of the Course as above.

Stabling: 40 boxes, allotted on arrival. Limited accommodation for lads and lasses. Apply: (01291) 623414.

By Road: 1 mile North-West of the town on the A466. (1 mile from Junction 22 of the M4 (Severn Bridge) or M48 Junction 2. There is a free public car park opposite the Stands entrance.

By Rail: Chepstow Station (from Paddington, change at Gloucester or Newport). The course is 1 mile from station.

By Air: Helicopter landing facility in the centre of the course.

CHESTER (L.H)

Flat: A level, sharp, left-handed, circular course of 1m 73y, with a short run-in of 230y.
Chester is a specialists' track which generally suits the sharp-actioned horse.

Address: The Racecourse, Chester CH1 2LY Tel: (01244) 304600 Fax: (01244) 304649
www.chester-races.co.uk

Clerk of the Course: Ed Gretton (07855) 807710

Chief Executive: Richard Thomas

Going Reports: Contact Main Office (01244) 304600

Stabling: (175 boxes) and accommodation. Tel: (01244) 324880

By Road: The course is near the centre of the city on the A548 (Queensferry Road). The Owners and Trainers car park is adjacent to the County Stand. There is a public car park in the centre of the course.

By Rail: Chester Station (¾ mile from the course). Services from Euston, Paddington and Northgate.

By Air: Hawarden Airport (2 miles).

DONCASTER (L.H)

Flat: A left-handed, flat, galloping course of 1m 7f 110y, with a long run-in which extends to a straight mile.

N.H. Conical, 2m (11) 247y run-in. A very fair, flat track ideally suited to the long-striding galloper.

Address: Doncaster Racecourse, Leger Way, Doncaster DN2 6BB Tel: (01302) 304200,
Fax: (01302) 323271 E-mail: info@britishracing.com, Email: info@doncaster-racecourse.co.uk
Website: www.doncaster-racecourse.com

Clerk of the Course: David Williams

Managing Director: Adam Waterworth

Operations Manager: Matt Clayton

Going Reports: Contact Clerk of the Course as above.

Stabling: Free stabling and accommodation. Mr M Taylor Tel: (01302) 349337

By Road: East of the town, off the A638 (M18 Junctions 3 & 4). Club members car park reserved. Large public car park free and adjacent to the course.

By Rail: Doncaster Central Station (from King's Cross). Special bus service from the station (1 mile).

By Air: Helicopter landing facility by prior arrangement only.

EPSOM (L.H)

Flat: Left-handed and undulating with easy turns, and a run-in of just under 4f. The straight 5f course is also undulating and downhill all the way, making it the fastest 5f in the world.

Address: The Racecourse, Epsom Downs, Surrey, KT18 5LQ. Tel: (01372) 726311, Fax (01372) 748253
www.epsomderby.co.uk

Clerk of the Course: Andrew Cooper. Tel: (01372) 726311, Mobile (07774) 230850.

Acting Managing Director: Nick Blofeld

Going Reports: Contact Clerk of the Course as above.

Stabling: Free stabling and accommodation. Tel: (01372) 460454

By Road: 2 miles South of the town on the B290 (M25 Junctions 8 & 9). For full car park particulars apply to: The Club Secretary, Epsom Grandstand, Epsom Downs, Surrey KT18 5LQ. Tel: (01372) 726311.

By Rail: Epsom, Epsom Downs or Tattenham Corner Stations (trains from London Bridge, Waterloo, Victoria). Regular bus services run to the course from Epsom and Morden Underground Station.
By Air: London (Heathrow) and London (Gatwick) are both within 20 miles of the course. Heliport (Derby Meeting only) apply to Hascombe Aviation. Tel: (01279) 680291.

EXETER (R.H)

N.H.: Oval, 2m (11) 300y run-in uphill. Undulating with a home straight of half a mile. A good test of stamina, suiting the handy, well-balanced sort.
Address: Exeter Racecourse, Kennford, Exeter, Devon EX6 7XS Tel: (01392) 832599 Fax: (01392) 833454
Email: info@exeter-races.co.uk Website: www.exeter-racecourse.co.uk
Clerk of the Course: Barry Johnson
Managing Director: Stephen Clarke
Club Secretary: Mrs Robinson
Going Reports: Contact Clerk of the Course as above.
Stabling: 81 loose boxes on the course. Sleeping accommodation and canteen for both lads and lasses by prior arrangement. Apply to Mrs J. Browning. Tel: (01392) 832816 or (01392) 832599.
By Road: The course is at Haldon, 5 miles South-West of Exeter on the A38 (Plymouth) road, 2 miles East of Chudleigh.
By Rail: Exeter (St Davids) Station.
By Air: Helicopters can land by prior arrangement.

FAKENHAM (L.H)

N.H.: Square, 1m (6) 200y run-in. On the turn almost throughout and undulating, suiting the handy front-runner. The going rarely becomes heavy.
Address: The Racecourse, Fakenham, Norfolk NR21 7NY Tel: (01328) 862388 Fax: (01328) 855908
email: info@fakenhamracecourse.co.uk Website: www.fakenhamracecourse.co.uk
Clerk of the Course & Chief Executive: David Hunter Tel: (01328) 862388 Mobile (07767) 802206.
Going Reports: Contact Clerk of the Course as above.
Stabling: 68 boxes available. Tel: (01328) 862388 Fax (01328) 855908.
By Road: 1 mile South of the town on the B1146 (East Dereham) road.
By Rail: Norwich Station (26 miles) (Liverpool Street line), King's Lynn (22 miles) (Liverpool Street).
By Air: Helicopter landing facility in the centre of the course.

FOLKESTONE (R.H)

Flat: Right-handed, undulating, circuit of 1m 3f, with a two and a half furlong run-in. There is a straight 6f course.
N.H.: Oval, 1m 3f (8) chases 220y run-in, hurdles 250y run-in. An undulating course with easy fences, not particularly suitable for the long-striding galloper.
Address: Folkestone Racecourse, Westenhanger, Hythe, Kent CT21 4HX Tel (01303) 266407
Fax: (01303) 260185 Website: www.folkestone-racecourse.co.uk
Acting Managing Director: Kevan Hodges
Clerk of the Course: Neil Mackenzie Ross
Going Reports: Contact Clerk of the Course as above
Stabling: 90 boxes allotted in rotation. Advance notice required for overnight accommodation, from 2pm on the day prior to racing. (01303) 266407 or 268449 (racedays).
By Road: 6 miles West of town at Westenhanger. Easy access from Junction 11 of the M20. Car park adjoins stands. (Free, except course enclosure £4).
By Rail: Westenhanger Station adjoins course. Trains from Charing Cross.
By Air: Helicopter landing facility by prior arrangement.

FONTWELL (Fig. 8)

N.H.: 2m (7) 230y run-in with left-hand bend close home. The figure-of-eight chase course suits handy types and is something of a specialists' track. The left-handed hurdle course is oval, one mile round with nine hurdles per two and a quarter miles.
Address: Fontwell Park Racecourse, nr Arundel, West Sussex BN18 0SX Tel: (01243) 543335
Fax: (01243) 543904 www.fontwellpark.co.uk
Clerk of the Course: Edward Arkell
General Manager: Phil Bell
Going Reports: (01243) 543335 during office hours.
Stabling: 77 boxes. Limited accommodation. If arriving the day before the meeting, contact:
Tel: (01243) 543370.

By Road: South of village at the junction of the A29 (Bognor) and A27 (Brighton-Chichester) roads.
By Rail: Barnham Station (2 miles). Brighton-Portsmouth line (access via London Victoria).
By Air: Helicopter landing facility by prior arrangement with the Clerk of the Course.

GOODWOOD (R.H)

Flat: A sharp, undulating, essentially right-handed track with a long run-in. There is also a straight six furlong course.
Address: Goodwood Racecourse Ltd., Goodwood, Chichester, West Sussex PO18 0PX
Tel: (01243) 755022, Fax: (01243) 755025 www.goodwood.co.uk
Managing Director: Rod Fabricius Tel: Mobile (07836) 321254
Clerk of the Course: Seamus Buckley (07774) 100223
Going Reports: (01243) 755022 (recorded message)
Stabling: Free stabling and accommodation for runners (115 well equipped boxes at Goodwood House). Subsidised canteen and recreational facilities. Tel: (01243) 755022/755036.
By Road: 6 miles North of Chichester between the A286 & A285. There is a car park adjacent to the course. Ample free car and coach parking.
By Rail: Chichester Station (from Victoria or London Bridge). Regular bus service to the course (6 miles).
By Air: Helicopter landing facility by prior arrangement with Martin Fiddler. Tel: (01279) 850750.
Fax (01279) 850459 Goodwood Airport 2 miles (taxi to the course).

GREAT LEIGHS (L.H)

Flat: Left-handed, 8 furlong polytrack circuit with 2 extended chutes to provide starts for 7 and 8 furlong races. There is a 2 furlong home straight.
Address: Moulsham Hall Lane, Great Leighs, Chelmsford, Essex, CM3 1QP. Tel: 01245 362412
Website: www.greatleighs.com
Clerk of the Course: TBA
By Road: The racecourse lies about 5 miles north of Chelmsford on the A131 and is approachable from both M11 (exit Junction 8, Stansted, and follow brown tourist signs from A120 eastbound) and A12. Free car park.
By Rail: Chelmsford (5 miles from course), Braintree (3 miles from course) or Stansted (12 miles from course).
By Air: Stansted; Helicopter landing on course by prior arrangement.

HAMILTON (R.H)

Flat: Sharp, undulating, right-handed course of 1m 5f with a five and a half furlong, uphill run-in. There is a straight track of 6f.
Address: Hamilton Park Racecourse, Bothwell Road, Hamilton, Lanarkshire ML3 0DW Tel: (01698) 283806
Fax: (01698) 286621 www.hamilton-park.co.uk
Racing Manager & Clerk of the Course: Hazel Peplinski (01698) 283806. Mobile (07774) 116733.
Fax (01698) 286621
Chief Executive: Alastair Warwick Tel: (01698) 283806
Going Reports: Head Groundsman: (07850) 609037 (mobile).
Stabling: Free stabling (120 boxes) and accommodation on request. Tel: (01698) 248892 or Office.
By Road: Off the A74 on the B7071 (Hamilton-Bothwell road). (M74 Junction 5). Free parking for cars and buses.
By Rail: Hamilton West Station (1 mile).
By Air: Glasgow Airport (20 miles).

HAYDOCK (L.H)

Flat: A galloping, almost flat, oval track, 1m 5f round, with a run-in of four and a half furlongs and a straight six furlong course.
N.H. Oval, 1m 5f (10) 440y run-in. Flat, galloping chase course. The hurdle track, which is sharp, is inside the chase course and has some tight bends.
Address: Haydock Park Racecourse, Newton-le-Willows, Merseyside WA12 0HQ Tel: (01942) 725963
Fax: (01942) 270879 www.haydock-park.co.uk
Clerk of the Course: Kirkland Tellwright
Managing Director: Dickon White
Going Reports: Contact Clerk of the Course as above
Stabling: Applications to be made to the Racecourse for stabling and accommodation.
Tel (01942) 725963 or (01942) 402615 (racedays).
By Road: The course is on the A49 near Junction 23 of the M6.

By Rail: Newton-le-Willows Station (Manchester-Liverpool line) is 2.5 miles from the course. Earlstown 3 miles from the course. Warrington Bank Quay and Wigan are on the London to Carlisle/ Glasgow line.
By Air: Landing facilities in the centre of the course for helicopters and planes not exceeding 10,000lbs laden weight. Apply to the Sales Office.

HEREFORD (R.H)

N.H. Square, 1m 4f (9) 300y run-in. The turns, apart from the final one that is on falling ground, are easily negotiated, placing the emphasis on speed rather than stamina. A handy position round the home turn is vital, as winners rarely come from behind. The hurdle track is on the outside of the chase course.
Address: Hereford Racecourse, Roman Road, Holmer, Hereford HR4 9 QU Tel: (01432) 273560,
Fax (01432) 352807 Website: www.hereford-racecourse.co.uk
Clerk of the Course and General Manager: Katie Stephens
Executive Director: Simon Lee
Going Reports: (01432) 352807 (Recorded) or website as listed above
Stabling: 90 boxes allocated on arrival. Apply to the Stabling Manager, The Racecourse House, Roman Road, Holmer, Hereford. Tel: (01432) 273560.
By Road: 1 mile North West of the City centre off the A49 (Leominster) road.
By Rail: Hereford Station (1 mile from the course).
By Air: Helicopter landing facility in the centre of the course by arrangement with the Clerk of the Course, and entirely at own risk.

HEXHAM (L.H)

N.H.: Oval, 1m 4f (10) 220y run-in. An undulating course that becomes very testing when the ground is soft, it has easy fences and a stiff uphill climb to the finishing straight, which is on a separate spur.
Address: Hexham Racecourse, The Riding, Hexham, Northumberland NE46 2JP Tel: (01434) 606881
Fax (01434) 605814, Racedays (01434) 603738. Email: hexrace@aol.com Website: www.hexham-racecourse.co.uk
Managing Director, Secretary: Charles Enderby
Clerk of the Course: Jonny Fenwicke-Clennell
Going Reports: Contact Clerk of the Course as above
Stabling: Boxes allocated in rotation. Tel: (01434) 603738.
By Road: 1.5 miles South-West of the town off the B6305.
By Rail: Hexham Station (Newcastle-Carlisle line). Free bus to the course.
By Air: Helicopter landing facility in centre of course (by special arrangement only).

HUNTINGDON (R.H)

N.H.: Oval, 1m 4f (9) 200y run-in. Perfectly flat, galloping track with a tricky open ditch in front of the stands. The two fences in the home straight can cause problems for novice chasers. Suits front runners.
Address: The Racecourse, Brampton, Huntingdon, Cambridgeshire PE28 4NL Tel: (01480) 453373
Fax: (01480) 455275 www.huntingdon-racecourse.co.uk
Clerk of the Course: Fiona Needham Tel: (01638) 675559 (mobile)
Racecourse Manager: Amy Starkey
Going Reports: Tel: (01480) 453373
Stabling: 100 boxes available. Allotted on arrival. Tel Racecourse Office.
By Road: The course is situated at Brampton, 2 miles West of Huntingdon on the A14. Easy access from the A1 (½ mile from the course).
By Rail: Huntingdon Station. Buses and taxis to course.
By Air: Helicopter landing facility by prior arrangement.

KELSO (L.H)

N.H.: Oval, 1m 3f (9) 440y run-in uphill. Rather undulating with two downhill fences opposite the stands, Kelso suits the nippy, front-running sort, though the uphill run to the finish helps the true stayer. The hurdle course is smaller and very sharp with a tight turn away from the stands.
Address: Kelso Racecourse, Kelso, Roxburghshire TD5 7SX Tel: (01573) 224767 www.kelso-races.co.uk
Clerk of the Course: Anthea Morshead (07789) 697241
Managing Director & Secretary: Richard M. Landale, c/o Sale & Partners, 18-20 Glendale Road, Wooler, Northumberland NE71 6DW. Tel: (01688) 281041.
Going Reports: Racecourse: (01573) 22767 Groundsman Tel: (07774) 172527

Stabling: Boxes allotted in rotation. Reservations for stabling and accommodation for lads and lasses at the racecourse. Please phone Head Groundsman Tel: (01573) 224767 or Racecourse stables: (01573) 224822 from 3pm the day before racing.
By Road: 1 mile North of the town, off the B6461.
By Rail: Berwick-upon-Tweed Station. 23 mile bus journey to Kelso.
By Air: Helicopters can land at course by arrangement, fixed wing aircraft Winfield, regular aircraft Edinburgh

KEMPTON (R.H)

Flat: A floodlit Polytrack circuit opened in March 2006. A 10f outer track accommodates races over 6f, 7f, 1m, 1m 3f, 1m 4f and 2m. The 8f inner track caters for races over 5f and 1m 2f.
N.H. Triangular, 1m 5f (10) 175y run-in. Practically flat; sharp course where the long run between the last obstacle on the far side and the first in the home straight switches the emphasis from jumping to speed. The hurdles track is on the outside of the chase track. The fences have been rebuilt and the water jump removed. The course crosses the Polytrack at two points on each circuit.
Address: Kempton Park Racecourse, Sunbury-on-Thames, Middlesex TW16 5AQ Tel: (01932) 782292 Fax: (01932) 782044 Raceday Fax: (01932) 779525 Website: www.kempton.co.uk Email: kempton@rht.net
Clerk of the Course: Brian Clifford (07880) 784484
Managing Director: Steve Tully
Raceday Office Manager: Beverley Frith
Going Reports: (01932) 782292 if unavailable contact Clerk of the Course as above
Stabling: Allocated on arrival. Prior booking required for overnight stay. Tel: (01932) 783334
By Road: On the A308 near Junction 1 of the M3.
By Rail: Kempton Park Station (from Waterloo).
By Air: London (Heathrow) Airport 6 miles.

LEICESTER (R.H)

Flat: Stiff, galloping, right-handed oval of 1m 5f, with a 5f run-in. There is a straight course of seven furlongs.
N.H. Rectangular, 1m 6f (10) 250y run-in uphill. An undulating course with an elbow 150y from the finish, Leicester can demand a high degree of stamina, for the going can become extremely heavy and the last three furlongs are uphill.
Address: Leicester Racecourse, Oadby, Leicester LE2 4AL. Tel: (0116) 2716515 Fax (0116) 2711746 www.leicester-racecourse.com
Clerk of the Course: Jimmy Stevenson (0116) 2712115
General Manager: David Maykels (0116) 2716515
Going Reports: Recorded message (0116) 2710875 or contact Head Groundsman (0116) 2712115 (07774) 497281 (mobile).
Stabling: Allocated on arrival. canteen opens at 7.30a.m. tel: (0116) 271 2115.
By Road: The course is 2.5 miles South-East of the City on the A6 (M1, Junction 21). The car park is free.
By Rail: Leicester Station (from St Pancras) is 2.5 miles.
By Air: Helicopter landing facility in the centre of the course.

LINGFIELD (L.H)

Flat, Turf: A sharp, undulating left-handed circuit, with a 7f 140y straight course.
Flat, Polytrack: The left-handed all-weather polytrack is 1m 2f round, with an extended chute to provide a 1m 5f start. It is a sharp, level track with a short run-in.
N.H. Conical, 1m 5f (10) 200y run-in. Severely undulating with a tight downhill turn into the straight, the chase course suits front runners and those of doubtful resolution.
Address: Lingfield Park Racecourse, Lingfield, Surrey RH7 6PQ Tel: (01342) 834800 Fax: (01342) 832833 www.lingfield-racecourse.co.uk
Clerk of the Course: Neil Mackenzie Ross
Acting Managing Director: Kevan Hodges
Going Reports: Contact Clerk of the Course as above
Stabling: 180 boxes. For details of accommodation tel (01342) 831720. Advance notice for overnight accommodation required before 12 noon on the day before racing.
By Road: South-East of the town off the A22 (M25 Junction 6). Ample free parking.
By Rail: Lingfield Station (regular services from London Bridge and Victoria). ½m walk to the course.
By Air: London (Gatwick) Airport 10 miles. Helicopter landing facility south of wind-sock.

LUDLOW (R.H)

N.H. Oval, 1m 4f (9) 185y run-in. The chase course is flat and has quite sharp bends into and out of the home straight, although long-striding horses never seem to have any difficulties. The hurdle course is on the outside of the chase track and is not so sharp.

Address: Ludlow Race Club Ltd, The Racecourse, Bromfield, Ludlow, Shropshire SY8 2BT
Tel: (01584) 856221 (Racedays) or see below.

Secretary & Clerk of the Course: Bob Davies. Tel: (01981) 580260 (Home), Mobile (07970) 861533,
Fax (01981) 580181 (home), 01584 856217 (course) Email: bobdavies@ludlowracecourse.co.uk
www.ludlowracecourse.co.uk

Going Reports: Contact Clerk Of Course as above or Groundsman Tel: (01584) 856269

Stabling: Free and allocated on arrival. 100 stables, mainly shavings with a limited number of paper and straw. Tel: (01584) 856269.

By Road: The course is situated at Bromfield, 2 miles North of Ludlow on the A49.

By Rail: Ludlow Station (Hereford-Shrewsbury line) 2 miles.

By Air: Helicopter landing facility in the centre of the course by arrangement with the Clerk of the Course and entirely at own risk.

MARKET RASEN (R.H)

N.H. Oval, 1m 2f (8) 250y run-in. A sharp, undulating course with a long run to the straight, Market Rasen favours the handy, front-running type. The fences are not as easy as they used to be.

Address: Market Rasen Racecourse, Legsby Road, Market Rasen, Lincolnshire LN8 3EA
Tel: (01673) 843434 Fax: (01673) 844532 Website: www.marketrasenraces.co.uk

Clerk of the Course: Nick Patton Tel: (07775) 704822

Managing Director: Pip Kirkby

Going Reports: Contact Clerk of the Course as above.

Stabling: 90 boxes at the course, allocated on arrival. Accommodation for lads and lasses is by reservation only. Tel: (01673) 842307 (racedays only)

By Road: The town is just off the A46, and the racecourse is one mile East of the town on the A631. Free car parks and racecards.

By Rail: Market Rasen Station 1 mile (King's Cross - Cleethorpes line).

By Air: Helicopter landing facility by prior arrangement only.

MUSSELBURGH (R.H)

Flat: A sharp, level, right-handed oval of 1m 2f, with a run-in of 4f. There is an additional 5f straight course.

N.H. Rectangular, 1m 3f (8) 150y run-in (variable). A virtually flat track with sharp turns, suiting the handy, front-running sort. Drains well.

Address: Musselburgh Racecourse, Linkfield Road, Musselburgh, East Lothian EH21 7RG
Tel: (0131) 665 2859 (Racecourse) Fax: (0131) 653 2083

Clerk of the Course: Anthea Morshead (07789) 697241

General Manager: Bill Farnsworth (07710) 536134

Going Reports: Contact main office as above.

Stabling: Free stabling. Accommodation provided. Tel: (0131) 665 4955,
Stables (racedays) (0131) 665 2796.

By Road: The course is situated at Musselburgh, 5 miles East of Edinburgh on the A1. Car park, adjoining course, free for buses and cars.

By Rail: Waverley Station (Edinburgh). Local Rail service to Musselburgh.

By Air: Edinburgh (Turnhouse) Airport 30 minutes

NEWBURY (L.H)

Flat: Left-handed, oval track of about 1m 7f, with a slightly undulating straight mile. The round course is level and galloping with a four and a half furlong run-in. Races over the round mile and 7f 60y start on the adjoining chute.

N.H. Oval, 1m 6f (11) 255y run-in. Slightly undulating, wide and galloping in nature. The fences are stiff and sound jumping is essential. One of the fairest tracks in the country.

Address: The Racecourse, Newbury, Berkshire RG14 7NZ Tel: (01635) 40015 Fax: (01635) 528354

Managing Director & Clerk of the Course: Mark Kershaw Racecourse Office (01635) 40015 or 550354
Website: www.newbury-racecourse.co.uk

Raceday Clerk: Richard Osgood

General Manager: Stephen Higgins

Going Reports: Clerk of the Course as above.
Stabling: Free stabling and accommodation for lads and lasses. Tel: (01635) 40015.
By Road: East of the town off the A34 (M4, Junction 12 or 13). Car park, adjoining enclosures, free.
By Rail: Newbury Racecourse Station, adjoins course.
By Air: Light Aircraft landing strip East/West. 830 metres by 30 metres wide. Helicopter landing facilities.

NEWCASTLE (L.H)

Flat: Galloping, easy, left-handed oval of 1m 6f, with an uphill 4f run-in. There is a straight course of 1m 8y.
N.H. Oval, 1m 6f (11) 220y run-in. A gradually rising home straight of four furlongs makes this galloping track a true test of stamina, especially as the ground can become very heavy. The fences are rather stiff.
Address: High Gosforth Park, Newcastle-Upon-Tyne NE3 5HP Tel: (0191) 236 2020 Fax 0191 236 7761
www.newcastle-racecourse.co.uk
Clerk of the Course: James Armstrong (07801) 166820
Stabling: Stabling Free. It is essential to book accommodation in advance. Apply via the Racecourse Office.
Going Reports: Contact Clerk of the Course as above.
By Road: 4 miles North of city on the A6125 (near the A1). Car and coach park free.
By Rail: Newcastle Central Station (from King's Cross), a free bus service operates from South Gosforth and Regent Centre Metro Station.
By Air: Helicopter landing facility by prior arrangement. The Airport is 4 miles from the course.

NEWMARKET (R.H)

Rowley Mile Course: There is a straight ten furlong course, which is wide and galloping. Races over 12f or more are right-handed. The Rowley course has a long run-in and a stiff finish.
July Course: Races up to a mile are run on the Bunbury course, which is straight. Races over 10f or more are right-handed, with a 7f run-in. Like the Rowley course, the July track is stiff.
Address: Newmarket Racecourse, Newmarket, Suffolk CB8 0TG Tel: (01638) 663482 (Main Office), (01638) 663762 (Rowley), (01638) 662752 (July) Fax: Rowley (01638) 675340. Fax: July (01638) 667839
www.newmarketracecourse.co.uk
Clerk of the Course: Michael Prosser, Westfield House, The Links, Newmarket. Tel: (01638) 662933
Managing Director: Stephen Wallis
Going Reports: Contact main office or Clerk Of Course as above
Stabling: Free accommodation available at the Links Stables. Tel: (01638) 662200
By Road: South-West of the town on the A1304 London Road (M11 Junction 9). Free car parking at the rear of the enclosure. Members car park all days; Free courtesy bus service from Newmarket Station, Bus Station and High Street, commencing 90 minutes prior to the first race, and return trips up to 60 minutes after the last race.
By Rail: Infrequent rail service to Newmarket Station from Cambridge (Liverpool Street) or direct bus service from Cambridge (13 mile journey).
By Air: Landing facilities for light aircraft and helicopters on racedays at both racecourses. See Flight Guide. Cambridge Airport 11 miles.

NEWTON ABBOT (L.H)

N.H. Oval, 1m 2f (7) 300y run-in. Flat with two tight bends and a water jump situated three fences from home. The nippy, agile sort is favoured. The run-in can be very short on the hurdle course.
Address: Newton Abbot Races Ltd., Kingsteignton Road, Newton Abbot, Devon TQ12 3AF
Tel: (01626) 353235 Fax: (01626) 336972 www.newtonabbotracing.com
Clerk of the Course/Estate Manager: Jason Loosemore (07788) 101250
Managing Director: Pat Masterson. Tel: (01626) 353235 Fax: (01626) 336972 Mobile: (07778) 463207.
Going reports: Clerk of the Course as above, or Head Groundsman: (0374) 914403
Stabling: 90 boxes, allocated on arrival. Tel: (07467) 264796
By Road: North of the town on the A380. Torquay 6 miles, Exeter 17 miles.
By Rail: Newton Abbot Station (from Paddington) ¾ mile. Buses and taxis operate to and from the course.
By Air: Helicopter landing pad in the centre of the course.

NOTTINGHAM (L.H)

Flat: Left-handed, galloping, oval of about 1m 4f, and a run-in of four and a half furlongs. Flat with easy turns.
Address: Nottingham Racecourse, Colwick Park, Nottingham NG2 4BE Tel: (0115) 958 0620
Fax: (0115) 958 4515 www.nottinghamracecourse.co.uk
Clerk of the Course: Nick Patton (07775) 704822
Going Reports: Contact main office as above

Managing Director: Nina Coverley
Stabling: 120 boxes allotted on arrival. Hostel for lads and lasses. Tel: (0115) 950 1198
By Road: 2 miles East of the City on the B686. The car park is free. Silver Ring Picnic Car Park £12 (admits car and four occupants).
By Rail: Nottingham (Midland) Station. Regular bus service to course (2 miles).
By Air: Helicopter landing facility in the centre of the course.

PERTH (R.H)

N.H.: Rectangular, 1m 2f (8) 283y run-in. A flat, easy track with sweeping turns. Not a course for the long-striding galloper. An efficient watering system ensures that the ground rarely gets hard.
Address: Perth Racecourse, Scone Palace Park, Perth PH2 6BB Tel (01738) 551597 Fax: (01738) 553021
Website: www.perth-races.co.uk
Clerk of the Course: Anthea Morshead Tel: (07789) 697241
General Manager: Sam Morshead Tel: (01738) 551597 Mobile: (07768) 868848 Home: (01764) 652658.
Secretary: Mrs M Reid
Going Reports: Groundsman: (07899 034 012) or contact Clerk of the Course as above.
Stabling: 96 boxes and accommodation for lads and lasses Tel: (01738) 551597. Stables
Tel: (01738) 621604 (racedays only).
By Road: 4 miles North of the town off the A93.
By Rail: Perth Station (from Dundee) 4 miles. There are buses to the course.
By Air: Scone Airport (3.75 miles). Edinburgh Airport 45 minutes.

PLUMPTON (L.H)

N.H.: Oval, 1m 1f (7) 200y run-in uphill. A tight, undulating circuit with an uphill finish, Plumpton favours the handy, fast jumper. The ground often gets heavy, as the course is based on clay soil.
Address: Plumpton Racecourse, Plumpton, East Sussex, BN7 3AL Tel: (01273) 891550/890383
Fax: (01273) 891557 www.plumptonracecourse.co.uk
Clerk of the Course: Mark Cornford
Chief Executive: Patrick Davis
Going Reports: Tel: (01273) 891550, or (07771) 660115.
Stabling: 75 boxes. Advance notice required for overnight arrival. Tel: (01273) 890522
By Road: 2 miles North of the village off the B2116.
By Rail: Plumpton Station (from Victoria) adjoins course.
By Air: Helicopter landing facility by prior arrangement with the Clerk of the Course.

PONTEFRACT (L.H)

Flat: Left-handed oval, undulating course of 2m 133y, with a short run-in of 2f. It is a particularly stiff track with the last 3f uphill.
Address: Pontefract Park Race Co. Ltd., The Park, Pontefract, West Yorkshire Tel: (01977) 703224 (Admin Office) (01977) 781307 (Racedays) www.pontefract-races.co.uk
Clerk of the Course, Managing Director & Secretary: Norman Gundill, 33 Ropergate, Pontefract, West Yorkshire. WF8 1LE. Tel: (01977) 703224 (Office), (01977) 620649 (Home), (01977) 702210 (racedays)
Going Reports: Contact Admin Office as above, or Racedays number
Stabling: Stabling and accommodation must be reserved. They will be allocated on a first come-first served basis. Tel: (01977 702323)
By Road: 1 mile North of the town on the A639. Junction 32 of M62. Free car park adjacent to the course.
By Rail: Pontefract Station (Tanshelf, every hour to Wakefield), 1½ miles from the course. Regular bus service from Leeds.
By Air: Helicopters by arrangement only. (Nearest Airfields: Doncaster, Sherburn-in-Elmet, Yeadon (Leeds/Bradford).

REDCAR (L.H)

Flat: Left-handed, level, galloping, oval course of 14f with a straight run-in of 5f. There is also a straight 8f.
Address: Redcar Racecourse, Redcar, Cleveland TS10 2BY Tel: (01642) 484068 Fax: (01642) 488272
www.redcarracing.com
Clerk of the Course: James Sanderson Tel: (01642) 484068 Mobile (07770) 613049
Chief Executive: Neil Etherington (07768) 405464
Going Reports: Contact main office as above
Stabling: 142 Boxes available. Tel Stables (01642) 484068 or racedays only (01642) 484254).

By Road: In town off the A1085. Free parking adjoining the course for buses and cars.
By Rail: Redcar Station (¼ mile from the course).
By Air: Landing facilities at Turners Arms Farm (600y runway) Yearby, Cleveland. 2 miles South of the racecourse - transport available. Teeside airport (18 miles west of Redcar).

RIPON (R.H)

Flat: A sharp, undulating, right-handed oval of 1m 5f, with a 5f run-in. There is also a 6f straight course.
Address: Ripon Racecourse, Boroughbridge Road, Ripon, North Yorkshire HG4 1UG Tel: (01765) 602156
Fax: (01765) 690018 E-mail: info@ripon-races.co.uk Website: www.ripon-races.co.uk
Clerk of the Course & Managing Director: James Hutchinson, 77 North Street, Ripon HG4 1DS. Tel: (01765) 602156, Mobile (07860) 679904. Racedays (01765) 603696
Going Reports: Tel: (01765) 603696
Stabling: Trainers requiring stabling (104 boxes available) are requested to contact Stable Manager prior to 11a.m. the day before racing. Tel: (01765) 604135/603696
By Road: The course is situated 2 miles South-East of the city, on the B6265. There is ample free parking for cars and coaches. For reservations apply to the Secretary.
By Rail: Harrogate Station (11 miles), or Thirsk (15 miles). Bus services to Ripon.
By Air: Helicopters only on the course. Otherwise Leeds/Bradford airport.

SALISBURY (R.H)

Flat: Right-handed and level, with a run-in of 4f. There is a straight 8f track. The last half mile is uphill, providing a stiff test of stamina.
Address: Salisbury Racecourse, Netherhampton, Salisbury, Wiltshire SP2 8PN Tel: (01722) 326461
Fax: 01722 412710 www.salisburyracecourse.co.uk
Clerk of the Course & General Manager: Jeremy Martin (07880) 744999 mobile
Going Reports: Contact main office as above
Stabling: Free stabling (112 boxes) and accommodation for lads and lasses, apply to the Stabling Manager (01722) 327327.
By Road: 3 miles South-West of the city on the A3094 at Netherhampton. Free car park adjoins the course.
By Rail: Salisbury Station is 3.5 miles (from London Waterloo). Bus service to the course.
By Air: Helicopter landing facility near the ten furlong start.

SANDOWN (R.H)

Flat: An easy right-handed oval course of 1m 5f with a stiff straight uphill run-in of 4f. Separate straight 5f track is also uphill. Galloping.
N.H. Oval, 1m 5f (11) 220y run-in uphill. Features seven fences on the back straight, the last three (Railway Fences) are very close together and can often decide the outcome of races. The stiff uphill climb to the finish puts the emphasis very much on stamina, but accurate-jumping, free-running sorts are also favoured. Hurdle races are run on the Flat course.
Address: Sandown Park Racecourse, Esher, Surrey KT10 9AJ Tel: (01372) 464348 Fax: (01372) 470427
www.sandown.co.uk
Clerk of the Course: Andrew Cooper, Sandown Park, Esher, Surrey. Tel: (01372) 463072
Mobile (0374) 230 850.
Managing Director: David Mackinnon
Going Reports: (01372) 461212.
Stabling: Free stabling and accommodation for lads and lasses. Tel: (01372) 463511.
By Road: 4 miles South-West of Kingston-on-Thames, on the A307 (M25 Junction 10). The members' car park is £5. All other car parking is free.
By Rail: Esher Station (from Waterloo) adjoins the course.
By Air: London (Heathrow) Airport 12 miles.

SEDGEFIELD (L.H)

N.H. Oval, 1m 2f (8) 200y run-in: Hurdles 200y run-in. Undulating with fairly tight turns and does not suit the big, long-striding horse.
Address: Sedgefield Racecourse, Sedgefield, Stockton-on-Tees, Cleveland TS21 2HW
Tel: (01740) 621925 (Office) Fax: (01740) 620663
Clerk of the Course: Charlie Moore Tel: (01287) 711233, (07764) 255500 mobile
General Manager: Jill Williamson
Going Reports: Tel: (01740) 621925 or contact Clerk Of Course as above

Stabling: 115 boxes filled in rotation. No forage. Accommodation for horse attendants: Tel: (01740) 621925
By Road: ¾ mile South-West of the town, near the junction of the A689 (Bishop Auckland) and the A177 (Durham) roads. The car park is free.
By Rail: Darlington Station (9 miles). Durham Station (12 miles).
By Air: Helicopter landing facility in car park area by prior arrangement only.

SOUTHWELL (L.H)
Flat, Turf: Tight left-handed track.
Flat, Fibresand: Left-handed oval, Fibresand course of 1m 2f with a 3f run-in. There is a straight 5f. Sharp and level, Southwell suits front-runners.
N.H. Oval, 1m 1f (7) 220y run-in. A tight, flat track with a short run-in, suits front-runners.
Address: Southwell Racecourse, Rolleston, Newark, Nottinghamshire NG25 0TS Tel: (0870) 2202332 Fax: (01636) 812271 www.southwell-racecourse.co.uk
Clerk of the Course: Jon Pullin (07775) 943341
General Manager: Nathan Corden
Going Reports: Contact Clerk of the Course as above.
Stabling: 110 boxes at the course. Applications for staff and horse accommodation to be booked by noon the day before racing on (01636) 814481.
By Road: The course is situated at Rolleston, 3 miles South of Southwell, 5 miles from Newark.
By Rail: Rolleston Station (Nottingham-Newark line) adjoins the course.
By Air: Helicopters can land by prior arrangement with Mr David Williams Tel: (07968) 306373

STRATFORD-ON-AVON (L.H)
N.H. Triangular, 1m 2f (8) 200y run-in. Virtually flat with two tight bends, and quite a short home straight. A sharp and turning course, Stratford-on-Avon suits the well-balanced, handy sort.
Address: Stratford Racecourse, Luddington Road, Stratford-upon-Avon, Warwickshire CV37 9SE
Tel: (01789) 267949 Fax: (01789) 415850 www.stratfordracecourse.net
Clerk of the Course: Stephen Lambert. Mobile (07836) 384932. Home (01608) 674354
Assistant Clerk of the Course: Ilona Barnett
Going reports: Contact main office as above or Head Groundsman Tel: (07770) 623366.
Stabling: Allotted on arrival. Advance notice must be given for overnight stays. Tel: (01789) 267949.
By Road: 1 mile from the town centre, off the A429 (Evesham road).
By Rail: Stratford-on-Avon Station (from Birmingham New Street or Leamington Spa) 1 mile.
By Air: Helicopter landing facility by prior arrangement.

TAUNTON (R.H)
N.H. Elongated oval, 1m 2f (8) 150y run-in uphill. Sharp turns, especially after the winning post, with a steady climb from the home bend. Suits the handy sort.
Address: Taunton Racecourse, Orchard Portman, Taunton, Somerset TA3 7BL Tel: (01823) 337172 (Office) Fax: (01823) 325881 www.tauntonracecourse.co.uk
Clerk of the Course: Michael Trickey, The Racecourse, Taunton, Somerset TA3 7BL. Tel: (01823) 337172 (07774) 620717 mobile
Managing Director: John Hills
Going reports: Contact Clerk of the Course as above, or head Groundsman (after 4.30pm) (07971) 695132.
Stabling: 98 boxes allotted on arrival. Advance bookings for long journeys. Apply to the Stable Manager, c/o The Racecourse (01823) 337172
By Road: 2 miles South of the town on the B3170 (Honiton) road (M5 Junction 25).
By Rail: Taunton Station 2½ miles. There are buses and taxis to course.
By Air: Helicopter landing facility by prior arrangement.

THIRSK (L.H)
Flat: Left-handed, oval of 1m 2f with sharp turns and an undulating run-in of 4f. There is a straight 6f track.
Address: The Racecourse, Station Road, Thirsk, North Yorkshire YO7 1QL Tel: (01845) 522276   Fax: (01845) 525353.
Clerk of the Course: & Racecourse Manager Christopher Tetley (07860) 919661 mobile
Going reports: Contact main office as above
Club Secretary: Mr J McNaught

Stabling: For stabling and accommodation apply to the Racecourse Tel: (01845) 522276 or (01845) 522096 (racedays).
By Road: West of the town on the A61. Free car park adjacent to the course for buses and cars.
By Rail: Thirsk Station (from King's Cross). 1/2 mile from the course.
By Air: Helicopters can land by prior arrangement. Tel: Racecourse (01845) 522276. Fixed wing aircraft can land at RAF Leeming. Tel: (01677) 423041. Light aircraft at Bagby. Tel: (01845) 597385 or (01845) 537555.

TOWCESTER (R.H)

N.H. Square, 1m 6f (10) 200y run-in uphill. The final six furlongs are uphill. One of the most testing tracks in the country with the emphasis purely on stamina.
Address: The Racecourse, Easton Neston, Towcester, Northants NN12 7HS Tel: (01327) 353414
Fax: (01327) 358534 www.towcester-racecourse.co.uk
Clerk of the course: Robert Bellamy (07836) 241458
General Manager: Kevin Ackerman.
Chief Executive: Chris Palmer.
Going Reports: Tel: (01327) 353414 or contact Clerk of the Course as above.
Stabling: Being re-built at time of going to press. Contact racecourse office for details
By Road: 1 mile South-East of the town on the A5 (Milton Keynes road). M1 (Junction 15a).
By Rail: Northampton Station (Euston) 9 miles, buses to Towcester; or Milton Keynes (Euston) 12 miles, taxis available.
By Air: Helicopters can land by prior arrangement with the Racecourse Manager.

UTTOXETER (L.H)

N.H. Oval, 1m 2f (8) 170y run-in. A few undulations, easy bends and fences and a flat home straight of over half a mile. Suits front-runners, especially on the two mile hurdle course.
Address: The Racecourse, Wood Lane, Uttoxeter, Staffordshire ST14 8BD Tel: (01889) 562561
Fax: (01889) 562786 Website: www.uttoxeter-racecourse.co.uk
Clerk of the Course Keith Ottesen (07813) 043453
General Manager: David MacDonald
Going Reports: Contact main office or Clerk of the Course, as above.
Stabling: 90 boxes, allotted on arrival. Tel: (01889) 562561.
By Road: South-East of the town off the B5017 (Marchington Road).
By Rail: Uttoxeter Station (Crewe-Derby line) adjoins the course.
By Air: Helicopters can land by prior arrangement with the raceday office.

WARWICK (L.H)

Flat: Left-handed, sharp, level track of 1m 6f 32y in circumference, with a run-in of two and a half furlongs. A new 6f straight course opens in 2007..
N.H. Circular, 1m 6f (10) 240y run-in. Undulating with tight bends, five quick fences in the back straight and a short home straight, Warwick favours handiness and speed rather than stamina.
Address: Warwick Racecourse, Hampton Street, Warwick CV34 6HN Tel: (01926) 491553
Fax: (01926) 403223 www.warwickracecourse.co.uk
Clerk of the Course: Fiona Needham
Managing Director: Huw Williams
Going Reports: Contact main office as above
Stabling: 112 boxes allocated on arrival or by reservation (01926) 493803.
By Road: West of the town on the B4095 adjacent to Junction 15 of the M40.
By Rail: Warwick or Leamington Spa Station.
By Air: Helicopters can land by prior arrangement with the Clerk of the Course.

WETHERBY (L.H)

N.H. Oval, 1m 4f (9) 200y run-in slightly uphill. A flat, very fair course which suits the long-striding galloper. The track layout has been altered slightly for 2007/8 and the water jump has been removed.
Address: The Racecourse, York Road, Wetherby, LS22 5EJ Tel: (01937) 582035 Fax: (01937) 588021
www.wetherbyracing.co.uk
Clerk of the Course & Chief Executive: James Sanderson
Going reports: Tel: (01937) 582035, or Course Foreman: (07880) 722586
Stabling: 98 boxes allocated on arrival. Accommodation available. Tel: (01937) 582035 or from 2pm day before racing (01937) 582074.

By Road: East of the town off the B1224 (York Road). Adjacent to the A1. Excellent bus and coach facilities. Car park free.
By Rail: Leeds Station 12 miles. Buses to Wetherby.
By Air: Helicopters can land by prior arrangement

WINCANTON (R.H)

N.H. Rectangular, 1m 3f (9) 200y run-in. Good galloping course where the going rarely becomes heavy. The home straight is mainly downhill.
Address: Wincanton Racecourse, Wincanton, Somerset BA9 8BJ Tel: (01963) 32344 Fax: (01963) 34668
www.wincantonracecourse.co.uk
Clerk of the Course: Rebecca Morgan (07767) 612931
Managing Director: Stephen Clarke
Going Reports: Contact Racecourse Office as above.
Stabling: 92 boxes allocated on arrival, overnight accommodation must be booked in advance. Apply to the Stable Manager, Wincanton Racecourse. Tel: (01963) 32344.
By Road: 1 mile North of the town on the B3081.
By Rail: Gillingham Station (from Waterloo) or Castle Cary Station (from Paddington). Buses and taxis to the course.
By Air: Helicopter landing area is situated in the centre of the course.

WINDSOR (Fig. 8)

Flat: Figure eight track of 1m 4f 110y. The course is level and sharp with a long run-in. The 6f course is essentially straight.
Address: Royal Windsor Racecourse, Maidenhead Road, Windsor, Berkshire SL4 5JJ Tel: (01753) 498400
Fax: (01753) 830156. Website: www.windsor-racecourse.co.uk
Clerk of the Course: Gemma Charrington
Managing Director: Jon Pullin
Going Reports: Contact Clerk of the Course as above.
Stabling: 120 boxes available. Reservation required for overnight stay and accommodation only.
Tel: (01753) 498400 or (01753) 498405 (racedays).
By Road: North of the town on the A308 (M4 Junction 6). Car parks adjoin the course (£1, £1.50, £2).
By Rail: Windsor Central Station (from Paddington) or Windsor & Eton Riverside Station (from Waterloo).
By Air: London (Heathrow) Airport 15 minutes. Also White Waltham Airport (West London Aero Club) 15 minutes.
River Bus: 7 mins from Barry Avenue promenade at Windsor

WOLVERHAMPTON (L.H)

Flat: Left-handed oval of 1m, with a run-in of 380y. A level track with sharp bends, the Polytrack surface, in use since October 2004, generally rides slower than that at Lingfield.
Address: Wolverhampton Racecourse, Dunstall Park, Gorsebrook Road, Wolverhampton WV6 0PE
Tel: (08702) 202442 Fax: 0870 220 0107 www.wolverhampton-racecourse.co.uk
Clerk of the Course: Fergus Cameron (07971) 531162
General Manager: Dave Roberts
Going Reports: Contact Main Office as above
Stabling: 100 boxes allotted on arrival. Applications for lads and lasses, and overnight stables must be made to Racecourse by noon on the day before racing. Tel: (01902) 421421. Fax: (01902) 421621.
By Road: 1 mile North of city on the A449 (M54 Junction 2 or M6 Junction 12). Car parking free of charge.
By Rail: Wolverhampton Station (from Euston) 1 mile.
By Air: Halfpenny Green Airport 8 miles.

WORCESTER (L.H)

N.H. Elongated oval, 1m 5f (9) 220y run-in. Flat with easy turns, Worcester is a very fair, galloping track.
Address: Worcester Racecourse, Pitchcroft, Worcester WR1 3EJ Tel: (0870) 220 2772
Fax: (08702) 202882 www.worcester-racecourse.co.uk
Clerk of the Course: Fergus Cameron, Wolverhampton Racecourse. Tel: (07971) 531162.
Managing Director: Dave Roberts Tel: (01905) 25364.
Going Reports: Contact Clerk of the Course as above, or (01905) 25364.
Stabling: 100 boxes allotted on arrival. Overnight accommodation for lads and lasses in Worcester.
Tel: (01905) 25364.
By Road: West of the city off the A449 (Kidderminster road) (M5 Junc 8).

By Rail: Foregate Street Station, Worcester (from Paddington) ¾ mile.
By Air: Helicopter landing facility in the centre of the course, by prior arrangement only.

YARMOUTH (L.H)

Flat: Left-handed, level circuit of 1m 4f, with a run-in of 5f. The straight course is 8f long.
Address: The Racecourse, Jellicoe Road, Great Yarmouth, Norfolk NR30 4AU Tel: (01493) 842527
Fax: (01493) 843254 www.greatyarmouth-racecourse.co.uk
Clerk of the Course: Charlie Moore
General Manager: Glenn Tubby
Going Reports: Contact Main Office as above
Stabling: Allocated on arrival. Tel: (01493) 855651.
By Road: 1 mile East of town centre (well sign-posted from A47 & A12). Large car park adjoining course £1.
By Rail: Great Yarmouth Station (1 mile). Bus service to the course.
By Air: Helicopter landing available by prior arrangement with Racecourse Office

YORK (L.H)

Flat: Left-handed, level, galloping track, with a straight 6f. There is also an adjoining course of 6f 214y.
Address: The Racecourse, York YO23 1EX Tel: (01904) 620911 Fax: (01904) 611071 Website:
www.yorkracecourse.co.uk
Clerk of the Course and Chief Executive: William Derby
Going Reports: Contact Main Office as above
Stabling: 200 boxes available Tel: (01904) 706317 (Racedays).
By Road: 1 mile South-East of the city on the A1036.
Car parking: Free, except May and August meetings when £5 per vehicle.
By Rail: 1½ miles York Station (from King's Cross). Special bus service from station to the course.
By Air: Light aircraft and helicopter landing facilities available at Rufforth aerodrome (5,000ft tarmac
runway). £20 landing fee-transport arranged to course. Leeds/Bradford airport (25 miles).

THE DERBY STAKES (CLASS 1)
EPSOM, SATURDAY, JUNE 7TH

HORSE	TRAINER	HORSE	TRAINER
AATHER (IRE)		CELT	
ACHILL ISLAND (IRE)	A. P. O'Brien, Ireland	CELTIC DRAGON	Mrs A. J. Perrett
AENEID		CHAMPAGNE SQUALL (IRE)	
AJLOUN (USA)		CHAMPION BREEZE	D. R. C. Elsworth
AKARSHAN (IRE)	John M. Oxx, Ireland	CHANGING WORLD (IRE)	
AL AMAAN		CHECKLOW (USA)	J. Noseda
AL AZY (IRE)	J. L. Dunlop	CHERRY LINX (IRE)	A. Fabre, France
AL JATHAB (IRE)		CHESAPEAKE BAY	A. P. O'Brien, Ireland
AL SAMHA (USA)	M. Johnston	CITY STABLE (IRE)	Sir Michael Stoute
ALAKAM (IRE)	A. de Royer Dupre, France	CLEAR DAYLIGHT	
ALAN DEVONSHIRE	M. H. Tompkins	COFFEE TEA OR ME	W. P. Mullins, Ireland
ALANDI (IRE)	John M. Oxx, Ireland	COIN OF THE REALM (IRE)	E. A. L. Dunlop
ALANEED		COLLECTION (IRE)	W. J. Haggas
ALESSANDRO VOLTA	A. P. O'Brien, Ireland	COLONY (IRE)	Sir Michael Stoute
ALEXANDER SEVERUS (IRE)	A. P. O'Brien, Ireland	CONDUIT (IRE)	Sir Michael Stoute
ALLIED POWERS (IRE)	M. L. W. Bell	CONFEDERATE	R. Charlton
ALLOW ME		COOL JUDGEMENT (IRE)	M. A. Jarvis
ALMONAFIS (IRE)	Sir Michael Stoute	CRAIGSTOWN	
ALMOUTAZ (USA)	B. W. Hills	CRUSOE'S RETURN	
ALQAFFAY (IRE)	A. P. O'Brien, Ireland	CURTAIN CALL (FR)	L. M. Cumani
ARABIAN GEM (IRE)	M. Johnston	DAASIJ (IRE)	
ARCTIC CAPE		DALCERAS	
ARROW FLIGHT (IRE)		DANCER IN DEMAND (IRE)	Sir Michael Stoute
ART PROFIT (IRE)	D. R. C. Elsworth	DANCERS DILEMMA (IRE)	
ASKAR TAU (FR)	M. P. Tregoning	DANEHILL STORM	
AT ALL	John M. Oxx, Ireland	DARAAHEM (IRE)	B. W. Hills
ATSO (USA)	P. Bary, France	DARK PROSPECT	
AUGMENTATION	P. W. D'Arcy	DASHING PATRIARCH	
AZEER (USA)	P. W. Chapple-Hyam	DAWAL (IRE)	John M. Oxx, Ireland
AZTLAN (USA)	P. Bary, France	DEADLY SILENCE (USA)	
BANQUET (IRE)		DECREE (IRE)	A. P. O'Brien, Ireland
BARKING WOLF (IRE)		DEER LAKE (IRE)	J. Noseda
BASHKIROV	A. P. O'Brien, Ireland	DELTA BRAVO (FR)	J. M. Beguigne, France
BAVARIAN NORDIC (USA)	Mrs A. Duffield	DEO VALENTE (USA)	B. J. Meehan
BEAUCHAMP WINNER	G. A. Butler	DISTANT PEAK (IRE)	
BEAUJEU (IRE)	M. Johnston	DIVINE SONG	
BEHRAR (IRE)	A. Fabre, France	DIXIE DEAN (USA)	Sir Michael Stoute
BENEDETTO	Mrs A. J. Perrett	DOCTOR ROBERT	Tom Dascombe
BETTER HAND (IRE)	M. R. Channon	DOVE (IRE)	
BLACK TOR FIGARRO (IRE)	B. W. Duke	DOWNHILLER (IRE)	J. L. Dunlop
BLIMEY O'RILEY (IRE)	M. H. Tompkins	DRUM MAJOR (IRE)	Sir Michael Stoute
BOLD CHOICE (IRE)	M. A. Jarvis	DUBAI SAMURAI	J. W. Hills
BOUGUEREAU	P. W. Chapple-Hyam	DUBROVNICK (IRE)	J. Noseda
BOX HILL (USA)	D. Wachman, Ireland	DUNCAN	
BOY ON A SWING (USA)	J. A. Osborne	DUNTULM	H. Candy
BRAVO BOLIVAR (IRE)		DUNVEGAN (IRE)	John M. Oxx, Ireland
BRIGHT FALCON		E MAJOR	Sir Michael Stoute
BRONZE CANNON (USA)	J. H. M. Gosden	EASTERN HILLS	
BUDAPEST (IRE)	A. P. O'Brien, Ireland	EBADIYAN (IRE)	John M. Oxx, Ireland
BUGAKU	Sir Michael Stoute	EDGBASTON (IRE)	M. Johnston
BY COMMAND	J. L. Dunlop	EL DUENDE (USA)	W. Jarvis
CAESAR'S SONG (IRE)		ELECTROLYSER (IRE)	C. G. Cox
CALABASH (IRE)	A. P. O'Brien, Ireland	EMIL (IRE)	
CALISTOS QUEST	M. Botti	EMIRATES WORLD (UAE)	
CALMING INFLUENCE (IRE)		EMMROOZ	
CAPE EXPRESS (IRE)	M. A. Jarvis	ENROLLER (IRE)	
CARDIFF (IRE)	A. P. O'Brien, Ireland	EPHORUS (USA)	Sir Michael Stoute
CARLIOR (FR)	Jean Claude Rouget, France	EQBAAL	J. L. Dunlop
CASINO DRIVE (USA)		ERZEN (IRE)	John M. Oxx, Ireland
CATS IN BOOTS (IRE)		ETOSHA (IRE)	
CEDAR FALLS (USA)	A. P. O'Brien, Ireland	EVERYBODY KNOWS	

HORSE	TRAINER
EXCAPE (IRE)	D. R. C. Elsworth
EXPRESSO STAR (USA)	J. H. M. Gosden
FALCATIV	
FANJURA (IRE)	J. Noseda
FAST COMPANY (IRE)	Saeed bin Suroor, United Arab Emirates
FATEH FIELD (USA)	
FEARED IN FLIGHT (IRE)	B. W. Hills
FILUN	L. M. Cumani
FINISTERRE	A. P. O'Brien, Ireland
FIRESIDE	P. W. Chapple-Hyam
FIRST AVENUE	M. A. Jarvis
FLIGHT TO QUALITY	M. Johnston
FOOLIN MYSELF	
FRANCESCO PETRARCH (FR)	J. S. Bolger, Ireland
FREDDIES FONG	I. W. McInnes
FRENCH ART	D. R. C. Elsworth
FRENCH RIVIERA	Sir Michael Stoute
FROZEN FIRE (GER)	A. P. O'Brien, Ireland
GAIA PRINCE (USA)	Mrs A. J. Perrett
GALIYAN	John M. Oxx, Ireland
GENERAL TING (IRE)	
GEORGE GERSHWIN (IRE)	
GHAIYATH	M. P. Tregoning
GIANT AMONG MEN (USA)	A. P. O'Brien, Ireland
GIANT LOVE (USA)	M. Johnston
GREAT RUMPUSCAT (USA)	A. P. O'Brien, Ireland
HANOVERIAN BARON	John M. Oxx, Ireland
HAWAANA (IRE)	
HAWK AND I (IRE)	
HAWK FLIGHT (IRE)	
HELLZAPOPPIN	
HENRYTHENAVIGATOR (USA)	A. P. O'Brien, Ireland
HEX (FR)	A. Fabre, France
HIGH STEPPING (USA)	E. A. L. Dunlop
HINDU KUSH (IRE)	A. P. O'Brien, Ireland
HISTORICAL GIANT (USA)	A. P. O'Brien, Ireland
HOUGHTON (IRE)	Sir Michael Stoute
HOWDIGO	J. R. Best
IBN BATTUTA (USA)	
IBN KHALDUN (USA)	
IBN QUTAIBA (USA)	
ICY COOL (IRE)	J. Noseda
IN CLOSE (USA)	J. Noseda
INTERNATIONALDEBUT (IRE)	
INVENTOR (IRE)	B. J. Meehan
ISTIQDAAM	J. H. M. Gosden
JACQUES MARQUETTE (IRE)	A. P. O'Brien, Ireland
JAMES POLLARD (IRE)	D. R. C. Elsworth
JUDPOT (USA)	H. R. A. Cecil
KADABI (IRE)	A. Fabre, France
KALAN (FR)	Jean Claude Rouget, France
KARASHAR (IRE)	John M. Oxx, Ireland
KENSINGTON OVAL	Sir Michael Stoute
KHALEEQ (USA)	
KHATEEB (IRE)	M. A. Jarvis
KILSHANNIG (IRE)	John M. Oxx, Ireland
KING KENNY	D. J. Murphy
KING OF PENTACLES	
KING OF QUEENS (IRE)	John M. Oxx, Ireland
KING OF ROME (IRE)	A. P. O'Brien, Ireland
KING OF WESTPHALIA (USA)	A. P. O'Brien, Ireland
KING O'THE GYPSIES (IRE)	R. Charlton
KINGDOM OF FIFE	
KINGDOM OF NAPLES (USA)	A. P. O'Brien, Ireland
KING'S ALCHEMIST	
KIRKUM (IRE)	J. Noseda
KOSSACK	L. M. Cumani

HORSE	TRAINER
KRISTAL GLORY (IRE)	J. L. Dunlop
KRYPTONITE (IRE)	J. W. Hills
LATHEETHA	
LATIN AMERICA (IRE)	A. P. O'Brien, Ireland
LATIN LAD	R. Hannon
LISANI (IRE)	John M. Oxx, Ireland
LISSELAN PROSPECT (USA)	
LOVE EMPIRE (USA)	M. Johnston
LUCIFER SAM (USA)	A. P. O'Brien, Ireland
LUNAYEF (IRE)	A. Fabre, France
MAGISTRATE (IRE)	M. A. Jarvis
MAGNA CUM LAUDE (IRE)	A. P. O'Brien, Ireland
MAIDSTONE MERCURY (FR)	
MAIDSTONE MIXTURE (FR)	
MANASSAS (IRE)	B. J. Meehan
MANSHOOR (IRE)	
MANYRIVERSTOCROSS (IRE)	A. King
MARAASED	M. A. Jarvis
MARCO POLO (USA)	Sir Michael Stoute
MARTYR	R. Hannon
MASQOOL (USA)	
MAWATHEEQ (USA)	
MAZE (IRE)	B. Smart
MCCONNELL (USA)	J. R. Best
MEETHAAQ (USA)	Sir Michael Stoute
METTERNICH (USA)	J. H. M. Gosden
MEYDAN CITY (USA)	
MIKHAIL FOKINE (USA)	A. P. O'Brien, Ireland
MINNEAPOLIS	A. P. O'Brien, Ireland
MISSISSIPPI RIVER (IRE)	A. P. O'Brien, Ireland
MISTA ROSSA	H. Morrison
MOGHAAYER	
MOIQEN (IRE)	
MONTAGNE D'OR (IRE)	
MONTELAGO (IRE)	John M. Oxx, Ireland
MONTEVETRO	R. Hannon
MONTFJORD (IRE)	E. J. O'Neill
MOOSLEY (IRE)	P. W. Chapple-Hyam
MOUNTAIN PRIDE (IRE)	J. L. Dunlop
MOURAD (IRE)	John M. Oxx, Ireland
MUBROOK (USA)	L. M. Cumani
MUTHEEB (USA)	
MYSTERY STAR (IRE)	M. H. Tompkins
NATIONAL HERITAGE	A. P. O'Brien, Ireland
NAWAKHIDA (USA)	M. Johnston
NEMO SPIRIT (IRE)	
NEW APPROACH (IRE)	J. S. Bolger, Ireland
NEW ZEALAND (IRE)	A. P. O'Brien, Ireland
NEXUS (IRE)	
NISAAL (IRE)	J. L. Dunlop
NORTH PARADE	B. J. Meehan
NORTHERN MELODY (IRE)	
ODIN'S RAVEN (IRE)	John M. Oxx, Ireland
OMNICAT (USA)	Saeed bin Suroor, United Arab Emirates
OPTIMO MAXIMO (USA)	A. P. O'Brien, Ireland
OPTIMUS MAXIMUS (IRE)	P. F. I. Cole
OUTER CONTINENT (USA)	P. Bary, France
PAGAN LIGHTNING (USA)	B. J. Meehan
PATKAI (IRE)	Sir Michael Stoute
PEAK OIL	
PENFOLD	N. I. M. Rossiter
PEREZ PRADO (USA)	W. Jarvis
PINK IVORY	Saeed bin Suroor, United Arab Emirates
PLAN (USA)	A. P. O'Brien, Ireland
PLAVIUS (USA)	
POET	A. P. O'Brien, Ireland
PRAIRIE HAWK (USA)	A. P. O'Brien, Ireland

HORSE	TRAINER
PRIME EXHIBIT	R. Charlton
PSI (USA)	J. E. Pease, France
QANAWAAT	
RAGTIME (IRE)	A. P. O'Brien, Ireland
RAMONA CHASE	
RED KESTREL (USA)	
RED ROCK PRINCE (IRE)	P. F. I. Cole
RED SHOOTER (IRE)	
RELATIVE STRENGTH (IRE)	A. M. Balding
RESPLENDENT LIGHT	
RIDGE DANCE	J. H. M. Gosden
RIPPLE (FR)	Jean Claude Rouget, France
RIQAAB (IRE)	E. A. L. Dunlop
RIVER DRAGON (IRE)	A. P. O'Brien, Ireland
ROCK PEAK (IRE)	H. Morrison
ROYAL AVENUE (IRE)	T. D. Easterby
ROYAL DESTINATION (IRE)	J. Noseda
SAINGLEND	
SAVARAIN	L. M. Cumani
SCARAB (IRE)	
SCEPTRE ROUGE (IRE)	A. de Royer Dupre, France
SCHOPENHAUER (USA)	L. M. Cumani
SEA'S LEGACY (IRE)	John M. Oxx, Ireland
SEVENTH CAVALRY (IRE)	H. R. A. Cecil
SHAKANI (IRE)	A. Fabre, France
SHAMIRAN (IRE)	John M. Oxx, Ireland
SHUBBAAN (USA)	
SILVER REGENT (USA)	Mrs A. J. Perrett
SIMARIAN (IRE)	John M. Oxx, Ireland
SINBAD THE SAILOR	J. W. Hills
SINDAJAN (IRE)	A. Fabre, France
SIR ROYAL (USA)	
SIYABONA (USA)	
SIYASA (USA)	
SKYCAP (IRE)	
SKYCRUISER (IRE)	Saeed bin Suroor, United Arab Emirates
SKYSURFERS	
SLANEY WAVE (IRE)	J. S. Bolger, Ireland
SLIGO	A. P. O'Brien, Ireland
SMETANA	H. Morrison
SMOOTH SOVEREIGN (IRE)	M. Johnston
SOLAR MAX (IRE)	C. R. Egerton
SONG OF FREEDOM (IRE)	D. K. Weld, Ireland
SOOMAR	T. G. Mills
SOVIET (IRE)	M. Johnston
SPECIAL BRANCH AMI (IRE)	C. R. Egerton
SPECIAL RESERVE (IRE)	R. Hannon
SPIRIT OF ST LOUIS (USA)	L. M. Cumani
SPIRITONTHEMOUNT (USA)	B. W. Hills
SQUIRE BOLDWOOD (IRE)	D. R. C. Elsworth
ST JEAN CAP FERRAT	G. Wragg
STONE OF SCONE	E. A. L. Dunlop
STUBBS ART (IRE)	D. R. C. Elsworth
SUMMER LOVE	
TAARESH (IRE)	J. L. Dunlop
TABAAHI (IRE)	
TAJAAWEED (USA)	Sir Michael Stoute
TAKWEEN (IRE)	
TALE OF TWO CITIES (IRE)	A. P. O'Brien, Ireland
TALLEST PEAK (USA)	A. P. O'Brien, Ireland
TAMAYUZ	
TANTO FAZ (IRE)	W. J. Haggas
TANWEER (USA)	Sir Michael Stoute
TARBOLTON (IRE)	
TARBRAX	
TARTAN BEARER (IRE)	Sir Michael Stoute
TEJWAAL	
THARAWAAT (IRE)	B. W. Hills
THAT'S ALL (IRE)	
THE BOGBERRY (USA)	A. P. O'Brien, Ireland
THE TARTAN ARMY (IRE)	C. Collins, Ireland
THOROUGHLY RED (IRE)	John M. Oxx, Ireland
THREE ROCKS (IRE)	J. S. Bolger, Ireland
TIGHNABRUAICH (IRE)	M. A. Jarvis
TILABAY (IRE)	John M. Oxx, Ireland
TIMARI (IRE)	John M. Oxx, Ireland
TOLLISHILL (IRE)	J. A. Osborne
TORPHICHEN	M. A. Jarvis
TOUCHDOWN	M. Johnston
TRIANGULAR (USA)	P. Bary, France
TROJAN WARRIOR (USA)	A. P. O'Brien, Ireland
TUAOI (IRE)	Dominique Sepulchre, France
TURJUMAN (USA)	
ULTIMATE QUEST (IRE)	Sir Mark Prescott
UNNEFER (FR)	H. R. A. Cecil
URBAN FARMER	
VASCO MARENGO	D. Smaga, France
VIA GALILEI (IRE)	J. S. Bolger, Ireland
VISIO	A. Fabre, France
VIVALDI (IRE)	A. P. O'Brien, Ireland
VOICE COACH (IRE)	Sir Michael Stoute
WALHALLA (IRE)	M. P. Tregoning
WALLACE SADDIE	
WARRINGAH	Sir Michael Stoute
WASAN	E. A. L. Dunlop
WASHINGTON IRVING (IRE)	A. P. O'Brien, Ireland
WASSILY KANDINSKY	A. P. O'Brien, Ireland
WATAR (IRE)	
WILLIAM HOGARTH	A. P. O'Brien, Ireland
WINE 'N DINE	
WORLD OF CHOICE (USA)	Saeed bin Suroor, United Arab Emirates
WORLD OF EVENTS (USA)	
XI (USA)	
YATHREB (USA)	J. L. Dunlop
YELLOW THUNDER (IRE)	Luke Comer, Ireland
YS (FR)	J. E. Hammond, France
ZAFRANAGAR (IRE)	A. Fabre, France
ZAKHAAREF	M. Johnston
ZULU CHIEF (USA)	A. P. O'Brien, Ireland
ZUWAAR	J. H. M. Gosden
EX ARTISTIQUE (IRE)	A. de Royer Dupre, France
EX ASHARNA (IRE)	A. de Royer Dupre, France
EX CARLING (FR)	
EX DABARA (IRE)	Mrs E. Mader, Germany
EX DANCE DESIGN (IRE)	
EX FLOWER BAY (USA)	W. P. Mullins, Ireland
EX FOLGORE (USA)	
EX GLAMOROUS GIRL (IRE)	B. W. Duke
EX MAID OF DAWKINS (USA)	A. de Royer Dupre, France
EX SERENA'S SONG (USA)	
EX SHAWARA (IRE)	A. de Royer Dupre, France
EX SHEMALA (IRE)	A. de Royer Dupre, France
EX VAYEVA (IRE)	A. de Royer Dupre, France
EX ZAINTA (IRE)	A. de Royer Dupre, France

EUROPEAN FREE HANDICAP
NEWMARKET CRAVEN MEETING 2008
(ON THE ROWLEY MILE COURSE)
WEDNESDAY, APRIL 16TH

The Free Handicap (Class A) (Listed race) with total prize fund of £30,000 added for two-years old only of 2007 (including all two-year-olds in the 2007 European two-year-old Thoroughbred Racehorse Rankings), to run as three-year-olds; lowest weight 7st 12lb; highest weight 9st 7lb.
Penalty for winner after December 31, 2007, 5lb. Seven furlongs.

Rating		st	lb	Rating		st	lb
126	NEW APPROACH (IRE)	9	7	110	LIANG KAY (GER)	8	5
125	FAST COMPANY (IRE)	9	6	110	MAD ABOUT YOU (IRE)	8	5
122	MYBOYCHARLIE (IRE)	9	3	110	MAGRITTE (ITY)	8	5
120	RAVEN'S PASS (USA)	9	1	110	MODERN LOOK (GB)	8	5
120	RIO DE LA PLATA (USA)	9	1	110	NAHOODH (IRE)	8	5
119	ZARKAVA (IRE)	9	0	110	REDOLENT (GB)	8	5
118	KINGSGATE NATIVE (IRE)	8	13	110	RIVER PROUD (USA)	8	5
118	NATAGORA (FR)	8	13	110	SPIRIT OF SHARJAH (IRE)	8	5
118	THEWAYYOUARE (USA)	8	13	109	ALEXANDER CASTLE (USA)	8	4
117	FLEETING SPIRIT (IRE)	8	12	109	FAT BOY (IRE)	8	4
117	HELLO MORNING (FR)	8	12	109	GREAT BARRIER REEF (USA)	8	4
117	IBN KHALDUN (USA)	8	12	109	GREATWALLOFCHINA (USA)	8	4
117	LISTEN (IRE)	8	12	108	CELTIC SLIPPER (IRE)	8	3
116	ALEXANDROS (GB)	8	11	108	CONFRONT (GB)	8	3
116	YOUNG PRETENDER (FR)	8	11	108	PENCIL HILL (IRE)	8	3
115	CURTAIN CALL (IRE)	8	10	108	RIDGE DANCE (GB)	8	3
115	DECLARATION OF WAR (IRE)	8	10	108	SENSE OF JOY (GB)	8	3
115	MCCARTNEY (GER)	8	10	108	SPACIOUS (GB)	8	3
115	PROVISO (GB)	8	10	108	SWISS FRANC (GB)	8	3
115	SHEDIAK (FR)	8	10	108	VISIT (GB)	8	3
114	DARK ANGEL (IRE)	8	9	107	ALFATHAA (GB)	8	2
114	HENRYTHENAVIGATOR (USA)	8	9	107	ART MASTER (GB)	8	2
114	LAURELDEAN GALE (USA)	8	9	107	BEACON LODGE (IRE)	8	2
114	POMELLATO (GER)	8	9	107	BERBICE (IRE)	8	2
114	SCINTILLO (GB)	8	9	107	EASTERN ROMANCE (GB)	8	2
114	WINKER WATSON (GB)	8	9	107	GOTHENBURG (UAE)	8	2
113	ACHILL ISLAND (IRE)	8	8	107	KOTSI (IRE)	8	2
113	CONFERENCE CALL (GB)	8	8	107	LADY AQUITAINE (USA)	8	2
113	FULL OF GOLD (FR)	8	8	107	PHILARIO (IRE)	8	2
113	GLADIATORUS (USA)	8	8	107	RED ALERT DAY (GB)	8	2
113	HATTA FORT (GB)	8	8	107	YAHRAB (IRE)	8	2
113	LIZARD ISLAND (USA)	8	8	106	DRAWNFROMTHEPAST (IRE)	8	1
113	LUCK MONEY (IRE)	8	8	106	DUBAI TIME (GB)	8	1
112	GAGNOA (IRE)	8	7	106	FESTOSO (IRE)	8	1
112	SAVETHISDANCEFORME (IRE)	8	7	106	ONE GREAT CAT (USA)	8	1
112	STERN OPINION (USA)	8	7	106	STIMULATION (IRE)	8	1
112	STRIKE THE DEAL (USA)	8	7	106	UNILATERAL (IRE)	8	1
111	BLUE CHAGALL (FR)	8	6	106	YANKADI (USA)	8	1
111	CAPTAIN GERRARD (IRE)	8	6	106	YOU'RESOTHRILLING (USA)	8	1
111	CITY LEADER (IRE)	8	6	105	ALBABILIA (IRE)	8	0
111	FEARED IN FLIGHT (IRE)	8	6	105	CENTENNIAL (IRE)	8	0
111	PRECIOUS BOY (GER)	8	6	105	CUTE ASS (IRE)	8	0
111	SAOIRSE ABU (USA)	8	6	105	ELLETELLE (IRE)	8	0
111	SIR GERRY (USA)	8	6	105	IGUAZU FALLS (USA)	8	0
111	STARLIT SANDS (GB)	8	6	105	KANDAHAR RUN (GB)	8	0
111	TAJDEEF (USA)	8	6	105	KITTY MATCHAM (IRE)	8	0
110	ALNADANA (IRE)	8	5	105	LADY DEAUVILLE (FR)	8	0
110	FARREL (IRE)	8	5	105	NIJOOM DUBAI (GB)	8	0
110	GOLDIKOVA (IRE)	8	5	104	ACHILLES OF TROY (IRE)	7	13
110	INDIAN DAFFODIL (IRE)	8	5	104	DREAM EATER (IRE)	7	13

Rating		st	lb
104	**EMMROOZ** (GB)	7	13
104	**EXHIBITION** (IRE)	7	13
104	**FATEH FIELD** (USA)	7	13
104	**FLORISTRY** (GB)	7	13
104	**LET US PREY** (GB)	7	13
104	**MISSIT** (IRE)	7	13
104	**NEWLY ELECTED** (IRE)	7	13
104	**PERFECT POLLY** (GB)	7	13
104	**SUGAR MINT** (IRE)	7	13
103	**ATLANTIC SPORT** (USA)	7	12
103	**BOUGUEREAU** (GB)	7	12
103	**BROKEN APPLAUSE** (IRE)	7	12
103	**DON'T FORGET FAITH** (USA)	7	12
103	**HAMMADI** (IRE)	7	12
103	**MAJOR EAZY** (IRE)	7	12
103	**MANASSAS** (IRE)	7	12
103	**MUTHABARA** (IRE)	7	12
103	**QUEEN OF NAPLES** (GB)	7	12
103	**SIBERIAN TIGER** (IRE)	7	12
103	**THE LOAN EXPRESS** (IRE)	7	12
102	**BAZERGAN** (IRE)	7	11
102	**CAKE** (IRE)	7	11
102	**EXCLAMATION** (GB)	7	11
102	**FRANCESCA D'GORGIO** (USA)	7	11
102	**HITCHENS** (IRE)	7	11
102	**MAZE** (IRE)	7	11
102	**ROYAL CONFIDENCE** (GB)	7	11
102	**SWEEPSTAKE** (IRE)	7	11

Rating		st	lb
102	**TUSCAN EVENING** (IRE)	7	11
101	**ALMAJD** (IRE)	7	10
101	**BOBS SURPRISE** (GB)	7	10
101	**BRAVE PROSPECTOR** (GB)	7	10
101	**FRED'S LAD** (GB)	7	10
101	**GROUP THERAPY** (GB)	7	10
101	**NACHO LIBRE** (GB)	7	10
101	**RAYMI COYA** (CAN)	7	10
101	**ROCK OF ROCHELLE** (USA)	7	10
101	**SHARP NEPHEW** (GB)	7	10
101	**SPINNING LUCY** (IRE)	7	10
100	**ANNIE SKATES** (USA)	7	9
100	**ARIEGE** (USA)	7	9
100	**DONEGAL** (USA)	7	9
100	**EASY TARGET** (FR)	7	9
100	**ELLMAU** (GB)	7	9
100	**EVA'S REQUEST** (IRE)	7	9
100	**FASHION ROCKS** (IRE)	7	9
100	**IMPERIAL MINT** (IRE)	7	9
100	**IRISH JIG** (IRE)	7	9
100	**LATIN LAD** (GB)	7	9
100	**LOCH JIPP** (USA)	7	9
100	**SKADRAK** (USA)	7	9
100	**SOUTH DAKOTA** (IRE)	7	9
100	**STEP SOFTLY** (GB)	7	9
100	**STRATEGIC MOVER** (USA)	7	9
100	**WARSAW** (IRE)	7	9
100	**WESTERN ART** (USA)	7	9

WORLD THOROUGHBRED RACEHORSE RANKINGS

For three-year-olds rated 110 or greater by the International Federation of Horseracing Authorities.

Rating		Trained
129	AUTHORIZED (IRE)	GB
129	CURLIN (USA)	USA
126	STREET SENSE (USA)	USA
125	SOLDIER OF FORTUNE (IRE)	IRE
124	ANY GIVEN SATURDAY (USA)	USA
123	LITERATO (FR)	FR
123	RAGS TO RICHES (USA)	USA
122	DARJINA (FR)	FR
122	EAGLE MOUNTAIN (GB)	IRE
122	EXCELLENT ART (GB)	IRE
122	HARD SPUN (USA)	USA
122	PEEPING FAWN (USA)	IRE
122	SAGARA (FR)	FR
121	INDIAN INK (IRE)	GB
120	COCKNEY REBEL (IRE)	GB
120	DUKE OF MARMALADE (IRE)	IRE
120	GRASSHOPPER (USA)	USA
120	LAWMAN (FR)	FR
120	SAKHEE'S SECRET (GB)	GB
119	ADLERFLUG (GER)	GER
119	FINSCEAL BEO (IRE)	IRE
119	ASTRONOMER ROYAL (USA)	IRE
118	CREACHADOIR (IRE)	IRE/GB
118	DUTCH ART (GB)	GB
118	MRS LINDSAY (USA)	FR
118	NOBIZ LIKE SHOBIZ (USA)	USA
118	TIAGO (USA)	USA
118	ZAMBEZI SUN (GB)	FR
117	HOLOCENE (USA)	FR
117	LIGHT SHIFT (USA)	GB
117	RED GIANT (USA)	USA
117	SCAT DADDY (USA)	USA
117	VADAPOLINA (FR)	FR
117	VODKA (JPN)	JPN
117	YELLOWSTONE (IRE)	IRE
116	DAAHER (CAN)	USA
116	DREAM RUSH (USA)	USA
116	HE'S A DECOY (USA)	IRE
116	LADY JOANNE (USA)	USA
116	LEAR'S PRINCESS (USA)	USA
116	MAJESTIC ROI (USA)	GB
116	OCTAVE (USA)	USA
116	PANTY RAID (USA)	USA
116	SIGHTSEEING (USA)	USA
116	TOUGH TIZ'S SIS (USA)	USA
116	VITAL EQUINE (IRE)	GB
116	WEST WIND (GB)	FR
115	ASAKUSA KINGS (JPN)	JPN
115	BIT OF WHIMSY (USA)	USA
115	BOSCOBEL (GB)	GB
115	C P WEST (USA)	USA
115	CIRCULAR QUAY (USA)	USA
115	COASTAL PATH (GB)	FR
115	DAIWA SCARLET (JPN)	JPN
115	DAYTONA (IRE)	USA
115	DOMINICAN (USA)	USA
115	DREAMING OF ANNA (USA)	USA
115	GOLDEN TITUS (IRE)	ITY

Rating		Trained
115	HALICARNASSUS (IRE)	GB
115	HONOLULU (IRE)	IRE
115	IDIOT PROOF (USA)	USA
115	LEGERETE (USA)	FR
115	LUCARNO (USA)	GB
115	MI EMMA (GER)	GER
115	PASSAGE OF TIME (GB)	GB
115	POET LAUREATE (GB)	FR
115	PROMISING LEAD (GB)	GB
115	RED ROCK CANYON (IRE)	IRE
115	ROC DE CAMBES (NZ)	JPN
115	RUTHERIENNE (USA)	USA
115	SEALY HILL (CAN)	CAN
115	SHAMDINAN (FR)	FR/USA
115	SILKWOOD (GB)	GB
115	STORMELLO (USA)	USA
115	TARIQ (GB)	GB
115	TASHELKA (FR)	FR
114	ALEXANDER OF HALES (USA)	IRE
114	ARABIAN GLEAM (GB)	GB
114	BEAUTY IS TRUTH (IRE)	FR
114	CONILLON (GER)	GER
114	FIRST STREAM (GER)	GER
114	FOLLOWMYFOOTSTEPS (USA)	IRE
114	HONOURED GUEST (IRE)	IRE
114	MAJOR CADEAUX (GB)	GB
114	MISS LUCIFER (FR)	GB
114	MISSVINSKI (USA)	FR/USA
114	SIMPLY PERFECT (GB)	GB
114	SPIRIT ONE (FR)	FR
114	US RANGER (USA)	FR/IRE
113	ALL IS VANITY (FR)	FR
113	ALL MY LOVING (IRE)	IRE
113	AQALEEM (GB)	GB
113	ARCH SWING (USA)	IRE
113	HARLAND (GB)	GB
113	MAHLER (GB)	GB
113	MORES WELLS (GB)	IRE
113	MYSTIC LIPS (GER)	GER
113	STONESIDE (IRE)	FR/USA
113	ZAHAM (USA)	GB
112	ALEXANDER TANGO (IRE)	IRE
112	ARCHIPENKO (USA)	IRE
112	COQUERELLE (IRE)	FR
112	DALVINA (GB)	GB/USA
112	DANSANT (GB)	GB
112	EZIMA (IRE)	IRE
112	HEARTHSTEAD MAISON (IRE)	GB
112	HELLVELYN (GB)	GB
112	INDIAN CHOICE (USA)	FR
112	MACARTHUR (IRE)	IRE
112	PERSIAN STORM (GER)	GER
112	REGAL FLUSH (GB)	GB
112	REGIME (IRE)	GB
112	SHREK (GER)	GER
112	VERACITY (GB)	GB
111	AVISO (GER)	GER
111	BELIEVE ME (IRE)	FR

Rating	Trained	Rating	Trained
111 CELESTIAL HALO (IRE)	GB	110 DIMENTICATA (IRE)	IRE
111 HAATEF (USA)	IRE	110 DIYAKALANIE (FR)	FR
111 KIRKLEES (IRE)	GB	110 DUBAI'S TOUCH (GB)	GB
111 NOBLE PRINCE (GER)	FR	110 FASHION STATEMENT (GB)	GB
111 RAHIYAH (USA)	GB	110 FRISTON FOREST (IRE)	FR
111 ROYAL AND REGAL (IRE)	FR	110 LE CADRE NOIR (IRE)	ITY
111 SALFORD MILL (IRE)	GB	110 LION SANDS (GB)	GB
110 ACAPULCO (IRE)	IRE	110 MOLLY MAX (GER)	GER
110 ADAGIO (GB)	GB/USA	110 PER INCANTO (USA)	ITY/GB
110 ADMIRALOFTHEFLEET (USA)	IRE	110 PIPEDREAMER (GB)	GB
110 ALASKA RIVER (GB)	GER	110 RED MOLONEY (USA)	IRE
110 APPEL AU MAITRE (FR)	NOR	110 SHUJOON (FR)	FR
110 ARABIAN GULF (GB)	GB	110 SWEET LILLY (GB)	GB
110 AXXOS (GER)	GER	110 THOUSAND WORDS (GB)	GB
110 CHICHI CREASY (FR)	FR	110 TRANQUIL TIGER (GB)	GB
110 COSTUME (GB)	GB/USA	110 TURFROSE (GER)	ITY

OLDER HORSES 2007

For four-year-olds and up rated 110 or greater by the International Federation of Horseracing Authorities.

Rating	Age	Trained	Rating	Age	Trained
131 MANDURO (GER)	5	FR	118 JAMBALAYA (CAN)	5	USA
129 DYLAN THOMAS (IRE)	4	IRE	118 MANDESHA (FR)	4	FR
129 INVASOR (ARG)	5	USA	118 SHOWING UP (USA)	4	USA
125 ADMIRE MOON (JPN)	4	JPN	118 SKY CONQUEROR (CAN)	5	CAN
125 ENGLISH CHANNEL (USA)	4	USA	118 SMOKEY STOVER (USA)	4	USA
124 LAWYER RON (USA)	4	USA	118 SOLDIER HOLLOW (GB)	7	GER
124 YOUMZAIN (IRE)	4	GB	118 SOLDIER'S TALE (USA)	6	GB
123 NOTNOWCATO (GB)	5	GB	118 SUPER HORNET (JPN)	4	JPN
123 RAMONTI (FR)	5	GB	118 TOYLSOME (GB)	8	GER
122 GETAWAY (GER)	4	FR	118 VERMILION (JPN)	5	JPN
122 KIP DEVILLE (USA)	4	USA	117 AGNES ARK (JPN)	4	JPN
122 LAVA MAN (USA)	6	USA	117 ASIATIC BOY (ARG)	4	UAE
122 MEISHO SAMSON (JPN)	4	JPN	117 CHOSAN (JPN)	5	JPN
122 POP ROCK (JPN)	6	JPN	117 DISTANT WAY (USA)	6	ITY
122 SEPTIMUS (IRE)	4	IRE	117 EINSTEIN (BRZ)	5	USA
121 DAIWA MAJOR (JPN)	6	JPN	117 GEORDIELAND (FR)	6	GB
121 MATSURIDA GOGH (JPN)	4	JPN	117 HYSTERICALADY (USA)	4	USA
121 MIDNIGHT LUTE (USA)	4	USA	117 IRISH WELLS (FR)	4	FR
121 YEATS (IRE)	6	IRE	117 JEREMY (USA)	4	GB
120 CESARE (GB)	6	GB	117 LAHUDOOD (GB)	4	USA
120 CORINTHIAN (USA)	5	USA	117 LINNGARI (IRE)	5	UAE/FR
120 FABULOUS STRIKE (USA)	4	USA	117 MARAAHEL (IRE)	6	GB
120 MISS ANDRETTI (AUS)	6	AUS	117 MARCHAND D'OR (FR)	4	FR
120 RED ROCKS (IRE)	4	GB	117 POLITICAL FORCE (USA)	4	USA
120 SCORPION (IRE)	5	IRE	117 PRECIOUS KITTEN (USA)	4	USA
119 AFTER MARKET (USA)	4	USA	117 PRICE TAG (GB)	4	USA
119 ASK (GB)	4	GB	117 RED CLUBS (IRE)	5	GB
119 BENBAUN (IRE)	6	GB	117 REMARKABLE NEWS (VEN)	5	USA
119 BETTER TALK NOW (USA)	8	USA	117 SCHIAPARELLI (GER)	4	GER
119 CLOUDY'S KNIGHT (USA)	7	USA	117 SIR PERCY (GB)	4	GB
119 DOCTOR DINO (FR)	5	FR	117 SPIRITO DEL VENTO (FR)	4	FR
119 GEORGE WASHINGTON (IRE)	4	IRE	117 SUNRIVER (USA)	4	USA
119 KONGO RIKISHIO (IRE)	5	JPN	117 SURF CAT (USA)	5	USA
119 MOUNTAIN HIGH (IRE)	5	GB	117 SUZUKA PHOENIX (JPN)	4	JPN
119 QUIJANO (GER)	5	GER	117 TAKEOVER TARGET (AUS)	8	AUS
119 SADDEX (GB)	4	GER	117 TURTLE BOWL (IRE)	4	FR
119 SIXTIES ICON (GB)	4	GB	116 ADMIRE FUJI (JPN)	5	JPN
119 THE TIN MAN (USA)	9	USA	116 BUSSONI (GER)	6	GER
118 DELTA BLUES (JPN)	6	JPN	116 COMPANY (JPN)	6	JPN
118 GINGER PUNCH (USA)	4	USA	116 COSMONAUT (USA)	5	USA

Rating	Age	Trained	Rating	Age	Trained
116 DANDY MAN (IRE)	4	IRE	113 ALLEGRETTO (IRE)	4	GB
116 GRAND COUTURIER (GB)	4	USA	113 ANNA PAVLOVA (GB)	4	GB
116 GREG'S GOLD (USA)	6	USA	113 ARCH REBEL (USA)	6	IRE
116 IN SUMMATION (USA)	4	USA	113 BALTHAZAAR'S GIFT (IRE)	4	GB
116 LAVEROCK (IRE)	5	UAE/GB	113 BORIS DE DEAUVILLE (IRE)	4	FR
116 MOLENGAO (BRZ)	6	USA	113 DUFF (IRE)	4	IRE
116 MY TYPHOON (IRE)	5	USA	113 FORMAL DECREE (GER)	4	UAE/GB
116 NASHOBA'S KEY (USA)	4	USA	113 GREEK RENAISSANCE (IRE)	4	GB
116 PAPAL BULL (GB)	4	GB	113 HATTAN (IRE)	5	GB
116 PASSAGER (FR)	4	FR	113 LE MIRACLE (GER)	6	GER
116 PRESSING (IRE)	4	ITY/GB	113 MACLEYA (GER)	5	FR
116 PRINCE FLORI (GER)	4	GER	113 MONACHESI (IRE)	4	ITY
116 PURIM (USA)	5	USA	113 SANTIAGO (GER)	5	GER
116 RACINGER (FR)	4	FR	113 WELSH EMPEROR (IRE)	8	GB
116 ROYAL HIGHNESS (GER)	5	USA	112 AMADEUS WOLF (GB)	4	GB
116 SATWA QUEEN (FR)	5	FR	112 BLUE KSAR (IRE)	4	GB
116 SHADOW GATE (JPN)	5	JPN	112 CRIME SCENE (IRE)	4	GB
116 SPRING AT LAST (USA)	4	USA	112 DESERT LORD (GB)	7	GB
116 STREAM OF GOLD (IRE)	6	USA	112 DONALDSON (GER)	5	GER
116 STUDENT COUNCIL (USA)	5	USA	112 FRACAS (IRE)	5	IRE
116 WAIT A WHILE (USA)	4	USA	112 KANDIDATE (GB)	5	GB
115 ARSON SQUAD (USA)	4	USA	112 KOCAB (GB)	5	FR
115 ASSET (IRE)	4	GB	112 MASHAAHED (GB)	4	GB
115 AWESOME GEM (USA)	4	USA	112 MUNADDAM (USA)	5	GB
115 BALANCE (USA)	4	USA	112 POSEIDON ADVENTURE (IRE)	4	GER
115 BENNY THE BULL (USA)	4	USA	112 ROWE PARK (GB)	4	GB
115 BLUE CONCORDE (JPN)	7	JPN	112 ROYAL OATH (USA)	4	GB
115 BUZZARDS BAY (USA)	5	USA	112 STORMY RIVER (FR)	4	FR
115 CITRONNADE (USA)	4	USA	112 TAKE A BOW (GB)	6	GB
115 ECHELON (GB)	5	GB	112 TAM LIN (GB)	4	GB
115 ECHO OF LIGHT (GB)	5	GB	112 VISON CELEBRE (IRE)	4	FR
115 ERIMO EXPIRE (JPN)	5	JPN	112 WAKE UP MAGGIE (IRE)	4	GB
115 FIELD ROUGE (JPN)	5	JPN	111 ADVANCED (GB)	4	GB
115 GARNICA (FR)	4	FR	111 APOLLO STAR (GER)	5	GER
115 HONEY RYDER (USA)	6	USA	111 APPALACHIAN TRAIL (IRE)	6	GB
115 INTI RAIMI (JPN)	5	JPN	111 BALKAN KNIGHT (GB)	7	GB
115 IRRIDESCENCE (SAF)	6	UAE	111 BORDERLESCOTT (GB)	5	GB
115 KELLY'S LANDING (USA)	6	USA	111 BRISANT (GER)	5	GER
115 MAGNUS (AUS)	5	AUS	111 DARAMSAR (FR)	4	FR
115 MASTER COMMAND (USA)	5	USA	111 DECADO (IRE)	4	IRE
115 MISS SHOP (USA)	4	USA	111 DISTINCTION (IRE)	8	GB
115 NANNINA (GB)	4	GB	111 DRAGON DANCER (GB)	4	GB
115 ORACLE WEST (SAF)	5	UAE	111 EASTERN APPEAL (IRE)	4	IRE
115 PROSPECT PARK (GB)	6	USA	111 FAIRMILE (GB)	5	GB
115 RED EVIE (IRE)	4	GB	111 FINALMENTE (GB)	5	IRE
115 SERGEANT CECIL (GB)	8	GB	111 JUMBAJUKIBA (GB)	4	GB
115 SHAKESPEARE (USA)	5	USA	111 LORD ADMIRAL (USA)	6	IRE
115 SILENT NAME (JPN)	5	USA	111 MACORVILLE (USA)	4	GB
115 SILVER WAGON (USA)	6	USA	111 MIGHTY (GB)	4	GB
115 STAGE GIFT (IRE)	5	UAE/GB	111 MONTARE (FR)	5	FR
115 SUN BOAT (GB)	5	GB	111 MULTIDIMENSIONAL (GB)	4	GB
115 SUNRISE BACCHUS (JPN)	5	JPN	111 MUSTAMEET (USA)	6	IRE
115 TAKE D' TOUR (USA)	5	USA	111 SECRET WORLD (IRE)	4	GB
115 TOKAI TRICK (JPN)	5	JPN	111 SHAHIN (USA)	4	GB
115 UNBRIDLED BELLE (USA)	4	USA	111 SOAPY DANGER (GB)	4	GB
115 WANDERIN BOY (USA)	6	USA	111 STRONGHOLD (GB)	5	GB
114 AL QASI (IRE)	4	GB	111 TELL (GB)	4	GB
114 ATLANTIC AIR (FR)	5	FR	111 WIESENPFAD (FR)	4	GER
114 CHAMPS ELYSEES (GB)	4	FR/USA	110 ADMIRAL'S CRUISE (USA)	5	GB
114 DANAK (IRE)	4	IRE	110 AREYOUTALKINGTOME (GB)	4	GB
114 EGERTON (GER)	6	GER	110 ASPECTUS (IRE)	4	GER
114 LORD DU SUD (FR)	6	FR	110 BAHIA BREEZE (GB)	5	GB
114 PURPLE MOON (IRE)	4	GB	110 BLUE BAJAN (GB)	5	GB
114 SPECIOSA (IRE)	4	GB	110 BLYTHE KNIGHT (IRE)	7	GB
114 SUDAN (IRE)	4	FR	110 CHERRY MIX (FR)	6	GB
114 TIZA (SAF)	5	FR	110 CLASSIC PUNCH (IRE)	4	GB
114 WINDSOR KNOT (IRE)	5	GB	110 ELECTRIC BEAT (GB)	4	GER

Rating		Age	Trained
110	**GALACTIC STAR** (GB)	4	GB
110	**HARVEST QUEEN** (IRE)	4	GB
110	**IVY CREEK** (USA)	4	GB
110	**KAPIL** (SAF)	5	SAF
110	**KONIG TURF** (GER)	5	GER
110	**LA BOUM** (GER)	4	FR
110	**MHARADONO** (GER)	4	GER
110	**MOORHOUSE LAD** (GB)	4	GB
110	**MUSICAL WAY** (FR)	5	FR
110	**MUTAWAAJID** (AUS)	4	GB
110	**OLYMPIAN ODYSSEY** (GB)	4	UAE/GB

Rating		Age	Trained
110	**PEACE OFFERING** (IRE)	7	GB
110	**PONTE TRESA** (FR)	4	FR
110	**REDSTONE DANCER** (IRE)	5	IRE
110	**RHENUS** (GB)	4	FR
110	**SILVER TOUCH** (IRE)	4	GB
110	**SOMMERTAG** (GER)	4	GER
110	**STEPPE DANCER** (IRE)	4	GB
110	**STOTSFOLD** (GB)	4	GB
110	**TAX FREE** (IRE)	5	GB
110	**TUNGSTEN STRIKE** (USA)	6	GB
110	**TURBO LINN** (GB)	4	GB

RACEFORM CHAMPIONS 2007
THREE-YEAR-OLDS AND UP

5f-6f

SACRED KINGDOM	129
MIDNIGHT LUTE	126
SAKHEE'S SECRET	126
BENBAUN	125
MISS ANDRETTI	125
DUTCH ART	124
BENTLEY BISCUIT	123
SOLDIER'S TALE	123
TAKEOVER TARGET	123
DANDY MAN	122
FABULOUS STRIKE	122
RED CLUBS	122
US RANGER	122
ABSOLUTE CHAMPION	121
AREYOUTALKINGTOME	121
ASSET	121
MAGNUS	121
SPARK OF LIFE	121

7f-9f

LAWYER RON	128
MANDURO	128
ADMIRE MOON	127
INVASOR	125
RAMONTI	125
ARMADA	124
COCKNEY REBEL	124
CREACHADOIR	124
DARJINA	124
EXCELLENT ART	124
GOOD BA BA	124
LINNGARI	124
PEEPING FAWN	124

10f-12f

MANDURO	133
INVASOR	132
AUTHORIZED	131
DYLAN THOMAS	131
CURLIN	131
PREMIUM TAP	128
SOLDIER OF FORTUNE	127
STREET SENSE	127
LAVA MAN	126
LAWYER RON	126
NOTNOWCATO	126
YOUMZAIN	126
RED ROCKS	125

13+f

SEPTIMUS	124
YEATS	124
EFFICIENT	123
GETAWAY	122
HONOLULU	121
LUCARNO	121
SCORPION	121
PAPAL BULL	120
PURPLE MOON	120
ASK	119
BLUE MONDAY	119
GEORDIELAND	119
MAHLER	119
SERGEANT CECIL	119

Raceform
INTERACTIVE

Compile your own horse comments, ratings and lists to
follow and form your OWN opinion.

RACEFORM CHAMPIONS 2007
TWO-YEAR-OLDS

5f-6f

MYBOYCHARLIE	118
NATAGORA	117
POMELLATO	117
FLEETING SPIRIT	116
WINKER WATSON	116
KINGSGATE NATIVE	115
DARK ANGEL	114
SIR GERRY	112
STRIKE THE DEAL	112
ALEXANDROS	111
RIVER PROUD	111
TAJDEEF	111
CAPTAIN GERRARD	110
HENRYTHENAVIGATOR	110
SAOIRSE ABU	110

7f+

NEW APPROACH	125
FAST COMPANY	124
WAR PASS	123
RIO DE LA PLATA	119
ZARKAVA	119
IBN KHALDUN	118
RAVEN'S PASS	118
THEWAYYOUARE	117
HELLO MORNING	116
MCCARTNEY	115
INDIAN BLESSING	114
MYBOYCHARLIE	114
TALL POPPY	114

RACEFORM FASTEST PERFORMERS
THREE-YEAR-OLDS AND UP 2007

5f-6f Turf

MISS ANDRETTI	123
DANDY MAN	120
MAGNUS	119
SAKHEE'S SECRET	118
TAKEOVER TARGET	118
DUTCH ART	117
GARNICA	117
RED CLUBS	117
ENTICING	116
AMADEUS WOLF	115
BALTHAZAAR'S GIFT	115
BEAUTY IS TRUTH	115
BEL CANTOR	115
HAATEF	115
LE CADRE NOIR	115
MARCHAND D'OR	115
RIPPLES MAID	115
SIERRA VISTA	115

7f-9f Turf

FORMAL DECREE	118
INDIAN INK	118
ACE	117
ADMIRE MOON	117
COCKNEY REBEL	117
DARJINA	117
JUMBAJUKIBA	117
ORACLE WEST	117
BLYTHE KNIGHT	116
CREACHADOIR	116
FINSCEAL BEO	116
LINNGARI	116
OLYMPIAN ODYSSEY	116
ORDNANCE ROW	116
STREAM OF GOLD	116

7f-9f AW

ASIATIC BOY	115
FOLK	115
GENTLEMAN'S DEAL	115
EXPENSIVE	114
PARTY BOSS	114
SPRING AT LAST	114
VENTURA	114
CEREMONIAL JADE	113
KANDIDATE	113
SPEEDY SAM	113
WORLD SPIRIT	113
BINNION BAY	112
CALIFORNIA LAWS	112
LES FAZZANI	112
PREMIO LOCO	112
SUPER FRANK	112
UHOOMAGOO	112

10f-12f Turf

DYLAN THOMAS	120
NOTNOWCATO	118
SOLDIER OF FORTUNE	118
YOUMZAIN	118
GETAWAY	117
PEEPING FAWN	117
SAGARA	117
DUKE OF MARMALADE	116
GALACTIC STAR	116
GEORGE WASHINGTON	116
ZAMBEZI SUN	116
BORIS DE DEAUVILLE	115
DOCTOR DINO	115
HEARTHSTEAD MAISON	115
KING RAMA	115
MONTARE	115
MOUNTAIN HIGH	115
RED ROCK CANYON	115
STAGE GIFT	115
TASHELKA	115
VAN GOSH	115
YELLOWSTONE	115

10f-12f AW

INVASOR	120	MIGHTY	114
PREMIUM TAP	118	WATAMU	114
CUSOON	116	COEUR DE LIONNE	113
STEPPE DANCER	116	BULLISH LUCK	112
AL THARIB	115	GEORDIELAND	112
BLUE BAJAN	115	GRAND PASSION	112
DANSANT	115	HERNANDO ROYAL	112
IMPERIAL STAR	114	ILLUSTRIOUS BLUE	112
LION SANDS	114	PIVOTAL ANSWER	112

13f+ Turf

ALLEGRETTO	118	VAREVEES	116
BRISANT	117	GETAWAY	115
LE MIRACLE	117	MAJESTIC CONCORDE	115
MACLEYA	117	SOAPY DANGER	115
PONTE TRESA	117	FINALMENTE	114
YEATS	117	MORES WELLS	114
ANNA PAVLOVA	116	ORBIT O'GOLD	114
ATHLUMNEY LAD	116	VERACITY	114
SCORPION	116		

RACEFORM FASTEST PERFORMERS TWO-YEAR-OLDS OF 2007

5f-6f Turf

CAPTAIN GERRARD	111	NATAGORA	111
KINGSGATE NATIVE	111	FLEETING SPIRIT	110

7f+ Turf

NEW APPROACH	115	RAVEN'S PASS	111
FAST COMPANY	114	ZARKAVA	111
RIO DE LA PLATA	112	LISTEN	110
ALEXANDROS	111		

MEDIAN TIMES 2007

The following Raceform median times are used in the calculation of the Split Second speed figures. They represent a true average time for the distance, which has been arrived at after looking at the winning times for all races over each distance within the past five years, except for those restricted to two or three-year-olds.

Some current race distances have been omitted as they have not yet had a sufficient number of races run over them to produce a reliable average time.

ASCOT

5f 1m 0.50	1m Straight 1m 40.60	1m 4f 2m 35.50
6f 1m 14.40	1m Round 1m 40.80	2m 3m 32.60
7f 1m 28.00	1m 2f 2m 9.80	2m 4f 4m 20.60

AYR

5f 1m 0.10	1m 1m 43.80	1m 5f 13y 2m 56.60
6f 1m 13.60	1m 1f 20y 1m 58.40	1m 7f 3m 20.40
7f 50y 1m 33.40	1m 2f 2m 12.00	2m 1f 105y 4m 05.70

BATH

5f 11y 1m 2.50	1m 2f 46y 2m 11.00	1m 5f 22y 2m 52.00
5f 161y 1m 11.20	1m 3f 144y 2m 30.60	2m 1f 34y 3m 51.90
1m 5y 1m 40.80		

BEVERLEY

5f 1m 3.50	1m 100y 1m 47.60	1m 4f 16y 2m 40.90
7f 100y 1m 33.80	1m 1f 207y 2m 7.00	2m 35y 3m 39.80

BRIGHTON

5f 59y 1m 2.30	6f 209y 1m 23.10	1m 1f 209y 2m 3.60
5f 213y 1m 10.20	7f 214y 1m 36.00	1m 3f 196y 2m 32.70

CARLISLE

5f 1m 0.80	7f 200y 1m 40.00	1m 6f 32y 3m 7.50
5f 193y 1m 13.70	1m 1f 61y 1m 57.60	2m 1f 52y 3m 53.00
6f 192y 1m 27.10	1m 3f 107y 2m 23.10	

CATTERICK

5f 59.80	7f 1m 27.00	1m 5f 175y 3m 3.60
5f 212y 1m 13.60	1m 3f 214y 2m 38.90	1m 7f 177y 3m 32.00

CHEPSTOW

5f 16y 59.30	1m 14y 1m 36.20	2m 49y 3m 38.90
6f 16y 1m 12.90	1m 2f 36y 2m 10.60	2m 2f 4m 03.60
7f 16y 1m 23.20	1m 4f 23y 2m 39.00	

CHESTER

5f 16y 1m 1.00	1m 2f 75y 2m 12.20	1m 5f 89y 2m 55.70
6f 18y 1m 13.80	1m 3f 79y 2m 26.60	1m 7f 195y 3m 29.90
7f 2y 1m 26.50	1m 4f 66y 2m 41.00	2m 2f 147y 4m 10.90
7f 122y 1m 33.80		

DONCASTER

5f 1m 0.50	1m str 1m 39.30	1m 6f 132y 3m 6.70
5f 140y 1m 7.40	1m rnd 1m 41.00	2m 110y 3m 55.50
6f 1m 13.60	1m 2f 60y 2m 11.12	2m 2f 3m 58.20
7f 1m 26.30	1m 4f 2m 35.10	

EPSOM

5f 55.70	7f 1m 23.30	1m 2f 18y 2m 9.70
6f 1m 9.40	1m 114y 1m 46.10	1m 4f 10y 2m 38.90

FOLKESTONE

5f 1m 0.00	1m 1f 149y 2m 4.90	1m 7f 92y 3m 29.70
6f 1m 12.77	1m 4f 2m 40.90	2m 93y 3m 37.20
7f Straight 1m 27.30		

GOODWOOD

5f 58.40	1m 1f 1m 56.30	1m 6f 3m 3.60
6f 1m 12.20	1m 1f 192y 2m 8.00	2m 3m 33.20
7f 1m 27.40	1m 3f 2m 28.30	2m 5f 4m 33.10
1m 1m 39.90	1m 4f 2m 38.40	

HAMILTON

5f 4y 1m 0.00	1m 1f 36y 1m 59.70	1m 4f 17y 2m 38.60
6f 5y 1m 12.20	1m 3f 16y 2m 25.60	1m 5f 9y 2m 53.90
1m 65y 1m 48.40		

HAYDOCK

5f 1m 0.50	1m 30y 1m 43.80	1m 6f 3m 4.30
6f 1m 14.00	1m 2f 120y 2m 16.70	2m 45y 3m 37.00
7f 30y 1m 30.20	1m 3f 200y 2m 33.20	

KEMPTON (A.W)

5f 1m 0.50	1m 1m 39.80	1m 4f 2m 34.50
6f 1m 13.10	1m 2f 2m 8.00	2m 3m 30.10
7f 1m 26.00	1m 3f 2m 21.90	

LEICESTER

5f 2y 1m 0.00	7f 9y 1m 26.20	1m 1f 218y 2m 7.90
5f 218y 1m 13.00	1m 60y 1m 45.10	1m 3f 183y 2m 33.90

LINGFIELD

5f 58.20	7f 140y 1m 32.30	1m 3f 106y 2m 31.50
6f 1m 11.20	1m 1f 1m 56.60	1m 6f 3m 10.00
7f 1m 23.30	1m 2f 2m 10.50	2m 3m 34.80

LINGFIELD (A.W)

5f 58.80	1m 1m 38.20	1m 5f 2m 46.00
6f 1m 11.90	1m 2f 2m 6.60	2m 3m 25.70
7f 1m 24.80	1m 4f 2m 33.00	

MUSSELBURGH

5f 1m 0.40	1m 1f 1m 54.70	1m 6f 3m 5.30
7f 30y 1m 30.30	1m 4f 2m 39.70	2m 3m 36.10
1m 1m 41.20	1m 5f 2m 52.00	

NEWBURY

5f 34y 1m 1.40	1m 1f 1m 55.50	1m 4f 5y 2m 35.50
6f 8y 1m 13.00	1m 2f 6y 2m 8.80	1m 5f 61y 2m 52.00
7f Straight 1m 25.70	1m 3f 5y 2m 21.20	2m 3m 36.90
1m Straight 1m 39.70		

NEWCASTLE

5f 1m 0.70	1m 3y Straight 1m 43.70	1m 4f 93y 2m 45.60
6f 1m 15.20	1m 1f 9y 1m 58.10	1m 6f 97y 3m 11.30
7f 1m 29.00	1m 2f 32y 2m 13.50	2m 19y 3m 35.20
1m Round 1m 43.70		

NEWMARKET

5f Rowley ... 59.10	1m 1f Rowley ... 1m 50.60	1m 6f Rowley ... 2m 58.50
6f Rowley ... 1m 12.20	1m 2f Rowley ... 2m 5.80	2m Rowley ... 3m 30.80
7f Rowley ... 1m 25.40	1m 4f Rowley ... 2m 33.50	2m 2f Rowley ... 3m 54.80
1m Rowley ... 1m 38.60		

NEWMARKET (JULY)

5f July ... 59.10	1m July ... 1m 40.00	1m 6f 175y July ... 3m 11.30
6f July ... 1m 12.50	1m 2f July ... 2m 5.50	3m 24y July ... 3m 27.00
7f July ... 1m 25.70	1m 4f July ... 2m 32.90	

NOTTINGHAM

5f 13y ... 1m 0.70	1m 54y ... 1m 45.60	1m 6f 15y ... 3m 7.30
6f 15y ... 1m 15.10	1m 1f 213y ... 2m 10.70	2m 9y ... 3m 33.60

PONTEFRACT

5f ... 1m 3.30	1m 2f 6y ... 2m 13.70	1m 1f 216y ... 4m 3.90
6f ... 1m 16.90	1m 4f 8y ... 2m 40.80	2m 5f 122y ... 5m 8.80
1m 4y ... 1m 45.90	2m 1f 22y ... 3m 51.60	

REDCAR

5f ... 58.60	1m ... 1m 38.00	1m 3f ... 2m 21.70
6f ... 1m 11.80	1m 1f ... 1m 53.00	1m 6f 19y ... 3m 4.70
7f ... 1m 24.50	1m 2f ... 2m 7.10	2m 4y ... 3m 31.40

RIPON

5f ... 1m 0.70	1m ... 1m 41.40	1m 4f 10y ... 2m 36.70
6f ... 1m 13.00	1m 1f 170y ... 2m 5.40	2m ... 3m 31.80

SALISBURY

5f ... 1m 0.80	1m ... 1m 43.50	1m 4f ... 2m 38.00
6f ... 1m 14.80	1m 1f 198y ... 2m 9.90	1m 6f 15y ... 3m 7.40
6f 212y ... 1m		

SANDOWN

5f 6y ... 1m 1.60	1m 1f ... 1m 56.30	2m 78y ... 3m 39.50
7f 16y ... 1m 29.50	1m 2f 7y ... 2m 10.50	
1m 14y ... 1m 43.30	1m 6f ... 3m 6.60	

SOUTHWELL

6f ... 1m 15.80	1m 2f ... 2m 13.10	1m 4f ... 2m 41.70
7f ... 1m 29.40	1m 3f ... 2m 27.80	2m ... 3m 38.60

SOUTHWELL (A.W)

5f ... 59.70	1m ... 1m 43.70	1m 6f ... 3m 8.30
6f ... 1m 16.50	1m 3f ... 2m 28.00	2m ... 3m 45.50
7f ... 1m 30.30	1m 4f ... 2m 41.00	

THIRSK

5f ... 59.60	7f ... 1m 27.20	1m 4f ... 2m 36.20
6f ... 1m 12.70	1m ... 1m 40.10	2m ... 3m 33.40

WARWICK

5f ... 59.60	1m 22y ... 1m 41.00	1m 6f 213y ... 3m 19.00
5f 110y ... 1m 5.90	1m 2f 188y ... 2m 21.10	2m 39y ... 3m 33.80
7f 26y ... 1m 24.60	1m 4f 134y ... 2m 44.60	

WINDSOR

5f 10y	1m 0.30	1m 67y	1m 44.70	1m 3f 135y	2m 29.50
6f	1m 13.00	1m 2f 7y	2m 8.70		

WOLVERHAMPTON (A.W)

5f 20y	1m 2.30	1m 141y	1m 50.50	1m 5f 194y	3m 6.00
5f 216y	1m 15.00	1m 1f 103y	2m 1.70	2m 119y	3m 41.80
7f 32y	1m 29.60	1m 4f 50y	2m 41.10		

YARMOUTH

5f 43y	1m 2.20	1m 3y	1m 40.60	1m 6f 17y	3m 7.60
6f 3y	1m 14.40	1m 2f 21y	2m 10.50	2m	3m 34.60
7f 3y	1m 26.60	1m 3f 101y	2m 28.70		

YORK

5f	59.30	1m	1m 38.80	1m 4f	2m 33.20
6f	1m 11.90	1m 208y	1m 52.00	1m 6f	3m 00.20
7f	1m 25.30	1m 2f 88y	2m 12.50	2m 2f	3m 58.40

RACEFORM RECORD TIMES (FLAT)

ASCOT

DISTANCE	TIME	AGE	WEIGHT	GOING	HORSE	DATE		
5f	59.77 secs	2	9-3	Good To Firm	**DRAWNFROMTHEPAST**	Jun	19	2007
5f	57.44 secs	6	9-1	Good To Firm	**MISS ANDRETTI**	Jun	19	2007
6f	1m 12.46	2	9-1	Good To Firm	**HENRYTHENAVIGATOR**	Jun	19	2007
7f	1m 27.9	2	7-12	Good To Firm	**RELATIVE ORDER**	Aug	11	2007
7f	1m 25.89	4	8-9	Good To Firm	**DABBERS RIDGE**	July	29	2006
1m (Rnd)	1m 39.14	3	9-0	Good To Firm	**NANNINA**	Jun	23	2006
1m (Str)	1m 37.21	5	9-0	Good To Firm	**RAMONTI**	Jun	17	2007
1m 2f	2m 04.15	4	8-7	Good To Firm	**I'M SO LUCKY**	Jun	23	2006
1m 4f	2m 27.24	3	8-9	Good To Firm	**LINAS SELECTION**	Jun	23	2006
2m	3m 25.52	6	9-0	Good To Firm	**TUNGSTEN STRIKE**	May	2	2007
2m 4f	4m 18.29	8	9-1	Good	**FULL HOUSE**	Jun	22	2006
2m 5f 159y	5m 04.60	4	9-0	Good To Firm	**BADDAM**	Jun	24	2006

AYR

DISTANCE	TIME	AGE	WEIGHT	GOING	HORSE	DATE		
5f	56.9 secs	2	8-11	Good	BOOGIE STREET	Sep	18	2003
5f	57.2 secs	4	9-5	Good To Firm	SIR JOEY	Sep	16	1993
6f	1m 09.7	2	7-10	Good Sir	BERT	Sep	17	1969
6f	1m 08.9	7	8-8	Good To Firm	SOBERING THOUGHTS	Sep	18	1993
7f 50y	1m 28.9	2	9-0	Good	TAFAAHUM	Sep	19	2003
7f 50y	1m 28.2	4	9-2	Good To Firm	FLUR NA H ALBA	Jun	21	2003
1m	1m 39.2	2	9-0	Good To Firm	KRIBENSIS	Sep	17	1986
1m	1m 36.0	4	7-13	Firm	SUFI	Sep	16	1959
1m 1f 20y	1m 50.3	4	9-3	Good	RETIREMENT	Sep	19	2003
1m 2f	2m 04.0	4	9-9	Good To Firm	ENDLESS HALL	July	17	2000
1m 2f 192y	2m 13.3	4	9-0	Good To Firm	AZZAAM	Sep	18	1991
1m 5f 13y	2m 45.8	4	9-7	Good To Firm	EDEN'S CLOSE	Sep	18	1993
1m 7f	3m 13.1	3	9-4	Good	ROMANY RYE	Sep	19	1991
2m 1f 105y	3m 45.0	4	6-13	Good	CURRY	Sep	16	1955

BATH

DISTANCE	TIME	AGE	WEIGHT	GOING	HORSE	DATE		
5f 11y	1m 00.1	2	8-11	Firm	**DOUBLE FANTASY**	Aug	25	2000
5f 11y	58.75 secs	3	8-12	Firm	**ENTICING**	May	1	2007
5f 161y	1m 09.1	2	8-7	Firm	**SIBLA**	Aug	25	2000
5f 161y	1m 08.1	6	9-0	Firm	**MADRACO**	May	22	1989
1m 5y	1m 40.3	2	8-12	Good To Firm	**KHASSAH**	Sep	9	1999
1m 5y	1m 37.2	5	8-12	Good To Firm	**ADOBE**	Jun	17	2000
1m 2f 46y	2m 05.6	3	9-0	Good To Firm	**CONNOISSEUR BAY**	May	29	1998
1m 3f 144y	2m 25.74	4	9-0	Hard	**TOP OF THE CHARTS**	Sep	8	2005
1m 5f 22y	2m 47.2	4	10-0	Firm	**FLOWN**	Aug	13	1991
2m 1f 34y	3m 43.4	6	7-9	Firm	**YAHESKA**	Jun	14	2003

BEVERLEY

DISTANCE	TIME	AGE	WEIGHT	GOING	HORSE	DATE		
5f	1m 01.0	2	8-2	Good To Firm	ADDO	July	17	2001
5f	1m 00.1	4	9-5	Firm	PIC UP STICKS	Apr	16	2003
7f 100y	1m 31.1	2	9-0	Firm	MAJAL	July	30	1991
7f 100y	1m 29.5	3	7-8	Firm	WHO'S TEF	July	30	1991
1m 100y	1m 43.3	2	9-0	Firm	ARDEN	Sep	24	1986
1m 100y	1m 42.2	3	8-4	Firm	LEGAL CASE	Jun	14	1989
1m 1f 207y	2m 01.8	3	9-7	Firm	ROSE ALTO	July	5	1991
1m 3f 216y	2m 30.8	3	8-1	Hard	COINAGE	Jun	18	1986
2m 35y	3m 29.5	4	9-2	Good To Firm	RUSHEN RAIDER	Aug	14	1996

BRIGHTON

DISTANCE	TIME	AGE	WEIGHT	GOING	HORSE	DATE		
5f 59y	1m.00.1	2	9-0	Firm	BID FOR BLUE	May	6	1993
5f 59y	59.3 secs	3	8-9	Firm	PLAY HEVER GOLF	May	26	1993
5f 213y	1m 08.1	2	8-9	Firm	SONG MIST	July	16	1996
5f 213y	1m 07.3	3	8-9	Firm	THIRD PARTY	Jun	3	1997
5f 213y	1m 07.3	5	9-1	Good To Firm	BLUNDELL LANE	May	4	2000
6f 209y	1m 19.9	2	8-11	Hard	RAIN BURST	Sep	15	1988
6f 209y	1m 19.4	4	9-3	Good To Firm	SAWAKI	Sep	3	1991
7f 214y	1m 32.8	2	9-7	Firm	ASIAN PETE	Oct	3	1989
7f 214y	1m 30.5	5	8-11	Firm	MYSTIC RIDGE	May	27	1999
1m 1f 209y	2m 04.7	2	9-0	Good To Soft	ESTEEMED MASTER	Nov	2	2001
1m 1f 209y	1m 57.2	3	9-0	Firm	GET THE MESSAGE	Apr	30	1984
1m 3f 196y	2m 25.8	4	8-2	Firm	NEW ZEALAND	July	4	1985

CARLISLE

DISTANCE	TIME	AGE	WEIGHT	GOING	HORSE	DATE		
5f	1m 00.1	2	8-5	Firm	LA TORTUGA	Aug	2	1999
5f	59.3 secs	5	8-12	Firm	FRIAR TUCK	July	21	2000
5f 193y	1m 12.45	2	9-6	Good To Firm	MUSICAL GUEST	Sep	11	2005
5f 193y	1m 10.83	4	9-0	Good To Firm	BO MCGINTY	Sep	11	2005
6f 206y	1m 26.5	2	9-4	Hard	SENSE OF PRIORITY	Sep	10	1991
6f 206y	1m 25.3	4	9-1	Firm	MOVE WITH EDES	July	6	1996
7f 200y	1m 37.34	5	9-7	Good To Firm	HULA BALLEW	Aug	17	2005
7f 214y	1m 44.6	2	8-8	Firm	BLUE GARTER	Sep	9	1980
1m 1f 61y	1m 53.8	3	9-0	Firm	LITTLE JIMBOB	Jun	14	2004
1m 3f 206y	2m 29.13	5	9-8	Firm	TEMPSFORD	Sep	19	2005
1m 6f 32y	3m 02.2	6	8-10	Firm	EXPLOSIVE SPEED	May	26	1994

CATTERICK

DISTANCE	TIME	AGE	WEIGHT	GOING	HORSE	DATE		
5f	57.7 secs	2	9-0	Good To Firm	VERDE ALITALIA	Sep	21	1991
5f	57.1 secs	4	8-7	Firm	KABCAST	July	7	1989
5f 212y	1m 11.4	2	9-4	Firm	CAPTAIN NICK	July	11	1978
5f 212y	1m 09.8	9	8-13	Good To Firm	SHARP HAT	May	30	2003
7f	1m 24.1	2	8-11	Firm	LINDAS FANTASY	Sep	18	1982
7f	1m 22.5	6	8-7	Firm	DIFFERENTIAL	May	31	2003
1m 3f 214y	2m 30.5	3	8-8	Good To Firm	RAHAF	May	30	2003
1m 5f 175y	2m 54.8	3	8-5	Firm	GERYON	May	31	1984
1m 7f 177y	3m 20.8	4	7-11	Firm	BEAN BOY	July	8	1982

CHEPSTOW

DISTANCE	TIME	AGE	WEIGHT	GOING	HORSE	DATE		
5f 16y	57.6 secs	2	8-11	Firm	MICRO LOVE	July	8	1986
5f 16y	56.8 secs	3	8-4	Firm	TORBAY EXPRESS	Sep	15	1979
6f 16y	1m 09.4	2	9-0	Firm	ROYAL FIFI	Sep	9	1989
6f 16y	1m 08.8	4	8-6	Firm	AFRICAN REX	May	12	1987
7f 16y	1m 20.8	2	9-0	Good To Firm	ROYAL AMARETTO	Sep	12	1996
7f 16y	1m 19.3	3	9-0	Firm	TARANAKI	Sep	18	2001
1m 14y	1m 33.1	2	8-11	Good To Firm	SKI ACADEMY	Aug	28	1995
1m 14y	1m 31.6	3	8-13	Firm	STOLI	Sep	18	2001
1m 2f 36y	2m 04.1	5	8-9	Hard	LEONIDAS	July	5	1983
1m 2f 36y	2m 04.1	5	7-8	Good To Firm	IT'S VARADAN	Sep	9	1989
1m 2f 36y	2m 04.1	3	8-5	Good To Firm	ELA ATHENA	July	23	1999
1m 4f 23y	2m 31.0	3	8-9	Good To Firm	SPRITSAIL	July	13	1989
1m 4f 23y	2m 31.0	7	9-6	Hard	MAINTOP	Aug	27	1984
2m 49y	3m 27.7	4	9-0	Good To Firm	WIZZARD ARTIST	July	1	1989
2m 2f	3m 56.4	5	8-7	Good To Firm	LAFFAH	July	8	2000

CHESTER

DISTANCE	TIME	AGE	WEIGHT	GOING	HORSE	DATE		
5f 16y	1m 00.06	2	8-9	Good To Firm	NOT FOR ME	July	14	2006
5f 16y	59.2 secs	3	10-0	Firm	ALTHREY DON	July	10	1964
6f 18y	1m 13.2	2	8-11	Good To Firm	ACE OF PARKES	July	11	1998
6f 18y	1m 12.7	3	8-3	Good To Firm	PLAY HEVER GOLF	May	4	1993
6f 18y	1m 12.7	6	9-2	Good	STACK ROCK	Jun	23	1993
7f 2y	1m 26.2	2	8-4	Good To Firm	BY HAND	Aug	31	1991
7f 2y	1m 23.75	5	8-13	Good To Firm	THREE GRACES	July	9	2005
7f 122y	1m 35.0	2	9-0	Firm	DOUBLE VALUE	Sep	1	1972
7f 122y	1m 30.91	3	8-12	Good To Firm	CUPID'S GLORY	Aug	18	2005
1m 2f 75y	2m 7.15	3	8-8	Good To Firm	STOTSFOLD	Sep	23	2006
1m 3f 79y	2m 22.5	3	8-9	Good To Firm	ROCKERLONG	May	9	2001
1m 4f 66y	2m 34.2	3	8-11	Good To Firm	OLD VIC	May	9	1989
1m 5f 89y	2m 45.4	5	8-11	Firm	RAKAPOSHI KING	May	7	1987
1m 7f 195y	3m 24.5	7	7-11	Good To Firm	MOONLIGHT QUEST	July	30	1995
2m 2f 147y	3m 58.59	7	9-2	Good To Firm	GREENWICH MEANTIME	May	9	2007

DONCASTER

DISTANCE	TIME	AGE	WEIGHT	GOING	HORSE	DATE		
5f	58.4 secs	2	9-5	Firm	SING SING	Sep	11	1959
5f	57.2 secs	6	9-12	Good To Firm	CELTIC MILL	Sep	9	2004
5f 140y	1m 07.2	2	9-0	Good To Firm	CARTOGRAPHY	Jun	29	2003
5f 140y	1m 05.6	9	9-10	Good	HALMAHERA	Sep	8	2004
6f	1m 09.6	2	8-11	Good	CAESAR BEWARE	Sep	8	2004
6f	1m 09.7	3	8-9	Good To Firm	ILTIMAS	July	26	1995
6f 110y	1m 17.42	2	8-2	Good To Firm	ROYAL CONFIDENCE	Sep	12	2007
7f	1m 22.6	2	9-1	Good To Firm	LIBRETTIST	Sep	8	2004
7f	1m 21.6	3	9-4	Good To Firm	PASTORAL PURSUITS	Sep	9	2004
1m Str	1m 36.5	2	8-6	Good To Firm	SINGHALESE	Sep	9	2004
1m Rnd	1m 35.4	2	9-0	Good To Firm	PLAYFUL ACT	Sep	9	2004
1m Str	1m 36.6	7	9-9	Good To Firm	INVADER	Jun	29	2003
1m Rnd	1m 36.7	3	8-10	Good To Firm	MUSHAHID	July	17	1996
1m 2f 60y	2m 13.4	2	8-8	Good	YARD BIRD	Nov	6	1981
1m 2f 60y	2m 04.81	4	8-13	Good To Firm	RED GALA	Sep	12	2007
1m 4f	2m 27.7	3	8-12	Good To Firm	TAKWIN	Sep	9	2000
1m 6f 132y	3m 01.07	3	8-7	Good To Firm	HI CALYPSO	Sep	13	2007
2m 110y	3m 34.4	4	9-12	Good To Firm	FARSI	Jun	12	1992
2m 2f	3m 48.41	4	9-4	Good To Firm	SEPTIMUS	Sep	14	2007

EPSOM

DISTANCE	TIME	AGE	WEIGHT	GOING	HORSE	DATE		
5f	55.0 secs	2	8-9	Good To Firm	PRINCE ASLIA	Jun	9	1995
5f	53.6 secs	4	9-5	Firm	INDIGENOUS	Jun	2	1960
6f	1m 07.8	2	8-11	Good To Firm	SHOWBROOK	Jun	5	1991
6f	1m 07.3	5	8-12	Good	LOYAL TYCOON	Jun	7	2003
7f	1m 21.3	2	8-9	Good To Firm	RED PEONY	July	29	2004
7f	1m 20.1	4	8-7	Firm	CAPISTRANO	Jun	7	1972
1m 114y	1m 42.8	2	8-5	Good To Firm	NIGHTSTALKER	Aug	30	1988
1m 114y	1m 40.7	3	8-6	Good To Firm	SYLVA HONDA	Jun	5	1991
1m 2f 18y	2m 03.5	5	7-13	Good	CROSSBOW	Jun	7	1967
1m 4f 10y	2m 32.3	3	9-0	Good To Firm	LAMMTARRA	Jun	10	1995

FOLKESTONE

DISTANCE	TIME	AGE	WEIGHT	GOING	HORSE	DATE		
5f	58.4 secs	2	9-2	Good To Firm	PIVOTAL	Nov	6	1995
5f	58.23 secs	3	9-4	Good To Firm	MILLISECOND	Sep	2	2007
6f	1m 10.8	2	8-9	Good	BOOMERANG BLADE	July	16	1998
6f	1m 09.38	4	9-6	Good To Firm	MUNADDAM	Sep	18	2006
6f 189y	1m 23.7	2	8-11	Good	HEN HARRIER	July	3	1996
6f 189y	1m 22.0	4	10-0	Firm	NEUWEST	Jun	28	1996
7f (str)	1m 25.01	2	9-0	Good To Firm	DONNA ALBA	Sep	2	2007
7f (str)	1m 23.76	3	8-11	Good To Firm	WELSH CAKE	Sep	18	2006
1m 1f 149y	1m 59.7	3	8-6	Good To Firm	DIZZY	July	23	1991
1m 4f	3m 33.2	4	8-8	Hard	SNOW BLIZZARD	Jun	30	1992
1m 7f 92y	3m 23.1	3	9-11	Firm	MATA ASKARI	Sep	12	1991
2m 93y	3m 34.9	3	8-12	Good To Firm	CANDLE SMOKE	Aug	20	1996

GOODWOOD

DISTANCE	TIME	AGE	WEIGHT	GOING	HORSE	DATE		
5f	57.5 secs	2	8-12	Good To Firm	POETS COVE	Aug	3	1990
5f	56.0 secs	5	9-0	Good To Firm	RUDI'S PET	July	27	1999
6f	1m 09.8	2	8-11	Good To Firm	BACHIR	July	28	1999
6f	1m 09.18	4	9-0	Good	TAX FREE	Sep	9	2006
7f	1m 24.9	2	8-11	Good To Firm	EKRAAR	July	29	1999
7f	1m 23.8	3	8-7	Firm	BRIEF GLIMPSE	July	25	1995
1m	1m 37.21	2	9-0	Good	CALDRA	Sep	9	2006
1m	1m 35.61	4	8-9	Good To Firm	SPECTAIT	Aug	4	2006
1m 1f	1m 52.8	3	9-6	Good	VENA	July	27	1995
1m 1f 192y	2m 02.81	3	9-3	Good To Firm	ROAD TO LOVE	Aug	3	2006
1m 2f	2m 04.9	3	8-6	Firm	KARTAJANA	Aug	4	1990
1m 3f	2m 23.0	3	8-8	Good To Firm	ASIAN HEIGHTS	May	22	2001
1m 4f	2m 31.5	3	8-10	Firm	PRESENTING	July	25	1995
1m 6f	2m 58.5	4	9-2	Good To Firm	MOWBRAY	July	27	1999
2m	3m 21.55	5	9-10	Good To Firm	YEATS	Aug	3	2006
2m 4f	4m 11.7	3	7-10	Firm	LUCKY MOON	Sep	2	1990

HAMILTON

DISTANCE	TIME	AGE	WEIGHT	GOING	HORSE	DATE		
5f 4y	58.0 secs	3	7-8	Firm	FAIR DANDY	Sep	25	1972
5f 4y	58.0 secs	4	8-6	Firm	GOLDEN SLEIGH	Sep	6	1972
6f 5y	1m 10.0	2	8-12	Good To Firm	BREAK THE CODE	Aug	24	1999
6f 5y	1m 09.3	4	8-7	Firm	MARCUS GAME	July	11	1974
1m 65y	1m 45.8	2	8-11	Firm	HOPEFUL SUBJECT	Sep	24	1973
1m 65y	1m 42.7	6	7-7	Firm	CRANLEY	Sep	25	1972
1m 1f 36y	1m 53.6	3	9-6	Good To Firm	REGENT'S SECRET	Aug	10	2005
1m 3f 16y	2m 19.8	3	8-1	Good To Firm	MCELDOWNEY	Aug	22	2005
1m 3f 16y	2m 20.7	5	9-8	Good To Firm	WADI	July	20	2000
1m 4f 17y	2m 32.0	4	7-4	Firm	FINE POINT	Aug	24	1981
1m 5f 9y	2m 45.1	6	9-6	Firm	MENTALASANYTHIN	Jun	14	1995

HAYDOCK

DISTANCE	TIME	AGE	WEIGHT	GOING	HORSE	DATE	
5f	59.2 secs	2	9-4	Firm	MONEY FOR NOTHING	Aug	21	1964
5f	58.2 secs	5	8-9	Good	SIERRA VISTA	Sep	3	2005
6f	1m 09.9	4	9-0	Good To Firm	IKTAMAL	Sep	7	1996
7f 30y	1m 29.4	2	9-0	Good To Firm	APPREHENSION	Sep	7	1996
7f 30y	1m 27.2	4	9-4	Firm	INDIAN KING	Jun	5	1982
1m 30y	1m 40.6	2	8-12	Good To Firm	BESIEGE	Sep	7	1996
1m 30y	1m 40.1	3	9-2	Firm	UNTOLD RICHES	July	11	1999
1m 2f 120y	2m 08.5	3	8-7	Good To Firm	FAHAL	Aug	5	1995
1m 3f 200y	2m 26.4	5	8-2	Firm	NEW MEMBER	July	4	1970
1m 6f	2m 59.5	3	8-3	Good To Firm	CASTLE SECRET	Sep	30	1989
2m 45y	3m 27.0	4	8-13	Good	PRINCE OF PEACE	May	26	1984
2m 1f 130y	3m 55.0	3	8-12	Good	CRYSTAL SPIRIT	Sep	8	1990

KEMPTON (A.W)

DISTANCE	TIME	AGE	WEIGHT	GOING	HORSE	DATE	
5f	59.11	2	9-1	Standard	HADAF	Oct	6	2007
6f	1m 12.22	2	8-11	Standard	DHANYATA	Sep	2	2006
6f	1m 11.13	3	9-0	Standard	RABBIT FIGHTER	Dec	12	2007
7f	1m 24.73	2	9-3	Standard	STORM FORCE	Nov	3	2007
7f	1m 23.91	3	8-4	Standard	BOMBER COMMAND	Nov	24	2006
1m	1m 38.22	2	9-0	Standard	ART MASTER	Oct	6	2007
1m	1m 36.82	6	9-0	Standard	GENTLEMAN'S DEAL	Feb	4	2007
1m 2f	2m 4.44	3	8-11	Standard	STOTSFOLD	Sep	6	2006
1m 3f	2m 18.15	3	8-8	Standard	AL THARIB	Aug	27	2007
1m 4f	2m 30.48	3	8-11	Standard	DANSANT	Nov	3	2007
2m	3m 25.83	3	9-1	Standard	FEATHERLIGHT	Sep	29	2007

LEICESTER

DISTANCE	TIME	AGE	WEIGHT	GOING	HORSE	DATE	
5f 2y	58.4 secs	2	9-0	Firm	CUTTING BLADE	Jun	9	1986
5f 2y	57.85 secs	5	9-5	Good To Firm	THE JOBBER	Sep	18	2006
5f 218y	1m 10.1	3	9-0	Firm	THORDIS	Oct	24	1995
5f 218y	1m 09.4	3	8-12	Good To Firm	LAKELAND BEAUTY	May	29	1990
7f 9y	1m 22.8	2	8-6	Good	MISS DRAGONFLY	Sep	22	1997
7f 9y	1m 20.8	3	8-7	Firm	FLOWER BOWL	Jun	9	1986
1m 60y	1m 44.05	2	8-11	Good To Firm	CONGRESSIONAL	Sep	6	2005
1m 60y	1m 42.49	3	9-2	Good To Firm	STREET WARRIOR	Sep	18	2006
1m 1f 218y	2m 05.3	2	9-1	Good To Firm	WINDSOR CASTLE	Oct	14	1996
1m 1f 218y	2m 02.4	3	8-11	Firm	EFFIGY	Nov	4	1985
1m 1f 218y	2m 02.4	4	9-6	Good To Firm	LADY ANGHARAD	Jun	18	2000
1m 3f 183y	2m 27.1	5	8-12	Good To Firm	MURGHEM	Jun	18	2000

LINGFIELD (TURF)

DISTANCE	TIME	AGE	WEIGHT	GOING	HORSE	DATE	
5f	57.1 secs	2	8-9	Good	EMERALD PEACE	Aug	6	1999
5f	56.2 secs	3	9-1	Good To Firm	EVENINGPERFORMANCE	July	25	1994
6f	1m 08.6	2	9-3	Firm	THE RITZ	Jun	11	1965
6f	1m 08.2	6	9-10	Firm	AL AMEAD	July	2	1986
7f	1m 21.3	2	7-6	Firm	MANDAV	Oct	3	1980
7f	1m 20.1	3	8-7	Good To Firm	ZELAH	May	13	1998
7f 140y	1m 29.9	2	8-12	Firm	RATHER WARM	Nov	7	1978
7f 140y	1m 26.7	3	8-6	Good To Firm	HIAAM	Jul	11	1987
1m 1f	1m 52.4	4	9-2	Good To Firm	QUANDARY	July	15	1995
1m 2f	2m 04.6	3	9-3	Firm	USRAN	July	15	1989
1m 3f 106y	2m 23.9	3	8-5	Firm	NIGHT-SHIRT	July	14	1990
1m 6f	2m 59.1	5	9-5	Firm	IBN BEY	July	1	1989
2m	3m 23.7	3	9-5	Good To Firm	LAURIES CRUSADOR	Aug	13	1988

LINGFIELD (A.W)

DISTANCE	TIME	AGE	WEIGHT	GOING	HORSE	DATE		
5f	58.61 secs	2	8-12	Standard	**WAVERTREE PRINCESS**	Nov	04	2007
5f	57.26 secs	8	8-12	Standard	**MAGIC GLADE**	Feb	27	2007
6f	1m 11.03	2	9-0	Standard	**RAINBOW PROMISES**	Oct	5	2006
6f	1m 09.80	7	9-2	Standard	**MALTESE FALCON**	Nov	24	2007
7f	1m 23.96	2	9-1	Standard	**ROARING FORTE**	Nov	12	2007
7f	1m 22.7	6	9-12	Standard	**VORTEX**	Apr	9	2005
1m	1m 36.5	2	9-5	Standard	**SAN PIER NICETO**	Nov	30	1989
1m	1m 35.40	4	9-1	Standard	**MINA A SALEM**	Dec	19	2006
1m 2f	2m 01.79	5	9-0	Standard	**CUSOON**	Feb	24	2007
1m 4f	2m 28.22	4	9-5	Standard	**DESCARTES**	Oct	5	2006
1m 5f	2m 42.47	3	9-2	Standard	**RAFFAAS**	July	3	2007
2m	3m 20.07	4	9-0	Standard	**NIGHT**	Aug	8	1992

MUSSELBURGH

DISTANCE	TIME	AGE	WEIGHT	GOING	HORSE	DATE		
5f	57.7 secs	2	8-2	Firm	**ARASONG**	May	16	1994
5f	57.3 secs	3	8-12	Firm	**CORUNNA**	Jun	3	2000
7f 30y	1m 28.4	2	8-8	Firm	**SAND BANKES**	Jun	26	2000
7f 30y	1m 27.1	5	8-12	Good	**DIAMOND DECORUM**	Jun	18	2001
1m	1m 40.3	2	8-12	Good To Firm	**SUCESSION**	Sep	26	2004
1m	1m 38.8	6	9-4	Good To Firm	**SEA STORM**	May	29	2004
1m 1f	1m 51.7	4	9-7	Firm	**KID'Z'PLAY**	Jun	3	2000
1m 4f	2m 33.7	3	9-11	Firm	**ALEXANDRINE**	Jun	26	2000
1m 5f	2m 48.9	6	8-10	Good To Firm	**TOJONESKI**	July	27	2005
1m 6f	2m 59.2	3	9-7	Firm	**FORUM CHRIS**	July	3	2000
2m	3m 28.1	3	8-1	Good To Firm	**WARRING KINGDOM**	Sep	13	1999

NEWBURY

DISTANCE	TIME	AGE	WEIGHT	GOING	HORSE	DATE		
5f 34y	59.1 secs	2	8-6	Good To Firm	**SUPERSTAR LEO**	July	22	2000
5f 34y	59.2 secs	3	9-5	Good To Firm	**THE TRADER**	Aug	18	2001
6f 8y	1m 11.19	2	8-9	Good To Firm	**MIXED BLESSING**	July	23	2005
6f 8y	1m 09.42	3	8-11	Good To Firm	**NOTA BENE**	May	13	2005
7f	1m 24.1	2	8-11	Good To Firm	**HAAFHD**	Aug	15	2003
7f	1m 21.5	3	8-4	Good To Firm	**THREE POINTS**	July	21	2000
1m	1m 37.5	2	9-1	Good To Firm	**WINGED CUPID**	Sep	16	2005
1m	1m 33.59	6	9-0	Firm	**RAKTI**	May	14	2005
1m 1f	1m 49.6	3	8-0	Good To Firm	**HOLTYE**	May	21	1995
1m 2f 6y	2m 1.2	3	8-7	Good To Firm	**WALL STREET**	July	20	1996
1m 3f 5y	2m 16.5	3	8-9	Good To Firm	**GRANDERA**	Sep	22	2001
1m 4f 5y	2m 28.26	4	9-7	Good To Firm	**AZAMOUR**	Jul	23	2005
1m 5f 61y	2m 44.9	5	10-0	Good To Firm	**MYSTIC HILL**	July	20	1996
2m	3m 25.4	8	9-12	Good To Firm	**MOONLIGHT QUEST**	July	19	1996

NEWCASTLE

DISTANCE	TIME	AGE	WEIGHT	GOING	HORSE	DATE		
5f	58.8 secs	2	9-0	Firm	ATLANTIC VIKING	Jun	4	1997
5f	58.0 secs	4	9-2	Firm	PRINCESS OBERON	July	23	1994
6f	1m 12.18	2	9-0	Good To Firm	STEPPING UP	Sep	5	2005
6f	1m 10.6	8	9-5	Firm	TEDBURROW	July	1	2000
7f	1m 24.2	2	9-0	Good To Firm	ISCAN	Aug	31	1998
7f	1m 23.3	4	9-2	Good To Firm	QUIET VENTURE	Aug	31	1998
1m	1m 38.9	2	9-0	Good To Firm	STOWAWAY	Oct	2	1996
1m	1m 38.9	3	8-12	Firm	JACAMAR	July	22	1989
1m 3y	1m 37.1	2	8-3	Good To Firm	HOH STEAMER	Aug	31	1998
1m 3y	1m 37.3	3	8-8	Good To Firm	ITS MAGIC	May	27	1999
1m 1f 9y	2m 03.2	2	8-13	Soft	RESPONSE	Oct	30	1993
1m 1f 9y	1m 58.4	3	8-8	Good To Firm	INTRODUCING	Aug	6	2003
1m 2f 32y	2m 06.5	3	8-11	Firm	MISSIONARY RIDGE	July	29	1990
1m 4f 93y	2m 37.3	5	8-12	Firm	RETENDER	Jun	25	1994
1m 6f 97y	3m 06.4	3	9-6	Good To Firm	ONE OFF	Aug	6	2003
2m 19y	3m 24.3	4	8-10	Good	FAR CRY	Jun	26	1999

NEWMARKET (ROWLEY)

DISTANCE	TIME	AGE	WEIGHT	GOING	HORSE	DATE		
5f	58.76 secs	2	8-5	Good To Firm	VALIANT ROMEO	Oct	3	2002
5f	56.8 secs	6	9-2	Good To Firm	LOCHSONG	Apr	30	1994
6f	1m 09.61	2	8-11	Good To Firm	OASIS DREAM	Oct	3	2002
6f	1m 09.64	4	9-4	Good To Firm	ASSET	Apr	19	2007
7f	1m 22.9	2	8-11	Good To Firm	GROSVENOR SQUARE	Sep	21	2004
7f	1m 22.2	4	9-5	Good To Firm	PERFOLIA	Oct	17	1991
1m	1m 35.7	2	9-0	Good To Firm	FORWARD MOVE	Sep	21	2004
1m	1m 34.54	4	9-0	Good To Firm	DESERT DEER	Oct	3	2002
1m 1f	1m 47.26	5	8-12	Good To Firm	MANDURO	Apr	19	2007
1m 2f	2m 04.6	2	9-4	Good	HIGHLAND CHIEFTAIN	Nov	2	1985
1m 2f	2m 01.0	3	8-10	Good	PALACE MUSIC	Oct	20	1984
1m 4f	2m 27.1	5	8-12	Good To Firm	EASTERN BREEZE	Oct	3	2003
1m 6f	2m 51.59	3	8-7	Good	ART EYES	Sep	29	2005
2m	3m 19.5	5	9-5	Good To Firm	GREY SHOT	Oct	4	1997
2m 2f	3m 47.5	3	7-12	Hard	WHITEWAY	Oct	15	1947

NEWMARKET (JULY)

DISTANCE	TIME	AGE	WEIGHT	GOING	HORSE	DATE		
5f	58.5 secs	2	8-10	Good	SEDUCTRESS	July	10	1990
5f	57.3 secs	6	8-12	Good To Firm	RAMBLING BEAR	Jan	1	1999
6f	1m 10.6	2	8-10	Good To Firm	MUJTAHID	July	11	1990
6f	1m 09.5	3	8-13	Good To Firm	STRAVINSKY	July	8	1999
7f	1m 24.1	2	8-11	Good	MY HANSEL	Aug	27	1999
7f	1m 22.5	3	9-7	Firm	HO LENG	July	9	1998
1m	1m 39.0	2	8-11	Good	TRACEABILITY	Aug	25	1995
1m	1m 35.5	3	8-6	Good To Firm	LOVERS KNOT	July	8	1998
1m 110y	1m 44.1	3	8-11	Good	GOLDEN SNAKE	Apr	15	1999
1m 2f	2m 00.9	4	9-3	Good To Firm	ELHAYQ	May	1	1999
1m 4f	2m 25.2	4	9-2	Good	CRAIGSTEEL	July	6	1999
1m 6f 175y	3m 04.2	3	8-5	Good	ARRIVE	July	11	2001
2m 24y	3m 20.2	7	9-10	Good	YORKSHIRE	July	11	2001

NOTTINGHAM

DISTANCE	TIME	AGE	WEIGHT	GOING	HORSE	DATE		
5f 13y	57.9 secs	2	8-9	Firm	HOH MAGIC	May	13	1994
5f 13y	57.6 secs	6	9-2	Good To Firm	CATCH THE CAT	May	14	2005
6f 15y	1m 11.4	2	8-11	Firm	JAMEELAPI	Aug	8	1983
6f 15y	1m 10.0	4	9-2	Firm	AJANAC	Aug	8	1988
1m 54y	1m 40.8	2	9-0	Good To Firm	KING'S LOCH	Sep	2	1991
1m 54y	1m 39.6	4	8-2	Firm	BLAKE'S TREASURE	Sep	2	1991
1m 1f 213y	2m 02.3	2	9-0	Firm	AYAABI	July	21	1984
1m 6f 15y	2m 57.8	3	8-10	Firm	BUSTER JO	Oct	1	1985
2m 9y	3m 25.25	3	9-5	Good	BULWARK	Sep	27	2005
2m 2f 18y	3m 55.1	9	9-10	Good To Firm	PEARL RUN	May	1	1990

PONTEFRACT

DISTANCE	TIME	AGE	WEIGHT	GOING	HORSE	DATE		
5f	1m 01.1	2	9-0	Firm	GOLDEN BOUNTY	Sep	20	2001
5f	1m 00.8	4	8-9	Firm	BLUE MAEVE	Sep	29	2004
6f	1m 14.0	2	9-3	Firm	FAWZI	Sep	6	1983
6f	1m 12.6	3	7-13	Firm	MERRY ONE	Aug	29	1970
1m 4y	1m 42.8	2	9-13	Firm	STAR SPRAY	Sep	6	1970
1m 4y	1m 41.3	7	8-9	Firm	NIGRASINE	Sep	20	2001
1m 2f 6y	2m 12.8	2	9-0	Good To Firm	WARBROOK	Oct	2	1995
1m 2f 6y	2m 08.2	4	7-8	Hard	HAPPY HECTOR	July	9	1979
1m 4f 8y	2m 33.72	3	8-7	Firm	AJAAN	Aug	8	2007
2m 1f 22y	3m 40.67	4	8-7	Good To Firm	PARADISE FLIGHT	Jun	6	2005
2m 1f 216y	3m 51.1	3	8-8	Firm	KUDZ	Sep	9	1986
2m 5f 122y	4m 47.8	4	8-4	Firm	PHYSICAL	May	14	1984

REDCAR

DISTANCE	TIME	AGE	WEIGHT	GOING	HORSE	DATE		
5f	56.9 secs	2	9-0	Firm	MISTER JOEL	Oct	24	1995
5f	56.01 secs	10	9-3	Firm	HENRY HALL	Sep	20	2006
6f	1m 08.8	2	8-3	Good To Firm	OBE GOLD	Oct	2	2004
6f	1m 08.6	3	9-2	Good To Firm	SIZZLING SAGA	Jun	21	1991
7f	1m 21.28	2	9-3	Firm	KAROO BLUE	Sep	20	2006
7f	1m 21.0	3	9-1	Firm	EMPTY QUARTER	Oct	3	1995
1m	1m 34.37	2	9-0	Firm	MASTERSHIP	Sep	20	2006
1m	1m 32.42	4	10-0	Firm	NANTON	Sep	20	2006
1m 1f	1m 52.4	2	9-0	Firm	SPEAR	Sep	13	2004
1m 1f	1m 48.5	5	8-12	Firm	MELLOTTIE	July	25	1990
1m 2f	2m 10.1	2	8-11	Good	ADDING	Nov	10	1989
1m 2f	2m 01.4	5	9-2	Firm	ERADICATE	May	28	1990
1m 3f	2m 17.2	3	8-9	Firm	PHOTO CALL	Aug	7	1990
1m 5f 135y	2m 54.7	6	9-10	Firm	BRODESSA	Jun	20	1992
1m 6f 19y	2m 59.81	4	9-1	Good To Firm	ESPRIT DE CORPS	Sep	11	2006
2m 4y	3m 24.9	3	9-3	Good To Firm	SUBSONIC	Oct	8	1991

RIPON

DISTANCE	TIME	AGE	WEIGHT	GOING	HORSE	DATE		
5f	57.8 secs	2	8-8	Firm	SUPER ROCKY	July	5	1991
5f	57.6 secs	2	8-5	Good	BROADSTAIRS BEAUTY	May	21	1995
6f	1m 10.9	2	8-11	Good	KAHIR ALMAYDAN	Aug	28	1995
6f	1m 09.8	4	9-8	Good To Firm	TADEO	Aug	16	1997
6f	1m 09.8	5	7-10	Firm	QUOIT	July	23	1966
1m	1m 39.79	2	8-6	Good	TOP JARO	Sep	24	2005
1m	1m 36.62	4	8-11	Good To Firm	GRANSTON	Aug	29	2005
1m 1f	1m 50.4	3	9-2	Good To Firm	BOLD WORDS	Apr	9	1997
1m 2f	2m 02.6	3	9-4	Firm	SWIFT SWORD	July	20	1990
1m 4f 60y	2m 32.06	4	8-8	Good	HEARTHSTEAD WINGS	Apr	29	2006
2m	3m 27.07	5	9-12	Good To Firm	GREENWICH MEANTIME	Aug	30	2005

SALISBURY

DISTANCE	TIME	AGE	WEIGHT	GOING	HORSE	DATE		
5f	59.3 secs	2	9-0	Good To Firm	AJIGOLO	May	12	2005
5f	59.4 secs	3	8-11	Firm	BELLSABANGING	May	5	1993
6f	1m 12.1	2	8-0	Good To Firm	PARISIAN LADY	Jun	10	1997
6f	1m 11.3	3	8-1	Firm	BENTONG	May	7	2006
6f 212y	1m 25.9	2	9-0	Firm	MORE ROYAL	Jun	29	1995
6f 212y	1m 24.9	3	9-7	Firm	HIGH SUMMER	Sep	5	1996
1m	1m 40.48	2	8-13	Firm	CHOIR MASTER	Sep	17	2002
1m	1m 38.29	3	8-7	Good To Firm	LAYMAN	Aug	11	2005
1m 1f 198y	2m 04.9	3	8-6	Good To Firm	ZANTE	Aug	12	1998
1m 4f	2m 31.6	3	9-5	Good To Firm	ARRIVE	Jun	27	2001
1m 6f 15y	2m 59.4	3	8-6	Good To Firm	TABAREEH	Sep	2	1999

SANDOWN

DISTANCE	TIME	AGE	WEIGHT	GOING	HORSE	DATE		
5f 6y	59.4 secs	2	9-3	Firm	TIMES TIME	July	22	1982
5f 6y	58.8 secs	6	8-9	Good To Firm	PALACEGATE TOUCH	Sep	17	1996
7f 16y	1m 26.56	2	9-0	Good To Firm	RAVEN'S PASS	Sep	1	2007
7f 16y	1m 26.3	3	9-0	Firm	MAWSUFF	Jun	14	1983
1m 14y	1m 41.1	2	8-11	Firm	REFERENCE POINT	Sep	23	1986
1m 14y	1m 39.0	3	8-8	Firm	LINDA'S FANASTY	Aug	19	1983
1m 1f	1m 54.6	2	8-8	Good To Firm	FRENCH PRETENDER	Sep	20	1988
1m 1f	1m 52.4	7	9-3	Good To Firm	BOURGAINVILLE	Aug	11	2005
1m 2f 7y	2m 02.1	4	8-11	Firm	KALAGLOW	May	31	1982
1m 3f 91y	2m 21.6	4	8-3	Firm	AYLESFIELD	July	7	1984
1m 6f	2m 56.9	4	8-7	Good To Firm	LADY ROSANNA	July	19	1989
2m 78y	3m 29.9	6	9-2	Firm	SADEEM	May	29	1989

SOUTHWELL (TURF)

DISTANCE	TIME	AGE	WEIGHT	GOING	HORSE	DATE		
6f	1m 15.03	2	9-3	Good	TREPA	Sep	6	2006
6f	1m 13.48	4	8-10	Good	PARIS BELL	Sep	6	2006
7f	1m 27.56	2	9-7	Good	HART OF GOLD	Sep	6	2006
7f	1m 25.95	3	9-0	Good	AEROPLANE	Sep	6	2006
1m 2f	2m 7.47	3	8-11	Good To Firm	DESERT AUTHORITY	Sep	7	2006
1m 3f	2m 20.13	4	9-12	Good	SANCHI	Sep	6	2006
1m 4f	3m 34.4	5	9-3	Good To Firm	CORN LILY	Aug	10	1991
2m	3m 34.1	5	9-1	Good To Firm	TRIPLICATE	Sep	20	1991

SOUTHWELL (A.W)

DISTANCE	TIME	AGE	WEIGHT	GOING	HORSE	DATE		
5f	58.5 secs	2	8-1	Standard	PRIMROSE AND ROSE	Apr	4	2001
5f	57.35 secs	5	9-4	Standard To Fast	FYODOR	Jan	1	2006
6f	1m 14.0	2	8-5	Standard	PANALO	Nov	8	1989
6f	1m 13.3	3	9-2	Standard	RAMBO EXPRESS	Dec	16	1990
7f	1m 27.1	2	8-2	Standard	MYSTIC CRYSTAL	Nov	20	1990
7f	1m 26.8	5	8-4	Standard	AMENABLE	Dec	13	1990
1m	1m 38.0	2	8-9	Standard	ALPHA RASCAL	Nov	13	1990
1m	1m 38.0	3	8-10	Standard	ANDREW'S FIRST	Dec	30	1989
1m	1m 37.2	3	8-6	Standard	VALIRA	Nov	3	1990
1m 3f	2m 21.5	4	9-7	Standard	TEMPERING	Dec	5	1990
1m 4f	2m 33.9	4	9-12	Standard	FAST CHICK	Nov	8	1989
1m 6f	3m 01.6	3	7-7	Standard	QUALITAIR AVIATOR	Dec	1	1989
1m 6f	3m 01.6	3	7-8	Standard	EREVNON	Dec	29	1990
2m	3m 37.6	9	8-12	Standard	OLD HUBERT	Dec	5	1990

THIRSK

DISTANCE	TIME	AGE	WEIGHT	GOING	HORSE	DATE		
5f	57.2 secs	2	9-7	Good To Firm	PROUD BOAST	Aug	5	2000
5f	56.1 secs	5	8-0	Firm	SIR SANDROVITCH	Jun	26	2003
6f	1m 09.2	2	9-6	Good To Firm	WESTCOURT MAGIC	Jun	25	1995
6f	1m 08.8	6	9-4	Firm	JOHAYRO	July	23	1999
7f	1m 23.7	2	8-9	Firm	COURTING	July	23	1999
7f	1m 22.8	4	8-5	Firm	SILVER HAZE	May	21	1988
1m	1m 37.9	2	9-0	Good To Firm	SUNDAY SYMPHONY	Sep	4	2004
1m	1m 34.8	4	8-13	Firm	YEARSLEY	May	5	1990
1m 4f	2m 29.9	5	9-12	Firm	GALLERY GOD	Jun	4	2001
2m	3m 22.3	3	8-10	Firm	TOMASCHEK	Aug	1	1964

WARWICK

DISTANCE	TIME	AGE	WEIGHT	GOING	HORSE	DATE		
5f	58.4 secs	2	9-7	Good To Firm	PRENONAMOSS	Oct	9	1990
5f	57.8 secs	5	9-4	Good To Firm	ANOTHER EPISODE	Aug	29	1994
5f 110y	1m 03.6	5	8-6	Good To Firm	DIZZY IN THE HEAD	Jun	27	2004
6f	1m 11.22	2	9-3	Good To Firm	HURRICANE HYMNBOOK	Sep	15	2007
6f	1m 10.94	6	9-8	Good	STAMFORD BLUE	July	12	2007
6f 21y	1m 10.6	2	9-0	Good To Firm	VIKING SPIRIT	Sep	6	2004
6f 21y	1m 09.6	6	9-2	Firm	PARKSIDE PURSUIT	Jun	20	2004
6f 21y	1m 12.1	3	8-6	Good To Firm	GEMTASTIC	Jun	18	2001
7f 26y	1m 22.9	2	9-3	Good To Firm	COUNTRY RAMBLER	Jun	20	2004
7f 26y	1m 21.2	3	8-11	Good To Firm	LUCKY SPIN	Jun	19	2004
1m 22y	1m 37.1	3	8-11	Firm	ORINOCOVSKY	Jun	26	2002
1m 2f 188y	2m 16.2	7-12	8-9	Good To Firm	SCENTED AIR	Apr	21	2003
1m 4f 134y	2m 39.5	3	8-13	Good To Firm	MAIMANA	Jun	22	2002
1m 6f 135y	3m 07.5	3	9-7	Good To Firm	BURMA BAY	July	2	1999
2m 39y	3m 30.6	5	8-1	Good To Firm	RENAISSANCE LADY	Jun	27	2001

WINDSOR

DISTANCE	TIME	AGE	WEIGHT	GOING	HORSE	DATE		
5f 10y	58.75 secs	2	8-12	Good To Firm	HOH MIKE	May tab>15		2006
5f 10y	59.1 secs	4	8-13	Good	BEYOND THE CLOUDS	July	17	2000
5f 217y	1m 09.0	2	8-7	Good To Firm	OPTIONS OPEN	July	25	1994
5f 217y	1m 10.1	3	8-4	Firm	SWEET RELIEF	Sep	11	1978
6f	1m 10.5	2	9-5	Good To Firm	CUBISM	Aug	17	1998
6f	1m 10.06	6	8-11	Good To Firm	PRESTO SHINKO	Aug	4	2007
1m 67y	1m 44.38	2	9-1	Good To Firm	GENRE	Oct	3	2005
1m 67y	1m 40.27	4	9-3	Good To Firm	LIBRETTIST	July	1	2006
1m 2f 7y	2m 03.0	3	9-1	Firm	MOOMBA MASQUERADE	May	19	1990
1m 3f 135y	2m 21.5	3	9-2	Firm	DOUBLE FLORIN	May	19	1980

WOLVERHAMPTON (A.W)

DISTANCE	TIME	AGE	WEIGHT	GOING	HORSE	DATE		
5f 20y	1m 01.13	2	8-8	Standard To Fast	YUNGABURRA	Nov	8	2006
5f 20y	1m 00.56	3	8-10	Standard	KING ORCHISIOS	Oct	29	2006
5f 216y	1m 12.61	2	9-0	Standard To Fast	PRIME DEFENDER	Nov	8	2006
7f 32y	1m 27.7	2	9-5	Standard	BILLY DANE	Aug	14	2006
7f 32y	1m 26.86	6	9-3	Standard	BORDER MUSIC	Mar	10	2007
1m 141y	1m 48.08	2	8-9	Standard To Fast	WORLDLY	Aug	30	2006
1m 141y	1m 48.20	4	9-1	Standard	TRIFTI	Oct	1	2005
1m 1f 103y	1m 57.34	4	8-13	Standard	BAHAR SHUMAAL	Oct	28	2006
1m 4f 50y	2m 34.75	5	8-13	Standard To Fast	FANTOCHE	May	3	2007
1m 5f 194y	2m 59.85	6	9-12	Standard To Fast	VALANCE	Aug	30	2006
2m 119y	3m 35.85	5	8-11	Standard To Fast	MARKET WATCHER	Nov	21	2006

YARMOUTH

DISTANCE	TIME	AGE	WEIGHT	GOING	HORSE	DATE		
5f 43y	1m 00.4	2	8-6	Good To Firm	EBBA	July	26	1999
5f 43y	1m 00.2	3	8-11	Firm	CHARM BIRD	Sep	15	1988
6f 3y	1m 10.4	2	9-0	Firm	LANCHESTER	Aug	15	1988
6f 3y	1m 10.0	3	8-10	Good To Firm	TIPSY CREEK	Aug	10	1997
7f 3y	1m 22.2	2	9-0	Good To Firm	WARRSHAN	Sep	14	1988
7f 3y	1m 22.12	4	9-4	Good To Firm	GLENBUCK	Apr	26	2007
1m 3y	1m 36.3	3	8-2	Good To Firm	OUTRUN	Sep	15	1988
1m 3y	1m 33.9	3	8-8	Firm	BONNE ETOILE	Jun	27	1995
1m 2f 21y	2m 02.83	4	8-9	Firm	REUNITE	July	18	2006
1m 3f 101y	2m 23.1	3	8-9	Firm	RAHIL	July	1	1993
1m 6f 17y	2m 57.8	3	8-2	Good To Firm	BARAKAT	July	24	1990
2m	3m 26.7	4	8-2	Good To Firm	ALHESN	July	26	1999
2m 2f 51y	3m 56.8	4	9-10	Firm	PROVENCE	Sep	19	1991

YORK

DISTANCE	TIME	AGE	WEIGHT	GOING	HORSE	DATE		
5f 3y	58.4 secs	2	8-11	Good To Firm	HOWICK FALLS	Aug	20	2003
5f 3y	56.2 secs	3	9-9	Good To Firm	OASIS DREAM	Aug	21	2003
6f	1m 10.6	2	9-0	Good To Firm	CARRY ON KATIE	Aug	21	2003
6f	1m 08.58	7	9-4	Firm	CAPE OF GOOD HOPE	Jun	16	2005
7f	1m 23.29	2	8-12	Good	VITAL EQUINE	Sep	9	2006
7f	1m 21.98	5	9-6	Good	IFFRAAJ	Sep	9	2006
7f 202y	1m 37.2	2	9-4	Good To Firm	THE WIFE	Sep	2	1999
7f 205y	1m 36.0	5	8-7	Good To Firm	FAITHFUL WARRIOR	Jul	11	2003
1m 205y	1m 52.4	2	8-1	Good To Firm	ORAL EVIDENCE	Oct	6	1988
1m 208y	1m 46.76	5	9-8	Good To Firm	ECHO OF LIGHT	Sep	5	2007
1m 2f 88y	2m 06.09	4	8-11	Good To Firm	IMPERIAL STRIDE	Jun	17	2005
1m 3f 198y	2m 27.4	4	9-4	Good To Firm	ISLINGTON	Aug	20	2003
1m 5f 197y	2m 52.5	4	8-9	Good To Firm	MAMOOL	May	15	2003
1m 7f 195y	3m 18.4	3	8-0	Good To Firm	DAM BUSTERS	Aug	16	1988

TOP FLAT JOCKEYS IN BRITAIN 2007

Covering racing from January 1st - December 31st, Turf and AW.

W-R	%	JOCKEY	2ND	3RD	TOTAL PRIZE	WIN PRIZE
213-1242	17%	SEB SANDERS	167	146	1,499,323	971,222
207-1040	20%	JAMIE SPENCER	151	119	2,893,611	2,106,903
170-1135	15%	N CALLAN	154	132	1,264,543	803,953
139-869	16%	RICHARD HUGHES	115	108	1,878,210	1,013,598
128-675	19%	RYAN MOORE	100	72	2,511,814	1,636,719
112-1292	9%	CHRIS CATLIN	119	114	728,193	396,045
109-717	15%	JIMMY FORTUNE	83	92	2,358,117	1,464,420
106-970	11%	STEVE DROWNE	104	91	1,306,204	826,254
96-793	12%	TED DURCAN	96	74	1,372,825	845,571
93-524	18%	KERRIN MCEVOY	66	56	1,460,687	992,415
92-938	10%	DANE O'NEILL	92	107	645,319	375,323
92-943	10%	JIM CROWLEY	93	95	676,283	406,993
90-943	10%	PAUL HANAGAN	98	103	947,826	604,818
89-955	9%	EDDIE AHERN	114	90	1,090,526	540,276
88-701	13%	T P QUEALLY	72	50	705,749	463,649
79-770	10%	JOHN EGAN	87	83	771,096	416,028
77-376	20%	L DETTORI	52	42	3,108,640	2,359,489
76-579	13%	GREG FAIRLEY	52	43	483,883	356,825
75-595	13%	GEORGE BAKER	69	71	502,718	308,349
73-420	17%	R HILLS	55	51	1,413,834	814,490
73-462	16%	JOE FANNING	49	60	678,496	511,120
73-836	9%	PAUL MULRENNAN	73	82	623,611	432,751
70-657	11%	MARTIN DWYER	70	56	795,516	405,720
68-679	10%	DARRYLL HOLLAND	78	65	865,388	556,710
67-540	12%	WILLIAM BUICK	57	58	660,623	492,347
66-827	8%	TOM EAVES	72	75	603,128	337,719
65-622	10%	LIAM JONES	51	70	375,287	250,896
65-793	8%	MICKY FENTON	70	64	442,825	260,409
63-687	9%	ROYSTON FFRENCH	76	54	731,104	507,025
63-849	7%	JIMMY QUINN	78	75	890,755	610,577
62-387	16%	PHILIP ROBINSON	51	45	820,080	514,279
62-530	12%	K DARLEY	65	59	767,443	396,952
62-719	9%	FERGUS SWEENEY	64	51	415,689	293,146
60-593	10%	PHILLIP MAKIN	45	67	382,278	240,092
60-624	10%	PAT COSGRAVE	57	58	417,590	262,672
57-594	10%	FRANCIS NORTON	56	60	725,494	481,322
57-618	9%	DAVID ALLAN	58	63	501,744	317,813
56-719	8%	ADAM KIRBY	69	53	416,467	253,084
56-757	7%	HAYLEY TURNER	71	77	368,508	180,409
52-654	8%	STEPHEN DONOHOE	48	54	251,814	155,188
51-695	7%	ROBERT HAVLIN	79	72	363,224	184,562
50-455	11%	MICHAEL HILLS	44	50	1,344,385	969,965
49-787	6%	L P KENIRY	75	64	358,202	208,579
46-365	13%	NICKY MACKAY	40	45	358,691	218,340
46-367	13%	DANIEL TUDHOPE	36	33	237,267	160,202
45-534	8%	DEAN MCKEOWN	55	55	412,088	295,178
44-370	12%	RICHARD KINGSCOTE	40	51	281,948	191,980
43-532	8%	J-P GUILLAMBERT	54	55	422,340	238,801
42-512	8%	RICHARD MULLEN	38	46	282,001	164,408
41-432	9%	ADRIAN T NICHOLLS	47	43	379,879	229,463

TOP FLAT TRAINERS IN BRITAIN 2007

Covering racing from January 1st - December 31st, Turf and AW.

TRAINER	LEADING HORSE	W-R	2ND	3RD	4TH	TOTAL PRIZE	WIN PRIZE
A P O'BRIEN	Dylan Thomas	18-112	27	12	6	3,484,026	1,666,717
SIR MICHAEL STOUTE	Notnowcato	113-498	79	59	53	2,574,336	1,691,390
R HANNON	Indian Ink	148-1075	140	103	118	2,083,975	1,192,346
P W CHAPPLE-HYAM	Authorized	33-235	30	21	17	1,868,407	1,463,796
B W HILLS	Dark Angel	91-659	78	81	69	1,796,770	1,213,024
M R CHANNON	Youmzain	109-1086	116	119	99	1,703,200	986,798
SAEED BIN SUROOR	Ramonti	73-285	51	32	27	1,688,114	1,234,540
M JOHNSTON	Zaham	161-998	125	117	99	1,651,628	1,188,791
J H M GOSDEN	Lucarno	67-401	59	56	37	1,637,782	1,046,061
R A FAHEY	Charlie Tokyo	85-926	101	107	86	1,132,476	643,994
K A RYAN	Anosti	107-932	108	89	73	1,111,861	628,750
J NOSEDA	Soldier's Tale	56-258	39	27	26	1,054,363	723,671
B J MEEHAN	Exclamation	61-544	46	50	40	891,624	585,957
L M CUMANI	Purple Moon	56-301	38	48	27	860,684	581,284
W J HAGGAS	Candidato Roy	66-376	48	49	33	763,916	546,929
H R A CECIL	Light Shift	45-215	35	27	26	732,567	561,861
A M BALDING	Dream Eater	39-410	36	44	43	711,375	525,039
M L W BELL	Red Evie	47-351	45	42	31	710,809	556,868
J L DUNLOP	Shmookh	57-430	64	40	38	690,771	420,499
M A JARVIS	Silkwood	68-382	57	43	32	685,288	451,451
H MORRISON	Sakhee's Secret	51-366	47	35	31	656,405	488,549
D NICHOLLS	Tax Free	68-577	66	57	37	627,020	388,681
J A OSBORNE	Geordieland	61-380	56	46	26	616,309	330,669
E A L DUNLOP	King Of Argos	50-391	43	56	38	568,665	276,536
T D EASTERBY	Cristal Clear	58-702	70	70	55	548,335	321,822
J R FANSHAWE	Cesare	36-259	22	36	31	546,659	403,981
K R BURKE	Aahayson	62-583	65	49	46	541,784	305,531
R CHARLTON	Third Set	42-271	32	32	26	539,111	424,979
C E BRITTAIN	Lake Poet	37-423	54	43	43	536,995	267,308
B SMART	Captain Gerrard	43-346	44	38	26	522,986	374,770
D R C ELSWORTH	Balkan Knight	34-340	40	45	34	495,030	241,953
C G COX	Dansili Dancer	33-272	33	22	17	446,311	292,416
M P TREGONING	Aqaleem	34-205	21	20	21	426,552	179,769
J S MOORE	Dubai Dynamo	31-405	50	39	42	425,512	265,789
T D BARRON	Flipando	53-477	36	52	42	387,840	239,841
MRS A J PERRETT	Tungsten Strike	35-390	32	37	37	381,598	229,271
J S BOLGER	Finsceal Beo	2-6	0	1	0	375,172	348,288
P F I COLE	River Proud	37-311	22	30	22	375,167	251,821
B R MILLMAN	Sergeant Cecil	44-377	31	35	36	365,991	256,715
J R BEST	Kingsgate Native	35-391	38	41	28	362,772	253,779
J G GIVEN	Trick Or Treat	33-320	36	27	17	345,494	189,779
G A BUTLER	Dansant	35-205	26	22	10	343,896	263,981
SIR MARK PRESCOTT	Bee Eater	66-311	47	28	13	338,852	241,331
R M BECKETT	Lipocco	41-321	38	37	20	330,349	197,813
M W EASTERBY	Gentleman's Deal	40-477	31	42	29	327,282	239,559
M H TOMPKINS	Topatoo	39-400	44	48	32	326,970	195,450
A FABRE	Manduro	3-6	1	0	1	322,753	267,987
P D EVANS	Vhujon	53-587	50	60	44	320,454	171,771
I SEMPLE	Appalachian Trail	44-379	35	36	37	315,118	216,753
C F WALL	Wake Up Maggie	31-213	21	18	20	310,817	217,210

TOP FLAT OWNERS IN BRITAIN 2007

Covering racing from January 1st - December 31st, Turf and AW.

OWNER	HORSE	W-R	2ND	3RD	4TH	TOTAL PRIZE	WIN PRIZE
GODOLPHIN	RAMONTI	73-285	51	32	27	1,688,114	1,234,540
HAMDAN AL MAKTOUM	MARAAHEL	101-557	82	63	48	1,646,790	988,396
S AL HOMEIZI/I AL SAGAR	AUTHORIZED	10-35	5	2	6	1,375,201	1,263,870
CHEVELEY PARK STUD	ALLEGRETTO	46-195	35	28	19	1,272,108	891,120
MRS J MAGNIER/M TABOR	DYLAN THOMAS	3-20	5	1	3	987,563	590,512
D SMITH, MRS J MAGNIER, M TABOR	EAGLE MOUNTAIN	3-23	6	4	0	835,748	251,697
K ABDULLA	RAINCOAT	67-308	54	44	20	762,925	442,952
SHEIKH MOHAMMED	BOSCOBEL	58-329	46	38	27	750,144	539,664
JABER ABDULLAH	YOUMZAIN	24-175	11	28	19	657,068	384,651
GEORGE STRAWBRIDGE	LUCARNO	15-61	11	6	10	595,121	443,348
RAYMOND TOOTH	EXCLAMATION	14-93	10	7	6	491,186	394,655
J C SMITH	DREAM EATER	14-137	17	10	20	455,720	347,574
M TABOR/MRS J MAGNIER	PEEPING FAWN	2-14	3	3	0	420,090	278,222
SHEIKH AHMED AL MAKTOUM	HATTA FORT	43-230	35	21	15	385,168	283,983
GAINSBOROUGH	MISS LUCIFER	35-206	33	20	19	366,395	268,629
A D DE ROTHSCHILD	NOTNOWCATO	1-5	0	2	1	363,890	259,314
NIARCHOS FAMILY	LIGHT SHIFT	9-31	5	4	4	356,179	288,498
HRH PRINCESS HAYA OF JORDAN	DANDY MAN	23-158	19	32	8	353,483	125,325
THE HON MRS J CORBETT/C WRIGHT	DARK ANGEL	5-12	2	0	1	344,413	337,667
R J ARCULLI	RED CLUBS	2-30	3	2	5	289,305	182,265
MISS B SWIRE	SAKHEE'S SECRET	4-63	6	4	2	277,759	256,380
MOUNTGRANGE STUD	GEORDIELAND	24-124	22	13	9	262,595	114,065
MRS J MAGNIER	EXCELLENT ART	3-8	2	0	0	260,145	224,281
SAEED SUHAIL	ARABIAN GLEAM	14-71	11	12	8	258,828	164,675
MRS J MAGNIER, M TABOR D SMITH	MAHLER	1-14	2	1	1	251,601	34,068
BARON G VON ULLMANN	MANDURO	2-3	0	1	0	250,022	239,597
MRS FITRI HAY	DUBAI DYNAMO	12-111	8	11	11	249,952	200,244
JOHN LIVOCK	THIRD SET	4-7	0	0	0	228,510	227,835
SAEED MANANA	HATTAN	17-208	24	21	18	222,525	95,760
H MORIN	LITERATO	1-1	0	0	0	222,350	222,350
THE SEARCHERS	FLEETING SPIRIT	5-13	3	2	0	220,084	116,453
PHIL CUNNINGHAM	COCKNEY REBEL	1-2	0	0	0	218,077	211,352
M A RYAN	FINSCEAL BEO	1-4	0	0	2	215,462	198,730
BUDGET STABLE	SOLDIER'S TALE	1-3	0	2	0	212,515	198,730
M TABOR, D SMITH MRS J MAGNIER	YELLOWSTONE	2-21	3	2	3	203,414	38,105
D SMITH, M TABOR MRS J MAGNIER	SIMPLY PERFECT	2-7	0	1	2	202,921	141,950
BOX 41	HALICARNASSUS	11-67	6	8	6	186,538	153,116
TERRY NEILL	RED EVIE	4-18	1	2	0	172,694	168,947
JOHN MAYNE	KINGSGATE NATIVE	3-25	3	3	3	170,199	144,902
R C BOND	CAPTAIN GERRARD	16-144	12	18	8	168,975	109,732
NIGEL SHIELDS	QADAR	14-162	15	22	7	168,102	92,104
SANGSTER FAMILY	CITY LEADER	6-36	3	5	1	163,433	104,247
M SINES	GYPSY BABY	8-29	9	2	0	158,727	50,647
MRS ELIZABETH MORAN	JEREMY	3-10	3	3	0	156,280	56,229
PAUL J DIXON	DOCOFTHEBAY	16-193	20	19	7	156,228	76,164
MRS J S BOLGER	NEW APPROACH	1-3	0	0	0	152,933	149,558
MRS SARAH E WOODHEAD	LADY RANGALI	4-7	1	0	0	151,990	150,449
A D SPENCE	ERADICATE	18-138	11	16	13	149,302	102,662
CRAIG BENNETT	PURPLE MOON	2-3	0	0	1	144,627	141,674
MRS SUSAN ROY/CHEVELEY PARK STUD	DUTCH ART	0-4	2	1	1	144,543	0

TOP FLAT HORSES IN BRITAIN 2007

Covering racing from January 1st - December 31st, Turf and AW.

HORSE (AGE)	WIN & PLACE £	W-R	TRAINER	OWNER	BREEDER
AUTHORIZED (3)	1,191,296	3-4	P W Chapple-Hyam	S Al Homeizi/I Al Sagar	Marengo Inv/Knighton House
DYLAN THOMAS (4)	618,879	1-3	A P O'Brien	Mrs J Magnier M Tabor	Tower Bloodstock
LUCARNO (3)	516,904	4-8	J H M Gosden	George Strawbridge	Augustin Stable
RAMONTI (5)	489,333	3-4	Saeed Bin Suroor	Godolphin	S P A Siba
EAGLE MOUNTAIN (3)	384,805	0-4	A P O'Brien	D Smith/Mrs Magnier/M Tabor	London T'bred Services
NOTNOWCATO (5)	363,890	1-5	Sir Michael Stoute	A D de Rothschild	Southcourt Stud
PEEPING FAWN (3)	362,494	2-3	A P O'Brien	M Tabor Mrs J Magnier	Barnett Enterprises
DARK ANGEL (2)	341,306	4-9	B W Hills	The Hon J M Corbett/C Wright	Yeomanstown Stud
LIGHT SHIFT (3)	274,080	3-4	H R A Cecil	Niarchos Family	Flaxman Holdings Ltd
RED CLUBS (4)	272,607	1-6	B W Hills	R J Arculli	J Fike
SAKHEE'S SECRET (3)	264,861	4-5	H Morrison	Miss B Swire	Miss B Swire
EXCELLENT ART (3)	253,424	1-3	A P O'Brien	Magnier/Tabor/Smith/Green	Cheveley Park Stud
MARAAHEL (6)	251,353	3-6	Sir Michael Stoute	Hamdan Al Maktoum	Shadwell Estate Company
MANDURO (5)	239,597	2-2	A Fabre	Baron G Von Ullmann	Rolf Brunner
LITERATO (3)	222,350	1-1	J-C Rouget	H Morin	Bsh Of Administrativa
COCKNEY REBEL (3)	218,077	1-2	G A Huffer	Phil Cunningham	Oak Lodge Bloodstock
SOLDIER'S TALE (6)	212,515	1-3	J Noseda	Budget Stables	Budget Stables Inc
SCORPION (5)	208,393	1-4	A P O'Brien	Mrs John Magnier/M Tabor	Grangemore Stud
DREAM EATER (2)	204,048	1-8	A M Balding	J C Smith	Stone Ridge Farm
FINSCEAL BEO (3)	198,730	1-2	J S Bolger	M A Ryan	Rathberry Stud
THIRD SET (4)	198,602	3-6	R Charlton	John Livock	A Stroud/J Hanly
EXCLAMATION (2)	191,560	2-3	B J Meehan	Raymond Tooth	Exors Of The Late S Cohn
ALLEGRETTO (4)	181,987	2-6	Sir Michael Stoute	Cheveley Park Stud	Miss K Rausing/Airlie Stud
SEPTIMUS (4)	181,555	2-3	A P O'Brien	D Smith/Mrs. Magnier/M Tabor	Barronstown Stud/Orpendale
AQALEEM (3)	179,453	1-3	M P Tregoning	Hamdan Al Maktoum	Shadwell Estate Company
PIPEDREAMER (3)	175,016	4-6	J H M Gosden	Cheveley Park Stud	Cheveley Park Stud Ltd
SIMPLY PERFECT (3)	166,476	1-4	J Noseda	D Smith/M Tabor/Mrs Magnier	Trehedyn Stud/Quarry B'stock
RED EVIE (4)	161,823	2-4	M L W Bell	Terry Neill	Dermot Cantillon/Forenaghts
INDIAN INK (3)	161,694	1-3	R Hannon	Raymond Tooth	Killeen Castle Stud
YOUMZAIN (4)	161,400	0-1	M R Channon	Jaber Abdullah	Frank Dunne
ZAHAM (3)	160,511	5-10	M Johnston	Hamdan Al Maktoum	London T'bred Services Ltd
KINGSGATE NATIVE (2)	158,754	1-3	J R Best	John Mayne	Peter McCutcheon
MAHLER (3)	152,885	1-4	A P O'Brien	Mrs Magnier/M Tabor/D Smith	Pegasus Racing Ltd
LADY RANGALI (2)	151,990	4-7	Mrs A Duffield	Mrs Sarah E Woodhead	Mrs C Hartery
NEW APPROACH (2)	149,558	1-1	J S Bolger	Mrs J S Bolger	Lodge Park Stud
IBN KHALDUN (3)	147,169	4-5	Saeed Bin Suroor	Godolphin	Darley
BOSCOBEL (3)	145,059	4-6	M Johnston	Sheikh Mohammed	Darley
PURPLE MOON (4)	144,627	2-3	L M Cumani	Craig Bennett	Gestut Shohrenhof
DUTCH ART (3)	144,543	0-4	P W Chapple-Hyam	Mrs Roy/Cheveley Park Stud	Cromlech Bloodstock
JEREMY (4)	143,626	1-4	Sir Michael Stoute	Mrs Elizabeth Moran	Brookdale
ECHELON (5)	142,318	3-5	Sir Michael Stoute	Cheveley Park Stud	Cheveley Park Stud Ltd
DUBAI DYNAMO (3)	139,379	3-10	J S Moore	Mrs Fitri Hay	T K & Mrs P A Knox
TARIQ (3)	138,698	3-4	P W Chapple-Hyam	S Al Homeizi/I Al Sagar	D R Botterill
MAJESTIC ROI (3)	135,322	2-5	M R Channon	Jaber Abdullah	Gaines-Gentry Thoroughbreds
REGAL FLUSH (3)	133,715	2-6	Sir Michael Stoute	Cheveley Park Stud	Cheveley Park Stud Ltd
JUNIPER GIRL (4)	133,583	1-4	M L W Bell	M B Hawtin	Mrs E Kent
NANNINA (4)	129,751	1-5	J H M Gosden	Cheveley Park Stud	Cheveley Park Stud Ltd
CITY LEADER (2)	128,778	2-4	B J Meehan	Sangster Family	Swettenham Stud
YEATS (6)	127,755	1-1	A P O'Brien	Mrs John Magnier	Barrowsdale Stud/Orpendale
DUKE OF MARMALADE (3)	125,460	0-4	A P O'Brien	Mrs John Magnier/M Tabor	Southern Bloodstock

TOP NH JOCKEYS
IN BRITAIN 2006/7

W-R	%	JOCKEY	2ND	3RD	TOTAL PRIZE
184-758	24%	A P McCOY	117	97	2,271,123
154-847	18%	RICHARD JOHNSON	139	108	2,000,616
105-556	19%	T J O'BRIEN	82	67	921,914
99-551	18%	ROBERT THORNTON	77	66	1,617,999
98-542	18%	TIMMY MURPHY	71	53	1,452,637
89-675	13%	G LEE	97	65	1,029,922
80-512	16%	P J BRENNAN	59	62	925,397
75-291	26%	R WALSH	53	40	2,330,759
75-474	16%	NOEL FEHILY	65	65	841,444
73-462	16%	SAM THOMAS	68	40	765,327
69-401	17%	TONY DOBBIN	59	41	863,821
60-369	16%	MICK FITZGERALD	41	47	980,243
59-425	14%	WAYNE HUTCHINSON	39	54	524,404
59-473	12%	PAUL MOLONEY	37	56	618,240
59-614	10%	TOM SCUDAMORE	71	76	785,444
54-490	11%	LEIGHTON ASPELL	63	52	554,371
46-417	11%	PHIL KINSELLA	40	45	280,523
44-433	10%	MARK BRADBURNE	51	51	381,091
42-374	11%	DOMINIC ELSWORTH	46	35	388,843
42-443	9%	JAMIE MOORE	57	57	492,474
42-489	9%	RICHARD McGRATH	49	52	409,600
40-381	10%	DARYL JACOB	45	46	365,800
38-406	9%	JASON MAGUIRE	51	46	387,332
35-417	8%	ANDREW THORNTON	47	45	368,102
34-321	11%	S J CRAINE	35	40	252,303
31-265	12%	MR T GREENALL	30	28	141,771
31-323	10%	W T KENNEDY	38	29	200,243
31-369	8%	PETER BUCHANAN	27	38	248,064
30-204	15%	LIAM TREADWELL	20	16	250,968
30-260	12%	T J DREAPER	19	25	195,074
30-316	9%	DOUGIE COSTELLO	28	24	271,409
29-271	11%	BARRY FENTON	31	26	333,601
28-393	7%	PADDY ASPELL	27	34	198,130
27-289	9%	J A McCARTHY	24	19	222,631
27-296	9%	TONY EVANS	30	28	293,459
26-288	9%	BRIAN HARDING	19	27	186,094
26-327	8%	T J DOYLE	37	36	348,047
25-294	9%	JOE TIZZARD	32	20	245,416
24-237	10%	ANDREW GLASSONBURY	20	16	256,765
24-301	8%	WARREN MARSTON	29	23	172,072
24-341	7%	KEITH MERCER	35	37	228,976
23-278	8%	S P JONES	29	38	357,735
22-142	15%	DAVID ENGLAND	13	11	184,114
22-165	13%	P C O'NEILL	15	14	198,024
22-221	10%	P J McDONALD	21	16	237,433
22-224	10%	MICHAEL McALISTER	13	18	124,328
22-304	7%	BARRY KENIRY	21	27	148,443
21-174	12%	GERARD TUMELTY	11	12	100,658
21-268	8%	ROBERT LUCEY-BUTLER	7	18	114,769
21-319	7%	DAVE CROSSE	35	27	170,155

TOP NH TRAINERS IN BRITAIN 2006/7

TRAINER	LEADING HORSE	W-R	2ND	3RD	4TH	TOTAL PRIZE	WIN PRIZE
P F NICHOLLS	Kauto Star	126-539	99	68	42	2,972,659	2,160,448
JONJO O'NEILL	Exotic Dancer	126-821	112	95	66	1,692,487	1,107,406
D E PIPE	Our Vic	134-767	90	77	67	1,605,596	1,044,496
A KING	Voy Por Ustedes	92-414	72	52	34	1,569,089	1,208,532
P J HOBBS	Detroit City	111-608	94	66	58	1,511,238	941,170
N J HENDERSON	Afsoun	74-320	40	39	26	990,763	503,560
MISS VENETIA WILLIAMS	Idole First	76-417	55	41	52	940,601	628,870
FERDY MURPHY	Hot Weld	61-439	64	38	29	896,148	627,550
P BOWEN	Mckelvey	72-354	44	49	26	889,995	531,298
N G RICHARDS	Monet's Garden	64-320	58	41	22	787,139	472,688
J HOWARD JOHNSON	Inglis Drever	54-399	48	45	35	783,374	475,888
EVAN WILLIAMS	State Of Play	66-505	50	60	39	623,870	455,222
N A TWISTON-DAVIES	Knowhere	60-432	46	35	37	604,537	367,654
H D DALY	Mighty Man	36-250	38	32	21	537,198	318,211
G L MOORE	Heathcote	45-408	51	68	37	529,527	312,668
MRS S J SMITH	Omni Cosmo Touch	51-437	49	54	32	439,240	256,535
GORDON ELLIOTT	Silver Birch	4-22	3	6	2	429,374	413,453
CARL LLEWELLYN	Dempsey	34-184	14	23	15	406,448	256,886
J J QUINN	Crow Wood	33-141	30	18	11	375,510	269,398
D MCCAIN JNR	Regal Heights	40-366	49	46	36	364,672	207,024
MISS H C KNIGHT	Racing Demon	30-268	33	27	26	346,463	236,491
MISS E C LAVELLE	Labelthou	28-184	22	21	16	328,514	251,243
B G POWELL	Take A Mile	47-363	37	41	24	318,521	216,147
C J MANN	My Turn Now	33-182	26	23	15	295,769	182,134
R H ALNER	Sir Rembrandt	31-307	38	37	27	292,842	143,170
K G REVELEY	Ungaro	30-242	37	26	23	288,317	194,068
M SCUDAMORE	Heltornic	22-293	29	32	25	244,190	176,926
N J GIFFORD	Straw Bear	14-120	14	14	10	242,402	163,691
IAN WILLIAMS	Bambi De L'Orme	19-289	21	37	23	238,981	160,092
J W MULLINS	See You Sometime	21-269	28	20	22	238,052	142,611
J M JEFFERSON	Calatagan	31-199	22	15	11	228,918	159,740
T R GEORGE	Kilbeggan Blade	30-223	16	25	33	224,272	143,756
NICK WILLIAMS	Kings Brook	15-89	12	10	7	220,588	143,331
JOHN G CARR	Sublimity	2-17	1	1	1	209,763	208,012
R C GUEST	Shannon's Pride	27-352	37	27	28	199,700	111,658
DR R D P NEWLAND	Overstrand	6-36	8	5	5	196,978	140,009
M F HARRIS	Herecomestanley	24-255	24	34	20	194,416	117,521
MRS A M THORPE	Rushneeyriver	32-119	22	13	9	193,375	156,068
MISS LUCINDA V RUSSELL	Incas	24-295	27	34	32	192,002	113,300
C L TIZZARD	Flight Leader	20-179	27	15	18	171,801	110,958
L LUNGO	Wild Cane Ridge	23-155	19	15	9	165,302	96,758
NOEL T CHANCE	River City	11-104	12	12	10	161,526	55,825
P MONTEITH	Locksmith	21-190	24	25	22	160,512	86,352
MRS L WADHAM	United	13-99	10	6	10	158,236	115,275
R H BUCKLER	I Hear Thunder	14-152	20	21	17	153,980	94,356
O SHERWOOD	Caribou	20-140	21	19	8	153,963	92,740
V R A DARTNALL	Borehill Joker	21-113	19	11	10	146,319	94,311
S GOLLINGS	Royal Shakespeare	7-130	20	19	13	142,303	50,895
J L SPEARING	Simon	8-118	11	13	11	142,276	105,215
R J HODGES	Preacher Boy	9-126	22	22	14	138,617	39,143

TOP NH OWNERS IN BRITAIN IN 2006/7

OWNER	LEADING HORSE	W-R	2ND	3RD	4TH	TOTAL PRIZE	WIN PRIZE
JOHN P MCMANUS	Wichita Lineman	93-633	102	69	57	1,327,115	784,779
SIR ROBERT OGDEN	Exotic Dancer	27-97	17	9	9	941,932	695,517
D A JOHNSON	Acambo	59-316	46	37	32	845,925	546,274
TREVOR HEMMINGS	Afsoun	42-287	45	33	21	748,712	394,981
ANDREA & GRAHAM WYLIE	Inglis Drever	45-242	35	23	29	686,554	440,822
CLIVE D SMITH	Kauto Star	6-21	1	2	0	620,126	607,263
BRIAN WALSH	Silver Birch	5-15	4	0	1	445,058	416,788
THE STEWART FAMILY	My Will	18-84	17	12	7	379,505	205,872
MRS M FINDLAY & P K BARBER	Denman	10-18	3	0	0	254,768	241,251
ALAN PETERSON	Fair Along	6-22	4	2	1	219,279	137,937
DAVID WESLEY YATES	Monet's Garden	3-7	0	0	1	217,246	205,221
N ELLIOTT	Mckelvey	4-12	1	1	2	215,579	62,443
MRS A B YEOMAN & C R WHITTAKER	Taranis	3-6	1	1	0	212,799	153,954
TERRY WARNER	Detroit City	7-54	8	5	6	210,916	187,965
D S J P SYNDICATE	Katchit	7-8	1	0	0	206,578	202,300
W HENNESSY	Sublimity	1-1	0	0	0	205,272	205,272
S HUBBARD RODWELL	Hot Weld	3-22	2	2	2	197,252	192,285
MRS GAY SMITH	Black Jack Ketchum	28-139	15	17	8	174,769	117,962
E R HANBURY	Mighty Man	2-5	2	1	0	174,512	96,957
MRS T BROWN	Dempsey	2-21	2	2	2	159,214	85,530
WINFIELD LONGMAN WRIGHT FENTON	My Way De Solzen	4-6	2	0	0	157,417	141,374
PAUL GREEN	Eurotrek	5-39	9	4	2	140,320	105,487
M C PIPE	Gaspara	9-53	7	6	2	139,720	95,791
KEITH NICHOLSON	Ela Re	19-105	7	17	7	138,004	105,232
IAN PAYNE & KIM FRANKLIN	Halcon Genelardais	2-6	0	1	0	130,628	119,650
DR R D P AND MRS L J NEWLAND	Overstrand	2-5	1	0	0	127,805	95,720
MRS M FINDLAY	Desert Quest	4-23	4	5	1	123,772	62,075
LAURENCE BYRNE	Hardy Eustace	1-4	1	0	0	118,344	56,340
THREE LINE WHIP	Blazing Bailey	4-12	3	1	1	117,310	70,203
H R MOULD	Knowhere	7-43	5	4	5	113,717	39,118
C G ROACH	Thisthatandtother	7-27	4	0	0	112,556	49,566
B SIDDLE & B D HAYNES	Heathcote	4-12	1	2	0	110,699	98,202
J HALES	Neptune Collonges	5-19	4	3	0	108,922	50,995
JIM ENNIS	Faasel	6-40	5	7	5	108,642	23,377
MR & MRS WILLIAM RUCKER	State Of Play	2-10	0	2	2	107,377	89,285
MR & MRS R ANDERSON GREEN	King Barry	13-96	5	13	4	103,258	81,085
ASHLEYBANK INVESTMENTS LTD	Wild Cane Ridge	7-57	8	7	6	102,504	42,522
MRS T P RADFORD	Racing Demon	4-14	1	1	1	101,107	63,376
MRS MARIE TAYLOR	Crow Wood	5-14	2	2	0	100,415	66,428
STEPHEN W MOLLOY	Heltronic	3-7	1	1	0	99,787	96,489
WALTERS PLANT HIRE LTD	Blue Splash	16-67	9	6	6	99,781	79,570
MR & MRS DUNCAN DAVIDSON	Bohemian Spirit	12-74	15	14	6	99,661	51,449
MRS MERCY RIMELL	Simon	2-7	1	0	0	99,511	91,232
NIGEL BUNTER	D'Argent	2-10	2	1	1	97,717	64,625
MAURICE CHAPMAN	Chief Dan George	5-34	1	3	2	97,176	93,359
MRS DIANA WHATELEY	Boychuk	4-26	7	4	1	96,802	31,823
ELITE RACING CLUB	Penzance	9-39	7	7	1	93,815	63,126
M A RYAN	Al Eile	1-1	0	0	0	91,232	91,232
MS Y M HILL	Yes Sir	7-13	0	0	2	89,030	80,213
J B WEBB	Royal Shakespeare	5-54	10	8	6	88,636	30,706

TOP NH HORSES
IN BRITAIN 2006/7

HORSE (AGE)	WIN & PLACE £	W-R	TRAINER	OWNER	BREEDER
KAUTO STAR (7)	607,263	6-6	P F Nicholls	Clive D Smith	Mme Henri Aubert
EXOTIC DANCER (7)	429,382	4-7	Jonjo O'Neill	Sir Robert Ogden	G Gilles & Ecurie J Ouaki
SILVER BIRCH (10)	407,465	1-3	Gordon Elliott	Brian Walsh	J And Mrs Power
VOY POR USTEDES (6)	247,091	2-4	A King	Sir Robert Ogden	Ecurie Guillaume & F Picoulet
MONET'S GARDEN (9)	217,246	3-5	N G Richards	David Wesley Yates	William Delahunty
TARANIS (6)	212,799	3-6	P F Nicholls	Mrs Yeoman & C Whittaker	Pierre De Maleissye Melun
KATCHIT (4)	206,578	7-8	A King	D S J P Syndicate	D J Burke
MCKELVEY (8)	206,176	2-6	P Bowen	N Elliott	John Quane
SUBLIMITY (7)	205,272	1-1	John G Carr	W Hennessy	Stratford Place/Watership Down
INGLIS DREVER (8)	192,869	2-4	J Howard Johnson	Andrea & Graham Wylie	R J McAlpine & D O Pickering
HOT WELD (8)	188,166	2-6	Ferdy Murphy	S Hubbard Rodwell	Cartmel Bloodstock
MIGHTY MAN (7)	174,082	2-4	H D Daly	E R Hanbury	Evan Hanbury
DETROIT CITY (5)	173,033	3-5	P J Hobbs	Terry Warner	Edward J Kelly
MY WAY DE SOLZEN (7)	157,417	4-6	A King	Winfield,Longman,Wright,Fenton	C Ricous-Guerin & J Guerin
DEMPSEY (9)	156,346	2-6	Carl Llewellyn	Mrs T Brown	Seamus Larkin
DENMAN (7)	151,537	5-5	P F Nicholls	Mrs M Findlay & P K Barber	Colman O'Flynn
HALCON GENELARDAIS (7)	130,628	2-4	A King	Ian Payne & Kim Franklin	G Descours & Mlle Constance Des
ACAMBO (6)	127,945	2-4	D E Pipe	D A Johnson	A Groschler
OUR VIC (9)	126,473	1-4	D E Pipe	D A Johnson	Col W B Mullins
OVERSTRAND (9)	122,317	3-9	Dr R D P Newland	Dr & Mrs Newland, C Stedman	Airlie Stud
HARDY EUSTACE (10)	118,344	1-3	D T Hughes	Laurence Byrne	Patrick Joyce
FAIR ALONG (5)	118,222	3-8	P J Hobbs	Alan Peterson	Gestut Harzburg
GASPARA (4)	117,837	4-5	D E Pipe	M C Pipe	Jean-Pierre-Joseph Dubois
AFSOUN (5)	116,281	2-6	N J Henderson	Trevor Hemmings	S A Aga Khan
WICHITA LINEMAN (6)	116,056	4-6	Jonjo O'Neill	John P McManus	Pat Tobin
MY WILL (7)	105,173	1-6	P F Nicholls	The Stewart Family	Michel-Jacques Rivaillon
MASSINI'S MAGUIRE (6)	100,058	3-8	P J Hobbs	Alan Peterson	G Quirk
HELTORNIC (7)	99,787	3-7	M Scudamore	Stephen W Molloy	A W Buller
SIMON (8)	99,511	2-6	J L Spearing	Mrs Mercy Rimell	Mrs Mercy Rimell
STATE OF PLAY (7)	99,235	1-3	Evan Williams	Mr & Mrs William Rucker	Roland Lerner
HEATHCOTE (5)	97,645	1-7	G L Moore	B Siddle & B D Haynes	Miss K Rausing
STRAW BEAR (6)	96,743	2-5	N J Gifford	John P McManus	Cyril Humphris
CHIEF DAN GEORGE (7)	96,090	5-11	James Moffatt	Maurice Chapman	Matthew Brady
BLAZING BAILEY (5)	95,587	2-7	A King	Three Line Whip	A M Tombs
AL EILE (7)	91,232	1-1	John Queally	M A Ryan	Michael Ryan
YES SIR (8)	89,030	7-13	P Bowen	Ms Y M Hill	Louis Hill
DEMI BEAU (9)	87,190	1-5	Evan Williams	Cunningham Racing	Lord Howard De Walden
TWIST MAGIC (5)	85,977	2-4	P F Nicholls	B Fulton T Hayward M Lynch	Dr Georg Hastrich And Co
TURPIN GREEN (9)	81,237	1-5	N G Richards	Trevor Hemmings	Pat Leyden
UNITED (6)	80,809	3-7	Mrs L Wadham	R B Holt	Gestut Norina
TIDAL BAY (6)	79,692	4-6	J Howard Johnson	Andrea & Graham Wylie	John Dorgan
DUNBRODY MILLAR (9)	78,993	1-11	P Bowen	Dundon Else Partnership	Lord Donegall
D'ARGENT (10)	78,410	1-4	A King	Nigel Bunter	Navan Stables
SLIM PICKINGS (7)	77,650	0-2	T J Taaffe	Doubtful Five Syndicate	T A O'Donnell
MADISON DU BERLAIS (6)	77,278	3-10	D E Pipe	R Stanley & Y Reynolds II	Jean-Marc Lucas
BRAVE INCA (9)	77,004	0-1	C A Murphy	Novices Syndicate	D W Macauley
NOZIC (5)	75,563	2-5	P F Nicholls	S McVie	P Le Gloannec
IDOLE FIRST (8)	74,620	2-4	Miss Venetia Williams	D and J Racing Ltd	Ralph Alfandari
SEE YOU SOMETIME (12)	74,218	1-5	J W Mullins	J A G Meaden	J A G & Mrs S R B Meaden
PARSONS LEGACY (9)	73,703	1-5	P J Hobbs	R A S Offer	Frederick Woods

LEADING SIRES OF 2007 IN GREAT BRITAIN AND IRELAND

STALLION	BREEDING	RNRS	WNRS	WINS	WIN MONEY	PLACES	PLACE MONEY	TOTAL
DANEHILL (USA)	by Danzig (USA)	113	54	81	2490463	189	1258430	3748892
GALILEO (IRE)	by Sadler's Wells (USA)	117	52	80	2459634	145	478326	2937960
MONTJEU (IRE)	by Sadler's Wells (USA)	136	47	61	1720197	180	656099	2376296
DANEHILL DANCER (IRE)	by Danehill (USA)	193	79	117	1380456	305	911503	2291959
SADLER'S WELLS (USA)	by Northern Dancer	157	58	93	1414011	179	731045	2145056
PIVOTAL (GB)	by Polar Falcon (USA)	148	69	105	931062	257	594173	1525235
ROCK OF GIBRALTAR (IRE)	by Danehill (USA)	97	37	52	519216	157	885423	1404639
INDIAN RIDGE	by Ahonoora	83	31	47	1069583	128	236043	1295627
IN THE WINGS	by Sadler's Wells (USA)	102	40	70	715906	221	359165	1075070
ACCLAMATION (GB)	by Royal Applause (GB)	55	24	38	714179	100	345442	1059621
ROYAL APPLAUSE (GB)	by Waajib	159	63	93	724301	289	281901	1006203
DANSILI (GB)	by Danehill (USA)	110	56	85	605356	219	353328	958684
GREEN DESERT (USA)	by Danzig (USA)	117	52	84	570896	241	364392	935288
KINGMAMBO (USA)	by Mr Prospector (USA)	73	24	36	578343	111	337416	915759
MR GREELEY (USA)	by Gone West (USA)	22	12	18	656254	38	151559	807813
CADEAUX GENEREUX	by Young Generation	107	49	74	543466	183	256048	799514
CAPE CROSS (IRE)	by Green Desert (USA)	150	49	73	500621	225	280160	780781
INCHINOR (GB)BY AHONOORA	by Northern Dancer	71	22	39	559579	117	214058	773636
NIGHT SHIFT (USA)	by Danehill (USA)	87	39	63	565031	164	199026	764057
DANETIME (IRE)	by Danehill (USA)	127	48	75	349432	233	390799	740231
INVINCIBLE SPIRIT (IRE)	by Green Desert (USA)	102	37	53	431223	145	308007	739230
KYLLACHY (GB)	by Pivotal (GB)	107	38	54	533394	179	198399	731793
MEDICEAN (GB)	by Machiavellian (USA)	100	29	47	297610	125	421958	719568
NAMID (GB)	by Indian Ridge	135	48	68	477016	195	241549	718565
SELKIRK (USA)	by Sharpen Up	93	33	45	477561	145	232502	710063

LEADING SIRES OF 2007
(GREAT BRITAIN, IRELAND AND OVERSEAS)

STALLION	BREEDING	DOMESTIC WNRS	DOMESTIC WINS	WIN MONEY	OVERSEAS WNRS	OVERSEAS WINS	WIN MONEY	TOTAL
DANEHILL (USA)	by Danzig (USA)	54	81	2490463	43	68	1852428	4342890
GALILEO (IRE)	by Sadler's Wells (USA)	52	80	2459634	25	44	393089	2852723
SINGSPIEL (IRE)	by In The Wings	35	54	346913	64	104	2040016	2386928
MONTJEU (IRE)	by Sadler's Wells (USA)	47	61	1720197	41	64	581023	2301220
DANEHILL DANCER (IRE)	by Danehill (USA)	79	117	1380456	50	75	640086	2020542
SADLER'S WELLS (USA)	by Northern Dancer	58	93	1414011	33	42	530602	1944613
INDIAN RIDGE	by Ahonoora	31	47	1059583	27	46	607844	1667427
MARJU (IRE)	by Last Tycoon	25	39	190031	48	85	1368814	1558845
MACHIAVELLIAN (USA)	by Mr Prospector (USA)	35	55	341866	37	60	1129293	1471159
INVINCIBLE SPIRIT (IRE)	by Green Desert (USA)	37	53	431223	18	36	988329	1419552
DANSILI (GB)	by Danehill (USA)	56	85	605356	43	64	795779	1401135
PIVOTAL (GB)	by Polar Falcon (USA)	69	105	931062	27	46	390638	1321700
IN THE WINGS	by Sadler's Wells (USA)	40	70	715906	26	41	563989	1279895
MARTINO ALONSO (IRE)	by Marju (IRE)	1	3	446294	2	5	773422	1219716
FASLIYEV (USA)	by Nureyev (USA)	38	60	446304	66	117	714041	1160345
ROYAL APPLAUSE (GB)	by Waajib	63	93	724301	31	49	401334	1125635
CADEAUX GENEREUX	by Young Generation	48	74	543466	24	42	543060	1086526
ROCK OF GIBRALTAR (IRE)	by Danehill (USA)	37	52	519216	36	50	559020	1078236
BARATHEA (IRE)	by Sadler's Wells (USA)	30	39	336980	55	97	740639	1077619
KING'S BEST (USA)	by Kingmambo (USA)	45	63	430389	37	64	622460	1052850
INCHINOR (GB)	by Ahonoora	22	39	559979	35	61	453956	1013535
GRAND LODGE (USA)	by Chief's Crown	36	56	340158	41	72	658952	999110
SELKIRK (USA)	by Sharpen Up	33	45	477561	26	45	517479	995041
ZAMINDAR (USA)	by Gone West (USA)	12	18	56969	25	47	915689	972658
GREEN DESERT (USA)	by Danzig (USA)	52	84	570896	29	48	391987	962883

LEADING TWO-YEAR-OLD SIRES OF 2007 IN GREAT BRITAIN AND IRELAND

STALLION	BREEDING	RNRS	WNRS	WINS	WIN MONEY	PLACES	PLACE MONEY	TOTAL
GALILEO (IRE)	by Sadler's Wells (USA)	43	12	18	1112338	31	42073	1154410
†ACCLAMATION (GB)	by Royal Applause (GB)	55	24	38	714179	100	345442	1059621
DANEHILL DANCER (IRE)	by Danehill (USA)	49	22	31	413610	65	425205	833815
INDIAN RIDGE	by Ahonoora	13	3	4	681463	7	43327	724790
INVINCIBLE SPIRIT (IRE)	by Green Desert (USA)	46	17	25	253181	66	213345	466526
SADLER'S WELLS (USA)	by Northern Dancer	33	11	13	269946	30	160099	430045
MR GREELEY (USA)	by Gone West (USA)	12	5	7	271142	22	132139	403281
†OASIS DREAM (GB)	by Green Desert (USA)	54	19	26	180202	81	168884	349086
CHOISIR (AUS)	by Danehill Dancer (IRE)	57	21	28	198443	75	110345	308788
ROCK OF GIBRALTAR (IRE)	by Danehill (USA)	43	14	19	219552	48	81162	300715
KYLLACHY (GB)	by Pivotal (GB)	56	14	19	201150	70	93363	294513
NIGHT SHIFT (USA)	by Northern Dancer	22	7	7	226349	32	50681	277030
FASLIYEV (USA)	by Nureyev (USA)	50	15	23	183300	45	87082	270383
†DUBAI DESTINATION (USA)	by Kingmambo (USA)	50	12	18	210021	54	46510	256531
ROYAL APPLAUSE (GB)	by Waajib	49	22	31	156492	86	95570	252062
MUJADIL (USA)	by Storm Bird (CAN)	22	7	8	161839	26	86838	248677
†MODIGLIANI (USA)	by Danzig (USA)	14	3	5	122128	20	102366	224493
CAPE CROSS (IRE)	by Green Desert (USA)	55	20	26	167296	47	52986	220282
DESERT PRINCE (IRE)	by Green Desert (USA)	16	3	3	13926	16	200652	214577
STORM CAT (USA)	by Storm Bird (CAN)	14	8	9	158084	11	54643	212727
DR FONG (USA)	by Kris S (USA)	60	16	23	150856	42	57796	208652
†HAWK WING (USA)	by Woodman (USA)	59	19	19	112780	59	88783	201563
BERTOLINI (USA)	by Danzig (USA)	63	25	35	101215	87	93595	194809

† = indicates first crop sire

LEADING FIRST CROP SIRES OF 2007 IN GREAT BRITAIN AND IRELAND

STALLION	BREEDING	RNRS	WNRS	WINS	WIN MONEY	PLACES	PLACE MONEY	TOTAL
ACCLAMATION (GB)	by Royal Applause (GB)	55	24	38	714179	92	345442	1059634
OASIS DREAM (GB)	by Green Desert (USA)	54	19	26	180202	71	168884	349092
DUBAI DESTINATION (USA)	by Kingmambo (USA)	50	12	18	210021	51	46510	256535
MODIGLIANI (USA)	by Danzig (USA)	14	3	5	122128	19	102366	224495
HAWK WING (USA)	by Woodman (USA)	59	19	19	112780	54	88783	201568
CAPTAIN RIO (GB)	by Pivotal (GB)	75	24	27	113651	90	69816	183478
CLODOVIL (IRE)	by Danehill (USA)	25	11	16	147596	38	34744	182345
NAYEF (USA)	by Gulch (USA)	35	7	8	78238	17	45379	123619
STATUE OF LIBERTY (USA)	by Storm Cat (USA)	46	15	16	61819	48	49495	111322
DALAKHANI (IRE)	by Darshaan	18	8	9	56918	19	21776	78694
PROUD CITIZEN (USA)	by Gone West (USA)	5	3	4	51556	6	24959	76515
CHEVALIER (IRE)	by Danehill (USA)	18	6	8	43445	22	32321	75771
REEL BUDDY (USA)	by Mr Greeley (USA)	27	5	5	13188	24	59472	72662
SPARTACUS (IRE)	by Danehill (USA)	30	10	11	47152	31	18851	66005
CATCHER IN THE RYE (IRE)	by Danehill (USA)	24	8	10	46030	16	17572	63603
WHERE OR WHEN (IRE)	by Danehill Dancer (IRE)	22	2	2	9954	11	49438	59393
OKAWANGO (USA)	by Kingmambo (USA)	14	3	4	27397	9	24621	52019
HIGH CHAPARRAL (IRE)	by Sadler's Wells (USA)	18	2	2	10039	16	23231	33273
DOMEDRIVER (IRE)	by Indian Ridge	19	2	2	13111	21	13364	26477
STORMING HOME (GB)	by Machiavellian (USA)	12	5	5	13720	7	4607	17878
CARNIVAL DANCER (GB)	by Sadler's Wells (USA)	8	3	3	7877	13	5701	13579
KRIS KIN (USA)	by Kris S (USA)	8	3	3	7064	5	4159	11224
HARLAN'S HOLIDAY (USA)	by Harlan (USA)	3	2	2	7125	2	1825	8950
WISEMAN'S FERRY (USA)	by Hennessy (USA)	2	1	2	4297	3	1425	5723
HOLD THAT TIGER (USA)	by Storm Cat (USA)	7	0	0	0	9	5590	5590

LEADING MATERNAL GRANDSIRES OF 2007 IN GREAT BRITAIN AND IRELAND

STALLION	BREEDING	RNRS	WNRS	WINS	WIN MONEY	PLACES	PLACE MONEY	TOTAL
SADLER'S WELLS (USA)	by Northern Dancer	263	90	126	1832491	368	1378902	3211393
DARSHAAN	by Shirley Heightsby Sharpen Up	230	88	137	1491204	322	1318003	2809208
DIESIS	by Shirley Heightsby Sharpen Up	104	41	54	1539420	116	466021	2005441
MACHIAVELLIAN (USA)	by Mr Prospector (USA)	101	45	60	1277874	142	206198	1484072
ROYAL ACADEMY (USA)	by Nijinsky (CAN)	141	45	68	805024	207	508981	1314006
CADEAUX GENEREUX	by Young Generation	156	46	70	858296	256	346782	1205078
SAUMAREZ	by Rainbow Quest (USA)	8	2	4	1094380	5	103699	1198079
INDIAN RIDGE	by Ahonoora	130	46	74	610209	209	530703	1140912
SHIRLEY HEIGHTS	by Mill Reef (USA)	121	34	53	609955	191	368353	978308
DANEHILL (USA)	by Danzig (USA)	156	54	81	537533	248	396232	933765
NIGHT SHIFT (USA)	by Northern Dancer	185	67	103	502728	292	402699	905427
RAINBOW QUEST (USA)	by Blushing Groom (FR)	163	47	65	489966	202	389443	879409
CAERLEON (USA)	by Nijinsky (CAN)	159	58	69	472407	209	377148	849554
WOODMAN (USA)	by Mr Prospector (USA)	137	41	61	484247	194	341064	825312
SELKIRK (USA)	by Sharpen Up	96	37	50	521359	150	294353	815712
GREEN DESERT (USA)	by Danzig (USA)	167	64	97	444555	307	369900	814455
WARNING	by Known Fact (USA)	100	41	65	436302	184	329096	765398
NASHWAN (USA)	by Blushing Groom (FR)	106	31	47	435161	129	304157	739318
MR PROSPECTOR (USA)	by Raise A Native	93	40	59	439958	127	293962	733920
ANABAA (USA)	by Danzig (USA)	26	6	7	687693	38	34901	722595
ERINS ISLE	by Busted	5	2	4	619347	7	45876	665223
THATCHING	by Thatching (USA)	70	20	27	423703	120	202551	626254
PERSIAN BOLD	by Bold Lad (IRE)	117	38	62	405389	181	204414	609803
BE MY GUEST (USA)	by Northern Dancer	87	21	36	394228	118	212745	606973

FLAT STALLIONS' EARNINGS FOR 2007

(includes every stallion who sired a winner on the flat in Great Britain and Ireland in 2007)

STALLIONS	RNRS	STARTS	WNRS	WINS	PLACES	TOTAL
ABOU ZOUZ (USA)	5	37	1	1	12	12431.35
ACAMBARO (GER)	3	22	1	4	6	19266.43
ACATENANGO (GER)	12	44	3	3	11	17215.95
ACCLAMATION (GB)	55	282	24	38	100	1059620.95
ACT ONE (GB)	36	155	17	20	37	257184.65
AFFIRMED (USA)	2	8	1	1	3	6868.36
AFTERNOON DEELITES (USA)	1	11	1	2	1	4066.40
AGNES WORLD (USA)	30	158	9	15	32	75118.66
AIR EXPRESS (IRE)	1	7	1	1	1	2667.06
ALDEBARAN (USA)	4	8	1	1	1	5087.83
ALHAARTH (IRE)	93	414	21	30	118	275441.80
ALI-ROYAL (IRE)	6	46	1	3	10	14631.95
ALJABR (USA)	17	83	7	8	29	96399.79
ALLIED FORCES (USA)	8	64	3	4	12	28771.23
ALMATY (IRE)	4	40	2	6	15	34716.53
ALMUSHTARAK (IRE)	5	36	2	5	7	14467.14
ALMUTAWAKEL (GB)	29	177	10	16	52	139534.42
ALZAO (USA)	28	106	8	12	30	346047.73
AMONG MEN (USA)	6	21	1	1	4	10099.70
ANABAA (USA)	44	183	14	19	49	252364.17
ANITA'S PRINCE	4	32	1	2	3	6143.46
ANSHAN	4	20	1	1	8	48967.50
APTITUDE (USA)	5	17	3	4	8	22619.84
ARAGON	4	26	1	1	8	5708.84
ARCH (USA)	12	54	6	6	15	236098.18
ARKADIAN HERO (USA)	17	91	5	10	14	35907.81
ASHKALANI (IRE)	15	71	3	4	22	24616.40
ATRAF (GB)	50	326	16	32	89	245716.43
AUCTION HOUSE (USA)	58	316	10	13	82	97850.49
AVERTI (IRE)	100	544	33	37	143	249857.40
AWESOME AGAIN (CAN)	1	9	1	1	7	8120.94
BACH (IRE)	3	17	2	2	5	18291.55
BACHIR (IRE)	3	10	1	4	1	14219.35
BAD AS I WANNA BE (IRE)	5	29	1	1	8	8243.67
BAHAMIAN BOUNTY (GB)	101	621	30	53	204	446254.51
BAHHARE (USA)	36	243	14	23	60	152708.00
BAHRI (USA)	40	172	10	15	34	123889.98
BALLA COVE	2	8	1	1	0	14735.47
BARATHEA (IRE)	117	599	30	39	175	585215.16
BARATHEA GUEST (GB)	3	21	1	1	5	6200.25
BASANTA (IRE)	3	7	1	1	2	4681.08
BEAT ALL (USA)	9	53	5	5	19	24542.96
BEAT HOLLOW (GB)	27	120	10	14	39	85777.10
BECKETT (IRE)	26	84	4	4	2	13612.78
BEHRENS (USA)	1	2	1	1	0	2266.95
BELONG TO ME (USA)	5	33	3	6	10	48331.19
BE MY GUEST (USA)	7	40	1	2	13	26203.12
BENNY THE DIP (USA)	14	64	5	6	15	67350.82
BERING	14	58	4	7	19	37153.14
BERTOLINI (USA)	136	845	54	94	218	611414.73
BEST OF THE BESTS (IRE)	38	202	10	10	62	77261.15
BEVELED (USA)	6	64	5	6	16	25283.06
BIANCONI (USA)	3	19	1	1	4	5424.91
BIEN BIEN (USA)	9	79	3	5	21	31337.56
BIG SHUFFLE (USA)	12	51	1	3	12	28380.65
BIGSTONE (IRE)	5	39	3	4	6	48358.63
BIJOU D'INDE (GB)	5	19	1	2	2	5921.70
BIN AJWAAD (IRE)	6	51	3	4	11	78487.64
BISHOP OF CASHEL (GB)	11	49	2	3	11	19409.14
BLACK MINNALOUSHE (USA)	12	63	4	7	13	101331.94

STALLIONS	RNRS	STARTS	WNRS	WINS	PLACES	TOTAL
BLACK SAM BELLAMY (IRE)	2	6	1	1	0	2914.65
BLUEBIRD (USA)	23	150	6	9	43	120917.57
BLUEGRASS PRINCE (IRE)	9	59	4	8	11	35822.34
BLUE OCEAN (USA)	8	45	2	2	12	30399.64
BLUES TRAVELLER (IRE)	4	19	1	2	5	15890.05
BLUSHING FLAME (USA)	1	5	1	2	2	11063.70
BOB BACK (USA)	4	7	1	1	4	8779.73
BOB'S RETURN (IRE)	1	11	1	1	2	3245.25
BOLD EDGE (GB)	30	189	8	16	39	116824.74
BOLD FACT (USA)	37	189	13	16	38	123803.27
BOTANIC (USA)	2	9	1	1	2	2492.85
BOUNDARY (USA)	5	33	1	1	10	11662.88
BRAVE ACT (GB)	9	39	2	3	6	35560.16
BRIEF TRUCE (USA)	10	66	3	4	16	44576.28
BROCCO (USA)	1	6	1	1	2	7153.60
BUBBLE GUM FELLOW (JPN)	1	8	1	1	4	3666.34
BUDDHA (USA)	3	16	1	1	5	5869.71
BUSY FLIGHT (GB)	1	4	1	1	1	2313.14
CADEAUX GENEREUX	107	628	48	74	183	799513.73
CAERLEON (USA)	5	27	1	1	5	10116.32
CAPE CROSS (IRE)	150	702	49	73	225	780780.81
CAPTAIN RIO (GB)	75	355	24	27	93	183467.16
CARNEGIE (IRE)	1	7	1	1	2	3154.95
CARNIVAL DANCER (GB)	8	43	3	3	13	13577.51
CARSON CITY (USA)	4	16	2	4	5	91754.00
CASE LAW	6	50	2	2	8	12711.26
CATCHER IN THE RYE (IRE)	24	87	8	10	17	63601.90
CATIENUS (USA)	3	22	1	2	11	15451.37
CATRAIL (USA)	7	38	2	4	6	11356.78
CAT THIEF (USA)	1	4	1	1	2	3375.55
CAYMAN KAI (IRE)	12	85	2	2	20	16242.36
CELTIC SWING (GB)	40	221	15	18	75	280143.85
CHARNWOOD FOREST (IRE)	16	86	3	4	20	29953.14
CHEROKEE RUN (USA)	4	20	1	3	7	15340.08
CHESTER HOUSE (USA)	16	80	9	19	27	160606.38
CHEVALIER (IRE)	18	86	6	8	24	57766.04
CHOISIR (AUS)	57	242	21	28	75	308787.87
CIGAR	2	26	2	4	7	14192.48
CITY ON A HILL (USA)	32	191	7	10	44	60779.63
CLAN OF ROSES (GB)	4	34	1	1	4	5505.16
CLANTIME	5	35	1	1	5	3613.25
CLASSIC CLICHE (IRE)	5	19	1	1	5	21973.55
CLODOVIL (IRE)	25	127	11	16	41	182340.05
CLOUDINGS (IRE)	13	48	1	1	7	6026.48
COIS NA TINE (IRE)	5	30	1	2	7	14038.11
COLLEGE CHAPEL (GB)	12	90	4	10	20	75467.72
COMMON GROUNDS	5	63	1	1	23	20763.58
COMPTON ADMIRAL (GB)	12	53	2	3	11	14956.96
COMPTON PLACE (GB)	121	878	40	68	252	525990.90
CORONADO'S QUEST (USA)	4	17	2	2	2	7331.95
COZZENE (USA)	18	79	9	14	17	84852.47
CRAFTY PROSPECTOR (USA)	3	26	1	1	8	5956.12
CROCO ROUGE (IRE)	5	18	2	3	3	21132.03
CROWN JESTER (AUS)	1	10	1	2	0	4095.00
CRYPTOCLEARANCE (USA)	5	47	2	3	6	22842.62
CYRANO DE BERGERAC	6	25	1	1	4	8873.17
DAAWE (USA)	2	23	1	2	10	25729.35
DAGGERS DRAWN (USA)	67	349	22	40	68	211265.02
DALAKHANI (IRE)	18	43	8	9	19	78694.31
DANCING SPREE (USA)	6	54	4	8	17	74675.29
DANEHILL (USA)	113	560	54	81	189	3748892.13
DANEHILL DANCER (IRE)	193	977	79	117	305	2291959.36
DANETIME (IRE)	127	765	48	75	233	740231.27
DANSILI (GB)	110	690	56	85	219	958684.26

STALLIONS	RNRS	STARTS	WNRS	WINS	PLACES	TOTAL
DANZERO (AUS)	12	106	7	13	25	138695.39
DANZIG (USA)	21	117	10	17	36	313718.13
DANZIG CONNECTION (USA)	10	69	3	6	19	26295.52
DARNAY (GB)	9	45	3	9	11	38629.79
DARSHAAN	17	83	4	7	32	118696.89
DASHING BLADE	9	28	1	2	5	15421.94
DAYJUR (USA)	4	48	1	1	8	4970.44
DAYLAMI (IRE)	87	375	28	38	111	327904.75
DEFINITE ARTICLE (GB)	29	106	8	9	22	104467.71
DELTA DANCER (GB)	4	28	1	2	10	11842.84
DEPLOY	10	47	2	4	12	71874.33
DEPUTY MINISTER (CAN)	1	2	1	1	1	3250.39
DESERT KING (IRE)	20	105	7	10	37	175401.20
DESERT PRINCE (IRE)	99	571	35	51	165	591105.26
DESERT STORY (IRE)	30	186	7	12	53	71355.47
DESERT STYLE (IRE)	72	403	26	44	102	303223.98
DESERT SUN (GB)	49	397	22	31	100	293577.53
DIESIS	44	192	17	22	70	333040.12
DIKTAT (GB)	171	940	50	70	293	580337.42
DILSHAAN (GB)	16	90	5	6	23	33484.97
DISTANT MUSIC (USA)	52	287	13	17	71	118006.98
DISTANT RELATIVE	4	24	2	3	5	7535.18
DISTANT VIEW (USA)	27	116	6	7	32	42663.50
DISTINCTLY NORTH (USA)	3	8	1	1	1	3945.84
DISTORTED HUMOR (USA)	10	34	5	5	12	38090.98
DIVINE LIGHT (JPN)	1	1	1	1	0	102601.46
DIXIELAND BAND (USA)	9	41	3	5	16	56810.69
DIXIE UNION (USA)	10	47	4	4	12	36668.75
DOCKSIDER (USA)	29	176	10	19	52	177615.49
DOLPHIN STREET (FR)	10	85	5	8	21	40580.37
DOMEDRIVER (IRE)	19	77	2	3	21	26474.75
DONERAILE COURT (USA)	5	14	2	7	5	43506.29
DOUBLE TRIGGER (IRE)	6	18	2	2	1	7380.21
DOYOUN	2	12	2	2	5	16679.30
DR DEVIOUS (IRE)	15	53	3	5	10	46838.39
DREAMS END (GB)	3	17	1	1	5	4761.70
DR FONG (USA)	140	628	40	57	157	499716.62
DR MASSINI (IRE)	5	17	2	2	2	15179.72
DUBAI DESTINATION (USA)	50	176	12	18	54	256531.35
DUBAI MILLENNIUM (GB)	3	8	1	1	4	35799.30
DUSHYANTOR (USA)	4	12	1	1	3	15831.57
DYNAFORMER (USA)	21	73	7	10	28	579620.83
EAGLE EYED (USA)	10	63	4	8	17	81010.35
E DUBAI (USA)	2	3	1	1	0	4857.75
EFISIO	64	429	27	44	106	402112.89
ELA-MANA-MOU	4	15	2	2	6	13980.19
EL CORREDOR (USA)	3	12	1	1	4	8412.25
ELMAAMUL (USA)	14	79	2	3	14	38260.26
ELNADIM (USA)	60	322	16	29	99	369943.59
EL PRADO (IRE)	10	33	4	5	10	103469.16
ELUSIVE QUALITY (USA)	38	171	13	19	57	205185.22
EMARATI (USA)	6	42	2	4	7	13093.67
EMPEROR FOUNTAIN	3	30	1	1	7	10045.30
EMPEROR JONES (USA)	8	56	5	6	14	50017.26
ENTREPRENEUR (GB)	20	126	9	13	31	86224.14
ENVIRONMENT FRIEND (GB)	3	18	1	1	5	6903.45
ERHAAB (USA)	30	160	5	6	53	57903.20
FANTASTIC LIGHT (USA)	95	424	33	43	136	425545.62
FASLIYEV (USA)	140	733	38	60	186	650456.37
FATH (USA)	49	281	15	22	80	195771.23
FAVORITE TRICK (USA)	1	9	1	3	2	36155.07
FAYRUZ	36	253	11	17	74	118116.25
FIRST TRUMP (GB)	25	160	7	15	32	57982.50
FLEETWOOD (IRE)	15	58	3	3	10	16851.51

STALLIONS	RNRS	STARTS	WNRS	WINS	PLACES	TOTAL
FLYING SPUR (AUS)	11	55	2	4	15	65796.91
FLY TO THE STARS (GB)	1	12	1	2	5	12698.85
FORESTRY (USA)	7	13	1	1	3	4647.52
FOREST WILDCAT (USA)	13	48	6	8	16	41792.83
FORZANDO	38	197	9	11	33	47725.07
FOURSTARS ALLSTAR (USA)	4	12	1	1	3	6801.01
FOXHOUND (USA)	63	409	17	25	116	181802.34
FRAAM (GB)	68	316	15	23	66	171682.63
FRUITS OF LOVE (USA)	41	216	12	15	67	153341.48
FUMO DI LONDRA (IRE)	4	20	1	1	6	3799.80
FUSAICHI PEGASUS (USA)	22	87	6	8	32	74844.69
GALILEO (IRE)	117	418	52	80	145	2937960.39
GENERAL MONASH (USA)	11	63	1	1	13	9272.07
GENEROUS (IRE)	31	186	16	27	71	234899.39
GERMANY (USA)	3	8	1	1	4	7595.93
GHAZI (USA)	3	23	2	3	8	40710.49
GIANT'S CAUSEWAY (USA)	61	248	22	26	59	337403.29
GILDED TIME (USA)	3	42	2	6	22	40735.00
GLORY OF DANCER (GB)	2	20	1	1	7	10176.49
GOLAN (IRE)	36	179	11	16	52	148808.25
GOLD AWAY (IRE)	6	33	2	5	11	71344.46
GOLDEN SNAKE (USA)	18	95	6	6	29	34153.60
GOLDMARK (USA)	7	34	2	3	10	22431.14
GONE WEST (USA)	13	50	3	3	19	35175.17
GORSE (GB)	6	19	3	3	4	10163.03
GOTHENBERG (IRE)	3	13	1	1	3	6912.25
GRAND LODGE (USA)	118	595	36	56	138	551754.45
GRAND SLAM (USA)	22	109	5	5	38	59998.47
GREAT COMMOTION (USA)	5	23	1	1	8	8064.32
GREAT DANE (IRE)	3	22	1	2	2	6048.25
GREEN DESERT (USA)	117	644	52	84	241	935287.76
GREY DESIRE	4	19	1	1	2	2331.80
GROOM DANCER (USA)	52	210	10	14	51	93756.80
GULCH (USA)	26	117	6	13	29	117334.70
HALLING (USA)	82	417	26	45	138	569305.73
HAMAS (IRE)	6	43	1	1	6	6883.01
HANDSOME RIDGE (GB)	1	11	1	2	3	5900.14
HARLAN'S HOLIDAY (USA)	3	10	2	2	3	8950.42
HAWK WING (USA)	59	209	19	19	59	201562.72
HECTOR PROTECTOR (USA)	2	10	1	1	4	11657.50
HENNESSY (USA)	12	35	2	2	8	24303.86
HERNANDO (FR)	63	252	24	34	73	325952.39
HIGH CHAPARRAL (IRE)	18	55	2	2	19	33270.45
HIGH ESTATE	6	28	3	4	4	14057.65
HIGHEST HONOR (FR)	18	76	7	8	26	74350.35
HIGH YIELD (USA)	12	47	1	2	4	5813.76
HOLY BULL (USA)	1	2	1	1	1	4044.50
HONOUR AND GLORY (USA)	2	9	1	1	1	5111.70
HORSE CHESTNUT (SAF)	7	28	1	1	8	8505.94
HOUSEBUSTER (USA)	2	16	1	1	7	24105.99
HUNTING LION (IRE)	17	88	7	10	24	56766.79
HURRICANE SKY (AUS)	3	32	1	2	14	11193.96
HUSSONET (USA)	4	16	3	4	6	17921.68
IHTIRAM (IRE)	1	2	1	1	0	121259.38
IMPERIAL BALLET (IRE)	62	350	17	21	90	153902.68
INCHINOR (GB)	71	395	22	39	117	773636.44
IN COMMAND (IRE)	3	4	1	1	1	2201.42
INDIAN DANEHILL (IRE)	42	232	12	22	52	117888.56
INDIAN LODGE (IRE)	29	172	10	13	49	84835.78
INDIAN RIDGE	83	431	31	47	128	1295626.50
INDIAN ROCKET (GB)	18	135	9	14	23	66912.14
IN THE WINGS	102	573	40	70	221	1075070.46
INTIKHAB (USA)	67	340	27	41	91	628972.32
INVINCIBLE SPIRIT (IRE)	102	507	37	53	145	739230.49

STALLIONS	RNRS	STARTS	WNRS	WINS	PLACES	TOTAL
IRISH RIVER (FR)	4	16	1	1	11	6965.37
IRON MASK (USA)	55	277	11	14	51	74514.33
ISHIGURU (USA)	37	257	18	27	82	242153.97
JADE HUNTER (USA)	1	4	1	1	0	2184.00
JADE ROBBERY (USA)	23	121	10	14	35	112568.20
JOHANNESBURG (USA)	45	161	12	14	47	153298.13
JOSR ALGARHOUD (IRE)	75	458	17	29	102	177502.08
KABOOL (GB)	3	19	2	3	6	31690.69
KAFWAIN (USA)	1	3	1	1	0	2968.87
KAHYASI	16	79	7	15	28	156825.54
KALANISI (IRE)	42	157	11	17	50	214993.40
KALDOUNEVEES (FR)	3	10	1	1	0	2047.50
KASAKOV (GB)	2	6	1	1	0	2047.50
KAYF TARA (GB)	11	52	2	3	14	21679.33
KELTOS (FR)	7	52	3	4	22	77475.56
KENDOR (FR)	4	9	2	2	2	225808.96
KEY OF LUCK (USA)	69	353	18	27	76	176542.20
KILLER INSTINCT (GB)	11	55	1	1	8	6150.74
KING CHARLEMAGNE (USA)	58	279	14	18	59	103125.34
KINGMAMBO (USA)	73	294	24	36	111	915758.88
KING OF KINGS (IRE)	7	46	1	2	6	9510.33
KING'S BEST (USA)	133	593	45	63	176	707789.82
KING'S SIGNET (USA)	3	30	2	3	9	111299.55
KING'S THEATRE (IRE)	31	132	5	8	25	82671.74
KIRKWALL (GB)	5	24	1	1	10	28484.15
KOMAITE (USA)	30	237	11	18	59	169739.26
KORNADO (GB)	2	6	1	1	2	5738.08
KRIS	8	37	2	4	8	30240.73
KRIS KIN (USA)	8	26	3	3	5	11222.75
KRIS S (USA)	5	19	2	3	5	24358.38
KUTUB (IRE)	1	3	1	1	2	18516.90
KYLIAN (USA)	5	32	2	3	11	16959.15
KYLLACHY (GB)	107	610	38	54	179	731793.25
LABEEB (GB)	4	27	1	1	9	15225.33
LAHIB (USA)	23	105	5	5	15	25303.06
LAKE CONISTON (IRE)	29	195	10	20	41	126972.07
LANDO (GER)	7	27	1	1	9	52061.32
LANGFUHR (CAN)	9	31	3	5	8	45281.21
LARGESSE (GB)	11	66	2	3	17	31194.84
LEAR FAN (USA)	13	69	3	3	21	47913.64
LEAR SPEAR (USA)	7	30	1	1	8	5407.79
LEMON DROP KID (USA)	21	79	7	9	36	120687.14
LEND A HAND (GB)	42	208	11	15	37	89256.27
LIL'S BOY (USA)	31	120	4	8	27	105253.52
LIMNOS (JPN)	3	15	1	3	4	18812.35
LIMPID (GB)	1	11	1	2	1	4836.00
LINAMIX (FR)	32	103	5	6	27	81800.52
LION CAVERN (USA)	6	57	1	1	14	16874.66
LLANDAFF (USA)	1	6	1	2	0	3707.35
LOMITAS (GB)	43	219	16	25	73	372506.92
LORD OF MEN (GB)	3	24	2	3	4	17828.26
LOUP SAUVAGE (USA)	6	45	3	4	14	25615.67
LUCKY GUEST	3	8	1	1	3	20753.03
LUGANA BEACH	10	68	2	3	11	14469.31
LUHUK (USA)	3	10	1	1	1	4752.00
LUJAIN (USA)	67	470	26	39	136	254967.99
LURE (USA)	4	33	2	4	7	13926.40
LYCIUS (USA)	6	47	3	5	16	34950.72
MACHIAVELLIAN (USA)	81	483	35	55	140	538496.03
MAGIC RING (IRE)	20	195	11	21	57	136528.93
MAKBUL	27	166	8	15	30	87824.48
MALIBU MOON (USA)	4	10	1	1	3	4289.00
MAMALIK (USA)	4	41	2	2	7	8532.12
MARATHON (USA)	3	20	1	2	6	8562.45

STALLIONS	RNRS	STARTS	WNRS	WINS	PLACES	TOTAL
MARJU (IRE)	74	370	25	39	100	379618.53
MARK OF ESTEEM (IRE)	107	596	35	54	187	513720.77
MARTINO ALONSO (IRE)	1	4	1	3	1	489333.63
MATTY G (USA)	1	9	1	1	4	8477.62
MEDAALY (GB)	8	39	3	3	10	13646.70
MEDECIS (GB)	4	16	1	1	3	5470.51
MEDICEAN (GB)	100	452	29	47	125	719567.98
MENIFEE (USA)	2	7	1	1	5	16963.52
MERDON MELODY	2	13	1	2	4	24871.60
MIDHISH (GB)	5	22	2	2	4	7348.23
MIGHTY (USA)	1	20	1	3	5	11271.32
MILLKOM (GB)	12	71	4	7	24	37866.53
MINARDI (USA)	6	32	2	2	7	14423.88
MIND GAMES (GB)	51	364	18	30	86	179088.92
MISTER BAILEYS (GB)	24	143	9	17	48	144834.97
MISWAKI (USA)	10	60	4	7	14	31214.53
MIZZEN MAST (USA)	14	47	7	8	15	46549.50
MODIGLIANI (USA)	14	69	3	5	20	224493.42
MONARCHOS (USA)	4	20	2	2	0	5286.00
MONASHEE MOUNTAIN (USA)	58	334	19	26	88	278541.20
MONSAGEM (USA)	1	2	1	1	1	47675.68
MONSUN (GER)	11	35	5	8	17	347305.20
MONTJEU (IRE)	136	513	47	61	180	2376295.87
MON TRESOR	2	16	1	2	7	29989.09
MORE THAN READY (USA)	13	52	5	5	18	45100.47
MOST WELCOME	21	160	8	12	43	100129.73
MOZART (IRE)	30	194	12	18	58	374396.27
MR GREELEY (USA)	22	89	12	18	38	807813.30
MT LIVERMORE (USA)	9	62	2	3	14	25265.68
MTOTO	39	151	10	15	35	99185.54
MUHTARRAM (USA)	27	123	4	6	21	35569.88
MUHTATHIR (GB)	5	20	1	1	7	74786.13
MUJADIL (USA)	80	577	27	37	146	684586.49
MUJAHID (USA)	78	448	31	49	111	383639.79
MUJTAHID (USA)	1	6	1	1	2	24797.29
MUKADDAMAH (USA)	3	22	2	2	3	8534.88
MULL OF KINTYRE (USA)	99	475	20	29	98	217561.52
MUTAKDDIM (USA)	2	2	1	1	0	2047.50
MUTAMAM (GB)	3	22	1	1	5	5433.60
MY BEST VALENTINE (GB)	3	31	2	2	14	12413.26
NAMAQUALAND (USA)	14	74	4	4	23	23304.65
NAMID (GB)	135	745	48	68	195	718564.94
NASHWAN (USA)	20	109	5	9	26	55055.23
NAYEF (USA)	35	66	7	8	19	123617.40
NIGHT SHIFT (USA)	87	577	39	63	164	764057.23
NOT FOR LOVE (USA)	1	6	1	1	0	4807.20
NOVERRE (USA)	84	444	27	34	134	455089.84
OASIS DREAM (GB)	54	198	19	26	81	349085.98
OBSERVATORY (USA)	69	326	21	29	72	173349.54
OCTAGONAL (NZ)	6	16	1	2	6	63323.80
OFFICER (USA)	9	39	2	2	7	27412.38
OKAWANGO (USA)	14	35	3	4	10	52018.45
OLDEN TIMES (GB)	6	16	1	1	2	4611.19
OLD VIC	5	15	1	3	4	29802.70
OPENING VERSE (USA)	6	42	1	1	13	11918.52
ORIENTATE (USA)	5	26	2	2	10	15954.30
ORPEN (USA)	108	599	34	48	138	422513.32
OSCAR (IRE)	13	20	2	2	5	18755.79
OVERBURY (IRE)	13	48	3	4	12	56902.21
PARADE MARSHAL (USA)	1	9	1	2	3	6788.50
PARIS HOUSE (GB)	23	150	7	11	26	85974.89
PEINTRE CELEBRE (USA)	56	259	17	25	86	385519.05
PELDER (IRE)	2	10	1	2	4	13286.10
PENNEKAMP (USA)	16	76	3	6	13	25661.00

STALLIONS	RNRS	STARTS	WNRS	WINS	PLACES	TOTAL
PENTIRE (GB)	1	6	1	2	1	4971.53
PERPENDICULAR (GB)	2	13	1	1	4	3821.90
PERRYSTON VIEW (GB)	5	39	1	2	3	7184.74
PERUGINO (USA)	23	101	3	4	32	49976.80
PETARDIA (GB)	6	44	1	2	3	6327.59
PETONG	6	34	2	2	3	8040.80
PICCOLO (GB)	100	679	29	45	184	462869.82
PIPS PRIDE (GB)	1	13	1	1	3	3080.89
PISTOLET BLEU (IRE)	5	16	1	1	1	10199.36
PIVOTAL (GB)	148	738	69	105	257	1525234.86
PLATINI (GER)	3	7	1	1	1	4069.69
PLEASANT TAP (USA)	6	30	1	2	11	10386.56
POINT GIVEN (USA)	5	25	2	3	4	14938.80
POLAR FALCON (USA)	22	147	8	12	32	143244.52
POLAR PRINCE (IRE)	14	93	5	8	29	65373.71
POLIGLOTE (GB)	4	18	1	3	4	9831.34
POLISH PRECEDENT (USA)	53	256	9	14	48	112414.30
POMPEII COURT (USA)	1	8	1	1	1	2652.00
PRESENTING (GB)	2	8	1	1	2	3169.45
PRESIDIUM	11	101	4	9	14	27857.16
PRIMO DOMINIE	17	129	7	9	30	62261.21
PRIMO VALENTINO (IRE)	40	216	12	21	58	129391.14
PRINCELY HEIR (IRE)	23	148	6	12	35	67015.41
PRINCE SABO	15	108	7	10	24	59988.67
PRIOLO (USA)	11	56	4	5	13	31027.77
PRIZED (USA)	1	4	1	2	0	7772.40
PROFESSIONAL (IRE)	1	12	1	1	6	14347.85
PROUD CITIZEN (USA)	5	23	3	4	7	76515.20
PULPIT (USA)	5	8	2	2	1	11954.70
PURSUIT OF LOVE (GB)	44	306	17	24	78	232728.18
PYRAMUS (USA)	4	41	2	3	14	17061.73
QUIET AMERICAN (USA)	4	20	1	2	6	12857.96
QUWS (GB)	5	24	2	2	4	8455.73
RAHY (USA)	40	178	19	34	62	395808.06
RAINBOW QUEST (USA)	55	211	20	26	68	187665.92
RAISE A GRAND (IRE)	35	173	8	11	38	65087.00
RAPHANE (USA)	6	37	2	6	8	27610.10
REDBACK (GB)	48	268	18	24	69	173166.12
RED RANSOM (USA)	80	312	30	42	103	543825.51
RED SUNSET	2	3	1	1	0	3968.58
REEL BUDDY (USA)	27	109	5	5	26	72659.78
REVOQUE (IRE)	21	128	4	7	31	177998.39
RICHTER SCALE (USA)	1	3	1	1	0	2388.75
RIVERWISE (USA)	1	2	1	2	0	5596.50
ROBELLINO (USA)	34	153	5	7	38	57743.88
ROBERTICO (GB)	1	7	1	1	1	3500.00
ROCK CITY	10	58	4	5	5	17320.58
ROCK OF GIBRALTAR (IRE)	97	433	37	52	157	1404639.38
ROI NORMAND (USA)	1	9	1	1	2	7046.25
ROSSINI (USA)	56	279	11	18	55	117111.23
ROY (USA)	3	24	1	1	5	96986.55
ROYAL ABJAR (USA)	5	33	2	8	6	90609.56
ROYAL ACADEMY (USA)	26	113	7	10	19	141577.79
ROYAL ANTHEM (USA)	7	43	2	3	14	23987.93
ROYAL APPLAUSE (GB)	159	996	63	93	289	1006202.66
ROYAL DRAGON (USA)	1	3	1	1	1	2470.50
RUBIANO (USA)	1	5	1	2	2	7949.00
RUDIMENTARY (USA)	11	57	2	4	16	37189.58
SADDLERS' HALL (IRE)	11	32	1	2	4	15916.97
SADLER'S WELLS (USA)	157	554	58	93	179	2145056.33
SAFAWAN	5	44	2	3	18	24893.12
SAGACITY (FR)	1	4	1	1	1	2747.95
SAGAMIX (FR)	3	13	1	1	5	6822.98
SAHM (USA)	5	22	2	5	5	106297.39

STALLIONS	RNRS	STARTS	WNRS	WINS	PLACES	TOTAL
SAINT BALLADO (CAN)	1	11	1	1	4	14795.35
SAKHEE (USA)	38	165	15	26	60	563549.49
SANDPIT (BRZ)	2	22	1	3	2	8885.10
SANGLAMORE (USA)	3	31	2	6	9	18136.95
SECOND EMPIRE (IRE)	32	199	8	16	39	133973.90
SEEKING THE GOLD (USA)	24	92	13	17	28	99018.55
SELKIRK (USA)	93	416	33	45	145	710062.88
SESARO (USA)	6	34	1	2	7	9602.39
SHAHRASTANI (USA)	3	21	1	1	8	5328.46
SHERNAZAR	3	12	2	2	3	12407.44
SHINKO FOREST (IRE)	55	305	18	28	83	401928.63
SILVANO (GER)	2	13	1	1	7	69954.50
SILVER DEPUTY (CAN)	4	28	4	6	5	18209.78
SILVER HAWK (USA)	15	95	7	14	39	254598.16
SILVER PATRIARCH (IRE)	15	69	4	6	15	58163.60
SILVER WIZARD (IRE)	4	12	1	1	1	3444.30
SINGSPIEL (IRE)	100	469	35	54	155	503297.99
SINNDAR (IRE)	41	186	9	12	59	589884.35
SIR CAT (USA)	1	11	1	5	2	16746.94
SKY CLASSIC (CAN)	3	11	1	3	2	13805.41
SLIP ANCHOR	12	47	1	2	10	13507.30
SMART STRIKE (CAN)	6	27	3	4	9	68475.18
SMOKE GLACKEN (USA)	3	19	1	1	1	1899.90
SNURGE	2	10	1	1	5	17223.78
SONGANDAPRAYER (USA)	2	10	1	1	4	9287.55
SOVIET STAR (USA)	79	410	26	38	110	429896.19
SPARTACUS (IRE)	30	130	10	11	31	66002.47
SPECTRUM (IRE)	72	386	23	37	91	270197.17
SPINNING WORLD (USA)	46	245	21	37	77	338728.36
SRI PEKAN (USA)	17	80	5	9	16	104063.01
STARBOROUGH (GB)	7	32	3	5	10	26118.70
STATUE OF LIBERTY (USA)	46	164	15	16	52	111313.71
STERNKOENIG (IRE)	1	6	1	2	2	14714.30
STORM BOOT (USA)	1	9	1	1	6	9060.90
STORM CAT (USA)	32	110	14	17	28	303787.97
STORMIN FEVER (USA)	6	27	1	1	10	20751.17
STORMING HOME (GB)	12	27	5	5	7	17877.15
STORMY ATLANTIC (USA)	2	14	2	6	4	33241.56
STRAVINSKY (USA)	60	374	20	35	95	540992.95
STREET CRY (IRE)	27	89	6	7	27	189055.20
SUGARFOOT (GB)	12	53	2	2	6	7340.47
SUNDAY BREAK (JPN)	2	6	1	1	1	2413.12
SUNDAY SILENCE (USA)	4	24	3	3	2	22675.85
SUPERIOR PREMIUM (GB)	21	93	2	3	20	22279.64
SURE BLADE (USA)	7	58	1	2	9	15662.92
SWAIN (IRE)	19	84	10	13	22	95741.97
TACTICAL CAT (USA)	2	21	1	2	5	8545.74
TAGULA (IRE)	98	501	32	58	122	470045.32
TAKE RISKS (FR)	3	4	1	1	0	2817.49
TAKHLID (USA)	1	11	1	1	2	4428.75
TALE OF THE CAT (USA)	16	78	5	5	17	24459.87
TAMARISK (IRE)	5	19	1	1	5	4447.81
TAMURE (IRE)	5	42	2	2	17	21714.65
TECHNOLOGY (USA)	1	3	1	1	1	7818.92
TENBY (GB)	2	7	2	2	4	13096.99
TENDULKAR (USA)	20	77	2	4	15	36428.99
TERTULLIAN (USA)	5	26	2	2	3	8070.65
THEATRICAL (USA)	20	94	7	12	28	93084.57
THREE WONDERS (USA)	1	10	1	1	2	2601.90
THUNDER GULCH (USA)	8	43	3	5	10	26019.13
TIGER HILL (IRE)	10	27	2	2	9	11244.96
TIMELESS TIMES (USA)	12	75	2	3	15	16206.94
TIPSY CREEK (USA)	29	157	3	3	31	26854.97
TITUS LIVIUS (FR)	74	431	23	33	114	277639.40

STALLIONS	RNRS	STARTS	WNRS	WINS	PLACES	TOTAL
TOBOUGG (IRE)	98	509	28	43	129	391440.51
TOMBA (GB)	24	121	5	8	27	52731.20
TOP OF THE WORLD	1	6	1	1	2	2652.00
TORRENTIAL (USA)	1	1	1	1	0	11217.60
TRADITIONALLY (USA)	42	165	4	4	28	52391.70
TRANS ISLAND (GB)	56	323	14	24	94	288328.53
TREMPOLINO (USA)	11	61	3	5	19	33412.28
TRUE BRAVE (USA)	2	18	1	1	9	8321.60
TUMBLEWEED RIDGE (GB)	16	90	2	3	19	18440.96
TURBO SPEED	1	4	1	3	0	52637.10
TURTLE ISLAND (IRE)	20	83	3	4	22	25632.31
TWICE AS SHARP (GB)	1	9	1	1	1	2349.90
TWINING (USA)	1	17	1	1	4	4023.65
UNBRIDLED'S SONG (USA)	5	18	1	2	8	19621.44
UNFUWAIN (USA)	13	99	4	7	27	50835.69
UP AND AT 'EM (GB)	4	41	3	3	8	9289.37
VAL ROYAL (FR)	39	173	11	18	45	548982.42
VAN NISTELROOY (USA)	7	28	5	7	10	136075.63
VERGLAS (IRE)	13	51	3	3	11	29389.77
VETTORI (IRE)	74	413	22	34	97	198653.86
VICTORY GALLOP (CAN)	6	20	3	3	3	20223.70
VICTORY NOTE (USA)	25	171	11	18	53	122284.18
VIKING RULER (AUS)	9	29	2	2	8	15469.62
WADOOD (USA)	1	8	1	2	1	4699.50
WAKY NAO (GB)	5	44	3	4	6	28954.05
WAR CHANT (USA)	15	67	3	4	24	73647.55
WARNINGFORD (GB)	9	39	3	4	10	33771.49
WELDNAAS (USA)	3	19	1	1	2	5522.70
WHERE OR WHEN (IRE)	22	60	2	2	11	59392.38
WHITTINGHAM (IRE)	8	57	2	4	9	18061.60
WINNING GALLERY	1	11	1	2	5	15859.55
WISEMAN'S FERRY (USA)	2	8	1	2	3	5722.50
WITH APPROVAL (CAN)	5	19	4	5	3	14677.60
WIZARD KING (GB)	25	167	5	8	36	43570.79
WOLFHOUND (USA)	15	117	6	8	34	38333.69
WOODBOROUGH (USA)	23	124	4	5	19	25129.94
WOODMAN (USA)	18	81	5	7	16	28585.55
XAAR (GB)	97	461	27	35	121	522631.73
YANKEE GENTLEMAN (USA)	3	12	2	2	2	5505.50
ZAFONIC (USA)	50	302	15	19	98	186058.31
ZAHA (CAN)	34	203	11	12	40	56027.52
ZAMINDAR (USA)	37	188	12	18	50	118295.07
ZIETEN (USA)	2	16	1	1	4	9172.20
ZILZAL (USA)	35	205	11	12	51	86599.50
ZINAAD (GB)	1	3	1	1	1	12932.00

BY KIND PERMISSION OF WEATHERBYS

NH STALLIONS' EARNINGS FOR 2006/2007

(includes every stallion who sired a winner over jumps in Great Britain and Ireland in 2006/2007)

STALLIONS	RNRS	STARTS	WNRS	WINS	PLACES	TOTAL
AAHSAYLAD	21	61	1	2	13	28921.25
ACAMBARO (GER)	4	12	2	4	2	150160.79
ACATENANGO (GER)	22	93	9	12	40	175319.87
ACCONDY (IRE)	6	22	1	2	6	11043.64
ACCORDION	169	634	42	63	194	782949.00
ACTING BRAVE (GB)	3	15	1	1	5	6428.91
ADIEU AU ROI (IRE)	2	12	2	4	3	53684.77
AFFIRMED (USA)	3	15	1	2	2	8104.84
AFZAL	18	79	9	13	29	82216.81
AGENT BLEU (FR)	7	33	2	3	9	44277.73
AIR DISPLAY (USA)	4	18	1	1	3	4522.32
AJDAYT (USA)	3	20	1	1	10	29740.05
AJRAAS (USA)	8	33	1	1	7	17709.04
ALAMO BAY (USA)	4	18	1	2	9	26713.66
ALDERBROOK (GB)	81	297	27	43	79	423475.64
ALFLORA (IRE)	125	420	32	49	109	361240.74
ALHAARTH (IRE)	26	109	5	9	35	164874.30
ALHAATMI (GB)	1	8	1	3	1	30638.18
ALHIJAZ (GB)	8	33	2	2	12	17346.75
ALI-ROYAL (IRE)	14	65	4	5	16	27365.73
ALJABR (USA)	2	4	1	1	2	5757.40
ALKALDE (GER)	5	33	2	5	11	133092.75
ALLEGED (USA)	3	9	1	1	3	9356.20
ALLEGORIC (USA)	3	10	2	2	2	11137.61
ALLIED FORCES (USA)	4	18	1	1	5	6112.47
ALL MY DREAMS (IRE)	1	6	1	1	1	4515.18
ALMUTAWAKEL (GB)	6	23	3	3	7	20520.61
ALPHABATIM (USA)	30	96	4	8	17	40437.11
ALTOUNTASH	1	13	1	2	4	16374.50
ALWUHUSH (USA)	3	9	1	1	1	17141.89
ALYWAR (USA)	3	11	1	1	4	6690.45
ALZAO (USA)	26	110	12	13	34	180092.85
AMONG MEN (USA)	10	53	2	2	13	18414.78
ANABAA (USA)	17	71	3	4	15	30209.16
ANSHAN	190	643	37	44	169	633665.86
APELDOORN (FR)	3	9	1	1	5	24533.45
APRIL NIGHT (FR)	9	48	4	7	18	48350.15
APTITUDE (USA)	1	5	1	1	2	4720.44
ARCHITECT (USA)	1	5	1	1	2	19003.46
ARCHWAY (IRE)	5	30	3	5	9	221501.40
ARCTIC CIDER (USA)	7	30	2	3	8	78699.76
ARCTIC LORD	89	382	17	20	101	247117.65
ARISTOCRACY	20	69	2	3	13	34801.59
ART BLEU	3	12	1	1	2	11823.60
ARZANNI	19	50	4	4	15	36586.08
ASHKALANI (IRE)	16	30	2	2	9	12073.60
ASSESSOR (IRE)	6	19	3	6	2	171064.80
ASTARABAD (USA)	5	17	3	8	7	165073.09
ATRAF (GB)	20	73	5	7	14	51201.17
AVERTI (IRE)	5	20	1	1	4	6821.50
BABY TURK	12	41	3	3	16	44111.44
BACHIR (IRE)	4	28	2	3	6	17947.08
BADOLATO (USA)	1	6	1	1	3	7052.60
BAHHARE (USA)	34	154	12	21	47	167285.36
BAHRI (USA)	11	42	3	3	19	27450.51
BAKHAROFF (USA)	1	9	1	2	2	5540.72
BAL HARBOUR (GB)	13	36	3	3	9	21005.95

STALLIONS	RNRS	STARTS	WNRS	WINS	PLACES	TOTAL
BALLA COVE	8	30	2	3	1	35312.77
BALLEROY (USA)	4	12	1	2	1	11005.86
BALNIBARBI (GB)	3	10	2	2	1	24664.60
BANDMASTER (USA)	11	29	1	1	11	16653.80
BARATHEA (IRE)	44	160	8	10	47	79048.26
THE BART (USA)	3	15	1	3	5	27163.48
BASANTA (IRE)	8	40	2	3	15	34625.99
BATEAU ROUGE	2	12	2	4	3	26822.21
BEAT ALL (USA)	4	13	1	1	1	3466.89
BEAUCHAMP KING (GB)	5	19	1	1	1	4380.60
BEAU SHER	21	63	2	2	15	34133.90
BEAU ZAM (NZ)	1	7	1	1	2	6686.30
BELMEZ (USA)	2	6	1	2	2	24453.30
BE MY NATIVE (USA)	90	297	18	24	94	332309.06
BENEFICIAL (GB)	129	539	44	71	136	626333.85
BENNY THE DIP (USA)	22	71	4	6	16	41043.10
BERING	20	84	7	12	22	83227.77
BERTOLINI (USA)	6	13	1	1	3	4332.00
BEVELED (USA)	9	37	2	2	14	23022.14
BEYSSAC (FR)	12	47	6	11	16	102799.16
BIEN BIEN (USA)	12	48	4	6	25	82421.10
BIG SHUFFLE (USA)	9	26	2	3	7	54094.86
BIGSTONE (IRE)	23	92	10	14	26	190404.89
BIJOU D'INDE (GB)	11	38	2	2	6	9252.48
BIN AJWAAD (IRE)	7	18	1	2	3	11075.54
BISHOP OF CASHEL (GB)	9	29	1	1	7	8690.70
BLACK MONDAY	10	29	1	1	7	14813.07
BLUEBIRD (USA)	9	36	1	1	13	12040.65
BLUEGRASS PRINCE (IRE)	8	29	1	1	3	3831.93
BLUE OCEAN (USA)	10	23	1	1	5	11218.99
BLUES TRAVELLER (IRE)	13	44	2	3	9	20194.36
BLUSHING FLAME (USA)	6	30	3	7	7	34073.80
BOB BACK	137	488	42	48	131	434479.77
BOB'S RETURN (IRE)	68	258	12	18	78	196468.86
BOJADOR (FR)	1	9	1	1	5	12121.25
BOLD EDGE (GB)	5	19	2	4	6	31486.96
BOLD FACT (USA)	9	23	2	2	5	13334.91
BOLLIN WILLIAM (GB)	2	8	1	2	5	10791.45
BOSTON TWO STEP (USA)	3	14	1	3	2	18578.40
BOUNDARY (USA)	3	13	1	1	3	5886.47
BOYNE VALLEY	7	38	1	1	12	11101.80
BRAVE ACT (GB)	9	42	3	5	13	37804.01
BRAVEFOOT (GB)	15	42	2	2	10	11918.59
BRICASSAR (GB)	2	7	2	4	1	74710.10
BRIEF TRUCE (USA)	10	46	2	3	16	34460.82
BRIER CREEK (USA)	9	25	1	1	8	21019.15
BROADSWORD (USA)	6	12	1	1	1	13893.25
BROKEN HEARTED	63	242	8	12	54	119735.43
BUCKSKIN (FR)	10	26	2	2	4	13396.35
BULINGTON (FR)	9	48	4	7	21	75307.10
BUSTER KING	1	4	1	1	1	5134.44
BUSTINO	5	18	1	2	5	8586.70
BUSY FLIGHT (GB)	13	48	4	5	7	20149.15
CADEAUX GENEREUX	28	64	2	2	19	33528.73
CADOUBEL (FR)	2	9	1	2	6	23896.46
CADOUDAL (FR)	37	132	12	17	44	140026.72
CAERLEON (USA)	4	13	1	1	3	3639.50
CAJETANO (USA)	1	8	1	3	3	211966.92
CAMDEN TOWN	10	49	2	4	11	32726.97
CAPE CROSS (IRE)	18	50	2	3	18	40651.40
CAPOTE (USA)	2	14	1	1	7	17846.60
CARDINAL FLOWER	4	13	1	1	3	14753.80
CARLINGFORD CASTLE	6	23	2	3	8	36195.30
CARROLL HOUSE	76	300	17	24	66	267011.08
CASTLE KEEP	3	11	1	2	2	21814.49
CATALDI	4	22	1	2	5	18441.44

STALLIONS	RNRS	STARTS	WNRS	WINS	PLACES	TOTAL
CELIO RUFO	10	53	1	1	15	10201.99
CELTIC SWING (GB)	15	55	2	2	12	14717.74
CHADDLEWORTH (IRE)	7	27	2	3	3	15790.46
CHAMBERLIN (FR)	9	25	2	2	9	70648.45
CHARENTE RIVER (IRE)	11	40	1	1	10	9147.02
CHARMER	15	66	5	6	22	58667.02
CHARNWOOD FOREST (IRE)	30	113	6	8	26	55442.99
CHEF DE CLAN II (FR)	4	29	3	3	12	31651.61
CHESTER HOUSE (USA)	3	12	1	1	5	7500.99
CICERAO (IRE)	1	7	1	1	1	5177.25
CITY HONOURS (USA)	30	84	5	8	14	44755.71
CITY ON A HILL (USA)	6	25	2	2	7	12645.79
CLANTIME	2	10	2	3	4	11735.52
CLASSIC CLICHE (IRE)	91	354	25	36	100	276758.94
CLASSIC MEMORY	4	20	2	3	6	15229.07
CLEARLY BUST	2	17	2	5	5	424757.16
CLERKENWELL (USA)	8	32	1	1	6	12873.12
CLOUDINGS (IRE)	55	239	16	25	79	214331.32
COIS NA TINE (IRE)	5	13	1	1	2	3102.23
COLLEGE CHAPEL (GB)	8	56	2	2	15	19159.08
COLONEL COLLINS (USA)	2	11	1	1	3	5469.65
COMMANCHE RUN	49	172	8	10	37	97242.24
COMPTON ADMIRAL (GB)	4	13	1	2	2	8685.30
COMPTON PLACE (GB)	6	30	1	1	11	8781.85
CONVINCED	4	13	1	2	5	19148.37
CORROUGE (USA)	17	54	3	4	13	32725.80
COURTSHIP (GB)	14	45	2	4	11	24692.37
COZZENE (USA)	6	16	2	3	4	40807.33
CROCO ROUGE (IRE)	9	54	6	6	26	100424.53
CRUISE MISSILE	4	16	1	4	9	48093.35
CYBORG (FR)	27	120	11	20	41	204886.62
DADARISSIME (FR)	4	13	1	1	6	13622.29
DAGGERS DRAWN (USA)	16	48	4	5	13	31359.14
DANASINGA (AUS)	1	6	1	1	2	4568.00
DANCING HIGH	11	56	3	4	16	28756.88
DANEHILL (USA)	27	101	6	8	27	52634.38
DANEHILL DANCER (IRE)	40	123	8	12	31	96511.09
DANETIME (IRE)	10	35	1	2	8	15859.98
DANSILI (GB)	18	55	2	3	9	26921.00
DANSKE (NZ)	1	3	1	1	2	2914.60
DANZERO (AUS)	13	31	2	4	5	21021.12
DANZIG (USA)	2	8	2	3	3	16097.75
DANZIG CONNECTION (USA)	14	52	3	7	13	61662.80
DARAZARI (IRE)	39	123	6	9	28	51253.09
DARSHAAN	31	115	8	13	38	138295.52
DASHING BLADE	18	80	4	7	24	103481.51
DAYLAMI (IRE)	31	134	13	18	52	224258.72
DEAR DOCTOR (FR)	3	14	1	1	3	4139.42
DEEP SOCIETY	2	10	1	3	2	12787.79
DEFACTO (USA)	11	28	1	2	6	10672.80
DEFINITE ARTICLE (GB)	56	185	12	16	64	154364.83
DEMOCRATIC (USA)	2	6	1	1	2	10433.00
DENEL (FR)	19	64	4	4	16	28655.39
DENHAM RED (FR)	3	9	2	2	5	17546.66
DEPLOY	16	68	8	11	24	62658.61
DEPUTY MINISTER (CAN)	3	18	1	1	2	12038.75
DERNIER EMPEREUR (USA)	4	13	1	2	5	16185.85
DERRYLIN	8	33	2	3	7	17209.85
DESERT KING (IRE)	37	135	12	16	35	177227.46
DESERT OF WIND (USA)	2	12	1	1	2	17675.87
DESERT PRINCE (IRE)	32	108	8	11	35	85487.98
DESERT STORY (IRE)	22	59	4	5	6	37162.62
DESERT STYLE (IRE)	17	51	5	5	12	28066.74
DESERT SUN (GB)	27	72	2	2	12	21779.47
DESSE ZENNY (USA)	5	13	1	1	1	5020.00

STALLIONS	RNRS	STARTS	WNRS	WINS	PLACES	TOTAL
DETROIT SAM (FR)	2	14	2	3	6	27733.20
DIESIS	22	67	6	10	22	152458.32
DIKTAT (GB)	20	67	1	1	12	10360.85
DILUM (USA)	2	10	1	2	7	39452.70
DISCOVER D'AUTEUIL (FR)	3	14	2	5	4	35942.76
DISTANT MUSIC (USA)	4	12	1	1	3	5396.85
DISTANT VIEW (USA)	8	19	1	1	7	8053.91
DISTINCTLY NORTH (USA)	9	38	2	2	8	14921.68
DOLPHIN STREET (FR)	15	45	1	1	11	13729.00
DOM ALCO (FR)	8	52	4	5	23	265628.13
DOMITOR (USA)	1	6	1	1	1	3921.50
DOUBLE BED (FR)	13	43	3	7	14	57915.53
DOUBLE ECLIPSE (IRE)	9	20	2	2	6	16823.55
DOUBLETOUR (USA)	9	23	1	1	1	6549.66
DOUBLE TRIGGER (IRE)	40	123	9	11	31	82640.10
DOYOUN	6	16	1	1	5	11796.50
DR DEVIOUS (IRE)	30	120	5	9	32	140361.80
DREAMS END (GB)	6	25	2	3	4	8485.20
DR FONG (USA)	31	109	3	4	30	61121.38
DR MASSINI (IRE)	102	357	18	30	81	399333.98
DUKY	8	28	1	2	6	12913.15
DUNBEATH (USA)	1	7	1	1	1	4303.50
DYNAFORMER (USA)	8	32	3	5	10	51939.27
EAGLE EYED (USA)	20	87	5	5	39	71507.90
EARL OF BARKING (IRE)	3	24	1	2	6	15326.87
EASYCALL (GB)	2	8	1	1	3	3703.65
ECOSSAIS (FR)	1	3	1	1	0	2192.64
EFISIO	16	73	6	9	20	61756.32
ELA-MANA-MOU	3	8	1	1	5	14032.84
EL CONQUISTADOR	15	44	2	2	5	10479.80
ELNADIM (USA)	4	12	1	2	2	6619.40
EMARATI (USA)	4	16	1	1	4	8241.58
EMPEROR FOUNTAIN	14	52	1	1	16	13717.56
EMPEROR JONES (USA)	24	72	3	3	12	23602.20
EN CALCAT (FR)	1	7	1	1	4	23915.50
ENTREPRENEUR (GB)	29	89	1	1	24	24017.42
ENVIRONMENT FRIEND (GB)	31	126	7	12	35	87342.18
EPAPHOS (GER)	1	4	1	2	2	10791.00
EPERVIER BLEU	18	59	7	13	19	143871.61
EPISTOLAIRE (IRE)	2	10	1	1	5	7006.70
ERHAAB (USA)	8	33	3	4	12	25882.12
ERINS ISLE	33	117	5	10	28	166376.66
EUROBUS	23	67	5	5	19	92707.38
EVEN TOP (IRE)	6	20	2	2	5	16827.35
EVE'S ERROR	8	37	1	2	14	16677.46
EXATTIC (USA)	1	7	1	1	5	10243.65
EXECUTIVE PERK	68	233	16	22	53	148599.86
EXIT TO NOWHERE (USA)	33	100	3	4	27	34875.47
EZZOUD (IRE)	4	18	1	1	6	8975.95
FANTASTIC LIGHT (USA)	17	65	6	7	16	36537.05
FARHAAN	3	15	1	1	4	6864.85
FASLIYEV (USA)	15	67	5	11	19	103544.40
FAUSTUS (USA)	10	42	3	3	9	14976.90
FAVORITE TRICK (USA)	1	4	1	1	3	8905.39
FIJAR TANGO (FR)	4	21	1	1	10	10655.79
FIRST TRUMP (GB)	14	52	2	2	14	78893.60
FLAMING FEATHER (GB)	2	9	1	1	0	5956.90
FLEETWOOD (IRE)	21	73	7	10	16	50542.86
FLEMENSFIRTH (USA)	139	520	30	50	142	616401.34
FLORIDA SON	9	32	3	4	5	27208.87
FLYING LEGEND (USA)	13	66	5	6	16	66384.75
FLYING SPUR (AUS)	15	71	3	5	18	37404.54
FLY TO THE STARS (GB)	2	6	1	1	3	6246.42
FORZANDO	16	60	1	2	14	18672.93

STALLIONS	RNRS	STARTS	WNRS	WINS	PLACES	TOTAL
FOURSTARS ALLSTAR (USA)	96	375	16	30	101	346724.81
FOXHOUND (USA)	36	150	9	11	39	76684.89
FRAAM (GB)	27	133	8	12	48	76662.88
FRAMLINGTON COURT	1	5	1	1	2	4989.90
FRANC BLEU ARGENT (USA)	4	17	2	3	6	18638.19
FREEDOM CRY (GB)	2	6	1	2	0	22285.18
FRENCH GLORY	1	8	1	3	4	27525.85
FRESH BREEZE (USA)	8	24	1	1	8	12908.93
FRIMAIRE (GB)	8	30	1	1	11	15573.54
FRUITS OF LOVE (USA)	18	61	3	7	15	81369.09
FUJI KISEKI (JPN)	1	6	1	1	3	8311.96
FUMO DI LONDRA (IRE)	6	8	1	1	0	1370.40
FUNNY BABY (FR)	7	39	5	8	17	149597.93
GALILEO (IRE)	10	31	3	5	14	30242.02
GANGES (USA)	1	5	1	1	2	2617.25
GARDE ROYALE	17	74	7	9	30	124846.19
GENERAL HOLME (USA)	1	6	1	1	1	3483.00
GENERAL MONASH (USA)	18	86	1	1	17	16132.79
GENERAL VIEW	1	6	1	2	1	13984.83
GENEROUS (IRE)	16	52	5	7	19	48938.34
GERMANY (IRE)	36	136	6	6	23	59100.03
GIANT'S CAUSEWAY (USA)	17	80	8	11	24	119356.15
GILDORAN	13	40	2	2	9	19349.30
GLACIAL STORM (USA)	124	494	30	46	148	487373.01
GLAIEUL (USA)	4	15	2	2	7	58597.72
GLORY OF DANCER (GB)	2	12	1	1	3	7047.92
GOLD AND STEEL (FR)	2	9	1	1	2	4857.60
GOLD AWAY (IRE)	2	11	1	2	4	31981.23
GOLDEN TORNADO (IRE)	4	14	1	2	2	11882.83
GOLDMARK (USA)	23	79	5	5	17	39669.38
GOLDNEYEV (USA)	4	18	2	3	8	19603.18
GONE FISHIN	4	8	1	1	1	3341.25
GOOD THYNE (USA)	89	312	20	26	69	458725.72
GOOFALIK (USA)	5	25	2	4	6	33466.44
GOTHENBERG (IRE)	4	11	1	1	2	4357.40
GOTHLAND (FR)	21	70	3	3	14	16925.69
GRAND LODGE (USA)	64	194	7	9	51	98271.33
GRAND PLAISIR (IRE)	39	119	5	7	35	87720.38
GRAND TRESOR (FR)	8	37	4	8	14	64340.88
GRAPE TREE ROAD (GB)	2	9	2	3	2	14441.45
GREAT COMMOTION (USA)	8	36	2	2	10	17117.29
GREAT PALM (USA)	14	44	3	3	13	37480.26
GREEN DANCER (USA)	4	16	1	1	1	3190.05
GREEN DESERT (USA)	9	31	3	5	11	29446.10
GREENSMITH	8	31	3	5	9	49278.65
GREEN TUNE (USA)	4	23	1	1	6	6538.45
GROOM DANCER (USA)	37	150	9	13	37	109196.63
GROSVENOR (NZ)	2	7	1	2	3	19783.35
GULCH (USA)	9	30	2	2	10	15796.60
GUNNER B	40	133	6	9	40	90637.90
HALCON (GB)	1	4	1	2	1	130628.00
HALLING (USA)	27	103	9	12	32	206715.45
HATIM (USA)	8	31	1	1	11	17820.76
HAWKER'S NEWS (IRE)	1	4	1	1	1	2979.30
HECTOR PROTECTOR (USA)	12	36	2	5	4	26194.00
HERMITAGE (USA)	1	13	1	1	6	5655.80
HERNANDO (FR)	42	155	15	23	45	246681.14
HERON ISLAND (IRE)	24	76	6	10	19	71332.15
HIGH ESTATE	2	12	1	2	5	11231.65
HIGHEST HONOR (FR)	19	62	3	4	13	75068.75
HIGH ROLLER (IRE)	16	72	2	2	14	19915.52
HOLLOW HAND	6	18	2	2	5	15915.73
HOMME DE LOI (IRE)	4	21	2	3	9	15212.31
HOMO SAPIEN	16	61	1	1	15	10475.38

STALLIONS	RNRS	STARTS	WNRS	WINS	PLACES	TOTAL
HOUMAYOUN (FR)	18	53	3	6	8	28253.58
HOUSAMIX (FR)	1	2	1	1	1	8630.40
HUBBLY BUBBLY (USA)	22	99	4	5	26	76037.44
HUMBEL (USA)	24	79	2	3	9	23922.64
HUNTING LION (IRE)	3	8	1	1	0	2927.70
HUSYAN (USA)	4	30	3	4	11	36808.99
IDRIS (IRE)	14	50	1	1	7	5097.32
IMPERIAL BALLET (IRE)	30	92	4	4	26	70557.73
IMPERIAL FRONTIER (USA)	1	7	1	2	1	17377.15
IMP SOCIETY (USA)	2	3	1	1	0	2740.80
IN CAMERA (IRE)	2	8	1	3	2	10235.60
INCHINOR (GB)	33	105	6	7	32	75208.81
INDIAN DANEHILL (IRE)	14	66	4	4	22	50543.77
INDIAN LODGE (IRE)	9	28	1	1	4	3421.35
INDIAN RIDGE	16	47	4	5	18	54574.01
INDIAN RIVER (FR)	3	13	1	3	6	77278.00
INFANTRY	5	16	2	2	5	10250.13
INSAN (USA)	31	107	5	7	31	139219.44
IN THE WINGS	61	271	23	41	74	659176.08
INTIKHAB (USA)	10	28	1	1	6	6869.13
IRISH RIVER (FR)	5	27	2	2	13	19747.72
IRIS NOIR (FR)	2	10	1	1	4	8729.03
JENDALI (USA)	6	29	1	1	6	8764.73
JIMBLE (FR)	3	14	1	1	3	8664.29
JOHN FRENCH	10	27	2	2	7	12853.59
JOLLY JAKE (NZ)	16	57	1	1	16	36111.45
JOSR ALGARHOUD (IRE)	15	44	3	3	11	18718.34
JUMBO HIRT (USA)	9	45	2	2	11	15437.49
JUPITER ISLAND	7	25	1	1	12	7826.37
JURADO (USA)	37	182	12	18	48	128995.20
KADALKO (FR)	20	80	7	11	33	127113.72
KADEED (IRE)	12	49	3	5	9	46042.19
KAHTAN (GB)	1	2	1	1	1	1904.00
KAHYASI	47	175	15	25	54	354190.32
KALANISI (IRE)	15	56	3	10	12	222989.49
KALDOUN (FR)	1	6	1	1	1	4896.50
KALDOUNEVEES (FR)	10	38	1	3	8	20123.00
KALDOU STAR (GB)	1	4	1	1	1	7108.50
KALLISTO (GER)	2	9	1	2	4	26621.59
KARINGA BAY	67	250	20	27	67	246031.03
KASAKOV (GB)	2	15	1	2	7	15893.25
KASMAYO (GB)	3	14	1	2	3	21220.09
KAYF TARA (GB)	72	184	11	13	53	86705.23
KEEN	18	43	1	1	8	8028.20
KENDOR (FR)	3	14	2	2	2	16355.10
KEY OF LUCK (USA)	36	126	8	11	29	106512.57
KING CHARLEMAGNE (USA)	7	16	2	4	3	17336.98
KING LUTHIER	9	37	1	1	4	5385.17
KINGMAMBO (USA)	12	45	3	9	14	225717.10
KING OF KINGS (IRE)	12	39	1	2	7	7502.43
KING PERSIAN	4	15	1	1	4	5417.80
KING'S BEST (USA)	21	72	4	7	13	44370.14
KING'S RIDE	30	108	3	4	24	68019.22
KING'S SIGNET (USA)	2	13	1	2	5	8849.20
KING'S THEATRE (IRE)	64	240	20	31	76	430412.03
KIRKWALL (GB)	2	11	2	2	8	20764.30
KIZITCA (FR)	3	10	2	3	3	10351.40
KOMAITE (USA)	13	46	5	8	14	126864.42
KOTASHAAN (FR)	5	12	2	2	3	10648.96
KRIS	24	93	5	7	28	90221.82
KRIS S (USA)	8	29	3	5	9	54920.14
LAFONTAINE (USA)	2	7	1	3	2	56466.49
LAGUNAS	2	2	1	1	0	3578.30
LAHIB (USA)	26	91	7	12	21	79362.40

STALLIONS	RNRS	STARTS	WNRS	WINS	PLACES	TOTAL
LAHINT (USA)	1	5	1	2	3	21960.10
LAKE CONISTON (IRE)	14	45	4	6	10	38926.74
LAMMTARRA (USA)	1	5	1	1	2	5326.80
LANCASTRIAN	5	13	2	2	1	7493.50
LANDO (GER)	9	35	4	5	16	90550.36
LANGFUHR (CAN)	1	5	1	1	2	4744.60
LAPIERRE	3	12	1	2	4	12471.78
LAST TYCOON	2	13	1	2	4	9248.10
LAVIRCO (GER)	5	8	1	1	1	23132.40
LAW SOCIETY (USA)	8	25	1	2	5	36811.62
LEADING COUNSEL (USA)	40	171	12	18	57	297041.54
LEAD ON TIME (USA)	2	9	1	2	5	19142.15
LEAR FAN (USA)	14	65	5	7	25	106139.42
LE BALAFRE (FR)	5	20	3	4	7	20626.25
LE NAIN JAUNE (FR)	2	10	1	2	2	11135.20
LEND A HAND (GB)	12	43	2	2	9	12374.89
LESOTHO (USA)	2	8	1	2	2	6678.62
LIGHTS OUT (FR)	3	22	2	5	11	36299.80
LIMNOS (JPN)	3	8	1	2	3	32297.58
LINAMIX (FR)	41	155	11	19	44	154379.05
LION CAVERN (USA)	5	25	1	1	6	14856.25
LITTLE BIGHORN	15	55	2	2	9	27306.36
LOMITAS (GB)	17	75	7	12	28	179342.58
LORD AMERICO	193	743	46	65	186	901926.10
LORD OF APPEAL (GB)	22	72	2	2	22	29641.30
LORD OF MEN (GB)	3	15	1	1	7	13344.28
LOST WORLD (IRE)	6	27	2	8	7	164646.94
LOUP SAUVAGE (USA)	2	6	1	1	2	3022.00
LOUP SOLITAIRE (USA)	6	29	3	6	14	76113.13
LOWELL (USA)	1	5	1	1	1	3157.40
LUCHIROVERTE (IRE)	5	23	1	1	8	10379.87
LUCKY GUEST	4	12	1	2	2	11282.55
LUGANA BEACH	2	6	1	2	1	34011.00
LUSO (GB)	97	327	20	27	77	285366.31
LUTE ANTIQUE (FR)	22	81	6	9	29	152324.28
LYPHARD'S WISH (FR)	3	13	1	3	2	23486.50
MACHIAVELLIAN (USA)	38	159	9	11	46	90938.15
MAGICAL STRIKE (USA)	2	19	1	1	3	5771.93
MAGICAL WONDER (USA)	12	60	5	6	20	141068.05
MAGIC RING (IRE)	12	32	3	3	6	11603.00
MAJED (IRE)	1	11	1	2	4	16259.42
MAKBUL	16	69	3	6	15	41449.00
MANDALUS	21	71	4	9	19	157692.86
MANSONNIEN (FR)	16	55	8	13	20	388443.42
MARCHAND DE SABLE (USA)	2	6	1	1	3	68610.50
MARIGNAN (USA)	6	17	1	1	2	7234.19
MARJU (IRE)	27	140	10	17	55	210511.51
MARK OF ESTEEM (IRE)	27	83	5	5	25	68341.71
MARMATO	1	6	1	1	1	4926.00
MASTER WILLIE	15	46	4	5	15	53629.66
MAZAAD	4	20	1	1	9	10914.85
MEDAALY (GB)	9	37	2	2	9	28003.89
MEDICEAN (GB)	11	39	3	5	12	30178.77
MEDICUS (GER)	1	6	1	3	2	16578.10
MERDON MELODY	1	8	1	1	3	5666.39
MICHEL GEORGES (GB)	1	3	1	1	1	6403.00
MIDHISH (GB)	12	26	1	1	2	5878.83
MIDNIGHT LEGEND (GB)	35	130	8	12	33	89351.74
MILLFONTAINE	1	6	1	1	2	6988.60
MILLKOM (GB)	4	17	1	1	9	11424.96
MINER'S LAMP	3	7	1	1	1	2819.60
MINER'S MARK (USA)	1	4	1	1	1	6634.78
MINSTER SON	39	159	9	12	48	109202.68
MIRROR BOY	1	11	1	1	3	6183.25

STALLIONS	RNRS	STARTS	WNRS	WINS	PLACES	TOTAL
MISSED FLIGHT (GB)	10	48	2	5	12	48751.41
MISTER BAILEYS (GB)	19	60	2	3	16	110013.87
MISTER LORD (USA)	95	342	30	45	86	542163.11
MISTER MAT (FR)	26	78	3	3	14	19191.58
MISTERTOPOGIGO (IRE)	2	7	1	1	2	4961.80
MISWAKI (USA)	1	11	1	1	2	14510.00
MOHAAJIR (USA)	10	32	3	4	7	23739.26
MONASHEE MOUNTAIN (USA)	14	39	2	2	13	13184.20
MONSUN (GER)	22	70	7	11	18	72497.94
MONTELIMAR (USA)	44	187	10	13	76	180387.42
MONTJEU (IRE)	27	97	6	9	29	128352.68
MON TRESOR	5	13	1	2	1	7022.25
MOONAX (IRE)	47	155	8	9	41	82928.28
MORPETH (GB)	18	58	5	7	18	40989.82
MOSCOW SOCIETY (USA)	78	320	16	22	99	337389.65
MOSHAAJIR (USA)	6	37	3	3	10	18151.40
MOST WELCOME	14	51	2	5	15	32203.93
MR CONFUSION (IRE)	4	25	2	2	4	14162.07
MTOTO	36	169	7	10	49	91610.88
MUHARIB (USA)	4	17	1	1	4	10814.75
MUHTARRAM (USA)	18	71	4	6	26	52379.45
MUHTATHIR (GB)	4	14	1	1	6	5635.16
MUJADIL (USA)	26	82	4	5	17	39171.15
MUJAHID (USA)	10	32	2	2	16	40663.10
MUKADDAMAH (USA)	5	11	1	1	3	10049.98
MULL OF KINTYRE (USA)	14	37	1	1	9	18707.45
MURMURE (FR)	3	7	1	1	3	6594.45
MUROTO	20	92	2	3	25	35365.87
MYSTIKO (USA)	1	6	1	2	2	6249.80
NAHEEZ (USA)	26	89	9	11	22	99657.62
NALCHIK (USA)	1	3	1	1	2	4227.40
NAMAQUALAND (USA)	17	81	6	13	28	72445.63
NAMID (GB)	6	21	1	3	5	15291.91
NASHAMAA	3	9	1	2	2	12480.25
NASHWAN (USA)	25	95	9	15	19	88992.06
NAZAR (IRE)	2	4	1	1	0	5369.00
NEEDLE GUN (IRE)	55	181	7	14	38	175667.57
NELTINO	4	12	1	1	5	8672.40
NEUSTRIEN (FR)	1	5	1	1	1	5279.40
NEW FRONTIER (IRE)	34	122	5	5	22	39599.96
NICHOLAS BILL	8	22	2	2	5	11549.52
NICOLOTTE (GB)	5	26	1	1	4	4885.46
NIGHT SHIFT (USA)	31	117	6	9	31	127116.59
NIKOS	20	71	6	7	23	59024.19
NOMADIC WAY (USA)	25	91	6	11	31	58759.58
NOMINATION	2	6	1	1	2	3004.25
NONONITO (FR)	7	20	3	3	3	20030.29
NORDIC BRAVE	2	8	1	1	1	6783.80
NORWICH	82	317	20	32	75	411485.28
NUMEROUS (USA)	2	23	1	1	8	8225.20
OCTAGONAL (NZ)	13	69	4	8	26	77182.32
OLD VIC	193	676	50	67	182	1145113.92
OPERA GHOST	5	13	2	3	3	15752.99
ORPEN (USA)	46	154	9	20	32	149973.84
OSCAR (IRE)	262	935	61	87	241	1138376.44
OSCAR SCHINDLER (IRE)	25	78	2	4	13	122511.71
OVERBURY (IRE)	143	509	27	47	116	353640.87
OVER THE RIVER (FR)	35	128	11	14	44	144652.23
OWINGTON (GB)	1	9	1	1	3	7120.75
PANORAMIC	8	30	2	3	14	27980.05
PARIS HOUSE (GB)	11	37	3	3	3	8204.80
PARTHIAN SPRINGS (GB)	14	38	2	3	10	75047.09
PASSING SALE (FR)	15	59	6	9	23	128754.34
PASTERNAK (GB)	25	84	4	4	10	18569.59

STALLIONS	RNRS	STARTS	WNRS	WINS	PLACES	TOTAL
PAST GLORIES	9	44	5	6	12	58479.15
PEACOCK (FR)	2	11	1	2	5	17628.54
PEINTRE CELEBRE (USA)	9	40	5	5	7	32025.83
PELDER (IRE)	2	5	1	1	0	4879.50
PENNEKAMP (USA)	19	67	3	8	19	87432.94
PERPENDICULAR (GB)	16	78	4	8	23	47020.63
PERRAULT	5	23	2	2	12	24963.36
PERSIAN BOLD	13	43	4	5	17	47870.96
PERSIAN MEWS	3	10	1	1	2	2027.19
PERSONAL FLAG (USA)	1	10	1	2	2	15140.00
PERUGINO (USA)	38	162	8	12	48	138526.74
PETARDIA (GB)	14	54	2	3	11	21377.15
PETORIUS	3	11	1	1	3	7110.60
PETOSKI	47	138	6	15	33	94202.24
PHARDANTE (FR)	66	220	16	18	66	204370.89
PHARLY (FR)	12	43	5	5	9	18578.67
PICCOLO (GB)	17	56	3	7	15	32124.85
PIERRE (GB)	22	66	4	10	8	145649.16
PISTOLET BLEU (IRE)	71	231	19	25	69	234060.07
PIVOTAL (GB)	20	91	8	13	21	80683.68
PLATINI (GER)	14	50	5	9	16	56734.24
PLEASANT TAP (USA)	4	22	1	1	11	48196.73
POET'S DREAM (IRE)	1	1	1	1	0	2740.80
POLAR FALCON (USA)	14	46	5	5	16	53850.85
POLAR PRINCE (IRE)	12	41	2	2	8	11332.99
POLIGLOTE (GB)	9	38	5	11	18	211436.29
POLISH PRECEDENT (USA)	30	138	8	11	37	71793.41
PORT ETIENNE (FR)	2	5	1	1	1	6931.40
PORT LYAUTEY (FR)	6	22	2	3	12	87548.56
PORTRAIT GALLERY (IRE)	23	70	5	7	19	36153.71
POSIDONAS (GB)	9	26	1	1	7	10406.60
PRESENTING (GB)	268	950	71	106	265	1172658.33
PRESIDIUM	21	74	3	4	20	25003.42
PRIMITIVE RISING (USA)	48	155	12	15	48	96818.85
PRIMO DOMINIE	7	29	1	1	10	13973.75
PRINCE DANIEL (USA)	10	48	3	3	12	16924.25
PRINCE OF BIRDS (USA)	12	42	2	2	8	54957.47
PRINCE SABO	5	10	1	1	1	1926.20
PRINCETON (FR)	1	9	1	3	2	10163.45
PRIOLO (USA)	15	55	3	3	19	94582.27
PROJECT MANAGER	1	7	1	1	3	14787.59
PROTEKTOR (GER)	2	14	1	5	4	47448.32
PROUD PANTHER (FR)	1	8	1	1	4	8124.40
PUISSANCE	5	20	1	1	2	4355.43
PURE MELODY (USA)	1	10	1	4	3	21529.90
PURSUIT OF LOVE (GB)	19	70	3	3	13	18678.00
PYRAMUS (USA)	2	2	1	1	0	1561.50
QUWS (GB)	9	22	2	4	6	35003.50
RAGMAR (FR)	16	59	3	3	19	39218.44
RAHY (USA)	6	13	1	1	3	17411.05
RAINBOW QUEST (USA)	26	79	7	9	19	140251.66
RAINBOW REEF (GB)	1	6	1	1	1	2715.80
RAINBOWS FOR LIFE (CAN)	12	48	3	4	10	28235.96
RAISE A GRAND (IRE)	19	79	1	1	19	18408.00
RAJPOUTE (FR)	2	4	1	1	0	17080.20
RAKAPOSHI KING	55	210	7	8	59	79740.13
RASHAR (USA)	55	201	11	14	33	108266.06
REAL QUIET (USA)	3	16	1	1	7	27082.76
RED RANSOM (USA)	11	32	2	2	12	26618.90
RELIEF PITCHER	7	27	2	3	10	31034.25
RELIGIOUSLY (USA)	25	98	4	6	23	90958.10
REPRIMAND	12	66	2	2	27	35168.90
REVOQUE (IRE)	42	128	11	15	37	125862.64
RIBERETTO	5	16	2	2	4	7962.85

STALLIONS	RNRS	STARTS	WNRS	WINS	PLACES	TOTAL
RICHE MARE (FR)	1	5	1	1	2	6959.60
RICH REBEL (USA)	1	2	1	2	0	7863.09
RIDGEWOOD BEN (GB)	12	32	2	2	4	5125.80
RIGHT WIN (IRE)	19	71	5	6	24	56578.55
RIVER BAY (USA)	3	15	2	2	5	11538.57
RIVERMAN (USA)	2	17	1	1	3	4330.40
RIVER MIST (USA)	3	17	2	3	7	22404.20
ROBELLINO (USA)	33	111	10	12	35	88382.83
ROBIN DES CHAMPS (FR)	6	14	1	1	4	11176.22
ROBIN DES PRES (FR)	7	29	2	3	14	37634.25
ROCHESSON (FR)	1	6	1	2	2	12746.40
ROCK HOPPER	26	95	3	4	21	27996.60
ROI DE ROME (USA)	6	16	3	3	0	12408.70
ROLFE (USA)	2	11	1	1	1	2317.95
ROMANOV (IRE)	1	9	1	2	1	11182.35
ROSCOE BLAKE	2	6	1	1	2	5622.60
ROSEBERRY AVENUE (IRE)	1	3	1	1	0	2055.60
ROSELIER (FR)	135	511	37	55	153	962995.32
ROSSINI (USA)	27	126	5	7	33	47570.90
ROYAL ABJAR (USA)	5	36	2	3	11	19423.41
ROYAL ACADEMY (USA)	20	55	1	1	9	11663.45
ROYAL ANTHEM (USA)	10	34	2	4	13	16998.18
ROYAL APPLAUSE (GB)	18	66	5	6	13	32739.58
ROYAL CHARTER (FR)	7	32	3	4	10	56263.20
ROYAL COURT (IRE)	1	8	1	1	2	3360.90
ROYAL FOUNTAIN	10	39	3	4	10	14272.55
RUBIANO (USA)	1	8	1	1	3	4724.80
RUDIMENTARY (USA)	47	160	8	10	44	78182.72
RUNYON (IRE)	2	9	1	1	0	6671.72
RUSSIAN REVIVAL (USA)	4	22	2	5	4	33372.40
SABREHILL (USA)	12	65	3	6	22	74422.45
SADDLERS' HALL (IRE)	208	756	52	73	204	654965.33
SADLER'S WELLS (USA)	110	457	29	37	131	555101.56
SAFAWAN	6	13	1	1	2	10898.40
SAFETY CATCH (USA)	22	95	6	7	23	68245.71
SAGAMIX (FR)	4	11	2	2	7	12715.22
SAHM (USA)	2	9	1	1	3	4721.62
SAINT CYRIEN (FR)	3	5	1	1	1	4858.60
SAINT PREUIL (FR)	13	61	5	11	28	236202.50
SALSE (USA)	8	26	2	2	9	11556.47
SANDPIT (BRZ)	1	5	1	2	3	9904.00
SANGLAMORE (USA)	4	18	1	1	6	27988.26
SARATOGA SPRINGS (CAN)	2	13	1	3	1	14006.60
SARPEDON (FR)	1	2	1	1	1	3760.00
SASSANIAN (USA)	7	25	1	2	11	48864.30
SATCO (FR)	15	65	2	2	17	20491.50
SCRIBANO (GB)	19	62	3	5	16	108395.17
SCRIBE (IRE)	2	8	1	1	3	6898.00
SEA RAVEN (IRE)	21	59	2	3	12	26446.68
SECOND EMPIRE (IRE)	24	77	4	4	17	29529.11
SECOND SET (IRE)	3	18	2	2	6	10360.21
SECRET 'N CLASSY (CAN)	4	15	2	3	3	19688.58
SELKIRK (USA)	36	124	7	12	30	374138.96
SEMILLON (GB)	10	46	4	5	13	48645.71
SENDAWAR (IRE)	5	11	1	1	1	6418.90
SHAAB	4	33	2	2	5	14349.90
SHAAMIT (IRE)	17	63	1	1	9	9999.65
SHAHANNDEH	14	41	1	1	5	6385.53
SHAHRASTANI (USA)	21	54	1	1	11	10567.07
SHAMBO	20	56	4	6	15	47593.55
SHANTOU (USA)	1	7	1	3	2	63704.00
SHARDARI	30	101	2	4	22	30041.33
SHAREEF DANCER (USA)	5	27	3	3	7	22662.75
SHARP DEAL	1	5	1	1	4	74218.00

STALLIONS	RNRS	STARTS	WNRS	WINS	PLACES	TOTAL
SHEIKH ALBADOU (GB)	2	11	1	1	3	3251.02
SHERNAZAR	120	368	28	33	88	270440.30
SHEYRANN	6	18	1	1	2	7508.50
SHINKO FOREST (IRE)	13	46	1	4	9	23666.93
SHIRLEY HEIGHTS	2	17	1	2	8	17072.87
SHUAILAAN (USA)	1	12	1	1	4	4920.72
SIAM (USA)	1	7	1	1	1	3491.50
SIGNE DIVIN (USA)	5	25	2	2	12	18027.61
SILLERY (USA)	5	22	4	4	6	25807.52
SILVER CHARM (USA)	1	2	1	1	0	3253.00
SILVER HAWK (USA)	8	34	4	5	10	44133.53
SILVER OWL	1	8	1	3	3	19463.30
SILVER PATRIARCH (IRE)	87	299	17	20	74	128786.03
SILVER RAINBOW (GB)	2	8	1	3	4	26502.05
SILVINO (USA)	1	3	1	1	0	3253.00
SIMON DU DESERT (FR)	6	28	2	3	12	60490.97
SIMPLY GREAT (FR)	37	143	6	7	44	96522.63
SINGSPIEL (IRE)	23	75	5	6	29	50019.40
SINNDAR (IRE)	14	50	5	6	16	29484.57
SIR CAT (USA)	1	3	1	1	1	2638.00
SIR HARRY LEWIS (USA)	42	168	15	22	60	376579.37
SKY CLASSIC (CAN)	2	12	1	5	4	26508.83
SKY LAWYER (FR)	1	6	1	1	4	7674.70
SLEEPING CAR (FR)	14	37	3	3	15	25666.35
SLIP ANCHOR	36	130	9	11	41	85085.79
SMADOUN (FR)	4	12	1	1	4	12991.40
SNURGE	19	55	4	5	12	44670.51
SOLARSTERN (FR)	1	7	1	1	5	11178.80
SON OF SILVER	1	7	1	1	1	4714.54
SOUTHERN HALO (USA)	6	35	2	8	6	31035.79
SOUVENIR COPY (USA)	1	6	1	2	1	5226.15
SOVIET STAR (USA)	21	77	4	4	21	34303.63
SPADOUN (FR)	2	5	1	1	2	2403.25
SPANISH PLACE (USA)	5	19	2	2	7	22603.59
SPECTRUM (IRE)	51	197	14	21	58	198456.48
SPINNING WORLD (USA)	10	27	3	3	3	15438.79
SRI PEKAN (USA)	17	66	3	3	15	42667.03
STANDIFORD (USA)	4	15	2	2	3	15398.56
STARBOROUGH (GB)	8	27	2	3	6	11804.86
STARK SOUTH (USA)	3	14	1	2	6	17349.98
STAR QUEST	4	16	2	3	4	39971.45
STEP TOGETHER (USA)	1	2	1	1	1	3255.30
STORM BIRD (CAN)	2	15	1	1	3	8599.90
STRAVINSKY (USA)	5	17	1	1	2	10540.69
STRONG GALE	9	34	2	2	12	14166.00
SUAVE DANCER (USA)	1	3	1	1	1	6054.49
SUBOTICA (FR)	7	33	3	4	13	32592.65
SULA BULA	10	51	2	2	15	18914.45
SULTRY SONG (USA)	1	5	1	1	3	8069.99
SUNDAY SILENCE (USA)	5	31	2	3	15	42664.43
SUNLEY BUILDS	2	16	2	2	7	12382.62
SUPERIOR PREMIUM (GB)	1	4	1	1	2	6957.50
SUPREME LEADER	319	1092	89	122	321	1064453.08
SURE BLADE (USA)	9	30	1	4	8	28976.80
SWAIN (IRE)	10	29	2	2	10	21565.35
SYMBOLI HEIGHTS (FR)	6	20	2	2	4	10528.90
SYNEFOS (USA)	14	50	5	6	11	41315.84
TACTICAL CAT (USA)	1	4	1	1	1	4237.50
TAGULA (IRE)	16	46	2	3	6	32065.55
TAIPAN (IRE)	97	355	20	31	102	356302.78
TAKE RISKS (FR)	6	38	3	3	12	57095.99
TALE OF THE CAT (USA)	2	7	1	1	2	8552.42
TAMURE (IRE)	15	32	2	2	9	10690.84
TANNENKONIG (IRE)	4	12	1	1	2	4431.50

STALLIONS	RNRS	STARTS	WNRS	WINS	PLACES	TOTAL
TAWRRIFIC (NZ)	2	14	1	1	1	5018.57
TEAMSTER	12	42	1	1	11	12167.36
TECHNOLOGY (USA)	1	5	1	2	1	22927.85
TEENOSO (USA)	20	66	6	8	21	76486.67
TEL QUEL (FR)	8	40	3	4	15	30162.85
TEMPORAL (GER)	1	3	1	2	1	14827.52
TERIMON	47	174	11	16	36	114270.68
THEATRICAL	11	31	1	2	14	30757.80
THEATRICAL CHARMER	4	17	1	2	5	18837.70
THEN AGAIN	4	19	1	1	7	9564.25
THOWRA (FR)	29	82	5	6	21	44762.88
TIDARO (USA)	6	24	1	2	9	18407.65
TIGER HILL (IRE)	8	33	2	3	13	24156.19
TILDEN	1	6	1	1	1	3738.54
TIMELESS TIMES (USA)	4	11	1	1	4	8928.90
TINA'S PET	7	30	2	3	8	14001.01
TIRAAZ (USA)	11	33	2	4	9	15140.06
TITUS LIVIUS (FR)	30	85	5	6	14	47358.64
TOPANOORA	74	275	14	19	66	146295.36
TOP OF THE WORLD	6	13	1	1	1	5899.81
TORUS	12	49	1	1	17	57768.76
TOULON (GB)	31	131	11	15	39	180244.28
TRAGIC ROLE (USA)	17	55	2	2	10	19197.55
TRANS ISLAND (GB)	14	50	3	9	11	71949.28
TREASURE HUNTER	20	77	4	4	20	31690.16
TREMBLANT	2	17	2	2	7	19073.20
TREMPOLINO (USA)	17	95	5	9	34	116932.94
TRUE BRAVE (USA)	5	26	4	6	12	91288.95
TURBO SPEED	1	5	1	5	0	24437.64
TURGEON (USA)	15	75	8	16	30	562974.69
TURTLE ISLAND (IRE)	58	203	10	17	55	134652.32
UN DESPERADO (FR)	95	359	23	29	89	387989.98
UNFUWAIN (USA)	30	140	12	17	54	321496.59
UNGARO (GER)	5	20	3	4	3	19795.12
USEFUL (FR)	17	88	6	10	34	85160.32
VAGUELY PLEASANT (FR)	2	7	2	2	0	42408.54
VALANJOU (FR)	3	12	1	1	5	9370.35
VARESE (FR)	1	18	1	3	5	12519.26
VERGLAS (IRE)	2	10	1	1	3	9684.10
VESTRIS ABU	4	7	1	1	2	4882.00
VETTORI (IRE)	55	199	9	13	51	113519.96
VICTORY NOTE (USA)	24	84	4	6	16	77925.30
VIDEO ROCK (FR)	33	149	9	14	62	242565.52
VILLAGE STAR (FR)	1	6	1	6	0	607263.00
VILLEZ (USA)	19	105	9	18	36	476237.71
VISTO SI STAMPI (IRE)	3	10	1	1	2	8234.47
WACE (USA)	8	33	2	2	2	7362.80
WAKY NAO (GB)	6	29	3	3	7	19103.08
WARCRAFT (USA)	24	84	1	1	19	20424.98
WARNING	4	21	3	5	11	58265.89
WELD	21	69	3	6	19	279581.16
WELL BELOVED (GB)	2	8	1	1	0	3253.00
WELSH TERM	7	35	3	4	5	23825.09
WILLIE JOE (IRE)	1	5	1	1	2	3969.25
WINDSOR CASTLE (GB)	14	35	2	2	3	11991.48
WINGED LOVE (IRE)	13	40	5	9	9	130658.21
WITH APPROVAL (CAN)	2	7	1	1	2	4473.30
WITNESS BOX (USA)	24	69	3	3	15	30409.80
WIZARD KING (GB)	27	101	7	11	20	71915.98
WOLFHOUND (USA)	12	38	3	6	7	31934.71
WOODBOROUGH (USA)	14	46	1	1	8	21129.97
WOODMAN (USA)	15	60	3	6	17	36232.60
YAHEEB (USA)	4	18	1	1	2	2644.40
YAMANIN VITAL (NZ)	1	9	1	2	1	10512.37

STALLIONS	RNRS	STARTS	WNRS	WINS	PLACES	TOTAL
YASHGAN	9	36	1	1	4	9178.39
ZABEEL (NZ)	3	11	1	1	6	43753.00
ZAFFARAN (USA)	152	535	39	57	146	660697.24
ZAFONIC (USA)	26	87	4	5	19	47808.94
ZAHA (CAN)	9	24	1	1	7	5218.54
ZILZAL (USA)	20	82	8	13	28	73777.64
ZINAAD (GB)	2	7	1	1	3	5798.80

BY KIND PERMISSION OF WEATHERBYS

HIGH-PRICED YEARLINGS OF 2007 AT TATTERSALLS' SALES
The following yearlings realised 105,000 guineas and over at Tattersalls' Sales in 2007:-

Name and Breeding	Purchaser	Guineas
LIFFEY DANCER (IRE) B F SADLER'S WELLS (USA) - BRIGID (IRE)	C GORDON-WATSON BS	25000
FLAME OF HESTIA (IRE) CH F GIANT'S CAUSEWAY (USA) - ELLEN (IRE)	C GORDON-WATSON BS	10000
B C GONE WEST (USA) MYTH TO REALITY (FR)	JOHN FERGUSON BS	10000
GR C DALAKHANI (IRE) - BELLA LAMBADA (GB)	C GORDON-WATSON BS	10000
B C GALILEO (IRE) - SILVER COLOURS (USA)	D O'BYRNE	7500
BR F DANEHILL DANCER (IRE) - FLAWLY (GB)	S CHRISTIAN	70000
B C MONTJEU (IRE) - ZIVANIA (IRE)	D O'BYRNE	60000
LADY OF INTRIGUE (IRE) B F SADLER'S WELLS (USA) - DEDICATED LADY (IRE)	C GORDON-WATSON BS	54000
B C MONTJEU (IRE) - SECRET DREAM (IRE)	D O'BYRNE	52000
B C MONTJEU (IRE) - MILLENNIUM DASH (GB)	D O'BYRNE	50000
B F KYLLACHY (GB) - HALLAND PARK LASS (IRE)	BLANDFORD BS	48000
B C OASIS DREAM (GB) - WUNDERS DREAM (IRE)	J MAGNIER	48000
B C DALAKHANI (GB) - TIME HONOURED (GB)	JOHN FERGUSON BS	48000
B C PIVOTAL (GB) - MISS PINKERTON (GB)	D O'BYRNE	47500
CH C GALILEO (IRE) - LLIA (GB)	JOHN WARREN BS	45000
B F OASIS DREAM (GB) - SUNSET CAFE (IRE)	MISS M O'TOOLE	43000
B C OASIS DREAM (GB) - RUBIES FROM BURMA (USA)	JOHN FERGUSON BS	42500
MAFAAZ (GB) CH C MEDICEAN (GB) - COMPLIMENTARY PASS (IRE)	SHADWELL ESTATE	40000
B F PIVOTAL (GB) - PIETRA DURA (GB)	BLANDFORD BS	38000
ALANBROOKE (GB) BR/GR C HERNANDO (FR) - ALOUETTE (GB)	M JOHNSTON	38000
B C SADLER'S WELLS (USA) - GRECIAN BRIDE (IRE)	J MAGNIER	38000
B C SADLER'S WELLS (USA) - PEONY (GB)	D O'BYRNE	38000
MISS KHAYA (IRE) B F DANEHILL DANCER (IRE) - BENEVENTA (GB)	CHARLES EGERTON BS	38000
B F ROCK OF GIBRALTAR (IRE) - CHALICE WELLS (GB)	BBA (IRELAND)	38000
CH F DANEHILL DANCER (IRE) - STAGE PRESENCE (IRE)	HUGO LASCELLES BS	37500
ALADDIN'S LAMP (IRE) B C CAPE CROSS (IRE) - LUMINATA (IRE)	JOHN FERGUSON BS	37500
B C GALILEO (IRE) - GREEN ROSY (IRE)	J MAGNIER	37500
B C GIANT'S CAUSEWAY (USA) - SAREE (IRE)	M GOODBODY	37500
B F DANEHILL DANCER (IRE) - BEX (IRE)	NETHERFIELD HOUSE STUD	36000
B F ACCLAMATION (GB) - SNAP CRACKLE POP (IRE)	NETHERFIELD HOUSE STUD	35000
B C DANEHILL DANCER (IRE) - MODEL QUEEN (USA)	E DUNLOP	35000
RULER OF ALL (IRE) B C SADLER'S WELLS (USA) - SHABBY CHIC (USA)	M GOODBODY	34000
B C DANEHILL DANCER (IRE) - MOOD SWINGS (IRE)	BLANDFORD BS	34000
B F GALILEO (IRE) - FASCINATING RHYTHM (GB)	M V MAGNIER	32000
B C PIVOTAL (GB) - PRINCESS ATHENA	C GORDON-WATSON BS	32000
B F MONTJEU (IRE) - ECOUTILA (USA)	JOHN WARREN BS	31000
B C GALILEO (IRE) - BELLE ALLEMANDE (CAN)	J MAGNIER	31000
B F GALILEO (IRE) - ONE SO MARVELLOUS (GB)	NEWTOWN ANNER STUD	30000
ZAAQYA (GB) B F NAYEF (USA) - CLASSICAL DANCER (GB)	SHADWELL ESTATE	30000
B/BR C CAPE CROSS (IRE) - WIMPLE (USA)	B SMART	30000
B F DANSILI (GB) - ACHIEVE (GB)	BBA (IRELAND)	30000
B F OASIS DREAM (GB) - JACKIE'S OPERA (FR)	D WACHMAN	30000
B F SADLER'S WELLS (USA) - SPRING FLIGHT (USA)	D O'BYRNE	30000
B C ELUSIVE QUALITY (USA) - LUCKY (IRE)	B SMART	30000
SUMBE (USA) B/BR C GIANT'S CAUSEWAY (USA) - SUMOTO (USA)	M TREGONING	29000
B C CAPE CROSS (IRE) - HUMILIS (IRE)	JOHN FERGUSON BS	29000
B C SADLER'S WELLS (USA) - LA MOULINE (IRE)	JOHN WARREN BS	29000
B C DANEHILL DANCER (IRE) - DANCE LESSON (GB)	VENDOR	28500
OSTAADI (GB) B C NAYEF (USA) - BLODWEN (USA)	SHADWELL ESTATE	28000
HAPPY DAY (IRE) B C DANEHILL DANCER (IRE) - IN THE LIMELIGHT (IRE)	CHARLES EGERTON BS	28000
B C SADLER'S WELLS (USA) - ZARAWA (IRE)	CITYWEST INC	28000
HAZAYNA (GB) B F BARATHEA (IRE) - HAZAARADJAT (IRE)	KERN/LILLINGSTON ASS	28000
B C GALILEO (IRE) - KITE MARK (GB)	M GOODBODY	27000
B F DANETIME (IRE) - LINDFIELD BELLE (GB)	C GORDON-WATSON BS	26000
CH C GALILEO (IRE) - TREE TOPS (GB)	C GORDON-WATSON BS	26000
EXCELSIOR ACADEMY (GB) B C MONTJEU (IRE) - BIRTHDAY SUIT (IRE)	CHARLES EGERTON BS	26000
CH C PIVOTAL (GB) - JIVING (GB)	VENDOR	26000
B C CAPE CROSS (IRE) - LARAMIE (USA)	P NATAF	26000
AL TAMOOH (IRE) B F DALAKHANI (IRE) - CLAXON (GB)	SHADWELL ESTATE	26000
B F SADLER'S WELLS (USA) - MONEEFA (GB)	DE BURGH/FARRINGTON	25000
B C GIANT'S CAUSEWAY (USA) - SPIRITUAL AIR (GB)	D O'BYRNE	25000
PARK MELODY (IRE) B F REFUSE TO BEND (IRE) - PARK CHARGER (GB)	MCKEEVER ST LAWRENCE	25000
MAZIONA (GB) B F DANSILI (GB) - POLYGUEZA (FR)	SHADWELL ESTATE	25000
LIBERATION (IRE) B C REFUSE TO BEND (IRE) - MOSAIQUE BLEUE (IRE)	JOHN FERGUSON BS	24000
B F SADLER'S WELLS (USA) - SAGANECA (USA)	AL EILE STUD	24000
B F DANEHILL DANCER (IRE) - WANNABE (GB)	B O'RYAN	24000
B C OASIS DREAM (GB) - WENDYLINA (IRE)	C GORDON-WATSON BS	24000

Name and Breeding	Purchaser	Guineas
B C PEINTRE CELEBRE (USA) - TRICOTEUSE (GB)	M MAGNIER	230000
CH C PIVOTAL (GB) - FAIRY CONTESSA (IRE)	JOHN FERGUSON BS	230000
B C NAYEF (USA) - HYPERSPECTRA (GB)	JOHN FERGUSON BS	230000
B F INDIAN RIDGE - DAMSEL (GB)	C GORDON-WATSON BS	230000
HI FLING (GB) B C OASIS DREAM (GB) - CRAFTY BUZZ (USA)	CHARLES EGERTON BS	220000
B C MONTJEU (IRE) - GRAIN OF GOLD (GB)	J MAGNIER	220000
GHAAYER (GB) B C NAYEF (USA) - VALTHEA (FR)	VENDOR	220000
LAURENCIO (IRE) B C MONSUN (GER) - LAURENCIA (GB)	SHADWELL ESTATE	220000
ASATEER (IRE) B C ALHAARTH (IRE) - CATATONIC (GB)	JOHN WARREN BS	220000
B F GALILEO (IRE) - PALACOONA (FR)	SHADWELL ESTATE	220000
CH C LEMON DROP KID (USA) - COZY MARIA (USA)	SHADWELL ESTATE	220000
B C DANSILI (GB) - ANBELLA (FR)	JOHN FERGUSON BS	220000
B C DANEHILL DANCER (IRE) - CRUMPETSFORTEA (IRE)	C GORDON-WATSON BS	215000
B C DANEHILL DANCER (IRE) - LADY MILETRIAN (IRE)	JOHN WARREN BS	210000
BENEDICTE (IRE) B F GALILEO (IRE) - RACHELLE (IRE)	C MARNANE	210000
BURNS NIGHT (GB) CH C SELKIRK (USA) - NIGHT FROLIC (GB)	M JOHNSTON	210000
CH C RAHY (USA) - NO MORE IRONING (USA)	DAVID METCALFE BS	210000
B C MORE THAN READY (USA) - YOU AGAIN (USA)	J GOSDEN	210000
SOUTH EASTER (IRE) CH C GALILEO (IRE) - DANCE TREAT (USA)	ANTHONY STROUD BS	210000
AAKEF (IRE) B C EXCEED AND EXCEL (AUS) - BUSH BABY (GB)	SHADWELL ESTATE	210000
CH F DANEHILL DANCER (IRE) - LILISSA (IRE)	D O'BYRNE	210000
MOHALHAL (IRE) B C CAPE CROSS (IRE) - MADAME DUBOIS	SHADWELL ESTATE	210000
ARABIAN MIRAGE (GB) B F OASIS DREAM (GB) - BATHILDE (IRE)	BBA (IRELAND)	210000
B C REFUSE TO BEND (IRE) - STYLE OF LIFE (USA)	B SMART	200000
ITHINKBEST (GB) B C KING'S BEST (USA) - MONTURANI (IRE)	C GORDON-WATSON BS	200000
B C SADLER'S WELLS (USA) - MABROVA	D K WELD	200000
NEHAAM (GB) B C NAYEF (USA) - CHARM THE STARS (GB)	SHADWELL ESTATE	200000
LAAHEB (GB) B C CAPE CROSS (IRE) - MASKUNAH (IRE)	SHADWELL ESTATE	200000
B C CAPE CROSS (IRE) - SHIMNA (GB)	JOHN FERGUSON BS	200000
B C INVINCIBLE SPIRIT (IRE) - NOFA'S MAGIC (USA)	JOHN FERGUSON BS	200000
B C MONTJEU (IRE) - BRIGHT HALO (IRE)	J ALLISON	200000
B C KHELEYF (USA) - SEWARDS FOLLY (GB)	A O NERSES	200000
B C INDIAN RIDGE - CASTELLANE (FR)	SHADWELL ESTATE	200000
B C INDIAN HAVEN (GB) - SPECIFICALLY (USA)	KERN/LILLINGSTON ASS	200000
B F REFUSE TO BEND (IRE) - TOTAL ALOOF (GB)	BLANDFORD BS	200000
B C MONTJEU (IRE) - SOMEONE SPECIAL	C GORDON-WATSON BS	200000
HIGHLAND FLASH (GB) B C GALILEO (IRE) - SILK (IRE)	CHARLES EGERTON BS	200000
B C CAPE CROSS (IRE) - MARE NOSTRUM (GB)	JOHN FERGUSON BS	200000
CH C PIVOTAL (GB) - MISS QUEEN (IRE)	JOHN FERGUSON BS	200000
B F GREEN DESERT (USA) - INCHYRE (GB)	BRIAN GRASSICK BS	200000
B C DR FONG (USA) - MAIL THE DESERT (IRE)	B SMART	200000
KHAN TENGRI (IRE) GR C SADLER'S WELLS (USA) - ELA ATHENA (GB)	M TREGONING	190000
CH C MEDICEAN (GB) - PREFERENCE (GB)	C GORDON-WATSON BS	190000
B C DANEHILL DANCER (IRE) - LITTLETON ARWEN (GB)	EPONA MANAGEMENT	190000
CH C SELKIRK (USA) - PORTELET (GB)	C GORDON-WATSON BS	185000
ABIGAIL'S AUNT (GB) CH F EFISIO - ROHITA (IRE)	BLANDFORD BS	185000
METRAASH (GB) CH C DUBAI DESTINATION (USA) - BALLYMORE CELEBRE (IRE)	SHADWELL ESTATE	185000
B C SADLER'S WELLS (USA) - HOTELGENIE DOT COM (GB)	GILL RICHARDSON BS	180000
CH C BACHELOR DUKE (USA) - DAWN CHORUS (GB)	MRS A SKIFFINGTON	180000
B F OASIS DREAM (GB) - MISS PARTY LINE (USA)	CHARLES EGERTON BS	180000
GYR (IRE) CH C PIVOTAL (GB) - RAFHA	L STRATTON	180000
SILK MEADOW (GB) B F BARATHEA (IRE) - PERILS OF JOY (IRE)	MCKEEVER ST LAWRENCE	180000
ALKHAFIF (GB) B C ROYAL APPLAUSE (GB) - MY FIRST ROMANCE (GB)	SHADWELL ESTATE	180000
B F CADEAUX GENEREUX - BIANCA NERA (GB)	MEON VALLEY STUD	180000
HARBINGER (GB) B C DANSILI (GB) - PENANG PEARL (FR)	JOHN WARREN BS	180000
B F KHELEYF - VICTORIA REGIA (IRE)	M TREGONING	180000
ERROL FLYNN (IRE) B/BR C DANEHILL DANCER (IRE) - WARUSHA (GER)	MOUNTGRANGE STUD	180000
ATEEB (GB) B C RED RANSOM (USA) - DESIGN PERFECTION (USA)	SHADWELL ESTATE	180000
MEGAMIX (GB) GR F LINAMIX (FR) - KALAMBARA (IRE)	MEON VALLEY STUD	175000
B/BR C MEDAGLIA D'ORO (USA) - PONDERING (USA)	CITYWEST INC	175000
B C NAYEF (USA) - MAURI MOON (GB)	B SMART	175000
B C CAPE CROSS (IRE) - MENNETOU (IRE)	GILL RICHARDSON BS	175000
B C MEDICEAN (GB) - BLACK BELT SHOPPER (IRE)	K YOSHIDA	170000
CH C MR GREELEY (USA) - LAURENTINE (USA)	BLANDFORD BS	170000
FROSTED (GB) CH F DR FONG (USA) - ARCTIC AIR (GB)	CHEVELEY PARK STUD	170000
B/BR C STREET CRY (IRE) - AWAAMIR (GB)	JOHN FERGUSON BS	170000
B C DANEHILL DANCER (IRE) - ON FAIR STAGE (IRE)	D O'BYRNE	170000
B C FALBRAV (IRE) - CREAM TEASE (GB)	K YOSHIDA	170000
B F RED RANSOM (USA) - DANCE PARADE (USA)	C GORDON-WATSON BS	170000
B C SADLER'S WELLS (USA) - ZARAWA (IRE)	D O'BYRNE	170000
SILVER SHOON (IRE) GR F FASLIYEV (USA) - LIMPOPO (GB)	D K WELD	165000

Name and Breeding	Purchaser	Guineas
IN HER SHOES (GB) CH F PIVOTAL (GB) - EBARAYA (IRE)	J MCCALMONT	16500
ALYAZWA (GB) CH C SELKIRK (USA) - ROSE CROIX (USA)	SHADWELL ESTATE	16000
B C PIVOTAL (GB) - TEGGIANO (IRE)	JOHN FERGUSON BS	16000
FAREER (GB) CH C BAHAMIAN BOUNTY (GB) - SONGSHEET (USA)	SHADWELL ESTATE	16000
HIGHLAND LASSIE (IRE) B F OASIS DREAM (GB) - ARLESIANA (USA)	CHARLES EGERTON BS	16000
B C PIVOTAL (GB) - KIROV (GB)	HONG KONG JOCKEY CLUB	16000
B C ACCLAMATION (GB) - TASHA'S DREAM (USA)	C GORDON-WATSON BS	16000
SILVADOR (GB) GR C SELKIRK (USA) - DALI'S GREY (GB)	J BRUMMITT	16000
B C ROYAL APPLAUSE (GB) - NEEDWOOD EPIC (GB)	BBA (IRELAND)	16000
INFIRAAD (GB) CH C HAAFHD (GB) - RAZZLE (IRE)	SHADWELL ESTATE	16000
B C SADLER'S WELLS (USA) - MISS SATAMIXA (FR)	D O'BYRNE	16000
TALENT SCOUT (IRE) B C EXCEED AND EXCEL (AUS) - TAALLUF (USA)	JOHN FERGUSON BS	16000
B F DANETIME (IRE) - VILLA NOVA (IRE)	BBA (IRELAND)	16000
B C MONTJEU (IRE) - LADY LAHAR (GB)	BBA (IRELAND)	16000
B C DANSILI (GB) - MERLE (GB)	B O'RYAN	16000
B C MONTJEU (IRE) - AIM FOR THE TOP (USA)	JOHN MCCORMACK BS	16000
B C GALILEO (IRE) - SEVI'S CHOICE (USA)	B O'RYAN	15500
LA ZONA (IRE) B F SINGSPIEL (IRE) - REINE DE NEIGE (GB)	PETER DOYLE BS	15500
B C INDIAN RIDGE - VIOLET SPRING (IRE)	P F I COLE	15500
TWISTED (GB) CH C SELKIRK (USA) - WINDING (USA)	BLANDFORD BS	15500
KITANESTRA (IRE) B F SADLER'S WELLS (USA) - ANGELICA TREE (CAN)	LITEX COMMERCE	15500
CH F DALAKHANI (IRE) - SLAP SHOT (IRE)	C DE MOUBRAY	15000
B F GALILEO (IRE) - PILLARS OF SOCIETY (IRE)	MISS M O'TOOLE	15000
AMSAAR (GB) B/BR C KYLLACHY (GB) - SELKIRK ROSE (IRE)	SHADWELL ESTATE	15000
B C KING'S BEST (USA) - TIME SAVED (GB)	JOHN FERGUSON BS	15000
B F HAWK WING (USA) - HAMPTON LUCY (IRE)	ALLAN BLOODLINES	15000
B C DESERT STYLE (IRE) - SANPALA (IRE)	P F I COLE	15000
CYGNET (GB) B C DANSILI (GB) - BALLET PRINCESS (GB)	C GORDON-WATSON BS	15000
TAAMEER (GB) B C BEAT HOLLOW (GB) - VAYAVAIG (GB)	SHADWELL ESTATE	15000
B C SADLER'S WELLS (USA) - EDETANA (USA)	HUGO MERRY BS	15000
B F MARJU (IRE) - SZABO (IRE)	HUGO MERRY BS	15000
PENINSULA GIRL (IRE) B F CAPE CROSS (IRE) - RIO DE JUMEIRAH (GB)	GILL RICHARDSON BS	15000
CHEAP THRILLS (GB) CH F BERTOLINI (USA) - LICENCE TO THRILL (GB)	R DOYLE	15000
GR F DALAKHANI (IRE) - MASSARRA (GB)	BBA (IRELAND)	15000
B C OASIS DREAM (GB) - KANGRA VALLEY (GB)	C GORDON-WATSON BS	15000
REFLECTED IMAGE (IRE) B F REFUSE TO BEND (IRE) - ANGELIC SOUNDS (USA)	ANTHONY STROUD BS	15000
NEGOTIATION (IRE) B C REFUSE TO BEND (IRE) - DONA ROYALE (IRE)	JOHN FERGUSON BS	15000
ALBAHER (IRE) B C OASIS DREAM (GB) - DANCE SEQUENCE (USA)	SHADWELL ESTATES	15000
NOORDHOEK KID (GB) B C DANSILI (GB) - ANQOOD (IRE)	CHARLES EGERTON BS	15000
B C JOHANNESBURG (USA) - POLICY SETTER (USA)	DAVID METCALFE BS	15000
B C GIANT'S CAUSEWAY - ALSTEMERIA (IRE)	VENDOR	15000
LACROSSE (GB) B C CAPE CROSS (IRE) - LA SKY (IRE)	VENDOR	15000
CH C INDIAN RIDGE - SCRUPLE (IRE)	J GOSDEN	15000
TOO TALL (GB) B C MEDICEAN (GB) - EMBARK (GB)	C GORDON-WATSON BS	14500
SALFORD SPIRIT (GB) B C DESERT SUN (GB) - CRIBELLA (USA)	D ELSWORTH	14500
BR F GALILEO (IRE) - COMMON KNOWLEDGE (GB)	E DUNLOP	14500
LA ADELITA (IRE) B F ANABAA (USA) - AIMING (GB)	BBA (IRELAND)	14000
CH C DR FONG (USA) - PARTY DOLL	M JOHNSTON	14000
ALSHAFAFEYA (IRE) B F SAKHEE (USA) - KINCOB (USA)	A GOLD	14000
B C SADLER'S WELLS (USA) - CALADIRA (IRE)	C GORDON-WATSON BS	14000
B F DANSILI (GB) - AZUR (IRE)	MISS M O'TOOLE	14000
B C CELTIC SWING (GB) - MAGICAL PEACE (IRE)	D K WELD	14000
ABLIDA (GB) B F CAPE CROSS (IRE) - JANET (GB)	LITEX COMMERCE	14000
B C ROCK OF GIBRALTAR (IRE) - MARGOT (GB)	K YOSHIDA	14000
B F REFUSE TO BEND (IRE) - LIONNE (GB)	B O'RYAN	14000
SABISTAR (GB) B C GREEN DESERT (USA) - BALISADA (GB)	BLANDFORD BS	14000
CH C INDIAN RIDGE - MYSTIC TEMPO (USA)	J GOSDEN	14000
B F CAPE CROSS (IRE) - DINKA RAJA (USA)	HUGO MERRY BS	14000
B C CAPE CROSS (IRE) - VIOLA DA BRACCIO (IRE)	M BASTARD	14000
B F EXCEED AND EXCEL (AUS) - DAME BLANCHE (IRE)	BBA (IRELAND)	14000
B C DANSILI (GB) - MYLANIA (GB)	C GORDON-WATSON BS	14000
B C DANSILI (GB) - ROYAL FLAME (GB)	BLANDFORD BS	14000
MONITOR CLOSELY (IRE) B C OASIS DREAM (GB) - INDEPENDENCE (GB)	BLANDFORD BS	14000
ELIZA DOOLITTLE (GB) B F ROYAL APPLAUSE (GB) - GREEN SUPREME (GB)	J FANSHAWE	14000
B C CLODOVIL (IRE) - CAFE CREME (IRE)	BADGERS BS	13500
CH C SPINNING WORLD (USA) - RUN TO JANE (IRE)	JOHN WARREN BS	13500
HIGHTIME HEROINE (IRE) B F DANETIME (IRE) - ESTERLINA (IRE)	CHEVELEY PARK STUD	13500
ROCKY'S PRIDE (IRE) B C ROCK OF GIBRALTAR (IRE) - L'ANIMEE (GB)	CHEVELEY PARK STUD	13500
B C GALILEO (IRE) - BEHERA	C GORDON-WATSON BS	13000
CH F GIANT'S CAUSEWAY (USA) - AKUNA BAY (USA)	JOHN WARREN BS	13000
B C DANETIME (IRE) - LADY INGABELLE (IRE)	J GOSDEN	13000

Name and Breeding	Purchaser	Guineas
SIODUIL (IRE) GR F OASIS DREAM (GB) - INDIAN BELLE (IRE)	BBA (IRELAND)	130000
B C PEINTRE CELEBRE (USA) - INCHBERRY (GB)	BBA (IRELAND)	130000
BR C ROCK OF GIBRALTAR (IRE) - TWICE THE EASE (GB)	BLANDFORD BS	130000
B C KYLLACHY (GB) - TRIPLE SHARP (GB)	T NERSES	130000
B C SELKIRK (USA) - LEGEND HAS IT (IRE)	A BALDING	130000
WAAHEJ (GB) B C HAAFHD (GB) - MADAM NINETTE (GB)	SHADWELL ESTATE	130000
B C DALAKHANI (IRE) - PINAFLORE (FR)	J GOSDEN	130000
NORMANDIE ART (GB) B F RAINBOW QUEST (USA) - LIGHT WIND (GB)	S ROBERTS	125000
GR F VERGLAS (IRE) - FACTICE (USA)	VENDOR	125000
KAZBOW (IRE) B C RAINBOW QUEST (USA) - KASOTA (IRE)	C GORDON-WATSON BS	125000
CH C PIVOTAL (GB) - GRANDALEA (GB)	MCKEEVER ST LAWRENCE	125000
B C DANEHILL DANCER (IRE) - WILLOWBRIDGE (IRE)	CITYWEST INC	125000
HYDRANT (GB) B C HAAFHD (GB) - SPRING (GB)	JOHN WARREN BS	125000
CH F GALILEO (IRE) - ZIETORY (GB)	BBA (IRELAND)	125000
DANEHILL DESTINY (GB) B F DANEHILL DANCER (IRE) - COMERAINCOMESHINE (GB)	CHEVELEY PARK STUD	120000
B F EXCEED AND EXCEL (AUS) - KARAYB (IRE)	S HILLEN	120000
CROSSFIRE (IRE) B C CAPE CROSS (IRE) - CINNAMON ROSE (USA)	SIR M PRESCOTT	120000
SHAWEEL (GB) B C DANSILI (GB) - COODEN BEACH (GB)	SHADWELL ESTATES	120000
B C DANSILI (GB) - ROWAN FLOWER (IRE)	C GORDON-WATSON BS	120000
ALL ABOUT YOU (IRE) B C MIND GAMES (GB) - EXPECTATION (IRE)	C GORDON-WATSON BS	120000
B C DANEHILL DANCER (IRE) - GREEN SWALLOW (FR)	HONG KONG JOCKEY CLUB	120000
DUBAI CREST (GB) B C DUBAI DESTINATION (USA) - ON THE BRINK (GB)	MRS A PERRETT	120000
ALMUTAWAAZIN (GB) B C NAYEF (USA) - CROWN WATER (USA)	SHADWELL ESTATE	120000
DREAMCOAT (GB) CH C PIVOTAL (GB) - FOLLOW A DREAM (USA)	VENDOR	120000
MY SUPERSTAR (GB) B F SADLER'S WELLS (USA) - MADDIE MAY (USA)	VENDOR	120000
B C ELUSIVE QUALITY (USA) - OCEAN SILK (USA)	MCKEEVER ST LAWRENCE	120000
CH/GR C CADEAUX GENEREUX - MISS UNIVERSE (IRE)	JOHN FERGUSON BS	120000
CH F EXCEED AND EXCEL (AUS) - COOLRAIN LADY (IRE)	B SMART	120000
B C HAAFHD (GB) - SHANTY (GB)	C GORDON-WATSON BS	120000
CRIMEA (IRE) B C KHELEYF (USA) - RUSSIAN COUNTESS (USA)	M JOHNSTON	120000
CH C PIVOTAL (GB) - BLIXEN (USA)	BLANDFORD BS	120000
B C KYLLACHY (GB) - HASTE (GB)	J ALLISON	120000
CH C DANEHILL DANCER (IRE) - BRAVO DANCER (GB)	BBA (IRELAND)	120000
B F PIVOTAL (GB) - BOLSHAYA (GB)	HUGO MERRY BS	115000
LAVA STEPS (USA) B C GIANT'S CAUSEWAY (USA) - MIZNAH (IRE)	S MOORE	115000
B C WHERE OR WHEN (IRE) - SECRET FLAME (GB)	JOHN WARREN BS	115000
B F EXCEED AND EXCEL (AUS) - PANGLOSSIAN (IRE)	MCKEEVER ST LAWRENCE	115000
MY VERSE (GB) B F EXCEED AND EXCEL (AUS) - REEMATNA (GB)	ANTHONY STROUD BS	115000
CH F KING'S BEST (USA) - MISS HONORINE (USA)	T STEWART	115000
GALLAGHER (GB) CH C BAHAMIAN BOUNTY (GB) - ROO (GB)	CHARLES EGERTON BS	115000
B C BAHAMIAN BOUNTY (GB) - MONAIYA	H MORRISON	115000
CH F MEDICEAN (GB) - VENTO DEL ORENO (FR)	T O'BRIEN	115000
B/BR F HAWK WING (USA) - HAWALA (IRE)	W HAGGAS	115000
LA DE TWO (IRE) CH C GALILEO (IRE) - FIRECREST (USA)	VENDOR	115000
B F RED RANSOM (USA) - STRING QUARTET (USA)	ANTHONY STROUD BS	110000
CH C DR FONG (USA) - CARAMBOLA (IRE)	ANGIE SYKES BS	110000
GR F DALAKHANI (IRE) - CITY ZONE (IRE)	MISS M O'TOOLE	110000
MAWSEM (IRE) CH C MONSUN (GER) - IRTIFA (GB)	SHADWELL ESTATE	110000
B C DANEHILL DANCER (IRE) - LITTLETON ARWEN (USA)	S J LEAHY BS	110000
MASTOORA (IRE) B F ACCLAMATION (GB) - SACRED LOVE (IRE)	SHADWELL ESTATE	110000
CH F NAMID (GB) - DUNDEL (IRE)	PETER DOYLE BS	110000
ASSIGNMENT (IRE) B C BARATHEA (IRE) - URGENT LIAISON (IRE)	JOHN WARREN BS	110000
MAGALING (IRE) CH C MEDICEAN (GB) - FLING (GB)	L CUMANI	110000
B C ROCK OF GIBRALTAR (IRE) - TAKING LIBERTIES (IRE)	P F I COLE	110000
B F MARJU (GB) - LUNDA (IRE)	HUNTINGDON/NORRIS	110000
CARTOON (GB) BR F DANEHILL DANCER (IRE) - ELFIN LAUGHTER (GB)	JOHN WARREN BS	110000
HOLAMO (IRE) BR F MONTJEU (IRE) - HOLY NOLA (USA)	VENDOR	110000
B F ROCK OF GIBRALTAR (IRE) - PURPLE SPIRIT (IRE)	D O'BYRNE	105000
STRAWBERRYDAIQUIRI (GB) GR F DANSILI (GB) - STRAWBERRY MORN (CAN)	HUGO MERRY BS	105000
CH F GIANT'S CAUSEWAY (USA) - ZAPPEUSE (USA)	LITEX COMMERCE	105000
HALLIWELL HOUSE (GB) CH F SELKIRK (USA) - DUSTY ANSWER (GB)	CHEVELEY PARK STUD	105000
B F MONTJEU (IRE) - CHILD PRODIGY (IRE)	SHEEHY BROS	105000
B C OASIS DREAM (GB) - SUNSHINE N'SHOWERS (GB)	D MURPHY	105000

HIGH-PRICED YEARLINGS OF 2007 AT GOFFS

The following yearlings realised 72,000 euros and over at Goffs Sales in 2007:-

Name and Breeding	Purchaser	Euro
GR F SADLER'S WELLS (USA) - ALBANOVA (GB)	D L O'BYRNE	2400C
B F ROCK OF GIBRALTAR (IRE) - SPIRIT OF TARA (IRE)	DE BURGH/FARRINGTON	9000
B C MONTJEU (IRE) - MASKAYA (IRE)	D L O'BYRNE	6500
B C GALILEO (IRE) - ONEREUSE (GB)	D L O'BYRNE	6500
CH C INDIAN RIDGE - ALLELUIA (GB)	C GORDON-WATSON BS	600C
B C MONTJEU (IRE) - PARK CRYSTAL (IRE)	D L O'BYRNE	575C
CH C GALILEO (IRE) - CORRINE (IRE)	C GORDON-WATSON BS	550C
B C MONTJEU (IRE) - CRAFTY EXAMPLE (USA)	D L O'BYRNE	450C
B F INVINCIBLE SPIRIT (IRE) - WATCH THE CLOCK (GB)	NEWTOWN ANNER STUD	440C
SOLAS NA GEALAI (IRE) B C GALILEO (IRE) - LUNAR LUSTRE (IRE)	J S BOLGER	435C
B C SADLER'S WELLS (USA) - KATIYFA	D L O'BYRNE	420C
B C SADLER'S WELLS (USA) - WELSH LOVE	D L O'BYRNE	380C
B C MONTJEU (IRE) - DANCE DESIRE (IRE)	D L O'BYRNE	370C
B C HAWK WING (USA) - ANNOUNCING PEACE (GB)	D L O'BYRNE	350C
INTENSE FOCUS (IRE) B C GIANT'S CAUSEWAY (USA) - DANELETA (IRE)	J S BOLGER	340C
CH F KINGMAMBO (USA) - PIQUETNOL (USA)	J ALBRECHT	325C
B F MONTJEU (IRE) - MAJINSKAYA (FR)	HERBAGE STUD	320C
ALMEDAWAR (IRE) B C ELUSIVE QUALITY (USA) - LUCKY RAINBOW (USA)	SHADWELL ESTATE	310C
B F SADLER'S WELLS (USA) - TARASCON (IRE)	J MAGNIER	300C
B C MONTJEU (IRE) - CHEAL ROSE (IRE)	BIG RED FARM	3000
B F INVINCIBLE SPIRIT (IRE) - NASSMA (IRE)	BBA (IRELAND)	3000
FORTUNI (IRE) B C MONTJEU (IRE) - DESERT EASE (IRE)	SIR M PRESCOTT	3000
B C DANEHILL DANCER (IRE) - PAY THE BANK	D L O'BYRNE	280C
CH C RAHY (USA) - TANGO CHARLIE (USA)	JOHN FERGUSON BS	2800
B F OASIS DREAM (GB) - HABARIYA (IRE)	VENDOR	2800
COMBAT ZONE (IRE) B C REFUSE TO BEND (IRE) - ZEITING (IRE)	J FERGUSON	280C
GR C JOHANNESBURG (USA) - PAIUTE PRINCESS (FR)	BRIAN GRASSICK BS	2750
B F ROCK OF GIBRALTAR (IRE) - QUIET MOUSE (USA)	GILL RICHARDSON BS	2700
B C DANEHILL DANCER (IRE) - MOUNTAIN LAW (USA)	KERRI RADCLIFFE BS	2700
HIGH CIAN (IRE) B C HIGH CHAPARRAL (IRE) - QUEEN'S MUSIC (USA)	KERRI RADCLIFFE BS	2700
DISCREET AFFAIR (IRE) B F INVINCIBLE SPIRIT (IRE) - LADY ELYSEES (USA)	D K WELD	2700
B C DANEHILL DANCER (IRE) - ZAGREB FLYER (GB)	PEGASUS FARMS	260C
B/BR F STREET CRY (IRE) - SOMETHING MON (USA)	EUGO MONTGOMERY BS	260C
B C KYLLACHY (GB) - POLISH DESCENT (IRE)	C GORDON-WATSON BS	2600
CH F PIVOTAL (GB) - MY GIDDY AUNT (IRE)	NEWTOWN ANNER STUD	2600
B F MONTJEU (IRE) - BONHEUR (IRE)	KERRI RADCLIFFE BS	2600
B/BR C JOHANNESBURG (USA) - NAJIYA (GB)	F STACK	2550
CH C ROCK OF GIBRALTAR (IRE) - CLAXTON'S SLEW (USA)	D K WELD	2550
B C INDIAN RIDGE - NATIVE QUEEN (FR)	D K WELD	2500
B C DANEHILL DANCER (IRE) - LABRUSCA (GB)	D K WELD	2400
B C DANETIME (IRE) - OPTIONAL (GB)	B O'RYAN	2400
RAWAADAH (GB) CH F MONSIEUR BOND (IRE) - AMAZED (GB)	SHADWELL ESTATE	2400
CH F DANEHILL DANCER (IRE) - RIVER FLOW (USA)	BBA (IRELAND)	2400
B F DANSILI (GB) - KALLAVESI (USA)	BBA (IRELAND)	2300
CH C EXCEED AND EXCEL (AUS) - ROYAL FIZZ (IRE)	HONG KONG JOCKEY CLUB	2300
B F KHELEYF (USA) - SILVER ARROW (USA)	B SMART	2300
BR F JOHANNESBURG (USA) - GRABLE (IRE)	M A JARVIS	2300
CH C REFUSE TO BEND (IRE) - BELLA BELLA (USA)	B SMART	2300
PRECIOUS GEM (IRE) B F SADLER'S WELLS (USA) - RUBY (IRE)	D K WELD	2300
B F ONE COOL CAT (USA) - LATEST CHAPTER (IRE)	D L O'BYRNE	2300
MARINA OF VENICE (IRE) CH F GALILEO (IRE) - DAME'S VIOLET (IRE)	J S BOLGER	2300
B F CAPE CROSS (IRE) - ROYAL DEVOTION (IRE)	P EDDIS	2200
CH C INDIAN RIDGE - UPPERVILLE (IRE)	D K WELD	2200
LADY LUACHMHAR (IRE) B F GALILEO (IRE) - RADHWA (FR)	GILL RICHARDSON BS	2200
B C INVINCIBLE SPIRIT (IRE) - BUCKLE (IRE)	M O'TOOLE	2200
LIVALEO (IRE) B C GALILEO (IRE) - LIVADIYA (IRE)	H ROGERS	2200l
B F WAR CHANT - WOODLAND ORCHID (USA)	BBA (IRELAND)	2100
C DANEHILL DANCER (IRE) - VERONICA COOPER (USA)	C GORDON-WATSON BS	2100
CH C GALILEO (IRE) - FOUR GREEN (FR)	D L O'BYRNE	2100
B C DANSILI (GB) - OVAL OFFICE (GB)	PEGASUS FARMS	2100
ALYSTAR (IRE) CH F ROCK OF GIBRALTAR (IRE) - ARPEGE (IRE)	P COLE	2000
LEXCEN (IRE) B C EXCEED AND EXCEL (AUS) - CIDARIS (IRE)	JOHN FERGUSON BS	2000
CAREFREE SMILE (IRE) B F INVINCIBLE SPIRIT (IRE) - FRIPPET (IRE)	D K WELD	2000
MEDICIO (FR) B C MEDICEAN (GB) - COSPICUA (IRE)	SHADWELL ESTATE	2000
B C REFUSE TO BEND (IRE) - KARDASHINA (FR)	M A JARVIS	2000
B F DUBAI DESTINATION (USA) - ESCAPE TO VICTORY (GB)	D WACHMAN	2000
B C MONTJEU (IRE) - MILETRIAN (IRE)	D L O'BYRNE	2000

Name and Breeding	Purchaser	Euros
B F REFUSE TO BEND (IRE) - ATNAB (USA)	B SMART	200000
ROCK RELIEF (IRE) GR C DAYLAMI (IRE) - SHEER BLISS (IRE)	SIR M PRESCOTT	200000
B C DANETIME (IRE) - EXPONENT (USA)	B O'RYAN	200000
CH C GIANT'S CAUSEWAY (USA) - MADEIRA MIST (IRE)	P COLE	200000
MODERN DAY ICON (IRE) B C INVINCIBLE SPIRIT (IRE) - FA E DESFA (GB)	PLANTATION STUD	195000
ALECTRONA (FR) B F INVINCIBLE SPIRIT (IRE) - DOM PENNION (GB)	W SWINBURN	195000
B F DANEHILL DANCER (IRE) - FEATHER BRIDE (IRE)	HALYCON BS	195000
MAR SIN DE (IRE) B F DANETIME (IRE) - SHALL WE TELL (GB)	BBA (IRELAND)	190000
B C INVINCIBLE SPIRIT (IRE) - BELLA MICHELA (IRE)	B SMART	190000
B C GALILEO (IRE) - SILLY GAME (IRE)	D K WELD	190000
B F DANETIME (IRE) - SHEILA BLIGE (GB)	D L O'BYRNE	190000
AIM TO ACHIEVE (IRE) B F GALILEO (IRE) - SABANDER BAY (USA)	BBA (IRELAND)	190000
B F ROYAL APPLAUSE (GB) - RAINBOWS FOR ALL (IRE)	BBA (IRELAND)	190000
B F ROYAL APPLAUSE (GB) - LEUKIPPIDS (IRE)	NEWTOWN ANNER STUD	185000
B C PIVOTAL (GB) - COLLEGE FUND GIRL (IRE)	MCKEEVER ST LAWRENCE	180000
CH C KHELEYF (USA) - SAPHIRE (GB)	J ALLISON	180000
B F EXCEED AND EXCEL (AUS) - SHESASMARTLADY (IRE)	M O'TOOLE	180000
B F ROCK OF GIBRALTAR (IRE) - PATRIMONY (IRE)	J S BOLGER	180000
CH C DANEHILL DANCER (IRE) - RAIN FLOWER (IRE)	BBA (IRELAND)	175000
CH F PIVOTAL (GB) - RASH (GB)	FORM BS	170000
CH C REFUSE TO BEND (IRE) - MISS A NOTE (USA)	B O'RYAN	170000
AL MUGTAREB (IRE) B C ACCLAMATION (GB) - BILLIE BAILEY (USA)	SHADWELL ESTATE	170000
B F MONTJEU (IRE) - CONCEPT (USA)	S & M SYNDICATE	170000
B C KING'S BEST (USA) - SHARPLAW VENTURE (GB)	HONG KONG JOCKEY CLUB	170000
B F ROCK OF GIBRALTAR (IRE) - SPEAK SOFTLY TO ME (USA)	HUGO MERRY BS	165000
BRAVEHEART MOVE (IRE) B C CAPE CROSS (IRE) - TOKEN GESTURE (IRE)	SIR M PRESCOTT	160000
B F KING'S BEST (USA) - LUNGTA (USA)	BBA (GERMANY)	160000
CH C JOHANNESBURG (USA) - PEROVSKIA (USA)	BLANDFORD BS	160000
B F DANEHILL DANCER (IRE) - DOCTRINE (USA)	D L O'BYRNE	160000
VERGLAS DELIGHT (IRE) GR F VERGLAS (IRE) - YOUR VILLAGE (IRE)	F BARRY	160000
B F INVINCIBLE SPIRIT (IRE) - BAILEYS CREAM (GB)	PETER DOYLE BS	160000
CEIST EILE (IRE) B F NOVERRE (USA) - SHARAFANYA (IRE)	BBA (IRELAND)	160000
B F DANETIME (IRE) - DALAL (GB)	D L O'BYRNE	160000
CH F BACHELOR DUKE (USA) - MOOD INDIGO (IRE)	D K WELD	160000
B F ONE COOL CAT (USA) - LOVE EMERALD (USA)	J MAGNIER	160000
B F DANEHILL DANCER (IRE) - KYLEMORE (IRE)	BBA (IRELAND)	155000
B F EXCEED AND EXCEL (AUS) - PACIFIC GROVE (GB)	D K WELD	155000
B F DANEHILL DANCER (IRE) - IGREJA (ARG)	FORM BS	150000
CHERISH THE MOMENT (IRE) B C GALILEO (IRE) - BELLECLAIRE (IRE)	BBA (IRELAND)	150000
STEEL FREE (IRE) B F DANEHILL DANCER (IRE) - CANDELABRA (GB)	RICHARD FRISBY BS	150000
B C KHELEYF (USA) - SAFE CARE (IRE)	JOHN FERGUSON BS	150000
B/BR C CAPE CROSS (IRE) - TSHUSICK (GB)	CASTLEMARTIN & SKYMARC	150000
BR C LINAMIX (FR) - HINT OF HUMOUR (USA)	D K WELD	150000
B F HAWK WING (USA) - THAIDAH (CAN)	DE BURGH/FARRINGTON	150000
GR F VERGLAS (IRE) - LITTLE WHISPER (IRE)	B O'RYAN	150000
DEVOTION TO DUTY (IRE) B C MONTJEU (IRE) - CHARMANTE (USA)	BBA (IRELAND)	150000
B C VAN NISTELROOY (USA) - FABULIST (USA)	F BARRY	150000
B F CAPE CROSS (IRE) - ASPIRATION (IRE)	BBA (IRELAND)	150000
B/BR F MR GREELEY (USA) - PARTY STRIPES (USA)	B O'RYAN	150000
B C MONTJEU (IRE) - CHECK BID (USA)	BBA (IRELAND)	150000
B C GALILEO (IRE) - ALL'S FORGOTTEN (USA)	J S BOLGER	145000
B F DANSILI (GB) - EVENING PROMISE (GB)	B O'RYAN	145000
B/BR C GIANT'S CAUSEWAY (USA) - DARABANKA (IRE)	A BULLRICH	145000
LITTLE CALLA (IRE) CH F INDIAN RIDGE - QUEEN OF PALMS (IRE)	BLANDFORD BS	145000
B F FASLIYEV (USA) - RIBOT'S GUEST (IRE)	SHEEHY BROS	145000
BR F ONE COOL CAT (USA) - TERMANIA (USA)	D L O'BYRNE	145000
SHY APPEAL (IRE) B F BARATHEA (IRE) - SPECIAL CAUSE (IRE)	S BURNS	140000
MUNSAAB (IRE) B C ALHAARTH (IRE) - CLAUSTRA (FR)	SHADWELL ESTATE	140000
B C TIGER HILL (IRE) - SAGAMARTHA (GB)	BLANDFORD BS	140000
B C SADLER'S WELLS (USA) - SUMMER TRYSTING (USA)	D K WELD	140000
GRANSKI (IRE) B C ALHAARTH (IRE) - PURPLE HAZE (IRE)	J WARREN	140000
CHAPTER AND VERSE (IRE) GR C ONE COOL CAT (USA) - BEAUTIFUL HILL (IRE)	BBA (IRELAND)	140000
SULTANS WAY (IRE) B C INDIAN RIDGE - ROSES FROM RIDEY (IRE)	O COLE	140000
FANDITHA (IRE) CH F DANEHILL DANCER (IRE) - SPLENDID (USA)	PETER DOYLE BS	140000
B C EXCEED AND EXCEL (AUS) - STRINGS (GB)	J ALBRECHT	140000
B F ELUSIVE QUALITY (USA) - MISTLE SONG (USA)	B SMART	135000
CHERISH THE MOMENT (IRE) B C GALILEO (IRE) - BELLECLAIRE (IRE)	T HYDE	135000
B F GALILEO (IRE) - BEAUTIFUL NOTE (USA)	R BLACOE	130000
B F EXCEED AND EXCEL (AUS) - ANNALETTA (GB)	BBA (IRELAND)	130000
B C KING'S BEST (USA) - JULIE JALOUSE (USA)	JOHN FERGUSON BS	130000
GR C EL PRADO (IRE) - CINDERELLASLIPPER (USA)	BBA (IRELAND)	130000

Name and Breeding	Purchaser	Euro
B F ROYAL APPLAUSE (GB) - MOHICAN PRINCESS (GB)	C MCCORMACK BS	13000
CH F DANEHILL DANCER (IRE) - WONDROUS STORY (USA)	BBA (IRELAND)	13000
TOMAS AN TSIODA (IRE) BR C BACHELOR DUKE (USA) - KIMOLA (IRE)	J S BOLGER	12500
B F ROCK OF GIBRALTAR (IRE) - MARCH HARE (GB)	D K WELD	12500
GR F CLODOVIL (IRE) - ZARIYBA (IRE)	E LYNAM	12500
LUVMEDO (IRE) B F ONE COOL CAT (USA) - DRESS CODE (IRE)	PETER DOYLE BS	12500
CHIEF SIZEMATTERS (USA) B C BROKEN VOW (USA) - GREY MATTER (USA)	BBA (IRELAND)	12000
CH C OFFICER (USA) - STORMY SURPRISE (USA)	MURAYAMA BS	12000
BORN TO ROCK (IRE) B C STATUE OF LIBERTY (USA) - DAZIYRA (IRE)	J GORMAN	12000
B C DANEHILL DANCER (IRE) - BE DIGNIFIED (IRE)	F SAITO	12000
B F SAKHEE (USA) - EQUITY PRINCESS (GB)	R HAGGAS	12000
CH F MARK OF ESTEEM (IRE) - DREAM TIME (GB)	F BARRY	12000
B C HIGH CHAPARRAL (IRE) - LILI CUP (FR)	M A JARVIS	12000
CH F ROCK OF GIBRALTAR (IRE) - LINDESBERG (IRE)	BBA (IRELAND)	12000
B F STORMING HOME (GB) - TITHCAR (GB)	HUGO MERRY BS	12000
B F FASLIYEV (USA) - OCTAGLEAM (GB)	F BARRY	12000
B F REFUSE TO BEND (IRE) - FOLLOW THAT DREAM (GB)	F BARRY	12000
B F SAHM (USA) - LULUA (USA)	F BARRY	12000
CRUIKADYKE (GB) B C KYLLACHY (GB) - SHOSHONE (GB)	S MOORE	12000
B C HAWK WING (USA) - ON THE NILE (IRE)	SHEEHY BROS	12000
B C SELKIRK (USA) - LEGEND HAS IT (IRE)	RATHBARRY STUD	12000
B F CAPE CROSS (IRE) - INDABA (IRE)	B O'RYAN	11500
GR C VERGLAS (IRE) - HALICARDIA (GB)	MCKEEVER ST LAWRENCE	11500
B C INVINCIBLE SPIRIT (IRE) - TURTULLA (IRE)	PRIME EQUESTRIAN	11500
CH C CHOISIR (AUS) - THERE WITH ME (USA)	PRIME EQUESTRIAN	11500
BR F ONE COOL CAT (USA) - ALAZIMA (USA)	GLENVALE STUD	11500
GLEN MOLLY (IRE) B F DANETIME (IRE) - SONOROUS (IRE)	BBA (IRELAND)	11000
B F INVINCIBLE SPIRIT (IRE) - DOITMYWAY (IRE)	MCKEEVER ST LAWRENCE	11000
B C PROUD CITIZEN (USA) - ENDLESS REWARD (USA)	VENDOR	11000
B F XAAR (GB) - TAROUDANNT (IRE)	BBA (IRELAND)	11000
B F DANEHILL DANCER (IRE) - AN MOSEY (USA)	IRISH RACING SHARES	11000
B C NAYEF (USA) - MY FUNNY VALENTINE (IRE)	BBA (IRELAND)	11000
B F BARATHEA (IRE) - CACHE CREEK (IRE)	B O'RYAN	11000
B F HIGH CHAPARRAL (IRE) - UNCHARTED HAVEN (GB)	BBA (IRELAND)	11000
B F DANEHILL DANCER (IRE) - GOLD SCRIPT (FR)	NEWTOWN ANNER STUD	11000
SUNSHINE ALWAYS (IRE) B/GR C VERGLAS (IRE) - EASY SUNSHINE (USA)	HAWTHORN VILLA STUD	11000
B/BR F TALE OF THE CAT (USA) - OUT OF SYNC (USA)	PRIME EQUESTRIAN	10500
B F BACHELOR DUKE (USA) - PHARAOH'S DELIGHT	R COLLET	10500
SOLASAI (USA) B F MALIBU MOON (USA) - TWIN SAILS (USA)	J S BOLGER	10500
BR F ONE COOL CAT (USA) - ALAZIMA (USA)	FORM BS	10500
B F ACCLAMATION (GB) - SPECIAL DANCER (GB)	BRIAN GRASSICK BS	10500
B C ROYAL APPLAUSE (GB) - ANNA FRED (GER)	W SWINBURN	10500
CH C COMPTON PLACE (GB) - RAINBOW SPECTRUM (FR)	C MCCORMACK BS	10500
B C SADLER'S WELLS (USA) - JAYA (USA)	HIGHFORT STUD	10000
B F BARATHEA (IRE) - SUBITO (GB)	BBA (IRELAND)	10000
B C DANEHILL DANCER (IRE) - PUCK'S CASTLE (USA)	C GORDON-WATSON BS	10000
LA CREME (IRE) B F CLODOVIL (IRE) - DAWIYDA (IRE)	GILL RICHARDSON BS	10000
B F MONTJEU (IRE) - ANOTHER DANCER (FR)	EMERALD BS	10000
B F MARJU (IRE) - NIGHT EYES (IRE)	BBA (IRELAND)	10000
BR F HAWK WING (USA) - HOITY TOITY (GB)	BRIAN GRASSICK BS	10000
KAYFIAR (USA) CH C LION HEART (USA) - IVOR JEWEL (USA)	P COLE	10000
B F OFFICER (USA) - INN BETWEEN (USA)	S MOORE	10000
CH F MR GREELEY (USA) - LAPTOP (USA)	J S BOLGER	10000
B/BR C RAHY (USA) - WENDY VAALA (USA)	F BARRY	10000
ALHABAN (IRE) GR C VERGLAS (IRE) - ANNE TUDOR (USA)	SHADWELL ESTATE	10000
B C EXCEED AND EXCEL (AUS) - HARIYA (IRE)	JOHN WARREN BS	10000
B C CELTIC SWING (GB) - SHENKARA (IRE)	B O'RYAN	10000
QUATERMAIN (GB) CH C PEINTRE CELEBRE (USA) - FANCY LADY (GB)	PRIME EQUESTRIAN	10000
ROYAL TROOPER (IRE) B C HAWK WING (USA) - STRAWBERRY ROAN (USA)	ALLAN BLOODLINES	10000
B/BR C HOLD THAT TIGER (USA) - THE FUR FLEW (USA)	B O'RYAN	10000
MEAN LAE (IRE) B F JOHANNESBURG (USA) - PLUME ROUGE (USA)	VENDOR	10000
B C HAWK WING (USA) - SAVIGNANO (GB)	MCKEEVER ST LAWRENCE	9500
B C SOVIET STAR (USA) - PUTOUT (GB)	MCKEEVER ST LAWRENCE	9500
B F CATCHER IN THE RYE (IRE) - HAUT VOLEE (GB)	BBA (IRELAND)	9500
BRIGHT WIRE (IRE) B C ELUSIVE CITY (USA) - ALINGA (IRE)	RICHARD FRISBY BS	9500
POINTILLIST (IRE) B F PEINTRE CELEBRE (USA) - FOR EXAMPLE (USA)	D REDVERS	9500
B C STROLL (USA) - AFLEET SUMMER (USA)	D REDVERS	9000
B C DANEHILL DANCER (IRE) - GENTLE NIGHT (GB)	JOHN WARREN BS	9000
B C HIGH CHAPARRAL (IRE) - PRINCESSA (GER)	M O'TOOLE	9000
CH F DUBAI DESTINATION (USA) - WILAYIF (USA)	J GORMAN	9000
B F DANEHILL DANCER (IRE) - SNIFFLE (IRE)	D L O'BYRNE	9000

Name and Breeding	Purchaser	Euros
B F ALHAARTH (IRE) - PILGRIM'S WAY (USA)	RICHARD FRISBY BS	90000
CH F SPINNING WORLD (USA) - HIGH SPOT (GB)	S HILLEN	90000
RYAN STYLE (IRE) B C DESERT STYLE (IRE) - WESTLIFE (IRE)	KERRI RADCLIFFE BS	90000
CH F ROYAL ACADEMY (USA) - SUPER SUPREME (IND)	D REVDERS	90000
CH F ROCK OF GIBRALTAR (IRE) - BELSAY (GB)	J ALBRECHT	90000
B F CAPE CROSS (IRE) - KARRI VALLEY (USA)	GILL RICHARDSON BS	90000
B F REFUSE TO BEND (IRE) - FOR EVVA SILCA (GB)	COOLBAY HOUSE STUD	90000
B F GALILEO (IRE) - ALMARAI (USA)	VENDOR	90000
B C ONE COOL CAT (USA) - CONGRESS (IRE)	PETER DOYLE BS	90000
B C MONTJEU (IRE) - INCHOATE (GB)	BBA (IRELAND)	90000
B C ROCK OF GIBRALTAR (IRE) - TAMMANY HALL (IRE)	S KIRK	90000
CH F HALLING (USA) - CAIRNS (UAE)	L M SYNDICATE	90000
B C ELUSIVE CITY (USA) - SAVAGE (IRE)	PETER DOYLE BS	88000
B F ROYAL APPLAUSE (GB) - TRULY YOURS (IRE)	CASTLEMARTIN STUD	88000
B C ROYAL APPLAUSE (GB) - NOBLE LADY (GB)	D REVDERS	85000
B F DANEHILL DANCER (IRE) - LAC DESSERT (USA)	EIRE OG THOROUGHBREDS	85000
B C DANSILI (GB) - HECKLE (GB)	DAVID MCGREAVY BS	85000
B C STRONG HOPE (USA) - SOCCORY (USA)	BBA (IRELAND)	85000
B F CHOISIR (AUS) - ROYAL MISTRESS (GB)	D NICHOLLS	85000
CH F KHELEYF (USA) - GIFT OF SPRING (USA)	BBA (IRELAND)	82000
B C INVINCIBLE SPIRIT (IRE) - TAPPEN ZEE	PETER DOYLE BS	80000
CH F ROCK OF GIBRALTAR (IRE) - WOODYOUSMILEFORME (USA)	DERRYLUSKIN STUD	80000
CH F ALMUTAWAKEL (GB) - AL EURO (FR)	E LYNAM	80000
B F ELUSIVE QUALITY (USA) - VIA BORGHESE (USA)	PRIME EQUESTRIAN	80000
CH C DANEHILL DANCER (IRE) - CASTILIAN QUEEN (USA)	INDEPENDENT TRADERS	80000
B F GALILEO (IRE) - DESERT BLUEBELL	VENDOR	80000
B F MR GREELEY (USA) - QUARREL OVER HALO (USA)	TREE VIEW STUD	80000
CH C DR FONG (USA) - SUBLIME BEAUTY (USA)	ALLAN BLOODLINES	80000
B C DANETIME (IRE) - LODEMA (IRE)	D K WELD	80000
MONACO DREAM (IRE) B F HAWK WING (USA) - PARVENUE (IRE)	BLANDFORD BS	80000
B F DALAKHANI (IRE) - GREEN LASSY (FR)	CHURCHFARM BS	80000
B C HIGH CHAPARRAL (IRE) - GO OUT BACKWARDS (FR)	HONG KONG JOCKEY CLUB	80000
B C PIVOTAL (GB) - LA GANDILIE (FR)	PETER DOYLE BS	80000
B F SADLER'S WELLS (USA) - LADY PROMINENCE (IRE)	VENDOR	80000
CH C GIANT'S CAUSEWAY (USA) - CHIMING (IRE)	Y DE MILAGRO	80000
B C MONTJEU (IRE) - ULIANA (USA)	OAK TREE FARM	80000
B C RESET (AUS) - SCENIC VENTURE (IRE)	B O'RYAN	80000
B C ROCK OF GIBRALTAR (IRE) - OUIJA'S SISTER (GB)	M HALFORD	80000
B F DANETIME (IRE) - SARAH STOKES (IRE)	IRISH RACING SHARES	78000
B F ACCLAMATION (GB) - ALMAVIVA (IRE)	VENDOR	75000
B F ONE COOL CAT (USA) - BEAUTIFUL FRANCE (IRE)	P COLE	75000
B F BACHELOR DUKE (USA) - SHIGERU SUMMIT (GB)	E LYNAM	75000
RAPID RELEASE (CAN) CH C ACTION THIS DAY (USA) - BAIL MONEY (USA)	SIR M PRESCOTT	75000
B F EXCEED AND EXCEL (AUS) - GUJARAT (USA)	J DEWBERRY	75000
CH F ACTION THIS DAY (USA) - LEVER TO HEAVEN (IRE)	D K WELD	75000
B F BERTOLINI (USA) - NIRVANA (USA)	J FLYNN	75000
B C FALBRAV (IRE) - AMATHIA (IRE)	T TATE	75000
B C KEY OF LUCK (USA) - DISREGARD THAT (IRE)	D REVDERS	75000
B C BAHAMIAN BOUNTY (GB) - CLASSIC FAN (USA)	B O'RYAN	75000
B C JOHANNESBURG (USA) - PINA COLADA (GB)	C GORDON-WATSON BS	72000
B C SAFFRON WALDEN (FR) - EZILLA (IRE)	J RYAN	72000
B C NAYEF (USA) - AGONY AUNT (GB)	D REVDERS	72000
CH C DANEHILL DANCER (IRE) - BRAARI (USA)	GLENVALE STUD	72000

HIGH-PRICED YEARLINGS OF 2007 AT DONCASTER SALES
The following yearlings realised 40,000 guineas and over at Doncaster Sales in 2007:-

Name and Breeding	Purchaser	Guineas
B C ACCLAMATION (GB) - CHANGING PARTNERS (GB)	J FERGUSON	1850
CH C RAHY (USA) - HELWA (USA)	RICHARD O'GORMAN BS	1750
B C PIVOTAL (GB) - RED TULLE (USA)	J WARREN	1650
B C DR FONG (USA) - ATLANTIC DESTINY (IRE)	J FERGUSON	1600
OUQBA (GB) B C RED RANSOM (USA) - DANCING MIRAGE (USA)	SHADWELL ESTATES	1400
B F INVINCIBLE SPIRIT (IRE) - OATEY (GB)	BLANDFORD BS	1300
BAWAARDI (IRE) B C ACCLAMATION (GB) - GLOBAL TREND (GB)	SHADWELL ESTATES	1300
B C KYLLACHY (GB) - PALACEGATE EPISODE (IRE)	E LYNAM	1300
B C FAYRUZ - GRANDEL (GB)	J GOSDEN	1200
B C TIGER HILL (IRE) - CARAFE (GB)	DE BURGH FARRINGTON	1200
B C DANETIME (IRE) - MUCKROSS PARK (GB)	STEPHEN HILLEN BS	1150
B C DANSILI (GB) - MARAAMI (GB)	J MCCALMONT	1150
BR F OASIS DREAM (GB) - FEARN ROYAL (IRE)	VENDOR	1150
NAIZAK (GB) CH F MEDICEAN (GB) - SUNNY DAVIS (IRE)	SHADWELL ESTATES	1100
CH F EXCEED AND EXCEL (AUS) - IKAN (IRE)	B SMART	1100
B C CAPE CROSS (IRE) - RAVINE (GB)	C MCCORMACK	1100
HANTA YO (IRE) CH C ALHAARTH (IRE) - TEKINDIA (FR)	J WARREN	1050
CH F BERTOLINI (USA) - ARIAN DA (GB)	BBA (IRELAND)	1000
B C DANETIME (IRE) - DANZ DANZ (GB)	J O'BYRNE	1000
B F GALILEO (IRE) - ROSA DELLE ALPI (USA)	BBA (IRELAND)	1000
CH C JOHANNESBURG (USA) - GOLDEN FLYER (FR)	P CHAPPLE HYAM	1000
DENICES DESERT (GB) B F GREEN DESERT (USA) - DENICE (GB)	HUGO MERRY BS	1000
CH F EXCEED AND EXCEL (AUS) - QUIZ SHOW (GB)	B SMART	960
B C HAWKEYE (IRE) - CANARY BIRD (IRE)	B O'RYAN	950
B C ONE COOL CAT (USA) - CATCH THE MOON (IRE)	J O'BYRNE	950
B F REFUSE TO BEND (IRE) - IKTIDAR (GB)	RICHARD O'GORMAN BS	950
GR C INTIKHAB (USA) - CAYMAN SUNRISE (IRE)	KERN/LILLINGSTON ASS	900
MURAWEG (IRE) B C KHELEYF (USA) - LADY MORANBON (USA)	SHADWELL ESTATES	900
MASSILAH (GB) B F NAMID (GB) - LOVELEAVES (GB)	SHADWELL ESTATES	900
B C CHOISIR (AUS) - EASTERN EMBER	PETER DOYLE BS	850
B C TOBOUGG (IRE) - MARGARET'S GIFT (GB)	M JARVIS	850
B C HAAFHD (GB) - EGO (GB)	BLANDFORD BS	850
SHOOTING PARTY (IRE) B C NOVERRE (USA) - L-WAY FIRST (IRE)	PETER DOYLE BS	840
B C EXCEED AND EXCEL (AUS) - SPINAMIX (GB)	B SMART	840
MAHAAWER (GB) B C ROYAL APPLAUSE (GB) - FOREST PRIZE (GB)	SHADWELL ESTATES	820
REDHEAD (IRE) CH F REDBACK (GB) - RINNEEN (IRE)	PETER DOYLE BS	800
CH F COMPTON PLACE (GB) - SHIFTING MIST (GB)	MCKEEVER ST LAWRENCE	800
B/BR C KHELEYF (USA) - LOVE AND ADVENTURE (USA)	BLANDFORD BS	800
B F REFUSE TO BEND (IRE) - GOLLY GOSH (GB)	R DOYLE	760
B C ACCLAMATION (GB) - KHAFAYA (GB)	W MCKAY	710
B C CENTURY CITY (IRE) - JAY'S RENNY (USA)	B O'RYAN	700
CH C MEDICEAN (GB) - NEFELI (GB)	C MARNANE	700
CH F KYLLACHY (GB) - MISS MELTEMI (IRE)	D ARMSTRONG	700
B F INVINCIBLE SPIRIT (IRE) - TARBELA (IRE)	D REDVERS	680
RETRO (IRE) B C TAGULA (IRE) - CABCHARGE PRINCESS (IRE)	PETER DOYLE BS	680
B C KYLLACHY (GB) - CUTTING REEF (IRE)	A SMITH	660
B C COMPTON PLACE (GB) - RUSH HOUR (IRE)	J BRUMMITT	650
B C ACCLAMATION (GB) - TEODORA (IRE)	B SMART	650
RED ROSSINI (IRE) B C ROSSINI (USA) - LA SCALA (USA)	PETER DOYLE BS	650
KINGSGATE STORM (IRE) GR C MUJADIL (USA) - IN THE HIGHLANDS (GB)	HIGHFLYER BS	650
ARFAJAH (IRE) B F INVINCIBLE SPIRIT (IRE) - BANADIYKA (IRE)	SHADWELL ESTATES	640
GR F DANSILI (GB) - MRS GRAY	BBA (IRELAND)	640
B C KYLLACHY (GB) - GO BETWEEN (GB)	B SMART	640
B C OASIS DREAM (GB) - FINITY (USA)	R O'GORMAN	620
B F AUCTION HOUSE (USA) - ELLWAY QUEEN (USA)	MCKEEVER ST LAWRENCE	600
MASAMAH (IRE) GR C EXCEED AND EXCEL (AUS) - BETHESDA (GB)	SHADWELL ESTATES	600
CH C FUSAICHI PEGASUS (USA) - TO ACT (USA)	EMERALD BS	600
RIPTIDE (GB) B C VAL ROYAL (FR) - GLITTERING IMAGE (IRE)	B O'RYAN	600
B C VAL ROYAL (FR) - RACHEL GREEN (GB)	R O'RYAN	600
CELTIC REBEL (IRE) B C BAHRI (USA) - FARJAH (IRE)	BLANDFORD BS	600
B F KYLLACHY (GB) - ELSIE PLUNKETT (GB)	D BROWN	600
CH C PICCOLO (GB) - FIAMMA ROYALE (FR)	MCKEEVER ST LAWRENCE	580
B C ROYAL APPLAUSE (GB) - WILDWOOD FLOWER (GB)	B SMART	580
SUN SHIP (IRE) B C XAAR (GB) - SILKY DAWN (IRE)	PETER DOYLE BS	580
B C CATCHER IN THE RYE (IRE) - BRAVE DANCE (IRE)	E LYNAM	570
MONACO MISTRESS (IRE) B F ACCLAMATION (GB) - BENDIS (GER)	B HASLAM	570
B C BERTOLINI (USA) - MALCESINE (IRE)	D REDVERS	560

Name and Breeding	Purchaser	Guineas
CH C MEDICAN (GB) - GIUSINA MIA (USA)	E LYNAM	55000
NOBLE JACK (IRE) B C ELUSIVE CITY (USA) - BEGINE (IRE)	PETER DOYLE BS	55000
B C ROYAL APPLAUSE (GB) - QUEEN OF DANCE (IRE)	D REDVERS	55000
B C ACCLAMATION (GB) - STARRY NIGHT (GB)	MR BROWN	55000
CH C SAKHEE (USA) - LATIN REVIEW (IRE)	C BURKE	54000
B C MONSIEUR BOND (IRE) - SONG OF SKYE (GB)	DE BURGH FARRINGTON	54000
GR C VERGLAS (IRE) - AZIA (IRE)	B O'RYAN	53000
RIMTAH (IRE) B F REDBACK (GB) - MIDNIGHT SPECIAL (IRE)	SHADWELL ESTATES	52000
B C FASLIYEV (USA) - NATALIE TOO (USA)	BLANDFORD BS	52000
B C DESERT STYLE (IRE) - DOUBLE EIGHT (IRE)	SHADWELL ESTATES	52000
KNOW BY NOW (GB) B C PICCOLO (GB) - ADDICTED TO LOVE (GB)	T TATE	52000
B C KYLLACHY (GB) - OPENING CEREMONY (USA)	R O'RYAN	52000
B C ROYAL APPLAUSE (GB) - CORINIUM (IRE)	BLANDFORD BS	52000
B F ACCLAMATION (GB) - CARABINE (USA)	JOHN WARREN BS	52000
WOODLARK ISLAND (IRE) B C TAGULA (IRE) - BE MY LOVER (GB)	PETER DOYLE BS	50000
B C HAWK WING - LYRIC FANTASY (IRE)	J WARREN	50000
B F INVINCIBLE SPIRIT (IRE) - TO THE WOODS (IRE)	BLANDFORD BS	50000
CH C BACHELOR DUKE (USA) - TRULY BEWITCHED (USA)	W MUIR	50000
B F WAR CHANT (USA) - SHINING JEWEL (GB)	J MOORE	50000
B C PEACE RULES (USA) - LA CAT (USA)	TALL TREES	50000
B C INVINCIBLE SPIRIT (IRE) - NEED YOU BADLY (GB)	M O'TOOLE	50000
CH C DANEHILL DANCER (IRE) - SILVER SKATES (IRE)	HUGO MERRY BS	50000
JONNY MUDBALL (GB) B C OASIS DREAM - WAYPOINT (GB)	N VAUGHAN	50000
ROSIE TWO (GB) B F ACCLAMATION (GB) - JUST A GLIMMER (USA)	S KITTOW	50000
CH F DANEHILL DANCER (IRE) - BLUEBELL WOOD (IRE)	J O'BYRNE	50000
B C TOBOUGG (IRE) - ALEXANDER BALLET (GB)	ANGELA SYKES BS	50000
CH C TAGULA (IRE) - CARPET LADY (IRE)	WALTER SWINBURN RACING	50000
CH C BIG SHUFFLE (USA) - ROMANZE (GER)	GREEN & GOLD SYNDICATE	50000
B C FASLIYEV (USA) - SAVIERES (IRE)	B O'RYAN	50000
B F ACCLAMATION (GB) - FINAL TRICK (GB)	DAVID REDVERS BS	50000
B C MULL OF KINTYRE (USA) - SERIOUS CONTENDER (IRE)	TALL TREES	48000
B C INVINCIBLE SPIRIT (IRE) - SPECIAL PARK (USA)	MCKEEVER ST LAWRENCE	47000
CH F SPARTACUS (IRE) - PARTY BAG (GB)	S HILLEN	47000
B C NOVERRE (USA) - IT TAKES TWO (IRE)	J DELAHOOKE	47000
B C EXCEED AND EXCEL (AUS) - HIGH STANDARD (GB)	W BROWNE	47000
OCEANS EDGE (GB) BR C NEEDWOOD BLADE (GB) - LADY ROXANNE (GB)	KERN/LILLINGSTON ASS	46000
CH F ALHAARTH (IRE) - NOBLE DANE (IRE)	D REDVERS	46000
FROGNAL (IRE) B C KHELEYF (USA) - SHANNON DORE (IRE)	MCKEEVER ST LAWRENCE	46000
B C NAMID (GB) - CORPS DE BALLET (IRE)	D ARMSTRONG	46000
B F NAMID (GB) - BYE BOLD AILEEN (IRE)	E LYNAM	46000
EAGER TO BOW (IRE) B C ACCLAMATION (GB) - TULLAWADGEEN (IRE)	KERN/LILLINGSTON ASS	46000
CH C NOVERRE (USA) - HARTSTOWN HOUSE (IRE)	DAVID REDVERS BS	46000
B C EXCEED AND EXCEL (AUS) - ANGEL ALYDAR (USA)	IRISH RACING SHARES	46000
CH C INTIKHAB (USA) - SCOTTISH EXILE (IRE)	WILL EDMEADES BS	46000
B F DR FONG (USA) - MYSTIFY (GB)	PETER DOYLE BS	45000
B C ACCLAMATION (GB) - RAZOR SHARP (GB)	J BRUMMITT	45000
B C SPARTACUS (IRE) - HALOMIX (GB)	DE BURGH FARRINGTON	44000
MILIEMIL (GB) B F ACCLAMATION (GB) - LADY BETAMBEAU (IRE)	P COLE	44000
MAWAASEM (IRE) B C ELUSIVE CITY (USA) - JUSTINE AU JARDIN (USA)	SHADWELL ESTATES	44000
SOLIS (GB) B C JOSR ALGARHOUD (IRE) - PASSIFLORA (GB)	J QUINN	44000
CH C MEDECIS (GB) - GREEN BELT (FR)	B O'RYAN	44000
IVOR NOVELLO (IRE) B C NOVERRE (USA) - PEARLY BROOKS (GB)	A SKIFFINGTON	43000
B C DEFINITE ARTICLE (GB) - FORTUNE'S GIRL (GB)	R HAGGAS	43000
B C ROYAL APPLAUSE (GB) - INCISE (GB)	B SMART	42000
DALMUNZIE (IRE) CH F CHOISIR (AUS) - BERENICE (ITY)	J QUINN	42000
GR/RO C EL PRADO (IRE) - VICEREINE (GB)	J MCCARTAN	42000
WEST LEAKE (IRE) B C ACCLAMATION (GB) - KILSHANNY (GB)	BBA (IRELAND)	42000
SHAJEE (IRE) B C ELUSIVE CITY (USA) - NAGIDA (GB)	SHADWELL ESTATES	42000
GR C VERGLAS (IRE) - DAZZLING DANCER (GB)	BBA (IRELAND)	42000
NASSAU BEACH (IRE) B C BAHAMIAN BOUNTY (GB) - OH'CECILIA (IRE)	T EASTERBY	42000
B C TOBOUGG (IRE) - FLEUVE D'OR (IRE)	G HOWSON BS	42000
B C CATCHER IN THE RYE (IRE) - NO WAY (IRE)	IRISH RACING SHARES	41000
CH C BAHAMIAN BOUNTY (GB) - AMANIY (USA)	BLANDFORD BS	40000
CH C EXCEED AND EXCEL (AUS) - ONLY IN DREAMS (GB)	BLANDFORD BS	40000
CH F MONSIEUR BOND (IRE) - FEELING BLUE (GB)	BLANDFORD BS	40000
B C MONSIEUR BOND (IRE) - MAY LIGHT (GB)	E JOHNSON HOUGHTON	40000
LIVELY BLADE (GB) CH C NEEDWOOD BLADE (GB) - BREEZY DAY	R BEDDING	40000
CH C AMERICAN POST (GB) - MARGI (FR)	DE BURGH FARRINGTON	40000
B C ALHAARTH (IRE) - GINTILGALLA (GB)	VENDOR	40000
MYTHICISM (GB) B F OASIS DREAM - ROMANTIC MYTH (USA)	MCKEEVER ST LAWRENCE	40000
B F ROCK OF GIBRALTAR (IRE) - THREE DAYS IN MAY (GB)	R O'RYAN	40000
B C PURSUIT OF LOVE (GB) - SOCIETY ROSE (GB)	A BALDING	40000

HIGH-PRICED YEARLINGS OF 2007 AT TATTERSALLS IRELAND SALE

The following yearlings realised 35,000 euros and over at Tattersalls Ireland Sales in 20

Name and Breeding	Purchaser	E
B F DANEHILL DANCER (IRE) - DANIYSHA (IRE)	EDWARD DALY BS	150
B G MILAN (GB) - I REMEMBER IT WELL (IRE)	B O'RYAN	130
B C DANETIME (IRE) - COLOMA (JPN)	W BROWN	110
B F MONTJEU (IRE) - ALMOND MOUSSE (FR)	S HILLEN	110
CH C PIVOTAL (GB) - CLEAR SPRING (USA)	C MARNANE	90
BR C CATCHER IN THE RYE (IRE) - EJDER (IRE)	B O'RYAN	90
B F JOHANNESBURG (USA) - MARGAY (IRE)	P MASON	85
KING OF TARA (USA) B/BR C SAHM (USA) - LADY PAN JAMMER (IRE)	K ROSS	85
B C SAKHEE (USA) - CANTERLOUPE (IRE)	G LYONS	85
MARTIAL JACK (FR) CH G AGENT BLEU (FR) - LINE SAJ (FR)	S GORMAN	82
B C ELUSIVE CITY (USA) - YA YA (IRE)	A KENNEDY	80
B F PRESENTING (GB) - COOLSHAMROCK (IRE)	KENNYCOURT STUD	75
B C KING'S THEATRE (IRE) - WICKED CRACK (IRE)	A MURPHY	75
BR G PRESENTING (GB) - COOLSILVER (IRE)	HIGHFLYER BS	72
CH C PRESENTING (GB) - KINDLY LIGHT (IRE)	J O'BYRNE	72
ZAVAALA (IRE) CH F ROCK OF GIBRALTAR - ZAVALETA (IRE)	EDWARD DALY BS	72
BR G KALANISI (IRE) - SPECIFIEDRISK (IRE)	VENDOR	72
HEART OF FIRE (IRE) B C MUJADIL (USA) - HEART'S DESIRE (IRE)	F BARRY	70
CH C NAMID (GB) - BINT ALHAARTH (IRE)	D REDVERS	70
GR/RO F DAYLAMI (IRE) - ACTORIS (USA)	B O'RYAN	70
B F REFUSE TO BEND (IRE) - FLYING MILLIE (IRE)	F BARRY	70
SACRAL NIRVANA (FR) CH F MANSONNIEN (FR) - AUBANE (FR)	VENDOR	70
GR F DAYLAMI (IRE) - ATHLUMNEY LADY (GB)	E O'NEILL	68
B G OSCAR (IRE) - LA LUNA (IRE)	HIGHFLYER BS	68
B F EXCEED AND EXCEL (AUS) - LADY OF KILDARE (IRE)	DE BURGH FARRINGTON	65
B C EXCEED AND EXCEL (AUS) - GLYMPSE (GB)	GLOBAL BS	65
B F SOVIET STAR (USA) - FIFE (IRE)	B O'RYAN	64
CH C BAHAMIAN BOUNTY (GB) - PASCALI (GB)	GILL RICHARDSON BS	63
B G FAIR MIX (IRE) - POSH PEARL (GB)	J KEATLEY	63
B C DESERT STYLE (IRE) - SAMARITAN WOMAN (IRE)	M PITMAN	62
CH C CHOISIR (AUS) - TIP TAP TOE (IRE)	HUGO MERRY BS	62
B G KING'S THEATRE (IRE) - GEORGES GIRL (IRE)	BRENDAN BASHFORD BS	60
CH C TAGULA (IRE) - ERNE PROJECT (IRE)	PRIME EQUESTRIAN	60
B C MEDICEAN (GB) - AL SHADEEDAH (USA)	B O'RYAN	60
BR G PRESENTING (GB) - HOLLYGROVE CLICHE (GB)	HIGHFLYER BS	60
B F HAWKEYE (IRE) - BURNIN' MEMORIES (USA)	F BARRY	60
B G KALANISI (IRE) - AKARIYDA (IRE)	P TONERY	60
B G ACCORDION - VUL GALE	HIGHFLYER BS	56
B G FLEMENSFIRTH (USA) - SILVA VENTURE (IRE)	C SWAN	55
B G OSCAR (IRE) - COUMEENOOLE LADY	GLENVIEW HOUSE STUD	55
B G KING'S THEATRE (USA) - GALVINA (FR)	W F CODD	55
BR C INDIAN HAVEN (GB) - LADY CINDERS (IRE)	M THOMPKINS	54
B F DEFINITE ARTICLE (GB) - BELLE MAGELLO (FR)	M TALLON	52
B G FLEMENSFIRTH (USA) - HEATHER BREEZE (IRE)	I FERGUSON	52
LATIN CONNECTION (IRE) B C SOVIET STAR (USA) - VIA VERBANO (IRE)	BBA (IRELAND)	52
B F BACHELOR DUKE (USA) - SOVIET BELLE (IRE)	W BROWNE	52
B/BR F PILSUDSKI (IRE) - FORGOTTEN STAR (IRE)	VENDOR	52
CH G FLEMENSFIRTH (USA) - ROYAL ROSY (IRE)	J O'BYRNE	50
B G OVERBURY (IRE) - SIBERIANSDAUGHTER (IRE)	HIGHFLYER BS	50
B C BAHAMIAN BOUNTY (GB) - DARK EYED LADY (IRE)	PRIME EQUESTRIAN	50
B C OASIS DREAM (GB) - FOREVER PHOENIX (GB)	BBA (IRELAND)	50
B/BR G PRESENTING (GB) - REGAL HOLLY (GB)	G GALVIN (P.S.)	50
B G BENEFICIAL (GB) - FLORIDA (IRE)	KENNYCOURT STUD	50
B G OSCAR (IRE) - SHAPING	J O'BYRNE	50
B G OLD VIC - DRAMATIC DAME (IRE)	BBA (IRELAND)	50
B C DANETIME (IRE) - SCARLET EMPRESS (GB)	S HILLEN	50
B F GROOM DANCER (USA) - KAYDEE QUEEN (IRE)	BEECHES STUD	50
B G BENEFICIAL (GB) - EUROCURRENCY (IRE)	J O'BYRNE	49
B G MILAN (GB) - STRONG PROFIT (IRE)	HIGHFLYER BS	48
B G BAHRI (USA) - PRIVATE COLLECTION (IRE)	D REDVERS	48
B F GALILEO (IRE) - DEUXIEME (IRE)	OAKTREE FARM	48
B G FLEMENSFIRTH (USA) - COMPLAININGBUT (IRE)	W DENNISON	48
B C OLD VIC - DIPPERS DAUGHTER	J O'BYRNE	48
B G SHANTOU (USA) - BACK LOG (IRE)	J O'BYRNE	47
CH G OLD VIC - CLODY GIRL (IRE)	BROWNSTOWN HOUSE STUD	47
CH F NOVERRE (USA) - TWIGGY'S SISTER (IRE)	PRIME EQUESTRIAN	47
B F FANTASTIC LIGHT (USA) - LAMARQUE (IRE)	L STRATTAN	47

Name and Breeding	Purchaser	Euros
B G OLD VIC - LAMBOURNE LACE (IRE)	OAK TREE FARM	47000
B G BOB BACK (USA) - MRS AVERY (IRE)	HIGHFLYER BS	46000
CH C CHOISIR (AUS) - BAHRAIN PEARL (IRE)	W BROWNE	46000
BR G PRESENTING (GB) - GLEN EILE (IRE)	J KEATLEY	46000
B G PRESENTING (GB) - MISTRIC (GB)	VENDOR	46000
CH G FLEMENSFIRTH (USA) - CASTLEHAVEN (IRE)	FUTURATE LTD	45000
B F BAHRI (USA) - MIRWARA (IRE)	E LYNAM	45000
BR G DEFINITE ARTICLE (GB) - ROYAL MOLLY (IRE)	J O'BYRNE	45000
B F ONE COOL CAT (USA) - SAN LUIS REY (GB)	ONEWAY	45000
B C HAWK WING (USA) - MESMERIST (USA)	BBA (IRELAND)	44000
B C HALLING (USA) - SIX NATIONS (USA)	J BOLGER	44000
B G FLEMENSFIRTH (USA) - MY BALOO	G GRIFFIN	44000
B C ELUSIVE CITY (USA) - GLENARFF (USA)	E O'GORMAN	43000
B G FLEMENSFIRTH (USA) - SADDLERS GREEN (IRE)	J O'BYRNE	43000
B C KING'S THEATRE (IRE) - GUEST OF ANCHOR (GB)	J O'BYRNE	43000
B G EXIT TO NOWHERE (USA) - PHARLENG (USA)	DAVID REDVERS BS	42000
B G ANSHAN - DAIZINNI (GB)	S CHRISTIAN	42000
GR F VERGLAS (IRE) - LADYLISHANDRA (IRE)	D REDVERS	42000
B C MUJADIL (USA) - DANESTAR (GB)	D REDVERS	42000
B F OLD VIC - DEE-ONE-O-ONE (GB)	BBA (IRELAND)	42000
CH F ECTON PARK (USA) - DEAR ABIGAIL (USA)	GORDIAN TROELLER BS	41000
B F ELUSIVE CITY (USA) - KING OF ALL (IRE)	D REDVERS	41000
B F FASLIYEV (USA) - SOLTURA (IRE)	J O'BYRNE	40000
ACCLABEN (IRE) B C ACCLAMATION (GB) - JOUR DE GRACE (SWE)	J GLOVER	40000
CH C DEFINITE ARTICLE (GB) - DAPRIKA (FR)	BRENDAN BASHFORD BS	40000
CH C OLD VIC - VITALITY	DEERFIELD STUD	40000
BALLARINA (GB) B F COMPTON PLACE (GB) - MISS ULUWATU (IRE)	S ALSTON	40000
BR C INVINCIBLE SPIRIT (IRE) - MUGHETTA (IRE)	JENSEN BS	40000
BR C TOUT SEUL (IRE) - THORBELLA (GB)	B O'RYAN	40000
B G OSCAR (IRE) - SAMEERZA (FR)	C SWAN	40000
OMNIUM DUKE (IRE) CH C INDIAN HAVEN (GB) - PLEASE BE GOOD (IRE)	A SKIFFINGTON	40000
GR F MARJU (IRE) - LEGAL STEPS (IRE)	E LYNAM	40000
B C FRAAM (GB) - LA PANTHERE (USA)	B O'RYAN	40000
CH C HAWK WING (USA) - SHOOOZ (IRE)	R WILLIAMSON	40000
GR F CLODOVIL (IRE) - KRAYYALEI (IRE)	KILTEELAGH STUD	40000
B F KEY OF LUCK (USA) - MESSINA (IRE)	DE BURGH FARRINGTON	40000
B F KING CHARLEMAGNE (USA) - MISS SERENDIPITY (IRE)	VENDOR	40000
B F OSCAR (IRE) - DEEP SUPREME (IRE)	C O'BRIEN	38000
B F INVINCIBLE SPIRIT (IRE) - IRINATINVIDIO (GB)	E O'GORMAN	38000
BR C KYLLACHY (GB) - KELSO MAGIC (IRE)	BRIERYHILL BS	38000
CH G PRESENTING (GB) - BELMARITA (IRE)	D HASSETT	38000
B C MILAN (GB) - LA CABRILLA	K MCMANUS	38000
B F KING'S THEATRE (IRE) - BOBNVAL (IRE)	P CONDRON	37000
B F ACCLAMATION (GB) - LAMZENA (IRE)	R DOYLE	37000
CH C DAYLAMI (IRE) - DALLAAH (GB)	D REDVERS	37000
CH C INTIKHAB (USA) - ALJEEZA (GB)	M PITMAN	37000
B F INVINCIBLE SPIRIT (IRE) - ELBA (IRE)	E O'GORMAN	37000
GR C ALFLORA (IRE) - CHEEKY MARE (GB)	BALLYDUANE STUD	37000
B F ROYAL APPLAUSE (GB) - FIRST DEGREE (GB)	ALLAN BLOODLINES	36000
B C INVINCIBLE SPIRIT (IRE) - ALEXANDER RIDGE (IRE)	C MARNANE	36000
B G FLEMENSFIRTH (USA) - CASLAIN OG (IRE)	D FLOOD	36000
CH F SHINKO FOREST (IRE) - LAWLESS BRIDGET (GB)	P NEARY	36000
B G FLEMENSFIRTH (USA) - ANOTHER FAIRY (IRE)	O MURPHY	36000
B C ELUSIVE CITY (USA) - HANDY STATION (IRE)	ALLAN BLOODLINES	36000
CH C DEFINITE ARTICLE (GB) - GLENVIEW LAKE (IRE)	DR J O'CONNOR	36000
B F FLEMENSFIRTH (USA) - THE BOAT INN (IRE)	C O'BRIEN	36000
B F DANETIME (IRE) - CLANDOLLY (IRE)	D REDVERS	36000
B F KING'S THEATRE (IRE) - LA GRANDE DAME	M LYNCH	36000
B G MILAN (GB) - GARDEN CITY (IRE)	NOVEMBER BS	36000
CH G OLD VIC - ZAROTE (IRE)	M BROWNE	35000
GR/BR F VERGLAS (IRE) - GOOGOOSH (IRE)	M BASTARD	35000
B C MARJU (IRE) - MAC MELODY (IRE)	E LYNAM	35000
BL C ARTAN (IRE) - NAMORA (GER)	VENDOR	35000
B G MILAN (GB) - HATI ROY (IRE)	GLEADHILL HOUSE STUD	35000
B/BR C CLODOVIL (IRE) - SON CHOU (GB)	D REDVERS	35000
B C KEY OF LUCK (USA) - DESERT ORDER (IRE)	I KALLITHEAS	35000
BR G OSCAR (IRE) - QUENNIE MO GHRA (IRE)	ARGLO ABBEY	35000
B C KING'S THEATRE (IRE) - KEEP HUNTING (IRE)	L CUSACK	35000

1000 GUINEAS STAKES (3y fillies) Newmarket-1 mile

Year	Owner	Winner and Price	Jockey	Trainer	Second	Third	Ran	Time
1967	R Boucher's	FLEET (11/2)	G Moore	N Murless	St Paul Girl	Lacquer	16	1 44.76
1968	Mrs N Murless's	CAERGWRLE (4/1)	A Barclay	N Murless	Photo Flash	Sovereign	14	1 40.38
1969	R Moller's	FULL DRESS (7/1)	R Hutchinson	H Wragg	Hecuba	Motionless	13	1 44.53
1970	Jean, Lady Ashcombe's	HUMBLE DUTY (3/1)	L Piggott	P Walwyn	Gleam	Black Satin	12	1 42.13
1971	Mrs R Stanley's	ALTESSE ROYALE (25/1)	Y Saint Martin	N Murless	Super Honey	Catherine Wheel	10	1 40.90
1972	G Pope's	WATERLOO (8/1)	E Hide	J W Watts	Marisela	Rose Dubarry	18	1 39.49
1973	The Queen's	MYSTERIOUS (11/1)	G Lewis	N Murless	Jacinth	Shellshock	14	1 42.12
1974	Mrs D O' Kelly's	HIGHCLERE (12/1)	J Mercer	R Hern	Polygamy	Mrs Twiggywinkle	15	1 40.32
1975	D Wildenstein's	NOCTURNAL SPREE (14/1)	J Roe	S Murless	Girl Friend	Joking Apart	16	1 41.65
1976	Mrs E Kettlewell's	FLYING WATER (2/1)	Y Saint Martin	A Penna	Konata	Kesar Queen	25	1 37.83
1977	R Bonnycastle's	MRS MCARDY (16/1)	E Hide	B Hills	Freeze the Secret	Sanedtki	18	1 40.07
1978	Helena Springfield Ltd's	ENSTONE SPARK (35/1)	E Johnson	M W Easterby	Fair Salinia	Seraphima	16	1 41.56
1979	O Phipps's	ONE IN A MILLION (evens)	J Mercer	H Cecil	Abbeydale	Yanuka	17	1 43.06
1980	H Joel's	QUICK AS LIGHTNING (12/1)	B Rouse	J Dunlop	Our Home	Mrs Penny	23	1 41.89
1981	Sir P Oppenheimer's	FAIRY FOOTSTEPS (6/4)	L Piggott	H Cecil	Tolmi	Go Leasing	14	1 40.43
1982	Maktoum Al-Maktoum's	ON THE HOUSE (33/1)	J Reid	H Wragg	Time Charter	Dione	15	1 40.45
1983	M Lemos's	MA BICHE (5/2)	F Head	Mme C Head	Favoridge	Habibti	14	1 41.71
1984	Sheikh Mohammed's	PEBBLES (8/1)	P Robinson	C Brittain	Meis El-Reem	Desirable	15	1 36.18
1985	R Ranier's	OH SO SHARP (2/1)	S Cauthen	H Cecil	Al Bahathri	Bella Colora	17	1 36.85
1986	S Niarchos's	MIDWAY LADY (10/1)	R Cochrane	B Hanbury	Maysoon	Sonic Lady	15	1 41.54
1987	E Aland's	MIESQUE (15/8)	F Head	F Boutin	Milligram	Interval	14	1 38.48
1988	Sheikh Mohammed's	RAVINELLA (4/5)	G W Moore	Mme C Head	Dabaweyaa	Diminuendo	12	1 40.88
1989	Hamdan Al-Maktoum's	MUSICAL BLISS (7/2)	W R Swinburn	M Stoute	Kerrera	Aldbourne	7	1 42.69
1990	Hamdan Al-Maktoum's	SALSABIL (6/4)	W Carson	J Dunlop	Heart of Joy	Negligent	10	1 38.06
1991	Maktoum Al-Maktoum's	SHADAYID (4/6)	W Carson	J Dunlop	Kooyonga	Crystal Gazing	14	1 38.18
1992	Maktoum Al-Maktoum's	HATOOF (5/1)	W R Swinburn	Mme C Head	Marling	Kenbu	14	1 39.45
1993	Mohamed Obaida's	SAYYEDATI (4/1)	W R Swinburn	C Brittain	Niche	Aljan	15	1 37.34
1994	R Sangster's	LAS MENINAS (12/1)	J Reid	J Stack	Balanchine	Coup de Genie	15	1 36.72
1995	Hamdan Al-Maktoum's	HARAYIR (5/1)	Pat Eddery	Major W R Hern	Aqaarid	Moonshell	13	1 36.71
1996	Wafic Said's	BOSRA SHAM (10/11)	Pat Eddery	H Cecil	Matiya	Bint Shadayid	13	1 37.75
1997	Greenbay Stables Ltd's	SLEEPYTIME (5/1)	L Dettori	H Cecil	Oh Nellie	Dazzle	16	1 37.66
1998	Godolphin's	CAPE VERDI (100/30)	L Dettori	S bin Suroor	Shahtoush	Exclusive	16	1 37.86
1999	K Abdulla's	WINCE (4/1)	K Fallon	H Cecil	Wannabe Grand	Valentine Waltz	22	1 37.91
2000	Hamdan Al-Maktoum's	LAHAN (4/1)	R Hills	J Gosden	Princess Ellen	Petrushka	18	1 36.38
2001	Sheikh Ahmed Al Maktoum's	AMEERAT (11/1)	P Robinson	M Jarvis	Muwakleh	Toroca	15	1 36.38
2002	Godolphin's	KAZZIA (14/1)	L Dettori	Saeed bin Suroor	Snowfire	Alaska	17	1 37.85
2003	Cheveley Park Stud's	RUSSIAN RHYTHM (12/1)	K Fallon	Sir M Stoute	Six Perfections	Intercontinental	19	1 38.43
2004	Duke of Roxburghe's	ATTRACTION (11/4)	K Darley	M Johnston	Sundrop	Hathah	16	1 36.70
2005	Mrs John Magnier & M M Tabor's	VIRGINIA WATERS (12/1)	K Fallon	A O'Brien	Maids Causeway	Vista Bella	13	1 36.50
2006	M Sly, Dr Davies & Mrs P Sly's	SPECIOSA (10/1)	M Fenton	Mrs P Sly	Confidential Lady	Nasheej	20	1 40.50
2007	M Ryan's	FINSCEAL BEO (5/4)	K Manning	J Bolger	Arch Swing	Simply Perfect	21	1 34.94

2000 GUINEAS STAKES (3y) Newmarket-1 mile

Year	Owner	Winner and Price	Jockey	Trainer	Second	Third	Ran	Time
1967	H Joel's	ROYAL PALACE (100/30)	G Moore	N Murless	Taj Dewan	Missile	18	1 39.37
1968	R Guest's	SIR IVOR (11/8)	L Piggott	V O'Brien	Petingo	Jimmy Reppin	10	1 39.26
1969	J Brown's	RIGHT TACK (15/2)	G Lewis	J Sutcliffe	Tower Walk	Welsh Pageant	13	1 41.65
1970	C Engelhard's	NIJINSKY (4/7)	L Piggott	V O'Brien	Yellow God	Roi Soleil	14	1 41.54
1971	Mrs J Hislop's	BRIGADIER GERARD (11/2)	J Mercer	R Hern	Mill Reef	My Swallow	6	1 39.20
1972	Sir J Thorn's	HIGH TOP (85/40)	W Carson	B Van Cutsem	Roberto	Sun Prince	12	1 40.82
1973	Mrs B Davis's	MON FILS (50/1)	F Durr	R Hannon	Noble Decree	Sharp Edge	18	1 42.97
1974	Mme M Berger's	NONOALCO (19/2)	Y Saint Martin	F Boutin	Giacometti	Apalachee	12	1 39.53
1975	C d'Alessio's	BOLKONSKI (33/1)	G Dettori	H Cecil	Grundy	Dominion	24	1 39.53
1976	C d'Alessio's	WOLLOW (evens)	G Dettori	H Cecil	Vitiges	Thieving Demon	17	1 38.09
1977	N Schibbye's	NEBBIOLO (20/1)	G Curran	K Prendergast	Tachypous	The Minstrel	18	1 38.54
1978	J Hayter's	ROLAND GARDENS (28/1)	F Durr	D Sasse	Remainder Man	Weth Man	19	1 47.33
1979	A Shead's	TAP ON WOOD (20/1)	S Cauthen	B Hills	Kris	Young Generation	20	1 43.60
1980	K Abdulla's	KNOWN FACT (14/1)	W Carson	J Tree	Posse	Night Alert	14	1 40.46

(Nureyev in first disqualified)

Year	Owner	Winner and Price	Jockey	Trainer	Second	Third	Ran	Time
1981	Mrs A Munos's	TO-AGORI-MOU (5/2)	G Starkey	G Harwood	Mattaboy	Bel Bolide	19	1 41.43
1982	G Oldham's	ZINO (8/1)	F Head	F Boutin	Wind and Wuthering	Tender King	26	1 37.13
1983	R Sangster's	LOMOND (9/1)	Pat Eddery	V O'Brien	Tolomeo	Muscatite	16	1 43.87
1984	R Sangster's	EL GRAN SENOR (15/8)	Pat Eddery	V O'Brien	Chief Singer	Lear Fan	9	1 37.41
1985	Maktoum Al Maktoum's	SHADEED (15/8)	L Piggott	M Stoute	Bairn	Supreme Leader	15	1 37.41
1986	K Abdulla's	DANCING BRAVE (15/8)	G Starkey	G Harwood	Green Desert	Huntingdale	15	1 40.00
1987	J Horgan's	DON'T FORGET ME (9/1)	W Carson	R Hannon	Bellotto	Midyan	13	1 36.74
1988	H H Aga Khan's	DOYOUN (4/5)	W R Swinburn	M Stoute	Charmer	Bellefella	9	1 41.73
1989	Hamdan Al-Maktoum's	NASHWAN (3/1)	W Carson	R Hern	Ezbourne	Danehill	14	1 36.44
1990	John Horgan's	TIROL (9/1)	M Kinane	R Hannon	Machiavellian	Anshan	14	1 35.84
1991	Lady Beaverbrook's	MYSTIKO (13/2)	M Roberts	C Brittain	Lycius	Ganges	14	1 37.83
1992	R Sangster's	RODRIGO DE TRIANO (6/1)	L Piggott	P Chapple-Hyam	Lucky Lindy	Pursuit of Love	16	1 38.37
1993	K Abdulla's	ZAFONIC (5/6)	Pat Eddery	A Fabre	Barathea	Bin Ajwaad	14	1 35.32
1994	G R Bailey Ltd's	MISTER BAILEYS (16/1)	J Weaver	M Johnston	Grand Lodge	Colonel Collins	23	1 35.08
1995	Sheikh Mohammed's	PENNEKAMP (9/2)	T Jarnet	A Fabre	Celtic Swing	Bahri	11	1 35.16
1996	Godolphin's	MARK OF ESTEEM (11/2)	L Dettori	S bin Suroor	Even Top	Bijou D'Inde	16	1 37.59
1997	M Tabor & Mrs J Magnier's	ENTREPRENEUR (11/2)	M Kinane	M Stoute	Revoque	Poteen	16	1 35.64
1998	M Tabor & Mrs J Magnier's	KING OF KINGS (7/2)	M Kinane	A O'Brien	Lend A Hand	Border Arrow	18	1 39.25
1999	Godolphin's	ISLAND SANDS (10/1)	L Dettori	S Bin Suroor	Enrique	Mujahid	16	1 37.74
2000	Saeed Suhail's	KINGS BEST (13/2)	K Fallon	Sir M Stoute	Giant's Causeway	Barathea Guest	27	1 37.77
2001	Lord Weinstock's	GOLAN (9/1)	K Fallon	Sir M Stoute	Tamburlaine	Frenchmans Bay	18	1 37.48
2002	Sir A Ferguson & Mrs J Magnier's	ROCK OF GIBRALTAR (9/1)	J Murtagh	A O'Brien	Hawk Wing	Redback	22	1 36.50
2003	Moyglare Stud Farm's	REFUSE TO BEND (9/2)	P J Smullen	D Weld	Zafeen	Norse Dancer	20	1 37.98
2004	Hamdan Al Maktoum's	HAAFHD (11/2)	R Hills	B Hills	Snow Ridge	Azamour	14	1 36.60
2005	M M Tabor & Mrs John Magnier's	FOOTSTEPSINTHESAND (13/2)	K Fallon	A O'Brien	Rebel Rebel	Kandidate	19	1 36.10
2006	Mrs J, M M Tabor, Mr M Tabor &	GEORGE WASHINGTON (6/4)	K Fallon	A O'Brien	Sir Percy	Olympian Odyssey	14	1 36.80
2007	Mr D Smith's	COCKNEY REBEL (25/1)	O Peslier	G Huffer	Vital Equine	Dutch Art	24	1 35.28

DERBY STAKES (3y) Epsom-1 mile 4 furlongs 10 yards

Year	Owner	Winner and Price	Trainer	Jockey	Second	Third	Ran	Time
1966	Lady Z Wernher's	CHARLOTTOWN (5/1)	G Smyth	A Breasley	Pretendre	Black Prince	25	2 37.63
1967	H Joel's	ROYAL PALACE (7/4)	N Murless	G Moore	Ribocco	Dart Board	22	2 38.36
1968	H Guest's	SIR IVOR (4/5)	V O'Brien	L Piggott	Connaught	Mount Athos	13	2 38.73
1969	A Budgett's	BLAKENEY (15/2)	A Budgett	E Johnson	Shoemaker	Prince Regent	26	2 40.30
1970	C Engelhard's	NIJINSKY (11/8)	V O'Brien	L Piggott	Gyr	Stintino	11	2 34.68
1971	P Mellon's	MILL REEF (100/30)	I Balding	G Lewis	Linden Tree	Irish Ball	21	2 37.14
1972	J Galbreath's	ROBERTO (3/1)	V O'Brien	L Piggott	Rheingold	Pentland Firth	22	2 36.09
1973	A Budgett's	MORSTON (25/1)	A Budgett	E Hide	Cavo Doro	Freefoot	25	2 35.92
1974	Mrs N. Phillips's	SNOW KNIGHT (50/1)	P Nelson	B Taylor	Imperial Prince	Giacometti	18	2 35.04
1975	Dr C Vittadini's	GRUNDY (5/1)	P Walwyn	Pat Eddery	Nobiliary	Hunza Dancer	18	2 35.35
1976	N B Hunt's	EMPERY (10/1)	M Zilber	L Piggott	Relkino	Oats	23	2 35.69
1977	R Sangster's	THE MINSTREL (5/1)	V O'Brien	L Piggott	Hot Grove	Blushing Groom	22	2 36.44
1978	Lord Halifax's	SHIRLEY HEIGHTS (8/1)	J Dunlop	G Starkey	Hawaiian Sound	Remainder Man	25	2 35.30
1979	Sir M Sobell's	TROY (6/1)	R Hern	W Carson	Dickens Hill	Northern Baby	23	2 36.59
1980	Mrs A Plesch's	HENBIT (7/1)	R Hern	W Carson	Master Willie	Rankin	24	2 34.77
1981	H H Aga Khan's	SHERGAR (10/11)	M Stoute	W Swinburn	Glint of Gold	Scintillating Air	18	2 44.21
1982	R Sangster's	GOLDEN FLEECE (3/1)	V O'Brien	Pat Eddery	Touching Wood	Silver Hawk	18	2 34.27
1983	E Moller's	TEENOSO (9/2)	G Wragg	L Piggott	Carlingford Castle	Shearwalk	21	2 49.07
1984	L Miglitti's	SECRETO (14/1)	D O'Brien	C Roche	El Gran Senor	Mighty Flutter	17	2 39.12
1985	Lord H. de Walden's	SLIP ANCHOR (9/4)	H Cecil	S Cauthen	Law Society	Damister	14	2 36.23
1986	H H Aga Khan's	SHAHRASTANI (11/2)	M Stoute	W Swinburn	Dancing Brave	Mashkour	17	2 37.13
1987	L Freedman's	REFERENCE POINT (6/4)	H Cecil	S Cauthen	Most Welcome	Bellotto	19	2 33.90
1988	H H Aga Khan's	KAHYASI (11/1)	L Cumani	R Cochrane	Glacial Storm	Doyoun	14	2 33.84
1989	Hamdan Al-Maktoum's	NASHWAN (5/4)	R Hern	W Carson	Terimon	Cacoethes	12	2 34.90
1990	K Abdulla's	QUEST FOR FAME (7/1)	R Charlton	Pat Eddery	Blue Stag	Elmaamul	18	2 37.26
1991	F Salman's	GENEROUS (9/1)	P Cole	A Munro	Marju	Star of Gdansk	13	2 34.00
1992	Sidney H Craig's	DR DEVIOUS (8/1)	P Chapple-Hyam	J Reid	St Jovite	Silver Wisp	18	2 36.19
1993	K Abdulla's	COMMANDER IN CHIEF (15/2)	H Cecil	M Kinane	Blue Judge	Blues Traveller	16	2 34.51
1994	Hamdan Al-Maktoum's	ERHAAB (7/2)	J Dunlop	W Carson	King's Theatre	Colonel Collins	25	2 34.16
1995	Saeed Maktoum Al Maktoum's	LAMMTARRA (14/1)	S Bin Suroor	W Swinburn	Tamure	Presenting	15	2 32.31
1996	C Dismal's	SHAAMIT (12/1)	W Haggas	M Hills	Dushyantor	Shantou	20	2 35.05
1997	L Knight's	BENNY THE DIP (11/1)	J Gosden	W Ryan	Silver Patriarch	Romanov	13	2 35.77
1998	Obaid Al Maktoum's	HIGH-RISE (20/1)	L Cumani	O Peslier	City Honours	Border Arrow	15	2 33.88
1999	Thoroughbred Corporation's	OATH (13/2)	H Cecil	K Fallon	Daliapour	Beat All	16	2 37.43
2000	H H Aga Khan's	SINNDAR (7/1)	J Oxx	J Murtagh	Sakhee	Beat Hollow	15	2 36.75
2001	M Tabor & Mrs J Magnier's	GALILEO (11/4)	A O'Brien	M Kinane	Golan	Tobougg	12	2 33.27
2002	M Tabor & Mrs J Magnier's	HIGH CHAPARRAL (7/2)	A O'Brien	J Murtagh	Hawk Wing	Moon Ballad	12	2 39.45
2003	Saeed Suhail's	KRIS KIN (6/1)	Sir M Stoute	K Fallon	The Great Gatsby	Alamshar	20	2 33.35
2004	Ballymacoll Stud's	NORTH LIGHT (7/2)	Sir M Stoute	K Fallon	Rule Of Law	Let The Lion Roar	14	2 33.70
2005	The Royal Ascot Racing Club's	MOTIVATOR (3/1)	M Bell	J Murtagh	Walk In The Park	Dubawi	13	2 35.60
2006	A E Pakenham's	SIR PERCY (6/1)	M Tregoning	M Dwyer	Dragon Dancer	Dylan Thomas	18	2 35.20
2007	Saleh Al Homaizi & Imad Al Sagar's	AUTHORIZED (5/4)	P Chapple-Hyam	L Dettori	Eagle Mountain	Aqaleem	17	2 34.77

OAKS STAKES (3y fillies) Epsom-1 Mile 4 furlongs 10 yards

Year	Owner	Winner and Price	Jockey	Trainer	Second	Third	Ran	Time
1972	C St George's	GINEVRA (8/1)	A Murray	R Price	Regal Exception	Arkadina	17	2 39.35
1973	G Pope's	MYSTERIOUS (13/8)	G Lewis	N Murless	Where You Lead	Aureoletta	10	2 36.31
1974	L Freedman's	POLYGAMY (3/1)	Pat Eddery	P Walwyn	Furioso	Matuta	15	2 39.39
1975	J Morrison's	JULIETTE MARNY (12/1)	L Piggott	J Tree	Val's Girl	Moonlight Night	12	2 39.10
1976	D Wildenstein's	PAWNEESE (6/5)	Y Saint Martin	A Penna	Roses for the Star	African Dancer	14	2 35.25
1977	The Queen's	DUNFERMLINE (6/1)	W Carson	M Stoute	Freeze the Secret	Vaguely Deb	13	2 36.53
1978	S Hanson's	FAIR SALINIA (8/1)	G Starkey	M Stoute	Dancing Maid	Suni	15	2 36.82
1979	J Morrison's	SCINTILLATE (20/1)	Pat Eddery	J Tree	Bonnie Isle	Britannia's Rule	14	2 43.74
1980	R Hollingsworth's	BIREME (9/2)	W Carson	H Hern	Vielle	The Dancer	11	2 34.33
1981	Mrs B Firestone's	BLUE WIND (3/1)	L Piggott	D Weld	Madam Gay	Leap Lively	12	2 40.93
1982	R Barnett's	TIME CHARTER (12/1)	W Newnes	H Candy	Slightly Dangerous	Last Feather	13	2 34.21
1983	Sir M Sobell's	SUN PRINCESS (6/1)	W Carson	H Hern	Acclimatise	New Coins	15	2 40.98
1984	Sir R McAlpine's	CIRCUS PLUME (4/1)	L Piggott	J Dunlop	Media Luna	Poquito Queen	15	2 38.97
1985	Sheikh Mohammed's	OH SO SHARP (6/4)	S Cauthen	H Cecil	Triptych	Dubian	15	2 41.37
1986	H Ranier's	MIDWAY LADY (15/8)	R Cochrane	B Hanbury	Untold	Maysoon	15	2 35.60
1987	Sheikh Mohammed's	UNITE (11/1)	W R Swinburn	M Stoute	Bourbon Girl	Three Tails	11	2 38.17
1988	Sheikh Mohammed's	DIMINUENDO (7/4)	S Cauthen	H Cecil	Sudden Love	Animatrice	11	2 35.02
1989	S M Al Maktoum's	SNOW BRIDE (13/2)	S Cauthen	H Cecil	Roseate Tern	Mamaluna	9	2 34.22

(Aliysa finished first but was disqualified)

Year	Owner	Winner and Price	Jockey	Trainer	Second	Third	Ran	Time
1990	Hamdan Al-Maktoum's	SALSABIL (2/1)	W Carson	J Dunlop	Game Plan	Knight's Baroness	8	2 38.70
1991	Maktoum Al-Maktoum's	JET SKI LADY (50/1)	C Roche	J Bolger	Shamshir	Shadayid	9	2 37.30
1992	W J Gredley's	USER FRIENDLY (5/1)	G Duffield	C Brittain	All Al Sea	Pearl Angel	7	2 39.77
1993	Sheikh Mohammed's	INTREPIDITY (5/1)	M Roberts	A Fabre	Royal Ballerina	Oakmead	14	2 34.19
1994	Godolphin's	BALANCHINE (3/1)	L Dettori	H Ibrahim	Wind In Her Hair	Hawajiss	10	2 40.37
1995	Maktoum Al Maktoum/ Godolphin's	MOONSHELL (3/1)	L Dettori	S Bin Suroor	Dance A Dream	Pure Grain	10	2 35.44
1996	Wafic Said's	LADY CARLA (100/30)	Pat Eddery	H Cecil	Pricket	Mezzogiorno	11	2 35.55
1997	K Abdulla's	REAMS OF VERSE (5/6)	K Fallon	H Cecil	Gazelle Royale	Crown of Light	12	2 35.59
1998	Mrs D Nagle & Mrs J Magnier's	SHAHTOUSH (12/1)	M Kinane	A O'Brien	Bahr	Midnight Line	8	2 38.23
1999	F Salman's	RAMRUMA (3/1)	K Fallon	H Cecil	Noushkey	Zahrat Dubai	10	2 38.72
2000	Lordship Stud's	LOVE DIVINE (9/4)	T Quinn	H Cecil	Kalypso Katie	Melikah	16	2 43.11
2001	Mrs D. Nagle & Mrs J. Magnier's	IMAGINE (3/1)	M Kinane	A O'Brien	Flight of Fancy	Relish The Thought	14	2 36.70
2002	Godolphin's	KAZZIA (100/30)	L Dettori	S Bin Suroor	Quarter Moon	Shadow Dancing	14	2 44.52
2003	W S Farish III's	CASUAL LOOK (10/1)	M Dwyer	A Balding	Yesterday	Summitville	15	2 38.07
2004	Lord Derby's	OUIJA BOARD (7/2)	K Fallon	E Dunlop	All Too Beautiful	Punctilious	13	2 35.40
2005	Hamdan Al Maktoum's	ESWARAH (11/4)	R Hills	M Jarvis	Something Exciting	Pictavia	12	2 39.00
2006	Mrs J Magnier, Mr M Tabor & Mr D Smith's	ALEXANDROVA (9/4)	K Fallon	A O'Brien	Rising Cross	Short Skirt	10	2 37.70
2007	Niarchos Family's	LIGHT SHIFT (13/2)	T Durcan	H Cecil	Peeping Fawn	All My Loving	14	2 40.38

ST LEGER STAKES (3y) Doncaster-1 mile 6 furlongs 132 yards

Year	Owner	Winner and Price	Jockey	Trainer	Second	Third	Ran	Time
1966	R Sigtia's	SODIUM (7/1)	F Durr	G Todd	Charlottown	David Jack	9	3 9.80
1967	C Engelhard's	RIBOCCO (7/2)	L Piggott	R Houghton	Hopeful Venture	Ruysdael	8	3 5.40
1968	C Engelhard's	RIBERO (100/30)	L Piggott	R Houghton	Canterbury	Cold Storage	8	3 19.80
1969	G Oldham's	INTERMEZZO (7/1)	R Hutchinson	H Wragg	Ribofilio	Prince Consort	11	3 11.80
1970	C Engelhard's	NIJINSKY (2/7)	L Piggott	V O'Brien	Meadowville	Politico	9	3 6.40
1971	Mrs J Rogerson's	ATHENS WOOD (5/2)	L Piggott	H T Jones	Homeric	Falkland	8	3 14.90
1972	O Phipps's	BOUCHER (3/1)	L Piggott	V O'Brien	Our Mirage	Ginevra	7	3 28.71
1973	W Behrens's	PELEID (28/1)	F Durr	W Elsey	Buoy	Duke of Ragusa	13	3 8.21
1974	Lady Beaverbrook's	BUSTINO (11/10)	J Mercer	R Hern	Giacometti	Riboson	10	3 9.02
1975	C St George's	BRUNI (9/1)	A Murray	R Price	King Pellinore	Libra's Rib	12	3 9.02
1976	D Wildenstein's	CROW (6/1)	Y Saint-Martin	A Penna	Secret Man	Scallywag	15	3 13.17
1977	The Queen's	DUNFERMLINE (10/1)	W Carson	R Hern	Alleged	Classic Example	13	3 5.17
1978	M Lemos's	JULIO MARINER (28/1)	E Hide	C Brittain	Le Moss	M-Lolshan	14	3 4.94
1979	A Rolland's	SON OF LOVE (20/1)	A Lequeux	R Collet	Soleil Noir	World Leader	17	3 9.02
1980	H Joel's	LIGHT CAVALRY (3/1)	J Mercer	H Cecil	Water Mill	Niniski	7	3 11.48
1981	Sir J Astor's	CUT ABOVE (28/1)	J Mercer	R Hern	Glint of Gold	Bustomi	15	3 11.60
1982	Maktoum Al Maktoum's	TOUCHING WOOD (7/1)	P Cook	H T Jones	Zilos	Diamond Shoal	15	3 3.53
1983	Sir M Sobell's	SUN PRINCESS (11/8)	W Carson	R Hern	Esprit du Nord	Carlingford Castle	11	3 16.65
1984	I Allan's	COMMANCHE RUN (7/4)	L Piggott	L Cumani	Baynoun	Alphabatim	10	3 16.93
1985	Sheikh Mohammed's	OH SO SHARP (8/11)	S Cauthen	H Cecil	Phardante	Lanfranco	6	3 7.13
1986	Duchess of Norfolk's	MOON MADNESS (9/2)	Pat Eddery	J Dunlop	Celestial Storm	Untold	8	3 5.03
1987	L Freedman's	REFERENCE POINT (4/11)	S Cauthen	H Cecil	Mountain Kingdom	Dry Dock	8	3 5.91
1988	Lady Beaverbrook's	MINSTER SON (15/2)	W Carson	N A Graham	Diminuendo	Sheriff's Star	7	3 6.80
1989	C St George's (Run at Ayr)	MICHELOZZO (6/4)	S Cauthen	H Cecil	Sapience	Rosate Tern	8	3 20.72
1990	M Arbib's	SNURGE (7/2)	T Quinn	P Cole	Hellenic	River God	8	8.78
1991	K Abdulla's	TOULON (5/2)	Pat Eddery	A Fabre	Saddlers' Hall	Michelletti	10	3 3.12
1992	W J Gredley's	USER FRIENDLY (7/4)	G Duffield	C Brittain	Sonus	Bonny Scot	10	3 5.48
1993	Mrs G A E Smith's	BOB'S RETURN (3/1)	P Robinson	M Tompkins	Armiger	Edbaysaan	9	3 7.85
1994	Sheikh Mohammed's	MOONAX (40/1)	Pat Eddery	B Hills	Broadway Flyer	Double Trigger	7	4.19
1995	Godolphin's	CLASSIC CLICHE (100/30)	L Dettori	S Bin Suroor	Minds Music	Istirdaad	10	3 9.74
1996	Sheikh Mohammed's	SHANTOU (8/1)	L Dettori	J Gosden	Dushyantor	Samraan	11	3 5.10
1997	P Winfield's	SILVER PATRIARCH (5/4)	Pat Eddery	J Dunlop	Vertical Speed	The Fly	11	3 6.92
1998	Godolphin's	NEDAWI (11/2)	J Reid	S Bin Suroor	High and Low	Sunshine Street	9	3 5.61
1999	Godolphin's	MUTAFAWEQ (11/2)	R Hills	S Bin Suroor	Ramruma	Adair	9	3 2.75
2000	N Jones's	MILLENARY (11/4)	T Quinn	J Dunlop	Air Marshall	Chimes At Midnight	11	3 2.58
2001	M Tabor & Mrs J Magnier's	MILAN (13/8)	M Kinane	A O'Brien	Demophilos	Mr Combustible	11	3 5.16
2002	Sir Neil Westbrook's	BOLLIN ERIC (7/1)	K Darley	T Easterby	Highest	Bandari	8	2.92
2003	Mrs J Magnier's	BRIAN BORU (5/4)	J P Spencer	A O'Brien	High Accolade	Phoenix Reach	12	3 4.64
2004	Godolphin's	RULE OF LAW (3/1)	K McEvoy	S Bin Suroor	Quiff	Tycoon	8	3 6.20
2005	Mrs J Magnier & M Tabor's	SCORPION (10/1)	L Dettori	A O'Brien	The Geezer	Tawqeet	6	3 19.00
2006	Mrs S Roy's	SIXTIES ICON (11/8)	L Dettori	J Noseda	The Last Drop	Red Rocks	11	2 57.20
2007	G Strawbridge's (Run at York)	LUCARNO (7/2)	J Fortune	J Gosden	Mahler	Honolulu	10	3 1.90

KING GEORGE VI AND QUEEN ELIZABETH STAKES Ascot-1 mile 4 furlongs

Year	Owner	Winner and Price	Jockey	Trainer	Second	Third	Ran	Time
1968	H Joel's	ROYAL PALACE 4-9-7 (7/4)	A Barclay	N Murless	Felicio	Topyo	7	2 33.22
1969	Duke of Devonshire's	PARK TOP 5-9-4 (9/4)	L Piggott	B van Cutsem	Crozier	Hogarth	9	2 32.46
1970	C Engelhard's	NIJINSKY 3-8-7 (40/85)	L Piggott	V O'Brien	Blakeney	Crepellana	6	2 36.16
1971	P Mellon's	MILL REEF 3-8-7 (8/13)	G Lewis	I Balding	Ortis	Acclimatization	10	2 32.56
1972	Mrs J Hislop's	BRIGADIER GERARD 4-9-7 (8/13)	J Mercer	R Hern	Parnell	Riverman	10	2 32.91
1973	N B Hunt's	DAHLIA 3-8-4 (10/1)	W Pyers	M Zilber	Rheingold	Our Mirage	12	2 30.43
1974	N B Hunt's	DAHLIA 4-9-4 (15/8)	L Piggott	M Zilber	Highclere	Dankaro	10	2 33.03
1975	Dr C Vittadini's	GRUNDY 3-8-7 (4/5)	P Eddery	P Walwyn	Bustino	Dahlia	11	2 26.98
1976	R Sangster's	PAWNEESE 3-8-5 (9/4)	Y Saint Martin	A Penna	Bruni	Orange Bay	10	2 29.36
1977	R Sangster's	THE MINSTREL 3-8-8 (7/4)	L Piggott	V O'Brien	Orange Bay	Exceller	11	2 30.48
1978	D McCall's	ILE DE BOURBON 3-8-8 (12/1)	J Reid	R F Houghton	Hawaiian Sound	Montcontour	14	2 30.53
1979	Sir M Sobell's	TROY 3-8-8 (2/5)	W Carson	R Hern	Gay Mecene	Ela-Mana-Mou	7	2 33.75
1980	S Weinstock's	ELA-MANA-MOU 4-9-7 (11/4)	W Carson	R Hern	Mrs Penny	Gregorian	7	2 35.39
1981	H H Aga Khan's	SHERGAR 3-8-8 (2/5)	W Swinburn	M Stoute	Madam Gay	Fingals Cave	7	2 35.40
1982	A Ward's	KALAGLOW 4-9-7 (13-2)	G Starkey	G Harwood	Asset	Glint of Gold	9	2 31.58
1983	R Barnett's	TIME CHARTER 4-9-4 (5/1)	J Mercer	H Candy	Diamond Shoal	Sun Princess	9	2 30.78
1984	E Moller's	TEENOSO 4-9-7 (13/2)	L Piggott	G Wragg	Sadler's Wells	Tolomeo	13	2 27.95
1985	Lady Beaverbrook's	PETOSKI 3-8-8 (12/1)	W Carson	R Hern	Oh So Sharp	Rainbow Quest	12	2 27.61
1986	K Abdulla's	DANCING BRAVE 3-8-8 (6/4)	Pat Eddery	G Harwood	Shardari	Triptych	9	2 29.49
1987	L Freedman's	REFERENCE POINT 3-8-8 (11/10)	S Cauthen	H Cecil	Celestial Storm	Triptych	9	2 34.63
1988	Hamdan Al-Maktoum's	MTOTO 5-9-7 (4/1)	M Roberts	A C Stewart	Untuwain	Tony Bin	7	2 37.33
1989	Sheikh Ahmed Al Maktoum's	NASHWAN 3-8-8 (2/9)	W Carson	R Hern	Cacoethes	Top Class	7	2 32.27
1990	Sheikh Mohammed's	BELMEZ 3-8-9 (15/2)	M Kinane	H Cecil	Old Vic	Assatis	11	2 30.76
1991	F Salman's	GENEROUS 3-8-9 (4/6)	A Munro	P Cole	Sanglamore	Rock Hopper	9	2 28.99
1992	Mrs V K Payson's	ST JOVITE 3-8-9 (4/5)	S Craine	J Bolger	Saddlers' Hall	Opera House	8	2 30.85
1993	Sheikh Mohammed's	OPERA HOUSE 5-9-7 (8/1)	M Roberts	M Stoute	White Muzzle	Commander in Chief	10	2 33.94
1994	Sheikh Mohammed's	KING'S THEATRE 3-8-9 (12/1)	M Kinane	H Cecil	White Muzzle	Wagon Master	12	2 28.92
1995	Saeed Maktoum Al Maktoum's	LAMMTARRA 3-8-9 (9/4)	L Dettori	S Bin Suroor	Pentire	Strategic Choice	7	2 31.01
1996	Mollers Racing's	PENTIRE 4-9-7 (100/30)	M Hills	G Wragg	Classic Cliche	Shaamit	8	2 28.11
1997	Godolphin's	SWAIN 5-9-7 (16/1)	J Reid	S Bin Suroor	Pilsudski	Helissio	8	2 36.45
1998	Godolphin's	SWAIN 6-9-7 (11/2)	L Dettori	S Bin Suroor	High-Rise	Royal Anthem	8	2 29.06
1999	Godolphin's	DAYLAMI 5-9-7 (3/1)	L Dettori	S Bin Suroor	Nedawi	Fruits Of Love	8	2 29.35
2000	M Tabor's	MONTJEU 4-9-7 (1/3)	M Kinane	J Hammond	Fantastic Light	Daliapour	8	2 29.98
2001	Mrs J Magnier & M Tabor's	GALILEO 3-8-9 (1/2)	M Kinane	A O'Brien	Fantastic Light	Hightori	12	2 27.71
2002	Exors of the late Lord Weinstock's	GOLAN 4-9-7 (1/2)	K Fallon	Sir M Stoute	Nayef	Zindabad	9	2 29.70
2003	H H Aga Khan's	ALAMSHAR 3-8-9 (13/2)	J Murtagh	J Oxx	Sulamani	Kris Kin	11	2 33.10
2004	Godolphin's	DOYEN 4-9-7 (11/10)	L Dettori	S Bin Suroor	Hard Buck	Sulamani	11	2 33.00
2005	H H Aga Khan's	AZAMOUR 4-9-7 (5/2)	M Kinane	J Oxx	Norse Dancer	Bago	12	2 28.20
	(Run at Newbury)							
2006	M Tabor's	HURRICANE RUN 4-9-7 (5/6)	C Soumillon	A Fabre	Electrocutionist	Heart's Cry	6	2 30.20
2007	Mrs J Magnier & M Tabor's	DYLAN THOMAS 4-9-7 (5/4)	J Murtagh	A O'Brien	Youmzain	Marahel	7	2 31.10

PRIX DE L'ARC DE TRIOMPHE Longchamp-1 mile 4 furlongs

Year	Owner	Winner and Price	Jockey	Trainer	Second	Third	Ran	Time
1966	W Burmann's	BON MOT 3-8-10 (53/10)	F Head	W Head	Sigebert	Lionel	24	2 39.80
1967	Mme S Volterra's	TOPYO 3-8-10 (10/1)	W Pyers	M Bartholomew	Salvo	Ribocco	30	2 38.20
1968	Mrs W Franklyn's	VAGUELY NOBLE 3-8-10 (5/2)	W Williamson	E Pollet	Sir Ivor	Carmarthen	17	2 35.20
1969	S McGrath's	LEVMOSS 4-9-6 (52/1)	W Williamson	S McGrath	Park Top	Grandier	24	2 29.00
1970	A Plesch's	SASSAFRAS 3-8-10 (19/1)	Y Saint Martin	F Mathet	Nijinsky	Miss Dan.	15	2 29.70
1971	P Mellon's	MILL REEF 3-8-10 (7/10)	G Lewis	I Balding	Pistol Packer.	Cambrizzia	18	2 28.30
1972	Countess M Batthyany's	SAN SAN 3-8-7 (3/2)	F Head	A Penna	Rescousse.	Homeric.	19	2 28.30
1973	J Zeisel's	RHEINGOLD 4-9-6 (77/10)	L Piggott	B Hills	Allez France.	Hard to Beat.	27	2 35.80
1974	D Wildenstein's	ALLEZ FRANCE 4-9-3 (1/2)	Y Saint Martin	A Penna	Comtesse de Loir.	Margouillat.	20	2 36.90
1975	W Zeilehack's	STAR APPEAL 5-9-6 (119/1)	G Starkey	T Grieper	On My Way.	Comtesse de Loir.	24	2 33.60
1976	J Wertheimer's	IVANJICA 4-9-1 (71/10)	F Head	A Head	Crow.	Youth.	20	2 39.40
1977	R Sangster's	ALLEGED 3-8-11 (38/10)	L Piggott	V O'Brien	Balmerino.	Crystal Palace	26	2 30.60
1978	R Sangster's	ALLEGED 4-9-4 (7/5)	L Piggott	V O'Brien	Trillion	Dancing Maid	18	2 36.50
1979	Mme G Head's	THREE TROIKAS 3-8-8 (88/10)	F Head	Mme C Head.	Le Marmot	Troy.	22	2 28.90
1980	J Wertheimer's	DETROIT 3-8-8 (67/10)	Pat Eddery	O Doueb	Argument.	Ela-Mana-Mou.	20	2 28.00
1981	J Wertheimer's	GOLD RIVER 4-9-1 (53/1)	G W Moore	A Head.	Bikala	April Run.	24	2 35.20
1982	H H Aga Khan's	AKIYDA 3-8-8 (43/4)	Y Saint Martin	F. Mathet	Ardross.	Awaasif	17	2 34.90
1983	D Wildenstein's	ALL ALONG 4-9-1 (173/10)	W Swinburn.	P Biancone.	Sun Princess.	Luth Enchantee	26	2 28.10
1984	D Wildenstein's	SAGACE 4-9-4 (29/1)	Y Saint Martin	P Biancone.	Northern Trick	All Along	22	2 39.10
1985	K Abdulla's	RAINBOW QUEST 4-9-4 (71/10)	Pat Eddery	J Tree	Sagace	Kozana	15	2 29.50
1986	K Abdulla's	DANCING BRAVE 3-8-11 (11/10)	Pat Eddery	G Harwood.	Bering.	Triptych.	15	2 27.70
1987	P de Moussac's	TREMPOLINO 3-8-11 (20/1)	Pat Eddery	F Camici.	Tony Bin	Triptych.	11	2 26.30
1988	Mrs V Gaucci del Bono's.	TONY BIN 5-9-4 (14/1)	J Reid	L Camici	Mtoto	Boyalino.	24	2 27.30
1989	A Balzarini's	CARROLL HOUSE 4-9-4 (19/1)	M Kinane	M Jarvis.	Behera	Saint Andrews	19	2 30.80
1990	B McNall's	SAUMAREZ 3-8-11 (15/1)	G Mosse.	N Clement.	Epervier Bleu.	Snurge.	21	2 29.80
1991	H Chalhoub's	SUAVE DANCER 3-8-11 (37/10)	C Asmussen.	J Hammond	Magic Night	Pistol Bleu	14	2 31.40
1992	O Lecerf's	SUBOTICA 4-9-4 (88/10)	T Jarnet	A Fabre.	User Friendly.	Vert Amande.	18	2 39.00
1993	D Tsui's	URBAN SEA 4-9-1 (37/1)	E Saint Martin	J Lesbordes	White Muzzle.	Opera House	23	2 37.90
1994	Sheikh Mohammed's	CARNEGIE 3-8-11 (3/1)	T Jarnet	A Fabre.	Hernando	Apple Tree.	20	2 31.10
1995	Saeed Maktoum Al Maktoum's	LAMMTARRA 3-8-11 (2/1)	L Dettori	S Bin Suroor.	Freedom Cry	Swain	16	2 31.80
1996	E Sarasola's	HELISSIO 3-8-11 (18/10)	O Peslier	E Lellouche	Pilsudski	Oscar Schindler	16	2 29.60
1997	D Wildenstein's	PEINTRE CELEBRE 3-8-11 (22/10)	O Peslier	A Fabre.	Pilsudski	Borgia	18	2 24.60
1998	J-L Lagardere's.	SAGAMIX 3-8-11 (5/2)	O Peslier	A Fabre.	Leggera.	Tiger Hill	14	2 34.50
1999	M Tabor's.	MONTJEU 3-8-11 (6/4)	M Kinane	J Hammond	El Condor Pasa.	Croco Rouge.	14	2 38.50
2000	H H Aga Khan's	SINNDAR 3-8-11 (6/4)	J Murtagh	J Oxx.	Egyptband.	Volvoreta	17	2 25.80
2001	Godolphin's.	SAKHEE 4-9-5 (22/10)	L Dettori	S Bin Suroor.	Aquarelliste	Sagacity.	17	2 36.10
2002	Godolphin's.	MARIENBARD 4-9-5 (158/10)	L Dettori	S Bin Suroor.	Sulamani	High Chaparral.	16	2 26.70
2003	H H Aga Khan's.	DALAKHANI 3-8-11 (9/4)	C Soumillon.	A De-Royer-Dupre.	Mubtaker.	High Chaparral.	13	2 32.30
2004	Niarchos Family's.	BAGO 3-8-11 (10/1)	T Gillet.	J E Pease.	Cherry Mix.	Ouija Board.	13	2 25.00
2005	M Tabor's.	HURRICANE RUN 3-8-11 (11/4)	K Fallon.	A Fabre.	Westerner.	Bago.	18	2 27.40
2006	K Abdulla's	RAIL LINK 3-8-11 (8/1)	S Pasquier.	A Fabre.	Pride.	Deep Impact.	15	2 26.30
2007	Mrs J Magnier & M Tabor's.	DYLAN THOMAS 4-9-5 (11/2)	K Fallon	A O'Brien	Youmzain.	Sagara.	12	2 28.50

GRAND NATIONAL STEEPLECHASE Aintree 4½ m 4f

Year	Winner and Price	Age & Weight	Jockey	Second	Third	Ran	Time
1964	TEAM SPIRIT (18/1)	12 10 3	G W Robinson	Purple Silk	Peacetown	33	9 47.00
1965	JAY TRUMP (100/8)	8 11 5	Mr C Smith, jun.	Freddie	Mr. Jones	47	9 30.60
1966	ANGLO (50/1)	8 10 0	T Norman	Freddie	Forest Prince	47	9 52.80
1967	FOINAVON (100/1)	9 10 0	J Buckingham	Honey End	Red Alligator	44	9 49.60
1968	RED ALLIGATOR (100/7)	9 10 0	B Fletcher	Moidore's Token	Different Class	45	9 28.60
1969	HIGHLAND WEDDING (100/9)	12 10 4	E Harty	Steel Bridge	Rondetto	30	9 30.80
1970	GAY TRIP (15/1)	8 11 5	P Taaffe	Vulture	Miss Hunter	28	9 38.00
1971	SPECIFY (28/1)	9 10 13	J Cook	Black Secret	Astbury	38	9 34.20
1972	WELL TO DO (14/1)	9 10 1	G Thorner	Gay Trip	Black Secret	42	10 08.40
1973	RED RUM (9/1)	8 10 5	B Fletcher	Crisp	L'Escargot	38	9 01.90
1974	RED RUM (11/1)	9 12 0	B Fletcher	L'Escargot	Charles Dickens	42	9 20.30
1975	L'ESCARGOT (13/2)	12 11 3	T Carberry	Red Rum	Spanish Steps	31	9 31.10
1976	RAG TRADE (14/1)	10 10 12	J Burke	Red Rum	Eyecatcher	32	9 20.90
1977	RED RUM (9/1)	12 11 8	T Stack	Churchtown Boy	Eyecatcher	42	9 30.30
1978	LUCIUS (14/1)	9 10 9	B R Davies	Sebastian V.	Drumroan	37	9 33.90
1979	RUBSTIC (25/1)	10 10 0	M Barnes	Zongalero	Rough & Tumble	34	9 52.90
1980	BEN NEVIS (40/1)	12 10 12	Mr C Fenwick	Rough & Tumble	The Pilgarlic	30	10 17.40
1981	ALDANITI (10/1)	11 10 13	R Champion	Spartan Missile	Royal Mail	39	9 47.20
1982	GRITTAR (7/1)	9 11 5	E Saunders	Hard Outlook	Loving Words	39	9 12.60
1983	CORBIERE (13/1)	8 11 4	B de Haan	Greasepaint	Yer Man	41	9 47.04
1984	HALLO DANDY (13/1)	10 10 2	N Doughty	Greasepaint	Corbiere	40	9 21.04
1985	LAST SUSPECT (50/1)	11 10 5	H Davies	Mr Snugfit	Corbiere	40	9 42.70
1986	WEST TIP (15/2)	9 10 11	R Dunwoody	Young Driver	Classified	40	9 33.00
1987	MAORI VENTURE (28/1)	11 10 13	S C Knight	The Tsarevich	Lean Ar Aghaidh	40	9 19.30
1988	RHYME N'REASON (10/1)	9 11 0	B Powell	Durham Edition	Monanore	40	9 53.50
1989	LITTLE POLVEIR (28/1)	12 10 3	J Frost	West Tip	The Thinker	40	10 06.80
1990	MR FRISK (16/1)	11 10 6	Mr M Armytage	Durham Edition	Rinus	38	8 47.80
1991	SEAGRAM (12/1)	11 10 6	N Hawke	Garrison Savanah	Auntie Dot	40	9 29.90
1992	PARTY POLITICS (14/1)	8 10 7	C Llewellyn	Romany King	Laura's Beau	40	9 06.30
1993	Race Void						
1994	MINNEHOMA (16/1)	11 10 8	R Dunwoody	Just So	Moorcroft Boy	36	10 18.80
1995	ROYAL ATHLETE (40/1)	12 10 6	J Titley	Party Politics	Over The Deel	35	9 04.00
1996	ROUGH QUEST (7/1)	10 10 7	M Fitzgerald	Encore Un Peu	Superior Finish	27	9 00.80
1997	LORD GYLLENE (14/1)	9 10 0	A Dobbin	Suny Bay	Camelot Knight	36	9 05.80
1998	EARTH SUMMIT (7/1)	10 10 5	C Llewellyn	Suny Bay	Samlee	37	10 51.40
1999	BOBBYJO (10/1)	9 10 0	P Carberry	Blue Charm	Call It A Day	32	9 14.00
2000	PAPILLON (10/1)	9 10 12	R Walsh	Mely Moss	Niki Dee	40	9 09.70
2001	RED MARAUDER (33/1)	11 10 11	R Guest	Smarty	Blowing Wind	40	11 00.10
2002	BINDAREE (16/1)	8 10 4	J Culloty	What's Up Boys	Blowing Wind	40	9 09.00
2003	MONTY'S PASS (16/1)	10 10 7	B J Geraghty	Supreme Glory	Amberleigh House	40	9 21.70
2004	AMBERLEIGH HOUSE (16/1)	12 10 10	G Lee	Clan Royal	Lord Atterbury	39	9 20.30
2005	HEDGEHUNTER (7/1)	9 11 1	R Walsh	Royal Auclair	Simply Gifted	40	9 20.80
2006	NUMBERSIXVALVERDE (11/1)	10 10 8	N Madden	Hedgehunter	Clan Royal	40	9 41.00
2007	SILVER BIRCH (33/1)	10 10 6	R M Power	McKelvey	Slim Pickings	40	9 13.60

WINNERS OF GREAT RACES

LINCOLN HANDICAP
Doncaster-1m
1998	HUNTERS OF BRORA 8-9-0	23
1999	RIGHT WING 5-9-5	24
2000	JOHN FERNELEY 5-8-10	24
2001	NIMELLO 5-8-9	23
2002	ZUCCHERO 6-8-13	23
2003	PABLO 4-8-11	24
2004	BABODANA 4-9-10	24
2005	STREAM OF GOLD 4-9-10	22
*2006	BLYTHE KNIGHT 6-8-10	30
**2007	VERY WISE 5-8-11	20

*Run at Redcar
**Run at Newcastle

GREENHAM STAKES (3y)
Newbury-7f
1998	VICTORY NOTE 9-0	6
1999	ENRIQUE 9-0	6
*2000	BARATHEA GUEST 9-0	7
2001	MUNIR 9-0	7
2002	REDBACK 9-0	10
2003	MUQBIL 9-0	8
2004	SALFORD CITY 9-0	10
2005	INDESATCHEL 9-0	9
2006	RED CLUBS 9-0	5
2007	MAJOR CADEAUX 9-0	6

*Run at Newmarket

EUROPEAN FREE HANDICAP (3y)
Newmarket-7f
1998	DESERT PRINCE 9-5	9
1999	BERTOLINI 9-7	6
2000	CAPE TOWN 9-2	8
2001	CLEARING 9-6	10
2002	TWILIGHT BLUES 9-5	8
2003	INDIAN HAVEN 9-1	6
2004	BRUNEL 8-13	11
2005	KAMAKIRI 8-10	8
2006	MISU BOND 8-13	8
2007	PRIME DEFENDER 9-5	7

CRAVEN STAKES (3y)
Newmarket-1m
1998	XAAR 8-12	6
1999	COMPTON ADMIRAL 8-9	7
2000	UMISTIM 8-9	9
2001	KING'S IRONBRIDGE 8-9	6
2002	KING OF HAPPINESS 8-9	6
2003	HURRICANE ALAN 8-9	5
2004	HAAFHD 8-9	7
2005	DEMOCRATIC DEFICIT 8-12	8
2006	KILLYBEGS 8-12	9
2007	ADAGIO 8-12	8

JOCKEY CLUB STAKES
Newmarket-1m 4f
1998	ROMANOV 4-8-9	9
1999	SILVER PATRIARCH 5-9-0	11
2000	BLUEPRINT 5-8-9	11
2001	MILLENARY 4-9-0	7
2002	MARIENBARD 5-8-9	9
2003	WARRSAN 5-8-9	6
2004	GAMUT 5-8-9	7

2005	ALKAASED 5-8-9	
2006	SHIROCCO 5-9-3	
2007	SIXTIES ICON 4-9-3	

CHESTER VASE (3y)
Chester-1m 4f 66yds
1998	GULLAND 8-10	
1999	PESHTIGO 8-10	
2000	MILLENARY 8-10	
2001	MR COMBUSTIBLE 8-10	
2002	FIGHT YOUR CORNER 8-10	
2003	DUTCH GOLD 8-10	
2004	RED LANCER 8-10	
2005	HATTAN 8-10	
2006	PAPAL BULL 8-12	
2007	SOLDIER OF FORTUNE 9-2	

CHESTER CUP
Chester-2m 2f 147yds
1998	SILENCE IN COURT 7-9-0	1
1999	RAINBOW HIGH 4-9-0	1
2000	BANGALORE 4-7-10	1
2001	RAINBOW HIGH 6-9-13	1
2002	FANTASY HILL 6-8-9	1
2003	HUGS DANCER 6-8-11	1
2004	ANAK PEKAN 4-8-2	1
2005	ANAK PEKAN 5-9-6	1
2006	ADMIRAL 5-8-1	1
2007	GREENWICH MEANTIME 7-9-2	1

OAKS TRIAL (3y fillies)
Lingfield-1m 3f 106yds
1998	BRISTOL CHANNEL 8-8	
1999	RAMRUMA 8-8	
2000	FILM SCRIPT 8-8	
2001	DOUBLE CROSSED 8-8	
2002	BIRDIE 8-8	
2003	SANTA SOPHIA 8-8	
2004	BARAKA 8-8	
2005	CASSYDORA 8-10	
2006	SINDIRANA 8-10	1
2007	KAYAH 8-12	

DERBY TRIAL (3y)
Lingfield-1m 3f 106yds
1998	HIGH-RISE 8-7	
1999	LUCIDO 8-7	
2000	SADDLER'S QUEST 8-7	
2001	PERFECT SUNDAY 8-7	
2002	BANDARI 8-7	
2003	FRANKLINS GARDENS 8-7	
2004	PERCUSSIONIST 8-7	
2005	KONG 8-10	
2006	LINDA'S LAD 9-3	
2007	AQALEEM 8-12	

MUSIDORA STAKES (3y fillies)
York-1m 2f 88yds
1998	BAHR 8-8	
1999	ZAHRAT DUBAI 8-8	
2000	KALYPSO KATIE 8-8	
2001	TIME AWAY 8-8	1
2002	ISLINGTON 8-8	
2003	CASSIS 8-8	

2004	PUNCTILIOUS 8-8	6
2005	SECRET HISTORY 8-10	6
2006	SHORT SKIRT 8-12	6
2007	PASSAGE OF TIME 9-1	5

DANTE STAKES (3y)
York-1m 2f 88yds

1998	SARATOGA SPRINGS 8-11	6
1999	SALFORD EXPRESS 8-11	8
2000	SAKHEE 8-11	5
2001	DILSHAAN 8-11	6
2002	MOON BALLAD 8-11	6
2003	MAGISTRETTI 8-11	10
2004	NORTH LIGHT 8-11	10
2005	MOTIVATOR 8-11	6
2006	SEPTIMUS 9-0	6
2007	AUTHORIZED 9-0	6

YORKSHIRE CUP
York-1m 5f 194yds

1998	BUSY FLIGHT 5-8-9	6
1999	CHURLISH CHARM 4-8-9	8
2000	KAYF TARA 6-9-0	8
2001	MARIENBARD 4-8-9	8
2002	ZINDABAD 6-8-9	7
2003	MAMOOL 4-8-9	8
2004	MILLENARY 7-8-13	10
2005	FRANKLINS GARDENS 5-8-10	9
2006	PERCUSSIONIST 5-8-12	7
2007	SERGEANT CECIL 8-9-3	10

DUKE OF YORK STAKES
York-6f

1998	BOLLIN JOANNE 5-8-11	10
1999	SAMPOWER STAR 3-8-5	14
2000	LEND A HAND 5-9-5	10
2001	PIPALONG 5-9-6	14
2002	INVINCIBLE SPIRIT 5-9-5	12
2003	TWILIGHT BLUES 4-9-2	15
2004	MONSIEUR BOND 4-9-2	15
2005	THE KIDDYKID 5-9-2	11
2006	STEENBERG 7-9-2	16
2007	AMADEUS WOLF 4-9-2	17

LOCKINGE STAKES
Newbury-1m

1998	CAPE CROSS 4-9-0	10
1999	FLY TO THE STARS 5-9-0	6
2000	ALJABR 4-9-0	7
2001	MEDICEAN 4-9-0	7
2002	KELTOS 4-9-0	10
2003	HAWK WING 4-9-0	6
2004	RUSSIAN RHYTHM 4-8-11	15
2005	RAKTI 6-9-0	8
2006	PEERESS 5-8-11	8
2007	RED EVIE 4-8-11	8

HENRY II STAKES
Sandown-2m 78yds

1998	PERSIAN PUNCH 5-9-1	11
1999	ARCTIC OWL 5-9-3	11
2000	PERSIAN PUNCH 7-8-12	7
2001	SOLO MIO 7-9-1	11
2002	AKBAR 6-9-0	11
2003	MR DINOS 4-9-3	10
2004	PAPINEAU 4-8-12	9

2005	FIGHT YOUR CORNER 6-9-0	16
2006	TUNGSTEN STRIKE 5-9-2	7
2007	ALLEGRETTO 4-9-0	7

TEMPLE STAKES
Sandown-5f 6yds

1998	BOLSHOI 6-9-3	8
1999	TIPSY CREEK 5-9-3	8
2000	PERRYSTON VIEW 8-9-3	9
2001	CASSANDRA GO 5-9-0	10
2002	KYLLACHY 4-9-3	11
2003	AIRWAVE 3-9-0	7
*2004	NIGHT PROSPECTOR 4-9-4	12
2005	CELTIC MILL 7-9-4	13
2006	REVERENCE 5-9-4	12
2007	SIERRA VISTA 7-9-1	8

*Run at Epsom

BRIGADIER GERARD STAKES
Sandown-1m 2f 7yds

1998	INSATIABLE 5-8-10	9
1999	CHESTER HOUSE 4-8-10	6
2000	SHIVA 5-9-0	8
2001	BORDER ARROW 6-8-10	5
2002	POTEMKIN 4-8-10	4
2003	SIGHTS ON GOLD 4-8-10	8
2004	BANDARI 5-8-10	6
2005	NEW MORNING 4-8-7	5
2006	NOTNOWCATO 4-9-3	6
2007	TAKE A BOW 6-9-0	7

CORONATION CUP
Epsom-1m 4f 10yds

1998	SILVER PATRIARCH 4-9-0	7
1999	DAYLAMI 5-9-0	7
2000	DALIAPOUR 4-9-0	4
2001	MUTAFAWEQ 5-9-0	6
2002	BOREAL 4-9-0	6
2003	WARRSAN 5-9-0	9
2004	WARRSAN 6-9-0	11
2005	YEATS 4-9-0	7
2006	SHIROCCO 5-9-0	6
2007	SCORPION 5-9-0	7

WILLIAM HILL TROPHY (HANDICAP) (3y)
York-6f

1998	FRIAR TUCK 8-11	22
1999	PEPPERDINE 8-3	23
2000	COTTON HOUSE 8-13	23
2001	ORIENTOR 9-2	20
2002	ARTIE 7-10	20
2003	DAZZLING BAY 8-2	19
2004	TWO STEP KID 8-9	20
2005	TAX FREE 8-9	20
2006	PRINCE TAMINO 8-13	18
2007	ABANDONED	

QUEEN ANNE STAKES
Ascot-1m

1998	INTIKHAB 4-9-2	9
1999	CAPE CROSS 5-9-7	8
2000	KALANISI 4-9-2	11
2001	MEDICEAN 4-9-7	10
2002	NO EXCUSE NEEDED 4-9-2	12
2003	DUBAI DESTINATION 4-9-0	10
2004	REFUSE TO BEND 4-9-0	16
*2005	VALIXIR 4-9-0	7

2006 **AD VALOREM** 4-9-0 7
2007 **RAMONTI** 5-9-0 8
*Run at York

PRINCE OF WALES'S STAKES
Ascot-1m 2f
1998 **FAITHFUL SON** 4-9-3 8
1999 **LEAR SPEAR** 4-9-3 8
2000 **DUBAI MILLENNIUM** 4-9-0 6
2001 **FANTASTIC LIGHT** 5-9-1 9
2002 **GRANDERA** 4-9-0 12
2003 **NAYEF** 5-9-0 10
2004 **RAKTI** 5-9-0 10
*2005 **AZAMOUR** 4-9-0 10
2006 **OUIJA BOARD** 5-8-11 7
2007 **MANDURO** 5-9-0 6
*Run at York

ST JAMES'S PALACE STAKES (3y)
Ascot-1m
1998 **DR FONG** 9-0 8
1999 **SENDAWAR** 9-0 11
2000 **GIANT'S CAUSEWAY** 9-0 11
2001 **BLACK MINNALOUSHE** 9-0 11
2002 **ROCK OF GIBRALTAR** 9-0 11
2003 **ZAFEEN** 9-0 11
2004 **AZAMOUR** 9-0 11
*2005 **SHAMARDAL** 9-0 8
2006 **ARAAFA** 9-0 11
2007 **EXCELLENT ART** 9-0 8
*Run at York

COVENTRY STAKES (2y)
Ascot-6f
1998 **RED SEA** 8-12 17
1999 **FASLIYEV** 8-12 18
2000 **CD EUROPE** 8-12 12
2001 **LANDSEER** 8-12 20
2002 **STATUE OF LIBERTY** 8-12 16
2003 **THREE VALLEYS** 8-12 13
2004 **ICEMAN** 8-12 13
*2005 **RED CLUBS** 8-12 14
2006 **HELLVELYN** 9-1 21
2007 **HENRYTHENAVIGATOR** 9-1 20
*Run at York

KING EDWARD VII STAKES (3y)
Ascot-1m 4f
1998 **ROYAL ANTHEM** 8-8 10
1999 **MUTAFAWEQ** 8-8 10
2000 **SUBTLE POWER** 8-8 7
2001 **STORMING HOME** 8-8 12
2002 **BALAKHERI** 8-10 8
2003 **HIGH ACCOLADE** 8-11 8
2004 **FIVE DYNASTIES** 8-11 5
*2005 **PLEA BARGAIN** 8-11 5
2006 **PAPAL BULL** 8-12 9
2007 **BOSCOBEL** 8-12 9
*Run at York

JERSEY STAKES (3y)
Ascot-7f
1998 **DIKTAT** 8-10 16
1999 **LOTS OF MAGIC** 8-11 12
2000 **OBSERVATORY** 8-11 19
2001 **MOZART** 8-11 18
2002 **JUST JAMES** 8-11 15
2003 **MEMBERSHIP** 8-10 14

2004 **KHELEYF** 8-10 15
*2005 **PROCLAMATION** 8-13 21
2006 **JEREMY** 9-1 14
2007 **TARIQ** 9-1 15
*Run at York

WINDSOR FOREST STAKES
(fillies & mares)
Ascot-1m
2004 **FAVOURABLE TERMS** 4-8-12 10
*2005 **PEERESS** 4-8-9 8
2006 **SOVIET SONG** 6-8-12 10
2007 **NANNINA** 4-8-12 9
*Run at York

QUEEN MARY STAKES (2y fillies)
Ascot-5f
1998 **BINT ALLAYL** 8-8 17
1999 **SHINING HOUR** 8-8 13
2000 **ROMANTIC MYTH** 8-8 20
2001 **QUEEN'S LOGIC** 8-8 20
2002 **ROMANTIC LIASON** 8-8 13
2003 **ATTRACTION** 8-10 14
2004 **DAMSON** 8-10 17
*2005 **FLASHY WINGS** 8-10 17
2006 **GILDED** 8-12 15
2007 **ELLETELLE** 8-12 21
*Run at York

CORONATION STAKES (3y fillies)
Ascot-1m
1998 **EXCLUSIVE** 9-0 9
1999 **BALISADA** 9-0 9
2000 **CRIMPLENE** 9-0 9
2001 **BANKS HILL** 9-0 13
2002 **SOPHISTICAT** 9-0 9
2003 **RUSSIAN RHYTHM** 9-0 11
2004 **ATTRACTION** 9-0 11
*2005 **MAIDS CAUSEWAY** 9-0 9
2006 **NANNINA** 9-0 15
2007 **INDIAN INK** 9-0 13
*Run at York

ROYAL HUNT CUP
Ascot-1m
1998 **REFUSE TO LOSE** 4-7-11 32
1999 **SHOWBOAT** 5-8-6 32
2000 **CARIBBEAN MONARCH** 5-8-10 32
2001 **SURPRISE ENCOUNTER** 5-8-9 30
2002 **NORTON** 5-8-9 32
2003 **MACADAMIA** 4-8-13 32
2004 **MINE** 6-9-5 31
*2005 **NEW SEEKER** 5-9-0 22
2006 **CESARE** 5-8-8 30
2007 **ROYAL OATH** 4-9-0 26
*Run at York

QUEEN'S VASE (3y)
Ascot-2m
1998 **MARIDPOUR** 8-11 8
1999 **ENDORSEMENT** 8-6 11
2000 **DALAMPOUR** 8-11 13
2001 **AND BEYOND** 8-11 16
2002 **MAMOOL** 8-11 14
2003 **SHANTY STAR** 8-11 12
2004 **DUKE OF VENICE** 8-11 10
*2005 **MELROSE AVENUE** 8-11 10

2006 **SOAPY DANGER** 9-1 11
2007 **MAHLER** 9-1 15
Run at York

GOLDEN JUBILEE STAKES
Ascot-6f
(Cork and Orrery Stakes before 2002)
1998 **TOMBA** 4-9-0 12
1999 **BOLD EDGE** 4-9-0 9
2000 **SUPERIOR PREMIUM** 6-9-0 16
2001 **HARMONIC WAY** 9-0 21
2002 **MALHUB** 4-9-4 12
2003 **CHOISIR** 4-9-4 17
2004 **FAYR JAG** 5-9-4 14
2005 **CAPE OF GOOD HOPE** 7-9-4 15
2006 **LES ARCS** 4-9-4 18
2007 **SOLDIER'S TALE** 6-9-4 21
Run at York

NORFOLK STAKES (2y)
Ascot-5f
1998 **ROSSELLI** 8-12 15
1999 **WARM HEART** 8-12 13
2000 **SUPERSTAR LEO** 8-7 11
2001 **JOHANNESBURG** 8-12 10
2002 **BARON'S PIT** 8-12 8
2003 **RUSSIAN VALOUR** 8-12 8
2004 **BLUE DAKOTA** 8-12 9
2005 **MASTA PLASTA** 8-12 12
2006 **DUTCH ART** 9-1 11
2007 **WINKER WATSON** 9-1 11
Run at York

GOLD CUP
Ascot-2m 4f
1998 **KAYF TARA** 4-9-0 16
1999 **ENZELI** 4-9-0 17
2000 **KAYF TARA** 6-9-2 11
2001 **ROYAL REBEL** 5-9-2 12
2002 **ROYAL REBEL** 6-9-2 12
2003 **MR DINOS** 4-9-0 12
2004 **PAPINEAU** 4-9-0 12
*2005 **WESTERNER** 6-9-2 17
2006 **YEATS** 5-9-2 12
2007 **YEATS** 6-9-2 14
*Run at York

RIBBLESDALE STAKES (3y fillies)
Ascot-1m 4f
1998 **BAHR** 8-8 9
1999 **FAIRY QUEEN** 8-8 12
2000 **MILETRIAN** 8-8 9
2001 **SAHARA SLEW** 8-8 14
2002 **IRRESISTIBLE JEWEL** 8-8 15
2003 **SPANISH SUN** 8-11 9
2004 **PUNCTILIOUS** 8-11 9
*2005 **THAKAFAAT** 8-11 9
2006 **MONT ETOILE** 8-12 11
2007 **SILKWOOD** 8-12 9
*Run at York

HARDWICKE STAKES
Ascot-1m 4f
1998 **POSIDONAS** 6-8-9 7
1999 **FRUITS OF LOVE** 4-8-12 8
2000 **FRUITS OF LOVE** 5-8-12 9
2001 **SANDMASON** 4-8-9 7

2002 **ZINDABAD** 6-8-12 7
2003 **INDIAN CREEK** 5-8-9 9
2004 **DOYEN** 4-8-9 6
*2005 **BANDARI** 6-8-9 6
2006 **MARAAHEL** 5-9-0 8
2007 **MARAAHEL** 6-9-0 7
*Run at York

WOKINGHAM STAKES
Ascot-6f
1998 **SELHURSTPARK FLYER** 7-9-7 29
1999 **DEEP SPACE** 4-8-7 30
2000 **HARMONIC WAY** 9-0 29
2001 **NICE ONE CLARE** 5-9-3 30
2002 **CAPRICHO** 5-9-3 28
2003 **RATIO** 5-9-3 dead heated with
      FAYR JAG 4-9-6 29
2004 **LAFI** 5-8-13 29
*2005 **IFFRAAJ** 4-9-6 17
2006 **BALTIC KING** 6-9-10 28
2007 **DARK MISSILE** 4-8-6 26
*Run at York

KING'S STAND STAKES
Ascot-5f
1998 **BOLSHOI** 6-9-2 19
1999 **MITCHAM** 3-8-10 17
2000 **NUCLEAR DEBATE** 5-9-2 23
2001 **CASSANDRA GO** 5-8-13 22
2002 **DOMINICA** 3-8-7 15
2003 **CHOISIR** 4-9-7 20
2004 **THE TATLING** 7-9-2 19
*2005 **CHINEUR** 4-9-2 16
2006 **TAKEOVER TARGET** 7-9-7 28
2007 **MISS ANDRETTI** 6-9-1 20
*Run at York

NORTHUMBERLAND PLATE
Newcastle-2m 19yds
1998 **CYRIAN** 4-7-13 20
1999 **FAR CRY** 4-8-10 20
2000 **BAY OF ISLANDS** 8-8-4 18
2001 **ARCHDUKE FERDINAND** 3-8-4 18
2002 **BANGALORE** 6-9-5 16
2003 **UNLEASH** 4-8-11 20
2004 **MIRJAN** 8-8-3 19
2005 **SERGEANT CECIL** 6-8-8 20
2006 **TOLDO** 4-8-2 20
2007 **JUNIPER GIRL** 4-8-11 20

ECLIPSE STAKES
Sandown-1m 2f 7yds
1998 **DAYLAMI** 4-9-7 7
1999 **COMPTON ADMIRAL** 3-8-10 8
2000 **GIANT'S CAUSEWAY** 3-8-10 8
2001 **MEDICEAN** 4-9-7 8
2002 **HAWK WING** 3-8-10 5
2003 **FALBRAV** 5-9-7 15
2004 **REFUSE TO BEND** 4-9-7 12
2005 **ORATORIO** 3-8-10 7
2006 **DAVID JUNIOR** 4-9-7 9
2007 **NOTNOWCATO** 5-9-7 8

LANCASHIRE OAKS (fillies and mares)
Haydock-1m 3f 200yds
1998 **CATCHASCATCHCAN** 3-8-4 6
1999 **NOUSHKEY** 3-8-4 7
2000 **ELA ATHENA** 4-9-3 11

2001 **SACRED SONG** 4-9-6 8
2002 **MELLOW PARK** 3-8-5 8
2003 **PLACE ROUGE** 4-9-3 12
2004 **PONGEE** 4-9-3 8
2005 **PLAYFUL ACT** 3-8-5 8
2006 **ALLEGRETTO** 3-8-6 8
*2007 **TURBO LINN** 4-9-5 12
*Run at Newmarket

CHERRY HINTON STAKES (2y fillies)
Newmarket-6f
1998 **WANNABE GRAND** 8-9 10
1999 **TORGAU** 8-9 12
2000 **DORA CARRINGTON** 8-9 9
2001 **SILENT HONOR** 8-9 7
2002 **SPINOLA** 8-9 9
2003 **ATTRACTION** 8-12 8
2004 **JEWEL IN THE SAND** 8-9 10
2005 **DONNA BLINI** 8-9 8
2006 **SANDER CAMILLO** 8-12 10
2007 **YOU'RESOTHRILLING** 8-12 14

BUNBURY CUP
Newmarket-7f
1998 **HO LENG** 3-9-7 20
1999 **GRANGEVILLE** 4-9-3 19
2000 **TAYSEER** 6-8-9 19
2001 **ATAVUS** 4-8-9 19
*2002 **MINE** 4-8-12 16
2003 **PATAVELLIAN** 5-9-1 20
2004 **MATERIAL WITNESS** 7-9-3 19
2005 **MINE** 7-9-9 18
2006 **MINE** 8-9-10 19
2007 **GIGANTICUS** 4-8-8 18
* Capricho disqualified from first place dead-heat

PRINCESS OF WALES'S STAKES
Newmarket-1m 4f
1998 **FRUITS OF LOVE** 3-8-3 7
1999 **CRAIGSTEEL** 4-9-2 8
2000 **LITTLE ROCK** 4-9-2 6
2001 **MUTAMAM** 6-9-2 9
2002 **MILLENARY** 5-9-2 7
2003 **MILLENARY** 6-9-2 6
2004 **BANDARI** 5-9-2 8
2005 **GAMUT** 6-9-2 5
2006 **SOAPY DANGER** 3-8-3 4
2007 **PAPAL BULL** 4-9-2 12

JULY STAKES (2y)
Newmarket-6f
1998 **BERTOLINI** 8-10 6
1999 **CITY ON A HILL** 8-13 7
2000 **NOVERRE** 8-13 6
2001 **MESHAHEER** 8-10 5
2002 **MISTER LINKS** 8-10 10
2003 **NEVISIAN LAD** 8-10 8
2004 **CAPTAIN HURRICANE** 8-10 7
2005 **IVAN DENISOVICH** 8-10 11
2006 **STRATEGIC PRINCE** 8-12 9
2007 **WINKER WATSON** 9-1 13

FALMOUTH STAKES (fillies & mares)
Newmarket-1m
1998 **LOVERS KNOT** 3-8-6 13
1999 **RONDA** 3-8-6 8
2000 **ALSHAKR** 3-8-6 10

2001 **PROUDWINGS** 5-9-4 11
2002 **TASHAWAK** 3-8-6 9
2003 **MACADAMIA** 4-9-1 8
2004 **SOVIET SONG** 4-9-1 7
2005 **SOVIET SONG** 5-9-1 7
2006 **RAJEEM** 3-8-10 7
2007 **SIMPLY PERFECT** 3-8-10 7

JULY CUP
Newmarket-6f
1998 **ELNADIM** 4-9-5 17
1999 **STRAVINSKY** 3-8-13 17
2000 **AGNES WORLD** 5-9-5 10
2001 **MOZART** 3-8-13 18
2002 **CONTINENT** 5-9-5 14
2003 **OASIS DREAM** 3-8-13 16
2004 **FRIZZANTE** 5-9-2 20
2005 **PASTORAL PURSUITS** 4-9-5 19
2006 **LES ARCS** 6-9-5 19
2007 **SAKHEE'S SECRET** 3-8-13 18

PRINCESS MARGARET STAKES (2y fillies)
Ascot-6f
1998 **MYTHICAL GIRL** 8-9 6
1999 **SAINTLY SPEECH** 8-9 8
2000 **ENTHUSED** 8-9 8
2001 **LEGGY LOU** 8-9 6
2002 **RUSSIAN RHYTHM** 8-9 8
2003 **RIVER BELLE** 8-9 9
2004 **SOAR** 8-9 6
*2005 **MIXED BLESSING** 8-9 12
2006 **SCARLET RUNNER** 8-12 10
2007 **VISIT** 8-12 13
*Run at Newbury

STEWARDS' CUP
Goodwood-6f
1998 **SUPERIOR PREMIUM** 4-8-12 29
1999 **HARMONIC WAY** 4-8-6 30
2000 **TAYSEER** 6-8-11 30
2001 **GUINEA HUNTER** 5-9-0 30
2002 **BOND BOY** 5-8-2 28
2003 **PATAVELLIAN** 5-8-11 29
2004 **PIVOTAL POINT** 4-8-11 28
2005 **GIFT HORSE** 5-9-7 27
2006 **BORDERLESCOTT** 4-9-5 27
2007 **ZIDANE** 5-9-1 27

GORDON STAKES (3y)
Goodwood-1m 4f
1998 **RABAH** 8-10 dead heated with
          NEDAWI 8-10 6
1999 **COMPTON ACE** 8-10 6
2000 **MILLENARY** 8-13 10
2001 **ALEXIUS** 8-10 11
2002 **BANDARI** 8-13 4
2003 **PHOENIX REACH** 8-10 10
2004 **MARAAHEL** 8-10 8
2005 **THE GEEZER** 8-10 5
2006 **SIXTIES ICON** 9-0 7
2007 **YELLOWSTONE** 9-0 9

SUSSEX STAKES
Goodwood-1m
1998 **AMONG MEN** 4-9-7 10
1999 **ALJABR** 3-8-13 8

2000	GIANT'S CAUSEWAY 3-9-0	10
2001	NOVERRE 3-9-0	10
2002	ROCK OF GIBRALTAR 3-8-13	5
2003	REEL BUDDY 5-9-7	9
2004	SOVIET SONG 4-9-4	11
2005	PROCLAMATION 3-8-13	12
2006	COURT MASTERPIECE 6-9-7	7
2007	RAMONTI 5-9-7	8

RICHMOND STAKES (2y)
Goodwood-6f

1998	MUQTARIB 8-11	4
1999	BACHIR 8-11	7
*2000	PYRUS 8-11	8
2001	MISTER COSMI 8-11	8
**2002	REVENUE 8-11	9
2003	CARRIZO CREEK 8-11	7
2004	MONTGOMERY'S ARCH 8-11	8
2005	ALWAYS HOPEFUL 8-11	6
2006	HAMOODY 9-0	7
2007	STRIKE THE DEAL 9-0	9

*Endless Summer disqualified from first place
**Elusive City disqualified from first place

KING GEORGE STAKES
Goodwood-5f

1998	LAND OF DREAMS 3-8-7	15
1999	RUDI'S PET 5-9-0	15
2000	CASSANDRA GO 4-8-10	13
2001	DIETRICH 3-8-12	15
2002	AGNETHA 3-8-7	14
2003	THE TATLING 6-9-0	9
2004	RINGMOOR DOWN 5-8-11	13
2005	FIRE UP THE BAND 6-9-0	12
2006	LA CUCARACHA 5-8-11	18
2007	MOORHOUSE LAD 4-9-0	17

GOODWOOD CUP
Goodwood-2m

1998	DOUBLE TRIGGER 7-9-5	9
1999	KAYF TARA 5-9-7	7
2000	ROYAL REBEL 4-9-2	8
2001	PERSIAN PUNCH 8-9-5	12
2002	JARDINES LOOKOUT 5-9-2	9
2003	PERSIAN PUNCH 10-9-4	9
2004	DARASIM 4-9-2	9
2005	DISTINCTION 6-9-5	10
2006	YEATS 5-9-10	15
2007	ALLEGRETTO 4-9-5	15

MOLECOMB STAKES (2y)
Goodwood-5f

1998	INYA LAKE 8-7	9
1999	MISTY MISS 8-7	10
2000	MISTY EYED 8-10	9
2001	WHITBARROW 9-1	14
2002	WUNDERS DREAM 8-7	13
2003	MAJESTIC MISSILE 8-12	9
2004	TOURNEDOS 8-12	13
2005	STRIKE UP THE BAND 9-1	15
2006	ENTICING 8-11	13
2007	FLEETING SPIRIT 8-11	16

NASSAU STAKES (fillies and mares)
Goodwood-1m 1f 192yds

1998	ALBORADA 3-8-9	9
1999	ZAHRAT DUBAI 3-8-6	8

2000	CRIMPLENE 3-8-6	7
2001	LAILANI 3-8-6	7
2002	ISLINGTON 3-8-6	10
2003	RUSSIAN RHYTHM 3-8-6	8
2004	FAVOURABLE TERMS 4-9-2	6
2005	ALEXANDER GOLDRUN 4-9-3	11
2006	OUIJA BOARD 5-9-5	7
2007	PEEPING FAWN 3-8-10	8

HUNGERFORD STAKES
Newbury-7f

1998	MUHTATHIR 3-8-8	9
1999	LEND A HAND 4-9-0	7
2000	ARKADIAN HERO 5-9-2	8
2001	ATAVUS 4-8-13	7
2002	REEL BUDDY 5-8-13	10
2003	WITH REASON 5-8-13	11
2004	CHIC 4-8-11	13
2005	SLEEPING INDIAN 4-9-0	9
2006	WELSH EMPEROR 7-9-3	7
2007	RED EVIE 4-9-4	10

GEOFFREY FREER STAKES
Newbury-1m 5f 61yds

1998	MULTICOLOURED 5-9-3	6
1999	SILVER PATRIARCH 5-9-9	6
2000	MURGHEM 5-9-3	6
2001	MR COMBUSTIBLE 3-8-6	5
2002	MUBTAKER 5-9-3	7
2003	MUBTAKER 6-9-3	5
2004	MUBTAKER 7-9-3	4
2005	LOCHBUIE 4-9-3	5
2006	ADMIRAL'S CRUISE 4-9-3	5
2007	PAPAL BULL 4-9-7	5

INTERNATIONAL STAKES
York-1m 2f 88yds

1998	ONE SO WONDERFUL 4-9-2	8
1999	ROYAL ANTHEM 4-9-5	12
2000	GIANT'S CAUSEWAY 3-8-11	6
2001	SAKHEE 3-8-11	8
2002	NAYEF 4-9-5	7
2003	FALBRAV 5-9-5	8
2004	SULAMANI 5-9-5	9
2005	ELECTROCUTIONIST 4-9-5	7
2006	NOTNOWCATO 4-9-5	7
2007	AUTHORIZED 3-8-11	7

GREAT VOLTIGEUR STAKES (3y)
York-1m 4f

1998	SEA WAVE 8-9	6
1999	FANTASTIC LIGHT 8-9	6
2000	AIR MARSHALL 8-9	5
2001	MILAN 8-9	9
2002	BANDARI 3-8-9	6
2003	POWERSCOURT 8-9	7
2004	RULE OF LAW 8-9	6
2005	HARD TOP 8-9	6
2006	YOUMZAIN 8-12	10
2007	LUCARNO 8-12	9

YORKSHIRE OAKS (fillies and mares)
York-1m 4f

1998	CATCHASCATCHCAN 3-8-8	6
1999	RAMRUMA 3-8-8	11
2000	PETRUSHKA 3-8-8	6
2001	SUPER TASSA 5-9-4	9

2002	ISLINGTON 3-8-8	11
2003	ISLINGTON 4-9-4	8
2004	QUIFF 3-8-8	8
2005	PUNCTILIOUS 4-9-4	11
2006	ALEXANDROVA 3-8-11	6
2007	PEEPING FAWN 3-8-11	7

EBOR HANDICAP
York-1m 5f 197yds

1998	TUNING 3-8-7	21
1999	VICIOUS CIRCLE 5-8-4	21
2000	GIVE THE SLIP 3-8-4	22
2001	MEDITERRANEAN 3-8-4	22
2002	HUGS DANCER 5-8-5	22
2003	SAINT ALEBE 4-8-8	22
2004	MEPHISTO 5-9-4	19
2005	SERGEANT CECIL 6-8-12	20
2006	MUDAWIN 5-8-4	19
2007	PURPLE MOON 4-9-4	19

GIMCRACK STAKES (2y)
York-6f

1998	JOSR ALGARHOUD 8-11	8
1999	MULL OF KINTYRE 8-11	10
2000	BANNISTER 8-11	10
2001	ROCK OF GIBRALTAR 9-0	9
2002	COUNTRY REEL 8-11	11
2003	BALMONT 8-11	10
2004	TONY JAMES 8-11	11
2005	AMADEUS WOLF 8-11	13
2006	CONQUEST 8-12	6
2007	SIR GERRY 8-12	8

NUNTHORPE STAKES
York-5f

1998	LOCHANGEL 4-9-6	17
1999	STRAVINSKY 3-9-7	16
2000	NUCLEAR DEBATE 5-9-9	13
2001	MOZART 3-9-7	10
2002	KYLLACHY 4-9-11	17
2003	OASIS DREAM 3-9-9	9
2004	BAHAMIAN PIRATE 9-9-11	12
2005	LA CUCARACHA 4-9-8	16
2006	REVERENCE 5-9-11	14
2007	KINGSGATE NATIVE 2-8-1	16

PRESTIGE STAKES (2y fillies)
Goodwood-7f

1998	CIRCLE OF GOLD 8-9	9
1999	ICICLE 8-9	9
2000	FREEFOURRACING 8-9	6
2001	GOSSAMER 8-9	6
2002	GEMINIANI 8-9	8
2003	GRACEFULLY 8-9	6
2004	DUBAI SURPRISE 8-9	12
2005	NANNINA 8-9	9
2006	SESMEN 9-0	10
2007	SENSE OF JOY 9-0	7

CELEBRATION MILE
Goodwood-1m

1998	MUHTATHIR 3-8-9	9
1999	CAPE CROSS 5-9-7	5
2000	MEDICEAN 3-8-9	6
2001	NO EXCUSE NEEDED 3-8-9	6
2002	TILLERMAN 6-9-1	7
2003	PRIORS LODGE 5-9-1	6

2004	CHIC 4-8-12	7
2005	CHIC 5-8-12	8
2006	CARADAK 5-9-1	6
2007	ECHELON 5-8-12	8

SOLARIO STAKES (2y)
Sandown-7f 16yds

1998	RAISE A GRAND 8-11	7
1999	BEST OF THE BESTS 8-11	7
2000	KING'S IRONBRIDGE 8-11	7
2001	REDBACK 9-0	10
2002	FOSS WAY 8-11	11
2003	BARBAJUAN 8-11	8
2004	WINDSOR KNOT 8-11	8
2005	OPERA CAPE 8-11	7
2006	DRUMFIRE 9-0	8
2007	RAVEN'S PASS 9-0	9

SPRINT CUP
Haydock-6f

1998	TAMARISK 3-8-12	13
1999	DIKTAT 4-9-0	16
2000	PIPALONG 4-8-11	13
2001	NUCLEAR DEBATE 6-9-0	12
2002	INVINCIBLE SPIRIT 5-9-0	14
2003	SOMNUS 3-8-12	10
2004	TANTE ROSE 4-8-11	19
2005	GOODRICKE 3-8-12	17
2006	REVERENCE 5-9-3	11
2007	RED CLUBS 4-9-3	14

SEPTEMBER STAKES
Kempton-1m polytrack (1m 4f on turf before 2006)

*1998	CRIMSON TIDE 4-9-5	5
*1999	YAVANA'S PACE 7-9-0	5
2000	MUTAMAM 5-9-0	7
2001	MUTAMAM 6-9-8	4
2002	ASIAN HEIGHTS 4-9-3	6
2003	MUBTAKER 6-9-8	5
2004	MAMOOL 5-9-3	4
**2005	IMPERIAL STRIDE 4-9-8	6
2006	KANDIDATE 4-9-4	6
2007	STEPPE DANCER 4-9-4	7

* Run at Epsom
** Run at Newmarket

MAY HILL STAKES (2y fillies)
Doncaster-1m

1998	CALANDO 8-9	10
1999	TEGGIANO 8-9	12
2000	KARASTA 8-9	12
2001	HALF GLANCE 8-9	10
2002	SUMMITVILLE 8-9	8
2003	KINNAIRD 8-9	10
2004	PLAYFUL ACT 8-10	8
2005	NASHEEJ 8-13	8
*2006	SIMPLY PERFECT 8-12	12
2007	SPACIOUS 8-12	9

*Run at York

PORTLAND HANDICAP
Doncaster-5f 140yds

1998	CADEAUX CHER 4-8-7	21
1999	ASTONISHED 3-9-6	21
2000	COMPTON BANKER 3-8-8	22
2001	SMOKIN BEAU 4-9-4	22
2002	HALMAHERA 7-8-13	22

2003	HALMAHERA 8-9-4	22
2004	HALMAHERA 9-9-10	22
2005	OUT AFTER DARK 4-8-12	21
*2006	FANTASY BELIEVER 8-8-13	19
2007	FULLANDBY 5-8-13	21

*Run at York

PARK HILL STAKES (fillies and mares)
Doncaster-1m 6f 132yds

1998	DELILAH 4-9-6	9
1999	MISTLE SONG 3-8-5	10
2000	MILETRIAN 3-8-10	11
2001	RANIN 3-8-5	13
2002	ALEXANDER THREE D 3-8-5	9
2003	DISCREET BRIEF 3-8-5	8
2004	ECHOES IN ETERNITY 4-9-3	10
2005	SWEET STREAM 5-9-3	11
*2006	RISING CROSS 3-8-7	7
2007	HI CALYPSO 3-8-7	14

*Run at York

DONCASTER CUP
Doncaster-2m 2f

1998	DOUBLE TRIGGER 7-9-5	6
1999	FAR CRY 4-9-0	6
2000	ENZELI 5-9-7	9
2001	ALLELUIA 3-7-11	11
2002	BOREAS 7-9-1	8
2003	PERSIAN PUNCH 10-9-4	6
2004	MILLENARY 7 9-4 dead heated with	
	KASTHARI 5-9-1	8
2005	MILLENARY 8-9-4	7
*2006	SERGEANT CECIL 7-9-4	8
2007	SEPTIMUS 4-9-4	8

*Run at York

CHAMPAGNE STAKES (2y)
Doncaster-7f

1998	AUCTION HOUSE 8-10	8
1999	DISTANT MUSIC 8-10	6
2000	NOVERRE 9-0	8
2001	DUBAI DESTINATION 8-10	8
2002	ALMUSHAHAR 8-10	11
2003	LUCKY STORY 9-0	6
2004	ETLAALA 8-10	10
2005	CLOSE TO YOU 8-10 dead heated with	
	SILENT TIMES 8-10	7
*2006	VITAL EQUINE 8-12	8
2007	MCCARTNEY 8-12	10

*Run at York

FLYING CHILDERS STAKES (2y)
Doncaster-5f

1998	SHEER VIKING 8-12	13
1999	MRS P 8-7	14
2000	SUPERSTAR LEO 8-12	11
2001	SADDAD 8-12	13
2002	WUNDERS DREAM 8-12	14
2003	HOWICK FALLS 8-12	13
2004	CHATEAU ISTANA 8-12	11
2005	GODFREY STREET 8-12	9
*2006	WI DUD 9-0	9
2007	FLEETING SPIRIT 8-11	8

*Run at York

AYR GOLD CUP
Ayr-6f

1998	ALWAYS ALIGHT 4-8-7	29
1999	GRANGEVILLE 4-9-0	28
2000	BAHAMIAN PIRATE 5-8-0	28
2001	CONTINENT 4-8-10	28
2002	FUNFAIR WANE 3-9-3	28
2003	QUITO 6-8-6	26
2004	FUNFAIR WANE 5-8-6	24
2005	PRESTO SHINKO 4-9-2	27
2006	FONTHILL ROAD 6-9-2	23
2007	ADVANCED 4-9-9	28

MILL REEF STAKES (2y)
Newbury-6f 8yds

1998	GOLDEN SILCA 8-12	5
1999	PRIMO VALENTINO 8-12	4
2000	BOUNCING BOWDLER 8-12	7
2001	FIREBREAK 9-1	10
2002	ZAFEEN 9-1	8
2003	BYRON 8-12	10
2004	GALEOTA 8-12	9
2005	COOL CREEK 8-12	13
2006	EXCELLENT ART 9-1	6
2007	DARK ANGEL 9-1	6

CUMBERLAND LODGE STAKES
Ascot-1m 4f

1998	CAPRI 3-8-7	9
1999	ABANDONED	
2000	MUTAMAM 5-9-3	6
2001	NAYEF 3 8-9	7
2002	SYSTEMATIC 3-8-6	5
2003	HIGH ACCOLADE 3-8-11	5
2004	HIGH ACCOLADE 4-9-0	9
*2005	MUBTAKER 8-9-0	6
2006	YOUNG MICK 4-9-0	8
2007	ASK 4-9-3	8

*Run at Newmarket

FILLIES' MILE (2y fillies)
Ascot-1m

1998	SUNSPANGLED 8-10	8
1999	TEGGIANO 8-10	6
2000	CRYSTAL MUSIC 8-10	10
2001	GOSSAMER 8-10	7
2002	SOVIET SONG 8-10	10
2003	RED BLOOM 8-10	7
2004	PLAYFUL ACT 8-10	9
*2005	NANNINA 8-10	6
2006	SIMPLY PERFECT 8-12	8
2007	LISTEN 8-12	7

*Run at Newmarket

DJADEM STAKES
Ascot-6f

1998	BIANCONI 3-8-12	9
1999	BOLD EDGE 4-9-4	11
2000	SAMPOWER STAR 4-9-0	11
2001	NICE ONE CLARE 5-8-11	15
2002	CRYSTAL CASTLE 4-9-0	11
2003	ACCLAMATION 4-9-0	14
2004	PIVOTAL POINT 4-9-0	12
*2005	BARON'S PIT 5-9-0	13
2006	RED CLUBS 3-8-12	10
2007	HAATEF 3-8-12	17

*Run at Newmarket

QUEEN ELIZABETH II STAKES
Ascot-1m

1998	DESERT PRINCE 3-8-11	7
1999	DUBAI MILLENNIUM 3-8-11	4
2000	OBSERVATORY 3-8-11	12
2001	SUMMONER 4-9-1	8
2002	WHERE OR WHEN 3-8-11	5
2003	FALBRAV 5-9-1	8
2004	RAKTI 5-9-1	11
*2005	STARCRAFT 5-9-1	6
2006	GEORGE WASHINGTON 3-8-13	8
2007	RAMONTI 5-9-3	7

*Run at Newmarket

ROYAL LODGE STAKES (2y)
Ascot-1m

1998	MUTAAHAB 8-11	6
1999	ROYAL KINGDOM 8-11	6
2000	ATLANTIS PRINCE 8-11	8
2001	MUTINYONTHEBOUNTY 8-11	9
2002	AL JADEED 8-11	9
2003	SNOW RIDGE 8-11	10
2004	PERFECTPERFORMANCE 8-11	8
*2005	LEO 8-11	8
2006	ADMIRALOFTHEFLEET 8-12	7
2007	CITY LEADER 8-12	11

*Run at Newmarket

CHEVELEY PARK STAKES (2y fillies)
Newmarket-6f

1998	WANNABE GRAND 8-11	9
1999	SEAZUN 8-11	14
2000	REGAL ROSE 8-11	13
2001	QUEEN'S LOGIC 8-11	8
2002	AIRWAVE 8-11	6
2003	CARRY ON KATIE 8-11	10
2004	MAGICAL ROMANCE 8-11	7
2005	DONNA BLINI 8-11	10
2006	INDIAN INK 8-12	11
2007	NATAGORA 8-12	14

MIDDLE PARK STAKES (2y)
Newmarket-6f

1998	LUJAIN 8-11	7
1999	PRIMO VALENTINO 8-11	6
2000	MINARDI 8-11	10
2001	JOHANNESBURG 8-11	7
2002	OASIS DREAM 8-11	10
*2003	BALMONT 8-11	13
2004	AD VALOREM 8-11	9
2005	AMADEUS WOLF 8-11	6
2006	DUTCH ART 8-12	6
2007	DARK ANGEL 8-12	9

*Three Valleys disqualified from first place

SUN CHARIOT STAKES
(fillies and mares)
Newmarket-1m (1m 2f before 2000)

1998	KISSOGRAM 3-8-8	5
1999	LADY IN WAITING 4-8-13	8
2000	DANCEABOUT 3-8-9	9
2001	INDEPENDENCE 3-8-10	16
2002	DRESS TO THRILL 3-8-10	10
2003	ECHOES IN ETERNITY 3-8-10	10
2004	ATTRACTION 3-8-11	5
2005	PEERESS 4-9-0	10
2006	SPINNING QUEEN 3-8-12	5
2007	MAJESTIC ROI 3-8-13	9

CAMBRIDGESHIRE
Newmarket-1m 1f

1998	LEAR SPEAR 3-7-13	35
*1999	SHE'S OUR MARE 6-7-12	33
2000	KATY NOWAITEE 4-8-8	35
2001	I CRIED FOR YOU 6-8-6	35
2002	BEAUCHAMP PILOT 4-9-5	30
2003	CHIVALRY 4-8-1	34
2004	SPANISH DON 6-8-7	32
2005	BLUE MONDAY 4-9-3	30
2006	FORMAL DECREE 3-8-9	33
2007	PIPEDREAMER 3-8-12	34

* Run over 1m 2f

JOCKEY CLUB CUP
Newmarket-2m

1998	ARCTIC OWL 4-9-5	7
1999	RAINBOW HIGH 4-9-0	3
2000	PERSIAN PUNCH 7-9-5	9
2001	CAPAL GARMON 3-8-4	7
2002	PERSIAN PUNCH 9-9-0	8
2003	PERSIAN PUNCH 10-9-0	6
2004	MILLENARY 7-9-5	9
2005	COVER UP 8-9-0	10
2006	HAWRIDGE PRINCE 6-9-0	7
2007	ROYAL AND REGAL 3-8-4	8

CORNWALLIS STAKES (2y)
Ascot-5f

1998	SHOW ME THE MONEY 8-8	12
1999	KIER PARK 8-12	13
*2000	DANEHURST 8-7	17
2001	DOMINICA 8-7	11
2002	PEACE OFFERING 8-12	11
2003	MAJESTIC MISSILE 9-1	11
**2004	CASTELLETTO 8-9	11
***2005	'HUNTER STREET 8-12	12
2006	ALZERRA 8-1	10
2007	CAPTAIN GERRARD 9-0	12

*Run at Newbury
**Run at Newmarket
***Run at Salisbury

DEWHURST STAKES (2y)
Newmarket-7f

1998	MUJAHID 9-0	7
1999	DISTANT MUSIC 9-0	5
2000	TOBOUGG 9-0	10
2001	ROCK OF GIBRALTAR 9-0	8
2002	TOUT SEUL 9-0	16
2003	MILK IT MICK 9-0	12
2004	SHAMARDAL 9-0	9
2005	SIR PERCY 9-0	8
2006	TEOFILO 9-1	15
2007	NEW APPROACH 9-1	10

ROCKFEL STAKES (2y fillies)
Newmarket-7f

1998	HULA ANGEL 8-9	14
1999	LAHAN 8-9	12
2000	SAYEDAH 8-9	16
2001	DISTANT VALLEY 8-9	10
2002	LUVAH GIRL 8-9	11
2003	CAIRNS 8-9	10
2004	MAIDS CAUSEWAY 8-12	8
2005	SPECIOSA 8-9	14
2006	FINSCEAL BEO 9-2	14
2007	KITTY MATCHAM 8-12	10

CHALLENGE STAKES
Newmarket-7f

1998	DECORATED HERO 6-9-4	10
1999	SUSU 6-8-11	10
2000	LAST RESORT 3-8-9	9
2001	MUNIR 3-8-12	14
2002	NAYYIR 4-9-0	17
2003	JUST JAMES 4-9-0	11
2004	FIREBREAK 5-9-4	12
2005	LE VIE DEI COLORI 5-9-0	15
2006	SLEEPING INDIAN 5 9-3	16
2007	MISS LUCIFER 3-8-12	15

TWO-YEAR-OLD TROPHY (2y)
Redcar-6f

1998	PIPALONG 7-13	22
1999	KHASAYL 8-8	26
2000	DIM SUMS 8-4	23
2001	CAPTAIN RIO 8-10	25
2002	SOMNUS 8-12	18
2003	PEAK TO CREEK 9-0	23
2004	OBE GOLD 8-3	24
2005	MISU BOND 9-0	24
2006	DANUM DANCER 8-3	24
2007	DUBAI DYNAMO 9-2	23

CHAMPION STAKES
Newmarket-1m 2f

1998	ALBORADA 3-8-8	10
1999	ALBORADA 4-8-13	13
2000	KALANISI 4-9-2	15
2001	NAYEF 3-8-11	12
2002	STORMING HOME 4-9-2	11
2003	RAKTI 4-9-2	12
2004	HAAFHD 3-8-11	11
2005	DAVID JUNIOR 3-8-11	15
2006	PRIDE 6-9-0	8
2007	LITERATO 3-8-12	12

CESAREWITCH
Newmarket-2m 2f

1998	SPIRIT OF LOVE 3-8-8	29
1999	TOP CEES 9-8-10	32
2000	HEROS FATAL 6-8-1	33
2001	DISTANT PROSPECT 4-8-8	31
2002	MISS FARA 7-8-0	36

2003	LANDING LIGHT 8-9-4	36
2004	CONTACT DANCER 5-8-2	34
2005	SERGEANT CECIL 6-9-8	34
2006	DETROIT CITY 4-9-1	31
2007	LEG SPINNER 6-8-11	33

HORRIS HILL STAKES (2y)
Newbury-7f

1998	BRANCASTER 8-9	6
1999	UMISTIM 8-9	9
2000	CLEARING 8-9	9
2001	RAPSCALLION 8-9	10
2002	MAKHLAB 8-9	10
2003	PEAK TO CREEK 8-9	9
2004	CUPID'S GLORY 8-9	13
2005	HURRICANE CAT 8-9	13
2006	DIJEERR 8-12	10
2007	BEACON LODGE 8-12	11

RACING POST TROPHY (2y)
Doncaster-1m

1998	COMMANDER COLLINS 9-0	6
1999	ARISTOTLE 9-0	9
2000	DILSHAAN 9-0	9
2001	HIGH CHAPARRAL 9-0	6
2002	BRIAN BORU 9-0	9
2003	AMERICAN POST 9-0	4
2004	MOTIVATOR 9-0	8
2005	PALACE EPISODE 9-0	7
*2006	AUTHORIZED 9-0	14
2007	IBN KHALDUN 9-0	12

*Run at Newbury

NOVEMBER HANDICAP
Doncaster-1m 4f

1998	YAVANA'S PACE 6-9-10	23
1999	FLOSSY 3-7-7	16
2000	BATSWING 5-8-8	20
2001	ROYAL CAVALIER 4-7-10	24
2002	RED WINE 3-8-1	23
2003	TURBO 4-9-2	24
2004	CARTE DIAMOND 3-9-6	24
2005	COME ON JONNY 3-8-0	21
*2006	GROUP CAPTAIN 4-9-5	20
2007	MALT OR MASH 3-8-10	21

*Run at Windsor

WINNERS OF PRINCIPAL RACES IN IRELAND

IRISH 2000 GUINEAS (3y)
The Curragh-1m
1998	DESERT PRINCE 9-0	7
1999	SAFFRON WALDEN 9-0	10
2000	BACHIR 9-0	8
2001	BLACK MINNALOUSHE 9-0	12
2002	ROCK OF GIBRALTAR 9-0	7
2003	INDIAN HAVEN 9-0	16
2004	BACHELOR DUKE 9-0	8
2005	DUBAWI 9-0	8
2006	ARAAFA 9-0	11
2007	COCKNEY REBEL 9-0	12

TATTERSALLS GOLD CUP
The Curragh-1m 2f 110yds
1998	DAYLAMI 4-9-4	5
1999	SHIVA 4-8-11	6
2000	MONTJEU 4-9-0	5
2001	FANTASTIC LIGHT 5-9-0	6
2002	REBELLINE 4-8-11	8
2003	BLACK SAM BELLAMY 4-9-0	8
2005	GREY SWALLOW 4-9-0	6
2006	HURRICANE RUN 4-9-0	3
2007	NOTNOWCATO 5-9-0	9

IRISH 1000 GUINEAS (3y fillies)
The Curragh-1m
1998	TARASCON 9-0	13
1999	HULA ANGEL 9-0	17
2000	CRIMPLENE 9-0	13
2001	IMAGINE 9-0	16
2002	GOSSAMER 9-0	15
2003	YESTERDAY 9-0	18
2004	ATTRACTION 9-0	15
2005	SAOIRE 9-0	18
2006	NIGHTIME 9-0	15
2007	FINSCEAL BEO 9-0	11

IRISH DERBY (3y)
The Curragh-1m 4f
1998	DREAM WELL 9-0	10
1999	MONTJEU 9-0	10
2000	SINNDAR 9-0	11
2001	GALILEO 9-0	12
2002	HIGH CHAPARRAL 9-0	9
2003	ALAMSHAR 9-0	9
2004	GREY SWALLOW 9-0	10
2005	HURRICANE RUN 9-0	9
2006	DYLAN THOMAS 9-0	8
2007	SOLDIER OF FORTUNE 9-0	11

IRISH OAKS (3y fillies)
The Curragh-1m 4f
1998	WINONA 9-0	9
1999	RAMRUMA 9-0	7
2000	PETRUSHKA 9-0	10
2001	LAILANI 9-0	12
2002	MARGARULA 9-0	12
2003	VINTAGE TIPPLE 9-0	11
2004	OUIJA BOARD 9-0	7

2005	SHAWANDA 9-0	13
2006	ALEXANDROVA 9-0	6
2007	PEEPING FAWN 9-0	12

PHOENIX STAKES (2y)
Leopardstown-6f
1998	LAVERY 9-0	11
1999	FASLIYEV 9-0	6
2000	MINARDI 9-0	10
2001	JOHANNESBURG 9-0	11
2002	SPARTACUS 9-0	9
2003	ONE COOL CAT 9-0	7
2004	DAMSON 8-11	6
2005	GEORGE WASHINGTON 9-0	7
2006	HOLY ROMAN EMPEROR 9-1	7
2007	SAOIRSE ABU 8-12	6

IRISH CHAMPION STAKES
Leopardstown-1m 2f
1998	SWAIN 6-9-4	8
1999	DAYLAMI 5-9-4	7
2000	GIANT'S CAUSEWAY 3-8-11	7
2001	FANTASTIC LIGHT 5-9-4	7
2002	GRANDERA 4-9-4	7
2003	HIGH CHAPARRAL 4-9-4	7
2004	AZAMOUR 3-8-11	8
2005	ORATORIO 3-8-11	10
2006	DYLAN THOMAS 3-9-0	5
2007	DYLAN THOMAS 4-9-7	6

IRISH CAMBRIDGESHIRE
The Curragh-1m
1998	LADY ORANSWELL 4-7-3	21
1999	SEEFINN 4-7-7	14
2000	SILVERWARE 4-7-11	24
2001	OSPREY RIDGE 8-8-13	22
2002	MASANI 3-9-7	21
2003	DEFINITE BEST 5-8-5	15
2004	DUE RESPECT 4-8-10	18
2005	KESTREL CROSS 3-9-1	20
2006	QUINMASTER 4-10-1	22
2007	JALMIRA 6-8-13	24

MOYGLARE STUD STAKES (2y fillies)
The Curragh-7f
1998	EDABIYA 8-11	13
1999	PRESELI 8-11	10
2000	SEQUOYAH 8-11	10
2001	QUARTER MOON 8-11	17
2002	MAIL THE DESERT 8-11	9
2003	NECKLACE 8-11	11
2004	CHELSEA ROSE 8-11	9
2005	RUMPLESTILTSKIN 8-11	9
2006	MISS BEATRIX 8-12	12
2007	SAOIRSE ABU 8-12	7

NATIONAL STAKES (2y)
The Curragh-7f
(1m before 2000)
1998	MUS-IF 9-0	9
1999	SINNDAR 9-0	9
2000	BECKETT 9-0	9

2001	HAWK WING 9-0	7
2002	REFUSE TO BEND 9-0	7
2003	ONE COOL CAT 9-0	8
2004	DUBAWI 9-0	7
2005	GEORGE WASHINGTON 9-0	7
2006	TEOFILO 9-1	6
2007	NEW APPROACH 9-1	9

IRISH ST LEGER
The Curragh-1m 6f

1998	KAYF TARA 4-9-8	7
1999	KAYF TARA 5-9-8	5
2000	ARCTIC OWL 6-9-8	8
2001	VINNIE ROE 3-8-12	8
2002	VINNIE ROE 4-9-9	8
2003	VINNIE ROE 5-9-9	6
2004	VINNIE ROE 6-9-8	13
2005	COLLIER HILL 7-9-8	9
2006	KASTORIA 5-9-7	8
2007	YEATS 6-9-11	9

IRISH CESAREWITCH
The Curragh-2m

1998	SWEETNESS HERSELF 5-9-6	15
1999	MILTONFIELD 10-9-6	13
2000	TRAGIC LOVER 4-9-7	24
2001	RAPID DEPLOYMENT 4-8-13	19
2002	AMERICAN GOTHIC 4-9-0	18
2003	ZIMBABWE 3-8-0	17
2004	ESSEX 4-7-9	20
2005	CLARA ALLEN 7-8-0	17
2006	IKTITAF 5-8-8	16
2007	SANDYMOUNT EARL 4-9-3	21

PIERSE HURDLE
Leopardstown-2m
(Ladbroke Hurdle before 2001)

1999	ARCHIVE FOOTAGE 7-11-8	25
2000	MANTLES PRINCE 6-9-12	14
2001	GRINKOV 6-10-7	24
2002	ADAMANT APPROACH 8-11-1	26
2003	XENOPHON 7-10-11	28
2004	DROMLEASE EXPRESS 6-10-4	19
2005	ESSEX 5-10-8	21

2006	STUDMASTER 6-10-3	27
2007	SPRING THE QUE 8-10-3	30
2008	BARKER 7-10-6	28

AIG EUROPE CHAMPION HURDLE
Leopardstown-2m

1999	ISTABRAQ 7-11-10	6
2000	ISTABRAQ 8-11-10	6
2001	ISTABRAQ 9-11-10	7
2002	NED KELLY 6-11-10	8
2003	LIKE-A-BUTTERFLY 9-11-5	5
2004	FOREMAN 6-11-10	8
2005	MACS JOY 6-11-10	6
2006	BRAVE INCA 8-11-10	7
2007	HARDY EUSTACE 10-11-10	8
2008	SIZING EUROPE 6-11-10	6

HENNESSY COGNAC GOLD CUP
Leopardstown-3m

1998	DORANS PRIDE 9-12-0	8
1999	FLORIDA PEARL 7-12-0	7
2000	FLORIDA PEARL 8-12-0	7
2001	FLORIDA PEARL 9-12-0	7
2002	ALEXANDER BANQUET 9-12-0	5
2003	BEEF OR SALMON 7-12-0	5
2004	FLORIDA PEARL 12-11-12	7
2005	RULE SUPREME 9-11-12	7
2006	BEEF OR SALMON 10-11-12	7
2007	BEEF OR SALMON 11-11-12	5
2008	THE LISTENER 9-11-10	8

IRISH GRAND NATIONAL
Fairyhouse-3m 5f

1998	BOBBYJO 8-11-3	22
1999	GLEBE LAD 7-10-0	18
2000	COMMANCHE COURT 7-11-4	24
2001	DAVIDS LAD 7-10-0	19
2002	THE BUNNY BOILER 8-9-9	17
2003	TIMBERA 9-10-12	21
2004	GRANIT D'ESTRUVAL 10-10-0	28
2005	NUMBERSIXVALVERDE 9-10-1	26
2006	POINT BARROW 8-10-8	26
2007	BUTLER'S CABIN 7-10-4	29

WINNERS OF PRINCIPAL RACES IN FRANCE

PRIX GANAY
Longchamp-1m 2f 110yds
1998	**ASTARABAD** 4-9-2	4
1999	**DARK MOONDANCER** 4-9-2	5
2000	**INDIAN DANEHILL** 4-9-2	4
2001	**GOLDEN SNAKE** 5-9-2	9
2002	**AQUARELLISTE** 4-8-13	7
2003	**FAIR MIX** 5-9-2	9
2004	**EXECUTE** 7-9-2	8
2005	**BAGO** 4-9-2	9
2006	**CORRE CAMINOS** 4-9-2	7
2007	**DYLAN THOMAS** 4-9-2	8

POULE D'ESSAI DES POULAINS (3y)
Longchamp-1m
1998	**VICTORY NOTE** 9-2	12
1999	**SENDAWAR** 9-2	15
2000	**BACHIR** 9-2	7
*2001	**VAHORIMIX** 9-2	12
2002	**LANDSEER** 9-2	13
2003	**CLODOVIL** 9-2	10
2004	**AMERICAN POST** 9-2	9
2005	**SHAMARDAL** 9-2	15
2006	**AUSSIE RULES** 9-2	11
2007	**ASTRONOMER ROYAL** 9-2	14

* Noverre disqualified from first place

POULE D'ESSAI DES POULICHES
(3y fillies)
Longchamp-1m
1998	**ZALAIYKA** 9-0	14
1999	**VALENTINE WALTZ** 9-0	14
2000	**BLUEMAMBA** 9-0	11
2001	**ROSE GYPSY** 9-0	15
2002	**ZENDA** 9-0	17
2003	**MUSICAL CHIMES** 9-0	12
2004	**TORRESTRELLA** 9-0	13
2005	**DIVINE PROPORTIONS** 9-0	8
*2006	**TIE BLACK** 9-0	13
2007	**DARJINA** 9-0	13

*Price Tag disqualified from first place

PRIX SAINT-ALARY (3y fillies)
Longchamp-1m 2f
1998	**ZAINTA** 9-0	9
1999	**CERULEAN SKY** 9-0	10
2000	**REVE D'OSCAR** 9-0	7
2001	**NADIA** 9-0	7
2002	**MAROTTA** 9-0	12
2003	**FIDELITE** 9-0	7
2004	**ASK FOR THE MOON** 9-0	7
2005	**VADAWINA** 9-0	8
2006	**GERMANCE** 9-0	8
2007	**COQUERELLE** 9-0	6

PRIX JEAN PRAT (3y)
Chantilly-1m (1m 1f before 2005)
1998	**ALMUTAWAKEL** 8-11	6
1999	**GOLDEN SNAKE** 9-2	6
2000	**SUANCES** 9-2	7

2001	**OLDEN TIMES** 9-2	5
2002	**ROUVRES** 9-2	8
2003	**VESPONE** 9-2	8
2004	**BAGO** 9-2	8
2005	**TURTLE BOWL** 9-2	8
2006	**STORMY RIVER** 9-2	11
2007	**LAWMAN** 9-2	7

PRIX D'ISPAHAN
Longchamp-1m 1f 55yds
1998	**LOUP SAUVAGE** 4-9-2	7
1999	**CROCO ROUGE** 4-9-2	8
2000	**SENDAWAR** 4-9-2	5
2001	**OBSERVATORY** 4-9-2	5
2002	**BEST OF THE BESTS** 5-9-2	4
2003	**FALBRAV** 5-9-2	8
2004	**PRINCE KIRK** 4-9-2	5
2005	**VALIXIR** 4-9-2	8
2006	**LAVEROCK** 4-9-2	11
2007	**MANDURO** 5-9-2	5

PRIX DU JOCKEY CLUB (3y)
Chantilly-1m 2f 110yds (1m 4f before 2005)
1998	**DREAM WELL** 9-2	13
1999	**MONTJEU** 9-2	8
2000	**HOLDING COURT** 9-2	14
2001	**ANABAA BLUE** 9-2	14
2002	**SULAMANI** 9-2	15
2003	**DALAKHANI** 9-2	7
2004	**BLUE CANARI** 9-2	15
2005	**SHAMARDAL** 9-2	17
2006	**DARSI** 9-2	15
2007	**LAWMAN** 9-2	20

PRIX DE DIANE (3y fillies)
Chantilly-1m 2f 110yds
1998	**ZAINTA** 9-2	11
1999	**DARYABA** 9-2	14
2000	**EGYPTBAND** 9-2	14
2001	**AQUARELLISTE** 9-0	12
2002	**BRIGHT SKY** 9-0	15
2003	**NEBRASKA TORNADO** 9-0	10
2004	**LATICE** 9-0	17
2005	**DIVINE PROPORTIONS** 9-0	10
2006	**CONFIDENTIAL LADY** 9-0	14
2007	**WEST WIND** 9-0	14

GRAND PRIX DE PARIS (3y)
Longchamp-1m 4f (1m 2f before 2005)
1998	**LIMPID** 9-2	7
1999	**SLICKLY** 9-2	8
2000	**BEAT HOLLOW** 9-2	7
2001	**CHICHICASTENANGO** 9-2	5
2002	**KHALKEVI** 9-2	6
2003	**VESPONE** 9-2	11
2004	**BAGO** 9-2	4
2005	**SCORPION** 9-2	9
2006	**RAIL LINK** 9-2	9
2007	**ZAMBEZI SUN** 9-2	7

GRAND PRIX DE SAINT-CLOUD
Saint-Cloud-1m 4f
1998	**FRAGRANT MIX** 4-9-8	9
1999	**EL CONDOR PASA** 4-9-8	10
2000	**MONTJEU** 4-9-8	4
2001	**MIRIO** 4-9-9	9
2002	**ANGE GABRIEL** 4-9-8	6
2003	**ANGE GABRIEL** 5-9-9	10
2004	**GAMUT** 5-9-9	10
2005	**ALKAASED** 5-9-2	11
2006	**PRIDE** 6-8-13	6
2007	**MOUNTAIN HIGH** 5-9-2	6

PRIX MAURICE DE GHEEST
Deauville-6f 110yds
1998	**SEEKING THE PEARL** 4-8-13	12
1999	**DIKTAT** 4-9-2	10
2000	**BOLD EDGE** 5-9-2	11
2001	**KING CHARLEMAGNE** 3-8-12	9
2002	**MAY BALL** 5-8-13	9
2003	**PORLEZZA** 4-8-12	12
2004	**SOMNUS** 4-9-2	18
2005	**WHIPPER** 4-9-2	13
2006	**MARCHAND D'OR** 3-8-11	17
2007	**MARCHAND D'OR** 4-9-2	13

PRIX JACQUES LE MAROIS
Deauville-1m
1998	**TAIKI SHUTTLE** 4-9-4	8
1999	**DUBAI MILLENNIUM** 3-8-11	5
2000	**MUHTATHIR** 5-9-4	11
*2001	**VAHORIMIX** 3-8-13	9
2002	**BANKS HILL** 4-9-1	8
2003	**SIX PERFECTIONS** 3-8-9	12
2004	**WHIPPER** 3-8-11	10
2005	**DUBAWI** 3-8-11	6
2006	**LIBRETTIST** 4-9-4	10
2007	**MANDURO** 5-9-4	6
*Proudwings disqualified from first place

PRIX MORNY (2y)
Deauville-6f
1998	**ORPEN** 9-0	13
1999	**FASLIYEV** 9-0	7
2000	**BAD AS I WANNA BE** 9-0	6
2001	**JOHANNESBURG** 9-0	11
2002	**ELUSIVE CITY** 9-0	6
2003	**WHIPPER** 9-0	8
2004	**DIVINE PROPORTIONS** 8-11	9
2005	**SILCA'S SISTER** 8-11	7
2006	**DUTCH ART** 9-0	7
2007	**MYBOYCHARLIE** 8-13	6

PRIX DU MOULIN DE LONGCHAMP
Longchamp-1m
1998	**DESERT PRINCE** 3-8-11	7
1999	**SENDAWAR** 3-8-11	9
2000	**INDIAN LODGE** 4-9-2	8
2001	**SLICKLY** 5-9-2	9
2002	**ROCK OF GIBRALTAR** 3-8-11	7
2003	**NEBRASKA TORNADO** 3-8-8	14
2004	**GREY LILAS** 3-8-8	11
2005	**STARCRAFT** 5-9-2	9
2006	**LIBRETTIST** 4-9-2	8
2007	**DARJINA** 3-8-8	9

CRITERIUM INTERNATIONAL (2y)
Saint-Cloud-1m
2001	**ACT ONE** 9-0	6
2002	**DALAKHANI** 9-0	5
2003	**BAGO** 9-0	7
2004	**HELIOS QUERCUS** 9-0	8
2005	**CARLOTAMIX** 9-0	6
2006	**MOUNT NELSON** 9-0	10
2007	**THEWAYYOUARE** 9-0	6

PRIX VERMEILLE (fillies and mares)
Longchamp-1m 4f
(for 3yo fillies only prior to 2004)
1998	**LEGGERA** 9-0	11
1999	**DARYABA** 9-0	11
2000	**VOLVORETA** 9-0	11
2001	**AQUARELLISTE** 9-0	12
2002	**PEARLY SHELLS** 9-0	11
2003	**MEZZO SOPRANO** 9-0	11
2004	**SWEET STREAM** 4-9-2	13
2005	**SHAWANDA** 3-8-7	8
2006	**MANDESHA** 3-8-7	11
2007	**MRS LINDSAY** 3-8-9	10

PRIX DU CADRAN
Longchamp-2m 4f
1998	**INVERMARK** 4-9-2	9
1999	**TAJOUN** 5-9-2	8
2000	**SAN SEBASTIAN** 6-9-2	9
2001	**GERMINIS** 7-9-2	9
2002	**GIVE NOTICE** 5-9-2	16
2003	**WESTERNER** 4-9-2	10
2004	**WESTERNER** 5-9-6	8
2005	**REEFSCAPE** 4-9-2	10
2006	**SERGEANT CECIL** 7-9-2	7
2007	**LE MIRACLE** 6-9-2	6

PRIX DE L'ABBAYE DE LONGCHAMP
Longchamp-5f
1998	**MY BEST VALENTINE** 8-9-10	14
1999	**AGNES WORLD** 4-9-10	14
2000	**NAMID** 4-9-11	11
2001	**IMPERIAL BEAUTY** 5-9-8	19
2002	**CONTINENT** 5-9-11	20
2003	**PATAVELLIAN** 5-9-11	19
2004	**VAR** 5-9-11	15
2005	**AVONBRIDGE** 5-9-11	17
2006	**DESERT LORD** 6-9-11	14
2007	**BENBAUN** 6-9-11	17

PRIX MARCEL BOUSSAC (2y fillies)
Longchamp-1m
1998	**JUVENIA** 8-11	11
1999	**LADY OF CHAD** 8-11	11
2000	**AMONITA** 8-11	10
2001	**SULK** 8-11	9
2002	**SIX PERFECTIONS** 8-11	10
2003	**DENEBOLA** 8-11	16
2004	**DIVINE PROPORTIONS** 8-11	10
2005	**RUMPLESTILTSKIN** 8-11	15
2006	**FINSCEAL BEO** 8-11	13
2007	**ZARKAVA** 8-11	10

PRIX JEAN-LUC LAGARDERE (2y)
(Grand Criterium before 2003)
Longchamp-7f (1m before 2001)
1998	WAY OF LIGHT 9-0	7
1999	CIRO 9-0	3
2000	OKAWANGO 9-0	7
2001	ROCK OF GIBRALTAR 9-0	5
2002	HOLD THAT TIGER 9-0	14
2003	AMERICAN POST 9-0	6
2004	ORATORIO 9-0	6
2005	HORATIO NELSON 9-0	6
2006	HOLY ROMAN EMPEROR 9-0	9
2007	RIO DE LA PLATA 9-0	8

PRIX DE LA FORET
Longchamp-7f
1998	TOMBA 4-9-2	9
1999	FIELD OF HOPE 4-8-12	11
2000	INDIAN LODGE 4-9-2	11
2001	MOUNT ABU 4-9-2	11
2002	DEDICATION 3-8-11	10
2003	ETOILE MONTANTE 3-8-11	10
2004	SOMNUS 4-9-2	7
2005	COURT MASTERPIECE 5-9-2	8
2006	CARADAK 5-9-3	14
2007	TOYLSOME 8-9-2	13

PRIX ROYAL-OAK
Longchamp-1m 7f 110yds
1998	TIRAAZ 4-9-4	7
1999	AMILYNX 3-8-9	7
2000	AMILYNX 4-9-4	11
2001	VINNIE ROE 3-8-9	13
2002	MR DINOS 3-8-9	7
2003	WESTERNER 4-9-4	14
2004	WESTERNER 5-9-4	8
2005	ALCAZAR 10-9-4	11
2006	MONTARE 4-9-1	10
2007	ALLEGRETTO 4-9-1	11

CRITERIUM DE SAINT-CLOUD (2y)
Saint-Cloud-1m 2f
1998	SPADOUN 9-0	6
1999	GOLDAMIX 8-10	7
2000	SAGACITY 9-0	8
2001	BALLINGARRY 9-0	10
2002	ALBERTO GIACOMETTI 9-0	10
2003	VOIX DU NORD 9-0	10
2004	PAITA 8-11	7
2005	LINDA'S LAD 9-0	5
2006	PASSAGE OF TIME 8-11	13
2007	FULL OF GOLD 9-0	6

WINNERS OF OTHER OVERSEAS RACES

DUBAI WORLD CUP
Nad Al Sheba-1m 2f dirt
1998	SILVER CHARM 4-9-0	9
1999	ALMUTAWAKEL 4-9-0	8
2000	DUBAI MILLENNIUM 4-9-0	13
2001	CAPTAIN STEVE 4-9-0	12
2002	STREET CRY 4-9-0	11
2003	MOON BALLAD 4-9-0	11
2004	PLEASANTLY PERFECT 6-9-0	12
2005	ROSES IN MAY 5-9-0	12
2006	ELECTROCUTIONIST 5-9-0	11
2007	INVASOR 5-9-0	7

KENTUCKY DERBY
Churchill Downs-1m 2f dirt
1998	REAL QUIET 9-0	15
1999	CHARISMATIC 9-0	19
2000	FUSAICHI PEGASUS 9-0	19
2001	MONARCHOS 9-0	17
2002	WAR EMBLEM 9-0	18
2003	FUNNY CIDE 9-0	16
2004	SMARTY JONES 9-0	18
2005	GIACOMO 9-0	20
2006	BARBARO 9-0	20
2007	STREET SENSE 9-0	20

BREEDERS' CUP TURF
Various courses-1m 4f
1998	BUCK'S BOY 5-9-0	13
1999	DAYLAMI 5-9-0	14
2000	KALANISI 4-9-0	13

2001	FANTASTIC LIGHT 5-9-0	11
2002	HIGH CHAPARRAL 3-8-9	8
2003	JOHAR 4-9-0 dead heated with	
	HIGH CHAPARRAL 4-9-0	9
2004	BETTER TALK NOW 5-9-0	8
2005	SHIROCCO 4-9-0	13
2006	RED ROCKS 3-8-10	11
2007	ENGLISH CHANNEL 5-9-0	8

BREEDERS' CUP CLASSIC
Various courses-1m 2f dirt
1998	AWESOME AGAIN 4-9-0	10
1999	CAT THIEF 3-8-10	14
2000	TIZNOW 3-8-10	13
2001	TIZNOW 4-9-0	13
2002	VOLPONI 4-9-0	12
2003	PLEASANTLY PERFECT 5-9-0	10
2004	GHOSTZAPPER 4-9-0	13
2005	SAINT LIAM 5-9-0	13
2006	INVASOR 4-9-0	13
2007	CURLIN 3-8-9	9

MELBOURNE CUP
Flemington-2m
1998	JEZABEEL 6-8-0	24
1999	ROGAN JOSH 7-7-12	24
2000	BREW 6-7-10	22
2001	ETHEREAL 3-8-2	22
2002	MEDIA PUZZLE 5-8-4	23
2003	MAKYBE DIVA 4-8-0	23
2004	MAKYBE DIVA 5-8-11	24

2005 **MAKYBE DIVA** 6-9-2 24
2006 **DELTA BLUES** 5-8-11 23
2007 **EFFICIENT** 4-8-8 21

JAPAN CUP
Tokyo-1m 4f
1998 **EL CONDOR PASA** 3-8-5 15
1999 **SPECIAL WEEK** 4-9-0 14
2000 **T M OPERA O** 4-9-0 16
2001 **JUNGLE POCKET** 3-8-10 15
2002 **FALBRAV** 4-9-0 16

2003 **TAP DANCE CITY** 6-9-0 18
2004 **ZENNO ROB ROY** 4-9-0 16
2005 **ALKAASED** 5-9-0 18
2006 **DEEP IMPACT** 4-9-0 11
2007 **ADMIRE MOON** 4-9-0 18

WINNERS OF PRINCIPAL NATIONAL HUNT RACES

HENNESSY COGNAC GOLD CUP H'CAP CHASE
Newbury-3m 2f 110yds
1998 **TEETON MILL** 9-10-5 16
1999 **EVER BLESSED** 7-10-0 13
2000 **KING'S ROAD** 7-10-7 17
2001 **WHAT'S UP BOYS** 7-10-12 14
*2002 **GINGEMBRE** 8-10-13 25
2003 **STRONG FLOW** 6-11-0 21
2004 **CELESTIAL GOLD** 6-10-5 14
2005 **TRABOLGAN** 7-11-12 19
2006 **STATE OF PLAY** 6-11-4 16
2007 **DENMAN** 7-11-12 18
*Be My Royal disqualified from first place

KING GEORGE VI CHASE
Kempton-3m
1998 **TEETON MILL** 9-11-10 9
1999 **SEE MORE BUSINESS** 9-11-10 9
2000 **FIRST GOLD** 7-11-10 9
2001 **FLORIDA PEARL** 9-11-10 8
2002 **BEST MATE** 7-11-10 10
2003 **EDREDON BLEU** 11-11-10 12
2004 **KICKING KING** 6-11-10 13
*2005 **KICKING KING** 7-11-10 9
2006 **KAUTO STAR** 6-11-10 9
2007 **KAUTO STAR** 7-11-10 7
*Run at Sandown

WELSH NATIONAL H'CAP CHASE
Chepstow-3m 5f 110yds
1998 **KENDAL CAVALIER** 8-10-0 14
1999 **EDMOND** 7-10-0 16
2000 **JOCKS CROSS** 9-10-4 19
2001 **SUPREME GLORY** 8-10-0 13
2002 **MINI SENSATION** 9-10-4 16
2003 **BINDAREE** 9-10-9 14
2004 **SILVER BIRCH** 7-10-5 17
2005 **L'AVENTURE** 6-10-4 18
2006 **HALCON GENELARDAIS** 6-11-3 18
2007 **MIKO DE BEAUCHENE** 7-10-5 18

VICTOR CHANDLER CHASE
(Handicap before 2008)
Ascot-2m 1f (2m before 2008)
*1999 **CALL EQUINAME** 9-11-3 7
2000 **NORDANCE PRINCE** 9-10-0 10
2001 **FUNCTION DREAM** 9-10-11 10

2002 **TURGEONEV** 7-10-4 8
2003 ABANDONED
2004 **ISIO** 8-10-5 13
2005 **WELL CHIEF 6-11-10 10
***2006 **TYSOU** 9-11-2 10
2007 ABANDONED
2008 **TAMARINBLEU** 8-11-7 7
*Run at Kempton
**Run at Cheltenham
***Run at Sandown

TOTESPORT TROPHY H'CAP HURDLE
Newbury-2m 110yds
1998 **SHARPICAL** 6-11-1 14
1999 **DECOUPAGE** 7-11-10 18
2000 **GEOS** 5-11-3 17
2001 **LANDING LIGHT** 6-10-2 20
2002 **COPELAND** 7-11-7 16
2003 **SPIRIT LEADER** 7-10-0 27
2004 **GEOS** 9-10-9 25
2005 **ESSEX** 5-11-6 25
2006 ABANDONED
2007 **HEATHCOTE** 5-10-6 20
2008 **WINGMAN** 6-10-0 24

RACING POST H'CAP CHASE
Kempton-3m
1998 **SUPER TACTICS** 10-10-10 7
1999 **DR LEUNT** 8-11-5 8
2000 **GLORIA VICTIS** 6-11-10 13
2001 **YOUNG SPARTACUS** 8-11-3 15
2002 **GUNTHER MCBRIDE** 7-10-3 14
2003 **LA LANDIERE** 8-11-7 12
2004 **MARLBOROUGH** 12-11-12 11
2005 **FARMER JACK** 9-11-12 16
*2006 **INNOX** 10-11-0 15
2007 **SIMON** 8-11-5 10
*Run at Sandown

SUPREME NOVICES' HURDLE
Cheltenham-2m 110yds
1998 **FRENCH BALLERINA** 5-11-3 30
1999 **HORS LA LOI III** 4-11-0 20
2000 **SAUSALITO BAY** 6-11-8 16
2001 ABANDONED
2002 **LIKE-A-BUTTERFLY** 8-11-3 28
2003 **BACK IN FRONT** 6-11-8 19
2004 **BRAVE INCA** 6-11-7 19
2005 **ARCALIS** 5-11-7 20

2006　**NOLAND** 5-11-7......................................20
2007　**EBAZIYAN** 6-11-7....................................22

ARKLE CHALLENGE TROPHY (NOVICES' CHASE)
Cheltenham-2m
1998　**CHAMPLEVE** 5-11-0..............................16
1999　**FLAGSHIP UBERALLES** 5-11-0..............14
2000　**TIUTCHEV** 7-11-8.................................12
2001　ABANDONED
2002　**MOSCOW FLYER** 8-11-8........................12
2003　**AZERTYUIOP** 6-11-8...............................9
2004　**WELL CHIEF** 5-11-3..............................16
2005　**CONTRABAND** 7-11-7............................19
2006　**VOY POR USTEDES** 5-11-2...................14
2007　**MY WAY DE SOLZEN** 7-11-7.................13

CHAMPION HURDLE
Cheltenham-2m 110yds
1998　**ISTABRAQ** 6-12-0.................................18
1999　**ISTABRAQ** 7-12-0.................................14
2000　**ISTABRAQ** 8-12-0.................................12
2001　ABANDONED
2002　**HORS LA LOI III** 7-12-0.........................15
2003　**ROOSTER BOOSTER** 9-12-0.................17
2004　**HARDY EUSTACE** 7-11-10.....................14
2005　**HARDY EUSTACE** 8-11-10.....................14
2006　**BRAVE INCA** 8-11-10............................18
2007　**SUBLIMITY** 7-11-10...............................10

QUEEN MOTHER CHAMPION CHASE
Cheltenham-2m
1998　**ONE MAN** 10-12-0....................................8
1999　**CALL EQUINAME** 9-12-0.......................13
2000　**EDREDON BLEU** 8-12-0...........................9
2001　ABANDONED
2002　**FLAGSHIP UBERALLES** 8-12-0...............12
2003　**MOSCOW FLYER** 9-12-0........................11
2004　**AZERTYUIOP** 7-11-10...............................8
2005　**MOSCOW FLYER** 11-11-10.......................8
2006　**NEWMILL** 8-11-10...................................12
2007　**VOY POR USTEDES** 6-11-10...................10

BALLYMORE PROPERTIES NOVICES' HURDLE
(Royal & SunAlliance Hurdle before 2007)
Cheltenham-2m 5f
1998　**FRENCH HOLLY** 7-11-7...........................18
1999　**BARTON** 6-11-7.....................................18
2000　**MONSIGNOR** 6-11-7.............................14
2001　ABANDONED
2002　**GALILEO** 6-11-7.....................................27
2003　**HARDY EUSTACE** 6-11-7.......................19
2004　**FUNDAMENTALIST** 6-11-7....................15
2005　**NO REFUGE** 5-11-7................................20
2006　**NICANOR** 5-11-7...................................17
2007　**MASSINI'S MAGUIRE** 6-11-7.................15

ROYAL & SUNALLIANCE NOVICES' CHASE
Cheltenham-3m
1998　**FLORIDA PEARL** 6-11-4..........................10
1999　**LOOKS LIKE TROUBLE** 7-11-4...............14
2000　**LORD NOELIE** 7-11-4...............................9
2001　ABANDONED
2002　**HUSSARD COLLONGES** 7-11-4...............19
2003　**ONE KNIGHT** 7-11-4.................................9

2004　**RULE SUPREME** 8-11-4..........................10
2005　**TRABOLGAN** 7-11-4.................................9
2006　**STAR DE MOHAISON** 5-10-8..................15
2007　**DENMAN** 7-11-4.....................................17

WORLD HURDLE
(Stayers' Hurdle before 2005)
Cheltenham-3m
1998　**PRINCEFUL** 7-11-10..................................9
1999　**ANZUM** 8-11-10......................................12
2000　**BACCHANAL** 6-11-10.............................10
2001　ABANDONED
2002　**BARACOUDA** 7-11-10.............................16
2003　**BARACOUDA** 8-11-10.............................11
2004　**IRIS'S GIFT** 7-11-10.................................10
2005　**INGLIS DREVER** 6-11-10.........................12
2006　**MY WAY DE SOLZEN** 6-11-10.................20
2007　**INGLIS DREVER** 8-11-10.........................14

TRIUMPH HURDLE (4y)
Cheltenham-2m 1f
1998　**UPGRADE** 11-0..25
1999　**KATARINO** 11-0......................................14
2000　**SNOW DROP** 10-9..................................28
2001　ABANDONED
2002　**SCOLARDY** 11-0.....................................28
2003　**SPECTROSCOPE** 11-0...........................27
2004　**MADE IN JAPAN** 11-0.............................23
2005　**PENZANCE** 11-0.....................................23
2006　**DETROIT CITY** 11-0.................................17
2007　**KATCHIT** 11-0..23

CHELTENHAM GOLD CUP
Cheltenham-3m 2f 110yds
1998　**COOL DAWN** 10-12-0..............................17
1999　**SEE MORE BUSINESS** 9-12-0...............12
2000　**LOOKS LIKE TROUBLE** 8-12-0...............12
2001　ABANDONED
2002　**BEST MATE** 7-12-0.................................18
2003　**BEST MATE** 8-12-0.................................15
2004　**BEST MATE** 9-11-10...............................10
2005　**KICKING KING** 7-11-10...........................15
2006　**WAR OF ATTRITION** 7-11-10...................22
2007　**KAUTO STAR** 7-11-10.............................18

FESTIVAL TROPHY CHASE
Cheltenham-2m 5f
2005　**THISTHATANDTOTHER** 9-11-3.................4
2006　**FONDMORT** 10-11-0................................11
2007　**TARANIS** 6-11-0..9

BETFAIR BOWL CHASE
(Martell Cup Chase before 2005)
Aintree-3m 1f
1998　**ESCARTEFIGUE** 6-11-13..........................8
1999　**MACGEORGE** 9-11-5................................5
2000　**SEE MORE BUSINESS** 10-12-0................4
2001　**FIRST GOLD** 8-12-0..................................7
2002　**FLORIDA PEARL** 10-11-12........................6
2003　**FIRST GOLD** 10-11-12..............................7
2004　**TIUTCHEV** 11-11-12.................................8
2005　**GREY ABBEY** 11-11-12.............................8
2006　**CELESTIAL GOLD** 8-11-8..........................9
2007　**EXOTIC DANCER** 7-11-12.........................5

AINTREE HURDLE
Aintree-2m 4f

1998	**PRIDWELL** 8-11-7	6
1999	**ISTABRAQ** 7-11-7	7
2000	**MISTER MOROSE** 10-11-7	10
2001	**BARTON** 8-11-7	8
2002	**ILNAMAR** 6-11-7	14
2003	**SACUNDAI** 6-11-7	11
2004	**RHINESTONE COWBOY** 8-11-7	11
2005	**AL EILE** 5-11 7	9
2006	**ASIAN MAZE** 7-11-0	9
2007	**AL EILE** 7-11-7	11

SCOTTISH GRAND NATIONAL (H'CAP CHASE)
Ayr-4m 1f

1998	**BARONET** 8-10-0	18
1999	**YOUNG KENNY** 8-11-10	15
2000	**PARIS PIKE** 8-11-0	18
2001	**GINGEMBRE** 7-11-2	30
2002	**TAKE CONTROL** 8-10-6	18
2003	**RYALUX** 10-10-5	19
2004	**GREY ABBEY** 10-11-12	28

2005	**JOES EDGE** 8-9-11	20
2006	**RUN FOR PADDY** 10-10-2	30
2007	**HOT WELD** 8-9-9	23

GOLD CUP (H'CAP CHASE)
(Whitbread Gold Cup until 2001, Attheraces Gold Cup in 2002-3, Betfred Gold Cup 2004-7)
Sandown-3m 5f 110yds

1998	**CALL IT A DAY** 8-10-10	19
1999	**EULOGY** 9-10-0	19
2000	**BEAU** 7-10-9	20
2001	**AD HOC** 7-10-4	25
2002	**BOUNCE BACK** 6-10-9	20
2003	**AD HOC** 9-10-10	16
2004	**PUNTAL** 8-11-4	18
2005	**JACK HIGH** 10-10-0	19
2006	**LACDOUDAL** 7-11-5	18
2007	**HOT WELD** 8-10-0	10

DISTANCE CONVERSION

5f	1,000m	10f	2,000m	15f	3,000m	20f	4,000m
6f	1,200m	11f	2,200m	16f	3,200m	21f	4,200m
7f	1,400m	12f	2,400m	17f	3,400m	22f	4,400m
8f	1,600m	13f	2,600m	18f	3,600m		
9f	1,800m	14f	2,800m	19f	3,800m		

LEADING TRAINERS ON THE FLAT: 1897-2007

1897 R Marsh	1934 Frank Butters	1971 I Balding
1898 R Marsh	1935 Frank Butters	1972 W Hern
1899 J Porter	1936 J Lawson	1973 C F N Murless
1900 R Marsh	1937 C Boyd-Rochfort	1974 P Walwyn
1901 J Huggins	1938 C Boyd-Rochfort	1975 P Walwyn
1902 R S Sievier	1939 J L Jarvis	1976 H Cecil
1903 G Blackwell	1940 F Darling	1977 M V O'Brien
1904 P P Gilpin	1941 F Darling	1978 H Cecil
1905 W T Robinson	1942 F Darling	1979 H Cecil
1906 Hon G Lambton	1943 W Nightingall	1980 W Hern
1907 A Taylor	1944 Frank Butters	1981 M Stoute
1908 C Morton	1945 W Earl	1982 H Cecil
1909 A Taylor	1946 Frank Butters	1983 W Hern
1910 A Taylor	1947 F Darling	1984 H Cecil
1911 Hon G Lambton	1948 C F N Murless	1985 H Cecil
1912 Hon G Lambton	1949 Frank Butters	1986 M Stoute
1913 R Wootton	1950 C H Semblat	1987 H Cecil
1914 A Taylor	1951 J L Jarvis	1988 H Cecil
1915 P P Gilpin	1952 M Marsh	1989 M Stoute
1916 R C Dawson	1953 J L Jarvis	1990 H Cecil
1917 A Taylor	1954 C Boyd-Rochfort	1991 P Cole
1918 A Taylor	1955 C Boyd-Rochfort	1992 R Hannon
1919 A Taylor	1956 C F Elsey	1993 H Cecil
1920 A Taylor	1957 C F N Murless	1994 M Stoute
1921 A Taylor	1958 C Boyd-Rochfort	1995 J Dunlop
1922 A Taylor	1959 C F N Murless	1996 Saeed bin Suroor
1923 A Taylor	1960 C F N Murless	1997 M Stoute
1924 R C Dawson	1961 C F N Murless	1998 Saeed bin Suroor
1925 A Taylor	1962 W Hern	1999 Saeed bin Suroor
1926 F Darling	1963 P Prendergast	2000 Sir M Stoute
1927 Frank Butters	1964 P Prendergast	2001 A O'Brien
1928 Frank Butters	1965 P Prendergast	2002 A O'Brien
1929 R C Dawson	1966 M V O'Brien	2003 Sir M Stoute
1930 H S Persse	1967 C F N Murless	2004 Saeed bin Suroor
1931 J Lawson	1968 C F N Murless	2005 Sir M Stoute
1932 Frank Butters	1969 A M Budgett	2006 Sir M Stoute
1933 F Darling	1970 C F N Murless	2007 A O'Brien

CHAMPION JOCKEYS ON THE FLAT: 1895-2007

1896 M Cannon	164	1917 S Donoghue	42	1937 G Richards	216
1897 M Cannon	145	1918 S Donoghue	66	1938 G Richards	206
1898 O Madden	161	1919 S Donoghue	129	1939 G Richards	155
1899 S Loates	160	1920 S Donoghue	143	1940 G Richards	68
1900 L Reiff	143	1921 S Donoghue	141	1941 H Wragg	71
1901 O Madden	130	1922 S Donoghue	102	1942 G Richards	67
1902 W Lane	170	1923 S Donoghue	89	1943 G Richards	65
1903 O Madden	154	C Elliott	89	1944 G Richards	88
1904 O Madden	161	1924 C Elliott	106	1945 G Richards	104
1905 E Wheatley	124	1925 G Richards	118	1946 G Richards	212
1906 W Higgs	149	1926 T Weston	95	1947 G Richards	269
1907 W Higgs	146	1927 G Richards	164	1948 G Richards	224
1908 D Maher	139	1928 G Richards	148	1949 G Richards	261
1909 F Wootton	165	1929 G Richards	135	1950 G Richards	201
1910 F Wootton	137	1930 F Fox	129	1951 G Richards	227
1911 F Wootton	187	1931 G Richards	145	1952 G Richards	231
1912 F Wootton	118	1932 G Richards	190	1953 G Richards	191
1913 D Maher	115	1933 G Richards	259	1954 D Smith	129
1914 S Donoghue	129	1934 G Richards	212	1955 D Smith	168
1915 S Donoghue	62	1935 G Richards	217	1956 D Smith	155
1916 S Donoghue	43	1936 G Richards	174	1957 A Breasley	173

1958 D Smith	165	1975 Pat Eddery	164	1992 M Roberts	206
1959 D Smith	157	1976 Pat Eddery	162	1993 Pat Eddery	169
1960 L Piggott	170	1977 Pat Eddery	176	1994 L Dettori	233
1961 A Breasley	171	1978 W Carson	182	1995 L Dettori	211
1962 A Breasley	179	1979 J Mercer	164	1996 Pat Eddery	186
1963 A Breasley	176	1980 W Carson	166	1997 K Fallon	196
1964 L Piggott	140	1981 L Piggott	179	1998 K Fallon	185
1965 L Piggott	160	1982 L Piggott	188	1999 K Fallon	200
1966 L Piggott	191	1983 W Carson	159	2000 K Darley	152
1967 L Piggott	117	1984 S Cauthen	130	2001 K Fallon	166
1968 L Piggott	139	1985 S Cauthen	195	2002 K Fallon	144
1969 L Piggott	163	1986 Pat Eddery	176	2003 K Fallon	208
1970 L Piggott	162	1987 S Cauthen	197	2004 L Dettori	192
1971 L Piggott	162	1988 Pat Eddery	183	2005 J Spencer	163
1972 W Carson	132	1989 Pat Eddery	171	2006 K Moore	180
1973 W Carson	164	1990 Pat Eddery	209	2007 S Sanders	190
1974 Pat Eddery	148	1991 Pat Eddery	165	J Spencer	190

LEADING OWNERS ON THE FLAT: 1895-2007

1895 Ld de Rothschild	1933 Ld Derby	1971 Mr P Mellon
1896 Ld de Rothschild	1934 H.H. Aga Khan	1972 Mrs J Hislop
1987 Mr J Gubbins	1935 H.H. Aga Khan	1973 Mr N B Hunt
1898 Ld de Rothschild	1936 Ld Astor	1974 Mr N B Hunt
1899 Duke of Westminster	1937 H.H. Aga Khan	1975 Dr C Vittadini
1900 H.R.H. The Prince of Wales	1938 Ld Derby	1976 Mr D Wildenstein
1901 Sir G Blundell Maple	1939 Ld Rosebery	1977 Mr R Sangster
1902 Mr R S Sievier	1940 Lord Rothermere	1978 Mr R Sangster
1903 Sir James Miller	1941 Ld Glanely	1979 Sir M Sobell
1904 Sir James Miller	1942 His Majesty	1980 S Weinstock
1905 Col W Hall Walker	1943 Miss D Paget	1981 H.H. Aga Khan
1906 Ld Derby (late)	1944 H.H. Aga Khan	1982 Mr R Sangster
1907 Col W Hall Walker	1945 Ld Derby	1983 Mr R Sangster
1908 Mr J B Joel	1946 H.H. Aga Khan	1984 Mr R Sangster
1909 Mr "Fairie"	1947 H.H. Aga Khan	1985 Sheikh Mohammed
1910 Mr "Fairie"	1948 H.H. Aga Khan	1986 Sheikh Mohammed
1911 Ld Derby	1949 H.H. Aga Khan	1987 Sheikh Mohammed
1912 Mr T Pilkington	1950 M M Boussac	1988 Sheikh Mohammed
1913 Mr J B Joel	1951 M M Boussac	1989 Sheikh Mohammed
1914 Mr J B Joel	1952 H. H. Aga Khan	1990 Mr Hamdan Al-Maktoum
1915 Mr L Neumann	1953 Sir Victor Sassoon	1991 Sheikh Mohammed
1916 Mr E Hulton	1954 Her Majesty	1992 Sheikh Mohammed
1917 Mr "Fairie"	1955 Lady Zia Wernner	1993 Sheikh Mohammed
1918 Lady James Douglas	1956 Maj L B Holliday	1994 Mr Hamdan Al-Maktoum
1919 Ld Glanely	1957 Her Majesty	1995 Mr Hamdan Al-Maktoum
1920 Sir Robert Jardine	1958 Mr J McShain	1996 Godolphin
1921 Mr S B Joel	1959 Prince Aly Khan	1997 Sheikh Mohammed
1922 Ld Woolavington	1960 Sir Victor Sassoon	1998 Godolphin
1923 Ld Derby	1961 Maj L B Holliday	1999 Godolphin
1924 H.H. Aga Khan	1962 Maj L B Holliday	2000 H.H. Aga Khan
1925 Ld Astor	1963 Mr J R Mullion	2001 Godolphin
1926 Ld Woolavington	1964 Mrs H E Jackson	2002 Mr Hamdan Al-Maktoum
1927 Ld Derby	1965 M J Ternynck	2003 K Abdullah
1928 Ld Derby	1966 Lady Zia Wernher	2004 Godolphin
1929 H.H. Aga Khan	1967 Mr H J Joel	2005 Mr Hamdan Al-Maktoum
1930 H.H. Aga Khan	1968 Mr Raymond R Guest	2006 Godolphin
1931 Mr J A Dewar	1969 Mr D Robinson	2007 Godolphin
1932 H.H. Aga Khan	1970 Mr C Engelhard	

LEADING SIRES ON THE FLAT: 1895-2007

1895 St Simon	1900 St Simon	1905 Gallinule
1896 St Simon	1901 St Simon	1906 Persimmon
1897 Kendal	1902 Persimmon	1907 St Frusquin
1898 Galopin	1903 St Frusquin	1908 Persimmon
1899 Orme	1904 Gallinule	1909 Cyllene

1910 Cyllene	1943 Fairway	1976 Wolver Hollow
1911 Sundridge	1944 Fairway	1977 Northern Dancer
1912 Persimmon	1945 Hyperion	1978 Mill Reef (USA)
1913 Desmond	1946 Hyperion	1979 Petingo
1914 Polymelus	1947 Nearco	1980 Pitcairn
1915 Polymelus	1948 Big Game	1981 Great Nephew
1916 Polymelus	1949 Nearco	1982 Be My Guest (USA)
1917 Bayardo	1950 Fair Trial	1983 Northern Dancer
1918 Bayardo	1951 Nasrullah	1984 Northern Dancer
1919 The Tetrarch	1952 Tehran	1985 Kris
1920 Polymelus	1953 Chanteur II	1986 Nijinsky (CAN)
1921 Polymelus	1954 Hyperion	1987 Mill Reef (USA)
1922 Lemberg	1955 Alycidon	1988 Caerleon (USA)
1923 Swynford	1956 Court Martial	1989 Blushing Groom (FR)
1924 Son-in-Law	1957 Court Martial	1990 Sadler's Wells (USA)
1925 Phalaris	1958 Mossborough	1991 Caerleon (USA)
1926 Hurry On	1959 Petition	1992 Sadler's Wells (USA)
1927 Buchan	1960 Aureole	1993 Sadler's Wells (USA)
1928 Phalaris	1961 Aureole	1994 Sadler's Wells (USA)
1929 Tetratema	1962 Never Say Die	1995 Sadler's Wells (USA)
1930 Son-in-Law	1963 Ribot	1996 Sadler's Wells (USA)
1931 Pharos	1964 Chamossaire	1997 Sadler's Wells (USA)
1932 Gainsborough	1965 Court Harwell	1998 Sadler's Wells (USA)
1933 Gainsborough	1966 Charlottesville	1999 Sadler's Wells (USA)
1934 Blandford	1967 Ribot	2000 Sadler's Wells (USA)
1935 Blandford	1968 Ribot	2001 Sadler's Wells (USA)
1936 Fairway	1969 Crepello	2002 Sadler's Wells (USA)
1937 Solario	1970 Northern Dancer	2003 Sadler's Wells (USA)
1938 Blandford	1971 Never Bend	2004 Sadler's Wells (USA)
1939 Fairway	1972 Queen's Hussar	2005 Danehill (USA)
1940 Hyperion	1973 Vaguely Noble	2006 Danehill (USA)
1941 Hyperion	1974 Vaguely Noble	2007 Danehill (USA)
1942 Hyperion	1975 Great Nephew	

LEADING BREEDERS ON THE FLAT: 1910-2007

1910 Mr "Fairie"	1941 Ld Glanely	1971 Mr P Mellon
1911 Ld Derby (late)	1942 National Stud	1972 Mr J Hislop
1912 Col. W Hall Walker	1943 Miss D Paget	1973 Claiborne Farm
1913 Mr J B Joel	1944 Ld Rosebery	1974 Mr N B Hunt
1914 Mr J B Joel	1945 Ld Derby	1975 Overbury Stud
1915 Mr L Neumann	1946 Lt- Col H Boyd-Rochfort	1976 Dayton Ltd
1916 Mr E Hulton	1947 H.H. Aga Khan	1977 Mr E P Taylor
1917 Mr "Fairie"	1948 H.H. Aga Khan	1978 Cragwood Estates Inc
1918 Lady James Douglas	1949 H.H. Aga Khan	1979 Ballymacoll Stud
1919 Ld Derby	1950 M M Boussac	1980 P Clarke
1920 Ld Derby	1951 M M Boussac	1981 H.H. Aga Khan
1921 Mr S B Joel	1952 H. H. Aga Khan	1982 Someries Stud
1922 Ld Derby	1953 Mr F Darling	1983 White Lodge Stud
1923 Ld Derby	1954 Maj L B Holliday	1984 Mr E P Taylor
1924 Lady Sykes	1955 Someries Stud	1985 Dalham Stud Farms
1925 Ld Astor	1956 Maj L B Holliday	1986 H.H. Aga Khan
1926 Ld Woolavington	1957 Eve Stud	1987 Cliveden Stud
1927 Ld Derby	1958 Mr R Ball	1988 H. H. Aga Khan
1928 Ld Derby	1959 Prince Aly Khan and the late	1989 Mr Hamdan Al- Maktoum
1929 Ld Derby	H.H. Aga Khan	1990 Capt. Macdonald- Buchanan
1930 Ld Derby	1960 Eve Stud Ltd	1991 Barronstown Stud
1931 Ld Dewar	1961 Eve Stud Ltd	1992 Swettenham Stud
1932 H.H. Aga Khan	1962 Maj L B Holliday	1993 Juddmonte Farms
1933 Sir Alec Black	1963 Mr H F Guggenheim	1994 Shadwell Farm & Estate Ltd
1934 H.H. Aga Khan	1964 Bull Run Stud	1995 Shadwell Farm & Estate Ltd
1935 H.H. Aga Khan	1965 Mr J Ternynck	1996 Sheikh Mohammed
1936 Ld Astor	1966 Someries Stud	1997 Sheikh Mohammed
1937 H.H. Aga Khan	1967 Mr H J Joel	1998 Sheikh Mohammed
1938 Ld Derby	1968 Mill Ridge Farm	1999 H. H. The Aga Khan's Studs
1939 Ld Rosebery	1969 Lord Rosebery	2000 H. H. The Aga Khan's Studs
1940 Mr H E Morriss	1970 Mr E P Taylor	

2001 Shadwell Farm & Estate Ltd
2002 Gainsborough Stud
2003 Juddmonte

2004 Juddmonte
2005 Shadwell Farm & Estate Ltd
2006 Darley

2007 Darley

LEADING TRAINERS OVER JUMPS: 1946-2007

1946-47 F T T Walwyn
1947-48 F T T Walwyn
1948-49 F T T Walwyn
1949-50 P V F Cazalet
1950-51 T F Rimell
1951-52 N Crump
1952-53 M V O'Brien
1953-54 M V O'Brien
1954-55 H R Price
1955-56 W Hall
1956-57 N Crump
1957-58 F T T Walwyn
1958-59 H R Price
1959-60 P V F Cazalet
1960-61 T F Rimell
1961-62 H R Price
1962-63 K Piggott
1963-64 F T T Walwyn
1964-65 P V F Cazalet
1965-66 H R Price
1966-67 H R Price

1967-68 Denys Smith
1968-69 T F Rimell
1969-70 T F Rimell
1970-71 F T Winter
1971-72 F T Winter
1972-73 F T Winter
1973-74 F T Winter
1974-75 F T Winter
1975-76 T F Rimell
1976-77 F T Winter
1977-78 F T Winter
1978-79 M H Easterby
1979-80 M H Easterby
1980-81 M H Easterby
1981-82 M W Dickinson
1982-83 M W Dickinson
1983-84 M W Dickinson
1984-85 F T Winter
1985-86 N J Henderson
1986-87 N J Henderson
1987-88 D R C Elsworth

1988-89 M C Pipe
1989-90 M C Pipe
1990-91 M C Pipe
1991-92 M C Pipe
1992-93 M C Pipe
1993-94 D Nicholson
1994-95 D Nicholson
1995-96 M C Pipe
1996-97 M C Pipe
1997-98 M C Pipe
1998-99 M C Pipe
1999-00 M C Pipe
2000-01 M C Pipe
2001-02 M C Pipe
2002-03 M C Pipe
2003-04 M C Pipe
2004-05 M C Pipe
2005-06 P F Nicholls
2006-07 P F Nicholls

CHAMPION JOCKEYS OVER JUMPS: 1901-2007

Prior to the 1925-26 season the figure relates to racing between January and December

1901	F Mason	58
1902	F Mason	67
1903	P Woodland	54
1904	F Mason	59
1905	F Mason	73
1906	F Mason	58
1907	F Mason	59
1908	P Cowley	65
1909	R Gordon	45
1910	E Piggott	67
1911	W Payne	76
1912	I Anthony	78
1913	E Piggott	60
1914	Mr J R Anthony	60
1915	E Piggott	44
1916	C Hawkins	17
1917	W Smith	15
1918	G Duller	17
1919	Mr H Brown	48
1920	F B Rees	64
1921	F B Rees	65
1922	J Anthony	78
1923	F B Rees	64
1924	F B Rees	108
1925	E Foster	76
1925-26	T Leader	61
1926-27	F B Rees	59
1927-28	W Stott	88
1928-29	W Stott	65
1929-30	W Stott	77
1930-31	W Stott	81
1931-32	W Stott	77
1932-33	G Wilson	61
1933-34	G Wilson	56
1934-35	G Wilson	73

1935-36	G Wilson	57
1936-37	G Wilson	45
1937-38	G Wilson	59
1938-39	T F Rimell	61
1939-40	T F Rimell	24
1940-41	G Wilson	22
1941-42	R Smyth	12
1942-43	No racing	
1943-44	No racing	
1944-45	H Nicholson	15
	T F Rimell	15
1945-46	T F Rimell	54
1946-47	J Dowdeswell	58
1947-48	B Marshall	66
1948-49	T Moloney	60
1949-50	T Moloney	95
1950-51	T Moloney	83
1951-52	T Moloney	99
1952-53	F Winter	121
1953-54	R Francis	76
1954-55	T Moloney	67
1955-56	F Winter	74
1956-57	F Winter	80
1957-58	F Winter	82
1958-59	T Brookshaw	83
1959-60	S Mellor	68
1960-61	S Mellor	118
1961-62	S Mellor	80
1962-63	J Gifford	70
1963-64	J Gifford	94
1964-65	T Biddlecombe	114
1965-66	T Biddlecombe	102
1966-67	J Gifford	122
1967-68	J Gifford	82
1968-69	B R Davies	77

	T Biddlecombe	77
1969-70	B R Davies	91
1970-71	G Thorner	74
1971-72	B R Davies	89
1972-73	R Barry	125
1973-74	R Barry	94
1974-75	T Stack	82
1975-76	J Francome	96
1976-77	T Stack	97
1977-78	J J O'Neill	149
1978-79	J Francome	95
1979-80	J J O'Neill	117
1980-81	J Francome	105
1981-82	J Francome	120
	P Scudamore	120
1982-83	J Francome	106
1983-84	J Francome	131
1984-85	J Francome	101
1985-86	P Scudamore	91
1986-87	P Scudamore	123
1987-88	P Scudamore	132
1988-89	P Scudamore	221
1989-90	P Scudamore	170
1990-91	P Scudamore	141
1991-92	P Scudamore	175
1992-93	R Dunwoody	173
1993-94	R Dunwoody	197
1994-95	R Dunwoody	160
1995-96	A P McCoy	175
1996-97	A P McCoy	190
1997-98	A P McCoy	253
1998-99	A P McCoy	186
1999-00	A P McCoy	245
2000-01	A P McCoy	191
2001-02	A P McCoy	289

2002-03 A P McCoy 256
2003-04 A P McCoy 209
2004-05 A P McCoy 200
2005-06 A P McCoy 178
2006-07 A P McCoy 184

LEADING OWNERS OVER JUMPS: 1946-2007

(Please note that prior to the 1994-95 season the leading owner was determined by win prizemoney only)

1946-47 Mr J J McDowell	1967-68 Mr H S Alper	1988-89 Mr R Burridge
1947-48 Mr J Proctor	1968-69 Mr B P Jenks	1989-90 Mrs Harry J Duffey
1948-49 Mr W F Williamson	1969-70 Mr E R Courage	1990-91 Mr P Piller
1949-50 Mrs L Brotherton	1970-71 Mr F Pontin	1991-92 Whitcombe Manor
1950-51 Mr J Royle	1971-72 Capt T A Forster	Racing Stables Ltd
1951-52 Miss D Paget	1972-73 Mr N H Le Mare	1992-93 Mrs J Mould
1952-53 Mr J H Griffin	1973-74 Mr N H Le Mare	1993-94 Pell-Mell Partners
1953-54 Mr J H Griffin	1974-75 Mr R Guest	1994-95 Roach Foods Limited
1954-55 Mrs W H E Welman	1975-76 Mr P B Raymond	1995-96 Mr A T A Wates
1955-56 Mrs L Carver	1976-77 Mr N H Le Mare	1996-97 Mr R Ogden
1956-57 Mrs Geoffrey Kohn	1977-78 Mrs O Jackson	1997-98 Mr D A Johnson
1957-58 Mr D J Coughlan	1978-79 Snailwell Stud Co Ltd	1998-99 Mr J P McManus
1958-59 Mr J E Bigg	1979-80 Mr H J Joel	1999-00 Mr R Ogden
1959-60 Miss W H Wallace	1980-81 Mr R J Wilson	2000-01 Sir R Ogden
1960-61 Mr C Vaughan	1981-82 Sheikh Ali Abu Khamsin	2001-02 Mr D A Johnson
1961-62 Mr N Cohen	1982-83 Sheikh Ali Abu Khamsin	2002-03 Mr D A Johnson
1962-63 Mr P B Raymond	1983-84 Sheikh Ali Abu Khamsin	2003-04 Mr D A Johnson
1963-64 Mr J K Goodman	1984-85 T Kilroe and Son Ltd	2004-05 Mr D A Johnson
1964-65 Mrs M Stephenson	1985-86 Sheikh Ali Abu Khamsin	2005-06 Mr J P McManus
1965-66 Duchess of Westminster	1986-87 Mr H J Joel	2006-07 Mr J P McManus
1966-67 Mr C P T Watkins	1987-88 Miss Juliet E Reed	

LEADING AMATEUR RIDERS OVER JUMPS: 1946-2007

1946-47 Ld Mildmay 32	1966-67 Mr C Collins 33	1986-87 Mr T Thomson Jones ... 19
1947-48 Ld Mildmay 22	1967-68 Mr R Tate 30	1987-88 Mr T Thomson Jones ... 15
1948-49 Ld Mildmay 30	1968-69 Mr R Tate 17	1988-89 Mr P Fenton 18
1949-50 Ld Mildmay 38	1969-70 Mr M Dickinson 23	1989-90 Mr M McMahon 15
1950-51 Mr P Chisman 13	1970-71 Mr J Lawrence 17	1990-91 Mr K Johnson 24
1951-52 Mr C Straker 19	1971-72 Mr W Foulkes 26	1991-92 Mr M P Hourigan 24
1952-53 Mr A H Moralee 22	1972-73 Mr R Smith 56	1992-93 Mr A Thornton 26
1953-54 Mr A H Moralee 22	1973-74 Mr A Webber 21	1993-94 Mr J Greenall 21
1954-55 Mr A H Moralee 16	1974-75 Mr R Lamb 22	1994-95 Mr D Parker 16
1955-56 Mr R McCreery 13	1975-76 Mr P Greenall 25	1995-96 Mr J Culloty 40
Mr A H Moralee 13	Mr G Jones 25	1996-97 Mr R Thornton 30
1956-57 Mr R McCreery 23	1976-77 Mr P Greenall 27	1997-98 Mr S Durack 41
1957-58 Mr J Lawrence 18	1977-78 Mr G Sloan 23	1998-99 Mr A Dempsey 47
1958-59 Mr J Sutcliffe 18	1978-79 Mr T G Dun 26	1999-00 Mr P Flynn 41
1959-60 Mr G Kindersley 22	1979-80 Mr O Sherwood 29	2000-01 Mr T Scudamore 24
1960-61 Sir W Pigott-Brown 28	1980-81 Mr P Webber 32	2001-02 Mr D Crosse 19
1961-62 Mr A Biddlecombe 30	1981-82 Mr D Browne 28	2002-03 Mr C Williams 23
1962-63 Sir W Pigott-Brown 20	1982-83 Mr D Browne 33	2003-04 Mr O Nelmes 14
1963-64 Mr S Davenport 32	1983-84 Mr S Sherwood 28	2004-05 Mr T Greenall 31
1964-65 Mr M Gifford 15	1984-85 Mr S Sherwood 30	2005-06 Mr T O'Brien 32
1965-66 Mr C Collins 24	1985-86 Mr T Thomson Jones... 25	2006-07 Mr T Greenall 31

LEADING SIRES OVER JUMPS: 1986-2007

1986 Deep Run	1993-94 Strong Gale	2001-02 Be My Native (USA)
1987 Deep Run	1994-95 Strong Gale	2002-03 Be My Native (USA)
1988 Deep Run	1995-96 Strong Gale	2003-04 Be My Native (USA)
1989 Deep Run	1996-97 Strong Gale	2004-05 Supreme Leader
1989-90 Deep Run	1997-98 Strong Gale	2005-06 Supreme Leader
1990-91 Deep Run	1998-99 Strong Gale	2006-07 Presenting
1991-92 Deep Run	1999-00 Strong Gale	
1992-93 Deep Run	2000-01 Be My Native (USA)	

JOCKEYS' AGENTS

Jockeys' Agents and their Contact Details

Agent	Telephone	Mobile/Email	Fax
NICKY ADAMS	01488 72004/72964	07796 547659	
W ADAMS	01656 734416	07767 847025 welshwizard@wadams.fsbusiness.co.uk	01656 731915
NEIL ALLAN	01903 883797	07985 311141	
SARAH BOSLEY	01672 861200	07899 952295	
KEITH BRADLEY	01638 666350	07754 690050 keith.bradley2@ntlworld.com	
CHRIS BROAD	01452 760482/447	07836 622858 c.j.broad@talk21.com	01452 760394
RUTH BURCHELL	01495 302551	07773 790885	
GLORIA CHARNOCK	01653 695004/690097	07951 576912	
PAUL CLARKE	01638 660804	07885 914306 paul.clarke79@btinternet.com	
T E CLAYDON	01206 330880	07866 597559 tim@headquarterspartnership.co.uk	01206 330880
RAY COCHRANE	01223 812008	07798 651247	
RAY DODDS	0208 2451273	07952 226092 rayandzoe@blueyonder.co.uk	
SIMON DODDS	01509 502650/01509 503887	07974 924735	

Agent	Telephone	Mobile/Email	Fax
MS J S DOYLE	01488 72222	07831 880678 doyleracing@yahoo.co.uk	01488 72223
SHIPPY ELLIS	01638 668484	07860 864864 shippy.jockeys@virgin.net	01638 660946
JOHN W FORD	01954 261122	07830 294210	01954 261565
DR STEPHEN FOSTER	01386 871904	07768 415609 sfoster@markcoumbe.co.uk	
MARK GILCHRIST	01903 883356	07810 821787/ 07985 311141 gll677@aol.com	01903 883797
W P GRUNDY	01845 597850	07973 817634	01845 597945
RICHARD HALE	01768 886990/887320	07909 520542 richardhale77@hotmail.co.uk	
MISS SUSAN HARDING	01635 281166	07884 065582	
ALAN HARRISON	01969 625006	07861 392097 alanharrison31@btinternet.com	
RICHARD HARRISON	01325 732186/182	richard694@btinternet.com	
TONY HIND	01353 665669	07807 908599 anthony945@btinternet.com	
GAVIN HORNE	01392 422852/01386 443319	07914 897170/07787 748712 gavin.horne@hotmail.co.uk	
RICHARD HUNTER	01377 259123	07801 248644 jockagent@btconnect.com	

Agent	Telephone	Mobile/Email	Fax
L R JAMES	01653 699466	07947 414001	01653 691455
GUY JEWELL	01672 861231	07765 248859 guyjewell@fsmail.net	01672 861231
A P JONES	01635 253150	07771 553242 apjonesracing@aol.com	
JON LEES	01306 888318	07711 972643	
GEOFF LESTER	01635 253150	07771 832788	
MRS E LUCEY-BUTLER	01273 890124	07973 873846/07989 124949 homewoodgate@aol.com	
MISS S METCALFE	01635 298067	07900 207018	
MENIN MUGGERIDGE		07850 203881/ 07706 786261 mpmuggeridge@hotmail.com	01342 715814
MISS A C MURRAY	01793 701365	07727 022961	
TERRY NORMAN	01279 419395	07900 525033 terry@tnorman19.freeserve.co.uk	01279 432619
GARETH OWEN	01638 669968	07958 335206 gareth.owen@ntlworld.com	
DAVE POLLINGTON	01751 477142	07850 015711	
SHASHI RIGHTON	01638 751938/01392 422852	07787 748712/07914 897170	
DAVE ROBERTS	01737 761369	07860 234342	

Agent	Telephone	Mobile/Email	Fax
JOHN ROBERTSON	01284 850805/850807	07860 235151 jockeys@btinternet.com	01284 850807
ANDREW SHERET	01642 713391	07876 558899/282283 andrew.sheret@btinternet.com	
MISS L SQUIRE	01883 373540	07914 932229	
SAM STRONGE	01488 72818	07775 727778 sam.stronge@virgin.net	01488 73790
HUGH TAYLOR	01483 858023	07736 635459	
I J TWISS	01942 602581	07793 863510	
JENNIFER WALSH	00 353 45883704	00 353 87258025	00 353 45871929
IAN WARDLE	01761 453555	07831 865974	
ANDY WATERWORTH	01132 600993	07974 262665 mail@topriders.co.uk	
LAURA WAY	01704 834488	07775 777494	
BOB WILLIAMS	01638 750032	07774 662278	

Are your contact details missing or incorrect?
If so please update us by
email: richard.lowther@racingpost.co.uk
or leave a message on 0500 007071

FLAT JOCKEYS

Riding weights and contact details.

An index of agents appears on page 719

AHERN, EDDIE	8-5	Terry Norman
ALLAN, DAVID	8-6	Gloria Charnock
ARNOLDA, GIHAN	8-7	Neil Allan/Bob Williams
ASPELL, PADDY	9-0	Richard Hale
BAKER, GEORGE	9-0	Guy Jewell
BOWMAN, J H	8-6	Miss Susan Harding
BRADLEY, P	8-7	
BRISLAND, ROBYN	7-7	
CALLAN N,	8-5	Simon Dodds
CARSON, STEPHEN	8-4	Guy Jewell
CATLIN, CHRIS	8-0	Nicky Adams
CAVANAGH, CHRIS	8-6	
CHALMERS, NEIL	8-3	Miss S Metcalfe
COOPER, STEPHEN	8-4	
CORRIGAN, J	7-12	Bob Williams
COSGRAVE, PAT	8-7	Richard Hale/Guy Jewell
CREIGHTON, EDWARD	8-5	Miss A C Murray
CROWLEY, JIM	8-6	Guy Jewell
CULHANE, TONY	8-7	Mark Gilchrist
D'AVILA, WANDERSON	8-1	
DALY, ALAN	8-5	Guy Jewell
DE PAIVA, BENARIO	7-12	
DE SOUSA, SILVESTRE	8-0	Gareth Owen
DE SOUZA, JOSE	8-4	John W Ford
DE SOUZA, NELSON	7-12	Sam Stronge
DETTORI, L	8-7	R Cochrane
DOBBS, PAT	8-4	Nicky Adams/Tony Hind
DOE, PAUL	8-4	Mark Gilchrist
DONOHOE, STEPHEN	8-7	L R James
DOYLE, BRETT	8-6	Laura Way
DOYLE, JAMES	8-4	Ms J S Doyle
DROWNE, SEVE	8-6	Ian Wardle
DURCAN, TED	8-6	Laura Way
DWYER, MARTIN	8-3	Gareth Owen
EAVES, TOM	8-6	Richard Hale
EDDERY, PAUL	8-2	L R James
EDMUNDS, JASON	8-4	
EGAN, JOHN	8-3	Mark Gilchrist
ENSTONE, LEE	8-8	Alan Harrison
FAIRLEY, GREG	8-2	Simon Dodds/Richard Hale
FANNING, JOE	8-2	W P Grundy
FENTON, MICKY	8-6	Shashi Righton
FESSEY, PAUL	7-12	Richard Hale
FFRENCH, ROYSTON	8-0	Richard Hale
FITZSIMONS, PAUL	8-4	Guy Jewell
FORTUNE, JIMMY	8-7	Tony Hind
FOX, DOMINIC	7-10	L R James
FREDERICKS, P	8-9	
GANNON, CATHERINE	7-12	Simon Dodds
GAULE, OLIVE	7-0	Alan Harrison
GEMELOVA, NATALIA	7-7	Miss S Metcalfe
GHUNOWA, KEVIN	8-0	Nicky Adams
GIBBONS, GRAHAM	8-4	Laura Way
GIBSON, DALE	7-12	Mark Gilchrist
GOLAM, SALEEM	8-2	Neil Allan
GUILLAMBERT, J-P	8-6	Simon Dodds
HADDON, COLIN	8-6	
HALLIDAY, V	8-6	
HAMILTON, TONY	8-6	Richard Hale
HANAGAN, PAUL	8-0	Richard Hale
HANNON, G	8-2	Sarah Bosley

HAVLIN, ROBERT	8-6	Ian Wardle
HENRY, MATTHEW	8-2	Neil Allan
HILLS, MICHAEL	8-6	B J Robertson
HILLS, R	8-4	B J Robertson
HITCHCOTT, SAM	8-8	Nicky Adams
HOLLAND, DARRYLL	8-5	Laura Way
HUGHES, RICHARD	8-7	Geoff Lester
HUNTER, S	8-5	
JONES, LIAM	7-10	Mark Gilchrist
KELLY, SHANE	8-6	Richard Hunter
KENIRY, L P	8-5	Nicky Adams
KERTON, CHARLOTTE	7-6	L R James
KINSELLA, DAVID	7-12	Ian Wardle
KIRBY, ADAM	8-9	Nicky Adams
LAWSON, MARK	8-5	Richard Hale
LYNCH, FERGAL	8-9	Alan Harrison
MACKAY, JAMIE	7-12	Gareth Owen
MACKAY, NICKY	7-12	Terry Norman/Laura Way
MAKIN, PHILLIP	8-7	Richard Hale
MATHERS, PATRICK	8-1	Shashi Righton
MCAULEY, JOHN	7-10	
MCCARTHY, ADRIAN	7-13	Neil Allan
MCDONALD, FRANKIE	7-12	Gavin Horne
MCEVOY, KERRIN	8-5	Hugh Taylor
MCKEOWN, DEAN	8-3	Simon Dodds
MCLAUGHLIN, T G	8-10	Gavin Horne
MONGAN, IAN	8-6	Guy Jewell
MOORE, RYAN	8-6	Tony Hind
MULLEN, RICHARD	8-2	Tony Hind
MULRENNAN, PAUL	8-4	Richard Hale
MUNRO, ALAN	8-0	Laura Way
MYLONAS, D	8-4	Sarah Bosley
NEM, MANAV	7-5	
NICHOLLS, ADRIAN T	8-0	Shashi Righton
NORTON, FRANCIS	8-0	Ian Wardle
O'DONOHOE, D	8-3	Richard Hale
O'DWYER, JERRY	8-8	Paul Clarke
O'NEILL, DANE	8-6	Nicky Adams
O'SHEA, T P	8-2	Laura Way
POLLARD, NEIL	8-4	Richard Hunter
PROCTER, ANTONY	8-12	John W Ford
QUEALLY, T P	8-5	Keith Bradley
QUINN, AMIR	8-8	Neil Allan
QUINN, JIMMY	7-12	Gavin Horne
QUINN, PAUL	7-12	Alan Harrison
QUINN, T	8-4	J Lees
RANKIN, DAWN	8-2	
ROBINSON, PHILIP	8-5	Shippy Ellis
SANDERS, SEB	8-7	Keith Bradley
SCHOLES, ADRIAN	9-4	
SEMAAN, EDDIE	8-4	
SLATTERY, VINCE	8-11	c/o 07831 545789
SMITH, J D	8-6	Richard Hunter
SMITH, RICHARD	8-3	Guy Jewell
SMITH, TINA	8-4	
SPENCER, JAMIE	8-7	Andrew Sheret
STACK, EMMETT	8-2	Guy Jewell
STOKELL, ANN	8-4	c/o 07814 579982
STUBBS, KRISTIN	7-12	
SUPPLE, W		Laura Way
SWEENEY, FERGUS	8-6	Nicky Adams
TAHIR, F	8-5	
THOMAS, B	7-12	
THOMAS, RICHARD	8-2	Ian Wardle
TINKLER KIM	7-12	
TUDHOPE, DANIEL	8-4	Alan Harrison
TURNER, HAYLEY	7-12	Guy Jewell
URBINA, OSCAR	8-5	Guy Jewell
WHITWORTH, SIMON	8-4	Nicky Adams
WILLIAMS, DARREN	8-7	Neil Allan
WINSTON, ROBERT	8-5	Richard Hale

APPRENTICES

Their employers and contact details.

An index of agents appears on page 719

ATKINSON, ROSS (G L Moore)	7-4	Neil Allan
ATKINSON, TOBY (D R C Elsworth)	7-12	c/o 01638 665310
BAKER, AMY (Miss J Feilden)	7-7	John W Ford
BARTLEY GARY, (J S Goldie)	8-9	Richard Hale
BAZELEY, N (Mrs P N Dutfield)	8-4	c/o 01297 553560
BETTS, ANTHONY (N Wilson)	7-12	c/o 01904 468151
BETTS, LANCE (N Wilson)	7-10	Alan Harrison
BIRCH, MATTHEW (S Kirk)	8-3	c/o 01488 73215
BIRD, RYAN (H Morrison)	8-3	c/o 01635 281678
BLOCK, TRAVIS (H Morrison)	8-7	Nicky Adams
BROWN, NEIL (T D Barron)	8-6	Richard Hale
BRUNING, JOSEPHINE (J Pearce)	7-7	Sarah Bosley
BUBB, THOMAS (S Dow)	8-0	c/o 01372 721490
BUICK, WILLIAM (A M Balding)	7-0	Simon Dodds
BUSHBY, S (A D Brown)	7-12	Sarah Bosley
BYLES, ASHTON (B W Hills)	8-4	c/o 01488 71548
CAFFERTY, W J (P C Haslam)	9-0	Andy Waterworth
CANNON, DECLAN (K R Burke)	8-2	Alan Harrison
CARSON, WILLIAM (S C Williams)	8-2	Neil Allan
CAVANAGH, JOHN (M Dods)	8-3	John W Ford
CHEUNG, MARVIN (G C H Chung)	7-12	Miss S Metcalfe
CLARK, RYAN (R Simpson)	7-10	c/o 01488 73333
COSHAM, MATTHEW (Dr J R J Naylor)	7-12	c/o 01980 620804
COSTELLO, DOUGIE (J J Quinn)	9-5	Richard Hale
COUMBE, MARK (A W Carroll)	8-2	Dr Stephen Foster
COWLEY, RACHEL (J O'Reilly)	7-10	c/o 01302 724795
CRAVEN, IAN (Mrs G S Rees)	8-2	c/o 01722 812780
CRAY, BILLY (D J S ffrench Davis)	7-8	c/o 01488 73675
CREIGHTON, ALAN (E J Creighton)	8-4	L R James
CREIGHTON, S (E J Creighton)	8-0	Miss S Metcalfe
CUMINE, JULIE-ANNE (W M Brisbourne)	7-3	c/o 01743 741536
DA SILVA, D T (P F I Cole)	8-2	c/o 01488 638433
DAVIES, MATTHEW (M R Channon)	8-2	R T Harrison
DEAN, JACK (W G M Turner)	8-0	Neil Allan
DEAN, TOLLEY (J S Moore)	8-1	Neil Allan/Mark Gilchrist
DONAGHY, PATRICK (P C Haslam)	7-12	Alan Harrison
DOYLE, SOPHIE (Ms J S Doyle)	7-8	Ms J S Doyle
DRURY, SAMUEL (N Wilson)	7-12	c/o 01904 468151
EATON, NATASHA (A Bailey)	7-10	c/o 07808 734223
EATON, SONIA (B P J Baugh)	7-8	L R James
EDDERY, CHARLES (R Hannon)	6-8	c/o 01264 850254
EDWARDS, GARY (M Brittain)	8-2	Andy Waterworth
EGAN, ROBBIE (A J McCabe)	8-0	Simon Dodds
ELFORD, GEMMA (A B Haynes)	8-2	c/o 01264 850088
ELLIOTT, ANDREW (K R Burke)	7-13	Alan Harrison
ENGLAND, DEBRA (W J Musson)	7-6	Richard Hunter
EVANS, RICHARD (P D Evans)	7-13	01873 890837
FENTIMAN, DURAN (T D Easterby)	7-7	Alan Harrison
FOX, KIEREN (J R Best)	7-12	c/o 01622 880276
FRAZER, JONATHAN (J S Wainwright)	8-0	c/o 01653 658537
FROST, HADDEN (R Hannon)	8-3	Sam Stronge/Sarah Bosley
GERAN, M C (P W Chapple-Hyam)	7-4	L R James
GLENISTER, CHRIS (B W Hills)	7-12	John W Ford
GUEST, MARTIN (M A Jarvis)	8-5	Bob Williams
GUNDOWRY, KRISHLOVY (R C Guest)	8-0	c/o 01909 475962
HALFORD, MARC (D R C Elsworth)	8-4	Neil Allan
HAMBLETT, ASHLEY (L M Cumani)	8-2	Simon Dodds/Laura Way
HAMBLETT, JAMIE (Sir Michael Stoute)	8-2	Miss S Metcalfe
HARRISON, KELLY (K R Burke)	7-10	Alan Harrison

HEFFERNAN, ANDREW (Paul Green)	8-4	c/o 01515 260093
HESLOP, DEAN (T D Barron)	8-0	Richard Hunter
HILL, RYAN (Peter Grayson)	8-3	c/o 01704 830668
HILLS, PATRICK (M H Tompkins)	8-0	Gareth Owen/Laura Way
HOUGH, CHRIS (M L W Bell)	7-13	R T Dodds
HUNT, DAVID (J R Norton)	8-0	c/o 01266 387633
HUSSAIN, TALIB (M P Tregoning)	8-1	c/o 01488 73300
JONES, JAMIE (M G Quinlan)	8-7	Nicky Adams
KENNEMORE, RUSSELL (R Hollinshead)	8-4	L R James
KINGSCOTE, RICHARD (R Charlton)	8-4	Guy Jewell
KYNE, JAMIE (D Carroll)	6-5	Alan Harrison
LAWES, N S (M W Easterby)	8-0	Richard Hale
LEAPER, THOMAS (J O'Reilly)	7-2	c/o 01302 724795
LEPROHON, CHARLI (C E Brittain)	7-11	c/o 01638 664347
LOGUSH, SINEAD (J Gallagher)	8-1	c/o 01608 674492
LUSSIANA, MARIE (M Johnston)	7-10	c/o 01969 622237
MALONE, TOM (D E Pipe)	9-2	Dave Roberts
MANSER, KYLIE (Mrs H Sweeting)	8-3	Sarah Bosley
MARSHALL, JEMMA (G L Moore)	8-4	Paul Clarke
MAY, K (B J Meehan)	7-8	Ian Wardle
MCCREERY, DANIELLE (N Tinkler)	7-5	Miss S Metcalfe
MCDONALD, P J (G A Swinbank)	8-6	Richard Hale
MCDONNELL, KEITH (J J Quinn)	7-4	c/o 01944 768370
MCGEE, HEATHER (L M Cumani)	7-7	c/o 01638 665432
MEADOWS, TIMOTHY (W S Kittow)	8-2	Gavin Horne
MILCZAREK, KIRSTY (N A Callaghan)	7-12	Neil Allan
MILLMAN, JAMES (B R Millman)	8-4	Neil Allan
MITCHELL, JACK (P M Phelan)	8-4	Neil Allan
MORGAN, ASHLEY (M H Tompkins)	7-12	Neil Allan
MORIARTY, JAMIE (R A Fahey)	8-4	Richard Hale
MORRIS, LUKE (M L W Bell)	7-8	Neil Allan
MULLEN, ANDREW (K A Ryan)	8-0	Richard Hale
NOLAN, P (A B Haynes)	8-0	c/o 01264 850088
O'BRIEN, THOMAS (M R Channon)	8-2	R T Harrison
O'HARA, SLADE (G R Oldroyd)	8-6	Alan Harrison
O'REILLY, JAMES (J O'Reilly)	???	Andy Waterworth
PAYNE, JAKE (J M Bradley)	7-10	c/o 01291 622486
PICKARD, PAUL (J M Jefferson)	7-13	L R James
POLLI, NICOL (M Botti)	7-6	Paul Clarke
POULTON, HARRY (J R Boyle)	8-7	R T Harrison/Miss L Squire
PROBERT, DAVID (A M Balding)	7-0	Miss S Metcalfe
RAFTERY, RYAN (J A Osborne)	8-2	c/o 01488 73139
REVELEY, JAMES (N G Richards)	9-0	Richard Hale
ROGERS, JAMES (R A Fahey)	7-12	Richard Hale
ROMEO, PIETRO (J M Bradley)	8-2	c/o 01291 622486
ROPER, BRADLEY (N A Callaghan)	8-9	Neil Allan
ROTHERY, ADELE (D Nicholls)	7-7	c/o 01845 501470
ROWE, RICHARD (R ROWE)	7-10	c/o 01903 742871
SANTOS, VICTOR (H J L Dunlop)	8-0	c/o 01488 73584
SAVAGE, BARRY (J M Bradley)	7-12	c/o 01291 622486
SCALLAN, KATIA (M P Tregoning)	7-8	c/o 01488 73300
SCOTT, AMY (H Candy)	7-11	c/o 01367 820276
STAINTON, MICHAEL J (R M Whitaker)	8-2	John W Ford
TOBIN, KEVIN (C J Mann)	9-0	Chris Broad
TREADWELL, LIAM (Miss Venetia Williams)	9-2	Neil Allan
WISHART, BENJAMIN (M S Saunders)	7-10	c/o 01749 841011

JUMP JOCKEYS

Riding weights and contact details.

An index of agents appears on page 719

An index of agents appears on page 719

Name	Weight	Agent
PELL, PADDY	9-0	Richard Hale
LEY, TIMOTHY	9-11	
TCHELOR, MATTIE	9-7	Dave Roberts
RRIDGE, GARY	10-0	Richard Hale
LGER, COLIN	9-11	Chris Broad
ADBURNE, MARK	10-0	L R James
ENNAN, P J	10-0	Dave Roberts
CHANAN, PETER	9-7	Richard Hale
RNE, J P	10-0	Andy Waterworth
ARE, J E	10-0	
STELLO, DOUGIE	9-7	Richard Hale
AINE, S J	10-0	Sam Stronge
OSSE, DAVE	10-0	Dave Roberts
RRAN, SEAN	10-0	W Adams
VIES, JAMES	9-10	Dave Roberts
MPSEY, ALAN	10-0	Richard Hale
NNIS, DAVID	10-4	Chris Broad
MENT, JAMES	9-13	Sarah Bosley
BBIN, TONY	10-4	Richard Hale
YLE, JAMES	8-7	Ms J S Doyle
RACK, S E	10-0	Dave Roberts
LIOTT, SIMON	10-0	L R James
SWORTH, DOMINIC	10-0	Dave Roberts
ANS, TONY	10-0	Chris Broad
LTEJSEK, JAN	10-0	L R James
HILY, NOEL	10-2	Chris Broad
NTON, BARRY	10-0	Dave Roberts
TZGERALD, MICK	10-5	Dave Roberts
LEY, MARCUS	10-0	Sam Stronge
X, SEAN	10-7	c/o 01264 850218
UBUSSEAU, LUDOVIC	10-0	
LDSTEIN, JAMIE	10-0	L R James
ANT, MARK	10-0	Sam Stronge
EENE, R J	10-0	L R James
RDING, BRIAN	10-0	Richard Hale
RRIS, JAY	9-7	Andy Waterworth
WKINS, ADAM	9-5	
DE, PHILIP	10-0	L R James
BSON, RICHARD	10-4	Andy Waterworth
NOUR, CHRIS	10-0	L R James
GHES, RICHARD	8-7	Geoff Lester
TCHINSON, WAYNE	10-0	Chris Broad
COB, DARYL	10-0	Chris Broad
HNSON, KENNY	10-0	L R James
HNSON, RICHARD	10-0	Dave Roberts
ENIRY, BARRY	10-0	Dave Roberts
NNEDY, W T	9-10	Dave Roberts
NG, FERGUS	10-0	Richard Hale
VERTY, DEREK	9-10	L R James
E, GRAHAM	10-0	Richard Hale
EWELLYN, CARL	10-0	c/o 01488 73311
AGUIRE, JASON	10-3	Chris Broad
ARSTON, WARREN	10-3	Chris Broad
CCARTHY, J A	10-0	L R James
CCOY, A P	10-4	Dave Roberts
CGANN, DECLAN	9-10	L R James
CGRATH, LARRY	10-0	L R James
CGRATH, RICHARD	10-0	Richard Hale

MERCER, KEITH	10-0	Richard Hale
MOGFORD, JODIE	10-0	Dave Roberts
MOLONEY, PAUL	10-0	Chris Broad
MOORE, JAMIE	10-0	Dave Roberts
MULHOLLAND, NEIL	10-0	Dave Roberts
MURPHY, TIMMY	10-0	Chris Broad
NAUGHTON, M H	9-4	L R James
NELMES, OWYN	10-0	L R James
NICOLLS, MARK	9-9	L R James
O'BRIEN, T J	10-0	Dave Roberts
O'CONNOR, T	9-13	L R James
O'KEEFFE, ALAN	10-0	Dave Roberts
O'MEARA, DAVID	10-0	Richard Hale
O'NEILL, P C	10-0	Sam Stronge
O'REGAN, DENIS	10-0	Richard Hale
OLIVER, HENRY	10-0	Sam Stronge
PHELAN, T J	9-7	Dave Roberts
PRITCHARD, JOHN	9-0	R T Harrison
RENWICK, WILSON	10-0	Richard Hale
SCUDAMORE, TOM	10-0	Dave Roberts
SIDDALL, TOM	10-0	Dave Roberts
SLATTERY, VINCE	9-7	07831 545789
SPATE, RICHARD	9-7	L R James
STEPHENS, LEE	10-0	Dave Roberts
STEVENSON, J W	9-4	Andy Waterworth
STOKELL, ANN	9-9	07814 579982
STRETTON, CLAIRE	10-7	
STUDD, C M	9-4	L R James
SUPPLE, GERRY	10-0	L R James
THOMAS, GARETH	9-12	Andy Waterworth
THOMAS, SAM	10-6	Sam Stronge
THORNTON, ANDREW	10-2	Dave Roberts
THORNTON, ROBERT	10-0	Dave Roberts
TINKLER, ANDREW	10-0	Dave Roberts
TIZZARD, JOE	10-2	Sam Stronge
VICKERS, LEE	9-7	L R James
WALFORD, ROBERT	9-7	Dave Roberts
WALSH, R	10-2	Jennifer Walsh
WHELAN, PADGE	10-0	Richard Hale/Sam Stronge
WILLIAMS, CHRISTIAN	10-0	Dave Roberts
YOUNG, RICHARD	9-9	L R James

Are your contact details missing or incorrect?
If so please update us by email:
richard.lowther@racingpost.co.uk
or leave a message on 0500 007071

CONDITIONALS

Their employers and contact details.

An index of agents appears on page 719

ADAMS, ANDREW (Mrs S J Smith)	9-12	c/o 01274 564930
BENSON, P J (D McCain Jnr)	9-7	Richard Hale
BERRIDGE, LIAM (J Howard Johnson)	9-12	c/o 01388 762113
BURKE, KEIRAN (P R Rodford)	9-7	Sam Stronge
BURTON, WAYNE (J C Fox)	9-0	c/o 01264 850218
CAFFERTY, W J (P C Haslam)	10-0	Andy Waterworth
CARTER, N J (Miss Venetia Williams)	9-12	Dave Roberts
CHALLONER, HARRY (R Ford)	9-7	c/o 01829 760095
COLEMAN, A (Miss Venetia Williams)	9-0	Sam Stronge
COLLIER, TJADE (Mrs S J Smith)	9-9	Sam Stronge
CRAWLEY, MATT (K F Clutterbuck)	9-7	Sam Stronge
CULLINANE, DAVID (M C Chapman)	9-7	L R James
CUMMINGS, RYAN (D J Wintle)	9-4	L R James
DAVIES, CHRIS (B G Powell)	10-0	Ruth Burchell
DAVIS, FEARGHAL (N G Richards)	9-7	Richard Hale
DAYMAN, O (Dr P Pritchard)	9-9	c/o 01483 811989
DE GILES, FELIX (N J Henderson)	9-7	Dave Roberts
DEHDASHTI, EAMON (G L Moore)	10-0	Dave Roberts
DERWIN, GARY (G M Moore)	9-7	c/o 01969 623823
DICKINSON, MATHEW (G M Moore)	10-0	Andy Waterworth
DOYLE, JACK (A King)	9-12	Dave Roberts
DREAPER, T J (Ferdy Murphy)	10-6	Richard Hale
EDWARDS, LEE (T Wall)	9-12	Andy Waterworth
ENGLAND, DAVID (N A Twiston-Davies)	9-7	Chris Broad
FARRELLY, J W (D E Pipe)	9-9	Dave Roberts
FAVELL, J (Andrew Turnell)	9-5	c/o 01793 731841
FLAVIN, JOHN (Evan Williams)	9-7	c/o 01466 754069
FROST, HADDEN (R Hannon)	8-7	Sam Stronge/Sarah Bosley
GAGAN, STEVEN (Mrs S J Smith)	9-7	Richard Hunter
GILLIES, C I (Miss Lucinda V Russell)	9-7	c/o 01577 862482
GOLDSTEIN, MARC (Miss J S Davis)	9-7	Chris Broad
GREENWAY, TOM (R Ford)	9-11	Chris Broad
HALLIDAY, J (J M Jefferson)	9-9	c/o 01653 697225
HEARD, LIAM (P F Nicholls)	9-11	Sam Stronge
HUGHES, BRIAN (G A Swinbank)	9-10	Richard Hale
HUTCHISON, DANIEL (G L Moore)	9-12	c/o 01273 620405
JENKINSON, JAMIE (Noel T Chance)	10-0	Chris Broad
JONES, S P (B G Powell)	9-9	Dave Roberts
KAVANAGH, WAYNE (J W Mullins)	9-7	Dave Roberts
KILGARRIFF, LUKE (J R Gask)	9-5	c/o 07507 555303
KILLORAN, R J (N A Twiston-Davies)	9-7	Dave Roberts
KINGTON, JOHN (M Scudamore)	9-7	Dave Roberts
KINSELLA, PHIL (K G Reveley)	9-9	Richard Hale
LUCEY-BUTLER, ROBERT (Carl Llewellyn)	9-11	Sam Stronge
MALONE, TOM (D E Pipe)	9-11	Dave Roberts
MANIA, RYAN (A G Foster)	9-7	c/o 01361 810504
MARSHALL, JEMMA (G L Moore)	9-7	Paul Clarke
MARTIN, ANDREW (Miss A M Newton-Smith)	9-7	c/o 01323 488354
MCALISTER, MICHAEL (I McMath)	9-11	Richard Hale
MCAVOY, MICHAEL (Micky Hammond)	9-10	Andy Waterworth
MCCARTHY, WILLIE (T R George)	10-2	Chris Broad
MCLERNON, R P (Jonjo O'Neill)	9-4	c/o 01386 584209
MERRIGAN, PADDY (P Bowen)	10-0	Dave Roberts
MESSENGER, CRAIG (Mrs L C Jewell)	9-0	c/o 01622 842788
MESSENGER, TOM (B N Pollock)	9-7	L R James
MILCZAREK, JONJO (Carl Llewellyn)	9-4	c/o 01488 71065
MOLLOY, T (P J Hobbs)	9-12	Dave Roberts
MOORCROFT, BYRON (Mrs D A Hamer)	9-3	Ruth Burchell
MOORMAN, JONATHAN (A J McCabe)	9-7	c/o 01777 869300

MURPHY, MICHAEL (Ian Williams)	9-4	Dave Roberts
NOLAN, E (Jonjo O'Neill)	9-4	c/o 01386 584209
O'CONNELL, MICHAEL (Ferdy Murphy)	9-7	Richard Hale/Sam Stronge
O'DWYER, DARREN (P J Hobbs)	9-5	Dave Roberts
O'FARRELL, J P (J Howard Johnson)	10-0	Richard Hale
PALMOWSKI, JOSEPH (Ferdy Murphy)	9-0	c/o 01969 622289
PEMBERTON, JAY (N J Gifford)	9-5	Sam Stronge
POGSON, ADAM (C T Pogson)	10-1	Andy Waterworth
POSTE, CHARLIE (M F Harris)	9-9	Dave Roberts
QUINLAN, SEAN (R T Phillips)	9-4	Chris Broad
REVELEY, JAMES (N G Richards)	9-9	Richard Hale
RIDING, JENNY (P Monteith)	9-0	Richard Hale
ROBINSON, DANIEL (B G Powell)	9-7	c/o 01962 717705
ROE, MATTY (Mrs L Wadham)	9-4	L R James
RUTHERFORD, GARY (Mrs S J Smith)	9-7	c/o 01274 564930
SALMON, JACK (C L Tizzard)	10-7	c/o 01903 250598
SKELTON, HARRY (P F Nicholls)	9-7	Dave Roberts
SMITH, NATHAN (K C Bailey)	9-12	c/o 01242 890341
SWAN, D (Mrs N Macauley)	10-4	c/o 01476 860090
THOMAS, PHILIP (R Dickin)	9-0	c/o 01789 450052
THOMPSON, C D (Miss Venetia Williams)	9-7	Andy Waterworth
THOMPSON, THOMAS (G A Swinbank)	9-10	c/o 01325 377318
TIERNEY, RICHARD (J S Wainwright)	9-10	Richard Hale
TOBIN, KEVIN (C J Mann)	9-2	Chris Broad
TOLMAN, P J (Miss A M Thorpe)	9-10	c/o 01267 253595
TREADWELL, LIAM (Miss Venetia Williams)	9-11	Dave Roberts
TUMELTY, GERARD (A King)	9-9	Chris Broad
WALSH, S P (Mrs Norma Pook)	10-0	L R James
WATSON, KIERAN (Micky Hammond)	9-8	c/o 01969 625223
WHARFE, BERNIE (Miss H C Knight)	10-0	Sam Stronge
WHILLANS, EWAN (Ferdy Murphy)	9-10	Richard Hale
WHILLANS, GARRY (D W Whillans)	9-0	c/o 01450 373128
WHITE, JAMES (V R A Dartnall)	9-7	Dave Roberts
WILLIAMSON, CAREY (M J Gingell)	9-0	c/o 01553 842420
YOXALL, ANDREW (B De Haan)	9-2	c/o 01488 72163

AMATEUR RIDERS

Riding weights and contact details.

An index of agents appears on page 719

ADAMS, B 9-0	Shashi Righton
ALERS-HANKEY, D 11-9	07811 335979
ALEXANDER, J F 11-7	0131 3328850
ALLAN, MISS L 9-2	Andy Waterworth
ALLISON, MISS J 10-0	01488 73656
ARMSON, R 10-7	01332 865293
BALDOCK, M 10-0	07796 260429
BARBER, M 10-2	01437 763772/07977 778172
BARNES, ANGELA 9-0	07904 144018/01697 746675
BARNES, J 10-2	07763 384169
BARRETT, RAY 9-7	01507 463433/07930 933524
BARTLEY, MRS C 9-0	Simon Dodds
BASTIMAN, MISS R 9-7	01423 359397
BATES, LEE 10-5	01429 837087
BEDDOES, MISS S 9-0	c/o 01273 620106
BEVAN, MISS A 8-10	01531 634846
BIDDICK, W 10-0	Dave Roberts
BOSLEY, MRS S J 9-0	01367 820115/07778 938040
BRAMLEY, MISS FAYE 9-0	Sarah Bosley
BREWER, G C 10-12	01653 648166
BREWER, MISS L J 8-12	07974 765506
BRIDGES, MISS L H DOVETON 8-5	01747 852825
BROTHERTON, MISS S 8-12	c/o 01653 618620
BROWN, A C 10-0	01544 267322
BROWN, MISS F C 9-0	01638 577470
BULL, MISS M J 9-0	01636 816717
BULL, P	01634 235253
BURROWS, M 9-13	07773 317775
BURTON, D 9-11	L R James
BURTON, R P L 10-10	01743 709697
BYRNE, S W 10-0	Sam Stronge
CALLOW, C J 9-4	Richard Hale
CASSIDY, MISS S C 9-0	07985 296945
CHANIN, I 9-7	L R James
CHILTON, MISS K N 9-12	01743 741536
CLUBB, MRS H 8-10	R Harrison
COLLINGTON, P 9-3	Paul Clarke
COOK, J R F 10-0	01281 690864
COOKSON, E 9-2	L R James
COTTRILL, MISS V L 9-0	01829 760095
COWARD, JACQUELINE 9-10	07919 477619
COWLEY, P E 10-7	07775 943346
CRAGGS, T G 9-0	01740 620239
CULLIGAN, K T 9-0	01403 700911
CUMANI, MISS F 9-8	c/o 01638 665432
CUTHBERT, MISS H E 9-0	01228 560822
DAVIDSON, MISS R P 9-7	Richard Hale
DE BEST, MRS I 8-8	07836 799919
DENIEL, MISS A J 8-10	0795 1102441
DOBSON, S 9-10	A Harrison
DODD, K 10-7	01451 850496
DREW, MISS P 8-7	01954 250772/07986 325921
DUNCAN, MISS C 9-2	01638 663375
DUNSDON, D H 10-3	Sam Stronge
DURMAN, MISS S-J 8-7	c/o Jimmy Fox
	01264 850218
DYSON, MISS C 9-10	01527 821493/0780 3720183
EDE, A 10-7	01258 817271
EDWARDS, D M 10-7	01643 831549/07811 898002
ELLERBECK, JAMES 9-2	07793 539676
ELLIS, MISS JOEY B 8-5	07766 256918
ELLISON, MISS L L 8-8	01653 690005
ENRIGHT, MRS M 8-7	01273 479183
EVANS, L 9-7	L R James
EWART, J P L 10-2	07971 857068
FERGUSON, P K 9-13	01953 717224
FOLKES, MISS E 9-4	01743 741536
FORD, K R 9-10	01432 820604
FRIEZE, MISS ANGHARAD 9-4	T Claydon
GALTON, F F L A 8-12	07710 337350
GARDNER, MISS L J 9-12	07971 660190
GOSCHEN, MISS A B 10-9	07719 611301
GOSWELL, S G 9-7	01635 298210
GRACEY-DAVISON, MISS G D 9-6	L R James
GREEN, MISS R A 9-0	01258 817271
GREENALL, HON T E 10-0	Richard Hale
GUERRIERO, J 10-10	Dave Roberts
GUNDRY, MISS P-A B 10-0	W Adams
GUNSTONE, MISS M J 9-5	01488 73007
HAIGH, MISS V 10-0	01302 710235
HALL, G 9-0	07956 281 440
HANDLEY, MISS D M 10-4	01428 722528
HANLY, A F P 10-7	01584 874064
HANNAFORD, MISS C 9-4	01271 858647
HANSON, S P 9-7	Chris Broad/07817 275107
HARWOOD, MISS L J 8-7	01798 873011
HASLAM, B M R 10-10	c/o 01969 624351
HAYNES, HARRY 9-4	Richard Hale
HICKS, L W 11-4	07961 1557720
HOCKLEY, P 9-7	07793 539676
HORNER, MISS L V 9-2	01235 835888/01488 638636
HUGHES, RHYS S 10-0	Mrs R Burchell
HUTCHINSON, MISS A L 9-4	01638 577288
HUXLEY, C 9-10	Chris Broad
ILLMAN, MISS R 9-0	01428 722528
JAMES, K 9-11	L R James
JENNER, MISS J 8-10	07973 825149
JOHNSON, L 9-4	L R James
JOHNSON, P 11-4	0191 2674464
JONES, MISS E J 9-3	Mrs Ruth Burchell
KING, B A 9-12	L R James/01865 361260
KING, J A 9-9	01974 640532
KING, J J 9-12	01403 700911
KNELLER, MISS R 9-2	I Twiss
LANGLEY, R G 10-7	07866 532722
LILLY, MISS ZOE 9-0	Mrs E Lucey-Butler
LITTMODEN, MISS E P 9-2	01638 663375
LODGE, MISS JESSICA 9-3	I Twiss
LURCOCK, M J 10-7	07973 418257
MANN, MRS S M 9-3	c/o 01488 73118/71717
MACTAGGART, J 11-07	01450 860314
MCCARTHY, R I 10-0	C D Broad
MCCOURT, T M 9-6	01235 867453/01451 850182
MERRIAM, A 10-1	L R James
METCALFE, MISS C 10-0	0191 3736277
MILNE, MISS C P 9-0	01403 700911
MOORE, MRS S J 8-7	01488 648822

MORGAN, L 9-7.......................................07813 944107
MORRIS, MRS M A 8-10 01400 273930/07702 719902
MORRIS, S W 10-7...................................07771 922808
MULLINEAUX, MISS M J L 8-7 ....01829 261440
NEWBOLD, J D 10-0..............................01327 361733
NOSWORTHY, MISS C C 8-5.................07971 106044
PATTINSON, M I 8-12...........................01372 748800
PAYTER, L R 9-7...................................01327 860043
PEARCE, N A 9-10...........................Mrs R Burchell
PEARCE, S 8-5.....................................01638 664669
PEBODY, D M 9-7.......01295 750807/07909 834113
POOLES, R L 10-0.........01488 73032/07977 099953
PRICE, ASHLEE 9-6.............................A P Jones
PRITCHARD, DR P L J 9-11 ....01453 811881/
                                                              01453 811989
QUINN, R P 10-4..............................Dave Roberts
REES, S P 9-0......................................01638 577470
RICHARDSON, J A 10-4.........................0498 584711
RIMELL, M G 10-9.......01451 820819/07778 648303
ROBERTS, MRS M S 9-7.....................01305 761745/
                                                              07803 752831
ROWSELL, MISS L A 9-10 ....07814 148932
RUTTY, MISS L A 8-0...........................01969 640330
RYAN, MISS A 8-13...........................Richard Hale
SALAMAN, M B 10-0.....01672 541048/01488 72324
SCHOLFIELD, N 9-7...........................Dave Roberts

SESTON, M 10-4............................Andy Waterworth
SHARRATT, MISS S 10-5....................07966 467879
SOLLITT, M 10-4............................Andy Waterworth
SOUTHCOMBE, MISS W L 8-5.............0797 1225621
SOWERBY, MISS M N 8-10................Miss S Metcalfe
STOREY, C 10-0.............01573 420615/07976 587315
THOMPSON, MRS C A 9-001483 200135/0836 205579
TIZZARD, MISS C A 9-7........................01258 817271
TOMPSETT, MISS I G 9-7..................Mrs R Burchell
TROTTER, R J 10-3..............................07802 427351
TURNER, MISS A L 9-0..07939 585526/01664 464351
TURNER, D I 9-3..............01722 337399/07768 094908
WAKEHAM, R T H 10-5.........................0771 697452
WALEY-COHEN, S B 10-0....................07887 848425/
                                                              0131 4402309
WALFORD, M T 10-7....01653 648166 07734 265687
WALKER, S A 9-7.....................................S Dodds
WALLACE, MISS A 8-5.....................Wayne Hardie
WELLS, MISS A S 8-12..............................P Clarke
WILESMITH, M C 10-9...01531 890410/07768 431894
WILLIAMS, O 10-4.............................Sam Stronge
WILSON, MISS D Y 8-6........................01242 519008
WILSON, MISS F 9-0...........................01642 784587
WINTLE, A A 11-0................................07767 351144
YATES, K 9-7.....................................Sam Stronge
YORK, P 10-7...............01372 457102/07774 962168